Personal Finance

SECOND CANADIAN EDITION

JACK R. KAPOOR
College of DuPage

LES R. DLABAY
Lake Forest College

ROBERT J. HUGHES
Dallas County Community College

ARSHAD AHMAD
Concordia University

McGraw-Hill
Ryerson

Toronto   Montréal   Boston   Burr Ridge IL   Dubuque IA   Madison WI   New York   San Francisco
St Louis   Bangkok   Bogatá   Caracas   Kuala Lumpur   Lisbon   London   Madrid   Mexico City
Milan   New Delhi   Santiago   Seoul   Singapore   Sydney   Taipei

The McGraw·Hill Companies

McGraw-Hill Ryerson

Personal Finance,
Second Canadian Edition

ISBN: 0-07-091429-X

2 3 4 5 6 7 8 9 10 TCP 0 9 8 7 6 5 4

Printed and bound in Canada.

Care has been taken to trace ownership of copyright material contained in this text; however, the publisher will welcome any information that enables them to rectify any reference or credit for subsequent editions.

Vice President, Editorial and Media Technology: Patrick Ferrier
Executive Sponsoring Editor: Lynn Fisher
Developmental Editor: Maria Chu
Marketing Manager: Kelly Smyth
Supervising Editor: Anne Macdonald
Copy Editor: Rohini Herbert
Production Coordinator: Paula Brown
Cover Design: Sharon Lucas
Cover Image Credit: Burke/Triolo Productions/FoodPix
Permissions: Alison Derry, Permissions Plus
Composition: Lynda Powell
Printer: Transcontinental Printing Group
Chapter 4 Opening Photo: CP/Phill Snel
Chapter 6 Opening Photo: CP/Tom Hanson

National Library of Canada Cataloguing in Publication

Personal finance / Jack R. Kapoor ... [et al.]. — 2nd Canadian ed.

Includes index.
ISBN 0-07-091429-X

1. Finance, Personal. I. Kapoor, Jack R.

HG179.P455 2003   332.024   C2002-905023-5

To our extended family of students, eager to learn personal finance.

About the Authors

Jack Kapoor, COLLEGE OF DUPAGE

Jack Kapoor is a Professor of Business and Economics in the Business and Services Division. Dr. Kapoor has taught Business and Economics at College of DuPage since 1969. He received his B.A. and M.S. from San Francisco State College and his Ed.D. from Northern Illinois University. Professor Kapoor was awarded the Business and Services Division's Outstanding Professor Award for 1999–2000.

Dr. Kapoor is known internationally as a co-author of several textbooks including *Business: A Practical Approach* (Rand McNally), *Business* (Houghton Mifflin), and the forthcoming *Small Business Management* (Richard D. Irwin/McGraw-Hill).

Les Dlabay, LAKE FOREST COLLEGE

Les Dlabay teaches in the Department of Economics and Business at Lake Forest College, Lake Forest, Illinois. Over the past 25 years, he has taught more than 30 different courses in high school, community college, university, adult education, and teacher preparation programs. Dr. Dlabay has developed a wide variety of textbook materials, student activity guides, instructor manuals, testing programs, audio-visual materials, and software packages in the areas of Personal Finance, Consumer Economics, and International Business.

Dr. Dlabay has served as a consultant to corporations, educational institutions, and government agencies. He has presented more than 140 workshops and seminars in over 20 states to encourage teachers to actively involve students in the learning process with video presentations, newsletters, interviews, and Internet research activities.

Robert Hughes, RICHLAND COLLEGE

Robert Hughes teaches business, management, and finance courses at Richland College, which is part of the Dallas Community College system. In addition to *Personal Finance*, he has written college texts for Introduction to Business, Small Business Management and Entrepreneurship, and Business Math and presently has five books in publication. Dr. Hughes received his bachelor's degree from Southern Nazarene University and his master's and doctorate degrees from the University of North Texas.

Arshad Ahmad, CONCORDIA UNIVERSITY

Arshad Ahmad is Associate Professor and Director of the Finance Co-op Program at the John Molson School of Business at Concordia University. He completed his CGA designation in 1997, received an MBA and Ph.D from McGill University, and was awarded the George L.Geis Dissertation of the Year Award by the Canadian Society for the Study of Higher Education. Dr. Ahmad has received numerous faculty and university teaching awards. He was named a 3M teaching fellow in 1992 by the Society for Teaching and Learning in Higher Education and 3M Canada, and he now serves as Coordinator for the program.

Dr. Ahmad is the author of several texts, including *Canadian Financial Management* (5th Edition), and other pedagogical material, including study guides, case studies, video series, CD-ROMs, and various devices on the World Wide Web. He created and taught the business faculty's first Web-based undergraduate and graduate courses in Personal Finance, which have attracted over 3,000 students during the past two years.

Brief Contents

[1] Planning Your Personal Finances

1 Personal Financial Planning: An Introduction 2
2 Money Management Strategy: Financial Statements and Budgeting 35
3 Planning Your Tax Strategy 59

[2] Managing Your Credit

4 The Banking Services of Financial Institutions 98
5 Introduction to Consumer Credit 125
6 Choosing a Source Credit: The Costs of Credit Alternatives 155
7 The Finances of Housing 182

[3] Insuring Your Resources

8 Home and Automobile Insurance 210
9 Life, Health, and Disability Insurance 238

[4] Investing Your Financial Resources

10 Fundamentals of Investing 278
11 Investing in Stocks 312
12 Investing in Bonds 353
13 Investing in Mutual Funds 380

[5] Controlling Your Financial Future

14 Retirement Planning 408
15 Estate Planning 438

Appendix
The Time Value of Money 457

Glossary 468

Index 474

Contents

[1]
Planning Your Personal Finances

1 Personal Financial Planning: An Introduction   2

The Financial Planning Process   3
  Step 1: Determine Your Current Financial Situation   3
  Step 2: Develop Financial Goals   4
  Step 3: Identify Alternative Courses of Action   4
  Step 4: Evaluate Alternatives   5
  Step 5: Create and Implement a Financial Action Plan   6
  Step 6: Re-evaluate and Revise Your Plan   7

Developing Personal Financial Goals   8
  Types of Financial Goals   8
  Goal Setting Guidelines   9

Influences on Personal Financial Planning   10
  Life Situation and Personal Values   10
  Economic Factors   11

Opportunity Costs and the Time Value of Money   15
  Personal Opportunity Costs   15
  Financial Opportunity Costs   16

Achieving Financial Goals   20
  Components of Personal Financial Planning   20
  Developing a Flexible Financial Plan   23
  Implementing Your Financial Plan   23

Appendix: Financial Planners and Other Financial Planning Information Sources   29

2 Money Management Strategy: Financial Statements and Budgeting   35

Planning for Successful Money Management   36
  Opportunity Cost and Money Management   36
  Components of Money Management   36

A System for Personal Financial Records   37

Personal Financial Statements for Measuring Financial Progress   39
  The Personal Balance Sheet: Where Are You Now?   39
  Evaluating Your Financial Position   41
  The Cash Flow Statement: Where Did Your Money Go?   41

Budgeting for Skilled Money Management   45
  Starting the Budgeting Process   45
  Characteristics of Successful Budgeting   52

Saving to Achieve Financial Goals   52
  Selecting a Saving Technique   52
  Calculating Savings Amounts   54
  Two-Income Households   54

3 Planning Your Tax Strategy   59

Taxes and Financial Planning   60
  Taxes on Purchases   60
  Taxes on Property   60
  Taxes on Wealth   60
  Taxes on Earnings   61

Filing Your Federal and Provincial
Income Tax Return 61
Who Must File? 61
Filing Quebec Tax Returns 61

Income Tax Fundamentals 62
Step 1: Determining Total Income 62
Step 2: Calculating Net Income and
Taxable Income 63
Step 3: Calculating Taxes Owing 66
Making Tax Payments 74
Deadlines and Penalties 78

Tax Planning Strategies 81
Consumer Purchasing 83
Investment Decisions 84
Retirement Plans 85
Changing Tax Strategies 86

Tax Assistance and the Audit Process 87
Tax Information Sources 87
Tax Preparation Software and Electronic
Filing 89
Tax Preparation Services 89
What If Your Return Is Audited? 90

[2]
Managing Your Credit

4   The Banking Services of Financial
Institutions 98

A Strategy for Managing Cash 99
Meeting Daily Money Needs 97
Types of Financial Services 100
Electronic Banking Services 100
Methods of Payment 102
Opportunity Costs of Financial Services 102
Financial Services and Economic
Conditions 102

Types of Financial Institutions 103
Deposit-Type Institutions 104
Nondeposit Institutions 105
Cyberbanking 106
Comparing Financial Institutions 106

Types of Savings Plans 108
Regular Savings Accounts 109
Term Deposits and Guaranteed Investment
Certificates (GICs) 109
Interest-Earning Chequing Accounts 110
Canada Savings Bonds 110

Evaluating Savings Plans 111
Rate of Return 111
Nominal Interest Rate 111
Inflation 112
Tax Considerations 112
Liquidity 112
Safety 112
Restrictions and Fees 113

Selecting Payment Methods 113
Types of Chequing Accounts 113
Evaluating Chequing Accounts 114
Other Payment Methods 115

Appendix: Using a Chequing Account 122

5   Introduction to Consumer Credit 125

What is Consumer Credit? 126
Consumer Credit in Our Economy 126
Uses and Misuses of Credit 127
Advantages of Credit 127
Disadvantages of Credit 128
Summary: Advantages and Disadvantages
of Credit 129

Types of Credit 129
Closed-End Credit 129
Open-End Credit 130
Car Loans 134

Measuring Your Credit Capacity 136
Can You Afford a Loan? 136
General Rules of Credit Capacity 138
Co-signing a Loan 138
Building and Maintaining Your Credit
Rating 139

Applying for Credit 146
A Scenario from the Past 146
What Creditors Look For: The Five Cs of
Credit Management 146
What If Your Application Is Denied? 148

Avoiding and Correcting Credit
  Mistakes   150
  In Case of a Billing Error   150
  Identity Crisis: What to Do If Your Identity
    Is Stolen   150

6 Choosing a Source of Credit: The Costs of Credit Alternatives 155

Sources of Consumer Credit   156
  What Kind of Loan Should You Seek?   156

The Cost of Credit   158
  Finance Charge and Annual Percentage
    Rate (APR)   158
  Tackling the Trade-Offs   159
  Calculating the Cost of Credit   160
  Credit Insurance   164

Managing Your Debts   165
  Warning Signs of Debt Problems   166
  The Serious Consequences of Debt   167

Consumer Credit Counselling Services   168

Declaring Personal Bankruptcy   169
  Fending Off Bankruptcy: Consolidation
    Loans   170
  Bankruptcy and Insolvency Act   170
  Effects of Bankruptcy on Future Credit   171

Appendix: Other Methods of
  Determining the Cost of Credit   178

7 The Finances of Housing 182

Evaluating Housing Alternatives   183
  Your Lifestyle and Your Choice of
    Housing   183
  Opportunity Costs of Housing Choices   183
  Renting versus Buying Housing   184
  Housing Information Sources   185

Renting   186
  Selecting a Rental Unit   186
  Advantages of Renting   186

Disadvantages of Renting   187
Costs of Renting   189
Renting Rights   189

The Home-Buying Process   189
  Step 1: Determine Home Ownership
    Needs   189
  Step 2: Find and Evaluate a Property to
    Purchase   192
  Step 3: Price the Property   194

The Finances of Home Buying   195
  Step 4: Obtain Financing   195
  Step 5: Close the Purchase Transaction   200
  Home Buying: A Final Word   202

Selling Your Home   203
  Preparing Your Home for Selling   203
  Determining the Selling Price   204
  Sale by Owner   204
  Listing with a Real Estate Agent   204

[3]
Insuring Your Resources

8 Home and Automobile Insurance 210

Insurance and Risk Management: An
  Introduction   211
  What Is Insurance?   211
  Types of Risks   211
  Risk Management Methods   212
  Planning an Insurance Program   213

Property and Liability Insurance   217
  Potential Property Losses   217
  Liability Protection   217

Principles of Home and Property
  Insurance   220
  Homeowner's Insurance Coverages   220
  Tenant's Insurance   223
  Home Insurance Types   224
  Exclusions   225

Home Insurance Cost Factors   226
  Deductibles   226
  How Much Coverage Do You Need?   226

Factors That Affect Home Insurance
  Costs   227
Reducing Home Insurance Costs   228

Automobile Insurance Coverages   228
Motor Vehicle Bodily Injury Coverages   229
Other Automobile Insurance Coverages   231

Automobile Insurance Costs   231
Amount of Coverage   231
Automobile Insurance Premium Factors   232
Reducing Automobile Insurance
  Premiums   233

9 Life, Health, and Disability Insurance   238

Life Insurance: An Introduction   239
What Is Life Insurance?   239
The Purpose of Life Insurance   240
The Principle of Life Insurance   240

Determining Your Life Insurance Needs   242
Do You Need Life Insurance?   242
Determining Your Life Insurance
  Objectives   242
Estimating Your Life Insurance
  Requirements   242

Types of Life Insurance   244
Term Life Insurance   244
Permanent Life Insurance   246
Other Types of Life Insurance Policies   250

Important Provisions in a Life Insurance Contract   250
Naming Your Beneficiary   250
The Grace Period   251
Policy Reinstatement   251
Nonforfeiture Clause   251
Incontestability Clause   252
Suicide Clause   252
Automatic Premium Loans   252
Misstatement of Age Provision   252
Policy Loan Provision   252
Riders to Life Insurance Policies   252

Buying Life Insurance   253
From Whom to Buy?   253

Comparing Policy Costs   254
Obtaining a Policy   255
Examining a Policy   255
Choosing Settlement Options   256
Switching Policies   257

Financial Planning with Annuities   257
Why Buy Annuities?   258
Tax Considerations   259

Health Insurance and Financial Planning   259
What Is Health Insurance?   259
The Need for Supplemental Health
  Insurance   260
Group Health Insurance   260
Individual Health Insurance   261
Supplementing Your Group Insurance   261

Disability Income Insurance   261
Definition of Disability   262
Disability Insurance Trade-offs   263
Sources of Disability Income   262
Determining Your Disability Income
  Insurance Requirements   264
Critical Illness Insurance   264

Supplemental Health Insurance   266
Dental Expense Insurance   266
Vision Care Insurance   266
Long-Term Care Insurance   266
Major Provisions in a Health Insurance
  Policy   267
Health Insurance Trade-offs   269
Health Information Online   270

[4]
Investing Your Financial Resources

10 Fundamentals of Investing   278

Preparing for an Investment Program   279
Establishing Investment Goals   279
Performing a Financial Checkup   280

Getting the Money Needed to Start an
Investment Program 281
The Value of Long-Term Investment
Programs 282

Factors Affecting the Choice of Investments 284
Safety and Risk 284
Risk Tolerance Insurance 285
Components of the Risk Factor 286
Investment Income 289
Investment Growth 289
Investment Liquidity 290

An Overview of Investment Alternatives 290
Stock or Equity Financing 290
Corporate and Government Bonds 291
Mutual Funds 292
Real Estate 292
Other Investment Alternatives 293
Summary of Factors That Affect
Investment Choices 293
A Personal Investment Plan 295

Factors That Reduce Investment Risk 299
The Role of a Financial Planner 299
Your Role in the Investment Process 300
Tax Considerations 302

Sources of Investment Information 303
The Internet and Online Computer
Services 303
Newspapers and News Programs 304
Business Periodicals and Government
Publications 305
Corporate Reports 305
Statistical Averages 306
Investor Services and Newsletters 306
Desktop Information Services 307

11 Investing in Stocks 312

Common Stocks 313
How Are the Markets Doing? 313
Why Own Stocks 314
Why Corporations Issue Common Stocks 315
Why Investors Purchase Common Stocks 316

Preferred Stocks 318
The Cumulative Feature of Preferred
Stocks 320
The Participation Feature of Preferred
Stocks 320
The Conversion Feature of Preferred
Stocks 321

Evaluation of a Stock Issue 321
Classification of Stock Investments 322
How to Read the Financial Section of
the Newspaper 323
The Internet 323
Stock Advisory Services 325
Corporate News 326
Factors That Influence the Price of a
Stock 329

Buying and Selling Stocks 336
Primary Markets for Stocks 336
Secondary Markets for Stocks 337
Brokerage Firms and Account
Executives 337
Should You Use a Full-Service or a
Discount Brokerage Firm? 338
A Sample Stock Transaction 339
Computerized Transactions 340
Commission Charges 341
Securities Regulation 342

Long-Term and Short-Term Investment Strategies 342
Long-Term Techniques 342
Short-Term Techniques 343

12 Investing in Bonds 353

Characteristics of Corporate Bonds 354

Why Corporations Sell Corporate Bonds 356
Types of Bonds 356
Convertible Bonds 357
Provisions for Repayment 357

Why Investors Purchase Corporate Bonds 360
Interest Income 360
Dollar Appreciation of Bond Value 361

Bond Repayment at Maturity 362
A Typical Bond Transaction 362
The Mechanics of a Bond Transaction 364

Government Bonds and Debt Securities 365
Types of Bonds 365
Provincial Government Securities and
  Guarantees 368
Municipal Bonds/Installment
  Debentures 368
Other Types of Bonds 368

The Decision to Buy or Sell Bonds 370
Annual Reports 370
The Internet 370
Bond Ratings 371
Bond Yield Calculations 372
Other Sources of Information 375

13 Investing in Mutual Funds 380

Why Investors Purchase Mutual Funds 382
Characteristics of Mutual Funds 382
Management Expense Ratio 385
Special Fees 386

Classifications of Mutual Funds 388

How to Make a Decision to Buy or Sell Mutual Funds 390
How to Read the Mutual Funds Section
  of the Newspaper 391
Financial Objectives—Again 392
Mutual Fund Prospectus 392
Mutual Fund Annual Report 393
Financial Publications 393
The Internet 393

The Mechanics of a Mutual Fund Transaction 395
Return on Investment 396

Taxes and Mutual Funds 398
Purchase Options 398
Withdrawal Options 400

[5]
Controlling Your Financial Future

14 Retirement Planning 408

Why Retirement Planning? 409
Tackling the Trade-offs 409
The Importance of Starting Early 409
The Basics of Retirement Planning 411

Conducting a Financial Analysis 411
Review Your Assets 412

Retirement Living Expenses 414
Adjust Your Expenses for Inflation 416

Planning Your Retirement Housing 417
Type of Housing 417
Avoiding Retirement Housing Traps 418

Planning Your Retirement Income 419
Public Pensions 419
Employer Pension Plans 422
Personal Retirement Plans 423
Will You Have Enough Money during
  Retirement? 430

Living on Your Retirement Income 432
Tax Advantages 432
Working during Retirement 432
Investing for Retirement 433
Dipping into Your Nest Egg 433

15 Estate Planning   438

Why Estate Planning?   439
What Is Estate Planning?   439
Provincial Family Law   440
The Opportunity Cost of Rationalizing   440

Legal Aspects of Estate Planning   441
Wills   442

Types and Formats of Wills   444
Writing Your Will   444
Altering or Rewriting Your Will   447
A Living Will   447
Power of Attorney   448
Letter of Last Instruction   448

Types of Trusts and Estates   449
Benefits of Establishing Trusts   449
Types of Trusts   449
Estates   451
Estate Assets Not Distributed by a Will   451
Settling Your Estate   452

Appendix

The Time Value of Money   457

Glossary   468

Index   474

Preface

The Textbook as an Anchor

One of the most fulfilling parts of teaching is when past students single out your course or pedagogy as the reason for a profound lifestyle/career change. In one unsolicited letter, Shirley wrote: "Sir, I wish my boyfriend took your course. I have changed my spending habits that I now practise with ease, and I have come to believe that financial problems are challenges disguised as hidden opportunities. There was something about the textbook that made me feel that experts were ever present to guide me to issues that I had either avoided or was most puzzled by....".

Many of us receive e-mail or letters of this kind. And we can learn a lot from them. Shirley is referring to a Web-based course that attracts large numbers of undergraduate students every semester. The course stands out with respect to the access and convenience it provides students as well as to multimedia that was selected to enhance their learning experience (CD-ROMs, videos, PowerPoint presentations, Interactive Testing, and more).

Despite all this, Shirley pointed at certain aspects of her experience that we often take for granted. Shirley focuses on the textbook. While other valuable learning resources were provided, we often overlook the special role of a textbook. In this case, it was deliberately used as the centrepiece around which other media and activities were designed. It resonated the presence of guided expertise, which is a great metaphor for enabling student learning. It also drew the learner to attend to difficult issues. In fact, we are convinced that a well-designed textbook can be the anchor for meaningful learning environments.

Variety Makes for a Rich Learning Environment

A mosaic becomes functional when the pieces fit together and when the sum of the parts exceed the whole. We recognize that students have different learning styles and that a textbook can have features that help them understand and apply concepts. Beyond informing our readers, we wanted them to raise important questions that require further investigation. As well, we decided to limit coverage to 15 chapters grouped under five sections so that we could provide sufficient depth without pretending to give the last word on each topic. Thus, we took on the following triple challenge in revising each chapter for this edition. First, each chapter must qualify as being learner centred and provide examples and situations students can easily relate to. Second, multiple perspectives must raise the bar of content so that the learner begins to ask good questions and not simply accept material as prescription. Third, learning depends on the organization of material where important concepts jump out and are reinforced in as many different contexts as possible.

EXAMPLES

CHAPTER OPENING CASE typically describes a situation that the learner will face or is currently facing. It begins the conversation by presenting a problem, dilemma, or circumstance that clearly needs immediate attention highlighted by the Questions following the case. These questions guide the contents of the chapter and link procedures that may otherwise seem unrelated. For example, Chapter 3 presents the case of Stephanie Seymour, a young graduate planning her tax strategy.

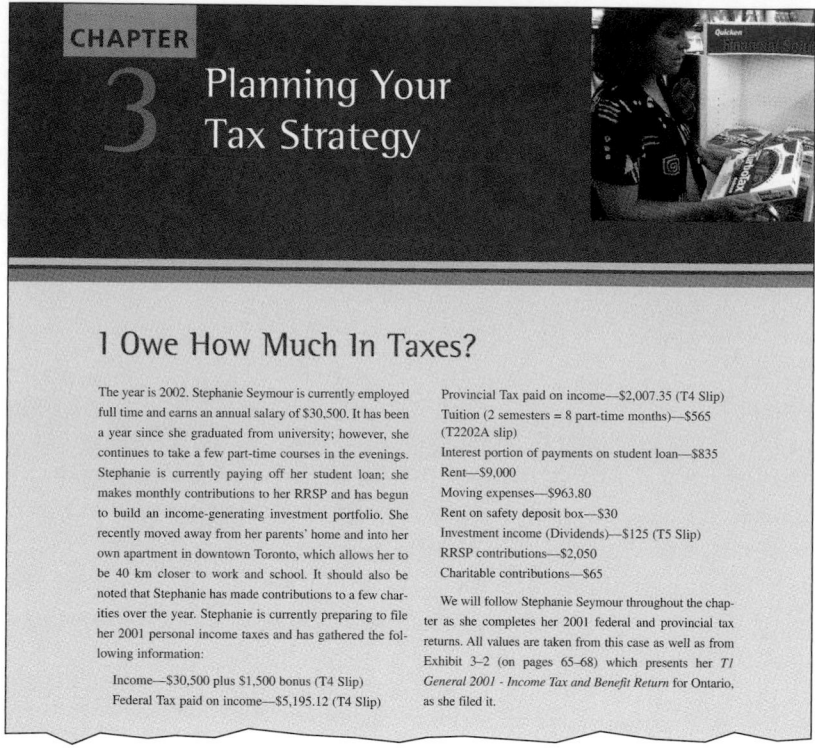

LEARNING OBJECTIVES structure the chapter with each objective repeated in the margin at the appropriate place in the main body of the chapter. The Learning Objectives appear again in the end of chapter summary and are used to organize end-of-chapter questions, problems, and exercises, as well as materials in the Instructor's Manual and the Test Bank.

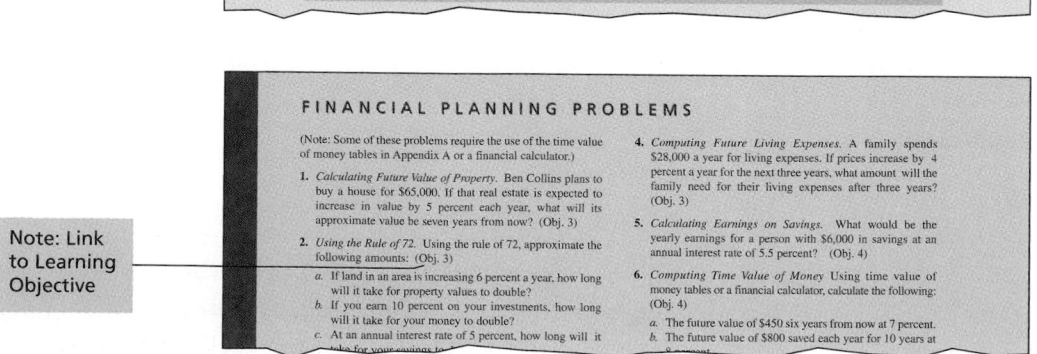

STUDENT WORK has been incorporated into the text and depicts how former students have approached a number of decisions relevant to them. They serve to model for their peers how they tackled difficult questions by highlighting their analyses and suggested courses of action.

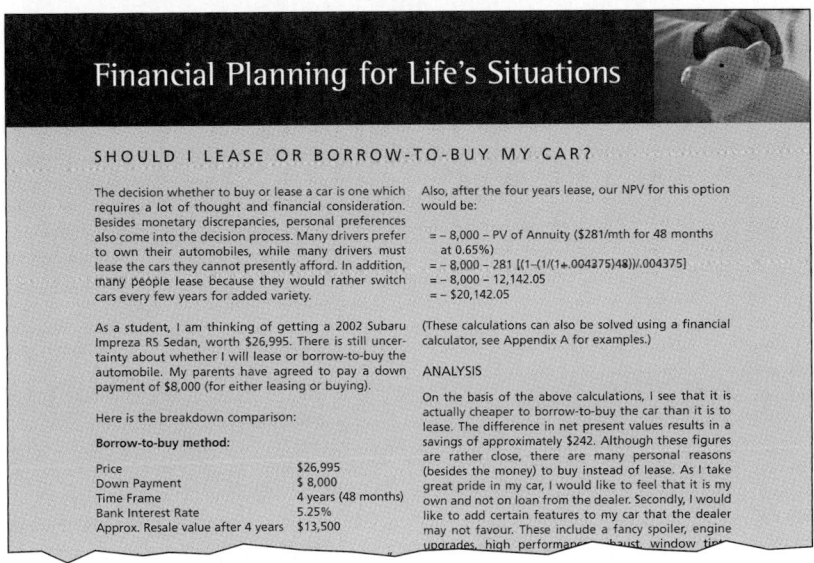

FINANCIAL PLANNING FOR LIFE'S SITUATIONS offers information that gets the learner to take action. It is based on the principle of active learning. It highlights special situations to prompt learners to apply concepts learned and make unique financial planning decisions.

FINANCIAL PLANNING CALCULATIONS features approximately 100 mathematical applications that the learner must master. All these calculations are situated in decisions that are typical of what learners encounter but may have shied away from due to the numbers behind these operations. The procedures illustrated in these calculations reinforce concepts introduced in the chapter in an applied setting. They are also tied to end-of-chapter questions and exercises.

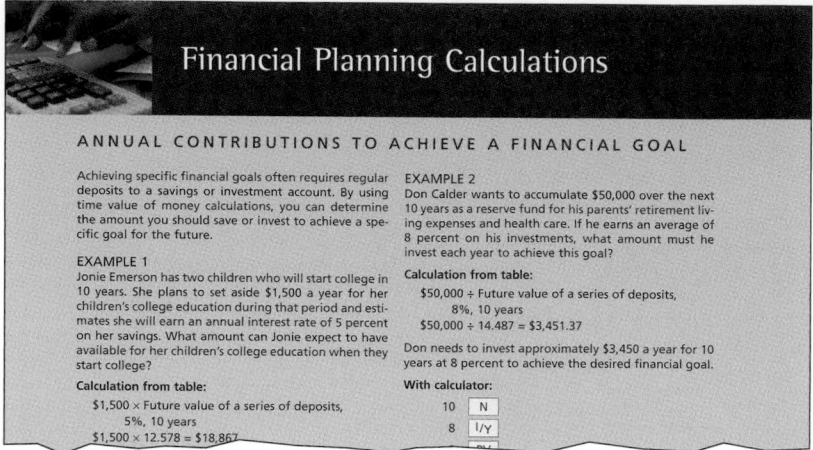

Financial Planning Calculations

ANNUAL CONTRIBUTIONS TO ACHIEVE A FINANCIAL GOAL

Achieving specific financial goals often requires regular deposits to a savings or investment account. By using time value of money calculations, you can determine the amount you should save or invest to achieve a specific goal for the future.

EXAMPLE 1
Jonie Emerson has two children who will start college in 10 years. She plans to set aside $1,500 a year for her children's college education during that period and estimates she will earn an annual interest rate of 5 percent on her savings. What amount can Jonie expect to have available for her children's college education when they start college?

Calculation from table:
$1,500 × Future value of a series of deposits, 5%, 10 years
$1,500 × 12.578 = $18,867

EXAMPLE 2
Don Calder wants to accumulate $50,000 over the next 10 years as a reserve fund for his parents' retirement living expenses and health care. If he earns an average of 8 percent on his investments, what amount must he invest each year to achieve this goal?

Calculation from table:
$50,000 ÷ Future value of a series of deposits, 8%, 10 years
$50,000 ÷ 14.487 = $3,451.37

Don needs to invest approximately $3,450 a year for 10 years at 8 percent to achieve the desired financial goal.

With calculator:

10	N
8	I/Y

ADVICE FROM A PRO is a great example of distributed expertise and multiple perspectives. In this box, industry professionals provide the kind of advice one can take home and internalize in order to make sense of the informational deluge that all of us face.

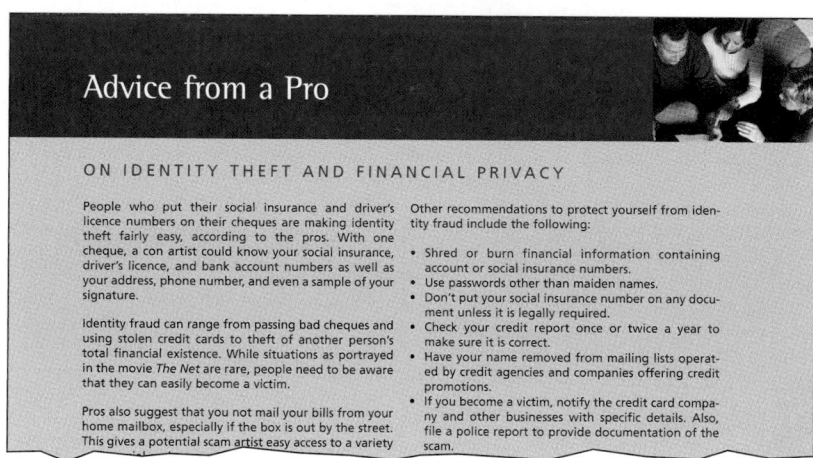

Advice from a Pro

ON IDENTITY THEFT AND FINANCIAL PRIVACY

People who put their social insurance and driver's licence numbers on their cheques are making identity theft fairly easy, according to the pros. With one cheque, a con artist could know your social insurance, driver's licence, and bank account numbers as well as your address, phone number, and even a sample of your signature.

Identity fraud can range from passing bad cheques and using stolen credit cards to theft of another person's total financial existence. While situations as portrayed in the movie *The Net* are rare, people need to be aware that they can easily become a victim.

Pros also suggest that you not mail your bills from your home mailbox, especially if the box is out by the street. This gives a potential scam artist easy access to a variety

Other recommendations to protect yourself from identity fraud include the following:

- Shred or burn financial information containing account or social insurance numbers.
- Use passwords other than maiden names.
- Don't put your social insurance number on any document unless it is legally required.
- Check your credit report once or twice a year to make sure it is correct.
- Have your name removed from mailing lists operated by credit agencies and companies offering credit promotions.
- If you become a victim, notify the credit card company and other businesses with specific details. Also, file a police report to provide documentation of the scam.

DID YOU KNOW boxes contain up-to-date facts, figures, and answers to frequently asked questions. They are featured several times within each chapter and typically elicit an "aha!" from the learner. These are not just catchy but provide well-researched insights that are often quoted by students in discussion forums.

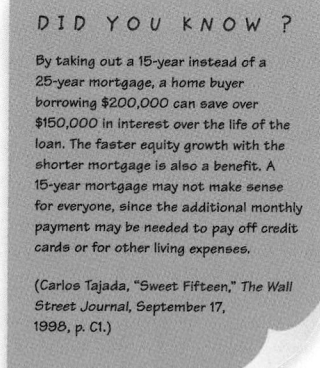

DID YOU KNOW?

By taking out a 15-year instead of a 25-year mortgage, a home buyer borrowing $200,000 can save over $150,000 in interest over the life of the loan. The faster equity growth with the shorter mortgage is also a benefit. A 15-year mortgage may not make sense for everyone, since the additional monthly payment may be needed to pay off credit cards or for other living expenses.

(Carlos Tajada, "Sweet Fifteen," *The Wall Street Journal*, September 17, 1998, p. C1.)

CONCEPT CHECKS are a valuable device to get the learner to digest conceptual chunks within a section before they proceed further into the chapter. They also serve to refocus the attention of the learning objectives that apply to that section.

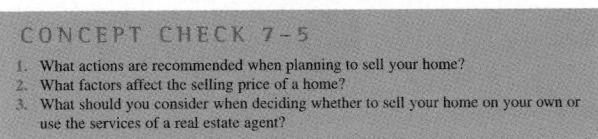

CONCEPT CHECK 7-5
1. What actions are recommended when planning to sell your home?
2. What factors affect the selling price of a home?
3. What should you consider when deciding whether to sell your home on your own or use the services of a real estate agent?

FINANCIAL PLANNING ACTIVITIES are the link for students to translate learning objectives into research which feeds into decisions they may be ready to make. It provides a "To Do" list using various procedures, techniques, and sources of information.

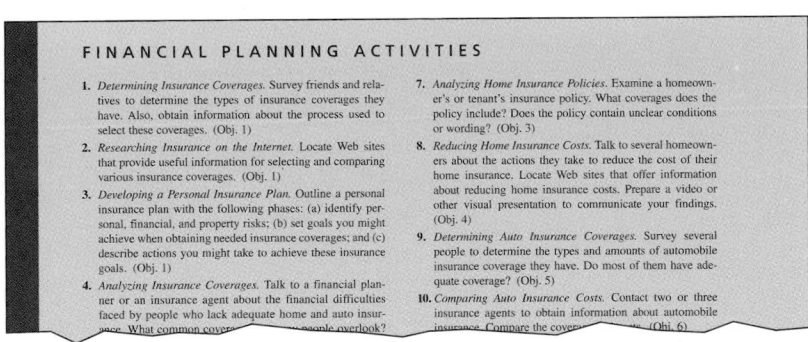

FINANCIAL PLANNING ACTIVITIES

1. *Determining Insurance Coverages.* Survey friends and relatives to determine the types of insurance coverages they have. Also, obtain information about the process used to select these coverages. (Obj. 1)
2. *Researching Insurance on the Internet.* Locate Web sites that provide useful information for selecting and comparing various insurance coverages. (Obj. 1)
3. *Developing a Personal Insurance Plan.* Outline a personal insurance plan with the following phases: (a) identify personal, financial, and property risks; (b) set goals you might achieve when obtaining needed insurance coverages; and (c) describe actions you might take to achieve these insurance goals. (Obj. 1)
4. *Analyzing Insurance Coverages.* Talk to a financial planner or an insurance agent about the financial difficulties faced by people who lack adequate home and auto insurance. What common coverages do people overlook?

7. *Analyzing Home Insurance Policies.* Examine a homeowner's or tenant's insurance policy. What coverages does the policy include? Does the policy contain unclear conditions or wording? (Obj. 3)
8. *Reducing Home Insurance Costs.* Talk to several homeowners about the actions they take to reduce the cost of their home insurance. Locate Web sites that offer information about reducing home insurance costs. Prepare a video or other visual presentation to communicate your findings. (Obj. 4)
9. *Determining Auto Insurance Coverages.* Survey several people to determine the types and amounts of automobile insurance coverage they have. Do most of them have adequate coverage? (Obj. 5)
10. *Comparing Auto Insurance Costs.* Contact two or three insurance agents to obtain information about automobile insurance. Compare the coverages. (Obj. 6)

LIFE SITUATION CASES provide opportunities for the learner to understand situations that individuals face which must be dealt with. These allow the student to become a consultant so that underlying problems are identified, a framework for analysis is established, and issues are clarified for possible solutions.

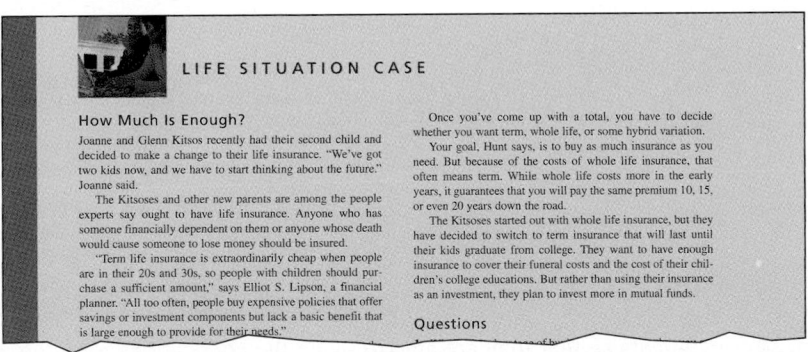

LIFE SITUATION CASE

How Much Is Enough?

Joanne and Glenn Kitsos recently had their second child and decided to make a change to their life insurance. "We've got two kids now, and we have to start thinking about the future," Joanne said.

The Kitsoses and other new parents are among the people experts say ought to have life insurance. Anyone who has someone financially dependent on them or anyone whose death would cause someone to lose money should be insured.

"Term life insurance is extraordinarily cheap when people are in their 20s and 30s, so people with children should purchase a sufficient amount," says Elliot S. Lipson, a financial planner. "All too often, people buy expensive policies that offer savings or investment components but lack a basic benefit that is large enough to provide for their needs."

Once you've come up with a total, you have to decide whether you want term, whole life, or some hybrid variation.

Your goal, Hunt says, is to buy as much insurance as you need. But because of the costs of whole life insurance, that often means term. While whole life costs more in the early years, it guarantees that you will pay the same premium 10, 15, or even 20 years down the road.

The Kitsoses started out with whole life insurance, but they have decided to switch to term insurance that will last until their kids graduate from college. They want to have enough insurance to cover their funeral costs and the cost of their children's college educations. But rather than using their insurance as an investment, they plan to invest more in mutual funds.

Questions

THE CONTINUOUS CASE reinforces the benefits of case-based teaching by pulling together the major concepts presented in each of the five sections in the text. It provides an opportunity to identify and analyze a range of personal financial decisions for several topics in a given section. Students begin to appreciate the broad links between chapters and sections.

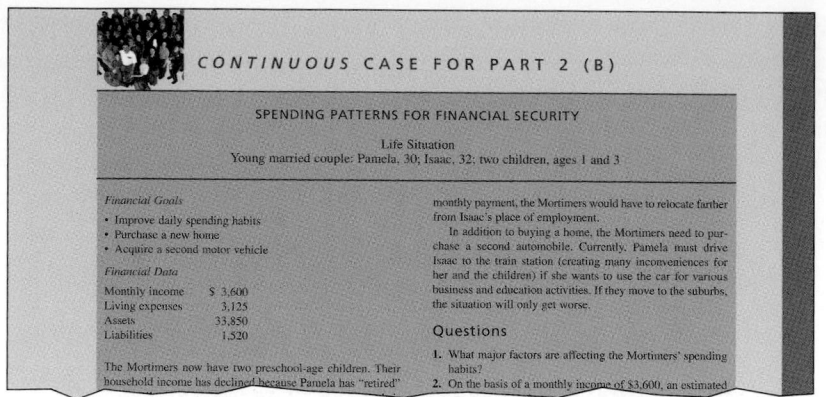

UPDATING CONTENT AND ADDITIONAL FEATURES

Overall, we have revised and updated Web sites, facts, and figures, including the *Did You Know* boxes, using relevant Canadian sources. We have introduced several examples of student work and cases that feature issues important to them. We have also illustrated financial calculations throughout the text detailing applications using a Texas Instrument BAII Plus calculator. A tutorial for the TI BAII Plus Calculator can be downloaded at the Kapoor Web site: **www.mcgrawhill.ca/college/kapoor**.

In addition to these features, we paid special attention to several chapters, including Chapter 3: *Planning Your Tax Strategy* and Chapters 10 to 13 under Part 4: *Investing Your Financial Resources*. With the use of up-dated references to the new budget, there is an increased emphasis on student sources of income, deductions, including loans, tips, gratuities, scholarships, grants, and so on. Similarly, we wanted to reflect changing economic realities. We have introduced brand new sections on "Mega Trends and Market Psychology," "How to Spot Online Investment Scams," and "Understanding the Enron Collapse" in Chapter 11 and more on desktop information services in Chapter 10. We have formulated new introductory cases that capture the pulse of what is of concern to many Canadians in managing their money.

In this spirit, this edition features practical tips on paying off your mortgage early (in Chapter 7); checklists highlighting advantages and disadvantages of different types of insurance (term-to-100, whole life, universal life, and term, as well as plans offered by universities in Chapters 8 and 9); the introduction of ETF index funds, costs of open- and closed-end mutual funds (in Chapter 13); more detailed information on annuities and potential pseudo-taxes that may be incurred on death (in Chapter 15).

We have been mindful of attending to detail, but more importantly, we have made a special effort to put ourselves in the mind of the reader. We are confident that this edition will meet the needs of students so that they are able to make the connections with the information, advice, and stories that unfold and gain the confidence to pursue further mastery of any of the 15 topics presented.

AN EYE ON THE SEAMLESS INTEGRATION OF TECHNOLOGY

Whether you are a technology buff or averse to it, most instructors in Canadian colleges and universities seem to be giving the same message: that the judicious use of technology which enhances learning must be promoted vigorously because it is clearly associated with student success (see Technology & Student Success Series http://www.mcgrawhill.ca/highereducation/administrators/research.php).

As mentioned earlier, our approach is to start with the textbook as the anchor around which several media are hosted. As authors, we are simply amazed at the menu of online and offline instructional resources for both instructors and for students. These complementary resources are also a testament to the commitment and deep level of support available for all users of *Personal Finance*.

By adopting this text, you also acquire a comprehensive teaching/learning package that includes the following:

Supplements for the Instructor

Your Integrated i-Learning Sales Specialist is a McGraw-Hill Ryerson representative who has the experience, product knowledge, training, and support to help you assess and integrate any of the below-noted products, technology, and services into your course for optimum teaching and learning performance. Whether it's how to use our test bank software, helping your students improve their grades, or how to put your entire course online, your i-Learning Sales Specialist is there to help. Contact your local i-Learning Sales Specialist today to learn how to maximize all McGraw-Hill Ryerson resources!

INSTRUCTOR'S ONLINE LEARNING CENTRE (OLC) The OLC at
www.mcgrawhill.ca/college/kapoor includes a password-protected Web site for Instructors. The site offers downloadable supplements and PageOut, the McGraw-Hill Ryerson course Web site development centre.

INSTRUCTOR'S CD-ROM This CD-ROM contains all the necessary Instructor
Supplements, including:

Instructor's Manual a "Course Planning Guide" with instructional strategies, course projects, and supplementary resource lists. The "Chapter Teaching Materials" section of the Instructor's Manual provides a chapter overview, the chapter objectives with summaries, introductory activities, and detailed lecture outlines with teaching suggestions. This section also includes concluding activities, ready-to-duplicate quizzes, supplementary lecture materials and activities, and answers to concept checks, end-of-chapter questions, problems, and cases.

Computerized Test Bank consists of over 1,000 true-false, multiple choice, and essay questions. These test items are organized by the learning objectives for each chapter, present different levels of difficulty, and are tied to concepts in the text.

PowerPoint Presentation prepared by Cyndi Hornby, of Fanshawe College, contains visual presentations that may be edited and manipulated to fit a particular course format.

CBC VIDEO CASES prepared by Rosemary Vanderhoeven, University of Guelph. These

videos, selected from CBC broadcasts, have been chosen to assist students in applying personal finance theory to real-world issues. A set of instructor notes for each video segment will be available at the Instructor's Online Learning Centre. The video segments are available in VHS format and through video-streaming at the Student's OLC.

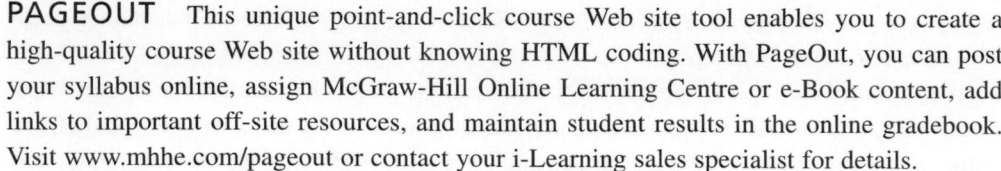

PAGEOUT This unique point-and-click course Web site tool enables you to create a high-quality course Web site without knowing HTML coding. With PageOut, you can post your syllabus online, assign McGraw-Hill Online Learning Centre or e-Book content, add links to important off-site resources, and maintain student results in the online gradebook. Visit www.mhhe.com/pageout or contact your i-Learning sales specialist for details.

In addition, content cartridges are also available for course management systems, such as *WebCT* and *Blackboard*, to expand the reach of your course and open up distance-learning options.

e-SERVICES McGraw-Hill Ryerson offers a unique services package designed for Canadian faculty. This includes technical support, access to our educational technology conferences, and custom e-Courses, to name just a few. Please speak to your i-Learning sales specialist for details.

Supplements for the Student

STUDENT ONLINE LEARNING CENTRE The electronic learning aid located at **www.mcgrawhill.ca/college/kapoor** offers a wealth of materials, including quick quizzes, extensive annotated Web resources, Internet Application Questions, and Electronic Lecture Notes, organized on a chapter-by-chapter basis. In addition, the site contains key terms and a searchable glossary, CBC video cases, and more.

One more thing...

Many instructors who have taught *Personal Finance* point out that many students select their elective course simply because the subject matter is intrinsically appealing to them. We agree. *Personal Finance* highlights authentic situations that every student encounters at some point, relating to setting goals, budgeting, taxes, insurance, investment, retirement, and so on. And yet, the subject matter lends itself to decision making that can be dreadful and wonderful at the same time.

Many surveys reveal that a majority of Canadians try to avoid, defer, or simply dread making financial decisions that have a way of popping up frequently, no matter how old you are and no matter what you do. Yet, as mentioned earlier, financial problems are really opportunities in disguise. We tend to make important lifestyle changes once we falter or when we have to. After taking the first steps in confronting difficult decisions, much of the anxiety dissipates, and alternative courses of action become feasible. We also wonder why we had not tackled these issues earlier. In fact, there is a strong argument to start learning about money, choices, and opportunity costs in high school and build on basic concepts during the college and university years and the rest of our careers.

We hope this textbook will help students take those first steps. We hope it will serve them to build a solid foundation. We also hope that their learning experience will be informative, enjoyable, and lifelong.

Acknowledgements

When we consider the efforts of contributors, we are truly humbled by their dedication and professionalism. Former students, friends, colleagues, and family members deserve many thanks and recognition for their sacrifices and especially for giving this textbook its own flavour and character. Some of them are acknowledged below.

We are also indebted and offer special thanks to Catherine Condoroussis who was the Research Assistant and contributor of many ideas that has made this edition extremely valuable to students. Catherine was first my student, then Teaching Assistant, and now has worked on this project as a peer. She has done excellent work and has always promoted the learner's perspective. I am confident she will continue to bring quality to whatever she endeavours to do in the future.

We also wish to thank Naz Rahman for her efforts to improve the Test Bank and to the following reviewers whose constructive suggestions have been incorporated as much as possible. They include reviewers of the First Canadian Edition:

Tov Assogbavi
Laurentian University

Dave Belford
Fanshawe College

Michael Bozzo
Mohawk College

Chuck Cox
St. Lawrence College

Paul Davies
Brock University

Jim Hebert
Red River College

Cyndi Hornby
Fanshawe College

Jon Levy, CA
McGill University

Cecilia Rodriquez-Hurabielle
Northern Alberta Institute of Technology

Martha Spence
Confederation College

Nancy Tait
Sir Sandford Fleming College

Eben Otuteye
University of New Brunswick, Fredericton

Rosemary Vanderhoeven
University of Guelph

Ellen Wilson
Northern Alberta Institute of Technology

Reviewers of the Second Canadian Edition:

Martin Beaudry
Concordia University

Michael Bozzo
Mohawk College

Jim Butko
Niagara College

Robert Campbell
Dawson College

Martha Cheney
Southern Alberta Institute of Technology

Don Cyr
Brock University

Michael Hlinka
George Brown College

Brain Hobson
Georgian College

Cyndi Hornby
Fanshawe College

Tom Jolly
Algonquin College

Doris Kochanek
Conaissance Technologies

Jon Levy, CA
McGill University

Alex Ng
University of Northern British Columbia

Omil Oloo
University of Lethbridge

Marie-Claude Savard
Peak Financial

Don Wheeler
College of North Atlantic

Ellen Wilson
Northern Alberta Institute of Technology

We would also like to acknowledge the professional contributions made by McGraw-Hill Higher Education and McGraw-Hill Ryerson. Thanks go to Lynn Fisher, Executive Sponsoring Editor, Maria Chu, Developmental Editor, Anne Macdonald, Supervising Editor, and Rohini Herbert, Copy Editor.

Finally, we look forward to your comments, suggestions, and questions. It is our hope that this textbook will make a difference in the lives of your students.

Arshad Ahmad
arshad@jmsb.concordia.ca

Online
Learning Centre

www.mcgrawhill.ca/college/kapoor

FOR THE STUDENT

- **Want to get higher grades?**

- **Want instant feedback on your comprehension *and* retention of the course material?**

- **Want to know how ready you *really* are to take your next exam?**

- **Want the extra help at *your* convenience?**

Of course you do!

Then check out your
Online Learning Centre!

- Online Quizzes: Pre- and Post-Tests
- Web Resources
- Internet Application Questions
- Electronic Lecture Notes and much more!

    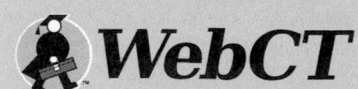

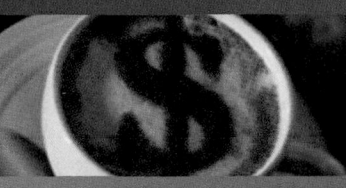

Personal Finance
SECOND CANADIAN EDITION

FOR THE INSTRUCTOR

- Want an easy way to test your students prior to an exam that *doesn't* create more work for you?

- Want to access your supplements *without* having to bring them all to class?

- Want an *easy* way to get your course on-line?

- Want to *free up more time* in your day to get more done?

Of course you do!

Then check out your
Online Learning Centre!

- Downloadable Supplements
- PageOut
- Online Resources

McGraw-Hill Ryerson

Higher Learning. Forward Thinking.™

PART 1

PLANNING YOUR PERSONAL FINANCES

CHAPTER 1
Personal Financial Planning: An Introduction

CHAPTER 2
Money Management Strategy: Financial Statements and Budgeting

CHAPTER 3
Planning Your Tax Strategy

Personal Financial Planning: An Introduction

Karen's Financial Plan

Karen Edwards, 23, completed her Bachelor of Science one year ago. The major cost of her tuition and books was covered by a scholarship. Through wise planning, she was able to save $15,000 from her part-time jobs. Acting on a suggestion from her parents, Karen met with a financial planner, who advised her to invest her money in low-risk bonds and saving certificates.

Karen works in an office in Toronto, Ontario, and she earns $25,000 a year. In approximately three years, she would like to return to school and start her master's degree. Then, she would like to buy a house. Karen wants to live on her salary and invest the $15,000 for her education and future home.

QUESTIONS

1 How did Karen benefit from her parents' advice and her own financial planning?

2 What decisions does Karen need to make regarding her future?

3 How could various personal and economic factors influence Karen's financial planning?

4 What would be the value of Karen's $15,000 in three years if it earned an annual interest rate of 7 percent?

5 Conduct a Web search to obtain information that Karen may find useful.

LEARNING OBJECTIVES

1 Analyze the process for making personal financial decisions.

2 Develop personal financial goals.

3 Assess personal and economic factors that influence personal financial planning.

4 Determine personal and financial opportunity costs associated with personal financial decisions.

5 Identify strategies for achieving personal financial goals for different life situations.

The Financial Planning Process

Everywhere you turn, someone is talking about money. When it comes to handling your finances, are you an *explorer*, someone who is always searching through uncharted areas? Are you a *passenger*, just along for the ride on the money decision-making trip of life? Or are you a *researcher*, seeking answers to the inevitable money questions of life?

Most people want to handle their finances so that they get full satisfaction from each available dollar. Typical financial goals include such things as a new car, a larger home, advanced career training, extended travel, and self-sufficiency during working and retirement years. To achieve these and other goals, people need to identify and set priorities. Financial and personal satisfaction are the result of an organized process that is commonly referred to as *personal money management* or *personal financial planning*.

Personal financial planning is the process of managing your money to achieve personal economic satisfaction. This planning process allows you to control your financial situation. Every person, family, or household has a unique financial position, and any financial activity, therefore, must also be carefully planned to meet specific needs and goals.

A comprehensive financial plan can enhance the quality of your life and increase your satisfaction by reducing uncertainty about your future needs and resources. The specific advantages of personal financial planning include:

- Increased effectiveness in obtaining, using, and protecting your financial resources throughout your lifetime.
- Increased control of your financial affairs by avoiding excessive debt, bankruptcy, and dependence on others for economic security.
- Improved personal relationships resulting from well-planned and effectively communicated financial decisions.
- A sense of freedom from financial worries obtained by looking to the future, anticipating expenses, and achieving your personal economic goals.

We all make hundreds of decisions each day. Most of these decisions are quite simple and have few consequences. Some are complex and have long-term effects on our personal and financial situations. While everyone makes decisions, few people consider how to make better decisions. As Exhibit 1–1 shows, the financial planning process is a logical, six-step procedure: (1) determining your current financial situation, (2) developing financial goals, (3) identifying alternative courses of action, (4) evaluating alternatives, (5) creating and implementing a financial action plan, and (6) re-evaluating and revising the plan.

STEP 1: DETERMINE YOUR CURRENT FINANCIAL SITUATION

In this first step of the financial planning process, you will determine your current financial situation with regard to income, savings, living expenses, and debts. Preparing a list of current asset and debt balances and amounts spent for various items gives you a foundation for financial planning activities. The personal financial statements discussed in Chapter 2 will provide the information you need to match your goals with your current income and potential earning power.

STEP 1 EXAMPLE: Within the next two months, Kent Mullins will complete his undergraduate studies with a major in international studies. He has worked part time in various sales jobs. He has a small savings fund ($1,700) and more than $8,500 in student loans. What additional information should Kent have available when planning his personal finances?

Objective 1

Analyze the process for making personal financial decisions.

personal financial planning
The process of managing your money to achieve personal economic satisfaction.

Visit the Web site
See the Weblinks under Chapter 1 on the online learning centre at www.mcgrawhill.ca/college/kapoor.

Exhibit 1–1

The Financial
Planning Process

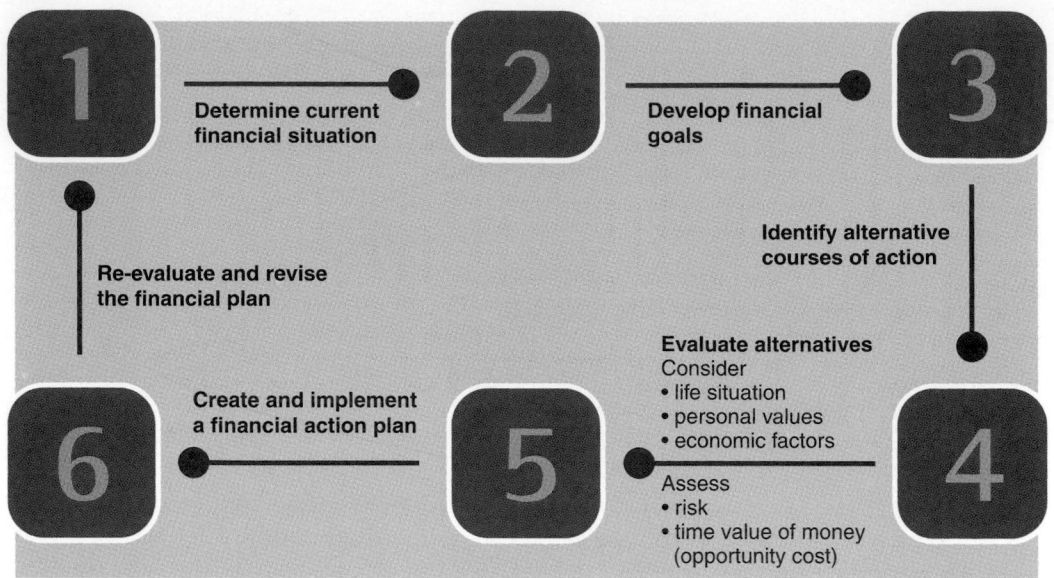

Visit the Web site

See Personal Financial
Planning worksheets
under Chapter 1 on the
online learning centre at
www.mcgrawhill.ca/
college/kapoor.

STEP 2: DEVELOP FINANCIAL GOALS

You should periodically analyze your financial values and goals. This involves identifying how you feel about money and why you feel that way. Are your feelings about money based on factual knowledge or on the influence of others? Are your financial priorities based on social pressures, household needs, or desires for luxury items? How will economic conditions affect your goals and priorities? The purpose of this analysis is to differentiate your needs from your wants.

Specific financial goals are vital to financial planning. Others can suggest financial goals for you; however, you must decide which goals to pursue. Your financial goals can range from spending all of your current income to developing an extensive savings and investment program for your future financial security.

STEP 2 EXAMPLE: Kent Mullins has several goals, including paying off his student loans, obtaining an advanced degree in global business management, and working in Latin America for a multinational company. What other goals might be appropriate for Kent?

STEP 3: IDENTIFY ALTERNATIVE COURSES OF ACTION

Developing alternatives is crucial for making good decisions. Although many factors will influence the available alternatives, possible courses of action usually fall into these categories:

- *Continue the same course of action.* For example, you may determine that the amount you have saved each month is still appropriate.
- *Expand the current situation.* You may choose to save a larger amount each month.
- *Change the current situation.* You may decide to use a money market account instead of a regular savings account.
- *Take a new course of action.* You may decide to use your monthly savings budget to pay off credit card debts.

Not all of these categories will apply to every decision situation; however, they do represent possible courses of action. For example, if you want to stop working full time to go to school, you must generate several alternatives under the category "Take a new course of action."

Creativity in decision making is vital to effective choices. Considering all of the possible alternatives will help you make more effective and satisfying decisions. For instance, most people believe they must own a car to get to work or school. However, they should consider other alternatives, such as public transportation, carpooling, renting a car, shared ownership of a car, or a company car.

Remember, when you decide not to take action, you elect to "do nothing," which can be a dangerous alternative.

STEP 3 EXAMPLE: Kent Mullins has several options available for the near future. He could work full time and save for graduate school; he could go to graduate school full time by taking out an additional loan; or he could go to school part time and work part time. What additional alternatives might he consider?

STEP 4: EVALUATE ALTERNATIVES

You need to evaluate possible courses of action, taking into consideration your life situation, personal values, and current economic conditions. How will the ages of dependants affect your saving goals? How do you like to spend leisure time? How will changes in interest rates affect your financial situation?

CONSEQUENCES OF CHOICES Every decision closes off alternatives. For example, a decision to invest in stocks may mean you cannot take a vacation. A decision to go to school full time may mean you cannot work full time. **Opportunity cost** is what you give up by making a choice. This cost, commonly referred to as the *trade-off* of a decision, cannot always be measured in dollars. It may refer to the money you forgo by attending school rather than working, but it may also refer to the time you spend shopping around to compare brands for a major purchase. In either case, the resources you give up (money or time) have a value that is lost.

opportunity cost
What a person gives up by making a choice.

Decision making will be an ongoing part of your personal and financial situations. Thus, you will need to consider the lost opportunities that will result from your decisions. Since decisions vary on the basis of each person's situation and values, opportunity costs will differ for each person.

EVALUATING RISK Uncertainty is a part of every decision. Selecting a college or university major and choosing a career field involve risk. What if you don't like working in this field or cannot obtain employment in it? Other decisions involve a very low degree of risk, such as putting money in a savings account or purchasing items that cost only a few dollars. Your chances of losing something of great value are low in these situations.

In many financial decisions, identifying and evaluating risk is difficult (see Exhibit 1–2). The best way to consider risk is to gather information based on your experience and the experiences of others and to use financial planning information sources.

FINANCIAL PLANNING INFORMATION SOURCES When you travel, you often need a road map. Travelling the path of financial planning requires a different kind of map. Relevant information is required at each stage of the decision-making process. This book provides the foundation you need to make personal financial planning decisions. Changing personal, social, and economic conditions will require that you continually supplement and update your knowledge. Exhibit 1–3 offers an overview of the informational resources available when making personal financial decisions. The Financial Planning for Life's Situations box on page 7 and the appendix to this chapter provide additional information.

Exhibit 1–2

Types of Risk

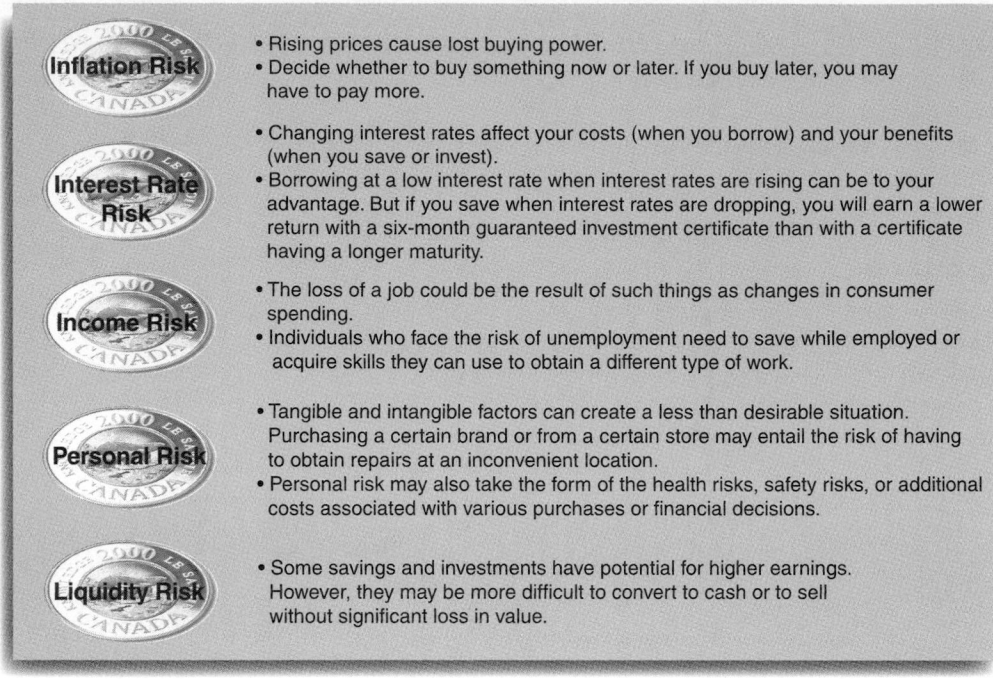

STEP 4 EXAMPLE: As Kent Mullins evaluates his alternative courses of action, he must consider his income needs for both the short term and the long term. He should also assess career opportunities with his current skills and his potential with advanced training. What risks and trade-offs should Kent consider?

STEP 5: CREATE AND IMPLEMENT A FINANCIAL ACTION PLAN

In this step of the financial planning process, you develop an action plan. This requires choosing ways to achieve your goals. For example, you can increase your savings by reducing your spending or by increasing your income through extra time on the job. If you are concerned about year-end tax payments, you may increase the amount withheld from each paycheque, file

Exhibit 1–3

Financial Planning Information Sources

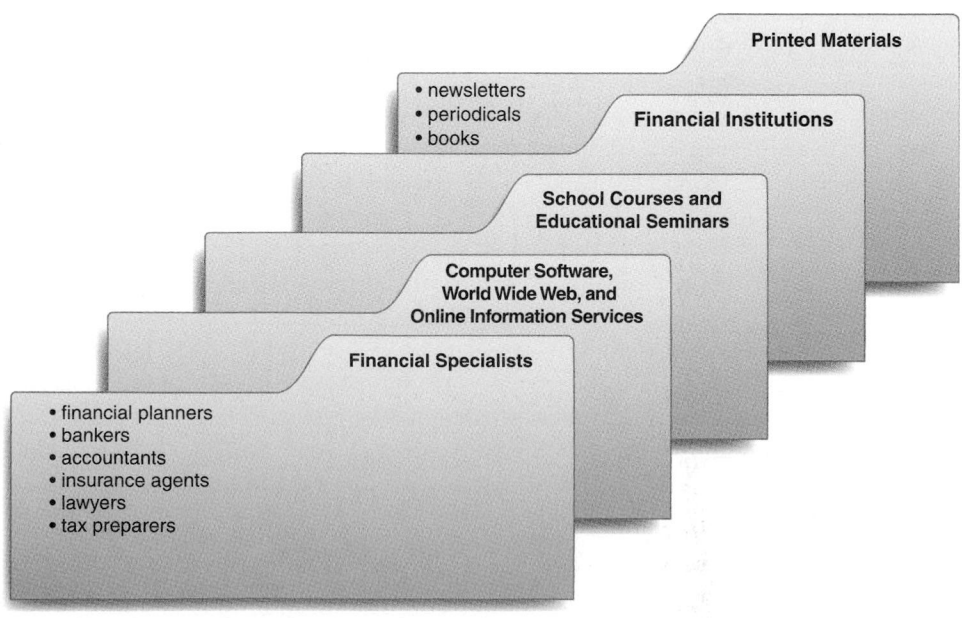

Financial Planning for Life's Situations

USING THE INTERNET FOR FINANCIAL PLANNING

Web . . . e-mail . . . URL . . . cybercash!

Just a few years ago, these terms made no sense to most people. Even now, many people are still not quite sure about all this stuff. However, most know that good financial planning requires information, and the Internet is the most efficient source of information.

Throughout this book, the financial planning content presented can be expanded and updated using the Internet. The Web sites we suggest, along with others you locate yourself, will allow you to quickly obtain information for making financial decisions appropriate to your life situation. In addition, at the end of each chapter, a feature called "Creating an E-Plan: Financial Decisions Using the Web" will give you an opportunity to plan, research, and implement various components necessary for a comprehensive financial plan.

As you study the personal financial topics discussed in this book, you will find the following Internet topic areas especially useful:

- *Cyber-info for personal financial planning:* With thousands of personal finance Web sites available, where does a person begin? Some of the most useful ones include www.webfin.com, www.quicken.ca, and www.cafp.org.
- *Online banking:* No more lines. No more rude bank tellers. No more inhaling exhaust fumes while waiting in the drive-through lane. In addition to existing banks that are online, there are Web-only banks, such as www.ingdirect.ca.

- *Online tax information and advice:* Tax planning should not occur only around April 30. For assistance, go to www.ccra-adrc.gc.ca and www.kpmg.ca.
- *Applying for a mortgage online:* Instead of waiting days or even weeks, prospective home buyers can now obtain financing online at www.webfin.com and www.scotiabank.ca.
- *Buying a car online:* Information that used to be difficult to get is now available to everyone. More than 70 percent of car buyers research their planned purchases online to obtain information about vehicle features and costs at such Web sites as www.carsbynet.com and www.sympatico.ca/contents/automotive.
- *Selecting investments online:* As everyone knows, "information is power." This axiom is especially true when investing. You can obtain company information and investment assistance at www.quicken.ca and www.mutfunds.com.
- *Being your own investment broker:* You already know which investments you want to buy? Then it's time to get into the market by going to www.bmoinvestorline.com.
- *Planning for retirement:* Whether you are 40 years or 40 minutes away from retiring, you can get lots of help at www.retireweb.com.

Note: Additional Web sites appear on the end sheets of this book and in the end-of-chapter exercises. Refer to the appendix for this chapter for information on conducting Internet searches. Also, be aware that Web sites may change or no longer be in use.

---

quarterly tax payments, or shelter current income in a tax-deferred retirement program. As you achieve your immediate or short-term goals, the goals next in priority will come into focus.

To implement your financial action plan, you may need assistance from others. For example, you may use the services of an insurance agent to purchase property insurance or the services of an investment broker to purchase stocks, bonds, or mutual funds. Your own efforts should be geared toward achieving your financial goals.

STEP 5 EXAMPLE: Kent Mullins has decided to work full time for a few years while he (1) pays off his student loans, (2) saves money for graduate school, and (3) takes a couple of courses in the evenings and on weekends. What are the benefits and drawbacks of this choice?

STEP 6: RE-EVALUATE AND REVISE YOUR PLAN

Financial planning is a dynamic process that does not end when you take a particular action. You need to regularly assess your financial decisions. You should do a complete review of your

7

finances at least once a year. Changing personal, social, and economic factors may require more frequent assessments.

When life events affect your financial needs, this financial planning process will provide a vehicle for adapting to those changes. Regularly reviewing this decision-making process will help you make priority adjustments that will bring your financial goals and activities in line with your current life situation.

STEP 6 EXAMPLE: Over the next six to 12 months, Kent Mullins should reassess his financial, career, and personal situations. What employment opportunities or family circumstances might affect his need or desire to take a different course of action?

CONCEPT CHECK 1–1

1. What are the main elements of every decision we make?
2. What are some risks associated with financial decisions?
3. What are some common sources of financial planning information?
4. Why should you re-evaluate your actions after making a personal financial decision?
5. What Web site feature of www.cafp.org or www.canadianfinance.com would provide assistance with your financial decisions?

Developing Personal Financial Goals

Objective 2

Develop personal financial goals

Since Canada is among the richest countries in the world, it is difficult to understand why so many Canadians have money problems. The answer seems to be the result of two main factors. The first is poor planning and weak money management habits in such areas as spending and the use of credit. The other is extensive advertising, selling efforts, and product availability. Achieving personal financial satisfaction starts with clear financial goals.

TYPES OF FINANCIAL GOALS

Two factors commonly influence your financial aspirations for the future. The first is the time frame in which you would like to achieve your goals. The second is the type of financial need that drives your goals.

TIMING OF GOALS What would you like to do tomorrow? Believe it or not, that question involves goal setting. *Short-term goals* are goals to be achieved within the next year or so, such as saving for a vacation or paying off small debts. *Intermediate goals* have a time frame of two to five years. *Long-term goals* involve financial plans that are more than five years off, such as retirement savings, money for children's college/university education, or the purchase of a vacation home.

Long-term goals should be planned in coordination with short-term and intermediate ones. Setting and achieving short-term goals is commonly the basis for moving toward success of long-term goals. For example, saving for a down payment to buy a house is a short-term goal that can be a foundation for a long-term goal: owning your own home.

Goal frequency is another ingredient in the financial planning process. Some goals, such as vacations or money for gifts, may be set annually. Other goals, such as a higher education, a car, or a house, occur less frequently.

GOALS FOR DIFFERENT FINANCIAL NEEDS A goal of obtaining increased career training is different from a goal of saving money to pay a semi-annual auto insurance premium. *Consumable-product goals* usually occur on a periodic basis and involve items that are used up relatively quickly, such as food, clothing, and entertainment. Such purchases, if made unwisely, can have a negative effect on your financial situation.

Durable-product goals usually involve infrequently purchased, expensive items, such as appliances, cars, and sporting equipment; these consist of tangible items. In contrast, many people overlook *intangible-purchase goals*. These goals may relate to personal relationships, health, education, and leisure. Goal setting for these life circumstances is also necessary for your overall well being.

GOAL SETTING GUIDELINES

An old saying goes, "If you don't know where you're going, you might end up somewhere else and not even know it." Goal setting is central to financial decision making. Your financial goals are the basis for planning, implementing, and measuring the progress of your spending, saving, and investing activities. Exhibit 1–4 offers typical goals and financial activities for various life situations.

Exhibit 1–4   Financial Goals and Activities for Various Life Situations

COMMON FINANCIAL GOALS AND ACTIVITIES		
• Obtain appropriate career training. • Create an effective financial recordkeeping system. • Develop a regular savings and investment program.	• Accumulate an appropriate emergency fund. • Purchase appropriate types and amounts of insurance coverage. • Create and implement a flexible budget.	• Evaluate and select appropriate investments. • Establish and implement a plan for retirement goals. • Make a will and develop an estate plan.

LIFE SITUATION	SPECIALIZED FINANCIAL ACTIVITIES
Young, single (18–35)	• Establish financial independence. • Obtain disability insurance to replace income during prolonged illness. • Consider home purchase.
Young couple with children under 18	• Carefully manage the increased need for the use of credit. • Obtain an appropriate amount of life insurance for the care of dependants. • Use a will to name a guardian for children.
Single parent with children under 18	• Obtain adequate amounts of health, life, and disability insurances. • Contribute to savings and investment funds for children's higher education. • Name a guardian for children and make other estate plans.
Young dual-income couple, no children	• Coordinate insurance coverage and other benefits. • Develop savings and investment programs for changes in life situation (larger house, children). • Consider tax-deferred contributions to retirement fund.
Older couple (+50), no dependent children at home	• Consolidate financial assets and review estate plans. • Obtain health insurance for post-retirement period. • Plan retirement housing, living expenses, recreational activities, and part-time work.
Mixed-generation household (elderly individuals and children under 18)	• Obtain long-term health care insurance and life/disability income for care of younger dependants. • Use dependent care service, if needed. • Provide arrangements for handling finances of elderly if they become ill. • Consider splitting of investment cost, with elderly getting income while alive and principal going to surviving relatives.
Older (+50), single	• Make arrangements for long-term health care coverage. • Review will and estate plan. • Plan retirement living facilities, living expenses, and activities.

Your financial goals should be stated to take the following factors into account:

[1] *Financial goals should be realistic.* Financial goals should be based on your income and life situation. For example, it is probably not realistic to expect to buy a new car each year if you are a full-time student.

[2] *Financial goals should be stated in specific, measurable terms.* Knowing exactly what your goals are will help you create a plan designed to achieve them. For example, the goal of "accumulating $5,000 in an investment fund within three years" is a clearer guide to planning than the goal of "putting money into an investment fund."

[3] *Financial goals should have a time frame.* In the preceding example, the goal is to be achieved in three years. A time frame helps you measure your progress toward your financial goals.

[4] *Financial goals should indicate the type of action to be taken.* Your financial goals are the basis for the various financial activities you will undertake.

The Financial Planning for Life's Situations box on page 12 gives you an opportunity to set financial goals.

CONCEPT CHECK 1–2

1. What are examples of long-term goals?
2. What are the four main characteristics of useful financial goals?

Influences on Personal Financial Planning

Objective 3

Assess personal and economic factors that influence personal financial planning.

Many factors influence daily financial decisions, ranging from age and household size to interest rates and inflation. Three main elements affect financial planning activities: life situation, personal values, and economic factors.

LIFE SITUATION AND PERSONAL VALUES

People in their 50s spend money differently from those in their 20s. Personal factors, such as age, income, household size, and personal beliefs, influence your spending and saving patterns. Your life situation or lifestyle is created by a combination of factors.

As our society changes, different types of financial needs evolve. Today, people tend to get married at a later age, and more households have two incomes. Many households are headed by single parents. More than two million women provide care for both dependent children and parents. We are also living longer: more than 80 percent of all Canadians now living are expected to live past age 65.

adult life cycle The stages in the family situation and financial needs of an adult.

As Exhibit 1–5 shows, the **adult life cycle**—the stages in the family situation and financial needs of an adult—is an important influence on your financial activities and decisions. Your life situation is also affected by marital status, household size, and employment, as well as such events as

- Graduation (at various levels of education).
- Engagement and marriage.
- The birth or adoption of a child.
- A career change or a move to a new area.
- Dependent children leaving home.
- Changes in health.
- Divorce.

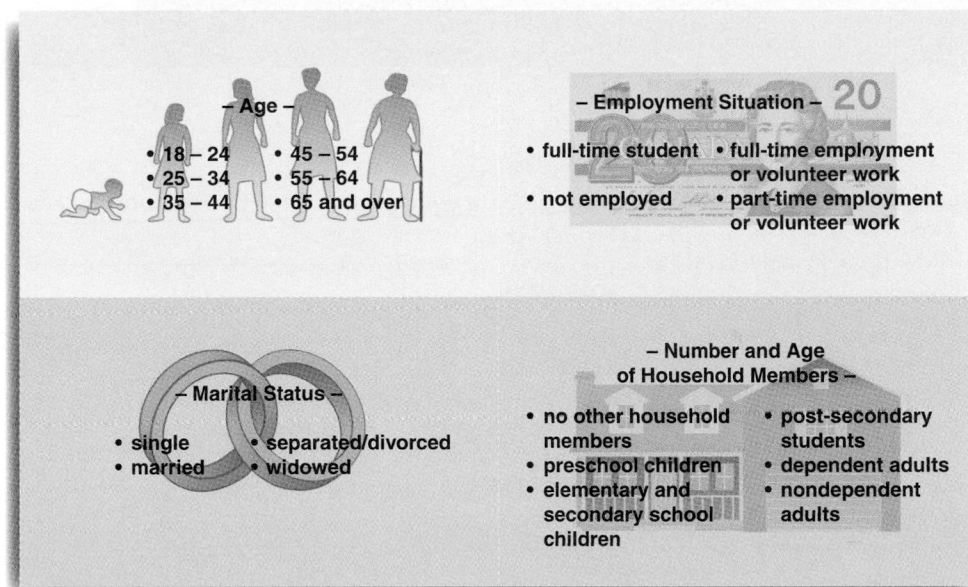

Exhibit 1-5

Life Situation
Influences on Your
Financial Decisions

- Retirement.
- The death of a spouse, family member, or other dependant.

In addition to being defined by your family situation, you are defined by your values—the ideas and principles that you consider correct, desirable, and important. **Values** have a direct influence on such decisions as spending now versus saving for the future or continuing school versus getting a job.

values Ideas and principles that a person considers correct, desirable, and important.

ECONOMIC FACTORS

Daily economic activities are another important influence on financial planning. In our society, the forces of supply and demand play an important role in setting prices. **Economics** is the study of how wealth is created and distributed. The economic environment includes various institutions, principally business, labour, and government, that must work together to satisfy our needs and wants.

economics The study of how wealth is created and distributed.

MARKET FORCES Prices of goods and services are generally determined by supply and demand. Just as a high demand for a consumer product forces its price up, a high demand for money pushes up interest rates. This price of money reflects the limited supply of money and the demand for it.

At times, the price of an item may seem to be unaffected by the forces of supply and demand, but in fact, at such times, other economic factors may also be influencing its price. Although such factors as production costs and competition influence prices, the market forces of supply and demand remain in operation.

FINANCIAL INSTITUTIONS Banks, trust companies, credit unions, insurance companies, and investment companies are the financial institutions with which most people do business. Financial institutions provide services that facilitate financial activities in our economy. They accept savings, handle chequing accounts, sell insurance, and make investments on behalf of others.

While various government agencies regulate financial activities, the Bank of Canada, our nation's central bank, has significant responsibility in our economy. The Bank of Canada is concerned with maintaining an adequate money supply. It achieves this by influencing borrowing, interest rates, and the buying or selling of government securities. The Bank of Canada attempts

Financial Planning for Life's Situations

CREATING FINANCIAL GOALS

On the basis of your current situation or expectations for the future, create two financial goals, one short-term and one long-term, using the following guidelines:

Step 1. Create realistic goals on the basis of your life situation.

A. SHORT-TERM GOAL

_____

_____

_____

_____

_____

B. LONG-TERM GOAL

_____

_____

_____

_____

_____

Step 2. State your goals in specific, measurable terms.

a. _____

_____

b. _____

_____

Step 3. Describe the time frame for accomplishing your goals.

a. _____

_____

b. _____

_____

Step 4. Indicate actions to be taken to achieve your goals.

a. _____

_____

b. _____

_____

to make adequate funds available for consumer spending and business expansion while keeping interest rates and consumer prices at an appropriate level.

GLOBAL INFLUENCES The global marketplace also influences financial activities. Our economy is affected by both the financial activities of foreign investors and competition from foreign companies. Canadian businesses compete against foreign companies for the spending dollars of Canadian consumers.

When the level of exports of Canadian-made goods is lower than the level of imported goods, more Canadian dollars leave the country than the dollar value of foreign currency coming into Canada. This reduces the funds available for domestic spending and investment. Also, if foreign companies decide not to invest their dollars in Canada, the domestic money supply is reduced. This reduced money supply may cause higher interest rates.

ECONOMIC CONDITIONS Newspapers and business periodicals regularly publish current economic statistics. Exhibit 1–6 provides an overview of some economic indicators that influence financial decisions. Your personal financial decisions are most heavily influenced by consumer prices, consumer spending, and interest rates.

> **DID YOU KNOW ?**
>
> A basket of goods and services that cost $100 in 1914 cost $1587.67 in 2001.
>
> (www.bankofcanada.com)

1. Consumer Prices Inflation is a rise in the general level of prices. In times of inflation, the buying power of the dollar decreases. For example, if prices increased 5 percent during the last year, items that cost $100 then would now cost $105. This means it now takes more money to buy the same amount of goods and services.

inflation A rise in the general level of prices.

The main cause of inflation is an increase in demand without a comparable increase in supply. For example, if people have more money to spend because of pay increases or borrowing but the same amounts of goods and services are available, the increased demand can bid up prices for those goods and services.

Exhibit 1-6 Changing Economic Conditions and Financial Decisions

Economic Factor	What It Measures	How It Influences Financial Planning
Consumer prices	The value of the dollar; changes in inflation	If consumer prices increase faster than your income, you are unable to purchase the same amount of goods and services; higher consumer prices will also cause higher interest rates.
Consumer spending	The demand for goods and services by individuals and households	Increased consumer spending is likely to create more jobs and higher wages; high levels of consumer spending and borrowing can also push up consumer prices and interest rates.
Interest rates	The cost of money; the cost of credit when you borrow; the return on your money when you save or invest	Higher interest rates make buying on credit more expensive; higher interest rates make saving and investing more attractive and discourage borrowing.
Money supply	The dollars available for spending in our economy	Interest rates tend to decline as more people save and invest; but higher saving (and lower spending) may also reduce job opportunities.
Unemployment	The number of people without employment who are willing and able to work	People who are unemployed should reduce their debt level and have an emergency savings fund for living costs while out of work; high unemployment reduces consumer spending and job opportunities.
Housing starts	The number of new homes being built	Increased home building results in more job opportunities, higher wages, more consumer spending, and overall economic expansion.
Gross domestic product (GDP)	The total value of goods and services produced within a country's borders, including items produced with foreign resources	The GDP provides an indication of a nation's economic viability resulting in employment and opportunities for personal financial wealth.
Trade balance	The difference between a country's exports and its imports	If a country exports more than it imports, interest rates may rise and foreign goods and foreign travel will cost more.
TSE 300 composite index and other stock market indexes	The relative value of stocks represented by the index	These indexes provide an indication of the general movement of stock prices.

Advice from a Pro

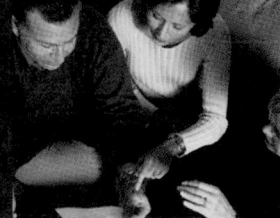

ON PERSONAL FINANCIAL PLANNING

"Spend less than you earn" is the foundation of long-term financial security, according to financial planner Ellen Rogin.

Although it sounds simple, most people do not follow this basic requirement for financial planning success. Ms. Rogin has been advising people about their money for more than 12 years. While the typical clients of her company range in age from 30 to 50, some are younger or older. Most of her clients are professionals and executives who have a common concern: a secure retirement. But Ms. Rogin is quick to point out that she works with people with a variety of needs, life situations, and investment philosophies. She has even advised a lottery winner, although she doesn't recommend that expectation as a steady path to long-term financial security!

The availability of information, Ms. Rogin believes, is the most significant change in the financial planning marketplace in recent years. With the Internet, television programs, and an extensive number of magazines and books, people can be better informed regarding personal finance topics and investments. However, Ms. Rogin warns that people must assess the validity of the information. She suggests "avoiding specific investment advice from magazines and other sources that may not be appropriate for your individual situation."

When planning your own financial direction, Ms. Rogin recommends three actions:

1. Set specific financial goals.
2. Reduce your debts.
3. Save for retirement.

Even if someone else is managing your finances, Ms. Rogin encourages you to "be involved." Be aware of your personal economic situation and the financial marketplace. Communicate your money views, risk acceptance, and financial priorities. Never let a financial planner, your spouse, or another family member have complete control.

Inflation is most harmful to people living on fixed incomes. Due to inflation, retired people and others whose incomes do not change are able to afford smaller amounts of goods and services.

Inflation can also adversely affect lenders of money. Unless an adequate interest rate is charged, amounts repaid by borrowers in times of inflation have less buying power than the money they borrowed. If you pay 10 percent interest on a loan and the inflation rate is 12 percent, the dollars you pay the lender have lost buying power. For this reason, interest rates rise in periods of high inflation.

The rate of inflation varies. During the late 1950s and early 1960s, the annual inflation rate was in the 1 to 3 percent range. During the late 1970s and early 1980s, the cost of living increased 10 to 12 percent annually.

More recently, the annual price increase for most goods and services as measured by the consumer price index has been in the 1 to 3 percent range. The *consumer price index* (CPI), published by Statistics Canada, is a measure of the average change in the prices urban consumers pay for a fixed "basket" of goods and services. For current CPI information, go to www.statcan.ca.

2. Consumer Spending Total demand for goods and services in the economy influences employment opportunities and the potential for income. As consumer purchasing increases, the financial resources of current and prospective employees expand. This situation improves the financial condition of many households.

DID YOU KNOW ?

To find out how fast prices double, you can use the rule of 72. Just divide 72 by the annual inflation rate (or interest rate). An annual inflation rate of 8 percent, for example, means prices will double in nine years (72 ÷ 8 = 9).

In contrast, reduced spending causes unemployment, since staff reduction commonly results from a company's reduced financial resources. The financial hardships of unemployment are a major concern of business, labour, and government. Retraining programs, income assistance, and job services can help people adjust.

3. Interest Rates In simple terms, interest rates represent the cost of money. Like everything else, money has a price. The forces of supply and demand influence interest rates. When consumer saving and investing increase the supply of money, interest rates tend to decrease. However, as consumer, business, government, and foreign borrowing increase the demand for money, interest rates tend to rise.

Interest rates affect your financial planning. The earnings you receive as a saver or an investor reflect current interest rates as well as a *risk premium* based on such factors as the length of time your funds will be used by others, expected inflation, and the extent of uncertainty about getting your money back. Risk is also a factor in the interest rate you pay as a borrower. People with poor credit ratings pay a higher interest rate than people with good credit ratings. Interest rates influence many financial decisions. Current interest rate data may be obtained at www.webfin.com.

> **DID YOU KNOW ?**
>
> Canadian households spent an average of $53,470 in 1999 on everything from furniture to entertainment.
>
> (www.statcan.ca)

CONCEPT CHECK 1-3

1. How do age, marital status, household size, employment situation, and other personal factors affect financial planning?
2. How might the uncertainty of inflation make personal financial planning difficult?
3. What factors influence the level of interest rates?

Opportunity Costs and the Time Value of Money

Have you noticed that you always give up something when you make choices? In every financial decision, you sacrifice something to obtain something else that you consider more desirable. For example, you might forgo current consumption to invest funds for future purchases or long-term financial security. Or you might gain the use of an expensive item now by making credit payments from future earnings. These *opportunity costs* may be viewed in terms of both personal and financial resources (see Exhibit 1–7).

Objective 4

Determine personal and financial opportunity costs associated with personal financial decisions.

PERSONAL OPPORTUNITY COSTS

An important personal opportunity cost involves time that when used for one activity cannot be used for other activities. Time used for studying, working, or shopping will not be available for other uses. The allocation of time should be viewed like any decision: Select your use of time to meet your needs, achieve your goals, and satisfy personal values.

Other personal opportunity costs relate to health. Poor eating habits, lack of sleep, or avoiding exercise can result in illness, time away from school or work, increased health care costs, and reduced financial security. Like financial resources, your personal resources (time, energy, health, abilities, knowledge) require management.

Exhibit 1–7

Opportunity Costs and Financial Results Should Be Evaluated When Making Financial Decisions

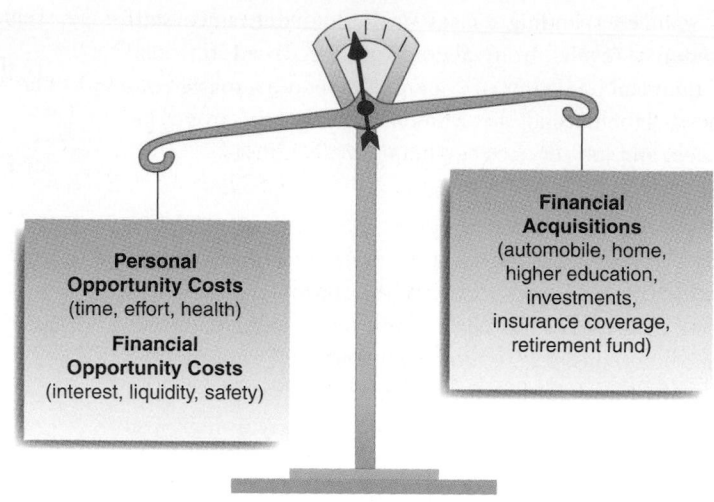

FINANCIAL OPPORTUNITY COSTS

time value of money
Increases in an amount of money as a result of interest earned.

You are constantly making choices among various financial decisions. In making those choices, you must consider the **time value of money**, the increases in an amount of money as a result of interest earned. Saving or investing a dollar instead of spending it today results in a future amount greater than a dollar. Every time you spend, save, invest, or borrow money, you should consider the time value of that money as an opportunity cost. Spending money from your savings account means lost interest earnings; however, what you buy with that money may have a higher priority than those earnings. Borrowing to make a purchase involves the opportunity cost of paying interest on the loan, but your current needs may make this trade-off worthwhile.

The opportunity cost of the time value of money is also present in these financial decisions:

- Setting aside funds in a savings plan with little or no risk has the opportunity cost of potentially higher returns from an investment with greater risk.
- Having extra money withheld from your paycheque in order to receive a tax refund has the opportunity cost of the lost interest the money could earn in a savings account.
- Making annual deposits in a Registered Retirement Savings Plan (RRSP) can help you avoid the opportunity cost of having inadequate funds later in life.
- Purchasing a new automobile or home appliance has the potential benefit of saving you money on future maintenance and energy costs.

INTEREST CALCULATIONS Three amounts are used to calculate the time value of money for savings in the form of interest earned:

- The amount of the savings (commonly called the *principal*).
- The annual interest rate.
- The length of time the money is on deposit.

simple interest
Interest computed on the principal, excluding previously earned interest

There are two methods of calculating interest: **simple interest** and compound interest. Simple interest is calculated as follows: $I = P \times r \times T$

For example, $500 on deposit at a 6 percent annual interest rate for two years would earn $60 ($500 × 0.06 × 2).

Compounding refers to interest that is earned on previously earned interest. Each time interest is added to the principal, the next interest amount is computed on the new balance. For example, the $500 on deposit at a 6 percent annual interest rate for two years would earn $61.80. ($500 × 0.06 = $30 the first year and [$500 + $30]× 0.06 = $31.80 the second year, $31.80 + $30 = $61.80)

> **compounding** A process that calculates interest based on previously earned interest.

Since you are earning interest on the principal as well as accumulated interest, the total amount is greater than what you would earn under simple interest ($61.80 > $60).

You can calculate the increased value of your money from interest earned in two ways: You can calculate the total amount that will be available later (future value), or you can determine the current value of an amount desired in the future (present value).

FUTURE VALUE OF A SINGLE AMOUNT Deposited money earns interest that will increase over time. **Future value** is the amount to which current savings will increase on the basis of a certain interest rate and a certain time period. Future value computations typically involve *compounding*, since interest is earned on previously earned interest. Compounding allows the future value of a deposit to grow faster than it would if interest were paid only on the original deposit. For example, $100 deposited in a 6-percent account for two years will grow to $112.36. This amount is computed as follows:

> **future value** The amount to which current savings will increase based on a certain interest rate and a certain time period; typically involves compounding.

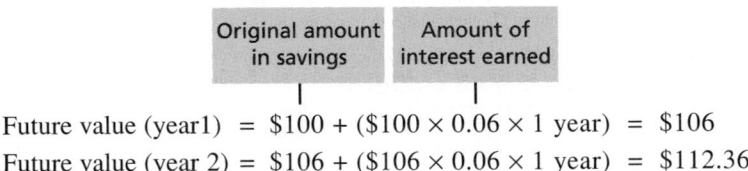

$$\text{Future value (year1)} = \$100 + (\$100 \times 0.06 \times 1 \text{ year}) = \$106$$
$$\text{Future value (year 2)} = \$106 + (\$106 \times 0.06 \times 1 \text{ year}) = \$112.36$$

The same process could be continued for a third, fourth, and fifth year, but the computations would be time consuming. Future value tables simplify the process (see Exhibit 1–8). To use a future value table, multiply the amount deposited by the factor for the desired interest rate and time period. For example, $650 at 8 percent for 10 years would have a future value of $1,403.35 ($650 × 2.159). The future value of an amount will always be greater than the original amount. As Exhibit 1–8A shows, all the future value factors are larger than 1.

The sooner you make deposits, the greater the future value will be. Depositing $1,000 in a 5-percent account at age 40 will give you $3,387 at age 65. However, making the $1,000 deposit at age 25 would result in an account balance of $7,040 at age 65.

FUTURE VALUE OF A SERIES OF DEPOSITS Quite often, savers and investors make regular deposits. An *annuity* is a series of equal deposits or payments. To determine the future value of equal yearly savings deposits, use Exhibit 1–8B. For this table to be used, the deposits must earn a constant interest rate. If you deposit $50 a year at 7 percent for six years, starting at the end of the first year, you will have $357.65 at the end of that time ($50 × 7.153). The Financial Planning Calculations box on page 20 presents examples of using future value to achieve financial goals.

PRESENT VALUE OF A SINGLE AMOUNT Another aspect of the time value of money involves determining the current value of a desired amount for the future. **Present value** is the current value for a future amount based on a certain interest rate and a certain time period. Present value computations, also called *discounting*, allow you to determine how much to deposit now to obtain a desired total in the future. Present value tables (Exhibit 1–8C) can be used to make the computations. If you want $1,000 five years from now and you earn 5 percent on your savings, you need to deposit $784 ($1,000 × 0.784).

> **present value** The current value for a future amount based on a certain interest rate and a certain time period; also referred to as discounting.

Exhibit 1–8

The Value of
Money Tables
(condensed)

A. FUTURE VALUE OF $1 (SINGLE AMOUNT)

Year	Percent				
	5%	6%	7%	8%	9%
5	1.276	1.338	1.403	1.469	1.539
6	1.340	1.419	1.501	1.587	1.677
7	1.407	1.504	1.606	1.714	1.828
8	1.477	1.594	1.718	1.851	1.993
9	1.551	1.689	1.838	1.999	2.172
10	1.629	1.791	1.967	2.159	2.367

B. FUTURE VALUE OF A SERIES OF ANNUAL DEPOSITS (ANNUITY)

Year	Percent				
	5%	6%	7%	8%	9%
5	5.526	5.637	5.751	5.867	5.985
6	6.802	6.975	7.153	7.336	7.523
7	8.142	8.394	8.654	8.923	9.200
8	9.549	9.897	10.260	10.637	11.028
9	11.027	11.491	11.978	12.488	13.021
10	12.578	13.181	13.816	14.487	15.193

C. PRESENT VALUE OF $1 (SINGLE AMOUNT)

Year	Percent				
	5%	6%	7%	8%	9%
5	0.784	0.747	0.713	0.681	0.650
6	0.746	0.705	0.666	0.630	0.596
7	0.711	0.665	0.623	0.583	0.547
8	0.677	0.627	0.582	0.540	0.502
9	0.645	0.592	0.544	0.500	0.460
10	0.614	0.558	0.508	0.463	0.422

D. PRESENT VALUE OF A SERIES OF ANNUAL DEPOSITS (ANNUITY)

Year	Percent				
	5%	6%	7%	8%	9%
5	4.329	4.212	4.100	3.993	3.890
6	5.076	4.917	4.767	4.623	4.486
7	5.786	5.582	5.389	5.206	5.033
8	6.463	6.210	5.971	5.747	5.535
9	7.108	6.802	6.515	6.247	5.995
10	7.722	7.360	7.024	6.710	6.418

See Appendix A at the end of the book for more complete future value and present value tables.

The present value of the amount you want in the future will always be less than the future value, since all of the factors in Exhibit 1–8C are less than 1 and interest earned will increase the present value amount to the desired future amount.

PRESENT VALUE OF A SERIES OF DEPOSITS You can also use present value computations to determine how much you need to deposit so that you can take a certain amount out of the account for a desired number of years. For example, if you want to take $400 out of an investment account each year for nine years and your money is earning an annual rate of 8 percent, you can see from Exhibit 1–8D that you would need to make a current deposit of $2,498.80 ($400 × 6.247).

FINANCIAL CALCULATORS Currently, financial calculators, with time value of money functions built in, are widely used to calculate future value, present values, and annuities. For the following examples, we will use the Texas Instrument BA II Plus financial calculator, which sells for approximately $50 and is recommended by the Canadian Institute of Financial Planning.

Important keys on a financial calculator for Time Value of Money Problems (Texas Instrument BA II Plus)

CPT – Compute key used to initiate financial calculations once all values are inputed.

N – Number of periods

I/Y – Interest rate per period

PV – Present value

PMT – Amount of payment, used only for annuities

FV – Future value

Let's try a problem. What is the future value of $100 after three years at a 10 percent annual interest rate?

First, you must enter the data:

3 N

10 I/Y

100 PV

0 PMT   (optional if registers are cleared)

To find the solution, the future value, press CPT FV, and the future value of –133.1 is displayed. The BA II Plus displays present value solutions as a (+) and future values as a (–) because it assumes one is an inflow and the other an outflow. The Financial Planning Calculations box on page 20 presents examples of using a financial calculator to solve future value problems.

The formulas for calculating future and present values, as well as tables and the use of the financial calculator covering a wider range of interest rates and time periods, are presented in Appendix A. Computer programs for calculating time value of money are also available.

CONCEPT CHECK 1–4

1. How can you use future value and present value computations to measure the opportunity cost of a financial decision?
2. Use the time value of money tables in Exhibit 1–8 or a financial calculator to calculate the following:
   a. The future value of $100 at 7 percent in 10 years.
   b. The future value of $100 a year for six years earning 6 percent.
   c. The present value of $500 received in eight years with an interest rate of 8 percent.

Financial Planning Calculations

ANNUAL CONTRIBUTIONS TO ACHIEVE A FINANCIAL GOAL

Achieving specific financial goals often requires regular deposits to a savings or investment account. By using time value of money calculations, you can determine the amount you should save or invest to achieve a specific goal for the future.

EXAMPLE 1

Jonie Emerson has two children who will start college in 10 years. She plans to set aside $1,500 a year for her children's college education during that period and estimates she will earn an annual interest rate of 5 percent on her savings. What amount can Jonie expect to have available for her children's college education when they start college?

Calculation from table:

$1,500 × Future value of a series of deposits,
5%, 10 years
$1,500 × 12.578 = $18,867

With calculator:

10	N
5	I/Y
0	PV
1,500	PMT

Then press CPT FV and the answer

= $18,866.84

EXAMPLE 2

Don Calder wants to accumulate $50,000 over the next 10 years as a reserve fund for his parents' retirement living expenses and health care. If he earns an average of 8 percent on his investments, what amount must he invest each year to achieve this goal?

Calculation from table:

$50,000 ÷ Future value of a series of deposits,
8%, 10 years
$50,000 ÷ 14.487 = $3,451.37

Don needs to invest approximately $3,450 a year for 10 years at 8 percent to achieve the desired financial goal.

With calculator:

10	N
8	I/Y
0	PV
50,000	FV

Then press CPT PMT and the answer

= $3,451.47

Achieving Financial Goals

Objective 5

Identify strategies for achieving personal financial goals for different life situations.

Throughout life, our needs usually can be satisfied with the intelligent use of financial resources. Financial planning involves deciding how to obtain, protect, and use those resources. By using the eight major areas of personal financial planning to organize your financial activities, you can avoid many common money mistakes.

COMPONENTS OF PERSONAL FINANCIAL PLANNING

This book is designed to provide a framework for the study and planning of personal financial decisions. Exhibit 1–9 presents an overview of the eight major personal financial planning areas. To achieve a successful financial situation, you must coordinate these components through an organized plan and wise decision making.

OBTAINING (CHAPTER 1) You obtain financial resources from employment, investments, or ownership of a business. Obtaining financial resources is the foundation of financial planning, since these resources are used for all financial activities.

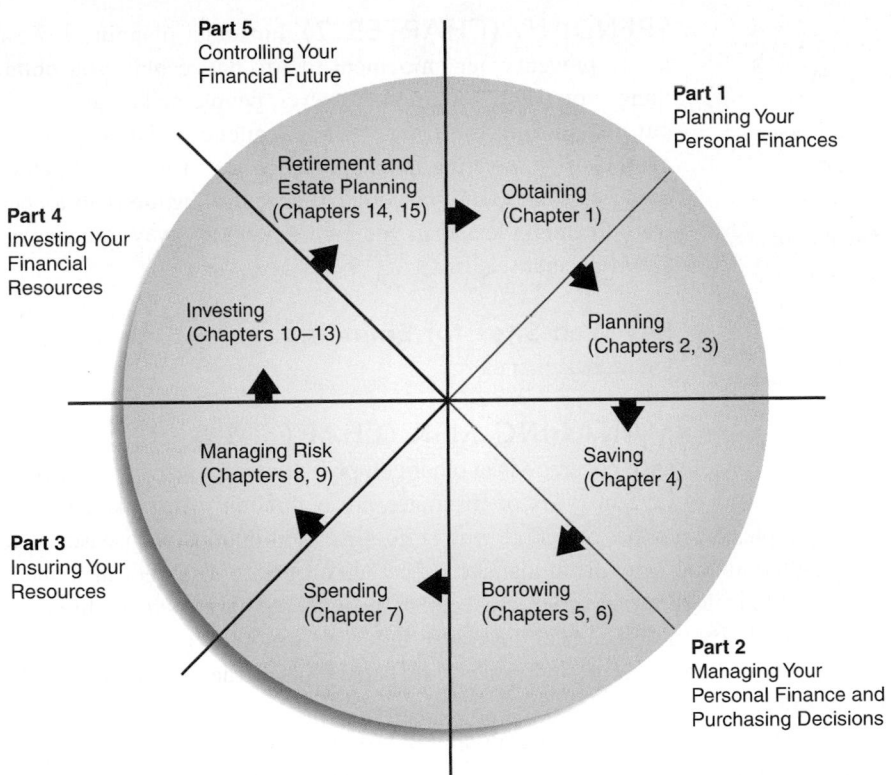

Exhibit 1–9

Components of
Personal Financial
Planning

Key Web Sites for Obtaining: www.quicken.ca www.monster.com

PLANNING (CHAPTERS 2, 3) Planned spending through budgeting is the key to achieving goals and future financial security. Efforts to anticipate expenses and financial decisions can also help reduce taxes. The ability to pay your fair share of taxes—no more, no less—is vital to increasing your financial resources.

Key Web Sites for Planning: www.cafp.org www.quicken.ca

SAVING (CHAPTER 4) Long-term financial security starts with a regular savings plan for emergencies, unexpected bills, replacement of major items, and the purchase of special goods and services, such as a higher education, a boat, or a vacation home. Once you have established a basic savings plan, you may use additional money for investments that offer greater financial growth.

   An amount of savings must be available to meet current household needs. **Liquidity** refers to the ability to readily convert financial resources into cash without a loss in value. The need for liquidity will vary on the basis of a person's age, health, and family situation. Savings plans, such as interest-earning chequing accounts, money market accounts, and money market funds, earn money on your savings while providing liquidity.

liquidity The ability to readily convert financial resources into cash without a loss in value.

Key Web Sites for Saving: www.webfin.com

BORROWING (CHAPTERS 5, 6) Maintaining control over your credit-buying habits will contribute to your financial goals. The overuse and misuse of credit may cause a situation in which a person's debts far exceed the resources available to pay those debts. **Bankruptcy** is a set of federal laws that allow you to either restructure your debts or remove certain debts. The people who declare bankruptcy each year may have avoided this trauma with wise spending and borrowing decisions. Chapter 6 discusses bankruptcy in detail.

bankruptcy A set of federal laws that allow you to either restructure your debts or remove certain debts.

Key Web Sites for Borrowing: www.cibc.com www.scotiabank.ca

SPENDING (CHAPTER 7) Financial planning is designed not to prevent your enjoyment of life but to help you obtain the things you want. Too often, however, people make purchases without considering the financial consequences. Some people shop compulsively, creating financial difficulties. You should detail your living expenses and your other financial obligations in a spending plan. Spending less than you earn is the only way to achieve long-term financial security.

Key Web Sites for Spending: www.consumerworld.org; www.consumer.ca

MANAGING RISK (CHAPTERS 8, 9) Adequate insurance coverage is another component of personal financial planning. Certain types of insurance are commonly overlooked in financial plans. For example, the number of people who suffer disabling injuries or diseases at age 50 is greater than the number who die at that age, so people may need disability insurance more than they need life insurance. Yet surveys reveal that most people have adequate life insurance but few have disability insurance. The insurance industry is more aggressive in selling life insurance than in selling disability insurance, thus putting the burden of obtaining adequate disability insurance on you.

Many households have excessive or overlapping insurance coverage. Insuring property for more than it is worth may be a waste of money, as may both a husband and a wife having similar health insurance coverage.

Key Web Sites for Managing Risk: www.canadalife.com   www.canlink.com/imperial

INVESTING (CHAPTERS 10–13) While many types of investment vehicles are available, people invest for two primary reasons. Those interested in current income select investments that pay regular dividends or interest. In contrast, investors who desire long-term growth choose stocks, mutual funds, real estate, and other investments with potential for increased value in the future.

You can achieve investment diversification by including a variety of assets in your portfolio—for example, stocks, bond mutual funds, real estate, and collectibles, such as rare coins. Obtaining general investment advice is easy; however, it is more difficult to obtain specific investment advice to meet your individual needs and goals.

Key Web Sites for Investing: www.canadafinance.com   www.webfin.com

RETIREMENT AND ESTATE PLANNING (CHAPTERS 14, 15) Most people desire financial security upon completion of full-time employment. But retirement planning also involves thinking about your housing situation, your recreational activities, and possible part-time or volunteer work.

Key Web Sites for Retirement and Estate Planning: www.elderweb.org www.fiftyplus.net

Transfers of money or property to others should be timed, if possible, to minimize the tax burden and maximize the benefits for those receiving the financial resources. A knowledge of property transfer methods can help you select the best course of action for funding current and future living costs, educational expenses, and retirement needs of dependants.

DEVELOPING A FLEXIBLE FINANCIAL PLAN

A **financial plan** is a formalized report that summarizes your current financial situation, analyzes your financial needs, and recommends future financial activities. You can create this document on your own, seek assistance from a financial planner, or use a money management software package (see the chapter appendix). Exhibit 1–10 offers a framework for developing and implementing a financial plan, along with examples for several life situations. (Also see the Financial Planning for Life's Situations box on pages 24 and 25.)

financial plan A formalized report that summarizes your current financial situation, analyzes your financial needs, and recommends future financial activities.

IMPLEMENTING YOUR FINANCIAL PLAN

You must have a plan before you can implement it. However, once you have clearly assessed your current situation and identified your financial goals, what do you do next?

The most important strategy for success is the development of financial habits that contribute to both short-term satisfaction and long-term financial security, including the following:

[1] Using a well-conceived spending plan will help you stay within your income while you save and invest for the future. The main source of financial difficulties is overspending.

[2] Having appropriate insurance protection will help you prevent financial disasters.

Exhibit 1–10   Financial Planning in Action

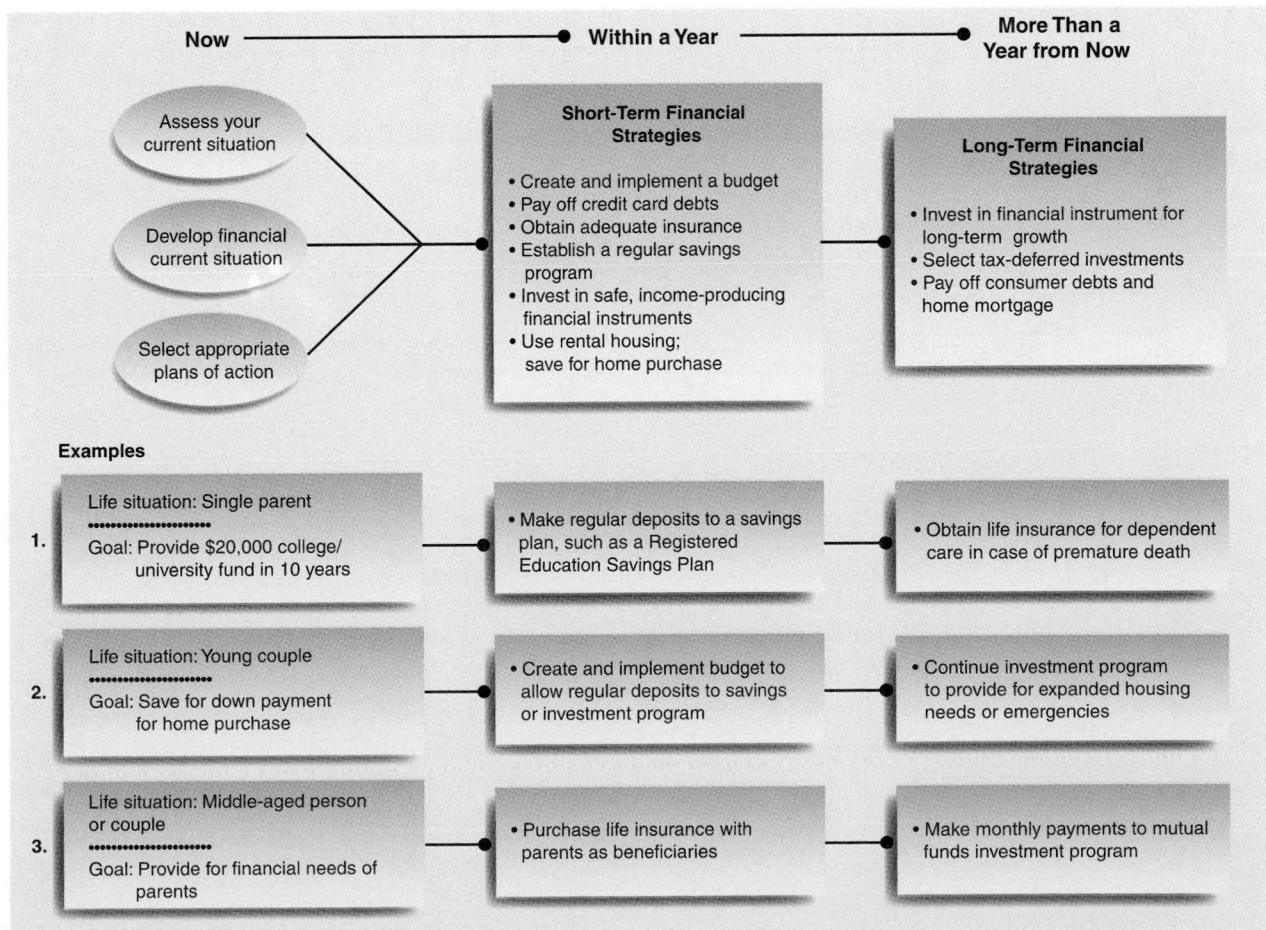

Financial Planning for Life's Situations

I NEED $20,000 FOR MY EDUCATION. SHOULD I BORROW OR WORK PART TIME?

Jim Stewarts is an Accounting Major at Concordia University; he takes five courses a semester and expects to graduate in three years. Jim came to the Financial Aid Office for help in deciding whether he should borrow money or work part time. Let's look at his situation:

Residential status: Jim lives with his parents and is free of food and board charges.

Potential amount of hours allotted for part-time work: Assuming 35 weeks in a school year and that Jim will be unable to work for four weeks; Jim is left with 31 work weeks. Considering Jim's grades are of primary importance, we advise him to work for a maximum of 15 hours a week.

Potential amount of hours allotted for full-time summer employment: Jim will have 17 weeks (52 less 35 weeks) during the summer, when he can work full time for 40 hours a week. We suggest he work only 15 of these weeks so that some time is set aside for a vacation.

Type of job: Assuming an entry level job in his discipline, he will earn roughly $10 an hour.

Personal savings: It is quite common for students to have poor saving habits; therefore, we will assume that Jim currently has no savings.

IF JIM WORKS PART TIME DURING SEMESTERS AND FULL TIME DURING THE SUMMER:

During the school year, Jim can earn $4,650 ($10/hr × 15 hrs × 31 wks = $4,650).

During the summer he can earn $6,000 ($10/hr × 40 hrs × 15 wks = $6,000).

Jim's yearly gross income would be $4,650 + $6,000 = $10,650.

Yet, Jim would not have use of the entire amount. His take-home pay or net pay, which is his gross income minus taxes would be $8,839.50 ($10,650 − [.17 × $10,650]) because he is in the low tax bracket (17%) in Quebec (see Chapter 3). However, when he files his income tax, he could receive a refund. This will be discussed later.

IF JIM TAKES OUT A STUDENT LOAN FOR $20,000:

There are student loans offered by both the federal and provincial governments; these loans are of greater advantage because they offer lower interest rates than the banks and you are only required to pay them back once you graduate. If Jim were to take out a loan today for $20,000 from the Quebec Government's Aide Financiere aux Etudes program, he would pay an annual interest rate of 6.875 percent. (www.afe.gouv.qc.ca/anglais/renseigner/taux.htm) Since he would want to pay the loan back in six years after graduation, using the Present Value formula, he would make monthly payments of $339.78. (See Appendix A for PV of an Annuity equation).

$$PV = Payments \times \frac{1 - \frac{1}{(1 + i)^n}}{i}$$

Where PV = $20,000, i = Interest Rate = .06875/12, n = # of Monthly Payments = 72.

Visit the Web site
See the Post-Test under Chapter 1 on the online learning centre at www.mcgrawhill.ca/college/kapoor.

[3] Becoming informed about tax and investment alternatives will help you expand your financial resources.

Achieving your financial objectives requires two things: (1) a willingness to learn, and (2) appropriate information sources. You must provide the first element; the chapters that follow will provide the second. For successful financial planning, know where you are now, know where you want to be, and be persistent in your efforts to get there.

Solving for the Payments, we get $339.78. Jim would be able to make these monthly payments when he graduates, assuming he earns an accountant's starting salary of $33,000. (www.careers-in-accounting.com/ascal.htm). Overall, this loan would cost Jim roughly $24,500 ($339.78 × 72 months).

RECOMMENDATION:

We recommend that Jim work part time during the school year and full time during the summer. We have come to this conclusion on the basis of the following results:

As mentioned above, Jim's net pay will be $8,839.50. However, if he gets his parents to do his income tax for him, they will be able to show him as a dependent and receive a refund from the government. With that, they can simply reimburse Jim the $1,810.50 that was originally deducted from his paycheque. With this strategy, Jim actually has $10,650 as his net pay. Since he needs $20,000 to finance his education (or $6,666.66 in each of his three years of university), will he still have enough money left over for his additional expenses? The following table suggests that he will:

EXPENSES OF AN AVERAGE STUDENT WHO LIVES AT HOME:		
Expense	Amount (monthly) $	Amount (yearly) $
Clothing	50	600
Entertainment	80	960
Videos & CD's	35	420
Miscellaneous	20	240
Total	185	2,220

$10,650 − $6,666.66 = $3,983.34 (amount of money left over after paying for school)
$3,983.34 − $2,220 = $1,763.34 (balance left over for saving)

By working part time, we recognize that Jim will forgo the additional time available for his studies. However, in our experience, students tend to squander additional time and procrastinate in completing their assigned work.

If Jim works instead of taking out a loan, he will earn enough money to finance his education, pay for additional personal expenses, and still save an amount, which he can use toward such expenditures as a car or house. Although one advantage of credit is that you can enjoy a good or service now and only pay for it later, it may be more prudent to avoid loans, if possible. The advantage of working part time is to avoid the cost of borrowed money as well as gain experience in the field. With our recommendation, Jim will be debt free upon graduation and with the money he has saved, he can start building a solid savings foundation (see Chapter 10).

SOURCE: Assignment was written by and reproduced with permission from the following students: Vikram Kotecha, Matthew Berry, Mili De Silva, and Rikesh Shah—Introductory Course in Personal Finance , JMSB, Concordia University, Winter 2002

CONCEPT CHECK 1–5

1. What are the main components of personal financial planning?
2. What is the purpose of a financial plan?
3. Identify some common actions taken to achieve financial goals.

SUMMARY OF OBJECTIVES

Objective 1
Analyze the process for making personal financial decisions.
Personal financial planning involves the following process: (1) determine your current financial situation; (2) develop financial goals; (3) identify alternative courses of action; (4) evaluate alternatives; (5) create and implement a financial action plan; and (6) re-evaluate and revise the financial plan.

Objective 2
Develop personal financial goals.
Financial goals should (1) be realistic; (2) be stated in specific, measurable terms; (3) have a time frame; and (4) indicate the type of action to be taken.

Objective 3
Assess personal and economic factors that influence personal financial planning.
Financial decisions are affected by a person's life situation (income, age, household size, health), personal values, and economic factors (prices, interest rates, and employment opportunities).

Objective 4
Determine personal and financial opportunity costs associated with personal financial decisions.
Every decision involves a trade-off with things given up. Personal opportunity costs include time, effort, and health. Financial opportunity costs are based on the time value of money. Future value and present value calculations enable you to measure the increased value (or lost interest) that results from a saving, investing, borrowing, or purchasing decision.

Objective 5
Identify strategies for achieving personal financial goals for different life situations.
Successful financial planning requires specific goals combined with spending, saving, investing, and borrowing strategies based on your personal situation and various social and economic factors.

KEY TERMS

adult life cycle 10

bankruptcy 21

compounding 17

economics 11

financial plan 23

future value 17

inflation 13

liquidity 21

opportunity cost 5

personal financial planning 3

present value 17

simple interest 16

time value of money 16

values 11

FINANCIAL PLANNING PROBLEMS

(Note: Some of these problems require the use of the time value of money tables in Appendix A or a financial calculator.)

1. *Calculating Future Value of Property.* Ben Collins plans to buy a house for $65,000. If that real estate is expected to increase in value by 5 percent each year, what will its approximate value be seven years from now? (Obj. 3)

2. *Using the Rule of 72.* Using the rule of 72, approximate the following amounts: (Obj. 3)

   a. If land in an area is increasing 6 percent a year, how long will it take for property values to double?

   b. If you earn 10 percent on your investments, how long will it take for your money to double?

   c. At an annual interest rate of 5 percent, how long will it take for your savings to double?

3. *Determining the Inflation Rate.* In the late 1980s, selected automobiles had an average cost of $12,000. The average cost of those same automobiles is now $15,000. What was the rate of increase for these automobiles between the two time periods? (Obj. 3)

4. *Computing Future Living Expenses.* A family spends $28,000 a year for living expenses. If prices increase by 4 percent a year for the next three years, what amount will the family need for their living expenses after three years? (Obj. 3)

5. *Calculating Earnings on Savings.* What would be the yearly earnings for a person with $6,000 in savings at an annual interest rate of 5.5 percent? (Obj. 4)

6. *Computing Time Value of Money* Using time value of money tables or a financial calculator, calculate the following: (Obj. 4)

   a. The future value of $450 six years from now at 7 percent.

   b. The future value of $800 saved each year for 10 years at 8 percent.

   c. The amount a person would have to deposit today (present value) at a 6-percent interest rate to have $1,000 five years from now.

   d. The amount a person would have to deposit today to be able to take out $500 a year for 10 years from an account earning 8 percent.

7. *Calculating Future Value of a Series of Amounts.* Elaine Romberg prepares her own income tax return each year. A tax preparer would charge her $60 for this service. Over a period of 10 years, how much does Elaine gain from preparing her own tax return? Assume she can earn 6 percent with a savings certificate. (Obj. 4)

FINANCIAL PLANNING ACTIVITIES

1. *Researching Personal Finance on the Internet.* Using Web sites, such as www.canadianfinance.com, www.cafp.org, or www.quicken.ca, and search engines, obtain information about commonly suggested actions related to various personal financial planning decisions. What are some of the best sources of information on the Internet to assist you with financial planning? (Obj. 1)

2. *Comparing Financial Planning Actions.* Survey friends, relatives, and others to determine the process they use when making financial decisions. How do these people measure risk when making financial decisions? (Obj. 1)

3. *Using Financial Planning Experts.* Prepare a list of financial planning specialists (investment advisers, credit counsellors, insurance agents, real estate brokers, tax preparers) in your community who can assist people with personal financial planning. Prepare a list of questions that might be asked of these financial planning professionals by (a) a young person just starting out on his or her own, (b) a young couple planning for their children's education and for their own retirement, and (c) a person nearing retirement. (Obj. 1, 3)

4. *Setting Financial Goals.* Create one short-term goal and one long-term goal for people in these life situations: (a) a young single person, (b) a single parent with a child aged eight years, (c) a married person with no children, and (d) a retired person. (Obj. 2)

5. *Analyzing Changing Life Situations.* Ask friends, relatives, and others how their spending, saving, and borrowing activities changed when they decided to continue their education, change careers, or have children. (Obj. 3)

6. *Researching Economic Conditions.* Use library resources or Web sites to determine recent trends in interest rates, inflation, and other economic indicators. Information about the consumer price index (measuring changes in the cost of living) may be obtained at www.statcan.com. Report how this economic information might affect your financial planning decisions. (Obj. 3)

7. *Comparing Alternative Financial Actions.* What actions would be necessary to compare a financial planner who advertises "One Low Fee Is Charged to Develop Your Personal Financial Plan" and one that advertises "You Are Not Charged a Fee, My Services Are Covered by the Investment Company for Which I Work"? (Obj. 4, 5)

8. *Determining Opportunity Costs.* What is the relationship between current interest rates and financial opportunity costs? Using time value of money calculations, state one or more goals in terms of an annual savings amount and the future value of this savings fund. (Obj. 2, 4)

9. *Researching Financial Planning Software.* Visit software retailers to obtain information about the features and costs of various personal financial planning activities. Information about such programs as Microsoft Money and Quicken may be obtained on the Internet. (Obj. 5)

LIFE SITUATION CASE

Triple Trouble for the "Sandwich Generation"

Until recently, Fran and Ed Blake's personal finances ran smoothly. Both have maintained well-paying jobs while raising two children. The Blakes have a daughter who is completing her first year of college and a son three years younger. Currently, they have $22,000 in various savings and investment funds set aside for the children's education. With education costs increasing faster than inflation, they are uncertain whether this amount is adequate.

In recent months, Fran's mother has required extensive medical attention and personal care assistance. Unable to live alone, she is now a resident of a long-term-care facility. The cost of this service is $2,050 a month, with annual increases of about 7 percent. While a major portion of the cost is covered by the Canada Pension Plan and Old Age Security, Fran's mother is unable to cover the entire cost. Their desire to help adds to the Blakes' financial burden.

The Blakes are like many other Canadians who have financial responsibilities for both dependent children and aging parents. Commonly referred to as the "sandwich generation," this group is squeezed on one side by the cost of raising and educating children and on the other side by the financial demands of caring for aging parents.

Finally, the Blakes, ages 47 and 43, are also concerned about saving for their own retirement. While they have consistently made annual deposits to a Registered Retirement Savings Plan (RRSP), various current financial demands may force them to tap into this money.

Questions

1. What actions have the Blakes taken that would be considered wise financial planning choices?
2. What areas of financial concern do the Blakes face? What actions might be appropriate to address these concerns?
3. Using time value of money calculations (tables in the Appendix or a financial calculator), compute the following:
   a. At 12 percent, what would be the value of the $22,000 education funds in three years?
   b. If the cost of long-term care is increasing at 7 percent a year, what will be the approximate monthly cost for Fran's mother eight years from now?
   c. Fran and Ed plan to deposit $1,500 a year to their RRSPs for 35 years. If they earn an average annual return of 9 percent, what will be the value of their RRSPs after 35 years?

 CREATING A FINANCIAL PLAN

Starting Your Financial Plan

Planning is the foundation for success in every aspect of life. Assessing your current financial situation along with setting goals is the key to successful financial planning.

Web Sites for Financial Planning
- Investing information at **www. investorlearning.ca** and **www.independentfinancial.on.ca**.
- Selected articles from Canadian MoneySaver magazine at www.canadianmoneysaver.ca, from MoneySense magazine at **www.moneysense.ca**, and IE:Money magazine at **www.iemoney.ca**.
- Information on credit cards, car loans, and mortgages at **www.scotiabank.ca** and **www.royalbank.com**.

- Current consumer price index and inflation information from Statistics Canada at **www.statcan.ca**.
- Information on Bank of Canada activities and publications at **www.bank-banque-canada.ca**.
- Retirement planning at **www.retireweb.com** and **www.elderweb.org**.

(Note: Addresses and content of Web sites change, and new sites are created daily. Use the search engines discussed in the chapter appendix to update and locate Web sites for your current financial planning needs.)

APPENDIX: 1

Financial Planners and Other Financial Planning Information Sources

"ATM fees rise."

"Global currency fluctuations may affect consumer prices."

"Mortgage interest rates remain constant."

These are just a few of the possible influences on personal financial decisions that occur each day. While this book offers the foundation for successful personal financial planning, changing social trends, economic conditions, and technology influence the decision-making environment. Your ability to continually supplement and update your knowledge is a skill that will serve you for a lifetime.

Various resources are available to assist you with personal financial decisions. These resources include printed materials, financial institutions, courses and seminars, the Internet, computer software, and financial planning specialists.

Current Periodicals

As Exhibit 1–A shows, a variety of personal-finance periodicals are available to expand and update your knowledge. These periodicals, along with books on various personal-finance topics, can be found in libraries.

Financial Institutions

Some financial advisers, such as insurance agents and investment brokers, are affiliated with companies that sell financial services. Through national marketing efforts or local promotions, banks, trust companies, credit unions, insurance companies, investment brokers, and real estate offices offer suggestions on budgeting, saving, investing, and other aspects of financial planning. These organizations frequently offer booklets, financial planning worksheets, Web sites, and other materials and information.

Courses and Seminars

Colleges and universities offer courses in investments, real estate, insurance, taxation, and estate planning to enhance your knowledge of personal financial planning.

Civic clubs and community business organizations often schedule free or inexpensive programs featuring speakers and workshops on career planning, small-business management, budgeting, life insurance, tax return preparation, and investments. Financial institutions and financial service trade associations present seminars for current and prospective customers and members.

29

Exhibit 1–A Personal Financial Planning Periodicals

The area of personal finance is constantly changing. You can keep up with changes by reading the following periodicals. You can subscribe to them, read them at your school or community library, or access them on the Internet.

CA Magazine 277 Wellington Street West Toronto, ON M5V 3H2 www.camagazine.com	*The Globe and Mail* 444 Front Street West Toronto, ON M5V 2S9 www.globeandmail.com	*MoneySense Magazine* 156 Front Street West Toronto, ON M5J 2L6 www.moneysense.ca
Canadian Business 777 Bay Street, Fifth Floor Toronto, ON M5W 1A7 www.canadianbusiness.com	*IE:Money* 25 Sheppard Avenue West, Suite 100 Toronto, ON M2N 6S7 www.iemoney.ca	*National Post* 300–1450 Don Mills Road Don Mills, ON M3B 3R5 www.nationalpost.com
Canadian MoneySaver P.O. Box 370 Bath, ON K0H 1G0 www.canadianmoneysaver.ca	*Maclean's* 777 Bay Street Toronto, ON M5W 1A7 www.macleans.ca	

Personal Finance Software

Personal computer software is available to help you perform a variety of personal financial planning activities, from selecting a career to writing a will. These programs help you analyze your current financial situation and project your future financial position. Specialized computer programs are also available for conducting investment analyses, preparing tax returns, and determining the costs of financing and owning a home. Remember, a personal computer cannot change your saving, spending, and borrowing habits; only *you* can do that. However, your computer can provide fast and current analyses of your financial situation and progress. For information about the latest software, visit a computer store or read the articles and advertisements in magazines, such as *PC Computing*, *PC Magazine*, *Computer Life*, *Windows*, *Family PC*, and *Home PC*.

SPREADSHEETS

A spreadsheet program, such as Excel or Lotus 1-2-3, can assist with various financial planning tasks. Spreadsheet software can store, manipulate, create projections, and report data for such activities as

- Creating budget categories and recording spending patterns.
- Maintaining tax records for different types of expenses, such as mileage, travel expenses, materials and supplies, and business-related costs.
- Calculating the growth potential of savings accounts and investments.
- Monitoring changes in the market value of investments.
- Keeping records of the value of items for a home inventory.
- Projecting needed amounts of life insurance and retirement income.

MONEY MANAGEMENT AND FINANCIAL PLANNING PROGRAMS

Integrated financial planning programs can help you maintain home financial records, create a budget, observe spending patterns, write cheques, keep tax records, select and monitor investments, and project retirement needs. The most popular of these software packages are

Microsoft Money
Microsoft
1-800-668-7975
(www.microsoft.com/money)

Quicken
Intuit
1-888-829-8684
(www.quicken.ca)

TAX SOFTWARE

Each year, the software available to prepare tax returns becomes more helpful. Besides preparation and printing of the various forms and schedules, programs include tax-planning tips (with audio and video clips), audit warnings, and the ability to file your tax return electronically. The most readily available tax software includes

Quicktax
Intuit
1-888-829-8684
(www.intuit.com/canada)

Hometax
CCH Canadian Limited
1-905-624-0303
(www.hometax.com)

INVESTMENT ANALYSIS PROGRAMS

Software designed for researching, trading, and monitoring an investment portfolio is also available. Most of these programs may be connected to online services to obtain current stock quotes and to buy and sell investments.

The World Wide Web and Personal Financial Planning

The World Wide Web makes it possible to access more information from your home or office than libraries offer. You may use the Web for a variety of personal financial planning activities, including (1) researching current financial information; (2) obtaining programs to do financial planning calculations; (3) monitoring current stock and investment values; and (4) asking questions of experts and others through help lines, bulletin board services, and discussion forums. Some of the most useful Web sites providing current information on various personal finance topics include:

- *Canadian MoneySaver* magazine at www.canadianmoneysaver.ca; *IE:Money* magazine at www.iemoney.com; and *MoneySense* magazine at www.moneysense.ca.
- Current consumer price index and inflation information from Statistics Canada at www.statcan.ca.
- The Quicken Web site at www.quicken.ca.
- Information on Bank of Canada activities and publications at www.bank-banque-canada.ca.
- Investing information at www.webfin.com.

Additional Web sites are offered at the end of each chapter in the "Creating a Financial Plan."

Using Search Engines

A search engine is a Web site that allows you to locate information related to specific topics. Some of the most commonly used search engines include

www.altavista.ca
www.ca.msn.com
www.Canada.com
www.overture.com

www.searchCanada.ca
www.webcity.ca
www.webcrawler.com
www.yahoo.ca

Search engines operate in different ways and provide various features. Some search engines look for topic areas; others seek specific words. When conducting Web searches, be precise with your descriptive words. For example, use "mortgage rates" instead of "interest rates" to obtain information on the cost of borrowing to buy a home. Use "résumés" instead of "career planning" for assistance on developing a personal data sheet.

Financial Planning Specialists

Various specialists provide specific financial assistance and advice:

- *Accountants* specialize in tax matters and financial documents.
- *Bankers* assist with financial services and trusts.
- *Credit counsellors* suggest ways to reduce spending and eliminate credit problems.
- *Certified financial planners* coordinate financial decisions into a single plan.
- *Insurance agents* sell insurance coverage to protect your wealth and property.
- *Investment brokers* provide information and handle transactions for stocks, bonds, and other investments.
- *Lawyers* help in preparing wills, estate planning, tax problems, and other legal matters.
- *Real estate agents* assist with buying and selling a home or other real estate.
- *Tax preparers* specialize in the completion of income tax returns and other tax matters.

Many of these specialists offer services that include various aspects of financial planning. A financial planner's background or the company he or she represents is a good gauge of the financial planner's principal area of expertise. An accountant is likely to be most knowledgeable about tax laws, while an insurance company representative will probably emphasize how to use insurance for achieving financial goals.

WHO ARE THE FINANCIAL PLANNERS?

Many financial planners represent major insurance companies or investment businesses. Financial planners may also be individuals whose primary profession is tax accounting, real estate, or law. Financial planners are commonly categorized on the basis of three methods of compensation:

[1] **Fee-only planners** charge an hourly rate that may range from $75 to $200, or may charge a fixed fee of between less than $500 and several thousand dollars. Other fee-only planners may charge an annual fee ranging from .04 percent to 1 percent of the value of your assets.

[2] **Fee-and-commission planners** earn commissions from the investment and insurance products purchased and charge a fixed fee (ranging from $250 to $2,000) for a financial plan.

[3] **Commission-only planners** receive their revenue from the commissions on sales of insurance, mutual funds, and other investments.

Consumers must be cautious about the fees charged and how these fees are communicated. A recent study revealed that more than half of financial planners who told "mystery shoppers" that they offer "fee-only" services actually earned commissions or other financial rewards for implementing the recommendations made to their clients.

DO YOU NEED A FINANCIAL PLANNER?

The two main factors that determine whether you need financial planning assistance are (1) your income, and (2) your willingness to make independent decisions. If you earn less than $40,000 a year, you probably do not need a financial planner. Income of less than this amount does not allow for many major financial decisions once you have allocated for the spending, savings, insurance, and tax elements of your personal financial planning.

Taking an active role in your financial affairs can reduce the need for a financial planner. Your willingness to keep up to date on developments related to investments, insurance, and taxes can reduce the amount you spend on financial advisers. This will require an ongoing investment of time and effort; however, it will enable you to control your own financial direction.

When deciding whether to use a financial planner, also consider the services he or she provides. First, the financial planner should assist you in assessing your current financial position with regard to spending, saving, insurance, taxes, and potential investments. Second, the financial planner should offer a clearly written plan with different courses of action. Third, the planner should take time to discuss the components of the plan and help you monitor your financial progress. Finally, the financial planner should guide you to other experts and sources of financial services as needed.

HOW SHOULD YOU SELECT A FINANCIAL PLANNER?

You can locate financial planners by using a telephone directory, contacting financial institutions, or obtaining references from friends, business associates, or professionals with whom you currently deal, such as insurance agents or real estate brokers.

When evaluating a financial planner, ask the following:

- Is financial planning your primary activity, or are other activities primary?
- Are you licensed as an investment broker or as a seller of life insurance?
- What is your educational background and formal training?
- What are your areas of expertise?
- Do you use experts in other areas, such as taxes, law, or insurance, to assist you with financial planning recommendations?
- What professional titles and certifications do you possess?
- Am I allowed a free initial consultation?
- How is the fee determined? (Is this an amount I can afford?)
- Do you have an independent practice, or are you affiliated with a major financial services company?
- What are sample insurance, tax, and investment recommendations you make for clients?
- My major concern is _____. What would you suggest?
- May I see a sample of a written financial plan?
- May I see the contract you use with clients?
- Who are some of your clients whom I might contact?

Also, make sure you are comfortable with the planner and that the planner can clearly communicate. This type of investigation takes time and effort; however, remember that you are considering placing your entire financial future in the hands of one person.

HOW ARE FINANCIAL PLANNERS CERTIFIED?

Currently, there are few regulations governing financial planners in Canada. A financial planner may be a professional lawyer, accountant, investment adviser, insurance salesperson, mutual fund specialist, or none of the above. Financial planners are bound by the same statutes and common law that apply to anyone selling services. They must perform their work with due care, and they cannot misrepresent their work or their qualifications. Financial planners should be willing and knowledgeable enough to call on an expert when advanced knowledge or licensing is required to meet the client's needs.

The Canadian Securities Administration (CSA) offers the Financial Planning Proficiency Exam (FPPE). The full-day exam includes multiple-choice questions in the morning session and essay-style questions in the afternoon portion. Anyone who uses such terms as *planner*, *consultant*, or *adviser* in combination with *wealth*, *retirement*, *money*, or *financial* has to pass the FPPE. They also need two years of industry experience and have to commit to a continuing education plan.

The following organizations and agencies can be contacted for further information about certification and regulation of financial planners:

- *The Canadian Institute of Financial Planning* offers six correspondence courses leading to the designation of Certified Financial Planner (CFP) (www.mutfunds.com/cifp)
- *The Canadian Association of Financial Planners* (www.cafp.org)
- *The Canadian Securities Institute* offers a Professional Financial Planning course (www.csi.ca)
- *The Life Underwriters Association of Canada* offers a course of studies that leads to the CFP designation
- *The Institute of Canadian Bankers* offers programs in personal finance
- *The Canadian Association of Insurance and Financial Advisors* (www.caifa.com)

Money Management Strategy: Financial Statements and Budgeting

"We Spent How Much on What?"

"Here we go again," complained Ben. "Every time we try to use a budget, we end up arguing and still don't have enough money."

Yolanda replied, "Maybe if we kept track of everything we spend, we would have some idea of where our money goes."

"No, not that!" Ben exclaimed. "I have a friend who keeps a notebook and lists everything he spends. That would drive me crazy."

"Well, we can't keep going like we have," responded Yolanda. "A year ago, we owed $4,500 on the credit cards. Now it's up to $7,000. And we don't have anything in savings. How will we ever be able to have a down payment for a house?"

Ben and Yolanda decided to sort all their cheque stubs, receipts, and credit card statements to see where their money was going. Last year, they spent more than $2,000 in restaurants and charged more than $800 on their vacation.

"I didn't realize we spent that much on those things," commented Ben. "We also had auto maintenance costs of $1,650 and donated $1,800 to the homeless shelter and church. Those are things we had to do and wanted to do."

Yolanda replied, "But now that we know how we spend our money, what do we do next?"

"Maybe we should get a computerized money management program," Ben suggested.

Yolanda countered, "Maybe we should just start with spending a few dollars on a notebook and file folders to record and sort our receipts."

QUESTIONS

1 What would Ben and Yolanda learn by sorting their expenses into various categories? What categories should they use?

2 How can knowing where their money goes help Ben and Yolanda plan their spending?

3 What financial goals might Ben and Yolanda consider to address some of their money management concerns?

4 Locate a Web site that would help Ben and Yolanda improve their money management skills.

LEARNING OBJECTIVES

1 Recognize relationships among financial documents and money management activities.

2 Create a system for maintaining personal financial records.

3 Develop a personal balance sheet and cash flow statement.

4 Create and implement a budget.

5 Calculate savings needed to achieve financial goals.

Planning for Successful Money Management

Objective 1

Recognize relationships among financial documents and money management activities.

money management
Day-to-day financial activities necessary to manage current personal economic resources while working toward long-term financial security.

Visit the Web site
See the Pre-Test under Chapter 2 on the online learning centre at www.mcgrawhill.ca/college/kapoor.

"Each month I have too much month and not enough money. If the month were only 20 days long, budgeting would be easy." Most of us have heard a comment like this when it comes to budgeting and money management.

Your daily spending and saving decisions are at the centre of financial planning. You must coordinate these decisions with your needs, goals, and personal situation. When people watch a baseball or football game, they usually know the score. In financial planning also, knowing the score is important. Maintaining financial records and planning your spending are essential to successful personal financial management. The time and effort you devote to these record-keeping activities will yield benefits. **Money management** refers to the day-to-day financial activities necessary to manage current personal economic resources while working toward long-term financial security.

OPPORTUNITY COST AND MONEY MANAGEMENT

Consumers can choose from more than 25,000 items in a supermarket, from more than 11,000 periodicals, and from as many as 500 cable television stations. Daily decision making is a fact of life, and trade-offs are associated with each choice made. Selecting an alternative means you give up something else. In terms of money management decisions, examples of trade-off situations, or *opportunity costs*, include the following:

- Spending money on current living expenses reduces the amount you can use for saving and investing for long-term financial security.
- Saving and investing for the future reduces the amount you can spend now.
- Buying on credit results in payments later and a reduction in the amount of future income available for spending.
- Using savings for purchases results in lost interest earnings and an inability to use savings for other purposes.
- Comparison shopping can save you money and improve the quality of your purchases but uses up something of value you cannot replace: your time.

As you develop and implement various money management activities, you need to assess financial and personal costs and benefits associated with financial decisions.

COMPONENTS OF MONEY MANAGEMENT

As Exhibit 2–1 shows, the three major money management activities are interrelated. Personal financial records and documents are the foundation of systematic resource use. They provide written evidence of business transactions, ownership of property, and legal matters. Personal financial statements enable you to measure and assess your financial position and progress. Your spending plan, or budget, is the basis for effective money management.

CONCEPT CHECK 2–1

1. What opportunity costs are associated with money management activities?
2. What are the three major money management activities?

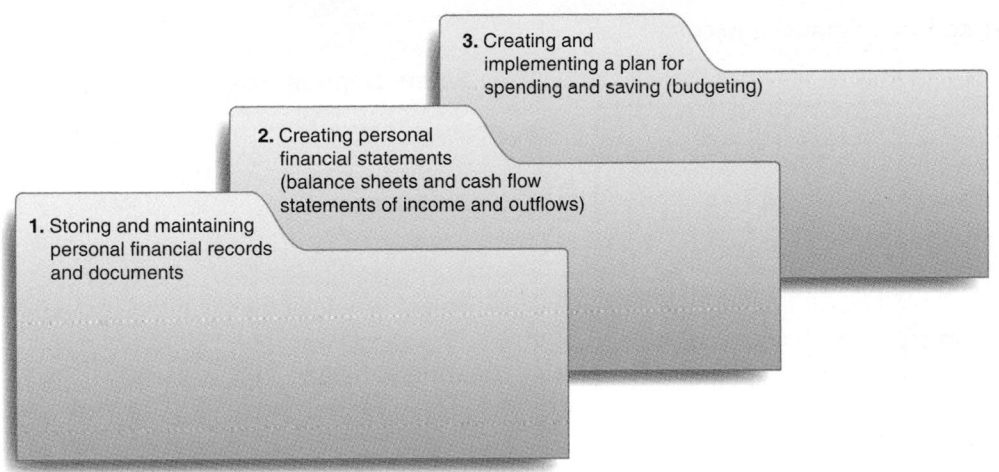

Exhibit 2-1
Money
Management
Activities

3. Creating and implementing a plan for spending and saving (budgeting)

2. Creating personal financial statements (balance sheets and cash flow statements of income and outflows)

1. Storing and maintaining personal financial records and documents

A System for Personal Financial Records

Experts once predicted that computers would result in fewer paper documents. How wrong they were! Today, computers are generating more paperwork than ever. Much of that paperwork relates to financial matters. Invoices, credit card statements, insurance policies, and tax records are the basis of financial recordkeeping and personal economic choices.

An organized system of financial records provides a basis for:

- Handling daily business affairs, including payment of bills on time.
- Planning and measuring financial progress.
- Completing required tax reports.
- Making effective investment decisions.
- Determining available resources for current and future buying.

As Exhibit 2–2 shows, most financial records are kept in one of three places: a home file, a safety deposit box, or a home computer. A home file should be used to keep records for current needs and documents with limited value. Your home file may be a series of folders, a cabinet with several drawers, or even a cardboard box. Whatever method you use, it is most important that your home file be organized to allow quick access to required documents and information.

Important financial records and valuable articles should be kept in a location that provides better security than a home file. A **safety deposit box** is a private storage area at a financial institution with maximum security for valuables and difficult-to-replace documents. Access to the contents of a safety deposit box requires two keys. One key is issued to you; the other is kept by the financial institution where the safety deposit box is located. Items commonly kept in a safety deposit box include stock certificates, contracts, a list of insurance policies, and valuables, such as rare coins and stamps.

The number of financial records and documents may seem overwhelming; however, they can easily be organized into 10 categories (see Exhibit 2–2). These groups correspond to the major topics covered in this book. You may not need to use all of these records and documents at present. As your financial situation changes, you will add others.

How long should you keep personal finance records? The answer to this question differs for various documents. Such records as birth certificates and wills should be kept permanently. Records on property and investments should be kept as long as you own these items. Federal tax laws dictate the length of

Objective 2

Create a system for maintaining personal financial records.

safety deposit box
A private storage area at a financial institution with maximum security for valuables.

DID YOU KNOW ?

In Canada, people keep various documents and valuables in safety deposit boxes in banks, trust companies, and credit unions. While these boxes are usually very safe, each year a few people lose the contents of their safety deposit boxes through theft, fire, or natural disasters. Such losses are usually, but not always, covered by the financial institution's insurance.

Exhibit 2–2   Where to Keep Financial Records

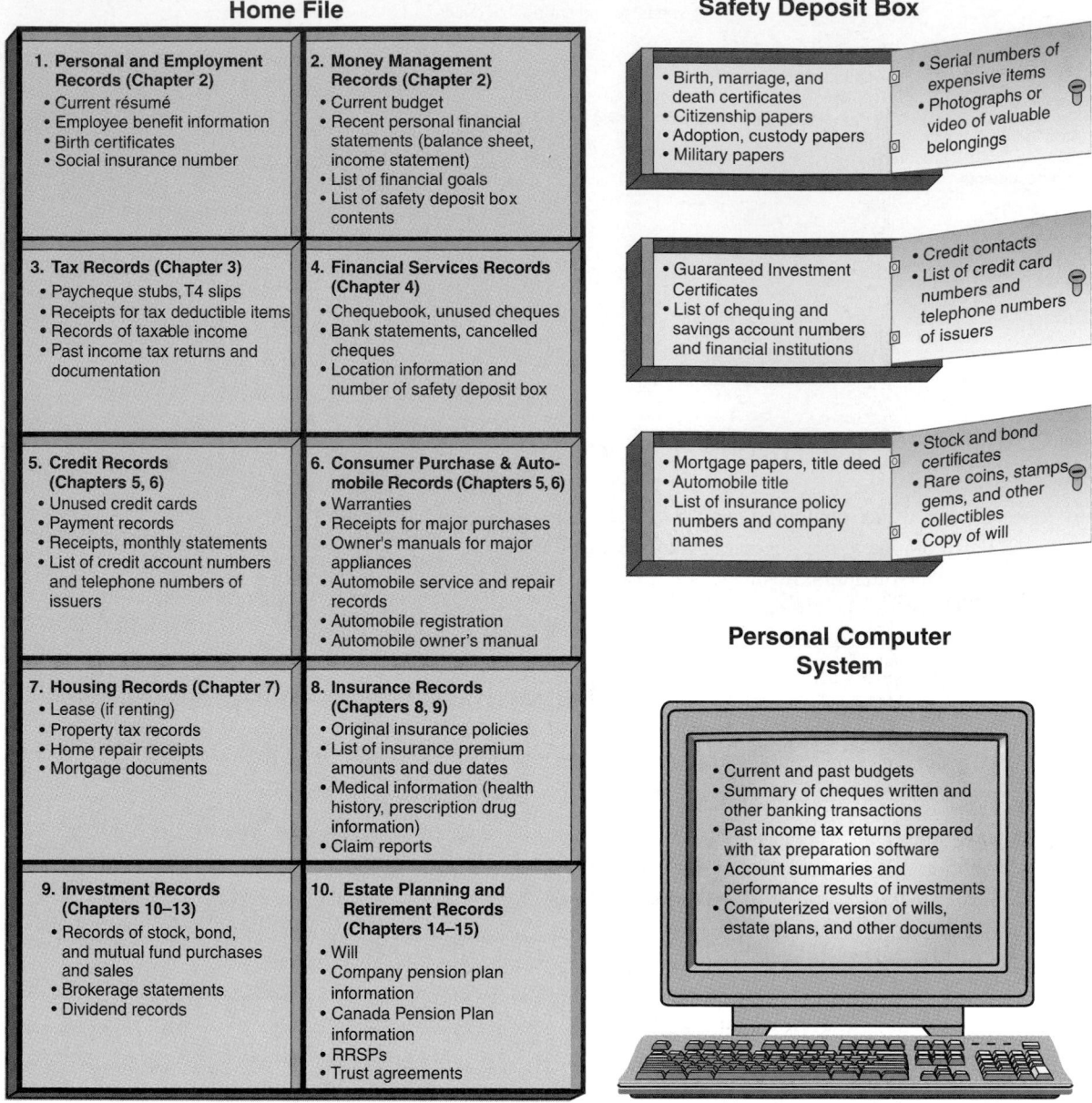

Home File

1. Personal and Employment Records (Chapter 2)
- Current résumé
- Employee benefit information
- Birth certificates
- Social insurance number

2. Money Management Records (Chapter 2)
- Current budget
- Recent personal financial statements (balance sheet, income statement)
- List of financial goals
- List of safety deposit box contents

3. Tax Records (Chapter 3)
- Paycheque stubs, T4 slips
- Receipts for tax deductible items
- Records of taxable income
- Past income tax returns and documentation

4. Financial Services Records (Chapter 4)
- Chequebook, unused cheques
- Bank statements, cancelled cheques
- Location information and number of safety deposit box

5. Credit Records (Chapters 5, 6)
- Unused credit cards
- Payment records
- Receipts, monthly statements
- List of credit account numbers and telephone numbers of issuers

6. Consumer Purchase & Automobile Records (Chapters 5, 6)
- Warranties
- Receipts for major purchases
- Owner's manuals for major appliances
- Automobile service and repair records
- Automobile registration
- Automobile owner's manual

7. Housing Records (Chapter 7)
- Lease (if renting)
- Property tax records
- Home repair receipts
- Mortgage documents

8. Insurance Records (Chapters 8, 9)
- Original insurance policies
- List of insurance premium amounts and due dates
- Medical information (health history, prescription drug information)
- Claim reports

9. Investment Records (Chapters 10–13)
- Records of stock, bond, and mutual fund purchases and sales
- Brokerage statements
- Dividend records

10. Estate Planning and Retirement Records (Chapters 14–15)
- Will
- Company pension plan information
- Canada Pension Plan information
- RRSPs
- Trust agreements

Safety Deposit Box

- Birth, marriage, and death certificates
- Citizenship papers
- Adoption, custody papers
- Military papers
- Serial numbers of expensive items
- Photographs or video of valuable belongings

- Guaranteed Investment Certificates
- List of chequing and savings account numbers and financial institutions
- Credit contacts
- List of credit card numbers and telephone numbers of issuers

- Mortgage papers, title deed
- Automobile title
- List of insurance policy numbers and company names
- Stock and bond certificates
- Rare coins, stamps, gems, and other collectibles
- Copy of will

Personal Computer System

- Current and past budgets
- Summary of cheques written and other banking transactions
- Past income tax returns prepared with tax preparation software
- Account summaries and performance results of investments
- Computerized version of wills, estate plans, and other documents

time you should keep tax-related information. Copies of tax returns and supporting data should be saved for six years. Normally, an audit will go back only three years; however, under certain circumstances, the Canada Customs and Revenue Agency may request information from six years back. Financial experts recommend keeping documents related to the purchase and sale of real estate indefinitely.

CONCEPT CHECK 2-2

1. What are the benefits of an organized system of financial records and documents?
2. What suggestions would you give for creating a system for organizing and storing financial records and documents?
3. What influences the length of time you should keep financial records and documents?

Personal Financial Statements for Measuring Financial Progress

Every journey starts somewhere. You need to know where you are before you can go somewhere else. Personal financial statements tell you the starting point of your financial journey.

Most of the financial documents we have discussed come from financial institutions, other business organizations, or the government. Two documents that you create yourself, the personal balance sheet and the cash flow statement, are called *personal financial statements*. These reports provide information about your current financial position and present a summary of your income and spending. The main purposes of personal financial statements are to

- Report your current financial position in relation to the value of the items you own and the amounts you owe.
- Measure your progress toward your financial goals.
- Maintain information about your financial activities.
- Provide data you can use when preparing tax forms or applying for credit.

THE PERSONAL BALANCE SHEET: WHERE ARE YOU NOW?

The current financial position of an individual or a family is a common starting point for financial planning. A **balance sheet**, also called a *net worth statement* or *statement of financial position*, reports what you own and what you owe. You prepare a personal balance sheet to determine your current financial position using the following process:

Items of value (what you own)	−	Amounts owed (what you owe)	=	Net worth (your wealth)

For example, if your possessions are worth $4,500 and you owe $800 to others, your net worth is $3,700.

STEP 1: LISTING ITEMS OF VALUE Available cash and money in bank accounts combined with other items of value are the foundation of your current financial position. **Assets** are cash and other tangible property with a monetary value. The balance sheet for Rose and Edgar Gomez (Exhibit 2–3) lists their assets under four categories:

[1] **Liquid assets** are cash and items of value that can easily be converted to cash. Money in chequing and savings accounts is liquid and is available to the Gomez family for current spending. The cash value of their life insurance may be borrowed, if needed. While assets other than liquid assets can also be converted into cash, the process is not quite as easy.

[2] *Real estate* includes a home, a condominium, vacation property, or other land that a person or family owns.

[3] *Personal possessions* are a major portion of assets for most people. Included in this category are automobiles and other personal belongings. While these items have value, they may be difficult to convert to cash. You may decide to list your possessions on the balance sheet at their original cost. However, these values probably need to be revised over time, since a five-year-old television set, for example, is worth less now than when it was new. Thus, you may wish to list your possessions at their current value (also referred to as *market value*). This method takes into account the fact that such things as a home or rare jewellery may increase in value over time. You can estimate current value by looking at ads for the selling price of comparable automobiles, homes, or other possessions. Or you may use the services of an appraiser.

Objective 3

Develop a personal balance sheet and cash flow statement.

balance sheet
A financial statement that reports what an individual or a family owns and owes; also called a *net worth statement*.

assets Cash and other property with a monetary value.

liquid assets Cash and items of value that can easily be converted to cash.

Visit the Web site
See Personal Financial Planning worksheets under Chapter 2 on the online learning centre at www.mcgrawhill.ca/college/kapoor.

most important *cash inflow*; however, other income, such as interest earned on a savings account, should also be considered. In contrast, payments for such items as rent, food, and loans are *cash outflows*.

cash flow statement
A financial statement that summarizes cash receipts and payments for a given period.

A **cash flow statement**, also called a *personal income and expenditure statement*, (Exhibit 2–4) is a summary of cash receipts and payments for a given period, such as a month or a year. This report provides data on your income and spending patterns, which will be helpful when preparing a budget. A chequing account can provide information for your cash flow statement. Deposits to the account are your *inflows*; cheques written are your *outflows*. Of course, in using this system, when you do not deposit the entire amounts received you must also note the spending of undeposited amounts in your cash flow statement.

The process for preparing a cash flow statement is

| Total cash received during the time period | – | Cash outflows during the time period | = | Cash surplus or deficit |

Exhibit 2–4   Creating a Cash Flow Statement of Income and Outflows

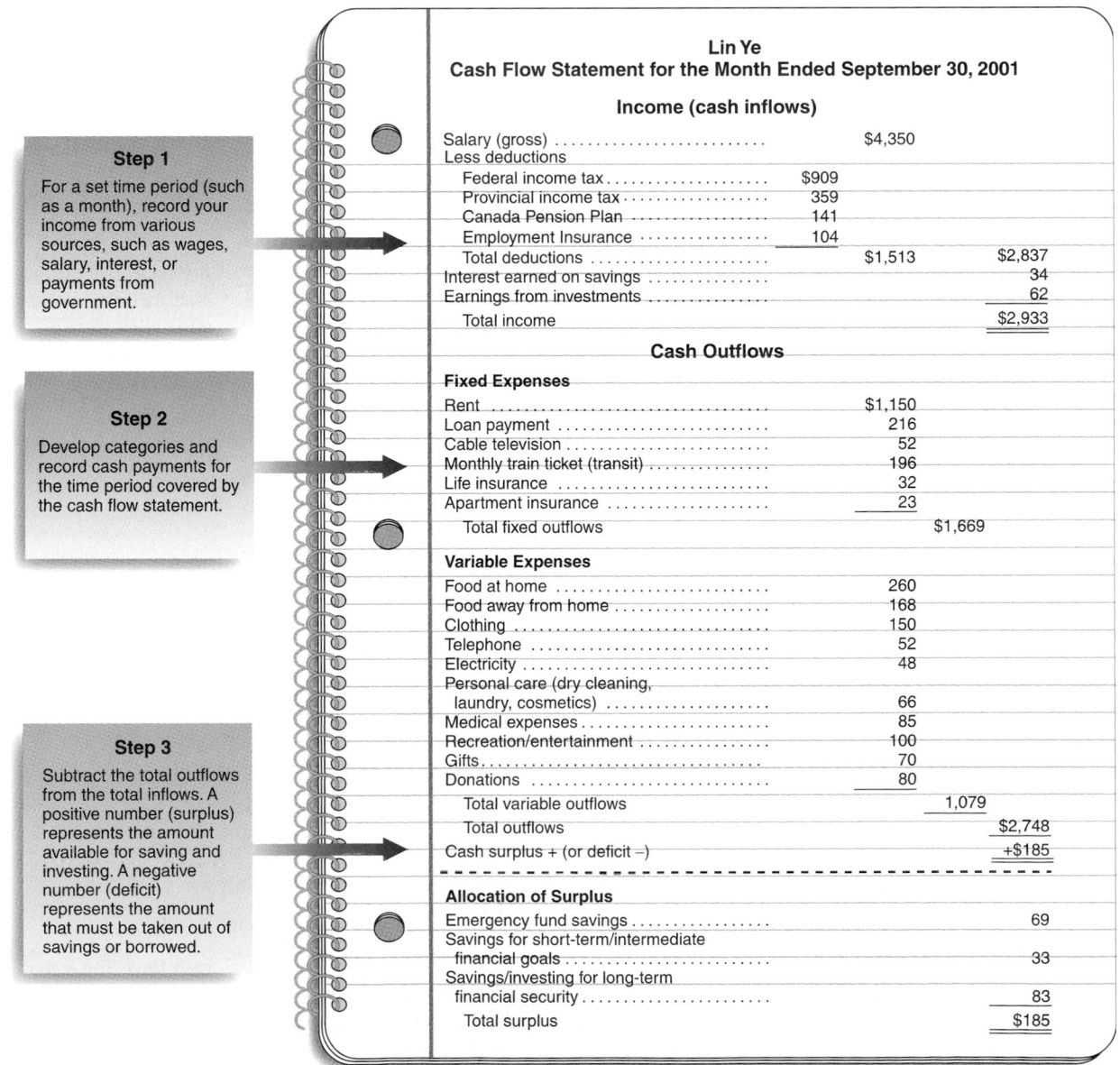

Step 1
For a set time period (such as a month), record your income from various sources, such as wages, salary, interest, or payments from government.

Step 2
Develop categories and record cash payments for the time period covered by the cash flow statement.

Step 3
Subtract the total outflows from the total inflows. A positive number (surplus) represents the amount available for saving and investing. A negative number (deficit) represents the amount that must be taken out of savings or borrowed.

Lin Ye
Cash Flow Statement for the Month Ended September 30, 2001

Income (cash inflows)

Salary (gross)		$4,350	
Less deductions			
Federal income tax....................	$909		
Provincial income tax.................	359		
Canada Pension Plan	141		
Employment Insurance	104		
Total deductions	$1,513	$2,837	
Interest earned on savings		34	
Earnings from investments		62	
Total income		$2,933	

Cash Outflows

Fixed Expenses

Rent	$1,150	
Loan payment	216	
Cable television	52	
Monthly train ticket (transit).............	196	
Life insurance	32	
Apartment insurance	23	
Total fixed outflows	$1,669	

Variable Expenses

Food at home	260	
Food away from home	168	
Clothing	150	
Telephone	52	
Electricity	48	
Personal care (dry cleaning, laundry, cosmetics)	66	
Medical expenses......................	85	
Recreation/entertainment	100	
Gifts.................................	70	
Donations	80	
Total variable outflows	1,079	
Total outflows		$2,748
Cash surplus + (or deficit –)		+$185

Allocation of Surplus

Emergency fund savings		69
Savings for short-term/intermediate financial goals		33
Savings/investing for long-term financial security......................		83
Total surplus		$185

Financial Planning Calculations

RATIOS FOR EVALUATING FINANCIAL PROGRESS

Financial ratios provide guidelines for measuring changes in your financial situation. These relationships can indicate progress toward an improved financial position.

Ratio	Calculation	Example	Interpretation
Debt ratio	Liabilities divided by net worth	$25,000/$50,000 = 0.5	Shows relationship between debt and net worth; a low debt ratio is best.
Current ratio	Liquid assets divided by current liabilities	$4,000/$2,000 = 2	Indicates $2 in liquid assets for every $1 of current liabilities; a high current ratio is desirable to have cash available to pay bills.
Liquidity ratio	Liquid assets divided by monthly expenses	$10,000/$4,000 = 2.5	Indicates the number of months in which living expenses can be paid if an emergency arises; a high liquidity ratio is desirable.
Debt-payments ratio	Monthly credit payments divided by take-home pay	$540/$3,600 = 0.15	Indicates how much of a person's earnings goes for debt payments (excluding a home mortgage); most financial advisers recommend a debt-payments ratio of less than 20 percent.
Savings ratio	Amount saved each month divided by gross income	$648/$5,400 = 0.12	Financial experts recommend monthly savings of at least 10 percent.

These financial ratios, and other financial analysis methods, can assist you in assessing your spending and saving patterns to help you reach your financial goals.

STEP 1: RECORD INCOME Creating a cash flow statement starts with identifying the cash received during the time period involved. **Income** is the inflows of cash to an individual or a household. For most people, the main source of income is money received from a job. Other common income sources include

income Inflows of cash to an individual or a household.

- Wages, salaries, and commissions.
- Self-employment business income.
- Savings and investment income (interest, dividends, rent).
- Gifts, grants, scholarships, and educational loans.
- Government payments, such as Canada Pension Plan, welfare, and Employment Insurance benefits.
- Amounts received from pension and retirement programs.
- Alimony and child support payments.

In Exhibit 2–4, note that Lin Ye's monthly salary (or *gross income*) of $4,350 is her main source of income. However, she does not have use of the entire amount. **Take-home pay**, also called *net pay* or *net income*, is a person's earnings after deductions for taxes and other items. Lin's deductions for federal and provincial taxes, Canada Pension Plan contributions, and Employment Insurance are $1,513. Her take-home pay is $2,933. This amount, plus earnings from savings and investments, is the income she has available for use during the current month.

take-home pay Earnings after deductions for taxes and other items; also called *disposable income.*

43

discretionary income
Money left over after paying for housing, food, and other necessities.

Take-home pay is also called *disposable income*, the amount a person or household has available to spend. **Discretionary income** is money left over after paying for housing, food, and other necessities. Studies report that discretionary income ranges from less than 5 percent for people under age 25 to more than 40 percent for older people.

STEP 2: RECORD CASH OUTFLOWS Cash payments for living expenses and other items make up the second component of a cash flow statement. Lin Ye divides her cash outflows into two major categories: fixed expenses and variable expenses. While every individual and household has different cash outflows, these main categories, along with the sub-groupings Lin uses, can be adapted to most situations.

[1] *Fixed expenses* are payments that do not vary from month to month. Rent or mortgage payments, installment loan payments, cable television service fees, and a monthly train ticket for commuting to work are examples of constant or fixed cash outflows.

For Lin, another type of fixed expense is the amount she sets aside each month for payments due once or twice a year. For example, Lin pays $384 every March for life insurance. Each month, she records a fixed outflow of $32 for deposit in a special savings account so that the money will be available when her insurance payment is due.

[2] *Variable expenses* are flexible payments that change from month to month. Common examples of variable cash outflows are food, clothing, utilities (such as electricity and telephone), recreation, medical expenses, gifts, and donations. The use of a chequebook or some other recordkeeping system is necessary for an accurate total of cash outflows.

DID YOU KNOW ?

The most common advice from financial planners: "Save more." "Save all you can." "Cut your spending so you can save more."

STEP 3: DETERMINE NET CASH FLOW The difference between income and outflows can be either a positive (surplus) or a negative (deficit) cash flow. A deficit exists if more cash goes out than comes in during a given month. This amount must be made up by withdrawals from savings or by borrowing. The effect of a net cash flow on net worth is shown in the Financial Planning for Life's Situations feature on page 45.

When you have a cash surplus, as Lin did (Exhibit 2–4), this amount is available for saving, investing, or paying off debts. Each month, Lin sets aside money for her emergency fund in a savings account that she would use for unexpected expenses or to pay living costs if she did not receive her salary. She deposits the rest of the surplus in savings and investment plans that have two purposes. The first is the achievement of short-term and intermediate financial goals, such as a new car, a vacation, or re-enrollment in school; the second is long-term financial security—her retirement.

A cash flow statement provides the foundation for preparing and implementing a spending, saving, and investment plan, discussed in the next section.

CONCEPT CHECK 2–3

1. What are the main purposes of personal financial statements?
2. What does a personal balance sheet tell about your financial situation?
3. How can you use a balance sheet for personal financial planning?
4. What information does a cash flow statement present?

Financial Planning for Life's Situations

MEASURING YOUR FINANCIAL PROGRESS

People commonly prepare a balance sheet on a periodic basis, such as every three or six months. Between those points in time, use your budget and cash flow statement to plan and measure spending and saving activities. For example, during a certain calendar year, you might prepare a balance sheet on March 1, June 30, and December 31. Your budget would serve to plan your spending and saving between these points in time, and your cash flow statement of income and outflows would document your actual spending and saving. This relationship may be illustrated as shown below.

Changes in your net worth are the result of the relationship between cash inflows and outflows. In periods when your outflows exceed your inflows, you must draw on savings or borrow (buy on credit). When this happens, lower assets (savings) or higher liabilities (due to the use of credit) result in a lower net worth.

When inflows exceed outflows, putting money into savings or paying off debts will result in a higher net worth. In general, the relationship between the cash flow statement and the balance sheet may be expressed as follows:

Cash Flow Statement	Balance Sheet
If cash inflows (income) are greater than cash outflows	Net worth increases
If cash outflows (payments) are greater than cash inflows (income)	Net worth decreases

Using a budget, creating a cash flow statement, and developing a balance sheet on a periodic basis can help you improve your financial situation.

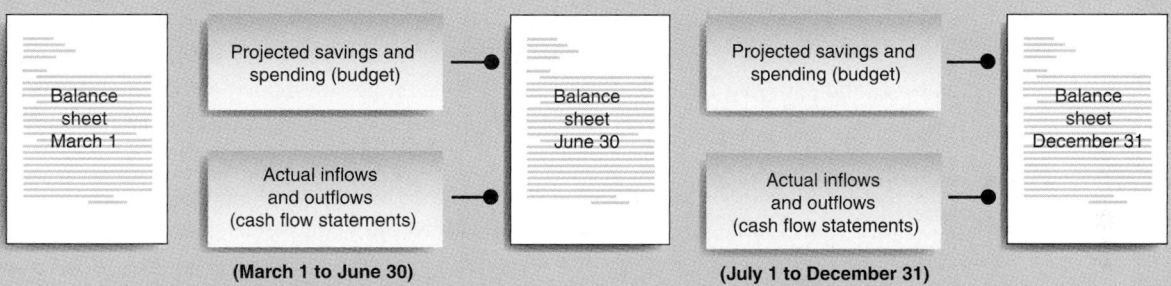

Budgeting for Skilled Money Management

A **budget**, or *spending plan*, is necessary for successful financial planning. The common financial problems of overusing credit, lacking a regular savings program, and failing to ensure future financial security can be minimized through budgeting. The main purposes of a budget are to help you

- Live within your income.
- Spend your money wisely.
- Reach your financial goals.
- Prepare for financial emergencies.
- Develop wise financial management habits.

Budgeting may be viewed in four major phases as shown in Exhibit 2–5.

STARTING THE BUDGETING PROCESS

The financial statements and documents discussed in the first sections of this chapter provide a starting point for your daily money management activities. A personal balance sheet is an

Exhibit 2–5

Creating and
Implementing a
Budget

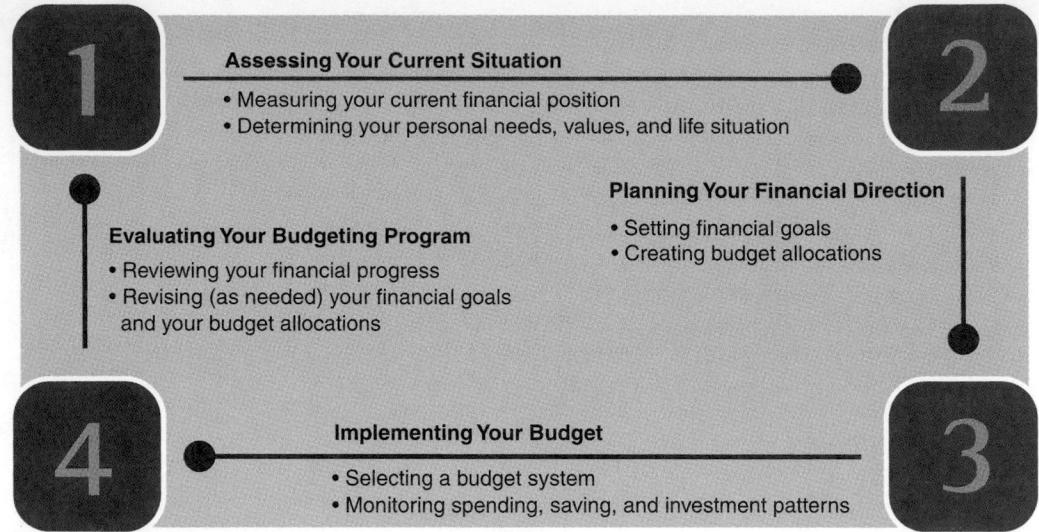

effective scorecard for measuring financial progress. Increases in net worth as a result of increased assets or decreased debt are evidence of an improved financial position. A regular assessment of your financial standing using a personal balance sheet can provide a point of reference for money management decisions.

Each day, you make many decisions that communicate your *lifestyle* by indicating how you spend your time and money. The clothes you wear, the food you eat, and the interests you pursue contribute to your lifestyle. Some people spend time and money on automobiles or stereo equipment; other people travel, plant gardens, or engage in church or community activities. These actions reflect a lifestyle influenced by three factors:

- *Career.* Your job situation will influence the amount of your income, the way you spend your leisure time, and even the people with whom you associate.
- *Family.* The size of your household and the ages of its members will also affect your lifestyle. The spending priorities of a couple without children will differ from those of a couple with several youngsters.
- *Values.* Ideas and beliefs you regard as important will strongly influence your interests, activities, and purchasing habits.

These factors combine to create planned spending patterns that your financial goals reflect.

STEP 1: SETTING FINANCIAL GOALS Future plans are an important dimension of your financial direction. Financial goals are plans for future activities that require you to plan your spending, saving, and investing. Exhibit 2–6 gives examples of common financial goals based on life situation and time.

As discussed in Chapter 1, financial goals should be realistic; be stated in specific, measurable terms; have a definite time frame; and imply the type of action to be taken. Your personal financial statements and budgeting allow you to achieve your financial goals with

[1] Your cash flow statement: telling you what you received and spent over the past month.
[2] Your balance sheet: reporting your current financial position—where you are now.
[3] Your budget: planning spending and saving to achieve financial goals.

STEP 2: ESTIMATING INCOME As Exhibit 2–7 on page 48 shows, you should first estimate available money for a given time period. A common budgeting period is a month, since many payments, such as rent or mortgage, utilities, and credit cards, are due each month.

Exhibit 2-6   Common Financial Goals

Personal Situation	Short-Term Goals (less than 2 years)	Intermediate Goals (2–5 years)	Long-Term Goals (more than 5 years)
Single person	• Complete college/university • Pay off auto loan	• Take a vacation to Europe • Pay off education loan • Return to school for graduate degree	• Buy a vacation home in the mountains • Provide for retirement income
Married couple (no children)	• Take an annual vacation • Buy a new car	• Remodel home • Build a stock portfolio	• Buy a retirement home • Provide for retirement income
Parent (young children)	• Increase life insurance • Increase savings	• Increase investments • Buy a new car	• Accumulate a college/university fund for children • Move to a larger home

NOTE: As discussed in Chapter 1, your goals should be realistic, specific, and measurable for a definite time frame.

In determining available income, include only money that you are sure you'll receive. Bonuses, gifts, or unexpected income should not be considered until the money is actually received.

If you get paid once a month, planning is easy since you will work with a single amount. But if you get paid weekly or twice a month, you will need to plan how much of each paycheque will go for various expenses. If you get paid every two weeks, plan your spending based on the two paycheques you will receive each month. Then, during the two months each year that have three paydays, you can put additional amounts into savings, pay off some debts, or make a special purchase.

Budgeting income may be difficult if your earnings vary by season or your income is irregular, as with sales commissions. In these situations, attempt to estimate your income based on the past year and on your expectations for the current year. Estimating your income on the low side will help you avoid overspending and other financial difficulties.

STEP 3: BUDGETING EMERGENCY FUND AND SAVINGS To set aside money for unexpected expenses as well as future financial security, the Fraziers (see Exhibit 2–7) have budgeted several amounts for savings and investments. Financial advisers suggest that an emergency fund representing three to six months of living expenses be established for use in periods of unexpected financial difficulty. This amount will vary on the basis of a person's life situation and employment stability. A three-month emergency fund is probably adequate for a person with a stable income or secure employment, while a person with erratic or seasonal income may need to set aside an emergency fund sufficient for six months or more of living expenses.

The Fraziers also set aside an amount each month for their automobile insurance payment, which is due every six months. Both this amount and the emergency fund are put into a savings account that will earn interest. The *time value of money*, discussed in Chapter 1, refers to increases in an amount of money as a result of interest earned. Savings methods for achieving financial goals are discussed later in this chapter.

A very common budgeting mistake is to save the amount you have left at the end of the month. When you do that, you often have *nothing* left for savings. Since savings are vital to long-term financial security, advisers suggest that an amount be budgeted as a fixed expense.

STEP 4: BUDGETING FIXED EXPENSES Definite obligations are the basis for this portion of a budget. As Exhibit 2–7 shows, the Fraziers have fixed expenses for housing, taxes, and loan payments. They make a monthly payment of $29 for life insurance. The budgeted total for the Fraziers' fixed expenses is $806, or 28 percent of estimated available income.

Exhibit 2-7   The Fraziers Develop and Implement a Monthly Budget

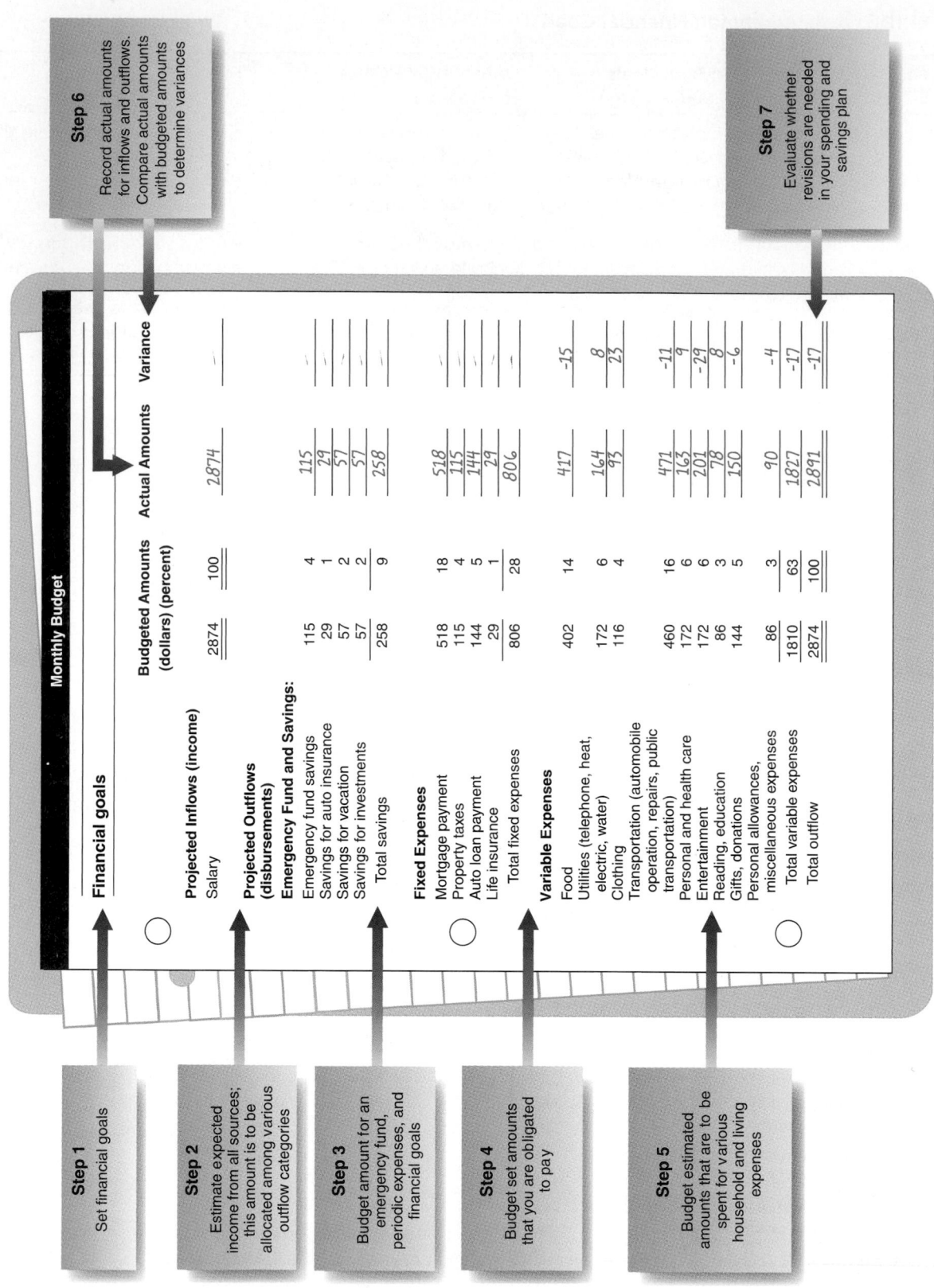

Step 6
Record actual amounts for inflows and outflows. Compare actual amounts with budgeted amounts to determine variances

Step 7
Evaluate whether revisions are needed in your spending and savings plan

Step 1
Set financial goals

Step 2
Estimate expected income from all sources; this amount is to be allocated among various outflow categories

Step 3
Budget amount for an emergency fund, periodic expenses, and financial goals

Step 4
Budget set amounts that you are obligated to pay

Step 5
Budget estimated amounts that are to be spent for various household and living expenses

Monthly Budget

	Budgeted Amounts (dollars) (percent)		Actual Amounts	Variance
Financial goals				
Projected Inflows (income)				
Salary	2874	100	2874	
Projected Outflows (disbursements)				
Emergency Fund and Savings:				
Emergency fund savings	115	4	115	
Savings for auto insurance	29	1	29	
Savings for vacation	57	2	57	
Savings for investments	57	2	57	
Total savings	258	9	258	
Fixed Expenses				
Mortgage payment	518	18	518	
Property taxes	115	4	115	
Auto loan payment	144	5	144	
Life insurance	29	1	29	
Total fixed expenses	806	28	806	
Variable Expenses				
Food	402	14	417	-15
Utilities (telephone, heat, electric, water)	172	6	164	8
Clothing	116	4	93	23
Transportation (automobile operation, repairs, public transportation)	460	16	471	-11
Personal and health care	172	6	163	9
Entertainment	172	6	201	-29
Reading, education	86	3	78	8
Gifts, donations	144	5	150	-6
Personal allowances, miscellaneous expenses	86	3	90	-4
Total variable expenses	1810	63	1827	-17
Total outflow	2874	100	2891	-17

Assigning amounts to spending categories requires careful consideration. The amount you budget for various items will depend on your current needs and plans for the future. The following sources can help you plan your spending:

- Your cash flow statement.
- Consumer expenditure data (www.statcan.ca).
- Articles in magazines such as *MoneySaver*.
- Estimates of future income and expenses and anticipated changes in inflation rates.

Exhibit 2–8 provides suggested budget allocations for different life situations. Although this information can be of value when creating budget categories, maintaining a detailed record of your spending for several months is a better source for your personal situation. However, don't become discouraged. Use a simple system, such as a notebook or your chequebook. This "spending diary" will help you know where your money is going. Remember, a budget is an *estimate* for spending and saving intended to help you make better use of your money, not to reduce your enjoyment of life.

DID YOU KNOW ?

Only 16 percent of Canadian consumers prepare a monthly budget on paper. (Fédération des ACEF du Québec—survey of 1902 Canadians, June 2001)

STEP 5: BUDGETING VARIABLE EXPENSES Planning for variable expenses is not as easy as budgeting for savings or fixed expenses. Variable expenses will fluctuate by household situation, time of year, health, economic conditions, and a variety of other factors. A major portion of the Fraziers' planned spending—more than 60 percent of their budgeted income—is for variable living costs.

Exhibit 2–8   Typical After-Tax Budget Allocations for Different Life Situations

Budget Category	Student	Working Single (no dependants)	Couple (children under 18)	Single Parent (young children)	Parents (children over 18 in college/ university)	Couple (over 55, no dependent children)
Housing (rent or mortgage payment; utilities; furnishings and appliances)	0–25%	30–35%	25–35%	20–30%	25–30%	25–35%
Transportation	5–10	15–20	15–20	10–18	12–18	10–18
Food (at home and away from home)	15–20	15–25	15–25	13–20	15–20	18–25
Clothing	5–12	5–15	5–10	5–10	4–8	4–8
Personal and health care (including child care)	3–5	3–5	4–10	8–12	4–6	6–12
Entertainment and recreation	5–10	5–10	4–8	4–8	6–10	5–8
Reading and education	10–30	2–4	3–5	3–5	6–12	2–4
Personal insurance and pension payments	0–5	4–8	5–9	5–9	4–7	6–8
Gifts, donations, and contributions	4–6	5–8	3–5	3–5	4–8	3–5
Savings	0–10	4–15	5–10	5–8	2–4	3–5

SOURCES: U.S. Bureau of Labor Statistics (http://stats.bls.gov); American Demographics; Money; The Wall Street Journal

The Fraziers base their estimates on their needs and desires for the items listed and on expected changes in the cost of living. The *consumer price index (CPI)* is a measure of the general price level of consumer goods and services in Canada. This government statistic indicates changes in the buying power of a dollar. As consumer prices increase due to inflation, people must spend more to buy the same amount. Changes in the cost of living will vary depending on where you live and what you buy.

As mentioned in Chapter 1, the *rule of 72* can help you budget for price rises. At a 6-percent inflation rate, prices will double in 12 years (72/6); at an 8-percent inflation rate, prices will double in only 9 years (72/8).

STEP 6: RECORDING SPENDING AMOUNTS
After you have established your spending plan, you will need to keep records of your actual income and expenses similar to those you keep in preparing an income statement. In Exhibit 2–7, note that the Fraziers estimated specific amounts for income and expenses. These are presented under "Budgeted Amounts." The family's actual spending was not always the same as planned. A **budget variance** is the difference between the amount budgeted and the actual amount received or spent. The total variance for the Fraziers was a $17 **deficit**, since their actual spending exceeded their planned spending by this amount. The Fraziers would have had a **surplus** if their actual spending had been less than they had planned.

Variances for income should be viewed as the opposite of variances for expenses. Less income than expected would be a deficit, while more income than expected would be a surplus.

Spending more than planned for an item may be justified by reducing spending for another item or putting less into savings. However, it may be necessary to revise your budget and financial goals.

STEP 7: REVIEWING SPENDING AND SAVING PATTERNS
Like most decision-making activities, budgeting is a circular, ongoing process. You will need to review and perhaps revise your spending plan on a regular basis.

Reviewing Your Financial Progress The results of your budget may be obvious: having extra cash in chequing, falling behind in your bill payments, and so on. However, such obvious results may not always be present. Occasionally, you will have to sit down (with other household members, if appropriate) and review areas where spending has been more or less than expected.

As Exhibit 2–9 shows, you can prepare an annual summary to compare actual spending with budgeted amounts. This type of summary may also be prepared every three or six months. A spreadsheet computer program can be useful for this purpose. The summary will help you see areas where changes in your budget may be necessary. This review process is vital to both successful short-term money management and long-term financial security.

Revising Your Goals and Budget Allocations What should you cut first when a budget shortage occurs? This question doesn't have easy answers, and the answers will vary for different household situations. The most common overspending areas are entertainment and food, especially away-from-home meals. Purchasing less expensive brand items, buying quality used products, avoiding credit card purchases, and renting rather than buying are common budget adjustment techniques.

At this point in the budgeting process, you may also revise your financial goals. Are you making progress toward achieving your objectives? Have changes in personal or economic conditions affected

---

budget variance The difference between the amount budgeted and the actual amount received or spent.

deficit The amount by which actual spending exceeds planned spending.

surplus The amount by which actual spending is less than planned spending.

DID YOU KNOW ?

Seventeen percent of Canadians aged 18-30 reported not having met some of their monthly payments on bank loans over the preceding 12 months.

(Fédération des ACEF du Québec— survey of 1902 Canadians, June 2001)

Exhibit 2–9   An Annual Budget Summary

Item	Monthly Budget	Actual Spending (cash outflows)												Annual Totals	
		Jan.	Feb.	Mar.	Apr.	May	June	July	Aug.	Sept.	Oct.	Nov.	Dec.	Actual	Budgeted*
Income	2,730	2,730	2,730	2,730	2,940	2,730	2,730	2,730	2,730	2,850	2,850	2,850	2,850	33,450	32,760
Savings	150	150	150	200	150	90	50	30	100	250	250	150	40	1,610	1,800
Mortgage/rent	826	826	826	826	826	826	826	826	826	826	826	826	826	9,912	9,912
Housing costs (insurance, utilities)	190	214	238	187	176	185	188	146	178	198	177	201	195	2,283	2,230
Telephone	50	43	45	67	56	54	52	65	45	43	52	49	47	618	600
Food (at home)	280	287	277	245	234	278	267	298	320	301	298	278	324	3,407	3,360
Food (away from home)	80	67	78	84	87	123	109	89	83	67	76	83	143	1,089	960
Clothing	100	98	78	123	156	86	76	111	124	87	95	123	111	1,268	1,200
Transportation (auto operation, public transportation)	340	302	312	333	345	297	287	390	373	299	301	267	301	3,807	4,080
Credit payments	249	249	249	249	249	249	249	249	249	249	249	249	249	2,988	2,988
Insurance (life, health, other)	45	—	—	135	—	—	135	—	—	135	—	—	135	540	540
Health care	140	176	145	187	122	111	156	186	166	134	189	193	147	1,912	1,680
Recreation	80	67	98	123	98	67	45	87	98	65	87	87	111	1,033	960
Reading, education	40	52	54	44	34	39	54	12	38	54	34	76	45	516	480
Gifts, donations	100	102	110	94	87	123	89	95	94	113	87	99	134	1,227	1,200
Personal miscellaneous expense	60	89	45	67	54	98	59	54	49	71	65	90	56	797	720
Total	2,730	2,702	2,705	2,964	2,674	2,626	2,642	2,638	2,743	2,892	2,786	2,771	2,864	33,007	32,760
Surplus (deficit)		28	25	(254)	266	104	88	92	(13)	(42)	64	79	(14)	443	—

*Actual spending times 12.

the desirability of certain goals? Have new goals surfaced that should be given a higher priority than those that have been your major concern? Addressing these issues while creating an effective saving method will help ensure accomplishment of your financial goals.

CHARACTERISTICS OF SUCCESSFUL BUDGETING

Having a spending plan will not eliminate financial worries. A budget will work only if you follow it. Changes in income, expenses, and goals will require changes in your spending plan. Money management experts advise that a successful budget should be

- *Well planned.* A good budget takes time and effort to prepare. Planning a budget should involve everyone affected by it. Children can learn important money management lessons by helping to develop and use the family budget.
- *Realistic.* If you have a moderate income, don't immediately expect to save enough money for an expensive car or a lavish vacation. A budget is designed not to prevent you from enjoying life but to help you achieve what you want most.
- *Flexible.* Unexpected expenses and changes in your cost of living will require a budget that you can easily revise. Also, special situations, such as two-income families or the arrival of a baby, may require an increase in certain types of expenses.
- *Clearly communicated.* Unless you and others involved are aware of the spending plan, it will not work. The budget should be written and available to all household members. Many variations of written budgets are possible, including a notebook or a computerized system (see the Financial Planning for Life's Situations box on the next page).

CONCEPT CHECK 2-4

1. What are the main purposes of a budget?
2. How does a person's life situation affect goal setting and amounts allocated for various budget categories?
3. What are the main steps in creating a budget?
4. What are commonly recommended qualities of a successful budget?
5. What actions might you take when evaluating your budgeting program?

Saving to Achieve Financial Goals

Objective 5

Calculate savings needed to achieve financial goals.

Saving of current income (as well as investing, which is discussed in Part 4) is the basis for an improved financial position and long-term financial security. Common reasons for saving include the following:

- To set aside money for irregular and unexpected expenses.
- To pay for the replacement of expensive items, such as appliances or an automobile, or to have money for a down payment on a house.
- To buy special items, such as home video or recreational equipment, or to pay for a vacation.
- To provide for long-term expenses, such as the education of children or retirement.
- To earn income from the interest on savings for use in paying living expenses.

SELECTING A SAVING TECHNIQUE

Traditionally, Canada ranks fairly low among industrial nations in savings rate. A low savings rate tends to slow economic growth with fewer funds available for business borrowing and for

Financial Planning for Life's Situations

SELECTING A BUDGETING SYSTEM

Although your chequebook will give you a fairly complete record of your expenses, it does not serve the purpose of planning for spending. A budget requires that you outline how you will spend available income. Various types of budgeting systems exist, from informal procedures to computerized spending plans.

A *mental budget* exists only in a person's mind. This simple system may be appropriate if you have limited resources and minimal financial responsibilities. The major drawback of a mental budget is the danger of forgetting what amounts you plan to spend on various items.

A *physical budget* involves the use of envelopes, folders, or containers to hold the money or slips of paper that represent amounts allocated for spending categories. This system allows you to actually see where your money goes. Envelopes would contain the amount of cash or a note listing the amount to be used for "Food," "Rent," "Clothing," "Auto Payment," "Entertainment," and other expenses.

Experienced financial advisers recommend a *written budget*. The exact system and the amount of detail will depend on the time, effort, and information that you put into the budgeting process. A written budget can be kept on notebook paper or in a specialized budgeting book available in office supply stores. A common budget format is a spreadsheet that has several monthly columns for comparing budgeted and actual amounts for various expense items.

The use of *computerized budgeting systems* is increasing. In addition to creating a spreadsheet budget, a home computer is capable of doing other financial recordkeeping tasks, such as writing cheques and projecting the future value of savings accounts. Software packages, such as Microsoft Money (www.microsoft.com/money) and Quicken (www.quicken.ca), can assist you. While it takes time and effort to learn the software and enter data, a computerized budgeting and recordkeeping procedure can yield fast and accurate financial planning data.

---

creation of new jobs. Low savings also affect the personal financial situations of people. Studies reveal that the majority of Canadians do not have an adequate amount set aside for emergencies.

Since most people find saving difficult, financial advisers suggest several methods to make it easier. One method is to write a cheque each payday and deposit it in a special savings account at a distant financial institution. This savings deposit can be a percentage of income, such as 5 or 10 percent, or a specific dollar amount. Always "pay yourself first." To guarantee setting something aside for savings, view savings as a fixed expense in your spending plan.

Another method is *payroll deduction*, which is available at many places of employment. Under a *direct deposit* system, an amount is automatically deducted from your salary and deposited in a savings or investment account.

Finally, saving coins or spending less on certain items can help you save. Each day, put your change in a container. In a short time, you will have enough money to make a substantial deposit in a savings account. You can also increase your savings by taking a sandwich to work instead of buying lunch or refraining from buying snacks or magazines.

How you save, however, is less important than making regular periodic savings deposits that will help you achieve financial goals. Small amounts of savings can grow faster than most people

DID YOU KNOW ?

Canadians are finally getting richer. The average Canadian household in 1999 gained 1.5 percent in net income and 3 percent in net worth, largely concentrated in the wealthiest homes. But in the wake of the 1990s recession, it was only in 2000 that net income surpassed the 1989 level. During the 1990s, Canadians did see a 20-percent rise in their net worth after inflation.

("Financial Outlook," Maclean's, May 22, 2000, p. 39)

realize. For example, at 5 percent interest, compounded daily, just $1 a day for 10 years will give you $4,700.

CALCULATING SAVINGS AMOUNTS

To achieve your financial objectives, you should convert your savings goals into specific amounts. While certain saving methods involve keeping money at home, those funds should be deposited in an interest-earning savings plan on a regular basis. To earn interest, you must learn to "hide" money, not in your home but in an account at a financial institution or with an investment company.

Your use of a savings or investment plan is vital to the growth of your money. As Exhibit 2–10 shows, using the time value of money calculations, introduced in Chapter 1, can help you achieve your financial goals.

TWO-INCOME HOUSEHOLDS

Since the 1970s, there has been a large shift in the financial structure of the family from single-earner households to dual-earner households. When women entered the workforce, budgeting strategies underwent a significant change. It was no longer reasonable for all resources to be pooled. Here are some suggestions for dual-income households.

[1] *Pooled Income:* Both incomes are combined, and bills are paid from the pool. This method requires trust and shared goals and values.

[2] *Sharing the Bills:* Each person is responsible for paying predetermined bills.

[3] *50/50:* Each person contributes an equal amount into the pool to cover shared expenses.

[4] *Proportionate Contributions:* This method is similar to the 50/50 method; however, each partner contributes a percentage of his/her income. This method is favourable when one partner earns a higher income than the other.

Exhibit 2–10

Using Savings to Achieve Financial Goals

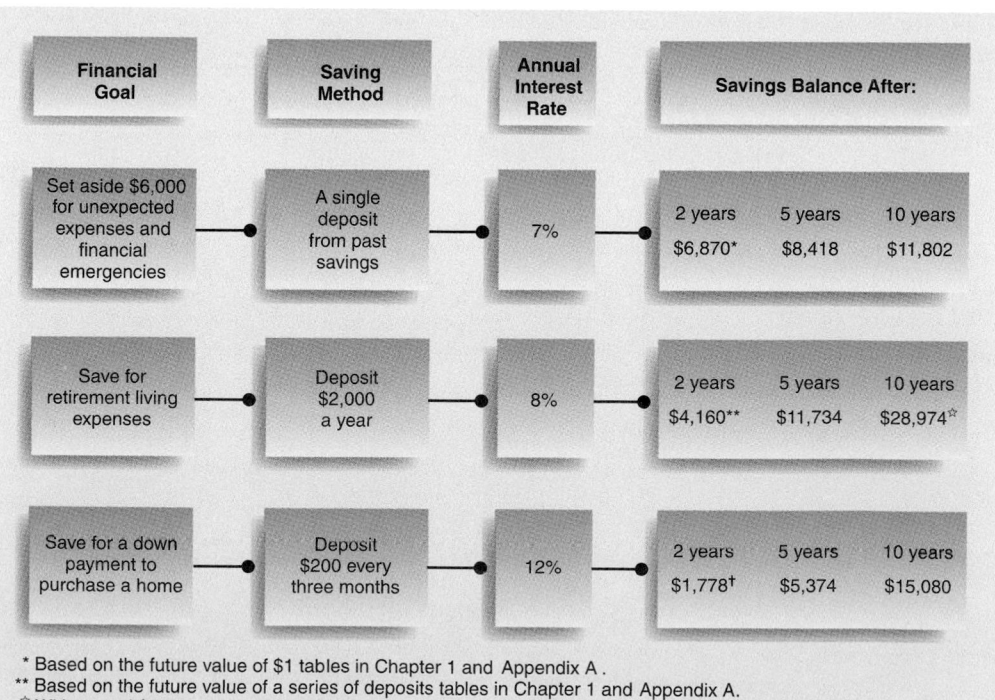

Financial Goal	Saving Method	Annual Interest Rate	Savings Balance After:		
			2 years	5 years	10 years
Set aside $6,000 for unexpected expenses and financial emergencies	A single deposit from past savings	7%	$6,870*	$8,418	$11,802
Save for retirement living expenses	Deposit $2,000 a year	8%	$4,160**	$11,734	$28,974☆
Save for a down payment to purchase a home	Deposit $200 every three months	12%	$1,778†	$5,374	$15,080

* Based on the future value of $1 tables in Chapter 1 and Appendix A.
** Based on the future value of a series of deposits tables in Chapter 1 and Appendix A.
☆ With annual $2,000 deposits, this same retirement account would grow to over $500,000 in 40 years.
† Based on quarterly compounding, explained in Chapter 4.

Learning to share financial responsibilities is something many households must face these days. The best solution is the sit down and discuss goals and values in order to make the right decision.

CONCEPT CHECK 2–5

1. What are some suggested methods to make saving easy?
2. What methods are available to calculate amounts needed to reach savings goals?

Visit the Web site
See the Post-Test under Chapter 2 on the online learning centre at www.mcgrawhill.ca/ college/kapoor.

SUMMARY OF OBJECTIVES

Objective 1
Recognize relationships among financial documents and money management activities.
Successful money management requires effective coordination of personal financial records, personal financial statements, and budgeting activities.

Objective 2
Create a system for maintaining personal financial records.
An organized system of financial records and documents is the foundation of effective money management. This system should provide ease of access as well as security for financial documents that may be impossible to replace.

Objective 3
Develop a personal balance sheet and cash flow statement.
A personal balance sheet, also known as a net worth statement, is prepared by listing all items of value (assets) and all amounts owed to others (liabilities). The difference between your total assets and your total liabilities is your net worth. A cash flow statement, also called a personal income and expenditure statement, is a summary of cash receipts and payments for a given period, such as a month or a year. This report provides data on your income and spending patterns.

Objective 4
Create and implement a budget.
The budgeting process involves four phases: (1) assessing your current personal and financial situation, (2) planning your financial direction by setting financial goals and creating budget allowances, (3) implementing your budget, and (4) evaluating your budgeting program.

Objective 5
Calculate savings needed to achieve financial goals.
Future value and present value calculations may be used to compute the increased value of savings for achieving financial goals.

KEY TERMS

assets 39

balance sheet 39

budget variance 50

budget 45

cash flow statement 42

cash flow 41

current liabilities 41

deficit 50

discretionary income 44

income 43

insolvency 41

liabilities 40

liquid assets 39

long-term liabilities 41

money management 36

net worth 41

safety deposit box 37

surplus 50

take-home pay 43

KEY FORMULAS

Page	Topic	Formula
41	Net worth	Net worth = Total assets − Total liabilities *Example:* = $125,000 − $53,000 = $72,000
43	Debt ratio	Debt ratio = Liabilities/Net worth *Example:* = $7,000/$21,000 = 0.33
43	Current ratio	Current ratio = Liquid assets/Current liabilities *Example:* = $8,500/$4,500 = 1.88
43	Liquidity ratio	Liquidity ratio = Liquid assets/Monthly expenses *Example:* = $8,500/$3,500 = 2.4
43	Debt-payments ratio	Debt-payments ratio = Monthly credit payments/Take-home pay *Example:* = $760/$3,800 = 0.20
43	Savings ratio	Savings ratio = Amount saved per month/Gross monthly income *Example:* = $460/$3,800 = 0.12
42	Cash surplus (or deficit)	Cash surplus (or deficit) = Total inflows − Total outflows *Example:* = $5,600 − $4,970 = $630 (surplus)

FINANCIAL PLANNING PROBLEMS

1. *Creating Personal Financial Statements.* On the basis of the procedures presented in the chapter, prepare your current personal balance sheet and a cash flow statement for the next month. (Obj. 3)

2. *Calculating Balance Sheet Amounts.* On the basis of the following data, compute the total assets, total liabilities, and net worth: (Obj. 3)
   - Liquid assets, $3,670
   - Investment assets, $8,340
   - Current liabilities, $2,670
   - Household assets, $89,890
   - Long-term liabilities, $76,230

3. *Preparing a Personal Balance Sheet.* Use the following items to prepare a balance sheet and a cash flow statement. Determine the total assets, total liabilities, net worth, total cash inflows, and total cash outflows. (Obj. 3)
   - Rent for the month, $650
   - Monthly take-home salary, $1,950
   - Cash in chequing account, $450
   - Savings account balance, $1,890
   - Spending for food, $345
   - Balance of educational loan, $2,160
   - Current value of automobile, $7,800
   - Telephone bill paid for month, $65
   - Credit card balance, $235
   - Loan payment, $80
   - Auto insurance, $230
   - Household possessions, $3,400
   - Stereo equipment, $2,350
   - Payment for electricity, $90
   - Lunches/parking at work, $180
   - Donations, $70
   - Home computer, $1,500
   - Value of stock investment, $860
   - Clothing purchase, $110
   - Restaurant spending, $130

4. *Computing Balance Sheet Amounts.* For each of the following situations, compute the missing amount: (Obj. 3)
   a. Assets $45,000; liabilities $16,000; net worth $_____
   b. Assets $76,500; liabilities $_____; net worth $18,700.
   c. Assets $34,280; liabilities $12,965; net worth $_____
   d. Assets $_____; liabilities $38,345; net worth $52,654

5. *Determining Budget Variances.* Fran Bowen created the following budget:
   Food, $350
   Transportation, $320
   Housing, $950
   Clothing, $100
   Personal expenses and recreation, $275
   She actually spent $298 for food, $337 for transportation, $982 for housing, $134 for clothing, and $231 for personal expenses and recreation. Calculate the variance for each of these categories, and indicate whether it was a *deficit* or a *surplus.* (Obj. 4)

6. *Calculating the Effect of Inflation.* Bill and Sally Kaplan have an annual spending plan that amounts to $36,000. If inflation is 5 percent a year for the next three years, what amount will the Kaplans need for their living expenses three years from now? (Obj. 4)

7. *Computing Time Value of Money for Savings.* Use future value and present value calculations (see examples in Appendix A) to determine the following: (Obj. 5)
   a. The future value of a $500 savings deposit after eight years at an annual interest rate of 7 percent.
   b. The future value of saving $1,500 a year for five years at an annual interest rate of 8 percent.
   c. The present value of a $2,000 savings account that will earn 6 percent interest for four years.

8. *Calculating Present Value of a Savings Fund.* Hal Thomas wants to establish a savings fund from which a community organization could draw $800 a year for 20 years. If the account earns 6 percent, what amount would he have to deposit now to achieve this goal? (Obj. 5)

FINANCIAL PLANNING ACTIVITIES

1. *Researching Money Management Information.* Using Web sites, library sources, friends, relatives, and others, obtain information on common suggestions for successful money management. (Obj. 1)
2. *Developing a Financial Document System.* Working with two or three others in your class, develop a system for filing and maintaining personal financial records. (Obj. 2)
3. *Comparing Financial Record Systems.* Conduct a survey of people of various ages to determine the system they use to keep track of various financial documents and records. (Obj. 2)
4. *Creating Personal Financial Statements.* Prepare a personal balance sheet and cash flow statement. (Obj. 3)
5. *Researching Household Asset Information on the Internet.* Using the World Wide Web or library research, find information about the assets commonly held by households in Canada. How have the values of assets, liabilities, and net worth of Canadian consumers changed in recent years? (Obj. 3)
6. *Researching Money Management Software.* Use the World Wide Web, store visits, or advertisements to determine the software a person might use to prepare personal financial statements, create a budget, and monitor spending, saving, and investing. (Obj. 3, 4)
7. *Analyzing Budgeting Situations* Discuss with several people how the budget in Exhibit 2–7 (p. 48) might be changed on the basis of various budget variances. If the household faced a decline in income, what spending areas might be reduced first? (Obj. 4)
8. *Comparing Budgeting Systems.* Ask two or three friends or relatives about their budgeting systems. Obtain information on how they maintain their spending records. Create a visual presentation (video or slide presentation) that communicates wise budgeting techniques. (Obj. 4)
9. *Analyzing Saving Habits.* Interview a young single person, a young couple, and a middle-aged person about their financial goals and savings habits. What actions do they take to determine and achieve various financial goals? (Obj. 5)

Out of Work but Not Out of Bills

Due to lower sales, the company for which Ed Weston works was cutting back on its workforce. Even though Ed had been with the company for seven years, most of his duties were being performed by new, automated equipment.

After getting the word about losing his job, Ed talked with his wife, Alice, and their two children (ages 12 and 9) about ways they could reduce spending. The Westons started by making up a list of three things: (1) bills they had to pay each month, (2) areas where they could reduce spending, and (3) sources of funds to help them pay current expenses. Each family member had several ideas to help them cope with the difficult financial burden that was likely to occur over the next few weeks and months.

Before Ed was unemployed, the Westons had a monthly take-home income of $3,165. Each month, the money went for the following items: $880 for rent, $180 for utilities, $560 for food, $480 for automobile expenses, $300 for clothing, $280 for insurance, $250 for savings, and $235 for personal and other items. After the loss of Ed's job, the household's monthly income is $1,550, from his wife's wages and his employment insurance (EI). The Westons also have savings accounts, investments, and retirement funds of $28,000.

Questions

1. What budget items might the Westons consider reducing to cope with their financial difficulties?
2. How should the Westons use their savings and retirement funds during this financial crisis? What additional sources of funds might be available to them during this period of unemployment?
3. What other current and future financial actions would you recommend to the Westons?

CREATING A FINANCIAL PLAN

Developing Personal Financial Statements and a Spending Plan

Money management activities are the basis for most financial planning activities. Creation of a financial document filing system, a personal balance sheet, a cash flow statement, and a budget provide you with tools for setting, implementing, and achieving financial goals.

Web Sites for Money Management

- Goal-setting and money management information at **www.canadianfinance.com** and **www.quicken.ca**.

- Budgeting and savings information at **www.royal bank.com/rmf** and **www.webfin.com**.

(Note: Addresses and content of Web sites change, and new sites are created daily. Use search engines to update and locate Web sites for your current financial planning needs.)

3 Planning Your Tax Strategy

I Owe How Much In Taxes?

The year is 2002. Stephanie Seymour is currently employed full time and earns an annual salary of $30,500. It has been a year since she graduated from university; however, she continues to take a few part-time courses in the evenings. Stephanie is currently paying off her student loan; she makes monthly contributions to her RRSP and has begun to build an income-generating investment portfolio. She recently moved away from her parents' home and into her own apartment in downtown Toronto, which allows her to be 40 km closer to work and school. It should also be noted that Stephanie has made contributions to a few charities over the year. Stephanie is currently preparing to file her 2001 personal income taxes and has gathered the following information:

Income—$30,500 plus $1,500 bonus (T4 Slip)

Federal Tax paid on income—$5,195.12 (T4 Slip)

Provincial Tax paid on income—$2,007.35 (T4 Slip)

Tuition (2 semesters = 8 part-time months)—$565 (T2202A slip)

Interest portion of payments on student loan—$835

Rent—$9,000

Moving expenses—$963.80

Rent on safety deposit box—$30

Investment income (Dividends)—$125 (T5 Slip)

RRSP contributions—$2,050

Charitable contributions—$65

We will follow Stephanie Seymour throughout the chapter as she completes her 2001 federal and provincial tax returns. All values are taken from this case as well as from Exhibit 3–2 (on pages 65–68) which presents her *T1 General 2001 - Income Tax and Benefit Return* for Ontario, as she filed it.

LEARNING OBJECTIVES

1 Describe the importance of taxes for personal financial planning.

2 Prepare federal and provincial income tax returns by calculating taxable income and the amount owed for federal and provincial income taxes.

3 Select appropriate tax strategies for different financial and personal situations.

4 Identify tax assistance sources.

Taxes and Financial Planning

Objective 1

Describe the importance of taxes for personal financial planning.

Visit the Web site
See the Chapter Overview under Chapter 3 on the online learning centre at www.mcgraw hill.ca/college/kapoor.

Taxes are an everyday financial fact of life. You pay some taxes every time you get a paycheque or make a purchase. However, most people concern themselves with taxes only in April. With about one-third of each dollar you earn going for taxes, an effective tax strategy is vital for successful financial planning. Familiarity with the tax rules and regulations can help you reduce your tax liability.

This financial obligation includes the many types of taxes discussed later in this section. To help you cope with these taxes, common goals related to tax planning include

- Knowing the current tax laws and regulations that affect you.
- Maintaining complete and appropriate tax records.
- Making purchase and investment decisions that can reduce your tax liability.

You should gear tax planning efforts toward paying your fair share of taxes while taking advantage of tax benefits appropriate to your personal and financial situation.

The principal purpose of taxes is to finance government activities. As citizens, we expect the government to provide such services as police and fire protection, schools, road maintenance, parks and libraries, and safety inspection of food, drugs, and other products. Most people pay taxes in four major categories: taxes on purchases, taxes on property, taxes on wealth, and taxes on earnings.

TAXES ON PURCHASES

excise tax A tax imposed on specific goods and services, such as gasoline, cigarettes, alcoholic beverages, tires, and air travel.

You probably pay sales tax on many of your purchases. These federal and provincial taxes are added to the purchase price of products. Many provinces exempt food and drugs from sales tax to reduce the economic burden of this tax on the poor. An **excise tax** is imposed by the federal and provincial governments on specific goods and services, such as gasoline, cigarettes, alcoholic beverages, tires, air travel, and telephone service.

TAXES ON PROPERTY

Real estate property tax is a major source of revenue for local governments. This tax is based on the value of land and buildings. The increasing amount of real estate property taxes is a major concern of homeowners. Retired people with fixed incomes may encounter financial difficulties when local property taxes increase rapidly.

Some areas also impose personal property taxes. Provincial and municipal governments may assess taxes on the value of automobiles, boats, furniture, and farm equipment.

DID YOU KNOW ?

In 2000, the average Canadian family had an income of $51,174 and paid $24,309 (47.5%) in federal, provincial, and municipal taxes. According to The Fraser Institute's annual Tax Freedom Day calculations, Canadians worked until June 29, 2001, to pay the total tax bill imposed on them by all levels of government. Forty years earlier, in 1961, Tax Freedom Day arrived a full 57 days sooner, on May 3. That means that on the average, every dollar you earned in the first half of 2001 was not for you, but for the government.

SOURCE: www.fraserinstitute.ca

TAXES ON WEALTH

Currently, the federal and provincial governments do not impose estate or inheritance taxes. However, federal tax liabilities may arise when income-generating investments are transferred to beneficiaries. An estate's executor(s) files a final "terminal" income tax return as of the date of death, which includes a deemed disposition of all assets owned by the individual as of that date.

In addition, the deceased is deemed to have disposed of all capital property upon death, which may trigger capital gains or losses. Thus, money and property passed on to heirs (other than a spouse) are subject to tax.

TAXES ON EARNINGS

Income taxes are used by the federal government to support a number of social benefit programs, such as the Canada Pension Plan and Employment Insurance. Income tax is a major financial planning factor for most people. Most workers are subject to federal and provincial income taxes.

Throughout the year, your employer will withhold income tax amounts from your paycheque, and you may be required to make income tax installments if you earn income from other sources, such as a business. Both types of payments are only estimates of your income taxes payable. You may need to pay an additional amount when you file your income tax return, or you may get a tax refund. The following sections will assist you in preparing your federal income tax return and planning your future tax strategies.

> **DID YOU KNOW ?**
>
> Personal Taxes paid in Canada in 2000 totalled $5.8 billion.
>
> SOURCE: www.cba.ca

> **CONCEPT CHECK 3-1**
>
> 1. How should you consider taxes in your financial planning?
> 2. What types of taxes do people frequently overlook when making financial decisions?

Filing Your Federal and Provincial Income Tax Return

As you stare at those piles of papers, you know it's time to do your taxes! Submitting your federal income tax return requires several decisions and actions. First, you must determine whether you are required to file a return. Next, you need to decide which basic form best serves your needs and whether you are required to submit additional schedules or supplementary forms. Finally, you must prepare your return. Note that students should file a return, even if they do not expect to pay tax, to get GST and QST refunds and, if applicable, other housing refunds.

WHO MUST FILE?

All residents and citizens of Canada must file a tax return for any year in which they have a balance of taxes owing. In addition, the federal government will tax Canadian citizens who are nonresidents of Canada on certain income from Canadian sources.

If you are a resident of Quebec on December 31 of a given taxation year, you will be able to choose between either the general tax filing system or the simplified system. While the former allows a series of Quebec deductions as well as nonrefundable tax credits, the simplified system allows you to claim a single lump-sum amount of $2,625. Obviously, you will want to choose the system that gives you the greater tax savings, so you should estimate your payable taxes under both systems to establish the one that is more advantageous for your situation.

FILING QUEBEC TAX RETURNS

Quebec is the only province that does not "piggyback" on the federal system of personal taxation, and as a result, its residents must file both a federal tax return and a separate Quebec tax return.

> **DID YOU KNOW ?**
>
> Budget 2001 will protect the five year, $100-billion tax cut plan and the $23.4 billion in increased support for health care and early childhood development.
>
> SOURCE: www.fin.gc.ca

While the Quebec *Taxation Act* has a number of similarities with the federal *Income Tax Act*, there are still a number of differences. If you must file a return in the province of Quebec, it is imperative that you contact the Québec Ministère du Revenu for further information. Quebec tax forms and guides are available in both French and English from the provincial government's Web site at www.gouv.qc.ca.

Income Tax Fundamentals

Objective 2

Prepare federal and provincial income tax returns by calculating taxable income and the amount owed for federal and provincial taxes

taxable income The net amount of income, after allowable deductions, on which income tax is computed.

employment income Money received for personal effort, such as wages, salary, commission, fees, tips, or bonuses.

investment income Money received in the form of dividends, interest, capital gains, or rent from investments. Also called *portfolio income.*

passive income Income resulting from business activities in which one does not actively participate.

exclusion An amount not included in total income.

tax-deferred income Income that will be taxed at a later date.

tax shelter An investment that provides immediate tax benefits and a reasonable expectation of a future profit.

Each year, millions of Canadians are required to pay their share of income taxes to the federal government. The process involves computing taxable income, determining the amount of income tax owed, and comparing this amount with the income tax payments withheld or made during the year.

STEP 1: DETERMINING TOTAL INCOME

Taxable income is the net amount of income, after allowable deductions and expenses are deducted, on which income tax is computed. Exhibit 3–1 presents the components of taxable income and the process used to compute it.

TYPES OF INCOME Most, but not all, income is subject to taxation. Your total income can consist of four main components:

[1] Employment income is money received for personal effort. Employment income is usually in the form of salary, commission, fees, tips, or bonuses.

> Stephanie's T4 slip shows that her employment income for the year 2001 is $32,000 ($30,500 salary + $1,500 bonus) (see line 101 in Exhibit 3–2 on page 66).

[2] Investment income, sometimes referred to as *portfolio income*, is money received in the form of dividends, interest, capital gains, or rent from investments.

> Stephanie's T5 slip shows that her investment income for the year 2001 is $156.25 in dividends. As seen on line 120 in Exhibit 3–2, this "grossed-up" amount is calculated by multiplying the actual dividend received by 125 percent ($125 x 125% = $156.25). See Chapter 10 for more details on the dividend gross-up calculation.

[3] Passive income results from business activities in which you do not actively participate, such as a limited partnership.

[4] Other income amounts for scholarships, bursaries, study grants, fellowships and artist grants.

Total income is unaffected by exclusions. An **exclusion** (also referred to as tax-exempt income) is an amount received but not included in total income for tax purposes. For example, the first $10,000 of a death benefit paid in recognition of a deceased employee's service by a company to the spouse of the deceased is exempt from tax.

Tax-deferred income is income that will be taxed at a later date. Common examples of tax-deferred income are the returns on investments held in Registered Retirement Savings Plans (RRSPs), Registered Pension Plans (RPPs), and Individual Pension Plans (IPPs). In addition, capital gains can be considered tax-deferred income since taxes are normally paid once a gain is realized on a sale. While these earnings are credited to the account now, you do not pay taxes on them until you withdraw them.

Certain adjustments to income, such as tax-deferred retirement plans, are a type of tax shelter. **Tax shelters** are investments that provide immediate tax benefits and a reasonable expectation of a future profit. In recent years, tax court rulings and changes in the tax code have disallowed various types of tax shelters that were considered excessive.

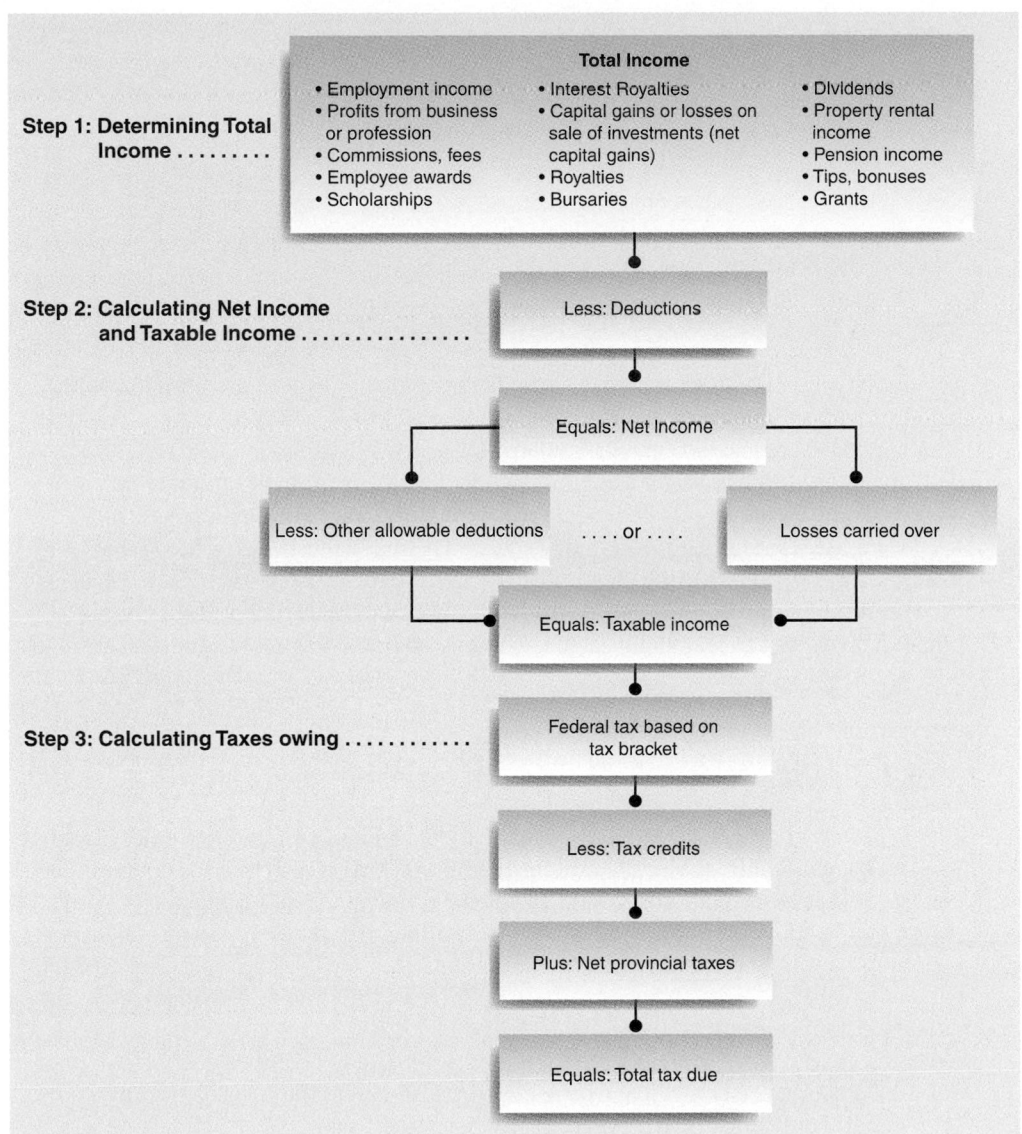

Exhibit 3–1

Computing
Taxable Income
and Your Tax
Liability

STEP 2: CALCULATING NET INCOME AND TAXABLE INCOME

Net income is total income after certain reductions have been made and is used as the basis for computing various income tax credits, such as medical expenses.

Deductions are expenses that a taxpayer is allowed to deduct from total income. Common deductions include the following:

- *Contributions* to registered deferred income plans, such as pension funds and registered saving plans.

> Stephanie is able to deduct $2,050 from her total income because she invested this amount in an RRSP before March 1, 2002. In order to calculate her maximum RRSP deduction, she has to determine the lower of the following two amounts:
>
> 1. The unused RRSP contribution shown on her *Notice of Assessment* or *Notice of Reassessment* for 2000 (that is, the amount she contributed to her RRSP in 2000 but did not claim as a deduction) **plus** the total of her RRSP contributions made in 2001.
> 2. Her RRSP deduction limit for 2001 plus the amounts she transferred to her RRSP on or before March 1, 2002.

net income Total income reduced by certain adjustments, such as contributions to an RRSP or RPP.

deductions Expenses that can be deducted from total income, such as certain medical expenses, child care expenses, union dues, attendant fees, investment counselling fees, and certain employment-related expenses.

Stephanie could not remember what her unused contributions were because she could not find her *Notice of Assessment* or *Notice of Reassessment* for 2000. Luckily, the CCRA offers a service called "T.I.P.S" (Tax Information Phone Service) which can be accessed by phone 1-800-267-6999 or online at www.ccra.gc.ca/tips. This service tells you what your RRSP deduction limit was as well as your unused contributions; it also allows you to track the status of your refund and offers plenty of useful information.

By calling T.I.P.S. Stephanie found out that her unused contributions for 2000 totalled $450 and her deduction limit was $7,450. Therefore, the maximum contributions she can deduct is $2,500 (option A $450 unused contribution + $2,050 contribution made prior to March 1, 2002) (see line 208 in Exhibit 3–2).

- *Union and professional dues* are generally deductible. Union dues are normally withheld at source and reported on the T4 and Québec Relevé 1 you receive from your employer. Dues required to maintain a legally recognized professional status are deductible, even if you do not need to maintain that status for your current job.
- *Moving expenses* are largely deductible if you move to start working at a new location, to move closer to school, or to start a business. The move must be to a home that is 40 km closer to your new work location than your old home. The 40-km distance is measured according to the shortest normal route of travel, not as a straight line between points. The deduction is not allowable if you are moving either to or from Canada.

Stephanie moved more than 40 km in order to start her new job; therefore, she can deduct the moving expenses from her $32, 000 salary for the year 2001. Please see Exhibit 3–2a on page 69 for Stephanie's calculation of allowable moving expenses. (See line 219 in Exhibit 3–2.)

- *Child care expenses* can be deducted, usually by the spouse with the lower net income in a two-parent family, subject to various limitations. This is also true for common-law couples who meet certain criteria. Single parents can deduct child care expenses from their own income. These expenses include babysitting, day nursery service, day camps, boarding schools, and camps. The criteria for eligibility are that these services free the parents to work, to carry on business, to attend school full time or part time, or to conduct grant-funded research.
- *Expenses to pay for an attendant for disabled people* may be either deducted as such or may be claimed as a medical expense credit. The deduction is limited to two-thirds of your earned income, which is essentially the sum of your salary and business income.
- *Other deductions* might include interest paid on loans, the proceeds of which are used to earn investment income; legal fees, if paid for specific purposes, such as disputed support or severance payments; a deduction for residents of northern Canada; and deductions for allowable business expenses, capital gains, carrying changes and interest expenses, and others.

Stephanie is allowed to deduct her safety deposit box fees because it is a deductible expense (she stores her bonds, her bond indenture, and other valuables in the safety deposit box). (See 221 in Exhibit 3–2.)

Your deductions are subtracted from total income to obtain your net income. Finally, other allowable deductions, such as the capital gains deduction (see below) and losses carried forward from other years, are deducted from net income to arrive at taxable income. The Financial Planning for Life's Situations box on page 71 can help you determine which items to include in your taxable income when you calculate your federal income tax.

You are required to maintain sufficient records to support tax deductions. Financial advisers recommend a home filing system (see Exhibit 3–3a on page 71) for storing receipts and other tax documents. Travel expenses can be documented in a daily log with records of mileage, tolls, parking fees, and away-from-home costs.

Generally, you should keep tax records for three years from the date you receive your notice of assessment. However, you may be required to provide backup documentation for up to six years from filing. Certain records, such as housing documents, should be kept indefinitely.

Stephanie's net income is $31, 662.45
Total income = $35, 156.25
Deductions = $ 3, 493.80 ($2, 500 RRSP + $963.80 moving expenses + $30 safety deposit box fees)
Net income = $31, 662.45
(See line 236 in Exhibit 3–2.)

CAPITAL GAINS EXEMPTION Capital gains arising from the sale of an individual's principal residence are exempt from taxes. A $100,000 capital gains exemption on all kinds

Exhibit 3–2

Canada Customs and Revenue Agency / Agence des douanes et du revenu du Canada

T1 GENERAL 2001

Income Tax and Benefit Return

Identification

ON 8

Attach your personal label here. Correct any wrong information.
If you are not attaching a label, print your name and address below.

First name and initial: Stephanie A.
Last name: Seymour
Mailing address: Apt. No. – Street No. Street name: 1414 King Street #6
P.O. Box, R.R.
City: Toronto Prov./Terr.: ON Postal code: M6J 3B1

Information about you

Enter your social insurance number (SIN) if it is not on the label, or if you are not attaching a label: 671 234 567

Enter your date of birth: Year Month Day

Your language of correspondence: / Votre langue de correspondance : English [X] Français [ ]

Check the box that applies to your marital status on December 31, 2001: (see the "Marital status" section in the guide for details)

1 [ ] Married 2 [ ] Living common law 3 [ ] Widowed
4 [ ] Divorced 5 [ ] Separated 6 [X] Single

Information about your spouse or common-law partner (if you checked box 1 or 2 above)

Enter his or her SIN if it is not on the label, or if you are not attaching a label:

Enter his or her first name:

Enter his or her net income for 2001 to claim certain credits: (see the guide for details)

Check this box if he or she was self-employed in 2001: 1 [ ]

If this return is for a deceased person, enter the date of death: Year Month Day

Do not use this area

Information about your residence

Enter your province or territory of residence on **December 31, 2001**:

Enter the province or territory where you **currently** reside if it is not the same as that shown above for your mailing address:

If you were self-employed in 2001, enter the province or territory of self-employment:

If you became or ceased to be a resident of Canada **in 2001**, give the date of: entry (Month Day) or departure (Month Day)

Elections Canada (Canadian citizens only; see the guide for details)

Do you authorize the Canada Customs and Revenue Agency to provide your name, address, and date of birth to Elections Canada for the **National Register of Electors**? .... Yes [X] 1 No [ ] 2
Your authorization is needed each year. This information will be used for electoral purposes only.

Goods and services tax / Harmonized sales tax (GST/HST) credit application

Are you applying for the GST/HST credit? (see the guide for details).. Yes [X] 1 No [ ] 2

If *yes*, we will now get the number of children for purposes of this credit from the Canada Child Tax Benefit information we have on file.

Your guide contains valuable information to help you complete your return.

When you come to a line on the return that applies to you, look up the line number in the guide for more information.

Do not use this area 172 171

SOURCE: www.ccra-adrc.gc.ca

of property was available before February 22, 1994. However, current regulations entitle the individual to a $500,000 lifetime "capital gains exemption" on qualified small business corporation shares and farm property. Note that under the *Income Tax Act*, and on all forms from the Canada Customs and Revenue Agency (CCRA; formerly Revenue Canada), this exemption is referred to as a capital gains *deduction* because the realized capital gains are included in determining total income but are then offset as a deduction to arrive at taxable income. After deducting the amounts for exemptions, you obtain your taxable income, which is the amount used to determine taxes owed.

STEP 3: CALCULATING TAXES OWING

Your taxable income is the basis for computing the amount of your income tax owing. Tax rates and the benefits of tax credits are the final phase of the tax computation process.

Exhibit 3–2

(continued)

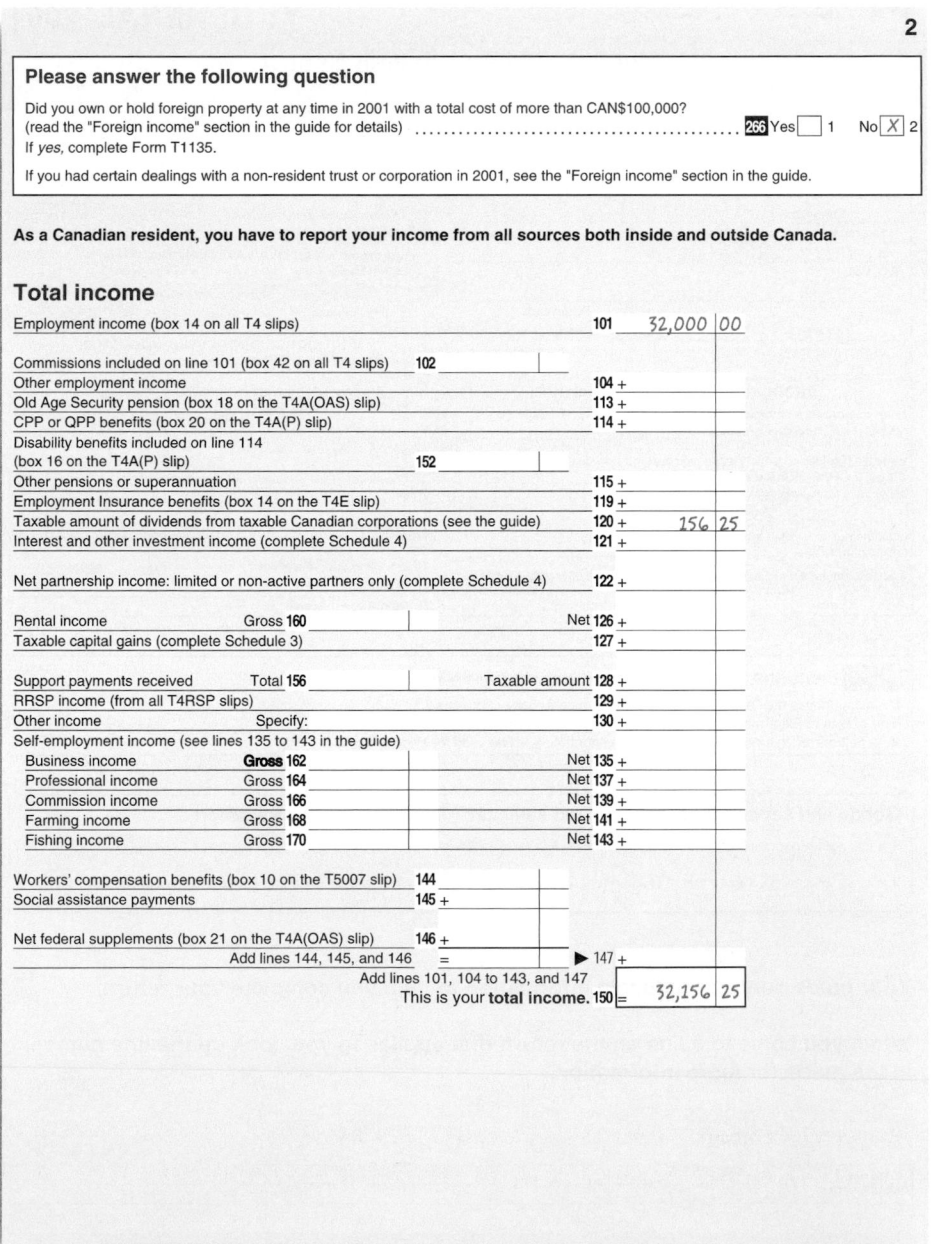

SOURCE: www.ccra-adrc.gc.ca

TAX RATES Using your taxable income, the appropriate federal, provincial and combined marginal rates can be determined. With the exception of Quebec, all provinces and territories have adopted the Tax on Income also known as the TONI system. TONI is a method of calculating provincial and territorial personal income tax, which parallels the federal calculations with taxable income as the starting point. The TONI system replaces the tax on tax calculations. The province of Quebec continues to administer its own provincial income taxes (more on page 61). Ontario figures are presented to illustrate these marginal rates. Note that these rates take into account the Economic Statement and Budget tabled by the federal government on October 18, 2000, which intends to gradually reduce marginal income tax rates over the next five years. See the table at the top of the next page.

> ### DID YOU KNOW ?
>
> The reductions announced in the Federal October 2000 economic statement will lower the personal income tax burden on average by 21 percent and by 27 percent for families with children by 2004-2005.
>
> SOURCE: Department of Finance Canada www.fin.gc.ca.

Exhibit 3-2
(continued)

Attach here all of the schedules, information slips, forms, receipts, and other documents that you need to attach to your return.   3

Net income

Enter your **total income** from line 150	150	35,156 25
Pension adjustment (box 52 on all T4 slips and box 34 on all T4A slips) 206		
Registered pension plan deduction (box 20 on all T4 slips and box 32 on all T4A slips)	207	
RRSP deduction (see Schedule 7; attach receipts)	208 +	2,500 00
Saskatchewan Pension Plan deduction (maximum $600)	209 +	
Annual union, professional, or like dues (box 44 on all T4 slips, or from receipts)	212 +	
Child care expenses (complete Form T778)	214 +	
Attendant care expenses	215 +	
Business investment loss Gross **228** Allowable deduction	217 +	
Moving expenses *(See EXHIBIT 3-2a)*	219 +	963 80
Support payments made Total **230** Allowable deduction	220 +	
Carrying charges and interest expenses (complete Schedule 4)	221 +	30 00
Deduction for CPP or QPP contributions on self-employment and other earnings (complete Schedule 8)	222 +	
Exploration and development expenses (complete Schedule 4)	224 +	
Other employment expenses	229 +	
Clergy residence deduction (complete Form T1223)	231 +	
Other deductions Specify:	232 +	
Add lines 207 to 224, 229, 231, and 232.	233 = ▶ −	3,493 80
Line 150 minus line 233 (if negative, enter "0"). This is your **net income before adjustments.**	234 =	
Social benefits repayment (if you reported income on line 113, 119, or 146, see line 235 in the guide)	235 −	
Line 234 minus line 235 (if negative, enter "0"). If you have a spouse or common-law partner, see line 236 in the guide. This is your **net income.**	236 =	31,662 45

Taxable income

Employee home relocation loan deduction (box 37 on all T4 slips)	248	
Stock option and shares deductions	249 +	
Other payments deduction (if you reported income on line 147, see line 250 in the guide)	250 +	
Limited partnership losses of other years	251 +	
Non-capital losses of other years	252 +	
Net capital losses of other years	253 +	
Capital gains deduction	254 +	
Northern residents deductions (complete Form T2222)	255 +	
Additional deductions Specify:	256 +	
Add lines 248 to 256.	257 = ▶ −	
Line 236 minus line 257 (if negative, enter "0") This is your **taxable income.**	260 =	31,662 45

Use your taxable income to calculate your federal tax on Schedule 1.

Starting this year you will also use Schedule 1 to claim your federal non-refundable tax credits.

SOURCE: www.ccra-adrc.gc.ca

2001 Income Tax Rates for Ontario residents

Income Tax bracket ($)	Fed. Marginal Rate (%) [2]	Ont. Marginal Rate (%)	Combined Rate (%)
30,754 or less	16	6.16	22.16
30,754–30,813	22	6.16	28.16
30,814–53,801	22	9.22	31.22
53,802–61,508[1]	22	9.22	33.06
61,509–61,628	26	9.22	37.06
61,629–63,505	26	11.16	39.39
63,506–99,999[1]	26	11.16	43.41
100,000 or more	29	11.16	46.41

[1] Ontario's marginal tax rate reflects the basic personal amount as well as the 20 percent surtax on provincial tax in excess of $3,560 (applicable to a taxable income of $53,802 or more) and the 36 percent surtax on provincial tax in excess of $4,491 (applicable to a taxable income of $63, 506 or more), but does not take into account the provincial tax reduction for low-income taxpayers.
[2] The federal marginal tax rate takes into account the basic personal amount.

SOURCE: www.taxprep.com 2001 Income Tax Rates for Ontario Residents. From "Things to Remember," Booklet published by CCH Canadian Tax Compliance Group. © 2001. Reprinted with permission.

Exhibit 3–2

(continued)

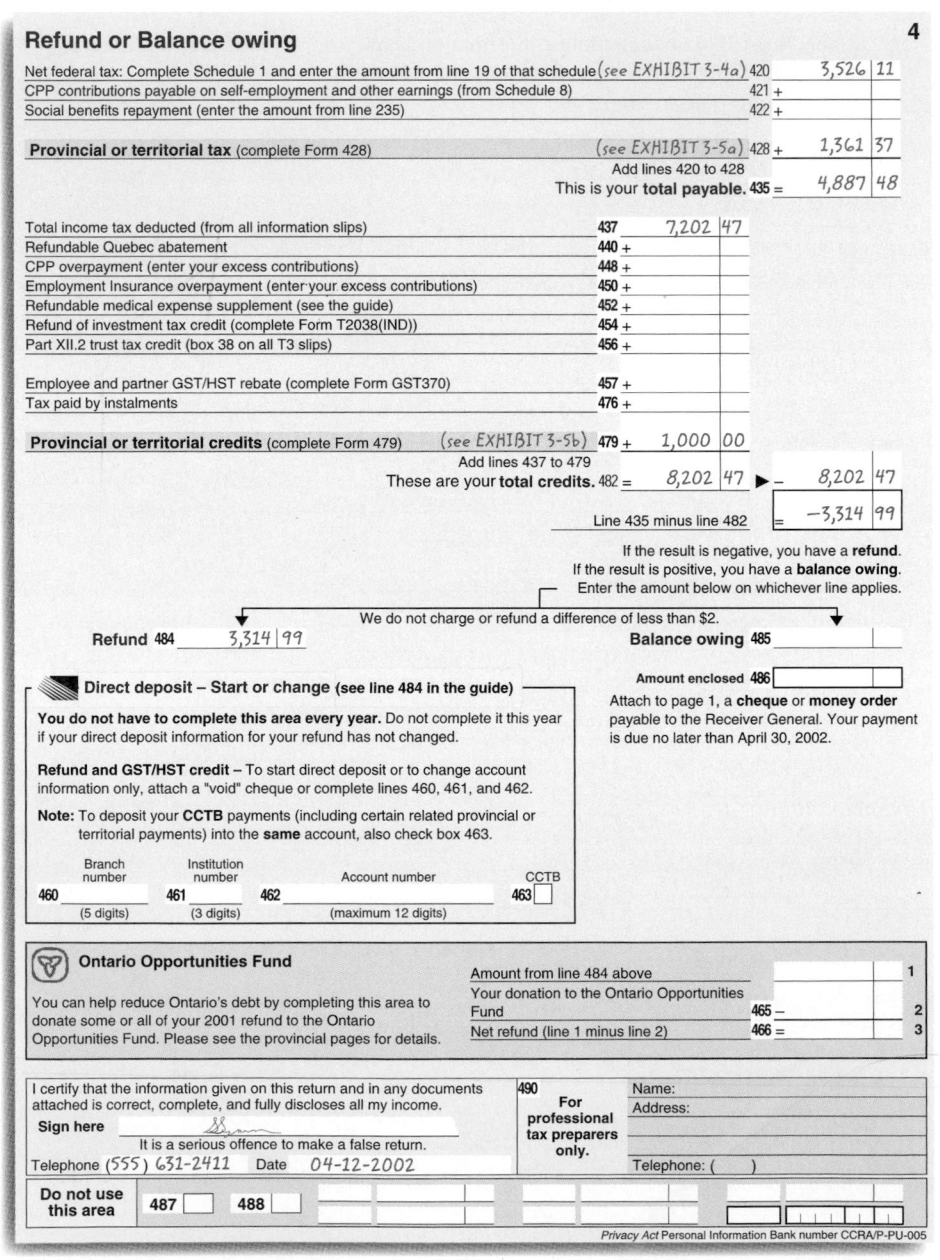

Your **marginal tax rate** is the rate you pay on the last dollar earned. For example, suppose you earned taxable income of $35,000 per year in Ontario. The first $30,754 will be taxed at 16 percent, while the remainder of your income will be taxed at 22 percent. The next dollar you earn will be taxed by the federal government at a rate of 22 percent (or a combined federal and provincial marginal tax rate of 31.22 percent).

In contrast, the **average tax rate** is based on the total tax due divided by total income. Except for taxpayers in the 16 percent tax bracket, this rate is less than a person's marginal tax rate. For example, an Ontario resident with total income of $40,000 and total tax bill of $8,057 (see Exhibit 3–9 on page 87 which computes the total federal and provincial taxes) would have an *average tax rate* of 21.15%. Exhibit 3–2b, on the next page, shows provincial tax rates, surtaxes, and the maximum combined marginal tax rate for all provinces and territories.

marginal tax rate The rate of tax paid on the last (and next) dollar of taxable income.

average tax rate Total tax due divided by total income.

Exhibit 3–2a

Calculation of allowable moving expences

Transportation and storage costs for household effects	650 00 1
Name of mover ABC Movers	
Travelling expenses from old residence to new residence	
Travel costs (other than accommodation and meals) For ONTARIO 42.5¢/km	+ 23 80 2
Number of household members in move 1	
Method of travel car	
Number of kilometres 56km	
Accommodation	+ 185 00 3
Number of nights 2	
Meals	+ 105 00 4
Number of days 3	
Temporary living expenses near new or old residence (maximum 15 days)	
Accommodation	+ 5
Number of nights	
Meals	+ 6
Number of days	
Cost of cancelling the lease for your old residence	+ 7
Incidental costs related to the move (specify)	+ 8
Costs to maintain your old residence when vacant (maximum $5,000)	+ 9
Cost of selling old residence	
Selling price $	
Real estate commission	+ 10
Legal or notarial fees	+ 11
Advertising	+ 12
Other selling costs (specify)	+ 13
Cost of purchasing new residence	
Purchase price $	
Legal or notarial fees	+ 14
Taxes paid for the registration or transfer of title (Do not include GST/HST or property taxes)	+ 15
Add lines 1 to 15 **Total moving expenses**	= 963 80 16
Enter any reimbursement or allowance that is not included in your income, and that you received for moving expenses that you claimed on line 16	= 17
Line 16 minus line 17 **Net moving expenses**	= 963 80 18
If you moved to start a job or a business, enter your net income for the year from employment or self-employment in the new work location. If you moved to study full time, enter your income for the year from scholarships, bursaries, fellowships, research grants, and prizes for achievement **Eligible income**	32,000 00 19
Enter the amount from line 18 or line 19, whichever is **less**.	
Enter the result on line 219 of your return **Allowable moving expenses**	963 80 20

If line 18 is more than line 19, you can carry forward the unused part (line 18 minus line 19) and deduct it from eligible income for the year after you move.

SOURCE: Calculation of allowable moving expenses. www.ccra-adrc.gc.ca Reproduced with permission of the Minister of Public Works and Government Services Canada 2002.

Exhibit 3–2b

Pro./Terr.	Taxable Income	Provincial Rate	Max. Combined Rate
NF	0–$29,590 $29,591–$59,180 Over $59,181	10.57% 16.16% 18.02% Surtax: 9% of PT > $7,032	48.64%
PE	0–$30,754 $30,755–$61,509 Over $61,510	9.8% 13.8% 16.7% Surtax:10% of PT> $5,200	47.37%
NS	0–$29,590 $29,591–$59,180 Over $59,181	9.77% 14.95% 16.67% Surtax:10% of PT>$10,000	47.34%
NB	0–$30,754 $30,75–$61,509 $61,510–$100,000 Over $ 100,000	9.68% 14.82% 16.52% 17.84%	46.84%
QC	0–$26,000 $26,001–$52,000 Over $52,001	17.00% 21.25% 24.50%	48.72%
ON	0–$30,814 $30,815–$61,629 Over $61,630	6.16% 9.22% 11.16% Surtax: 20% of PT> $3,560 Surtax: 36% of PT> $4,491	46.41%
MB	0–$30,544 $30,54–$61,089 Over $61,090	10.9% 16.2% 17.4%	46.40%
SK	0–$30,000 $30,001–$60,000 Over $60,001	11.5% 13.5% 16.0%	45.00%
AB		10% flat rate applicable on taxable income	39.00%
BC	0–$30,484 $30,485–$60,969 $60,970–$70,000 $70,001–$85,000 Over $ 85,001	7.3% 10.5% 13.7% 13.7% 16.7%	45.70%
YT	0–$30,754 $30,754–$61,509 $61,510–$100,000 Over $100,000	7.36% 10.12% 11.96% 13.34% Surtax: 5% of TT > $6,000	43.01%
NT / NU	0 – $30,754 $30,754–$61,509 $61,510–$100,000 Over $100,000	7.2% 9.9% 11.7% 13.05%	42.05%
Non-residents of Canada		48% of BFT	42.92%

Note: BFT = Basic Federal Tax; PT=Provincial Tax; TT= Territorial Tax
SOURCE: www.taxprep.com Personal Tax Credits. From "Things to Remember," Booklet published by CCH Canadian Tax Compliance Group. © 2001. Reprinted with permission.

Stephanie's net income of $31,662.45 is equal to her taxable income because she has no additional deductions to claim. Thus, her first $30,754 will be taxed by the federal government at 16% and the remaining $908.45 will be taxed at 22% (see the 2001 Income Tax Rates for Ontario residents table). Therefore, she owes $5,120.86 in taxes prior to subtracting her tax credits ($30,754 × 16% = $4,921.00 and $ 908.45 × 22% = $199.86; this gives $4,921.00 + $199.86 = $5,120.86) See line 8 in Exhibit 3–4a on page 73. In addition she can use her taxable income to calculate her provincial taxes which will total $1,976.22 ($30,814 × 6.16% = $1,898.00 and $848.45 × 9.22% = $78.23; this gives $1,898.00 + $78.23 = $1,976.22) See line 8 in Exhibit 3–5a on pages 76 and 77.

Financial Planning for Life's Situations

IS IT TAXABLE INCOME? IS IT DEDUCTIBLE?

Certain financial benefits individuals receive are not subject to federal income tax. Indicate whether each of the following items would or would not be included in taxable income when you compute your federal income tax.

	Yes	No
Is it taxable income . . . ?		
1. Lottery winnings	____	____
2. Child support received	____	____
3. Workers' compensation benefits	____	____
4. Life insurance death benefits	____	____
5. Provincial bond interest earnings	____	____
6. Bartering income	____	____
7. GST/HST Credit	____	____

Note: These taxable income items and deductions are based on the 2001 tax year and may change due to changes in the *Income Tax Act*.

Indicate whether each of the following items would or would not be deductible when you compute your federal income tax.

	Yes	No
Is it deductible . . . ?		
8. Life insurance premiums	____	____
9. Cosmetic surgery for improved looks	____	____
10. Fees for traffic violation tickets	____	____
11. Mileage for driving to volunteer work	____	____
12. A notary's fee for preparing a will	____	____
13. Income tax preparation fee	____	____

Answers: 3, 5, 6, 9—yes; 1, 2, 4, 7, 8, 10, 11, 12,13 —no.

Exhibit 3–3a   A Tax Recordkeeping System

Tax Returns and Tax Filing Information

- Current tax returns and instruction booklets
- Reference books on current tax laws and tax-saving techniques
- Social insurance numbers of household members
- Copies of federal tax returns from previous years

Income Records

- T4 slips reporting salary and taxes withheld at source
- T4 slips reporting pension income
- T5 slips reporting interest, dividends, and capital gains and losses from savings and investments
- Other slips for Employment Insurance benefits, royalty income, retirement, and other support payments

Expense Records

- Receipts for medical, dependant care, charitable donations, and employment-related expenses
- Business, investment, and rental-property expense documents

Exhibit 3–3b   Personal Tax Credits

PERSONAL TAX CREDITS (FEDERAL)

Under the definition provided by the Income Tax Act, personal tax credits are equal to the prescribed amount multiplied by the basic rate for the year. The basic rate is 16 percent.

	2001
Basic personal amount	$7,412.00
Amount with respect to age	$3,619.00
Reduced by net income in excess of	$26,941.00
Amount for an eligible dependant	$6,293.00
Reduced by net income in excess of	$630.00
Amount for infirm dependants	$3,500.00
Reduced by net income in excess of	$4,966.00
Caregiver amount	$3,500.00
Reduced by net income in excess of	$11,953.00
Contributions to QPP/CPP	
Employee	$1,496.40
Self-employed	$3,500.00
Employment insurance	$877.50
Pension income amount	$1,000.00
Disability amount	$6,000.00
Disability amount supplement for children	$3,500.00
Tuition fee	Amount paid
Amount of full-time education	$400.00
Amount of part-time education	$120.00
Interest on student loans	Amount paid
Charitable donations, gifts to government and cultural or ecological gifts	Amount paid
Medical expenses	Amount paid

SOURCE: www.taxprep.com Personal Tax Credits. From "Things to Remember," Booklet published by CCH Canadian Tax Compliance Group. © 2001. Reprinted with permission.

Financial Planning Calculations

TAX CREDITS VERSUS TAX DEDUCTIONS

Many people confuse *tax credits* with *tax deductions*. Is one better than the other? A tax *credit*, such as tuition fees or medical expenses, results in a dollar-for-dollar reduction in the amount of taxes owed. A tax *deduction*, such as an RRSP contribution, reduces the taxable income on which your taxes are based.

All tax credits reduce taxes payable with the limitation that taxes payable cannot be reduced below zero. Aside from political donations and the dividend tax credit (which require additional procedural calculations), the amount claimed is multiplied by 16 percent to arrive at the tax credit. For example, if $100 is spent on tuition, then about $16 can be claimed as a direct reduction of taxes ($100 × .16).

On the other hand, a deduction of $100 may or may not reduce your taxes by $16 because the tax savings arising from the deduction will depend on your marginal tax rate. Note that tax savings are simply equal to the deduction multiplied by the marginal tax rate. Thus, it

should be apparent that a tax credit of one dollar is worth more than a deduction worth one dollar. However, making a comparison of whether spending on a deductible item is better than spending on an item that generates tax credits requires a careful specification of several variables, including your marginal federal rate, the province you reside in, the rules attributed to the tax credit in question, and so on. Careful financial planning will help you use both tax credits and tax deductions to your maximum advantage.

> **$100 Tax Deduction**
>
> ↓
>
> Reduces your taxable income by $100. The amount of your tax reduction depends on your tax bracket. Your federal taxes will be reduced by $16 if you are in the 16 percent tax bracket and by $22 if you are in the 22 percent tax bracket.

Taxpayers who benefit from the special treatment given to certain income and receive special deductions may be subject to an additional tax. The *alternative minimum tax (AMT)* is designed to ensure that those who receive tax breaks also pay their fair share of taxes. Further discussion of the AMT is beyond the scope of this book; you may obtain information from the Canada Customs and Revenue Agency.

tax credit An amount subtracted directly from the amount of taxes owing.

TAX CREDITS The tax owing may be reduced by a **tax credit**, an amount subtracted from the amount of taxes owed. (See the Financial Planning Calculations feature above.) Personal credits, such as the basic, spousal, dependants, age, and disability credits, will reduce your payable income tax directly according to how each may apply to your situation. Some of the other credits that might also be claimed are for charitable or political donations, caregiver and medical expenses, tuition fees, interest on student loans, and dividend tax credits (see Exhibit 3–3b on the previous page).

In addition, every individual gets a federal tax credit of $1,186 (the basic personal amount), which offsets the federal tax on your first $7,412 of taxable income. People with a severe and prolonged mental or physical disability receive an additional federal tax credit of $6,000.

Note that while most of the amounts claimed are multiplied by 16 percent to arrive at the tax credit, certain tax credits, such as political donations and the dividend tax credit, require additional calculations (see Chapter 10 for examples of how the dividend tax credit is computed).

> ## DID YOU KNOW ?
>
> The Government's tax cuts have put $17 billion back into the pockets of Canadian families in 2001, and this figure will grow to $20 billion for 2002.
>
> SOURCE: www.fin.gc.ca

Ontario has its own nonrefundable tax credits which reduces the amount of provincial tax that one owes. However, if the total of these credits is greater than the amount of provincial tax you owed, you will not receive a refund. The rules for claiming the Ontario nonrefundable tax credits are the same as for the federal nonrefundable tax credits. However, the values and calculations are different. Each province and territory has a different way of calculating tax credits. Visit the CCRA website at www.ccra-adrc.gc.ca for information on your tax credits.

Federal tax credits:

As illustrated on the Federal Tax Schedule 1 Exhibit 3–4a, Stephanie can claim total federal nonrefundable tax credits of $1,594.75. These credits include the basic personal amount of $7,412.00, the interest paid on her student loan of $835 and her tuition and education amounts of $1,525 (from Schedule 11 Exhibit 3–4b on page 75). These credits add up to $9,772.00 ($7,412 + $835 + $1,525). This amount of $9,772.00 is then multiplied by 16 percent

Exhibit 3–4a

to give $1, 563.52. At this point, Stephanie can add $10.40 for her donations from Schedule 9 Exhibit 3–4c ($65 × 16%) plus the 13.33 percent dividend tax credit of $20.83 ($156.25 × 13.33%). This adds up to a total of $1,594.75 mentioned above ($1, 563.52 + $10.40 + $20.83).

Provincial tax credits:

As illustrated on Schedule ON428 Exhibit 3–5a (on pages 76–77), Stephanie can claim similar nonrefundable tax credits in Ontario as she did on her federal forms. There is a small difference in the values and calculations used. In addition, an Ontario resident can also claim an Ontario tax reduction of $156, and property and sales tax credits of $1,000 (see Schedule ON479 Exhibit 3–5b on pages 78–79).

MAKING TAX PAYMENTS

SOURCE WITHHOLDING Source withholding occurs as your employer and others are required to withhold tax at source and remit it to the CCRA as well as the Québec Ministère du Revenu if you live in Quebec. These withholdings will be applied toward all

EXHIBIT 3–4a

(continued)

Enter the amount from line 8 on the other side	5,120 86	9
Federal tax on split income (from line 4 of Form T1206)	424 +	10
Add lines 9 and 10 =		11
Enter your total federal non-refundable tax credits from line 350 on the other side	350 1,573 92	
Federal dividend tax credit (13.3333% of the amount on line 120 of your return)	425 + 20 83	
Overseas employment tax credit (complete Form T626)	426 +	
Minimum tax carry-over	427 +	
Add lines 350, 425, 426, and 427 =	1,594 75 ▶ − 1,594 75	12
Basic federal tax: Line 11 minus line 12 (if negative, enter "0") 429 =	3,526 11	13
Federal foreign tax credit: Complete the federal foreign tax credit calculation below and enter the amount from line (i) or line (ii), whichever is **less** −		14
Federal tax: Line 13 minus line 14 (if negative, enter "0") 406 =	3,526 11	15
Total federal political contributions (attach receipts) 409		
Federal political contribution tax credit (see the guide)	410	
Investment tax credit (complete Form T2038(IND))	412 +	
Labour-sponsored funds tax credit Net cost 413 Allowable credit 414 +		
Add lines 410, 412, and 414. 416 =	▶ −	16
Line 15 minus line 16 (if negative, enter "0") (if you have an amount on line 424 above, see Form T1206) 417 =	3,526 11	17
Additional tax on RESP accumulated income payments (complete Form T1172) 418 +		18
Net federal tax: Add lines 17 and 18 Enter this amount on line 420 of your return. 420 =	3,526 11	19

(see Line 420 in EXHIBIT 3-2)

Federal foreign tax credit: (see lines 431 and 433 in the guide)

Make a separate calculation for each foreign country.

Non-business-income tax paid to a foreign country	431	(i)
Net foreign non-business income * 433	X Basic federal tax ***	= (ii)
Net income **		

* Reduce this amount by any income from that foreign country for which you claimed a capital gains deduction, and by any income from that country that was, under a tax treaty, either exempt from tax in that country or deductible as exempt income in Canada (included on line 256). Also reduce this amount by the lesser of lines E and F on Form T626.

** Line 236 plus the amount on line 3 of Form T1206, minus the total of the amounts on lines 248, 249, 250, 253, 254, and minus any foreign income deductible as exempt income under a tax treaty or any income deductible as net employment income from a prescribed international organization (included on line 256). If the result is less than the amount on line 433, enter your **Basic federal tax***** on line (ii).

*** Line 429 plus the amount on lines 425 and 426, and minus any refundable Quebec abatement (line 440) and any federal refundable First Nations abatement (line 441 on the return for residents of Yukon).

SOURCE: T1-2001 Federal Tax Schedule 1. www.ccra-adrc.gc.ca Reproduced with permission of the Minister of Public Works and Government Services Canada 2002.

Exhibit 3-4b

T1-2001   **Federal Tuition and Education Amounts**   **Schedule 11**

If you are a student, complete this schedule to:
    calculate your tuition and education amounts to claim on line 323 of Schedule 1; and
    determine the amount, if any, available for you to carry forward to a future year.
In both cases, attach a copy of this schedule to **your** return.

Transferring your unused 2001 amounts:
    If you are a student, you can use this schedule to calculate the maximum amount available for transfer. Attach this schedule to **your** return if you are filing a return. If you are not filing a return, keep it for your records.
    You can transfer your unused 2001 amounts to ONE individual, either your spouse or common-law partner, or your or your spouse or common-law partner's parent or grandparent.
    You cannot transfer your unused 2001 amounts to your or your spouse or common-law partner's parent or grandparent if your spouse or common-law partner is claiming an amount for you on line 303 or line 326 of his or her Schedule 1.

Make sure that the person to whom you transfer your unused 2001 amounts does not attach this schedule, or a photocopy of this schedule, to his or her return.

See line 323 in the guide for more information.

Unused tuition and education amounts from your 2000 *Notice of Assessment* or *Notice of Reassessment* _____ **1**

Eligible tuition fees paid for 2001 _____ **320** 565 00 **2**
Education amount for 2001:
Use columns B and C of Forms T2202 and T2202A;
count each month only once to a maximum of 12 months in total
    Enter the number of months from column **B** _08_   x $120 = **321** + 960 00 **3**
    Enter the number of months from column **C** _____   x $400 = **322** + _____ **4**

    Total 2001 tuition and education amounts: Add lines 2, 3, and 4   = 1,525 00 ▶ + 1,525 00 **5**

    Total tuition and education amounts: Add lines 1 and 5   = 1,525 00 **6**

Taxable income from line 260 of your return _____ 31,662 45 **7**
Total of lines 300 to 318 of Schedule 1   − 7412 00 **8**
    Line 7 minus line 8 (if negative, enter "0")   = 24,250 45 **9**
Unused tuition and education amounts claimed for 2001:
Enter the amount from line 1 or line 9, whichever is **less** − ▶ _____ **10**
    Line 9 minus line 10   = 24,250 45 **11**
2001 tuition and education amounts claimed for 2001:
Enter the amount from line 5 or line 11, whichever is **less** + 1,525 00 **12**
    Total tuition and education amounts claimed for 2001: Add lines 10 and 12
    Enter this amount on line 323 of Schedule 1.   1,525 00 ▶ − 1,525 00 **13**

    Total unused tuition and education amounts: Line 6 minus line 13   = _____ **14**

Note: If the amount on line 14 is "0", you do not have to complete the rest of this schedule.

Enter $5,000, or the amount from line 5, whichever is **less** _____ **15**
Enter the amount from line 12 above   − _____ **16**
    Maximum amount available for transfer: Line 15 minus line 16   = _____ **17**
If you are transferring all or a part of the amount on line 17 to another individual, *
enter one of the following amounts:
    the amount from line 4 of your spouse or common-law partner's Schedule 2; **or**
    the amount from line 324 of your or your spouse or common-law partner's parent's or grandparent's
    Schedule 1 that relates to you, whichever applies.   **327** − _____ **18**

    Your unused tuition and education amounts available to carry forward to a future year: Line 14 minus line 18   = _____ **19**

* If you are not filing a return, keep this schedule for your records. In any case, this schedule, or a photocopy of this schedule, is **not to be attached** to the other individual's return.

SOURCE: T1-2001 Federal Tuition and Education Amounts, Schedule 11. www.ccra-adrc.gc.ca Reproduced with permission of the Minister of Public Works and Government Services Canada 2002.

Exhibit 3-4c

T1-2001   **Donations and Gifts**   **Schedule 9**

Be sure to attach a copy of this schedule to your return along with those official receipts that support your claim. Remember, you may have charitable donations shown on your T4 and T4A slips. See line 349 in the guide for more information.

Total charitable donations and government gifts _____ 65 00 **1**

Enter your **net income** from line 236 of your return   31,662 45 ×75% =   23,746 84 **2**

Note: If the amount on line 1 is less than the amount on line 2, enter the amount from line 1 on line 340 below and continue completing the schedule from line 340.

Gifts of depreciable property
(from Chart 2 in the pamphlet called *Gifts and Income Tax*)   **337** _____ **3**
Gifts of capital property
(from Chart 1 in the pamphlet called *Gifts and Income Tax*)   **339** + _____ **4**
    Add lines 3 and 4   = _____ × 25% = + _____ **5**
    Total donations limit: Add lines 2 and 5
    (not to exceed the amount on line 236 of your return)   = _____ **6**

Allowable charitable donations and government gifts
(enter the amount from line 1 or line 6, whichever is **less**)   **340** 65 00

Cultural and ecological gifts (see line 349 in the guide)   **342** + _____
    Add lines 340 and 342. 344 = 65 00
Enter $200, or the amount from line 344, whichever is **less** 345 − 65 00 ×16% = 346 10 40 **7**
    Line 344 minus line 345. 347 = _____ ×29% = 348 + _____ **8**
    Donations and gifts: Add lines 7 and 8
    Enter this amount on line 349 of Schedule 1.   10 40 **9**

(see Line 349 in EXHIBIT 3-4a)

SOURCE: T1-2001 Donation and Gifts, Schedule 9. www.ccra-adrc.gc.ca Reproduced with permission of the Minister of Public Works and Government Services Canada 2002.

forms of taxable income. Generally, there is no withholding of tax on interest, dividends, rent, or royalties paid to Canadian residents.

Tax withheld from a payment to you is considered to have been paid by you to the tax authorities, even if your employer never remits it. It is also considered to have been paid *to* you in the sense that it forms part of your total income.

After the end of the year, you will receive a T4 form (see Exhibit 3–6 on page 81), which reports your annual earnings and the amounts that have been deducted for income tax, social benefits, and other taxes. A copy of the T4 form is filed with your tax return to document your earnings and the amount you have paid in taxes. The difference between the amount withheld and the tax owed is either the additional amount you must pay or the refund you will receive.

Many taxpayers view an annual tax refund as a "windfall," extra money they can count on each year. However, these taxpayers are forgetting the opportunity cost of withholding excessive amounts. Others view their extra tax withholding as "forced savings." However, a

Exhibit 3–5a

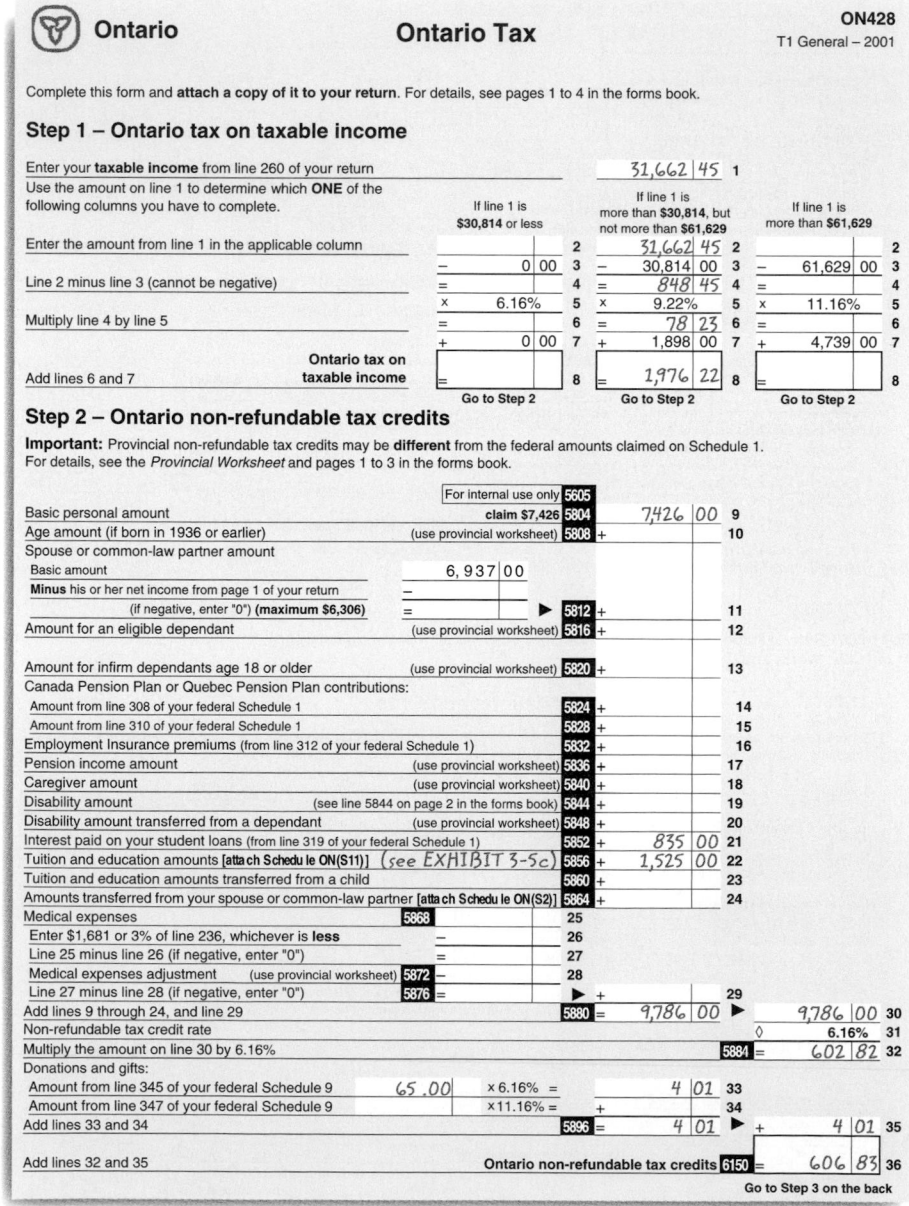

SOURCE: Ontario Tax T1-General-2001, ON428, www.ccra-adrc.gc.ca

payroll deduction plan for savings could serve the same purpose and would enable them to earn the interest instead of giving the government an interest-free loan.

REDUCTIONS OF SOURCE WITHHOLDINGS It is possible to reduce source withholdings if you prove that you are paying more withholding tax than necessary. In any situation where you expect to receive a refund after filing your return, you can request to have your source withholdings reduced. This type of situation can arise due to personal tax credits, RRSP contributions, charitable donations, medical expenses, and alimony and support payments. The CCRA form used to request this is the TD-1, the Personal Tax Credit Return.

INSTALLMENT PAYMENTS Your tax payments must be paid in installments if the difference between your payable taxes (including provincial tax) and the amount you have

Exhibit 3–5a

(continued)

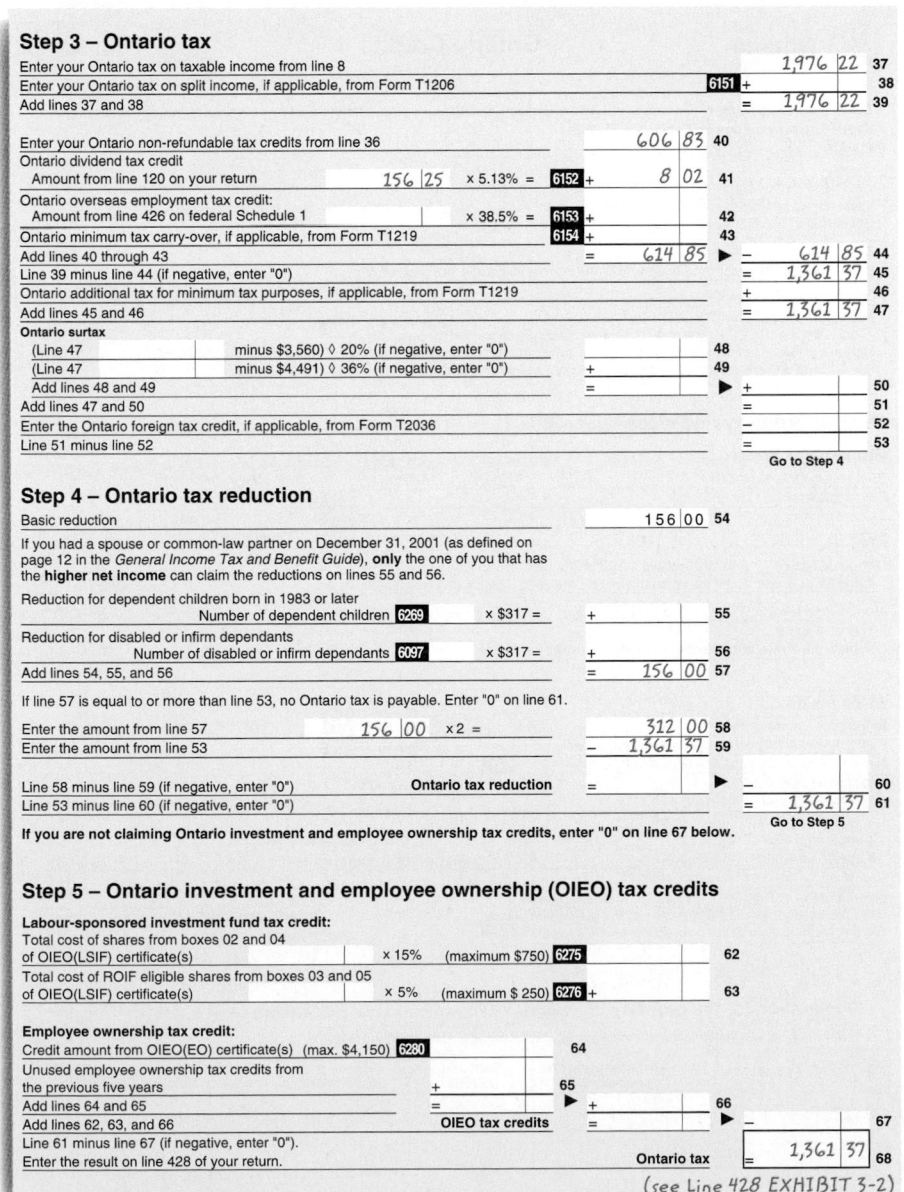

SOURCE: Ontario Tax T1-General-2001, ON428, www.ccra-adrc.gc.ca Reproduced with permission of the Minister of Public Works and Government Services Canada 2002.

already had withheld at source is more than $2,000 in both the current year and either of the two preceding years. In Quebec, where the federal government does not collect the provincial tax, the threshold is $1,200 of provincial tax instead of $2,000. The payments, which must be made quarterly, are due on the 15th day of March, June, September, and December.

DEADLINES AND PENALTIES

Most people are required to file their federal and Quebec tax returns by April 30 each year. If you or your spouse (or common-law spouse) has business income, then you have until June 15 to file your return. Note, however, that even though the return is not due until June 15, you will be required to pay any balance of tax owing by April 30. In cases where you have no tax to pay for the year, and neither the CCRA nor the Québec Ministère du Revenu

Exhibit 3–5b

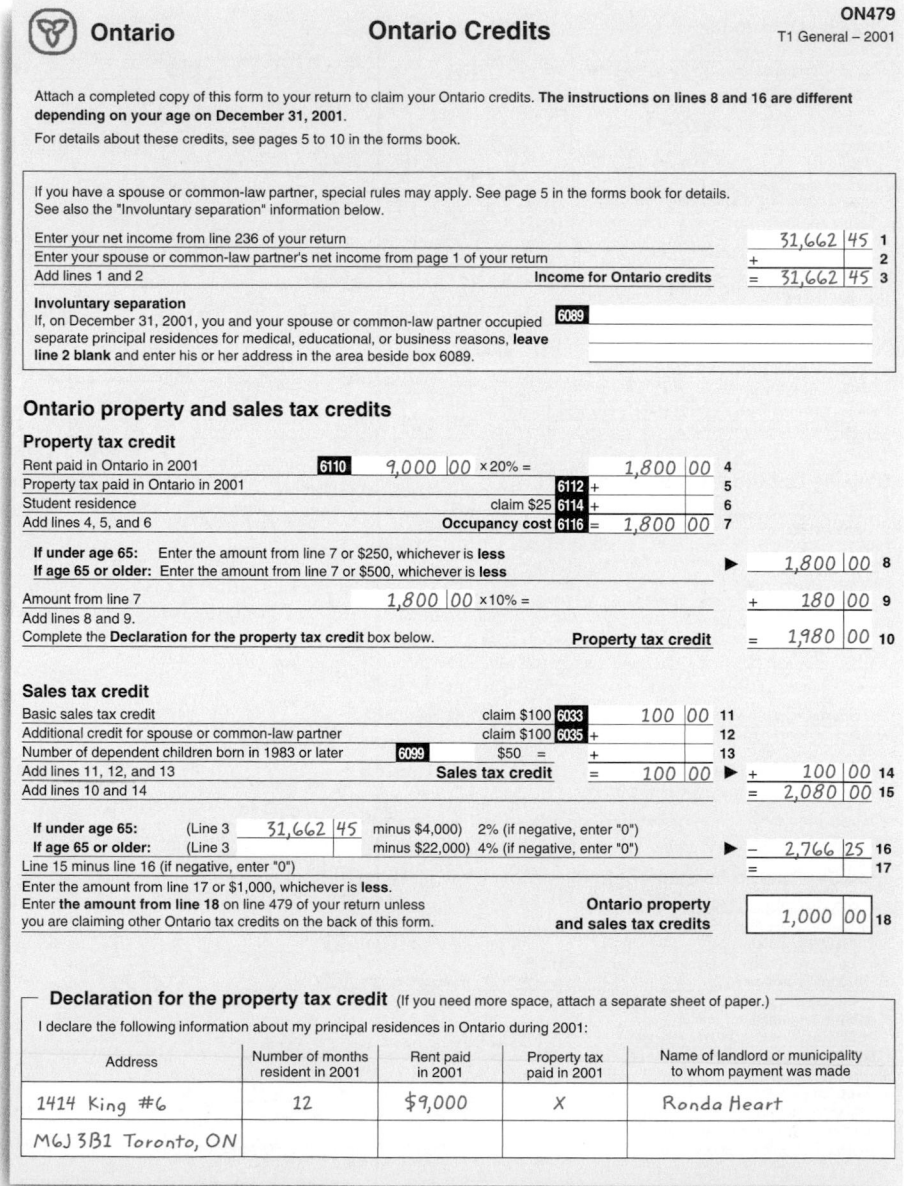

SOURCE: Ontario Credits ON 479, T1 General - 2001, www.ccra-adrc.gc.ca

has requested it, you have no obligation to file a return. Despite this, it is often still to your advantage to do so as it may affect your allowable RRSP contribution and other factors in future returns. Note that both parents must file a return to qualify for family support payments and GST and QST refunds.

Your return must be postmarked or transmitted electronically by the due date. Failure to do this will incur an automatic 5-percent penalty on any balance owing. In addition, 1 percent of the unpaid balance will be added for each full month that your return is late, to a maximum of 12 months. If you repeatedly fail to file your returns on time, you may incur even higher penalties.

DID YOU KNOW ?

In 1997, 14.4 million Canadians paid taxes, with an average income of $36,900 and an average tax bill from Ottawa of $5,100.

SOURCE: Canada Customs and Revenue Agency

Exhibit 3–5b

(continued)

Enter your Ontario property and sales tax credits from line 18 on the front of this form — 1,000 | 00 18

Ontario political contribution tax credit

Ontario political contributions made in 2001 — 6310 — 19
Credit calculated on the *Provincial Worksheet*
(maximum $1,000)   **Ontario political contribution tax credit** + — 20

Ontario home ownership savings plan (OHOSP) tax credit

OHOSP qualifying income:
If you lived with your spouse or common-law partner on December 31, 2001, or you claimed an amount for an eligible dependant on line 5816 of Form ON428, enter one-half of the amount from line 3. Otherwise, enter the amount from line 3. — 6315 — 21

Enter contributions to your plan in 2001   (maximum $2,000) 6236 — 22
Contributions to your spouse or common-law partner's plan in 2001   (max. $2,000) 6237 + — 23
Total contributions: Add lines 22 and 23 — = — 24
Look up the amount from line 21 in the table on page 10 in the forms book and enter the tax credit factor here — x — 25
Multiply line 24 by the factor on line 25
Attach the T1C-OHOSP receipt   **OHOSP tax credit** = ▶ + — 26

Ontario focused flow-through share tax credit

Enter the total expenses reported on Form T1221 6266 — x 5% = — + — 27
Add lines 18, 20, 26, and 27. **If you are claiming Ontario tax credits for self-employed individuals, complete the next section. Otherwise, enter the amount from line 28 on line 479 of your return.** = 1,000 | 00 28

Ontario tax credits for self-employed individuals

For details, see pages 7 to 9 in the forms book.

Number of eligible work placements your business or partnership is claiming under the Ontario co-operative education tax credit program 6325

Number of eligible post-secondary graduates your business or partnership hired under the Ontario graduate transitions tax credit program 6328

Number of eligible individuals with a disability your business or partnership incurred an expense for under the Ontario workplace accessibility tax credit program 6329

Are you claiming one or more of these tax credits as a member of a partnership? 6326 1 ☐ Yes 2 ☐ No

If *yes*, enter the first nine digits of your Business Number. 6327

Ontario co-operative education tax credit
Credit calculated on page 9 in the forms book   (maximum $1,000 per qualifying workplacement) 6320 + — 29

Ontario graduate transitions tax credit
Credit calculated on page 9 in the forms book   (maximum $4,000 per qualifying employment) 6321 + — 30
Ontario workplace child care tax credit
Qualifying expenditures 6332 — x 5% = — + — 31
Ontario workplace accessibility tax credit
Eligible expenditures 6334 — x 15% = — + — 32
Ontario educational technology tax credit
Eligible donations and price discounts 6330 — x 5% = — + — 33

(see Line 479 EXHIBIT 3-2)
Add lines 28 to 33. Enter the result on line 479 of your return.   **Ontario credits** = 1,000 | 00 34

SOURCE: Ontario Credits ON 479, T1 General - 2001, www.ccra-adrc.gc.ca Reproduced with permission of the Minister of Public Works and Government Services Canada 2002.

You should file your return on time even if you are unable to pay the balance owing since doing so will allow you to avoid the 5-percent automatic penalty. (Remember, though, that interest will continue to accrue on your unpaid balance.) Exhibit 3–7 on page 82 recaps the general section of your Federal return.

Stephanie has already paid a total of $8,202.47 in taxes this year ($5,195.12 + $2,007.35 + $1,000 [property and sales tax]). However according to her balance owing, she should have paid only $4,887.48. This means that Stephanie will receive a refund of $3,314.99.

Exhibit 3–5c

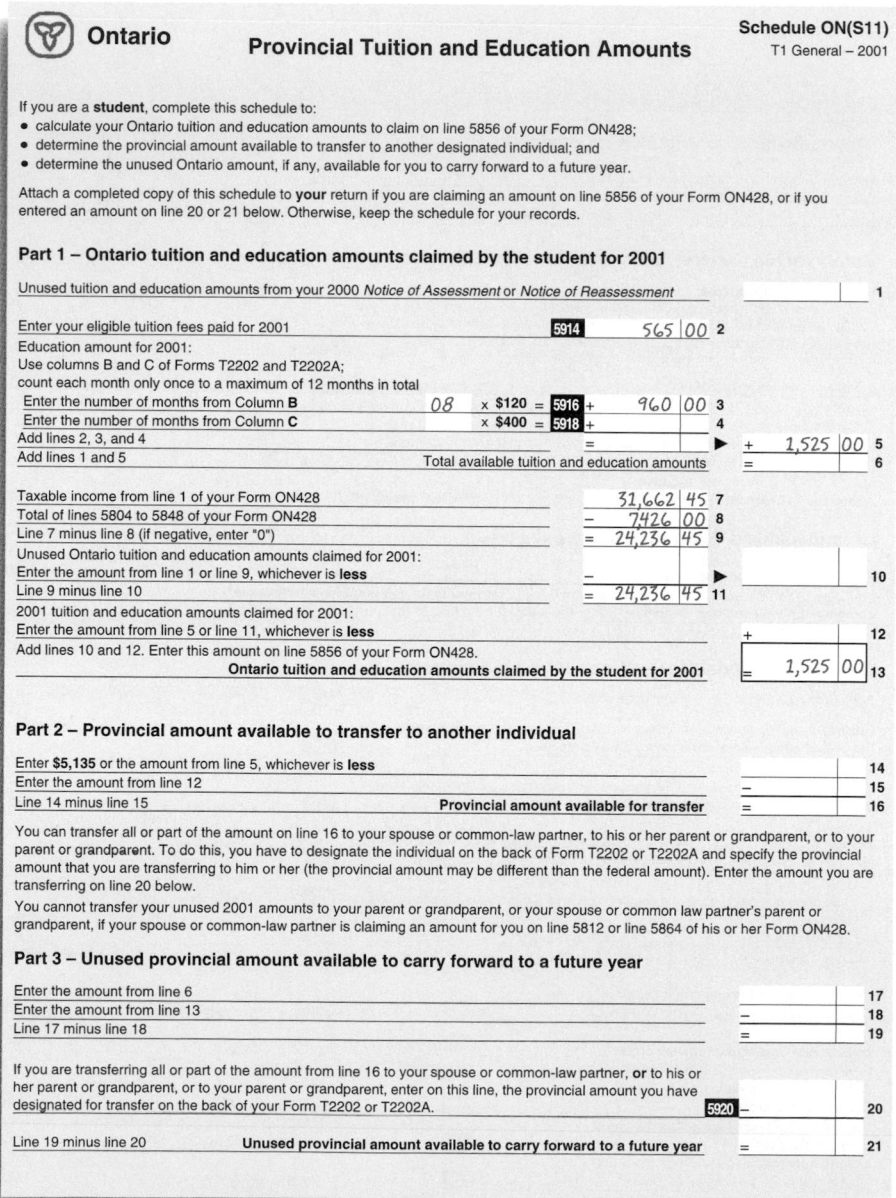

SOURCE: www.ccra-adrc.gc.ca Reproduced with permission of the Minister of Public Works and Government Services Canada 2002.

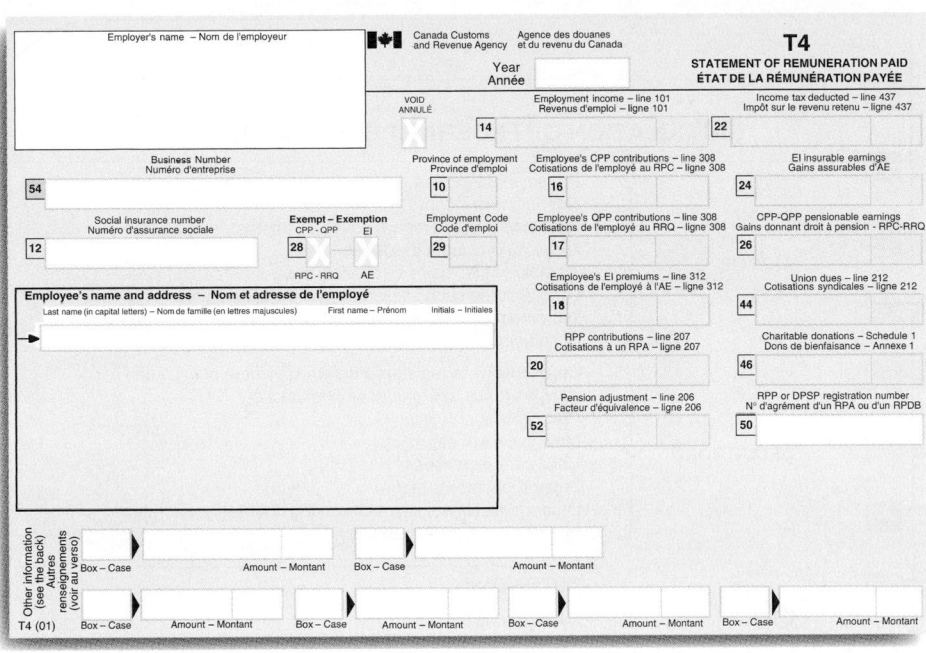

Exhibit 3–6

SOURCE: Statement of Remuneration Paid. www.ccra-adrc.gc.ca Reproduced with permission of the Minister of Public Works and Government Services Canada 2002.

CONCEPT CHECK 3–2

1. Who must file a tax return?
2. What are the five sections of the federal tax return?
3. How does tax-exempt income differ from tax-deferred income?
4. What information is needed to compute taxable income?
5. What is the difference between your marginal tax rate and your average tax rate?
6. How does a tax credit affect the amount owed for federal and provincial income taxes?

Tax Planning Strategies

Most people want to pay their fair share of taxes—no more, no less. They do this by practising **tax planning**, the use of legitimate methods to reduce one's taxes. In contrast, **tax evasion** is the use of illegal actions to reduce one's taxes. To minimize taxes owing, follow these guidelines:

- If you expect to have the *same* or a *lower* tax rate next year, *accelerate deductions* into the current year.
- If you expect to have a *lower* or the *same* tax rate next year, *delay the receipt of income* until next year. This means income will be taxed at a lower rate or at a later date.
- If you expect to have a *higher* tax rate next year, consider *delaying deductions,* since they will have a greater benefit. A $1,000 deduction at 22 percent lowers your taxes by $220; at 26 percent, your taxes are lowered by $260.
- If you expect to have a *higher* tax rate next year, *accelerate the receipt of income* to have it taxed at the current year's lower rate.

Objective 3

Select appropriate tax strategies for different financial and personal situations.

tax planning The use of legitimate methods to reduce one's taxes.

tax evasion The use of illegal actions to reduce one's taxes.

Exhibit 3–7

Five General
Sections of Your
Federal Tax
Return Form

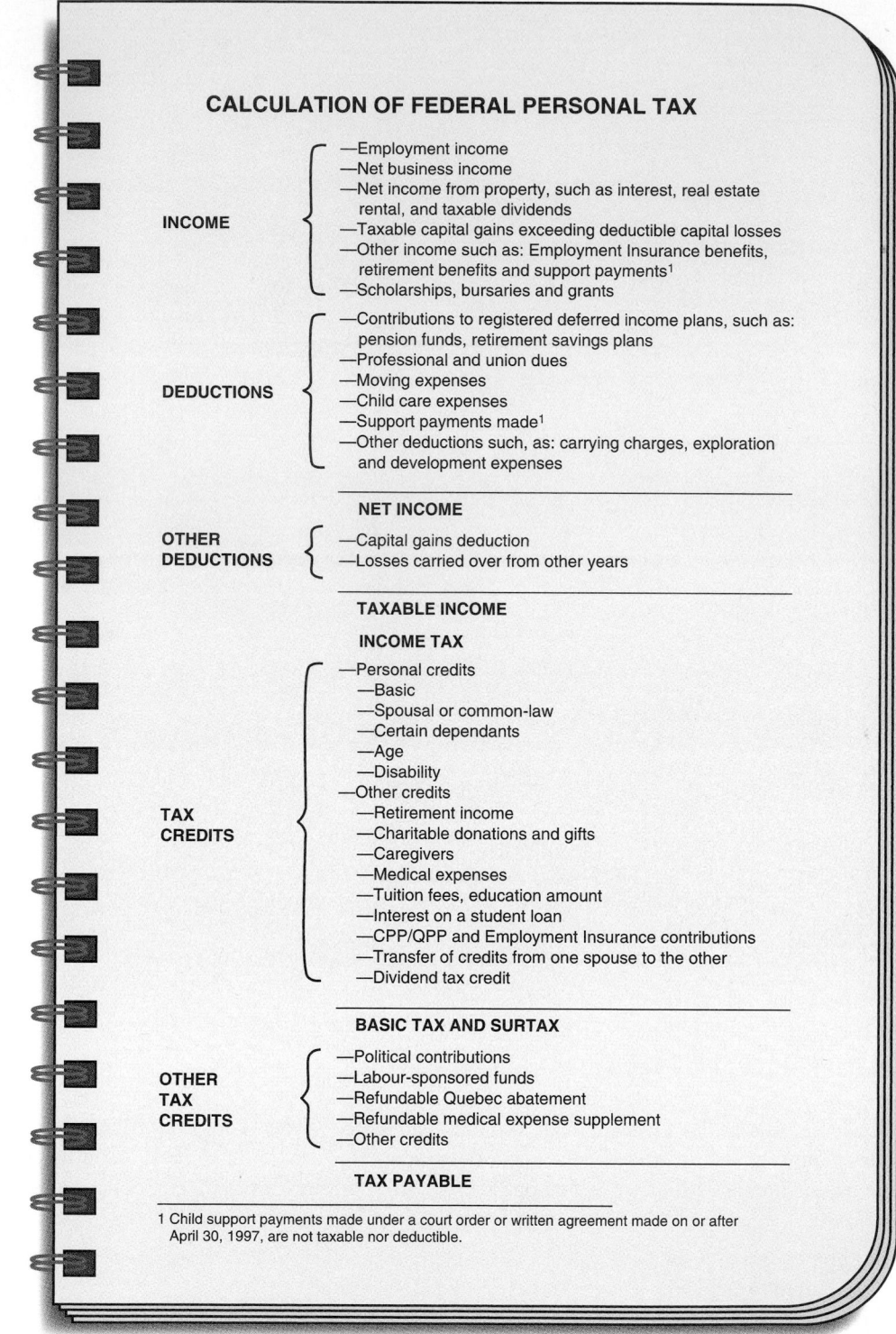

CALCULATION OF FEDERAL PERSONAL TAX

INCOME
—Employment income
—Net business income
—Net income from property, such as: interest, real estate rental, and taxable dividends
—Taxable capital gains exceeding deductible capital losses
—Other income such as: Employment Insurance benefits, retirement benefits and support payments[1]
—Scholarships, bursaries and grants

DEDUCTIONS
—Contributions to registered deferred income plans, such as: pension funds, retirement savings plans
—Professional and union dues
—Moving expenses
—Child care expenses
—Support payments made[1]
—Other deductions such, as: carrying charges, exploration and development expenses

---

NET INCOME

OTHER DEDUCTIONS
—Capital gains deduction
—Losses carried over from other years

TAXABLE INCOME

INCOME TAX

TAX CREDITS
—Personal credits
  —Basic
  —Spousal or common-law
  —Certain dependants
  —Age
  —Disability
—Other credits
  —Retirement income
  —Charitable donations and gifts
  —Caregivers
  —Medical expenses
  —Tuition fees, education amount
  —Interest on a student loan
  —CPP/QPP and Employment Insurance contributions
  —Transfer of credits from one spouse to the other
  —Dividend tax credit

BASIC TAX AND SURTAX

OTHER TAX CREDITS
—Political contributions
—Labour-sponsored funds
—Refundable Quebec abatement
—Refundable medical expense supplement
—Other credits

TAX PAYABLE

---

1 Child support payments made under a court order or written agreement made on or after April 30, 1997, are not taxable nor deductible.

SOURCE: Five General Sections of Your Federal Tax Return Form. From "Things to Remember," Booklet published by CCH Canadian Tax Compliance Group © 2001. Reprinted with permission.

As Exhibit 3–8 shows, people in different life situations can take advantage of various tax rules. When considering financial decisions in relation to your taxes, remember that purchasing, investing, and retirement planning are the areas most heavily affected by tax laws.

CONSUMER PURCHASING

The buying decisions most directly affected by taxes are the purchase of a residence, the use of credit, and job-related expenses.

PLACE OF RESIDENCE Owning a home is one of the best tax shelters, primarily because it is exempt from capital gains taxes as long as it qualifies as your principal residence. In addition, a home can be a reliable hedge against inflation and a retirement savings vehicle. While renting may seem less expensive than owning, the latter may be financially advantageous in the long run. Chapter 7 presents specific calculations for comparing renting and buying.

HOME BUYERS' PLAN If you qualify as a first-time buyer, this plan allows you to withdraw up to $20,000 as a loan from your RRSP to build or buy a home, without it counting

Visit the Web site

See Personal Financial Planning worksheets under Chapter 3 on the online learning centre at www.mcgrawhill.ca/college/kapoor.

Exhibit 3–8   Special Tax Situations

Business in your home	• If you have an office in your home, you can claim a portion of your home expenses as business expenses, subject to certain restrictions. The proportional expenses you can claim include rent if you are a tenant, mortgage interest if you are a homeowner, utilities, telephone, and home insurance. The portion you will be allowed to claim will depend on the fraction of your home that is used for business purposes, excluding any common areas.
Divorced persons	• Before a ruling on May 1, 1997, alimony, child support, and spousal maintenance payments were deductible to the payer and taxable to the recipient. No longer. Under the newer rules, the child support payments are generally calculated as a percentage of the support-paying parent's income, and adjusted to account for the impact of taxes, certain special child care expenses, and undue hardship. The rules for alimony and maintenance remain the same, earning a deduction for the payer and taxable income for the payee.
Single parents	• If you are single, widowed, divorced, or separated, and you support another family member (such as a child), you will be allowed to claim that person under the amount for elegible dependant credit. This will allow you to claim a credit worth up to $1,006.88.
Retired persons	• Between the ages of 60 and 70, you can apply to begin receiving your monthly benefits under the Canada Pension Plan (CPP) or Quebec Pension Plan (QPP), with some restrictions if you are less than 65 years old. At this point you may strategically direct that up to half of your CPP benefits be paid to your spouse, provided that you are both over the age of 60. If you are 65 or older by the end of the year you will also be allowed to claim an additional federal credit of up to $579, with the exact amount depending on your net income under $26,941.

NOTE: Individual circumstances and changes in the tax laws can affect these examples.
SOURCE: Income Tax table 2001. From "Things to Remember," Booklet published by CCH Canadian Tax Compliance Group © 2001. Reprinted with permission.

as a withdrawal. You must then repay the loan, without interest, over the next 15 years. Further, the funds you withdraw must have been in the plan for at least 90 days prior. This plan will be discussed more fully in later chapters.

STUDENT LOANS Students and former students can claim a 16-percent, nonrefundable federal tax credit on the interest on their student loans under the *Canada Student Loans Act* or equivalent provincial programs. You may claim this credit for any interest paid in the current year and in the five preceding years (after 1997). The credit is not transferable, but it can be carried forward for up to five years.

EMPLOYMENT-RELATED EXPENSES As previously mentioned, certain work expenses, such as union dues, some travel and education costs, and business tools, may be deducted if the employer has completed the required authorization forms.

INVESTMENT DECISIONS

A major area of tax planning involves the wide variety of decisions related to investing.

TAX-EXEMPT INVESTMENTS All individuals in Canada are entitled to a lifetime $500,000 capital gains exemption on qualified small business corporation shares and farm property. This exemption is limited to the total gains on both small business shares and family farms over a person's lifetime.

A gain on selling your home is normally completely exempt from taxation, provided that the home served as your principal residence. This single residence can be a house, a condominium, a share in a co-operative housing corporation, or something else. The value of the land up to one-half hectare will also be included.

TAX-DEFERRED INVESTMENTS Although from a tax standpoint tax-deferred investments, whose income will be taxed at a later date, are less beneficial than tax-exempt investments, they also have financial advantages. According to basic opportunity cost, paying a dollar in the future instead of today gives you the opportunity to invest (or spend) it now. In addition, an individual could withdraw tax-deferred income in years that his/her marginal tax rate is low.

Registered Education Savings Plans (RESPs) allow you to build an education fund for a child by earning tax-deferred investment income. Your contributions are not tax deductible, but any and all income in the plan grows tax-free until withdrawn by the recipient. You may invest up to $4,000 per year up to a lifetime contribution limit of $42,000, and the government will provide a direct grant to the RESP of 20 percent of the first $2,000 in annual contributions. The maximum period over which income generated in an RESP may be sheltered is 26 years.

capital gains Profits from the sale of a capital asset, such as stocks, bonds, or real estate.

Capital gains, profits from the sale of a capital asset, such as stocks, bonds, or real estate, are tax deferred; you do not have to pay the tax on these profits until the asset is sold. Fifty percent of the capital gain is taxable. The sale of an investment for less than its purchase price is, of course, a *capital loss*. Capital losses can be used to offset capital gains. Unused capital losses may be carried back up to three years or forward indefinitely to offset capital gains. Capital losses are recognized only on nondepreciable assets, such as land and securities.

SELF-EMPLOYMENT Owning your own business has certain tax advantages. Self-employed persons may deduct such expenses as health insurance as business costs.

CHILDREN'S INVESTMENTS Given the Canadian tax system's use of progressive tax rates, with the marginal rates increasing with higher incomes, many taxpayers attempt to minimize taxes by investing in the name of their children under age 18. Given that children generally have little or no income, this is an attempt at income splitting whereby the tax rate paid on the investment is lower or even nothing.

Despite the apparent logic of this scheme, this strategy is not a good one. The federal *Income Tax Act* contains a number of "attribution rules" to prevent income splitting, and states that any payment or transfer made "pursuant to the direction of, or with the concurrence of" a taxpayer to some other person is to be included in the taxpayer's income to the extent it would have been if paid to the taxpayer. That signifies that any income earned on an investment resulting from your transfer of money, property, or other to your child will be attributed back to you and will be taxed at your marginal rate.

Exceptions to this "attribution" rule with regard to children's investments occur when the money given to your child is classified as being lent, with interest on the loan being paid back to you. In this case, if the interest charged is at least equal to the CCRA's prescribed interest rate at the time and the interest is actually paid for that year before January 30, then the returns on investment will be taxed in the hands of your child. In any case, where the interest payment is not made by the January 30 deadline, that year's income and all future income from the loaned property will be attributed back to the lender. As well, capital gains are not attributed to parents.

RETIREMENT PLANS

A major tax strategy of benefit to working people is the use of tax-deferred retirement plans, such as RRSPs, RPPs, IPPs, and Deferred Profit Sharing Plans (DPSPs).

RRSP Registered Retirement Savings Plans are the quintessential tool in the Canadian taxpayer's toolbox. Virtually all taxpayers benefit from having these, and setting them up can be easily done at almost any bank or trust company or through a stockbroker or life insurance agent. The basic concept is simple: If you agree to put some of your salary away and not have immediate access to it, the tax system will tax that income and all proceeds from its investment when it is withdrawn from the RRSP, rather than when it is earned by the taxpayer.

Contributions to an RRSP are deductible for any year in which they are made or for the prior year if made within the first 60 days of the year. The contribution that you are allowed to make will depend on three factors. First, the most that can be contributed in any year is $13,500 through 2003, and then $14,500 for 2004 and $15,500 for 2005. Second, you can only contribute up to 18 percent of your prior year's earned income, subject to the above limitations, plus any contribution room that you may have carried forward from prior years. Third is your pension adjustment, defined as the deemed value of your pension earned for the previous year. In other words, the amount you will be allowed to contribute to your RRSP will be diminished by the amount that you and your employer put aside for your retirement pension. The amount of your pension adjustment will be shown on your T4 slip.

RPP A Registered Pension Plan is set up for employees by their employers. Larger companies and many smaller ones have such plans, in which your employer contributes an annual amount on your behalf. Occasionally, you will be required or allowed to contribute to the plan and you will be able to deduct your contribution in the year that it is made.

In general, there are two types of registered pension plans: money-purchase and defined benefit. The former is much like an

DID YOU KNOW ?

The value of your RRSP contribution in terms of tax savings will depend on your marginal rate of tax. Roughly speaking, with the rates varying due to different provincial tax rates, the value of your contribution will be:

27% on income up to $29,590
41% on income from $29,590 to $59,180
50% on income over $59,180

SOURCE: KPMG's Tax Planning for You and Your Family, 1999.

RRSP in that the amount of your pension will depend on the contributions made and the growth achieved with those funds. Large and public employers often provide the latter, defined benefit plans. With this type of plan, the amount you will receive as a pension is known in advance and is usually based on a percentage of your actual salary over a specified number of years.

If you are allowed to contribute to a money-purchase RPP, consider making your payment to an RRSP instead. Though the benefits in terms of taxes are the same, the amount you hold in your RPP will be locked in and inaccessible.

If you terminate your employment but are not yet eligible to receive pension income, you are allowed to transfer a lump-sum payment from your RPP to a locked-in RRSP or Registered Retirement Income Fund (RRIF). The amount allowed for transfer is limited, however, and you may be required to accept an immediate partial cash payment on which you will be taxed.

IPP   An individual pension plan is a defined-benefit registered pension plan designed and structured for one individual. IPP contributions are made according to the benefit payable at retirement. This type of plan may be to your advantage if you are already in your employer's group RPP but the benefits are not as high as you would want. Generally, this type of plan is optimal for executives or owner-managers, people over 53, or those earning more than $100,000 as a base salary.

DPSP Deferred Profit Sharing Plans are less common than RPPs but they operate in essentially the same way. Your employer makes contributions, and you are taxed only when you receive the funds. The contributions are based on current or accrued company profits but may have a defined minimum contribution amount. Further, they are limited to no more than 18 percent of your earnings in a year or a set maximum amount. You are not allowed to contribute to this type of plan and the amounts contributed by your employer will be reported as a pension adjustment on your T4, thereby reducing your RRSP contribution allowance.

CHANGING TAX STRATEGIES

Someone once said that "death and taxes are the only certainties of life." Changing tax laws seem to be another certainty. Each year, the CCRA modifies the tax return and filing procedures. In addition, the government frequently passes legislation that changes the *Income Tax Act*. These changes require that you regularly determine how to best consider the tax laws for personal financial planning. Carefully consider changes in your personal situation and your income level. You should monitor your personal tax strategies to best serve your daily living needs and your long-term financial goals.

CONCEPT CHECK 3-3

1. How does tax avoidance differ from tax evasion?
2. What common tax-saving methods are available to most individuals and households?

Tax Assistance and the Audit Process

In the process of completing your federal income tax return, you may seek additional information or assistance. After filing your return, you may be identified for a tax audit. If this happens, several policies and procedures protect your rights.

TAX INFORMATION SOURCES

As with other aspects of personal financial planning, many resources are available to assist you with your taxes. Both the Canada Customs and Revenue Agency and the Québec Ministère du Revenu offer comprehensive guides to help you plan and complete your tax return. Libraries and bookstores offer books and other publications that are updated yearly and that will help you create a strategy to effectively and legally minimize your total taxes paid. In addition, most daily newspapers frequently contain articles related to personal taxes and their various effects. See Exhibit 3–10 for an example of a tax-planning system.

The fastest way to find information on the various rules and regulations for both the CCRA and the Québec Ministère du Revenu is by searching online at their respective Internet sites.

Objective 4

Identify tax assistance sources

Visit the Web site
See the Weblinks under Chapter 3 on the online learning centre at www.mcgrawhill.ca/college/kapoor.

Exhibit 3–9   Tax Tables and Tax Rate Schedules

3. INCOME TAX TABLE (2001)[1,2]

Taxable Income	Newfoundland[3] Tax	%	P.E.I.[4] Tax	%	Nova Scotia[5] Tax	%	N. Brunswick[6] Tax	%
20,000	3,345	26.6	3,248	25.8	3,262	25.8	3,233	25.7
22,000	3,876	26.6	3,764	25.8	3,777	25.8	3,746	25.7
24,000	4,408	26.6	4,280	25.8	4,292	25.8	4,260	25.7
26,000	4,939	26.6	4,796	25.8	4,808	25.8	4,773	25.7
28,000	5,470	26.6	5,312	25.8	5,323	25.8	5,287	25.7
30,000	6,025	32.2	5,828	25.8	5,860	30.9	5,801	25.7
30,754	6,268	38.2	6,022	35.8	6,093	37.0	5,994	36.8
32,000	6,743	38.2	6,469	35.8	6,554	37.0	6,453	36.8
34,000	7,507	38.2	7,185	35.8	7,293	37.0	7,190	36.8
36,000	8,270	38.2	7,901	35.8	8,032	37.0	7,926	36.8
38,000	9,033	38.2	8,617	35.8	8,771	37.0	8,663	36.8
40,000	9,796	38.2	9,333	35.8	9,510	37.0	9,399	36.8
42,000	10,559	38.2	10,049	35.8	10,249	37.0	10,135	36.8
44,000	11,323	38.2	10,765	35.8	10,988	37.0	10,872	36.8
46,000	12,086	38.2	11,481	35.8	11,727	37.0	11,608	36.8
48,000	12,849	38.2	12,197	35.8	12,466	37.0	12,345	36.8
50,000	13,612	38.2	12,913	35.8	13,205	37.0	13,081	36.8
52,000	14,375	38.2	13,631	37.2	13,944	37.0	13,817	36.8
54,000	15,139	38.2	14,374	37.2	14,683	37.0	14,554	36.8
56,000	15,902	38.2	15,118	37.2	15,422	37.0	15,290	36.8
58,000	16,665	38.2	15,862	37.2	16,161	37.0	16,027	36.8
60,000	17,464	41.6	16,605	37.2	16,914	38.7	16,763	36.8
61,509	18,093	45.6	17,166	44.3	17,498	42.7	17,319	42.5
62,000	18,317	45.6	17,384	44.4	17,707	42.7	17,527	42.5
64,000	19,230	45.6	18,271	44.4	18,561	42.7	18,378	42.5
66,000	20,143	45.6	19,159	44.4	19,414	42.7	19,228	42.5
68,000	21,055	45.6	20,046	44.4	20,268	42.7	20,079	42.5
70,000	21,968	45.6	20,933	44.4	21,121	42.7	20,929	42.5
75,000	24,250	45.6	23,152	44.4	23,254	42.7	23,055	42.5
80,000	26,532	45.6	25,370	44.4	25,396	44.3	25,181	42.5
85,000	28,814	45.6	27,589	44.4	27,613	44.3	27,307	42.5
90,000	31,097	45.6	29,807	44.4	29,830	44.3	29,433	42.5
95,000	33,379	45.6	32,026	44.4	32,046	44.3	31,559	42.5
100,000	35,661	48.6	34,244	47.4	34,263	47.3	33,685	46.8
105,000	38,093	48.6	36,613	47.4	36,630	47.3	36,028	46.8
110,000	40,525	48.6	38,982	47.4	38,997	47.3	38,370	46.8
115,000	42,957	48.6	41,350	47.4	41,364	47.3	40,712	46.8
120,000	45,389	48.6	43,719	47.4	43,731	47.3	43,054	46.8
125,000	47,822	48.6	46,087	47.4	46,098	47.3	45,396	46.8
130,000	50,254	48.6	48,456	47.4	48,465	47.3	47,738	46.8

PROVINCES OTHER THAN QUEBEC

Ontario[7] Tax	%	Manitoba[8] Tax	%	Sask.[9] Tax	%	Alberta[10] Tax	%	B.C.[11] Tax	%
2,789	22.2	3,386	26.9	3,394	27.5	2,724	26.0	2,890	23.3
3,232	22.2	3,924	26.9	3,944	27.5	3,244	26.0	3,356	23.3
3,675	22.2	4,462	26.9	4,494	27.5	3,764	26.0	3,822	23.3
4,118	22.2	5,000	26.9	5,044	27.5	4,284	26.0	4,288	23.3
4,561	22.2	5,538	26.9	5,594	27.5	4,804	26.0	4,754	23.3
5,005	22.2	6,076	26.9	6,144	29.5	5,324	26.0	5,220	23.3
5,172	30.9	6,290	38.2	6,367	35.5	5,520	32.0	5,405	32.5
5,559	31.2	6,766	38.2	6,809	35.5	5,919	32.0	5,809	32.5
6,184	31.2	7,530	38.2	7,519	35.5	6,559	32.0	6,459	32.5
6,808	31.2	8,294	38.2	8,229	35.5	7,199	32.0	7,109	32.5
7,432	31.2	9,058	38.2	8,939	35.5	7,839	32.0	7,759	32.5
8,057	31.2	9,822	38.2	9,649	35.5	8,479	32.0	8,409	32.5
8,681	31.2	10,586	38.2	10,359	35.5	9,119	32.0	9,059	32.5
9,306	31.2	11,350	38.2	11,069	35.5	9,759	32.0	9,709	32.5
9,930	31.2	12,114	38.2	11,779	35.5	10,399	32.0	10,359	32.5
10,554	31.2	12,878	38.2	12,489	35.5	11,039	32.0	11,009	32.5
11,179	31.2	13,642	38.2	13,199	35.5	11,679	32.0	11,659	32.5
11,803	31.2	14,406	38.2	13,909	35.5	12,319	32.0	12,309	32.5
12,431	33.1	15,170	38.2	14,619	35.5	12,959	32.0	12,959	32.5
13,092	33.1	15,934	38.2	15,329	35.5	13,599	32.0	13,609	32.5
13,754	33.1	16,698	38.2	16,039	35.5	14,239	32.0	14,259	32.5
14,415	33.1	17,462	38.2	16,749	38.0	14,879	32.0	14,909	32.5
14,914	38.6	18,044	43.4	17,323	42.0	15,362	36.0	15,417	39.7
15,104	39.4	18,257	43.4	17,529	42.0	15,539	36.0	15,612	39.7
15,912	43.4	19,125	43.4	18,369	42.0	16,259	36.0	16,406	39.7
16,780	43.4	19,993	43.4	19,209	42.0	16,979	36.0	17,200	39.7
17,648	43.4	20,861	43.4	20,049	42.0	17,699	36.0	17,994	39.7
18,517	43.4	21,729	43.4	20,889	42.0	18,419	36.0	18,788	41.7
20,687	43.4	23,899	43.4	22,989	42.0	20,219	36.0	20,873	41.7
22,858	43.4	26,069	43.4	25,089	42.0	22,019	36.0	22,958	41.7
25,028	43.4	28,239	43.4	27,189	42.0	23,819	36.0	25,043	42.7
27,198	43.4	30,409	43.4	29,289	42.0	25,619	36.0	27,178	42.7
29,369	43.4	32,579	43.4	31,389	42.0	27,419	36.0	29,313	42.7
31,540	46.4	34,749	46.4	33,489	45.0	29,219	39.0	31,448	45.7
33,860	46.4	37,070	46.4	35,739	45.0	31,169	39.0	33,733	45.7
36,181	46.4	39,390	46.4	37,989	45.0	33,119	39.0	36,018	45.7
38,501	46.4	41,710	46.4	40,239	45.0	35,069	39.0	38,303	45.7
40,822	46.4	44,030	46.4	42,489	45.0	37,019	39.0	40,588	45.7
43,142	46.4	46,350	46.4	44,739	45.0	38,969	39.0	42,873	45.7
45,463	46.4	48,670	46.4	46,989	45.0	40,919	39.0	45,158	45.7

1. This table reflects the basic federal credit ($7,412 x 16% = $1,186). Use Table 8 to find out the value of the other amounts converted to credits to subtract from the federal tax, as established above.
2. The marginal rate applies to each additional dollar of income.
3. This table reflects the basic credit ($7,410 x 10.57% = $783.24) and the 9% surtax on provincial tax in excess of $7,050.
4. This table reflects the basic credit ($7,412 x 9.8% = $726.38) and the 10% surtax on provincial tax in excess of $5,200.
5. This table reflects the basic credit ($7,231 x 9.77% = $706.47) and the 10% surtax on provincial tax in excess of $10,000, but does not reflect the tax reduction.
6. This table reflects the basic credit ($7,412 x 9.68% = $717.48).

7. This table reflects the basic credit ($7,426 x 6.2% = $460.41), the 20% surtax on provincial tax in excess of $3,560 and the 36% surtax on provincial tax in excess of $4,491, but does not reflect the tax reduction.
8. This table reflects the basic credit ($7,412 x 10.94% = $807.91.48), but does not reflect the tax reduction.
9. This table reflects the basic credit ($8,000 x 11.5% = $920.00).
10. This table reflects the basic credit ($12,900 x 10% = $1,290.00).
11. This table reflects the basic credit ($8,000 x 7.3% = $582.00).

The CCRA is available at www.ccra-adrc.gc.ca, while the Québec Ministère du Revenu site can be found at www.revenu.gouv.qc.ca. Both can also be reached by telephone: you will find the telephone number for the closest service office in the blue pages of your local phone book.

TAX PUBLICATIONS Each year, several personal tax guides are published; most are available either directly from the issuers, in the case of various tax planning companies, or at a bookstore or library in the case of others. Some of the better-known publications from the financial-services sector include Deloitte & Touche's *How to Reduce the Tax You Pay*, KPMG's *Tax Planning for You and Your Family*, and CCH Canadian's *Preparing Your Income Tax Returns*. In various bookstores, you may also find Evelyn Jacks' annual *Jacks on Tax Savings*, Prentice Hall Canada's annual *Canadian Guide to Personal Financial Management*, and a number of other books on the topic. Though current taxation rules often change, since the basics usually remain the same you will also find that many non–current-year tax advisory and information publications are very relevant.

Exhibit 3–10

Tax-Planner Calendar

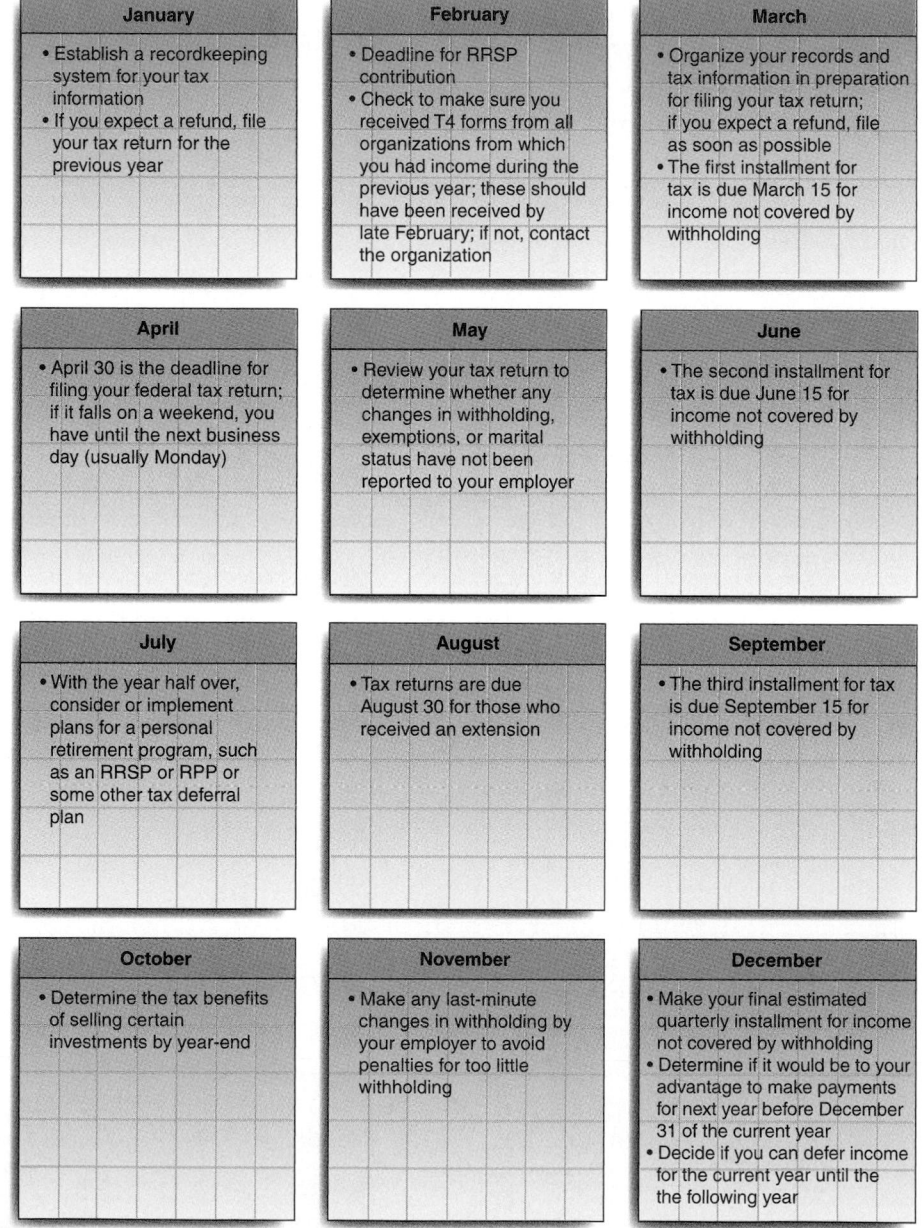

January
- Establish a recordkeeping system for your tax information
- If you expect a refund, file your tax return for the previous year

February
- Deadline for RRSP contribution
- Check to make sure you received T4 forms from all organizations from which you had income during the previous year; these should have been received by late February; if not, contact the organization

March
- Organize your records and tax information in preparation for filing your tax return; if you expect a refund, file as soon as possible
- The first installment for tax is due March 15 for income not covered by withholding

April
- April 30 is the deadline for filing your federal tax return; if it falls on a weekend, you have until the next business day (usually Monday)

May
- Review your tax return to determine whether any changes in withholding, exemptions, or marital status have not been reported to your employer

June
- The second installment for tax is due June 15 for income not covered by withholding

July
- With the year half over, consider or implement plans for a personal retirement program, such as an RRSP or RPP or some other tax deferral plan

August
- Tax returns are due August 30 for those who received an extension

September
- The third installment for tax is due September 15 for income not covered by withholding

October
- Determine the tax benefits of selling certain investments by year-end

November
- Make any last-minute changes in withholding by your employer to avoid penalties for too little withholding

December
- Make your final estimated quarterly installment for income not covered by withholding
- Determine if it would be to your advantage to make payments for next year before December 31 of the current year
- Decide if you can defer income for the current year until the the following year

NOTE: Children born before the end of the year give you a full-year exemption.

THE INTERNET As with other personal finance topics, extensive information may be found on the Internet, especially the World Wide Web. The Web sites for the CCRA and the Québec Ministère du Revenu are great places to start. As mentioned before, the CCRA is available at www.ccra-adrc.gc.ca, while the Québec Ministère du Revenu site can be found at www.revenu.gouv.qc.ca. Both agencies can also be reached by telephone. Such sites as *IE:Money* magazine at www.iemoney.com and Canoe Webfin at www.webfin.com, the Fraser Institute at www.fraserinstitute.ca, CANTAX at www.cantax.com, and the Canadian Taxpayer Federation at www.taxpayer.com are all excellent sources of Canadian tax information. Two of Canada's largest accounting firms, Ernst & Young and KPMG, provide quality links to many other Internet resources and can be found at www.eycan.com and www.kpmg.ca/tax, respectively. In addition, the Web sites of companies that sell tax software and tax-related organizations can be useful (see the Web sites suggested in the next section).

TAX PREPARATION SOFTWARE AND ELECTRONIC FILING

More and more taxpayers are using personal computers for tax recordkeeping and income tax preparation. A spreadsheet program can be very helpful in maintaining and updating tax data on various income and expense categories. There are also a number of different software packages that allow you to complete your return and then either file online or print the completed form for mailing. Popular choices are QuickTax, TaxWiz, and the Macintosh-based GriffTax. For more information, see www.quicktax.ca, www.taxwiz.ca, and www.grifftax.com, respectively.

ELECTRONIC FILING The CCRA allows most taxpayers to file their returns in electronic form using a personal computer. The system is called EFILE and is available across the country. It permits authorized tax return preparers or transmitters to file returns using tax return preparation and transmission software. The system is not complete, however, and as a result you will incur a small transmission fee charged by EFILE preparers to transmit your return even if you prepare it yourself.

There are many advantages to using this method to file your return. Besides the obvious benefit to the environment, filing this way will allow you to receive a refund within as little as two weeks, versus the six to eight weeks it might normally take. Also, you can keep all your records and are required to send them in only if expressly asked, thus reducing the paper burden. The Québec Ministère du Revenu offers a similar service, the details of which are available at its Web site.

Under the CCRA's TELEFILE program, qualifying wage earners, students, seniors and credit or benefit filers can file their returns by telephone. If you are eligible for this program you will be sent an invitation to use TELEFILE and your personalized income tax package will include an access code: you use a touch-tone phone to call the service and enter your information as prompted. As with EFILE, you are not required to send in supporting documents and you will likely receive your refund much sooner. NETFILE is a new service introduced by the CCRA which allows you to file your return directly to the CCRA over the internet. Visit www.netfile.gc.ca for more information.

TAX PREPARATION SERVICES

Many Canadian taxpayers pay someone to prepare their income tax returns. The fee for this service can range from $40 at a tax preparation service for a simple return to several thousand dollars to a chartered accountant for a complicated return.

Many people prepare their own tax returns. This experience can help you improve your understanding of your financial situation. Doing your own taxes can be complicated, however, particularly if you have sources of income other than salary. The sources available for professional tax assistance include the following:

- Tax services ranging from local services to national firms with many offices, such as H&R Block.
- Many accountants who offer tax assistance along with other business services. A chartered accountant (CA), a certified general account (CGA), or a certified management account (CMA) with special training in taxes can help with tax planning and the preparation of your annual tax return.
- Tax lawyers usually do not complete tax returns; however, you can use legal services when you are involved in a complicated tax-related transaction or when you have a difference of opinion with the government.

Even if you hire a professional tax preparer, you are responsible for supplying accurate and complete information and for the contents of your income tax return. Hiring a tax preparer will not guarantee that you pay the *correct* amount. A U.S. study conducted by *Money* magazine of 41 tax preparers reported fees ranging from $375 to $3,600, with taxes due ranging from $31,846 to $74,450 for the same fictional family. If you owe more tax because your return contains errors or you have made entries that are disallowed, it is your responsibility to pay that additional tax, plus any interest and penalties.

Be wary of tax preparers and other businesses that offer your refund in advance. These "refund anticipation loans" frequently charge very high interest rates for this type of consumer credit. Studies reveal that interest rates sometimes exceed 300 percent (on an annualized basis).

WHAT IF YOUR RETURN IS AUDITED?

tax audit A detailed examination of your tax return by the Canada Customs and Revenue Agency.

Canada Customs and Revenue Agency (CCRA) reviews all returns for completeness and accuracy. If you make an error, your tax is automatically recalculated and you receive either a bill or a refund. If you make an entry that is disallowed, you will be notified by mail. A **tax audit** is a detailed examination of your tax return by the CCRA. In most audits, the revenue department requests more information to support the entries on your tax return. Be sure to keep accurate records to support your return. Keep receipts, cancelled cheques, and other evidence to support the amounts that you claim. Avoiding common filing mistakes (see Exhibit 3–11) helps to minimize your chances of an audit.

TYPES OF AUDITS The simplest and most common type of audit is the *desk audit*. This mail inquiry requires you to clarify or document minor questions about your tax return. You usually have 30 days to provide the requested information.

Exhibit 3–11

Top Ten Filing Errors

1. Mathematical errors, such as adding or subtracting amounts incorrectly.
2. Forgetting to reduce income by identifying workers' compensation, social assistance payments, and net federal supplements.
3. Calculating and claiming provincial tax credits incorrectly.
4. Not including pension adjustments, which affect RRSP contribution room for the coming year.
5. Claiming GST/HST credits incorrectly by using incorrect spousal income amounts.
6. Entering the wrong amounts on lines referring to Canada Pension Plan, Quebec Pension Plan, and Employment Insurance contribution and overpayments.
7. Claiming incorrect amounts as RRSP contributions.
8. Forgetting to claim the basic personal amount.
9. Claiming the spousal amount incorrectly.
10. Forgetting to claim the age amount, or claiming it incorrectly.

Advice from a Pro

A PRO SPEAKS ON TAX PLANNING

Any attempt to calculate your investment return must include the least exciting, most annoying financial subject: taxes. Even the word makes me cringe!

The government *will* get their share of your money—no exceptions. Smart tax planning helps you pay less tax legally. The federal government isn't fooling around: Those who use illegitimate techniques to avoid paying taxes get socked with high-priced penalties or jail time. Pay your taxes on time.

Toward the first of the year, you will begin to receive a series of statements from the jobs at which you have worked or financial institutions where you hold accounts. This includes brokerage firms, banks, mutual funds, and other intermediaries. Scrounge up the receipts from any charitable donations you've made

and proof of any employment-related expenses you plan on writing off. Keep these materials together: Lost forms waste time and money!

Your tax return has several sections to be aware of. Generally, your income should be added up, including any losses. Figure your taxable income, factor in additional credits or taxes, and write a cheque. *You've just paid your taxes!*

For those with a home business, complicated returns, or sketchy paperwork, some professional tax guidance is highly recommended—*and worth it!* Spending some money on a tax preparer or CA might seem daunting but will ensure that your return is filed accurately and rapidly.

The *field audit* is more complex. An auditing agent visits you at your home, your business, or the office of your accountant so you have access to records. A field audit may be done to verify whether an individual has an office in the home as claimed.

If you use EFILE, TELEFILE, or NETFILE you won't need to file receipts with your return. However, the CCRA or the Québec Ministère du Revenu may later ask to check certain claims, such as donations, RRSP contributions, or tuition fees. This is normally just a formality designed to maintain the integrity of the electronic filing system.

YOUR AUDIT RIGHTS While most audits of individual taxpayers are desk audits, some are field audits. In either case, you should be aware of your rights. The auditor is not entitled to scrutinize all of your documents at will. He or she may request only specific information, and you have a right to ask why that information is needed. In any situation where you anticipate that you will have problems, you have the right to and should seek assistance from professional advisers. Generally, however, an audit is a simple verification and should not be cause for alarm if you have filed your return in good faith.

If either an audit of your return or an audit of another person's return gives an indication that your tax payable is not what you have calculated and declared, the CCRA will issue a reassessment. In cases where this means that you will need to pay more taxes, you will normally be contacted first and given the opportunity to make representations on your behalf. The reassessment cannot be issued if more than three years have passed from the last assessment, except in cases of fraud or misrepresentation stemming from "neglect, carelessness, or wilful default," whereby a reassessment can be issued at any time.

Another situation where the three-year limitation might not apply is where you have signed a waiver regarding a specific disputed issue, as asked by the CCRA. You have the right to refuse to sign and can also revoke a signed waiver if you give six months' notice. Refusing to sign may be a sound strategy if the three-year limit is almost up, as it means that the reassessment may not be made if the revenue department does not have adequate time to complete its audit.

If you find yourself unable to pay your taxes or make a tax filing on time due to a natural or human-made disaster, serious illness, or accident, the *Income Tax Act*'s fairness rules give a degree of latitude to the CCRA to waive penalties and interest on overdue payments. You should be aware, however, that your past compliance to taxation rules may be considered if you make a fairness-related request.

OBJECTIONS AND APPEALS You have the right to file a Notice of Objection through your local Chief of Appeals in cases where you do not agree with an assessment. Doing so will allow you to have your objection considered by the independent Appeals Officer, but you must file your notice within 90 days of the disputed assessment or one year after the due date of the return.

The Appeals Officer is normally your highest possible level of appeal within the CCRA. The next step would be to appeal to the Tax Court of Canada, at which point you would be just two steps and extensive legal wrangling away from the Supreme Court of Canada.

Be aware that it is usually best to pay your full taxes, including items in dispute. Doing so will avoid late charges if you lose your appeal, and interest on your payment will be returned to you if you win. Paying disputed amounts in advance of an appeals decision is not an admission of guilt, but rather a sound financial decision that should have no legal bearing on your dispute.

CONCEPT CHECK 3–4

1. What are the main sources available to help people prepare their taxes?
2. What actions can reduce the chances of an audit?
3. What appeal options do taxpayers have if they disagree with an audit decision?

SUMMARY OF OBJECTIVES

Objective 1
Describe the importance of taxes for personal financial planning.
Tax planning can influence spending, saving, borrowing, and investing decisions. A knowledge of tax laws and maintenance of accurate tax records allows you to take advantage of appropriate tax benefits. An awareness of income taxes, sales taxes, excise taxes, property taxes, estate taxes, and other taxes is vital for successful financial planning.

Objective 2
Prepare federal and provincial income tax returns by calculating taxable income and the amount owed for federal and provincial income taxes.
The major sections of your tax return require you to calculate (1) your filing status, (2) income, (3) deductions, (4) other

deductions, (5) tax credits, and (6) your refund or the additional amount you owe.

Objective 3
Select appropriate tax strategies for different financial and personal situations.
You may reduce your tax burden through careful planning and making financial decisions related to consumer purchasing, the use of debt, investments, and retirement planning.

Objective 4
Identify tax assistance sources.
The main sources of tax assistance are CCRA services and publications, other publications, the Internet, computer software, and professional tax preparers, such as commercial tax services, accountants, and attorneys.

KEY TERMS

average tax rate 69

capital gains 84

deductions 63

employment income 62

excise tax 60

exclusion 62

investment income 62

marginal tax rate 69

net income 63

passive income 62

tax audit 90

tax credit 72

tax evasion 81

tax planning 81

tax shelter 62

taxable income 62

tax-deferred income 62

FINANCIAL PLANNING PROBLEMS

1. *Computing Taxable Income.* Franklin Stewart arrived at the following tax information:

   Gross salary, $47,780
   Interest earnings, $225
   Dividend income, $80
   Basic personal amount, $7,412
   Deductions, $3,890
   Other losses, $1,150

   What amount would Franklin report as taxable income? (Obj. 1)

2. *Calculating the Average Tax Rate.* What would be the average tax rate for a person who paid taxes of $4,864.14 on a total income of $39,870? (Obj. 2)

3. *Determining a Refund or Taxes Owed.* On the basis of the following data, would Ann and Carl Wilton receive a refund or owe additional taxes? (Obj. 2)

   Net income, $48,190
   Deductions, $11,420
   Child care tax deduction, $80
   Federal income tax withheld, $6,784
   Basic personal amount, $7,412
   Tax rate on taxable income, 22 percent

4. *Comparing Taxes on Investments.* Would you prefer a fully taxable investment earning 10.7 percent or a tax-exempt investment earning 8.1 percent? Why? (Obj. 3)

5. *Future Value of a Tax Savings.* On December 30, you decide to make a $1,000 charitable donation. If you are in the 22-percent tax bracket, how much will you save in taxes for the current year? If you deposit that tax savings in a savings account for the next five years at 8 percent, what will be the future value of that account? (Obj. 3)

FINANCIAL PLANNING ACTIVITIES

1. *Searching the Internet for Tax Information* Using Web sites such as the Virtual Tax Resource Centre at www.tax.ca, the Canadian Tax Foundation at www.ctf.ca, or Webfin at www.webfin.com, or library resources, obtain information about the tax implications of various financial planning decisions. (Obj. 1)

2. *Researching Tax-Exempt Income.* Using library resources or the World Wide Web, determine the types of income that are exempt from federal income tax. (Obj. 2)

3. *Planning Your Tax Payment.* Survey several people about whether they get a federal tax refund or owe taxes each year. Obtain information about the following: (a) Do they usually get a refund or owe taxes when they file their federal tax return? (b) Is their situation (refund or payment) planned? (c) What are the reasons they want to get a refund each year? (d) Are there situations where getting a refund may not be a wise financial decision? (Obj. 2)

4. *Determining Tax Planning Activities.* Survey friends and relatives about their tax planning strategies. (Obj. 3)

5. *Researching Current Tax Forms.* Obtain samples of current tax forms you would use to file your federal income tax return. These may be ordered by mail, obtained at a local CCRA office or post office, or obtained on the Internet at www.ccra-adrc.gc.ca. (Obj. 4)

6. *Researching Tax Questions.* Use CCRA publications and other reference materials to answer a specific tax question. Contact a CCRA office to obtain an answer for the same question. What differences, if any, exist between the information sources? (Obj. 4)

7. *Analyzing Tax Preparation Software.* Visit a retailer that sells tax preparation software, such as www.intuit.com, or visit the Web sites of software companies to determine the costs and features of programs you may use to prepare and file your federal income tax return. (Obj. 4)

8. *Reducing Tax Errors.* Create a visual presentation (video or slide presentation) that demonstrates actions a person might take to reduce errors when filing a federal tax return. (Obj. 4)

LIFE SITUATION CASE

A Single Father's Tax Situation

Ever since his wife's death, Eric Armano has faced difficult personal and financial circumstances. His job provides him with a fairly good income but keeps him away from his daughters, ages 8 and 10, nearly 20 days a month. This requires him to use in-home child care services that consume a large portion of his income. Since the Armanos live in a small apartment, this arrangement has been very inconvenient.

Due to the costs of caring for his children, Eric has only a minimal amount withheld from his salary for federal income taxes. This makes more money available during the year, but for the last few years he has had to make large payments in April—another financial burden.

Although Eric has created an investment fund for his daughters' education and for his retirement, he has not sought to select investments that offer tax benefits. Overall, he needs to look at several aspects of his tax planning activities to find strategies that will best serve his current and future financial needs.

Eric has assembled the following information for the current tax year:

Earnings from wages, $47,590
Interest earned on savings, $125

RRSP deduction, $2,000
Chequing account interest, $65
Basic personal amount, $7,412
Other deductions, $6,350
Amount withheld for federal income tax, $3,178
Child care deduction, $1,400
Filing status: head of household

Questions

1. What are Eric's major financial concerns in his current situation?
2. In what ways might Eric improve his tax planning efforts?
3. Is Eric typical of many people in our society with regard to tax planning? Why, or why not?
4. What additional actions might Eric investigate with regard to taxes and personal financial planning?
5. Calculate the following
   a. What is Eric's taxable income? (Refer to Exhibit 3–1, p. 63.)
   b. What is his total tax liability? (Use Exhibit 3–9, p. 87.) What is his average tax rate?
   c. On the basis of his withholding, will Eric receive a refund or owe additional tax? What is the amount?

CREATING A FINANCIAL PLAN

Tax Planning Activities

Taxes are a fact of financial planning. However, various actions can be taken to reduce the time and money that goes toward taxes.

Web Sites for Tax Planning

- For access to federal tax forms, CCRA regulations and other tax information, go to the CCRA's Web site at **www.ccra-adrc.gc.ca.** You may also find information at the Government of Canada site at **www.gc.ca**, and the Department of Finance Canada site, at **www.fin.gc.ca**.
- For access to provincial tax forms, regulations, and other tax information, go to the Québec Ministère du Revenu's Web site at **www.revenu.gouv.qc.ca**. You may also find information at the Government of Quebec site at **www.gouv.qc.ca**, and the Department of Finance site at **www.finances.gouv. qc.ca**.
- You will find a tremendous amount of investment and accounting company sites with tax information on the Web. Among the better known are Ernst & Young at **www.eycan. com**, Deloitte & Touche at **www.deloitte.ca**, H & R Block Canada at **www.hrblock.ca**, KPMG Canada at **www.kpmg. ca**, and Evancic Perreault Robertson at **www.epr.ca**.
- Online tax statistics and information is available at the Fraser Institute site at **www.fraserinstitute.ca**, the Canoe Webfin site at **www.webfin.com**, the Virtual Tax Resource Centre at **www.tax.ca**, the Canadian Taxpayer Federation at

www.taxpayer.com, the CANTAX site at **www.cantax. com**, and the Canadian Tax Foundation site at **www.ctf.ca**.
- Information about tax return software is available at the GriffTax site at **www.grifftax.com**, the Intuit Canada site at **www.intuit.com/canada**, and the TaxWiz site at **www. taxwiz.ca**.
- In cases where you may have a dispute with the CCRA regarding your taxes, the Tax Court of Canada at **www.tcc-cci.gc.ca** is a government organization operating independently to settle tax disputes.

(Note: Addresses and content of Web sites change, and new sites are created daily. Use search engines to update and locate Web sites for your current financial planning needs.)

Short-Term Financial Planning Activities

1. Develop a system for filing and storing various tax records related to income, deductible expenses, and current tax forms (see Exhibit 3–2).
2. Using the CCRA site and other Web sites, identify recent changes in tax laws that may affect your financial planning decisions.
3. Using current CCRA tax forms and tax tables, estimate your tax liability for the current year.
4. Compare the cost of tax preparation services.

Long-Term Financial Planning Activities

1. Identify saving and investing decisions that would minimize future income taxes.
2. Develop a plan for actions to take related to your current and future tax situation.

Government Web Sites:
Government of Canada **www.gc.ca**
Department of Finance Canada **www.fin.gc.ca**
Canada Customs and Revenue Agency **www.ccra-adrc.gc.ca**
Government of Quebec **www.gouv.qc.ca**
Department of Finance **www.finances.gouv.qc.ca**
Department of Revenue **www.revenu.gouv.qc.ca**

Other provincial and territorial governments:
Alberta **www.gov.ab.ca**

British Columbia **www.gov.bc.ca**
Manitoba **www.gov.mb.ca**
New Brunswick **www.gov.nb.ca**
Newfoundland **www.gov.nf.ca**
Northwest Territories **www.gov.nt.ca**
Nova Scotia **www.gov.ns.ca**
Nunavut **www.gov.nu.ca**
Ontario **www.gov.on.ca**
Prince Edward Island **www.gov.pe.ca**
Saskatchewan **www.gov.sk.ca**
Yukon **www.gov.yk.ca**

United States **www.info.gov**
Internal Revenue Service **www.irs.ustreas.gov**

Other countries **www.intergov.gc.ca**

CONTINUOUS CASE FOR PART 1

Getting started: planning for the future

Life Situation
Single; age 22; starting a career; no dependants

Financial Goals

- Evaluate current financial situation
- Establish a personal financial plan
- Develop a budgeting system for spending and savings

Financial Data

Monthly income	$2,400
Living expenses	1,980
Assets	6,200
Liabilities	1,270
Emergency fund	300

While in college, Pamela Jenkins worked part time and was never concerned about long-term financial planning. Rather than creating a budget, she used her chequebook and savings account (which usually had a very low balance) to handle her financial needs.

After completing college, Pamela began her career as a sales representative for a clothing manufacturer located in Montreal. After one year, her assets consist of a 1995 Chevrolet, a television set, a stereo, and some clothing and other personal belongs, with a total value of $6,200.

Since a portion of her income is based on commissions, her monthly income varies from one month to the next. This situation has made it difficult for Pamela to establish a realistic budget. During lean months, she has had to resort to using her credit card to make ends meet. In fact, her credit card debt, $1,270, is her only liability at this time. Her only other source of income is a large tax refund. In the past, she has always used tax refunds to finance major purchases (a vacation or furniture) or pay off credit card debt.

Questions

1. What financial decisions should Pamela be thinking about at this point in her life?
2. What are some short-term, intermediate, and long-term financial goals that Pamela might want to develop?
3. How should Pamela budget for fluctuations in her income caused by commission earnings?
4. Assume Pamela's federal tax refund is $1,100. Given her current situation, what should she do with the refund?
5. On the basis of her life situation, what type of tax planning should Pamela consider?

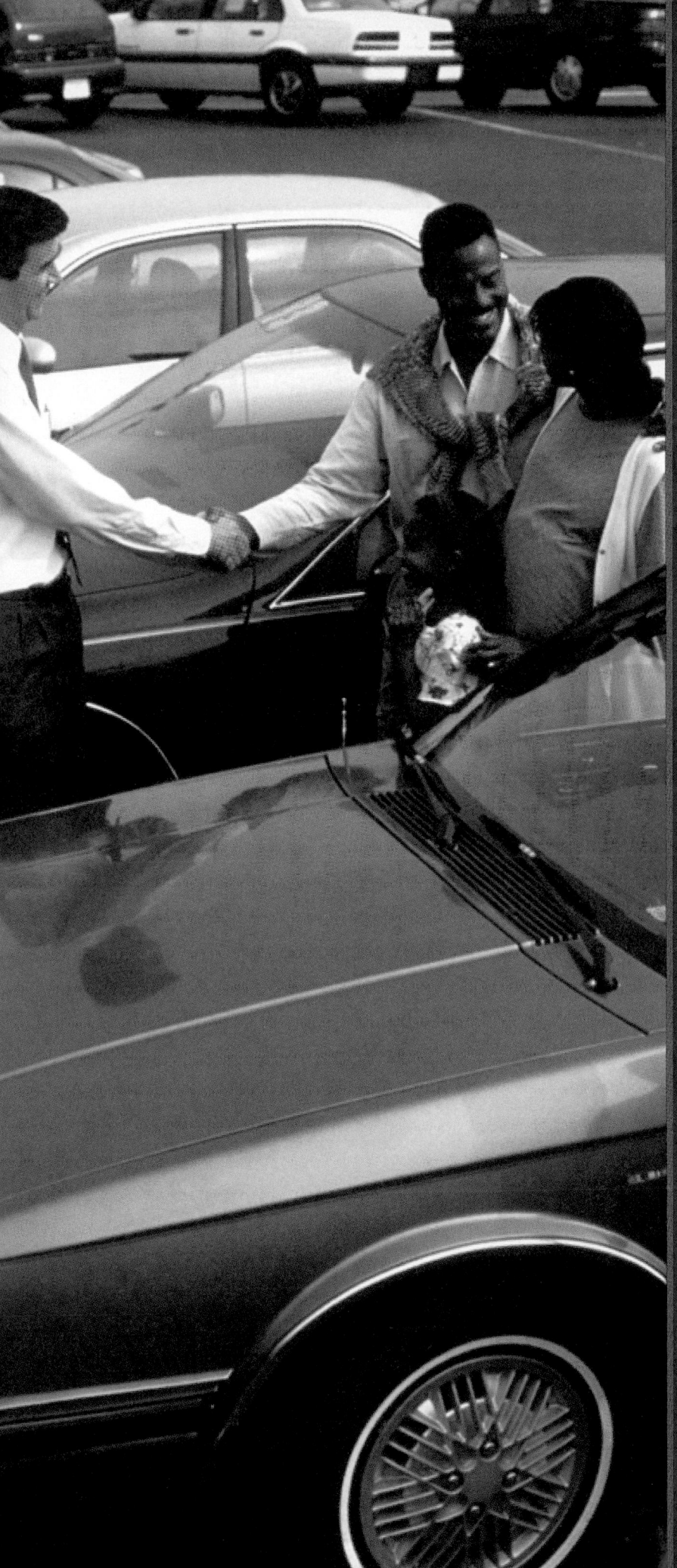

PART 2

MANAGING YOUR CREDIT

CHAPTER 4
**The Banking
Services of
Financial Institutions**

CHAPTER 5
**Introductiion to
Consumer Credit**

CHAPTER 6
**Choosing a Source of
Credit: The Costs of
Credit Alternatives**

CHAPTER 7
**The Finances of
Housing**

4 The Banking Services of Financial Institutions

Press One to Withdraw Cash...
Press Two to Deposit Cash...
Press Three for High Banking Fees!

Chris Carter was visiting the cash machine near his place of work for the third time this week. "Wow! Another cash withdrawal," commented his friend Edwin. "You must have tonnes of money in that chequing account."

"Well, not really," Chris confessed. "I can use this ATM card to access either my chequing or savings account."

"You mean after you've used up everything in your chequing account, you start taking money out of your savings?" asked Edwin. "Doesn't this machine make it too easy for you to overspend?"

"It's just that I've been very busy at work the last few weeks. I've been eating at restaurants a lot, and my cash is used up quickly," replied Chris.

A couple of weeks later, Chris received his bank statement, which included a couple of surprises. "Oh no!" he exclaimed. "Withdrawing cash from my chequing account made me fall below the minimum balance for the account, so they charged me $8.50. My 11 cash withdrawals resulted in more fees. And what's this? Another charge for an overdraft! All those cash withdrawals and fees really hit me hard! And my savings account is down to $78!"

QUESTIONS

1 What benefits and costs are associated with automated teller machines?

2 How does the use of financial services like ATMs affect a person's overall financial plan?

3 What could Chris do to reduce his banking fees and manage his money more wisely?

4 Locate a Web site that provides information suggesting methods for reducing banking fees.

LEARNING OBJECTIVES

1 Analyze factors that affect selection and use of financial services.

2 Compare the types of financial institutions.

3 Compare the costs and benefits of various savings plans.

4 Identify the factors used to evaluate different savings plans.

5 Compare the costs and benefits of different types of chequing accounts.

A Strategy for Managing Cash

With 53 banks, 55 trust and loan companies, and 2,440 credit unions and caisses populaires, an extensive financial services market exists. These organizations provide a variety of services for your daily payment and savings needs. Today, a trip to "the bank" may mean a visit to a credit union, an automated teller machine (or automatic banking machine), or checking an account balance on the Web. In recent years, financial services have expanded. A bank is not the only source of chequing accounts. Mortgages are available from several types of financial institutions.

While some financial decisions relate directly to goals, your daily activities require the use of financial services for various business transactions. Exhibit 4–1 provides an overview of financial services for managing cash flows and moving toward financial goals. In simplest terms, you can increase current savings only by spending less than you take in.

Objective 1

Analyze factors that affect selection and use of financial services.

MEETING DAILY MONEY NEEDS

Buying groceries, paying the rent, and other routine spending activities require a cash management plan.

MANAGING CASH   Cash, cheque, credit card, or automated teller machine (ATM) card (*debit card*) are the common payment choices. While most people desire ease of payment, they must also consider fees and the potential for impulse buying and overspending. For example, in recent years ATM fees have risen from nothing to $1 or $2 per cash withdrawal and even higher charges for balance inquiries. If you are charged two $1 transaction fees a week and could invest your money at 5 percent, this convenience will cost you more than $570 over a five-year period.

Common mistakes made when managing current cash needs include

- Overspending as a result of impulse buying and using credit cards.
- Having insufficient liquid assets (cash, chequing account) to pay current bills.
- Using savings or borrowing to pay for current expenses.

Exhibit 4–1

Financial Services for Managing Cash Flow

Financial Services for Short-Term Needs
- Daily purchases
- Living expense payments
- Emergency fund

Cash Availability	Savings	Chequing	Credit Cards
• Cheque cashing • Automated teller machines • Traveller's cheques • Foreign currency exchange	• Regular savings account • Money market account	• Regular chequing • Online payments • Automatic payments • Cashier's cheques • Money orders	• All-purpose cards • Cash advances

Financial Services for Long-Term Goals
- Major purchases
- Long-term financial security

Savings	Credit Services	Investment Services	Other Services
• Guaranteed Investment Certificates • Canada Savings Bonds (CSB)	• Cash loans for autos, education, and other purposes • Mortgages • Home equity loans	• Registered Retirement Savings Plans (RRSPs) • Brokerage service (Full service or discount) • Investment advice Mutual funds	• Insurance (auto, home, life, health) • Trust service • Tax preparation • Safety deposit boxes • Budget counselling • Estate planning

• Failing to put unneeded funds in an interest-earning savings account or investment plan to achieve long-term goals.

SOURCES OF QUICK CASH No matter how carefully you manage your money, there may be times when you will need more cash than you currently have available. To cope with that situation, you have two basic choices: liquidate savings or borrow. A savings account, Guaranteed Investment Certificates, mutual fund, or other investment may be raided when you need funds. Alternatively, a credit card cash advance or a personal loan may be appropriate. Remember, however, that both using savings and increasing borrowing reduce your net worth and your potential to achieve long-term financial security.

TYPES OF FINANCIAL SERVICES

Banks and other financial institutions offer services to meet a variety of needs. These services fall into four main categories.

1. SAVINGS Safe storage of funds for future use is a basic need for everyone. These services, commonly referred to as *time deposits*, include money in savings accounts and investment certificates. Selection of a savings plan is commonly based on the interest rate earned, liquidity, safety, and convenience. These factors are discussed later in the chapter.

2. PAYMENT SERVICES The ability to transfer money to other parties is a necessary part of daily business activities. Chequing accounts and other payment methods, commonly called *demand deposits*, are also covered later in the chapter.

3. BORROWING Most people use credit at some time during their lives. Credit alternatives range from short-term accounts, such as credit cards and cash loans, to long-term borrowing, such as a home mortgage. Chapters 5 and 6 discuss the types and costs of credit.

4. OTHER FINANCIAL SERVICES Insurance protection, investment for the future, real estate purchases, tax assistance, and financial planning are additional services you may need for successful financial management. With some financial plans, someone else manages your funds. A **trust** is a legal agreement that provides for the management and control of assets by one party for the benefit of another. This type of arrangement is most commonly created through a commercial bank or a lawyer. Parents who want to set aside certain funds for their children's education may use a trust or an RESP (Registered Education Savings Plan). The investments and money in the trust are managed by a bank, and the necessary amounts go to the children for their educational expenses. Trusts are covered in more detail in Chapter 5.

trust A legal agreement that provides for the management and control of assets by one party for the benefit of another.

ELECTRONIC BANKING SERVICES

Years ago, people had to conduct banking activities only during set business hours, usually 10 in the morning to three in the afternoon. Today, things are different. Several million Canadians bank or pay bills online. Computerized financial services (see Exhibit 4–2) provide fast, convenient, and efficient systems for recording inflows and outflows of funds.

DIRECT DEPOSIT Each year, more and more workers are receiving only a pay stub on payday. Their earnings are automatically deposited into chequing or savings accounts. This process saves time, effort, and money. Government agencies are

Exhibit 4–2

Electronic Banking
Transactions

also increasing use of direct deposits to reduce costs. Provincial and federal government cheques going to contractors and to Canada Pension Plan, Old Age Security, and welfare recipients are deposited electronically into the payees' bank accounts.

AUTOMATIC PAYMENTS Many utility companies, lenders, and other businesses allow customers to use an automatic payment system, with bills paid through direct withdrawal from a bank account. Experts recommend that you stagger your payments on the basis of when paycheques are received. This allows you to pay bills in an orderly fashion while stabilizing your cash flow. Be sure to check bank statements regularly to ensure that the correct amounts have been deducted from your account. A minor error can result in an overdrawn account and expensive fees.

AUTOMATED TELLER MACHINES **Automated teller machine (ATM)** convenience can be expensive. As the opening case points out, a person who uses an ATM several times a week can incur service charges of several hundred dollars a year. Surveys reveal that in casinos, ATM surcharges often add up to $3 to $5 per transaction. An ATM transaction on a cruise ship can cost $9 or more.

To reduce ATM fees, experts suggest that you

- Compare ATM fees at different financial institutions before opening an account. Get the fee schedule in writing.
- Use your own bank's ATM, whenever possible, to avoid surcharges imposed when using the ATM of another financial institution.
- Consider purchasing a monthly service package that includes ATM activity.
- Withdraw larger cash amounts, as needed, to avoid fees on several small transactions.
- Consider using personal cheques, traveller's cheques, credit cards, and prepaid cash cards when away from home.

Visit the Web site
See the CBC video exercise under Chapter 4 on the online learning centre at www.mcgraw hill.ca/college/kapoor.

automated teller machine (ATM)
A computer terminal used to conduct banking transactions.

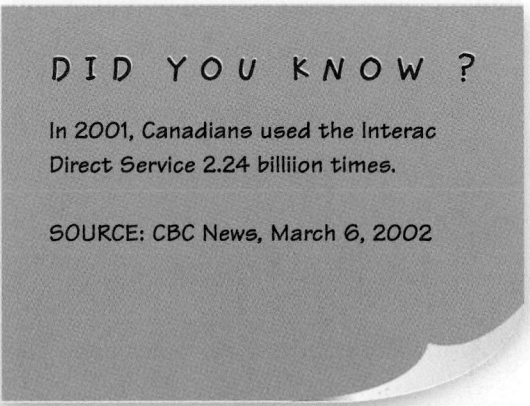

D I D   Y O U   K N O W ?

In 2001, Canadians used the Interac Direct Service 2.24 billiion times.

SOURCE: CBC News, March 6, 2002

METHODS OF PAYMENT

1. POINT-OF-SALE TRANSACTIONS

ATM cards are accepted by many retail stores and restaurants. Your financial institution may issue two types of debit cards for these transactions. An *online card* operates like an ATM card, with an instant transfer of funds from your account. Online transactions require that you enter your personal identification number (PIN) to authorize the transaction.

Offline card transactions are processed like credit card charges; your PIN is not required. However, these transactions do not increase the amount owed. Instead, the funds are deducted from your bank account after a day or two.

2. STORED-VALUE CARDS

Prepaid cards for buying telephone service, transit fares, laundry service, library fees, and school lunches are becoming very common. While some of these access cards, such as phone cards, are disposable (or become collector's items), others are reloadable "stored-value" cards.

3. SMART CARDS

"Smart cards," sometimes called "electronic wallets," look like ATM cards; however, they also include a microchip. This minicomputer stores prepaid amounts for buying goods and services. In addition, the card stores data about a person's account balances, transaction records, insurance information, and medical history. Smart cards are expected to see expanded use in the future as the services they offer increase.

4. ELECTRONIC CASH

SecurNat, offered by the National Bank of Canada (www.nbc.ca) is a payment solution that enables you to safely pay for a Web purchase, from a National Bank–approved merchant, using your credit card. In addition, recently developed electronic cash registers accept all forms of payment transactions, including cash, cheque, debit, and credit.

DID YOU KNOW ?

Generic ATMs are everywhere, with surcharges that are added to the regular transaction fees. These additional fees usually start at $1.50 and can climb much higher. Since the machines warn you about the service charge before your transaction is complete, however, you can cancel your transaction if you think the fee is excessive.

OPPORTUNITY COSTS OF FINANCIAL SERVICES

When making decisions about spending and saving, consider the trade-off between current satisfaction and long-term financial security. In a similar manner, you consider opportunity cost—what you give up—when you evaluate, select, and use financial services. The money you save by shopping around for a low-cost chequing account must be balanced against the value of the time you spend gathering information. Other common trade-offs related to financial services include the following:

- Higher returns of long-term savings and investment plans may be achieved at the cost of *low liquidity*, the inability to obtain your money quickly.
- The convenience of a 24-hour automated teller machine or a bank branch office near your home or place of work must be weighed against service fees.
- The "no fee" chequing account that requires a non–interest-bearing $500 minimum balance means lost interest of nearly $400 at 6 percent compounded over 10 years.

You should evaluate costs and benefits in both monetary and personal terms to choose the financial services that best serve your needs.

FINANCIAL SERVICES AND ECONOMIC CONDITIONS

Changing interest rates, rising consumer prices, and other economic factors also influence financial services. For successful financial planning, be aware of the current trends and future prospects for interest rates (see Exhibit 4–3 and the Financial Planning for Life's Situations

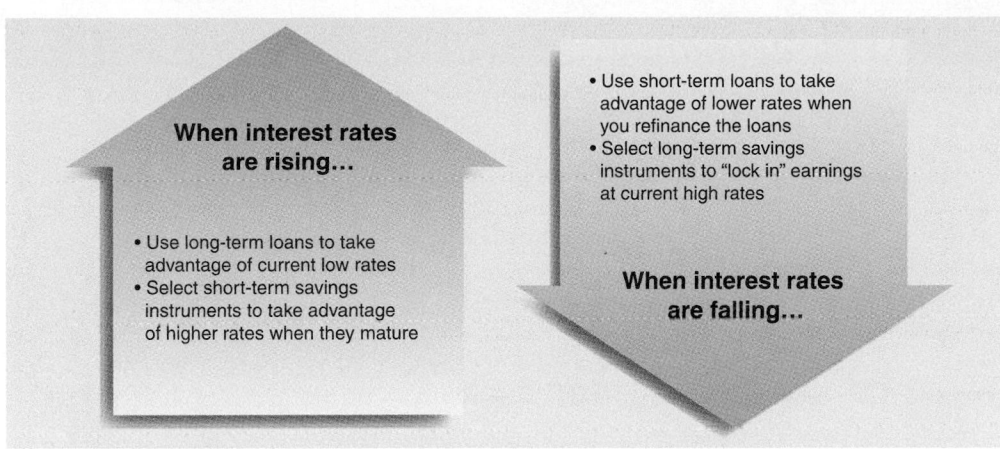

Exhibit 4–3

Changing Interest Rates and Decisions Related to Financial Services

When interest rates are rising...

• Use long-term loans to take advantage of current low rates
• Select short-term savings instruments to take advantage of higher rates when they mature

• Use short-term loans to take advantage of lower rates when you refinance the loans
• Select long-term savings instruments to "lock in" earnings at current high rates

When interest rates are falling...

box on page 104). You can learn about these trends and prospects by reading *The Financial Post* (www.nationalpost.com/financialpost/), the business section of daily newspapers, and business periodicals such as *Business Week* (www.businessweek.com), *IE:Money* (www.iemoney.com), and *Fortune* (www.fortune.com).

CONCEPT CHECK 4–1

1. What is the relationship between financial services and overall financial planning?
2. What are the major categories of financial services?
3. What financial services are available through electronic banking systems?
4. Why shouldn't you select financial services on the basis of only monetary factors?
5. How do changing economic conditions affect the use of financial services?

Types of Financial Institutions

Many types of businesses, such as insurance companies, investment brokers, and credit card companies, have become involved in financial services previously limited to banks. Such companies as GM Canada and the Hudson's Bay Company now issue or sponsor credit cards. Banks have also expanded their competitive efforts by opening offices that specialize in financial services, such as investments, insurance, or real estate. Increased competition has brought about the opening of many limited-service offices, sometimes called *nonbanks*. These limited-service offices specialize in a particular banking activity, such as savings or personal loans.

Despite changes in the banking environment, many familiar financial institutions still serve your needs. Most of these institutions have expanded their services. As Exhibit 4–4 shows, financial institutions fall into two major categories: deposit-type institutions and nondeposit institutions.

Objective 2

Compare the types of financial institutions.

Deposit-Type Institutions	Nondeposit Institutions
• Chartered banks • Trust companies • Credit unions/caisses populaires	• Life insurance companies • Investment companies • Mortgage and loan companies • Pawnshops • Cheque-cashing outlets

Exhibit 4–4

Types of Financial Institutions

Financial Planning for Life's Situations

UNDERSTANDING INTEREST RATES

When people discuss higher or lower interest rates, they could be talking about one of many types of interest rates. Some interest rates refer to the cost of borrowing by a business; others refer to the cost of buying a home. Your awareness of various types of interest rates can help you plan your spending, saving, borrowing, and investing. The accompanying table describes the most commonly reported interest rates and gives their *annual average* for selected years.

Using the business section of a newspaper or other business information sources, obtain current numbers for some or all of these interest rates. How might the current trend in interest rates affect your financial decisions?

	1970	1975	1980	1985	1990	1995	2000	Current
Prime rate—an indication of the rate banks charge large corporations	8.17	9.42	14.25	10.58	14.02	8.65	6.81	____%
Bank rate—an indication of the rate banks charge for loans	7.13	8.50	12.89	9.65	13.05	7.31	5.31	____
91-day T-bill rate—the yield on 91-day government treasury bills	5.99	7.40	12.79	9.43	12.81	6.89	5.21	____
30-yr T-bond rate—the yield on 30-year government treasury bonds	7.91	9.04	12.48	11.05	10.85	8.28	6.08	____
5-yr mortgage rate—the amount individuals are paying to borrow for the purchase of a home	10.45	11.43	14.32	12.18	13.41	9.22	8.31	____
5-yr term deposit rate—the amount that individuals are receiving for 5-year term deposits	7.63	8.27	11.25	9.63	10.33	6.70	5.48	____
Savings deposit rate—the amount that individuals are receiving for regular savings deposits	6.17	7.00	11.15	6.08	8.77	0.50	0.10	____

DEPOSIT-TYPE INSTITUTIONS

For many years, government policies prohibited cross-ownership and foreign control of the four major types of businesses in financial services. This division, referred to as the "four pillars," separated banks, trust companies, insurance companies, and investment dealers, where rules were established to protect their core business (deposit taking and lending, fiduciary services, insurance protection and underwriting, and securities trading, respectively).

However, spurred by the deregulation efforts in the United States, since 1980, services provided by Canadian companies have broadened and overlapped, blurring the separation of the four pillars. Keeping up with international developments, the federal government passed legislation on June 1, 1992, permitting banks, trust and loan companies, and insurance companies to compete more directly with one another.

CHARTERED BANKS Operating under the provisions of the Bank Act, the principal activity of the banks is to loan funds to businesses and consumers at interest rates that are higher than those the banks pay on deposits and other borrowings. **Chartered banks** own a range of other types of corporations, including brokerage firms, information service firms, and special financing corporations. This diversity enables banks to offer investment counselling and portfolio management services under one roof.

SCHEDULE I BANKS These include the six big banks (RBC Financial, CIBC, Bank of Montreal, Bank of Nova Scotia, TD Canada Trust, and the National Bank of Canada), smaller Canadian-owned banks, and other nonbank financial institutions.

SCHEDULE II BANKS These are subsidiaries of foreign banks in Canada that have restrictions on asset growth as well as on lending activities, which are a function of their local capital base, rather than the parent bank. They tend to focus on commercial corporate loans, rather than retail banking services to individuals.

TRUST COMPANIES Trust companies offer a broad range of financial services similar to those provided by banks. In addition, they are the only corporations allowed to act as a trustee in charge of corporate or individual property, stocks, and bonds. Most trust companies are owned by banks, except the large independents, such as Sunlife, Clarica, Maritime Life, and Great West Life.

CREDIT UNIONS AND CAISSES POPULAIRES A **credit union** (or *caisse populaire* in Quebec) is a user-owned, nonprofit, co-operative financial instiution. Traditionally, credit union members had to have a common bond, such as work, church, or community affiliation. As the common bond restriction was loosened, the membership of credit unions increased.

Each year, surveys conducted by consumer organizations and others report lower fees for chequing accounts, lower loan rates, and higher levels of user satisfaction for credit unions, compared with other financial institutions. Most credit unions offer credit cards, mortgages, home equity loans, direct deposit, cash machines, safety deposit boxes, and investment services.

NONDEPOSIT INSTITUTIONS

Financial services are also available from such institutions as life insurance companies, investment companies, mortgage and loan companies, pawnshops, and cheque-cashing outlets.

LIFE INSURANCE COMPANIES While the main purpose of life insurance is to provide financial security for dependants, many life insurance policies contain savings and investment features. Chapter 9 discusses these policies. In recent years, life insurance companies have expanded their financial services to include investment and retirement planning.

INVESTMENT COMPANIES Investment companies, also referred to as *mutual funds,* offer banking-type services. A common service of these organizations is the **money market fund**, a combination savings-investment plan in which the investment company uses your money to purchase a variety of short-term financial instruments. Your earnings are based on the interest the investment company receives. Unlike accounts at most banks, trust companies, and credit unions, investment company accounts are not covered by federal deposit insurance.

chartered bank A financial institution that offers a full range of financial services to individuals, businesses, and government agencies.

credit union /caisse populaire A user-owned, nonprofit co-operative financial institution that is organized for the benefit of its members.

money market fund A savings-investment plan offered by investment companies, with earnings based on investments in various short-term financial instruments.

DID YOU KNOW ?

In comparing the various service fees payable at different financial institutions, you will generally find that credit unions or *caisses populaires* offer a better deal than chartered banks and trust companies.

A good way to choose the best financial institution and package for you is by using the Financial Service Charges Calculator offered by Industry Canada. You can find it on the Internet at http://strategis.ic.gc.ca under the heading Consumer Information.

MORTGAGE AND LOAN COMPANIES These companies provide real estate mortgage loans as well as financing opportunities for individuals and small businesses. In general, the loans provided have short and intermediate terms with higher rates than most other lenders charge. Some of these companies have expanded their activities to also offer other financial planning services.

PAWNSHOPS Pawnshops make loans based on the value of tangible possessions, such as jewellery or other valuable items. Many low- and moderate-income families use these organizations to obtain cash loans quickly. Pawnshops charge higher fees than other financial institutions.

CHEQUE-CASHING OUTLETS Most financial institutions will not cash a cheque unless the person has an account. Cheque-cashing outlets (CCOs) charge anywhere from 1 to 20 percent of the face value of a cheque; the average cost is between 2 and 3 percent. However, for a low-income family, that can be a significant portion of the total household budget (see the Financial Planning for Life's Situations box on page 107).

CCOs offer a wide variety of services, including electronic tax filing, money orders, and private postal boxes. You can usually obtain most of these services for less expense at other locations.

CYBERBANKING

Banking through the telephone, the personal computer, and online services continues to expand. Most banks now have "cyber" branches where customers can check balances, pay bills, transfer funds, compare savings plans, and apply for loans on the Internet. The Bank of Montreal (www.bmo.com) and the TD Canada Trust (www.tdcanadatrust.com) were among the first Canadian banks to do business on the Internet. Citizens Bank of Canada (www.citizensbank.ca) was one of the first Canadian financial institutions to operate exclusively on the Internet. Access to all accounts and transactions is available 24 hours a day, seven days a week. (See the Financial Planning for Life's Situations box on page 109.)

One of the main deterrents to banking online is a lack of technical and computer expertise. Most banking transactions require specialized software for securely encrypting data. Do not worry, most financial Web sites show you how and where to download the required software free of charge.

COMPARING FINANCIAL INSTITUTIONS

DID YOU KNOW ?

The stark reality of services offered by cheque-cashing outlets is that the fees you pay are substantially higher than what you might be charged at other financial institutions. Studies reveal that poor consumers (who form the bulk of the outlets' clientele) can spend up to 10 times as much at a cheque-cashing outlet as they would with a basic account. Despite this fact, other studies have proposed that banks often poorly promote the availability of low-cost accounts.

The basic concerns of a financial services customer are simple:

- Where can I get the best return on my savings?
- How can I minimize the cost of chequing and payments services?
- Will I be able to borrow money when I need it?

As you use financial services, decide what you want from the organization that will serve your needs. With the financial marketplace constantly changing, you must assess the various services and other factors before selecting an organization (see Exhibit 4–5).

The services the financial institution offers are likely to be a major factor. Personal service is important to many customers. Convenience may be provided by business hours, branch offices, automated teller machines, and online service. Convenience and service have a cost, so be sure to compare fees and other charges at several financial institutions.

Financial Planning for Life's Situations

BEWARE OF HIGH-COST FINANCIAL SERVICES

Would you pay $8 to cash a $100 cheque? Or pay $20 to borrow $100 for two weeks? Many people without ready access to financial services (especially low-income consumers) commonly use the services of cheque-cashing outlets, pawnshops, payday loan stores, and rent-to-own centres. Offers of "quick cash" and "low payments" attract consumers without a bank account or credit cards.

PAWNSHOPS

Despite a thriving economy in recent years, thousands of consumers are increasingly in need of small loans—usually $50 to $75, to be repaid in 30 to 45 days. Pawnshops have become the "neighbourhood bankers" and the "local shopping malls," since they provide both lending and retail shopping services, selling items that owners do not redeem.

PAYDAY LOANS

Payday loans are also referred to as *cash advances, cheque advance loans, postdated cheque loans,* and *delayed deposit loans*. Desperate borrowers pay annual interest rates of as much as 780 percent and more to obtain needed cash from payday loan companies. The most common users of payday loans are workers who have become trapped by debts run up by free spending or who have been driven into debt by misfortune.

In a typical payday loan, a consumer writes a personal cheque for $115 to borrow $100 for 14 days. The payday lender agrees to hold the cheque until the next payday. This $15 finance charge for the 14 days translates into an annual percentage rate of 391 percent. Some consumers "roll over" their loans, paying another $15 for the $100 loan for the next 14 days. After a few rollovers, the finance charge can exceed the amount borrowed.

RENT-TO-OWN CENTRES

Years ago, people who rented furniture and appliances found few deluxe items available. Today, rental businesses offer big-screen televisions, seven-piece cherrywood bedroom sets, and personal computers. The rental-purchase industry—defined as stores that lease products to consumers who can then own the item if they complete a certain number of monthly or weekly payments—is in rapid growth.

Buyer beware, however. The rental agreements drawn up in this industry are not necessarily in the consumer's best interests, and interest rates are often very high.

Finally, you should consider safety factors and interest rates. Obtain information about earnings you will receive on savings and chequing accounts and the rate you will pay for borrowed funds. Most financial institutions have deposit insurance to protect customers against losses; however, not all of them are insured by federal government programs. Investigate the type of protection you will have.

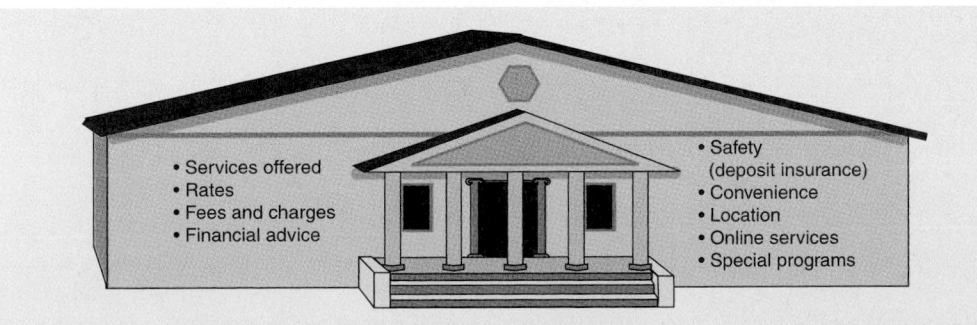

- Services offered
- Rates
- Fees and charges
- Financial advice

- Safety (deposit insurance)
- Convenience
- Location
- Online services
- Special programs

Exhibit 4–5

How Should You Choose a Financial Institution?

Your selection of a financial institution should be based on valid information. Never assume that one will provide a better interest rate or service than another. You need to compare banks, trust companies, and credit unions with other providers of financial services.

> ## CONCEPT CHECK 4–2
>
> 1. What are examples of deposit-type financial institutions?
> 2. What factors do consumers usually consider when selecting a financial institution to meet their saving and chequing needs?

Types of Savings Plans

Objective 3

Compare the costs and benefits of various savings plans.

As Chapter 2 emphasized, you need a savings program to attain financial goals. Evaluation of various savings plans is the starting point of this process.

Changes in financial services have created a wide choice of savings alternatives (see Exhibit 4–6). While the number of savings plans may seem overwhelming, they can be grouped into these main categories: regular savings accounts, term deposits and GICs, interest-earning chequing accounts, and Canada Savings Bonds. Investment vehicles, such as Canadian treasury bills, are discussed in later chapters.

Exhibit 4–6   Savings Alternatives

Type of Alternative	Benefits	Drawbacks
Regular savings accounts/ passbook accounts	Low minimum balance Ease of withdrawal Insured to $60,000	Low rate of return
Guaranteed Investment Certificates (GICs)	Guaranteed rate of return for time of GIC Insured	Possible penalty for early withdrawal Minimum deposit
Interest-earning chequing accounts	Chequing privileges Interest earned Insured to $60,000	Possible service charge for going below minimum balance Cost for printing cheques; other fees may apply
Money market accounts	Favourable rate of return (based on current interest rates) Allows some cheque writing	Higher minimum balance than regular savings accounts No interest or service charge, if below a certain balance
Money market funds	Favourable rate of return (based on current interest rates)	Minimum balance Not insured
Canada Savings Bonds (CSBs)	Rate of return varies with current interest rates Low minimum deposit Government guaranteed	No interest paid if redeemed before three months

BANKING ONLINE

"We never close." "Highest savings rates anywhere." "Lowest chequing account fees ever."

These impressive banking services are now possible with the use of the World Wide Web. Banks, like other businesses and financial service companies, are now online with cyber-versions of their traditional activities.

COMPARING BANKING SERVICES

As you start or expand your use of online banking services, several Web sites provide a wide range of banking information. These include www.iemoney.com and www.quicken.ca.

ONLINE BANK BRANCHES

Traditional banks are expanding to offer services online. Some examples include www.bmo.com and www.tdcanadatrust.com.

PAYING BILLS ONLINE

Internet delivery of household bills will soon occur; you might someday hear "You have bills" as you log on to a Web site or access your e-mail. Paperless bill delivery is currently limited in use to a few banks. However, several financial, utility, and technology companies are planning systems that will enable consumers to view, pay, scan details, and summarize monthly charges with the click of a mouse. For information on paying bills online, go to www.quicken.ca, www.yahoo.com, or www.aol.ca.

WEB-ONLY BANKS

Many of today's best chequing and savings deals come from branchless banks doing business solely on the Internet. Web banks usually require little or no minimum balance on chequing accounts. Many Internet banks also pay higher interest on chequing accounts than traditional banks. While ATMs are not readily available from Web banks, these online financial companies usually offer banking and customer service over the telephone. Some Internet banks include www.citizensbank.com and President's Choice Financial (www.preschoicefinancial.com) and ING Direct (www.ingdirect.ca)

Be cautious! You may access the Web site of the Canadian Deposit Insurance Corporation (www.cdic.ca) to obtain information on fraudulent cyber-banks. The CDIC can tell you if a Web bank has a legitimate charter to operate as a financial institution.

REGULAR SAVINGS ACCOUNTS

Regular savings accounts, traditionally called *passbook accounts*, usually involve a low or no minimum balance. Today, instead of a passbook showing deposits and withdrawals, savers may elect to receive a monthly or quarterly statement with a summary of transactions.

A regular savings account usually allows you to withdraw money as needed. However, *time deposits* may require a waiting period to obtain your funds.

TERM DEPOSITS AND GUARANTEED INVESTMENT CERTIFICATES (GICS)

Higher earnings are commonly available to savers when they leave money on deposit for a set time period.

TERM DEPOSITS Contrary to a savings account, which does not have a guaranteed interest rate of return, **term deposits** guarantee a rate of interest for a specified term. The trade-off is very simply that your money becomes less accessible for a time.

Some term deposits require a minimum deposit, and if you are willing to sacrifice some of the interest you might have earned, you will usually be permitted to withdraw your funds

term deposits A deposit that is made for a specified term in exchange for a higher rate of return. Can be redeemed before maturity by earning a reduced rate of interest (paying a penalty).

before maturity. The amount of interest you will earn is inversely related to the term of the investment, which will typically be between 30 and 364 days.

GUARANTEED INVESTMENT CERTIFICATES (GICS)

Guaranteed Investment Certificates (GICs)
Term deposits made for a longer period, usually from one to five years. These are non-redeemable before maturity; the only way to retrieve funds prematurely is to sell the GIC to a broker at a discount. There is an active secondary market for GICs.

Guaranteed Investment Certificates are essentially term deposits with a longer term, ranging from one to five years. They are equally safe and the interest is guaranteed. Interest is generally paid out semi-annually or annually, and some GICs allow for compounding.

As in the case of term deposits, a minimum deposit is often required and you trade off ease of access for a higher return. In this case, however, you will not be allowed to cash in the certificate before it matures. If you require your funds before the maturity date, you may be forced to sell your certificate through a brokerage house, and the return you earn will depend on the prevailing market valuation of your investment.

MANAGING YOUR TERM DEPOSITS AND GICS

When a term deposit or GIC reaches maturity, it is important to assess all earnings and costs. Do not allow your financial institution to automatically roll your money over into another deposit for the same term. If interest rates have dropped, you should consider investing in a term deposit for a shorter term in hopes that rates will rise. Alternatively, if you believe that rates are peaking and you do not think you will need your money for a time, then your best choice will be a longer-term GIC.

Rates will often vary slightly from one financial institution to the next. It is wise to comparison-shop for the best available rates. Current rates at most financial institutions are available at www.webfin.com/en/mymoney/rates/.

INTEREST-EARNING CHEQUING ACCOUNTS

Chequing accounts can also be savings vehicles. These interest-earning accounts, which usually pay a low interest rate, are discussed in the next section.

CANADA SAVINGS BONDS

Historically, Canada Savings Bonds (CSBs) developed from Victory bonds, which were offered between 1940 and 1944 in an effort to raise funds for the Canadian military action of the Second World War. Though crucial at the time and in the half century that followed, CSBs now have a declining role in the federal government's borrowing as the government's need for funds has diminished.

Unlike most investments, CSBs are sold only once a year, in October. They have a fixed rate of interest and the interest rates are usually adjusted for later years. Two types are available: the *regular interest bond* and the *compound interest bond*.

Visit the Web site
See Personal Financial Planning worksheets under Chapter 4 on the online learning centre at www.mcgrawhill.ca/college/kapoor.

REGULAR INTEREST BOND

This bond pays regular annual interest by cheque or direct deposit to an investor's account on November 1 of each year. Denominations for this bond issue are $300, $500, $1,000, $5,000, and $10,000. Only cash is permitted in buying this bond.

COMPOUND INTEREST BOND

This bond reinvests payable interest automatically until redemption or maturity. It is available in denominations of $100, $300, $500, $1,000, $5,000, and 10,000. This bond can be purchased by cash, by a monthly payment plan through a financial institution, or through a payroll savings plan.

CONCEPT CHECK 4–3

1. What are the main types of savings plans offered by financial institutions?
2. What are the benefits of Canada Savings Bonds?

Evaluating Savings Plans

Your selection of a savings plan will be influenced by the rate of return, inflation, tax considerations, liquidity, safety, and restrictions and fees.

RATE OF RETURN

Earnings on savings can be measured by the **rate of return**, or *yield*: the percentage of increase in the value of your savings from earned interest. For example, a $100 savings account that earned $5 after a year would have a rate of return, or yield, of 5 percent. This rate of return was determined by dividing the interest earned ($5) by the amount in the savings account ($100).

COMPOUNDING The yield on your savings usually will be greater than the stated interest rate. The more frequent the compounding, the higher your rate of return will be. For example, $100 in a savings account that earns 6 percent compounded annually will increase $6 after a year. But the same $100 in a 6-percent account compounded daily will earn $6.19 for the year. Although this difference may seem slight, large amounts held in savings for long periods of time will result in far higher differences (see Exhibit 4–7).

EFFECTIVE ANNUAL RATE (EAR) To incorporate the compounding effect, the **effective annual rate (EAR)** formula is used. Using the notation that m is the number of periods in a year and k_m is the rate of return for one period,

$$EAR = (1 + k_m)^m - 1$$

   It is important to note the effects of compounding. Imagine a simple case where you pay interest on a $100 loan at 12 percent yearly, compounded monthly. Not accounting for the compounding effect will lead you to conclude that you are paying 12 percent, or $12 per year in interest charges.
   The reality is that you are paying more. Using the EAR formula, which allows for compounding, will show that you will actually pay 12.68 percent, or $12.68. EAR can also be calculated with a financial calculator; see Appendix A for examples.

NOMINAL INTEREST RATE

The nominal interest rate is the periodic rate multiplied by the number of compounding periods in a year. For example, if a saving account pays 2 percent interest every three months, the

Objective 4

Identify the factors used to evaluate different savings plans.

rate of return The percentage of increase in the value of savings as a result of interest earned; also called *yield*.

effective annual rate (EAR) A formula that calculates the effective return, taking compounding into account.

$EAR = (1 + k_m)^m - 1$
   m = number of periods in a year
   k_m = rate of return for one period.

Shorter compounding periods result in higher yields. This chart shows the growth of $10,000, five-year GICs paying the same nominal rate of 8 percent, but with different compounding methods.

Exhibit 4–7

Compounding Frequency Increases the Savings Yield

	COMPOUNDING METHOD			
End of Year	Daily	Monthly	Quarterly	Annually
1	$10,832.78	$10,830.00	$10,824.32	$10,800.00
2	11,743.91	11,728.88	11,716.59	11,664.00
3	12,712.17	12,702.37	12,682.41	12,597.12
4	13,770.82	13,756.66	13,727.85	13,604.89
5	14,917.62	14,898.46	14,859.46	14,693.28
Effective rate	8.33%	8.30%	8.24%	8.00%

nominal interest rate is 2 × 4 because there are four three month periods in one year. The EAR for the same problem would be;

$$EAR = (1+2\%)^4 - 1$$
$$= 8.24\%$$

INFLATION

The rate of return you earn on your savings should be compared with the inflation rate. When the inflation rate was more than 10 percent, people with money in savings accounts earning 5 or 6 percent were experiencing a loss in the buying power of that money. In general, as the inflation rate increases, the interest rates offered to savers also increase. This gives you an opportunity to select a savings option that will minimize the erosion of your dollars on deposit.

TAX CONSIDERATIONS

Like inflation, taxes reduce interest earned on savings. For example, a 10-percent return for a saver in a 26-percent tax bracket means a real return of 7.4 percent (the Financial Planning Calculations feature on the next page shows how to compute the after-tax savings rate of return). As discussed in Chapter 3 and discussed further in Part 4, several tax-exempt and tax-deferred savings plans and investments can increase your real rate of return.

LIQUIDITY

Liquidity refers to the ease with which you can access cash or convert investments to cash with a minimal loss of principal. Some savings plans impose penalties for early withdrawal or have other restrictions. With certain types of savings certificates and accounts, early withdrawal may be penalized by a loss of interest or a lower earnings rate.

You should consider the degree of liquidity you desire in relation to your savings goals. To achieve long-term financial goals, many people trade off liquidity for a higher return.

SAFETY

Most savings plans at banks, trust companies, and credit unions or caisses populaires are insured by agencies affiliated with the federal government. This protection prevents loss of money due to the failure of the insured institution.

The Canadian Deposit Insurance Corporation (CDIC) will protect eligible deposits up to a maximum of $60,000 per person, including principal and interest, for each different member institution involved. Eligible deposits include savings and chequing accounts, term deposits, Guaranteed Investment Certificates, debentures, and other obligations issued by institutions that are members of the CDIC.

In the event that a member institution becomes insolvent, your insured funds will be secure up to $60,000. In the case of a joint deposit, the funds insured will be $60,000 divided among all the names in the account.

Be aware that deposits in different branches of the same institution will be counted as a single account and will be insured only to $60,000. If you have more than this amount to deposit, it would be wise to spread your money among different members of the CDIC, although chartered banks offer a variety of products that may be insured separately. To find out more about eligible deposits, you can access the CDIC site at www.cdic.ca.

Since not all financial institutions have federal deposit insurance, investigate this matter when you are selecting a savings plan.

Financial Planning Calculations

AFTER-TAX SAVINGS RATE OF RETURN

The taxability of interest on your savings reduces your real rate of return. In other words, you lose some portion of your interest to taxes. This calculation consists of the following steps:

1. Determine your top tax bracket for federal income taxes.
2. Subtract this rate, expressed as a decimal, from 1.0.
3. Multiply the result by the yield on your savings account.
4. This number, expressed as a percentage, is your after-tax rate of return.

For example,

1. You are in the 26 percent tax bracket (federally).
2. $1.0 - 0.26 = 0.74$.
3. If the yield on your savings account is 6.25 percent, $0.0625 \times 0.74 = 0.046$.
4. Your after-tax rate of return is 4.6 percent.

You may use the same procedure to determine the real rate of return on your savings based on inflation. For example, if you are earning 6 percent on savings and inflation is 5 percent, your real rate of return (after inflation) is 5.7 percent: $0.06 \times (1 - 0.05) = 0.057$.

RESTRICTIONS AND FEES

Other limitations can affect your choice of a savings program. For example, there may be a delay between the time interest is earned and the time it is added to your account. This means it will not be available for your immediate use. Also, some institutions charge a transaction fee for each deposit or withdrawal and pay interest only if you maintain a minimum monthly balance.

In the past, some financial institutions had promotions offering a "free" gift when a certain savings amount was deposited. To receive this gift, you had to leave your money on deposit for a certain time period or you may have received less interest, since some of the earnings were used to cover the cost of the "free" items. Economists tell us that "there is no such thing as a free lunch"; the same holds true for toasters and television sets.

CONCEPT CHECK 4–4

1. When would you prefer a savings plan with high liquidity over one with a high rate of return?
2. What is the relationship between compounding and the future value of an amount?
3. How do inflation and taxes affect earnings on savings?

Selecting Payment Methods

With about 90 percent of business transactions conducted by cheque, a chequing account is a necessity for most people.

TYPES OF CHEQUING ACCOUNTS

Chequing accounts fall into three major categories: regular chequing accounts, activity accounts, and interest-earning chequing accounts.

Objective 5

Compare the costs and benefits of different types of chequing accounts.

REGULAR CHEQUING ACCOUNTS *Regular chequing accounts* usually have a monthly service charge that you may avoid by keeping a minimum balance in the account. Some financial institutions will waive the monthly fee if you keep a certain amount in savings. Avoiding the monthly service charge can be beneficial. For example, a monthly fee of $7.50 results in $90 a year. However, you lose interest on the minimum-balance amount in a non–interest-earning account.

ACTIVITY ACCOUNTS *Activity accounts* charge a fee for each cheque written and sometimes a fee for each deposit, in addition to a monthly service charge. However, you do not have to maintain a minimum balance. An activity account is most appropriate for people who write only a few cheques each month and are unable to maintain the required minimum balance.

INTEREST-EARNING CHEQUING ACCOUNTS *Interest-earning chequing accounts* usually require a minimum balance. If the account balance goes below this amount, you may not earn interest and will likely incur a service charge.

EVALUATING CHEQUING ACCOUNTS

Would you rather have a chequing account that pays interest and requires a $1,000 minimum balance or an account that doesn't pay interest and requires a $300 minimum balance? This decision requires evaluating such factors as restrictions, fees and charges, interest, and special services (see Exhibit 4–8).

DID YOU KNOW ?

"Rubber cheques" mean big money for the banking industry. Every year, banks make billion-dollar profits from bounced-cheque fees. Studies have shown that some institutions charge up to 32 times what it actually costs them to process a cheque that is issued with insufficient funds.

RESTRICTIONS The most common limitation on chequing accounts is the amount you must keep on deposit to earn interest or avoid a service charge.

FEES AND CHARGES Nearly all financial institutions require a minimum balance or impose service charges for chequing accounts. When using an interest-bearing chequing account, compare your earnings with any service charge or fee. Also, consider the cost of lost or reduced interest due to the need to maintain the minimum balance.

Chequing account fees have increased in recent years. Such items as cheque printing, overdraft fees, and stop-payment orders have doubled or tripled in price at some financial institutions. Some institutions will try to entice you with fancy cheques at a low price and then charge a much higher price when you reorder. You may be able to purchase cheques at a lower cost from a mail-order company that advertises in magazines or the Sunday newspaper.

INTEREST As discussed earlier, the interest rate, the frequency of compounding, and the interest computation method will affect the earnings on your chequing account.

SPECIAL SERVICES Financial institutions commonly offer chequing account customers services such as 24-hour ATM machines and home banking services. Financial institutions are also attempting to reduce the paper and postage costs associated with chequing accounts. One solution is to not return cancelled cheques to customers. The financial institution then uses microfilm to store cheques and provides customers with detailed statements summarizing the cheques written. If a customer requests a copy of a cancelled cheque, the institution reproduces the copy from its microfilm file for a fee.

Overdraft protection is an automatic loan made to chequing account customers for cheques written in excess of the available balance. This service is convenient but costly. Most

overdraft protection
An automatic loan made to chequing account customers to cover the amount of cheques written in excess of the available balance in the account.

CHEQUING ACCOUNT SELECTION FACTORS

Restrictions	Fees and Charges
• Minimum balance	• Monthly fee
• Federal deposit insurance	• Fees for each cheque or deposit
• Hours and location of branch offices	• Printing of cheques
• Holding period for deposited cheques	• Fee to obtain cancelled cheque copy
	• Overdraft, stop-payment order, certified cheque fee
	• Fees for preauthorized bill payment, fund transfer, or home banking activity

Special Services	Interest
• Direct deposit of payroll and government cheques	• Interest rate
• ATM machines	• Minimum deposit to earn interest
• Overdraft protection	• Method of compounding
• Banking-at-home	• Portion of balance used to compute interest
• Discounts or free chequing for certain groups (students, senior citizens, employees of certain companies)	• Fee charged for falling below necessary balance to earn interest
• Free or discounted services, such as traveller's cheques	

Exhibit 4–8

Chequing Account Selection Factors

overdraft plans make loans based on $50 or $100 increments. An overdraft of just $1 might trigger a $50 loan and corresponding finance charges of perhaps 18 percent. But overdraft protection can be less costly than the fee charged for a cheque you write when you do not have enough money on deposit to cover it. That fee may be $20 or more. Many financial institutions will allow you to cover chequing account overdrafts with an automatic transfer from a savings account for a nominal fee.

Beware of chequing accounts that offer several services (safety deposit box, traveller's cheques, low-rate loans, and travel insurance) for a single monthly fee. This may sound like a good value; however, financial experts observe that such accounts benefit only a small group of people who make constant use of the services offered.

The Financial Planning Calculations box on page 117 offers a method for comparing the costs of various types of chequing accounts.

OTHER PAYMENT METHODS

While personal cheques are the most common payment form, other methods are available. A *certified cheque* is a personal cheque with guaranteed payment. The amount of the cheque is deducted from your balance when the financial institution certifies the cheque. You may purchase a *money order* in a similar manner from financial institutions, post offices, and stores. Certified cheques, cashier's cheques, and money orders allow you to make a payment that the recipient knows is valid.

Traveller's cheques allow you to make payments when you are away from home. This payment form requires you to sign each cheque twice. First, you sign the traveller's cheques when you purchase them. Then, to identify you as the authorized person, you sign them again as you cash them.

Prepaid travel cards are becoming more common. The card allows travellers visiting other nations to get local currency from an ATM.

Advice from a Pro

ON IDENTITY THEFT AND FINANCIAL PRIVACY

People who put their social insurance and driver's licence numbers on their cheques are making identity theft fairly easy, according to the pros. With one cheque, a con artist could know your social insurance, driver's licence, and bank account numbers as well as your address, phone number, and even a sample of your signature.

Identity fraud can range from passing bad cheques and using stolen credit cards to theft of another person's total financial existence. While situations as portrayed in the movie *The Net* are rare, people need to be aware that they can easily become a victim.

Pros also suggest that you not mail your bills from your home mailbox, especially if the box is out by the street. This gives a potential scam artist easy access to a variety of financial and personal information.

The ease of obtaining social insurance numbers and more than three billion credit solicitations a year make identity theft a fairly simple scam. Each day, more than a thousand people have their identities stolen by a con artist applying for credit in the victim's name. After obtaining a loan or racking up credit card charges, the thief disappears, leaving a ruined credit rating that may take years to correct.

Banks and other financial institutions work to protect the identities and privacy of their depositors. The pros remind bank customers that the slight inconvenience of being asked for identification or having an account balance checked protects you and others from financial losses.

Other recommendations to protect yourself from identity fraud include the following:

- Shred or burn financial information containing account or social insurance numbers.
- Use passwords other than maiden names.
- Don't put your social insurance number on any document unless it is legally required.
- Check your credit report once or twice a year to make sure it is correct.
- Have your name removed from mailing lists operated by credit agencies and companies offering credit promotions.
- If you become a victim, notify the credit card company and other businesses with specific details. Also, file a police report to provide documentation of the scam.

You can find out more about financial privacy and identity theft online. Industry Canada's interactive Consumer Connection Internet site (http://consumerconnection.ic.gc.ca) offers access to innovative products and to consumer information on a range of topics.

The Public Interest Advocacy Centre (PIAC) provides legal and research services on behalf of consumer interests concerning the provision of public services, especially telecommunications, broadcasting, energy, and banking, and with regard to privacy and competition. Access its site at www.piac.ca.

Visit the Web site
See the Post-Test under Chapter 4 on the online learning centre at www.mcgrawhill.ca/college/kapoor.

CONCEPT CHECK 4–5

1. What factors are commonly considered when selecting a chequing account?
2. Are chequing accounts that earn interest preferable to regular chequing accounts? Why, or why not?

Financial Planning Calculations

COMPARING CHEQUING ACCOUNT COSTS

Comparisons of interest earned and service charges and fees for chequing accounts can be confusing. To assist with this analysis, use the following calculation.

Remember: Not all items listed here will apply to every type of chequing account.

INFLOWS	OUTFLOWS
Step 1.	**Step 2.**
Multiply average monthly balance $ _____ by average rate of return _____ percent to determine annual earnings	Monthly service charge $ _____ × 12 $ _____
	Average number of cheques written per month _____ × charge per cheque × 12 $ _____
	Average number of deposits per month _____ × charge per deposit × 12 $ _____
	Fee for dropping below minimum balance $ _____ × number of times below minimum $ _____
	Lost interest: Opportunity cost _____ percent × required minimum balance $ _____ $ _____
Total estimated annual inflow $ _____	Total estimated annual outflow $ _____

Step 3.

Estimated annual inflows less annual outflows =

+ Net earnings for account (Step 1) $ _____

− Net cost for account (Step 2) $ _____

+/− $ _____

NOTE: This calculation does not take into account charges and fees for such services as overdrafts, stop-payments, ATM use, and cheque printing. Be sure to also consider these costs when selecting a chequing account.

SUMMARY OF OBJECTIVES

Objective 1
Analyze factors that affect selection and use of financial services.
Financial products, such as savings plans, chequing accounts, loans, and trust services, are used for managing daily financial activities. Technology, opportunity costs, and economic conditions affect the selection and use of financial services.

Objective 2
Compare the types of financial institutions.
Chartered banks, trust companies, credit unions and caisses populaires, life insurance companies, investment companies, mortgage and loan companies, pawnshops, and cheque-cashing outlets may be compared on the basis of services offered, rates and fees, safety, convenience, and special programs available to customers.

Objective 3
Compare the costs and benefits of various savings plans.
Commonly used savings plans include regular savings accounts, term deposits and Guaranteed Investment Certificates, interest-earning chequing accounts, and Canada Savings Bonds.

Objective 4
Identify the factors used to evaluate different savings plans.
Savings plans may be evaluated on the basis of rate of return, inflation, tax considerations, liquidity, safety, and restrictions and fees.

Objective 5
Compare the costs and benefits of different types of chequing accounts.
Regular chequing accounts, activity accounts, and interest-earning chequing accounts can be compared with regard to restrictions (such as a minimum balance), fees and charges, interest, and special services.

KEY TERMS

automated teller machine (ATM) 101

chartered bank 105

credit union/caisse populaire 105

effective annual rate (EAR) 111

Guaranteed Investment Certificates 110

money market fund 105

overdraft protection 114

rate of return 111

term deposits 109

trust 100

KEY FORMULAS

Page	Topic	Formula
111	Effective annual rate (EAR)	$EAR = (1 + k_m)^m - 1$ m = the number of periods in year k_m = the rate of return for one period.
113	After-tax rate of return	Interest rate $\times$ (1 – Tax rate) Example: $0.05 \times (1 - 0.26) = 0.037 = 3.7\%$

FINANCIAL PLANNING PROBLEMS

1. *Determining Savings Goals.* What would be common savings goals for a person who buys a five-year GIC paying 8.75 percent instead of an 18-month savings certificate paying 7.5 percent? (Obj. 4)

2. *Computing Future Value.* What would be the value of a savings account started with $500, earning 6 percent (compounded annually) after 10 years? (Obj. 5)

3. *Calculating Present Value.* Brenda Young desires to have $10,000 eight years from now for her daughter's college fund. If she will earn 7 percent (compounded annually) on her money, what amount should she deposit now? Use the present value of a single amount calculation. (Obj. 5)

4. *Computing Future Value of Annual Deposits.* What amount would you have if you deposited $1,500 a year for 30 years at 8 percent (compounded annually)? (Use Appendix A.) (Obj. 5)

5. *Comparing Taxable and Tax-Free Yields.* With a 26-percent marginal tax rate, would a tax-free yield of 7 percent or a taxable yield of 9.5 percent give you a better return on your savings? Why? (Obj. 5)

6. *Calculating Opportunity Cost.* What is the annual opportunity cost of a chequing account that requires a $350 minimum balance to avoid service charges? Assume an interest rate of 6.5 percent. (Obj. 5)

7. *Comparing Costs of Chequing Accounts.* What would be the net annual cost of the following chequing accounts? (Obj. 5)

   a. Monthly fee, $3.75; processing fee, 25 cents per cheque; cheques written, an average of 22 a month.
   b. Interest earnings of 6 percent with a $500 minimum balance; average monthly balance, $600; monthly service charge of $15 for falling below the minimum balance, which occurs three times a year (no interest earned in these months).

8. *Computing Chequing Account Costs.* On the basis of the following information, determine the true balance in your chequing account. (Ch. App.)

   Balance in your chequebook, $356
   Balance on bank statement, $472
   Service charge and other fees, $15
   Interest earned on the account, $4
   Total of outstanding cheques, $187
   Deposits in transit, $60

FINANCIAL PLANNING ACTIVITIES

1. *Researching Financial Services.* Using the World Wide Web or library resources, obtain information about new developments in financial services. How have technology, changing economic conditions, and new legislation affected the types and availability of various saving and chequing financial services? (Obj. 1)

2. *Monitoring Economic Conditions.* Research current economic conditions (interest rates, inflation) using *The Financial Post*, other library resources, or Web sites. On the basis of current economic conditions, what actions would you recommend to people who are saving and borrowing money? (Obj. 1)

3. *Comparing Financial Institutions.* Collect advertisements and promotional information from several financial institutions, or locate the Web sites of financial institutions, such as The Bank of Montreal (www.bmo.com) and the TD Canada Trust (www.tdcanadatrust.com). Create a list of factors that a person might consider when comparing costs and benefits of various savings plans and chequing accounts. (Obj. 2)

4. *Obtaining Opinions about Financial Services.* Survey several people to determine awareness and use of various financial services, such as online banking, "smart cards," and cheque-writing software. (Obj. 2)

5. *Researching Credit Unions.* Using the Web site for the Credit Union Central of Canada (www.cucentral.ca) or other sources, obtain information about joining a credit union and the services this type of financial institution offers. (Obj. 2)

6. *Comparing Savings Plans.* Collect advertisements from several financial institutions with information about the savings plans they offer. (You may do this using the Web sites of various financial institutions.) Compare the features and potential earnings of two or three savings plans. (Obj. 3, 4)

7. *Researching Current Savings Rates.* Using library sources (such as *The Financial Post* and other current business periodicals) or Web sites (such as www. webfin.com), prepare a summary of current rates of return for various savings accounts, money market accounts, Guaranteed Investment Certificates, and Canada Savings Bonds. (Obj. 3, 4)

8. *Analyzing Cheque-Writing Software.* Visit software retailers to obtain information about the features in various personal computer programs used for maintaining a chequing account. Information about such programs as Managing Your Money, Microsoft Money, and Quicken may be obtained on the Internet. (Obj. 5)

LIFE SITUATION CASE (1)

Checking Out Financial Services

Carla and Ed Johnson have separate chequing accounts. Each pays part of the household and living expenses. Carla pays the mortgage and telephone bill, while Ed pays for food and utilities and makes the insurance and car payments. This arrangement allows them the freedom to spend whatever extra money they have each month without needing to explain their actions to each other. Carla and Ed believe their separate accounts have minimized disagreements about money. Since both spend most of their money each month, they have low balances in their chequing accounts, resulting in a monthly charge totalling $15.

In the same financial institution where Carla has her chequing account, the Johnsons have $600 in a passbook savings account that earns 2.2 percent interest. If the savings account balance exceeded $1,000, they would earn 3.15 percent. If the balance stayed above $1,000, they would not have to pay the monthly service charge on Carla's chequing account. The financial institution has a program that moves money from chequing to savings. This program would allow the Johnsons to increase their savings and work toward a secure financial future.

Ed has his chequing account at a bank that offers an electronic banking system allowing a customer to obtain cash at many locations 24 hours a day. Ed believes this feature is valuable when cash is needed to cover business expenses and personal spending. For an additional monthly fee, the bank would also provide Ed with a credit card, a safety deposit box, and a single monthly statement summarizing all transactions.

While most people plan their spending for living expenses, few plan their use of financial services. Therefore, many people are charged high fees for chequing accounts and earn low interest on their savings. Despite a wide choice of financial institutions and services, you can learn to compare their costs and benefits. Your awareness of financial services and your ability to evaluate them are vital skills for a healthy personal economic future.

Questions

1. Which financial services are most important to Carla and Ed Johnson?
2. What efforts are the Johnsons currently making to assess their use of financial services in relation to their other financial activities?
3. How should the Johnsons assess their needs for financial services? On what bases should they compare financial services?
4. What should the Johnsons do to improve their use of financial services?

LIFE SITUATION CASE (2)

Selecting Online Financial Services

Each month, Margo Bostrom becomes more frustrated with the fees she pays for financial services. Recently, her chequing account and ATM fees were over $15 a month. In addition, Margo is frustrated by the lower quality of customer service.

Margo is considering a "Web-only" bank that offers continuous access to account information along with electronic bill-paying service. She would earn 6 percent interest on funds in her chequing account, which is about three times higher than what she currently earns. But since the Web-only bank doesn't have its own ATMs, she could incur significant fees when obtaining cash. On the positive side, she would have access to low-cost, online investment trading.

The Web-only bank will require direct deposit of paycheques. Cash deposits would have to be handled through an ATM or through an electronic transfer at a traditional bank.

Margo's current bank is expanding its services to include 24-hour access to account balances and electronic bill paying through its Web site. This added service might entice her to continue doing business with the bank. She is also concerned about deposit insurance with the Web-only bank.

Questions

1. What factors should Margo consider when comparing a "Web-only" bank and online banking with her current financial institution?
2. Locate Web sites that Margo might use while considering online banking.
3. What actions would you recommend for Margo?

CREATING A FINANCIAL PLAN

Assessing Market Conditions

Most of your personal finance decisions will be influenced by current market conditions as well as your own variable wishes and desires. While the text can't help you with the latter, the following are some online resources that may help you assess the former:

- **www.FinanCenter.com**—Provides information and calculations about budgeting, automobiles, housing, savings, investments, and credit.
- **www.webfin.com**—Allows you to figure out where you currently stand financially and to plan future strategies.
- **www.cba.ca**—Provides information on planning for your retirement and highlights various aspects.
- **http://strategis.ic.gc.ca**—Includes the Financial Service Charges Calculator: If you have a chequing or savings account at a Canadian financial institution, the calculator will allow you to compare your monthly service charges with those you would pay for various accounts or service packages at other financial institutions. Offered by Industry Canada (Office of Consumer Affairs).
- **www.cdic.ca**—The Canadian Deposit Insurance Corporation insures your eligible funds up to $60,000 for each member institution within which you have deposits. Find out more about what is and is not eligible and some useful deposit strategies at this site.
- **www.scotiabank.ca**—A fully searchable site with significant information on most facets of financial planning,

- **www.royalbank.com**—The Royal Bank of Canada's Web site for up-to-date news and information about banking services and programs.
- **www.citizens.com**—Canada's first independent online bank.
- **www.tdcanadatrust.com**—A wealth of information on banking at TD Canada Trust.
- **www.desjardins.com**—The leading credit union in Quebec, the Caisse Populaire Desjardins.
- **www.cwbank.com**—The Canadian Western Bank, the only Schedule I chartered bank with its headquarters and principal operations in Western Canada.
- **www.bmo.com**—The Bank of Montreal; visit here for information about the BMO's banking and investment services.
- **www.cibc.com**—The Canadian Imperial Bank of Commerce allows you to test-drive online banking and provides product and fee information.
- **www.lbcdirect.laurentianbank.ca**—The Laurentian Bank of Canada.
- **www.manulifebank.com**—The Manulife Bank of Canada has product and rates listings as well as a mortgage and investment calculator for you to test different payment and investment scenarios.
- **www.nbc.ca**—The National Bank of Canada allows you to have a personalized access page providing information that is specific to your needs.

4

APPENDIX: Using a Chequing Account

OPENING A CHEQUING ACCOUNT

Deciding who the owner of the account will be is your starting point for opening a chequing account. Only one person is allowed to write cheques on an *individual account*. A *joint account* has two or more owners, with any authorized person allowed to write cheques if it is specified as an "or" account. In contrast, an "and" account with two owners requires the signatures of both owners on cheques. This arrangement is commonly used by businesses and other organizations.

Both an individual account and a joint account require a signature card. This document is a record of the official signatures of the person or persons authorized to write cheques on the account.

MAKING DEPOSITS

A *deposit form* is used for adding money to your chequing account (see Exhibit 4–A). On this document, you list the amounts of the cash and cheques being deposited. Each cheque you deposit requires an *endorsement*—your signature on the back of the cheque—to authorize the transfer of the funds into your account. The following are three common endorsement forms:

- A *blank endorsement* is your signature. Use this endorsement form only when you are actually depositing or cashing a cheque, since a cheque could be cashed by anyone once its back has been signed.
- A *restrictive endorsement* consists of the words for *deposit only*, followed by your signature. This endorsement form is especially useful when you are depositing cheques by mail.
- A *special endorsement* allows you to transfer a cheque to an organization or another person. On this endorsement form, the words *pay to the order of* are followed by the name of the organization or person and then by your signature.

Exhibit 4-A

Deposit Slip

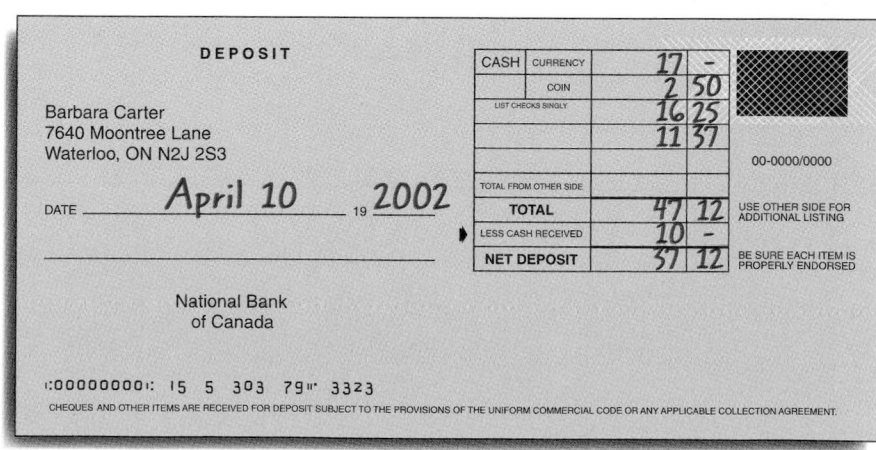

WRITING CHEQUES

Before writing a cheque, record the information in your cheque register and deduct the amount of the cheque from your balance; otherwise, you will think you have more money available than you really do. Many chequing account customers use duplicate cheques to maintain a record of their current balance.

The procedure for proper cheque writing, displayed in Exhibit 4–B, consists of the following steps:

[1] Record the current date.

[2] Write the name of the person or organization receiving the payment.

[3] Record the amount of the cheque in figures.

[4] Write the amount of the cheque in words; cheques for less than a dollar should be written as "only 79 cents," for example, with the word *dollars* on the cheque crossed out.

[5] Sign the cheque in the same way you signed the signature card when you opened your account.

[6] Make a note of the reason for payment to assist with budget and tax preparation.

Cheque-writing software is available as a separate program or as part of a financial planning package, such as Quicken (www.quicken.ca). These programs can easily prepare cheques while maintaining your financial records, such as the cheque register, personal financial statements, and a budget.

A *stop-payment order* may be necessary if a cheque is lost or stolen or if a business transaction was not completed in a satisfactory manner. The fee for a stop-payment commonly ranges from $0 to $20. If several cheques are missing or you lose your chequebook, the bank may suggest closing that account and opening a new one. This action is likely to be less costly than paying several stop-payment fees.

MAINTAINING A CHEQUING ACCOUNT

Each month you can receive a *bank statement*, a summary of the transactions for a chequing account. This document reports deposits made, cheques paid, interest earned, and fees for such items as service charges and printing of cheques. The balance reported on the bank statement probably will differ from the balance in your chequebook. Reasons for a difference are cheques that you have written but have not yet cleared, deposits you have made since the bank statement was prepared, interest added to your account, and deductions for fees and charges.

To determine your true balance, you should prepare a *bank reconciliation*. This report accounts for differences between the bank statement and your chequebook balance. The steps you take in this process, shown in the Financial Planning Calculations box on page 124, are as follows:

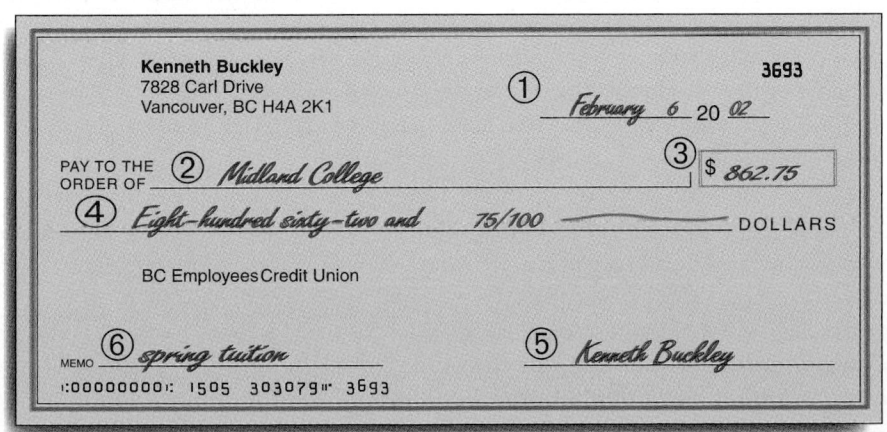

Exhibit 4-B

A Personal Cheque

Financial Planning Calculations

RECONCILING YOUR CHEQUING ACCOUNT

The process of comparing your chequebook balance to the bank statement is vital for determining any errors that may have ocurred. Use the following steps to reconcile your account:

THE BANK STATEMENT		
Balance on current bank statement	$	643.96
Step 1.	**Date**	**Amount**
Add up outstanding	10-4	70.00
cheques (cheques that you	10-6	130.00
have written but have	10-7	111.62
not yet cleared the banking		
system) and withdrawals		
still outstanding.		
Subtract the total.	$	−311.62
Step 2.	**Date**	**Amount**
Add up deposits in transit	10-2	60.00
(deposits that have been	10-5	90.00
made but are not reported		
on the current statement).		
Add the total.	$	+150.00
Adjusted bank balance	$	482.34

YOUR CHEQUEBOOK		
Current balance in your chequebook	$	295.91
Step 3.		
Subtract total of fees or other charges listed on bank statement.	$	−15.75
Subtract ATM withdrawals.	$	−100.00
Step 4.		
Add interest earned.	$	+2.18
Add direct deposits.	$	+300.00
Adjusted chequebook balance	$	482.34

[1] Compare the cheques you have written over the past month with those reported as paid on your bank statement. Use the cancelled cheques from the financial institution, or compare your cheque register with the cheque numbers reported on the bank statement (many financial institutions no longer return cancelled cheques to customers). *Subtract* from the *bank statement balance* the total of the cheques written but not yet cleared.

[2] Determine whether any recent deposits are not on the bank statement. If so, *add* the amount of the outstanding deposits to the *bank statement balance*.

[3] *Subtract* any fees or charges on the bank statement and ATM withdrawals from your *chequebook balance*.

[4] *Add* any interest earned to your *chequebook balance*.

At this point, the revised balances for both your chequebook and the bank statement should be the same. If the two do not match, check your math, making sure every cheque and deposit was recorded correctly in your chequebook and on the bank statement.

Many people do not take the time to reconcile their accounts; however, failure to do this could cost you money. If the bank subtracts more for a cheque than the amount for which you wrote it and you don't complain within a year, the bank may not be liable for correcting the error.

A Rising House of Cards?
Poorer Borrowers Use More Plastic

The strong economy of late 1990s was for the most part a result of the technology boom. However, mid-2000 marked the beginning of a downturn. This mild recession has been different from those in the past; it is primarily driven by the technology slump and a reduction in corporate profits, whereas the consumer has remained very resilient. This downturn has resulted in bankruptcies and excessive use of credit. A recent survey conducted by Leger Marketing showed that 75 percent of Canadians have at least one credit card and cardholders mentioned having an average of 2.5 cards with an average debt load of $1,269.

Recent trend analyses have shown that as credit card debt has risen, a new class of borrowers has come to the fore. The growing use and convenience of credit cards has facilitated the process of borrowing, and even those who can't really afford to borrow still do. Where at one time credit cards might have been reserved for those with the capacity to handle credit appropriately, they are now available to all.

Recent studies have shown that as ownership of cards has risen, the proportion of cards held by people with lower incomes has gone up. In addition, debt due to credit cards has also risen. A recent study by the Office of Consumer Affairs at Industry Canada showed that credit card debt as a portion of total household debt has risen by more than 50 percent since 1977.

Debt obligations of people seeking credit, debt, and bankruptcy counselling are generally now $13,000 to $14,000, up from $10,000 to $11,000 in 1997. Some consumers are heading for the precipice, perhaps without realizing how close the danger actually is or how sharp the drop might be.

Poorer, riskier borrowers joined the credit card ranks in the 1990s and apparently took on a lot of debt in the process. This group, many of whose members have low-level blue-collar jobs, is highly vulnerable to even a modest cyclical slowdown.

QUESTIONS

1 Why are today's consumers spending and borrowing heavily?

2 Why do some experts suggest that a new class of borrowers may be especially at risk if economic growth slows down?

LEARNING OBJECTIVES

1 Define consumer credit and analyze its advantages and disadvantages.

2 Differentiate among various types of credit.

3 Assess your credit capacity and build your credit rating.

4 Describe the information creditors look for when you apply for credit.

5 Identify the steps you can take to avoid and correct credit mistakes.

What is Consumer Credit?

Objective 1

Define consumer credit and analyze its advantages and disadvantages.

credit An arrangement to receive cash, goods, or services now and pay for them in the future.

consumer credit The use of credit for personal needs (except a home mortgage).

Visit the Web site

See the Pre-Test under Chapter 5 on the online learning centre at www.mcgrawhill.ca/ college/kapoor.

"Charge it!" "Cash or credit?" "Put it on my account." As these phrases indicate, the use of credit is a fact of life in personal and family financial planning. When you use credit, you satisfy needs today and pay for this satisfaction in the future. While the use of credit is often necessary and even advantageous, responsibilities and disadvantages are associated with its use.

Credit is an arrangement to receive cash, goods, or services now and pay for them in the future. **Consumer credit** refers to the use of credit for personal needs (except a home mortgage) by individuals and families, in contrast to credit used for business purposes.

Although Polonius cautioned, "Neither a borrower nor a lender be," using and providing credit have become a way of life for many people and businesses in today's economy. In January, you pay a bill for electricity that you used in December. You write a cheque for $40, a minimum payment on a $300 department store bill. With a bank loan, you purchase a new car. These are all examples of using credit: paying later for goods and services obtained now.

Most consumers have three alternatives in financing current purchases: They can draw on their savings, use their present earnings, or borrow against their expected future income. Each of these alternatives has trade-offs. If you continually deplete your savings, little will be left for emergencies or retirement income. If you spend your current income on luxuries instead of necessities, your well being will eventually suffer. And if you pledge your future income to make current credit purchases, you will have little or no spendable income in the future.

Consumer credit is based on trust in people's ability and willingness to pay bills when due. It works because people, by and large, are honest and responsible. But how does consumer credit affect our economy, and how is it affected by our economy?

CONSUMER CREDIT IN OUR ECONOMY

Consumer credit dates back to colonial times. While credit was originally a privilege of the affluent, farmers came to use it extensively. No direct finance charges were imposed; instead, the cost of credit was added to the prices of goods. With the advent of the automobile in the early 1900s, installment credit, in which the debt is repaid in equal installments over a specified period of time, exploded on the North American scene.

All economists now recognize consumer credit as a major force in the North American economy. Any forecast or evaluation of the economy includes consumer spending trends and consumer credit as a sustaining force. To paraphrase an old political expression, as the consumer goes, so goes the economy.

The aging of the baby boom generation has added to the growth of consumer credit. This generation currently represents almost 30 percent of the population but holds nearly 60 percent of the outstanding debt. The people in this age group have always been disproportionate users of credit, since consumption is highest as families are formed and homes are purchased and furnished. Thus, while the extensive use of debt by this generation is nothing new, the fact that it has grown rapidly has added to overall debt use.

USES AND MISUSES OF CREDIT

Using credit to purchase goods and services may allow consumers to be more efficient or more productive or to lead more satisfying lives. There are many valid reasons for using credit. A medical emergency may leave a person strapped for funds. A homemaker returning to the workforce may need a car. It may be possible to buy an item now for less money than it will cost later. Borrowing for a higher education is another valid reason. But it probably is not reasonable to borrow for everyday living expenses or to finance a Corvette on credit when a Ford Escort is all your budget allows.

> **DID YOU KNOW ?**
>
> Mortgage debts, personal loans, and credit card bills now represent 92 percent of Canadians' after-tax income, compared with 25 percent in 1982.
>
> SOURCE: *Insolvency Bulletin*, Industry Canada, 1998-1999

"Shopaholics" and young adults are most vulnerable to misusing credit. Post-secondary students are a prime target for credit card issuers, and issuers make it very easy for students to get credit cards. Tanya Svetlana, a 25-year-old teacher in Victoria, knows this all too well. As a university first-year student, she applied for and got seven credit cards, all bearing at least an 18.9-percent interest rate and a $20 annual fee. Although unemployed, she used the cards freely, buying expensive clothes for herself, extravagant presents for friends and family, and even a one-week vacation in the Bahamas. "It got to a point where I didn't even look at the price tag," she said. By her senior year, Tanya had amassed $9,000 in credit card debt and couldn't make the monthly payments of nearly $200. She eventually turned to her parents to bail her out. "Until my mother sat me down and showed me how much interest I had to pay, I hadn't even given it a thought. I was shocked," Tanya said. "I would have had to pay it off for years."

Using credit increases the amount of money a person can spend to purchase goods and services now. But the trade-off is that it decreases the amount of money that will be available to spend in the future. However, many people expect their incomes to increase and therefore expect to be able to make payments on past credit purchases and still make new purchases.

Here are some questions you should consider before you decide how and when to make a major purchase, for example, a car:

- Do I have the cash I need for the down payment?
- Do I want to use my savings for this purchase?
- Does the purchase fit my budget?
- Could I use the credit I need for this purchase in some better way?
- Could I postpone the purchase?
- What are the opportunity costs of postponing the purchase? (Alternative transportation costs, a possible increase in the price of the car.)
- What are the dollar costs and the psychological costs of using credit? (Interest, other finance charges, being in debt and responsible for making a monthly payment.)

If you decide to use credit, make sure the benefits of making the purchase now (increased efficiency or productivity, a more satisfying life, and so on) outweigh the costs (financial and psychological) of using credit. Thus, credit, when effectively used, can help you have more and enjoy more. When misused, credit can result in default, bankruptcy, and loss of creditworthiness.

ADVANTAGES OF CREDIT

Consumer credit enables people to enjoy goods and services now—a car, a home, an education, help in emergencies—and pay for them through payment plans based on future income.

Credit cards permit the purchase of goods even when funds are low. Customers with previously approved credit may receive other extras, such as advance notice of sales and the right to order by phone or to buy on approval. In addition, many shoppers believe it is easier to return merchandise they have purchased on account. Credit cards also provide shopping convenience and the efficiency of paying for several purchases with one monthly payment.

Credit is more than a substitute for cash. Many of the services it provides are taken for granted. Every time you flick the light switch or telephone a friend, you are using credit.

It is safer to use credit, since charge accounts and credit cards let you shop and travel without carrying a large amount of cash. You need a credit card to make a hotel reservation, rent a car, and shop by phone. You may also use credit cards for identification when cashing cheques, and the use of credit provides you with a record of expenses.

The use of credit cards can provide up to a 30-day "float," the time lag between when you make the purchase and when the lender deducts the balance from your chequing account when the payment is due. This float, offered by many credit card issuers, includes a grace period of 21 to 30 days. During the grace period, no finance charges are assessed on current purchases if the balance is paid in full each month.

Some large corporations, such as General Motors Corporation and Canadian Tire, issue either co-branded or their own Visa and MasterCard and offer rebates on purchases. For example, shopping with a TD Canada Trust/GM Visa allows you to earn 3 percent of every purchase, for a maximum of $1,500 to 3,500, to be applied to the total purchase price or lease down payment of any eligible new GM vehicle. A Canadian Tire Options MasterCard allows you to earn 20 percent more Canadian Tire money per dollar spent at Canadian Tire, and 1 percent earned per dollar spent outside of Canadian Tire. Points can be redeemed instantly at the point of sale in Canadian Tire on all merchandise in the store. Similarly, a Diners/En Route Aeroplan Miles card will give you one Aeroplan mile for each dollar you spend.

Platinum credit cards offered by American Express provide emergency medical evacuation for travellers. In 1994, Nathan Aman of Winnipeg was vacationing in a tiny, isolated town in Brazil. He ate something that made him gravely ill. With no doctor nearby, a friend frantically called Aman's credit card company about its guarantee to arrange emergency medical evacuation and treatment for card users. The company moved fast: It lined up a car to rush Aman to the nearest large town, managed to book a room in a sold-out hotel, and sent a doctor there to make a house call. The physician even accompanied Aman's travel partner, Carlos Piet, to a local pharmacy for medicine. "When we went home to see our doctor, he told us she had saved Nathan's life," recalls Piet. "For the last five years we have been indebted to the company."

Finally, credit indicates stability. The fact that lenders consider you a good risk usually means you are a responsible individual. However, if you do not repay your debts in a timely manner, you will find that credit has many disadvantages.

DISADVANTAGES OF CREDIT

Perhaps the greatest disadvantage of using credit is the temptation to overspend, especially during periods of inflation. It seems easy to buy today and pay tomorrow using cheaper dollars. But continual overspending can lead to serious trouble.

Whether or not credit involves security (something of value to back the loan), failure to repay a loan may result in loss of income, valuable property, and your good reputation. It can even lead to court action and bankruptcy. Misuse of credit can create serious long-term financial problems, damage to family relationships, and a slowing of progress toward financial goals. Therefore, you should approach credit with caution and avoid using it more extensively than your budget permits.

Although credit allows more immediate satisfaction of needs and desires, it does not increase total purchasing power. Credit purchases must be paid for out of future income; therefore, credit ties up the use of future income. Furthermore, if your income does not increase to cover rising costs, your ability to repay credit commitments will diminish. Before buying goods and services on credit, consider whether they will have lasting value, whether they will increase your personal satisfaction during present and future income periods, and whether your current income will continue or increase.

Finally, credit costs money. It is a service for which you must pay. Paying for purchases over a period of time is more costly than paying for them with cash. Purchasing with credit, rather than cash, involves one very obvious trade-off: the fact that it will cost more due to monthly finance charges and the compounding effect of interest on interest.

SUMMARY: ADVANTAGES AND DISADVANTAGES OF CREDIT

The use of credit provides immediate access to goods and services, flexibility in money management, safety and convenience, a cushion in emergencies, a means of increasing resources, and a good credit rating if you pay your debts back in a timely manner. But remember, the use of credit is a two-sided coin. An intelligent decision as to its use demands careful evaluation of your current debt, your future income, the added cost, and the consequences of overspending.

CONCEPT CHECK 5–1

1. How might consumers with credit card debt fare if a cyclical slowdown occurs?
2. What is consumer credit?
3. Why is consumer credit important to our economy?
4. What are the uses and misuses of credit?
5. What are the advantages and disadvantages of credit?

Types of Credit

Two basic types of consumer credit exist: closed-end credit and open-end credit. With **closed-end credit**, you pay back one-time loans in a specified period of time and in payments of equal amounts. With **open-end credit**, loans are made on a continuous basis and you are billed periodically for at least partial payment. Exhibit 5–1 shows examples of closed-end and open-end credit.

CLOSED-END CREDIT

Closed-end credit (also known as "direct" or "fixed" credit) is used for a specific purpose and involves a specified amount. Mortgage loans, automobile loans, and installment loans for purchasing furniture or appliances are examples of closed-end credit. An agreement, or contract, lists the repayment terms: the number of payments, the payment amount, and how much the credit will cost. Closed-end payment plans usually involve a written agreement for each credit purchase. A down payment or trade-in may be required, with the balance to be

Objective 2
Differentiate among various types of credit.

closed-end credit One-time loans that the borrower pays back in a specified period of time and in payments of equal amounts.

open-end credit A line of credit in which loans are made on a continuous basis and the borrower is billed periodically for at least partial payment.

Exhibit 5–1
Examples of Closed-End and Open-End Credit

Closed-End Credit	Open-End Credit
• Mortgage loans • Automobile loans • Installment loans	• Cards issued by department stores, bank cards (Visa, MasterCard, American Express) • Travel & entertainment (T&E) • Overdraft protection

repaid in equal weekly or monthly payments over a period of time. Generally, the seller holds title to the merchandise until the payments have been completed.

Exhibit 5–2 shows that consumer credit reached over $150 billion in 1998.

OPEN-END CREDIT

Using a credit card issued by a department store, using a bank credit card (Visa, MasterCard) to make purchases at different stores, charging a meal at a restaurant, and using overdraft protection are examples of open-end or revolving credit. As you will soon see, you do not apply for open-end credit to make a single purchase, as you do with closed-end credit. Rather, you can use open-end credit to make any purchases you wish if you do not exceed your **line of credit**, the maximum dollar amount of credit the lender has made available to you. You may have to pay **interest**, a periodic charge for the use of credit, or other finance charges. Some creditors allow you a grace period to pay a bill in full before you incur any interest charges.

You may have had an appointment with a dentist or chiropractor that you did not pay for until later. Professionals and small businesses often do not demand immediate payment but will charge interest if you do not pay the bill in full within 30 days. *Incidental credit* is a credit arrangement that has no extra costs and no specific repayment plan.

Many retailers use open-end credit. Customers can purchase goods or services up to a fixed dollar limit at any time. Usually, you have the option to pay the bill in full within 30 days without interest charges or to make set monthly installments based on the account balance plus interest.

Many banks extend a **bank line of credit**, a pre-arranged loan for a specified amount that you can use by writing a special cheque. Repayment is made in installments over a set period. The finance charges are based on the amount of credit used during the month and on the outstanding balance.

CREDIT CARDS Credit cards are extremely popular: 83 percent of Canadian households carry one or more credit cards.

One-third of all credit card users generally pay off their balances in full each month. These cardholders are often known as *convenience users*. Others are borrowers; they carry balances beyond the grace period and pay finance charges. Consumers use more than 1.4 billion credit cards to buy clothing, meals, vacations, gasoline, groceries, and other goods and services on credit.

While cash advances on credit cards can look attractive, remember that interest usually accrues from the moment you accept the cash, and you must also pay a transaction fee. One

line of credit The dollar amount, which may or may not be borrowed, that a lender makes available to a borrower.

interest A periodic charge for the use of credit.

bank line of credit A prearranged loan from a bank for a specified amount.

Exhibit 5–2

Volume of Consumer Credit

Economists now recognize consumer credit as a major force in the Canadian economy.

SOURCE:
www.economagic.com

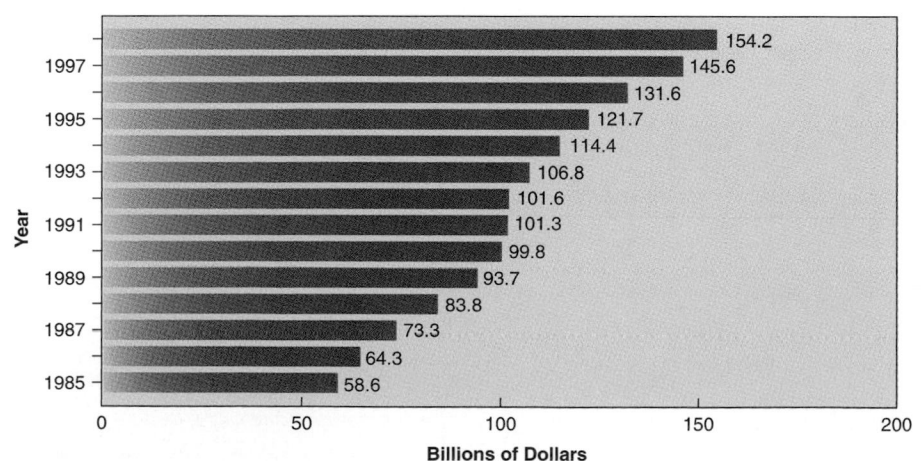

cash advance could cost you the money you were saving for a birthday gift for that special someone.

Most financial institutions participate in the credit card business, and the vast majority of them are affiliated with Visa International or the Interbank Card Association, which issues MasterCard. The Financial Planning for Life's Situations box on page 132 provides a few helpful hints for choosing a credit card.

Co-branding is the linking of a credit card with a business trade name offering "points" or premiums toward the purchase of a product or service. Co-branding has become increasingly popular since the success of General Motors Corporation's credit card. Co-branded credit cards offer rebates on products and services, such as health clubs, tax preparation services, and gasoline purchases. Banks are realizing that co-branded credit cards help build customer loyalty. *Smart cards*, the ultimate plastic, embedded with a computer chip that can store 500 times the data of a credit card, have been introduced into the market.

Smart cards combine credit cards, a driver's licence, a health care ID with your medical history and insurance information, frequent-flyer miles, and telephone cards. A single smart card, for example, can be used to buy an airline ticket, store it digitally, and track frequent-flyer miles. In the near future, smart cards will provide a crucial link between the World Wide Web and the physical world. In 1997, Visa Canada and Scotiabank launched Canada's first field trial of a reloadable chip-based Visa Cash card in Barrie, Ontario. The card's "take-up rate" in the first three months of the trial exceeded all expectations, and to date, over 130,000 purchase transactions have been made totalling over CND$380,000 and more than 500 merchants are participating in the trial. In addition, Visa announced a multifunction chip card, which was introduced at Georgian College campuses in Barrie, Orillia, and Owen Sound, Ontario.

PROTECTING YOURSELF AGAINST DEBIT/CREDIT CARD FRAUD

Credit fraud losses, when compared against the total debt owned by consumers on their credit cards, represents less than one-hundredth of 1 percent of the total owed. As a result, fraud losses related to credit may not seem all that terrible. But it *is* terrible for victims of fraud. Though they may be protected financially, they are forced to endure major inconvenience. Many fraud victims are devastated emotionally. The negative effects can linger for years. Moreover, all of us pay the costs of credit card fraud through higher prices, higher interest rates, and increased inconvenience.

How can you protect yourself against credit card fraud? You can take several measures:

- Sign your new card as soon as it arrives.
- Treat your card like money. Store it in a secure place.
- Shred anything with your account number before throwing it away.
- Don't give your card number over the phone or online unless you initiate the call.
- Don't write your card number on a postcard or on the outside of an envelope.
- Remember to get your card and receipt after a transaction, and double-check to be sure it's yours.

DID YOU KNOW ?

Thirty years after its introduction in Canada as Chargex, the Visa brand remains a consumer card of choice among Canadians. More than 23 million Visa cards are in circulation in Canada, and they can be used to make purchases at more than 562,000 locations across the country.

In 2000, Visa cardholders in Canada used their cards to pay for a record CDN$93.6 billion in purchases. This was an increase of almost 15 percent over 1999 and accounted for more than 15.6 percent of all purchases made by Canadian consumers during the year.

SOURCE: Visa Canada
http://corporate.visa.com

DID YOU KNOW ?

There are 40 million credit cards in circulation in Canada, and 18.4 million of those have an outstanding balance.

SOURCE: www.cba.com

Financial Planning for Life's Situations

CHOOSING A CREDIT CARD?

When choosing a credit card, it pays to shop around. Follow these suggestions to select the card that best meets your needs.

1. Department stores and gasoline companies are good places to obtain your first credit card. Pay your bills in full and on time, and you will begin to establish a good credit history.
2. Bank cards are offered through banks and credit unions. Fees and finance charges vary considerably (from 8 to 21.6 percent), so shop around.
3. If you usually pay your bill in full, try to deal with a financial institution with an interest-free grace period, which is the time after a purchase has been made and before a finance charge is imposed, typically 21 to 30 days.
4. If you're used to paying monthly installments, look for a card with a low monthly finance charge. Be sure you understand how that finance charge is calculated.
5. Consider obtaining a card from an out-of-province financial institution if it offers better terms than those offered locally.
6. Be aware of some credit cards that offer "no fee" or low interest but start charging interest from the day you purchase an item.
7. Watch out for credit cards that do not charge annual fees but instead charge a "transaction fee" each time you use the card.
8. If you're paying only the minimum amounts on your monthly statement, you need to plan your budget more carefully. The longer it takes for you to pay off a bill, the more interest you pay. The finance charges you pay on an item could end up being more than the item is worth.
9. With a grace period of 25 days, you actually get a free loan when you pay bills in full each month.
10. To avoid delays that may result in finance charges, follow the card issuer's instructions as to where, how, and when to make bill payments.
11. Beware of offers of easy credit. No one can guarantee to get you credit.
12. Be aware of credit cards offered by "credit repair" companies or "credit clinics." These firms may also offer to clean up your credit history for a fee. But remember, only time and good credit habits will repair your credit report if you have a poor credit history.
13. If you don't have a list of your credit issuers' telephone numbers, you may be able to obtain them by calling the 800 number directory assistance at 1-800-555-1212.
14. Travel and entertainment (T&E) cards often charge higher annual fees than most credit cards. Usually, you must make payment in full within 30 days of receiving your bill or typically no further purchases will be approved on the account.
15. Often, additional credit cards on your account for a spouse or child (over 18) are available with a minimum additional fee or no fee at all.
16. Be aware that debit cards are not credit cards but simply a substitute for a cheque or cash. The amount of the sale is subtracted from your chequing account.

SOURCES: American Institute of Certified Public Accountants; U.S. Office of Consumer Affairs; Federal Trade Commission

---

- If your billing statement is incorrect or your credit cards are lost or stolen, notify your card issuers immediately.
- If you don't receive your billing statement, notify the company immediately.
- If you are a victim of credit card fraud, call your lender immediately.
- Request a copy of your credit report every few years. Reviewing your report will tell you if anyone has applied for credit in your name and whether any accounts are being used without your knowledge, with the billing statement being sent to a different address.[1]

The Internet has joined the telephone and television as an important part of our lives. Every day, more consumers use the Internet for financial activities, such as investing, banking, and shopping.

When you make purchases online, make sure your transactions are secure, your personal information is protected, and your fraud sensors are sharpened. Although you can't control

---

[1] Experian Consumer Education Department, *Reports on Credit*, 1997.

Advice from a Pro

A PRO'S VIEWS ON CREDIT CHAOS

According to Jonathan Hoenig, a radio show host and a columnist, "the bubonic plague of personal finance comes in the form of a 17-percent or higher interest rate on your credit card. You'll have to do a lot of bargain shopping and coupon clipping to compensate for your constantly compounding finance charges. Bummer? *Yes.* Your fault? *Yes.* Just because you have access to credit doesn't mean you should necessarily partake of the plastic." He cautions that credit cards can be a useful part of personal finance or a painful experience. A good rule to live by: *Don't buy things you can't afford.*

Thankfully, most young people seem to be following the rules these days. Compared with the majority of cardholders, most of whom carry a balance, young people are demonstrating their financial savvy in record numbers.

Paying cash? You'll still deal with debt. Certain types, like school loans, car payments, and mortgages, are designed to be paid over longer periods of time. This is reflected in a lower interest rate. A credit card bill, and other types of "unsecured" debt, however, should be paid as soon as possible, advises Hoenig.

Various surveys suggest young people are headed in the right direction. Most college/university students recognize the importance of establishing and maintaining a good credit history.

---

fraud or deception on the Internet, you can take steps to recognize it, avoid it, and report it if it does occur. Here's how:

- *Use a secure browser*, software that encrypts or scrambles the purchase information you send over the Internet, to guard the security of your online transactions. Most computers come with a secure browser already installed. You can also download some browsers for free over the Internet.
- *Keep records of your online transactions.* Read your e-mail. Merchants may send you important information about your purchases.
- *Review your monthly bank and credit card statements* for any billing errors or unauthorized purchases. Notify your credit card issuer or bank immediately if your credit card or chequebook is lost or stolen.
- *Read the policies of Web sites you visit*, especially the disclosures about a site's security, its refund policies, and its privacy policy on collecting and using your personal information. Some Web sites' disclosures are easier to find than others; look at the bottom of the home page, on order forms, or in the "About" or "FAQ" section of a site. If you can't find a privacy policy, consider shopping elsewhere.
- *Keep your personal information private.* Don't disclose personal information—your address, telephone number, social insurance number, or e-mail address—unless you know who's collecting the information, why they're collecting it, and how they'll use it.
- *Give payment information only to businesses you know and trust*, and only in appropriate places, such as electronic order forms.
- *Never give your password to anyone online*, even your Internet service provider.
- *Do not download files sent to you by strangers or click on hyperlinks from people you don't know.* Opening a file could expose your computer system to a virus.[2]

---
[2] Adapted from Guide to Online Payments, Federal Trade Commission, March 1999 (www.ftc.gov).

DID YOU KNOW ?

Sixty-one percent of Canadian consumers have Internet access, and only 14 percent are currently shopping online.

SOURCE: ACEF du Quebec survey of 1,902 Canadians, June 2001

The Financial Planning for Life's Situations box on the next page describes what American Express and other card issuers have planned for online buyers.

TRAVEL AND ENTERTAINMENT (T&E) CARDS T&E cards are really not credit cards but charge cards because the monthly balance is due in full. However, most people think of Diners/En Route or American Express cards as credit cards because they don't pay the moment they purchase goods or services.

home equity loan A loan based on the current market value of a home less the amount still owed on the mortgage.

HOME EQUITY LOANS A **home equity loan** is based on the difference between the current market value of your home and the amount you still owe on your mortgage. With such a loan, you can borrow up to $100,000 or more on your home. Depending on the value of the home, you can borrow up to 85 percent of its appraised value, less the amount you still owe on your mortgage. The interest you pay on a home equity loan is tax deductible, unlike interest on other types of loans, but only if the proceeds are used for investment purposes and the investment is held outside of a registered plan.

A home equity loan is usually set up as a revolving line of credit, typically with a variable interest rate. A *revolving line of credit* is an arrangement whereby borrowings are permitted up to a specified limit and for a stated period, usually 5 to 10 years. Once the line of credit has been established, you draw from it only the amount you need at any one time (see the Financial Planning Calculations box on page 136). Today, many lenders offer home equity lines of credit. Remember, your home is your largest asset. You should use the home equity loan only for major items, such as education, home improvements, or medical bills, and not for daily expenses. If you miss payments on a home equity loan, you can lose your home. Furthermore, when you sell your home, you probably will be required to pay off your equity line in full. If you plan to sell your house in the near future, consider whether annual fees to maintain the account and other costs of setting up an equity credit line make sense.

CAR LOANS

Buying a vehicle is the second largest investment you will probably make after buying a house. There are many options available for financing your purchase. Here is a brief description of the financing available.

FINANCING AT THE DEALER Most car dealers offer financing in affiliation with car manufacturers (also referred to as factory financing) or financial institutions (also referred to as conditional sales contract). Factory financing enables you to get a loan directly from the car manufacturer and you can expect to pay significantly lower interest rates on the models they are trying to move. If you choose the conditional sales contract, you will receive a loan from a bank which normally has a lower interest rate or some other incentive and the dealer takes care of all the paper work.

LEASING Lower monthly payments associated with car leasing have resulted in its increased popularity during the last decade of rising car costs. There are two types of leases: closed-end leases and open-end leases. The Royal Bank of Canada Web site describes the two as follows (www.royalbank.com):

Closed-end lease: The leasing company is responsible for the residual value of the vehicle at lease-end. You can choose to buy the vehicle for that price and any other charges or fees stipulated in the contact, or return it to the leasing company.

A NEW BLUE CARD FOR THE TECHIES

American Express wants tech-savvy customers for its new Blue credit card, designed for online buyers. AmEx is pitching its Blue card as an ultrasafe way to shop online. Equipped with a built-in smart chip the card can be inserted into a special Reader attached to the user's computer to verify the shopper's identity and unlock the digital wallet. The digital wallet service, offered in late 1990, provides a secure, temporary transaction number to use instead of your actual credit card number. Simply insert the Blue in the Reader, enter your personal identification number (PIN) and shop online with confidence. For "e-tailers" that accept the wallet, including Gap.com, BlueLight.com, and Six Flags, Amex will zap that information to the merchant.

Not to be outdone by AmEx, other Internet credit card issuers are aiming at online buyers. NextCard, the Internet credit card issuer based in San Francisco, has high hopes for its Dilbert card, which features characters from the popular comic strip. The card features instant approvals, no late fees, and double frequent-flier miles, and if you don't need paper statements, the card pays you a "reverse" fee. Applicants who apply through the Dilbert.com Web site can adorn their cards with a picture of a Dilbert character and a title under their own name.

SOURCES: Mike McNamee, "Don't Leave Home Without a Freebie," *Business Week*, November 8, 1999. pp. 150–51; Pamela Black, "Just Put It on My Dilbert," *Business Week*, October 18, 1999, p. 8. www.americanexpress.com and www.nextcard.com

Open-end lease: You are responsible for the residual value of the vehicle and must pay that amount and any other charges or fees stipulated in the lease at lease-end.

Remember that the car is still owned and registered to the leasing company while you are leasing it. Also, you are responsible for all maintenance and repairs during the lease. Finally, you should pay attention to mileage restrictions when negotiating your lease agreement.

PAYING CASH This is the least expensive method to pay for your new or used vehicle because you avoid the cost of borrowed money (interest charges). Of course, if you are able to place the amount in an investment which earns a higher rate of return than the cost of borrowing the money, it is better to invest it. For example, if you were faced with the option to finance a car at 1.7 percent interest or invest the amount at 6 percent. The best solution would be to invest the amount at 6 percent, not only do you pocket a return of 4.3 percent but you can apply the interest earned on your investment toward your car loan. See the Financial Planning for Life's Situations on page 137 with an example on how one chooses between buying and leasing a car.

CONCEPT CHECK 5–2

1. What are the two main types of consumer credit?
2. What is a home equity loan?

Financial Planning Calculations

HOW MUCH CAN YOU BORROW WITH A HOME EQUITY LOAN?

Depending on your income and the equity in your home, you can apply for a line of credit for anywhere from $10,000 to $250,000 or more.

Some lenders let you borrow only up to 75 percent of the value of your home, less the amount of your first mortgage. At some banks you may qualify to borrow up to 85 percent! This higher lending limit may make the difference in your ability to get the money you need for home improvements, education, or other expenses.

Use the following chart to calculate your home loan value, which is the approximate amount of your home equity line of credit.

	Example	Your Home
Approximate market value of your home	$100,000	$_____
Multiply by .85	× .85	× .85
Approximate loan value	85,000	_____
Subtract balance due on mortgage(s)	50,000	_____
Approximate credit limit available	$35,000	$_____

In the above example, your home loan value (the amount for which you could establish your account) is $35,000.

Once your account is established, you can write a cheque for any amount you need up to $35,000.

In choosing a home equity loan,

1. Find out if your lending institution protects you against rising interest rates.
2. Compare the size of your lender's fee with those of other institutions.
3. Find out if your lender charges an inactivity fee.
4. Be wary of interest-only payments on home equity loans.
5. Find out whether your lender has the right to change the terms and conditions of your plan or to terminate your plan.
6. Carefully evaluate your reasons for using the equity in your home for loans.
7. Know the full costs and risks of home equity loans before you make a commitment to a lending institution.

Measuring Your Credit Capacity

Objective 3

Assess your credit capacity and build your credit rating.

The only way to determine how much credit you can assume is to first learn how to make an accurate and sensible personal or family budget. Budgets, as you learned in Chapter 2, are simple, carefully considered spending plans. With budgets, you first provide for basic necessities, such as rent or mortgage, food, and clothing. Then you provide for such items as home furnishings and other heavy, more durable goods.

CAN YOU AFFORD A LOAN?

Before you take out a loan, ask yourself whether you can meet all of your essential expenses and still afford the monthly loan payments. You can make this calculation in two ways. One is to add up all of your basic monthly expenses and then subtract this total from your take-home pay. If the difference will not cover the monthly payment and still leave funds for other expenses, you cannot afford the loan.

A second and more reliable method is to ask yourself what you plan to give up to make the monthly loan payment. If you currently save a portion of your income that is greater than the monthly payment, you can use these savings to pay off the loan. But if you do not, you will have to forgo spending on entertainment, new appliances, or perhaps even necessities. Are you

Financial Planning for Life's Situations

SHOULD I LEASE OR BORROW-TO-BUY MY CAR?

The decision whether to buy or lease a car is one which requires a lot of thought and financial consideration. Besides monetary discrepancies, personal preferences also come into the decision process. Many drivers prefer to own their automobiles, while many drivers must lease the cars they cannot presently afford. In addition, many people lease because they would rather switch cars every few years for added variety.

As a student, I am thinking of getting a 2002 Subaru Impreza RS Sedan, worth $26,995. There is still uncertainty about whether I will lease or borrow-to-buy the automobile. My parents have agreed to pay a down payment of $8,000 (for either leasing or buying).

Here is the breakdown comparison:

Borrow-to-buy method:

Price	$26,995
Down Payment	$ 8,000
Time Frame	4 years (48 months)
Bank Interest Rate	5.25%
Approx. Resale value after 4 years	$13,500

After placing these figures into the "loan calculator" at www.canadiandriver.com, my monthly payments work out to $530 for 48 months (see Appendix 6 monthly payments equation). Also, after four years, the NPV for this option would be (See Appendix A for PV Annuity and PV equations):

= Down Payment – PV Annuity + PV
= – 8,000 – PV Annuity ($530/mth for 48 months at 0.4375%) + PV($13,500 over 4 years at 5.25)
= – 8,000 – $530[(1–(1/(1+.004375)48))/.004375] + 13,500 (1/(1+.0525)4)
= – 8,000 –22,901.38 + 11,001.33
= – $19,900.05

Leasing method:

Down Payment	$8,000
Time of Lease	4 years (48 months)
Security deposit	$500
Dealer Interest Rate	7.8%

After placing these figures into the "lease calculator" at www.canadiandriver.com, my monthly payments work out to be $281 for 48 months.

Also, after the four years lease, our NPV for this option would be:

= – 8,000 – PV of Annuity ($281/mth for 48 months at 0.65%)
= – 8,000 – 281 [(1–(1/(1+.004375)48))/.004375]
= – 8,000 – 12,142.05
= – $20,142.05

(These calculations can also be solved using a financial calculator, see Appendix A for examples.)

ANALYSIS

On the basis of the above calculations, I see that it is actually cheaper to borrow-to-buy the car than it is to lease. The difference in net present values results in a savings of approximately $242. Although these figures are rather close, there are many personal reasons (besides the money) to buy instead of lease. As I take great pride in my car, I would like to feel that it is my own and not on loan from the dealer. Secondly, I would like to add certain features to my car that the dealer may not favour. These include a fancy spoiler, engine upgrades, high performance exhaust, window tints, new gauges, pedals, suspension, and so on.

Next, as I drive frequently and partake on road-trips, I would not want to worry about costly distance limitations placed by the dealer. Finally, I would very much like the option of keeping the car beyond the four years without having to negotiate for it with the dealership.

"Dealers will tell you that a lease is good for people who want to drive a new car all the time. Leasing also appeals to people who prefer lower monthly payments and want to drive something they cannot otherwise afford. I say it's not worth it, unless you have money to burn. You have all the responsibilities of ownership with none of its advantages." This quote, from www.smartcarguide.com, clearly illustrates my feelings on the matter, especially since I have no problems committing to one car for the long term.

SOURCE: Assignment written by and reproduced with permission from Alan Bogos and Bram Goldstein — Introductory Personal Finance Course John Molson School of Business, Concordia University, Winter 2002.

prepared to make this trade-off? Although it is difficult to precisely measure your credit capacity, you can follow certain guidelines.

GENERAL RULES OF CREDIT CAPACITY

DEBT-PAYMENTS-TO-INCOME RATIO The debt-payments-to-income ratio is calculated by dividing your monthly debt payments (not including house payment, which is a long-term liability) by your net monthly income. Experts suggest that you spend no more than 20 percent of your net (after-tax) income on consumer credit payments. Thus, as Exhibit 5–3 shows, a person making $1,068 per month after taxes should spend no more than $213 on credit payments per month.

The 20 percent estimate is the maximum; however, 15 percent is much better. The 20 percent estimate is based on the average family, with average expenses; it does not take major emergencies into account. If you are just beginning to use credit, you should not consider yourself safe if you are spending 20 percent of your net income on credit payments.

Visit the Web site

See Personal Financial Planning worksheets under Chapter 5 on the online learning centre at www.mcgrawhill.ca/college/kapoor.

DEBT-TO-EQUITY RATIO The debt-to-equity ratio is calculated by dividing your total liabilities by your net worth. In calculating this ratio, do not include the value of your home and the amount of its mortgage. If your debt-to-equity ratio is about 1—that is, if your consumer installment debt roughly equals your net worth (not including your home or the mortgage)—you have probably reached the upper limit of debt obligations.

The debt-to-equity ratio for business firms in general ranges between 0.33 and 0.50. The larger this ratio, the riskier the situation for lenders and borrowers. Of course, you can lower the debt-to-equity ratio by paying off debts.

None of the above methods is perfect for everyone; the limits given are only guidelines. Only you, on the basis of the money you earn, your current obligations, and your financial plans for the future, can determine the exact amount of credit you need and can afford. You must be your own credit manager.

Keep in mind that you adversely affect your credit capacity if you co-sign a loan for a friend or a relative.

CO-SIGNING A LOAN

What would you do if a friend or a relative asked you to co-sign a loan? Before you give your answer, make sure you understand what co-signing involves.

Exhibit 5–3

How to Calculate Debt-Payments-to-Income Ratio

Spend no more than 20 percent of your net (after-tax) income on credit payments.

Monthly gross income	**$1,500**
Less:	
All taxes	270
Canada Pension Plan contribution	112
Monthly RRSP contribution	50
Monthly net income	**$ 1,068**
Monthly installment credit payments:	
Visa	25
MasterCard	20
Diners/En Route card	15
Education loan	—
Personal bank loan	—
Auto loan	153
Total monthly payments	**$ 213**
Debt-payments-to-income ratio ($213/$1,068)	19.94%

You are being asked to guarantee a debt. Think carefully before you do. If the borrower doesn't pay the debt, you will have to. Be sure you can afford to pay if you have to and that you want to accept this responsibility.

You may have to pay up to the full amount of the debt if the borrower does not pay. You may also have to pay late fees or collection costs, which increase this amount.

The creditor can use the same collection methods against you that can be used against the borrower, such as suing you, garnishing your wages, and so on. If this debt is ever in default, that fact may become a part of your credit record.[3]

CO-SIGNERS OFTEN PAY Some studies of certain types of lenders show that as many as three of four co-signers are asked to wholly or partially repay the loan. That statistic should not surprise you. When you are asked to co-sign, you are being asked to take a risk that a professional lender will not take. The lender would not require a co-signer if the borrower met the lender's criteria for making a loan.

If you do co-sign and your friend or relative misses a payment, the lender can collect the entire debt from you immediately without pursuing the borrower first. Also, the amount you owe may increase if the lender decides to sue to collect. If the lender wins the case, it may be able to take your wages and property.

IF YOU DO CO-SIGN Despite the risks, at times you may decide to co-sign. Perhaps your child needs a first loan or a close friend needs help. Here are a few things to consider before you co-sign:

[1] Be sure you can afford to pay the loan. If you are asked to pay and cannot, you could be sued or your credit rating could be damaged.

[2] Consider that even if you are not asked to repay the debt, your liability for this loan may keep you from getting other credit you want.

[3] Before you pledge property, such as your automobile or furniture, to secure the loan, make sure you understand the consequences. If the borrower defaults, you could lose the property you pledge.

[4] Check your provincial law. Some provinces have laws giving you additional rights as a co-signer.

[5] Request that a copy of overdue-payment notices be sent to you so that you can take action to protect your credit history.

BUILDING AND MAINTAINING YOUR CREDIT RATING

If you apply for a charge account, credit card, car loan, personal loan, or mortgage, your credit experience, or lack of it, will be a major consideration for the creditor. Your credit experience may even affect your ability to get a job or buy life insurance. A good credit rating is a valuable asset that should be nurtured and protected. If you want a good rating, you must use credit with discretion: Limit your borrowing to your capacity to repay, and live up to the terms of your contracts. The quality of your credit rating is entirely up to you.

In reviewing your creditworthiness, a creditor seeks information from a credit bureau. Most creditors rely heavily on credit reports in considering loan applications.

CREDIT BUREAUS **Credit bureaus** collect credit and other information about consumers. There are two main credit bureaus in Canada: Equifax Canada (www.equifax.ca, 1-800-465-7166) and Trans Union of Canada (www.tuc.ca, 1-800-663-9980). In addition, several thousand regional credit bureaus collect credit information about consumers. These firms sell the data to creditors that evaluate credit applications.

credit bureau A reporting agency that assembles credit and other information about consumers.

---

[3] *Cosigning Loan: Facts for Consumers* (Washington, DC: Federal Trade Commission, Bureau of Consumer Protection, January 1988), p. 1.

WHO PROVIDES DATA TO CREDIT BUREAUS? Credit bureaus obtain their data from banks, finance companies, merchants, credit card companies, and other creditors. These sources regularly send reports to credit bureaus containing information about the kinds of credit they extend to customers, the amounts and terms of that credit, and customers' paying habits. Credit bureaus also collect some information from other sources, such as court records.

WHAT IS IN YOUR CREDIT FILES? As the sample credit report in Exhibit 5–4a shows, the credit bureau file contains your name, address, social insurance number, and birth-date. It may also include the following information:

- Your employer and position.
- Your former address.
- Your former employer.
- Your spouse's name, social insurance number, and employer.

Exhibit 5–4a

Sample Credit Report

All credit reports contain your name, address, social insurance number, and birthdate.

SOURCE: Sample Credit Report. Used with permission of Equifax Canada Inc.

EQUIFAX
Consumer Services Canada

Equifax Credit Report

Personal Information

Personal Data		Other Names	
Name:	RICHARD DENTON	Also Known as: C RICHARD DENTON	
SIN:	899XXX157		
Date of Birth:	1967-04-XX		

CurrentAddress		Previous Address	
Address:	11TH AVE WILLOW ST TORONTO, ON	Address:	WILLOW ST TORONTO, ON
Date Reported:	2001-12	Date Reported:	2000-12
		Address:	WESTMARR RD REGINA, SK
		Date Reported:	1999-06

Current Employment		Previous Employment	
Employer:	MCDOUGLAS HAULAGE	Employer:	PRIORITY TRUCKING
Occupation:	SUPERVISOR	Occupation:	DRIVER
		Employer:	MIDTOWN CATERING
		Occupation:	SUPERVISOR

Consumer Statement

Date Reported:	2002-02	Date to Be Removed: 2009-09
Statement:	CONSUMER STATES SLOW PAYMENTS ON ACCOUNT ARE DUE TO BEING UNEMPLOYED	

Credit Information

This section contains information on each account that you've opened in the past. It is retained in our database for not more than 6 years from the date of last activity.

An installment loan is a fixed-payment loan in which the monthly payment does not change from month to month. Examples of such loans are a mortgage, car loan or a student loan. A revolving loan is a loan in which the balance or amount owed changes from month to month, such as a credit card.

Note: The account numbers have been partially masked for your security.

HUDSONS BAY

Phone Number:	Not Available	High Credit/Credit Limit:	$4,500.00
Account Number:	XXX...890	Payment Amount:	$910.00
Association to Account:	Individual account	Balance:	$6,700.00
Type of Account:	Revolving	Past Due:	$6,700.00
Date Opened:	1999-01	Date of Last Activity:	2002-03
Status:		Date Reported:	2002-05
Months Reviewed:	36		
Payment History:	No payment 30 days late		
	No payment 60 days late		
	No payment 90 days late		
Prior Paying History:	Meaning two payments past due(2002-05)		
	Meaning one payment past due(2002-02)		
	Meaning at least 120 days past due(2001-12)		
Comments:	Subject disputes this account		
	Employee account		

Banking Information
Bank Account Information

Date Reported:	2002-03	Account Number:	423156
Financial Institution:	BQE NATIONALE	Account Type:	Savings Account
Date Opened:	2000-01	Balance:	$5,255.00
Telephone Number:	Not Available	# of NSF:	2 NSF IN 2001
Status:			
Comments:	Overdraft		

Public Records and Other Information

This section includes bankruptcies, judgments, voluntary repayment programs and secured loans. Public record information is retained in our database for a maximum of 7 years from the date filed, except in the case of multiple bankruptcies, which results in retention of bankruptcy information for 14 years. P.E.I is an exception to this and displays Public Records for 7 to 10 years and Bankruptcies for 14 years.

Bankruptcy

Date Filed:	1998-03
Name of Court:	MIN OF ATTORNEY GEN
Case Number and Trustee:	456789 ABC ASSOCIATES
Assets:	$1,500.00
Liabilities:	$55,000.00
Type:	Individual
Filer:	Subject
Date Discharged:	1999-12
Comments:	

Legal Item

Date Filed:	1998-12	Legal Item Status:	
Case Number:	321245	Date Verified:	
Court Name:	COLL MTL	Satisfied Date:	1998-12
Amount:	$255.00	Lawyer:	
Plaintiff:	CITY OF TORONTO		
Defendant:	RICHARD DENTON		
Comments:			

Secured Loans

Court Name:	COLL MTL	Date Filed:	1998-09
Industry Class:	Credit Unions	Creditor's Name and Amount:	TRANS CANADA CREDIT 9 ELLIS AVE TOR 3600
Maturity Date:	2002-04		
Comments:			

Collections

The following accounts have been turned over to an agency for collection. Collection information stays on file for a maximum period of 6 years from date of last payment to the creditor, or if none, 5 years from the date assigned to the collection agency.

32145 TIM HORTON

Date Assigned:	1998-05	Account Number:	32415678
Collection Agency:	COLL MTL	Reason:	Unknown
Amount:	$1,260.00	Balance:	$1,260.00
Date of Last Payment:	1998-12	Date Paid:	
Date Verified:			
Comments:			

Credit Inquiries

The following inquiries were generated because the listed company requested a copy of your credit report.

2002-02-15	FIRST DATA RESOURCES (402)777-9729
2001-04-27	FUTURE MORTGAGE CORP (416)783-1808
2001-03-24	BANK OF MONTREAL (Phone Number Not Available)

The following "soft" inquiries were also generated. These soft inquiries do not appear when lenders look at your file; they are only displayed to you and do not affect your credit score.

2002-06-11	EQUIFAX CONS SERV CP (Phone Number Not Available)
2002-06-10	EQUIFAX CONS SERV CP (Phone Number Not Available)
2002-06-07	EQUIFAX CONS SERV CP (Phone Number Not Available)

Investigate your File

Your confirmation number is 0010627347. Please keep this number in your records for future communication with us.

To launch an investigation of information contained in your credit report, you will need to complete a Consumer Credit Report Update Form.

Exhibit 5–4a

(continued)

- Public records and information.
- Cheques returned for insufficient funds.

Your credit file may also contain detailed credit information. Each time you buy from a reporting store on credit or take out a loan at a bank, a finance company, or some other reporting creditor, a credit bureau is informed of your account number and the date, amount, terms, and type of credit. As you make payments, your file is updated to show the outstanding balance, the number and amounts of payments past due, and the frequency of 30-, 60-, or 90-day delinquencies. Any suits, judgments, or tax liens against you may appear as well. However, a federal law protects your rights if the information in your credit file is erroneous. Figure 5–4b shows the consumer update form; you can use this form to make changes or inquiries to your credit report.

CREDIT BUREAU REGULATION IN CANADA Besides Alberta, New Brunswick, and the territories, each province has legislation regarding consumer reporting agencies, such as credit bureaus. The principal concerns of these regulations are the protection of consumer

EXHIBIT 5–4b

Consumer Update Form

Form used to make changes or inquiries to your credit report.

SOURCE: Consumer Credit Report Update Form. Used with permission of Equifax Canada Inc.

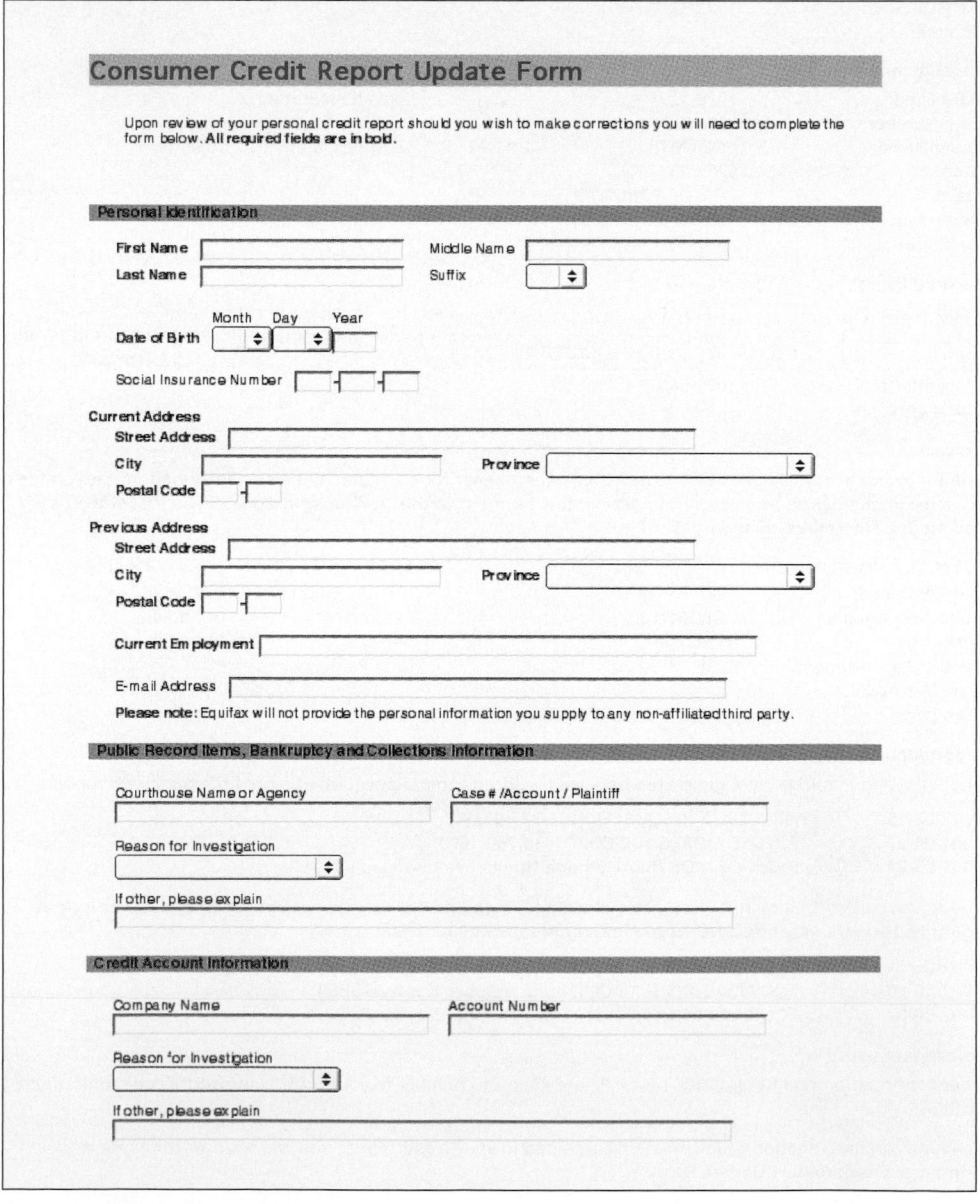

privacy with respect to credit information and the consumer's right not to suffer from false credit and personal information.

In addition, these laws stipulate the nature of the information that can be used in a credit report; a distinction is made between consumer information and personal data. While the former might include such details as your name, address, occupation, income, paying habits, and a number of other pertinent issues, personal information, such as character, reputation, and other characteristics, may not be included in a credit report.

ACCESS TO CREDIT REPORTS While you have a right to know the contents of your credit bureau file at any time, others may view your file only if you have given written consent or if you have been sent a written notice that your report has been obtained. Generally, you will find that a request for permission to access your report is included in a credit application.

In the event that you do not apply for credit but a request for information is made, the credit bureau must inform you of the request and provide you with the name and address of the requestor.

Though access to information is well legislated and despite the claims to the contrary by credit bureaus, many consumer organizations have expressed concerns that credit bureau files are less than secure. The relatively recent shift to electronic files has created a whole new level of vulnerability in terms of privacy and consumer groups are worried that anyone with a computer and a modem will be able to access confidential files.

credit reporting legislation
Credit Reporting Act—Applicable in British Columbia, Ontario, Nova Scotia, and Prince Edward Island
Credit Reporting Agencies Act—Applicable in Saskatchewan and Newfoundland
Personal Investigations Act—Applicable in Manitoba
Consumer Protection Act—Applicable in Quebec

TIME LIMITS ON ADVERSE DATA

There are limitations to the inclusion of detrimental information in a credit report. As an example, in Ontario, a first bankruptcy can be reported only within seven years of its occurrence. In the event of a second bankruptcy, however, that information is never deleted from the file. In Saskatchewan, the limit is 14 years for bankruptcy and seven years for any other adverse data. The actual limits may vary slightly from province to province, but the common goal is to limit the credit-damaging effect of past events.

There are also rules in place to protect the consumer's privacy, including restrictions on the situations in which a credit report agency may make a report. Your data can be divulged only in the event of a court order or a legitimate request from a person or organization concerned with extending credit, employment, or insurance to you.

INCORRECT INFORMATION IN YOUR CREDIT FILE
Credit bureaus are required to follow reasonable procedures to ensure that subscribing creditors report information

DID YOU KNOW ?

Consumers are given one of the following ratings in their credit report. This ranking can be arrived at in many ways.

RATING	WHAT IT MEANS
R0	Too new to rate; approved but not used
R1	Pays (or paid) within 30 days of payment due date or not over one payment past due
R2	Pays (or paid) in more than 30 days from payment due date, but not more than 60 days, or not more than two payments past due
R3	Pays (or paid) in more than 60 days from payment due date, but not more than 90 days, or not more than three payments past due
R4	Pays (or paid) in more than 90 days from payment due date, but not more than 120 days, or four payments past due
R5	Account is at least 120 days overdue, but is not yet rated "9"
R7	Making regular payments through a special arrangement to settle your debts
R8	Repossession (voluntary or involuntary return of merchandise)
R9	Bad debt; placed for collection; moved without giving a new address

R = Revolving credit (includes line of credits, overdraft, credit cards, charge cards, etc.)
SOURCE: www.equifax.com Used with permission of Equifax Canada Inc.

accurately. However, mistakes may occur. Your file may contain erroneous data or records of someone with a name similar to yours. When you notify the credit bureau that you dispute the accuracy of its information, it must reinvestigate and modify or remove inaccurate data. You should give the credit bureau any pertinent data you have concerning an error. If you contest an item on your credit report, the reporting agency must remove the item unless the creditor verifies that the information is accurate (see Exhibit 5–5).

You should review your credit files every few years even if you are not planning to apply for a big loan. Married women and young adults should make sure that all accounts for which they are individually and jointly liable are listed in their credit files. Exhibit 5–6 shows how you can obtain a copy of your credit report.

CONCEPT CHECK 5–3

1. What are the general rules for measuring credit capacity?
2. What can happen if you co-sign a loan?
3. What can you do to build and maintain your credit rating?
4. How do you correct erroneous information in your credit file?

EXHIBIT 5–5

Sample Dispute Letter

The law requires credit card companies to correct inaccurate or incomplete information in your credit report.

SOURCE: U.S. Federal Trade Commission, June 1999.

Date
Your Name
Your Address
Your City, Province, Postal Code

Complaint Department
Name of Credit Reporting Agency
Address
City, Province, Postal Code

Dear Sir or Madam:

I am writing to dispute the following information in my file. The items I dispute are also encircled on the attached copy of the report I received. (Identify item(s) disputed by name of source, such as creditor or tax court, and identify type of item, such as credit account, judgment, etc.)

This item is (inaccurate or incomplete) because (describe what is inaccurate or incomplete and why). I am requesting that the item be deleted (or request another specific change) to correct the information.

Enclosed are copies of (use this sentence if applicable and describe any enclosed documentation, such as payment records, court documents) supporting my position. Please reinvestigate this (these) matter(s) and (delete or correct) the disputed item(s) as soon as possible.

Sincerely,
Your name

Enclosures: (List what you are enclosing)

EQUIFAX Personal Solutions

YOUR CREDIT REPORT AS OF 04/09/2001

This Credit Report is available for you to view for 30 days. If you would like a current Credit Report, you may order another from MyEquifax.

Personal Data

John Q. Public
2351 N 85th Ave
Phoenix, AZ 85037

Social Security Number: 022-22-2222
Date of Birth: 1/11/1960

Previous Address(es):
133 Third Avenue
Phoenix, AZ 85037

Employment History

Cendant Hospitality FR

Location: Phoenix,AZ	Employment Date: 2/1/1989	Verified Date: 1/3/2001

Previous Employment(s):
SOFTWARE Support Hospitality Franch

Location: Atlanta, GA	Employment Date: 01/3/2001	Verified Date: 01/3/2001

Public Records
No bankruptcies on file
No liens on file
No judgements on file
No garnishments on file
No secured loans on file
No marital statuses on file
No financial counseling on file
No foreclosures on file
No non-responsibility entries on file

Collection Accounts
No collections on file.

Credit Information

Company Name	Account Number and Whose Account	Date Opened	Last Activity	Type of Account and Status	High Credit	Items as of Date Reported Terms	Balance	Past Due	Date Reported
Americredit Financial Services	40404XXXX JOINT ACCOUNT	03/1999	03/2000	Installment REPOSSESION	$16933	$430	$9077	$128	2/2000

Prior Paying History
30 days past due 07 times; 60 days past due 05 times; 90+ days past due 03 times

INVOLUNTARY REPOSSESION AUTO

Capital One	412174147128XXXX INDIVIDUAL ACCOUNT	10/1997	01/2001	Revolving PAYS AS AGREED	$777	15	$514		01/2001

Prior Paying History
30 days past due 02 times; 60 days past due 1 times; 90+ days past due 00 times
CREDIT CARD

Credit Inquiries

Companies that Requested your Credit File

04/29/2001 EFX Credit Profile Online
06/30/2001 Automotive
06/16/2000 AR-Associates National Bank

THE FOLLOWING INQUIRIES ARE NOT REPORTED TO BUSINESSES:
PRM - This is a promotional inquiry in which only your name and address were given to a credit grantor so you could be solicited you with an offer such as a credit card. (PRM inquiries remain on file for 12 months.)
AM or AR - These inquiries indicate a periodic review of your credit history by one of your creditors (AM and AR inquiries remain on file for 12 months.)
EQUIFAX, ACIS or UPDATE - These inquiries indicate Equifax's activity in response to your contact with us for either a copy of your credit file or a request for research.
PRM, AM, AR, INQ, EQUIFAX, ACIS and UPDATE inquiries do not show on credit files that businesses receive, only on copies provided to you.

Your confirmation number is 109933931. Please keep this number in your records for future communication with us.

EXHIBIT 5–6

Obtaining Your Credit Report

Equifax Canada Inc. (www.equifax.ca) is a recognized leader in the consumer and commercial credit reporting and information services industry. Equifax also delivers sophisticated decisioning, data, fraud, and e-commerce solutions to the business community. It is a subsidiary of Atlanta-based Equifax Inc. (NYSE: EFX), a worldwide leader in enabling and securing global commerce.

SOURCE: Your Credit Report. Used with permission of Equifax Canada Inc.

Applying for Credit

Objective 4

Describe the information creditors look for when you apply for credit.

A SCENARIO FROM THE PAST

Marie and Jerome Mangan have a joint income that is more than enough for them to make payments on their dream house, yet they are turned down for a mortgage loan. The lender says Marie might become pregnant and leave her job.

In fact, however, it is illegal for a creditor to ask or assume anything about a woman's childbearing plans. It is even illegal to discourage the Mangans from applying for a loan because Marie is of childbearing age. Also, the lender must fully acknowledge Marie's income.

When you are ready to apply for credit, you should know what creditors think is important in deciding whether you are creditworthy. You should also know what they cannot legally consider in their decisions. By law, race, colour, age, gender, marital status, and certain other factors may not be used to discriminate against you in any part of a credit dealing. Women should build and protect their own credit histories, using the checklist shown in the Financial Planning for Life's Situations box on page 148.

WHAT CREDITORS LOOK FOR: THE FIVE C'S OF CREDIT MANAGEMENT[4]

When a lender extends credit to its customers, it recognizes that some customers will be unable or unwilling to pay for their purchases. Therefore, lenders must establish policies for determining who will receive credit. Most lenders build their credit policies around the five Cs of credit: character, capacity, capital, collateral, and conditions (see the Financial Planning for Life's Situations box on page 149).

character The borrower's attitude toward credit obligations.

Character is the borrower's attitude toward credit obligations. Most credit managers consider character the most important factor in predicting whether you will make timely payments and ultimately repay your loan.

capacity The borrower's financial ability to meet credit obligations.

Capacity is your financial ability to meet credit obligations; that is, to make regular loan payments as scheduled in the credit agreement. Therefore, the lender checks your salary statements and other sources of income, such as dividends and interest. Your other financial obligations and monthly expenses are also considered before credit is approved. Typically, the gross debt service (GDS) ratio is approximately 30 percent and the total debt service (TDS) ratio 40 percent. See Chapter 7 for more information on GDS and TDS ratios.

capital The borrower's assets or net worth.

Capital refers to your assets or net worth. Generally, the greater your capital, the greater your ability to repay a loan. The lender determines your net worth by requiring you to complete a credit application (see Exhibit 5–7). You must authorize your employer and financial institutions to release information to confirm the claims made in the credit application.

collateral A valuable asset that is pledged to ensure loan payments.

Collateral is an asset that you pledge to a financial institution to obtain a loan. If you fail to honour the terms of the credit agreement, the lender can repossess the collateral and then sell it to satisfy the debt.

conditions The general economic conditions that can affect a borrower's ability to repay a loan.

Conditions refer to general economic conditions that can affect your ability to repay a loan. The basic question focuses on security—of both your job and the firm that employs you.

Creditors use different combinations of the five Cs to reach their decisions. Some creditors set unusually high standards, and others simply do not make certain kinds of loans. Creditors also use different kinds of rating systems. Some rely strictly on their own instinct and experience. Others use a credit-scoring or statistical system to predict whether an applicant is a good credit risk. They assign a certain number of points to each characteristic that has proven to be a reliable sign that a borrower will repay. Then they rate the applicant on this scale.

[4] Adapted from William M. Pride, Robert J. Hughes, and Jack R. Kapoor, *Business*, 6th ed. (Boston: Houghton Mifflin, 1999), pp. 498–500.

- Amount of loan requested
- Proposed use of the loan
- Your name and birthdate
- Social insurance number and driver's licence number
- Present and previous street addresses
- Present and previous employers and their addresses
- Present salary
- Number and ages of dependants
- Other income and sources of other income
- Have you ever received credit from us?

- If so, when and at which office?
- Chequing account number, institution, and branch
- Savings account number, institution, and branch
- Name of nearest relative not living with you
- Relative's address and telephone number
- Your marital status
- Information regarding joint applicant: same questions as above

EXHIBIT 5–7

Sample Credit Application Questions

Typical questions in a credit application appear in Exhibit 5–7. Exhibit 5–8 shows how your credit application might be scored. In addition, during the loan application process, the lender may evaluate many of the following criteria to determine whether you are a good credit risk.

AGE Gene and Melissa Marchand, a retired couple, and many older people have complained that they were denied credit because they were over a certain age or that when they retired, their credit was suddenly cut off or reduced.

The law is very specific about how a person's age may be used in credit decisions. A creditor may ask about your age, but if you're old enough to sign a binding contract, a creditor may not

- Turn you down or decrease your credit because of your age.
- Ignore your retirement income in rating your application.
- Close your credit account or require you to reapply for it because you have reached a certain age or retired.
- Deny you credit or close your account because credit life insurance or other credit-related insurance is not available to people of your age.

PUBLIC ASSISTANCE You may not be denied credit because you receive Old Age Security or public assistance. But, as with age, certain information related to this source of income could have a bearing on your creditworthiness.

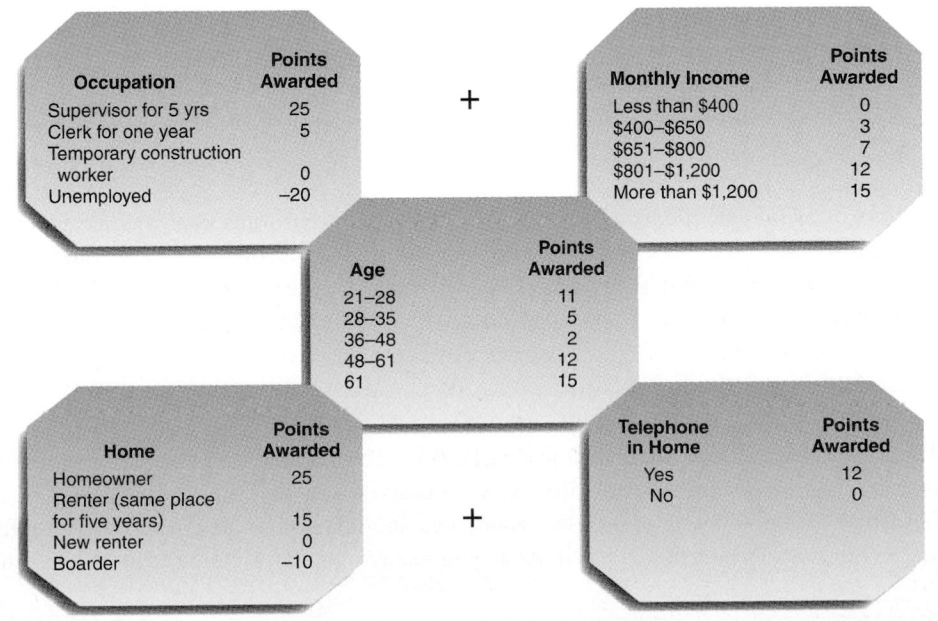

EXHIBIT 5–8

How a Consumer's Application Is Scored

Creditors use different kinds of rating systems to grant credit.

Occupation	Points Awarded
Supervisor for 5 yrs	25
Clerk for one year	5
Temporary construction worker	0
Unemployed	–20

Monthly Income	Points Awarded
Less than $400	0
$400–$650	3
$651–$800	7
$801–$1,200	12
More than $1,200	15

Age	Points Awarded
21–28	11
28–35	5
36–48	2
48–61	12
61	15

Home	Points Awarded
Homeowner	25
Renter (same place for five years)	15
New renter	0
Boarder	–10

Telephone in Home	Points Awarded
Yes	12
No	0

Financial Planning for Life's Situations

WOMEN'S CHECKLIST FOR BUILDING AND PROTECTING THEIR CREDIT HISTORIES

It is simple and sensible to build and protect your own credit history. Here are some steps to get you started.

If you are single:
- Open a chequing or savings account, or both.
- Apply for a local department store card.
- Take out a small loan from your bank. Make timely payments.

If you are married:
- Establish credit in your maiden name or your first name.
- Open your own accounts.
- Try to have separate credit card accounts in your own name.
- Review your joint accounts.
- Make sure that creditors report your credit history to credit bureaus in both names.

If you are getting married:
- Write to your creditors and ask them to continue maintaining your credit file separately.

If you have recently been separated or divorced:
- Close all of your joint accounts. Your credit record could suffer if your ex-partner is delinquent.
- Meet with your creditors and clear your credit record if your ex-partner has hurt your credit rating.

If you are widowed:
- Notify all creditors and tell them whether you or the executor of the estate will handle payment.
- Transfer all existing joint loans to your name alone. You may also want to renegotiate repayment terms.

- Transfer joint credit card accounts to your name alone or reapply for new accounts.
- Seek professional advice, if needed.

And remember that a creditor *cannot:*
1. Refuse you individual credit in your own name if you are creditworthy.
2. Require a spouse to co-sign a loan. Any creditworthy person can be your co-signer if one is required.
3. Ask about your birth control practices or family plans or assume that your income will be interrupted to have children.
4. Consider whether you have a telephone listing in your own name.

A creditor *must:*
5. Evaluate you on the same basis as applicants who are male or who have a different marital status.
6. Consider income from part-time employment.
7. Consider reliable alimony, child support, or separate-maintenance payments.
8. Consider the payment history of all joint accounts that accurately reflects your credit history.
9. Report the payment history on an account if you use the account jointly with your spouse.
10. Disregard information on accounts if you can prove that it does not reflect your ability or willingness to repay.

Source: Reprinted courtesy of office of Public Information, Federal Reserve Bank of Minneapolis, Minneapolis, MN 55480

HOUSING LOANS Federal laws ban discrimination due to such characteristics as your race, colour, or gender or to the race or national origin of the people in the neighbourhood where you live or want to buy your home. Creditors may not use any appraisal of the value of your property that considers the race of the people in your neighbourhood.

WHAT IF YOUR APPLICATION IS DENIED?

ASK QUESTIONS IF YOUR APPLICATION IS DENIED
If you receive a notice that your application has been denied, you should ask to know the specific reasons for denial. If the denial is based on a credit report, you should enquire about the specific information in the credit report that led to it. After you receive this information from the creditor,

Financial Planning for Life's Situations

THE FIVE C'S OF CREDIT

Here is what lenders look for in determining your creditworthiness.

CREDIT HISTORY

1. Character: Will you repay the loan?   Yes   No

	Yes	No
Do you have a good attitude toward credit obligations?	___	___
Have you used credit before?	___	___
Do you pay your bills on time?	___	___
Have you ever filed for bankruptcy?	___	___
Do you live within your means?	___	___

STABILITY

How long have you lived at your present address? _____ yrs.

Do you own your home? ___ ___

How long have you been employed by your present employer? _____ yrs.

INCOME

2. Capacity: Can you repay the loan?

Your salary and occupation? $_____ ; _____

Place of occupation? _____

Is your income reliable? ___ ___

Any other sources of income? $_____

EXPENSES

Number of dependants? _____

Do you pay any alimony or child support? ___ ___

Current debts? $_____

NET WORTH

3. Capital: What are your assets and net worth?

What are your assets? $_____

What are your liabilities? $_____

What is your net worth? $_____

LOAN SECURITY

4. Collateral: What if you don't repay the loan?

What assets do you have to secure the loan? (Car, home, furniture?) _____

What sources do you have besides income? (Savings, stocks, bonds, insurance?) _____

JOB SECURITY

5. Conditions: What general economic conditions can affect your repayment of the loan?

How secure is your job?   Secure ___   Not secure ___

How secure is the firm you work for?   Secure ___   Not secure ___

SOURCE: Adapted from William M. Pride, Robert J. Hughes, and Jack R. Kapoor, *Business*, 6th ed. (Boston: Houghton Mifflin, 1999), pp. 498–500.

you should contact the local credit bureau to find out what information it reported. You may ask the bureau to investigate any inaccurate or incomplete information and correct its records.

CONCEPT CHECK 5–4

1. What are the five Cs of credit?
2. What can you do if your credit application is denied?

Avoiding and Correcting Credit Mistakes

Objective 5

Identify the steps you can take to avoid and correct credit mistakes.

Has a department store's computer ever billed you for merchandise that you returned to the store or never received? Has a credit company ever charged you for the same item twice or failed to properly credit a payment on your account?

The best way to maintain your credit standing is to repay your debts on time. But complications may still occur. To protect your credit and save your time, money, and future credit rating, you should learn how to correct any mistakes and misunderstandings that crop up in your credit accounts. If a snag occurs, first try to deal directly with the creditor.

IN CASE OF A BILLING ERROR

First, notify the creditor. Give the creditor your name and account number, say that you believe the bill contains an error, and explain what you believe the error to be. State the suspected amount of the error or the item you want explained.

Lending institutions in general will review all contested material within a stated time frame, and will specify the grace period they allow for any complaints or requests for changes. They will usually ask that you pay all amounts in full pending the results of their investigation of your complaint, with the agreement that they will refund any erroneous billing amounts.

While billing errors are generally rare, it is important to work with your creditor to set things right if they do happen. Most companies will investigate and address errors if they occur, but it is your responsibility to verify every billing for accuracy (see Exhibit 5–9). In most cases, the source of the error will be with the seller, not the creditor.

IDENTITY CRISIS: WHAT TO DO IF YOUR IDENTITY IS STOLEN

Visit the Web site

See the CBC video exercises under Chapter 5 on the online learning centre at www.mcgraw hill.ca/college/kapoor.

"I don't remember charging those items. I've never even been in that store."

Maybe you never charged those goods and services, but someone else did—someone who used your name and personal information to commit fraud. When impostors take your name, social insurance number, credit card number, or some other piece of your personal information for their use, they are committing a crime.

The biggest problem is that you may not know your identity has been stolen until you notice that something is amiss: You may get bills for a credit card account you never opened, your credit report may include debts you never knew you had, a billing cycle may pass without your receiving a statement, or you may see charges on your bills that you didn't sign for, didn't authorize, and know nothing about.

If someone has stolen your identity, you should:

[1] *Contact the fraud departments of each of the two major credit bureaus* (see the table that follows). Tell them to flag your file with a fraud alert, including a statement that creditors should call you for permission before they open any new accounts in your name.

	To Report Fraud or To Order Credit Report	Web Site
Equifax	1-800-465-7166	www.equifax.ca
Trans Union	1-800-663-9980	www.tuc.ca

[2] *Contact the creditors for any accounts that have been tampered with or opened fraudulently.* Ask to speak with someone in the security or fraud department, and follow up in writing.

[3] *File a police report.* Keep a copy in case your creditors need proof of the crime.

STEP 1 **The Phone Call**

- Be organized: Record specific details (time, date, names, and titles of people spoken to)
- Collect written materials (warranties, guarantees, receipts, bills)
- Phone the company in question when you know what you would like done to rectify the problem
- Start at the bottom of the authority hierarchy (speak to the sales/service person involved in the situation)
- Remain calm, pleasant, and concise
- State the specific problem
- Supply details concerning the purchase, delivery, and service calls
- Negotiate a satisfactory solution and obtain a specific promise and a specific completion date

If the problem is not resolved
- Ask for someone who has more authority to make decisions
- Continue up the management ladder until the complaint is resolved to your satisfaction
- Do not hang up until you feel you have accomplished all you can over the telephone

STEP 2 **The Letter**

- State the problem
- Clarify the make, model, brand name, and serial number
- Clarify the price, date, place of purchase
- Clarify the name of the salesperson
- Clarify the conditions of the warranty and the date the problem was discovered
- Clarify the complaint and list the injuries (if any) caused by the problem
- Attach photocopies of any advertisements deemed necessary
- Clarify the agencies contacted regarding the complaint
- Describe a settlement that would be acceptable to rectify the problem (refund, exchange, repair)
- Specify a date by which the company is to comply with your demand (two to three weeks is reasonable)
- Explain any further action to be taken should the company not satisfy your demand
- Clarify the agencies to be contacted:
  —Goverment: Consumers' Bureau, Industry and Science Canada
  —Nongovernment: Better Business Bureau

STEP 3 **Other Alternatives**

If a satisfactory solution is not obtained by letter, try appropriate alternatives, such as independent agencies like your local Better Business Bureau. Complaining effectively will benefit not only you, but other consumers as well.

EXHIBIT 5–9

Steps in the Process of Resolving a Billing Dispute

The Consumers' Association of Canada (www.consumer.ca) offers advice about effective complaining in *Don't Be a Puppet in the Marketplace— Complain Effectively!*

To prevent an identity thief from picking up your trash to capture your personal information, tear or shred your charge receipts, copies of credit applications, insurance forms, bank cheques and statements, expired charge cards, and credit offers you get in the mail.

If you believe an unauthorized person has accessed your bank accounts, chequing account, or ATM card, close the accounts immediately. When you open new accounts, insist on password-only access. If your cheques have been stolen or misused, stop payment. If your ATM card has been lost, stolen, or otherwise compromised, cancel the card and get another with a new personal identification number (PIN).

If, after taking all these steps, you are still having identity problems, stay alert to new instances of identity theft. Notify the company or creditor immediately and follow up in writing.

SUMMARY OF OBJECTIVES

Objective 1
Define consumer credit and analyze its advantages and disadvantages.

Consumer credit is borrowing money to obtain goods or services by individuals and families for personal needs. Among the advantages of using credit are the ability to purchase goods when needed and pay for them gradually, the ability to deal with financial emergencies, convenience in shopping, and establishment of a credit rating. Disadvantages are that credit costs money, encourages overspending, and ties up future income.

Objective 2
Differentiate among various types of credit.

Closed-end (installment) and open-end (revolving) credit are two types of consumer credit. With closed-end credit, the borrower pays back a one-time loan in a stated period of time and with a specified number of payments. With open-end credit, the borrower is permitted to take loans on a continuous basis and is billed for partial payments periodically.

Objective 3
Assess your credit capacity and build your credit rating.

Two general rules for measuring credit capacity are the debt-payments-to-income ratio and the debt-to-equity ratio. In reviewing your creditworthiness, a creditor seeks information from one of the two national credit bureaus or a regional credit bureau.

Objective 4
Describe the information creditors look for when you apply for credit.

Creditors determine creditworthiness on the basis of the five Cs: character, capacity, capital, collateral, and conditions.

Objective 5
Identify the steps you can take to avoid and correct credit mistakes.

If a billing error occurs on your account, notify the creditor in writing within 60 days. If the dispute is not settled in your favour, you can place your version of it in your credit file. You may also withhold payment on any defective goods or services you have purchased with a credit card as long as you have attempted to resolve the problem with the merchant.

KEY TERMS

bank line of credit 130

capacity 146

capital 146

character 146

closed-end credit 129

collateral 146

conditions 146

consumer credit 126

credit 126

credit bureaus 139

credit reporting legislation 143

home equity loan 134

interest 130

line of credit 130

open-end credit 129

FINANCIAL PLANNING PROBLEMS

1. *Calculating the Amount for a Home Equity Loan.* A few years ago, Misha Azim purchased a home for $100,000. Today, the home is worth $150,000. His remaining mortgage balance is $50,000. Assuming Misha can borrow up to 80 percent of the market value of his home, what is the maximum amount he can borrow? (Obj. 2)

2. *Determining the Debt-Payments-to-Income Ratio.* Louise Gendron's monthly gross income is $2,000. Her employer withholds $400 in federal and provincial income taxes and $160 in Canada Pension Plan contributions per month. Louise contributes $80 per month for her RRSP. Her monthly credit payments for Visa, MasterCard, and Diners/En

Route cards are $35, $30, and $20, respectively. Her monthly payment on an automobile loan is $285. What is Louise's debt-payments-to-income ratio? Is Louise living within her means? Explain. (Obj. 3)

3. *Calculating the Debt-to-Equity Ratio.* Robert Thomas owns a $140,000 townhouse and still has an unpaid mortgage of $110,000. In addition to his mortgage, he has the following liabilities:

Visa	$565
MasterCard	480
Diners/En Route card	395
Student loan	920
Personal bank loan	800
Auto loan	4,250
Total	$7,410

Robert's net worth (not including his home) is about $21,000. This equity is in mutual funds, an automobile, a coin collection, furniture, and other personal property. What is Robert's debt-to-equity ratio? Has he reached the upper limit of debt obligations? Explain. (Obj. 3)

4. *Calculating Net Worth and Determining a Safe Credit Limit.*
   a. Calculate your net worth on the basis of your present assets and liabilities.
   b. Refer to your net worth statement and determine your safe credit limit. Use the debt-payments-to-income and debt-to-equity formulas. (Obj. 3)

5. *Using Credit Cards as Identification.* Dinesh Dani flew to Toronto to attend his brother's wedding. Knowing that his family would be busy, he did not ask anyone to meet him at the airport. Instead, he planned to rent a car to use while in Toronto. He has no nationally known credit cards but is prepared to pay cash for the rental car. The car rental agency refuses to rent him a car, even though it has several cars available. Why do you think Dinesh is unable to rent a car? (Obj. 4)

6. *Determining What Creditors Look for in Approving Loans.* Juan Villavera, a recent college graduate, has accepted a teaching position at Brockville High School. Jim moved to Brockville and applied for a car loan at the Royal Bank. He had never used credit or obtained a loan. The bank notified him that it will not approve the loan unless he has a co-signer. On what basis has the bank denied Juan credit? (Obj. 4)

7. *Analyzing Feasibility of a Loan.* Friedrich Reine has had a student loan, two auto loans, and three credit cards. He has always made timely payments on all obligations. He has a savings account of $2,400 and an annual income of $25,000. His current payments for rent, insurance, and utilities are about $1,100 per month. Friedrich has accumulated $12,800 in an individual retirement account. Friedrich's loan application asks for $10,000 to start up a small restaurant with some friends. Friedrich will not be an active manager; his partner will run the restaurant. Will he get the loan? Explain your answer. (Obj. 4)

FINANCIAL PLANNING ACTIVITIES

1. *Determining Whether or Not to Use Credit.* Survey friends and relatives to determine the process they used in deciding whether or not to use credit to purchase an automobile or a major appliance. What risks and opportunity costs did they consider? (Obj. 1)
2. *Analyzing Opportunity Costs Using Credit.* Think about the last three major purchases you made. (Obj. 1)
   a. Did you pay cash? If so, why?
   b. If you paid cash, what opportunity costs were associated with the purchase?
   c. Did you use credit? If so, why?
   d. What were the financial and psychological opportunity costs of using credit?
3. *Comparing Reasons for Using Credit.* Prepare a list of similarities and differences in the reasons the following individuals might have for using credit. (Obj. 2)
   a. A teenager.
   b. A young adult.
   c. A growing family of four.
   d. A retired couple.
4. *Using the Internet to Obtain Information about Credit Cards.* Choose one of the following organizations and visit its Web site. Then prepare a report that summarizes the information the organization provides. How could this information help you in choosing your credit card?

   a. Canoe Webfin provides information on credit card rates. (www.webfin.com)
   b. The Canadian Broadcasting Corporation provides information on how to regain financial health, uses and misuses of credit cards, and many other related topics. (www. cbc.ca/consumers) (Obj. 2)
5. *Using your Home Equity to Obtain a Loan.* Visit your local financial institutions, such as banks, trust companies, and credit unions, to obtain information about getting a home equity loan. Compare their requirements for the loan. (Obj. 2)
6. *Determining Whether to Co-sign a Loan.* Talk to a person who has co-signed a loan or to a representative from a financial institution. What experiences did this person have as a co-signer? (Obj. 3)
7. *Determining Net Worth and Credit Capacity.* What changes might take place in your personal net worth during different stages of your life? How might these changes affect your credit capacity? (Obj. 4)
8. *Assessing How Lenders Determine Creditworthiness.* Survey credit representatives, such as bankers, managers of credit departments in retail stores, managers of finance companies, credit union officers, managers of credit bureaus, and loan officers. Ask what procedures they follow in granting or refusing a loan. Write a report of your survey. (Obj. 4)

9. *Analyzing Credit-Related Problems.* Bring to class examples of credit-related problems of individuals or families. Suggest ways in which these problems might be solved. (Obj. 5)

10. *Evaluating Creditors and Seeking Help with Credit-Related Problems.* Compile a list of places a person can call to report dishonest credit practices, get advice and help with credit problems, and check out a creditor's reputation before signing a contract. (Obj. 6)

LIFE SITUATION CASE

A Hard Lesson on Credit Cards

Parents of post-secondary students, beware: The empty-nest syndrome you're experiencing may end up as empty-wallet syndrome. The moment your kids step on campus, they become highly-sought-after credit card customers. To establish relationships they hope will extend well beyond the post-secondary years, card marketers are offering students everything from free T-shirts to chances to win airline tickets as enticements to sign up. As a result, some students now have heavy credit card debts.

"Students who have no history with credit are being handed it on a silver platter," say Gina Orente, education adviser for a consumer advocacy group in Hull, Quebec. As long as they are over 18, students can get a card without asking mom or dad to co-sign. But when they get into trouble, they often go running to their folks for help. Huan Kwo did—and then some. Now 21 and in his final year at McGill University in Montreal, Kwo racked up $21,000 in debt on 16 cards over four years. "When I first started, my attitude was: 'I'll get a job after college to pay off all my debt,'" he says. He realized he dug himself into a hole when he couldn't meet the minimum monthly payments. Now he works three part-time jobs, and his parents are helping him pay his tuition and loans.

Questions

1. Why should parents of students be wary?
2. How do credit card marketers entice students?
3. Where do students turn for help when they get into debt trouble?

CREATING A FINANCIAL PLAN

Establishing and Maintaining A Credit Record

The wise use of credit requires a knowledge of the process for establishing credit. In addition, you should develop an awareness of credit reports and the legal rights associated with using consumer credit.

Web Sites for Wise Use of Credit
- The Canadian Broadcasting Corporation provides a great site at **http://cbc.ca/consumers**. Surf here for the latest consumer news and issues, including credit, credit fraud, and strategies for consumer protection.
- The BankruptcyCanada.com site (**www.bankruptcycanada.com**) provides information on all aspects of insolvency, including business, personal bankruptcy, consumer proposals, and choosing a trustee.

- Information on credit reports is available from Equifax Canada at **www.equifax.ca**.
- IE:Money magazine, at **www.iemoney.com**, suggests ways of improving your credit rating.
- Canoe Webfin, at **www.webfin.com**, has a credit quiz that can help you assess your credit situation and find out if it is time to get help.
- Finally, Industry Canada, at **www.strategis.ic.gc.ca/oca**, offers a calculator that helps you determine the real rate you are being charged on your credit cards so you can differentiate between good cards and bad ones.

(Note: Addresses and content of Web sites change, and new sites are created daily. Use search engines to update and locate Web sites for your current financial planning needs.)

6 Choosing a Source of Credit: The Costs of Credit Alternatives

The Perils of Teaser Rates

Remember Huan Kwo from the previous chapter, who racked up $21,000 in credit card debt? Having educated himself on the pitfalls of credit, Kwo now speaks to student groups on the issue. Since card issuers' pitches may be confusing, he and other experts offer this advice: Beware of teaser rates. Credit card marketers may advertise a low annual percentage rate (APR), but it often jumps substantially after three to nine months. One group that is often targeted by marketers is the student population. The incentive offered is a discounted rate for the first few months, which then leaps upward afterwards. Many students, eager for credit and receptive to the notion of "fast cash," will sign up without fully understanding the risks involved.

Because students move often and may not get their mail forwarded quickly, bills can get lost. Then, the students fall prey to late-payment fees. Some cards have late fees as high as $30. If one or two payments are overdue, many cards bump interest rates up as well.

Students are often unaware that rates on cash advances are much higher than those on card balances. Some cards also impose a fee of as much as 4 percent of the advance.

The moral? *Don't ask for extra credit.* Instead, find a card that has a restrictive credit line. Another option: Get a secured credit card. Its credit limit depends on your savings at the issuing bank. Debt advisers say students should hold only a credit card on which they can carry a small balance and a charge card they must pay off monthly. They should pay more than the minimum on credit cards. And they should not charge purchases they can pay for in cash, such as pizza and gas.

If you are a parent, talk to your kids about responsible credit card use. Make sure your kids know a card isn't a way of getting items they can't afford.

QUESTIONS

1 What is Huan Kwo's advice to student groups?

2 Are teaser rates unique to student credit cards?

3 Should you get a secured credit card? Why, or why not?

LEARNING OBJECTIVES

1   Analyze the major sources of consumer credit.

2   Determine the cost of credit by calculating interest using various interest formulas.

3   Develop a plan to manage your debts.

4   Evaluate various private and governmental sources that assist consumers with debt problems.

5   Assess the choices in declaring personal bankruptcy.

Sources of Consumer Credit

Objective 1

Analyze the major sources of consumer credit.

Credit costs got you down? Well, you are not alone. Credit costs money; therefore, always weigh the benefits of buying an item on credit now versus waiting until you have saved enough money to pay cash. We can all get into credit difficulties if we do not understand how and when to use credit.

Financial and other institutions, the sources of credit, come in all shapes and sizes. They play an important role in our economy, and they offer a broad range of financial services. By evaluating your credit options, you can reduce your finance charges. You can reconsider your decision to borrow money, discover a less expensive type of loan, or find a lender that charges a lower interest rate.

Before deciding whether to borrow money, ask yourself these three questions: Do I need a loan? Can I afford a loan? Can I qualify for a loan? We discussed the affordability of loans and the qualifications required to obtain loans in the last chapter. Here we wrestle with the first question.

You should avoid credit in two situations. The first situation is one in which you do not need or really want a product that will require financing. Easy access to installment loans or possession of credit cards sometimes encourages consumers to make expensive purchases they later regret. The solution to this problem is simple: After you have selected a product, resist any sales pressure to buy immediately and take a day to think it over.

The second situation is one in which you can afford to pay cash. Consider the trade-offs and opportunity costs involved. Paying cash is almost always cheaper than using credit. In fact, some stores even offer a discount for payment in cash.

WHAT KIND OF LOAN SHOULD YOU SEEK?

As discussed in the last chapter, two types of credit exist: closed-end and open-end credit. Because installment loans may carry a lower interest rate, they are the less expensive credit option for loans that are repaid over a period of many months or years. However, because credit cards usually provide a float period—a certain number of days during which no interest is charged—they represent the cheaper way to make credit purchases that are paid off in a month or two. Also, once you have a credit card, using it is always easier than taking out an installment loan. An alternative to a credit card is a travel and entertainment (T&E) card, such as an American Express or Diners/En Route card. A T&E card requires full payment of the balance due each month but does not impose a finance charge. Annual fees, however, can be high.

In seeking an installment loan, you may think first of borrowing from a bank or a credit union. However, less expensive credit sources are available.

INEXPENSIVE LOANS Parents or family members are often the source of the least expensive loans. They may charge you only the interest they would have earned had they not made the loan—as little as the percentage they would have earned on a passbook account. Such loans, however, can complicate family relationships. All loans to or from family members should be in writing and state the interest rate, if any, repayment schedule, and the final payment date.

Also relatively inexpensive is money borrowed on financial assets held by a lending institution, for example, a bank guaranteed investment certificate or the cash value of a whole life insurance policy. The interest rate on such loans typically ranges from 7 to 10 percent. But the trade-off is that your assets are tied up until you have repaid the loan.

MEDIUM-PRICED LOANS Often, you can obtain medium-priced loans from banks, trust companies, and credit unions. New-car loans, for example, may cost 8 to 12 percent; used-car loans and home improvement loans may cost slightly more.

Borrowing from credit unions has several advantages. These institutions provide credit life insurance, are generally sympathetic to borrowers with legitimate payment problems, and provide personalized service. Credit unions can now offer the same range of consumer loans that banks and other financial institutions do. More than 10 million Canadians belong to credit unions, and the number of credit union members has been growing steadily. About 800 credit unions exist in Canada today.

EXPENSIVE LOANS Though convenient to obtain, the most expensive loans available are from finance companies, retailers, and banks through credit cards. Finance companies often lend to people who cannot obtain credit from banks or credit unions. Typically, the interest ranges from 12 to 25 percent, although a card from The Bay or Canadian Tire can cost up to 29 percent. Other organizations, such as Money Mart, provide cheque cashing and related financing services that can cost up to 1 percent per week. If you are denied credit by a bank or a credit union, you should question your ability to afford the higher rate a loan company charges.

Borrowing from car dealers, appliance stores, department stores, and other retailers is also relatively expensive. The interest rates retailers charge are usually similar to those charged by finance companies, frequently 20 percent or more.

Banks lend funds not only through installment loans but also through cash advances on MasterCard or Visa cards. Credit card co-branding has become increasingly popular with banks and industries. Co-branded credit cards, such as the Yahoo! Visa card, will make shopping over the Internet easier and faster. Yahoo! will designate Visa as its "preferred card" and will promote Visa throughout its Web sites and to online merchants worldwide.

One type of loan from finance companies is currently less expensive than most other credit. Loans of this kind, which often can be obtained at a rate of under 8 percent, are available from the finance companies of major automakers. But a car dealer that offers you such a rate may be less willing to discount the price of the car or throw in free options.

CONCEPT CHECK 6-1

1. Why do students fall prey to late-payment fees?
2. What are the major sources of consumer credit?
3. What are some advantages and disadvantages of securing a loan from a credit union? from a finance company?

The Cost of Credit

Objective 2

Determine the cost of credit by calculating interest using various interest formulas.

If you are thinking of borrowing money or opening a credit account, your first step should be to figure out how much it will cost you and whether you can afford it. Then, you should shop for the best terms. Two key concepts that you should remember are the finance charge and the annual percentage rate.

FINANCE CHARGE AND ANNUAL PERCENTAGE RATE (APR)

Credit costs vary. If you know the finance charge and the annual percentage rate (APR), you can compare credit prices from different sources.

finance charge The total dollar amount paid to use credit.

annual percentage rate (APR) The percentage cost (or relative cost) of credit on a yearly basis. The APR yields a true rate of interest for comparisons with other sources of credit.

The **finance charge** is the total dollar amount you pay to use credit. It includes interest costs and sometimes other costs, such as service charges, credit-related insurance premiums, or appraisal fees.

For example, borrowing $100 for a year might cost you $10 in interest. If there is also a service charge of $1, the finance charge will be $11. The **annual percentage rate (APR)** is the percentage cost (or relative cost) of credit on a yearly basis. The APR is your key to comparing costs, regardless of the amount of credit or how much time you have to repay it.

Suppose you borrow $100 for one year and pay a finance charge of $10. If you can keep the entire $100 for the whole year and then pay it all back at once, you are paying an APR of 10 percent.

On average, you had full use of $100 throughout the year. To calculate the average use, add the loan balance during the first and last month, then divide by 2:

$$\text{Average balance} = \frac{\$100 + \$100}{2} = \$100$$

But if you repay the $100 and the finance charge (a total of $110) in 12 equal monthly payments, you don't get use of the $100 for the whole year. In fact, as shown next, you get use of less and less of that $100 each month. In this case, the $10 charge for credit amounts to an APR of 18.5 percent. The following table illustrates the difference:

Amount Borrowed	Month Number	Payment Made in Equal Installments ($100 ÷ 12)	Loan Balance
$100	1	0	$100.00
	2	8.33	91.67
	3	8.33	83.34
	4	8.33	75.01
	5	8.33	66.68
	6	8.33	58.35
	7	8.33	50.02
	8	8.33	41.69
	9	8.33	33.36
	10	8.33	25.03
	11	8.33	16.70
	12	8.33	8.37

Note that you are paying 10 percent interest even though you had use of only $91.67 during the second month, not $100. During the last month, you owed only $8.37 (and had use of $8.37), but the $10 interest is for the entire $100. As calculated in the previous example, the average use of the money during the year is $100 + $8.37 ÷ 2, or $54.18. The APR in the second case

Financial Planning Calculations

THE ARITHMETIC OF THE ANNUAL PERCENTAGE RATE (APR)

There are two ways to calculate the APR: using an APR formula and using the APR tables. The APR tables are more precise than the formula. The formula, given below, only approximates the APR:

$$r = \frac{2 \times n \times I}{P(N + 1)}$$

where

r = Approximate APR
n = Number of payment periods in one year (12, if payments are monthly; 52, if weekly)
I = Total dollar cost of credit
P = Principal, or net amount of loan
N = Total number of payments scheduled to pay off the loan

Let us compare the APR when the $100 loan is paid off in one lump sum at the end of the year and when the same loan is paid off in 12 equal monthly payments.

The stated annual interest rate is 10 percent for both loans.

Using the formula, the APR for the lump-sum loan is

$$r = \frac{2 \times 1 \times \$10}{\$100(1 + 1)} = \frac{\$20}{\$100(2)} = \frac{\$20}{\$200} = 0.10$$

or 10 percent

Using the formula, the APR for the monthly payment loan is

$$r = \frac{2 \times 12 \times \$10}{\$100(12 + 1)} = \frac{\$240}{\$100(13)} = \frac{\$240}{\$1,300}$$

= 0.1846, or 18.46 percent (rounded to 18.5 percent)

is 18.5 percent ($10/$54.18). The EAR (effective annual rate), as discussed in Chapter 3, for the same case, is 10.47 percent.

$$\left(1 + \tfrac{.10}{12}\right)^{12} - 1$$

The Financial Planning Calculations feature above shows how to calculate the APR using a formula.

All creditors—banks, stores, car dealers, credit card companies, and finance companies—should state the cost of their credit in terms of the finance charge and the APR. The law does not set interest rates or other credit charges, but it does require their disclosure so that you can compare credit costs and tackle the trade-offs.

TACKLING THE TRADE-OFFS

When you choose your financing, there are trade-offs between the features you prefer (term, size of payments, fixed or variable interest, or payment plan) and the cost of your loan. Here are some of the major trade-offs you should consider.

TERM VERSUS INTEREST COSTS Many people choose longer-term financing because they want smaller monthly payments. But the longer the term for a loan at a given interest rate, the greater is the amount you must pay in interest charges. Consider the following analysis of the relationship between the term and interest costs.

A COMPARISON Even when you understand the terms a creditor is offering, it's easy to underestimate the difference in dollars that different terms can make. Suppose you're buying a $7,500 used car. You put $1,500 down, and you need to borrow $6,000. Compare the following three credit arrangements:

	APR	Length of Loan	Monthly Payment	Total Finance Charge	Total Cost
Creditor A	14%	3 years	$205.07	$1,382.52	$7,382.52
Creditor B	14	4 years	163.96	1,870.08	7,870.08
Creditor C	15	4 years	166.98	2,015.04	8,015.04

How do these choices compare? The answer depends partly on what you need. The lowest-cost loan is available from creditor A. If you are looking for lower monthly payments, you could repay the loan over a longer period of time. However, you would have to pay more in total costs. A loan from creditor B—also at a 14 percent APR, but for four years—would add about $488 to your finance charge.

If that four-year loan were available only from creditor C, the APR of 15 percent would add another $145 to your finance charges. Other terms, such as the size of the down payment, will also make a difference. Be sure to look at all the terms before you make your choice.

LENDER RISK VERSUS INTEREST RATE You may prefer financing that requires low fixed payments with a large final payment or only a minimum of upfront cash. But both these requirements can increase your cost of borrowing because they create more risk for your lender.

If you want to minimize your borrowing costs, you may need to accept conditions that reduce your lender's risk. Here are a few possibilities.

VARIABLE INTEREST RATE A variable interest rate is based on fluctuating rates in the banking system, such as the prime rate. With this type of loan, you share the interest rate risks with the lender. Therefore, the lender may offer you a lower initial interest rate than it would with a fixed-rate loan.

Visit the Web site

See Personal Financial Planning worksheets under Chapter 6 on the online learning centre at www.mcgrawhill.ca/college/kapoor.

A SECURED LOAN If you pledge property or other assets as collateral, you'll probably receive a lower interest rate on your loan.

UPFRONT CASH Many lenders believe you have a higher stake in repaying a loan if you pay cash for a large portion of what you are financing. Doing so may give you a better chance of getting the other terms you want. Of course, by making a large down payment, you forgo interest that you might earn in a savings account.

A SHORTER TERM As you have learned, the shorter the period of time for which you borrow, the smaller the chance that something will prevent you from repaying and the lower the risk to the lender. Therefore, you may be able to borrow at a lower interest rate if you accept a shorter-term loan, but your payments will be higher.

In the next section, you will see how the above-mentioned trade-offs can affect the cost of closed-end and open-end credit.

CALCULATING THE COST OF CREDIT

The two most common methods of calculating interest are compound and simple interest formulas. Perhaps the most basic method is the simple interest calculation. Simple interest on the declining balance, add-on interest, bank discount, and compound interest are variations of simple interest.

SIMPLE INTEREST *Simple interest* is the interest computed on principal only excluding compounding; it is the dollar cost of borrowing money.

Financial Planning for Life's Situations

BANK OF CANADA RATE AND CREDIT CARD INTEREST RATES

In Canada, from 1980 to 1995, credit card interest rates generally moved up and down with the Bank rate, with a time lag. However, this trend has not been evident in the past few years. Generally, the interest rates on standard cards have not moved along with the Bank rate since 1995, and low-rate cards have not followed suit since 1999. Moreover, retail credit card rates have not changed in the last 18 years (see chart below).

THE BANK OF CANADA RATE AND CREDIT CARD INTEREST RATES

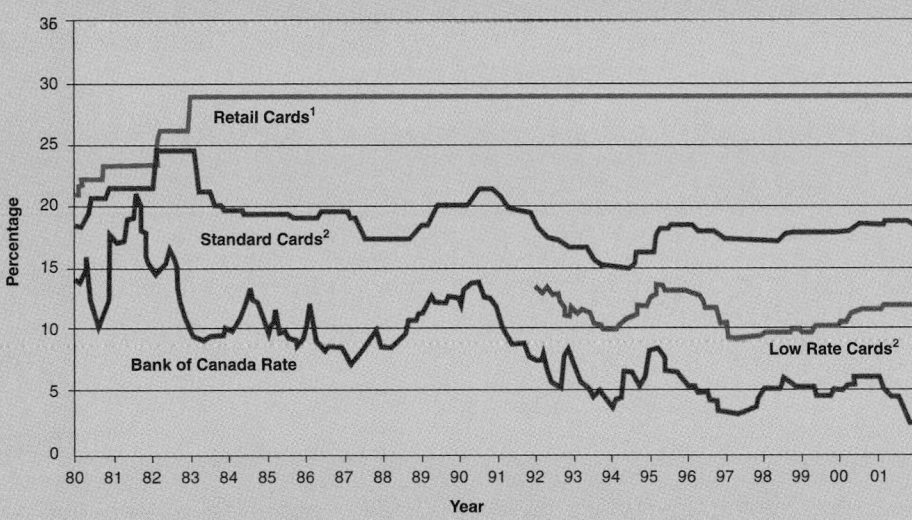

[1] Based on the average of the Sears card and the Hudson's Bay card
[2] Based on the average of the six major banks (for purchases)

SOURCE: Federal Consumer Agency of Canada (FCAC), "Credit Cards and You." Quarterly Credit Card Cost Report, December 2001. www.fcac-acfc.gc.ca.

Example 1 Suppose you have persuaded a relative to lend you $1,000 to purchase a laptop computer. Your relative agreed to charge only 5 percent interest, and you agreed to repay the loan at the end of one year. Using the simple interest formula, the interest will be 5 percent of $1,000 for one year, or $50, since you have the use of $1,000 for the entire year:

$$I = P \times r \times T$$
$$I = \$1,000 \times 0.05 \times 1$$
$$= \$50$$

Using the APR formula discussed earlier,

$$APR = \frac{2 \times n \times I}{P(N + 1)} = \frac{2 \times 1 \times \$50}{\$1,000(1 + 1)} = \frac{\$100}{\$2,000} = 0.05, \text{ or 5 percent}$$

Note that the stated rate, 5 percent, is also the annual percentage rate.

SIMPLE INTEREST ON THE DECLINING BALANCE When more than one payment is made on a simple interest loan, the method of computing interest is known as the **declining balance method**. Since you pay interest only on the amount of the original principal that you have not yet repaid, the more frequent the payments, the lower the interest you will pay. Most banks and credit unions use this method for their loans.

declining balance method A method of computing interest when more than one payment is made on a simple interest loan.

Example 2 Using simple interest on the declining balance to compute interest charges, the interest on a 5 percent, $1,000 loan repaid in two payments, one at the end of the first half-year and another at the end of the second half-year, would be $37.50, as follows:

First payment:

$$I = P \times r \times T$$
$$= \$1,000 \times 0.05 \times \frac{1}{2}$$
$$= \$25 \text{ interest plus } \$500, \text{ or } \$525$$

Second payment:

$$I = P \times r \times T$$
$$= \$500 \times 0.05 \times \frac{1}{2}$$
$$= \$12.50 \text{ interest plus the remaining balance of } \$500, \text{ or } \$512.50$$

Total payment on the loan:

$$\$525 + \$512.50 = \$1,037.50$$

Using the APR formula,

$$APR = \frac{2 \times n \times I}{P(N + 1)} = \frac{2 \times 2 \times \$37.50}{\$1,000(2 + 1)} = \frac{\$150}{\$3,000} = 0.05, \text{ or } 5 \text{ percent}$$

Note that using simple interest under the declining balance method, the stated rate, 5 percent, is also the annual percentage rate. The add-on interest, bank discount, and compound interest calculation methods differ from the simple interest method as to when, how, and on what balance interest is paid. For these methods, the real annual rate, or the annual percentage rate, differs from the stated rate.

adjusted balance method The assessment of finance charges after payments made during the billing period have been subtracted.

The appendix to this chapter presents various other methods of determining the cost of credit, such as the bank discount method, the compound interest formula, amortization, and the use of a financial calculator.

COST OF OPEN-END CREDIT As discussed earlier, open-end (revolving) credit includes credit cards, department store charge cards, and cheque overdraft accounts that allow you to write cheques for more than your actual balance. You can use open-end credit again and again until you reach a prearranged borrowing limit.

previous balance method A method of computing finance charges that gives no credit for payments made during the billing period.

Creditors will tell you how they calculate the finance charge. Creditors use various systems to calculate the balance on which they assess finance charges. Some creditors add finance charges after subtracting payments made during the billing period; this is called the **adjusted balance method**. Other creditors give you no credit for payments made during the billing period; this is called the **previous balance method**. Under the third—and the fairest—method, the **average daily balance method**, creditors add your balances for each day in the billing period and then divide by the number of days in the period. The average daily balance may include or exclude new purchases during the billing period.

average daily balance method A method of computing finance charges that uses a weighted average of the account balance throughout the current billing period.

Here is how some different methods of calculating finance charges affect the cost of credit:

	Average Daily Balance (*including* new purchases)	Average Daily Balance (*excluding* new purchases)
Monthly rate	$1\frac{1}{2}$%	$1\frac{1}{2}$%
APR	18%	18%
Previous balance	$400	$400
New purchases	$50 on 18th day	$50 on 18th day
Payments	$300 on 15th day (new balance = $100)	$300 on 15th day (new balance = $100)
Average daily balance	$270*	$250**
Finance charge	$4.05 ($1\frac{1}{2}$% × $270)	$3.75 ($1\frac{1}{2}$% × $250)

*To figure average daily balance (*including* new purchases):
($400 × 15 days) + ($100 × 3 days) + ($150 × 12 days) ÷ 30 days
= ($6,000 + $300 + $1,800) ÷ 30 or, $8,100 ÷ 30 days = $270
**To figure average daily balance (*excluding* new purchases):
[($400 × 15 days) + ($100 × 15 days)] ÷ 30 days = $7,500 ÷ 30 days = $250

	Adjusted Balance	Previous Balance
Monthly rate	$1\frac{1}{2}$%	$1\frac{1}{2}$%
APR	18%	18%
Previous balance	$400	$400
Payments	$300	$300
Average daily balance	N/A	N/A
Finance charge	$1.50 ($1\frac{1}{2}$% × $100)	$6 ($1\frac{1}{2}$% × $400)

As the example shows, the finance charge varies for the same pattern of purchases and payments.

Second, creditors must tell you when finance charges on your credit account begin so that you know how much time you have to pay your bills before a finance charge is added. Some creditors, for example, give you a 20- to 25-day grace period to pay your balance in full before imposing a finance charge. But in most cases, the grace period applies only if you have no outstanding balance on your card. Therefore, if you want to take advantage of the interest-free period on your card, you must pay your bill in full every month.

COST OF CREDIT AND EXPECTED INFLATION
As you have seen, interest rates dictate when you must pay future dollars to receive current dollars. Borrowers and lenders, however, are less concerned about dollars, present or future, than about the goods and services those dollars can buy—that is, their purchasing power.

Inflation erodes the purchasing power of money. Each percentage point increase in inflation means a decrease of approximately 1 percent in the quantity of goods and services you can purchase with a given quantity of dollars. As a result, lenders, seeking to protect their purchasing power, add the expected rate of inflation to the interest rate they charge. You are willing to pay this higher rate because you expect inflation to enable you to repay the loan with cheaper dollars.

For example, if a lender expects a 4-percent inflation rate for the coming year and desires an 8-percent return on its loan, it will probably charge you a 12-percent nominal or stated rate (a 4-percent inflation premium plus an 8-percent "real" rate).

Return to Example 1, in which you borrowed $1,000 from your relative at the bargain rate of 5 percent for one year. If the inflation rate was 4 percent during that year, your relative's real rate of return was only 1 percent (5 percent stated interest minus 4 percent inflation rate) and your "real" cost was not $50 but only $10 ($50 minus $40 inflation premium).

AVOID THE MINIMUM MONTHLY PAYMENT TRAP The "minimum monthly payment" is the smallest amount you can pay and still be a cardholder in good standing. Banks often encourage you to make the minimum payment, such as 3–5 percent of your outstanding balance or a minimum of $10. Some statements refer to the minimum as the "cardholder amount due." But that is not the total amount you owe.

Consider the following examples. In each example, the minimum payment is based on $1/36$ of the outstanding balance or $20, whichever is greater.

Example 1 You are buying new books for your courses. If you spend $500 on textbooks using a credit card charging 19.8 percent interest and make only the minimum payment, it will take you more than $2\frac{1}{2}$ years to pay off the loan, adding $150 in interest charges to the cost of your purchase. The same purchase on a credit card charging 12 percent interest will cost only $78 extra.

Example 2 You purchase a $2,000 stereo system using a credit card with 19 percent interest and a 2-percent minimum payment. If you pay just the minimum every month, it will take you 265 months—more than 22 years—to pay off the debt and will cost you nearly $4,800 in interest payments. Doubling the amount paid each month to 4 percent of the balance owed would allow you to shorten the payment time to 88 months from 265 months—or 7 years as opposed to 22 years—and save you about $3,680.

Example 3 You charge $2,000 in tuition and fees on a credit card charging 18.5 percent interest. If you pay off the balance by making the minimum payment each month, it will take you more than 11 years to repay the debt. By the time you have paid off the loan, you will have spent an extra $1,934 in interest alone—almost the actual cost of your tuition and fees. Again, to be prudent, pay off the balance as quickly as possible.

See the Financial Planning for Life's Situations feature on the next page for guidance in choosing the card that is right for you.

CREDIT INSURANCE

credit insurance Any type of insurance that ensures repayment of a loan in the event the borrower is unable to repay it.

Credit insurance ensures the repayment of your loan in the event of death, disability, or loss of property. The lender is named the beneficiary and directly receives any payments made on submitted claims.

There are three types of credit insurance: credit life, credit accident and health, and credit property. The most commonly purchased type of credit insurance is credit life insurance, which provides for the repayment of the loan if the borrower dies. According to many consumer organizations, most borrowers don't need credit life insurance. Those who don't have life insurance can buy term life insurance for less. Term life insurance is discussed in Chapter 9.

Credit accident and health insurance, also called *credit disability insurance*, re-pays your loan in the event of a loss of income due to illness or injury. Credit property insurance provides coverage for personal property purchased with a loan. It may also insure collateral property, such as a car or furniture. However, premiums for such coverage are quite high.

CONCEPT CHECK 6–2

1. Distinguish between the finance charge and the annual percentage rate.
2. What are the three variations of the simple interest formula?
3. Distinguish among the adjusted balance, previous balance, and average daily balance methods of calculating the cost of open-end credit.

Financial Planning for Life's Situations

TO CHOOSE IT, FIRST DECIDE HOW YOU PLAN TO USE IT

Many bank cards offer added value through enhancements, such as discounts on merchandise, rebates on purchases, travel and accident insurance, frequent-flyer points, emergency card replacement, donations to non-profit groups, and 24-hour customer service. The trick to finding the bank card that's right for you is to balance the benefits with the right price. You should consider interest rates and fees on the basis of how you plan to use the card.

- *Annual fee.* If you plan to pay your balance in full each month, shop for a card that has a grace period and carries no annual fee, or a low annual fee, even if the trade-off is a higher interest rate. You plan to pay little or no interest anyway. Gold or platinum cards often charge $100 or more in annual fees.
- *Low rates.* If you prefer to stretch out repayment, aim for a card with a lower interest rate. In general, lower-interest-rate cards tend to have tougher credit approval requirements, may not offer a grace period, and often have slightly higher annual fees. But if you qualify, the money you save on interest is likely to offset a higher fee.
- *Variable rates.* Some credit cards promote variable interest rates tied to the prime rate. You may benefit from lower interest rates when the rate is low, but remember that when the rate rises, you'll pay the higher rate even on purchases you've already made.
- *Grace period.* Not all credit cards offer a grace period. When you use such a card, the bank begins charging you interest on the day you make the purchase or the day the purchase is recorded on your account. Try to pay off your balance in full each month to maintain the grace period and avoid paying interest.

- *Other fees.* Most credit cards charge a special fee when you take a cash advance. Usually, the fee is about 2 or 3 percent of the amount borrowed.

Many banks impose late fees even when payment arrives a day after the due date. Some banks charge a set fee, such as $25 or $30, while others charge a percentage, such as 5 percent, of the minimum payment due.

Most cards assess an over-credit-limit fee. For instance, if you charge $400 over your limit and the penalty is 5 percent, you will pay a $20 fee in addition to interest charges. A few companies charge lost-card replacement fees, usually $5 or $10.

Some credit card issuers allow you to skip a payment without a penalty. While this sounds like the bank is giving you a break, you will be charged interest during this period and will owe more in interest than you did before.

Once you decide on the right combination of features and price, you can begin shopping. Federal law requires that every mail solicitation, "take one" application, and application brochure carry a special box listing the interest rate, annual fee, length of grace period, and other fees. This will allow you to easily compare the costs of different card plans.

SOURCES: American Bankers Association; *Understanding Credit Card Costs* (San Francisco: Consumer Action, March 1994); *Choosing and Using Credit Cards* (Washington, DC: Federal Trade Commission, January 1999). © American Bankers Association. Reprinted with permission.

Managing Your Debts

A sudden illness or the loss of your job may make it impossible for you to pay your bills on time. If you find you cannot make your payments, contact your creditors at once and try to work out a modified payment plan with them. If you have paid your bills promptly in the past, they may be willing to work with you. Do not wait until your account is turned over to a debt collector. At that point, the creditor has given up on you.

Automobile loans present special problems. Most automobile financing agreements permit your creditor to repossess your car anytime you are in default on your payments. No advance notice is required. If your car is repossessed and sold, you will still owe the difference between the selling price and the unpaid debt, plus any legal, towing, and storage charges. Try to solve

Objective 3

Develop a plan to manage your debts.

165

the problem with your creditor when you realize you will not be able to meet your payments. It may be better to sell the car yourself and pay off your debt than to incur the added costs of repossession.

If you are having trouble paying your bills, you may be tempted to turn to a company that claims to offer assistance in solving debt problems. Such companies may offer debt consolidation loans, debt counselling, or debt reorganization plans that are "guaranteed" to stop creditors' collection efforts. Before signing with such a company, investigate it. Be sure you understand what services the company provides and what they will cost you. Do not rely on verbal promises that do not appear in your contract. Also, check with the Better Business Bureau and your provincial or local consumer protection office. It may be able to tell you whether other consumers have registered complaints about the company.

WARNING SIGNS OF DEBT PROBLEMS

Jerome Olsen, in his early 30s, has a steady job with an annual income of $40,000. Jerome, his wife, and their two children enjoy a comfortable life. A new car is parked in the driveway of their home, which is furnished with such modern conveniences as a new microwave oven, a new freezer, an electric washer and dryer, a videocassette recorder, and a large-screen colour television set.

However, Jerome Olsen is in debt. He is drowning in a sea of bills, with most of his income tied up in repaying debts. Foreclosure proceedings on his home have been instituted, and several stores have court orders to repossess practically every major appliance in it. His current car payment is overdue, and three charge accounts at local stores are several months delinquent.

This case is neither exaggerated nor isolated. Unfortunately, a large number of people are in the same floundering state. These people's problem is immaturity. Mature consumers have certain information; they demonstrate self-discipline, control their impulses, and use sound judgment; they accept responsibility for money management; and they are able to postpone and govern expenditures when overextension of credit appears likely.

Referring to overindebtedness as one of the nation's main family financial problems, an expert on consumer affairs lists the following as frequent reasons for indebtedness:[1]

[1] *Emotional problems*, such as the need for instant gratification, as in the case of a man who can't resist buying a costly suit or a woman who impulsively purchases an expensive dress in a trendy department store.
[2] *The use of money to punish*, such as a husband who buys a new car without consulting his wife, who, in turn, buys a diamond watch to get even.
[3] *The expectation of instant comfort* among those who assume that by use of the installment plan, they can immediately have the possessions their parents acquired after years of work.
[4] *Keeping up with the Joneses*, which is more apparent than ever, not only among prosperous families but also among limited-income families.

---

[1] Judy Hammond, "Consumer Credit Counselors Say Debt Recovery Can Take Three to Five Years," *Knight-Ridder/Tribune Business News*, February 16, 1999.

[5] *Overindulgence of children*, often because of the parents' own emotional needs, competition with each other, or inadequate communication regarding expenditures for the children.

[6] *Misunderstanding or lack of communication among family members.* For example, a salesperson visited a Calgary family to sell them an expensive freezer. Although the freezer was beyond the means of this already overindebted family and too large for their needs anyway, the husband thought his wife wanted it. Not until later, in an interview with a debt counsellor, did the wife relate her concern when she signed the contract; she had wanted her husband to say no.

[7] *The amount of the finance charges*, which can push a family over the edge of their ability to pay, especially when they borrow from one company to pay another and these charges pyramid.

Exhibit 6–1 lists some danger signals of potential debt problems.

THE SERIOUS CONSEQUENCES OF DEBT

Just as the causes of indebtedness vary, so too does a mixture of other personal and family problems that frequently result from overextension of credit.

Loss of a job because of garnishment proceedings may occur in a family that has a disproportionate amount of income tied up in debts. Another possibility is that such a family is forced to neglect vital areas. In the frantic effort to rob Peter to pay Paul, skimping may seriously affect the family's health and neglect the educational needs of children. Excessive indebtedness may also result in heavy drinking, neglect of children, marital difficulties, and drug abuse. But help is available to those debtors who seek it.

See the Financial Planning for Life's Situations feature on page 168 to find out where you can obtain free credit information on the Internet.

CONCEPT CHECK 6–3

1. What are the most frequent reasons for indebtedness?
2. What are common danger signals of potential debt problems?

Exhibit 6–1

Danger Signals of Potential Debt Problems

Seek help from a consumer credit counselling service if you experience these danger signals.

According to the the Government of Canada's Office of the Superintendent of Bankruptcy, in its December 1998 publication "Dealing with Debt: A Consumer's Guide," you have—or are going to have—a debt problem if:

- You continually go over your spending limit or you use your credit cards as a necessity, rather than a convenience;
- You are always borrowing money to make it from one payday to the next;
- Your wages have been garnisheed or appropriated to pay for outstanding debts;
- You pay only interest or service charges monthly and do not reduce your total debt over many months;
- Creditors pressure you for payment, threaten to sue or repossess your car, furniture or television, or hire a collection agency to recover the money for them; or
- Utility companies cut off service because your bills have gone unpaid.

SOURCE: Based on "Dealing with Debt: A Consumer's Guide," Office of the Superintendent of Bankruptcy, December 1998.

MONEY MANAGEMENT IN CYBERSPACE

Whether you're developing a plan for reaching your financial goals or searching for a low-interest credit card, you can look to the Internet for a world of free information. Many Web sites provide interactive worksheets that allow you to plug in personal information and obtain customized reports. Here are some suggestions.

FinanCenter, at www.financenter.com, provides nifty payment calculators that help you figure out the actual dollars paid in interest over the period of a credit card debt or the maximum amount you should borrow at your current income. If your payments have been piling up, take a deep breath before travelling here.

Canoe Webfin, at www.webfin.com, provides you with everything you need to successfully manage your personal finances. News and reference materials allow you stay up to date on money matters. You can also use analytical tools to track your investments and plan your finances, and there are discussion groups and real-time chats with experts.

Industry Canada's Java calculator at http://strategis.ic.gc.ca/SSG/ca00491e.html will identify the cards that will cost you least in interest and other charges based on the way you have used your credit card recently. All you need to do is to identify your average monthly outstanding balance from recent credit card statements.

IE:Money magazine, at www.iemoney.com, suggests ways to manage your finances and improve your credit rating.

The Canadian Association of Financial Planners, at www.cafp.org, offers consumer information on what to expect from a financial planner, as well as how and why to choose one. A handy search tool lets you pinpoint an adviser close to home.

The Quicken Financial Network, at www.quicken.ca, is the developer of the popular software programs Quicken and QuickTax, which encompass a financial fitness test, expert advice, investment tracking, and other financial help.

The National Foundation for Consumer Credit at www.nfcc.org is a Web site for a network of local nonprofit organizations that provide consumer credit education and services.

Consumer Credit Counselling Services

Objective 4

Evaluate various private and governmental sources that assist consumers with debt problems.

If you are having problems paying your bills and need help, you have several options. You can contact your creditors and try to work out an adjusted repayment plan yourself, or you can check your telephone directory for a nonprofit financial counselling program to get help.

Various provincial authorities provide debt counselling services for families and individuals with financial problems. For example, the Government of Alberta's Web site provides a consumer tip sheet (www2.gov.ab.ca/gs/information/publications).

Credit counsellors are aware that most people who are in debt over their heads are basically honest people who want to clear up their indebtedness. Too often, the problems of such people arise from a lack of planning or a miscalculation of what they earn. Therefore, the counsellor is as concerned with preventing the problems as with solving them. As a result, credit counselling activities are divided into two parts:

[1] Aiding families with serious debt problems by helping them manage their money better and setting up a realistic budget and plan for expenditures.

[2] Helping people prevent debt problems by teaching them the necessity of family budget planning, providing education to people of all ages regarding the pitfalls of unwise credit buying, suggesting techniques for family budgeting, and encouraging credit institutions to provide full information about the costs and terms of credit and to withhold credit from those who cannot afford to repay it.

Universities, military bases, credit unions, and provincial and federal housing authorities sometimes provide nonprofit counselling services. These organizations usually charge little or nothing for such assistance. You can also check with your local bank or consumer protection office to see whether it has a listing of reputable, low-cost financial counselling services.

But what if a debtor suffers from an extreme case of financial woes? Is there any relief? The answer is yes: bankruptcy proceedings.

CONCEPT CHECK 6-4

1. What is a credit counselling service?
2. What are the two major activities of credit counselling services?
3. What options do consumers have for financial counselling?

Declaring Personal Bankruptcy

Janine Leclaire typifies the new face of bankruptcy. A 43-year-old freelance commercial photographer from Victoria, British Columbia, she was never in serious financial trouble until she began incurring big dental costs last year and reached for her credit cards to pay the bills. Since Janine didn't have dental insurance, her debt quickly mounted. It was too much for her to pay off with her $25,000-a-year freelance income. Her solution: Declare personal bankruptcy for the immediate freedom it would bring from creditors' demands.

Ms. Leclaire's move put her in familiar company, demographically speaking. An increasing number of bankruptcy filers are well-educated, middle-class baby boomers with an overwhelming level of credit card debt. These baby boomers make up 44 percent of the adult population, but they account for 59 percent of personal bankruptcies. In that group, the people most likely to be in bankruptcy are between 40 and 44 years old, an age group that is usually assumed to be economically established. Increasingly, too, the bankruptcy debtor is likely to be female.

Unfortunately for some debtors, bankruptcy has become an acceptable tool of credit management. During the last nine years, the personal bankruptcy rate has increased almost 8 percent annually (see Exhibit 6–2).

Objective 5

Assess the choices in declaring personal bankruptcy.

Exhibit 6–2

Canadian Bankruptcies and Proposals 1980-2001

SOURCE: As reproduced on the Bankruptcy Canada Web site at http://www.bankruptcy canada.com/bankstats1. htm and as adapted from Industry Canada statistics. Reproduced with permission of the Minister of Public Works and Government Services, 2002

Visit the Web site

See the Weblinks under Chapter 6 on the online learning centre at www.mcgrawhill.ca/ college/kapoor.

FENDING OFF BANKRUPTCY: CONSOLIDATION LOANS

It may sometimes be possible to avoid declaring bankruptcy. If you are under an excessive debt load and would like to regularize and control your payments, you may be able to obtain a consolidation loan. This is a new loan that is used to discharge a collection of existing debts and it may have different advantages and disadvantages.

The advantages of a consolidation loan are that it will have a single interest rate on the full amount of your selected debts and you may be able to extend the term of the loan beyond that of your initial debts, allowing you to make smaller payments as you repay your loan.

The disadvantages of this type of loan are twofold: cost and term. In general, you will be asked to pay a higher interest rate because you are considered to be a higher risk for the lender. In addition, as you extend the term of the loan you will find that the total of what you pay might be considerably higher than the sum of your debt load.

If you do decide to use a consolidation loan, it is best to limit it to paying off only your highest interest debts. It would be unwise to use this option to pay off any debt that is low– or non–interest-bearing.

BANKRUPTCY AND INSOLVENCY ACT

The decision to declare bankruptcy is a hard one, but each year sees at least 100,000 Canadian consumers choosing this route when all else fails. The *Bankruptcy and Insolvency Act*, a federal law initiated in 1992 and amended in 1997, regulates bankruptcy (a straight declaration of insolvency) and proposal (a wage earner plan) proceedings in Canada. It falls under the responsibility of the Office of the Superintendent of Bankruptcy at Industry Canada. By this Act you are allowed to declare insolvency either through a consumer proposal or through an assignment in bankruptcy.

consumer proposal
A maximum five-year plan for paying creditors all or a portion of a debt owed.

CONSUMER PROPOSALS A **consumer proposal** is a maximum five-year plan for paying creditors all or a portion of the total debt owed. To be eligible for this type of insolvency protection application, you must be insolvent and be less than $75,000 in debt (excluding a mortgage on your principal residence). Initiating the process involves applying to an administrator of consumer proposals, who may be a trustee in bankruptcy or another person appointed to the task. The administrator will provide you with counselling and guidance and will disburse paid funds to your creditors.

Both the court and your creditors must approve a consumer proposal. Once approved, it becomes binding for both you and your creditors. While, in general, this type of agreement will not release you from certain obligations, such as fines, alimony, or co-signer responsibilities, what it will do is protect you from a number of types of harassment or abuse. Your creditors will be restricted from demanding accelerated payments; any pre-existing wage-garnishment arrangements will be annulled; and your employer cannot subject you to any type of disciplinary action resulting from your consumer proposal. When all the conditions of your consumer proposal have been met, you will be issued a "certificate of performance."

The advantage of a consumer proposal is that it will save you from bankruptcy if it is approved. If it is not approved, either by the court or by your creditors, you may then need to seek a trustee in bankruptcy. This person will be a federally licensed individual (generally a chartered accountant) who will carry out the insolvency process.

DID YOU KNOW ?

Declaring bankruptcy does not eliminate all of your obligations. For example, alimony or support payments, debts incurred through fraud, and court costs must still be paid.

BANKRUPTCY Approximately 90 percent of all bankruptcies in Canada are by consumers, rather than businesses. If you are forced to take this choice, the first step will be the assignment of your assets to a licensed trustee. From this time until you are released from your debt by the courts, you will be considered an undischarged bankrupt.

A meeting will then be held among your creditors, who will need to prove their claim against your estate. Your secured creditors, such as your mortgage and your car-loan lenders, will be paid first, as their claims will be against specific assets. After that, your remaining assets will be distributed by specified order with the costs of the bankruptcy administration taking precedence over all other claims. Once this process is complete, the court can grant you a discharge. This document will free you from all claims from creditors, with some exceptions, such as court costs, alimony or support payments, and certain debts incurred through fraud.

PROTECTED ASSETS It is important to realize that not all of your assets will be seized or considered in a bankruptcy proceeding. Some of your property will be protected from creditors by provincial law. Typically, items that you may require to live and earn a living will be exempt from the tally of your assets.

EFFECTS OF BANKRUPTCY ON FUTURE CREDIT

Different people have different experiences in obtaining credit after they file bankruptcy. Some find obtaining credit more difficult. Others find obtaining credit easier because they have relieved themselves of their prior debts or because creditors know they cannot file another bankruptcy case for a period of time. Obtaining credit may be easier for people who file a consumer proposal and repay some of their debts than for people who file a straight bankruptcy and make no effort to repay. The bankruptcy law prohibits your employer from discharging you simply because you have filed a bankruptcy case.

WHAT ARE THE COSTS? According to the Office of the Superintendent of Bankruptcy (strategis.ic.gc.ca/sc_mrksv/bankrupt/engdoc/superint.html), the costs associated with submitting a consumer proposal are a basic fee of $1,500, a filing fee of $100 plus an additional 20 percent of the amount of your assets that are distributed to creditors. In addition, there is a fee of $170 for budget counselling. In the case of bankruptcy, the trustee may charge 100 percent of the first $975 of receipts plus 35 percent of receipts between $975 and $2,000 plus 50 percent of receipts in excess of $2,000. The filing fee is $75, and there is a fee of $170 for budget counselling.

Visit the Web site
See the Post-Test under Chapter 6 on the online learning centre at www.mcgrawhill.ca/college/kapoor.

There are also intangible costs to bankruptcy. For example, obtaining credit in the future may be difficult, since bankruptcy reports are retained in credit bureaus for 7 years. Therefore, you should take the extreme step of declaring personal bankruptcy only when no other options for solving your financial problems exist.

For a quick test of your credit IQ, read the Financial Planning for Life's Situations feature on the next page.

CONCEPT CHECK 6–5

1. What is the purpose of a consumer proposal?
2. What is the difference between a consumer proposal and bankruptcy?
3. How does bankruptcy affect your job and future credit?
4. What are the costs of declaring bankruptcy?

Financial Planning for Life's Situations

WHAT'S YOUR CREDIT IQ?

CREDIT-ABILITY SCORECARD

Test your credit IQ. For each question, circle the letter that best describes your credit habits.

1. I pay my bills when they are due.

   (A) Always (B) Almost always (C) Sometimes

2. After paying my regular bills each month, I have money left from my income.

   (A) Yes (B) Sometimes (C) Never

3. I know how much I owe on my credit cards each month before I receive my bills.

   (A) Yes (B) Sometimes (C) No

4. When I get behind in my payments, I ignore the past-due notices.

   (A) Never or not applicable (B) Sometimes
   (C) Always

5. When I need more money for my regular living expenses, I take out a loan or use my line of credit on my credit card or chequing account.

   (A) Never (B) Sometimes (C) Often

6. If I wanted to see a copy of my credit report, I would contact . . .

   (A) A credit reporting agency (B) My lenders
   (C) My lawyer

7. My credit record shows that I am current on all my loans and charge accounts.

   (A) Yes (B) Don't know (C) No

8. I pay more than the minimum balance due on my credit card accounts.

   (A) Always (B) Sometimes (C) Never

9. To pay off my current credit and charge card accounts, it would take me . . .

   (A) 4 months or less (B) 5 to 8 months
   (C) More than 8 months

10. My consumer loans (including auto loans, but not mortgage payment) and credit card bills each month average more than 20 percent of my take-home pay.

    (A) No (B) Sometimes (C) Always

11. If I had serious credit problems, I would contact my creditors to explain the problem.

    (A) Yes (B) Probably (C) No

12. If I default (don't repay) on a loan, that fact can stay on my credit report for . . .

    (A) 7 years (B) 3 years (C) 1 year

Assign a score of 3 for each "A" answer, 2 for each "B" answer, and 1 for each "C" answer. Total the score.

If you scored:

31–36 You have an excellent knowledge of credit and its responsible use.

24–30 You should take steps toward a better understanding of your personal finances and of the credit process.

18–23 You probably need to take a serious look at your personal finances; consider controlling your spending and staying on a tight budget.

12–17 You may be heading for serious trouble; consider seeking help, such as nonprofit consumer credit counselling services.

SOURCE: *How to Be Credit Smart*, AFSA Education Foundation, 1997.

SUMMARY OF OBJECTIVES

Objective 1
Analyze the major sources of consumer credit.
The major sources of consumer credit are banks, trust companies, credit unions, finance companies, life insurance companies, and family and friends. Each of these sources has unique advantages and disadvantages.

Parents or family members are often the source of the least expensive loans. They may charge you only the interest they would have earned had they not made the loan. Such loans, however, can complicate family relationships.

Objective 2
Determine the cost of credit by calculating interest using various interest formulas.
Compare the finance charge and the annual percentage rate (APR) as you shop for credit.

For a borrower, the most favourable method of calculating the cost of open-end credit is the adjusted balance method. In this period, creditors add finance charges after subtracting payments made during the billing period.

Objective 3
Develop a plan to manage your debts.
Debt has serious consequences if a proper plan for managing it is not implemented.

Most experts agree that emotional problems, the use of money to punish, the expectation of instant comfort, keeping up with the Joneses, overindulgence of children, misunderstanding or lack of communication among family members, and the amount of finance charges are common reasons for indebtedness.

Objective 4
Evaluate various private and governmental sources that assist consumers with debt problems.
If you cannot meet your obligations, contact your creditors immediately. Before signing up with a debt consolidation company, investigate it thoroughly. Better yet, contact a credit counselling service or other debt counselling organization.

Such organizations help people manage their money better by setting up a realistic budget and planning for expenditures. These organizations also help people prevent debt problems by teaching them the necessity of family budget planning and providing education to people of all ages.

Objective 5
Assess the choices in declaring personal bankruptcy.
A debtor's last resort is to declare bankruptcy. Consider the financial and other costs of bankruptcy before taking this extreme step. A debtor can declare insolvency either through a consumer proposal or through an assignment in bankruptcy.

Some people find obtaining credit more difficult after filing bankruptcy. Others find obtaining credit easier because they have relieved themselves of their prior debts or because creditors know they cannot file another bankruptcy case for a period of time.

KEY TERMS

adjusted balance method 162
annual percentage rate (APR) 158
average daily balance method 162

consumer proposal 170
credit insurance 164
declining balance method 162

finance charge 158
previous balance method 162

KEY FORMULAS

Page	Topic	Formula
159	Calculating annual percentage rate (APR)	$APR = \dfrac{2 \times \text{Number of payment periods in one year} \times \text{Dollar cost of credit}}{\text{Loan amount (Total number of payments to pay off the loan} + 1)}$ $= \dfrac{2 \times n \times I}{P(N+1)}$ *Example:* P = Principal borrowed, \$100; n = number of payments in one year, 1; I = Dollar cost of credit, \$8 $APR = \dfrac{2 \times 1 \times \$8}{\$100(1+1)} = \dfrac{\$192}{\$200} = 0.08$, or 8 percent For 12 equal monthly payments, $APR = \dfrac{2 \times 12 \times \$8}{\$100(12+1)} = \dfrac{\$192}{\$1,300} = 0.1476$, or 14.76 percent

Page	Topic	Formula
161	Calculating simple interest	$\dfrac{\text{Interest}}{\text{(in dollars)}} = $ Principal borrowed $\times$ Interest rate $\times$ Length of loan in years

$$I = P \times r \times T$$

Example:

From above: $P = \$100; r = 0.08; T = 1$

$$I = \$100 \times 0.08 \times 1 = \$8$$

| 177 | Calculating compound interest | Total future value of a loan $=$ Principal $(1 + \text{Rate of interest})^{\text{Time in years}}$ |

$$F = P(1 + r)^T$$

Example:

From above: $P = \$100; r = 0.08; T = 1$

$$F = \$100(1 + 0.08)^1 = \$100(1.08) = \$108$$

| 180 | Calculating total monthly payment (principal + interest) on a conventional loan | $\dfrac{\text{Monthly}}{\text{payment}} = \dfrac{\text{Loan} \times \text{Monthly interest rate} \times (1 + \text{Monthly interest rate})^{\text{Time in months}}}{(1 + \text{Monthly interest rate})^{\text{Time in months}} - 1}$ |

$$MP = P \times \frac{i \times (1 + i)^T}{(1 + i)^T - 1}$$

Example:

From above: $P = \$100; i = 0.08$

In a 12-month loan,

$$MP = \frac{\$100 \times 0.08(1 + 0.08)^{12}}{(1 + 0.08)^{12} - 1} = \frac{\$100 \times 0.08/12 \times (1 + 0.0066)^{12}}{(+ 0.0066)^{12} - 1} = \$8.70$$

FINANCIAL PLANNING PROBLEMS

1. *Calculating the Finance Charge on a Loan.* Dave borrowed $500 for one year and paid $50 in interest. The bank charged him a $5 service charge. What is the finance charge on this loan? (Obj. 2)

2. *Calculating the Annual Percentage Rate.* In problem 1, Dave borrowed $500 on January 1, 2001, and paid it all back at once on December 31, 2001. What was the APR? (Obj. 2)

3. *Calculating the Annual Percentage Rate.* If Dave paid the $500 in 12 equal monthly payments, what was the APR? (Obj. 2)

4. *Comparing the Costs of Credit Cards.* Bobby is trying to decide between two credit cards. One has no annual fee and an 18-percent interest rate, and the other has a $40-annual fee and an 8.9-percent interest rate. Should he take the card that's free or the one that costs $40? (Obj. 2)

5. *Calculating Cash Advance Fee and the Dollar Amount of Interest.* Sidney took a $200 cash advance by using cheques linked to her credit card account. The bank charges a 2-percent cash advance fee on the amount borrowed and offers no grace period on cash advances. Sidney paid the balance in full when the bill arrived. What was the cash advance fee? What was the interest for one month at an 18-percent APR? What was the total amount she paid? What if she had made the purchase with her credit card (assuming no overcredit limit) and paid off the bill in full promptly? (Obj. 2)

6. *Comparing the Cost of Credit during Inflationary Periods.* Dorothy lacks cash to pay for a $600-dishwasher. She could buy it from the store on credit by making 12 monthly payments of $52.74. The total cost would then be $632.88. Instead, Dorothy decides to deposit $50 a month in the bank until she has saved enough money to pay cash for the dishwasher. One year later, she has saved $642—$600 in deposits plus interest. When she goes back to the store, she finds the dishwasher now costs $660. Its price has gone up 10 percent, the current rate of inflation. Was postponing her purchase a good trade-off for Dorothy? (Obj. 2)

7. *Comparing Costs of Credit Using Three Calculation Methods.* You have been pricing a compact disc player in several stores. Three stores have the identical price of $300. Each store charges 18 percent APR, has a 30-day grace period, and sends out bills on the first of the month. On further investigation, you find that store A calculates the finance charge by using the average daily balance method, store B uses the adjusted balance method, and store C uses the previous balance method. Assume you

purchased the disc player on May 5 and made a $100 payment on June 15. What will the finance charge be if you made your purchase from store A? from store B? from store C? (Obj. 2)

8. *Determining Interest Cost Using the Simple Interest Formula.* What are the interest cost and the total amount due on a six-month loan of $1,500 at 13.2-percent simple annual interest? (Obj. 2)

FINANCIAL PLANNING ACTIVITIES

1. *Determining Criteria If a Loan Is Needed.* Survey friends and relatives to find out what criteria they have used to determine the need for credit. (Obj. 1)

2. *Comparing Costs of Loans from Various Lenders.* Prepare a list of sources of inexpensive loans, medium-priced loans, and expensive loans in your area. What are the trade-offs in obtaining a loan from an "easy" lender? (Obj. 1)

3. *Using the Internet to Obtain Information about the Costs of Credit.* As pointed out at the beginning of this chapter, credit costs money; therefore, you must conduct a cost/benefit analysis before making any major purchase. While most people consider credit costs, others simply ignore them and eventually find themselves in financial difficulties. To help consumers avoid this problem, each of the following organizations provides information on a Web site:

   - The Quicken Financial Network, at www.quicken.ca, helps consumers save money when purchasing, financing, or refinancing by keeping them up to date on news, views, and rates.
   - CCC Consumer Credit Counselling, at www.iamdebtfree.com, offers financial counselling and debt consolidation services.
   - Canoe Webfin, at www.webfin.com, brings you the latest rates for mortgages, credit cards, auto loans, home equity loans, and personal loans, as well as a slew of financial advice.

   Choose one of the above organizations and visit its Web site. Then, prepare a report that summarizes the information the organization provides. Finally, decide how this information could help you better manage your credit and its costs. (Obj. 2)

5. *Choosing between the Features and Costs of a Loan.* When you choose financing, what are the trade-offs between the features you prefer (term, size of payments, fixed or variable interest, or payment plan) and the cost of your loan? (Obj. 2)

6. *Calculating the Cost of Credit Using Two APR Formulas.* How are the simple interest and simple interest on the declining balance, formulas used in determining the cost of credit? (Obj. 2)

7. *Handling Harassment from Debt Collection Agencies.* Your friend is drowning in a sea of overdue bills and is being harassed by a debt collection agency. Prepare a list of the steps your friend should take if the harassment continues. (Obj. 3)

8. *Seeking Assistance from Consumer Credit Counselling Services.* Visit a local office of a credit counselling service. What assistance can debtors obtain from this office? What is the cost of this assistance, if any? (Obj. 4)

9. *Assessing the Choices in Declaring Personal Bankruptcy.* What factors would you consider in assessing the choices in declaring personal bankruptcy? Why should personal bankruptcy be the choice of last resort? (Obj. 4)

LIFE SITUATION CASE

Financing Sophie's Geo Metro

After shopping around, Sophie Aman decided on the car of her choice, a used Geo Metro. The dealer quoted her a total price of $8,000. Sophie decided to use $2,000 of her savings as a down payment and borrow $6,000. The salesperson wrote this information on a sales contract that Sophie took with her when she set out to find financing.

When Sophie applied for a loan, she discussed loan terms with the bank lending officer. The officer told her that the bank's policy was to lend only 80 percent of the total price of a used car. Sophie showed the officer her copy of the sales contract, indicating that she had agreed to make a $2,000, or 25 percent, down payment on the $8,000 car, so this requirement caused her no problem. Although the bank was willing to make 48-month loans at an annual percentage rate of 15 percent on used cars, Sophie chose a 36-month repayment schedule. She believed she could afford the higher payments, and she knew she would not have to pay as much interest if she paid off the loan at a faster rate. The bank lending officer provided Sophie with a copy of the statement shown here.

Statement (Loans)

Annual Percentage Rate The cost of your credit as a yearly rate.	Finance Charge The dollar amount the credit will cost you.	Amount Financed The amount of credit provided to you or on your behalf.	Total of Payments 36 The amount you will have paid after you have made all payments as scheduled.
15%	$1,487.64	$6,000.00	$7,487.64

You have the right to receive at this time an itemization of the Amount Financed.

☒ I want an itemization.   ☐ I do not want an itemization.

Your payment schedule will be:

Number of Payments	Amount of Payments	When Payments Are Due
36	$207.99	1st of each month

Sophie decided to compare the APR she had been offered with the APR offered by another bank, but the 20 percent APR of the second bank (bank B) was more expensive than the 15 percent APR of the first bank (bank A). Here is her comparison of the two loans:

	Bank A 15% APR	Bank B 20% APR
Amount financed	$6,000.00	$6,000.00
Finance charge	1,487.64	2,027.28
Total of payments	7,487.64	8,027.28
Monthly payments	207.99	222.98

The 5 percent difference in the APRs of the two banks meant Sophie would have to pay $15 extra every month if she got her loan from the second bank. Of course, she got the loan from the first bank.

Questions

1. What is perhaps the most important item shown on the statement? Why?
2. What is included in the finance charge?
3. What amount will Sophie receive from the bank?
4. Should Sophie borrow from bank A or bank B? Why?

CREATING A FINANCIAL PLAN

Comparing Credit Sources and Costs

Credit is available from many sources. Becoming aware of the differences among financial institutions related to borrowing costs and other factors while wisely managing your debt will help you avoid financial difficulties.

Web Sites for Comparing Credit Costs

- The Quicken Financial Network, at **www.quicken.ca**, provides the latest rates and has analytical tools to help you assess your financial decisions.
- Canoe Webfin, at **www.webfin.com**, has the latest rates, exhaustive financial advice, and various comparative capacities.

- Industry Canada, at **http://strategis.ic.gc.ca,** is a federal government site that gives both topical and historical facts to help you understand the various applicable laws as well as the variety of options you may have when choosing where to apply for credit.
- IE:Money magazine, at **www.iemoney.com**, is a personal finance magazine that suggests ways to manage your finances and improve your credit rating. Check out its archived articles for important advice about credit, debt, and finances.

(Note: Addresses and content of Web sites change, and new sites are created daily. Use search engines to update and locate Web sites for your current financial planning needs.)

CONTINUOUS CASE FOR PART 2 (A)

USING FINANCIAL SERVICES: SAVINGS, CHEQUING, AND CREDIT

Life Situation
Recently married couple: Pamela, 26; Isaac, 28; renting an apartment

Financial Goals

- Develop a savings fund for emergencies and long-term financial security
- Reduce monthly debt payments

Financial Data

Monthly income	$ 5,840
Living expenses	3,900
Assets	13,500
Liabilities	7,800
Emergency Fund	1,000

Pamela Wall recently married Isaac Mortimer. Pamela continues to work as a sales representative for a clothing manufacturer, and her monthly income has averaged $2,840 a month over the past year. Isaac is employed as a computer programmer and earns $3,000 a month.

The Mortimers' combined monthly income, $5,840, allows them to enjoy a comfortable lifestyle. Yet, they have been unable to save any money for emergencies. According to Isaac, "It's hard to believe, but we don't even have a savings account because we spend everything we make each month." Every month, they deposit each of their paycheques in separate chequing accounts. Isaac pays the rent and makes the car payment. Pamela buys the groceries and pays the monthly utilities. They use the money left over to purchase new clothes and the other "necessities" of life that they both want. To make matters worse, they often resort to using their seven credit cards for everyday purchases when they both run out of money at the end of the month. As a result, they have credit card debts totalling $2,800.

Questions

1. What is the minimum amount that the Mortimers should have in an emergency fund?
2. What should the Mortimers do to increase the amount of money they set aside for emergencies?
3. Pamela and Isaac have separate chequing accounts. Do you think they should give up their separate chequing accounts and open a joint chequing account?
4. If you were Pamela or Isaac, how would you go about paying off your credit card debts and other liabilities?
5. What would you recommend to the Mortimers regarding their future use of credit?

Pure Discount Loan

A *pure discount loan* is the simplest form of a loan. This loan allows you to borrow an amount of money today, which you must pay back in the future in a single lump sum including interest.

Example 1 Suppose you are expecting to receive $1,051.16 at the end of the year but require funds today. If a lender will charge you a 5-percent annual interest rate compounded monthly, the amount of money you could borrow today would be equal to the present value of $1,051.16 at the effective rate (see Appendix A for more details).

FORMULA

$$P = F \times \frac{1}{(1 + i)^n}$$

$$= 1,051.16 \frac{1}{(1 + \frac{.05}{12})^{1 \times 12}}$$

$$= 1,051.16 [.9513]$$

$$= 1,000$$

CALCULATOR

2ND	CLRTVM
1051.16	FV
5	I/Y
1	N
CPT	PV

$$= 1,000$$

Therefore, you are paying $51.16 in interest after one year. Using the APR formula, the APR is equal to 5.12 percent, since the interest is compounded monthly:

$$P = \frac{2 \times n \times I}{P(n+1)}$$

$$= \frac{2 \times 1 \times \$51.16}{\$1,000(1+1)}$$

$$= \frac{\$102.32}{\$2,000}$$

$$= .0512 \text{ or } 5.12\%$$

Bank Discount Method

When the *bank discount rate* method is used, interest is calculated on the amount to be paid back and you receive the difference between the amount to be paid back and the interest amount. For instance, if your relative lends you $1,000 less $50 (interest at 5 percent), you receive $950.

Example 1 Using the APR formula, you find the true interest rate, or the annual percentage rate, is 5.263 percent, not the stated 5 percent:

$$\text{APR} = \frac{2 \times n \times I}{P(N + 1)} = \frac{2 \times 1 \times \$50}{\$950(1 + 1)} = \frac{\$100}{\$1,900} = 0.05263, \text{ or } 5.263 \text{ percent}$$

Compound Interest

Unlike simple interest, *compound interest* is the interest paid on the original principal *plus* the accumulated interest. With interest compounding, the greater the number of periods for which interest is calculated, the more rapidly the amount of interest on interest and interest on principal builds.

Annual compounding means there is only *one* period annually for the calculation of interest. With such compounding, interest charges on a *one-year* loan are identical whether they are figured on a simple interest basis or on an annual compound basis. However, a new interest formula, based on the simple interest formula, must be used if there is annual compounding for two or more years or compounding with more than one compound period per year.

Compound Formula

A compact formula that describes compound interest calculations is

$$F = P(1 + r)^T$$

where

F = Total future repayment value of a loan (principal *plus* total accumulated or compound interest)

P = Principal

r = Rate of interest per year, or annual interest rate

T = Time in years

Before the compound interest formula can be used for *multiple*-period compounding, two important adjustments must be made.

First, adjust the *annual* interest rate (r) to reflect the number of compounding periods per year. For example, a 5-percent annual rate of interest, compounded half-yearly, works out to 2.5 percent (5 percent divided by 2) per half-year.

Second, adjust the time factor (T), which is measured in years, to reflect the *total* number of compounding periods. For example, your loan for one year compounded half-yearly works out to two compound periods (1 year multiplied by 2 compounding periods per year) over the length of the loan.

Example 2 Suppose your relative compounds interest semi-annually and you make two payments, six months apart. Using the compound interest formula and financial calculator, here is the annual percentage rate:

FORMULA

$$F = P(1 + r)T$$
$$F = \$1,000(1 + 0.05)^{1 \times 2}$$
$$= \$1,000(1 + 0.025)^2$$
$$= \$1,000(1.050625)$$
$$= \$1,050.625$$

CALCULATOR

2ND	CLRTVM
2	N
2.5	I/Y
1000	PV
CPT	FV

$$= \$1,050.625$$

That is, you are paying $50.63 in interest for a one-year, $1,000 loan. Now, using the APR formula, you find the APR is 6.75 percent:

$$\text{APR} = \frac{2 \times n \times I}{P(N + 1)}$$

$$= \frac{2 \times 2 \times \$50.63}{\$1,000(2 + 1)}$$

$$= \frac{\$202.52}{\$3,000}$$

$$= 0.0675, \text{ or } 6.75 \text{ percent}$$

If your relative chose to compound interest daily (365 compounding periods per year), the solution to this problem would be quite complicated. A calculator or a compound interest table can make interest calculations more manageable. See Appendix A for compound interest tables and the financial calculator.

The following table summarizes the effects on the APR when the interest on a one-year, $1,000 loan is calculated using the simple interest, declining balance, pure discount loan, bank discount, and compound interest methods:

Borrowed	Amount Interest	Stated Interest	Total Payments	Number of APR	Method
Simple interest*	$1,000	5%	$50.00	1	5.00%
Declining balance*	1,000	5	37.50	2	5.00
Pure discount loan*	1,000	5	51.16	1	5.12
Bank discount	1,000(–50)	5	50.00	1	5.26
Compound interest	1,000	5	50.63	2	6.75

*Discussed in the chapter.

The methods of calculating interest described here are just some of the more common methods in use. As you have seen, the method of interest calculation can substantially affect the amount of interest paid, and you should be aware not only of the stated or nominal interest rates but also of how the stated rates are used in calculating total interest charges. Furthermore, the simple interest, pure discount loan and bank discount methods assume you have the full use of the principal over the length of the loan. Rather than making periodic payments, you are obligated to repay the loan in one or two lump sums. Most borrowers, however, are unable to repay loans, especially home loans (mortgages) and auto loans, in one or two lump-sum payments. They must make equal periodic payments to pay off a loan and interest over the length of the loan. This concept is known as amortization.

Amortization

Amortization is the process of gradually reducing a debt through scheduled periodic payments. For example, if a five-year auto loan is repaid in 60 equal monthly payments, each of these payments is applied to reduce the principal and pay interest on the total amount borrowed. Over the initial years of the loan, most of the monthly payment is used to pay interest; the rest reduces the principal. As the loan approaches maturity, more of the monthly payment is used to pay off the principal than to pay interest.

The following formula can be used to calculate the monthly payment (principal and interest) on an installment loan or a conventional mortgage loan:

$$\text{Monthly payment} = \text{Loan} \times \frac{\text{Monthly interest rate} \times (1 + \text{Monthly interest rate})^{T \times 12}}{(1 + \text{Monthly interest rate})^{T \times 12} - 1}$$

Because a monthly mortgage payment is required, both the annual interest rate and the total length of the loan must be adjusted by 12 (months).

Example 3 On a 30-year mortgage loan for $60,000 at a 12-percent annual interest rate, what is the monthly payment (MP)? Substitute the numbers into the formula:

$$MP = \$60,000 \times \frac{\frac{0.12}{12} \times \left(1 + \frac{0.12}{12}\right)^{30 \times 12}}{\left(1 + \frac{0.12}{12}\right)^{30 \times 12} - 1}$$

$$= \$60,000 \times \frac{0.01 \times (1 + 0.01)^{360}}{(1 + 0.01)^{360} - 1}$$

$$= \$60,000 \times \frac{0.01 \times 35.9496}{35.9496 - 1}$$

$$= \$60,000 \times \frac{0.359496}{34.9496}$$

$$= \$60,000 \times 0.010286$$

$$= \$617.17$$

Use of Tables

Finding the monthly payment on a mortgage or consumer instalment loan may become rather complicated when the problem is solved manually. Fortunately, the use of the Present Value of an Annuity tables in Appendix A or a financial calculator can simplify the task.

USE OF TABLES (found in Appendix A)

$60,000 = PMT (PVA 12%, 30 years) × 12 (because they are monthly payments)
$60,000 = PMT (8.055) × 12
$60,000/96.66 = PMT

Therefore, the monthly payment is equal to $620.73
This value is fairly close to the $617.17 found by using the formula.

USE OF A FINANCIAL CALCULATOR

2ND		CLRTVM
(30 × 12) = 360		N
(12 / 12) = 1		I/Y
$60,000		PV
CPT		PMT

Therefore, your monthly payments are—$617.16. (The value is negative because the BAII Plus considers a payment as an outflow of money.)

Note: Always remember to clear the calculator before performing a new calculation: 2ND CLRTVM.

7 The Finances of Housing

Two Can Buy More Cheaply Than One

During a time when mortgage rates were fairly high, Ana Chen and her sister, Yvonne, were unable to buy the house they wanted. Their parents had given them $4,000 for a down payment, but that was not enough for the type of house they wanted.

After finishing college, Ana rented an apartment for seven years. During that time, she was able to save $8,000 for a down payment on a home. She now earns enough money to afford the monthly costs of a home.

During the past eight months, mortgage rates in their area of the country have declined 1.5 percentage points. Ana and Yvonne have decided to combine their resources to purchase a home. The *co-ownership* arrangement allows them to buy a home valued at $15,000 more than they could have afforded a year ago.

However, Ana and Yvonne should ask themselves a few questions before buying the house. What happens to the house if one of them marries or accepts a job transfer to another city? What if one of them can no longer meet the financial requirements of the home? How will they share maintenance responsibilities and costs?

Ana and Yvonne need to answer these and other questions before entering a co-ownership housing arrangement.

QUESTIONS

1 What factors affect a person's ability to buy a house?

2 What are common sources for a down payment? Why should home buyers not use all of their savings to make the down payment on a home?

3 What problems could arise in a co-ownership housing arrangement?

4 Locate Web sites that provide housing information that would be of value to Ana and Yvonne during their home-buying activities.

LEARNING OBJECTIVES

1 Evaluate available housing alternatives.

2 Analyze the costs and benefits associated with renting.

3 Implement the home-buying process.

4 Calculate the costs associated with purchasing a home.

5 Develop a strategy for selling a home.

Evaluating Housing Alternatives

As you walk around various neighbourhoods, you are likely to see a variety of housing types. When you assess housing alternatives, you need to identify the factors that will influence your choice.

YOUR LIFESTYLE AND YOUR CHOICE OF HOUSING

While the concept of lifestyle—how you spend your time and money—may seem intangible, it materializes in consumer purchases. Every buying decision is a statement about your lifestyle. Your lifestyle, needs, desires, and attitudes are reflected in your choice of a place to live. For example, some people want a kitchen large enough for family gatherings. Career-oriented people may want a lavish bathroom or a home spa where they can escape the pressures of work. As you select housing, you might consider the alternatives in Exhibit 7–1.

While personal preferences are the foundation of a housing decision, financial factors may modify the final choice. Traditional financial guidelines suggest that "you should spend no more than 25 or 30 percent of your take-home pay on housing" or "your home should cost about 2½ times your annual income." While changes in our economy and our society no longer make these guidelines completely valid, you need some sort of financial guideline to determine the amount to spend on housing. A budget and other financial records discussed in Chapter 2 can help you evaluate your income, living costs, and other financial obligations to determine an appropriate amount for your housing expenses.

OPPORTUNITY COSTS OF HOUSING CHOICES

Although the selection of housing is usually based on life situations and financial factors, you should also consider what you might have to give up. While the opportunity costs of your housing decision will vary, some common trade-offs include:

- The interest earnings lost on the money used for a down payment on a home or the security deposit for an apartment.
- The time and cost of commuting to work when you live in an area that offers less expensive housing or more living space.

Objective 1

Evaluate available housing alternatives.

Visit the Web site

See the Pre-Test under Chapter 7 on the online learning centre at www.mcgrawhill.ca/ college/kapoor.

Exhibit 7–1

Possible Housing for Different Life Situations

Life Situation	Possible Housing Types
Young single	Rental housing requires limited maintenance activities and offers mobility in the event of a job transfer Purchase a home or a condominium for financial benefits
Single parent	Rental housing provides a suitable environment for children and some degree of home security Purchase low-maintenance housing that meets the financial and social needs of family members
Young couple, no children	Rental housing offers convenience and flexibility of lifestyle Purchase housing for financial benefits and to build long-term financial security
Couple, young children	Rental housing can provide appropriate facilities for children in a family-oriented area Purchase a home to meet financial and other family needs
Couple, children no longer at home	Rental housing offers convenience and flexibility for changing needs and financial situations Purchase housing that requires minimal maintenance and meets lifestyle needs
Retired person	Rental housing can meet financial, social, and physical needs Purchase housing that requires minimal maintenance, offers convenience, and provides needed services

- The loss of equity growth when you rent a city apartment to be close to your work.
- The time and money you spend when you repair and improve a lower-priced home.
- The time and effort involved when you have a home built to your personal specifications.

Like every other financial choice, a housing decision requires consideration of what you give up in time, effort, and money.

RENTING VERSUS BUYING HOUSING

The choice between renting and buying your residence should be analyzed on the basis of lifestyle and financial factors. Exhibit 7–2 can help you assess renting and buying alternatives. Mobility is a primary motivator of renters, while buyers usually want permanence.

Exhibit 7–2

Evaluating Housing Alternatives

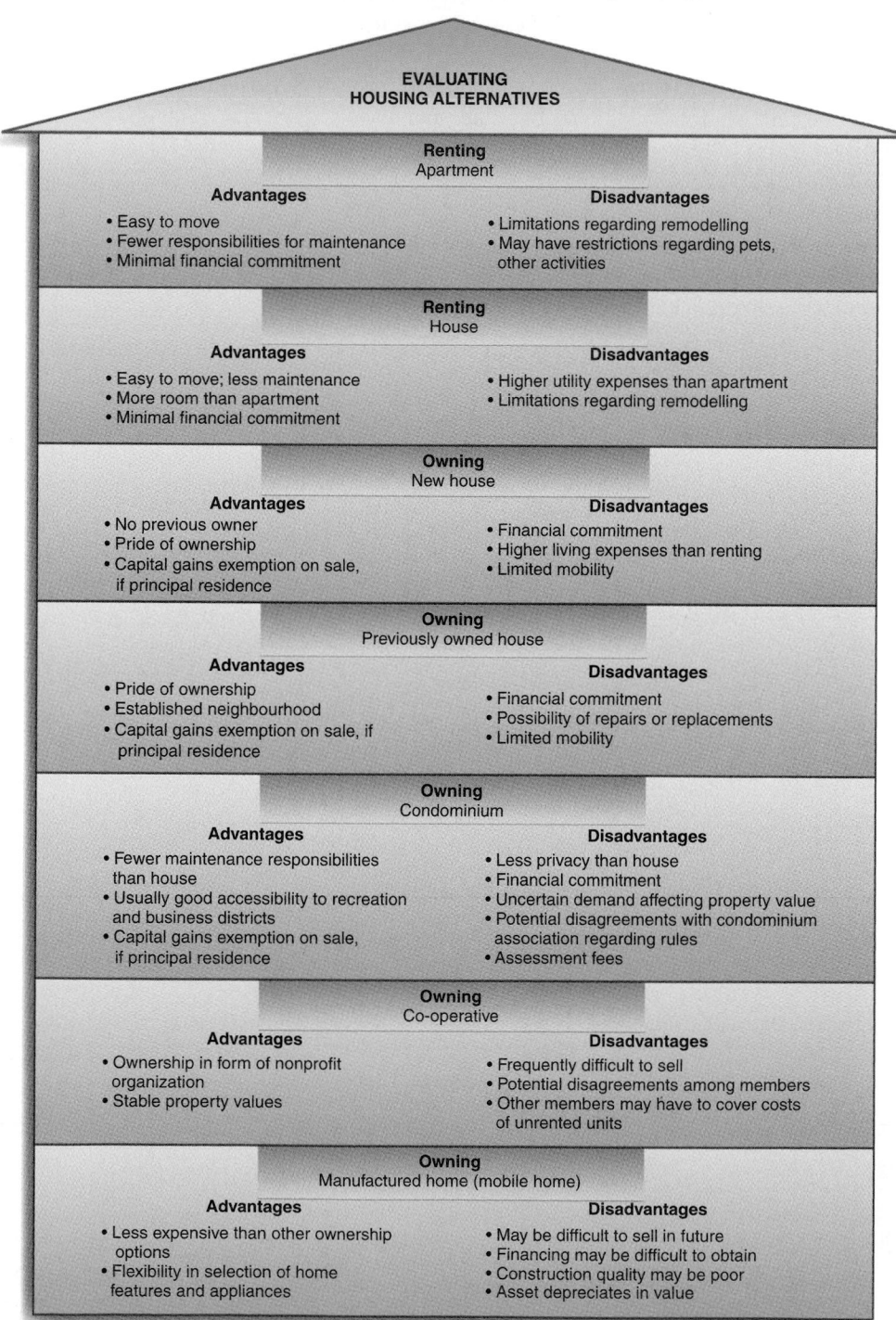

EVALUATING HOUSING ALTERNATIVES

Renting
Apartment

Advantages	Disadvantages
• Easy to move • Fewer responsibilities for maintenance • Minimal financial commitment	• Limitations regarding remodelling • May have restrictions regarding pets, other activities

Renting
House

Advantages	Disadvantages
• Easy to move; less maintenance • More room than apartment • Minimal financial commitment	• Higher utility expenses than apartment • Limitations regarding remodelling

Owning
New house

Advantages	Disadvantages
• No previous owner • Pride of ownership • Capital gains exemption on sale, if principal residence	• Financial commitment • Higher living expenses than renting • Limited mobility

Owning
Previously owned house

Advantages	Disadvantages
• Pride of ownership • Established neighbourhood • Capital gains exemption on sale, if principal residence	• Financial commitment • Possibility of repairs or replacements • Limited mobility

Owning
Condominium

Advantages	Disadvantages
• Fewer maintenance responsibilities than house • Usually good accessibility to recreation and business districts • Capital gains exemption on sale, if principal residence	• Less privacy than house • Financial commitment • Uncertain demand affecting property value • Potential disagreements with condominium association regarding rules • Assessment fees

Owning
Co-operative

Advantages	Disadvantages
• Ownership in form of nonprofit organization • Stable property values	• Frequently difficult to sell • Potential disagreements among members • Other members may have to cover costs of unrented units

Owning
Manufactured home (mobile home)

Advantages	Disadvantages
• Less expensive than other ownership options • Flexibility in selection of home features and appliances	• May be difficult to sell in future • Financing may be difficult to obtain • Construction quality may be poor • Asset depreciates in value

Financial Planning Calculations

RENTING VERSUS BUYING YOUR PLACE OF RESIDENCE

Comparing the costs of renting and buying involves consideration of a variety of factors. The following framework and example provides a basis for assessing these two housing alternatives. The apartment in the example has a monthly rent of $800, and the home costs $85,000. A 29-percent tax rate is assumed.

Although the numbers in this example favour renting, remember that in any financial decision calculations provide only part of the answer. You should also consider your needs and values and assess the opportunity costs associated with renting and buying.

	Example	Your Figures
Rental Costs		
Annual rent payments	$ 9,600	$ _____
Renter's insurance	170	_____
Total annual cost of renting	$ 9,770	_____
Buying Costs		
Annual mortgage payments	$10,500	_____
Property taxes (annual costs)	2,000	_____
Homeowner's insurance (annual premium)	400	_____
Estimated maintenance and repairs (1%)	850	_____
After-tax interest lost on down payment and closing costs	1,030	_____
Less (financial benefits of home ownership):		
Growth in equity	2,264	− _____
Estimated annual appreciation (3%)*	2,550	− _____
Total annual cost of buying	$ 9,966	_____

*This is a nationwide average; actual appreciation of property will vary by geographic area and economic conditions.

As you can see above in the Financial Planning Calculations feature the choice between renting and buying usually is not clear-cut. In general, renting is less costly in the short run, but home ownership usually has long-term financial advantages.

HOUSING INFORMATION SOURCES

As with other consumer purchases, housing information is available. Start your data search with basic resources, such as this book and books available in libraries. Consult the real estate section of your newspaper for articles about renting, buying, financing, remodelling, and other housing topics. Other helpful information sources are friends, real estate agents, and government agencies.

The World Wide Web has become an important source of housing information. In addition to providing home-buying tips and mortgage rates, online sites can be used to access available housing in an area (see the Financial Planning for Life's Situations feature on page 187).

CONCEPT CHECK 7–1

1. How does a person's employment and household situation influence the selection of housing?
2. What are some common opportunity costs associated with the selection of housing?

Renting

Objective 2

Analyze the costs and benefits associated with renting.

Are you interested in a "2-bd garden apt, a/c, crptg, mod bath, lndry"? Not sure? Translated, this means a two-bedroom garden apartment (at or below ground level) with air conditioning, carpeting, a modern bath, and laundry facilities.

At some point in your life, you are likely to rent your place of residence. You may rent when you are first on your own or later in life when you want to avoid the activities required to maintain your own home.

As a tenant, you pay for the right to live in a residence owned by someone else. Exhibit 7–3 presents the activities involved in finding and living in a rental unit.

SELECTING A RENTAL UNIT

An apartment is the most common type of rental housing. Apartments range from modern, luxury units with extensive recreational facilities to simple one- and two-bedroom units in quiet neighbourhoods.

If you need more room, you should consider renting a house. The increased space will cost more, and you will probably have some responsibility for maintaining the property. If you need less space, you may rent a room in a private house.

The main sources of information on available rental units are newspaper ads, real estate and rental offices, and people you know. When comparing rental units, consider the factors presented in Exhibit 7–4 on page 188.

ADVANTAGES OF RENTING

The three main advantages of renting are mobility, fewer responsibilities, and lower initial costs.

Exhibit 7–3   Housing Rental Activities

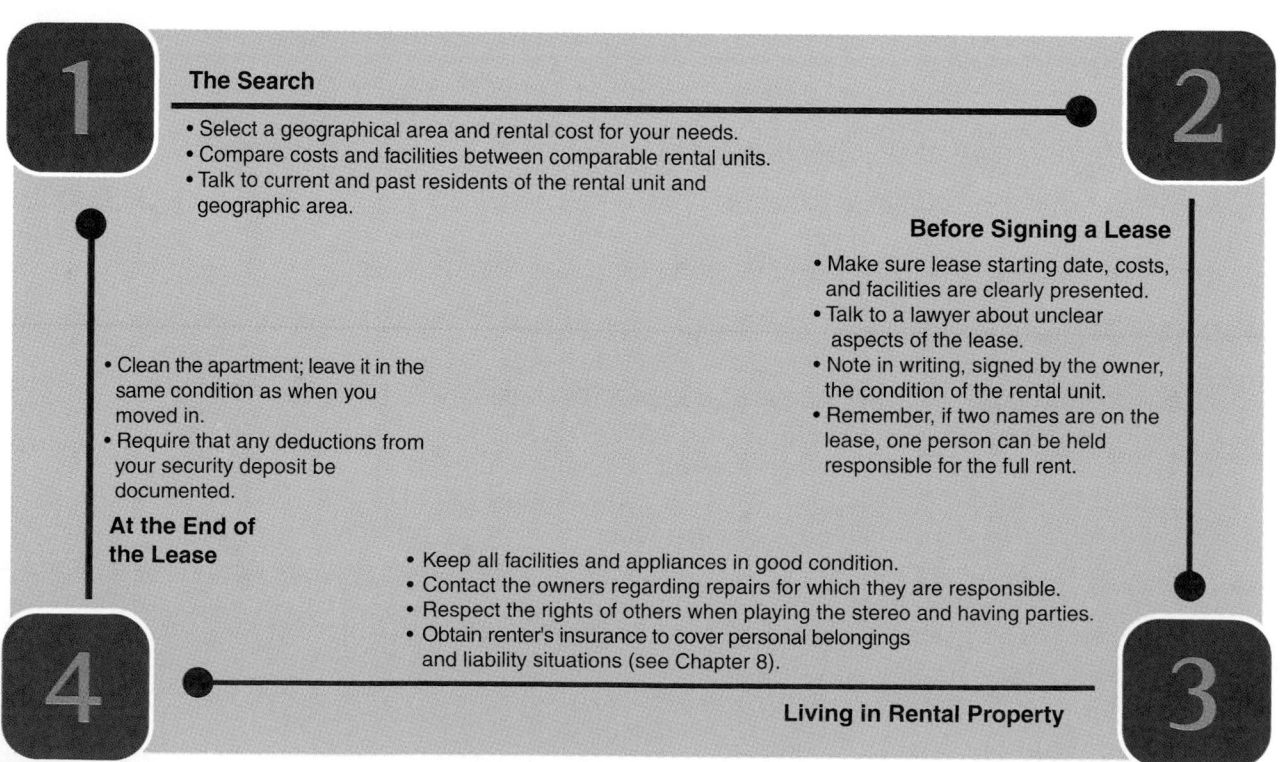

1 The Search
- Select a geographical area and rental cost for your needs.
- Compare costs and facilities between comparable rental units.
- Talk to current and past residents of the rental unit and geographic area.

2 Before Signing a Lease
- Make sure lease starting date, costs, and facilities are clearly presented.
- Talk to a lawyer about unclear aspects of the lease.
- Note in writing, signed by the owner, the condition of the rental unit.
- Remember, if two names are on the lease, one person can be held responsible for the full rent.

4 At the End of the Lease
- Clean the apartment; leave it in the same condition as when you moved in.
- Require that any deductions from your security deposit be documented.

3 Living in Rental Property
- Keep all facilities and appliances in good condition.
- Contact the owners regarding repairs for which they are responsible.
- Respect the rights of others when playing the stereo and having parties.
- Obtain renter's insurance to cover personal belongings and liability situations (see Chapter 8).

USING THE INTERNET FOR HOME BUYING

Instead of getting in the car on Sunday afternoon to go house hunting, home buyers are going online. The Web offers many home-buying services, including the following:

- The Canada Mortgage and Housing Corporation (CMHC) Web site (www.cmhc-schl.gc.ca) is one of the premier online resources for Canadians investigating housing. It offers a variety of housing-related information services, which include statistics, research, and a library of documents. Of particular interest is *The Newcomer's Guide to Canadian Housing*, a guide for new immigrants that is easy to understand and an extensive source of information for all types of housing.
- The Canoe Webfin (www.webfin.com) site offers extensive information on all aspects of personal finance in Canada. Also available are updated mortgage rates. Cannex Canada, at www.cannex.com/canada/english, has daily updated rates offered by banks, trust companies, life insurance companies,

mutual fund companies, and credit unions in Canada. The institutions themselves have online access to Cannex and are responsible for entering, updating, and maintaining their own interest rate and product information.
- Within the Personal Financial Tools section of www.moneycanada.com you will find a Home listing that provides several resources for calculating mortgage payments, the effects of lump-sum payments, and a number of other considerations. You can apply online for a mortgage at www.cibc.com/products/mortgage and www.citizensbank.ca/mortgage, as well as a number of other financial institutions.
- If you are interested in either buying or selling a home, MLS Online at www.mls.ca lists all residential and commercial MLS (Multiple Listing Service) property listings in Canada, including special features and prices. Similarly, visit www.remax.ca, www.sutton.com, and www.ireba.ca for listings with Remax Canada, Sutton Group Realty Canada, and the Independent Real Estate Brokers Association, respectively.

MOBILITY Renting offers mobility when a location change is necessary or desirable. A new job, a rent increase, the need for a larger apartment, or the desire to live in a different community can make relocation necessary. It is easier to move when you are renting than when you own a home. After you have completed school and started your career, renting makes it easier for job transfers.

FEWER RESPONSIBILITIES Renters have fewer responsibilities than homeowners since they usually do not have to be concerned with maintenance and repairs. However, they are expected to do regular household cleaning. Renters also have fewer financial concerns. Their main housing costs are rent and utilities, while homeowners incur expenses related to property taxes, property insurance, and upkeep.

LOWER INITIAL COSTS It is less expensive to take possession of a rental unit than to buy a home. While new tenants have only the first month's rent to pay, a new home buyer is likely to have a down payment and closing costs of several thousand dollars.

DISADVANTAGES OF RENTING

Renting has few financial benefits, may impose a restricted lifestyle, and involves legal details.

FEW FINANCIAL BENEFITS Renters are subject to rent increases, over which they have little control.

Exhibit 7–4

Selecting an
Apartment

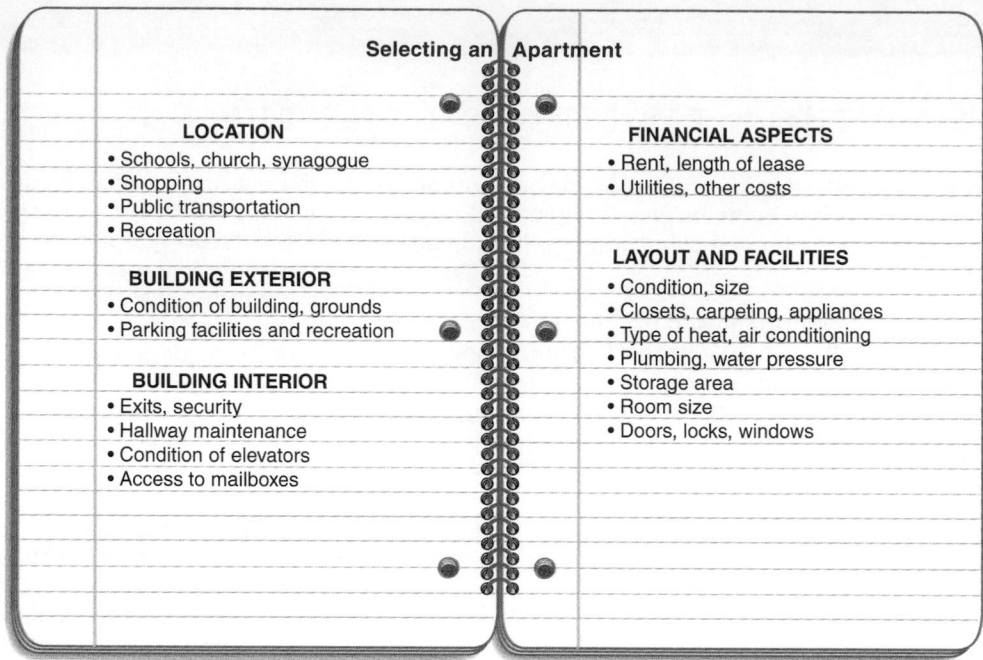

Selecting an Apartment	
LOCATION	**FINANCIAL ASPECTS**
• Schools, church, synagogue	• Rent, length of lease
• Shopping	• Utilities, other costs
• Public transportation	
• Recreation	**LAYOUT AND FACILITIES**
	• Condition, size
BUILDING EXTERIOR	• Closets, carpeting, appliances
• Condition of building, grounds	• Type of heat, air conditioning
• Parking facilities and recreation	• Plumbing, water pressure
	• Storage area
BUILDING INTERIOR	• Room size
• Exits, security	• Doors, locks, windows
• Hallway maintenance	
• Condition of elevators	
• Access to mailboxes	

RESTRICTED LIFESTYLE Renters are generally limited in the types of activities they can pursue in their place of residence. Noise from a stereo system or parties may be monitored closely. Tenants are often subject to restrictions regarding pets and decorating the property.

lease A legal document that defines the conditions of a rental agreement.

Visit the Web site

See Personal Financial Planning worksheets under Chapter 7 on the online learning centre at www.mcgrawhill.ca/ college/kapoor.

LEGAL DETAILS Most tenants sign a **lease**, a legal document that defines the conditions of a rental agreement. This document provides the following information:

- A description of the property, including the address.
- The name and address of the owner/landlord (the *lessor*).
- The name of the tenant (the *lessee*).
- The effective date of the lease.
- The length of the lease.
- The amount and due date of the monthly rent.
- The location at which the rent must be paid.
- The date and amount due of charges for late rent payments.
- A list of the utilities, appliances, furniture, or other facilities that are included in the rental amount.
- The restrictions regarding certain activities (pets, remodelling).
- The tenant's right to sublet the rental unit.
- The charges for damages or for moving out of the rental unit later (or earlier) than the lease expiration date.
- The conditions under which the landlord may enter the apartment.

Standard lease forms include conditions you may not want to accept. The fact that a lease is printed does not mean you must accept it as is. Negotiate with the landlord about lease terms you consider unacceptable.

Some leases give you the right to *sublet* the rental unit. Subletting may be necessary if you must vacate the premises before the lease expires. Subletting allows you to have another person take over rent payments and live in the rental unit.

Most leases are written, but oral leases are also valid. With an oral lease, one party must give a 30-day written notice to the other party before terminating the lease or imposing a rent increase.

A lease provides protection to both landlord and tenant. The tenant is protected from rent increases during the lease, term, unless the lease contains a provision allowing an increase. In most provinces, the tenant cannot be locked out or evicted without a court hearing. The lease gives the landlord the right to take legal action against a tenant for nonpayment of rent or destruction of property.

COSTS OF RENTING

As a renter, you will incur other living expenses besides monthly rent. For many apartments, water is covered by the rent; however, other utilities may not be covered. If you rent a house, you will probably pay for heat, electricity, water, and telephone. When you rent, you should obtain insurance coverage for your personal property. Renter's insurance is discussed in Chapter 8.

> ### DID YOU KNOW ?
>
> Renter's insurance is one of the most overlooked expenses of apartment dwellers. Damage or theft of personal property (clothing, furniture, stereo equipment, jewellery) usually is not covered by the landlord's insurance policy.

RENTING RIGHTS

The Canadian Charter of Human Rights recognizes and protects your rights to rent any apartment without discrimination based on race, colour, gender, pregnancy, sexual orientation, civil status, age, religion, political conviction, language, ethnic or national origin, social condition, or handicap. Renting is not hassle-free; problems can arise between tenants and landlords and/or roomates. The World Wide Web contains many helpful resources on how to deal with problems. See http://apartments.about.com. Visit your provincial and municipal government Web sites to find out the rules, regulations, and rights for renting that apply to you.

CONCEPT CHECK 7-2

1. What are the main benefits and drawbacks of renting a place of residence?
2. Which components of a lease are likely to be most negotiable?

The Home-Buying Process

Many people dream of having a place of residence they can call their own. Home ownership is a common financial goal. Exhibit 7–5 presents the process for achieving this goal.

Objective 3

Implement the home-buying process.

STEP 1: DETERMINE HOME OWNERSHIP NEEDS

In the first phase of the home-buying process, you should consider the benefits and drawbacks of this major financial commitment. Also, evaluate different types of housing units and determine the amount you can afford.

EVALUATE OWNING YOUR PLACE OF RESIDENCE

What Are the Benefits of Home Ownership? Whether you purchase a house, a condominium, or a manufactured home, you can enjoy the pride of ownership, financial benefits, and lifestyle flexibility of home ownership.

[1] *Pride of ownership.* Having a place to call their own is a primary motive of many home buyers. Stability of residence and a personalized living location can be important.
[2] *Financial benefits.* A potential benefit is increases in the value of the property: If the dwelling is your principal residence, there is no tax on any realized capital gain when you sell it. Finally, homeowners may be able to borrow against the equity in their homes. *Equity* is the home value less the amount owed on the mortgage.

Exhibit 7-5   The Home-Buying Process

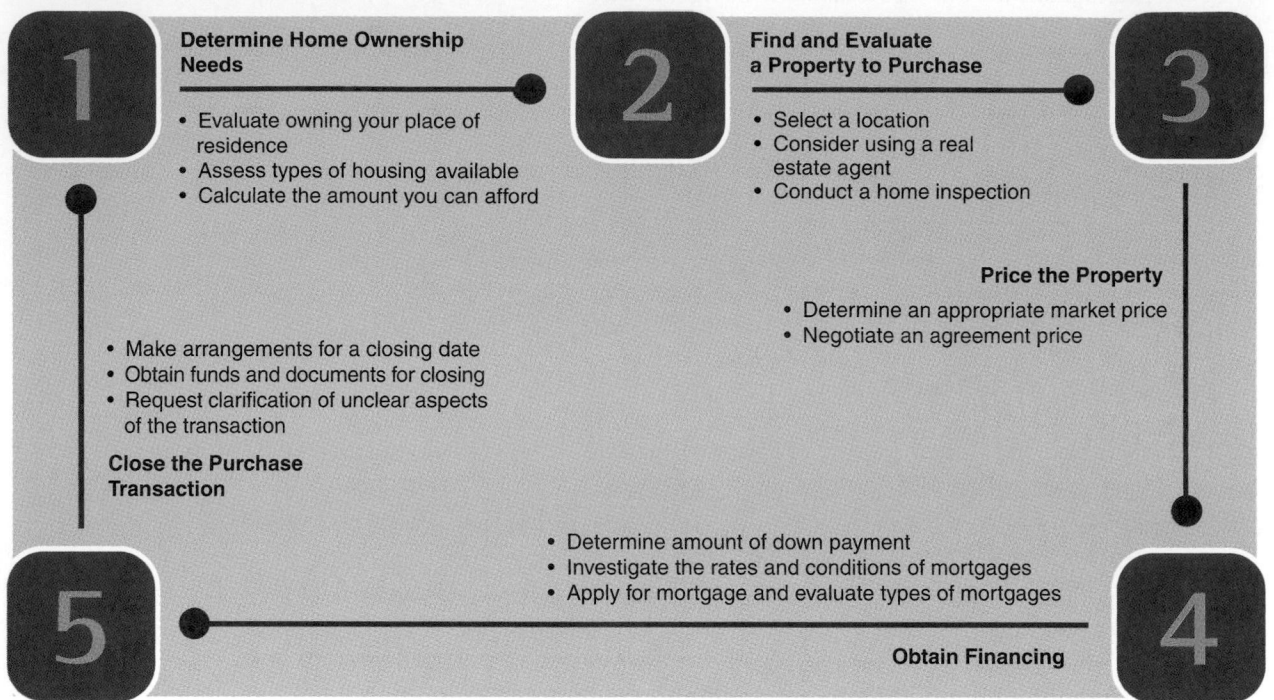

1

Determine Home Ownership Needs

- Evaluate owning your place of residence
- Assess types of housing available
- Calculate the amount you can afford

2

Find and Evaluate a Property to Purchase

- Select a location
- Consider using a real estate agent
- Conduct a home inspection

3

Price the Property

- Determine an appropriate market price
- Negotiate an agreement price

- Make arrangements for a closing date
- Obtain funds and documents for closing
- Request clarification of unclear aspects of the transaction

Close the Purchase Transaction

- Determine amount of down payment
- Investigate the rates and conditions of mortgages
- Apply for mortgage and evaluate types of mortgages

Obtain Financing

5

4

[3] *Lifestyle flexibility.* While renting gives you mobility, home ownership gives you more opportunity to express individuality. Homeowners have greater freedom than renters in decorating their dwellings and entertaining guests.

What Are the Drawbacks of Home Ownership? Buying one's own home does not guarantee a glamorous existence. This investment can result in financial uncertainty, limited mobility, and higher living costs.

[1] *Financial uncertainty.* Among the financial uncertainties associated with buying a home is obtaining money for a down payment. Obtaining mortgage financing may be a problem due to your personal situation or current economic conditions. Finally, changing property values in an area can affect your financial investment.

[2] *Limited mobility.* Home ownership does not provide ease of changing living location as does renting. If changes in your situation make it necessary to sell your home, doing so may be difficult. High interest rates and other factors can result in a weak demand for housing.

[3] *Higher living costs.* Owning your place of residence can be expensive. The home-owner is responsible for maintenance and costs of repainting, repairs, and home improvements.

[4] *Higher property taxes.* Even for homeowners who no longer have mortgage payments, higher property values and higher tax rates mean higher real estate taxes. Higher taxes affect homeowners more directly than renters, who pay them in the form of higher rent. It is harder for homeowners to counter the effects of high taxes by moving to less expensive housing.

ASSESS TYPES OF HOUSING AVAILABLE Seven common options are available to home buyers:

[1] *Single-family dwellings* are the most popular form of housing. These residences include previously owned houses, new houses, and custom-built houses. Older houses may be preferred by people who want a certain style and quality of housing.

[2] Multiunit dwellings, dwellings with more than one living unit, include duplexes and townhouses. A duplex is a building that contains two separate homes. A *townhouse* contains two, four, or six single-family living units.

[3] **Condominiums** are individually owned housing units in a building with several units. Individual ownership does not include the common areas, such as hallways, outside grounds, and recreational facilities. These areas are owned by the condominium association, which is run by the people who own the housing units. The condominium association oversees the management and operation of the housing complex. Condominium owners are charged a monthly fee to cover the maintenance, repairs, improvements, and insurance for the building and common areas. A condominium is not a type of building structure; it is a legal form of home ownership.

condominium An individually owned housing unit in a building with several such units.

[4] **Co-operative housing** is a type of subsidized housing. Rent for about half the units is geared to income (the rent is what the tenant can afford to pay), and the remaining portion of the available units are rented out at regular market prices. All tenants in a co-op are required to take part in managing and running the building. **Nonprofit housing** is rental housing owned by a community group, religious group, or nonprofit organization. The purpose is to provide affordable housing, not to produce a profit. Further information on both of these types of housing is available at your local library.

co-operative housing A type of subsidized housing in which half the units have geared-to-income rental prices.

nonprofit housing Rental housing owned by a community group, religious group, or nonprofit organization to provide affordable housing.

[5] **Manufactured homes** are housing units that are fully or partially assembled in a factory and then moved to the living site. There are two basic types of manufactured homes. One type is the *prefabricated home*, with components built in a factory and then assembled at the housing site. With this type of housing, mass production can keep building costs lower.

manufactured home A housing unit that is fully or partially assembed in a factory before being moved to the living site.

[6] *Mobile homes* are a second type of manufactured home. Since very few mobile homes are moved from their original sites, the term is not completely accurate. These housing units are typically less than 100 square metres in size; however, they usually offer the same features as a conventional house—fully equipped kitchens, fireplaces, cathedral ceilings, and whirlpool baths. The site for a mobile home may be either purchased or leased in a development specifically designed for such housing units.

The safety of mobile homes is continually debated. Fires occur no more frequently in these housing units than in other types of homes. But due to the construction of mobile homes, a fire spreads faster than in conventional houses. Manufacturers' standards for the fire safety of mobile homes are higher than in the past. Still, when a fire occurs in a mobile home, the unit is often completely destroyed. This type of housing is also vulnerable to wind forces.

Another common concern about mobile homes is their tendency to depreciate in value. When this occurs, an important benefit of home ownership is eliminated. Depreciation may make it difficult to obtain financing to purchase a mobile home.

[7] Building a home is another option. Some people want a home built to their specifications. Before you begin such a project, be sure you possess the necessary knowledge, money, and perseverance. When choosing a contractor to coordinate the project, consider the following:

- Does the contractor have the experience needed to handle the type of building project you require?
- Does the contractor have a good working relationship with the architect, materials suppliers, electricians, plumbers, carpenters, and other personnel needed to complete the project?
- What assurance do you have about the quality of materials?
- What arrangements must be made for payments during construction?
- What delays in the construction process will be considered legitimate?
- Is the contractor licensed and insured?
- Is the contractor willing to provide names, addresses, and phone numbers of satisfied customers?

• Have local consumer agencies received any complaints about this contractor?

Your written contract should include a time schedule, cost estimates, a description of the work, and a payment schedule.

You can save as much as 25 percent of the cost of a new house by supervising its construction. Home-building suppliers and owners of homes under construction can suggest quality tradespeople.

DETERMINE HOW MUCH YOU CAN AFFORD As you determine how much of your budget you will spend on a home, consider the price of the house along with its size and quality.

Price and Down Payment The amount you can spend is affected by funds available for a down payment, your income, and your current living expenses. Other factors you should consider are current mortgage rates, the potential future value of the property, and your ability to make monthly mortgage, tax, and insurance payments. To determine how much you can afford to spend on a home, have a loan officer at a mortgage company or other financial institution prequalify you. This service is provided without charge.

> **DID YOU KNOW ?**
>
> According to various surveys, the following housing features are most popular: modern kitchens; finished basements; big, modern bathrooms; fresh-looking and fresh-smelling living areas; large closets; fireplaces; and curb appeal created by plants and walkways.

Size and Quality You may not get all the features you want in your first home, but financial advisers suggest you get into the housing market by purchasing what you can afford. As you move up in the housing market, your second or third home can include more of the features you want.

Ideally, the home you buy will be in good condition. In certain circumstances, you may be willing to buy a *handyman's special*, a home that needs work and that you are able to get at a lower price because of its condition. You will then need to put more money into the house for repairs and improvements or to invest *sweat equity* by doing some of the work yourself. Home improvement information and assistance are available from hardware stores and other home product retailers.

STEP 2: FIND AND EVALUATE A PROPERTY TO PURCHASE

Next, you should select a location, consider using the services of a real estate agent, and conduct a home inspection.

SELECTING A LOCATION An old adage among real estate people is that the three most important factors to consider when buying a home are *location, location,* and *location!* Perhaps you prefer an urban, a suburban, or a rural setting. Or perhaps you want to live in a small town or in a resort area. In selecting a neighbourhood, compare your values and lifestyle with those of current residents.

zoning laws
Restrictions on how the property in an area can be used.

Be aware of **zoning laws**, restrictions on how the property in an area can be used. The location of businesses and the anticipated construction of industrial buildings or a highway may influence your buying decision.

If you have or plan to have a family, you should assess the school system. Educators recommend that schools be evaluated on program variety, achievement level of students, percentage of students who go on to post-secondary education, dedication of faculty members, facilities, school funding, and involvement of parents. Homeowners without children also benefit from strong schools, since the educational advantages of a community help maintain property values.

USING A REAL ESTATE AGENT A real estate agent can help you assess your housing needs and determine the amount you can afford to spend. Real estate agents have information about areas of interest to you and housing available to buy.

The main services a real estate agent provides include (1) presenting your offer to the seller, (2) negotiating a settlement price, (3) assisting you in obtaining financing, and (4) representing you at the closing. A real estate agent will also recommend lawyers, insurance agents, home inspectors, and mortgage companies to serve your needs.

Since the seller of the home usually pays the real estate agent's commission, the buyer may not incur a direct cost. However, this expense may be reflected in the price paid for the home. In some cases, the agent could be working for the seller. In others, the agent may be working for the buyer and may be a *dual agent*, working for both the buyer and the seller.

CONDUCTING A HOME INSPECTION Before reaching your decision about a specific home, conduct a complete evaluation of the property. An evaluation by a trained home inspector can minimize future problems. Do not assume everything is in proper working condition because someone lives there now. Being cautious and determined will save you headaches and unplanned expenses.

Some provinces, cities, and lenders require inspection documents. The mortgage company will usually conduct an *appraisal* to determine the fair market value of the property; although the appraisal is not a detailed inspection, it does help to assess the condition of the home. Exhibit 7–6 presents a detailed format for inspecting a home. A home purchase agreement may include the right to have a contractor or several professionals (roofer, plumber, electrician) inspect the property.

Exhibit 7–6 Conducting a Home Inspection

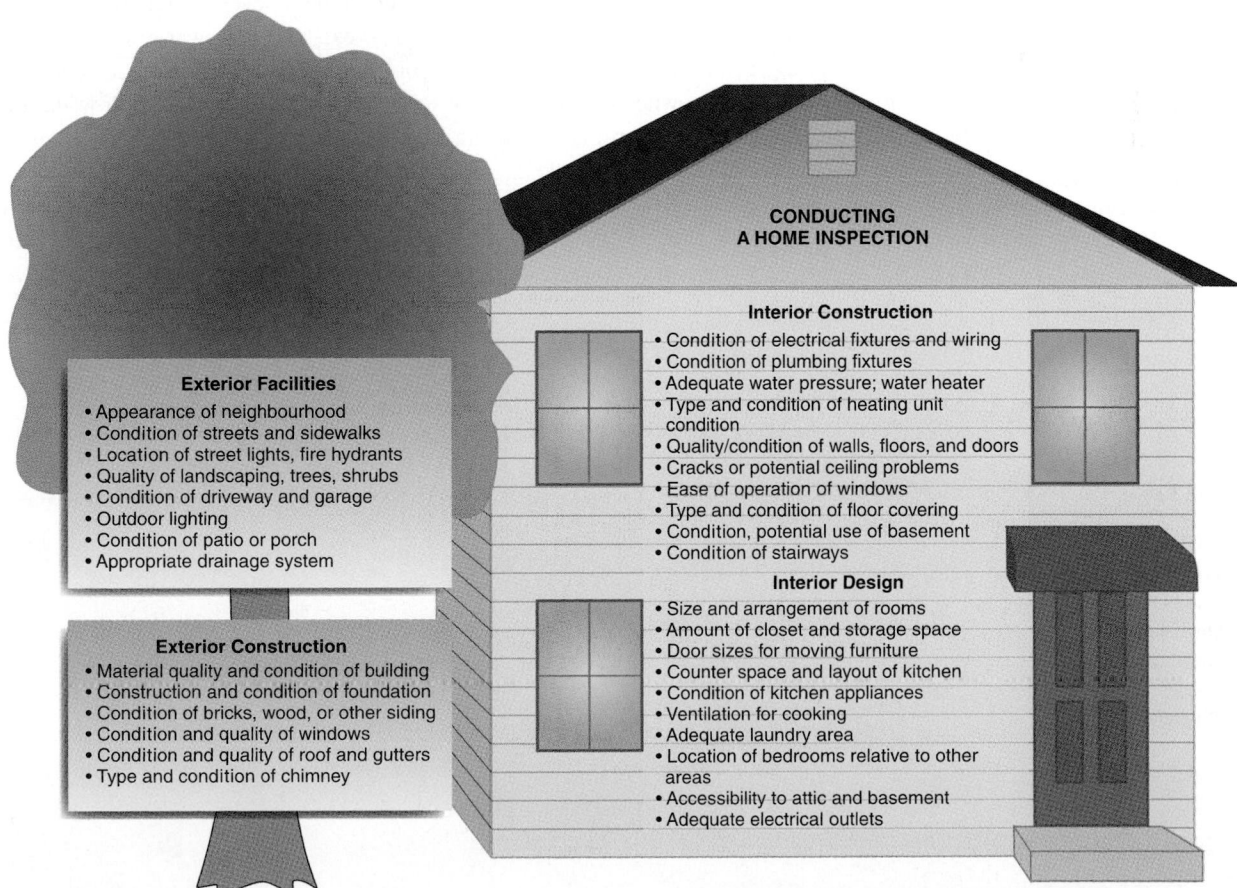

STEP 3: PRICE THE PROPERTY

After you have selected a home, determine an offer price and negotiate a final buying price.

DETERMINING THE HOME PRICE What price should you offer for the home? The main factors to consider are recent selling prices in the area, current demand for housing, the length of time the home has been on the market, the owner's need to sell, financing options, and features and condition of the home. Each of these factors can affect your offer price. For example, you will have to offer a higher price in times of low interest rates and high demand for homes. On the other hand, a home that has been on the market for over a year could mean an opportunity to offer a lower price. The services of a real estate agent or an appraiser can assist you in assessing the current value of the home.

Your offer will be in the form of an *offer to purchase*, or contract (see Exhibit 7–7). This document constitutes your legal offer to purchase the home. Your first offer price usually will not be accepted.

NEGOTIATING THE PURCHASE PRICE If your initial offer is accepted, you have a valid contract. If your offer is rejected, you have several options, depending on the seller. A counteroffer from the owner indicates a willingness to negotiate a price settlement. If the counteroffer is only slightly lower than the asking price, you are expected to move closer to that price with your next offer. If the counteroffer is quite a bit off the asking price, you are closer to the point where you might split the difference to arrive at the purchase price. If no counteroffer is forthcoming, you may wish to make another offer to see whether the seller is willing to do any negotiating. Be cautious in your negotiations if the seller is using a buyer agent. Remember, in that situation, the agent represents the interests of the seller.

In times of high demand for housing, negotiating may be minimized; this situation is referred to as a *seller's market*, since the current homeowner is likely to have several offers for the property. In contrast, when home sales are slow, a *buyer's market* exists and a lower price is likely.

When you buy a previously owned home, your negotiating power is based on current market demand and the current owner's need to sell. When you buy a new home, a slow market may mean lower prices or an opportunity to obtain various amenities (fireplace, higher-quality carpeting) from the builder at a lower cost.

Once a price has been agreed on, the purchase contract becomes the basis for the real estate transaction. As part of the offer, the buyer must present **earnest money**, a portion of the purchase price deposited as evidence of good faith to show that the purchase offer is serious. At

earnest money A portion of the price of a home that the buyer deposits as evidence of good faith to indicate a serious purchase offer.

Exhibit 7–7

The Components of an Offer to Purchase

SOURCE: *Homeownership: Guidelines for Buying and Owning a Home.* (Richmond, VA: Federal Reserve Bank of Richmond).

Components of an Offer to Purchase

In a real estate transaction, the contract between buyer and seller contains the following information:

- ❑ A description of the property
- ❑ The proposed price of the property
- ❑ The amount of the mortgage that will be needed
- ❑ The amount of the earnest money deposit
- ❑ The date and time of the closing
- ❑ Where the closing will take place
- ❑ A provision for extension of the closing date
- ❑ Time period for which the offer is in effect

- ❑ A provision for disposition of the deposit money if something goes wrong
- ❑ Adjustments to be made at the closing
- ❑ Details of what is included in the sale—home appliances, drapes, carpeting, and other items
- ❑ Special conditions of the sale
- ❑ Inspections the buyer can make before the closing

the closing of the home purchase, the earnest money is applied toward the down payment. This money is usually returned if the sale cannot be completed due to circumstances beyond the buyer's control.

Home purchase agreements often contain a *contingency clause*. This contract condition states that the agreement is binding only if a certain event occurs. For example, a real estate contract may stipulate that the contract will not be valid unless the buyer obtains financing for the purchase within a certain period of time, or it may make the purchase of a home contingent on the sale of the buyer's current home.

CONCEPT CHECK 7-3

1. What are the advantages and disadvantages of owning a home?
2. What guidelines can be used to determine the amount to spend for a home purchase?
3. How can the quality of a school system benefit even homeowners in a community who do not have school-age children?
4. What services are available to home buyers from real estate agents?
5. How does a *seller's* market differ from a *buyer's* market?

The Finances of Home Buying

After you have decided to purchase a specific home and have agreed on a price, you will probably obtain a loan. Financing a home purchase requires obtaining a mortgage, an awareness of types of mortgages, and settling the real estate transaction.

STEP 4: OBTAIN FINANCING

DETERMINE AMOUNT OF DOWN PAYMENT The amount of cash available for a down payment will affect the size of the mortgage loan you require. A large down payment, such as 20 percent or more, will make it easier for you to obtain a mortgage.

Personal savings, pension plan funds, sales of investments or other assets, and assistance from relatives are the most common sources of a down payment. Parents can help their children purchase a home by giving them a cash gift or a loan, depositing money with the lender to reduce the interest rate on the loan, co-signing the loan, or acting as co-mortgagors.

If you are a first-time buyer, you can use up to $20,000 of your RRSP holdings to help make a down payment. As an incentive, you will not be charged taxes on this withdrawal, provided that you pay back the money within a stated time period.

Making an immediate down payment of at least 25 percent of the purchase price will allow you to qualify for a conventional mortgage. Alternatively, you may qualify for what is known as a high-ratio mortgage if you are able to pay down only 5 to 25 percent of the purchase amount.

Federal law requires that you have mortgage insurance if your mortgage represents 75 percent or more of the total price you pay for your home. This coverage protects the lender from financial loss due to default and can be obtained through the Canada Mortgage and Housing Corporation (CMHC), a federal Crown corporation, or GE Capital Mortgage Insurance Company, a private company. The charge for this insurance will vary with the *loan-to-value* ratio of your mortgage (should remain 75 percent), which is the amount of your loan as a percentage of the total purchase price you will pay. Typically, the fee will be between 0.5 and 4.25 percent of your total loan in addition to an application fee, which may also be called an *underwriting fee*.

Objective 4

Calculate the costs associated with purchasing a home.

Visit the Web site

See the Weblinks under Chapter 7 on the online learning centre at www.mcgrawhill.ca/college/kapoor.

mortgage A long-term loan on a specific piece of property, such as a home or other real estate.

QUALIFYING FOR A MORTGAGE Do you have funds for a down payment? Do you earn enough to make mortgage payments while covering other living expenses? Do you have a good credit rating? Unless you pay cash for a home, a favourable response to these questions is necessary. A **mortgage** is a long-term loan on a specific piece of property, such as a home or other real estate. Payments on a mortgage are usually made over 15, 20, or 25 years. Banks, trust companies, credit unions, and mortgage companies are the most common home financing sources. *Mortgage brokers* can help home buyers obtain financing, since they are in contact with several financial institutions. A mortgage broker may charge higher fees than a lending institution with which you deal directly.

To qualify for a mortgage, you must meet criteria similar to those for other loans. The home you buy serves as security, or *collateral*, for the mortgage. The major factors that affect the affordability of your mortgage are your income, other debts, the amount available for a down payment, the length of the loan, and current mortgage rates. When looking at income, lenders use two ratios, the Gross Debt Service (GDS) ratio and the Total Debt Service (TDS) ratio. The GDS is your monthly mortgage payment, including principal, interest, heating, and taxes, as a percentage of your gross monthly income. The lender will not allow you to spend more than 30 to 32 percent of your gross income on shelter costs. The TDS ratio is your monthly mortgage payment, including any outstanding debt as a percentage of your gross monthly income. The amount the lender will allow you to spend on shelter and nonshelter financial obligations combined should not exceed 37 to 40 percent. The combined incomes of both spouses are usually considered, but excluding rental income. The results calculated in Exhibit 7–8 are (a) the monthly mortgage payment you can afford, (b) the mortgage amount you can afford, and (c) the home purchase price you can afford.

The procedures in Exhibit 7–8 include the following:

[1] Indicate your monthly gross income.
[2] Multiply your monthly gross income by 0.30 (or 0.40 if you have other debts, such as an auto loan). Lenders commonly use 30 percent (from the GDS ratio) and 40 percent (from the TDS ratio). These guidelines help determine the amount most people can comfortably afford for housing.
[3] After subtracting the monthly debt payments and an estimate of the monthly cost for property taxes and homeowner's insurance, you arrive at your *affordable monthly mortgage payment* (a).
[4] Divide (a) by the factor from Exhibit 7–9, based on your mortgage term (in years) and rate. Then multiply your answer by $1,000 to convert your figure to thousands of dollars. This gives you your *affordable mortgage amount* (b). Exhibit 7–9 provides the amount you need to pay back $1,000 over 15, 20, or 25 years based on various interest rates.
[5] To obtain your *affordable home purchase price* (c), divide (b) by the amount you will be financing, such as 0.9 when you make a 10 percent down payment.

These sample calculations are typical of those most financial institutions use; the actual qualifications for a mortgage may vary by lender and by the type of mortgage. In addition, current mortgage interest rates will affect the amount of the mortgage loan for which you qualify.

The mortgage loan for which you can qualify is larger when interest rates are low than when they are high. For example, a person who can afford a monthly mortgage payment of $700 will qualify for a 25-year loan of $100,000 at 7 percent.

As interest rates rise, fewer people are able to afford the cost of an average-priced home. See Exhibit 7–10 on page 198 for recent mortgage rates in Canada. A great wealth of information on mortgages can be found online at most banks' Web sites, such as www.royal bank, and at www.mortgageforless.com or www.ccra-adrc.gc.ca.

Exhibit 7–8 Housing Affordability and Mortgage Qualification Amounts

		Example A	Example B
Step 1:	Determine your monthly gross income (annual income divided by 12).	$36,000 ÷ 12	
Step 2:	With a down payment of at least 10 percent, lenders use 30 percent of monthly gross income as a guideline for the GDS ratio, and 40 percent of monthly gross income as a guideline for the TDS ratio.	$ 3,000 × .40 $ 1,200	$ 3,000 × .30 $ 900
Step 3:	Subtract other debt payments (e.g., payments on an auto loan) and an estimate of the monthly costs of property taxes and homeowner's insurance.	– 280 – 200	— – 200
(a) *Affordable monthly mortgage payment*		$ 720	$ 700
Step 4:	Divide this amount by the monthly mortgage payment per $1,000 based on current mortgage rates—a 10 percent, 25-year loan, for example (see Exhibit 7–9)—and multiply by $1,000.	÷ $ 8.95 × $ 1,000	÷ $ 8.95 × $ 1,000
(b) *Affordable mortgage amount*		$80,447	$78,212
Step 5:	Divide your affordable mortgage amount by 1 minus the fractional portion of your down payment (e.g., a 10 percent down payment).	÷ .9	÷ .9
(c) *Affordable home purchase price*		$89,385	$86,903

NOTE: The two ratios lending institutions use (step 2) and other loan requirements may vary based on a variety of factors, including the type of mortgage, the amount of the down payment, your income level, and current interest rates.

Term Rate	25 Years	20 Years	15 Years
6.0%	$ 6.40	$ 7.12	$ 8.40
6.5	6.62	7.40	8.66
7.0	7.00	7.69	8.93
7.5	7.32	7.99	9.20
8.0	7.63	8.28	9.48
8.5	7.95	8.58	9.76
9.0	8.25	8.90	10.05
9.5	8.62	9.21	10.34
10.0	8.95	9.52	10.63
10.5	9.29	9.84	10.92
11.0	9.63	10.16	11.22
11.5	9.98	10.49	11.52
12.0	10.32	10.81	11.82
12.5	10.68	11.15	12.13
13.0	11.03	11.48	12.44
13.5	11.39	11.82	12.75

Exhibit 7–9

Mortgage Payment Factors (principal and interest factors per $1,000 of loan amount)

Exhibit 7–10

Mortgage Rates through the Years

SOURCE: Bank of Canada
www.bankofcanada.ca

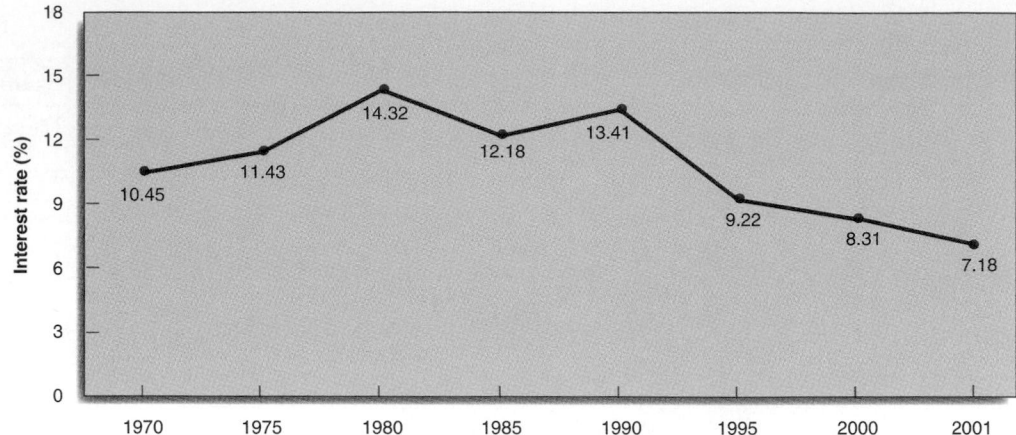

THE APPLICATION PROCESS Applying for a mortgage involves three main phases:

[1] After completing the mortgage application, a meeting between lender and borrower is scheduled. The borrower presents evidence of employment, income, ownership of assets, and amounts of existing debts. At this point, most lenders charge an application fee of between $100 and $300.

[2] The lender obtains a credit report and verifies other aspects of the borrower's application and financial status.

[3] The mortgage is either approved or denied. The decision is based on the potential borrower's credit and financial history and an evaluation of the home, including its location, condition, and value. This process will indicate the maximum mortgage for which you qualify. This amount may not be loaned on every house you are considering.

The loan commitment is the financial institution's decision to provide the funds needed to purchase a specific property. At this point, the purchase contract for the home becomes legally binding. The approved mortgage application usually *locks in* an interest rate for a certain period.

FIXED-RATE, FIXED-PAYMENT MORTGAGES Fixed-rate, fixed-payment mortgages are one of the two major types of mortgages.

Conventional Mortgages The conventional mortgage usually has equal payments over up to 25 years based on a fixed interest rate. This mortgage offers home buyers certainty about future loan payments. The mortgage payments are set at a level that allows **amortization** of the loan; that is, the balance owed is reduced with each payment. Since the amount borrowed is large, the payments made during the early years of the mortgage are applied mainly to interest, with only small reductions in the principal of the loan. As the amount owed declines, the monthly payments have an increasing impact on the loan balance. Near the end of the mortgage term, nearly all of each payment is applied to the balance.

For example, a $75,000, 25-year, 10-percent mortgage would have monthly payments of $671.25. The payments would be divided as follows:

amortization The reduction of a loan balance through payments made over a period of time.

	Interest		Principal	Remaining Balance	
For the first month	$625.00	($75,000 × 0.10 × $\frac{1}{12}$)	$ 46.25	$74,953.75	($75,000 − $46.25)
For the second month	624.61	($74,953.75 × 0.10 × $\frac{1}{12}$)	46.64	74,907.11	($74,953.75 − $46.64)

In the past, many conventional mortgages were *assumable*. This feature allowed a home buyer to continue with the seller's original agreement. Assumable mortgages were especially attractive if the mortgage rate was lower than market interest rates at the time of the sale. Today, due to volatile interest rates, few assumable mortgages are offered.

VARIABLE-RATE MORTGAGES Variable-rate mortgages are a second major category of financing available to home buyers. The **variable-rate mortgage (VRM)**, also referred to as a *flexible-rate mortgage*, has an interest rate that increases or decreases during the life of the loan. When mortgage rates were at record highs, many people took out variable-rate home loans, expecting rates would eventually go down. VRMs usually have a lower initial interest rate than fixed-rate mortgages; however, the borrower, not the lender, bears the risk of future interest rate increases.

A **rate cap** restricts the amount by which the interest rate can increase or decrease during the VRM term. This limit prevents the borrower from having to pay an interest rate significantly higher than the one in the original agreement. Most rate caps limit increases (or decreases) in the mortgage rate to one or two percentage points in a year and to no more than five points over the life of the loan. Most lenders charge a premium for this.

The monthly amount you pay will remain the same, regardless of the direction that interest rates may be going. What can change is the proportion of your payment that will go toward paying off your principal relative to the interest on the loan. If interest rates rise, then more of your money will be used against the interest than the principal, which will increase the total amount payable. This effect is called *negative amortization*, and it will extend the number of payments to be made to pay off the mortgage.

Consider several factors when you evaluate variable-rate mortgages: (1) determine the frequency of and restrictions on allowed changes in interest rates; (2) consider the frequency of and restrictions on changes in the monthly payment; (3) investigate the possibility that the loan will be extended due to negative amortization, and find out whether the mortgage agreement limits the amount of negative amortization; (4) find out what index the lending institution will use to set the mortgage interest rate over the term of the loan.

The rate for a variable- or flexible-rate mortgage will fluctuate from month to month according to the prime rate. If you believe that the prime rate will decline, then a variable-rate mortgage is advisable, as this will translate to more of your principal being paid down. Studies have also shown that a variable-rate mortgage can be less costly over the life of a mortgage as long as interest rates remain fairly stable.

Most institutions will allow you to convert your variable-rate mortgage to a fixed rate. If rates are rising, or if you do not wish to or are unable to keep track of rates, this would be a good strategy.

SPLIT OR MULTIRATE MORTGAGES This type of mortgage allows you to arrange part of your mortgage at one rate and term and another part at another rate and term. The advantage to this type of loan is that you will be getting at least a portion at a fixed rate if you do not qualify for the whole amount at that rate.

OPTIONS FOR PAYING BACK YOUR MORTGAGE
Most mortgage lenders offer options to your payment plan that will allow you to speed up your payment schedule. Alternatively,

> **DID YOU KNOW ?**
>
> Among different lenders, interest rates on a 25-year mortgage may vary up to a full percentage point within a single geographic region.

variable-rate mortgage (VRM) A home loan with an interest rate that can change during the mortgage term due to changes in market interest rates; also called a *flexible-rate mortgage*.

rate cap A limit on the increases and decreases in the interest rate charged on an adjustable-rate mortgage.

> **DID YOU KNOW ?**
>
> By taking out a 15-year instead of a 25-year mortgage, a home buyer borrowing $200,000 can save over $150,000 in interest over the life of the loan. The faster equity growth with the shorter mortgage is also a benefit. A 15-year mortgage may not make sense for everyone, since the additional monthly payment may be needed to pay off credit cards or for other living expenses.
>
> (Carlos Tajada, "Sweet Fifteen," *The Wall Street Journal*, September 17, 1998, p. C1.)

and subject to conditional rules, some institutions will also allow you to miss the occasional payment. In both cases, the details of the available options should be verified with the lender. (See the Financial Planning for Life's Situations feature on page 202.)

OTHER FINANCING METHODS Assuming an existing mortgage as part of the price you pay may give you a lower interest rate than the prevailing market rate. In addition, you'll save on appraisal and lawyer fees.

The vendor-take-back (VTB) mortgage is a loan extended to you as the buyer by the seller. This type of loan frequently has the advantage of a lower rate than most institutions offer.

> **second mortgage** A cash advance based on the paid-up value of home; also called a *home equity loan.*

Second Mortgages A **second mortgage**, also called a *home equity loan*, allows a home-owner to borrow on the paid-up value of the property. Traditional second mortgages allow a homeowner to borrow a lump sum against the equity and repay it in monthly installments. Recently, lending institutions have offered a variety of home equity loans, including a line of credit program that allows the borrower to obtain additional funds. You need to be careful when using a home equity line of credit. This revolving credit plan can keep you continually in debt as you request new cash advances.

> **reverse mortgage** A loan based on the equity in a home, which provides elderly homeowners with tax-free income and is paid back with interest when the home is sold or the homeowner dies.

Reverse Mortgages Programs are available to assist people who have a high equity in their homes and need cash. **Reverse mortgages** provide elderly homeowners with tax-free income in the form of a loan that is paid back (with interest) when the home is sold or the homeowner dies. A reverse mortgage has a *set term*, at the end of which the loan would be due. This format is likely to offer a higher monthly income; however, an elderly person faces the prospect of having to sell the home before he or she desires to do so. Reverse mort-gages are increasing in availability through both government programs and private lending institutions.

> **refinancing** The process of obtaining a new mortgage on a home to get a lower interest rate.

Refinancing During the term of your mortgage, you may want to **refinance** your home; that is, obtain a new mortgage on your current home at a lower interest rate. Before taking this action, be sure the costs of refinancing do not offset the savings of a lower interest rate. Refinancing is most advantageous when you can get a rate 2 or 3 percent lower than your cur-rent rate and when you plan to own your present home for at least two more years. Divide the costs of refinancing by the amount saved each month to determine the time you need to cover your costs.

STEP 5: CLOSE THE PURCHASE TRANSACTION

> **closing costs** Fees and charges paid when a real estate transaction is completed; also called settlement costs.
>
> **title insurance** Insurance that, during the mortgage term, protects the owner or the lender against financial loss resulting from future defects in the title and from other unforeseen property claims not excluded by the policy.

Before finalizing the transaction, do a *walk-through* to inspect the conditions and facilities of the home you plan to buy. You can use a Polaroid or video camera to collect evidence for any last-minute items you may need to negotiate.

The *closing* involves a meeting among the buyer, seller, and notary, or representatives of each party, to complete the transaction. Documents are signed, last-minute details are set-tled, and appropriate amounts are paid. A number of expenses are incurred at the closing. The **closing costs**, also referred to as settlement costs, are the fees and charges paid when a real estate transaction is completed (see Exhibit 7–11).

Title insurance is one closing cost. This coverage has two phases. First, the title company defines the boundaries of the property being purchased and conducts a search to determine whether the property is free of claims, such as unpaid real estate taxes. Second, during the mortgage term, the title company protects the owner and the lender against financial loss resulting from future defects in the title and from other unforeseen property claims not exclud-ed by the policy.

Exhibit 7–11   Common Additional Costs

When looking toward buying a home, it is important to prepare for other costs so there are no surprises. The following is a list of the most common costs of home purchasing, with an estimated price. Not all of these fees will apply to every situation or every province.

Item	Cost	Comments
Appraisal	$150–$200	Determines the value of your property; may be covered by your lender.
Home Inspection	$300	Can tell you what condition your home is in, and estimate the cost of repairs. It's a good idea to make your offer conditional on a home inspection.
Property Survey	$750–$1,000	A recent legal written/mapped description of your home, including its location and dimensions, is usually required by your mortgage lender (typically paid for by the seller).
Insurance for High-Ratio Mortgages	Varies	Up to 3 percent of your mortgage amount.
Home Insurance	$450	Your lender will require that you adequately insure to protect the investment.
Land Transfer Tax Interest Adjustment	$2,000 $100–$1,000	Tax levied by some provinces whenever property changes hands. In the event that your home purchase closing date does not coincide with the date when your mortgage payments start, you may be required to pay interest for this period. It is worthwhile to arrange for your mortgage payments to begin exactly one payment period after your closing date. You may also be able to negotiate to have your lender waive or reduce this payment.
Prepaid Property Tax and Utility Adjustments	$400–$1,500	If the previous owners prepaid property taxes and/or other utilities you will have to reimburse them, starting at the date your house sale closes.
Legal Fees	$350–$2,500	A real estate lawyer (a notary in Quebec) will bill you for conducting a title search, drafting the title deed, and preparing the mortgage. Registration fees and other disbursements are extra.
Moving Expenses	$200–$1,000	The cost of moving into your new home will vary, depending on whether you rent a truck and do it yourself or hire movers.
Service Charges	$150–$200	There may be additional charges for hooking up your gas, hydro, phone, cable, and so on.
GST	For new homes only	7 percent GST is charged on newly built homes. The builder often pays this tax, but it's a good idea to ask.
Life Insurance	Optional	This is optional, but it serves to cover your mortgage in the event of the insured's death.
Mortgage Application Fee	Varies	This amount varies from one institution to the next.

Also due at closing time is the deed recording fee. The **deed** (or **title**) is the document that transfers ownership of property from one party to another. This document certifies that the seller is the true owner of the property, there are no claims against the title, and the seller has the right to sell the property.

Mortgage insurance is another possible closing cost. If required, mortgage insurance protects the lender from loss resulting from a mortgage default.

deed or title A document that transfers ownership of property from one party to another.

SHOULD YOU PAY OFF YOUR MORTGAGE EARLY?

If you have a mortgage, you might consider paying it off early. Most mortgages include a *pre-payment penalty*, a fee you pay for the privilege of retiring a loan early. Before paying off your mortgage early, however, consider your lost earnings on the money you use to retire this debt.

Instead of paying off your entire mortgage early, consider paying an additional amount each month. This amount will be applied to the loan principal, so you will save interest and pay off the mortgage in a shorter time than the contracted period.

Beware of organizations that promise to help you make additional payments on your mortgage. This is something you could do on your own, and they are likely to charge you a fee for doing it. In addition, these organizations frequently collect money from you every two weeks but make a payment only once a month, which gives them the use of thousands of *your* dollars to invest for *their* gain.

TIPS TO PAY YOUR MORTGAGE OFF EARLY

Take a $100,000 mortgage at 8-percent interest over 25 years:

- Make weekly, rather than monthly, payments.
- Round off your payments (for example, from $190.80 to $200).
- Increase the weekly payment by $5 each year.
- Pay a lump sum of $500 (from income tax refund) on the first anniversary, increasing subsequent annual payments by $50 a year.

These small changes could help you retire your mortgage loan in approximately half the time and would cut interest bills in half!

SOURCE:
www.mortgageforless.com/tips/payoffearly.html.

---

escrow account
Money, usually deposited with the lending institution, for the payment of property taxes and homeowner's insurance.

At the closing and when you make your monthly payments, you will probably deposit money to be used for home expenses. For example, the lender will require that you have property insurance. An **escrow account** is money, usually deposited with the lending institution, for the payment of property taxes and homeowner's insurance. This account protects the lender from financial loss due to unpaid real estate taxes or damage from fire or other hazards.

As a new home buyer, you might also consider purchasing an agreement that gives you protection against defects in the home. *Implied warranties* created by federal and provincial laws may cover some problem areas; other repair costs can occur. Home builders and real estate sales companies offer warranties to buyers. Coverage offered commonly provides protection against structural, wiring, plumbing, heating, and other mechanical defects. Most home warranty programs have many limitations.

DID YOU KNOW ?

The Home Buyer Plan allows you to withdraw up to $20,000 from your RRSP to use as a down payment on your first home. For more information go to www.ccra-adrc.gc.ca.

HOME BUYING: A FINAL WORD

For most people, buying a home is the most expensive decision they will undertake. As a reminder, Exhibit 7–12 provides an overview of the major elements to consider when making this critical financial decision.

- **Location.** Consider the community and geographic region. A $150,000 home in one area may be an average-priced house, while in another part of the country it may be fairly expensive real estate. The demand for homes is largely affected by the economy and the availability of jobs.

- **Down payment.** While making a large down payment reduces your mortgage payments, you will also need funds for closing costs, moving expenses, repairs, or furniture.

- **Mortgage application.** When applying for a home loan, you will usually be required to provide copies of recent tax returns, a residence and employment history, information about bank and investment accounts, a listing of debts, and evidence of auto and any real estate ownership.

- **Closing costs.** Settlement costs can range from 2 to 6 percent of the loan amount. This means you could need as much as $6,000 to finalize a $100,000 mortgage; this amount is in addition to your down payment.

- **PIT.** Your monthly payment for principal, interest, and taxes is an important budget item. Beware of buying "too much house" and not having enough for other living expenses.

- **Maintenance costs.** As any homeowner will tell you, owning a home can be expensive. Set aside funds for repair and remodelling expenses.

Exhibit 7–12

The Main
Elements of
Buying a Home

CONCEPT CHECK 7–4

1. What are the main sources of money for a down payment?
2. What factors affect a person's ability to qualify for a mortgage?
3. How do changing interest rates affect the amount of mortgage a person can afford?
4. Under what conditions might a variable-rate mortgage be appropriate?
5. When might refinancing a mortgage be advisable?
6. How do closing costs affect a person's ability to afford a home purchase?

Selling Your Home

Most people who buy a home will eventually be on the other side of a real estate transaction. Selling your home requires preparing it for selling, setting a price, and deciding whether to sell it yourself or use a real estate agent.

Objective 5

Develop a strategy
for selling a home.

PREPARING YOUR HOME FOR SELLING

The effective presentation of your home can result in a fast and financially favourable sale. Real estate salespeople recommend that you make needed repairs and paint worn exterior and interior areas. Clear the garage and exterior areas of toys, debris, and old vehicles, and keep the lawn cut and the leaves raked. Keep the kitchen and bathroom clean. Avoid offensive odours by removing garbage and keeping pets and their areas clean. Remove excess furniture and dispose of unneeded items to make the house, closets, and storage areas look larger. When showing your home, open drapes and turn on lights to give it a pleasant atmosphere. This effort will give your property a positive image and make it attractive to potential buyers.

DETERMINING THE SELLING PRICE

appraisal An estimate
of the current value of
a property.

Putting a price on your home can be difficult. You risk not selling it immediately if the price is too high, and you may not get a fair amount if the price is too low. An **appraisal**, an estimate of the current value of the property, can provide a good indication of the price you should set. An asking price is influenced by recent selling prices of comparable homes in your area, demand in the housing market, and available financing based on current mortgage rates.

The home improvements you have made may or may not increase the selling price. A hot tub or an exercise room may have no value for potential buyers. Among the most desirable improvements are energy-efficient features, a remodelled kitchen, an additional or remodelled bathroom, added rooms and storage space, a converted basement, a fireplace, and an outdoor deck or patio.

The time to think about selling your home is when you buy it and every day you live there. Daily maintenance, timely repairs, and home improvements will increase the future sales price.

SALE BY OWNER

If you decide to sell your home without using a real estate professional, price the home and advertise it through local newspapers and with an information sheet describing it in detail. Obtain a listing sheet from a real estate office as an example of the information to include on your flier. Distribute the sheet at stores and in other public areas.

When selling your home on your own, obtain information about the availability of financing and financing requirements. This information will help you and potential buyers to determine whether a sale is possible. Use the services of a lawyer or title company to assist you with the contract, the closing, and other legal matters.

Require potential buyers to provide their names, addresses, telephone numbers, and background information, and show your home only by appointment. As a security measure, show it only when two or more adults are at home. Selling your own home can save you several thousand dollars in commission, but it requires an investment of time and effort.

LISTING WITH A REAL ESTATE AGENT

You may decide to sell your home with the assistance of a real estate agent. These businesses range from firms owned by one person to nationally franchised companies. Primary selection factors should be the real estate agent's knowledge of the community and the agent's willingness to actively market your home.

Your real estate agent will provide you with various services. These services include suggesting a selling price, making potential buyers and other agents aware of your home, providing advice on features to highlight, conducting showings of your home, and handling the financial aspects of the sale. A real estate agent can also help screen potential buyers to determine whether they will qualify for a mortgage.

Discount real estate brokers are available to assist sellers who are willing to take on certain duties and want to reduce selling costs.

CONCEPT CHECK 7-5

1. What actions are recommended when planning to sell your home?
2. What factors affect the selling price of a home?
3. What should you consider when deciding whether to sell your home on your own or use the services of a real estate agent?

SUMMARY OF OBJECTIVES

Objective 1
Evaluate available housing alternatives.
Your needs, life situation, and financial resources are the major factors that influence your selection of housing. Assess renting and buying alternatives in terms of their financial and opportunity costs.

Objective 2
Analyze the costs and benefits associated with renting.
The main advantages of renting are mobility, fewer responsibilities, and lower initial costs. The main disadvantages of renting are few financial benefits, a restricted lifestyle, and legal concerns.

Objective 3
Implement the home-buying process.
Home buying involves five major stages: (1) determining home ownership needs, (2) finding and evaluating a property

to purchase, (3) pricing the property, (4) financing the purchase, and (5) closing the real estate transaction.

Objective 4
Calculate the costs associated with purchasing a home.
The costs associated with purchasing a home include the down payment; mortgage origination costs; closing costs, such as a title fee, pre-paid interest, attorney's fees, payment for insurance, and a property survey.

Objective 5
Develop a strategy for selling a home.
When selling a home, you must decide whether to make certain repairs and improvements, determine a selling price, and choose between selling the home yourself and using the services of a real estate agent.

KEY TERMS

amortization 198

appraisal 204

closing costs 200

condominium 191

co-operative housing 191

deed or title 201

earnest money 194

escrow account 202

lease 188

manufactured home 191

mortgage 196

nonprofit housing 191

rate cap 199

refinancing 200

reverse mortgage 200

second mortgage 200

title insurance 200

variable-rate mortgage 199

zoning laws 192

FINANCIAL PLANNING PROBLEMS

1. *Determining Appropriate Housing.* What type of housing would you suggest for people in the following life situations? (Obj. 1)
   a. A single parent with two school-age children.
   b. A two-income couple without children.
   c. A person with both dependent children and a dependent parent.
   d. A couple near retirement with grown children.

2. *Comparing Renting and Buying.* On the basis of the following data, would you recommend buying or renting?

Rental Costs	Buying Costs
Annual rent, $7,380	Annual mortgage payments, $9,800
Insurance, $145	($9,575 is interest)
Security deposit, $650	Property taxes, $1,780
	Insurance/maintenance, $1,050
	Down payment/closing costs, $4,500
	Growth in equity, $225
	Estimated annual appreciation, $1,700

Assume an after-tax savings interest rate of 6 percent and a tax rate of 28 percent. (Obj. 2)

3. *Analyzing the Buy-versus-Rent Decision.* Use the buy-versus-rent analysis on p. 185 to compare two residences you might consider. (Obj. 2)

4. *Estimating a Monthly Mortgage Payment.* Estimate the affordable monthly mortgage payment, the affordable mortgage amount, and the affordable home purchase price for the following situation (see Exhibit 7–8). (Obj. 4)
   Monthly gross income, $2,950
   Down payment to be made—15 percent of purchase price
   Other debt (monthly payment), $160
   Monthly estimate for property taxes and insurance, $210
   25-year loan at 10.5 percent.

5. *Calculating Monthly Mortgage Payments.* On the basis of Exhibit 7–9, what would be the monthly mortgage payments for each of the following situations?

a. A $40,000, 15-year loan at 11.5 percent.

b. A $76,000, 25-year loan at 9 percent.

c. A $65,000, 20-year loan at 10 percent.

What relationship exists between the length of the loan and the monthly payment? How does the mortgage rate affect the monthly payment? (Obj. 4)

6. *Comparing Total Mortgage Payments.* Which mortgage would result in higher total payments? (Obj. 4)

Mortgage A: $985 a month for 25 years

Mortgage B: $780 a month for 5 years and $1,056 for 25 years

7. *Evaluating a Refinance Decision.* Kelly and Tim Johnson plan to refinance their mortgage to obtain a lower interest rate. They will reduce their mortgage payments by $56 a month. Their closing costs for refinancing will be $1,670. How long will it take them to cover the cost of refinancing? (Obj. 4)

8. *Future Value of an Amount Saved.* You estimate that you can save $3,800 by selling your home yourself, rather than using a real estate agent. What would be the future value of that amount if invested for five years at 7 percent? (Obj. 5)

FINANCIAL PLANNING ACTIVITIES

1. *Comparing Housing Alternatives.* Interview several people about the factors that influenced their current residence. (Obj. 1)

2. *Comparing Rental Situations.* Compare the costs, facilities, and features of apartments and other rental housing in your area. You may obtain this information through newspaper advertisements, rental offices, or online searches. (Obj. 2)

3. *Researching Rental Agreements.* Interview a tenant and a landlord to obtain their views about potential problems associated with renting. How do their views on tenant–landlord relations differ? (Obj. 2)

4. *Comparing Home-Buying Alternatives.* Visit the sales office for a condominium, a new home, and a mobile home. On the basis of the information obtained, prepare a written or an oral presentation comparing the benefits and potential concerns of these housing alternatives. (Obj. 3)

5. *Using a Real Estate Agent.* Interview a real estate agent about the process involved in selecting and buying a home. Ask about housing prices in your area and the services the agent provides. Also, find out the agent's opinion as to what

will happen to housing prices and interest rates over the next six months. (Obj. 3)

6. *Comparing Types of Mortgages.* Talk with people who have different types of mortgages. What suggestions do they offer about obtaining home financing? What were their experiences with closing costs when they purchased their homes? (Obj. 4)

7. *Comparing Mortgage Companies.* Contact several mortgage companies and other financial institutions to obtain information about current mortgage rates, application fees, and the process for obtaining a mortgage. (Obj. 4)

8. *Searching the Web for Mortgage Rates.* Using Web sites such as www.canadamortgage.com, www.cannex.com, or www.webfin.com, obtain information on current mortgage rates available in different parts of the country. (Obj. 4)

9. *Analyzing Homes for Sales.* Visit a couple of homes for sale. What features do you believe would appeal to potential buyers? What efforts were made to attract potential buyers to the open houses? (Obj. 5)

LIFE SITUATION CASE

Housing Decisions

When Marcel and Vanya St. Onge first saw the house, they didn't like it. However, it was a dark, rainy day. They viewed the house more favourably on their second visit, which they had expected to be a waste of time. Despite cracked ceilings, the need for a paint job, and a kitchen built in the 1950s, the St. Onges saw a potential to create a place they could call their own.

Brigitte Lavoie purchased her condominium four years ago. She obtained a mortgage rate of 9.75 percent, a very good rate then. Recently, when interest rates dropped, Brigitte was considering refinancing her mortgage at a lower rate.

Matthew and Petra Steward had been married for five years and were still living in an apartment. Several of the Stewards' friends had purchased homes recently. However, Matthew and Petra were not sure they wanted to follow this example.

Although they liked their friends' homes and had viewed photographs of homes currently on the market, they also liked the freedom from maintenance responsibility they enjoyed as renters.

Questions

1. How could the St. Onges have benefited from buying a home that needed improvements?

2. How might Brigitte Lavoie have found out when mortgage rates were at a level that would make refinancing her condominium more affordable?

3. Although the Stewards had good reasons for continuing to rent, what factors might make it desirable for an individual or a family to buy a home?

CREATING A FINANCIAL PLAN

Selecting and Financing Housing

Housing represents a major budget expenditure. This area of financial planning requires careful analysis of needs along with a comparison of the costs and benefits of housing alternatives.

Web Sites for Housing

Each of the following Web sites provides high-quality links to many other Internet resources.

- The Quicken Financial Network, at **www.quicken.ca**, provides a financial fitness test, expert advice, investment tracking, and other financial help, including mortgage information and "best-rate tracking."
- Retire Web, at **www.retireweb.com**, offers a mortgage vs. RRSP calculator that will help you understand whether you are better off investing an amount of money in your RRSP or using it to pay down your mortgage.

- The Mortgage Analyzer at **www.themortgage.com**, an excellent site for mortgage information, will give you payment information and an amortization schedule.
- Canada Mortgage, at **www.canmortgage.com**, offers a mortgage amortization calculator, which provides a graph to show the principal/interest payments over time, and shows the difference between lowering the price and reducing an interest rate (buying down the rate) to achieve equal monthly payments on the resulting mortgage.
- A key authority on all housing-related matters in Canada is the Canada Mortgage and Housing Corporation (CMHC), a Crown corporation. Visit **www.cmhc-schl.gc.ca** to find out more about mortgages, housing, and a variety of related regulations.

(Note: Addresses and content of Web sites change, and new sites are created daily. Use search engines to update and locate Web sites for your current financial planning needs.)

CONTINUOUS CASE FOR PART 2 (B)

SPENDING PATTERNS FOR FINANCIAL SECURITY

Life Situation
Young married couple: Pamela, 30; Isaac, 32; two children, ages 1 and 3

Financial Goals

- Improve daily spending habits
- Purchase a new home
- Acquire a second motor vehicle

Financial Data

Monthly income	$ 3,600
Living expenses	3,125
Assets	33,850
Liabilities	1,520

The Mortimers now have two preschool-age children. Their household income has declined because Pamela has "retired" for a while to care for the children. To compensate for their lower monthly income, Pamela and Isaac have cut back to the basics and purchase only the "necessities" each month. Still, their expenses total $3,125 a month. However, the Mortimers have managed to pay down their liabilities over the past four years; now their liabilities total $1,520.

Housing needs are also changing for the Mortimers as their family increases in size. At present, they pay $750 in rent for a two-bedroom apartment. To purchase a home for a comparable

monthly payment, the Mortimers would have to relocate farther from Isaac's place of employment.

In addition to buying a home, the Mortimers need to purchase a second automobile. Currently, Pamela must drive Isaac to the train station (creating many inconveniences for her and the children) if she wants to use the car for various business and education activities. If they move to the suburbs, the situation will only get worse.

Questions

1. What major factors are affecting the Mortimers' spending habits?
2. On the basis of a monthly income of $3,600, an estimated $240 per month for property taxes and homeowner's insurance, current mortgage interest rates of 9 percent, and a down payment of at least 10 percent, what would it cost the Mortimers to purchase a home?
3. What tax advantages will the Mortimers realize by purchasing a home, rather than renting?
4. What transportation alternatives should the Mortimers consider? If they decide that they need a second motor vehicle, how should they finance it?

PART 3

INSURING YOUR RESOURCES

CHAPTER 8
Home and Automoblie Insurance

CHAPTER 9
Life, Health, and Disability Insurance

Road Trips Are Fun, But Are You Insured?

José and Marty are excited about their spring break trip to the Rocky Mountains. They decided to rent a car because Marty drives an old car and José doesn't want to put kilometres on the Honda his parents gave him as a graduation gift. When they go to pick up the car, the sales agent asks them if they want a loss-damage and collision-damage waiver, which would cost them $10 per day. They don't want to spend an extra $70 on this trip, but neither one knows if his personal insurance covers rental cars. What should they do?

Motorists usually decline trip insurance. They get the same or better protection from their personal auto insurance. However, sometimes there are gaps in personal coverage. If you don't know the rules and decline the rental agency's offer, you may be driving uninsured. For example, Marty may not have comprehensive and collision coverage on his old car because he knows it isn't worth the additional coverage. This means he also won't be covered on the rental car.

If Marty's or José's auto policy doesn't cover collision or theft when driving a rental car, they have another option. Certain credit cards will protect them against damage or theft if the card is used when paying for the rental. But again, there may be limitations.

If José and Marty don't know their rental car insurance rules, they should check with their auto insurer or credit card company before signing the rental agreement. Otherwise, the safest thing might be to pay the additional $10 per day.

QUESTIONS

1 Why do most motorists decline additional coverage when they rent a car? What are the limitations of this strategy?

2 What other option do Marty and José have if their personal auto insurance does not cover rental cars?

3 What Web research could they do before they rent a car again?

LEARNING OBJECTIVES

1 Develop a risk management plan using insurance.

2 Discuss the importance of property and liability insurance.

3 Explain the insurance coverages and policy types available to homeowners and renters.

4 Analyze factors that influence the amount of coverage and cost of home insurance.

5 Identify the important types of automobile insurance coverages.

6 Evaluate factors that affect the cost of automobile insurance.

Insurance and Risk Management: An Introduction

You purchase insurance to control the effects of uncontrollable financial risk inherent to life and living (and for that matter even death). The idea is that certain bad things will happen, but you have no idea when or what, then your best bet is to be ready for them at all times. You do this by buying insurance, and the amount of insurance you buy should reflect the potential financial impact of the loss or partial loss of what you are insuring.

Objective 1

Develop a risk management plan using insurance.

WHAT IS INSURANCE?

Insurance is protection against possible financial loss. Although many types of insurance exist, they all have one thing in common: They give you the peace of mind that comes from knowing that money will be available to meet the needs of your survivors, pay medical expenses, protect your home and belongings, and cover personal or property damage.

Life insurance replaces income that would be lost if the policyholder died. Health insurance helps meet medical expenses when the policyholder becomes ill. Automobile insurance helps cover property and personal damage caused by the policyholder's car. Home insurance covers the policyholder's place of residence and its associated financial risks, such as damage to personal property and injuries to others.

An **insurance company**, or **insurer**, is a risk-sharing firm that agrees to assume financial responsibility for losses that may result from an insured risk. A person joins the risk-sharing group (the insurance company) by purchasing a **policy** (a contract). Under the policy, the insurance company agrees to assume the risk for a fee (the **premium**) that the person (the **insured**, or the **policyholder**) pays periodically.

Insurance mitigates the risks of financial uncertainty and unexpected losses. The financial consequences of failing to obtain the right amount and type of insurance can be disastrous.

insurance Protection against possible financial loss.

insurance company A risk-sharing firm that assumes financial responsibility for losses that may result from an insured risk.

insurer An insurance company.

policy A written contract for insurance.

premium The amount of money a policyholder is charged for an insurance policy.

insured A person covered by an insurance policy.

policyholder A person who owns an insurance policy.

TYPES OF RISKS

You face risks every day. You can't cross the street without some danger that you'll be hit by a car. You can't own property without taking the chance that it will be lost, stolen, damaged, or destroyed. Insurance companies offer financial protection against such dangers and losses by promising to compensate the insured for a relatively large loss in return for the payment of a much smaller but certain expense called the *premium*.

Risk, *peril*, and *hazard* are important terms in insurance. Each has a distinct, technical meaning in insurance terminology.

risk Chance or uncertainty of loss; may also mean "the insured."

Risk is the chance that something may be lost. When someone buys insurance, they assume that even if the associated risk happens, they will not be overly affected. For example, many people insure their car for loss and damage because they know the odds are good that risk may occur, and they know that repair or replacement costs could be very large. By buying insurance, they minimize the potential impact of a risk.

peril The cause of a possible loss.

Peril is the cause of a possible loss. It is the event that causes someone to take out insurance. People buy policies for financial protection against such perils as fire, windstorms, explosions, robbery, accidents, and premature death.

hazard A factor that increases the likelihood of loss through some peril.

Hazard increases the likelihood of loss through some peril. For example, defective house wiring is a hazard that increases the likelihood of the peril of fire.

The most common risks are classified as personal risks, property risks, and liability risks. *Personal risks* are the uncertainties surrounding loss of income or life due to premature death, illness, disability, old age, or unemployment. *Property risks* are the uncertainties of direct or indirect losses to property due to fire, windstorms, accidents, theft, and other hazards. *Liability risks* are loss possibilities due to negligence resulting in bodily harm or property damage to others. Such harm or damage could be caused by an automobile, professional misconduct, injury suffered on one's property, and so on.

pure risk A risk in which there is only a chance of loss; also called *insurable risk*.

Personal risks, property risks, and liability risks are types of **pure risk**, or *insurable risk*, since there would be a chance of loss only if the specified events occurred. Pure risks are accidental and unintentional risks for which the nature and financial cost of the loss can be predicted.

speculative risk A risk in which there is a chance of either loss or gain.

A **speculative risk** is a risk that carries a chance of either loss or gain. Starting a small business that may or may not succeed is an example of speculative risk. So is gambling. Speculative risks are legally defined as uninsurable.

RISK MANAGEMENT METHODS

Risk management is an organized strategy for protecting assets and people. It controls financial losses caused by destructive events. Risk management is a long-range planning process. People's risk management needs change at various points in their lives. If you understand risks and how to manage them, you can provide better protection for yourself and your family. You can reduce your financial losses and thereby improve your chances for economic, social, physical, and emotional well being. Since you will probably be unable to afford to cover all risks, you need to understand how to obtain the best protection you can afford.

Most people think of risk management as buying insurance. However, insurance is not the only method of dealing with risk; in certain situations, other methods may be less costly. Four general risk management techniques are commonly used.

1. RISK AVOIDANCE You can avoid the risk of an automobile accident by not driving to work. General Motors can avoid the risk of product failure by not introducing new cars. Risk avoidance would be practised in both instances, but at a very high cost. You might have to give up your job, and General Motors might lose out to competitors that introduce new models.

DID YOU KNOW ?

Alien abduction protection, pet insurance, and coverage if you turn into a werewolf are some of the strange but real-life policies available for a price. Wedding disaster insurance paid for an entire wedding party to reassemble at the original location—Hawaii—to recreate the scene for new photos when all the negatives were stolen from the photographer's car. One life insurance company gives fast runners discounts off their policies by submitting a certified race time for an event that's 5K or longer.

(Kimberly Lankford, "Weird Insurance," *Kiplinger's Personal Finance Magazine*, October, 1998, pp. 113–116.)

In some situations, however, risk avoidance is practical. At the personal level, people avoid risks by not smoking or by not walking through high-crime neighbourhoods. At the business level, jewellery stores avoid losses through robbery by locking their merchandise in vaults. Obviously, no person or business can avoid all risks.

2. RISK REDUCTION While avoiding risks completely may not be possible, reducing risks may be a cause of action. You can reduce the risk of injury in an auto accident by wearing a seat belt. You can install smoke alarms and fire extinguishers to protect life and reduce potential fire damage. You can reduce the risk of illness by eating a balanced diet and exercising.

3. RISK ASSUMPTION Risk assumption means taking on responsibility for the loss or injury that may result from a risk. Generally, it makes sense to assume a risk when the potential loss is small, when risk management has reduced the risk, when insurance coverage is expensive, and when there is no other way to obtain protection. For instance, you might decide not to purchase collision insurance on an older car. Then, if an accident occurs, you will bear the costs of fixing the car.

Self-insurance is the process of establishing a monetary fund to cover the cost of a loss. Self-insurance does not eliminate risks; it only provides means for covering losses. Many people self-insure by default, not by choice. Others take on as much insurance as they can afford and then self-insure the rest.

self-insurance The process of establishing a monetary fund to cover the cost of a loss.

4. RISK SHIFTING The most common method of dealing with risk is to shift, or transfer, it to an insurance company or some other organization. Insurance is the protection against loss afforded by the purchase of an insurance policy from an insurance company. Insurers, in their turn, usually insure themselves through what is known as re-insuring. By re-insuring the risks they have assumed by insuring your risk, they are acting very much like you: they are controlling the potential effects should risks actualize.

Exhibit 8–1 summarizes various risks and appropriate strategies for managing them.

PLANNING AN INSURANCE PROGRAM

Because all people have their own needs and goals, many of which change over the years, a personal insurance program should be tailored to those changes. In the early years of marriage, when the family is growing, most families need certain kinds of insurance protection. This protection may include property insurance on an apartment or a house, life and disability insurance for wage earners and caretakers of dependants, and adequate health insurance for the whole family.

Later, when the family has a higher income and a different financial situation, protection needs will change. There might be a long-range provision for the children's education, more life insurance to match higher income and living standards, and revised health insurance protection. Still later, when the children have grown and are on their own, retirement benefits will be a consideration, further changing the family's personal insurance program.

The Financial Planning for Life's Situations feature on page 215 suggests several guidelines to follow in planning your insurance program. Exhibit 8–2 outlines the steps in developing a personal insurance program.

> **DID YOU KNOW ?**
>
> Deductibles are a combination of risk assumption and risk shifting. The insured person assumes part of the risk, paying the first $100, $250, or $500 of a claim. The majority of the risk for a large claim is shifted to another party, the insurance company.

Exhibit 8–1   Examples of Risks and Risk Management Strategies

Risks		Strategies for Reducing Financial Impact		
Personal Events	Financial Impact	Personal Resources	Private Sector	Public Sector
Disability	Loss of one income Loss of services Increased expenses	Savings, investments Family observing safety precautions	Disability insurance	Disability insurance
Illness	Loss of one income Medical expenses	Health-enhancing behaviour	Health insurance	Medicare
Death	Loss of one income Loss of services Funeral expenses	Estate planning Risk reduction	Life insurance	Veteran's life insurance Government programs survivor's benefits
Retirement	Decreased income Unplanned living expenses	Savings Investments Hobbies, skills	Retirement and/or pensions	Public pensions Pension plan for government employees
Property loss	Catastrophic storm damage to property Repair or replacement cost of theft	Property repair and upkeep Security plans	Automobile insurance Homeowner's insurance Tenant's insurance	Basic disaster relief
Liability	Claims and settlement costs Lawsuits and legal expenses Loss of personal assets and income	Observing safety precautions Maintaining property	Homeowner's insurance Automobile insurance	

Exhibit 8–2

Creating a
Personal
Insurance
Program

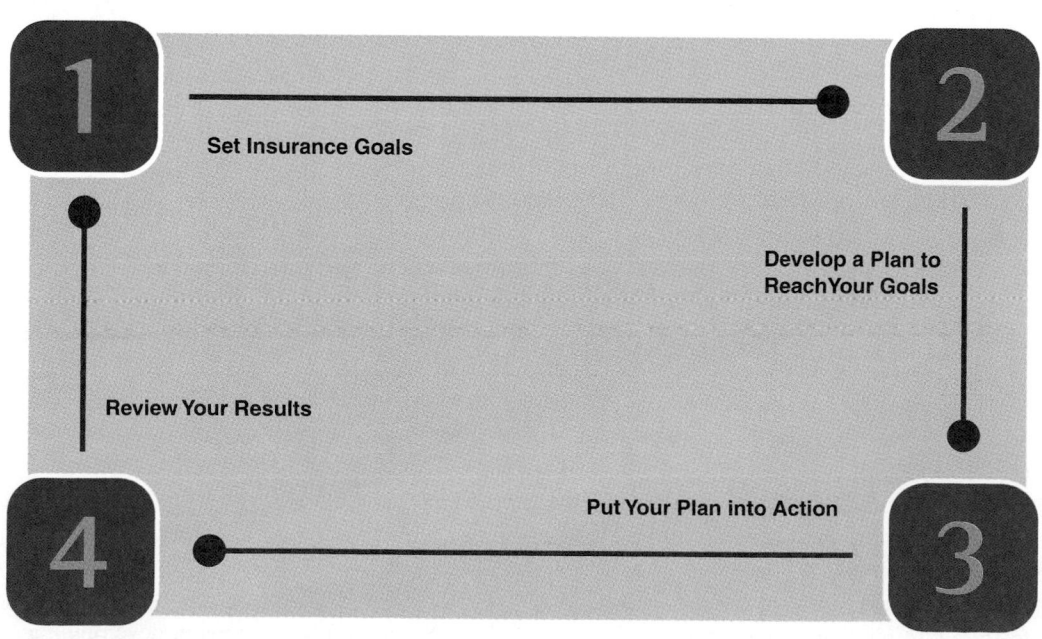

Financial Planning for Life's Situations

HOW CAN YOU PLAN AN INSURANCE PROGRAM?

Did you:	Yes	No
• Seek advice from a competent and reliable insurance adviser?	☐	☐
• Determine what insurance you need to provide your family with sufficient protection if you die?	☐	☐
• Consider what portion of the family protection is met by social assistance and by group insurance?	☐	☐
• Decide what other needs insurance must meet (funeral expenses, savings, retirement annuities, etc.)?	☐	☐
• Decide what types of insurance best meet your needs?	☐	☐
• Plan an insurance program and implement it except for periodic reviews of changing needs and changing conditions?	☐	☐
• Avoid buying more insurance than you need or can afford?	☐	☐
• Drop one policy for another that provides the same coverage for less money?	☐	☐

Note: *Yes* answers reflect wise actions for insurance planning.
SOURCE: Used with permission of Insurance Canada www.insurance-canada.ca.

STEP 1: SET INSURANCE GOALS In managing risks, your goal is to minimize personal, property, and liability risks. Your insurance goals should define what to do to cover the basic risks present in your life situation. Covering the basic risks means providing a financial resource to cover costs resulting from a loss.

Suppose your goal is to buy a new car. You must plan to make the purchase and to protect yourself against financial losses from accidents. Auto insurance on the car lets you enjoy the car without worrying that an auto accident might leave you worse off, financially, than before.

Each individual has unique goals. Income, age, family size, lifestyle, experience, and responsibilities influence the goals you set, and the insurance you buy must reflect those goals. In general, financial advisers say that a basic risk management plan must set goals to reduce the impact of the following events:

- Potential loss of income due to the premature death, illness, accident, or unemployment of a wage earner.
- Potential loss of income and extra expense resulting from the illness, disability, or death of a spouse.
- Additional expenses due to the injury, illness, or death of other family members.
- Potential loss of real or personal property due to fire, theft, or other hazards.
- Potential loss of income, savings, and property due to personal liability.

STEP 2: DEVELOP A PLAN TO REACH YOUR GOALS Planning is a sign of maturity, a way of taking control of life instead of letting life happen to you. What risks do you face? Which risks can you afford to take without having to back away from your goals? What resources—public programs, personal assets, or private risk-sharing plans—are available to you?

Visit the Web site
See Personal Financial Planning worksheets under Chapter 8 on the online learning centre at www.mcgrawhill.ca/college/kapoor.

215

To understand and use the resources at your command, you need good information. In terms of insurance, this means a clear picture of the available insurance, the reliability of different insurers, and the comparative costs of the coverage needed. See the Financial Planning for Life's Situations box on the next page for a list of key questions to ask your insurance provider before you purchase your home insurance.

STEP 3: PUT YOUR PLAN INTO ACTION As you carry out your plan, obtain financial and personal resources, budget them, and use them to reach your risk management goals. If, for example, you find the insurance protection you have is not enough to cover your basic risks, you may purchase additional coverage, change the kind of insurance coverage, restructure your budget to cover additional insurance costs, and strengthen your savings or investment programs to reduce long-term risk.

The best risk management plans have flexibility. Savings accounts or other cash, for example, should be available as emergency funds for unexpected financial problems. The best plans are also flexible enough to allow you to respond to changing life situations. Your goal should be an insurance program that expands (or contracts) with changing protection needs.

To put your risk management plan to work, you must answer four basic questions: (1) What should be insured, (2) for how much, (3) what kind of insurance should I buy, and (4) from whom?

STEP 4: REVIEW YOUR RESULTS Evaluate your insurance plan periodically, at least every two or three years or whenever your family circumstances change. Among the questions you should ask yourself are: Does it work? Does it adequately protect my plans and goals? An effective risk manager consistently checks the outcomes of decisions and is alert to changes that may reduce the effectiveness of the current risk management plan.

A young working couple may be entirely happy with their life and health insurance coverage. When they add an infant to the family, however, a review of protection is appropriate. Suddenly the risk of financial catastrophe to the family (should one or both parents die or become disabled) is much greater.

The needs of a single person differ from those of a family, a single parent, a couple, or a group of unrelated adults living in the same household. While these people face similar risks, their financial responsibility to others differs greatly. In each case, the vital question is: "Have I provided the financial resources and risk management strategy needed to take care of my basic responsibilities for my own well being and the well being of others?"

CONCEPT CHECK 8-1

1. What is the purpose of insurance?
2. How are the most common risks classified?
3. What is the difference between pure risk and speculative risk?
4. What are the methods of managing risk?
5. What are the steps in planning your personal insurance coverage?

Financial Planning for Life's Situations

HOMEOWNERS INSURANCE CHECKLIST

Following are some key questions to ask your insurance provider BEFORE you purchase your home insurance.

(Questions supplied by the *Insurance Bureau of Canada*)

- Who is covered under this policy?
- What property is covered?
- What "perils" are covered? (A peril is an event that can cause damage, such as fire, theft, or wind.)
- What is NOT covered? (This is called an "exclusion." Exclusions may apply to the persons who are covered, the property covered, the perils insured against, or the location where the coverage applies. Not every circumstance can be covered by an insurance policy. Normal wear-and-tear and deterioration of property are not insurable; you should check your policy for other exclusions.)

- What extensions of coverage are available? (Often called "riders," "forms," or "endorsements," some policy extensions are automatic, while others are optional and/or conditional.)
- What are the conditions of coverage, and what do you have to do to make sure that coverage continues?
- What do you do if there's a loss? How do you make a claim to recover a loss?

The preceding questions are intended as a guideline only and are not meant to be exhaustive.

SOURCE: http://www.insurance-canada.ca/

Property and Liability Insurance

Major disasters have caused catastrophic amounts of property loss. Some recent examples of these types of disasters are when a storm surge caused coastal flooding in the Gulf of St. Lawrence affecting P.E.I, New Brunswick, and Nova Scotia in 2000, the ice storm of 1998 that devastated parts of Ontario, Quebec, and the Maritimes, and the forest fires in British Columbia and elsewhere that frequently spring up in dry seasons and threaten to envelop entire villages.

Since most people invest large amounts of money in their homes and motor vehicles, protecting these assets from loss is a great concern. The cost of injuries and property damage caused by automobiles is also very great. Most people use insurance to reduce their chances of economic loss from these risks.

The price you pay for home and automobile insurance may be viewed as an investment in financial protection against these losses. Although the costs of home and automobile insurance may seem high, the financial losses from which insurance protects you are much higher. Property and liability insurance offer protection from financial losses that may arise from a wide variety of situations. See the Financial Planning for Life's Situations feature on page 218 to test your knowledge of what type of financial losses your insurance will cover.

The main risks related to homes and automobiles are (1) property damage or loss, and (2) your responsibility for injuries to others or damage to the property of others.

Objective 2

Discuss the importance of property and liability insurance.

POTENTIAL PROPERTY LOSSES

Houses, automobiles, furniture, clothing, and other personal belongings represent a substantial financial commitment. Property owners face two basic types of risks. The first is *physical*

Financial Planning for Life's Situations

ARE YOU COVERED?

Often people believe their insurance will cover various financial losses. For each of the following situations, name the type of home or automobile insurance that would protect you.

1. While you are on vacation, clothing and other personal belongings are stolen. _____

2. Your home is damaged by fire, and you have to live in a hotel for several weeks. _____

3. You and members of your family suffer injuries in an automobile accident caused by a hit-and-run driver. _____

4. A deliveryperson is injured on your property and takes legal action against you. _____

5. Your automobile is accidentally damaged by some people playing baseball. _____

6. A person takes legal action against you for injuries you caused in an automobile accident. _____

7. Water from a local lake rises and damages your furniture and carpeting. _____

8. Your automobile needs repairs because you hit a tree. _____

ANSWERS: (1) Personal property coverage of home insurance; (2) additional living expenses of home insurance; (3) accident benefits; (4) third-party liability coverage of home insurance; (5) comprehensive physical damage; (6) bodily injury liability; (7) flood insurance—requires coverage separate from home insurance; (8) collision.

---

damage caused by such hazards as fire, wind, water, and smoke. These hazards can cause destruction of your property or temporary loss of its use. For example, if a windstorm causes a large tree branch to break your windshield, you lose the use of the vehicle while it is being repaired. The second risk property owners face is *loss of use* due to robbery, burglary, vandalism, or arson.

LIABILITY PROTECTION

In many circumstances, a person may be judged legally responsible for injuries or damages. For example, if a child walks across your property, falls, and sustains severe injuries, the child's family may be able to recover damages from you as a result of the injuries. If you accidentally damage a rare painting while assisting a friend with home repairs, the friend may take legal action against you to recover the cost of the painting.

Liability is legal responsibility for the financial cost of another person's losses or injuries. Your legal responsibility is commonly caused by **negligence,** failure to take ordinary or reasonable care. Doing something in a careless manner, such as improperly supervising children at a swimming pool or failing to remove items from a frequently used staircase, may be ruled as negligence in a liability lawsuit.

liability Legal responsibility for the financial cost of another person's losses or injuries.

negligence Failure to take ordinary or reasonable care in a situation.

Advice from a Pro

A PRO SPEAKS ON INSURANCE

Ever been to a casino? Ever made a bet?

Buying insurance is essentially making a bet that you *don't* want to win. While you can't *plan* on experiencing many of life's calamities, you *should* plan for them. Without the appropriate insurance, a single event, such as a major accident, can completely trash your hard-earned assets.

Never smoked? Healthy as a horse? It doesn't matter! Insurance is specifically designed for those situations you hope will never occur. When those situations do occur, however, you'll find that savvy spending on appropriate insurance was money well spent.

Life insurance takes care of your dependants after you die. If you have a spouse, children, or other loved ones who are directly dependent on your income, life insurance is a *must*. Young people generally find they don't need life insurance.

Health insurance foots the medical bills if you get sick. If you've ever paid full price for a medical prescription, you are probably aware that health care costs have sky-rocketed. Even a seemingly simple procedure can often cost thousands of dollars. So, everyone needs health insurance, and thankfully, many employers offer group plans at reasonable rates. Be sure to inquire about health insurance when applying for a job; the level of insurance offered might affect your interest in working for a particular company. Working solo? Individuals who purchase private policies will pay more for equivalent coverage.

Keep in mind that there are insurance products available for any number of scenarios, so do your homework and evaluate your needs. As always, read everything and ask questions.

Despite taking great care, a person may still be held liable in a situation. **Strict liability** is present when a person is held responsible for intentional or unintentional actions. **Vicarious liability** occurs when a person is held responsible for the actions of another person. If the behaviour of a child causes financial or physical harm to others, the parent may be held responsible; if the activities of an employee cause damage, the employer may be held responsible.

strict liability A situation in which a person is held responsible for intentional or unintentional actions.

vicarious liability A situation in which a person is held legally responsible for the actions of another person.

CONCEPT CHECK 8-2

1. What property and liability risks might some people overlook?
2. How could a person's life situation influence the need for certain types of property and liability insurance?

Principles of Home and Property Insurance

Objective 3

Explain the insurance coverages and policy types available to home-owners and renters.

homeowner's insurance Coverage for a place of residence and its associated financial risks.

Your home and personal belongings are probably a major portion of your assets. Whether you rent your dwelling or own a home, property insurance is vital. **Homeowner's insurance** is coverage for your place of residence and its associated financial risks, such as damage to personal property and injuries to others (see Exhibit 8–3).

HOMEOWNER'S INSURANCE COVERAGES

A homeowner's policy provides coverages for the building and other structures, additional living expenses, personal property, personal liability and related coverages, and specialized coverages.

BUILDING AND OTHER STRUCTURES The main component of homeowner's insurance is protection against financial loss due to damage or destruction to a house or other structures. Your dwelling and attached structures are covered for fire and other damages. Detached structures on the property, such as a garage, toolshed, or gazebo, are also protected. The coverage may also include trees, shrubs, and plants.

ADDITIONAL LIVING EXPENSES If damage from a fire or other event prevents the use of your home, *additional living expense coverage* pays for the cost of living in a temporary location while your home is being repaired. Some policies limit additional living expense coverage to 10 to 20 percent of the home's coverage and limit payments to a maximum of six to nine months; other policies pay the full cost incurred for up to a year.

PERSONAL PROPERTY Typically, a home insurance policy will cover damage or destruction of the contents of your home—clothes, furniture, appliances, and similar items. The total value of the contents of your home may be calculated in one of two ways: as a percentage of the total value of your insurance coverage, or on an itemized basis that lists and values all the contents of your home. The limit coverage on your personal contents is usually an amount equal to 70 to 80 percent of the limit of insurance on the dwelling. This amount can be increased for an additional premium. Clearly, this method could be inadequate, as it might understate the value of certain items, such as a stamp or doll collection lying forgotten in the attic, that are valued at some astronomical sum.

The itemizing method, an approach generally recommended by insurance agents and companies, allows you to list and value all the items that you wish to protect and ensures adequate

Exhibit 8–3   Home Insurance Coverage

| Building and other structures | Personal property | Loss of use/additional living expenses while home is uninhabitable | Personal liability and related coverages |

coverage. This method will allow you to fully insure as much or as little as you wish within your home. It is recommended that you keep your list of items in a safety deposit box or some other location away from the insured property.

Personal property coverage commonly has limits for the theft of certain items, such as $1,000 for jewellery, $2,000 for firearms, and $2,500 for silverware. Items with a value exceeding these limits can be protected with a **personal property floater**, which covers the damage or loss of a specific item of high value. A floater requires a detailed description of the item and periodic appraisals to verify the current value. This coverage protects the item, regardless of location; thus, the item is insured while you are travelling or transporting it.

> **personal property floater** Additional property insurance to cover the damage or loss of a specific item of high value.

Floaters to protect home computers and other expensive equipment are recommended. This additional coverage can prevent financial loss due to damage or loss of your computer. Contact your insurance agent to determine whether the equipment is covered against damage from mischievous pets, spilled drinks, dropping, or power surges.

Personal property coverage usually provides protection against the loss or damage of articles taken with you when away from home. For example, possessions taken on vacation or used while at school are usually covered up to a policy limit. Property that you rent, such as some power tools or a rug shampoo machine, is insured while in your possession.

In the event of damage or loss of property, you must be able to prove both ownership and value. A **household inventory** is a list or other documentation of personal belongings, with purchase dates and cost information. You can get a form for such an inventory from an insurance agent. Exhibit 8–4 provides a reminder of the items you should include in the inventory. For items of special value, you should have receipts, serial numbers, brand names, model names, and written appraisals of value.

> **household inventory** A list or other documentation of personal belongings, with purchase dates and cost information.

Your household inventory can include photographs or a video recording of your home and contents. Make sure the closet and storage area doors are photographed open. On the backs of the photographs, indicate the date and the value of the objects. Regularly update your inventory, photos, and appraisal documents. Keep a copy of each document in a secure location, such as a safety deposit box.

REPLACEMENT VALUE OF YOUR HOME

Contrary to popular belief, the replacement value of your home for insurance purposes is not its current market value, principally because that type of valuation includes the value of the land and foundation, which are unlikely to be affected by typical disasters. As a result, the home insurance that you purchase will be based on the replacement value of your home's structure, which is the cost of rebuilding or otherwise replacing the structure of your home.

A professional appraisal will usually give you both the depreciated and the replacement value of the structure of your home. Your broker or agent, or your insurance company, can arrange an inspection of your property to assist you in calculating the rebuilding value of your home. Some insurance companies automatically set the amount of home insurance to the amount of the mortgage on the house. You should note, however, that insurance set at this amount protects the mortgage lender's interests and is not meant to cover your own interests in the structure as its owner.

THE 80-PERCENT RULE

In general, most insurance companies will refuse to pay in full for partial damage unless the insured has bought enough insurance to cover at least 80 percent of the home's replacement value. In cases where the coverage is less than 80 percent, the insurance company will only make payments that are proportional to the percentage of required minimum coverage taken. As an example, suppose that you bought a $70,000 home insurance policy on your $100,000 home (keeping in mind that this is the replacement value of the house, not including its foundation or the land it stands upon). If you then suffered a fire loss of $30,000, the insurance company would pay you only $26,250 (which is $70,000 ÷ $80,000 × $30,000). Had you bought insurance on at least 80 percent of your

Exhibit 8–4   Household Inventory Contents

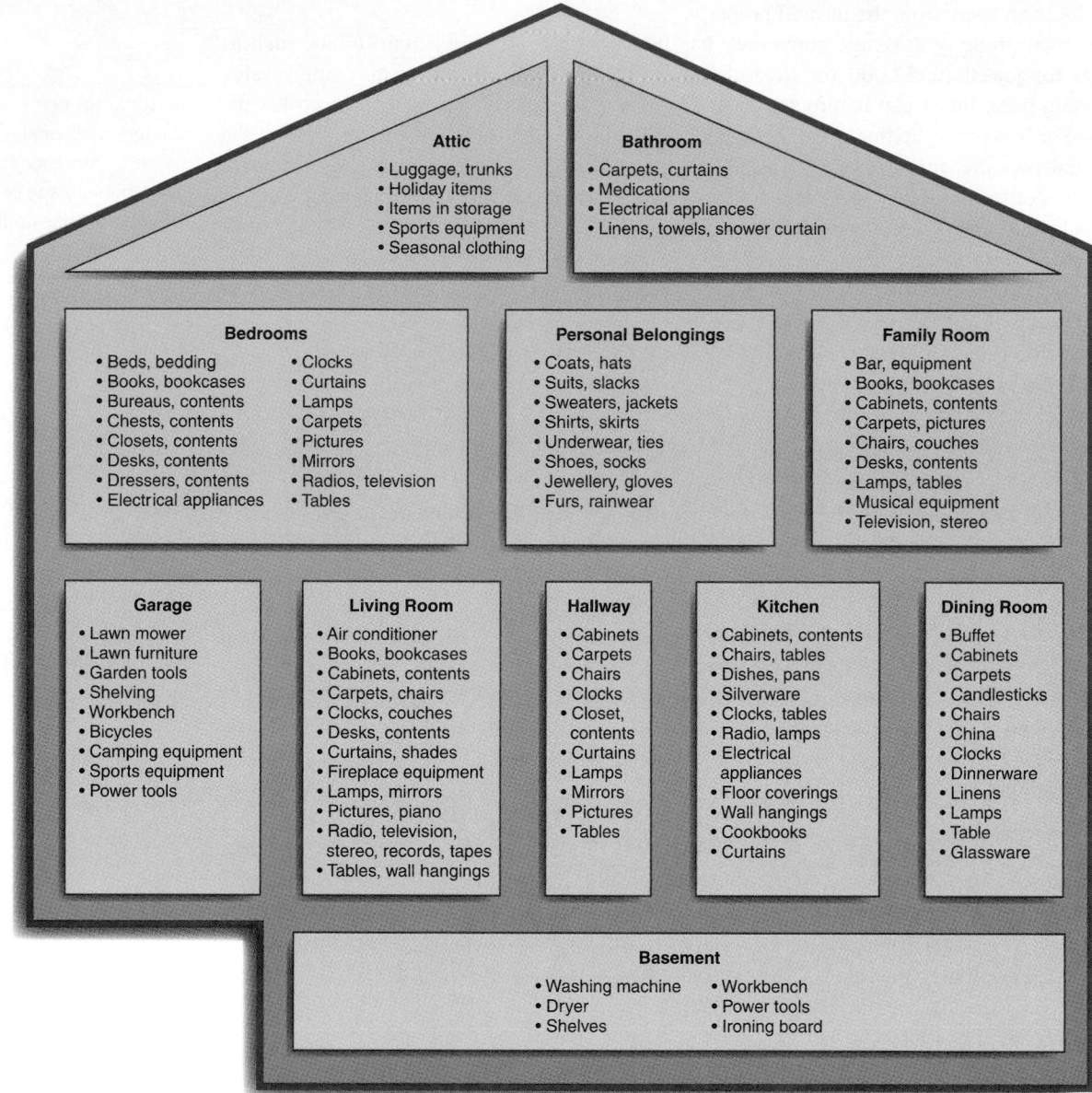

home's structural value, or $80,000 in this example, you would have received the full reimbursement from the insurance company.

The 80-percent rule is especially relevant when you consider inflation. The increasing dollar value of the replacement cost of homes puts you at risk of falling below the required coverage percentage if your policy does not take inflation into account. As a result, many insurance companies now offer an inflation protection provision that automatically increases the coverage amount in tandem with an inflation index, such as the Consumer Price Index. The additional premium you pay for this provision is often well worth it. Additionally, if you live in an area where the housing prices outstrip the rate of inflation, you will again want to insure yourself further, and most insurance companies will be happy to accept further premiums from you to do so.

PERSONAL LIABILITY AND RELATED COVERAGES

Each day, you face the risk of financial loss due to injuries to others or damage to property for which you are responsible. The following are examples of this risk:

- A neighbour or guest falls on your property, resulting in permanent disability.
- A spark from burning leaves on your property starts a fire that damages a neighbour's roof.
- A member of your family accidentally breaks an expensive glass statue while at another person's house.

In each of these situations, you could be held responsible for the costs incurred. The personal liability component of a homeowner's policy protects you from financial losses resulting from legal action or claims against you or family members due to damages to the property of others. This coverage includes the cost of legal defence.

Not all individuals who come to your property are covered by your liability insurance. While a babysitter or others who assist you occasionally are probably covered, regular employees, such as a housekeeper or a gardener, may require worker's compensation coverage.

Most homeowner's policies provide a basic personal liability coverage of $1,000,000, but additional amounts are frequently recommended. An **umbrella policy**, also called a *personal catastrophe policy*, supplements your basic personal liability coverage. This added protection covers you for personal injury claims, such as libel, slander, defamation of character, and invasion of property. Extended liability policies are sold in amounts of $1 million or more and are useful for individuals with substantial net worth. If you are a business owner, you may need other types of liability coverage.

umbrella policy Supplementary personal liability coverage; also called a *personal catastrophe policy*.

Voluntary medical payments pay the costs of minor accidental injuries on your property and minor injuries caused by you, family members, or pets away from home. Settlements under voluntary medical payments are made without determining fault. This protection allows fast processing of small claims, generally up to $5,000. Suits for more severe personal injuries are covered by the personal liability portion of the homeowner's policy. Voluntary medical payments coverage does not cover the people who live in the home being insured.

voluntary medical payments Home insurance that pays the cost of minor accidental injuries on one's property.

Should you or a family member accidentally damage another person's property, the voluntary property damages of homeowner's insurance will pay for these minor mishaps. This protection is usually limited to $500 or $1,000. Again, payments are made regardless of fault. Any property damage claims for greater amounts would require action under the personal liability coverage.

SPECIALIZED COVERAGES

Homeowners insurance and, in fact, most common insurance, is general. It won't cover special risks automatically. Area-specific risks include earthquakes, flooding, and brush-fires. Those with a need for that kind of assurance will need to have a related **rider**, or addition of coverage, added to their policies.

rider An addition of coverage to a standard insurance policy.

Insurance riders and policies can be purchased to cover just about anything, but something to keep in mind is that the costs of insurance are bound to rise wherever risks increase. Policy buyers must ensure that the risks of loss outweigh the costs of insurance at all times. It makes no sense to buy flood insurance in the desert, and it makes little sense not to in areas known for flash flooding.

TENANT'S INSURANCE

For people who rent, home insurance coverages include personal property protection, additional living expenses coverage, and personal liability and related coverages. Protection against financial loss due to damage or loss of personal property is the main component of tenant's insurance. Often, tenants believe they are

DID YOU KNOW ?

While more than 9 out of 10 homeowners have property insurance, only about 4 out of 10 renters are covered.

covered under the insurance policy of the building owner. In fact, the building owner's property insurance does not cover tenants' personal property unless the building owner can be proven liable. If faulty wiring causes a fire and damages a tenant's property, the renter may be able to collect for damages from the building owner. Tenant's insurance is relatively inexpensive and provides protection from financial loss due to many of the same risks covered in homeowner's policies. Your tenant's insurance should include third-party liability coverage. As with the contents of your rented space, the building owner's property insurance coverage will not be applicable if someone is hurt in your apartment and has sustained a significant injury, unless the building owner can be proven liable. Most importantly, the liability section of your tenant's package policy covers you for your Tenant's Legal Liability. Under any liability policy, you are not protected for loss to property in your care or control. If you cause damage to your apartment or unit because of fire, smoke, explosion, or water damage, you can be held liable for it. The Tenant's Legal Liability portion of your policy responds to this type of loss.

HOME INSURANCE TYPES

named perils A policy in which only those perils that are specifically listed will be covered should a loss occur.

all risk A policy in which any event that causes loss or damage to the insured property is covered unless it is specifically excluded.

To provide the consumer with the coverage best suited to their individual needs, insurance companies offer a number of policy forms. Each form differs in the number of perils, or events that could cause a loss, that it provides protection against. Essentially, there are two types of policies. The first is called a **named perils** policy. Only those perils that are specifically listed in the policy will be covered should a loss occur. If the consumer suffers a loss to their property, they must show that the cause of the loss was one of the perils named in order for the loss to be covered. The second type is known as an **all risk** policy. Any event that causes physical loss or damage to the insured property is covered unless it is specifically excluded. Most personal property policies do not cover, for example, damage to business or agricultural property, damage caused by wars, floods, or earthquakes, or intentional damage (see Exhibit 8–5). If

Exhibit 8–5

Not Everything Is Covered

Certain personal property is specifically excluded from the coverage provided by homeowner's insurance:

- Articles separately described and specifically insured, such as jewellery, furs, boats, or expensive electronic equipment.

- Animals, birds, or fish.

- Motorized land vehicles, except those used to service an insured's residence, that are not licensed for road use.

- Any device or instrument for the transmission and recording of sound, including any accessories or antennas, while in or on motor vehicles. This includes stereo tape players, stereo tapes, and citizens' band radios.

- Aircraft and parts.

- Property of roomers, boarders, and other tenants who are not related to any insured.

- Property contained in an apartment regularly rented or held for rental to others by any insured.

- Property rented or held for rental to others away from the residence premises.

- Business property in storage, or held as a sample, or for sale, or for delivery after sale.

- Business property pertaining to business actually conducted on the residence premises.

- Business property away from the residence premises.

the consumer suffers a loss to their property it is the responsibility of the insurance company to show that the cause of the loss is excluded, and if the company cannot do so, the loss is covered. Before purchasing insurance you should be aware of the types of losses or property that are not covered by your policy.

Insurance companies combine different types of coverage together in package policies so that you can choose the one that best suits your needs and your budget. A good guideline is the more extensive the coverage, the higher the premium you will pay. The following chart shows the common combinations of coverage:

Policy Form	Building	Contents
Standard form	Named perils	Named perils
Broad form	All risk	Named perils
Comprehensive form	All risk	All risk

Manufactured housing units and mobile homes usually qualify for insurance coverage with conventional policies. However, certain mobile homes may require a special arrangement and higher rates since their construction makes them more prone to fire and wind damage. The cost of mobile home insurance coverage is most heavily affected by location and by the method used to attach the housing unit to the ground. This type of property insurance is quite expensive; a $20,000 mobile home can cost as much to insure as a $60,000 house.

In addition to the property and liability risks previously discussed, home insurance policies include coverage for:

- Credit card fraud, cheque forgery, and counterfeit money.
- The cost of removing damaged property.
- Emergency removal of property to protect it from damage.
- Temporary repairs after a loss to prevent further damage.
- Fire department charges in areas with such fees.

Visit the Web site
See the Weblinks under Chapter 8 on the online learning centre at www.mcgrawhill.ca/college/kapoor.

EXCLUSIONS

Exclusions are like small print. Pay attention to them because they are part of what defines your insurance policy. Insurance companies use exclusions to help limit the risks they assure for the policy holder. In the wake of the terrorist attacks on the United States on September 11, 2001, for example, many insurers began including a terrorism exclusion in virtually any type of property insurance policy. To the average Canadian landowner, that may be no big deal, but you can be sure it caused concern for the owners of the CN Tower!

CONCEPT CHECK 8–3

1. What main coverages are included in home insurance policies?
2. What is the purpose of personal liability coverage?
3. How does tenant's insurance differ from other home insurance policies?

Home Insurance Cost Factors

Objective 4

Analyze factors that influence the amount of coverage and cost of home insurance.

Financial losses caused by fire, theft, wind, and other risks amount to billions of dollars each year. Since most homeowners have a mortgage on their property, their lending institutions usually require insurance. When purchasing insurance, you can get the best value by selecting the appropriate coverage amount and being aware of factors that affect insurance costs.

DEDUCTIBLES

Before an insurance company pays you any amount of your claim, it will ask that you pay a *deductible*, a fixed sum of money that is stipulated by your policy. The amount of your deductible is often $100, $250, or $500, and your insurance company will subtract that amount from your claim. For example, if you have a $2,000 claim resulting from a fire in your home and your policy stipulates that your deductible is $500, then the insurance company will pay you only $1,500, and you will pay the first $500. If, on the other hand, your insurable loss is $500 or less, then the insurance company will pay nothing.

In general, the higher a deductible you agree to pay, the lower the premium on your policy will be. The insurance company does this for three reasons: First, since you share more of your risk with the insurance company, it needs to pay less. Second, it is generally agreed that people are more careful if the costs of being careless are higher. Finally, a higher deductible means that the insurance company deals with fewer claims, thus saving administration fees.

A higher deductible can also be to your personal advantage as the effect of a higher deductible is to lower the premium cost per dollar of insurance and, thus, raise the amount of coverage. The ultimate result will be that your financial resources will be more secure.

There is a general rule that many financial experts use as a means to determine what an acceptable level of deductible would be for a given individual. The rule is that your deductible should total no more than 3 percent of your net worth. Accordingly, if your net worth were $25,000, your acceptable deductible on insurance should be no more than $750.

HOW MUCH COVERAGE DO YOU NEED?

Several factors affect the insurance coverage needed for your home and property (see Exhibit 8–6). Your insurance protection should be based on the amount needed to rebuild or repair your house, not the amount you paid for it. As construction costs rise, you should increase the amount of coverage. In recent years, most insurance policies have had a built-in inflation clause that increases coverage as property values increase.

In the past, most homeowner's policies contained a provision requiring that the building be insured for at least 80 percent of the replacement value. Under this **co-insurance clause**, the homeowner would have to pay for part of the losses if the property was not insured for the specified percentage of the replacement value. While a few companies still use a co-insurance clause, most companies today suggest full coverage.

If you are financing a home, the lending institution will require you to have property insurance in an amount that covers its financial investment. Remember, too, that the amount of insurance on your home will determine the coverage on the contents. Personal belongings are generally covered up to an amount ranging from 55 to 75 percent of the insurance amount on the dwelling.

co-insurance clause
A policy provision that requires a homeowner to pay for part of the losses if the property is not insured for the specified percentage of the replacement value.

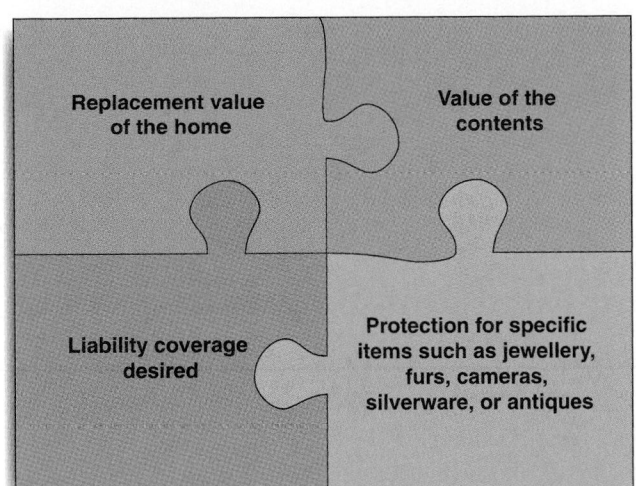

Exhibit 8–6

Determining the
Amount of Home
Insurance You
Need

Insurance companies base claim settlements on one of two methods. Under the **actual cash value (ACV)** method, the payment you receive is based on the current replacement cost of a damaged or lost item less depreciation. This means you would get $180 for a five-year-old television set that cost you $400 and had an estimated life of eight years if the same set now costs $480. Your settlement amount is determined by taking the current cost of $480 and subtracting five years of depreciation from it—$300 for five years at $60 a year.

Under the **replacement value** method for settling claims, you receive the full cost of repairing or replacing a damaged or lost item; depreciation is not considered. In order to receive the replacement value, the item lost must be replaced with an item of like kind and quality and for the same use. Certain items, such as antiques or memorabilia, will not qualify for replacement value. If the item is not replaced the insurance company will pay you the item's actual cash value at the time the loss occurred.

actual cash value (ACV) A claim settlement method in which the insured receives payment based on the current replacement cost of a damaged or lost item, less depreciation.

replacement value A claim settlement method in which the insured receives the full cost of repairing or replacing a damaged or lost item.

FACTORS THAT AFFECT HOME INSURANCE COSTS

The main influences on the premium paid for home and property insurance are the location of the home, the type of structure, the coverage amount and policy type, discounts, and differences among insurance companies.

LOCATION OF HOME
The location of the residence affects insurance rates. So do the efficiency of the fire department, distance from the fire station, the available water supply, and the frequency of thefts in the area. If more claims have been filed in an area, home insurance rates for people living there will be higher.

TYPE OF STRUCTURE
The type of home and the construction materials influence the costs of insurance coverage. A brick house, for example, would cost less to insure than a similar house made of wood. However, earthquake coverage is more expensive for a brick home than for a wood dwelling. Also, the age and style of the house can create potential risks and increase insurance costs. The source of heat especially auxiliary heating sources, such as a woodstove, affect the premium charged for your home. If you have an older home, it is important that the utilities, such as the wiring and plumbing, be updated regularly and meet current building codes. You roof should also be in good condition to ensure the best price on your insurance.

COVERAGE AMOUNT AND POLICY TYPE The policy you select and the financial limits of coverage affect the premium you pay. It costs more to insure a $150,000 home than a $100,000 home. The comprehensive form of homeowner's policy costs more than a tenant's policy.

As discussed, the *deductible* amount in your policy also affects the cost of your insurance. If you increase the amount of your deductible, your premium will be lower since the company will pay out less in claims. The most common deductible amount is $300. Increasing the deductible from $300 to $500 or $1,000 can reduce the premium 15 percent or more.

REDUCING HOME INSURANCE COSTS

HOME INSURANCE DISCOUNTS Most companies offer incentives that reduce home insurance costs. Your premium may be lower if you have smoke detectors or a fire extinguisher. Deterrents to burglars, such as deadbolt locks or an alarm system, can also save you money. Some companies offer home insurance discounts to policyholders who are nonsmokers or may give a discount for being "claim free" for a certain number of years.

COMPANY DIFFERENCES Studies show that you can save up to 25 percent on homeowner's insurance by comparing companies. Contact both insurance agents who work for one company and independent brokers who represent several. The information you obtain will enable you to compare rates. Home insurance rates may be compared using information from such Web sites as www.insuremarket.com.

Don't select a company on the basis of price alone. Also consider service and coverage. Not all companies settle claims in the same way. For example, a number of homeowners had two sides of their houses dented by hail. Since the type of siding used in these houses was no longer available, all of the siding had to be replaced. Some insurance companies paid for complete replacement of the siding, while others paid only for replacement of the damaged areas. Provincial insurance commissions, other government agencies, and consumer organizations can provide information about the reputations of insurance companies.

> ### CONCEPT CHECK 8-4
> 1. What major factors influence the cost of home insurance?
> 2. What actions can a person take to reduce the cost of home insurance?

Automobile Insurance Coverages

Objective 5

Identify the important types of automobile insurance coverages.

The potential damages associated with the risks of owning and operating an automobile can be very large, so much so that they may prove to be disastrous for your wealth and financial future. As a result, all provinces and territories require a minimum automobile insurance coverage if you are the owner or operator of an automobile. Your policy will protect you from three major financial risks (see Exhibit 8–7). The first is the risk of injury or death to you as owner and your passengers. The second is the possibility of damages, destruction, or theft. Finally, and perhaps most importantly, the third risk that an automobile insurance policy protects you against is third-party liability, the possibility that you will be held financially liable if you and your car injure someone else.

While the exact details of minimum coverage vary widely depending on the province or territory you live in, the following discussion is intended to provide you with an understanding of

Risk	Insurance Coverage
Injury to or death of yourself or your passengers	Accident benefits
Damage to your vehicle	Physical damage insurance, such as comprehensive or collision coverage
Liability to others for injury, death, or property damage	Third-party liability coverage

Exhibit 8-7

The Major Risks Assumed by Automobile Owners, and the Protective Insurance Coverage Available

the basic principles and concepts involved in automobile insurance. Every jurisdiction has minimum insurance laws because of the tremendous social and financial risks that are associated with automobiles. In fact, the risks are so significant that it is generally agreed that society cannot simply leave the task of automobile insurance protection to people's personal discretion.

To this effect, British Columbia, Manitoba, and Saskatchewan each provide basic automobile insurance coverage, with extra coverage available from private insurers. In Quebec, auto insurance coverage is split between the provincial government and private insurers. In all the other provinces and territories, provision of auto insurance is left in the hands of private insurers.

You should note that in areas where your insurance is publicly provided, you can expect to pay just one price for coverage and to get it in just one place. Conversely, if the insurance is provided privately through an insurance company, you will find a number of competing suppliers and the price you will be asked to pay may vary.

The main coverages provided by automobile insurance fall into two categories: bodily injury coverages and property damage coverages (see Exhibit 8-8). Other coverages include wage loss insurance, towing service, accidental death, and transportation replacement when a vehicle is undergoing repairs due to an accident.

MOTOR VEHICLE BODILY INJURY COVERAGES

Most of the money automobile insurance companies pay in claims goes for legal expenses of injury lawsuits, medical expenses, and related costs. The main bodily injury coverages are bodily injury liability, medical payments coverage, and uninsured motorist's protection.

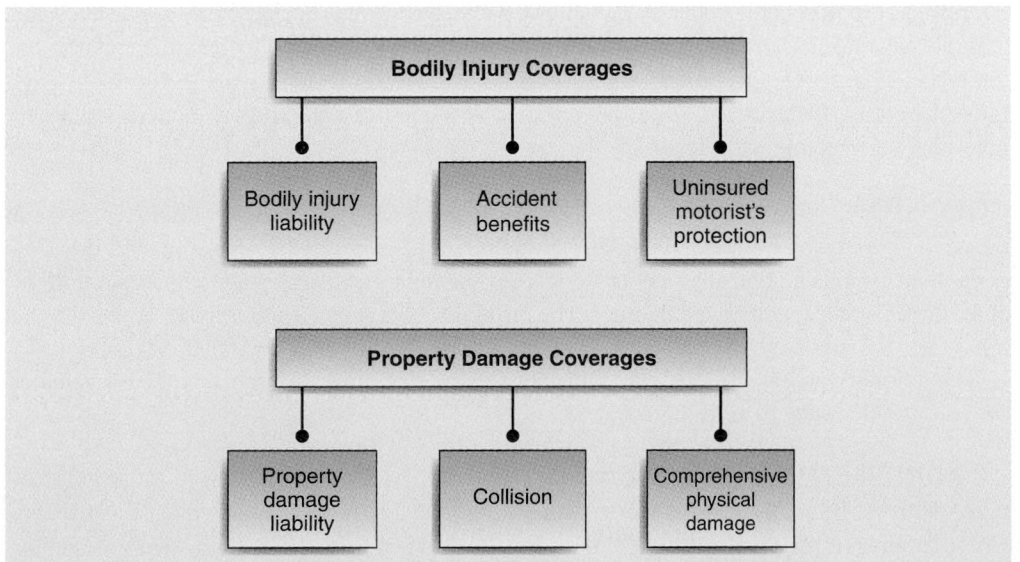

Exhibit 8-8

Two Major Categories of Automobile Insurance

No-fault systems in a number of provinces have influenced the process of settling bodily injury claims.

BODILY INJURY LIABILITY

bodily injury liability Coverage for the risk of financial loss due to legal expenses, medical costs, lost wages, and other expenses associated with injuries caused by an automobile accident for which the insured was responsible.

Bodily injury liability covers the risk of financial loss due to legal expenses, medical expenses, lost wages, and other expenses associated with injuries caused by an automobile accident for which you were responsible. This insurance protects you from extensive financial losses.

The automobile owner's policy covers both the owner and people who drive the vehicle with the owner's permission. As a result, if you are driving someone else's vehicle with their permission and have an accident causing bodily injury to other people, the automobile owner's policy will cover any liability claim. In cases where the owner is uninsured, your own policy will be needed to settle the claim.

ACCIDENT BENEFITS

accident benefits Automobile insurance that covers medical expenses for people injured in one's car.

While bodily injury liability pays for the costs of injuries to persons who were not in your automobile, **accident benefits** cover income replacement, medical, rehabilitation and attendant care expenses, and death and funeral costs for people who were injured in your automobile, including yourself. This protection covers friends, carpool members, and others who ride in your vehicle. These benefits are available if the related costs are the result of an automobile accident, regardless of fault.

UNINSURED MOTORIST'S PROTECTION

uninsured motorist coverage Automobile insurance coverage for the cost of injuries to a person and members of his or her family caused by a driver with inadequate insurance or by a hit-and-run driver.

If you are in an accident caused by an unidentified (unknown) or uninsured person, the **uninsured motorist coverage** protects the insured against the financial burden of injuries to you and your family up to $200,000. Protection is provided for bodily injury claims if the driver is unidentified or uninsured but covers only damage to your vehicle if the driver is identified but uninsured.

NO-FAULT INSURANCE

no-fault insurance An automobile insurance program in which drivers involved in accidents collect medical expenses, lost wages, and related injury costs from their own insurance companies.

As the cost to settle bodily injury claims accelerated relative to the premiums the insurance consumer had to pay, many provinces made the decision to implement no-fault insurance. **No-fault insurance** is widely misunderstood by the general public. Most think it has to do with whether their premium will go up following a claim, when, in fact, fault is determined in every incident for the purpose of premium calculation. No-fault insurance will allow you to collect payment from your own insurance company for bodily injury, and claim for damage to your own automobile no matter who is at fault in an accident. Despite its name, if you are at fault, your insurance premiums may increase. The system is intended to provide faster settlement of claims and reduce the cost associated with taking legal action against the at-fault third party. Manitoba, Saskatchewan, Quebec, and Ontario have all implemented variations of the no-fault system. In Quebec, the right to sue the at-fault party for your bodily injury losses has been removed, as the government pays injured parties. Ontario has a partial no-fault system that still allows suits in situations involving serious injury or death.

COLLISION

collision Automobile insurance that pays for damage to the insured's car when it is involved in an accident.

When your automobile is involved in an accident, **collision** insurance pays for the damage to the automobile, regardless of fault. However, if another driver caused the accident, your insurance company may try to recover the repair costs for your vehicle through the other driver's property damage liability. The insurance company's right to recover the amount it pays for the loss from the person responsible for the loss is called *subrogation*.

The amount you can collect with collision insurance is limited to the actual cash value of the automobile at the time of the accident.

COMPREHENSIVE PHYSICAL DAMAGE

comprehensive physical damage Automobile insurance that covers financial loss from damage to a vehicle caused by a risk other than a collision, such as fire, theft, glass breakage, hail, or vandalism.

Another protection for your automobile involves financial losses from damage caused by a risk other than a collision. **Comprehensive physical damage** covers you for such risks as fire, theft, glass breakage, falling objects, vandalism, wind, hail, flood, tornado, lightning, earthquake, avalanche, or damage caused by hitting an animal. Certain articles in your vehicle, such as some radios and stereo equipment, may be excluded from this insurance. These articles may be protected by the personal property coverage of your home insurance. Like collision insurance, comprehensive coverage applies only to your car, and claims are paid without considering fault. (See the Financial Planning Calculations feature on page 232.)

OTHER AUTOMOBILE INSURANCE COVERAGES

Towing and emergency road service coverage pays for the cost of breakdowns and mechanical assistance. This coverage can be especially beneficial on long trips or during inclement weather. Towing and road service coverage pays for the cost of getting the vehicle to a service station or starting it when it breaks down on the highway, not for the cost of repairs. If you belong to an automobile club, your membership may include towing coverage. Purchasing duplicate coverage as part of your automobile insurance could be a waste of money. Loss of use coverage pays for replacement transportation if your vehicle is stolen or is in the shop for repairs after an accident.

You can also purchase waiver of depreciation coverage for new vehicles. This insurance allows for the waiver of any depreciated value in your new car from the time of purchase for a limited period of time, usually 24 months. If you are in an accident, the insurance company will calculate the value of your loss based on the vehicle's retail value.

CONCEPT CHECK 8-5

1. What are the main coverages included in most automobile insurance policies?
2. What is no-fault insurance?
3. How does collision coverage differ from comprehensive physical damage coverage?

Automobile Insurance Costs

Automobile insurance premiums reflect the amounts insurance companies pay for injury and property damage claims. Your automobile insurance is directly related to coverage amounts and such factors as the vehicle, your place of residence, and your driving record.

The years 2001 and 2002 were an age of awakening for the automobile insurance industry in Canada. Costs related to insurance claims skyrocketed, and insurers scrambled to raise their prices quickly enough to cover the damage. Ontario and the Maritimes were the hardest hit by rising claims costs, but the resulting increases in insurance premiums were felt throughout the country.

Objective 6
Evaluate factors that affect the cost of automobile insurance.

AMOUNT OF COVERAGE

"How much coverage do I need?" This question affects the amount you pay for insurance. Our legal environment and increasing property values influence coverage amounts.

LEGAL CONCERNS As discussed earlier, every province has laws that mandate automobile liability insurance coverage.

Third-party liability (with a minimum limit by law of $200,000 in most provinces), accident benefits, and uninsured motorist coverage are mandatory in order to operate a motor

Financial Planning Calculations

CLAIM SETTLEMENTS AND DEDUCTIBLES

Both collision and comprehensive coverages are commonly sold with a deductible to help reduce insurance costs. If a broken windshield costs $250 to replace and you have a $100 deductible on your comprehensive coverage, the insurance company will pay $150 of the damages.

Deductibles keep insurance premiums lower by reducing the number of small claims companies pay. Going from full-coverage comprehensive insurance to a $100 deductible may reduce the cost of that coverage by as much as 40 percent.

vehicle in Canada. Driving without insurance can result in fines and criminal charges. Physical damage coverage is optional, but if your vehicle is being used as security for a loan, your lending contract may insist upon this coverage in order to protect the interests of the financial institution.

How much is enough? This, of course, depends on you. The minimum liability coverage required by all provinces except Quebec is $200,000. In Quebec, the minimum liability coverage is $50,000 for property damage, and as a Quebec resident, you are compensated for injury without regard to fault.

You may prefer to carry more insurance. Further, if you feel that your net worth is large enough for the liability risk of losing it to be too great, you will want to get more coverage. The prudent amount of coverage that is now commonly sought by Canadian drivers is $1,000,000. There are few liability cases involving amounts greater than this, and so it is usually possible to obtain this higher coverage at a good rate.

AUTOMOBILE INSURANCE PREMIUM FACTORS

Several factors influence the premium you pay for automobile insurance. The main factors are vehicle type, rating territory, and driver classification.

MAKE AND STYLE OF CAR CAN AFFECT INSURANCE COSTS The
type of car you drive generally does not affect the premium you pay for third-party liability insurance. It does, however, affect the cost of coverage for physical damage to your car. Insurance companies rate vehicles according to their safety record and cost to repair or replace them. The Canadian Loss Experience Automobile Rating (CLEAR) system rewards car owners with lower premiums for buying vehicles that experience fewer and smaller losses. For example, some vehicles may be more susceptible to theft than others; some may be better designed and less easily damaged; some are less expensive to repair; some protect their occupants better than others. The CLEAR system was developed by the nonprofit Vehicle Information Centre of Canada (VICC), which is sponsored by the automobile insurance industry. It also makes available to consumers pamphlets which you should check before buying your next vehicle: *Choosing Your Car*, *How Cars Measure Up*, and *Car Theft*. Checking before you buy could save you substantial insurance premium dollars. See www.vicc.com.

USE OF THE VEHICLE What you use your vehicle for has an impact on your premium. Insurance companies differ with regard to vehicles used for pleasure, business, or farming, the distance driven to work each day, and if you are using the vehicle for deliveries or carrying passengers.

RATING TERRITORY Your **rating territory** is the place of residence used to determine your automobile insurance premium. Various geographic locations have different costs due to differences in the number of claims made. For example, fewer accidents and less vandalism occur in rural areas than in large cities.

DRIVER CLASSIFICATION You are compared with other drivers to set your automobile insurance premium. **Driver classification** is a category based on the driver's age, gender, marital status, driving record, and driving habits; drivers' categories are used to determine automobile insurance rates. In general, young drivers (under 25) and those over 70 have more frequent and severe accidents. As a result, they pay higher premiums.

Accidents and traffic violations influence your driver classification. A poor driving record increases your insurance costs. Finally, you pay less for insurance if you do not drive to work than if you use your automobile for business.

The number of claims you file with your insurance company also affects your premiums. If you have many expensive claims or a poor driving record, your company may cancel your policy, making it difficult for you to obtain coverage from another company.

PROVINCIAL DIFFERENCES The factors used for determining the rate of your insurance premium will vary among provinces. In Quebec, you pay a set premium that is established for a given class of vehicle, rather than depending on your qualifications as the driver. In Manitoba, the rates depend on the make and model of your automobile, its use, geographical location, and your driving record, with no discrimination based on your age, gender, or marital status. In British Columbia, you pay premiums determined by the value of your automobile, its use, geography, and your history of claims.

HIGH-RISK-DRIVER INSURANCE Some drivers have accident records or other characteristics that make them very high-risk and thereby unacceptable to standard insurance companies. Nonetheless, some form of coverage must be made available to them if they are required by law to be insured. The insurance industry has solved this problem by creating an insurance pool that assigns high-risk cases to companies in proportion to their share of automobile insurance in each province. The result is that no company receives more than its fair share of bad risks and insurance is available to all drivers.

Having your policy assigned to the **high-risk pool** will not change any of the details of your application for insurance or of your claim. Both processes are the same as for other drivers, with the principal difference being that your premium will be considerably higher.

REDUCING AUTOMOBILE INSURANCE PREMIUMS

Methods for lowering automobile insurance costs include comparing companies and taking advantage of commonly offered discounts.

COMPARING COMPANIES Rates and service vary among automobile insurance companies. Among companies in the same area, premiums can vary as much as 100 percent. If you relocate, don't assume your present company will offer the best rates in your new living area.

Also consider the service the local insurance agent or broker provides. Will this company representative be available to answer questions, change coverages, and handle claims as needed?

PREMIUM DISCOUNTS The best way to keep your rates down is to establish and maintain a safe driving record. Taking steps to avoid accidents and traffic violations will mean

rating territory The place of residence used to determine a person's automobile insurance premium.

driver classification A category based on the driver's age, gender, marital status, driving record, and driving habits; used to determine automobile insurance rates.

high-risk pool Consists of people who are unable to obtain automobile insurance due to poor driving or accident records and must obtain coverage at high rates.

Financial Planning for Life's Situations

WHAT TO DO IF YOU HAVE AN AUTO ACCIDENT

No one plans to have an auto accident; nevertheless, thousands of accidents occur each year. If you are involved in an auto accident, you should take the following actions:

- Stop your vehicle, turn off your ignition, and remain at the scene of the accident.
- Seek medical assistance for anyone who is injured. Do not move an injured person; that should be done by medical personnel.
- Obtain the names and addresses of other drivers, passengers, and witnesses; make notes regarding the circumstances of the accident.

- Assist in the preparation of a police report, if required, by providing your name, address, licence number, and vehicle and insurance information. Do not admit fault.
- Obtain a copy of the police accident report, if any; file the necessary accident documents with your insurance company and provincial or local government agencies.

Visit the Web site

See the Post-Test under Chapter 8 on the online learning centre at www.mcgrawhill.ca/ college/kapoor.

lower automobile insurance premiums. In addition, most insurance companies offer various discounts.

Installing security devices, such as a fuel shutoff switch, a second ignition switch, or an alarm system, will decrease your chances of theft and lower your insurance costs. Being a non-smoker can qualify you for lower automobile insurance premiums. Discounts may also be offered for insuring two or more vehicles with the same company. Ask your insurance agent about other methods for lowering your automobile insurance rates.

Increasing the amount of deductibles will result in a lower premium. Also, some people believe an old car is not worth the amount paid for collision and comprehensive coverages and therefore dispense with them. However, before doing this, be sure to compare the value of your car for getting you to school or work with the cost of these coverages.

If you change your driving habits, get married, or alter your driving status in other ways, be sure to notify the insurance company. Premium savings can result. Also, some employers make group automobile insurance available to workers. And, before you buy a motor vehicle, find out which makes and models have the lowest insurance costs. This information can result in a purchasing decision with many financial benefits.

CONCEPT CHECK 8–6

1. What factors influence how much a person pays for automobile insurance?
2. What actions can a person take to reduce the cost of automobile insurance?

SUMMARY OF OBJECTIVES

Objective 1
Develop a risk management plan using insurance.
The four general risk management techniques are risk avoidance, risk reduction, risk assumption, and risk shifting. In planning a personal insurance program, set your goals, make a plan to reach your goals, put your plan into action, and review your results.

Objective 2
Discuss the importance of property and liability insurance.
Owners of homes and automobiles face the risks of (1) property damage or loss, and (2) legal actions by others for the costs of injuries or property damage. Property and liability insurance, offer protection from financial losses that may arise from a wide variety of situations faced by owners of homes and users of automobiles.

Objective 3
Explain the insurance coverages and policy types available to homeowners and renters.
Homeowner's insurance includes protection for the building and other structures, additional living expenses, personal property, and personal liability. Renter's insurance includes the same coverages excluding protection for the building and other structures, which is the concern of the building owner. The main types of home insurance policies are the basic, broad, special, tenant's, comprehensive, condominium, country home, and modified coverage forms. These policies differ in the risks and property they cover.

Objective 4
Analyze factors that influence the amount of coverage and cost of home insurance.
The amount of home insurance coverage is determined by the replacement cost of your dwelling and personal belongings. The cost of home insurance is influenced by the location of the home, the type of structure, the coverage amount, the policy type, discounts, and insurance company differences.

Objective 5
Identify the important types of automobile insurance coverages.
Automobile insurance is used to meet provincial minimum insurance laws and to protect drivers against financial losses associated with bodily injury and property damage. The major types of automobile insurance coverages are bodily injury liability, medical payments, uninsured motorist's, property damage liability, collision, and comprehensive physical damage.

Objective 6
Evaluate factors that affect the cost of automobile insurance.
The cost of automobile insurance is affected by the amount of coverage, automobile type, use of vehicle, rating territory, driver classification, differences among insurance companies, and premium discounts.

KEY TERMS

accident benefits 230
actual cash value (ACV) 227
all risk 224
bodily injury liability 230
co-insurance clause 226
collision 230
comprehensive physical damage 230
driver classification 233
hazard 212
high-risk pool 233
homeowner's insurance 220
household inventory 221

insurance 211
insurance company 211
insured 211
insurer 211
liability 218
named perils 224
negligence 218
no-fault insurance 230
peril 212
personal property floater 221
policy 211
policyholder 211
premium 211

pure risk 212
rating territory 233
replacement value 227
rider 223
risk 212
self-insurance 213
speculative risk 212
strict liability 219
umbrella policy 223
uninsured motorist coverage 230
vicarious liability 219
voluntary medical payments 223

FINANCIAL PLANNING PROBLEMS

1. *Calculating Property Loss Claim Coverage.* Most home insurance policies cover jewellery and silverware for a limited amount unless items are covered with additional insurance. If $3,500 worth of jewellery and $3,800 worth of silverware were stolen from a family, what amount of the claim would not be covered by insurance? (Obj. 3)

2. *Computing Actual Cash Value Coverage.* What amount would a person with actual cash value (ACV) coverage receive for two-year-old furniture destroyed by a fire? The furniture would cost $1,000 to replace today and had an estimated life of five years. (Obj. 3)

3. *Determining Replacement Cost.* What would it cost an insurance company to replace a family's personal property that originally cost $18,000? The replacement costs for the items have increased 15 percent. (Obj. 3)

4. *Calculating a Co-insurance Claim.* If Carissa Dalton has a $130,000 home insured for $100,000, on the basis of the 80-percent co-insurance provision how much would the insurance company pay on a $5,000 claim? (Obj. 3)

5. *Determining the Claim Amount (with Deductibles).* For each of the following situations, what amount would the insurance company pay? (Obj. 3)
   a. Wind damage of $785; the insured has a $500 deductible.
   b. Theft of a stereo system worth $1,300; the insured has a $250 deductible.
   c. Vandalism that does $375 of damage to a home; the insured has a $500 deductible.

6. *Calculating Future Value of Insurance Savings.* Beverly and Kyle Nelson currently insure their cars with separate companies, paying $450 and $375 a year. If they insured both cars with the same company, they would save 10 percent on the annual premiums. What would be the future value of the annual savings over 10 years on the basis of an annual interest rate of 6 percent? (Obj. 5)

FINANCIAL PLANNING ACTIVITIES

1. *Determining Insurance Coverages.* Survey friends and relatives to determine the types of insurance coverages they have. Also, obtain information about the process used to select these coverages. (Obj. 1)

2. *Researching Insurance on the Internet.* Locate Web sites that provide useful information for selecting and comparing various insurance coverages. (Obj. 1)

3. *Developing a Personal Insurance Plan.* Outline a personal insurance plan with the following phases: (a) identify personal, financial, and property risks; (b) set goals you might achieve when obtaining needed insurance coverages; and (c) describe actions you might take to achieve these insurance goals. (Obj. 1)

4. *Analyzing Insurance Coverages.* Talk to a financial planner or an insurance agent about the financial difficulties faced by people who lack adequate home and auto insurance. What common coverages do many people overlook? (Obj. 2)

5. *Maintaining a Household Inventory.* Survey several people about their household inventory records. In the event of damage or loss, would they be able to prove the value of their personal property and other belongings? (Obj. 3)

6. *Comparing Home Insurance Costs.* Contact two or three insurance agents to obtain information about home or tenant's insurance. Compare the coverage and costs. (Obj. 3)

7. *Analyzing Home Insurance Policies.* Examine a homeowner's or tenant's insurance policy. What coverages does the policy include? Does the policy contain unclear conditions or wording? (Obj. 3)

8. *Reducing Home Insurance Costs.* Talk to several homeowners about the actions they take to reduce the cost of their home insurance. Locate Web sites that offer information about reducing home insurance costs. Prepare a video or other visual presentation to communicate your findings. (Obj. 4)

9. *Determining Auto Insurance Coverages.* Survey several people to determine the types and amounts of automobile insurance coverage they have. Do most of them have adequate coverage? (Obj. 5)

10. *Comparing Auto Insurance Costs.* Contact two or three insurance agents to obtain information about automobile insurance. Compare the coverage and costs. (Obj. 6)

11. *Reducing Auto Insurance Costs.* Search the World Wide Web or talk to an insurance agent to obtain suggestions for reducing automobile insurance costs. (Obj. 6)

LIFE SITUATION CASE

We Rent, So Why Do We Need Insurance?

"Have you been down in the basement?" Nathan asked his wife, Erin, as he entered their apartment.

"No, what's up?" responded Erin.

"It's flooded because of all that rain we got last weekend!" he exclaimed.

"Oh no! We have the extra furniture my mom gave us stored down there. Is everything ruined?" Erin asked.

"The couch and coffee table are in a foot of water; the loveseat was the only thing that looked okay. Boy, I didn't realize the basement of this building wasn't waterproof. I'm going to call our landlady to complain."

As Erin thought about the situation, she remembered that when they moved in last fall, Kathy, their landlady, had informed them that her insurance policy covered the building but not the property belonging to each tenant. Because of this, they had purchased renter's insurance. "Nathan, I think our renter's insurance will cover the damage. Let me give our agent a call."

When Erin and Nathan purchased their insurance, they had to decide whether they wanted to be insured for cash value or for replacement costs. Replacement was more expensive, but it meant they would collect enough to go out and buy new household items at today's prices. If they had opted for cash value, the couch Erin's mother had paid $1,000 for five years ago would be worth less than $500 today.

Erin made the call and found out their insurance did cover the furniture in the basement, and at replacement value after they paid the deductible. The $300 they had invested in renter's insurance last year was well worth it!

Not every renter has as much foresight as Erin and Nathan. Fewer than four in 10 renters have tenant's insurance. Some aren't even aware they need it. They may assume they are covered by the landlord's insurance, but they aren't. This mistake can be costly.

Think about how much you have invested in your possessions and how much it would cost to replace them. Start with your stereo equipment or the colour television and VCR that you bought last year. Experts suggest that people who rent start thinking about these things as soon as they move into their first apartment. Your policy should cover your personal belongings and provide funds for living expenses if you are dispossessed by a fire or other disaster.

Questions

1. Why is it important for people who rent to have insurance?
2. Does the building owner's property insurance ever cover the tenant's personal property?
3. What is the difference between cash value and replacement value?
4. When shopping for renter's insurance, what coverage features should you look for?

CREATING A FINANCIAL PLAN

Obtaining Home and Auto Insurance

Creation of an insurance plan including appropriate coverage for your home, personal property, and motor vehicles helps to avoid financial difficulties.

Web Sites for Home and Auto Insurance

- The Insurance Bureau of Canada, at **www.ibc.ca**, has a useful resource page containing information on insurance regulations, safe driving, and related Ontario-specific advice.
- Insurance Canada, at **www.insurance-canada.ca**, offers insurance-related consumer information.
- The Insurance Adjusters Resource Centre, at **www.adjust-it.com**, has a database of services related to insurance coverage worldwide. Use the search engine to find a company, or subscribe to the newsletter.
- The Insurance Institute of Canada, at **www.iic-iac.org**, is the professional education arm of Canada's property and casualty insurance industry.
- Thompson's World Insurance News, at **www.thompsons news.com**, lays claim to being the Internet home of Canada's

only independent news weekly for insurance professionals. It also provides a useful and extensive list of links.

(Note: Addresses and content of Web sites change, and new sites are created daily. Use search engines to update and locate Web sites for your current financial planning needs.)

Short-Term Financial Planning Activities

1. List current and needed insurance coverages.
2. (a) Prepare an inventory of personal belongings. (b) Compare the cost of homeowner's or tenant's insurance from two or more companies.
3. Compare the cost of auto insurance from two or more companies.

Long-Term Financial Planning Activities

1. Identify buying decisions that could reduce your future home and auto insurance costs.
2. Develop a plan to monitor changes in your life situation that would affect the need to change home or auto insurance coverages.

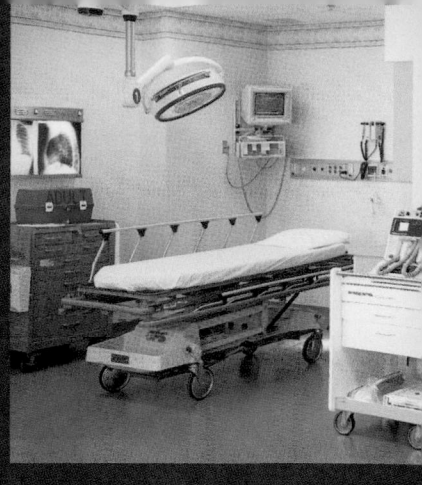

Staying Afloat When Your Health Sinks

Harry Mills had just bought a second dental practice when he was stricken with plasma cell cancer. For two years, he battled to make payments on his new office. By 1997, debilitated by both illness and intensive treatments, the dentist had fallen far behind.

But the Millses still had one big asset: a $250,000 life insurance policy. So, in 1998, Harry tapped it for $100,000. By the time he died in July of 1998, all his debts were paid off. "He didn't have to think he was a failure," says his widow Shirley, "He was able to die with dignity."

As the Millses learned, it is not easy to raise cash once you're diagnosed with a terminal illness. But there are ways to stay financially afloat in your final months. "Look at where the dollars are," says Herbert Daroff, a financial planner. "The value of your house, your life insurance, and your retirement assets." If you get a terminal diagnosis, give yourself time to absorb the doctor's words. Then, get in touch with a financial expert—a planner, broker, or lawyer you trust. The choices you make will depend on your family, resources, and life expectancy. If you have young children, holding on to assets may be a key goal. But if you have three years to live and can no longer work, you may need steady income to pay medical costs and living expenses.

An often overlooked source of income is life insurance. You can tap policies that have cash value, such as whole or universal life, in several ways. The simplest: Take a loan. Most are at near-market rates. And ask about accelerated death benefit riders. If you have less than six months to live, such policies will pay up to half their value before

you die. These options are not available if you have more common term insurance. But you can sell any policy to investors at a discount to its face value, an arrangement called a *viatical settlement*.

Check out the company; make sure it is regulated by an insurance commission. Shop around. Contact several different companies to get the best offer. Instead of selling a term policy, you can borrow using the policy as a collateral.

Some companies will lend up to 85 percent of a policy's value, depending on your life expectancy, and will pay your premiums. You repay nothing while you live, but your interest obligations will be compounding all the while. After you die, the company deducts interest and fees, and returns to your heirs any of the policy's remaining value. You may be charged an application fee of 2 or 3 percent of the total loan. Shirley Mills says her loan cost about $16,000. None of these alternatives is easy. And scrambling for money in the face of terminal illness may be the toughest financial decision you'll ever have to make.

QUESTIONS

1 How can the Internet help you create a life insurance program?

2 What was Harry Mills's biggest asset? Were all his debts paid off when he died?

3 What is an overlooked source of income for terminally ill people?

SOURCE: Adapted from "Staying Afloat When Your Health Sinks," *Business Week*, June 28, 1999, p. 134.

LEARNING OBJECTIVES

1   Define life insurance and describe its purpose and principle.

2   Determine your life insurance needs.

3   Distinguish between the two types of life insurance policies and analyze various types of life insurance.

4   Select important provisions in life insurance contracts.

5   Create a plan to buy life insurance.

6   Recognize how annuities provide financial security.

7   Define health insurance and explain its importance in financial planning.

8   Recognize the need for disability income insurance.

9   Understand the value of supplemental health and disability insurance.

Life Insurance: An Introduction

Canadians are among the most life-insured people in the world. By year-end 2000, we owned $2,078 billion in life insurance, we received $39.5 billion in payments from life and health insurance companies, and there were 120 active life insurance companies operating in Canada. In that year alone, Canadians paid a total of $44.4 billion in premiums on existing and new policies. About 17 million Canadians now have life insurance, and the average amount per insured individual in 2000 was about $121,400, with the average on a consistent rise since 1960.

The problem is that despite these figures, many families are still not adequately covered. All too often, either too little or too much insurance is purchased, or the wrong kind of coverage is sought for the wrong people. The consequence is that when a crisis situation arises, many find that their insurance coverage is inadequate, too stringent in its criteria for claims admissibility, or both.

The following chapter will introduce you to life insurance and will help you determine the level of your need for it as well as help you decide between different types of life insurance policies. It describes what life insurance is and how it works, as well as how you can use it to protect your family.

Objective 1

Define *life insurance* and describe its purpose and principle.

Visit the Web site
See the Pre-Test under Chapter 9 on the online learning centre at www.mcgrawhill.ca/college/kapoor.

WHAT IS LIFE INSURANCE?

Life insurance is neither mysterious nor difficult to understand. It works in the following manner: A person joins a risk-sharing group (an insurance company) by purchasing a contract (a policy). Under the policy, the insurance company promises to pay a sum of money at the time of the policyholder's death to the person or persons selected by him or her (the beneficiaries). In the case of an endowment policy, the money is paid to the policyholder (the insured) if he or she is alive on the future date (the maturity date) named in the policy. The insurance company makes this promise in return for the insured's agreement to pay it a sum of money (the premium) periodically.

THE PURPOSE OF LIFE INSURANCE

Most people buy life insurance to protect someone who depends on them from financial losses caused by their death. That someone could be the nonworking spouse and children of a single-income family. It could be the wife or husband of a two-income family. It could be an aging parent. It could be a business partner or a corporation.

Life insurance proceeds may be used to

- Pay off a home mortgage or other debts at the time of death.
- Provide lump-sum payments through an endowment to children when they reach a specified age.
- Provide an education or income for children.
- Make charitable bequests after death.
- Provide a retirement income.
- Accumulate savings.
- Establish a regular income for survivors.
- Set up an estate plan.
- Make estate and death tax payments.

Life insurance is one of the few ways to provide liquidity at the time of death.

THE PRINCIPLE OF LIFE INSURANCE

The principle of home insurance, discussed in Chapter 8, can be applied to the lives of people. From records covering many years and including millions of lives, mortality tables have been prepared to show the number of deaths among various age groups during any year. A standard mortality table is shown in Exhibit 9–1. A 30-year old man has a 0.001 probability of dying before his next birthday. If he wishes to buy a $200,000 term insurance policy for one year, the premium he will be asked to pay will be close to $200, or $0.001 \times \$200,000$, since this is the average amount of money the insurance company expects to need to pay out for every $200,000 of coverage for all of its male clients aged 30.

Of course, this amount will be adjusted for a number of factors, including particular characteristics that may put a person at higher or lower risk, the various administrative fees that each company must pay, and other factors. In general, it is best to look for a company that manages its resources efficiently, as this lower company cost may translate to a lower premium for you. You should also be aware that because your premiums must be paid at the start of the year but benefits might only be collected later, the insurance company should discount your premium to account for its extended opportunity to earn interest on the funds.

CONCEPT CHECK 9–1

1. How can the Internet help you create a life insurance plan?
2. What is the meaning of life insurance?
3. What is the purpose of life insurance?
4. What is the principle of life insurance?
5. What do mortality tables indicate?

Age	Alive at Start of Year	Deaths during Year	Probability of Survival	Probability of Death
<1 year	100,000	709	0.99291	0.00709
1 year	99,291	51	0.99949	0.00051
2 years	99,240	41	0.99959	0.00041
3 years	99,199	34	0.99966	0.00034
4 years	99,165	25	0.99975	0.00025
15 years	98,930	64	0.99935	0.00065
16 years	98,866	79	0.99920	0.00080
17 years	98,787	90	0.99909	0.00091
18 years	98,697	98	0.99901	0.00099
19 years	99,599	103	0.99895	0.00105
20 years	98,496	107	0.99891	0.00109
21 years	98,389	110	0.99888	0.00112
22 years	98,279	112	0.99886	0.00114
23 years	98,167	113	0.99885	0.00115
24 years	98,054	113	0.99885	0.00115
25 years	97,941	112	0.99886	0.00114
26 years	97,829	111	0.99886	0.00114
27 years	97,718	112	0.99886	0.00114
28 years	97,606	113	0.99884	0.00116
29 years	97,493	116	0.99881	0.00119
30 years	97,377	120	0.99878	0.00122
65 years	80,007	1,632	0.97960	0.02040
66 years	78,375	1,748	0.97770	0.02230
67 years	76,627	1,873	0.97556	0.02444
68 years	74,754	2,002	0.97322	0.02678
69 years	72,752	2,129	0.97073	0.02927
70 years	70,623	2,259	0.96801	0.03199
71 years	68,364	2,395	0.96498	0.03502
72 years	65,969	2,535	0.96156	0.03844
73 years	63,434	2,676	0.95782	0.04218
74 years	60,758	2,807	0.95380	0.04620
75 years	57,951	2,931	0.94942	0.05058
76 years	55,020	3,049	0.94458	0.05542
77 years	51,971	3,160	0.93920	0.06080
78 years	48,811	3,256	0.93330	0.06670
79 years	45,555	3,328	0.92695	0.07305
80 years	42,227	3,374	0.92009	0.07991
81 years	38,853	3,393	0.91268	0.08732
82 years	35,460	3,381	0.90466	0.09534
83 years	32,079	3,334	0.89606	0.10394
84 years	28,745	3,251	0.88692	0.11308
105 years	47	22	0.52616	0.47384
106 years	25	25	0.00000	1.00000

Exhibit 9–1

Mortality Table for Canadian Males

The table provides the number of deaths expected during any year of life for a hypothetical cohort of 100,000 Canadian males.

SOURCE: "Complete Life Table, Canada 1995–1997," adapted from the Statistics Canada publication "Life Tables, Canada and Territories." Catalogue 84–537, August 23, 2002.

Column 1, Age, is the starting age for the given year.

Column 2, Alive at Start of Year, shows how many of the cohort were alive at the start of the year at the age shown in column 1. For example, we see that in the third year, 99,199 of the original cohort were expected to be living.

Column 3, Deaths during Year, records the number of deaths expected to occur during the year starting on the birthday in Column 1. We see that, on average, 34 of the 99,199 alive on their fifth birthday are expected to die before their sixth birthday. In the entry for Column 2, Alive at Start of Year, Age 4 is equal to Column 2 minus Column 3 from the previous line, Age 3.

Column 4, Probability of Survival, is calculated as (Column 2 – Column 3) / Column 2, rounded to five decimal places. Thus, a three-year-old boy has a 0.99966 probability of surviving to his next birthday.

Column 5, Probability of Death, is calculated as Column 3 / Column 2, rounded to five decimal places.

Determining Your Life Insurance Needs

Objective 2

Determining your
life insurance needs.

You should consider a number of factors before you buy life insurance. These factors include your present and future sources of income, other savings and income protection, group life insurance, group annuities (or other pension benefits), net worth, and government benefits. First, however, you should determine whether you need life insurance.

DO YOU NEED LIFE INSURANCE?

If your death would cause financial stress for your spouse, children, parents, or anyone else you want to protect, you should consider purchasing life insurance. Your stage in the life cycle and the type of household you live in will influence this decision. Single persons living alone or with their parents usually have little or no need for life insurance. Consider Brian Brickman, 28, a bachelor who does not smoke, is in excellent health, and has no dependants. Brian owns a $100,000 condominium with a $90,000 mortgage. Since his employer provides a $100,000 group term life policy, he needs no additional life insurance. Larry Lucas, 32, and his wife, Liz, 30, are professionals, each earning $45,000 a year. The Lucases have no dependants. This two-earner couple may have a moderate need for life insurance, especially if they have a mortgage or other large debts. Parents with small children usually have the greatest need for life insurance.

DETERMINING YOUR LIFE INSURANCE OBJECTIVES

Visit the Web site

See Personal Financial Planning worksheets under Chapter 9 on the online learning centre at www.mcgrawhill.ca/college/kapoor.

Before you consider types of life insurance policies, you must decide what you want your life insurance to do for you and your dependants.

First, how much money do you want to leave to your dependants should you die today? Will you require more or less insurance protection to meet their needs as time goes on?

Second, when would you like to be able to retire? What amount of income do you believe you and your spouse would need then?

Third, how much will you be able to pay for your insurance program? Are the demands on your family budget for other living expenses likely to be greater or lower as time goes on?

When you have considered these questions and developed some approximate answers, you are ready to select the types and amounts of life insurance policies that will help you accomplish your objectives.

Once you have decided what you want your life insurance to accomplish, the next important decision is how much to buy.

ESTIMATING YOUR LIFE INSURANCE REQUIREMENTS

How much life insurance should you carry? This question is important for every person who owns or intends to buy life insurance. Because of the various factors involved, the question cannot be answered by mathematics alone. Nevertheless, an insurance policy puts a price on the life of the insured person, and therefore methods are needed to estimate what that price should be.

There are four general methods for determining the amount of insurance you may need: the easy method, the Dink method, the nonworking spouse method, and the family need method.

THE EASY METHOD Simple as this method is, it is remarkably useful. It is based on the insurance agent's general rule that a typical family will need approximately 70 percent of your salary for seven years before they adjust to the financial consequences of your death. In other words, for a simple estimate of your life insurance needs, just multiply your current gross income by 7 (7 years) and 0.70 (70 percent).

Example:

$30,000 current income × 7 = $210,000; $210,000 × 0.70 = $147,000

Your figures:

$_____ current income × 7 = $_____ × 0.70 = $_____

This method assumes your family is "typical." You may need more insurance if you have four or more children, if you have above-average family debt, if any member of your family suffers from poor health, or if your spouse has poor employment potential. On the other hand, you may need less insurance if your family is smaller.

THE DINK (DUAL INCOME, NO KIDS) METHOD If you have no dependants and your spouse earns as much as or more than you do, you have very simple insurance needs. Basically, all you need to do is ensure that your spouse will not be unduly burdened by debts should you die. Here is an example of the DINK method:

	Example	Your Figures
Funeral expenses	$ 6,000	$ _____
One-half of mortgage	60,000	_____
One-half of auto loan	7,000	_____
One-half of credit card balance	1,500	_____
One-half of personal debt	1,500	_____
Other debts	1,000	_____
Total insurance needs	$77,000	$ _____

This method assumes your spouse will continue to work after your death. If your spouse suffers poor health or is employed in an occupation with an uncertain future, you should consider adding an insurance cushion to see him or her through hard times.

THE NONWORKING SPOUSE METHOD Insurance experts have estimated that extra costs of up to $10,000 a year may be required to replace the services of a homemaker in a family with small children. These extra costs may include the cost of a housekeeper, child care, more meals out, additional carfare, laundry services, and so on. They do not include the lost potential earnings of the surviving spouse, who often must take time away from the job to care for the family.

To estimate how much life insurance a homemaker should carry, multiply the number of years before the youngest child reaches age 18 by $10,000:

Example:

10 years × $10,000 = $100,000

Your figures:

_____ years × $10,000 = $ _____

If there are teenage children, the $10,000 figure can be reduced. If there are more than two children under age 13 or anyone in the family suffers poor health or has special needs, the $10,000 figure should be adjusted upward.

THE FAMILY NEED METHOD The first three methods assume you and your family are "typical" and ignore important factors such as government benefits and your liquid assets. Exhibit 9–2 provides a detailed worksheet for making a thorough estimation of your life insurance needs.

Exhibit 9–2

A Worksheet to Calculate Your Life Insurance Needs

SOURCES: *About Life Insurance*, Metropolitan Life Insurance Company, February 1997, p. 3; *The TIAA Guide to Life Insurance Planning for People in Education* (New York: Teachers Insurance and Annuity Association, January 1997), p. 3.

1.	Five times your personal yearly income	_____ (1)
2.	Total approximate expenses above and beyond your daily living costs for you and your dependants (e.g., tuition, care for a disabled child or parent) amount to	+_____ (2)
3.	Your emergency fund (3 to 6 months of living expenses) amounts to	+_____ (3)
4.	Estimated amount for your funeral expenses (average is $6,000)	+_____ (4)
5.	Total estimate of your family's financial needs (add lines 1 through 4)	=_____ (5)
6.	Your total liquid assets (e.g., savings accounts, GICs, money market funds, existing life insurance both individual and group, pension plan death benefits, and government benefits	–_____ (6)
7.	Subtract line 6 from line 5 and enter the difference here.	=_____ (7)

The net result (line 7) is an estimate of the shortfall your family would face upon your death. Remember, these are just guidelines. For a complete analysis of your needs, consult a professional.

Although this method is quite thorough, you may believe it does not address all of your special needs. If so, you should obtain further advice from an insurance expert or a financial planner.

As you determine your life insurance needs, don't forget to consider the life insurance you may already have. You may have ample coverage through your employer and through any mortgage and credit life insurance you have purchased.

CONCEPT CHECK 9–2

1. How do you determine the need for life insurance?
2. What determines your life insurance objectives?
3. What are the four methods of estimating your life insurance requirements?

Types of Life Insurance

Objective 3

Distinguish between the two types of life insurance policies and analyze various types of life insurance.

term insurance Life insurance protection for a specified period of time; sometimes called *temporary life insurance.*

New insurance products are introduced to the market regularly, and there are many different types of life insurance available. However, they all fall into two basic types: term life or permanent life: Term insurance provides insurance coverage for a specific number of years. Permanent insurance provides protection for life. Both types pay a death benefit if you should die with the policy still in force. Exhibit 9–3 shows the types of policies issued in Canada recently, and Exhibit 9–4 shows major types and subtypes of life insurance.

TERM LIFE INSURANCE

Term insurance is like fire or auto insurance in that it provides protection against a specified financial risk for a finite period of time, often 10 or 20 years. It is pure insurance with no frills, and after the end of the specified term, you will not be eligible to collect any sum from the insurance company. A term insurance policy pays a benefit only if you die during the period it

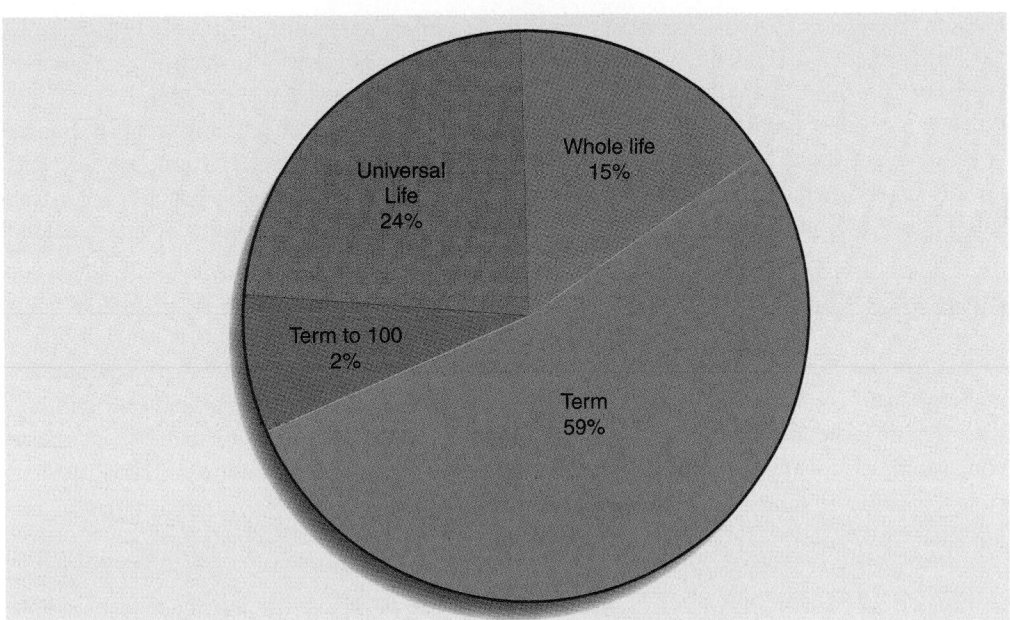

Exhibit 9–3

Types of Life
Insurance Policies
Issued

SOURCE: Reprinted
from "A Guide to Life
Insurance," 2002 with
the permission of the
*Canadian Life and
Health Insurance
Association Inc.*
www.clhia.ca

covers. If you stop paying the premiums, the insurance stops. Term insurance is, therefore, sometimes called *temporary life insurance*.

Term insurance is a basic, "no frills" form of life insurance and is the best value for most consumers. The premiums for people in their 20s and 30s are less expensive than those for whole life insurance, discussed in the next section.

You need insurance coverage most while you are raising young children. Although term life insurance premiums increase as you get older, you can reduce your coverage as your children grow up and your assets (the value of your savings, investments, home, autos, and so on) increase.

The various options in choosing your term insurance are outlined below.

RENEWABILITY OPTION The coverage of term insurance ends at the conclusion of the term, but you can continue it for another term if you have a renewability option.

CONVERSION OPTION If you have convertible term insurance, you can exchange it for a whole life policy without a medical examination and at a higher premium. The premium for the whole life policy stays the same for the rest of your life. Consider this option if you want cash-value life insurance and can't afford it now but expect to be able to in the future.

DECREASING TERM INSURANCE Term insurance is also available in a form that pays less to the beneficiary as time passes. The insurance period you select might depend on your age or on how long you decide you will need the coverage. For example, a decreasing term contract for 25 years might be appropriate as coverage of a mortgage loan balance on a house because the coverage will decrease as the balance on the mortgage decreases. You could get the same result by purchasing annual renewable term policies of diminishing

Term (temporary)	Permanent	Other Types
Level term	Whole life	Group life
Renewable term	Universal life	Credit life
Convertible term	Variable life	
Decreasing term	Adjustable life	
Term to 100	Limited payment	

Exhibit 9–4

Major Types and
Subtypes of Life
Insurance

amounts during the period of the mortgage loan. An annual renewable policy would offer more flexibility to change coverage if you were to sell or remortgage the house. Mortgage insurance therefore is a form of decreasing term insurance, decreasing to keep pace with the principal balance on your mortgage loan. *Term-to-100* policies are often seen as permanent insurance, but their main characteristics are similar to other term insurance policies. Term-to-100 plans usually do not include cash values or pay dividends. They provide a death benefit to age 100, if the policy is kept in force, and have level premiums, regardless of changes in age or health.

PERMANENT LIFE INSURANCE

Permanent insurance is purchased to cover lifelong needs, such as funeral expenses, supplementing a survivor's income, covering capital gains taxes at death, and providing for children who remain dependent for their lifetimes, often due to disability. Permanent life insurance comes in the following variations: whole life, limited payment, universal life, variable life, and adjustable life. Exhibit 9–5 compares some important features of the different types of life insurance.

whole life policy An insurance plan in which the policyholder pays a specified premium each year for as long as he or she lives; also called a *straight life policy, a cash-value life policy,* or an *ordinary life policy.*

cash value The amount received after giving up a life insurance policy.

WHOLE LIFE INSURANCE A common type of permanent life insurance is the **whole life policy** (also called a straight life policy, a cash-value life policy, or an ordinary life policy), for which you pay a specified premium each year for as long as you live. In return, the insurance company promises to pay a stipulated sum to the beneficiary when you die. The amount of your premium depends primarily on the age at which you purchase the insurance.

One important feature of the whole life policy is its cash value. **Cash value** (or *cash surrender value*) is an amount, which increases over the years, that you receive if you give up the insurance. Hence, cash-value policies provide a death benefit *and* a savings account. Insurance salespeople often emphasize the "forced savings" aspect of cash-value insurance. Cash-value policies provide a dubious benefit for individuals who have a proper personal finance plan. Besides the fact that these types of policies are often particularly expensive, the returns that you receive on your "forced savings" are difficult to calculate given the mix of savings and insurance that is difficult to separate into component parts. However, the cash value in a permanent life insurance policy can be used to keep your policy in force if you miss a premium. You can also use it directly as a loan. You can borrow any amount up to or close to the total cash value in your policy, depending on your agreement.

A policy loan requires no credit checks. You request it through your agent or the branch office of your life insurance company. If you have an irrevocable beneficiary, you'll also need their signature.

The loan can then be paid in a lump sum or in installments. Any unpaid balance plus interest is deducted from the proceeds of the policy at the time of your death. It may be fully or partially taxable. Check with your insurer about the tax consequences.

LIMITED PAYMENT POLICY One type of whole life policy is called the *limited payment policy*. With this plan, you pay premiums for a stipulated period, usually 20 years, or until you reach a specified age, such as 60 or 65 (unless your death occurs earlier). Your policy then becomes "paid up," and you remain insured for life. The company will pay the face amount of the policy at your death. Because the premium payment period for a limited payment policy is shorter than that for a whole life policy, the annual premium is higher. One important factor to be aware of if you are thinking of buying a limited payment policy is that the number of payments you will actually be required to make may vary. When pricing your limited payment policy, the insurance company will make a projection of both its costs and the investment value of the additional funds provided by your accelerated premium payments. If either of these projections falls short of reality, you will be required to make further payments. Thus, a policy that initially requires you to make payments for 20 years may later force you to

Exhibit 9-5 Types of Insurance

Policy Type	Permanent		Term to 100	Term
	Whole Life	Universal Life		
Period of coverage	Life	Life	To age 100	Depends on term in contract. Often renewable for additional terms but usually not past age 70 or 75.
Premiums	Guaranteed. Usually remain level.	Flexible. Can be increased or decreased by policyholder within certain limits.	Guaranteed. Usually remain level.	Guaranteed and remain level for term or policy (e.g. 1 year, 5 years, 10 years, etc.). Increase with each new term.
Death Benefits	Guaranteed in contract. Remain level. Dividends may be used to enhance death benefits in participating policies.	Flexible. May increase or decrease according to fluctuations in cash value fund.	Guaranteed in contract. Remain level.	Guaranteed in contract.
Cach Values	Guaranteed in contract.	Flexible. May increase or decrease according to investment returns and level of policyholder deposits.	Usually none. (Some policies have a small cash value of other nonforfeiture value after a long period, say, 20 years.)	Usually none. (Some long-term policies have a small cash value or either nonforfeiture value.)
Other Nonforfeiture Options	Guaranteed in contract.	Guaranteed in contract.	See above.	See above.
Dividends	Payable on "participating" policies. Not guaranteed.	Most policies are "nonparticipating' and do not pay dividends.	Most policies are "nonparticipating" and do not pay dividends.	Most policies are "nonparticipating" and do not pay dividends.
Advantages	• Provides protection for your entire lifetime—if kept in force. • Premium cost usually stays level, regardless of age or health problems. • Has cash values that can be borrowed, used to continue protection if premiums are missed, or withdrawn if the policy is no longer required. • Other nonforfeiture options allow the policyholder various possibilities of continuing coverage if premiums are missed or discontinued • If the policy is participating. It receives dividends that can be taken in cash, left to accumulate at interest, or used to purchase additional insurance		• Provides protection to age 100—if kept in force. • Premium cost usually stays level, regardless of age or health problems. • Premium cost is lower relative to traditional permanent policies.	• Suitable for short term insurance needs, or specific liabilities, such as a mortgage. • Provides more immediate protection because initially it is less expensive than permanent insurance • Can be converted to permanent insurance without medical evidence if it has a convertability option, often up to ages 65 or 70.
Disadvantages	• Initial cost may be too high for a sufficient amount of protection for your current needs • May be an efficient means of covering short-term needs. • Cash values tend to be small in the early years. You have to hold the policy for a long time, say over 10 years, before the cash values become sizable.		• Usually no cash values and no or limited nonforfieture values.	• If renewed, premiums increase with age and at some point higher premium costs may make it dificult or impossible to continue coverage. • Renewability of coverage will terminate at some point, commonly age 65 or age 75. • If premium is not paid, the policy terminates after 30 days and may not be reinstated if health is poor. • Usually no cash values and no nonforfieture options.

SOURCE: www.clhia.ca/, Canadian Life and Health Insurance Association Inc.

pay for several more years than you had planned. Policies can be either participating or non-participating, the difference being in the way the premiums are calculated.

PARTICIPATING AND NONPARTICIPATING POLICIES Participating policies have potential for earning dividends for the policy owner. Premiums are based on future expenses, the cost of claims settled over the course of the year, the number of policies that have been cancelled, and interest or other investment earnings. When returns are higher than these estimated expenses, a surplus is created and distributed to the policyholders in the form of dividends. You choose how you would like to use your dividends: You can be paid in cash or use them to buy additional coverage or to help pay part of your premiums. You should note that this dividend, being in reality a refund of the after-tax dollars you pay your bills with, is not considered taxable income.

participating policy
Life insurance that provides policy dividends.

In the case of a **nonparticipating policy**, premiums are calculated according to the insurance company's predicted future benefit payments. The amount of the premium cannot be altered, and in a case where an insurance company over- or underestimates its costs and efficiency, the difference will be felt in either the premiums of future customers or in the cash reserves of the company itself. You will receive no dividend payment even if the company overestimates its costs, but your premiums in general will be lower.

nonparticipating policy Life insurance that does not provide policy dividends.

UNIVERSAL LIFE Subject to certain minimums, **universal life** insurance is designed to let you pay premiums at any time in virtually any amount. The amount of insurance can be changed more easily in a universal life policy than in a traditional policy. The increase in the cash value of a universal life policy reflects the interest earned on short-term investments. Thus, the universal life policy clearly combines term insurance and investment elements. Universal life insurance policies accounted for almost two-thirds of the total annualized premiums for new individual policies sold in 2000. In 2000, universal life had its best year in terms of growth rates since the mid-1980s, although it is still far below its mid-1980s market share.

universal life A whole life policy that combines term insurance and investment elements.

Like the details of other types of policies, the details of universal life policies vary from company to company. The key distinguishing features of universal life policies are explicit, separate accounting reports to policyholders of (1) the charges for the insurance element, (2) the charges for company expenses (commissions, policy fees, and so on), and (3) the rate of return on the investment (cash value) of the policy. The rate of return is flexible; it is guaranteed to be not less than a certain amount (usually 4 percent), but it may be more, depending on the insurance company's decision.

What are the differences between universal life and whole life insurance? While whole life is a traditional life insurance policy that has level or guaranteed premiums and set death benefits and cash values, universal life is a newer, flexible form of whole life that was developed during the late 1970s when interest rates were high. A universal life policy uses current interest rates, which can be adjusted as prevailing rates change. It, therefore, is more sensitive to rate changes than whole life.

In its early days, universal life was promoted as "unbundling" the insurance and investment components of a whole life policy. The policyholder was portrayed as having some say in setting premiums, death benefits, and cash values. Despite this, however, many experts argue that the reality is that it is usually the insurance companies that will be adjusting the policies. An additional problem with the notion that universal life "unbundles" whole life is that you cannot cancel the life insurance while retaining the investment plan, and you cannot cancel the investment plan while retaining the life insurance policy.

VARIABLE INSURANCE The *variable life* insurance policy is another variation of permanent life insurance. Premiums are usually guaranteed in these policies; however, the cash values vary on the basis of the performance of an investment fund or other index. A minimum death benefit is guaranteed, but the death benefit can rise above the minimum, depending on

Financial Planning for Life's Situations

SO YOU THINK YOU'RE COVERED

If you bought universal life insurance in the 1980s or early 1990s, your mail may bring you unpleasant news: Your policy may be about to burst. Low interest rates have undermined millions of cash-value life insurance policies sold when rates were at historic double-digit highs. Insurers designed these policies around the premise that healthy investment earnings could reduce, or eventually eliminate, the premiums policyholders had to pay.

But as rates fell, insurers' investment returns couldn't keep up with the low-premium promise. The result was more holders getting notices that their policies' cash values are spiralling downward, forcing hefty boosts in costs. The alternative to paying more is to let the policy lapse—an option that may mean going without insurance for clients whose age or poor health makes them uninsurable.

The policies most likely to implode are those called universal, or adjustable-premium, life. Most universal life buyers took high interest rates as an opportunity to buy more insurance for less cost, paying the minimum premium necessary, based on rates when they bought the policy.

But those low premiums aren't guaranteed: If the insurance company suffers rising mortality costs (the funds needed to pay death benefits) or falling interest rates, you may be forced to pay more premium or reduce the death benefit. Mortality costs have actually trended down, but interest rates have fallen faster.

If you have a universal life policy, you will receive an annual statement showing how your policy is performing. Locate your latest statement and, if you can find it,

the sales illustration—the forecast your agent prepared when you bought your policy showing how its costs and cash value were projected to build over time. The illustration was probably based on a rosy view of interest rates at the time of purchase; the annual statement uses actual current rates. Compare what the illustration shows your cash value should be by now with the actual cash value from the statement. If your cash value isn't keeping up with the projection, your policy is headed for trouble. If you see trouble, call the agent who sold you the policy and ask for a set of "in-force illustrations" that recalculate the policy's future.

You want to know two things: how long the policy will last if you keep paying the current premium, and how much more you'd have to pay to maintain the current death benefit until your target age.

ANATOMY OF A LIFE INSURANCE IMPLOSION

Universal life policy: Bought by a 41-year-old man in 1984
Death benefit: $1 million
Interest rates at time of purchase: 12%
Annual premium: $4,720

Now the holder is told his policy will lapse when he's 68—not at age 95, as originally projected—because it is earning only 6% interest.

The policyholder's options:
  Boost annual premiums to $14,184.
  Cut the death benefit to $401,000.
  Let the policy lapse at age 68.

Reprinted from the August 30, 1999 issue of *Business Week* by special permission. © 1999 McGraw-Hill Companies, Inc.

---

the earning of the dollars invested in the separate fund. When you purchase a variable life policy, you assume the risk of poor investment performance.

ADJUSTABLE LIFE INSURANCE POLICY The *adjustable life* insurance policy is another relatively recent type of whole life insurance. You can change such a policy as your needs change. For example, if you want to increase or decrease your coverage, you can change either the premium payments or the period of coverage.

Over the years, variations on term and whole life insurance have been developed. The details of these policies may differ among companies. Therefore, check with individual companies to determine the best policy for your needs.

OTHER TYPES OF LIFE INSURANCE POLICIES

GROUP LIFE INSURANCE A group insurance plan insures a large number of persons under the terms of a single policy without requiring medical examinations. In general, the principles that apply to other forms of insurance also apply to group insurance.

Fundamentally, group insurance is term insurance, which was described earlier. Usually, the cost of group insurance is split between the employer and the employees so that the cost of insurance per $1,000 is the same for each employee, regardless of age. For older employees, the employer pays a larger portion of the costs of the group policy.

ENDOWMENT LIFE INSURANCE *Endowment life insurance* provides coverage from the beginning of the contract to maturity and guarantees payment of a specified sum to the insured, even if he or she is still living at the end of the endowment period. The face value of the policy is paid to beneficiaries upon the death of the insured. The endowment period typically has a duration of 10 to 20 years or the attainment of a specified age.

CREDIT LIFE INSURANCE *Credit life insurance* is a specialized version of group insurance that is purchased by creditors to cover the lives of a group of borrowers. The insurer agrees to reimburse to the creditor any outstanding debt in the event of the debtor's death. Ultimately, the cost for this coverage is borne by the borrower in the form of higher premiums.

Mortgage insurance, frequently purchased by homeowners as a requirement for obtaining a mortgage, is, in fact, a form of group insurance. Like credit life insurance, it protects the lender, in this case the institution providing your mortgage, from the possibility of your death.

Modern life insurance policies contain numerous provisions whose terminology can be confusing. Therefore, an understanding of these provisions is very important for the insurance buyer.

In our dynamic economy, inflation and interest rates change often. Therefore, experts recommend that you re-evaluate your insurance coverage every two years. Be sure to update your insurance whenever your situation changes substantially. For example, the birth of a child or an increase in your home mortgage can boost your insurance needs.

CONCEPT CHECK 9–3

1. What are the major types and subtypes of life insurance?

Important Provisions in a Life Insurance Contract

Objective 4

Select important provisions in life insurance contracts.

Your life insurance policy is valuable only if it meets your objectives. When your objectives change, however, it may not be necessary to give up the policy. Instead, study the policy carefully and discuss its provisions with your agent. Following are some of the most common provisions. Exhibit 9–6 shows the effects of inflation on a $100,000 policy.

NAMING YOUR BENEFICIARY

beneficiary A person designated to receive something, such as life insurance proceeds, from the insured.

An important provision in every life insurance policy is the right to name your beneficiary. A **beneficiary** is a person who is designated to receive something, such as life insurance proceeds, from the insured. In your policy, you can name one or more persons as contingent beneficiaries who will receive your policy proceeds if the primary beneficiary dies before you do.

Advice from a Pro

BE AN INFORMED INSURANCE BUYER

One pro, a fee-only insurance consultant, states that North Americans make thousands of costly decisions about life insurance. He advises that when you are in doubt about which life insurance to purchase, buy term. It is the least expensive, easy to understand, and a good start. If you want a whole life policy, buy a low-load cash-value policy. These policies are sold directly to the public or through fee-for-service advisers. Ask your agent to explain plausible risk in writing. Review annual statements and ask your agent for an in-force illustration every few years to determine if the current premium is still adequate.

THE GRACE PERIOD

When you buy a life insurance policy, the insurance company agrees to pay a certain sum of money under specified circumstances and you agree to pay a certain premium regularly. The *grace period* allows 28 to 31 days to elapse, during which time you may pay the premium without penalty. After that time, the policy lapses if you have not paid the premium.

POLICY REINSTATEMENT

A lapsed policy can be put back in force, or reinstated, if it has not been turned in for cash. To reinstate the policy, you must again qualify as an acceptable risk, and you must pay overdue premiums with interest. There is a time limit on reinstatement, usually one or two years.

NONFORFEITURE CLAUSE

One important feature of the whole life policy is the **nonforfeiture clause**. This provision prevents the forfeiture of accrued benefits if you choose to drop the policy. For example, if you decide not to continue paying premiums, you can exercise specified options with your cash value.

nonforfeiture clause A provision that allows the insured not to forfeit all accrued benefits.

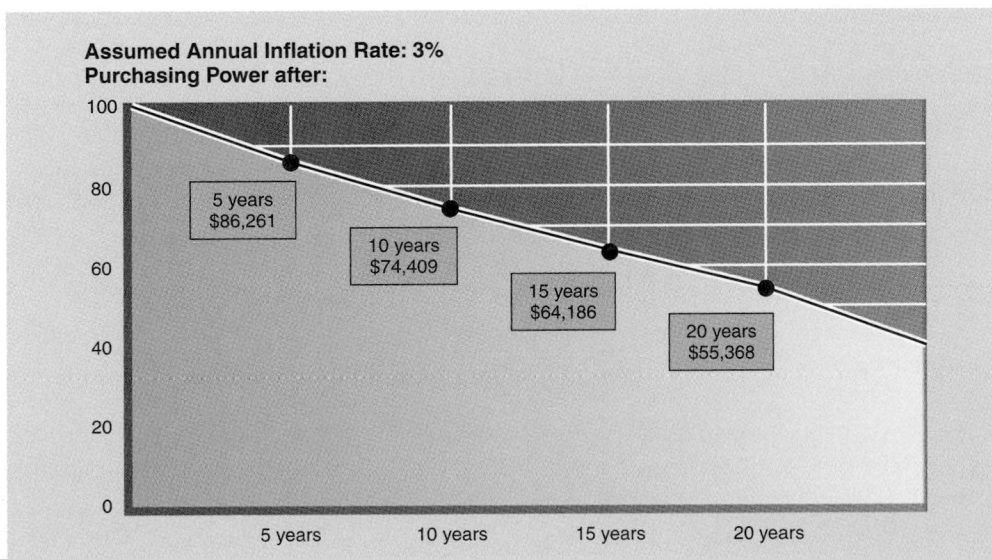

Assumed Annual Inflation Rate: 3%
Purchasing Power after:

5 years $86,261

10 years $74,409

15 years $64,186

20 years $55,368

Exhibit 9–6

Effects of Inflation on a $100,000 Life Insurance Policy

SOURCE: *The TIAA Guide to Life Insurance Planning for People in Education* (New York: Teachers Insurance and Annuity Association, January 1997), p. 8.

INCONTESTABILITY CLAUSE

The **incontestability clause** stipulates that after the policy has been in force for a specified period (usually two years), the insurance company cannot dispute its validity during the lifetime of the insured for any reason, including fraud. One reason for this provision is that the beneficiaries, who cannot defend the company's contesting of the claim, should not be forced to suffer because of the acts of the insured.

SUICIDE CLAUSE

The **suicide clause** provides that if the insured dies by suicide during the first two years the policy is in force, the death benefit will equal the amount of the premium paid. Generally, after two years, the suicide becomes a risk covered by the policy and the beneficiaries of a suicide receive the same benefit that is payable for death from any other cause.

AUTOMATIC PREMIUM LOANS

With an automatic premium loan option, if you do not pay the premium within the grace period, the insurance company automatically pays it out of the policy's cash value if that cash value is sufficient in your whole life policy. This prevents you from inadvertently allowing the policy to lapse.

MISSTATEMENT OF AGE PROVISION

The misstatement of age provision says that if the company finds out that your age was incorrectly stated, it will pay the benefits your premiums would have bought if your age had been correctly stated. The provision sets forth a simple procedure to resolve what could otherwise be a complicated legal matter.

POLICY LOAN PROVISION

A loan from the insurance company is available on a whole life policy after the policy has been in force for a time as stated in the policy. This feature, known as the *policy loan provision*, permits you to borrow any amount up to the cash value of the policy. However, a policy loan reduces the death benefit by the amount of the loan plus interest if the loan is not repaid.

RIDERS TO LIFE INSURANCE POLICIES

An insurance company can change the provisions of a policy by attaching a rider to it. A **rider** is any document attached to the policy that modifies its coverage by adding or excluding specified conditions or altering its benefits. A whole life insurance policy may include a waiver of premium disability benefit, an accidental death benefit, or both.

WAIVER OF PREMIUM DISABILITY Benefit Under this provision, the company waives any premiums that are due after the onset of total and permanent disability. In effect, the company pays the premiums. The disability must occur before you reach a certain age, usually 60.

The waiver of premium rider is sometimes desirable. Don't buy it, however, if the added cost will prevent you from carrying needed basic life insurance. Some insurance companies include this rider automatically in all policies issued through age 55.

ACCIDENTAL DEATH BENEFIT Under this provision, the insurance company pays twice the face amount of the policy if the insured's death results from an accident. The accidental death benefit is often called **double indemnity**. Accidental death must occur within a certain time period after the injury, usually 90 days, and before the insured reaches a certain age, usually 60 or 65.

> **double indemnity** A benefit under which the company pays twice the face value of the policy if the insured's death results from an accident.

The accidental death benefit is expensive. Moreover, your chances of dying in the exact manner stated in the policy are very small, as are the chances that your beneficiary will collect the double payment.

GUARANTEED INSURABILITY OPTION This option also refered to as future increase option, allows you to buy additional amounts of life insurance without proof of insurability. Thus, even if you do not remain in good health, you can increase the amount of your insurance as your income rises. This option is desirable if you anticipate the need for additional life insurance in the future.

CRITICAL ILLNESS *Critical illness* benefits are life insurance policy proceeds paid to a terminally ill policyholder *before* he or she dies. The benefits may be provided for directly in the policies, but more often, they are added by riders or attachments to new or existing policies.

JOINT, LAST TO DIE A *joint, last to die life insurance* policy, also called *survivorship life*, insures two lives, usually husband and wife. The death benefit is paid when the second spouse dies. Usually, a second-to-die policy is intended to pay estate taxes when both spouses die. However, some attorneys claim that with the right legal advice, you can minimize or avoid estate taxes completely.

Now that you know the various types of life insurance policies and the major provisions of and riders to such policies, you are ready to make your buying decisions.

CONCEPT CHECK 9–4

1. What are the most common provisions in life insurance contracts?
2. What is a beneficiary?
3. What is a rider?
4. What is the concept of double indemnity?

Buying Life Insurance

You should consider a number of factors before buying life insurance. As discussed earlier in this chapter, these factors include your present and future sources of income, other savings and income protection, group life insurance, group annuities (or other pension benefits), government benefits, and, of course, the financial strength of the company.

Objective 5

Create a plan to buy life insurance.

FROM WHOM TO BUY?

Look for insurance coverage from financially strong companies with professionally qualified representatives. It is not unusual for a relationship with an insurance company to extend over a period of 20, 30, or even 50 years. For that reason alone, you should choose carefully when deciding on an insurance company or an insurance agent. Fortunately, you have a choice of sources.

SOURCES Protection is available from a wide range of private and public sources, including insurance companies and their representatives; private groups, such as employers, labour unions, and professional or fraternal organizations; and financial institutions and manufacturers offering credit insurance.

RATING INSURANCE COMPANIES Some of the strongest, most reputable insurance companies in the nation provide excellent insurance coverage at reasonable costs. In fact, the financial strength of an insurance company may be a major factor in holding down premium costs for consumers.

Locate an insurance company by checking the reputations of local agencies. Ask members of your family, friends, or colleagues about the insurers they prefer.

CHOOSING YOUR INSURANCE PROVIDER Before you purchase your insurance, you'll need to consider whether you want to buy through a "direct" insurer, an agent, a broker, or a group plan. Agents and direct insurers represent one insurance company and offer only the products of that company. If that company has a range of products, then your needs will likely be met. It does, however, require that you have some knowledge of the products available in the marketplace so you can compare.

A broker, considered by most to be the better option, contracts with a limited number of insurance companies and can offer the products of those companies with which the broker has a contract.

A group plan can function either through an agent or a broker system. In some cases, while the plan may be serviced by a broker, the broker may use one insurance company almost exclusively for that plan. In this sense, the broker is really functioning more as an agent. Group plans may be offered through an employer, an alumni association, or another group affiliation.

Once you have found a provider, you must decide which policy is right for you. The best way to do this is to talk to your agent, which does not obligate you to buy insurance.

The Canadian Life and Health Insurance Association (www.clhia.ca) suggests you ask about the professional qualifications and training the agent has had. Agents with a CLU Chartered Life Underwriter) or CH.F.C. (Chartered Financial Consultant) demonstrate commitment to their profession. These programs require several years of study and examinations.

COMPARING POLICY COSTS

Each life insurance company designs the policies it sells to make them attractive and useful to many policyholders. One policy may have features another policy doesn't; one company may be more selective than another company; one company may get better returns on its investments than another company. These and other factors affect the prices of life insurance policies.

In brief, five factors affect the price a company charges for a life insurance policy: the company's cost of doing business, the returns on its investments, the mortality rate it expects among its policyholders, the features the policy contains, and competition among companies with comparable policies.

The prices of life insurance policies, therefore, vary considerably among life insurance companies. Moreover, a particular company will not be equally competitive for all policies. Thus, one company might have a competitively priced policy for 24-year-olds but not for 35-year-olds.

interest-adjusted index A method of evaluating the cost of life insurance by taking into account the time value of money.

Ask your agent to give you interest-adjusted indexes. An **interest-adjusted index** is a method of evaluating the cost of life insurance by taking into account the time value of money. Highly complex mathematical calculations and formulas combine premium payments, dividends, cash-value buildup, and present value analysis into an index number that makes possible a fairly accurate cost comparison among insurance companies. The lower the index number, the lower is the cost of the policy. The Financial Planning Calculations feature on page 256 shows how to use an interest-adjusted index to compare the costs of insurance.

Financial Planning for Life's Situations

LIFE INSURANCE CHECKLIST

Top 10 questions to ask your insurance provider BEFORE you purchase or renew your insurance:

1. What kind of homeowner's policy do I have, and who/what is covered under it?
2. How do I know if I am adequately insured?
3. What is NOT covered in my homeowner's policy? (What are the "exclusions"?)
4. Do I have replacement cost? guaranteed replacement cost?
5. What are the limitations on valuables, like jewellery, silverware, and computers?
6. What does my policy cover me for in terms of water damage?
7. What optional coverages should I consider?
8. What is my deductible? How much money can I save on my premium by choosing a higher deductible?
9. What safety features can I install that will help me save money and increase my protection?
10. Does the company offer 24-hour claims service?

When you have a claim . . .

1. Am I covered? For how much? (If not, why not? Show me where in the policy it explains that.)
2. Is there a deductible? How much?
3. Can I get assistance right now to make temporary repairs? How do I go about arranging the repairs?
4. What do I need to do to file my claim as soon as possible?
5. How long will it take to settle my claim?

(The preceding questions are intended as a guideline only and are not meant to be exhaustive.)

SOURCE: Homeowner's Insurance Checklist. Used with permission of Insurance Canada.
http://www.insurance-canada.ca/

OBTAINING A POLICY

A life insurance policy is issued after you submit an application for insurance and the insurance company accepts the application. The application usually has two parts. In the first part, you state your name, age, and gender, what type of policy you desire, how much insurance you want, your occupation, and so forth. In the second part, you give your medical history. While a medical examination is frequently required for ordinary policies, usually no examination is required for group insurance.

The company determines your insurability by means of the information on your application, the results of the medical examination, and the inspection report. Of all applicants, 98 percent are found to be insurable, though some may have to pay higher premiums because of an existing medical condition.

EXAMINING A POLICY

BEFORE THE PURCHASE When you buy a life insurance policy, read every word of the contract and, if necessary, ask your agent for a point-by-point explanation of the language. Many insurance companies have rewritten their contracts to make them more understandable. These are legal documents, and you should be familiar with what they promise, even though they use technical terms. Above all, ensure that your policy stipulates that your insurance provider will allow you some time to examine the policy properly and will allow you to cancel it without cost within a certain time limit, usually 10 days.

Financial Planning Calculations

DETERMINING THE COST OF INSURANCE

In determining the cost of insurance, don't overlook the time value of money. You must include as part of that cost the interest (opportunity cost) you would earn on money if you did not use it to pay insurance premiums. For many years, insurers did not assign a time value to money in making their sales presentations. Only recently has the insurance industry widely adopted interest-adjusted cost estimates.

If you fail to consider the time value of money, you may get the false impression that the insurance company is giving you something for nothing. Here is an example. Suppose you are 35 and have a $10,000 face amount, 20-year, limited-payment, participating policy. Your annual premium is $210, or $4,200 over the 20-year period. Your dividends over the 20-year payment period total $1,700, so your total net premium is $2,500 ($4,200 – $1,700). Yet the cash value of your policy at the end of 20 years is $4,600. If you disregard the interest your premiums could otherwise have earned, you might get the impression that the insurance company is giving you $2,100 more than you paid ($4,600 – $2,500). But if you consider the time value of money (or its opportunity cost), the insurance company is not giving you $2,100. What if you had invested the annual premiums in a conservative-stock mutual fund? At an 8-percent annual yield, your account would have accumulated to $6,180 in 20 years. Therefore, instead of having received $2,100 from the insurance company, you have paid the company $1,580 for 20 years of insurance protection:

Premiums you paid over 20 years	$4,200
Time value of money	1,980 ($6,180 – $4,200)
Total cost	6,180
Cash value	4,600
Net cost of insurance	1,580 ($6,180 – $4,600)

Be sure to request interest-adjusted indexes from your agent; if he or she doesn't give them to you, look for another agent. As you have seen in the example, you can compare the costs among insurance companies by combining premium payments, dividends, cash value buildup, and present value analysis into an index number.

AFTER THE PURCHASE After you buy new life insurance, you have a 10-day "free-look" period during which you can change your mind. If you do so, the company will return your premium without penalty.

It's a good idea to give your beneficiaries and your lawyer a photocopy of your policy. Your beneficiaries should know where the policy is kept because to obtain the insurance proceeds, they will have to send it to the company upon your death, along with a copy of the death certificate.

CHOOSING SETTLEMENT OPTIONS

A well-planned life insurance program should cover the immediate expenses resulting from the death of the insured. However, that is only one of its purposes. In most instances, the primary purpose of life insurance is to protect dependants against a loss of income resulting from the premature death of the primary wage earner. Thus, selecting the appropriate settlement option is an important part of designing a life insurance program. The most common settlement options are lump-sum payment, limited installment payment, life income option, and proceeds left with the company.

LUMP-SUM PAYMENT The insurance company pays the face amount of the policy in one installment to the beneficiary or to the estate of the insured. This form of settlement is the most widely used option.

LIMITED INSTALLMENT PAYMENT This option provides for payment of the life insurance proceeds in equal periodic installments for a specified number of years after your death.

LIFE INCOME OPTION Under the life income option, payments are made to the beneficiary for as long as she or he lives. The amount of each payment is based primarily on the gender and attained age of the beneficiary at the time of the insured's death.

PROCEEDS LEFT WITH THE COMPANY The life insurance proceeds are left with the insurance company at a specified rate of interest. The company acts as trustee and pays the interest to the beneficiary. The guaranteed minimum interest rate paid on the proceeds varies among companies.

SWITCHING POLICIES

Think twice if your agent suggests that you replace the whole life or universal life insurance you already own. Consumers lose millions of dollars each year because they don't hold onto their cash life insurance policies long enough or because they purchase the wrong policies. Half of those who buy whole or universal life policies drop them within 10 years.

Before you give up this protection, make sure you are still insurable (check medical and any other qualification requirements). Remember that you are now older than you were when you purchased your policy, and a new policy will therefore cost more. Moreover, the older policy may have provisions that are not duplicated in some of the new policies. This does not mean you should reject the idea of replacing your present policy; rather, you should proceed with caution. We recommend that you ask your agent or company for an opinion about the new proposal to get both sides of the argument.

The Financial Planning for Life's Situations feature on page 258 presents important guidelines for purchasing life insurance.

CONCEPT CHECK 9–5

1. How do insurance companies price their products?
2. How do insurance companies determine your insurability?
3. What should you do in examining a policy before and after the purchase?
4. What are the four most common settlement options?
5. Should you switch life insurance policies?

Financial Planning with Annuities

As you have seen so far, life insurance provides a set sum of money at your death. However, if you want to enjoy benefits while you are still alive, you might consider annuities. An annuity protects you against the risk of outliving your assets.

An **annuity** is a retirement-income option that provides you with pre-set installment payments for an agreed-upon period of time. Although we talk in terms of "purchasing" an annuity, you are actually *lending* your money to the issuer. The issuer then invests those funds and contracts to repay you, with interest, in predetermined installments over a set period of time. This may be for an agreed number of years, as in term-certain-to-age-90 annuities, or for life.

Objective 6

Recognize how annuities provide financial security.

annuity A contract that provides pre-set installment payments for an agreed-upon period of time.

TEN GOLDEN RULES OF BUYING LIFE INSURANCE

Remember that your need for life insurance coverage will change over time. Your income may go up or down, or your family size might change. Therefore, it is wise to review your coverage periodically to ensure that it keeps up with your changing needs.

Follow these rules when buying life insurance:	Done
1. Understand and know what your life insurance needs are before you make any purchase, and make sure the company you choose can meet those needs.	☐
2. Buy your life insurance from a company that is licensed in your province.	☐
3. Select an agent who is competent, knowledgeable, and trustworthy.	☐
4. Shop around and compare costs.	☐
5. Buy only the amount of life insurance you need and can afford.	☐
6. Ask about lower premium rates for nonsmokers.	☐
7. Read your policy and make sure you understand it.	☐
8. Inform your beneficiaries about the kinds and amount of life insurance you own.	☐
9. Keep your policy in a safe place at home, and keep your insurance company's name and your policy number in a safety deposit box.	☐
10. Check your coverage periodically, or whenever your situation changes, to ensure that it meets your current needs.	☐

SOURCE: American Council of Life Insurance, 1001 Pennsylvania Avenue, NW, Washington, DC 20004-2599.

The size of the installments you will receive depends on the amount you invest, how long you wish the payments to continue, and the prevailing rates at the time you buy your annuity. The number of years for which you choose to receive payments is called the term of the contract. The longer the *term* of your annuity, the smaller the installments will be. If you choose an annuity that will pay you until you die, the amount you receive will be based on actuarial estimates of your life expectancy at the age you are at the time of purchase.

The major drawback to buying annuities is that you sacrifice flexibility. Once you've purchased an annuity, you are locked in for the duration of the contract. That means you can't increase your installment payments to help fund a major purchase, or reinvest your funds to take advantage of better investment options, unless the issuer of your annuity is willing to let you cash it in—something that is usually done at the cost of a prohibitive interest penalty.

WHY BUY ANNUITIES?

An annuity can be a good post-retirement investment, especially when prevailing interest rates are strong. An annuity provides you with a means of deferring taxes on the proceeds of your RRSP or RPP, along with a predictable stream of income. It relieves you of the responsibility of making further investment decisions and can be tailored to suit your needs and preferences.

Annuities come with many features and options. A single-life annuity provides you with a stream of income for life. The size of the installment payments will be based on your life expectancy, calculated using actuarial information. Single-life annuities cease to provide benefits when you die. If you should die the week after purchasing your annuity, the issuer would keep all your money. *Guaranteed annuities* ensure that a life annuity will pay out for a minimum number of years. If you die before the agreed-upon time has passed, an amount representing the present value of the outstanding payments will go to the beneficiary you nominate when purchasing the annuity or to your estate.

Perhaps the simplest way to think of an annuity is as a wager. The insurance company is betting that you will not live as long as your life expectancy, while you are betting that you will actually exceed your life expectancy. For this reason, many experts suggest that annuities are not advisable for individuals in poor health, though there are exceptions. If you already have an annuity, for example, you should be aware that annuity contracts come with stipulations for a "surrender charge," the percentage fee you will be required to pay should you elect to cancel your contract. This fee can vary between 0 and 10 percent and generally decreases each year.

TAX CONSIDERATIONS

When you buy an annuity, the interest on the principal, as well as the interest compounded on that interest, builds up free of current income tax. With an annuity, there is no maximum annual contribution. Also, if you die during the accumulation period, your beneficiary is guaranteed no less than the amount invested.

CONCEPT CHECK 9-6

1. What is an annuity?
2. Why do people buy annuities?
3. How are annuities taxed?

Health Insurance and Financial Planning

In Canada, most basic medical procedures are provided for under provincial government health-care plans. This publicly financed health-care system is refered to as Medicare. You are assured of proper treatment that will not affect your financial situation to an overly large extent.

Because such items as semi-private or private hospital rooms, prescription drugs, eyeglasses, and dental care are either not covered or only partially covered by provincial insurance plans, you may want to supplement your health insurance through private medical insurance companies, such as Blue Cross, Greenshield Canada, Maritime Life, or Liberty Health.

When travelling outside Canada, it is important to remember that health-care costs outside the country can be very high and may not be fully covered by provincial health-care plans. In such cases, it is imperative to have adequate insurance protection.

Objective 7

Define *health insurance* and explain its importance in financial planning.

WHAT IS HEALTH INSURANCE?

Health insurance, like other forms of insurance, reduces the financial burden of risk by dividing losses among many individuals. It works in the same way as life insurance, homeowner's insurance, and automobile insurance. You pay the insurance company a specified premium, and the company guarantees you some degree of financial protection. Like the premiums and benefits of other types of insurance, the premiums and benefits of health insurance are figured on the basis of average experience. To establish rates and benefits, insurance company actuaries rely on general statistics that tell them how many people in a certain population group will become ill and how much their illnesses will cost.

Medical expense insurance and disability income insurance, discussed in the next section, are an important part of your financial planning. To safeguard your family's economic security, both protections should be a part of your overall insurance program.

THE NEED FOR SUPPLEMENTAL HEALTH INSURANCE

While the bulk of financial risks related to medical costs are minimized by the various provincial health-care insurance programs, you should establish your capacity to pay any costs that are not covered. Consider, for example, your willingness to share a room should you fall ill and require hospitalization. Basic provincial medical coverage will provide you with a room that will hold at least three other beds besides your own. This means that—at a time when you may be feeling less than sociable—you will be required to make concessions to the noise and occasional indiscretions of your roommates and their visitors. If this proposition is unappealing, you will want to request a private or at the least a semi-private room. Financially, this is where a problem can arise.

Since provincial medical coverage will not pay for the additional costs of a semi-private or private room, you will be asked to defray these costs yourself. For extended stays, this could translate to thousands of dollars. Similarly, once you leave the hospital, you will be required to assume either some or all of the costs for your medications. Again, this could prove costly.

Having thought out a few scenarios in which you might incur similar charges, you may choose to purchase supplemental medical coverage. Especially in cases where your personal wealth is small and might possibly be rapidly exhausted by the incidental costs of ill health, dental maintenance, and vision correction, buying supplemental medical coverage can be a sound financial planning decision.

GROUP HEALTH INSURANCE

Group plans comprise about 60 percent of all the health insurance issued by health and life insurance companies. Most of these plans are employer sponsored, and the employer often pays part or most of their cost. Group insurance will cover you and your immediate family. Group insurance seldom requires evidence that you are insurable if you enroll when you first become eligible for coverage.

The protection group insurance provides varies from plan to plan. The plan may not cover all of your health insurance needs; therefore, you will have to consider supplementing it with individual health insurance. Most universities offer health insurance coverage to full-time students. One of the leading providers for student health and dental plans in Canada is studentcare.net/work (aseq.com in Quebec).

Two factors to examine with group insurance are transferability and how the coverage is paid for. Many group plans do not allow for transfer of an insurance policy to the individual when an employee leaves the group. This is because underwriting for a group policy does not transfer well to individuals, but the consequence is that the departing employee loses both his or her benefits and coverage. He or she will need to replace his or her coverage privately and may find such factors as being older or having a degraded health status leading to heavy costs.

In the case of premium payments in a group plan, it matters who pays for what. Tax consequences will vary depending on payment source. With disability insurance, for example, if the premium is paid for by the employer, then the benefit received is taxed. If, instead, the

> ### DID YOU KNOW ?
>
> In 2000, Canadians paid $9.9 billion for health insurance.
>
> SOURCE: www.clhia.ca

individual makes the payments, then the benefit is not taxed. Be sure to discuss this with your plan administrator.

INDIVIDUAL HEALTH INSURANCE

Individual health insurance covers either one person or a family. If the kind of health insurance you need is not available through a group or if you need coverage in addition to the coverage a group provides, you should obtain an individual policy—a policy tailored to your particular needs—from the company of your choice. This requires careful shopping because coverage and cost vary from company to company.

Find out what your group insurance will pay for and what it won't. Make sure you have enough insurance, but don't waste money by overinsuring.

SUPPLEMENTING YOUR GROUP INSURANCE

A sign that your group coverage needs supplementing would be its failure to provide benefits for the major portion of your medical care bills. If, for example, your group policy will pay only $50 per day toward a hospital room and the cost in your area is $100, you should look for an individual policy that covers most of the remaining amount. In supplementing your group health insurance, also consider the health insurance benefits your employer-sponsored plan provides for family members.

If you have any questions about your group plan, you should be able to get answers from your employer, union, or association. If you have questions about an individual policy, talk with your insurance company representative.

CONCEPT CHECK 9–7

1. What is health insurance, and what is its purpose?

Disability Income Insurance

Because you feel healthy, you may overlook the very real need for disability income insurance. Disability income insurance protects your most valuable asset: your ability to earn income. Most people are more likely to lose their incomes due to disability than to death. The fact is that for all age groups, disability is more likely than death.

Disability income insurance provides regular cash income lost by employees as the result of an accident or illness. Disability income insurance is probably the most neglected form of insurance protection. Many people who insure their houses, cars, and other property fail to insure their most valuable resource: their earning power. Disability can cause much greater financial problems than death. In fact, disability is often called "the living death." Disabled persons lose earning power while expenses continue to rise. They often face huge expenses for the medical treatment and special care their disabilities require.

If you are between ages 35 and 65, your chances of being unable to work for 90 days or more due to a disabling illness or injury are about equal to your chances of dying. To be more specific, at age 40 you face a 12-percent chance of dying before reaching age 65 and a 19-percent chance of having at least one disability lasting 90 days or longer.[1] If you have no disability income protection, you are betting that you will not become disabled, and that could be a very costly bet.

Objective 8

Recognize the need for disability income insurance.

disability income insurance Provides payments to replace income when an insured person is unable to work.

---

[1] *The Consumer's Guide to Disability Insurance* (Washington, DC: Health Insurance Association of America, September 1991), p. 1.

The probability of a male becoming temporarily or permanently disabled between ages 20 and 30 is 1.3 percent, but between ages 20 and 60, it increases to 19.1 percent. Females are less prone to disability during their lifetimes and have only a 15.3 percent chance of becoming disabled between 20 and 60 years of age.[2]

DEFINITION OF DISABILITY

Disability has several definitions. Some policies define it simply as the inability to do your regular work. Others have stricter definitions. For example, a dentist who is unable to do his or her regular work because of a hand injury but can earn income through related duties, such as teaching dentistry, would not be considered permanently disabled under certain policies.

Good disability plans pay when you are unable to work at your regular job; poor disability plans pay only when you are unable to work at any job. A good disability plan will also make partial disability payments when you return to work on a part-time basis.

DISABILITY INSURANCE TRADE-OFFS

Following are some important trade-offs you should consider in purchasing disability income insurance.

WAITING OR ELIMINATION PERIOD Benefits don't begin on the first day you become disabled. Usually, there is a waiting or elimination period of between 30 and 90 days. Some waiting periods may be as long as 180 days. Generally, disability income policies with longer waiting periods have lower premiums. If you have substantial savings to cover three to six months of expenses, the reduced premiums of a policy with a long waiting period may be attractive. But if you need every paycheque to cover your bills, you are probably better off paying the higher premium for a short waiting period. Short waiting periods, however, are very expensive.

DID YOU KNOW ?

There are 3.3 million disabled Canadians, and a third of all people now aged 35 will be unable to work for six months before reaching age 65.

SOURCE: www.insurance-canada.ca "Shopping for Disability Insurance" by Jim Bullock, 1997.

DURATION OF BENEFITS The maximum time a disability income policy will pay benefits may be a few years, to age 65, or for life. You should seek a policy that pays benefits for life. If you became permanently disabled, it would be financially disastrous if your benefits ended at age 55 or 65.

AMOUNT OF BENEFITS You should aim for a benefit amount that, when added to your other income, will equal 60 to 70 percent of your gross pay. Of course, the greater the benefits, the greater is the cost.

ACCIDENT AND SICKNESS COVERAGE Consider both accident and sickness coverage. Some disability income policies will pay only for accidents, but you want to be insured for illness, too.

GUARANTEED RENEWABILITY Ask for noncancellable and guaranteed renewable coverage. Either coverage will protect you against your insurance company dropping you if your health becomes poor. The premium for these coverages is higher, but the coverages are well worth the extra cost. Furthermore, look for a disability income policy that waives premium payments while you are disabled.

---

[2] *Source Book of Health Data* (Washington, DC: Health Insurance Association of America, 1991), pp. 95–96.

SOURCES OF DISABILITY INCOME

Before you buy disability income insurance, remember that you may already have some form of such insurance. This coverage may come to you through your employer, government benefits, or worker's compensation. Use Exhibit 9–7 to determine how much income you will have available if you become disabled.

EMPLOYER Many, but not all, employers provide disability income protection for their employees through group insurance plans. Your employer may have some form of wage continuation policy that lasts a few months or an employee group disability plan that provides long-term protection. In most cases, your employer will pay part or all of the cost of this plan.

PRIVATE Most medical insurance policies offered by insurance companies will include limited coverage for disability. The exact details of coverage will depend on the cost of your premium, the company, and your policy details.

PUBLIC The provincial governments have established various social programs to provide some insurance against disability. The protection available may vary from one province to another, and eligibility requirements might include your having previously contributed to the program or your having suffered your injury either at work or during military service. The major social supports available to the disabled in Canada are outlined briefly below.

Employment Insurance This is a federal program that will provide short-term benefits to those who have previously contributed. While very helpful for short-term health issues, its benefits are limited by the relatively short term in which payments will be made.

Canada and Quebec Pension Plans Both these plans include a disability pension for contributors with a severe or prolonged disability. The funds can also be used in compensation for dependants and survivors. Again, however, the payments obtained from these

> **DID YOU KNOW ?**
>
> In 2001, the average Canada Pension Plan disability benefit was $699.84 per month.
>
> SOURCE: www.hrdc_drhc.gc.ca

How much income will you have available if you become disabled?

	Monthly Amount	After Waiting:	For a Period of:
Sick leave or short-term disability			
Group long-term disability			
Employment Insurance			
Other government programs			
Individual disability insurance			
Credit disability insurance			
Other income:			
Savings			
Spouse's income			
Total monthly income while disabled:	$		

Exhibit 9–7

Disability Income Worksheet

plans are inadequate to maintain a decent standard of living. The Canada Pension Plan, for example, provides a disability pension of up to a maximum of $956.05 monthly to age 65, after which a regular pension is paid. Furthermore, the rules and restrictions regarding these plans are very strict, and many disabilities do not qualify, particularly if they are only partial.

Worker's Compensation   These are provincial plans that provide medical, financial, and rehabilitative assistance to workers who suffer disability as a result of accidents or illness related to their work.

Short-term or Long-term Welfare   Provided at a municipal and provincial level, these programs are geared toward those with extremely limited alternative financial resources.

Whatever the form of social support you receive, it is virtually certain to be insufficient for your needs. At best, these government programs should be viewed as a supplement to your disability insurance coverage, rather than as a replacement.

DETERMINING YOUR DISABILITY INCOME INSURANCE REQUIREMENTS

Once you have found out what your benefits from the public and private disability income sources would be, you should determine whether those benefits are sufficient to meet your disability income needs. If the sum of your disability benefits approaches your after-tax income, you can safely assume that should disability strike, you'll be in good shape to pay your day-to-day bills while recuperating.

You should know how long you would have to wait before the benefits begin (the waiting or elimination period) and how long they would be paid (the benefit period).

What if, as is often the case, your disability benefits are not sufficient to support your family? In that case, you may want to consider buying disability income insurance to make up the difference.

Don't expect to insure yourself for your full salary. Most insurers limit benefits from all sources to no more than 70 to 80 percent of your take-home pay. For example, if you earn $400 a week, you could be eligible for disability insurance of about $280 to $320 a week. You will not need $400 because while you are disabled, your work-related expenses will be eliminated and your taxes will be far lower or may be even zero.

The Financial Planning for Life's Situations box on the next page shows you how to compare different features among disability income policies.

CRITICAL ILLNESS INSURANCE

Critical illness insurance is gaining recognition in Canada as a valuable insurance tool. Many are coming to realize that the probability of being struck by a critical illness at some point is actually very high. As a result, the costs of insurance coverage to provide for the eventuality become much more viable.

Critical illness insurance provides money for care if you are diagnosed with a serious illness or condition, like cancer, heart disease, stroke, multiple sclerosis, blindness, organ transplant, kidney failure, and paralysis, but not usually AIDS. There are also specialty programs, such as one product dealing specifically with women's cancers.

One in two men and one in three women will be struck by cancer, heart attack, or stroke at some point in their lives. For the most part, that will engender potentially devastating financial costs along with the emotional and physical trauma.

It is important to understand that while life insurance pays out when you die, critical illness does so while you are alive. It is a product you buy to protect yourself and your dependants, and it removes finances from the long list of concerns associated with critical illness.

DISABILITY INCOME POLICY CHECKLIST

Every disability income policy may have different features. The following checklist will help you compare policies you may be considering:

	Policy A	Policy B
1. How is disability defined?		
Inability to perform your own job?	____	____
Inability to perform any job?	____	____
2. Does the policy cover		
Accident?	____	____
Illness?	____	____
3. Are benefits available		
For total disability?	____	____
For partial disability?	____	____
Only after total disability?	____	____
Without a prior period of total disability?	____	____
4. Are full benefits paid, whether or not you are able to work, for loss of		
Sight?	____	____
Speech?	____	____
Hearing?	____	____
Use of limbs?	____	____

	Policy A	Policy B
5. What percentage of your income will the maximum benefit replace?	____	____
6. Is the policy noncancellable, guaranteed renewable, or conditionally renewable?	____	____
7. How long must you be disabled before premiums are waived?	____	____
8. Is there an option to buy additional coverage, without evidence of insurability, at a later date?	____	____
9. Does the policy offer an inflation adjustment feature?	____	____
If so, what is the rate of increase?	____	____
How often is it applied?	____	____
For how long?	____	____

	Policy A		Policy B	
	With Inflation Feature	Without Inflation Feature	With Inflation Feature	Without Inflation Feature
10. What does the policy cost?				
For a waiting period of				
_____ days and (30–180)	_____	_____	_____	_____
For a benefit period of				
_____ ? 1 yr.–lifetime	_____	_____	_____	_____
Total	_____	_____	_____	_____

SOURCE: Health Insurance Association of America, Washington DC.

Supplemental Health Insurance

Objective 9

Understand the value of supplemental health and disability insurance.

After duly considering the health and disability coverage currently available to you from the government, your employer, and other policies, you may decide to seek further coverage. You will be able to purchase insurance from a number of sources. You should consider a number of factors, including the cost of premiums, the precise coverage, and the amount of deductible that you may be required to pay on your claims. As with the auto insurance policies discussed in the previous chapter, the amount you agree to pay as a deductible on claims will affect the cost of your premiums. The greater your deductible, the lower your premiums will be.

While claim limits, deductibles, premiums, and other details will vary according to your policy, your basic coverage should include hospital costs, supplementary prescription drug charges (those not covered by your provincial plan), and dental maintenance. Many companies also offer vision coverage.

DENTAL EXPENSE INSURANCE

Dental expense insurance provides reimbursement for the expenses of dental services and supplies and encourages preventive dental care. The coverage normally provides or partially provides for oral examinations (including X-rays and cleanings), fillings, extractions, inlays, bridgework, and dentures, as well as oral surgery, root canal therapy, and orthodontics.

VISION CARE INSURANCE

A recent development in health insurance coverage is *vision care insurance*. An increasing number of insurance companies and pre-payment plans are offering this insurance, usually to groups.

Vision and eye health problems are prevalent chronic health-care concerns. Good vision care insurance should cover diagnosing and treating eye diseases, such as glaucoma, periodic eye examinations, eyeglasses, contact lenses, and eye surgery.

In considering vision and dental coverages, you should analyze their costs and benefits. Sometimes, these coverages cost more than they are worth.

LONG-TERM-CARE INSURANCE

long-term-care (LTC)
Provides day-in, day-out care for long-term illness or disability.

Long-term care is day-in, day-out assistance that you might need if you ever have an illness or a disability that lasts a long time and leaves you unable to care for yourself. You may or may not need lengthy care in a nursing home, but you may need help at home with daily activities, such as dressing, bathing, and doing household chores. While in the United States there is a large and growing market for long-term-care (LTC) insurance, Canadian consumers are generally unaware such insurance even exists.

Despite this, over the next five to 10 years it is expected that the giant baby-boom generation will gravitate to LTC insurance as it faces the reality that its parents are coming into the long-term-care years. For the moment, however, only a small percentage of the elderly are in assisted-living or LTC programs. The rest live by themselves or are supported by their families.

The families of people who receive LTC are well aware of the emotional cost of providing such care themselves and of the financial cost of hiring professionals. The insurance is not inexpensive, but should it prove necessary, it could be preferable to wiping out a family's assets or those of a future estate.

Advice from a Pro

LONG-TERM-CARE INSURANCE

Wendy Miller, head of benefits research at Merck & Company, laments that when offered LTC policies, Merck employees have been slow to purchase them. The company has offered LTC coverage since 1991, but fewer than 10 percent of its 18,500 eligible employees have signed on. "People think of it as old-age insurance," says Miller. "They tend to be overinsured in life insurance, yet don't have key elements of income protection, such as long-term care."

The best LTC policies cover both home care and nursing-home stays. Policies offer a range of benefits, from $50 per day for a year or $200 per day for a lifetime. You may need an inflation protection option, especially if you buy when you are young.

Long-term care can be expensive. Private Canadian nursing homes can cost from $3,000 to $6,000 a month, and even at $100 a day, the cumulative costs of long-term care can quickly eat into savings. Government nursing homes can cost less but have long waiting lists. Even with government subsidies, ward coverage in Ontario can cost $1,225 a month. Home care may cost between $35 and $48 an hour for a private registered nurse, or $70 an hour for an occupational therapist or physiotherapist. Less skilled personal care to help with eating or light housework may cost $15 an hour. If you depend on government programs, they may provide only 60 hours a month, or two hours a day, for home care.

Clearly, anticipating the costs of long-term care by considering insurance is sound financial planning, but there are various factors to consider. The cost of LTC insurance itself can be prohibitive, depending on your age and policy options.

The annual premium for LTC policies can range depending on your age and the choices you make. The older you are when you enroll, the higher is your annual premium. Typically, individual insurance plans are sold to the 50-to-80 age group, pay benefits for a maximum of two to six years, and carry a dollar limit on the total benefits they will pay.

The Financial Planning for Life's Situations box on page 268 can help you compare the features of long-term-care policies.

An insurance company usually allows you a minimum of 10 days to review your health insurance policy, so be sure to check the major provisions that affect your coverage. Other major provisions are described in the following sections.

MAJOR PROVISIONS IN A HEALTH INSURANCE POLICY

All health insurance policies have certain provisions in common. Be sure you understand what your policy covers. Even the most comprehensive policy may be of little value if a provision in small print limits or denies benefits.

DID YOU KNOW ?

Why do people buy long-term-care insurance?

- 25% To avoid dependence
- 23% To avoid losing savings and assets
- 15% To protect standard of living
- 12% To guarantee affordable services
- 25% For other reasons

SOURCES: Based on unpublished data from the Health Insurance Association, 1995 Long-Term Care Buyer/Non-Buyer Survey, and LifePlans, Inc., 1995; Teachers Insurance and Annuity Association, 1996.

Financial Planning for Life's Situations

LONG-TERM-CARE POLICY CHECKLIST

The following checklist will help you compare LTC policies you may be considering:

	Policy A	Policy B
1. What services are covered?		
Skilled care	___	___
Intermediate care	___	___
Custodial care	___	___
Home health care	___	___
Adult day care	___	___
Other	___	___
2. How much does the policy pay per day?		
For skilled care	___	___
For intermediate care	___	___
For custodial care	___	___
For home health care	___	___
For adult day care	___	___
3. How long will benefits last?		
In a nursing home for:		
Skilled nursing care	___	___
Intermediate nursing care	___	___
Custodial care	___	___
At home:	___	___
4. Does the policy have a maximum lifetime benefit? If so, what is it?		
For nursing home care	___	___
For home health care	___	___
5. Does the policy have a maximum length of coverage for each period of confinement? If so, what is it?		
For nursing home care	___	___
For home health care	___	___
6. How long must I wait before pre-existing conditions are covered?	___	___
7. How many days must I wait before benefits begin?		
For nursing home care	___	___
For home health care	___	___
8. Are Alzheimer's disease and other organic mental and nervous disorders covered?	___	___

	Policy A	Policy B
9. Does this policy require:		
Physician certification of need?	___	___
An assessment of activities of daily living?	___	___
A prior hospital stay for:		
Nursing home care?	___	___
Home health care?	___	___
A prior nursing home stay for home health care coverage?	___	___
Other?		
10. Is the policy guaranteed renewable?	___	___
11. What is the age range for enrollment?	___	___
12. Is there a waiver-of-premium provision:	___	___
For nursing home care?	___	___
For home health care?	___	___
13. How long must I be confined before premiums are waived?	___	___
14. Does the policy offer an inflation adjustment feature?		
If so:		
What is the rate of increase?	___	___
How often is it applied?	___	___
For how long?	___	___
Is there an additional cost?	___	___
15. What does the policy cost:		
Per year?		
With inflation feature	___	___
Without inflation feature	___	___
Per month?		
With inflation feature	___	___
Without inflation feature	___	___
16. Is there a 10-day free look?	___	___

SOURCE: *Guide to Long-Term Care Insurance* (Washington, DC: Health Insurance Association of America, 1994), pp. 11–12.

ELIGIBILITY The eligibility provision defines who is entitled to benefits under the policy. Age, marital status, and dependency requirements are usually specified in this provision. For example, foster children usually are not automatically covered under the family contract, but stepchildren may be. Check with your insurance company to be sure.

ASSIGNED BENEFITS When you assign benefits, you sign a paper allowing your insurance company to make payments to your hospital or doctor. Otherwise, the payments will be made to you when you turn in your bills and claim forms to the company.

INTERNAL LIMITS A policy with internal limits will pay only a fixed amount for your hospital, room no matter what the actual rate is. For example, if your policy has an internal limit of $200 per hospital day and you are in a $300-a-day hospital room, you will have to pay the difference.

CO-PAYMENT Co-payment is a type of cost sharing. Most major medical plans define co-payment as the amount the patient must pay for medical services after the deductible has been met. You pay a flat dollar amount each time you receive a covered medical service. Co-payments for prescriptions are common. The amount of co-payment does not vary with the cost of service.

> **co-payment** A provision under which the insured pays a flat dollar amount each time a covered medical service is received after the deductible has been met.

BENEFIT LIMITS The benefit limits provision defines the maximum benefits possible, in terms of either a dollar amount or a number of days in the hospital. Many policies today have benefit limits.

EXCLUSIONS AND LIMITATIONS The exclusions and limitations provision specifies the conditions or circumstances for which the policy does not provide benefits. For example, the policy may exclude coverage for pre-existing conditions or cosmetic surgery.

COORDINATION OF BENEFITS As discussed earlier, the coordination of benefits provision prevents you from collecting benefits from two or more group policies that would in total exceed the actual charges. Under this provision, the benefits from your own and your spouse's policies are coordinated to allow up to 100 percent payment of your covered charges.

GUARANTEED RENEWABLE With this policy provision, the insurance company cannot cancel a policy unless you fail to pay premiums when due. Also, it cannot raise premiums unless a rate increase occurs for all policyholders in that group.

CANCELLATION AND TERMINATION This provision explains the circumstances under which the insurance company can terminate your health insurance policy. It also explains your right to convert a group contract into an individual contract.

HEALTH INSURANCE TRADE-OFFS

The benefits of health insurance policies differ, and the differences can have a significant impact on your premiums. Consider the following trade-offs:

REIMBURSEMENT VERSUS INDEMNITY A reimbursement policy provides benefits based on the actual expenses you incur. An indemnity policy provides specified benefits, regardless of whether the actual expenses are greater or less than the benefits.

INTERNAL LIMITS VERSUS AGGREGATE LIMITS A policy with internal limits stipulates maximum benefits for specific expenses, such as the maximum reimbursement

Financial Planning for Life's Situations

HEALTH CARE WEB SITES

www.gov.on.ca/health is a site of the Ontario Ministry of Health and Long-Term Care that educates users about mental health, women's health, long-term care, drug programs, medical insurance, and health care professional regulations.

www.clhia.ca/ is the site for the Canadian Life & Health Insurance Association, which represents the majority of life and health insurance companies in Canada. Check here for facts and figures about insurance in Canada. They also provide a list of insurance companies that offer disability insurance.

www.compcorp.ca is the site of COMPCORP, the Canadian Life and Health Insurance Compensation Corporation, which was created by the life and health insurance industry in Canada to provide Canadian policyholders with protection, within limits, against loss of policy benefits in the event of the insolvency of their insurance company. Check here to discover the extent of protection afforded to you should your insurance company dissolve.

www.aon.ca/quicken/english/index.htm offers a health insurance primer by Quicken.ca. Also check here for province-specific information about government-provided health care coverage.

www.hc-sc.gc.ca/medicare is Health Canada's site to provide information about medicare and the Canada Health Act.

Visit the Web site

See the Post-Test under Chapter 9 on the online learning centre at www.mcgrawhill.ca/ college/kapoor.

for daily hospital room and board. Other policies may limit only the total amount of coverage, such as $1 million major expense benefits, or may have no limits.

DEDUCTIBLES AND CO-INSURANCE The cost of a health insurance policy can be greatly affected by the size of the deductible (the amount you must pay toward medical expenses before the insurance company pays), the degree of co-insurance, and the share of medical expenses you must pay (for example, 20 percent).

OUT-OF-POCKET LIMIT A policy that limits the total of the co-insurance and deductibles you must pay (for example, $2,000) will limit or eliminate your financial risk, but it will also increase the premium.

HEALTH INFORMATION ONLINE

Recent studies indicate that consumers are seeking information on health and health care online to supplement traditional medical counsel. Many legitimate providers of reliable health and medical information, including Health Canada, offer brochures and in-depth information on specific topics at their Web sites. The Financial Planning for Life's Situations feature above lists some good health care Web sites, and the feature on the next page provides some tips for consumers.

Financial Planning for Life's Situations

CONSUMER TIPS ON HEALTH, CRITICAL ILLNESS, AND DISABILITY INSURANCE

1. If you pay your own premiums directly, try to arrange to pay them on an annual or quarterly basis, rather than a monthly basis. It is cheaper.

2. Policies should be delivered to you within 30 days. If not, contact your insurer and find out, in writing, why.

3. When you receive a policy, take advantage of the free-look provision. You have 10 days to look it over and obtain a refund if you decide it is not for you.

4. Unless you have a policy with no internal limits, read over your contract every year to see whether its benefits are still in line with medical costs.

5. Don't replace a policy because you think it is out of date. Switching may subject you to new waiting periods and new exclusions. Rather, add to what you have, if necessary.

6. On the other hand, don't keep a policy because you've had it a long time. You don't get any special credit from the company for being an old customer.

7. Don't try to make a profit on your insurance by carrying overlapping coverages. Duplicate coverage is expensive. Besides, most group policies now contain a coordination of benefits clause limiting benefits to 100 percent.

8. Use your health emergency fund to cover small expenses.

9. If you're considering the purchase of a critical illness policy, such as cancer insurance, understand that it is supplementary and will pay for only certain diseases. You should have full coverage before you consider it. Otherwise, it's a gamble.

10. Don't lie on your insurance application. If you fail to mention a pre-existing condition, you may not get paid. You can usually get paid even for that condition after one or two years have elapsed if you have had no treatment for the condition during that period.

11. Keep your insurance up to date. Some policies adjust to inflation better than others. Some insurers check that benefits have not been outdistanced by inflation. Review your policies annually.

12. Never sign a health insurance application (such applications are lengthy and detailed for individually written policies) until you have recorded full and complete answers to every question.

SOURCE: Health Insurance Association of America.

CONCEPT CHECK 9–9

1. What are several types of health insurance coverage available under group and individual policies?
2. What are the major provisions of a health insurance policy?
3. How do you decide which coverage to choose?
4. How can you analyze the costs and benefits of your health insurance policy?

SUMMARY OF OBJECTIVES

Objective 1
Define *life insurance* and describe its purpose and principle.
Life insurance is a contract between an insurance company and a policyholder under which the company agrees to pay a specified sum to a beneficiary upon the insured's death. Most people buy life insurance to protect someone who depends on them from financial losses caused by their death. Fundamental to the life insurance principle is the predictable mortality experience of a large group of individuals.

Objective 2
Determine your life insurance needs.
In determining your life insurance needs, you must first determine your insurance objectives and then use the easy method, the DINK method, the nonworking spouse method, or the family need method. The family need method is recommended. You should consider a number of factors before you buy insurance, including your present and future sources of income, other savings and income protection, group life insurance, group annuities (or other pension benefits), and government benefits.

Objective 3
Distinguish between the two types of life insurance policies and analyze various types of life insurance.
The two types of life insurance policies are term life or permanent life. In general, term insurance provides protection against a specified financial risk for a finite period of time, often 10 or 20 years. Permanent life insurance is purchased to cover life-long needs, such as funeral expenses and supplementing a survivor's income. Many variations of these two types of life insurance policies are available. Term Life insurance is available with a renewability option, conversion option, or a decreasing option. Permanent life insurance is available in the following forms: whole life, universal life, variable insurance, and adjustable life. There are many additional options; therefore, you should check with your insurance company to determine which type offers the best policy for your particular needs at the lowest price.

As with other forms of insurance, price should not be your only consideration in choosing a life insurance policy. You should also consider the financial stability, reliability, and service the insurance company provides.

Objective 4
Select important provisions in life insurance contracts.
The naming of the beneficiary, the grace period, policy reinstatement, the incontestability clause, the suicide clause, automatic premium loans, the misstatement of age provision, and the policy loan provision are important provisions in most life insurance policies. Common riders in life insurance policies are the waiver of premium disability benefit, the accidental death benefit, the guaranteed insurability option, cost of living protection, and accelerated benefits.

Objective 5
Create a plan to buy life insurance.
Before buying life insurance, consider your present and future sources of income, group life insurance, group annuities (or other pension benefits), and government benefits. Then compare the costs of several life insurance policies. Examine your policy before and after the purchase, and choose appropriate settlement options. The most common settlement options are lump-sum payment, limited installment payment, life income option, and proceeds left with the company. Online services provide a wealth of information about all topics related to life insurance.

Objective 6
Recognize how annuities provide financial security.
An annuity is the opposite of life insurance: It pays while you live, whereas life insurance pays when you die. An annuity provides you with a regular income during your retirement years.

Objective 7
Define *health insurance* and explain its importance in financial planning.
Health insurance is protection that provides payment of benefits for a covered sickness or injury. Disability income insurance protects a person's most valuable asset: the ability to earn income. Critical illness insurance protects against the most common critical illness

Health insurance, critical illness, and disability income insurance are three protections against economic losses due to illness, accident, or disability. These should be a part of your overall insurance program to safeguard your family's economic security.

Disability can cause even greater financial problems than death. In fact, disability is often called "the living death." Disabled persons lose their earning power while continuing to incur normal expenses. In addition, they often face huge expenses for the medical treatment and special care their disabilities require.

Objective 8
Recognize the need for disability income insurance.
Disability income insurance provides regular cash income lost by employees as the result of an accident or illness. Sources of disability income insurance include the employer, government benefits, unions, and private insurance.

Objective 9
Understand the value of supplemental health insurance.
Supplemental health insurance is coverage that you can purchase in addition to the coverage available to you from the government, your employer, and other policies. Types of supplemental health insurance include dental expense insurance, vision care insurance, and long-term-care insurance.

KEY TERMS

annuity 257

beneficiary 250

cash value 246

co-payment 269

disability income insurance 261

double indemnity 253

incontestability clause 252

interest-adjusted index 254

long-term care 266

nonforfeiture clause 251

nonparticipating policy 248

participating policy 248

rider 252

suicide clause 252

term insurance 244

universal life 248

whole-life policy 246

FINANCIAL PLANNING PROBLEMS

1. *Illustrating the Principle of Life Insurance.* A group of 100,000 males, age 30, wish to contribute each year an amount to a common fund sufficient to pay $1,000 to the dependants of each group member who dies during the year. Use the mortality table in Exhibit 9–1 to determine the following: (Obj. 1)
   a. How many members of the group can be expected to die during the year?
   b. What amount must each of the 100,000 members contribute at the beginning of the year to provide $1,000 for the dependants of those who die before the end of the year?

2. *Calculating the Amount of Life Insurance Needed Using the Easy Method.* You are the wage earner in a "typical family," with $30,000 gross annual income. Use the easy method to determine how much life insurance you should carry. (Obj. 2)

3. *Estimating Life Insurance Needs Using the DINK Method.* You and your spouse are in good health and have reasonably secure careers. Each of you makes about $28,000 annually. You own a home with an $80,000 mortgage, and you owe $10,000 on car loans, $5,000 in personal debts, and $3,000 on credit card loans. You have no other debts. You have no

plans to increase the size of your family in the near future. Estimate your total insurance needs using the DINK method. (Obj. 2)

4. *Using the Nonworking Spouse Method to Determine Life Insurance Needs.* Tim and Allison are married and have two children, ages 4 and 7. Allison is a nonworking spouse who devotes all of her time to household activities. Estimate how much life insurance Tim and Allison should carry. (Obj. 2)

5. *Comparing the Costs of Life Insurance and Various Provisions in a Life Insurance Policy.* Obtain premium rates for $25,000 whole life, universal life, and term life policies from local insurance agents. Compare the costs and provisions of these policies. (Obj. 3)

6. *Calculating Your Life Insurance Needs.* Use Exhibit 9–2 to calculate your life insurance needs. (Obj. 3)

7. *Calculating the Amount of Disability Benefits.* Georgia Braxton, a widow, has take-home pay of $600 a week. Her disability insurance coverage replaces 70 percent of her earnings after a four-week waiting period. What amount would she receive in disability benefits if an illness kept Georgia off work for 16 weeks? (Obj. 8)

FINANCIAL PLANNING ACTIVITIES

1. *Assessing the Need for Life Insurance.* Interview relatives and friends to determine why they purchased life insurance. Prepare an essay summarizing your findings. (Obj. 1)

2. *Comparing the Methods of Determining Life Insurance Requirements.* Analyze the four methods of determining life insurance requirements. Which method is best, and why? (Obj. 2)

3. *Comparing Premiums for Life Insurance Policies.* Choose one stock company and one mutual life insurance company. Obtain and compare premiums for
   a. Term life insurance for $50,000.
   b. Whole life insurance for $50,000.
   c. Universal life insurance for $50,000.

Prepare a summary table indicating which policy you would consider and why. (Obj. 3)

4. *Reviewing an Employer's Health Benefit Package.* List the benefits included in your employee benefit package, such as health insurance, disability income insurance, and life insurance. Discuss the importance of such a benefit package to the consumer. (Obj. 7)

5. *Comparing Major Provisions in a Health-Care Insurance Policy.* Obtain sample health insurance policies from insurance agents or brokers, and analyze the policies for definitions, coverages, exclusions, limitations on coverage, and amounts of coverage. In what ways are the policies similar? In what ways do they differ? (Obj. 8)

LIFE SITUATION CASE

How Much Is Enough?

Joanne and Glenn Kitsos recently had their second child and decided to make a change to their life insurance. "We've got two kids now, and we have to start thinking about the future," Joanne said.

The Kitsoses and other new parents are among the people experts say ought to have life insurance. Anyone who has someone financially dependent on them or anyone whose death would cause someone to lose money should be insured.

"Term life insurance is extraordinarily cheap when people are in their 20s and 30s, so people with children should purchase a sufficient amount," says Elliot S. Lipson, a financial planner. "All too often, people buy expensive policies that offer savings or investment components but lack a basic benefit that is large enough to provide for their needs."

The amount you need isn't easy to determine because the total can be as little as five times and as much as 10 times your annual salary.

Jim Hunt, consultant to a major insurance group, says the total need for an average couple with two young children is close to six to eight times their salary. For example, the Kitsoses' combined income is $100,000, so they probably need a minimum of $600,000 in insurance and maybe a little more if they have no group life insurance at work.

Here are a few questions to ask when figuring how much life insurance you need:

- How much income will your dependants need every year if you die?
- How much income will your dependants have from other sources, such as investments, pensions, or savings, if you die?
- How much income will your dependants have access to from sources, such as your spouse's salary or government benefits?

Once you've come up with a total, you have to decide whether you want term, whole life, or some hybrid variation.

Your goal, Hunt says, is to buy as much insurance as you need. But because of the costs of whole life insurance, that often means term. While whole life costs more in the early years, it guarantees that you will pay the same premium 10, 15, or even 20 years down the road.

The Kitsoses started out with whole life insurance, but they have decided to switch to term insurance that will last until their kids graduate from college. They want to have enough insurance to cover their funeral costs and the cost of their children's college educations. But rather than using their insurance as an investment, they plan to invest more in mutual funds.

Questions

1. What is the advantage of buying life insurance when you are younger, and what is a good reason for having it?
2. What would be the total coverage needed for an average couple with two children and a combined income of $45,000?
3. What is one advantage of whole life insurance?
4. Is term insurance the right choice for the Kitsoses? Why, or why not?

SOURCES: Earl C. Gottschalk Jr., "Avoiding the Big Mistakes along Life's Path," *The Wall Street Journal*, May 27, 1997, p. C1; Candy McCampbell, "How Much Insurance to Carry Is a Question Not Easily Answered," *Gannett News Service*, July 9, 1997, p. S12.

CREATING A FINANCIAL PLAN

Comparing Health Insurance Plans

Changing programs and regulations influence your ability to be properly covered for health care and disability insurance coverage. Awareness of policy types, coverages, and limitations will help you plan this phase of your financial plan.

Web Sites for Life Insurance

- Find out more about the insurance industry by visiting the Canadian Life & Health Insurance Association at **www. clhia.ca.**
- Find out about the protection afforded to Canadian Insurance product buyers at **www.compcorp.ca/,** the site for COMP-CORP (the Canadian Life and Health Insurance Compensation Corporation).
- Quicken.ca has a very informative site at **www.aon.ca/quick en/english/index.html,** which provides information about a

variety of insurance products including life, health, and disability insurance.

- Robert Barney has written a number of articles strongly in favour of term insurance over whole life and universal life insurance for *Canadian MoneySaver* magazine. You can view these articles as well as contributions by other authors at **www.canadianmoneysaver.ca.**
- Another of Robert Barney's contributions to help people decide on life insurance is his company, Term4Sale, at **www.termcomparisons.cc/sale.com.** Visit the site to find a comparison of various term life insurance policies in Canada, as well as listing of current rates for different companies.

Web Sites for Health and Disability Insurance

- Visit the Health Canada site at **www.hc-sc.gc.ca/medicare** to learn more about medicare and the Canada Health Act.

- The Life and Health Insurance Foundation for Education (LIFE), at **www.life-line.org**, is an American nonprofit organization that provides information and education on life, health, and disability insurance. They also have a "disability needs" calculator to help you establish how much disability insurance you may need. Much of the information is applicable to Canada.
- You can visit the Blue Cross's Canadian site at **www.blue cross.ca** to find out about the health and disability insurance products it offers.

(Note: Addresses and content of Web sites change, and new sites are created daily. Use search engines to update and locate Web sites for your current financial planning needs.)

Short-Term Financial Planning Activities

1. Analyze current health insurance coverage in relation to family and household needs.
2. Compare the cost of health insurance programs available from various sources.

Long-Term Financial Planning Activities

1. Develop a plan for reducing health-care and disability insurance costs.

CONTINUOUS CASE FOR PART 3

MANAGING RISKS FOR EFFECTIVE FINANCIAL PLANNING

Life Situation
Pamela, 36; Isaac, 38; three children, ages 9, 7, and 4

Financial Goals

- Evaluate property and liability insurance needs
- Assess the need for disability insurance
- Determine additional life insurance needs

Financial Data

Monthly income	$4,300
Living expenses	4,075
Assets	150,850
Liabilities	99,520

Both Pamela and Isaac Mortimer are comfortable. They now have three children, are happy with their home, and are more financially secure than they were six years ago. In fact, everything seems to be right on track. Yet the Mortimers still have financial needs they must address. Several changes have affected their financial planning:

- The value of their home has increased due to inflation and home improvements.

- They have purchased a used car to meet additional transportation needs.
- Isaac's current employer offers him only 30 days of sick leave.
- Pamela's life insurance policy is for only $2,000. Isaac has life insurance coverage equal to approximately eight times his annual salary.

Questions

1. How should the Mortimers determine whether they have enough insurance coverage for their home?
2. What factors should the Mortimers consider in deciding whether to purchase collision insurance coverage for their used car?
3. When considering disability income insurance, what length of waiting period and duration of benefits should the Mortimers consider?
4. Do you think Pamela and Isaac Mortimer have enough life insurance? If not, what changes would you recommend? Explain your answer.

PART 4

INVESTING YOUR FINANCIAL RESOURCES

CHAPTER 10
Fundamentals
of Investing

CHAPTER 11
Investing in
Stocks

CHAPTER 12
Investing in
Bonds

CHAPTER 13
Investing in
Mutual Funds

10 Fundamentals of Investing

The Moneysense Personal Finance Web Site: Help You Can Use

Need some help establishing an investment program? Why not go to the Internet? That's what Jane and Brian Seward did. Six months ago, they purchased a computer for their two kids to use for schoolwork. Little did they realize how the computer would affect their investment planning and other financial decisions.

One afternoon, Jane was helping one of the kids with a homework assignment to determine the effect of compounding on savings. After looking at a number of different sites, they found the Moneysense personal finance Web site. As they wandered around through the site, they soon forgot about the assignment. The site, beyond current rates and various types of calculators, was a gold mine of personal finance information. There were no "get rich quick" schemes, but instead some solid financial advice and analysis that would help the Seward family with their finances.

Today, more and more Canadians are using the Internet to help plan their financial future, evaluate investment alternatives, and monitor the value of their investments. Although just one of many, the Moneysense Web site (www.moneysense.ca) is an excellent choice not only for beginning investors like Jane and Brian but also for more experienced investors. Within the site, the Sewards found information on credit, investing, tax planning, home mortgages, and a number of other important topics.

After reading the material on the Web site, both Jane and Brian decided it was time to take charge of their family's finances. They began by paying off some high-interest credit card bills and saving some money they could use for emergencies. Then, they started saving the money needed to finance an investment program. During this time, they also continued to learn. They studied additional material in the Moneysense Web site, visited other financial planning Web sites, and began to read *MoneySaver* and *IE:Money* magazines. They even began tracking some potential stock and mutual fund investments in anticipation of when they could actually purchase their first investments. According to Brian, their financial planning was not only rewarding but also fun. For the first time since they got married, they were getting their financial affairs in order.

QUESTIONS

1 How important is an investment program for financial planning?

2 Jane and Brian Seward began their search for investment information by examining the Moneysense Web site. If you were seeking help to establish an investment program, where would you obtain the needed information?

LEARNING OBJECTIVES

1   Explain why you should establish an investment program.

2   Describe how safety, risk, income, growth, and liquidity affect your investment decisions.

3   Identify the major types of investment alternatives.

4   Recognize the role of the professional financial planner and your role in a personal investment program.

5   Use various sources of financial information that can reduce risks and increase investment returns.

Preparing for an Investment Program

The old saying goes "I've been rich and I've been poor, but believe me, rich is better." While being rich doesn't guarantee happiness, the accumulation of money does provide financial security and is a worthy goal. Jane and Brian Seward, the couple in the opening case, began their financial planning and investment program by examining the material in the Moneysense site. Why not take a look and see the type of financial and investment information that it offers? View the material that the Sewards used to create their financial plan. Type in the following Web address: www.moneysense.ca. Within this page, you will find information on investments, stocks, and money management.

By studying the material contained in this Web site and following the basic investment principles presented in this chapter, along with the information on stocks, bonds, mutual funds, real estate, and other investments in the remaining chapters in Part 4, you can create a financial plan that is custom-made for you.

The decision to establish an investment plan is an important first step to accomplishing your long-term financial goals. Like other decisions, the decision to start an investment plan is one you must make for yourself. No one is going to make you save the money you need to fund an investment plan. These things won't be done unless you want to do them. In fact, the *specific* goals you want to accomplish must be the driving force behind your investment plan.

Objective 1

Explain why you should establish an investment program.

ESTABLISHING INVESTMENT GOALS

Some people say they want to be rich. Others say they want to be financially secure. But it takes more than just wishing. While it would be nice if you could magically accumulate wealth, it takes careful planning and discipline to achieve the financial freedom you desire. For most people, the first step is to establish investment goals. Without investment goals, you cannot know what you want to accomplish.

To be useful, investment goals must be specific and measurable. They must be tailored to your particular financial needs. Some financial planners suggest that investment goals be stated in terms of money: By December 31, 2008, I will have total assets of $120,000. Other financial planners believe investors are more motivated to work toward goals that are stated in terms of the particular things they desire: By January 1, 2008, I will have accumulated enough money to purchase a second home in the mountains. The following questions will help you establish valid investment goals:

[1] What will you use the money for?
[2] How much money do you need to satisfy your investment goals?

Here are some suggestions to help you obtain the money you need.

[1] *Pay yourself first.* Too often, people save or invest what is left over after they have paid everything else. As you might guess, nothing is left over in many cases, and the investment program is put on hold for another month. A second and much better approach is to (1) pay your monthly bills, (2) save a reasonable amount of money, and (3) use whatever money is left over for personal expenses, such as new clothes or entertainment.

[2] *Take advantage of employer-sponsored retirement programs.* Many employers will match part or all of the contributions you make to a retirement program. Here's how a matching program works. For every dollar the employee contributes, the employer matches it with a specified amount such as 25 cents, 50 cents, or even $1. To make this option even more attractive, many matching programs are often part of an employer-sponsored retirement program that receives favourable tax treatment. (The tax benefits of different types of retirement programs are discussed in Chapter 14.)

[3] *Participate in an elective savings program.* You can elect to have money withheld from your paycheque each payday and automatically deposited in a savings account. It is much easier to put money into the account than it is to get money out of it. You can also make investing easier by arranging with a mutual fund or brokerage firm to take a fixed sum from your bank account automatically every month and invest it. An elective savings program is an excellent way to fund an RRSP or RESP (both topics are discussed in Chapters 3 and 14).

[4] *Make a special savings effort one or two months each year.* Some financial planners recommend that you cut back to the basics for one or two months each year to obtain additional money for investment purposes.

[5] *Take advantage of gifts, inheritances, and windfalls.* During your lifetime, you will likely receive gifts, inheritances, salary increases, year-end bonuses, or income tax refunds. Often, people opt to spend this extra money on something they could not afford under normal circumstances. A better approach is to use the money to fund your investment program.

THE VALUE OF LONG-TERM INVESTMENT PROGRAMS

Visit the Web site

See Personal Financial Planning worksheets under Chapter 10 on the online learning centre at www.mcgrawhill.ca/college/kapoor.

Many people never start an investment program because they have only small sums of money. But even small sums grow over a long period of time. The Anopouloses, the couple described in the Financial Planning for Life's Situations feature on the next page, began their investment program by investing $2,000 each year when they were in their 20s; yet they expect their investment portfolio to be worth more than $1.5 million by the time Peter reaches age 65. How did they do it? Simple: They took advantage of the time value of money. You can achieve the same type of result. For instance, if you invest $2,000 each year for 40 years at a 6-percent annual rate of return, using the time value of money concepts in Chapter 1 and Appendix A, your investment will grow to $309,520. The rate of return and the length of time your money is invested *do* make a difference. Exhibit 10–1 shows how much your

Exhibit 10–1

Growth Rate for $2,000 Invested at the End of Each Year at Various Rates of Return for Different Time Periods

Rate of Return	BALANCE AT END OF YEAR					
	1	5	10	20	30	40
6%	$2,000	$11,274	$26,362	$73,572	$158,116	$309,520
7	2,000	11,502	27,632	81,990	188,922	399,280
8	2,000	11,734	28,974	91,524	226,560	518,120
9	2,000	11,970	30,386	102,320	272,620	675,780
10	2,000	12,210	31,874	114,550	328,980	885,180
11	2,000	12,456	33,444	128,406	398,040	1,163,660
12	2,000	12,706	35,098	144,104	482,660	1,534,180

Financial Planning for Life's Situations

REALITY 101: THE TIME VALUE OF MONEY

Should college and university students worry about planning for retirement? You bet! There is no better time to begin an investment program than when you are young. The reason is quite simple: If you start an investment program when you're young, let the time value of money work for you, and make sound investments, you won't have to worry about finances when you reach retirement age. With these facts in mind, it's even possible for a person with an average salary to retire early.

Take Maria and Peter Anopoulos. Mary, 32, is a high school history teacher. Peter, 35, runs his own computer consulting business. Together, they earn about $80,000 a year and enjoy their careers. Both want to make sure they have enough money to retire on when Peter reaches age 65.

When the Anopouloses married just over 10 years ago, they established a long-term goal to accumulate a retirement nest egg of $1.5 million. They consulted with Gina Anastas, a financial planner whom a friend recommended. Anastas explained that if they chose quality investments that earned a 12-percent average annual return and invested just $2,000 each year, their investment portfolio would be worth $1,534,180 at the end of 40 years, when Peter reached age 65. She explained that most of this amount was the result of the time value of money, an investment concept that allows all interest, dividends, and the dollar appreciation that occurs when investments increase in value to accumulate over a long period of time.

According to Anastas, there is no better time to begin an investment program than right now. To drive this point home, she calculated that if the Anopouloses waited 10 years before starting their investment program and made the same investments for a 30-year period, their investment portfolio would be worth only $482,660. They would lose over $1 million! Needless to say, the Anopouloses realized they had to start their investment program now.

Today, after 10 years of investing in long-term stocks and mutual funds, the Anopouloses estimate that their investments are worth approximately $45,000. And while the current value of their investment portfolio is a long way from $1.5 million, Gina Anastas forecasts that if they keep investing in the same types of investments, the time value of money will enable their portfolio to grow to more than $1.5 million by the time Peter reaches age 65.

---

investment portfolio will be worth at the end of selected time periods and with different rates of return.

Note that the value of your investments increases each year because of two factors. First, it is assumed you will invest another $2,000 each year. For example, at the end of 40 years, you will have invested a total of $80,000 ($2,000 × 40 years). Second, all investment earnings are allowed to accumulate and are added to your yearly deposits. Thus, the totals illustrated in Exhibit 10–1 are a result of continuous yearly deposits *plus* earnings on your investments.

Also, note that if investments earn a higher rate of return, total portfolio values increase dramatically. For example, a $2,000 annual investment that earns 6 percent a year is worth $309,520 at the end of 40 years. But if the same $2,000 annual investment earns 12 percent each year, your investment portfolio value increases to $1,534,180 at the end of the same 40-year period. The search for higher returns is one reason many investors choose stocks and mutual funds that offer higher potential returns compared with GICs or savings accounts. You should know that to earn higher returns, you must take more chances. In fact, the material in the next section will help you determine if you should invest in these higher-risk investments.

The investment earnings illustrated in Exhibit 10–1 are taxable as ordinary income. To avoid or postpone taxation, you may want to invest your money in an RRSP, RESP, or one of the tax-deferred investments described later in Part 5. The details about different types of

www.mcgrawhill.ca/college/kapoor

retirement accounts are presented in Chapter 14. Although taxes are always a consideration, this complication does not reduce the importance of the time value of money. In fact, the time value of money is so important for a successful investment program that you may want to review this concept (see Chapter 1 and Appendix A) before you begin to invest.

CONCEPT CHECK 10-1

1. How can the Internet help you create a financial plan or establish an investment program?
2. Why should an investor develop specific investment goals?
3. What factors should you consider when performing a financial checkup?
4. How can an investor accumulate the money needed to fund an investment program?
5. Explain the time value of money concept and how it could affect your investment program.

Factors Affecting the Choice of Investments

Objective 2

Describe how safety, risk, income, growth, and liquidity affect your investment decisions.

Millions of Canadians buy stocks, bonds, or mutual funds, purchase gold and silver, or make similar investments. And they all have reasons for investing their money. Some people want to supplement their retirement income when they reach age 65, while others want to become millionaires before age 40. Although each investor may have specific, individual goals for investing, all investors must consider a number of factors before choosing an investment alternative.

SAFETY AND RISK

The safety and risk factors are two sides of the same coin. You cannot evaluate any investment without assessing how safety relates to risk. Safety in an investment means minimal risk of loss. On the other hand, risk in an investment means a measure of uncertainty about the outcome. Investments range from very safe to very risky. At one end of the investment spectrum are very safe investments that attract conservative investors. Investments in this category include government bonds, savings accounts, guaranteed investment certificates, and certain stocks and bonds. Mutual funds and real estate may also be very safe investments. Investors pick such investments because they know there is very little chance that investments of this kind will become worthless. Although anyone can choose investments like those just listed, there is usually a reason someone chooses conservative investments. Many investors choose conservative investments because of the individual life situations in which they find themselves. As people approach retirement, for example, they usually choose more conservative investments with less chance of losing a large part of the nest egg they have built up over the years. Today, one interesting change in investment philosophy is that most financial planners recommend that retirees still invest a small portion of their money in investments that will increase in value. The reason is simple: People are living longer, and they need more money for their retirement years. Some people choose to invest one-time windfalls or inheritances in a conservative investment because they know it may be impossible to replace the money if it is lost. Finally, some investors simply dislike taking chances.

speculative investment
A high-risk investment made in the hope of earning a relatively large profit in a short time.

At the other end of the investment spectrum are speculative investments. A **speculative investment** is a high-risk investment made in the hope of earning a relatively large profit in a short time. Such investments offer the possibility of a larger dollar return, but if they are unsuccessful, you may lose most or all of your initial investment. Speculative stocks, certain bonds, mutual funds, real estate, derivatives, commodities, options, precious metals, precious stones, and collectibles are risk-oriented investments. Although many of these investments are discussed in detail in later chapters, they are often considered too risky for beginning investors.

By now, you probably realize that the safety and risk factors are more complex than the simple definitions just presented. From an investor's standpoint, one basic rule sums up the relationship between the factors of safety and risk: *The potential return on any investment should be directly related to the risk the investor assumes.* For example, Anne Landry was injured in a work-related accident three years ago. After a lengthy investigation, she received an insurance settlement totalling $420,000. As a result of the injury, she was no longer qualified to perform her old job as an assembler for an electronics manufacturer. When she thought about the future, she knew she needed to get a job but realized she would be forced to acquire new employment skills. She also realized she had received a great deal of money that could be invested to provide a steady source of income not only for the next two years while she obtained job training but also for the remainder of her life. Having never invested before, she quickly realized her tolerance for risk was minimal. She had to conserve her $420,000 settlement. Eventually, after much discussion with professionals and her own research, she chose to save about half her money in GICs. For the remaining half, she chose three stocks that offered a 4-percent average dividend, a potential for growth, and a high degree of safety because of the financial stability of the corporations that issued the stocks.

A more risk-oriented investor might have criticized Anne's decisions as too conservative. In fact, this second type of investor might have chosen to invest in more speculative stocks that offer a greater potential for growth and increase in market value even though the corporations issuing the stocks are not paying dividends at the present time. Often, beginning investors are afraid of the risk associated with many investments. But it helps to remember that without the risk, it is impossible to obtain the larger returns that really make an investment program grow. The key is to determine how much risk you are willing to assume and then choose quality investments that offer higher returns without an unacceptably high risk. The bottom line is this: What is right for one investor may not be right for another.

The problem of assessing safety and risk is further complicated by the large number of potential investments from which to choose. You must determine how much risk you are willing to assume. Once you have determined the amount of risk you are comfortable with, you can choose different investments that hopefully will provide the expected return.

RISK TOLERANCE

Risk tolerance is the amount of psychological pain you're willing to suffer from your investments. There are risks associated with investing, you could lose part or all of your principal, the purchasing power of your investment can decrease and you may not receive the returns you expected. In addition, unlike GICs, the money you invest in securities, mutual funds, and other similar investments are not insured by the Canada Deposit Insurance Corporation (CDIC). Therefore, it is important to determine your risk tolerance before you start investing your money. Since you have already determined your investment goals, you already have an idea of how much risk you can tolerate. For example, if you are saving for a short-term goal, you should choose a less risky investment because you need to guarantee that the cash will be available when you need it, you don't want to have to wait if the investment has decreased in value. To help you determine how much risk you are willing to assume, take the test for risk tolerance presented in the Financial Planning for Life's Situations feature on the next page. In addition, see the Advice from a Pro feature from Merrill Lynch on page 287.

Financial Planning for Life's Situations

A QUICK TEST TO MEASURE INVESTMENT RISK

The following quiz, adapted from one prepared by the T. Rowe Price group of mutual funds, can help you discover how comfortable you are with varying degrees of risk. Other things being equal, your risk tolerance score is a useful guide in deciding how heavily you should weight your portfolio toward safe investments versus more risk-oriented, speculative investments.

1. You're the winner on a TV game show. Which prize would you choose?
   - ☐ $2,000 in cash (1 point).
   - ☐ A 50-percent chance to win $4,000 (3 points).
   - ☐ A 20-percent chance to win $10,000 (5 points).
   - ☐ A 2-percent chance to win $100,000 (9 points).

2. You're down $500 in a poker game. How much more would you be willing to put up to win the $500 back?
   - ☐ More than $500 (8 points).
   - ☐ $500 (6 points).
   - ☐ $250 (4 points).
   - ☐ $100 (2 points).
   - ☐ Nothing—you'll cut your losses now (1 point).

3. A month after you invest in a stock, it suddenly goes up 15 percent. With no further information, what would you do?
   - ☐ Hold it, hoping for further gains (3 points).
   - ☐ Sell it and take your gains (1 point).
   - ☐ Buy more—it will probably go higher (4 points).

4. Your investment suddenly goes down 15 percent one month after you invest. Its fundamentals still look good. What would you do?

- ☐ Buy more. If it looked good at the original price, it looks even better now (4 points).
- ☐ Hold on and wait for it to come back (3 points).
- ☐ Sell it to avoid losing even more (1 point).

5. You're a key employee in a startup company. You can choose one of two ways to take your year-end bonus. Which would you pick?
   - ☐ $1,500 in cash (1 point).
   - ☐ Company stock options that could bring you $15,000 next year if the company succeeds, but will be worthless if it fails (5 points).

Your total score: _____

SCORING

5–18 points You are a more conservative investor. You prefer to minimize financial risks. The lower your score, the more cautious you are. When you choose investments, look for high credit ratings, well-established records, and an orientation toward stability. In stocks, bonds, and real estate, look for a focus on income.

19–30 points You are a less conservative investor. You are willing to take more chances in pursuit of greater rewards. The higher your score, the bolder you are. When you invest, look for high overall returns. You may want to consider bonds with higher yields and lower credit ratings, the stocks of newer companies, and real estate investments that use mortgage debt.

COMPONENTS OF THE RISK FACTOR

The risk factor associated with a specific investment does change from time to time. For example, the stock of Computer-Tabulating-Recording Company was once considered a high-risk investment. Then, this company changed its name to IBM and eventually became a leader in the computer industry. By the early 1980s, many conservative investors were purchasing IBM stock because of its safety and earnings potential. But in the early 1990s, many of these same investors sold their IBM stock because changes in the computer industry had brought financial problems for IBM. IBM was once again considered too risky for many investors. Now, as a result of solving many of its financial problems, IBM is once again considered a good choice for many investors.

When choosing an investment, you must carefully evaluate changes in the risk factor. In fact, the overall risk factor can be broken down into five components.

Advice from a Pro

RISK TOLERANCE

Your risk tolerance depends on many things, including:

Your goals and time frames. You most likely have several goals, such as your children's education, a vacation home, or an early retirement. You may be willing to take more risk with some goals than with others, depending on your time horizon for each goal.

Your income and asset base. The larger your income and asset base, the more risk you may be willing to take, again depending in part on your time frames. Some investors with a large asset base, however, may choose a more conservative approach, knowing they don't need to take on additional risk to meet their goals.

Your personality. Be frank and honest with yourself. Some people are simply predisposed to take lesser or greater risk. Making the right determination of your personal feelings in this regard will allow you to maintain a proper investment course, even in market storms.

STAYING CURRENT: THE IMPORTANCE OF PERIODIC REVIEW

Over time, you may need to adjust your portfolio's investment mix, depending on your life circumstances, your investing time frames, and market performance. Your tolerance for risk is likely to change with your age as well as with major life changes, such as marriage, children, or retirement. Your financial advisor can help you evaluate your portfolio periodically in light of your goals and tolerance for risk and can help determine if you are on track to achieving your goals.

SOURCE: Reprinted by permission of Merrill Lynch, Pierce, Fenner and Smith Incorporated. Copyright © 2002. Any further reproduction or redistribution is strictly prohibited.

INFLATION RISK Your investments can provide a way to keep up with or stay ahead of inflation. While inflation rates have fallen sharply from the high levels of the early 1980s, the dollar is still shrinking in value. As defined in Chapter 1, inflation is a rise in the general level of prices.

During periods of high inflation, there is a risk that the financial return on an investment will not keep pace with the inflation rate. To see how inflation reduces your buying power, let's assume you have deposited $10,000 in the bank at 4 percent interest. At the end of one year, your money will have earned $400 in interest ($10,000 × 4% = $400). Assuming an inflation rate of 6 percent, it will cost you an additional $600 ($10,000 × 6% = $600), or a total of $10,600, to purchase the same amount of goods you could have purchased for $10,000 a year earlier. Thus, even though you earned $400, you lost $200 in purchasing power. And after paying taxes on the $400 interest, your loss of purchasing power is even greater.

The rate of return when adjusted for inflation will vary from one investment to another. Before you rush out and invest in common stocks, however, realize that you should consider other factors when choosing an investment. On the other hand, rate of return is a major concern during periods of high inflation.

> **DID YOU KNOW ?**
>
> One dollar placed in a safety deposit box in early 1980 has a buying power of forty-three cents in early 2002.
>
> SOURCE: Bank of Canada
> www.bankofcanada.ca

INTEREST RATE RISK The interest rate risk associated with a fixed-return investment in preferred stocks or government or corporate bonds is the result of changes in the interest rates in the economy. The value of preferred stocks, government bonds, or corporate bonds decreases when overall interest rates increase. In contrast, the value of these same investments rises when overall interest rates decrease. For example, suppose you purchase a $1,000 corporate bond issued by Nortel (Northern Telecom Limited), which matures in 2012 and pays 9 percent interest until maturity. This means Nortel will pay $90 ($1,000 × 9% = $90) each year until the maturity date in 2012. If bond interest rates for comparable bonds increase to 11 percent, the market value of your 9-percent bond will decrease. No one will be willing to purchase your bond at the price you paid for it, since a comparable bond that pays 11 percent can be purchased for $1,000. As a result, you will have to sell your bond for less than $1,000 or hold it until maturity. If you decide to sell your Nortel bond, the approximate dollar price you could sell it for would be $818 ($90 ÷ 11% = $818). This price would provide the purchaser with an 11-percent return, and your initial investment is reduced by $182 ($1,000 − $818 = $182) because you owned a bond with a fixed interest rate of 9 percent during a period when overall interest rates in the economy increased.

Of course, if overall interest rates declined, your bond would increase in value. Let's assume that interest rates on comparable corporate bonds declined to 7 percent. As a result, the value of your Nortel bond that pays 9 percent would increase. The approximate price you could sell it for would be $1,286 ($90 ÷ 7% = $1,286). This price would provide the purchaser with a 7-percent return, and you would earn an additional $286 ($1,286 − 1,000 = $286) because you owned a bond with a fixed interest rate of 9 percent during a period when overall interest rates in the economy declined.

BUSINESS FAILURE RISK The risk of business failure is associated with investments in common stock, preferred stock, and corporate bonds. With each of these investments, you face the possibility that bad management, unsuccessful products, competition, or a host of other factors will cause the business to be less profitable than originally anticipated. Lower profits usually mean lower dividends or no dividends at all. If the business continues to operate at a loss, even interest payments and repayment of bonds may be questionable. The business may even fail and be forced to file for bankruptcy, in which case your investment may become totally worthless. Of course, the best way to protect yourself against such losses is to carefully evaluate the companies that issue the stocks and bonds you purchase. It also helps to purchase stock in more than one company and thus diversify your investments.

Visit the Web site
See the CBC video exercises under Chapter 10 on the online learning centre at www.mcgraw hill.ca/college/kapoor.

MARKET RISK The prices of stocks, bonds, mutual funds, and other investments may fluctuate because of the behaviour of investors in the marketplace. As a result, economic growth is not as systematic and predictable as most investors might believe. Generally, a period of rapid expansion is followed by a period of recession. During periods of recession, it may be quite difficult to sell such investments as real estate. Fluctuations in the market price for stocks and bonds may have nothing to do with the fundamental changes in the financial health of corporations. Such fluctuations may be caused by political or social conditions. For example, the price of petroleum stocks may increase or decrease as a result of political activity in the Middle East. In late 1997, the stock markets in Asia experienced substantial losses. As a result, investors who had purchased stocks listed on these exchanges lost money.

GLOBAL INVESTMENT RISK Today, more investors are investing in stocks and bonds issued by foreign firms and in global mutual funds. While we discuss these investments in more detail in the remainder of Part 4, you should know that investing in global securities creates additional risk. An investor can purchase stocks or bonds issued by individual foreign firms or, as most financial analysts recommend, purchase shares in a global mutual fund. For the small investor who has less than $200,000 to invest and is unaccustomed to the risks in foreign investments, global mutual funds offer more safety. Here are two factors to consider before taking the plunge.

First, *global investments must be evaluated just like domestic investments*. But evaluating foreign firms and global mutual funds may be difficult because reliable accounting information on foreign firms is often scarce. Of course, you can get an annual report, but you won't know whether the foreign firm uses the generally accepted accounting principles used by Canadian firms or follows its own national accounting rules.

Second, *changes in the currency exchange rate may affect the return on your investment.* The foreign currency exchange rate is applied whenever securities are bought and sold and whenever dividends are paid. For instance, if you want to purchase stock issued by a French firm, your Canadian currency must be converted into French francs. And the French francs you receive when you sell your shares in the foreign firm must be converted back to Canadian dollars. Your potential return is determined not only by how well your investment performed but also by whether the currency exchange rate became more or less favourable during the time you held the investment.

INVESTMENT INCOME

Investors sometimes purchase certain investments because they want a predictable source of income. The safest investments—passbook savings accounts, certificates of deposit, Canada Savings Bonds, and Canadian treasury bills—are also the most predictable sources of income. With these investments, you know exactly what the interest rate is and how much income will be paid on a specific date.

If investment income is a primary objective, you can also choose government bonds, corporate bonds, preferred stocks, utility stocks, or selected common stock issues. When purchasing stocks or corporate bonds for potential income, most investors are concerned about the issuing corporation's overall profits, future earnings picture, and dividend policies. For example, some corporations are very proud of their long record of consecutive dividend payments and will maintain that policy if at all possible (see Exhibit 10–2).

Other investments that may provide income potential are mutual funds and real estate rental property. Although the income from mutual funds is not guaranteed, you can choose funds whose primary objective is income. Income from rental property is not guaranteed because the possibility of either vacancies or unexpected repair bills always exists. The more speculative investments, such as commodities, options, precious metals, gemstones, and collectibles, offer little, if any, potential for regular income.

INVESTMENT GROWTH

To investors, *growth* means their investments will increase in value. Often, the greatest opportunity for growth is an investment in common stock. During the 1990s, investors found that stocks issued by corporations in the electronics, technology, energy, and health-care industries provided the greatest growth potential. In fact, goods and services provided by companies in these industries promise to be in even greater demand in the 21st century, eventhough, recently, there has been a slight decrease in growth resulting from the recessionary environment.

Corporation	Dividends Since	Type of Business
AT&T Corporation	1881	Telephone utility
E.I. DuPont de Nemours	1904	Chemicals
Exxon Mobil Corporation	1882	Chemical and petroleum products
General Electric Company	1899	Electrical equipment
Procter & Gamble Company	1891	Soap products
Chevron Texaco	1903	Chemical and petroleum products
Union Pacific Corporation	1900	Railroad

Exhibit 10–2

Corporations with Consecutive Dividend Payments for at Least 95 Years

When purchasing growth stocks, investors often sacrifice immediate cash dividends in return for greater dollar value in the future. Such companies as Nortel, BCE Inc., Research in Motion, and other technology firms are considered to be growth companies and pay few or no dividends. For most growth companies, profits that would normally be paid to shareholders in the form of dividends are re-invested in the companies in the form of retained earnings. The money the companies keep can provide at least part of the financing they need for future growth and expansion and control the cost of borrowing money. As a result, they grow at an even faster pace. Growth financed by *retained earnings* normally increases the dollar value of a share of stock for the investor.

Government bonds, corporate bonds, mutual funds, and real estate may also offer growth possibilities. Precious metals, gemstones, and collectibles are more speculative investments that offer less predictable growth potential. Investments in commodities and options are more speculative investments that usually stress immediate returns as opposed to continued long-term growth.

INVESTMENT LIQUIDITY

liquidity The ability to buy or sell an investment quickly without substantially affecting the investment's value.

Liquidity is the ability to buy or sell an investment quickly without substantially affecting the investment's value. Investments range from near-cash investments to frozen investments from which it is impossible to get your money. Chequing and savings accounts are very liquid because they can be quickly converted to cash. Guaranteed Investment Certificates impose penalties for withdrawing money before the maturity date.

With other investments, you may be able to sell quickly, but market conditions, economic conditions, or many other factors may prevent you from regaining the amount you originally invested. For example, the owner of real estate may have to lower the asking price to find a buyer. And it may be difficult to find a buyer for investments in collectibles, such as antiques and paintings.

> ### CONCEPT CHECK 10-2
> 1. Why are safety and risk two sides of the same coin?
> 2. What are the five components of the risk factor?
> 3. How do income, growth, and liquidity affect the choice of an investment?

An Overview of Investment Alternatives

Objective 3

Identify the major types of investment alternatives.

Once you have considered the risks involved, established your emergency fund, and have some money accumulated for investment purposes, it's time to consider the investment alternatives most people choose. you should begin by gathering as much information as possible about investment alternatives. Then you will be able to decide whether purchasing stocks, bonds, mutual funds, real estate, or other investments is a better use of your money than putting it in the bank. The remainder of this section provides a brief overview of different investment alternatives. The remaining chapters of Part 4 provide more detailed information on stocks, bonds, mutual funds, real estate, and other investment alternatives.

STOCK OR EQUITY FINANCING

equity capital Money that a business obtains from its owners.

Equity capital is money that a business obtains from its owners. If a business is a sole proprietorship or a partnership, it acquires equity capital when the owners invest their own money in the business. For a corporation, equity capital is provided by shareholders, who buy shares of its stock. Since all shareholders are owners, they share in the success of the corporation. This can make buying stock an attractive investment opportunity.

However, you should consider at least two factors before investing in stocks. First, a corporation is not required to repay the money obtained from the sale of stocks or to repurchase the stocks at a later date. Assume you purchased 100 shares of Air Canada stock. Later, you decide to sell your Air Canada stock. Your stocks are sold to another investor, not back to the company. In many cases, a shareholder sells his stocks because he or she thinks their price is going to decrease in value. The purchaser, on the other hand, buys those stocks because he or she thinks their price is going to increase. This creates a situation in which either the seller or the buyer earns a profit while the other party to the transaction experiences a loss.

Second, a corporation is under no legal obligation to pay dividends to shareholders. A **dividend** is a distribution of money, stocks, or other property that a corporation pays to shareholders. Dividends are paid out of earnings, but if a corporation that usually pays dividends has a bad year, its board of directors can vote to omit dividend payments to help pay necessary business expenses. Corporations may also retain earnings to make additional financing available for expansion, research and product development, or other business activities.

dividend A distribution of money, stocks, or other property that a corporation pays to shareholders.

There are two basic types of stocks: *common stocks* and *preferred stocks*. Both types have advantages and disadvantages that you should consider before deciding which to use for an investment program. A share of common stocks represents the most basic form of corporate ownership. People often purchase common stocks because this type of investment can provide (1) a source of income if the company pays dividends, (2) growth potential if the dollar value of the stocks increases, and (3) growth potential if the company splits its common stocks. And because it is a popular type of investment, most large corporations sell common stocks to satisfy a large part of their financing needs.

The most important priority an investor in preferred stocks enjoys is receiving cash dividends before common shareholders are paid any cash dividends. This factor is especially important when a corporation is experiencing financial problems and cannot pay cash dividends to both preferred and common shareholders. Other factors you should consider before purchasing both common or preferred stocks are discussed in Chapter 11.

CORPORATE AND GOVERNMENT BONDS

There are two types of bonds an investor should consider. A **corporate bond** is a corporation's written pledge to repay a specified amount of money, along with interest. A **government bond** is the written pledge of a government or a municipality to repay a specified sum of money, along with interest. Thus, when you buy a bond, you are loaning a corporation or government entity money for a period of time. Regardless of who issues the bond, you need to consider two major questions before investing in bonds. First, will the bond be repaid at maturity? The maturity dates for most bonds range between 1 and 30 years. An investor who purchases a bond has two options: keep the bond until maturity and then redeem it, or sell the bond to another investor. In either case, the value of the bond is closely tied to the ability of the corporation or government agency to repay the bond at maturity. Second, will the corporation or government agency be able to maintain interest payments to bondholders? Bondholders normally receive interest payments every six months. Again, if a corporation or government agency cannot pay the interest on its bonds, the value of those bonds will decrease.

corporate bond A corporation's written pledge to repay a specified amount of money, along with interest.

government bond The written pledge of a government or a municipality to repay a specified sum of money, along with interest.

Receiving periodic interest payments until maturity is one method of making money on a bond investment. Investors also use two other methods that can provide more liberal returns on bond investments. Chapter 12 discusses each of these methods.

Financial Planning for Life's Situations

RETURNS

Stocks have historically produced the highest average returns over the long-term. Fixed-income investments, like bonds, have historically earned lower long-term returns than stocks, while safe cash investments like treasury bills have generated the lowest returns.

From 1990 to 2000, no single type of asset has been the top performer for more than two consecutive years.

Top-performing asset types vary almost year-to-year.

Year	Canadian Equities	Canadian Bonds	Canadian T-bills
1990	−14.80%	7.54%	13.48%
1991	12.02%	22.14%	9.83%
1992	−1.43%	9.85%	7.08%
1993	32.55%	18.13%	5.50%
1994	−0.18%	−4.31%	5.36%
1995	14.53%	20.67%	7.39%
1996	28.35%	12.26%	5.02%
1997	14.98%	9.65%	3.18%
1998	−1.58%	9.17%	4.73%
1999	37.71%	−1.15%	4.66%
2000	7.41%	10.25%	5.47%

SOURCE: Standard & Poor's Micropal ®© Micropal, Inc. (2000); "Diversify your investments for portfolio success" Table provided by Royal Mutual Funds Inc., www.royalbank.com/investments

MUTUAL FUNDS

mutual fund An investment alternative chosen by people who pool their money to buy stocks, bonds, and other securities selected by professional managers employed by an investment company.

A **mutual fund** is an investment alternative chosen by people who pool their money to buy stocks, bonds, and other securities selected by professional managers employed by an investment company. Professional management is an especially important factor for investors with little or no previous experience in financial matters. Another reason investors choose mutual funds is *diversification*. Since mutual funds invest in a number of different securities, an occasional loss in one security is often offset by gains in other securities. As a result, the diversification provided by a mutual fund reduces risk.

The goals of one investor often differ from those of another. The managers of mutual funds realize this and tailor their funds to meet individual needs and objectives. Some invest in Canadian companies, while others invest in stocks and bonds issued by companies in foreign countries. As a result of all the different investment alternatives, mutual funds range from very conservative to extremely speculative investments.

Although investing money in a mutual fund provides professional management, even the best managers can make errors in judgment. The responsibility for choosing the right mutual fund is still based on the investor's evaluation of a mutual fund investment. Chapter 13 presents more information on the different types of mutual funds, the costs involved, and techniques for evaluating these investments.

REAL ESTATE

As a rule, real estate increases in value and eventually sells at a profit, but there are no guarantees. Although many beginning investors believe real estate values increase by 10 or

15 percent a year, in reality the nationwide average annual increase is about 3 percent. This growth rate makes real estate a long-term investment and not a get-rich-quick scheme.

Success in real estate investments depends on how well you evaluate alternatives. Experts often tell would-be investors that the three most important factors when evaluating a potential real estate investment are *location*, *location*, and *location*. While location may be the most important factor, other factors may determine whether or not a piece of real estate is a good investment. For example, you should answer the following questions before making a decision to purchase any property:

[1] Is the property priced competitively with similar properties?
[2] What type of financing is available, if any? What are the current interest rates?
[3] How much are the taxes?
[4] What is the condition of the buildings and houses in the immediate area?
[5] Why are the present owners selling the property?
[6] Is there a chance that the property will decrease in value?

Any investment has disadvantages, and real estate is no exception. Many people were "taken" by unscrupulous promoters who sold inaccessible land in the Florida Everglades. Poor location can cause a piece of property to decrease in value. Also, to sell your property, you must find an interested buyer who is able to obtain enough money or financing to complete the transaction. Finding a buyer can be difficult if loan money is scarce, the real estate market is in a decline, or you overpaid for the property. If you are forced to hold your investment longer than you originally planned, you must also consider taxes and loan payments.

OTHER INVESTMENT ALTERNATIVES

As defined earlier in this chapter, a speculative investment is a high-risk investment made in the hope of earning a relatively large profit in a short time. By its very nature, any investment may be speculative; that is, it may be quite risky. However, a true speculative investment is speculative because of the methods investors use to earn a quick profit. Typical speculative investments include:

- Call options
- Put options
- Derivatives
- Commodities
- Precious metals
- Gemstones
- Coins
- Stamps
- Antiques and collectibles

Without exception, investments of this kind are normally referred to as speculative for one reason or another. For example, the gold market has many unscrupulous dealers who sell worthless gold-plated lead coins to unsuspecting, uninformed investors. With any speculative investment, it is extremely important to deal with reputable dealers and recognized investment firms. It pays to be careful. While investments in this category can lead to large dollar gains, they should not be used by anyone who does not fully understand the risks involved. Chapter 11 presents information on options.

SUMMARY OF FACTORS THAT AFFECT INVESTMENT CHOICES

Earlier in this chapter, we examined how safety, risk, income, growth, and liquidity affect your investment choices. In the preceding section, we looked at available investment alternatives. Now, let's compare the factors that affect the choice of investments with each alternative. Exhibit 10–3 on page 296 ranks the alternatives in terms of safety, risk, income, growth, and liquidity.

Financial Planning for Life's Situations

BONDS OR STOCKS?

My projected savings are $5,000 for this year. Should I buy bonds or stocks?

The investment choice that is most appropriate for me depends primarily on three elements: My investment time horizon, my investment objectives, and my risk tolerance.

INVESTMENT GOALS AND RISK ANALYSIS (EXHIBIT 10-5)

At this point in my life, I have finished school, started a career, currently paying off student loans, and have already saved up for my emergency fund. My long-term investment goal is to save up $20,000 within four years for a down payment on my mortgage assuming I continue to save $5,000 a year. The return on my investment would be used to increase the down payment and reduce my mortgage further. From the questions posed on the risk and investment section of the Personal Finance CD ("The Personal Finance Course: An Interactive Guide for Your Financial Future"), I concluded that I primarily want my investment to produce income now but also some future growth. I would accept some fluctuations in the value of my investment as long as my losses were small and temporary. In addition, I understand that in order to achieve a good rate of return, I will have to tolerate some stock market volatility realizing that I am in for the long term. In conclusion, my investor profile is as follows:

Investment horizon: 3 to 5 years (the longer you invest the more risk you can take)
Investment objective: Income and growth
Risk tolerance: Fairly risk tolerant

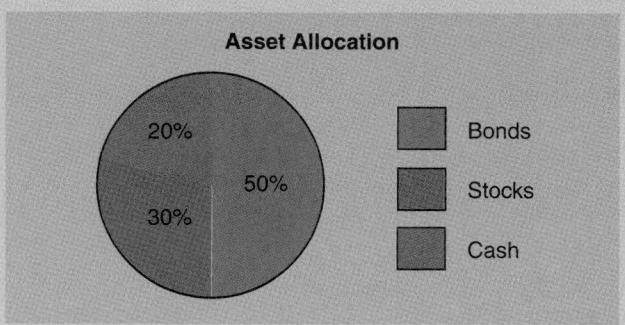

Asset Allocation

- 20% — Bonds
- 50% — Stocks
- 30% — Cash

The flaw with utilizing software is that it does not take into consideration present market conditions. It only provides you with a generalized solution, as does other risk analysis software on Internet, such as canadalife. com and scotiabank.com

Now let's look at the risks associated with the different kinds of investment options available.

BONDS

Bonds are a less risky type of investment than stocks and, in consequence, have a low potential for higher returns (see Safety and Risk). Bonds offer an even lower risk if you choose to hold them until maturity since there is no market risk and little risk of losing part or all of your capital. In this situation, the risk lies in the possibility of default of the issuer (see Business Failure Risk). However, if the issuer were the government, then that risk would be close to nothing (see Safety and Risk). Bonds have a fixed term with their yield affected by interest rates, inflation, the level of economic activity and the economy. An inverted relationship exists

---

diversification The process of spreading your assets among several types of investments to lessen risk.

It is now appropriate to introduce the topic of diversification. **Diversification** is the process of spreading your assets among several types of investments to lessen risk. In fact, diversification can reduce the risk associated with putting all your eggs in one basket—a common mistake made by investors. To avoid this mistake, many financial planners suggest that you think of your investment program as a pyramid consisting of four levels, as illustrated in Exhibit 10–4 on page 296. This approach to investing can provide financial growth and protection, regardless of your age, marital status, income, or level of financial sophistication.

In Exhibit 10–4, the investments in level 1 provide the foundation for an investment program. After the foundation is established in level 1, most investors choose from the investment alternatives in level 2 and level 3. Be warned: Many investors may decide the investments in

between interest rates and bond values...when one goes up, the other goes down.

The bond market has been faring very well since the beginning of the economic slowdown, as it usually does. However, looking forward, economic conditions will not be on the side of the bond market. Since interest rates have not been this low in almost 40 years (since 1962) (ROBtv), it would not be wise to invest in a bond for the long-term, as it is inevitable that the interest rates will rise again. Given present economic conditions, if I had to sell the bond for emergency purposes and interest rates had risen, I would have to sell my bond at a discount because the market rate would be higher than my coupon rate (see Interest Rate Risk). Because interest rates are so low, I am at higher risk because a change in interest rates will more greatly affect the price of a lower coupon bond (assuming all other characteristics are the same). Therefore, lower coupon bond prices are more volatile than higher coupon bond prices to changing interest rates (MyFinancialSite.com).

STOCKS

Stocks offer the potential for a higher return but are also associated with higher risk. Considering my young age, I am willing to take on a greater risk in exchange for a higher expected return. However, since I do want to maintain my capital as much as possible, my choice would be to invest in less risky stocks, blue-chip stocks, (see Classification of Stock Investments) companies that I have researched and can trust. This will provide me with the opportunity to receive income through dividends and the potential of a higher return. Stocks also act as a hedge against inflation (see Inflation risk) yet

have a high liquidity risk compared with bonds (see Liquidity Risk).

In conclusion, I would not invest in bonds or stocks but in both in order to reduce my risk through diversification. By spreading my assets among different investments, I can reduce the risk associated with putting all my eggs in one basket. (See Factors That Affect Investment Choices). I would begin by building a small cushion, with 25 percent of my investment in bonds and the remaining in low-risk equities and wait to build a stronger foundation in bonds when interest rates rise in the future (see graph below). (See Investment Pyramid.) In addition, I would seek financial help before buying the stocks for my portfolio.

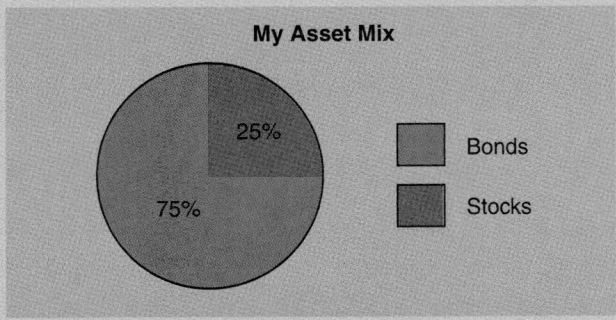

My Asset Mix

25%

75%

Bonds

Stocks

SOURCE: Catherine Condoroussis, Assignment— Introductory Personal Finance Course JMSB, Concordia University, Fall 2001.

level 4 are too speculative for their investment programs. While investments at this level may provide spectacular dollar gains, they pose the risk that they will lose value or even become totally worthless.

Once you understand the risk factors associated with different investment alternatives and the principle of diversification, the next step is to develop a personal investment plan.

A PERSONAL INVESTMENT PLAN

To be a successful investor, you must develop a plan and then implement it. Most people use a series of steps like those listed in Exhibit 10–5 on page 297 to develop their own personal plan for investing.

Exhibit 10–3

Factors Used to Evaluate Typical Investment Alternatives

	Type of Investment	FACTORS TO BE EVALUATED				
		Safety	Risk	Income	Growth	Liquidity
Traditional investments	Common stocks	Average	Average	Average	High	Average
	Preferred stocks	Average	Average	High	Average	Average
	Corporate bonds	Average	Average	High	Low	Average
	Government bonds	High	Low	Low	Low	High
	Mutual funds	Average	Average	Average	Average	Average
	Real estate	Average	Average	Average	Average	Low
Speculative investments	Options	Low	High	N/A	Low	Average
	Derivatives	Low	High	N/A	Low	Average
	Commodities	Low	High	N/A	Low	Average
	Precious metals, gemstones, and collectibles	Low	High	N/A	Low	Low

N/A = Not applicable.

You begin investment planning by establishing realistic goals. The second step is to determine the amount of money you will obtain by a specific date. The total amount of money specified in step 2 should be based on your goals. The amount of money you now have available for investment purposes is specified in step 3. For most investors, the money currently available for investment purposes has accumulated over a period of time. For example, Sharon and Derek Timmons began saving $200 a month to finance a future investment program more than three years ago. They deposited the money in an interest-bearing savings account. Now, after three years, they have accumulated more than $8,000, which they can use to purchase different investments. In step 4, you list specific investment alternatives that you want to evaluate.

Because of the relationship between risks and returns for each investment, step 5 is divided into two components. In step 5(a), you examine the risk factor for each investment alternative. In step 5(b), you examine the potential return associated with each alternative. The information needed to complete steps 5(a) and 5(b) should be based on your research of potential investments. At the very least, this requires some expert advice, careful study, and a commitment of your time. In step 6, you reduce potential investments to a reasonable number. In step 7, you make a final decision to choose at least two different investments. By choosing at least two alternatives, you build a certain amount of diversification into your

Exhibit 10–4

Possible Investments for Financial Security, Safety and Income, Growth, and Speculation

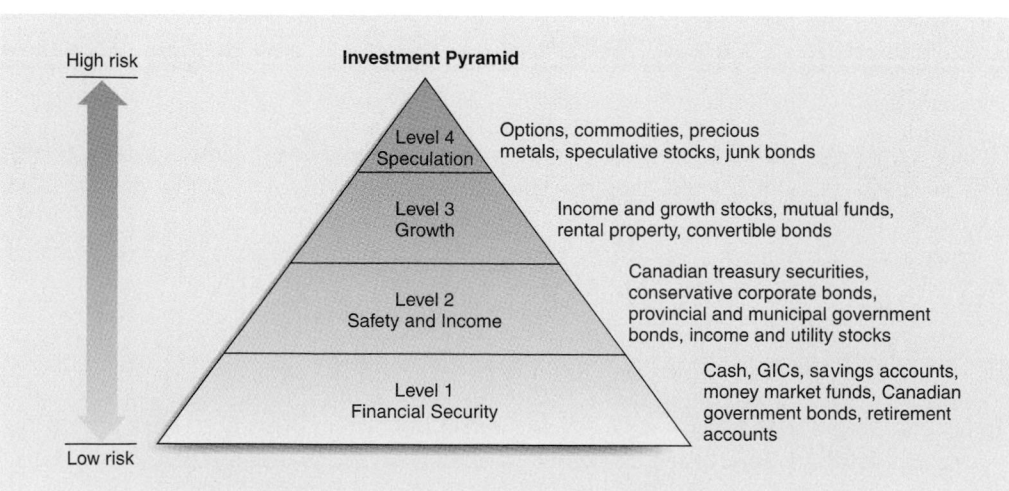

Advice from a Pro

PRESCRIPTION FOR A HEALTHY INVESTMENT PROGRAM

According to the pros, life is not a dress rehearsal. This is all we've got!! One host of a popular radio program on financial planning says that retiring means getting up in the morning and doing what *you* want to do. He often asks potential clients a basic question: What worthy goal would you pursue if money were no object? It is toward *this* goal that you start investing.

In addition to helping clients determine goals that are important, he also encourages clients to adopt the 15/15/70 rule. He recommends that you first give away 15 percent. You must learn that money is a servant, not a master. You must learn that it really is "more blessed to give than to receive." Then, give yourself 15 percent.

Most people say, I'll pay all the bills, then I'll invest whatever is left. It won't happen. Pay yourself off the top. Finally, live on the remaining 70 percent. Learn to discipline yourself in order to pay those bills.

Once a client has accumulated enough money to finance an investment program, he encourages his clients and radio listeners to choose long-term investments. For many beginning investors, he often suggests good mutual funds with a four-star or five-star rating, excellent long-term performance, and good management. Above all, this pro believes that you should pick investments that are suitable for your risk comfort level.

---

investment program. As the total dollar value of your investments grows, you will probably want to continue to consider additional investments. After all, spreading potential risks among different investments is a key factor in diversifying your investment program.

Step 8 provides for continued evaluation of your investments. Investors' circumstances often change as they go through life. As a result, investors are often forced to adapt their planning to new situations. For example, if you accept a new job at a substantially higher salary, changes in investment goals may make your present personal plan of action obsolete. Also, different investments may become more or less attractive because of changes in economic and financial conditions. During the early 1980s, for example, many investors sold their common stocks and placed their money in Guaranteed Investment Certificates (GICs) that paid high guaranteed interest. More recently, low interest rates have led investors to cash their bonds and GICs and purchase common stocks and mutual funds that offer more potential.

To illustrate the above planning process, let's use the case of Salomé Mari, who accepted a position in advertising after university. After two years, Salomé is earning $30,000 a year. Her take-home pay after deductions is $2,000 a month. Her living expenses are about $1,600 a month, which leaves a surplus of $400. After graduating from university, she immediately

---

1. Establish your investment goals.	**Exhibit 10–5**
2. Determine the amount of money you need to obtain your goals.	
3. Specify the amount of money you currently have available to fund your investments.	Steps for Effective Investment Planning
4. List different investments that you want to evaluate.	
5. Evaluate (a) the risk factor, and (b) the potential return for all investments.	
6. Reduce possible investments to a reasonable number.	
7. Choose at least two different investments.	
8. Continue to evaluate your investment program.	

began saving a portion of each month's surplus. First, she established an emergency fund. Now, she has $14,000 available for investment purposes. After much thought, Salomé developed the personal plan of action illustrated in Exhibit 10–6.

Your own plan may be quite different from Salomé's, but the principle is the same. Each person has different ideas and goals. Establish your investment goals first, and then follow through. Often, the follow-through is the most important component when it comes to developing a successful investment plan. Simply put: How important are your investment goals, and are you willing to work to attain them?

CONCEPT CHECK 10–3

1. Of all the investment alternatives presented in this chapter, which one do you think would help you obtain your investment goals? Why?
2. Why do investors purchase stocks?
3. What are two chief advantages of investing in mutual funds?
4. What factors should you consider before purchasing real estate for investment purposes?
5. How can the investment pyramid presented in Exhibit 10–4 help you build an investment program to reach your financial goals?
6. What are the steps required for a personal investment plan?

Exhibit 10–6

A Personal Investment Plan for Salomé Mari

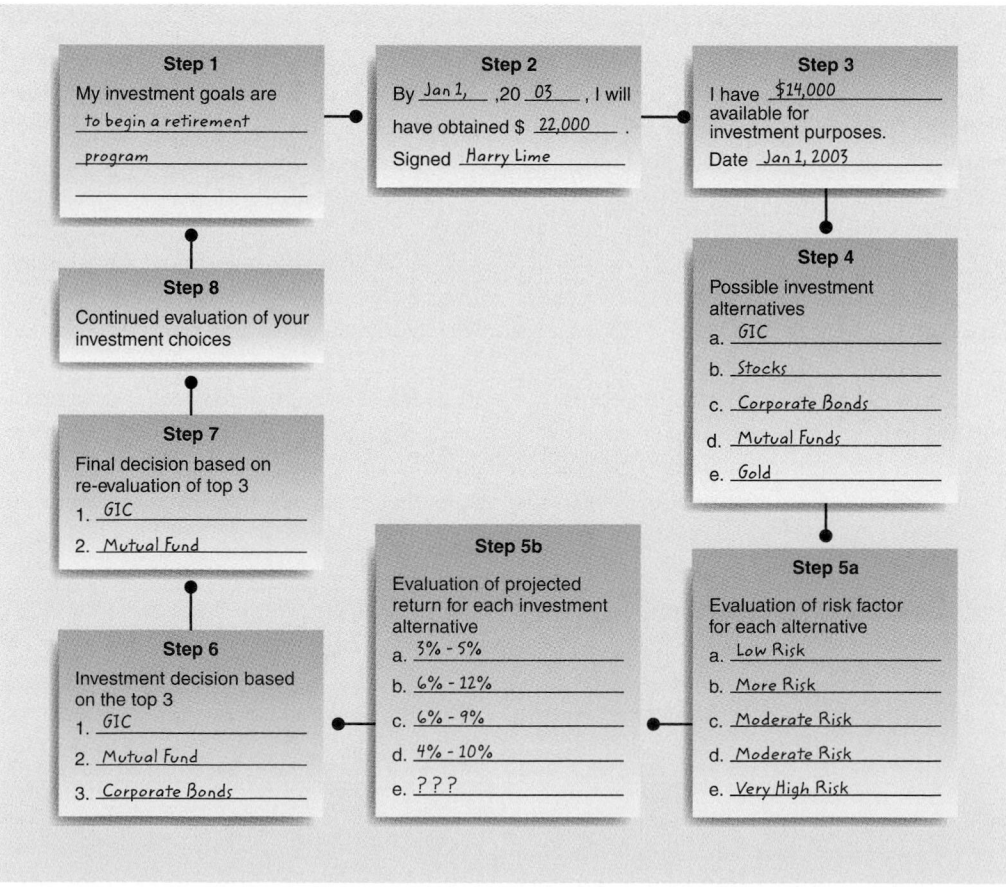

Advice from a Pro

THE PSYCHOLOGY OF INVESTING

Why do many investors fall prey to irrational financial thinking? The usual explanation is simple: fear and greed. Glen Whyte, a professor at the Rotman School of Management at the University of Toronto, specializes in the study of risky decision making. "For most people," he says, "the motive to get into the market is a simple desire to generate a gain. But once they're in, most investors make critically important decisions in a half-baked way, without valid information."

Which human characteristic causes the most problems? Stubbornness. All too often, investors desperately hold on to a loser in the hope it will pay off. Experts in behavioural finance call this loss aversion: Study after study shows that people are willing to run a greater risk to avoid a loss than to make a gain.

Another motive for hanging on too long is the so-called endowment effect—the belief that because we own something, it must be of superior value. Often, the price an investor pays for a stock becomes a kind of psychological line in the sand. If the owner is compelled to sell below that price, he or she experiences shame, denial, or regret. If, on the other hand, the market value is higher than the purchase price, the dominant emotions are pride, vindication, and satisfaction. Often, the real sting of investment losses is that we have no one to blame but ourselves. Investors tend to flock together when choosing their investments. Rather than basing their buy-and-sell decisions on their own research—in which case, they risk looking stupid as well as losing money—most people would rather tag along with the crowd. At least that way if they lose they can comfort themselves with the knowledge that everyone else was fooled, too. Yet another psychological tendency that gets in the way of profitable investing is cognitive bias. Our cognitive bias blinds us to potential dangers. When deciding where to put their money, most people consider the range of possible outcomes and decide which one they think is most likely. After arriving at that decision, however, they ignore all other possibilities.

One of the reasons people like to construct scenarios around their investments is that they are desperate to convince themselves that markets make sense. Human beings constantly seek meaning and patterns, and the markets don't offer much of either. In the absence of reliable information, investors become anxious and tend to rely on their emotions, which makes them vulnerable to rumours and hot tips.

How can investors stay out of trouble?

- Understand the extent to which your own personality can push you to make bad decisions.
- Follow a realistic investment plan that fits your needs and goals.
- Educate yourself. If your sense of self-efficiency is based on knowledge rather than ego, you're less likely to get carried away by your own success.
- Learn humility. A success rate of 60 to 70 percent in picking stocks is the best most people can expect to achieve.
- Finally, it is a good idea to develop a strong relationship with a trusted professional adviser or a group of fellow investors.

SOURCE: The Maclean's Guide to Personal Finance 2000, "Mind Games" by Vivian Smith, p. 28

Factors That Reduce Investment Risk

In this section, we examine the factors that can spell the difference between success and failure for an investor. We begin by reviewing the role of a financial planner. Then, we consider your role in the investment process.

THE ROLE OF A FINANCIAL PLANNER

To achieve their financial goals, many people seek professional help. In many cases, they turn to stockbrokers, lawyers, accountants, bankers, or insurance agents. However, these professionals are specialists in one specific field and may not be qualified to provide the type of advice required to develop a thorough financial plan.

Objective 4

Recognize the role of the professional financial planner and your role in a personal investment program.

While there is no such thing as a nationally designated "personal financial planner" in Canada, a number of organizations allow special designations after certain criteria have been met. The Canadian Association of Financial Planners (CAFP) requires that all Registered Financial Planners (RFP) must achieve an academic or professional standing recognized by the Association. The Member must be sponsored by other planners in the industry, be currently engaged in the profession and have demonstrated competence in financial planning. A minimum of two years' experience in the practice of financial planning is required. CAFP members must abide by the CAFP Code of Professional Ethics and make an ongoing commitment to maintaining professional standards through continuing education. The Canadian Institute of Financial Planning offers six correspondence courses to be completed as part of its requirements for the Chartered Financial Planner designation. Finally, the Canadian Securities Institute (CSI) and the Institute of Canadian Bankers (ICB) both offer a number of investment and personal finance courses.

In selecting a financial adviser, you will need to be aware of how they are being paid as well as how this might influence the advice you are given. Salaried employees of such institutions as banks or trust companies are sometimes designated as financial planners and will provide advice either free of charge or for a nominal fee. Commission planners receive their compensation from the sellers of the services and products that they recommend. In general, it would be a safe bet to assume that any advice you get from either of these types of planners will be biased in some way.

More objective advice might be available from fee-based planners and fee-only or fee-for-service planners. Fee-based planners receive their compensation partly in the form of fees paid by you and partly in the form of commissions from the institutions. Fee-only or fee-for-service planners will charge you directly on an hourly basis (typically from $50 to $250 per hour), and that will be their sole source of income for the service that they provide to you.

YOUR ROLE IN THE INVESTMENT PROCESS

Successful investors continually evaluate their investments. They never sit back and let their investments manage themselves. Obviously, different types of investments will require different methods of evaluation. Some factors to consider when choosing different investments are described next.

EVALUATE POTENTIAL INVESTMENTS

Let's assume you have $25,000 to invest. Also assume your investment will earn a 10-percent return the first year. At the end of one year, you will have earned $2,500 and your investment will be worth $27,500. Not a bad return on your original investment! Now ask yourself: How long would it take to earn $2,500 if I had to work for this amount of money at a job? For some people, it might take a month; for others, it might take longer. The point is that if you want this type of return, you should be willing to work for it, but the work takes a different form than a job. When choosing an investment, the work you invest is the time it takes to research different investments so that you can make an informed decision.

Some people invest large sums of money and never research the investments they purchase. Obviously, this is a flawed approach that can lead to large dollar losses. On the other hand, an informed investor has a much better chance of choosing the types of investments that will increase in value. In fact, much of the information in the remainder of Part 4 will help you learn how to evaluate different investment opportunities. But you have to be willing to work and learn if you want to be a successful investor. As you will see in the next section, evaluation doesn't stop once you make a decision to purchase an investment. It continues as long as you own the investment.

Financial Planning Calculations

CHARTING THE VALUE OF YOUR INVESTMENT

To monitor the value of their investments, many investors use a simple chart like the one illustrated here. To construct a chart like this one, place the original purchase price of your investment in the middle on the side of the chart. Then use price increments of a logical amount to show increases and decreases in dollar value.

Place individual dates along the bottom of the chart. For stocks, bonds, mutual funds, and similar investments, you may want to graph every two weeks and chart current values on, say, a Friday. For longer-term investments, such as real estate, you can chart current values every six months.

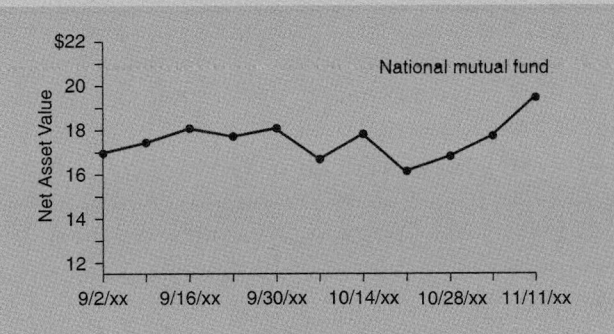

A WORD OF CAUTION

If an investment is beginning to have a large increase or decrease in value, you should watch that investment more closely. You can still continue to chart at regular intervals, but you may want to check dollar values more frequently—in some cases, daily.

MONITOR THE VALUE OF YOUR INVESTMENTS Would you believe that some people invest large sums of money and don't know what their investments are worth? They don't know if their investments have increased or decreased in value. They don't know if they should sell their investments or continue to hold them. A much better approach is to monitor the value of your investments. If you choose to invest in stocks, bonds, mutual funds, commodities, or options, you can determine the value of your holdings by looking at the price quotations reported on the Internet, on financial news television and radio programs, and in newspapers. Your real estate holdings may be compared with similar properties currently for sale in the surrounding area. Finally, you can determine the value of your precious metals, gemstones, and collectibles by checking with reputable dealers and investment firms. Regardless of which type of investment you choose, close surveillance will keep you informed of whether your investment increases or decreases in value. The Financial Planning Calculations box above presents further information on monitoring the value of your investments.

KEEP ACCURATE AND CURRENT RECORDS Accurate recordkeeping can help you spot opportunities to maximize profits or reduce dollar losses when you sell your investments. Accurate recordkeeping can also help you decide whether you want to invest additional funds in a particular investment. At the very least, you should keep purchase records for each of your investments that include the actual dollar cost of the investment, plus any commissions or fees you paid. It is also useful to keep a list of the sources of information (Internet addresses, business periodicals, research publications, and so on), along with copies of the material you used to evaluate each investment. Then, when it is time to re-evaluate an existing investment, you will know where to begin your search for current information. As you will see in the next section, accurate recordkeeping is also necessary for tax purposes.

TAX CONSIDERATIONS

Generally, investment income falls into three categories: tax-exempt, tax-deferred, and taxable. *Tax-exempt* income is often hard to come by, but it does exist in the form of specific tax-sheltered investments in resource activities, such as mining, and in labour-sponsored venture capital corporations. *Tax-deferred* investments have their income taxed at a later date to allow you to get an additional return on funds you might have otherwise paid as taxes. These include Registered Retirement Savings Plans (RRSPs), Registered Education Savings Plans (RESPs), and Registered Pension Plans (RPPs). The income from all other sorts of investments is *taxable income*.

As always in personal financial planning, it is important to realize all the consequences of your investment and tax decisions. Areas of concern for the former might include decisions about dividends, interest, rental income, and capital gains and losses. As for taxes, it's important to keep in mind the tax effect of all your sources of income, as some income may be more advantageous.

DIVIDENDS, INTEREST INCOME, AND RENTAL INCOME
As defined earlier in this chapter, a dividend is a distribution of money, stocks, or other property that a corporation pays to shareholders. Dividends are taxed in a peculiar way that is designed to reflect that the corporation paying you a dividend has already paid taxes on its profits (which it is sharing with you in the form of dividend payments). The total of the amount you receive in this form is "grossed-up" by 25 percent. This means that if you receive $100 in dividends, you will declare it as $125 in income. You are then taxed at your marginal rate minus a dividend tax credit at the rate of 13.33 percent. Capital dividends, or dividends derived from a corporation's capital gains, are the exception to this rule and will not be taxed.

Exhibit 10–7 demonstrates how dividends are taxed and the differences between marginal and effective rates depending on an individual's tax bracket.

Interest from banks, credit unions, and savings and loan associations is subject to federal taxation. Interest that you receive from promissory notes, loans, bonds, and Canadian securities must also be reported as income. You must report the total of such income as ordinary income on your tax return.

Exhibit 10–7

Calculation of Tax Rates on Dividend Income

	Federal tax rates			
	16%	**22%**	**26%**	**29%**
Dividends received	$1,000.00	$1,000.00	$1,000.00	$1,000.00
Gross-up (25 percent)	250.00	250.00	250.00	250.00
Grossed-up dividends	1,250.00	1,250.00	1,250.00	1,250.00
Federal tax	200.00	275.00	325.00	362.50
Less dividend tax credit (16.67% of dividends received)	(166.67)	(166.67)	(166.67)	(166.67)
Net federal tax	66.67	141.67	191.67	229.17
Add provincial tax (assume a provincial rate of 42.75%)	28.50	60.56	81.94	97.97
Total tax	95.17	202.23	273.61	327.14
Dividend after taxes	904.83	797.77	726.39	672.86
Effective tax rate (total tax ÷ dividends received)	9.52%	20.22%	27.36%	32.71%
Total marginal tax rate (federal rate × (1 + provincial rate))	22.84%	31.41%	37.12%	41.39%

NOTE: Note that although the effective tax rate on dividend income is lower than the total marginal tax rate in each income category, because the dividend tax credit remains constant, the marginal benefit of receiving dividend income reduces as the income tax bracket increases.

Net income from rental property is also subject to federal taxation and is treated as ordinary income like wages or salaries. Generally, you must report all income and expenses on rental property.

CAPITAL GAINS AND CAPITAL LOSSES Under current laws, profit resulting from the sale of stocks, mutual funds, bonds, land, and some personal property is considered a capital gain. For owners of certain small businesses and farm property, there is a $500,000 capital gains exemption. However, these two types of investments are defined very specifically, and you should check in advance to verify that your investment qualifies for the deduction. You will be taxed on 50 percent of all other capital gains you receive, minus any losses you may have incurred on nondepreciable assets, considered capital losses.

For example, assume Cody Shaw sold 100 shares of Ballard Power stocks for a profit of $1,000. If he is in the 26-percent tax bracket, the total tax he will pay on his profit will be $130 (26% × $500 = $130). Now suppose that he also incurred a capital loss of $200 upon selling 100 shares of Bid.com. Now his total taxes will be $104 (26% × (500 − 100)).

Under current taxation laws, an allowable capital loss is 50 percent of a capital loss; this amount can be used to offset taxable capital gains. Note, however, that if you do not have capital gains, then you will not be allowed to use your capital loss to offset other income.

Visit the Web site
See the Weblinks under Chapter 10 on the online learning centre at www.mcgrawhill.ca/college/kapoor.

CONCEPT CHECK 10-4

1. What type of training does a qualified financial planner have?
2. What is your role in the investment process?
3. How do dividends, interest, and rental income differ from capital gains and losses?

Sources of Investment Information

With most investments, more information is available than you can read and comprehend. Therefore, you must be selective in the type of information you use for evaluation purposes. With some investments, however, only a limited amount of information is available. For example, a wealth of information is available on individual stocks and mutual funds, whereas the amount of information on a metal, such as cobalt or manganese, may be limited to one source. Regardless of the number or availability of sources, always determine how reliable and accurate the information is. Following are sources of information you can use to evaluate present and future investments.

Objective 5

Use various sources of financial information that can reduce risks and increase investment returns.

THE INTERNET AND ONLINE COMPUTER SERVICES

While no one knows the exact number, experts estimate that there are more than 544 million Internet users worldwide.[1] Today, more people have access to information provided by computers located in their homes or at libraries, universities, or businesses than ever before, and this number is growing. More importantly, a wealth of information is available on most personal finance topics and different investment alternatives. For example, you can obtain interest rates for guaranteed investment certificates; current price information for stocks, bonds, and mutual funds; and brokers' recommendations to buy, hold, or sell a corporation's stocks. You can even trade securities online just by pushing the right button on your computer keyboard. You can also use computers and financial planning software to develop a personal financial plan.

---

[1] Forbes.com (www.forbes.com/asap/2002/1007/020tab.html)

To use your computer to generate information you really need, you must be selective. One of the best ways to access needed information is to use a search engine. Search engines, such as Yahoo Canada, AltaVista Canada, google.ca, and Canada.com, allow you to do a keyword search for either the personal finance topic or investment alternative that you want to explore. Federal, provincial, and local governments and most corporations also have Web sites where you can obtain valuable information.

Today, thousands of Internet service providers allow users to connect to the Internet and use search engines, newsgroups, mailing lists, and e-mail. If you're a beginner, you may find it easier to use one of the commercial online companies, such as Canada.com, AOLCanada, Bell Sympatico, and MSN.com. These companies usually provide subscribers with access to a broad range of information on a variety of topics, as well as a connection to the Internet. While it is impossible to list all of the Internet sites related to personal finance, those listed in Exhibit 10–8 will get you started. We will examine other specific Internet sites in the remaining chapters in Part 4. Also, read the appendix at the end of Chapter 1 for information on how to use the Internet for personal financial planning.

NEWSPAPERS AND NEWS PROGRAMS

One of the most readily available sources of information for the average investor is the financial page of a national newspaper or *The Financial Post*. There you will find a summary of the day's trading on the Montreal Stock Exchange, the TSX Venture Exchange, the Toronto Stock Exchange, and the two main U.S. exchanges, the Nasdaq Stock Market and the New York Stock Exchange. In addition to stock coverage, most newspapers provide information on

Exhibit 10–8

Useful Internet Sites for Personal Financial Planning

The following six Internet sites provide information that you can use to establish a financial plan and begin an investment program.

Sponsor and Description	Web Address
The **Canoe Webfin** Web site provides current financial news and material that can help both beginning and experienced investors sharpen their investment skills.	www.Webfin.com
The **Quicken** Web site provides information about investments, home mortgages, insurance, taxes, banking and credit, and different types of retirement programs.	www.quicken.ca
About Canada has an Investing: Canada link under its Business/Careers section. Click here to find a tremendous array of personal finance facts, advice, articles and more. There's also an Investing for Beginners section.	http://home.about.com/ aboutcanada/index.htm
Canadian Financial Network (CFN) has well over 6,000 international online financial resources gathered and saves time for investors by describing these resources in sufficient detail to allow you to stop surfing and start targeting the information that you want.	http://canadianfinance.com
Bell Sympatico has a section entitled Personal Finance that offers everything from family finance to current business and finance news to information on borrowing, budgeting, and more.	www.sympatico.ca
The **Investor Learning Centre of Canada** makes learning about investing easier than it has ever been before. Whether you're an absolute beginner or a seasoned investor, you'll find what you need.	www.investorlearning.ca

stocks traded in the over-the-counter markets, mutual funds, corporate and government bonds, commodities and options, and general economic news. Detailed information on how to read price quotations for stocks, bonds, mutual funds, and other investments is presented in the remaining chapters of Part 4.

It is also possible to obtain economic and investment information on radio or television. Many stations broadcast investment market summaries and economic information as part of their regular news programs. See Exhibit 10–9 for publications and news programs used by successful investors.

BUSINESS PERIODICALS AND GOVERNMENT PUBLICATIONS

Most business periodicals are published weekly, twice a month, or monthly. *The Globe and Mail's Report On Business*, *Business Week*, *Canadian Business*, *Fortune*, and similar business periodicals provide not only general news about the overall economy but also detailed financial information about individual corporations. Some business periodicals—for example, *Business 2.0* and *Canadian Banker*—focus on information about firms in a specific industry. In addition to business periodicals, more general magazines, such as *The Economist*, *Time*, and *Newsweek*, provide investment information as a regular feature. Finally, *Money*, *MoneySaver*, *Canadian MoneySaver*, *IE:Money* and similar periodicals provide information and advice designed to improve your investment skills.

The Canadian government is an excellent source of information that is often free or offered at low cost. Statistics Canada provides information compiled both nationally and regionally. Industry Canada's Strategis is also an excellent resource for businesses and consumers alike.

CORPORATE REPORTS

The federal government requires corporations selling new issues of securities to disclose information about corporate earnings, assets and liabilities, products or services, and the qualifications

---

While individual investors have their favourite sources for investment information, it is quite likely that most successful investors use some of the following newspapers, periodicals, and news programs on a regular basis.

Exhibit 10–9

A Personal Reading List for Successful Investing

Newspapers
- Larger local newspapers
- *The National Post*
- *The Globe and Mail*

Television
- CBC Business News, ROBtv, Business Television

Business Periodicals
- *The Globe and Mail's Report on Business* (ROB)
- *Business Week*
- *Canadian Business*
- *Fortune*
- *The Economist*
- *Newsweek*

Personal Financial Publications
- *Canadian MoneySaver*
- *IE:Money*
- *Money*
- *MoneySaver*
- *Maclean's Guide to Personal Finance*

of top management in a *prospectus* that they must give to investors. In addition to the prospectuses, all publicly owned corporations send their shareholders annual reports and quarterly reports that contain detailed financial data. Included in annual and quarterly corporate reports are statements of financial position, which describe changes in assets, liabilities, and owners' equity. Also included in these reports are income statements, which provide dollar amounts for sales, expenses, and profits or losses.

STATISTICAL AVERAGES

Investors often gauge the value of their investments by following one or more widely recognized statistical averages. Such an average is a statistical measure that indicates whether a broad investment category (stocks, bonds, mutual funds, and so on) is increasing or decreasing in value.

How much importance should you attach to statistical averages? These averages show trends and direction, but they do not pinpoint the actual value of a specific investment. The remaining chapters of Part 4 describe many of these averages.

INVESTOR SERVICES AND NEWSLETTERS

Many stockbrokers and financial planners mail a free monthly or quarterly newsletter to their clients. In addition, investors can subscribe to services that provide investment information. The fees for investor services generally range from $30 to $750 a year.

Five widely used services are available for investors who specialize in stocks, bonds, and mutual funds:

[1] *SEDAR.* The System for Electronic Document Analysis and Retrieval (SEDAR) is used for electronically filing securities information in Canada. Since January 1, 1997, it has been mandatory for Canadian companies to file electronically. SEDAR, therefore, provides access to all Canadian public companies and mutual fund filings, including annual reports, prospectuses, financial statements, press releases, and continuous disclosure documents. (See www.sedar.com.)

[2] *Stockhouse Canada.* Located at www.stockhouse.ca, this site offers free access to a number of newsletters, as well as quotes, charts, chats, and news.

[3] *The Fund Library.* The Fund Library, at www.fundlibrary.com, tracks more than 2,000 mutual funds and offers a number of tools and advice to help you compare them.

[4] *Value Line.* This service provides reports supplying detailed information, such as earnings, dividends, sales, liabilities, and other financial data, about major corporations. While the focus is the U.S. market, more than 100 Canadian corporations are also examined. (See www.valueline.com.)

Other investment publications that may help you evaluate potential investments are the Canadian Bond Rating Service's (CBRS) *Guide to Conservative Fixed-Income Investing*; the *Blue Book of CBS Stock Reports*; the *Investor's Digest of Canada* from MPL Communications; and publications by the International Monetary Fund.

In addition to the preceding publications, each of the following securities exchanges provides information through printed materials and the Internet:

• Toronto Stock Exchange (www.tse-cdnx.com)
• TSX Venture Exchange (www.tse-cdnx.com)
• Montreal Stock Exchange (www.m-x.ca)
• Winnipeg Stock Exchange (www.wse.ca)
• New York Stock Exchange (www.nyse.com)
• Nasdaq Stock Market (www.nasdaq.com)
• International Federation of Stock Exchanges (www.fibv.com)

Each of these Web sites provides basic information about the exchange, offers educational material and a glossary of important terms, and describes how investors can profit from transactions through the exchange.

The preceding discussion of investor services and newsletters is not exhaustive, but it gives you some idea of the amount and scope of information available to serious investors. Although most small investors find many of the services and newsletters described here too expensive for personal subscriptions, this information may be available from stockbrokers or financial planners. This type of information is also available at many public libraries.

DESKTOP INFORMATION SERVICES

Recently introduced into the financial services industry are desktop information services such as Bloomberg Professional service (http://about.bloomberg.com/), 3000 Xtra, Reuters (http://about.reuters.com/), which provide instantaneous access to real-time historical financial data, news, and many other services. These desktop information services have transformed the securities business and levelled the playing field between buyers and sellers.

CONCEPT CHECK 10-5

1. What do you think is the most readily available source of information for the average investor? Explain your answer.
2. What type of information can you obtain using the Internet?
3. Briefly describe the additional sources of information you can use to evaluate a potential investment and lessen risk.

SUMMARY OF OBJECTIVES

Objective 1
Explain why you should establish an investment program.
Investment goals must be specific and measurable and should be classified as short-term, intermediate, and long-term. Before beginning an investment program, you must make sure your personal financial affairs are in order. This process begins with learning to live within your means and obtaining adequate insurance protection. The next step is the accumulation of an emergency fund equal to three to nine months' living expenses. Then, and only then, is it time to save the money needed to establish an investment program.

Objective 2
Describe how safety, risk, income, growth, and liquidity affect your investment decisions.
Although each investor may have specific, individual reasons for investing, all investors must consider the factors of safety, risk, income, growth, and liquidity. Especially important is the relationship between safety and risk. Basically, this concept can be summarized as follows: The potential return for any investment should be directly related to the risk the investor assumes. The risk factor can be broken down into five components: inflation risk, interest rate risk, business failure risk, market risk, and global investment risk.

Objective 3
Identify the major types of investment alternatives.
Investment alternatives include stocks, bonds, mutual funds, and real estate. More speculative investment alternatives include options, derivatives, commodities, precious metals, gemstones, and collectibles. Before choosing a specific investment, you should evaluate all potential investments on the basis of safety, risk, income, growth, and liquidity. You should also diversify your investments to lessen risk. With all of these factors in mind, the next step is to develop a specific, personal investment plan to help you accomplish your goals.

Objective 4
Recognize the role of the professional financial planner and your role in a personal investment program.
There are no hard and fast rules that define what a person must do in order to use the designation of Personal Financial Planner. In general, however, there are a number of reputable associations that regulate the use of related designations, such as CFP (Certified Financial Planner), RFP (Registered Financial Planner), and FP (Financial Planner). These associations generally insist on formal training of some kind as well as a minimum of experience and commitment. Financial planners can help people achieve their investment goals, but

choosing a qualified planner is your responsibility. It is also your responsibility to evaluate and to monitor the value of your investments and to keep accurate and current records.

Objective 5

Use various sources of financial information that can reduce risks and increase investment returns.

Because more information on investments is available than most investors can read and comprehend, you must be selective in the type of information you use for evaluation purposes. Sources of information include the Internet, newspapers and news programs, business periodicals, government publications, corporate reports, statistical averages, and investor services.

KEY TERMS

corporate bond 291

diversification 294

dividend 291

emergency fund 280

equity capital 290

government bond 291

line of credit 281

liquidity 290

mutual fund 292

speculative investment 284

KEY FORMULAS

Page	Topic	Formula
287	Interest calculation for a corporate bond	Dollar amount of annual interest = Issue price × Interest rate
	Example:	Dollar amount of interest = $1,000 × 7% = $1,000 × 0.07 = $70
287	Approximate market price	Approximate market price = $\dfrac{\text{Annual interest amount}}{\text{Comparable interest rate}}$
	Example:	Approximate market price = $\dfrac{\$80}{9\%}$ = $\dfrac{\$80}{0.09}$ = $888.89

FINANCIAL PLANNING PROBLEMS

1. *Calculating the Amount for an Emergency Fund.* Beth-Anne and Martin Stewart have total take-home pay of $3,200 a month. Their monthly expenses total $2,800. Calculate the minimum amount this couple needs to establish an emergency fund. How did you calculate this amount? (Obj. 1)

2. *Determining Interest and Approximate Bond Value.* Assume that three years ago, you purchased a corporate bond that pays 9.5 percent. The purchase price was $1,000. Also assume that three years after your bond investment, comparable bonds are paying 8 percent. (Obj. 2)

   a. What is the annual dollar amount of interest that you receive from your bond investment?

   b. Assuming that comparable bonds are paying 8 percent, what is the approximate dollar price for which you could sell your bond?

   c. In your own words, explain why your bond increased or decreased in value.

3. *Analyzing Income and Growth Investments.*

   a. List three personal factors that might lead some investors to emphasize income rather than growth in their investment planning.

   b. List three personal factors that might lead some investors to emphasize growth rather than income. (Obj. 2)

4. *Comparing Investment Alternatives.* Choose three of the investment alternatives presented in this chapter, then rank them from high to low on safety, risk, and liquidity. Assume that 3 is the highest score and 1 is the lowest score for each factor. On the basis of your ranking, which of the three alternatives would you choose for your own investment program? Why? (Obj. 3)

5. *Developing a Financial Plan.* Assume you are single and have graduated from college. Your monthly take-home pay is $2,100, and your monthly expenses total $1,800, leaving you with a monthly surplus of $300. Develop a personal plan of action for investing like the one illustrated in Exhibit 10–6. (Obj. 3)

6. *Monitoring an Investment's Financial Performance.* On the basis of the following information, construct a graph that illustrates price movement for a share of the First Canadian T-Bill Mutual Fund. (Note: You may want to review the material presented in the Financial Planning Calculations feature on page 301.) (Obj. 4)

January	$18.70	July	$16.10
February	18.00	August	15.50
March	20.30	September	16.40
April	21.35	October	16.90
May	19.50	November	18.40
June	17.80	December	17.20

7. *Using Financial Information.* Suppose you just inherited 500 shares of General Motors of Canada stocks. List five sources of information you could use to evaluate your inheritance. Beside each source, briefly state how the information it contains could help in your evaluation. (Obj. 5)

FINANCIAL PLANNING ACTIVITIES

1. *Using Investment Information.* Choose a current issue of *MoneySaver, Canadian MoneySaver,* or *IE:Money* and summarize an article that provides suggestions on how you could use your money more effectively. (Obj. 1)

2. *Planning for an Investment Program.* Assume you are 28 years old, your take-home pay totals $2,200 a month, you have monthly living expenses that total $1,200, your monthly car payment is $300, and your credit card debts total $4,900. Using the information presented in this chapter, develop a three-part plan to (a) reduce your monthly expenses, (b) establish an emergency fund, and (c) save $4,000 to establish an investment program. (Obj. 1)

3. *Using the Internet to Obtain Information about Money Management.* As pointed out at the beginning of this chapter, it doesn't make sense to establish an investment program until credit card and installment purchases are reduced or eliminated. While most people are responsible and make payments when they're supposed to, some people get in trouble. To help avoid this problem, each of the following organizations has a site on the Internet:

   Credit Counselling Service of Sault Ste. Marie & District provides information on managing debt and credit, as well as a newsletter and other resources (www.soonet.ca). The National Foundation for Credit Counselling (NFCC) offers information about debt management, credit facts, and a budget calculator (www.nfcc.org). Equifax Canada is one of the two main credit bureaus in Canada (www.equifax.ca). Choose one of the above organizations and visit its Web site. Then, prepare a report that summarizes the information provided by the organization. Finally, indicate if this information could help you manage your consumer debt. (Obj. 1)

4. *Choosing Investment Alternatives.* From the investment alternatives described in this chapter, choose two specific investments you believe would help an individual who is 35 years old, is divorced, and earns $20,000 a year. Assume this person has $30,000 to invest at this time. As part of your recommendation, compare each of your investment suggestions on safety, risk, income, growth, and liquidity. (Obj. 2)

5. *Choosing Investment Alternatives.* Choose one of the investment alternatives presented in this chapter (stocks, bonds, mutual funds, real estate, or speculative investments) and prepare a two-page report describing why this investment would be appropriate for a woman who is 68 years old and has just lost her husband. Assume she is debt free and has inherited $175,000. (Obj. 3)

6. *Explaining the Principle of Diversification.* Prepare a two-minute presentation describing why the principle of diversification is important when establishing an investment program. (Obj. 3)

7. *Choosing a Financial Planner.* Many people call themselves financial planners. Describe the process you would use to choose one financial planner to help you develop an investment program. (Obj. 4)

8. *Reporting Investment Income for Tax Purposes.* Choose four of the following sources of investment income. Then, describe how each type is taxed by the federal government. (Obj. 4)
   a. Dividend income
   b. Interest income
   c. Rental income
   d. Capital gains
   e. Capital losses

9. *Using Investment Information.* Assume you have established an emergency fund and have saved an additional $12,000 to fund an investment in common stocks issued by Bell Canada. Using the sources of information discussed in this chapter, go to the library and obtain information about this company. Summarize your findings in a three-page report describing Bell's current operations and the firm's past and present financial performance. Finally, indicate if you would purchase Bell common stocks on the basis of the information in your report. (Obj. 5)

10. *Using Investment Information.* Each year the publishers of Maclean's provide a special edition called the Maclean's Guide to Personal Finance devoted to helping people learn about different investment alternatives. At the time of publication of this text, the latest guide was published for the year 2002. Obtain a copy of either this guide or one published at a later date and summarize one of the articles highlighting an investment that could help you reach your investment goals. (Obj. 5)

11. *Using the Internet to Obtain Investment Information.* One of the most useful Internet search engines available is Canada.com. Visit the Canada.com Finance site (http://finance.canada.com). Then, describe in a two-page report the type of information available and how it could help you become a better investor. (Obj. 5)

LIFE SITUATION CASE

First Budget, Then Invest for Success!

Jonathan and Meredith Faulk, married for 12 years, have an eight-year-old child. Six years ago, they purchased a home on which they owe about $110,000. They also owe $6,000 on their two-year-old automobile. All of their furniture is paid for, but they owe a total of $3,170 on two credit cards. Jonathan is employed as an engineer and makes $48,000 a year. Meredith works as a part-time computer analyst and earns about $18,000 a year. Their combined monthly income after deductions is $3,950.

About six months ago, the Faulks had what they now describe as a "financial meltdown." It all started one Monday afternoon when their air conditioner stopped cooling. Since their home was only six years old, they thought the repair ought to be a simple one—until the repair technician diagnosed their problem as a defective compressor. Unfortunately, the warranty on the compressor had run out about three months before the compressor broke down. According to the technician, it would cost more than $1,200 to replace the compressor. At the time, they had about $2,000 in their savings account, which they had been saving for their summer vacation, and now they had to use their vacation money to fix the air conditioner.

For the Faulks, the fact that they didn't have enough money to take a vacation was like a wake-up call. They realized they were now in their mid-30s and had serious cash problems. According to Jonathan, "We don't waste money, but there just never seems to be enough money to do the things we want to do." But according to Meredith, "The big problem is that we never have enough money to start an investment program that could pay for our daughter's post-secondary education or fund our retirement."

They decided to take a "big" first step in an attempt to solve their financial problems. They began by examining their monthly expenses for the past month. Here's what they found:

Income (cash inflow)

Jonathan's take-home salary	$2,800	
Meredith's take-home salary	1,150	
Total income		$3,950

Cash outflows

Monthly fixed expenses:		
Home mortgage payment,		
including taxes and insurance	$1,190	
Automobile loan	315	
Automobile insurance	130	
Life insurance premium	50	
Total fixed expenses		$1,685

Monthly variable expenses:		
Food and household necessities	$ 480	
Electricity	115	
Natural gas	50	
Telephone	55	
Family clothing allowance	130	
Gasoline and automobile repairs	120	
Personal and health care	100	
Recreation and entertainment	600	
Gifts and donations	300	
Minimum payment on credit cards	80	
Total variable expenses		$2,030
Total monthly expenses		**$3,715**
Surplus for savings or investments		**$ 235**

Once the Faulks realized they had a $235 surplus each month, they began to replace the $1,200 they had taken from their savings account to pay for repairing the air conditioner. Now it was time to take the next step.

Questions

1. How would you rate the financial status of the Faulks before the air conditioner broke down?
2. The Faulks have a $235 surplus at the end of each month. On the basis of their current financial condition, what do you think they should do with this money?
3. The Faulks' take-home pay is almost $4,000 a month. Yet, after all expenses are paid, there is only a $235 surplus each month. On the basis of the information presented in this case, what expenses, if any, seem out of line and could be reduced to increase the surplus at the end of each month?
4. Given that both Jonathan and Meredith Faulk are in their mid-30s and want to retire when they reach age 65, what type of investment goals would be most appropriate for them?
5. How does the time value of money concept affect the types of long-term goals and the investments that a couple like the Faulks might use to build their financial nest egg?
6. On the basis of the different investments described in this chapter, what specific types of investments (stocks, mutual funds, real estate, and so on) would you recommend for the Faulks? Why?

CREATING A FINANCIAL PLAN

Developing an Investment Plan

An investment program should consider safety, current income, growth potential, liquidity, and taxes. Your ability to set financial goals and select investment vehicles is crucial to long-term financial prosperity.

Web Sites for Investment Planning

*   Online investing information at **www.webfin.com**, **www. quicken.ca**, the Personal Finance link at **www.sympatico.ca**, **http://canadianfinance.com**, and in the Money section of **www.about.com/aboutcanada/index.htm**.
*   You can find investment articles from *IE:Money* magazine at www.iemoney.com, from *Canadian MoneySaver* magazine at **www.canadianmoneysaver.ca**, and from Canadian Business at **www.canadianbusiness.com**.
*   Market reports, corporate news and ratings, and various rates are all available online. Visit **www.fundlibrary.com**,

www.stockhouse.ca, **www.baystreet.com**, and **www.carl sononline.com**.
*   Online access to Canadian stock exchanges is at **www.tse-cdnx.com** for the Toronto Stock Exchange, and for the TSX Venture Exchange, and at **www.m-x.ca** for the Montreal Stock Exchange.

(NOTE: Addresses and content of Web sites change, and new sites are created daily. Use search engines to update and locate Web sites for your current financial planning needs.)

Long-Term Financial Planning Activities

1. Identify saving and investing decisions that would serve your changing life situations.
2. Develop a plan for revising investments as family and household situations change.

11 Investing in Stocks

Can Yahoo Canada Help You Pick Winning Stocks?

Can the Yahoo Canada Internet search engine help you pick stocks that will increase in value? The answer is a definite yes. Today, a wealth of information is available on the Internet, and the Yahoo Canada Finance Web site is an excellent place to start your search for a quality investment. That's what Jason Godwin did three years ago.

It all started when Jason, 26, moved to a small town in interior British Columbia. While he enjoyed the more relaxed lifestyle, he missed a lot of the conveniences he took for granted when he lived in the metropolitan Vancouver area. The convenience he missed the most was his trips to the public library. Ironically, he had never considered himself a bookworm, but he did enjoy researching different investments. Unfortunately, the local library in the nearest small town just didn't have the "stuff" that Jason used to make his investment decisions.

Jason quickly realized he would have to find other sources of information if he were to continue investing. A friend suggested that he consider going online, but Jason was reluctant. Just the thought of making important financial decisions on the basis of information from cyberspace was frightening. But if he wanted current and valid information, he had to do something. So, he purchased a computer and began surfing the Net for useful investment information. He found that by accessing the Internet, he could obtain more than enough information to evaluate stocks and other investments that caught his interest.

After five months of surfing the net and examining different Web sites, Jason now uses the Yahoo Canada Finance Web site as a starting point when evaluating potential stock investments. By simply entering Yahoo Canada's address (http://ca.finance.yahoo.com), typing in the name of a corporation or its stock symbol, and clicking his mouse, he can obtain information about management, new products and marketing activities, and financial data. Of particular interest to Jason are the recommendations made by brokers that follow a corporation's stock, the firm's earnings per share and earnings history, and access to research abstracts. And he can get current price information for a stock, along with graphs that show historical market values, current news about the firm, information submitted by the corporation to SEDAR, a profile of the company, and messages posted by investors. Now, Jason admits he has become a better investor than before he started using a computer. More importantly, his computer-based investment decisions have resulted in his investments increasing in value.

QUESTIONS

1 How important are evaluation of a stock issue and the financial condition of a company when making a decision to buy or sell the company's stocks? Explain your answer.

2 If you needed to obtain financial data to make a decision to buy or sell a company's stocks, would you go to the library or the Internet? Why?

LEARNING OBJECTIVES

1   Identify the most important features of common stocks.

2   Discuss the most important features of preferred stocks.

3   Explain how you can evaluate stock investments.

4   Describe how stocks are bought and sold.

5   Explain the trading techniques used by long-term investors and short-term speculators.

Common Stocks

Many beginning investors face two concerns when they begin an investment program. First, they don't know where to get the information they need to evaluate potential investments. In reality, more information is available than most investors can read. And, as pointed out in the opening case, quality investment information is available not only in libraries but also on the Internet. Jason Godwin found more information than he needed to make informed investment decisions by accessing the Yahoo Canada Finance Web site.

Second, beginning investors sometimes worry that they won't know what the information means when they do find it. Yet, common sense goes a long way when evaluating potential investments. For example, consider the following questions:

Objective 1

Identify the most important features of common stocks.

[1] Is an increase in sales a healthy sign for a corporation? (Answer: yes)

[2] Should a firm's profits increase or decrease over time? (Answer: increase)

[3] Should a corporation's earnings per share increase or decrease over time? (Answer: increase)

Although the answers to these questions are obvious, you will find more detailed answers to these and other questions in this chapter. In fact, that's what this chapter is all about. We want you to learn how to evaluate a stock and to make money from your investment decisions. That's the way it's supposed to work.

HOW ARE THE MARKETS DOING?

When people talk about "the market" they are actually referring to an **index**. With the growing importance of the stock market in our society, indexes, like the S&P/TSX Composite Index, DJIA, S&P 500 and NASDAQ composite, have grown to become a part of our everyday vocabulary.

Investors use indexes to track the performance of the stock market because it would be too difficult to try to track every single security trading in the country. Therefore, they take a smaller sample of the market that is representative of the whole.

The following are some of the most popular indexes:

index A statistical measure of the changes in a portfolio of stocks representing a portion of the overall market.

THE S&P/TSX COMPOSITE INDEX The S&P/TSX Composite Index comprises approximately 71 percent of market capitalization for Canadian-based companies listed by the Toronto Stock Exchange. The size of the S&P/TSX Composite (C$913.3 billion in float market capitalization as of October, 2000) and its broad economic sector coverage has made the S&P/TSX Composite the premier indicator of activity for equity markets since its launch on January 1, 1977.

See Exhibit 11–1 for more information on the S&P/TSX Composite Portfolio Characteristics.

DOW JONES INDUSTRIAL AVERAGE DJIA, often referred to as the Dow, is the best known and most widely reported indicator of the stock market's performance. The Dow tracks the price changes of 30 significant industrial stocks traded on the New York Stock Exchange.

NYSE COMPOSITE INDEX An index that covers the price movements of all stocks listed on the New York Stock Exchange.

NASDAQ COMPOSITE INDEX An index that covers the price movements of all stocks traded on the NASDAQ stock market. The NASDAQ Composite is heavily weighted in technology and Internet stocks. As such, the companies listed in the composite are considered to have high growth potential.

STANDARD & POOR'S 500 STOCK INDEX The S&P 500 is one of the best benchmarks in the world for large-cap stocks. By containing 500 companies, it has great *diversification*, and considered one of the best overall indicators of market performance.

WHY OWN STOCKS

Investors provide the money; the corporation uses the money to generate sales and earn profits; and the shareholders earn a return on their investment. Today a lot of people buy and sell stocks. Why? The most obvious answer is simple: They want larger returns than those that more conservative investments offer. As pointed out in the last chapter, significant differences exist between the rates of return offered by stock investments compared with those of corporate bonds and Canadian treasury bills. See Exhibit 11–2 for returns of different investments.

Before you decide to invest in stocks, you should realize that this type of investment involves more risk and greater potential for loss.

The term **securities** encompasses a broad range of investments, including stocks and bonds, mutual funds, options, and commodities, that are traded on security exchanges or the over-the-counter markets. In this chapter, we examine stocks. There are two types of stocks: common and preferred shares (the terms *stocks* and *shares* are used interchangeably throughout this text). We discuss common stocks in this section and preferred stocks in the next. Since common shareholders are the actual owners of the corporation, they share in its success. But before

securities Investments, including stocks and bonds, mutual funds, options, and commodities, traded on securities exchanges or the over-the-counter markets.

Exhibit 11–1

S&P/TSX Composite Portfolio Characteristics as of July 31, 2002

	($Mil US)	($Mil CN)
Largest company	$22,881	$36,019
Smallest company	18	29
Average company	1,413	2,224
Median company	418	658
Total MV	388,514	611,599

Sector	Weight	Number of Companies
Consumer discretionary	7.87%	35
Consumer staples	4.64%	19
Energy	14.59%	33
Financials	32.16%	30
Health care	2.57%	24
Industrials	9.59%	36
Information technology	4.73%	32
Materials	14.76%	52
Telecommunication services	4.46%	6
Utilities	4.63%	8

SOURCE; Standard & Poor's http://www.spglobal.com/indexmaincanada.html

If you invested $10,000 on January 31, 1988, you would have the returns shown in the table below on February 28, 2001.

Exhibit 11–2

Investment Returns

$10,000 INVESTED FROM JAN 31, 1988 TO FEB 28, 2001		
Index	Average Annual Return	Ending Value*
CPI - All Items (Inflation)	–2.52%	$ 6,157
Canada Savings Bonds Index	6.30%	$22,252
1-Year Average GIC Index	6.36%	$22,397
91 Day Treasury Bill Index	7.13%	$24,621
TSE 300 Composite Index	7.71%	$26,425
SCM Universe Bond Total Return Index	9.96%	$34,651
MSCI World ($CDN)	11.77%	$42,876
S&P 500 Composite ($CDN)	14.37%	$57,950
Dow Jones Industrial Average	15.30%	$64,393
Nasdaq Composite Principal ($CDN)	16.65%	$75,010

*Returns before tax and inflation (except CPI).

SOURCE: Globe HySales

What conclusion can be drawn from all these numbers? History shows that since 1988, if you kept your money in a sock under your bed, you lost buying power to inflation (CPI). If you had invested in Canada Savings Bonds, GICs, T-Bills, the TSE 300, or Canadian bonds, you probably would have slept well at night while gaining single-digit returns. If you had invested in global equities, S&P 500 stocks, Dow Jones 30 stocks, or Nasdaq stocks, you would have received double-digit returns, and because you were a long-term investor, you still would have slept well at night.

SOURCE: CI Funds, Connections Online, http://www.cifunds.com "The Benefits of Long-term Investing"

investing your money, it helps to understand why corporations issue common stocks and why investors purchase stocks.

WHY CORPORATIONS ISSUE COMMON STOCKS

Corporations issue common stocks to finance their business start-up costs and to help pay for their ongoing business activities. Today, corporations are classified as either private corporations or public corporations. A *private corporation* is a corporation whose stocks owned by relatively few people and not traded openly in stock markets. A *public corporation* is a corporation whose stocks traded openly in stock markets and may be purchased by individuals. Public corporations may have thousands or even millions of shareholders. Corporate managers prefer selling common stocks as a method of financing for several reasons.

A FORM OF EQUITY Corporations don't have to repay the money a shareholder pays for stocks. Generally, a shareholder in a public corporation may sell his or her stocks to another individual. The selling price is determined by how much a buyer is willing to pay for the stocks. Simply put, if the demand for a particular stock increases, the market value of the stock will increase. If the demand for a particular stock decreases, the market value of the stock will decrease. Demand for a stock changes when information about the firm or its future prospects is released to the general public. For example, information about expected sales revenues, earnings, expansions or mergers, or other important developments within the firm can increase or decrease the demand for, and ultimately the market value of, the firm's stocks.

DIVIDENDS NOT MANDATORY Dividends are paid out of profits, and dividend payments must be approved by the corporation's board of directors. Dividend policies vary among corporations, but most firms distribute between 30 and 70 percent of their earnings to shareholders. However, some corporations follow a policy of smaller or no dividend distributions to shareholders. In general, these are rapidly growing firms, such as Chapters (including Chapters Online), Gildan Activwear (Activwear), and Office Depot (office supplies), that retain a large share of their earnings for research and development, expansion, or major projects. On the other hand, utility companies and other financially secure enterprises may distribute 80 to 90 percent of their earnings. Always remember that if a corporation has had a bad year, dividend payments may be reduced or omitted. Although board members may vote to continue paying dividends when a corporation is operating at a loss, they often vote to completely omit dividend payments to shareholders.

VOTING RIGHTS AND CONTROL OF THE COMPANY In return for the financing provided by selling common stocks, management must make concessions to shareholders that may restrict corporate policies. For example, corporations are required by law to have an annual meeting at which shareholders have a right to vote, usually casting one vote per share of stock. Shareholders may vote in person or by proxy. A **proxy** is a legal form that lists the issues to be decided at a shareholders' meeting and requests that shareholders transfer their voting rights to some individual or individuals. The common shareholders elect the board of directors and must approve major changes in corporate policies. Typical changes in corporate policy include (1) an amendment of the corporate charter, (2) the sale of certain assets, (3) possible mergers, (4) the issuance of preferred stocks or corporate bonds, and (5) changes in the amount of common stocks.

Legally, a corporation may include a provision for pre-emptive rights in its corporate charter. A **pre-emptive right** is the right of current shareholders to purchase any new stock the corporation issues before it is offered to the general public. By exercising their pre-emptive rights, shareholders are able to maintain their current proportion of corporate ownership. This may be important when the corporation is small and management control is a matter of concern to shareholders.

Finally, corporations are required by law to distribute annual and quarterly reports to shareholders. These reports contain details about sales, earnings, and other vital information.

proxy A legal form that lists the issues to be decided at a shareholders' meeting and requests that shareholders transfer their voting rights to some individual or individuals.

pre-emptive right The right of current shareholders to purchase any new stocks the corporation issues before it is offered to the general public.

WHY INVESTORS PURCHASE COMMON STOCKS

How do you make money by buying common stocks? Basically, common stock investments can increase in three ways: income from dividends, dollar appreciation of stock value, and the possibility of increased value from stock splits.

INCOME FROM DIVIDENDS While the corporation's board members are under no legal obligation to pay dividends, most board members like to keep shareholders happy (and prosperous). Few things will unite shareholders into a powerful opposition force more rapidly than omitted or lowered dividends. Therefore, board members usually declare dividends if the corporation's after-tax profits are sufficient for them to do so. Since dividends are a distribution of profits, investors must be concerned about future after-tax profits. In short, how secure is the dividend?

Corporate dividends for common stocks may take the form of cash, additional stocks, or company products. However, the last type of dividend is extremely unusual. If the board of directors declares a cash dividend, each common shareholder receives an equal amount per share. Although dividend policies vary, most corporations pay dividends on a quarterly basis. Some corporations, particularly those experiencing large swings in earnings, declare special year-end or extra dividends in addition to their regular quarterly dividends.

Note in Exhibit 11–3 that Sobeys Inc. has declared a quarterly dividend of $0.06 per share to shareholders who own the stock on the record date of July 14. The **record date** is the date on which a shareholder must be registered on the corporation's books in order to receive dividend payments. When a stock is traded around the record date, the company must determine

record date The date on which a shareholder must be registered on the corporation's books in order to receive dividend payments.

DIVIDENDS

Corporate dividends declared Wednesday (quarterly unless otherwise indicated): **Sobeys Inc.**: Common, $0.06. Payable July 28. Record July 14.

Exhibit 11–3

Typical Information on Corporation Dividends as Presented in *The Montreal Gazette*

SOURCE: Adapted from *The Montreal Gazette*, Thursday, June 29, 2000.

whether the buyer or the seller is entitled to the dividend. To solve this problem, this rule is followed: *Dividends remain with the stock until two business days before the record date.* On the second day before the record date, the stock begins selling ex-dividend. An investor who purchases an ex-dividend stock is not entitled to receive dividends for that quarter, and the dividend is paid to the previous owner of the stock.

For example, Sobeys Inc. declared a quarterly dividend of $0.06 per share to shareholders who owned stocks on Friday, July 14. The stocks went ex-dividend on Wednesday, July 12, 2000, two *business* days before the July 14 date. A shareholder who purchased the stock on July 12 or after was not entitled to this quarterly dividend payment. Sobeys Inc. made the actual dividend payment on July 28 to shareholders who owned stocks on the record date. Investors are generally very conscious of the date on which a stock goes ex-dividend, and the dollar value of the stock may go down by the value of the quarterly dividend.

DOLLAR APPRECIATION OF STOCK VALUE In most cases, you purchase stocks and then hold on to them for a period of time. If the market value of the stocks increases, you must decide whether to sell them at the higher price or continue to hold them. If you decide to sell, the dollar amount of difference between the purchase price and the selling price represents your profit.

Let's assume that on June 4, 1999, you purchased 100 shares of Molson Inc. on the TSE at a cost of $13 a share. Your cost for the stocks was $1,300 plus $55 commission charges, for a total investment of $1,355. (Note: Commissions, a topic covered later in this chapter, are charged when you purchase stocks *and* when you sell stocks.) Let's also assume you held your 100 shares until June 4, 2002, and then sold them for $38 a share. During the two-year period you owned Molson Inc., the company paid dividends totalling $4.40 a share. Exhibit 11–4 shows your return on the investment. In this case, you made money because of quarterly dividend distributions and through an increase in stock value from $13 to $38 per share. As Exhibit 11–4 shows, your total return is $2,790. Of course, if the stock's value should decrease, or if the firm's board of directors reduces or votes to omit dividends, your return may be less than the original investment. For help in deciding if it's time to sell stocks, read the Financial Planning for Life's Situations box on page 319.

Visit the Web site
See Personal Financial Planning worksheets under Chapter 11 on the online learning centre at www.mcgrawhill.ca/college/kapoor.

POSSIBILITY OF INCREASED VALUE FROM STOCK SPLITS Investors can also increase potential profits through a stock split. A **stock split** is a procedure in which the shares of stock owned by existing shareholders are divided into a larger number of shares. In 2001, for example, Gildan Activwear's board of directors approved a 2-for-1 stock split. After the stock split, a shareholder who had previously owned 100 shares now owned 200 shares. The most common stock splits are 2-for-1, 3-for-1, and 4-for-1.

Why do corporations split their stocks? In many cases, a firm's management has a theoretical ideal price range for the firm's stocks. If the market value of the stocks rises above the ideal range, a stock split brings the market value back in line. In the case of Gildan Activwear, the 2-for-1 stock split reduced the market value to about one-half of the stock's

stock split A procedure in which the shares of common stocks owned by existing shareholders are divided into a larger number of shares.

Exhibit 11–4

Sample Stock
Transaction for
Seagram's

Assumptions			
100 shares of common stocks purchased June 4, 1999, sold June 4, 2002; dividends of $4 per share for the two-year period.			

Costs when purchased		Return when sold	
100 shares @ $13 =	$1,300	100 shares @ $38 =	$3,800
Plus commission	55	Minus commission	55
Total investment	$1,355	Total gain	$3,745

Transaction summary	
Total gain	$3,745
Minus total investment	– 1,355
Profit from stock sale	$2,390
Plus dividends	+ 400
Total gain for the transaction	$2,790

previous market value. The lower market value for each share of stock was the result of dividing the dollar value of the company by a larger number of shares of common stocks. Also, a decision to split a company's stocks and the resulting lower market value makes the stocks more attractive to the investing public. This attraction is based on the belief that most corporations split their stocks only when their financial future is improving and on the upswing. As a result, investors have an expectation of future financial growth. This expectation of future growth can mean increases in the firm's sales and profits *and* increases in the market value of the firm's stocks. *Be warned: There are no guarantees that a stock's market value will go up after a split.*

A less common type of stock split occurs when the number of outstanding shares of common stocks reduced. This usually occurs when the market value of a corporation's stocks has dropped to a point where the directors consider it too low. In a *reverse split*, shareholders exchange their shares for a proportionately smaller number of shares. As a result, the market value is adjusted upward by a proportionate amount.

CONCEPT CHECK 11–1

1. If you needed information about a stock investment, would you go the the library or the Internet? Why?
2. Why do corporations issue common stocks?
3. What are the typical issues on which shareholders vote?
4. Describe three reasons shareholders purchase common stocks.
5. Why do corporations split their stocks? Is a stock split good or bad for investors?

Preferred Stocks

Objective 2

Discuss the most
important features
of preferred stocks.

In addition to or instead of purchasing common stocks, you may purchase preferred stocks. The most important priority an investor in preferred stocks enjoys is receiving cash dividends before common shareholders are paid any cash dividends. This factor is especially important when a corporation is experiencing financial problems and cannot pay cash dividends to both preferred and common shareholders. Unlike the amount of the dividend on common stocks, the dollar amount of the dividend on preferred stocks is known before the stocks are purchased. The dividend amount is either a stated amount of money for each share of preferred stock or a

Financial Planning for Life's Situations

WHEN SHOULD YOU SELL A STOCK?

Assume that in January 2000, Marina Stahl purchased 100 shares of Royal Bank of Canada, one of Canada's big six banks, for $21.37 a share. According to Marina, all the financial information about the Royal Bank of Canada looked good. Two years later, when the value of Royal Bank of Canada had increased to $32.57 a share, Marina decided to sell the stocks for a profit. During that two-year period, she had thought about selling her stocks at least four times. But she just couldn't make the decision to sell.

According to financial experts, the value of a share of stock may go up or down, but investors like Marina Stahl always have trouble deciding when to sell. Generally, most investors have a reason for buying a stock, but when it is time to sell that same stock, they are often blinded by a sense of loyalty to "their" investments, whether deserved or not. Although no sure cures for this problem exist, the following suggestions may help:

1. *Follow your stock's value.* Too often, investors purchase a stock and then forget about it. They assume everything is okay and the stock will magically increase in value. A much better approach is to graph the dollar value of your stock on a weekly basis.
2. *Watch the company's financials.* Smart investors evaluate a stock investment before they make it. The smartest investors use all the available information to continuously evaluate their stocks. If the amounts reported or projected for sales, profits, or other important financial measures are declining or are well below industry averages, it may be time to sell the stocks. If you would not buy the same investment today, it's time to sell it no matter how much you have gained or lost.
3. *Track the firm's product line.* Simply put, if the firm's products become obsolete and the company fails to introduce state-of-the-art new products, its sales—and ultimately profits—may take a nosedive. The failure to introduce new products may destroy the firm's ability to compete.
4. *Monitor economic developments.* An economic recession or an economic recovery may cause the value of a stock investment to increase or decrease. For example, most consumers who are unemployed don't buy new cars. Therefore, manufacturing firms, such as General Motors or Ford, may experience lower sales, lower profits, and lower stock values until the employment outlook brightens. Also, watch the inflation rate, interest rates, productivity rates, and similar economic indicators that may be a red flag.
5. *Be patient.* The secret of success for making money with stocks is time. As pointed out earlier in this chapter, stocks have returned over 10 percent before adjusting for inflation each year for over a 40-year period and, assuming you purchased good stocks, your investments will eventually increase in value.

---

certain percentage of the par value of the stocks. The **par value** is an assigned (and often arbitrary) dollar value that is printed on a stock certificate. For example, if the par value for a preferred stock issue is $50 and the dividend rate is 6 percent, the dollar amount of the dividend is $3 ($50 × 6% = $3).

Preferred stocks are often referred to as "middle" investments because they represent an investment midway between common stocks (an ownership position) and corporate bonds (a creditor position). When compared with corporate bonds, the yield on preferred stocks is often smaller than the yield on bonds. When compared with common stocks, preferred stocks are safer investments that offer more secure dividends. They are often purchased by conservative investors wanting preferential tax treatment on the dividend and possible capital gains. They are also purchased by other corporations because corporations receive a tax break on the dividend income from preferred stocks. For all other investors, preferred stocks lack the growth potential that common stocks offer and the safety of many corporate bond issues. As a result, preferred stocks are generally considered a poor investment for most individuals.

While preferred stocks do not represent a legal debt that must be repaid, if the firm is dissolved or declares bankruptcy, preferred shareholders do have first claim to the corporation's assets after creditors (including bondholders).

par value An assigned (and often arbitrary) dollar value that is printed on a stock certificate.

www.mcgrawhill.ca/college/kapoor

callable preferred stocks Stocks that a corporation may exchange, at its option, for a specified amount of money.

Generally, preferred stocks are callable. **Callable preferred stocks** are stocks that a corporation may exchange, at its option, for a specified amount of money. To understand why a corporation would call in a preferred stock issue, you must first realize that dividend rates paid by similar investments increase and decrease. If dividends are decreasing and similar investments provide a smaller return than the corporation's preferred stock issue, management may decide to call in their existing preferred issue and substitute new preferred stocks that pay a lower dividend. Management may also decide to call in the preferred stocks and issue common stocks with no specified dividend. The dividend amount paid on a preferred issue can also affect the market value of the stock. For example, the preferred stock issue in the last example paid a 6-percent dividend. When the corporation issued preferred stocks, the 6-percent dividend was competitive with the dividends paid by corporations issuing preferred stocks at that time. If dividend rates on similar investments decrease, the market value of the 6-percent preferred stock issue will go up due to its higher dividend. On the other hand, if dividends paid on similar investments increase, the market value of the 6-percent preferred stock issue will fall due to its lower dividend rate.

When compared with corporations selling common stocks, preferred stocks are used less often by only a few corporations, yet it is an alternative method of financing that may attract investors who do not wish to buy common stocks. Preferred stocks, like common stocks, are equity financing that does not have to be repaid. And dividends on preferred stocks, as on common stocks, may be omitted by action of the board of directors.

Many small investors consider preferred stocks to be as safe as corporate bonds. Generally, however, it is less safe because corporate bonds represent borrowed money that must be repaid. Bondholders are more likely to receive interest payments until maturity and eventual repayment of their initial investment than preferred shareholders are to continue receiving dividends or recover their initial investment in the stocks. To make preferred stock issues more attractive, some corporations may offer three additional features.

THE CUMULATIVE FEATURE OF PREFERRED STOCKS

cumulative preferred stocks Stocks with unpaid dividends that accumulate and must be paid before any cash dividend is paid to common shareholders.

If the corporation's board of directors believes that omitting dividends is justified, it can vote to omit both the dividends paid to common shareholders and the dividends paid to preferred shareholders. One way preferred shareholders can protect themselves against omitted dividends is to purchase cumulative preferred stocks. **Cumulative preferred stocks** are stock with unpaid dividends that accumulate and must be paid before any cash dividend is paid to the common shareholders. If a corporation does not pay dividends to the cumulative preferred shareholders during one dividend period, the amount of the missed dividends is added to the following period's preferred dividends. If you own noncumulative preferred stocks, an omitted dividend will not be made up later.

THE PARTICIPATION FEATURE OF PREFERRED STOCKS

To make a preferred stock issue more attractive, corporations sometimes add a *participation feature*. This feature allows preferred shareholders to share with the common shareholders in the corporation's earnings. Participating preferred stocks are rare; this feature is used only when special measures are necessary to attract investors.

The participation feature of preferred stocks works like this: (1) The required dividend is paid to preferred shareholders; (2) a stated dividend, usually equal to the dividend amount paid to preferred shareholders, is paid to common shareholders; and (3) the remainder of the earnings available for distribution is shared by both preferred and common shareholders.

THE CONVERSION FEATURE OF PREFERRED STOCKS

Convertible preferred stocks can be exchanged, at the shareholder's option, for a specified number of shares of common stocks. The conversion feature provides the investor with the added safety of preferred stocks and the possibility of greater speculative gain through conversion to common stocks.

All the information relating to the number of shares of common stocks that may be obtained through conversion of preferred stocks is stated in the corporate records and is usually printed on the preferred stock certificate. For example, assume Martin & Martin Manufacturing Corporation has issued convertible preferred stocks. Each share of preferred stocks in this issue is convertible into two shares of common stocks. Assume the market price of Martin & Martin's convertible preferred stocks is $24 and the stocks pay an annual dividend of $1.60 a share. Also assume the market price of the company's common stocks is $9 and the common stocks currently pays an annual dividend of $0.54 a share. Under these circumstances, you would keep the preferred stocks. If the market price of the common stocks increased to above $12 a share, however, you would have an incentive to exercise the conversion option.

The decision to convert preferred stocks to common stocks is complicated by three factors. First, the dividends paid on preferred stocks are more secure than the dividends paid on common stocks. Second, the amount of the dividend for preferred stocks is generally higher than the amount of the dividend for common stocks. Third, because of the conversion option, the market value of convertible preferred stocks usually increases as the market value of common stocks increases.

The next section discusses additional factors you should evaluate before purchasing either preferred stocks or common stocks.

CONCEPT CHECK 11-2

1. What is the most important priority a preferred shareholder has compared with common shareholders?
2. Why would a corporation call in preferred stocks?
3. Why do corporations issue preferred stocks?
4. Describe three features corporations can offer to make preferred stocks more attractive.

Evaluation of a Stock Issue

Many investors expect to earn a 10-percent or higher return on their investments, yet they are unwilling to spend the time required to become a good investor. In fact, many people purchase investments without doing *any* research. They wouldn't buy a car without a test drive or purchase a residence without comparing different houses, but for some unknown reason they invest without doing their homework. The truth is that there is no substitute for a few hours of detective work when choosing an investment. This section explains how to evaluate a potential stock investment.

A wealth of information is available to stock investors. Sources of this information include newspapers, the Internet, business periodicals, corporate reports, and investor services. Most local newspapers carry several pages of business news. *The Financial Post* and *Canadian Business* are devoted almost entirely to financial and economic news. And following the economic upturn, more people are using the Internet to evaluate or monitor the value of their

Objective 3

Explain how you can evaluate stock investments.

investments. Obviously, different types of investments require different methods of evaluation, but a logical place to start the evaluation process for stock is with the classification of different types of stocks investments.

CLASSIFICATION OF STOCK INVESTMENTS

When evaluating a stock investment, stockbrokers, financial planners, and investors often classify stocks into different categories. We describe eight commonly used classifications.

blue-chip stock A safe investment that generally attracts conservative investors.

A **blue-chip stock** is a safe investment that generally attracts conservative investors. Stocks of this kind are issued by the strongest and most respected companies, such as Bell Canada, Royal Bank, and Power Corporation. Characteristics to watch for when evaluating this type of stock include leadership in an industrial group, a history of stable earnings, and consistency in paying dividends.

income stock A stock that pays higher-than-average dividends.

An **income stock** pays higher-than-average dividends. To be able to pay above-average dividends, a corporation must have a steady, predictable source of income. Stocks issued by Bristol-Myers Squibb, Dow Chemical, and Royal Dutch/Shell are often purchased for their higher-than-average dividends. Also, stocks issued by electric, gas, telephone, and other utility companies are generally classified as income stocks. Many investors seeking income may also include quality preferred stock issues in their portfolios.

growth stock A stock issued by a corporation that has the potential to earn profits above the average profits of all firms in the economy.

A **growth stock** is issued by a corporation that has the potential to earn profits above the average profits of all firms in the economy. Key factors to evaluate when choosing a growth stock include an expanding product line of quality merchandise and an effective research and development department. Retail expansion, state-of-the-art manufacturing facilities, and expansion into international markets are also characteristic of growth stocks. In fact, most growth companies retain a large part of their earnings to pay for their research and development efforts. As a result, such companies generally pay out less than 30 percent of their earnings in dividends to their shareholders. In the late 1990s, typical growth stocks included Adobe Systems, Southwest Airlines, and Home Depot.

cyclical stock A stock that follows the business cycle of advances and declines in the economy.

A **cyclical stock** follows the business cycle of advances and declines in the economy. When the economy expands, the market value of a cyclical stock increases; when the economy declines, the market value decreases. Most cyclical stocks are in basic industries, such as automobiles, steel, paper, and heavy manufacturing. Investors try to buy cyclical stocks just before the economy expands and sell them just before it declines. Assuming the economy continues to expand, most financial experts are predicting that Ballard Power (alternative fuel), Domtar (paper), and Oxford Properties Group (real estate) will increase in value because of increased demand for their products during the first part of the 21st century.

defensive stock A stock that remains stable during declines in the economy.

A **defensive stock** remains stable during declines in the economy. Generally, companies that issue such stocks have a history of stable earnings and are able to maintain dividend payments to shareholders during periods of economic decline. Many stocks that are classified as income stocks or blue-chip stocks are also classified as defensive stocks because of their stable earnings and consistent dividend policies. Stocks in this classification include Procter & Gamble, Kellogg, and stocks issued by utility companies.

large-cap stock A stock issued by a large corporation that has a large amount of stocks outstanding and a large amount of capitalization.

capitalization The total amount of securities—stocks and bonds—issued by a corporation.

Stocks may also be classified as large cap or small cap. A **large-cap stock** is issued by a large corporation that has a large amount of stocks outstanding and a large amount of capitalization. In financial circles, **capitalization** is usually defined as the total amount of securities—stocks and bonds—issued by a corporation. Typically, the companies listed in the Dow Jones averages are considered large caps. Because many large-cap stocks are often considered much more secure than small-cap stocks, they may appeal to more conservative investors. A **small-cap stock** is generally defined as a stock issued by a company that has a

small-cap stocks A stock issued by a company that has a capitalization of $150 million or less.

capitalization of $150 million or less. Since these stocks are issued by smaller companies, they tend to be more speculative and are often purchased by speculators hoping to make a quick profit.

A **penny stock** typically sells for less than $1 a share. These are stocks issued by new companies or companies with erratic sales and earnings. Therefore, penny stocks are more volatile than more conservative stocks. These stocks are classified as high-risk investments and are more difficult to research because information about them is hard to find. They are also more difficult to track, and dramatic increases and decreases in market value are common. Unfortunately, when the bubble bursts, these stocks can become worthless. As a result, penny stocks should be purchased only by investors who understand *all* the risks.

penny stock A stock that typically sells for less than $1 per share.

HOW TO READ THE FINANCIAL SECTION OF THE NEWSPAPER

Most metropolitan newspapers contain information about stocks listed on the Toronto Stock Exchange, the TSX Venture Exchange, and other major stock exchanges, and stocks of local interest. Although not all newspapers print exactly the same information, they usually provide the basic information. Stocks are listed alphabetically, so your first task is to move down the table to find the stocks you're interested in. Then, to read the stock quotation, you simply read across the table. The first row in Exhibit 11–5 gives detailed information about Finning International Inc. (Each numbered entry in the list below the enlarged stock table refers to a column of the stock table.)

If a corporation has more than one stock issue, the common stock issues are always listed first. Then the preferred stock issues are listed and are indicated by the letters *pf* behind the firm's name.

THE INTERNET

As pointed out in the previous chapter, it is impossible to describe all of the Web sites that deal with personal finance and investments. We will examine some Web sites that are logical starting points when evaluating a stock investment, but there are many more than those described in this section. Let's begin with information about a corporation that is available on the Internet.

Today, most corporations have a Web site, and the information these pages provide is especially useful. First, it is easily accessible. All you have to do is use a search engine to locate the corporation's site. Second, the information on the site may be more up to date than printed material obtained from the corporation or outside sources. Finally, this information may be more complete than that in the corporation's annual report, quarterly report, or other publications. Look at the financial information for Microsoft displayed in Exhibit 11–6. By clicking on a button, you can access Microsoft's latest annual report, information on the firm's earnings, and other factors that could affect the value of the company's stocks.

You can also use such Web sites as Canada.com and other search engines to obtain information about stock investments. Take a look at a portion of the opening page of the Canada.com Finance Web site in Exhibit 11–7 (on page 326). This Web site provides a wealth of information. Near the top of the page, you will notice 10 different subsections, including Mutual Funds, Stock Centre, and News. Each of these links will lead to more information and updates on each subject, as well as practical advice. The Portfolio/My News section allows you to track individually chosen stocks and to receive constant updates on news releases and industry events. You can also choose to be notified by e-mail whenever there is breaking news on a stock you have selected. To get the quote on a selected stock simply type in its symbol in the Enter Symbol(s) box. If you're not sure what the symbol is you can look it up by clicking on Symbol Search. A thorough search through this

Exhibit 11–5

Financial
Information about
Common Stock
Given in *The
Financial Post*

SOURCE: Adapted
from *The Financial
Post.* "FP Investing,"
Saturday, July 1, 2000.

THE FINANCIAL POST, SATURDAY, JULY 1, 2000

52W high	52W low	Stock	Ticker	Div	Yield %	P/E	Vol 00s	High /ask	Low /bid	Net chg	fiscal	Interim EPS	12 mth EPS	Vol 00s	High	Low	Cls/ last	Net chg
								—Friday—			—Earnings data—			—Week—				
15.40	11.50	Finning◇	FTT	0.20	1.6	14.9	413	12.75	12.50	–0.05	Ma 3M	0.17	0.84	8333	12.95	12.50	12.50	
n 10.50	8.00	FirmCap	FC	p0.67	7.3		nt	9.80	9.30					31	9.50	9.25	9.25	–0.25
5.95	4.20	1stAsia un	FAI	p0.52	10.2	14.7	26	5.20	5.10		Ma 3M	0.35	0.35	899	5.35	5.05	5.10	–0.10
9.90	7.10	1stAustPr	FAP	0.84	10.7	10.0	255	7.95	7.75	+0.05	Ja 3M	0.18	0.78	2065	8.00	7.75	7.85	–0.10
0.35	0.05	1stAust wt					z85	0.055	0.055					47	0.055	0.055	0.055	
2.70	0.35	1stCalg	FCP				648	0.85	0.82	–0.01	Ma 3M	d0.01	d0.22	13766	1.21	0.82	0.85	–0.13

1. Highest price paid for one share of Finning International during the past 52 weeks: $15.40

2. Lowest price paid for one share of Finning International in the past 52 weeks: $11.50

3. Name of the company: Finning International Inc.

4. Ticker symbol or letters that identify a stock for trading: FTT

5. Projected annual dividend for next year based on the amount of the firm's last dividend: $0.20

6. Yield percentage, or the percentage of return based on the dividend and current price of the stock: $0.20 ÷ $12.50 = 0.016 = 1.6%

7. Price–earnings (PE) ratio—the price of a share of stock divided by the corporation's earnings per share of stock outstanding over the last 12 months: 12.50 ÷ .84 = 14.9

8. Number of shares of Finning International traded during the previous business day, expressed in hundreds of shares: 413

9. Highest price paid for one share of Finning International during the previous business day: $12.75

10. Lowest price paid for one share of Finning International during the previous business day: $12.50

11. Price paid for the last transaction of the day: $12.50

12. Difference between the price paid for the last share today and the price paid for the last share on the previous day: minus $0.05 (in Bay Street terms, Finning International "closed down 0.05" on this day)

13. Fiscal year-end for reporting earnings: March (3 months)

14. Interim earnings per share: $0.17

15. Annual earnings per share: $0.84

16. Number of shares traded during the week, expressed in hundreds: 8,333

17. Highest price paid for one share during the week: $12.95

18. Lowest price paid for one share during the week: $12.50

19. Price paid for last transaction for the week: $12.50

20. Difference between the price paid for the last trading day and the price paid one week ago: $0

site may provide you with all the information you need to invest in stocks and track your investments. Begin the process by entering the Web address for the Canada.com finance site at http://finance.canada.com. From there you can explore the site fully: you'll be amazed at what a simple click of your mouse can bring you.

In addition, you can use professional advisory services like SEDAR (System Electronic Document Analysis and Retrieval) (www.sedar.com), Standard & Poor's Financial Information Services (www.standardpoor.com), Moody's Investors Service (www.moodys.com) and Value Line (www.valueline.com). While some of the information provided by these services is free, there is a charge for the more detailed information you may need to evaluate a stock investment. For more information about professional advisory services and the type of information they provide, read the next section.

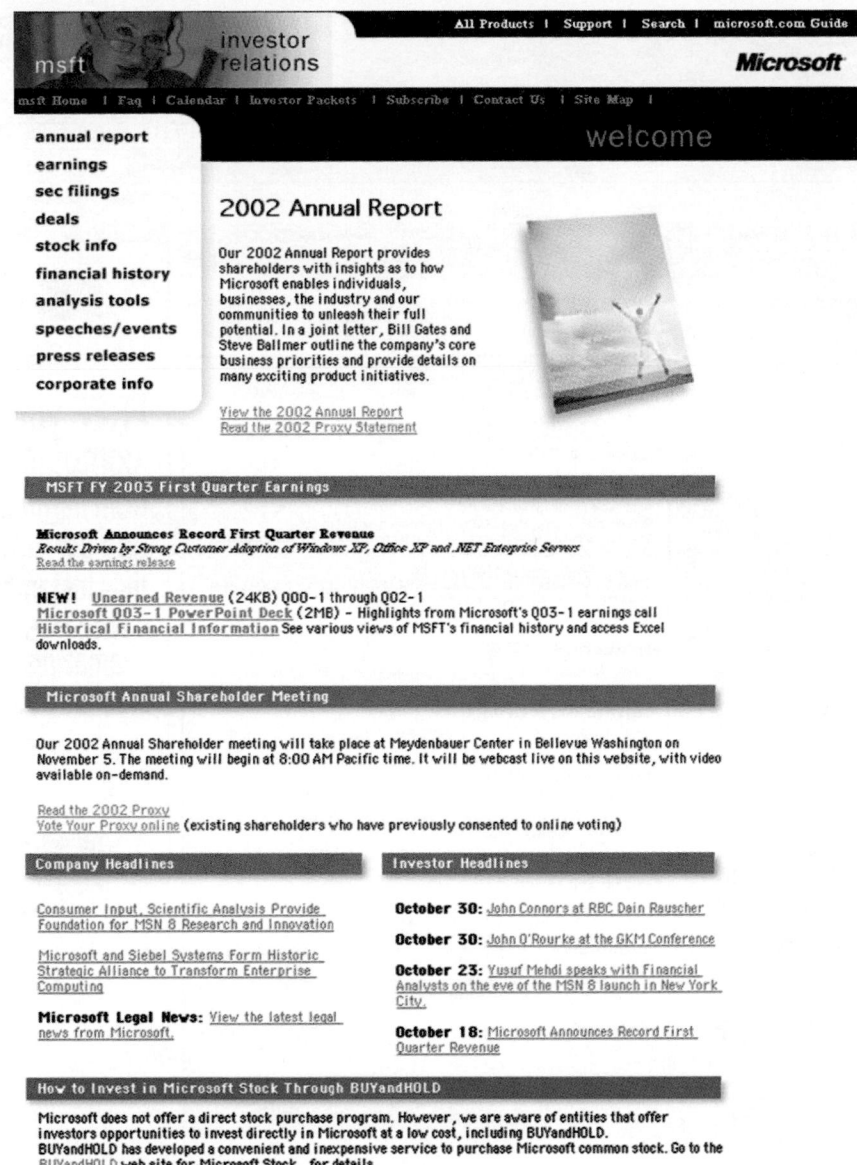

Exhibit 11–6

Financial
Information
Available on
Microsoft's
Investor Relations
Web Page

SOURCE: The
Microsoft Website
(www.microsoft. com)
October 29, 2002 ,
Microsoft Corporation,
One Microsoft Way,
Redmond, Washington,
98052.

STOCK ADVISORY SERVICES

In addition to newspapers and the Internet, sources of information you can use to evaluate potential stock investments are the printed materials provided by stock advisory services. In choosing among the hundreds of stock advisory services that charge fees for their information, you must consider both the quality and the quantity of the information they provide. The information ranges from simple alphabetical listings to detailed financial reports.

SEDAR, Standard & Poor's reports, and Value Line are briefly described in Chapter 10. A useful online service is found at www.zacks.com. Here we will examine a company report for BCE, Canada's largest communications company.

The report shown in Exhibit 11–8 (on page 328) is a document issued by Zacks Investment Research. The top section lists the company name and symbol on an exchange (here the New York Stock Exchange) and identifies the industry that BCE participates in.

Below the market information, such as the most recent price, price–earnings ratio (P/E), and dividend and capitalization values is a brief description of the company. This description displays the company's most prominent products and identifies its clientele.

Exhibit 11-7

A Portion of the Opening Page for the Canada.com Finance Site

SOURCE: Canada.com Web site, Tuesday, October 29, 2002. (http://finance.canada.com).

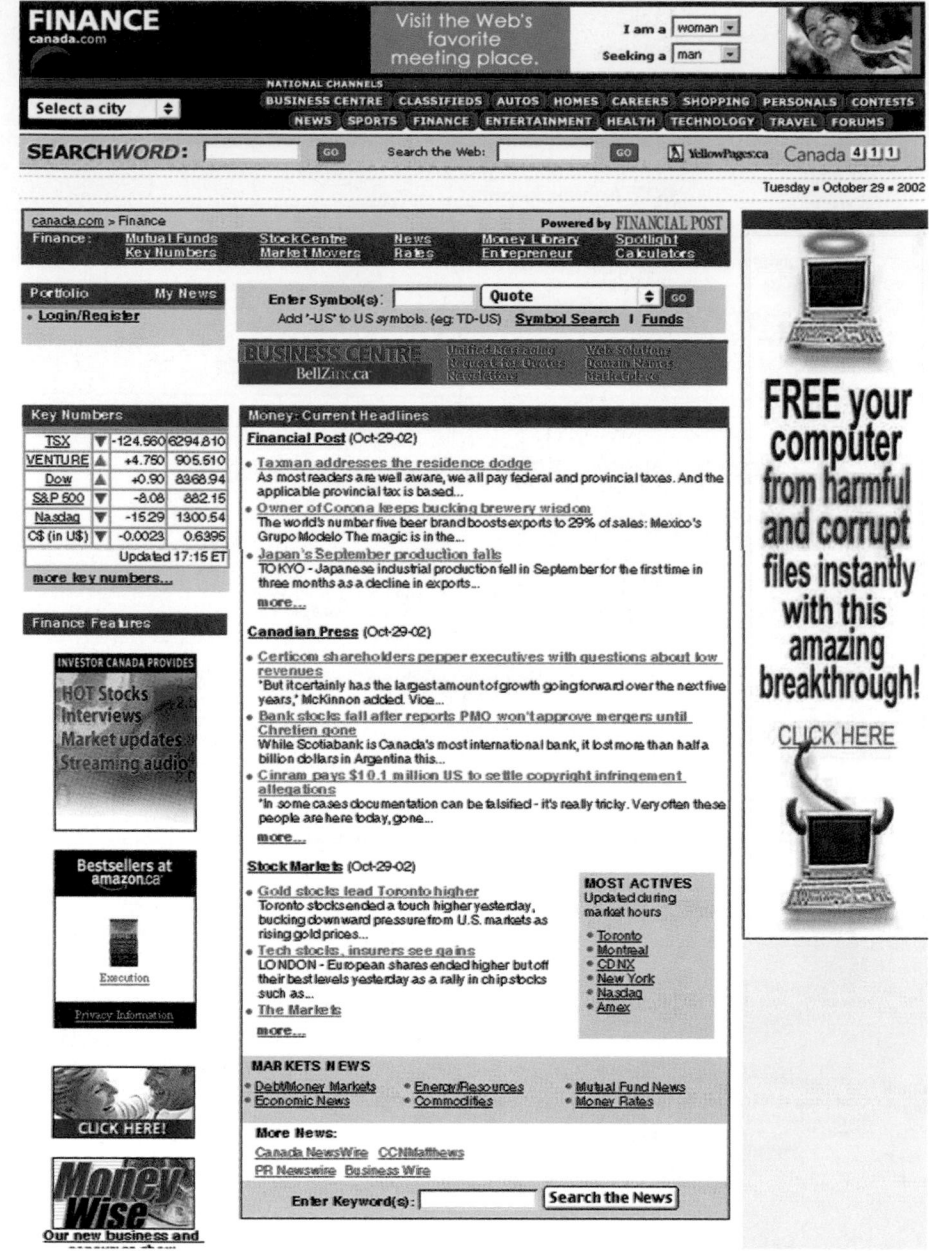

BCE Inc. shares trading on the New York Stock Exchange have been bought or sold for as little as $14.60 and as high as $27.23, at an average rate of 784,000 shares per day. To date, the share value has dropped by 19 percent and the earnings per share (EPS) have grown at a rate of 1 percent.

Exhibit 11–9 on page 330 presents a detailed four-page report on BCE issued by Globeinvestor GOLD. While other stock advisory services provide basically the same types of information as in Exhibits 11–8 and 11–9, it is the investor's job to interpret such information and decide whether the company's stocks are a good investment.

CORPORATE NEWS

As mentioned in Chapter 10, the federal government requires corporations selling new issues of securities to disclose information about corporate earnings, assets and liabilities, products or services, and the qualifications of top management in a prospectus that they must give to

Advice from a Pro

HOW TO SPOT ONLINE INVESTMENT SCAMS

There are signs that you can look out for before you invest in a company which is being promoted.

Beware of any stocks that you learn about on a bulletin board, chat room, newsgroup, or email. Promoters usually use these to promote stocks.

- Be on guard for high pressure tactics to buy from people you don't know. Promoters make their money from inflating the prices of stocks in order to allow them and insiders to sell their cheap stocks at higher prices. This is called pump and dump, and it is a favourite tactic of promoters who are improperly promoting stocks.
- Watch out for information that you see in online newsletters. Such information might appear to be unbiased and independent, but usually, such information is being provided by individuals paid to recommend the stocks.
- Look out for information contained in publications that contain good investment information along with recommendations or stories about praiseworthy stocks. These publications are veiled attempts to advertise a company; even though the articles appear to be unbiased commentary, the publishers, in fact, have been paid to promote a stock.
- Beware of promises of high profits and the sale relating to products of a new company. It takes time for businesses to become successful and usually the path to success is a gradual increase and not an overnight success. Be realistic when reviewing promises made by companies.
- Never be fooled by press releases or announcements of pending or imminent acquisitions. Unless such acquisitions become reality, this is a warning sign that there is nothing behind the announcement but an attempt to fool you into buying stocks.
- If the company has weak fundamentals, then its low stock price is a reflection of what its worth and not what a promoter tells you its worth. Review the financials of a company and rely on only what you see and not on what you are promised.
- Be on the lookout for small-cap companies that pay a generous executive salary or compensation package. This is a telltale sign that any money that the company is raising is going into the pockets of insiders and not into the company itself.
- Be leery of small-cap companies that are investing in projects unrelated to their businesses. Small-cap companies should not be changing their businesses when they have been created to pursue their original line of business.
- Beware of mining companies that change their focus, especially after another company has announced a large discovery. For example, you will have noticed that in the early 1990s, diamond stocks were very popular. Mining companies that were looking for gold suddenly started hinting in their news releases that they also had properties that could contain diamonds. This was an effort to fool investors into believing that their companies could be the ones to make the next big diamond find.
- Watch out for reverse splits. For example, a company that is trading at $2 per share consolidates its stocks, say on a 3-to-1 basis. Consequently, if you had 300 shares at $2, after the reverse split you would have 100 shares at $6. While the value of the stock seems to be the same, $600, you will begin to notice that the price of your stock will fall probably back to $2 and the value of your stock would be only $200. If the stock does not fall, it could be a sign that the company is trying to make its stocks look more attractive by making them appear that they are worth more. A good company with high profits doesn't need to consolidate its stocks to increase the value of its shares.
- Beware of companies that have been previously suspended or have had delinquent filings. This is an indication that the company is not well managed.
- Be leery of stocks that are thinly traded but have sporadic volume surges. This is an indication that heavy promotion is going on.
- Finally, if you think you have been scammed, report the scam to our *Complaint Centre* and your local *Better Business Bureau*. You may also want to contact your local Enforcement Agency to assist you in investigating the scam.

SOURCE: Based on http://www.fraudbureau.com/

Exhibit 11–8

Zacks Investment Research Report for BCE

SOURCE: Zacks Investment Research Inc., Company Reports, June 7, 2002.

June 7, 2002

Zacks Investment Research, Inc.
-Company Reports-

BCE INC

Ticker	BCE					Shares/ Outstanding			808.4 MM	
Exchange	NYSE									
Industry	UTIL-TELEPHONE					Institutions				
Type	Large					Insiders			16.69%	

Rec Price	P/E	Mkt Rate	Cap	Div (12Mo)	Yield Gr	Sales Gr	Sls Gr	EPS Rank	Div	Zacks
$18.51	18.5	$14963 MM	$1.20	6.5%	$14138	MM	–14%	1%	–6%	Hold

Price/Volume Data

52 Week High	$27.23
52 Week Low	$14.60
Price Change: Year to Date	–19%
Year to Date (Relative to S & P 500)	–13%
Average Daily Volume	784 000s
Beta	1.12

Zacks Company Profile

BCE Inc. is Canada's largest communications company. Through their operations in communications services, they provide residence and business customers in Canada with wireline and wireless communications products and applications, satellite communications and direct-to-home television services, systems integration expertise, electronic commerce solutions, Internet access, and high-speed data services and directories. Their shares are listed in Canada, the United States, and Europe. (press release)

Symbol
BCE
Previous Close
18.81
Yesterday's Volume
537500
Yesterday's Hi
19.03
Yesterday's Low
18.4

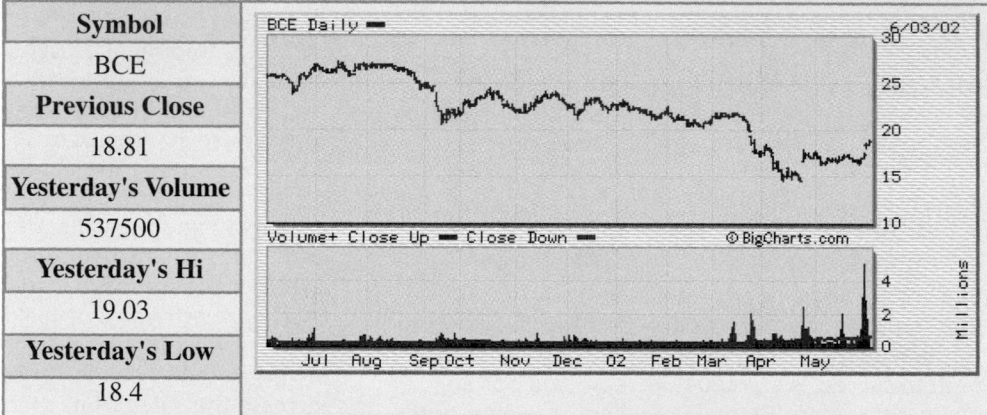

Numbers of Brokers Recommending (06/02/02)

Strong Buy	1
Moderate Buy	6
Hold	1
Moderate Sell	0
Strong Sell	0

Current Average Recommendation (1.0=Strong Buy, 5.0=Strong Sell)	2
Last Weeks Average Recommendation	1.9
Change In Average Recommendation	-.1

Earnings Estimates and Actuals

Actual Earnings Last Quarter	$0.24
EPS Surprise Last Quarter	4 %
Consensus Estimate for Current Quarter	$0.28
Consensus Estimate for Current Fiscal Year	$1.09
Consensus Estimate for Next Fiscal Year	$1.28

Industry Information

Company Industry Group	UTIL-TELEPHONE
Rank Within Industry Group	N/A of 158

Financial Planning for Life's Situations

GETTING TO THE BASICS OF ANNUAL REPORTS

One of the best resources you can use to determine the soundness of a stock investment is a corporation's annual report. These reports are an excellent tool for learning about a company, its management, its past performance, and its goals. But while thumbing through these glossy publications, you must always keep in mind that corporations use this medium to "toot their own horns." The letter from the chair of the board, the upbeat, smiling faces of the employees, and the artistic layout and beautiful photographs are nice to look at, but it's the accounting statements and footnotes that give the true picture of the financial health of a corporation. Understanding the items presented on these pages tucked away in the back of the report is the real key to determining if a company is making a profit. Once you know the basics of reading annual reports, you will be in a better position to evaluate different investment opportunities.

Experts recommend that before investing, you review and compare the annual reports a corporation has published

over the last three years. Read the shareholders' letters to see if they met their goals each year. Are any areas of concern mentioned? Are the facts presented in a straightforward manner, or do you have to struggle to interpret their meaning? Learn to read between the lines to separate the hype from the truth. And watch for words like *except for*, *challenges*, and *contingencies*.

Next, turn to the statement of financial position (sometimes called the balance sheet). This is where you can compare the corporation's financial position by noting changes in its current assets, current liabilities, inventories, total liabilities, and owners' equity. Information on the income statement will enable you to determine if the corporation earned a profit. Be sure to look at the amounts reported for sales, expenses, and profit or loss figures.

Finally, don't overlook the footnotes: They contain (and sometimes hide) important information.

---

investors. In addition to a prospectus, all publicly owned corporations send their shareholders an annual report and quarterly reports that contain detailed financial data. Even if you're not a shareholder, you can obtain an annual report from the corporation. For most corporations, all it takes is a call to a toll-free telephone number. A written request to the corporation's headquarters can also help you obtain an annual report. To see how the information contained in an annual report can help you choose stock investments, read the Financial Planning for Life's Situations feature above.

In addition to corporate publications, many periodicals can help you evaluate a corporation and its stock issues. *Report on Business*, *Canadian Business*, and *Business Week* provide not only general economic news but detailed financial information about individual corporations. Magazines, such as *IE:Money*, *MoneySense*, *MoneySaver*, and *Consumer Reports*, provide information to help you make informed investment decisions. Trade or industry publications, such as *Canadian Banker*, provide information about firms within a specific industry. Finally, news magazines, such as *The Economist*, *Maclean's*, and *Newsweek*, feature financial news on a regular basis.

FACTORS THAT INFLUENCE THE PRICE OF A STOCK

A **bull market** occurs when investors are optimistic about the nation's economy and buy stocks. In a bull market, the fact that more investors are buying stocks causes the value of both individual stocks and the stock market as a whole to increase. A **bear market** occurs when investors are pessimistic about the nation's economy and sell their stocks. Because more investors are selling their stocks, the value of both individual stocks and the stock market as a whole declines.

bull market Occurs when investors are optimistic about a nation's economy and buy stocks.

bear market Occurs when investors are pessimistic about a nation's economy and sell their stocks.

Exhibit 11-9

Globeinvestor GOLD Stock Report for BCE

SOURCE:
http://gold.globeinvestor.com/home1.html 2002 BCE Inc, Company snapshot. globeinvestgold.com

BCE INC. COMPANY SNAPSHOT

BCE-T:	Last: C$ 27.91	Net Change: C$ -0.340	% Change: -1.20	Volume: 1,170,800

Symbol:	Annual Income Statement	Annual Balance Sheet	Annual Cash Flow Statement
BCE-T	Annual Ratios	Quarterly Income Statement	Quarterly Balance Sheet
	Quarterly Cash Flow Statement		

Bottom of Form BCE INC. is a communications company. The company provides connections through wireline, wireless, data/Internet, and satellite services, largely under the Bell brand. BCE leverages those connections with extensive content creation capabilities through Bell Globemedia, which features CTV, *The Globe and Mail*, and Sympatico-Lycos.

Industry: Utilities (Telephone Utilities)
Symbol: BCE
Exchange(s): Toronto Stock Exchange, New York Stock Exchange

ANNUAL FINANCIALS

	Dec 31, 2001 12 Months C$	Dec 31, 2000 12 Months C$	Dec 31, 1999 12 Months C$	3Yr. Growth
Total Revenue ($000):	25,795,000	17,451,000	14,625,000	-7.41
Earnings before Interest & Tax ($000):	5,574,000	3,075,000	2,479,000	-8.54
Profit/Loss ($000):	523,000	4,851,000	5,459,000	-51.55
Earnings per Share:	0.57	7.43	8.35	-55.80
Total Assets ($000):	54,335,000	51,383,000	35,950,000	19.09
Dividends Per Share:	1.20	1.24	1.36	
Return on Com. Equity:	2.88	29.95	38.14	
Employees:	75,000	75,000	55,000	

Trailing 12 Month Results

	12 Months ended Sep 30, 2002, C$	12 Months ended Sep 30, 2001, C$	%Change
Total Revenue ($000):	21,083,000	23,816,000	-11.48
Profit/Loss ($000):	411,000	785,000	-47.71
Earnings per Share:	0.41	0.89	-53.93
Dividends Per Share:	1.20	1.20	
Number of Shares:	905,025,009	808,143,000	

COMPANY INFORMATION
Report on Business Magazine Top 1000 Ranking

Profit: 0030	Revenue: 0003	Assets: 0013

Key Personnel
CEO: Michael J. Sabia, President and CEO
CFO: Siim A. Vanaselja, Chief Financial Officer

Contact Information

Address:	1000 rue de La Gauchetiere O., Bureau 3700, Montreal, QC, H3B 4Y7	Phone:	514-870-8777
		Fax:	514-786-3970
		Web Address:	www.bce.ca
		E-Mail:	bcecomms@bce.ca
Investor Relations:	Maarika Paul, 800 3395353		

Company Type:	Public	Company Status:	Active
Auditors:	Deloitte & Touche		
Transfer Agent:	Computershare Trust Co. Of Can Montreal		
Incorporation:	Canada, Feb 25, 1970		

Securities: BCE.N BCE.T BCE.PR.A-T BCE.PR.P-T BCE.PR.R-T BCE.PR.S-T BCE.PR.Y-T

Top Companies in Telephone Utilities (Selected by Assets)

Bell Canada	TELUS	TELUS Communications
Aliant Inc.	Manitoba Telecom Services	Call-Net Enterprises
Bell Nordiq Group		

How do you determine whether it is the right time to buy or sell a particular stock? Many factors affect the market value of a stock. Therefore, you must also consider potential sales revenues, profits or losses, cash flow, and other important fundamentals when determining whether a stock will increase or decrease in value. In the remainder of this section, we examine numerical measures for a corporation and the fundamental, technical, and efficient market theories that investors use to determine whether a stock is priced right.

book value Determined by deducting all liabilities from the corporation's assets and dividing the remainder by the number of outstanding shares of common stocks.

NUMERICAL MEASURES FOR A CORPORATION Although little correlation may exist between the market value of a stock and its book value, book value is widely reported in financial publications. Therefore, it deserves mention. The **book value** for a share of stock is determined by deducting all liabilities from the corporation's assets and dividing the

Advice from a Pro

THE REAL MEANING OF THE ENRON COLLAPSE

The scandalous collapse of the Enron Corporation has alerted Americans (one would hope) to the inherent dangers of deregulating vital industries, such as energy. However, while the mainstream media focus on the question of whether corporate accounting firms should be held more accountable, they naturally miss the most important issue. Enron was more than just a corrupt corporation; it was functioning as part of the U.S. government.

Enron collapsed like a house of cards just when Wall Street was proclaiming it to be the very model of corporate perfection. Enron stocks were selling at over $80 a share at their peak last fall, and now those shares are worth less than a dollar. If there were justice in the world, we could all sit back and relax, knowing that Enron executives got what they deserved for their corruption and mismanagement. The problem is, Enron's collapse has put thousands of innocent Americans out of work and wiped out the retirement portfolios of thousands more.

When Enron stocks took a nosedive last fall, its corporate captains decided not to go down with the ship.

They and their top investors sold their stocks while hiding the true financial condition of the company from everyone else. In fact, Ken Lay, Enron's chairman, lied to Enron's small investors, telling them that the company's future had never looked brighter. As if that's not bad enough, after years of encouraging their employees to invest their retirement savings almost exclusively in Enron stocks, Enron's pension administrators blocked trading for those same employees for 90 days even as the prices plummeted. By the time, investors knew that the company was bankrupt, it was too late. Their stocks were worthless and their bosses had dumped and run. Enron employees weren't the only ones harmed. At least half a dozen state governments throughout the U.S. had also invested their employees' retirement savings in Enron stocks. Those portfolios, too, have lost nearly all their value. Thousands of Americans lost their life savings virtually overnight. Enron employees lost their jobs and their life savings.

SOURCE: The Email Activist, at www.theemailactivist. org/

---

remainder by the number of outstanding shares of common stocks. For example, assume XYZ Corporation has assets of $6 million and liabilities of $3 million and has issued 100,000 shares of common stocks. In this situation, the book value for a share of XYZ stock is $30 per share, as follows:

$$\frac{\overset{\textit{Assets}}{\$6,000,000} - \overset{\textit{Liabilities}}{\$3,000,000}}{100,000 \text{ shares of stock}} = \$30 \text{ per share}$$

Book value has two main uses: It is the value of the company's assets shareholders would theoretically receive if a company were liquidated, and it can be an indicator of an underpriced stock since a company's book value might be higher or lower than its market value. Some investors believe they have found a bargain when a stock's market value is about the same as or lower than its book value. *Be warned:* Book value calculations may be misleading because the dollar amount of assets used in the above formula may be understated or overstated on the firm's financial statements. For example, buildings are depreciated like the firm's other assets, yet buildings may increase, not decrease, in value. This dollar increase for buildings is not reported on a firm's financial statements. As a result, the book value may be incorrect. From a practical standpoint, most financial experts suggest that book value is just one piece of the puzzle and that you must consider other factors along with book value when evaluating a possible stock investment.

One of the most common calculations investors use to monitor the value of their investments is the current yield. The **current yield** is the yearly dollar amount of income generated by an investment divided by the investment's current market value. For example, assume you

current yield The yearly dollar amount of income generated by an investment divided by the investment's current market value.

purchase stock in Air Canada. Also assume Air Canada pays an annual dividend of $1.84 and is currently selling for $49 a share. The current dividend yield is 3.8 percent, calculated as follows:

$$\text{Current yield} = \frac{\text{Annual income amount}}{\text{Market value}}$$

$$= \frac{\$1.84}{\$49}$$

$$= 0.038, \text{ or 3.8 percent.}$$

As a general rule, an increase in current yield is a healthy sign for any investment. A current yield of 6 percent is better than a 3.8-percent current yield.

Although the current yield calculation is useful, you should also consider whether the investment is increasing or decreasing in dollar value. **Total shareholder return (TSR)** is a calculation that includes not only the yearly dollar amount of income but also any increase or decrease in the original purchase price of the investment. The following formula is used to calculate total shareholder return:

$$\text{TSR} = \text{Current return} + \text{Capital gain}$$

While this concept may be used for any investment, let's illustrate it by using the assumptions for a stock presented in the preceding example. Assume, in addition, that you own 100 shares that you purchased for $49 a share and hold your shares for two years before deciding to sell them at the current market price of $61.50 a share. Your total shareholder return for this investment would be $1,618, calculated as follows:

$$\text{TSR} = \text{Current return} + \text{Capital gain}$$

$$\$1,618 = \$368 + \$1,250$$

In this example, the current return of $368 results from the payment of dividends for two years ($1.84 per-share dividend $\times$ 100 shares $\times$ 2 years). The capital gain of $1,250 results from the increase in the stock price from $49 a share to $61.50 a share ($12.50 per-share increase $\times$ 100 shares = $1,250). (Of course, commissions to buy and sell your stocks, a topic covered in the next section, would reduce your total shareholder return.)

In this example, the investment increased in value and the TSR was greater than the current return. For an investment that decreases in value, the TSR will be less than the current return. And while it may be obvious, we should point out that the larger the dollar amount of total return, the better.

The **annualized holding period yield** calculation takes into account the TSR, the original investment, and the time the investment is held. The following formula is used to calculate the annualized holding period yield:

$$\text{Annualized holding period yield} = \frac{\text{TSR}}{\text{Original investment}} \times \frac{1}{N}$$

where

$$N = \text{Number of years investment is held}$$

To illustrate this concept, let's return to your Air Canada investment, for which the total return was $1,618, the original investment was $4,900, and the holding period was two years. As shown below, the annualized holding period yield for this investment is 16.5 percent for each of the two years you held the investment:

$$\text{Annualized holding period yield} = \frac{\$1,618}{\$4,900} \times \frac{1}{2}$$

$$= 0.165$$

$$= 16.5 \text{ percent}$$

total shareholder return (TSR) A calculation that includes the yearly dollar amount of income as well as any increase or decrease in the original purchase price of the investment.

annualized holding period yield A yield calculation that takes into account the total return, the original investment, and the time the investment is held.

There is no meaningful average for annualized holding period yield because individual investments vary. But an increase in annualized holding period yield is a healthy sign. For instance, an annualized holding period yield of 16.5 percent is better than one of 11 percent. If you are trying to decide whether to sell or hold a stock, the annualized holding period yield can help you decide if it is time to sell.

Earnings per share are a corporation's after-tax earnings divided by the number of outstanding shares of common stocks. For example, assume that in 2000, XYZ Corporation has after-tax earnings of $800,000. As mentioned previously, XYZ has 100,000 shares of common stocks. This means XYZ's earnings per share are $8 ($800,000 ÷ 100,000 = $8). Most shareholders consider the amount of EPS important because it is a measure of the company's profitability. No meaningful average for this measure exists, mainly because the number of shares of a firm's stocks is subject to change via stock splits and stock dividends. *As a general rule, however, an increase in earnings per share is a healthy sign for any corporation and its shareholders.*

The **price–earnings (P/E) ratio** is the price of a share of stock divided by the corporation's earnings per share of stocks outstanding over the last 12 months. For example, assume XYZ Corporation's common stocks are selling for $96 a share. As determined earlier, XYZ's earnings per share are $8. XYZ's price–earnings ratio is, therefore, 12 ($96 ÷ $8 = 12). For the most part, a high P/E means high projected earnings in the future. However, the P/E ratio doesn't tell a whole lot; it is useful, however, to compare the P/E ratios of other companies in the same industry, or with the market in general, or against the company's own historical P/E ratios. *A low price–earnings ratio indicates that a stock may be a good investment, and a high price–earnings ratio indicates that it may be a poor investment.* Generally, you should study the price–earnings ratio for a corporation over a period of time. For example, if XYZ's price–earnings ratio has ranged from 12 to 30 over the past three years, its current price–earnings ratio of 12 indicates that it is a potentially good investment. If XYZ's current price–earnings ratio were 27—toward the high end of the range—it may be a poor investment at this time. Although P/E ratios vary by industry, they range between 5 and 35 for most corporations.

The **beta** is an index reported in many financial publications that compares the risk associated with a specific stock issue with the risk of the stock market in general. The beta for the stock market in general (or the "average" stock) is 1.0. The majority of stocks have betas between 0.5 and 2.0. Generally, conservative stocks have low betas and speculative stocks have high betas. For example, assume XYZ Corporation's stocks have a beta of 0.50. This means its stocks are less responsive than the average stocks on the market. When the market in general increases by 10 percent, XYZ's stocks will go up 5 percent. If, on the other hand, ABC Corporation has a beta of 2.0, this means ABC's stocks are twice as responsive as the market. When the market in general decreases by 10 percent, ABC's stocks will go down 20 percent. Take another look at Zach's investment report in Exhibit 11–8. The beta for BCE is reported as 1.12. This means that if the stock market as a whole goes up 10 percent, the market value of BCE stocks will increase 11.2 percent. If the value of the stock market as a whole decreases by 10 percent, the market value of BCE's

earnings per share A corporation's after-tax earnings divided by the number of outstanding shares of common stocks.

price–earnings ratio the price of a share of stock divided by the corporation's earnings per share of stocks outstanding over the last 12 months.

beta an index that compares the risk associated with a specific stock issue with the risk of the stock market in general.

D I D   Y O U   K N O W ?

The chart below compares the five-year performance of the TSE 300, the Dow Jones Industrial Average, and the S&P 500, rebased.

Five-Year Index Performance (Rebased)

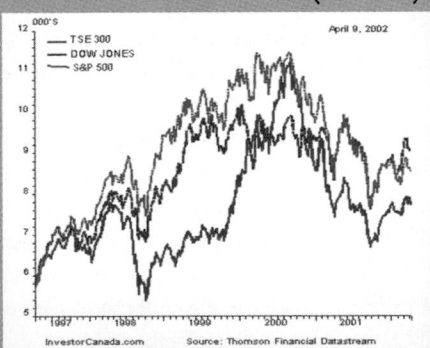

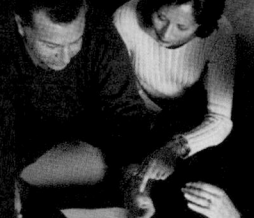
ON WHY PEOPLE SHOULD CHOOSE STOCKS

Investments in stocks are growth oriented, according to the pros. That is to say, stock investments generally don't pay interest like a GIC or a bond does, but in return they will grow in value. A healthy stock portfolio can grow 10 percent, maybe 15 percent a year.

The pros are quick to point out another reason for investing in stocks: They can grow on a tax-deferred basis. If you have income from a GIC or a bond, you stop at the end of each year and pay tax on it. The nice thing about stock investments is that you don't pay any tax until you actually sell the investments. And when you do, you pay taxes at a reduced rate. So, if you are growth oriented, if you have a job, and don't have immediate demands for even a small portion of your income, stocks are a great way to build wealth.

To help ensure success, the pros believe an investor must have reasonable expectations, be patient, and recognize the need for advice. Few individuals would sit down and draft their own will or even fix their own car. Acting independently without professional help when building a diversified investment portfolio can be just as catastrophic. Reasonable expectation, patience, and outside help have prove to be a winning combination.

---

stocks will decrease by 11.2 percent. Thus, the market value of BCE's stocks are slightly more volatile than the stock market as a whole. Because individual stocks generally move in the same direction as the stock market in general, most betas are positive, but it is possible for a stock to have a negative beta. A negative beta occurs when a corporation's stocks move in the opposite direction compared with the stock market in general.

INVESTMENT THEORIES Investors sometimes use three different investment theories to determine a stock's value. The **fundamental theory** is based on the assumption that a stock's intrinsic or real value is determined by the company's future earnings. If a corporation's expected earnings are higher than its present earnings, the corporation's stocks should increase in value. If its expected earnings are lower than its present earnings, the stocks should decrease in value. In addition to expected earnings, fundamentalists consider (1) the financial strength of the company, (2) the type of industry the company is in, (3) new-product development, and (4) the economic growth of the overall economy.

The **technical theory** is based on the assumption that a stock's market value is determined by the forces of supply and demand in the stock market as a whole. It is based not on the expected earnings or the intrinsic value of an individual corporation's stock but on factors found in the market as a whole. Typical technical factors are the total number of shares traded, the number of buy orders, and the number of sell orders over a period of time. Technical analysts, sometimes called *chartists*, construct charts that plot past price movements and other market averages. These charts allow them to observe trends and patterns for the market as a whole that enable them to predict whether a specific stock's market value will increase or decrease.

The **efficient market theory**, sometimes called the *random walk theory*, is based on the assumption that stock price movements are purely random. Advocates of the efficient market theory assume the stock market is completely efficient and buyers and sellers have considered all of the available information about an individual stock. Any news on an individual corporation, an oil embargo, or a change in the tax laws that may affect the value of a stock is quickly absorbed by all investors seeking a profit. Thus, a stock's current market price reflects its true value. The efficient market theory rejects both the fundamental theory and the technical theory. According to this theory, it is impossible for an investor to outperform the average for the stock market as a whole over a long period of time.

Before completing this section, you may want to examine the Financial Planning Calculations box on the next page.

---

fundamental theory An investment theory based on the assumption that a stock's intrinsic or real value is determined by the company's future earnings.

technical theory An investment theory based on the assumption that a stock's market value is determined by the forces of supply and demand in the stock market as a whole.

efficient market theory An investment theory based on the assumption that stock price movements are purely random; also called the *random walk theory*.

Financial Planning Calculations

EVALUATING CORPORATE STOCKS

No checklist can serve as a foolproof guide for choosing common or preferred stocks. However, the following questions will help you evaluate a potential stock investment.

CATEGORY 1: THE BASICS

1. What is the corporation's name? _____

2. What are the corporation's address and telephone number? _____

3. Have you requested the latest annual report and quarterly report? ☐ Yes ☐ No

4. What information about the corporation is available on the Internet? _____

5. Where are the stocks traded? _____

6. What types of products or services does this firm provide? _____

7. Briefly describe the prospects for this company. (Include significant factors like product development, plans for expansion, plans for mergers, etc.) _____

CATEGORY 2: DIVIDEND INCOME

8. Is the corporation currently paying dividends? If so, how much? _____

9. What is the current yield for this stock? _____

10. Has the dividend payout increased or decreased over the past seven years? _____

11. How does the yield for this investment compare with those for other potential investments? _____

CATEGORY 3: FINANCIAL PERFORMANCE

12. Is the corporation profitable? What are the firm's earnings per share for the last three years? _____

13. Have profits increased over the last seven years? ☐ Yes ☐ No

14. What is the 52-week high and low for these stocks? _____

What is the stocks' current price? _____

15. What is the firm's beta? _____

16. What is the firm's current P/E ratio? _____

17. How does the firm's P/E ratio compare with other firms in general? With other firms in the same industry? _____

18. Are this year's sales higher than last year's sales? ☐ Yes ☐ No

19. Have sales increased over the last seven years? ☐ Yes ☐ No

20. Briefly describe any other information that you obtained from SEDAR, Zacks, Standard & Poor's, or other stock advisory services. _____

A WORD OF CAUTION

When you use a checklist, there is always a danger of overlooking important relevant information. The above checklist is not all-inclusive, but it does provide some very sound questions that you should answer before making a decision to invest in stocks. Quite simply, it is a place to start. If you need other information, *you* are responsible for obtaining it and for determining how it affects your potential investment.

CONCEPT CHECK 11–3

1. What sources of information would you use to evaluate a stock issue?
2. How would you define (1) a blue-chip stock, (2) an income stock, (3) a growth stock, (4) a cyclical stock, (5) a defensive stock, (6) a penny stock, (7) a large-cap stock, and (8) a small-cap stock?
3. What are the formulas for current yield, total return, annualized holding period yield, book value, earnings per share, and price–earnings ratio?
4. Do you think the fundamental theory, the technical theory, or the efficient market theory best describes price movements for the stock market? Why?

Buying and Selling Stocks

Objective 4

Describe how stocks are bought and sold.

primary market A market in which an investor purchases financial securities, via an investment bank or other representative, from the issuer of those securities.

investment bank A financial firm that assists corporations in raising funds, usually by helping to sell new security issues.

initial public offering (IPO) Occurs when a corporation sells stocks to the general public for the first time.

secondary market A market for existing financial securities that are currently traded among investors.

To purchase a pair of Levi Strauss jeans, you simply walk into a store that sells Levi's, choose a pair, and pay for your purchase. To purchase common or preferred stocks, you generally have to work through a brokerage firm. In turn, your brokerage firm must buy the stocks in either the primary or secondary market. In the **primary market**, you purchase financial securities, via an investment bank or other representative, from the issuer of those securities. An **investment bank** is a financial firm that assists corporations in raising funds, usually by helping to sell new security issues.

New security issues sold through an investment bank can be issued by corporations that have sold stocks and bonds before and need to sell new issues to raise additional financing. The new securities can also be initial public offerings. An **initial public offering (IPO)** occurs when a corporation sells stocks to the general public for the first time. Highly visible companies that have sold stocks to raise capital include Research in Motion, and Quebecor. Investors bought these stocks through brokerage firms acting as agents for an investment banking firm, and the money they paid for common stocks flowed to the corporations that issued the stocks. Because these companies used the financing obtained through IPOs wisely, they have grown and prospered, and investors have profited from their IPO investments. However, not all companies that use IPOs to raise capital are good investments.

Be warned: The promise of quick profits often lures investors to purchase IPOs. An IPO is generally classified as a high-risk investment—one made in the hope of earning a relatively large profit in a short time. Depending on the corporation selling the new security, IPOs are usually too risky for most people.

After a stock has been sold through the primary market, it is traded through the secondary market. The **secondary market** is a market for existing financial securities that are currently traded among investors. Once the stocks are sold in the primary market, they can be sold time and again in the secondary market. The fact that stocks can be sold in the secondary market improves the liquidity of stock investments because the money you pay for stocks goes to the seller of the stocks.

PRIMARY MARKETS FOR STOCKS

How would you sell $100 million worth of common stocks or preferred stocks? For a large corporation, the decision to sell stocks is often complicated, time consuming, and expensive. There are basically two methods.

First, a large corporation may use an investment bank to sell and distribute the new stocks issue. Most large corporations that need a lot of financing use this method. If this method is used, analysts for the investment bank examine the corporation's financial position to determine whether the new issue is financially sound and how difficult it will be to sell.

If the investment bank is satisfied that the new stocks are a good risk, it will buy the stocks and then resell them to its customers—commercial banks, insurance companies, pension funds, mutual funds, and the general public. The investment bank's commission, or spread, ranges from less than 1 percent for a utility firm to as much as 25 percent for a small company selling stocks for the first time. The size of the spread depends on the quality and financial health of the issuing corporation. The commission allows the investment bank to make a profit while guaranteeing that the corporation will receive the financing it needs.

If the investment bank's analysts believe the new issue will be difficult to sell, the investment bank may agree to take the stocks on a best-efforts basis, without guaranteeing that the stocks will be sold. Because the corporation must take back any unsold stocks after a reasonable time, most large corporations are unwilling to accept this arrangement. If the stock issue is too large for one investment bank, a group of investment bankers may form an *underwriting syndicate*. Then, each member of the syndicate is responsible for selling only a part of the new issue.

The second method used by a corporation trying to obtain financing through the primary market is to sell directly to current shareholders. Usually, promotional materials describing the new stock issue are mailed to current shareholders. These shareholders may then purchase the stocks directly from the corporation.

You may ask, "Why would a corporation try to sell its own stocks?" The most obvious reason for doing so is to avoid the investment bank's commission. Of course, a corporation's ability to sell a new stock issue without the aid of an investment bank is tied directly to investors' perception of the corporation's financial health.

SECONDARY MARKETS FOR STOCKS

How do you buy or sell stocks in the secondary market? To purchase common or preferred stocks, you usually have to work with an employee of a brokerage firm who will buy or sell for you in a securities marketplace, at a securities exchange, or through the over-the-counter market.

SECURITIES EXCHANGES A **securities exchange** is a marketplace where member brokers who represent investors meet to buy and sell securities. The securities sold at a particular exchange must first be listed, or accepted for trading, at that exchange. Generally, the securities issued by nationwide corporations are traded at the Toronto Stock Exchange or the TSX Venture Exchange. The securities of regional corporations are traded at smaller, regional exchanges. The securities of very large corporations may be traded at more than one exchange. Canadian firms that do business abroad may also be listed on foreign securities exchanges—in Tokyo, the United States, London, or Paris, for example.

securities exchange A marketplace where member brokers who represent investors meet to buy and sell securities.

THE OVER-THE-COUNTER MARKET Not all securities are traded on organized exchanges. Stocks issued by several thousand companies are traded in the over-the-counter market. The **over-the-counter (OTC) market** is a network of dealers who buy and sell the stocks of corporations that are not listed on a securities exchange. Today, these stocks are not really traded over the counter. The term was coined more than 100 years ago when securities were sold "over the counter" in stores and banks.

over-the-counter (OTC) market A network of dealers who buy and sell the stocks of corporations that are not listed on a securities exchange.

Most over-the-counter securities are traded through **Nasdaq** (pronounced "nazzdack"). Nasdaq is an electronic marketplace for more than 4,100 different stocks. In addition to providing price information, this computerized system allows investors to buy and sell shares of companies listed on Nasdaq. When you want to buy or sell shares of a company that trades on Nasdaq—say, Research In Motion (RIM)—your account executive sends your order into the Nasdaq computer system, where it shows up on the screen with all the other orders from people who want to buy or sell RIM stocks. Then, a Nasdaq dealer (sometimes referred to as a *market maker*) sitting at a computer terminal matches buy and sell orders for RIM. Once a match is found, your order is completed.

Nasdaq (pronounced "nazzdack") An electronic marketplace for over 6,000 stocks.

Begun in 1971 and regulated by the National Association of Securities Dealers, Nasdaq is the third largest securities market in the world in terms of volume, trailing only the NYSE and Tokyo Stock Exchange. It is known for its innovative, forward-looking growth companies. Although many securities are issued by smaller companies, some large firms, including Intel, Microsoft, About.com, Apple Computer, and Ballard Power, also trade on Nasdaq.

BROKERAGE FIRMS AND ACCOUNT EXECUTIVES

An **account executive**, or *stockbroker*, is a licensed individual who buys or sells securities for his or her clients. (Actually, *account executive* is the more descriptive title because such individuals handle all types of securities, not just stocks.) While all account executives can buy or sell stocks for clients, most investors expect more from their account executives. Ideally, an

account executive A licensed individual who buys or sells securities for clients; also called a *stockbroker*.

account executive should provide information and advice to be used in evaluating potential investments. Many investors begin their search for an account executive by asking friends or business associates for recommendations. This is a logical starting point, but remember that some account executives are conservative, while others are more risk oriented.

Before choosing an account executive, you should have already determined your short-term and long-term financial objectives. Then, you must be careful to communicate those objectives to the account executive so that he or she can do a better job of advising you. Needless to say, account executives may err in their investment recommendations. To help avoid a situation in which your account executive's recommendations are automatically implemented, you should be *actively* involved in the decisions of your investment program and you should never allow your account executive to use his or her discretion without your approval. Watch your account for signs of churning. **Churning** is excessive buying and selling of securities to generate commissions. From a total-dollar-return standpoint, this practice usually leaves the client worse off or at least no better off. Churning is illegal under the rules established by the provincial securities exchange commissions; however, it may be difficult to prove. Finally, keep in mind that account executives generally are not liable for client losses that result from their recommendations. In fact, most brokerage firms require new clients to sign a statement in which they promise to submit any complaints to an arbitration board. This arbitration clause generally prevents a client from suing an account executive or a brokerage firm. Above all, remember you are investing *your* money and you should make the final decisions with the help of your account executive.

churning The excessive buying and selling of securities to generate commissions.

SHOULD YOU USE A FULL-SERVICE OR A DISCOUNT BROKERAGE FIRM?

Today, a healthy competition exists between full-serve brokerage firms and discount brokerage firms. While the most obvious difference between full-service and discount firms is the amount of the commissions they charge when you buy or sell stocks and other securities, there are at least three other factors to consider. First, consider how much research information is available and how much it costs. Both types of brokerage firms offer excellent research materials, but you are more likely to pay extra for information if you choose a discount brokerage firm. While most discount brokerage firms don't charge a lot of money for research reports, the fees can mount up over time and can offset the lower commissions they charge to buy or sell stocks.

Second, consider how much help you need when making an investment decision. Many full-service brokerage firms argue that you need a professional to help you make important investment decisions. While this may be true for some investors, most account executives employed by full-service brokerage firms are too busy to spend unlimited time with you on a one-on-one basis, especially if you are investing a small amount. Still, the full-service account executive is there to answer questions and make investment recommendations. On the other side, many discount brokerage firms argue that you alone are responsible for making your investment decisions. They are quick to point out that the most successful investors are the ones involved in their investment programs. And they argue that they have both personnel and materials dedicated to helping you learn how to become a better investor.

Third, consider how easy it is to buy and sell stocks and other securities when using either a full-service or discount brokerage firm. Questions to ask include:

[1] Can I buy or sell stocks over the phone?
[2] Can I trade stocks online?
[3] Where is your nearest office located?
[4] Do you have a toll-free telephone number for customer use?
[5] How often do I get statements?
[6] Is there a charge for statements, research reports, and other financial reports?
[7] Are there any fees in addition to the commissions I pay when I buy or sell stocks?

A SAMPLE STOCK TRANSACTION

Once you and your account executive have decided on a particular transaction, it is time to execute an order to buy or sell. Today, most investors either telephone their account executives or use the Internet and trade online. Let's begin by examining three types of orders used to trade stocks.

A **market order** is a request to buy or sell stocks at the current market value. Since the stock exchange is an auction market, the account executive's representative will try to get the best price available and the transaction will be completed as soon as possible.

Exhibit 11–10 illustrates one method for executing a market order to sell stocks. You should note two things. First, every stock listed on the TSE is traded at a specific computer-equipped trading post on the floor of the exchange. A computer monitor above the post indicates current price information for all stocks traded at each trading post. Second, each transaction is recorded, and the pertinent information (stock symbol, number of shares, and price) is transmitted to interested parties through a communications network called a *ticker tape*. Orders to buy or sell stocks, up to specified sizes in virtually all listed stocks, are transmitted electronically to the proper trading floor post. Then, a **specialist**, an individual on the floor of the exchange who buys or sells particular stocks in an effort to maintain an orderly market, executes the orders as quickly as market interest and activity permit. Payment for stocks is generally required within three business days of the transaction. Then, in about four to six weeks, a stock certificate is sent to the purchaser of the stock, unless the securities are left with the brokerage firm for safekeeping. Today, it is common practice for investors to leave stock certificates with a brokerage firm. Because the stock certificates are in the broker's care, transfers when the

market order A request to buy or sell stocks at the current market value.

specialist An individual on the floor of the exchange who buys or sells particular stocks in an effort to maintain an orderly market.

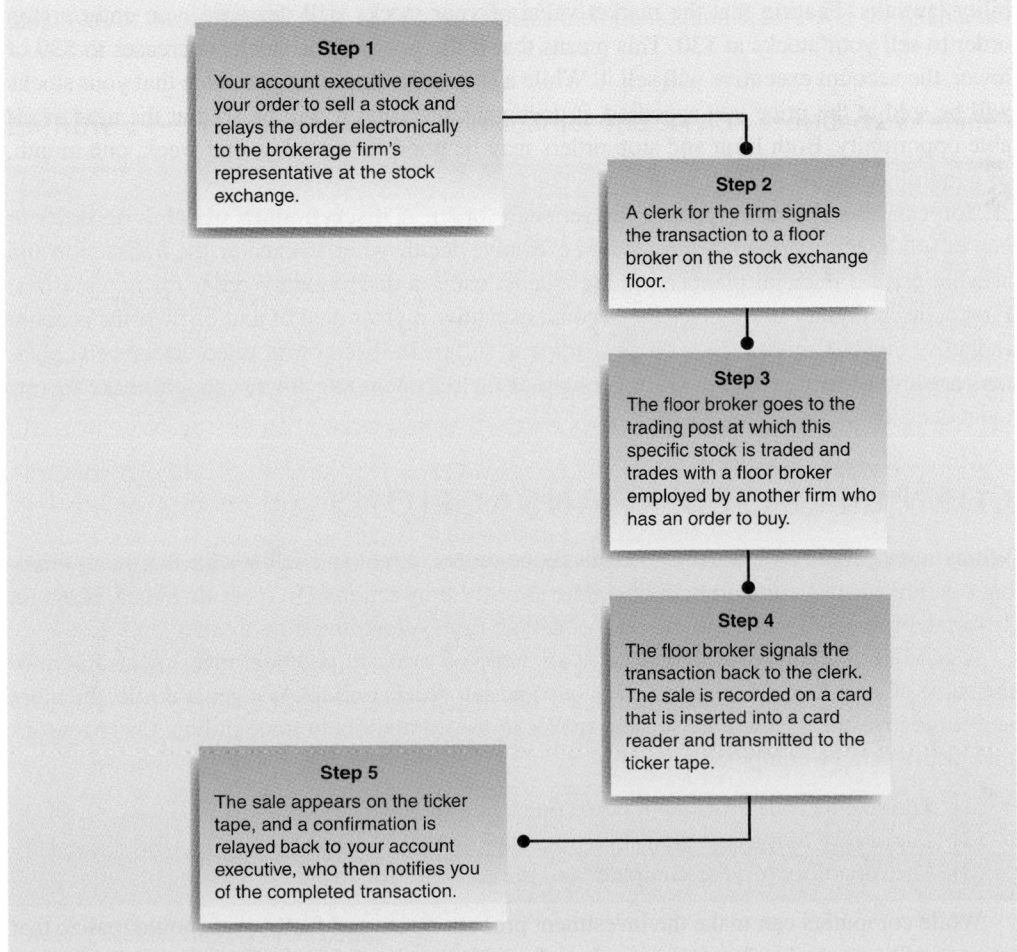

Step 1
Your account executive receives your order to sell a stock and relays the order electronically to the brokerage firm's representative at the stock exchange.

Step 2
A clerk for the firm signals the transaction to a floor broker on the stock exchange floor.

Step 3
The floor broker goes to the trading post at which this specific stock is traded and trades with a floor broker employed by another firm who has an order to buy.

Step 4
The floor broker signals the transaction back to the clerk. The sale is recorded on a card that is inserted into a card reader and transmitted to the ticker tape.

Step 5
The sale appears on the ticker tape, and a confirmation is relayed back to your account executive, who then notifies you of the completed transaction.

Exhibit 11–10

Steps in a Typical Transaction for Stock Traded on the Toronto Stock Exchange

Exhibit 11–14

An Example of
Selling Short

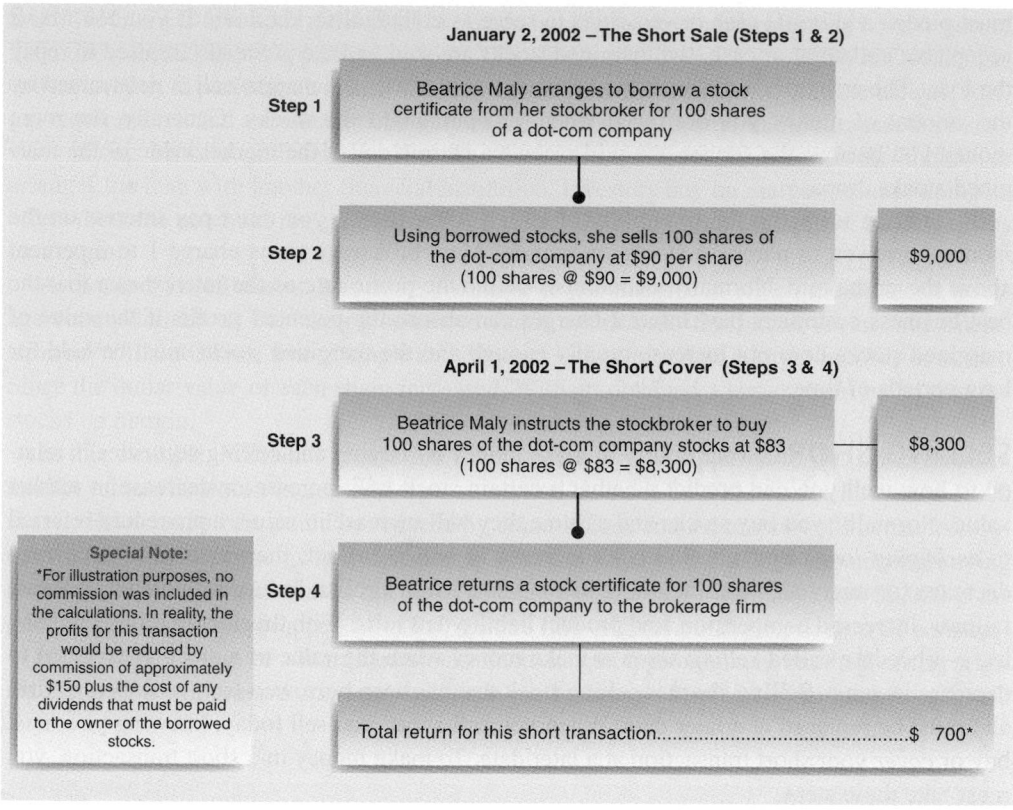

January 2, 2002 – The Short Sale (Steps 1 & 2)

Step 1   Beatrice Maly arranges to borrow a stock certificate from her stockbroker for 100 shares of a dot-com company

Step 2   Using borrowed stocks, she sells 100 shares of the dot-com company at $90 per share (100 shares @ $90 = $9,000)   — $9,000

April 1, 2002 – The Short Cover (Steps 3 & 4)

Step 3   Beatrice Maly instructs the stockbroker to buy 100 shares of the dot-com company stocks at $83 (100 shares @ $83 = $8,300)   — $8,300

Special Note:
*For illustration purposes, no commission was included in the calculations. In reality, the profits for this transaction would be reduced by commission of approximately $150 plus the cost of any dividends that must be paid to the owner of the borrowed stocks.

Step 4   Beatrice returns a stock certificate for 100 shares of the dot-com company to the brokerage firm

Total return for this short transaction..$ 700*

option The right to buy or sell stocks at a predetermined price during a specified period of time

TRADING IN OPTIONS An **option** gives you the right to buy or sell stocks at a predetermined price during a specified period of time. Options are usually available for three-, six-, or nine-month periods. If you think the market price of a stock will increase during a short period of time, you may decide to purchase a call option. A *call option* is sold by a shareholder and gives the purchaser the right to *buy* 100 shares at a guaranteed price before a specified expiration date.

It is also possible to purchase a put option. A *put option* is the right to sell 100 shares at a guaranteed price before a specified expiration date. With both call and put options, you are betting that the price of the stocks will increase or decrease in value before the expiration date. If this price movement does not occur before the expiration date, you lose the money you paid for your option.

Because of the increased risk involved in option trading, a more detailed discussion of how you profit or lose money with options is beyond the scope of this book. *Be warned:* Amateurs and beginning investors should stay away from options unless they fully understand all of the risks involved. For the rookie, the lure of large profits over a short period of time may be tempting, but the risks are real.

CONCEPT CHECK 11–5

1. How can an investor make money using the buy-and-hold technique?
2. What is the advantage of using dollar cost averaging?
3. Explain the difference between direct investment plans and dividend reinvestment plans.
4. Why would an investor buy stocks on margin?
5. Why would an investor use the selling-short technique?

Advice from a Pro

THEME INVESTING: MEGA TRENDS AND MARKET PSYCHOLOGY

Investing has always been a little bit like surfing. Successful investors spot key investment themes (waves) and ride them to profits. Sometimes, the waves are short and less than we expected. Other times, the waves take on a mind of their own and then fall under their own weight. The hardest but most profitable thing to do is to be the lone rider of a wave that others have deserted for the "next best thing" and wait for them to catch up. The key is to know when to get on and when to get off. Previous examples of trend investing include defence stocks during World War II; oil stocks in the 1970s; and, of course, the dot-coms.

How do you spot the next wave? You need to step back from the daily noise of the market and look at the long term—years, not weeks. You need to ask: What are the long-term forces that will propel some stocks and draw money from other sectors? In the early and mid-1990s, the focus was on demographic trends and the greying of the baby-boomers. In the second half of the 1990s, it was the Internet.

Demographics and the Internet also illustrate how long-term trends fall in and out of favour. Both are still with us, but both seem to have petered out. The profit potential of investing in companies that will benefit from the greying of the boomers is still here, but it was overshadowed by the Internet, obscured by market psychology that tends to focus on the current hot theme.

The events of September 11, 2001, are causing a major re-allocation of money into sectors that are expected to benefit from rebuilding infrastructure and making society safer from such attacks. For example, the market now has "new" investment themes. Prior to September 11, the market was focused on telecommunications inventory corrections, was still focused on old dot-com names, and lacked any new ideas to sell to investors. Post-attack, the spotlight is on security and defence stocks. While many of these previously unnoticed stocks have potential, many may not. A blind rush to buy any stocks with a "security theme" may result in another bubble.

Funds are moving out of the old favourites into these new hot sectors. However, for the most part, these new hot stocks are not in the major indexes. The result is that the headline indexes may not reflect the strength in the "new stocks" that were previously unnoticed.

These actions represent significant changes in investment policy in reaction to a key event, much like the re-allocation that occurred in the mid-1990s as investors were drawn to the promise of Internet stocks. The demand for increased security represents a long-term structural and psychological change that will provide a boost for stocks in that sector. The effects on insurance, airlines, and brokerages will reflect near-term concerns for profits, and as institutional investors raise cash to re-allocate funds to security stocks.

Other long-term trends remain intact, but market psychology tends to focus Wall Street's attention on one or two sectors at any one time. Patient investors can still make money on demographic trends, but the sectors noted above will take centre stage for the time being. Aggressive investors may make money by buying airline and brokerage stocks if the markets overreact.

There are three key things to remember:

1. Differentiate between knee-jerk reactions and fundamental structural changes.
2. Don't sell to avoid short-term losses. If you have decided that a sector/stock is a good long-term buy, don't try to avoid a short-term loss with panic selling. If a sector is falling, individual investors will not get the best prices, so it is better to stay put. You have a better chance of getting the stocks cheap by buying when everyone else is selling.
3. Stick with your game plan, but be vigilant for major structural changes. Demographic stocks may be a better buy today because we are all six years older, but a smarter investment would be airport security stocks with solid fundamentals. However, you need to do your homework before investing.

SOURCE: Rick Wayman (ResearchStock.com) http://www.investopedia.com/ December 14, 2001.

FINANCIAL PLANNING PROBLEMS

1. *Calculating Dividend Amounts.* Jennifer and Jeff Cooke own 220 shares of Petro-Canada common stocks. Assume that Petro-Canada's quarterly dividend is $10 per share. What is the amount of the dividend cheque the Cook couple will receive for this quarter? (Obj. 1)

2. *Determining the Number of Shares after a Stock Split.* In March, shareholders of Certicom Corporation approved a 2-for-1 stock split. After the split, how many Certicom stocks will an investor have if she or he owned 360 shares before the split? (Obj. 1)

3. *Calculating Total Return.* Tamara June purchased 100 shares of All-Canadian Manufacturing Company at 29\frac{1}{2}$ a share. One year later, she sold the stock for $38 a share. She paid her broker a $34 commission when she purchased the stocks and a $42 commission when she sold them. During the 12 months she owned the stocks, she received $184 in dividends. Calculate Tamara's total return on this investment. (Obj. 1)

4. *Calculating Total Return.* Marie and Brian Hume purchased 200 shares of a Canadian utility for $95 a share. One year later, they sold the stocks for $110 a share. They paid their broker a $130 commission when they purchased the stocks and a $150 commission when they sold them. During the 12 months they owned the stocks, they received $280 in dividends. Calculate the total return on this investment. (Obj. 1)

5. *Determining a Preferred Dividend Amount.* Thom Hayes owns Gaz Métropolitain preferred stocks. If this preferred stock issue pays 6$\frac{1}{4}$ percent based on a par value of $25, what is the dollar amount of the dividend for one share of Gaz Métropolitain? (Obj. 2)

6. *Calculating the Dividend for a Cumulative Preferred Stock Issue.* A sports equipment company issued a $3 cumulative preferred stock issue. In 2000, the firm's board of directors voted to omit dividends for both the company's common stock and its preferred stock issues. Also, the corporation's board of directors voted to pay dividends in 2001. (Obj. 2)
   a. How much did the preferred shareholders receive in 2000?
   b. How much did the common shareholders receive in 2000?
   c. How much did the preferred shareholders receive in 2001?

7. *Calculating Return on Investment.* Two years ago, you purchased 100 shares of a cola company. Your purchase price was $50 a share, plus a total commission of $55 to purchase the stocks. During the last two years, you have received the following dividend amounts: $0.56 per share for the first year and $0.68 per share the second year. Also, assume that at the end of two years, you sold your cola company stocks for $61 a share plus a total commission of $60 to sell the stocks. (Obj. 3)
   a. Calculate the current yield for your cola stocks at the time you purchased it.

   b. Calculate the current yield for your cola stocks at the time you sold it.
   c. Calculate the total return for your cola investment when you sold the stocks at the end of two years.
   d. Calculate the annualized holding period yield for your cola investment at the end of the two-year period.

8. *Calculating Book Value, Earnings per Share, and Price–Earnings Ratio.* As a shareholder of an oil company, you receive its annual report. In the financial statements, the firm has reported assets of $9 million, liabilities of $5 million, after-tax earnings of $2 million, and 750,000 outstanding shares of common stocks. (Obj. 3)
   a. Calculate the book value of a share of this oil company's common stocks.
   b. Calculate the earnings per share of this oil company's common stocks.
   c. Assuming a share of this oil company's common stocks have a market value of $40, what is the firm's price–earnings ratio?

9. *Using Dollar Cost Averaging.* For four years, Marie St. Louis invested $3,000 each year in a bank's stocks. The stock was selling for $34 in 1999, for $48 in 2000, $37 in 2001, and for $52 in 2002. (Obj. 5)
   a. What is Marie's total investment in this bank?
   b. After four years, how many shares does Marie own?
   c. What is the average cost per share of Marie's investment?

10. *Using Margin.* Brian Campbell invested $4,000 and borrowed $4,000 to purchase shares in a large retailing company. At the time of his investment, the stocks were selling for $45 a share. (Obj. 5)
    a. If Brian paid a $70 commission, how many shares could he buy if he used *only* his own money and did not use margin?
    b. If Brian paid a $100 commission, how many shares could he buy if he used his $4,000 and borrowed $4,000 on margin to buy these stocks?
    c. Assuming Brian did use margin, paid a $250 total commission to buy and sell his stocks, and sold his stocks for $53 a share, how much profit did he make on this investment?

11. *Selling Short.* After researching a software company's common stocks, Sarah Jackson is convinced the stocks are overpriced. She contacts her account executive and arranges to sell short 200 shares. At the time of the sale, a share of common stocks had a value of $35. Six months later, the stocks were selling for $23 a share, and Sarah instructs her broker to cover her short transaction. Total commissions to buy and sell the stocks were $120. What is her profit for this short transaction? (Obj. 5)

FINANCIAL PLANNING ACTIVITIES

1. *Surveying Investors.* Survey investors who own stocks. Then explain, in a short paragraph, their reasons for owning stocks. (Obj. 1)

2. *Determining the Effect of a Stock Split on a Stock's Market Value.* Use the *Reader's Guide to Periodical Literature*, the Internet, and/or issues of *The Financial Post* to locate a stock that has experienced a 2-for-1 split. (Obj. 1)

   a. What is the name of the corporation that had the 2-for-1 stock split?

   b. When did the stock split?

   c. What was the price the day before the stock split?

   d. What was the price the day after the stock split?

   e. What was the price a month after the stock split?

   f. At the end of one month, do you think the stock split was good for an individual investor?

3. *Interviewing an Account Executive.* Interview an account executive about the cumulative feature, participation feature, and conversion feature of a preferred stock. What do these features mean to preferred shareholders? (Obj. 2)

4. *Using Research Information.* Divide a sheet of paper into three columns. In the first column, list sources of information you can use to evaluate stock investments. In the second column, state where you would find each of these sources. In the third column, describe the types of information each source would provide. (Obj. 3)

5. *Using Stock Advisory Services.* Pick a stock that interests you and research the company at the library by examining the information contained in reports published by Moody's, Standard & Poor's, or Zacks, or business periodicals, such

as *Canadian Business, IE:Money, Money,* or *Business Week.* Then write a one- or two-page summary of your findings. On the basis of your research, would you still want to invest in these stocks? Why, or why not? (Obj. 3)

6. *Using the Internet.* Choose a stock that you think would be a good investment. Then research the stock using the Internet.

   a. On the basis of the information contained on the corporation's Web site, would you still want to invest in the stock? Explain your answer.

   b. What other investment information would you need to evaluate the stock? Where would you obtain this information?

7. *Conducting Library Research.* Conduct library research on the fundamental theory, the technical theory, and the efficient market theory described in this chapter. How do these theories explain the movements of a stock traded on the TSE or over-the-counter market? (Obj. 3)

8. *Exploring Career Opportunities.* Prepare a list of questions you could use to interview an account executive about career opportunities in the field of finance. (Obj. 4)

9. *Using Long-Term Investment Techniques.* Interview people who have used the long-term investment techniques of buy and hold, dollar cost averaging, direct investment plan, or dividend reinvestment plan. Describe your findings. (Obj. 5)

10. *Analyzing Short-Term Investments.* Prepare a chart that describes the similarities and differences among buying stocks on margin, selling short, and trading in options. (Obj. 5)

LIFE SITUATION CASE

Research Information Available from Zacks and Standard & Poor's

This chapter stressed the importance of evaluating potential investments. Now, it's your turn to try your skill at evaluating a potential investment in BCE. Assume you could invest $10,000 in the common stocks of this company. To help you evaluate this potential investment, carefully examine Exhibits 11–8 and 11–9, which reproduce the research reports on BCE from Zacks and Globeinvestor GOLD's, respectively.

Questions

1. On the basis of the research provided by Zacks and Globeinvestor GOLD's, would you buy BCE stock? Justify your answer.

2. What other investment information would you need to evaluate BCE common stocks? Where would you obtain this information?

3. On Friday, June 7, 2002, BCE common stocks were selling for $18.51 a share. Using a newspaper, determine the current price for a share of BCE common stocks. On the basis of this information, would your BCE investment have been profitable if you had purchased the common stocks for $18.51 a share? (Hint: BCE stock is listed on the NYSE.)

4. Assuming you purchased BCE stock on June 7, 2002, and on the basis of your answer to question 3, would you want to hold or sell your BCE stock? Explain your answer.

LEARNING OBJECTIVES

1 Describe the characteristics of corporate bonds.

2 Discuss why corporations issue bonds.

3 Explain why investors purchase corporate bonds.

4 Discuss why federal, provincial, and municipal governments issue bonds and why investors purchase government bonds.

5 Evaluate bonds when making an investment.

Visit the Web site

See the Pre-Test under Chapter 12 on the online learning centre at www.mcgrawhill.ca/ college/kapoor.

Opportunity costs! Bethan Jackson, the woman in the opening case, took a chance when she purchased 12 corporate bonds issued by a utility company. Her investment, which cost more than $12,000, could decrease in value. But because she took the time to evaluate the investment using reliable sources, she could be reasonably certain she would receive interest payments each year and eventual repayment when this bond issue reaches maturity in 2005.

The company that issued the bond also took advantage of the concept of opportunity costs when it sold bonds. It agreed to pay bondholders 7 percent interest until the bonds mature in 2005. It also agreed to repay Jackson's original investment when the bonds mature. In return, the company obtained the money it needed to provide telecommunications services to its customers, provide more jobs, and ultimately earn larger profits.

We begin this chapter by describing the basic characteristics of corporate bonds that define the relationship between investors, like Bethan Jackson, and corporations that sell bonds to obtain financing.

Characteristics of Corporate Bonds

Objective 1

Describe the characteristics of corporate bonds.

corporate bond A corporation's written pledge to repay a specified amount of money with interest.

face value The dollar amount the bondholder will receive at the bond's maturity.

maturity date For a corporate bond, the date on which the corporation is to repay the borrowed money.

A **corporate bond** is a corporation's written pledge to repay a specified amount of money with interest. Exhibit 12–1 shows a typical corporate bond. Note that it states the dollar amount of the bond, the interest rate, and the maturity date. The **face value** is the dollar amount the bondholder will receive at the bond's maturity. The usual face value of a corporate bond is $1,000, but the face value of some corporate bonds may be as high as $50,000. The total face value of all the bonds in an issue usually runs into millions of dollars (see Exhibit 12–2). Between the time of purchase and the maturity date, the corporation pays interest to the bondholder, usually every six months, at the stated interest rate (refered to as the coupon rate of the bond). For example, assume you purchase the bond shown in Exhibit 12–1, and the coupon rate for this bond is 8.5 percent. Using the following formula, you can calculate the annual interest amount for this bond:

$$
\begin{aligned}
\text{Dollar amount of annual interest} &= \text{Face value} \times \text{Interest rate} \\
&= \$1,000 \times 8.5 \text{ percent} \\
&= \$1,000 \times 0.085 \\
&= \$85
\end{aligned}
$$

In this situation, you receive interest of $85 a year from the corporation. The interest is paid semi-annually, or every six months, in $42.50 ($85 ÷ 2 = $42.50) installments until the bond matures.

The **maturity date** of a corporate bond is the date on which the corporation is to repay the borrowed money. At the maturity date, the bondholder returns the bond to the corporation and

Exhibit 12–1

A Typical
Corporate Bond

receives cash equal to the bond's face value. Maturity dates for bonds generally range from 1 to 30 years after the date of issue. Maturities for corporate bonds may also be classified as short term (under 5 years), intermediate term (5 to 15 years), and long term (over 15 years).

The actual legal conditions for a corporate bond are described in a bond indenture. A **bond indenture** is a legal document that details all of the conditions relating to a bond issue. Often containing over 100 pages of complicated legal wording, the bond indenture remains in effect until the bonds reach maturity or are redeemed by the corporation.

bond indenture A legal document that details all the conditions relating to a bond issue.

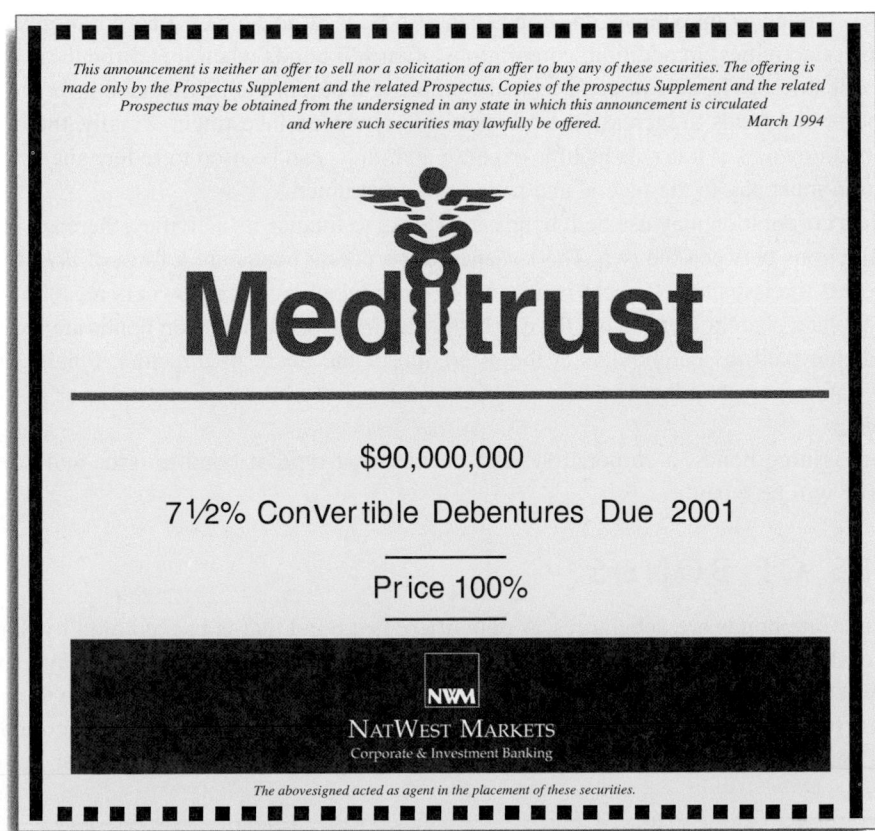

Exhibit 12–2

Advertisement for a 7 1/2-Percent Convertible Debenture Issued by Meditrust (Meditrust was renamed La Quintain 2001)

trustee A financially independent firm that acts as the bondholders' representative.

Since corporate bond indentures are very difficult for the average person to read and understand, a corporation issuing bonds appoints a trustee. The **trustee** is a financially independent firm that acts as the bondholders' representative. Usually, the trustee is a bank or some other financial institution. The corporation must report to the trustee periodically regarding its ability to make interest payments and eventually redeem the bonds. In turn, the trustee transmits this information to the bondholders along with its own evaluation of the corporation's ability to pay. If the corporation fails to live up to all the provisions in the indenture agreement, the trustee may bring legal action to protect the bondholders' interests. Certain bondholders are paid before others depending upon the class or type of bond, they are always paid after Revenue Canada and the employee payroll.

CONCEPT CHECK 12–1

1. If you needed information about a bond issue, would you go to the library or use the Internet?
2. What is the usual face value for a corporate bond?
3. What is the annual interest amount for a $1,000 bond issued by Power Corporation of Canada that pays $6\frac{1}{2}$ percent interest?
4. In your own words, define *maturity date* and *bond indenture*.
5. How does a trustee evaluate the provisions contained in a bond indenture?

Why Corporations Sell Corporate Bonds

Objective 2

Discuss why corporations issue bonds.

Let's begin this section with some basics of why corporations sell bonds. Corporations, such as Meditrust (see Exhibit 12–2), borrow when they don't have enough money to pay for major purchases—much as individuals do. Bonds can also be used to finance a corporation's ongoing business activities. In addition, corporations often sell bonds when it is difficult or impossible to sell stocks. The sale of bonds can also improve a corporation's financial leverage—the use of borrowed funds to increase the corporation's return on investment. Finally, the interest paid to bond owners is a tax-deductible expense and, thus, can be used to reduce the taxes the corporation must pay to the federal and provincial governments.

While a corporation may use both bonds and stocks to finance its activities, there are important distinctions between the two. The issuance of corporate bonds are a form of *debt financing*, whereas the issuance of stocks is a form of *equity financing*. Bond owners must be repaid at a future date; shareholders do not have to be repaid. Interest payments on bonds are required; dividends are paid to shareholders at the discretion of the board of directors. Finally, in the event of bankruptcy, bondholders have a claim to the assets of the corporation prior to that of shareholders.

Before issuing bonds, a corporation must decide what type of bond to issue and how the bond issue will be repaid.

TYPES OF BONDS

debenture A bond that is backed only by the reputation of the issuing corporation.

Most corporate bonds are debentures. A **debenture** is a bond that is backed only by the reputation of the issuing corporation. If the corporation fails to make either interest payments or repayment at maturity, debenture bondholders become general creditors, much like the firm's suppliers. In the event of corporate bankruptcy, general creditors, including debenture bondholders, can claim any asset not specifically used as collateral for a loan or other financial obligations.

To make a bond issue more appealing to conservative investors, a corporation may issue a mortgage bond. A **mortgage bond** (sometimes referred to as a *secured bond*) is a corporate bond secured by various assets of the issuing firm. A first mortgage bond may be backed by a lien on a specific asset, usually real estate. A corporation can also issue bonds that are backed by stocks and other bonds that it owns and, in some cases, even its operating equipment. A general mortgage bond is secured by all the fixed assets of the firm that are not pledged as collateral for other financial obligations. A secured bond is safer than a debenture because corporate assets or collateral may be sold to repay the bondholders if the corporation defaults on interest or repayment. Because of this added security, interest rates on mortgage bonds are usually lower than interest rates on debentures.

A third type of bond a corporation may issue is called a *subordinated* debenture. A **subordinated debenture** is an unsecured bond that gives bondholders a claim secondary to that of other designated bondholders with respect to interest payments, repayment, and assets. Investors who purchase subordinated debentures usually enjoy higher interest rates than other bondholders because of the increased risk associated with this type of bond.

> **mortgage bond** A corporate bond secured by various assets of the issuing firm.

> **subordinated debenture** An unsecured bond that gives bondholders a claim secondary to that of other designated bondholders with respect to both interest payments and assets.

CONVERTIBLE BONDS

A special type of bond a corporation may issue is a convertible bond. A **convertible bond** can be exchanged, at the owner's option, for a specified number of shares of the corporation's common stocks. This conversion feature allows investors to enjoy the lower risk of a corporate bond but also take advantage of the speculative nature of common stocks. For example, Noranda's $1,000 bond issue with a 2007 maturity date is convertible. Each bond can be converted to 28.9 shares of the company's common stocks. This means you could convert the bond to common stocks whenever the price of the company's common stocks is $34.60 ($1,000 ÷ 28.9 = $34.60) or higher.

In reality, there is no guarantee that Noranda bondholders will convert to common stocks even if the market value of the common stocks does increase to $34.60 or higher. The reason for choosing not to exercise the conversion feature in this example is quite simple. As the market value of the common stocks increases, the market value of the convertible bond also increases. By not converting to common stocks, bondholders enjoy the added safety of the bond and interest income in addition to the increased market value of the bond caused by the price movement of the common stocks.

The corporation gains three advantages by issuing convertible bonds. First, the interest rate on a convertible bond is often 1 to 2 percent lower than that on traditional bonds. Second, the conversion feature attracts investors who are interested in the possible gain that conversion to common stocks may provide. Third, if the bondholder converts to common stocks, the corporation no longer has to redeem the bond at maturity.

Convertible bonds, like all potential investments, must be carefully evaluated. Remember, not all convertible bonds are quality investments.

> **convertible bond** A bond that can be exchanged, at the owner's option, for a specified number of shares of the corporation's common stocks.

PROVISIONS FOR REPAYMENT

Today, most corporate bonds are callable. A **call feature** allows the corporation to call in or buy outstanding bonds from current bondholders before the maturity date. In the 1990s, investors saw a large number of bonds called because corporations could replace high-interest bond issues with new bond issues that have lower interest rates. The money needed to call a bond may come from the firm's profits, the sale of additional stocks, or the sale of a new bond issue that has a lower interest rate.

In most cases, corporations issuing callable bonds agree not to call them for the first 5 to 10 years after the bonds have been issued. When a call feature is used, the corporation may

> **call feature** A feature that allows the corporation to call in or buy outstanding bonds from current bondholders before the maturity date.

have to pay the bondholders a *premium*, an additional amount above the face value of the bond. The amount of the premium is specified in the bond indenture; a $10 to $50 premium over the bond's face value is common.

sinking fund A fund to which annual or semi-annual deposits are made for the purpose of redeeming a bond issue.

A corporation may use one of two methods to ensure that it has sufficient funds available to redeem a bond issue. First, the corporation may establish a sinking fund. A **sinking fund** is a fund to which annual or semi-annual deposits are made for the purpose of redeeming a bond issue. To retire a $100-million bond issue that matures in 2017, a Canadian corporation agreed to make annual sinking fund payments of $5 million on April 15 of each year beginning in 1998 and continuing through 2016. Note that the corporation will have made sinking fund payments totalling $90 million ($5 million × 18 years = $90 million) over the 18-year period. From a financial management standpoint, each annual sinking fund payment of $5 million can be invested and is an example of the time value of money (increases in an amount of money as a result of interest earned), a concept stressed throughout this text. At maturity, the $90 million contributed by the corporation *plus* the investment earnings will enable the corporation to pay off this $100 million bond issue.

A sinking fund provision in the bond indenture is generally advantageous to bondholders. Such a provision forces the corporation to make arrangements for bond repayment before the maturity date. If the terms of the provision are not met, the trustee or bondholders may take legal action against the company.

serial bonds Bonds of a single issue that mature on different dates.

Second, a corporation may issue serial bonds. **Serial bonds** are bonds of a single issue that mature on different dates. For example, Seaside Productions used a 20-year, $100 million bond issue to finance its expansion. None of the bonds mature during the first 10 years. Thereafter, 10 percent of the bonds mature each year until all the bonds are retired at the end of the 20-year period.

Detailed information about provisions for repayment, along with other vital information (including maturity date, interest rate, bond rating, call provisions, trustee, and details about collateral), is available from the Dominion Bond Rating Service (DBRS), the Canadian Bond Rating Service (CBRS), which was aquired by Standard and Poor's Corporation, Moody's Investors Service, and other financial service companies. Take a look at the information provided by the CBRS for the Canadian Tire bond rating illustrated in the Financial Planning for Life's Situations box on pages 359, 360.

CONCEPT CHECK 12-2

1. Why do corporations sell bonds?
2. What are the differences between a debenture, a mortgage bond, and a subordinated debenture?
3. Why would an investor purchase a Noranda convertible bond?
4. Describe three reasons a corporation would sell convertible bonds.
5. Explain the methods corporations can use to repay a bond issue.

STANDARD & POOR'S CANADIAN RATINGS

CANADIAN TIRE CORP. LTD.

ISSUER CREDIT RATING
Canadian Tire Corp. Ltd.
Corporate Credit Rating   BBB+/Stable/—

AFFIRMED RATINGS
Canadian Tire Corp. LTd.
Sr unsecd debt
Local currency   BBB+

Business Profile:
Average

Financial Policy:
Moderate

Debt Maturities:
2002 C$0 mil.
2003 C$200 mil.
2004 C$235 mil.
2005 C$0 mil.
2006+ C$875 mil.

Bank Lines:
Canadian Tire Corp. Ltd. has C$190 million in unsecured operating lines. Committed bank lines of C$630 million back the company's commercial paper program, Excluding Canadian Tire Receivables Trust, committed bank lines total C$389 million.

Corporate credit rating history:
Mar 21, 2001   BBB+

RATIONALE

The ratings reflect Canadian Tire Corp. Ltd.'s leading position in Canadian hard-goods retailing, a credit card operation that is a significant contributor to operating income, resilient earnings in the context of a very difficult economic and competitive environment, and improving credit protection measures and substantial liquidity in light of recent asset monetizations.

These factors are offset by profitability that remains quite low for the rating category, leverage that still reflects the company's heavy capital program, and an ambitious supply-chain program with an undefined payback.

OUTLOOK

Standard & Poor's expects Canadian Tire's profitability measures will improve and the company's leverage will remain stable. Risks to Canadian Tire include increasing competitive pressures in the home improvement channel, particularly in central Canada.

BUSINESS DESCRIPTION

Canadian Tire is one of Canada's largest retailers, specializing in automotive, sports and leisure, and housewares categories. The company operates 451 stores through 432 associate dealers, with 285 stores in Ontario and Quebec. Canadian Tire also operates 30 specialty Partsource stores and an agent-operated gas bar with 203 outlets. The company acquired Mark's Work Wearhouse Ltd., a 321-store chain of casual-and work-apparel stores, in February 2002. Canadian Tire also has a sizeable credit card operation, Canadian Tire Financial Services. Canadian Tire's three retail product segments consist of auto parts and accessories, sports and leisure, and home products. CustomerLink, a multi-layer supply-chain management program involving the development of crossdocking and flow through capability, is well under way.

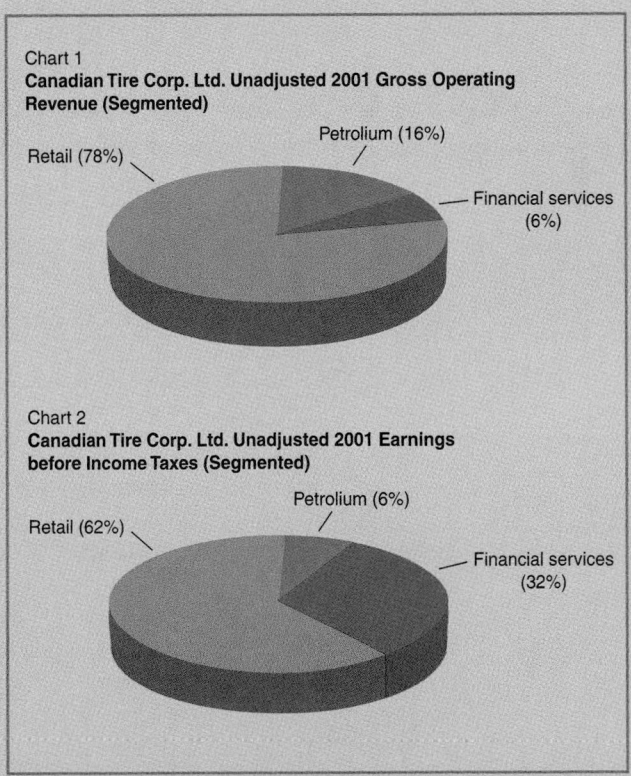

Chart 1
Canadian Tire Corp. Ltd. Unadjusted 2001 Gross Operating Revenue (Segmented)

Retail (78%)
Petrolium (16%)
Financial services (6%)

Chart 2
Canadian Tire Corp. Ltd. Unadjusted 2001 Earnings before Income Taxes (Segmented)

Retail (62%)
Petrolium (6%)
Financial services (32%)

(continued)

CANADIAN TIRE CORP. LT. FINANCIAL STATISTICS*					
	—Year ended Dec 31—				
(Mil. C$)	2001	2000	1999	1998	1997
Revenues	5,313.4	5,154.5	4,670.3	4,300.1	4,010.7
Net income from cont. oper.	170.7	142.9	140.3	162.3	144.1
Funds from operations (FFO)	391.8	370.5	342.2	275.7	250.4
Capital expenditures	358.2	382.2	377.3	303.1	253.5
Total debt	1351.1	1134.8	1470.4	1011.2	737.0
Shareholders' equity	1903.7	1459.4	1344.8	1261.6	1298.6
Oper. income/sales (%)	9.9	9.3	9.2	9.6	8.6
EBIT interest coverage (x)	3.8	3.2	3.2	4.1	4.1
EBITDA interest coverage (x)	5.5	4.6	4.5	5.5	5.6
FFO/total debt (%)	29.0	32.7	23.3	27.3	34.0
Return on capital (%)	12.6	12.6	12.6	15.0	11.6
Total debt/EBITDA (x)	2.4	2.2	3.0	2.2	1.8
Total debt/capital (%)	42.3	44.7	53.3	45.5	37.1

*Adjusted by capitalizing operating leases and captive finance. EBITDA—Earnings before interest, taxes, depreciation, and amortization.

SOURCE: Standard & Poor's

Why Investors Purchase Corporate Bonds

Objective 3

Explain why investors purchase corporate bonds.

In Chapters 10 and 11, we compared the historical returns provided by stocks and bonds. As you can see in Exhibit 11–2, stocks have had higher returns than most bonds and treasury bills. With this fact in mind, you may be wondering why you should consider bonds as an investment alternative. Why not just choose stocks because they provide the highest possible return of the three investment alternatives? The fact is that many corporate and government bonds are safer investments and are often considered a "safe harbour" in troubled economic times. And some investors use corporate and government bonds to diversify their investment portfolios. Basically, investors purchase corporate bonds for three reasons: (1) interest income, (2) possible increase in value, and (3) repayment at maturity.

INTEREST INCOME

As mentioned earlier in this chapter, bondholders normally receive interest payments every six months. As we saw earlier, the dollar amount of interest is determined by multiplying the interest rate by the face value of the bond. In fact, because interest income is so important to bond investors, let's review this calculation. If Canadian Tire issues a 7 1/2-percent bond with a face value of $1,000, the investor will receive $75 ($1,000 × 7.5% = $75) a year, paid in installments of $37.50 at the end of each six-month period.

The method used to pay bondholders their interest depends on whether they own registered bonds, registered coupon bonds, bearer bonds, or zero-coupon bonds. A **registered bond** is registered in the owner's name by the issuing company. Interest cheques for registered bonds are mailed directly to the bondholder of record. A variation of a registered bond is the registered coupon bond. A **registered coupon bond** is registered for principal only, not for interest. To collect interest payments on a registered coupon bond, the owner must present one of the detachable coupons to the issuing corporation or the paying agent.

A third type of bond is a **bearer bond**, which is not registered in the investor's name. As with a registered coupon bond, the owner of a bearer bond must detach a coupon and present it to the issuing corporation or the paying agent to collect interest payments. *Be warned:* If you own a bearer bond, you can be out of luck if it is lost or stolen. Anyone—the rightful owner or a thief—can collect interest payments and the face value at maturity if he or she has physical possession of the bearer bond or its detachable coupons. While some bearer bonds are still in circulation, corporations no longer issue them.

A zero-coupon bond is sold at a price far below its face value, makes no annual or semi-annual interest payments, and is redeemed for its face value at maturity. With a zero-coupon bond, the buyer receives a return based on the bond's increased market value as its maturity date approaches. For example, assume you purchased an Imasco Ltd. zero-coupon bond for $350 in 1995 and Imasco Ltd. will pay you $1,000 when the bond matures in 2012. For holding the bond for 18 years, you will receive interest of $650 ($1,000 face value – $350 purchase price = $650 interest) at maturity.

Before investing in **zero-coupon bonds**, you should consider at least two factors. First, even though all of the interest on these bonds is paid at maturity, the government requires you to report interest each year—that is, as you earn it, not when you actually receive it. Second, zero-coupon bonds are more volatile than other types of bonds. When evaluating such bonds, as in evaluating other types of bonds, the most important criterion is the quality of the issuer. It pays to be careful.

registered bond A bond that is registered in the owner's name by the issuing company.

registered coupon bond A bond that is registered for principal only, and not for interest.

bearer bond A bond that is not registered in the investor's name.

DOLLAR APPRECIATION OF BOND VALUE

Most beginning investors think that a $1,000 bond is always worth $1,000. In reality, the price of a corporate bond may fluctuate until the maturity date. Changes in overall interest rates in the economy are the primary cause of most bond price fluctuations. Changing bond prices that result from changes in overall interest rates in the economy are an example of interest rate risk, discussed in Chapter 10. In fact, there is an inverse relationship between a bond's market value and overall interest rates in the economy. When Canadian Tire issued the bond mentioned earlier, the 7 1/2 percent interest rate was competitive with the interest rates offered by other corporations issuing bonds at that time. If overall interest rates fall, the Canadian Tire bond will go up in market value due to its higher, 7 1/2 percent, interest rate. On the other hand, if overall interest rates rise, the market value of the Canadian Tire bond will fall due to its lower, 7 1/2 percent, interest rate.

When a bond is selling for less than its face value, it is said to be selling at a *discount*. When a bond is selling for more than its face value, it is said to be selling at a premium. Generally, investors consult *The Financial Post, Report on Business*, the Internet, or a newspaper to determine the price of a bond. Information on how to read bond quotations is provided later in this chapter.

It is also possible to approximate a bond's market value using the following formula:

zero-coupon bond A bond that is sold at a price far below its face value, makes no annual or semi-annual interest payments, and is redeemed for its face value at maturity.

Visit the Web site
See Personal Financial Planning worksheets under Chapter 12 on the online learning centre at www.mcgrawhill.ca/college/kapoor.

$$\text{Approximate market value} = \frac{\text{Dollar amount of annual interest}}{\text{Comparable interest rate}}$$

For example, assume you purchase a corporate bond that pays $4\frac{7}{8}$ percent interest based on a face value of $1,000. Also, assume that new corporate bond issues of comparable quality are currently paying 7 percent. The approximate market value is $696, as follows:

$$\text{Dollar amount of annual interest} = \$1,000 \times 4\frac{7}{8} \text{ percent}$$
$$= \$1,000 \times 4.875 \text{ percent}$$
$$= \$48.75$$

$$\text{Approximate market value} = \frac{\text{Dollar amount of annual interest}}{\text{Comparable interest rate}} = \frac{\$48.75}{7\%}$$
$$= \$696$$

The market value of a bond may also be affected by the financial condition of the company or government unit issuing the bond, the factors of supply and demand, an upturn or downturn in the economy, and the proximity of the bond's maturity date.

BOND REPAYMENT AT MATURITY

Corporate bonds are repaid at maturity. After you purchase a bond, you have two options: You may keep the bond until maturity and then redeem it, or you may sell the bond at any time to another investor. In either case, the value of your bond is closely tied to the corporation's ability to repay its bond indebtedness. For example, the telecommunication firm GT Group Telecom filed for reorganization under the provisions of the Bankruptcy Act. As a result, the bonds issued by GT Group Telecom immediately dropped in value due to questions concerning the prospects for bond repayment at maturity. On the other hand, if a corporation establishes a reputation as an aggressive firm with excellent and innovative products, experienced and capable managers, and increasing sales and profits, the value of your bond will increase. Simply put: Other investors will pay more money to get a quality bond that has excellent prospects of repayment at maturity.

A TYPICAL BOND TRANSACTION

Assume that on October 8, 1988, you purchased an 8.375 percent corporate bond issued by BCTel (BCTel merged with Telus in 1999). Your cost for the bond was $680 plus a $10 commission charge, for a total investment of $690. Also, assume that you held the bond until October 8, 1999, when you sold it at its current market value of $1,030. Exhibit 12–3 shows the return on your investment.

Exhibit 12–3

Sample Corporate Bond Transaction

Assumptions			
Interest, 8.375 percent; maturity date, 2016; purchased October 8, 1988; sold October 8, 1999			
Costs when purchased		**Return when sold**	
1 bond @ $680	$680	1 bond @ $1,030	$1,030
Plus commission	+ 10	Minus commission	– 10
Total investment	$690	Dollar return	$1,020
Transaction summary			
Dollar return	$1,020		
Minus total investment	– 690		
Profit from bond sale	$ 330		
Plus interest ($83.75 for 11 years)	+ 921		
Total return on the transaction	$1,251		

Financial Planning for Life's Situations

ARE BOND FUNDS RIGHT FOR YOU?

Simply put, bond funds are an indirect way of owning bonds, debt instruments, and IOUs issued by the Canadian treasury, corporations, or province, city, and local school districts. Many financial experts recommend bond funds for small investors because these investments offer diversification and professional management. Diversification spells safety because an occasional loss incurred with one bond issue is usually offset by gains from other bond issues in the fund. Also, professional managers should be able to do a better job of picking bonds than individual investors. But before investing, consider two factors. First, even the best managers make mistakes. Second, it may cost more to purchase bond funds than individual bonds. As with most investments, the key to making money with funds is evaluation.

EVALUATING BOND FUNDS

Marie Hamel, a working mother with one child, received $44,000 following the death of her grandmother. After some careful planning, she decided to invest $34,000 in two high-quality corporate bond funds. She used the remaining $10,000 to pay off some credit card debts and establish an emergency fund. During the next two years, she earned more than 11 percent on her bond investments each year—not bad during a period when GICs were paying between 1 and 4 percent.

Marie's 11 percent return wasn't just luck. She began by establishing an investment goal: Find a safe investment with minimal risk. After establishing her goal, she talked with an account executive at Yorkton Securities and asked for five suggestions that would enable her to attain her goal. Of the five original suggestions, three were conservative bond funds.

Next, Marie took a crucial step that many investors don't: She decided to do her own research and not just rely on the account executive's suggestions. She contacted the firms that managed each of the three bond funds and asked them to mail her a prospectus and an annual report. After receiving the information, she was able to (1) determine each fund's investment objective, (2) identify the investments each fund contained, and (3) calculate the approximate fees and expenses charged by each fund.

Then, she made a trip to the library, where she analyzed the performance of each of the three bond funds in the special mutual fund editions of Maclean's and Canadian Business. Each publication ranked the three bond funds according to the total return for the previous 12 months, three years, and five years. Although past performance is no guarantee of future performance, it may be one of the best predictors available. On the basis of the account executive's suggestions and her own research, she chose the "top" two bond funds.

Marie admits that she spent almost 30 hours researching her investments but believes the time was well spent. When you consider the amount of money she made on her bond fund investments during the first two years—more than $7,400—she made almost $250 an hour.

After paying commissions for buying and selling your BCTel bond, you experienced a capital gain of $330 because the market value of the bond increased from $680 to $1,030. The increase in the value of the bond resulted because overall interest rates in the economy declined during the 11-year period in which you owned the bond. Also, BCTel established a reputation for efficiency and productivity during this period. Increased efficiency and productivity help ensure that BCTel will be able to repay bondholders when the bond reaches maturity in 2016.

You also made money on your BCTel bond because of interest payments. For each of the 11 years you owned the bond, BCTel paid you $83.75 ($1,000 × 8.375% = $83.75) interest. Thus, you received interest payments totalling $921. In this example, you made a total shareholder return (TSR) of $1,251, as follows:

$$\text{TSR} = \text{Current return} + \text{Capital gain}$$
$$= \$921 + \$330$$
$$= \$1,251$$

363

Before investing in bonds, you should remember that the price of a corporate bond can decrease and that interest payments and eventual repayment may be a problem for a corporation that encounters financial difficulties or enters bankruptcy. In addition to purchasing individual bonds, some investors prefer to purchase bond funds. To help you decide whether you should purchase individual bonds or bond funds, read the Financial Planning for Life's Situations box on the previous page.

DID YOU KNOW ?

Typically, a bond trades over-the-counter. In July 2002, the TSX Group (TSX), through its trading services division, TSX Markets, purchased a 40-percent equity interest in CanDeal (http://www.candeal.ca/). Candeal is Canada's electronic trading system for institutional debt market professionals.

THE MECHANICS OF A BOND TRANSACTION

Most bonds are sold through full-service brokerage firms, discount brokerage firms, or the Internet. If you use a brokerage firm, your account executive should provide both information and advice about bond investments. Many experts urge you to remember one basic rule: It is always *your* money, and *you* should be the one who makes the final decision to buy or sell a bond. Your account executive's role is to make suggestions and provide information that may enable you to make a more informed decision. As with stock investments, the chief advantage of using a discount brokerage firm or trading online is lower commissions, but you must do your own research and make the decision to buy or sell a bond issue. As you will see later in this chapter, many sources of information can be used to evaluate bond investments.

The bond market is referred to as an "over-the-counter" (OTC) exchange. Unlike stock markets, there is no centralized floor. Rather, the market is decentralized and transactions are by phone or computer among buyers and sellers who might be continents apart or just next door to one another. Trading volumes are enormous and may average more than 20 times the volume of the stock markets.

Buyers and sellers trade bonds through bond or investment dealers, who are paid through a fee that is already represented in the price that buyers pay. There are about 190 dealers and a smaller number of banks and trust companies involved in this market, and all of the dealers are linked together by five inter-dealer bond brokers that are regulated by the Investment Dealers Association (IDA).

CONCEPT CHECK 12–3

1. Describe the three reasons investors purchase bonds.
2. What are the differences among a registered bond, a registered coupon bond, a bearer bond, and a zero-coupon bond?
3. In what ways can interest rates in the economy affect the price of a corporate bond?
4. Why is the value of a bond closely tied to the issuing corporation's ability to repay its bond indebtedness?
5. How are corporate bonds bought and sold?

Government Bonds and Debt Securities

In addition to corporations, the Canadian government and provincial and local governments issue bonds to obtain financing. In this section, we discuss bonds issued by these three levels of government and look at why investors purchase these bonds.

The federal government sells bonds and securities to finance both the national debt and the government's ongoing activities. The main reason investors choose Canadian government securities is that most investors consider them risk free. In fact, some financial planners refer to them as the ultimate safe investment because their quality is considered to be higher than that of any other investment. Because they are backed by the full faith and credit of the Canadian government and carry a decreased risk of default, they offer lower interest rates than corporate bonds.

Objective 4

Discuss why federal, provincial, and municipal governments issue bonds and why investors purchase government bonds.

TYPES OF BONDS

GOVERNMENT OF CANADA SECURITIES
The government of Canada issues three main types of securities in the form of marketable bonds, treasury bills, and Canada Savings Bonds. It is also the largest single issuer in the Canadian bond market, having direct marketable debt in the hundreds of billions of dollars.

MARKETABLE BONDS
These issues are referred to as marketable bonds because in addition to having a specific maturity date and interest rate, they are also transferable and, as a result, can be traded in the bond market. They are generally noncallable, which means that the government does not have the option of calling them in to be redeemed before maturity. As of 1991, there was also an issue of Government of Canada Real Return Bonds, which had their nominal return tied to the Consumer Price Index, a measure of inflation. With this type of bond, the maturity value is calculated by multiplying the original face value of the bond times the total inflation since the date of issue.

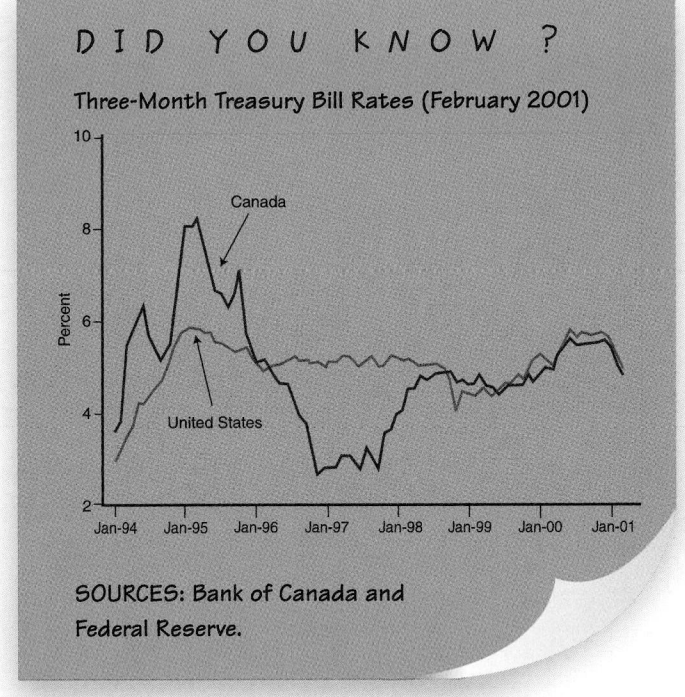

DID YOU KNOW ?

Three-Month Treasury Bill Rates (February 2001)

SOURCES: Bank of Canada and Federal Reserve.

TREASURY BILLS
A *treasury bill*, sometimes called a *T-bill*, is sold in a minimum unit of $1,000 with additional increments of $1,000 above the minimum. Treasury bills with terms to maturity of 91, 186, or 364 days are currently auctioned on a bi-weekly basis, generally on Tuesday for delivery on Thursday. See Exhibit 12–4 for an example of a treasury bill.

T-bills are discounted securities, and the actual purchase price you pay is less than the maturity value of the T-bill. Let's assume you purchased a 91-day T-bill with a purchase price of $990.13 and a face value of $1,000, this means that the discounted amount is $9.87 ($1,000 – $990.13). The convention in Canada is to quote T-bills in yield terms. In this example, you receive $9.87 on a $990.13 investment which produces an annualized rate of return equal to 4 per cent, computed as follows:

$$Y = [(F - P) / P] \times (365 / T)$$

where

Y = Current yield for a T-Bill
F = Face value of the T-Bill
P = Purchase price
T = Term

$Y = [(\$1,000 - \$990.13)/\$990.13] \times [365/91]$
$Y = [\$9.87 / \$990.13] \times 4$
$Y = .03987$ or approximately 4%

Exhibit 12–4

A Canadian
Treasury Bill

SOURCE: Bank of
Canada and Federal
Reserve

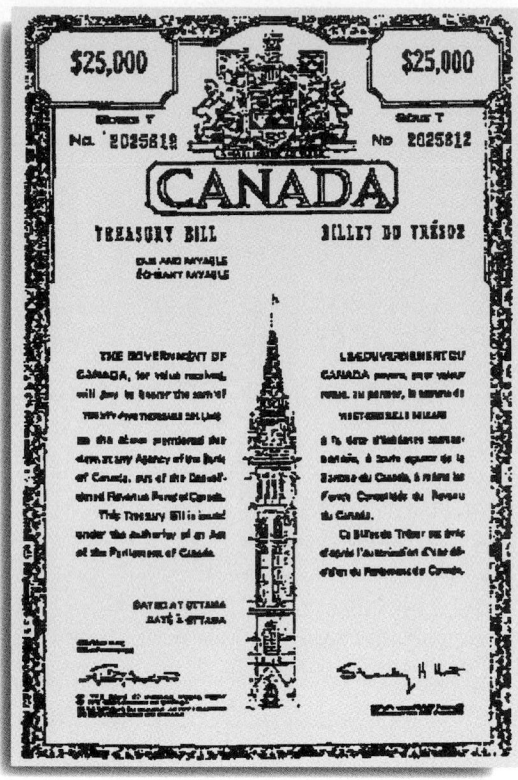

The price of the T-bill can be determined by rearranging the above equation and solving for (F-P)/P and then given F, solving for P.

CANADA SAVINGS BONDS (CSBs) These bonds first went on sale in the fall of 1946 and were developed from Victory bonds, which were issued between 1940 and 1944 to help Canada fight in World War II. Over the past half century or so, they have played an important role in the federal government's borrowing, though less so in recent times. The year 2002 marked the issue of Series 74. See Exhibit 12–5 for a sample CSB.

Since 1977, CSBs have been available as either a regular interest bond or a compound interest bond. The *regular interest bond* pays annual interest either by cheque or direct deposit to the holder's bank account on November 1 of each year. It is available in denominations of $300, $500, $1,000, $5,000, and $10,000, with a maximum of five each of the $300 and $500 bonds per registered owner. Interest is paid only on bonds held longer than three months from the date of issue. Should you choose to do so, you may also exchange your regular interest bond for a compound interest bond of the same series up to August 31 of the year following the issue.

The *compound interest bond* allows you to forfeit receipt of annual interest to allow the unpaid interest to compound annually and earn interest on the accumulated interest. This bond is available in

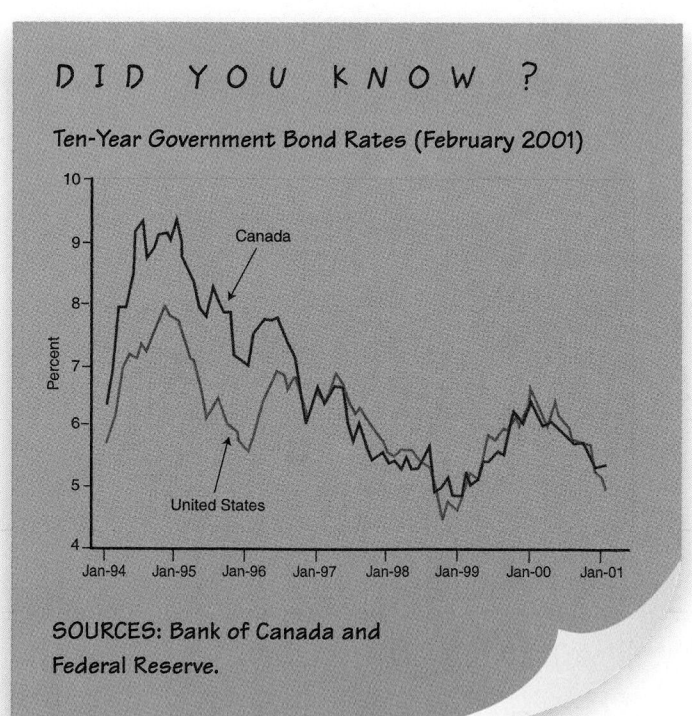

DID YOU KNOW?

Ten-Year Government Bond Rates (February 2001)

SOURCES: Bank of Canada and Federal Reserve.

Advice from a Pro

RELEASED FROM BONDAGE

Riddle me this: If a 7-Eleven is open 24 hours a day, seven days a week, 365 days a year, then *why* do the doors have locks? No answer?

Same question: If stocks have historically outperformed bonds, then why bother making bonds a part of your portfolio? Simple answer: *diversity.*

Buying bonds or other fixed-income investment diversifies a portfolio. By venturing outside the stock market, bond investors are purchasing securities that offer safety and stability. Corporate bonds, bank GICs, and Canadian treasury securities pay investors interest income. These interest payments can drastically boost your return, especially when the stock market sags. In addition to interest, the price of bonds itself fluctuates

with interest rates. When not held to "maturity," it is quite possible to make money investing in individual bonds.

Generally, you need serious cash to purchase a diversified portfolio of individual bonds, so those looking for fixed-income exposure might want to use bond mutual funds. These funds, which are not federally insured, are offered in a variety of risk profiles.

Thinking safety? In lieu of putting cash under your mattress, try a money market fund. Available through every major fund company, these investments function as really short-term bond funds and are perfect surrogates for the savings account.

denominations of $100, $300, $500, $1,000, $5,000, and $10,000, with a limit of five each of the $100, $300, and $500 bonds per registered owner. You may also exchange your compound interest bond for a regular interest bond of the same series at any time until maturity.

A consideration in buying this type of bond is that you must report compound interest as taxable income each year that you hold the bond, despite the fact that you will not actually receive those funds until you choose to redeem the bond. In planning your personal finance portfolio, this might be an important consideration if you anticipate investing a portion of your savings this way.

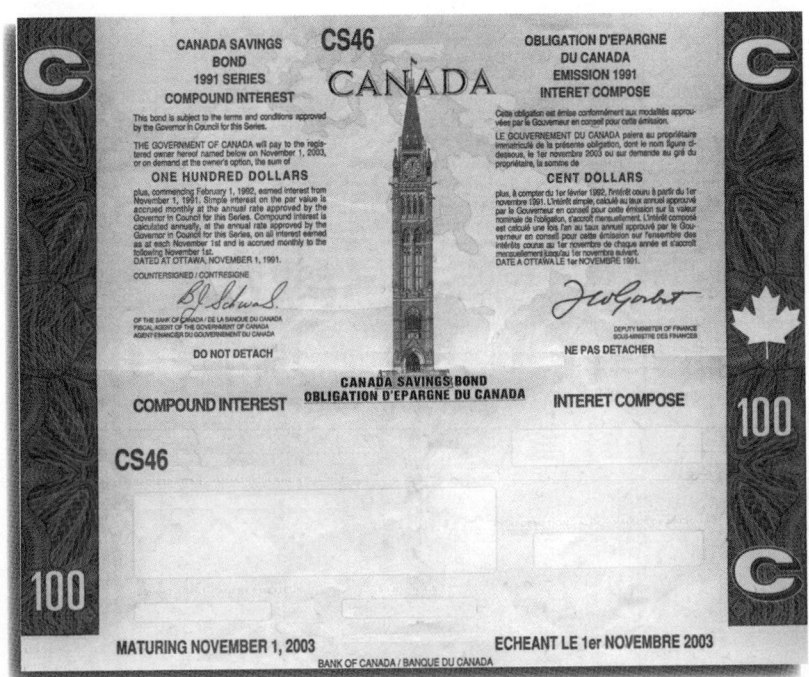

Exhibit 12–5

A Canada Savings Bond

SOURCE:
http://www.csb.gc.ca/eng/default.asp/lang=eng.

The convenience, safety, and liquidity of CSBs make them an attractive alternative to simple savings accounts. Additionally, you can also purchase these bonds as part of a payroll savings plan. This allows a type of "forced saving" that obeys the personal finance principle of "pay yourself first."

CANADA SAVINGS BONDS PAYROLL PROGRAM

For more than 55 years, the Payroll Savings Program has been Canada's easiest and safest way to save. The Payroll Savings Program allows you to save effortlessly through regular payroll deductions. The minimum you can deduct is $2 per weekly pay period (or $8 per monthly pay period). The Payroll Savings Program offers daily interest, competitive rates, one time sign-up, easy changes, RRSP option, easy redemptions, instant portability, and bond owner receipt. For more information, see Canada Savings Bonds Web site at www.csb.gc.ca.

PROVINCIAL GOVERNMENT SECURITIES AND GUARANTEES

Typically, a provincial bond or debenture issue is used to provide funds to the province for program spending and fund deficits, and all of the provinces have statutes covering how the raised funds are used. Virtually all provinces have bonds available in a wide range of denominations, with the most popular being $500, $1,000, $5,000, $10,000, and $25,000. The term will usually depend on the uses to which the proceeds from the bond sale will be put and the availability of investment funds.

MUNICIPAL BONDS/INSTALLMENT DEBENTURES

The market capital raising instrument most often used by municipalities is the installment debenture, or serial bond. With this type of bond issue, often called "munis," a part will mature every year for its term. As an example, a debenture issue of $100,000 would be arranged so that $10,000 becomes due each year for 10 years. In general, installment debentures are non-callable, such that the buyer of these bonds knows how long he or she can hold the investment.

OTHER TYPES OF BONDS

MORTGAGE BONDS This type of bond is an agreement that pledges land, buildings, or equipment as security for a loan and entitles the lender to take ownership of these assets if interest and principal payments are defaulted. This is fundamentally a loan of the same nature as a mortgage. A trustee, usually a trust company, manages the full loan and separates the total into convenient portions, usually $1,000 or multiples of $1,000.

FIRST MORTGAGE BONDS In general, these bonds are the most secure that a corporation can offer and are the debt that is considered foremost of all obligations a company may have. Often, this type of mortgage will apply against both current and future assets, a clause that is called the "after acquired" clause.

COLLATERAL TRUST BONDS These are secured bonds, but not by a pledge of real property as with a mortgage bond. Instead, these bonds are secured through securities, or collateral, and are usually issued by companies that do not own many fixed assets, but do own other securities. A typical example would be a holding company that issues a collateral trust bond secured by the securities of subsidiaries it may have.

DEBENTURES These issues are unsecured bonds. The issuing company promises to pay back the loan but does not offer any claim on assets or property to secure the loan to them.

CORPORATE NOTES This is an unsecured promise made by the issuing company, or borrower, to pay interest and principal at a specific date or dates.

DOMESTIC, FOREIGN, AND EUROBONDS Domestic bonds are issued in the country and currency of the issuer. Foreign bonds are, quite simply, bonds issued primarily in a currency and country other than the issuer's, allowing issuers access to huge sources of capital in other countries. Eurobonds differ from foreign bonds in that they are bonds issued on the international bond market in any currency. The international bond market is regulated by the International Securities Market Association (ISMA).

BONDS OR DEBENTURES CARRYING WARRANTS A warrant is an option to buy shares in the company from the issuer at a set price for a set period of time. This attachment is there to make a bond issue more attractive to buyers and to reward those who provide the business with long-term capital.

UNITS Units are packages of two or more corporate securities bundled by an investment dealer and sold at an overall price. In the past, the traditional bundle has usually included a bond or debenture bundled with a number of common shares.

REAL ESTATE BONDS These are bonds issued to finance real estate development and can vary in terms of return, maturity, and security.

STRIP BONDS This type of bond, also called a zero coupon bond, first appeared in Canada in 1982. It is the result of an investment dealer buying a block of existing high-quality bonds and then separating the individual interest coupons from the bonds. The coupons and bonds are then sold separately at significant discounts to their face values. You earn money by paying a discounted price and then redeeming them at the maturity date.

> **DID YOU KNOW ?**
>
> **CANADA MORTGAGE BONDS**
>
> The Canada Housing Trust recently began issuing Canada Mortgage Bonds. This initial issue totalled $2.2 billion dollars featuring a 5.527-percent coupon rate. This inaugural issue is the largest syndicated bond ever issued in a single turn in Canada. The five-year bond issue will mature on June 15, 2006, with interest payments being made semi-annually.
>
> SOURCE: http://www.cmhc-schl.gc.ca

CONCEPT CHECK 12–4

1. What are the maturities for different government securities?
2. How is the interest for Canada Savings Bonds calculated?
3. What risks are involved when investing in municipal bonds?

The Decision to Buy or Sell Bonds

Objective 5

Evaluate bonds
when making an
investment.

One basic principle we have stressed throughout this text is the need to evaluate any potential investment. Certainly, corporate *and* government bonds are no exception. Only after you have completed your evaluation should you purchase bonds. Of course, a decision to sell bonds also requires evaluation. In fact, evaluation may be even more critical for bond investments because there are fewer bonds to choose from. Although *The Financial Post* lists pages and pages of information on stocks, it provides less than a page for federal, provincial, and corporate bonds (see Exhibit 12–6). In bond quotations, prices are given as a percentage of the face value, which is typically $1,000. For example, BCTel (listed on the bottom of Exhibit 12–6) had a bid price of $132.86, which means a market price of $1,000 × 132.86% = $1,328.60. As this bond is selling at a premium, the yield on BCTel must be less than the fixed coupon interest rate that it offers. This can be confirmed by comparing the last column, "yield" (7.51%), with the second column, "coupon" (10.65%). Note that the opposite is true for bonds selling at a discount. These relationships are further explained under the heading Bond Yield Calculations on page 372. Finally, column three indicates that BCTel will mature on June 19, 2021. For the remainder of this section, we examine methods you can use to evaluate bond investments.

ANNUAL REPORTS

As pointed out earlier in this chapter, bondholders must be concerned about the financial health of the corporation or government unit that issues bonds. To understand how important financial information is when evaluating a bond issue, consider the following two questions:

- Will the bond be repaid at maturity?
- Will you receive interest payments until maturity?

While it may be difficult to answer these questions with 100 percent accuracy, the information contained in a firm's annual report is the logical starting point. Today, there are three ways to obtain a corporation's annual report. First, you can either write or telephone the corporation and request an annual report. (Hint: Many corporations have toll-free telephone numbers for your use.) Second, as mentioned in the next section, most corporations maintain a Web site that contains detailed information about their financial performance. Third, some financial publications provide a reader's service that allows you to use a toll-free telephone number or a postcard to obtain an annual report.

Regardless of how you obtain an annual report, you should look for signs of financial strength or weakness. Is the firm profitable? Are sales revenues increasing? Are the firm's long-term liabilities increasing? In fact, there are many questions you should ask before making a decision to buy a bond. To help you determine the right questions to ask when evaluating a bond issue, examine the Financial Planning Calculations feature on page 373. Also, you may want to examine the bond's rating and perform the calculations described on pp. 371–375 before investing your money.

THE INTERNET

Just as you can use the Internet to evaluate a stock investment, you can use much of the same financial information to evaluate a bond investment. By accessing a corporation's Web page and locating the topics "financial information," "annual report," or "investor relations," you can find many of the answers to the questions discussed in the last section. As an added bonus, a corporation may provide more than one year's annual report on its Web site, so you can make comparisons from one year to another.

When investing in bonds, you can use the Internet in three other ways. First, you can obtain price information on specific bond issues to track your investments. Especially, if you live in a small town or rural area without access to newspapers that provide bond coverage, the

BONDS

*Supplied by RBC Dominion Securities Inc.,
International from Reuters*

RBC DS Index	Index level	Total ret	Price ret	MTD tot.ret
Market	336.89	0.07	0.05	1.43
Short	287.97	0.02	0.00	1.08
Intermed	339.97	0.12	0.10	1.60
Long	413.73	0.07	0.05	1.82
Govts	335.36	0.05	0.03	1.46
Canadas	327.06	0.04	0.02	1.36
Provs	357.06	0.08	0.06	1.71
Munis	122.89	0.07	0.05	1.77
Corps	355.93	0.12	0.10	1.34

	Coupon	Mat. date	Bid $	Yld%
Canada	7.000	Sep 01/01	101.05	6.04
Canada	9.500	Oct 01/01	104.10	6.01
Canada	9.750	Dec 01/01	104.97	6.01
Canada	5.250	Dec 01/01	98.98	6.01
Canada	8.750	Feb 01/02	104.05	6.01
Canada	8.500	Apr 01/02	104.05	6.00
Canada	10.000	May 01/02	106.75	6.02
Canada	5.750	Jun 01/02	99.64	5.95
Canada	5.500	Sep 01/02	98.98	6.01
Canada	11.250	Dec 15/02	111.66	6.05
Canada	11.750	Feb 01/03	113.38	6.05
Canada	7.250	Jun 01/03	103.24	6.01
Canada	5.250	Sep 01/03	97.80	6.02
Canada	9.500	Oct 01/03	110.00	6.05
Canada	7.500	Dec 01/03	104.47	6.03
Canada	10.250	Feb 01/04	113.22	6.07
Canada	6.500	Jun 01/04	101.67	6.01
Canada	5.000	Sep 01/04	96.45	5.98
Canada	10.500	Oct 01/04	116.35	6.06
Canada	9.000	Dec 01/04	111.40	6.01
Canada	12.000	Mar 01/05	123.75	6.06
Canada	6.000	Sep 01/05	100.38	5.91

	Coupon	Mat. date	Bid $	Yld%
B C	9.000	Jan 09/02	104.07	6.13
B C	7.750	Jun 16/03	104.19	6.17
B C	9.000	Jun 21/04	109.67	6.21
B C	8.000	Aug 23/05	107.68	6.23
B C	5.250	Dec 01/06	94.92	6.22
B C	6.000	Jun 09/08	98.22	6.29
B C	6.250	Dec 01/09	99.63	6.30
B C	9.500	Jan 09/12	125.28	6.37
B C	8.500	Aug 23/13	118.83	6.36
B C	7.500	Jun 09/14	110.30	6.37
B C	9.950	May 15/21	139.49	6.47
B C	8.750	Aug 19/22	126.72	6.46
B C	8.000	Sep 08/23	118.54	6.45
B C	6.150	Nov 19/27	96.94	6.39
B C	5.700	Jun 18/29	91.69	6.33
B C MF	7.750	Dec 01/05	106.57	6.30
B C MF	5.500	Mar 24/08	94.73	6.37
HydQue	10.875	Jul25/01	104.78	8.13
HydQue	5.750	Feb 15/02	102.25	6.23
HydQue	5.500	May 15/03	98.15	6.21
HydQue	7.000	Jun01/04	102.58	6.24
HydQue	8.500	Aug 15/05	109.57	6.28
HydQue	13.250	Sep 30/05	101.56	6.27
HydQue	7.000	Feb 15/07	103.50	6.34
HydQue	6.000	Jul 15/09	97.20	6.41
HydQue	10.000	Sep 26/11	127.85	6.47
HydQue	10.250	Jul 16/12	131.15	6.48
HydQue	11.000	Aug 15/20	148.05	6.64
HydQue	10.500	Oct 15/21	143.90	6.62
HydQue	9.625	Jul 15/22	134.80	6.60
HydQue	6.000	Aug 15/31	94.00	6.45
Manit	6.500	Sep 04/01	100.41	6.12
Manit	9.750	Sep 03/02	107.12	6.17
Manit	7.875	Apr 07/03	104.27	6.16
Manit	5.650	Jul 15/04	98.02	6.21

	Coupon	Mat. date	Bid $	Yld%
Ontario	7.500	Jan 19/06	106.03	6.20
Ontario	7.750	Jul 24/06	107.71	6.20
Ontario	6.125	Sep 12/07	99.60	6.19
Ontario	5.700	Dec 01/08	96.45	6.25
Ontario	6.150	Apr 01/09	97.78	6.48
Ontario	6.200	Nov 19/09	99.63	6.25
Ontario	9.500	Jul 13/22	136.23	6.41
Ontario	8.100	Sep 08/23	120.56	6.39
Ontario	7.500	Feb 07/24	113.53	6.38
Ontario	8.500	Dec 02/25	126.60	6.37
Ontario	8.000	Jun 02/26	120.65	6.36
Ontario	8.000	Dec 02/26	120.59	6.38
Ontario	7.600	Jun 02/27	116.49	6.32
Ontario	6.250	Aug 25/28	99.11	6.32
Ontario	6.500	Mar 08/29	103.14	6.26
Ontario	6.200	Jun 02/31	99.69	6.22
OntHyd	8.625	Feb 06/02	103.70	6.13
OntHyd	9.000	Apr 16/02	104.75	6.13
OntHyd	9.000	Jun 24/02	105.23	6.13
OntHyd	12.500	Nov 30/02	102.49	6.03
OntHyd	5.375	Jun 02/03	97.95	6.15
OntHyd	7.750	Nov 03/05	106.93	6.20
OntHyd	14.250	Apr 21/06	106.12	6.18
OntHyd	5.600	Jun 02/08	95.94	6.26
OntHyd	10.000	May 10/09	103.00	6.28
OntHyd	10.500	Jan 15/10	116.22	6.32
OntHyd	13.250	May 14/10	117.73	6.35
OntHyd	13.000	Jan 29/11	120.63	6.43
OntHyd	10.000	Oct 17/14	133.96	6.35
OntHyd	10.125	Oct 15/21	142.69	6.42
OntHyd	8.900	Aug 18/22	129.25	6.41
OntHyd	9.000	May 26/25	132.50	6.38
OntHyd	8.500	May 26/25	126.37	6.37
OntHyd	8.250	Jun 22/26	123.83	6.36
Quebec	10.250	Oct 15/01	104.90	6.18
Quebec	5.250	Apr 01/02	98.55	6.14
Quebec	9.250	Apr 01/02	105.00	6.16
Quebec	13.000	Apr 07/03	116.85	6.24
Quebec	9.000	May 01/03	107.05	6.23

Exhibit 12–6

Financial Information about Corporate Bonds Available in *The Financial Post*

SOURCE: *The Financial Post*, Saturday, July 1, 2000, p. C17.

1. The first line of the first column shows information for a Government of Canada bond issue bearing a coupon value of 7 percent of the face value. It pays $1,000 × 0.07 = $70 per year and matures on September 1, 2001.
2. The current yield, or return, based on today's price is 6.04%.
3. The current bid to purchase a bond from this issue is for $1,010.50.

Internet can be a welcome source of current bond prices. Second, it is possible to trade bonds online and pay lower commissions than you would pay a full-service or discount brokerage firm. Third, you can get research about a corporation and its bond issues (including recommendations to buy or sell) by accessing specific bond Web sites. *Be warned:* Bond Web sites are not as numerous as Web sites that provide information on stocks, mutual funds, or personal financial planning. And many of the better bond Web sites charge a fee for their research and recommendations. Each of the following Web sites provides information and educational materials designed to make you a better bond investor:

www.cbrs.com   www.dbrs.com
www.bondcan.com   www.webfin.com
www.bondsonline.com   www.investinginbonds.com
www.moodys.com   www.standardpoor.com

BOND RATINGS

To determine the quality and risk associated with bond issues, investors rely on the bond ratings provided by the CBRS and the DBRS. Both companies rank thousands of corporate and municipal bonds.

As Exhibit 12–7 illustrates, bond ratings generally range from AAA (the highest) to D (the lowest). The first four individual categories represent investment-grade securities.

DID YOU KNOW ?

GOVERNMENT OF CANADA LONG-TERM CREDIT RATINGS

	Domestic debt Trend	Foreign debt Trend
Standard & Poor's Current	AAA Stable	AA+ Stable
Moody's Investors Service Current	Aa1 Stable	Aa1 Stable
Canadian Bond Rating Service Current	AA+ Stable	AA+ Stable
Dominion Bond Rating ServiceCurrent	AAA Stable	AA (high) Stable

SOURCE: Canada Savings Bonds Web site at www.csb.gc.ca.

Exhibit 12–7   Description of Bond Ratings Provided by the Dominion Bond Rating Service (DBRS)

Quality	Rating by DBRS	Description
Highest credit quality	AAA	Exceptionally strong protection for the timely repayment of principal and interest.
Superior credit quality	AA	Protection of interest and principal is considered high.
Satisfactory credit quality	A	Considered to be more susceptible to adverse economic conditions and have greater cyclical tendencies.
Adequate credit quality	BBB	Entity is more susceptible to adverse changes in financial and economic conditions, or there may be other adversities present.
Speculative	BB	The protection afforded interest and principal is uncertain. Small size or lack of competitive strength may be additional negative considerations.
Highly speculative	B	Reasonably high level of uncertainty as to ability of the entity to pay interest and principal on a continuing basis in the future, especially in periods of economic recession or industry adversity.
Very highly speculative	CCC	Bonds rated CCC often have characteristics which, if not remedied, may lead to default.
Extremely speculative	CC	Bonds rated CC have characteristics which, if not remedied, will lead to default.
Extremely speculative	C	In immediate danger of default. This is the lowest rating category provided to long-term instruments that are not in default.
In default of principal, interest, or both	D	Currently in default of interest, principal, or both.

SOURCE: Dominion Bond Rating Service, 2002.

Investment-grade securities are suitable for conservative investors who want a safe investment that provides a predictable source of income. Bonds in the next two categories are considered speculative in nature. Finally, the C and D categories are used to rank bonds that may be in default due to poor prospects of repayment or even continued payment of interest. Although bond ratings may be flawed or inaccurate, most investors regard the work of both the CBRS and the DBRS as highly reliable.

Generally, government securities are not graded because they are risk-free for practical purposes. The rating of long-term municipal bonds is similar to that of corporate bonds.

BOND YIELD CALCULATIONS

yield The rate of return earned by an investor who holds a bond for a stated period of time.

For a bond investment, the **yield** is the rate of return earned by an investor who holds a bond for a stated period of time. Two methods are used to measure the yield on a bond investment: the current yield and the yield to maturity.

current yield Determined by dividing the dollar amount of annual interest from an investment by its current market value.

The **current yield** is determined by dividing the dollar amount of annual interest from an investment by its current market value. For bonds, the following formula may help you complete this calculation:

$$\text{Current yield on a corporate bond} = \frac{\text{Dollar amount of annual interest}}{\text{Current market value}}$$

For example, assume you own a Rogers Telecom corporate bond that pays 7.5 percent interest on an annual basis. This means that each year you will receive $75 ($1,000 × 7.5% = $75). Also assume the current market price of the Rogers Telecom bond is $960. Because the current market value is less than the bond's face value, the current yield increases to 7.8 percent, as follows:

Financial Planning Calculations

EVALUATING CORPORATE BONDS

No checklist can serve as a foolproof guide for choosing a corporate or government bond. However, the following questions will help you evaluate a potential bond investment. (Usual sources of information include CBRS and DBRS.)

CATEGORY 1: INFORMATION ABOUT THE CORPORATION

1. What is the corporation's name? _____
2. What are the corporation's address and telephone number? _____
   _____
3. What type of products or services does this firm provide? _____
   _____
4. Briefly describe the prospects for this company. (Include significant factors, such as product development, plans for expansion, plans for mergers, etc.)
   _____
   _____
   _____
   _____

CATEGORY 2: BOND BASICS

5. What type of bond is this? _____
6. What is the face value for this bond? _____
7. What is the interest rate for this bond? _____
8. What is the annual interest amount for this bond?
   _____
9. When are interest payments made to bondholders?
   _____
10. Is the corporation currently paying interest as scheduled? ☐Yes ☐No
11. What is the maturity date for this bond? _____
12. What is the CBRS rating for this bond? _____
13. What is the DBRS rating for this bond? _____
14. What do these ratings mean? _____
   _____
   _____

15. What was the original issue date? _____
16. Who is the trustee for this bond issue? _____
   _____
17. Is the bond callable? If so, when? _____
   _____
18. Is the bond secured with collateral? If so, what?
   ☐Yes ☐No
19. How did the corporation use the money from this bond issue?
   _____
   _____

CATEGORY 3: FINANCIAL PERFORMANCE

20. Has the firm's total debt increased over the last three years? ☐Yes ☐No
21. Is the corporation profitable? If so, how profitable? ☐Yes ☐No $_____
22. Have profits increased over the last seven years? ☐Yes ☐No
23. Are this year's sales higher than last year's sales? ☐Yes ☐No
24. Have sales increased over the last seven years? ☐Yes ☐No
25. Briefly describe any other information that you obtained from Moody's, Standard & Poor's, or other advisory services. _____
   _____
   _____
   _____
   _____

A WORD OF CAUTION

When you use a checklist, there is always a danger of overlooking important relevant information. The above checklist is not a cure-all, but it does provide some very sound questions that you should answer before making a decision to invest in bonds. Quite simply, it is a place to start. If you need other information, *you* are responsible for obtaining it and for determining how it affects your potential investment.

$$\text{Current yield} = \frac{\$75}{\$960}$$
$$= 0.078, \text{ or } 7.8 \text{ percent}$$

This calculation allows you to compare the yield on a bond investment with the yields of other investment alternatives, which include Guaranteed Investment Certificates, common stocks, preferred stocks, and mutual funds. Naturally, the higher the current yield, the better it is! A current yield of 10 percent is better than a current yield of 7.8 percent.

yield to maturity A yield calculation that takes into account the relationships among a bond's maturity value, the time to maturity, the current price, and the dollar amount of interest.

The **yield to maturity** takes into account the relationships among a bond's maturity value, the time to maturity, the current price, and the dollar amount of interest. A formula for calculating the approximate yield to maturity is as follows:

$$\text{Yield to maturity} = \frac{\text{Dollar amount of annual interest} + \dfrac{\text{Face value} - \text{Market value}}{\text{Number of periods}}}{\dfrac{\text{Market value} + \text{Face value}}{2}}$$

For example, assume that on January 1, 1995, you purchased at the current market price of $830 a corporate bond with a $1,000 face value issued by Fruit of the Loom. The bond pays 7 percent annual interest, and its maturity date is 2011. The yield to maturity is 8.7 percent, as follows:

$$\text{Yield to maturity} = \frac{\$70 + \dfrac{\$1,000 - \$830}{17}}{\dfrac{\$830 + \$1,000}{2}}$$

$$= \frac{\$80}{\$915}$$

$$= 0.087, \text{ or } 8.7 \text{ percent}$$

In this situation, the yield to maturity takes into account two types of return on the bond. First, you will receive interest income from the purchase date until the maturity date. Second, at maturity you will receive a payment for the face value of the bond. If you purchased the bond at a price below the face value, the yield to maturity will be greater than the stated interest rate. If you purchased the bond at a price above the face value, the yield to maturity will be less than the stated interest rate. (Remember, the actual price you pay for a bond may be higher or lower than the face value because of many factors, including changes in the economy, increases or decreases in comparable interest rates on other investments, and the financial condition of the company.) Like the current yield, the yield to maturity allows you to compare returns on a bond investment with other investments. Also, like the current yield, the higher the yield to maturity, the better it is. A yield to maturity of 9 percent is better than a yield to maturity of 7 percent. The precise yield to maturiy (YTM) can be calculated using the time value of money concepts from Chapter 1, where the bond price is equated to the present value of coupon plus principal payments discounted at the YTM. In the above example, using a financial calculator, we can solve for the YTM.

$$\$830 = \$70 \times \frac{1 - 1 \div 1 + \text{YTM}^{17}}{\text{YTM}} + 1,000 \times 1 \div 1 + \text{YTM}^{17}$$

$$\text{YTM} = 8.98\%.$$

CALCULATOR

2ND	CLRTVM
FV	1,000
PMT	70
PV	−830
N	17
CPT	I/Y

YTM = 8.98%

Financial Planning Calculations

THE TIMES INTEREST EARNED RATIO: ONE TOOL TO HELP YOU EVALUATE BOND ISSUES

After evaluating a Canadian telecommunications utility, Bethan Jackson, the investor in the opening case, wanted to purchase the firm's corporate debentures. But she was concerned about the corporation's ability to make future interest payments. To determine the utility's ability to pay interest, she calculated a formula called the *times interest earned* ratio, illustrated below:

$$\text{Times interest earned} = \frac{\text{Operating income before interest and taxes}}{\text{Interest expense}}$$

Assume that the utility had interest expense of $837 million and operating income before interest and taxes of $6,588 million in 2001. The times interest earned ratio for the utility is 7.87 to 1, as follows:

$$\text{Times interest earned} = \frac{\$6,588 \text{ million}}{\$837 \text{ million}}$$
$$= 7.87 \text{ to } 1$$

Although the average for the times interest earned ratio varies from industry to industry, a higher number is better than a lower number. The utility is earning slightly over 7.87 times the amount required to pay the annual interest on its long-term notes, bonds, and other financial obligations. With a times interest earned ratio of 7.87 to 1, the utility could experience a "significant" drop in earnings and still meet its financial obligations.

One additional calculation, times interest earned, is described in the Financial Planning Calculations box above.

OTHER SOURCES OF INFORMATION

Investors can use two additional sources of information to evaluate potential bond investments. First, business periodicals can provide information about the economy and interest rates and detailed financial information about a corporation or government entity that issues bonds. You can locate many of these periodicals at your school or public library or on the Internet.

Second, a number of federal agencies provide information that may be useful to bond investors in either printed form or on the Internet. Reports and research published by the Bank of Canada and Department of Finance may be used to assess the nation's economy. You can also obtain information that corporations have reported to SEDAR by accessing the SEDAR Web site (www.sedar.com). Finally, provincial and municipal governments will provide information about specific provincial and municipal bond issues.

Visit the Web site

See the Post-Test under Chapter 12 on the online learning centre at www.mcgrawhill.ca/college/kapoor.

CONCEPT CHECK 12–5

1. What is the market value for a bond with a face value of $1,000 and a newspaper quotation of 77 1/4?
2. What type of information is contained in a corporation's annual report? On a corporation's Web site? How could this information be used to evaluate a bond issue?
3. How important are bond ratings when evaluating a bond issue?
4. Why should you calculate the current yield and yield to maturity on a bond investment?
5. How can business periodicals and government publications help you evaluate a bond issue?

SUMMARY OF OBJECTIVES

Objective 1
Describe the characteristics of corporate bonds.

A corporate bond is a corporation's written pledge to repay a specified amount of money with interest. All of the details about a bond (face value, interest rate, maturity date, repayment, etc.) are contained in the bond indenture. The trustee is the bondholder's representative.

Objective 2
Discuss why corporations issue bonds.

Corporations issue bonds and other securities to help finance their ongoing activities. Bonds may be debentures, mortgage bonds, subordinated debentures, or convertible bonds. Most bonds are callable. To ensure that the money will be available when needed to repay bonds, most corporations establish a sinking fund. Corporations can also issue serial bonds that mature on different dates.

Objective 3
Explain why investors purchase corporate bonds.

Investors purchase corporate bonds for three reasons: (1) interest income, (2) possible increase in value, and (3) repayment at maturity. The method used to pay bondholders their interest depends on whether they own registered bonds, registered coupon bonds, bearer bonds, or zero-coupon bonds. Because bonds can increase or decrease in value, it is possible to purchase a bond at a discount and hold the bond until it appreciates in value. Changes in overall interest rates in the economy are the primary causes of most bond price fluctuations. If you pay too much for a bond or it decreases in value, you can lose money on your investment. You can also choose to hold the bond until maturity and the corporation will repay the bond's face value. Corporate bonds can be bought or sold through account executives who represent brokerage firms.

Objective 4
Discuss why federal, provincial, and municipal governments issue bonds and why investors purchase government bonds.

Bonds issued by the Canadian government are used to finance the national debt and the ongoing activities of the federal government. The Canadian government issues three principal types of bonds: Treasury bills, marketable bonds, and Canada Savings Bonds. Provincial and local governments issue bonds to finance their ongoing activities and special projects, such as schools, roads, and toll bridges. Canadian government bonds can be purchased through banks, trust companies, and other financial institutions. Municipal bonds are generally sold through the government entity that issued them or through account executives.

Objective 5
Evaluate bonds when making an investment.

Some local newspapers, *The National Post*, and *The Globe and Mail* provide bond investors with information they need to evaluate a bond issue. Detailed financial information can be obtained by requesting a printed copy of the corporation's annual report or accessing its Web site. It is also possible to trade bonds online and obtain research information via the Internet. To determine the quality of a bond issue, most investors study the ratings provided by the CBRS and the DBRS. Investors can also calculate a current yield and a yield to maturity to evaluate bond issues.

The current yield is determined by dividing the dollar amount of annual interest of the bond by its current market value. The yield to maturity takes into account the relationship among a bond's maturity value, the time to maturity, the current price, and the dollar amount of interest.

KEY TERMS

bearer bond 361

bond indenture 355

call feature 357

convertible bond 357

corporate bond 354

current yield 372

debenture 356

face value 354

maturity date 354

mortgage bond 357

registered bond 361

registered coupon bond 361

serial bonds 358

sinking fund 358

subordinated debenture 357

trustee 356

yield 372

yield to maturity 374

zero-coupon bond 361

KEY FORMULAS

Page	Topic	Formula
354	Annual interest	Dollar amount of annual interest = Face value × Interest rate
	Example:	Dollar amount of annual interest = $1,000 × 6.75 percent
		= $1,000 × 0.0675
		= $67.50

Page	Topic	Formula
361	Approximate market value	Approximate market value = $\dfrac{\text{Dollar amount of annual interest}}{\text{Comparable interest rate}}$
	Example:	Approximate market value = $\dfrac{\$80}{0.095}$ = $\$842.11$
365	Current yield for a T-bill	Current yield = $\dfrac{\text{Face value} - \text{Purchase price}}{\text{Purchase price}} \times \dfrac{365}{T}$
	Example:	Current yield = $\dfrac{\$5}{\$945} \times \dfrac{365}{91}$ $= 0.021 = 2.12$ percent
372	Current yield for a corporate bond	Current yield = $\dfrac{\text{Dollar amount of annual interest}}{\text{Current market value}}$
	Example:	Current yield = $\dfrac{\$75}{\$800}$ $= 0.094 = 9.4$ percent
374	Yield to maturity	Yield to maturity = $\dfrac{\text{Dollar amount of annual interest} + \dfrac{\text{Face value} - \text{Market value}}{\text{Number of periods}}}{\dfrac{\text{Market value} + \text{Face value}}{2}}$
	Example:	Yield to maturity = $\dfrac{\$60 + \dfrac{\$1,000 - \$900}{10}}{\dfrac{\$900 + \$1,000}{2}}$ $= 0.074 = 7.4$ percent

Calculator:

2ND	CLRTVM
FV	1,000
PMT	60
PV	−900
N	10
CPT	I/Y

YTM = 7.45%

FINANCIAL PLANNING PROBLEMS

1. *Calculating Interest.* What is the annual interest amount for a $1,000 bond that pays 7¾ percent interest? (Obj. 1)

2. *Explaining Different Types of Corporate Bonds.* Dorothy Martin wants to invest $10,000 in corporate bonds. Her account executive suggested that she consider debentures, mortgage bonds, and convertible bonds. Since she has never invested in bonds, she is not sure how these types of bonds differ. How would you explain their differences to her? (Obj. 2)

3. *Evaluating Zero-Coupon Bonds.* List the reasons investors might want to buy zero-coupon bonds. Then, list the reasons investors might want to avoid zero-coupon bonds. On the basis of these lists, do you consider zero-coupon bonds a good alternative for your investment program? Why, or why not? (Obj. 2)

4. *Analyzing Why Investors Purchase Bonds.* In your own words, explain how each of the following factors is a reason to invest in bonds: (Obj. 3)
   a. Interest income.
   b. Possible increase in value.
   c. Repayment at maturity.

5. *Explaining Different Types of Government Securities.* Complete the following table: (Obj. 4)

	Minimum Amount	Maturity Range	How Interest Is Paid
Treasury bill	_____	_____	_____
Canada Savings Bond	_____	_____	_____

6. *Using the newspaper.* Use the information provided by a newspaper (for example, *The Globe and Mail*) to answer questions about the following bond issues: Manulife Financial and Power Corporation. (Obj. 4)
   a. What is the ticker symbol for each bond issue?
   b. Determine the current bond yield for each issue. What does the current yield calculation measure?
   c. Determine the yield to maturity for each issue. What does the yield to maturity mean?
   d. On the basis of your answers to the questions above, which bond would you select for your investment program? Briefly explain.
   e. Using the information on Standard & Poor's Web site, determine the current yield for each bond issue. What does the current yield calculation measure?
   f. Using the information on Standard & Poor's Web site, determine the yield to maturity for each bond issue. What does the yield to maturity calculation measure?

   g. What are the CBRS ratings for each bond? What do these ratings mean?
   h. On the basis of your answer to the above questions, which bond would you choose for your investment portfolio? Explain your answer. (Obj. 4)

7. *Calculating Tax-Equivalent Yield.* Assume you are in the 36-percent tax bracket and purchase a 7-percent, tax-exempt municipal bond. Use the formula presented in this chapter to calculate the taxable equivalent yield for this investment. (Obj. 4)

8. *Evaluating a Corporate Bond Issue.* Choose a corporate bond listed in *The Financial Post*, and use your online resources to answer the following questions about this bond issue: (Obj. 5)
   a. What is the CBRS and the DBRS rating for the issue?
   b. What is the purpose of the issue?
   c. Does the issue have a call provision?
   d. Who is the trustee for the issue?
   e. What collateral, if any, has been pledged as security for the issue?
   f. On the basis of the information you have obtained, would the bond be a good investment for you? Why, or why not?

9. *Calculating Yields.* Assume you purchased a corporate bond at its current market price of $850 on January 1, 1995. It pays 9 percent interest and will mature on December 31, 2004, at which time the corporation will pay you the face value of $1,000. (Obj. 5)
   a. Determine the current yield on your bond investment at the time of purchase.
   b. Determine the yield to maturity on your bond investment.

FINANCIAL PLANNING ACTIVITIES

1. *Explaining the Purpose of a Bond Indenture.* Prepare a one-minute oral presentation that describes the type of information contained in a bond indenture. (Obj. 1)

2. *Investigating a New Bond Issue.* Locate an advertisement for a new bond issue in *The Globe and Mail*, *The Financial Post*, or a local newspaper. Then, go to the library or use the Internet to research the corporation or government entity that is issuing the bonds. On the basis of your research, prepare a two-page report on the issuer. Be sure to describe its financial condition and how it will use the money raised by selling the bonds. (Obj. 2)

3. *Interviewing an Account Executive.* Talk to an account executive or a banker about the differences among debentures, mortgage bonds, and subordinated debentures. Describe your findings. (Obj. 2)

4. *Making Investment Decisions.* Assume you just inherited 10 Westcoast Energy Inc. bonds and each bond is convertible to 64.5 shares of the corporation's common stocks. (Obj. 2)
   a. What type of information would you need to help you decide whether to convert your bonds to common stocks?
   b. Where would you obtain this information?
   c. Under what conditions would you convert your bonds to common stocks?
   d. Under what conditions would you keep the bonds?

5. *Analyzing Why Investors Purchase Bonds.* Survey at least two investors who own either corporate or government bonds. Then answer the following questions: (Obj. 3)

   a. Why did these investors purchase the bonds?
   b. How long have they invested in bonds?
   c. Do they consider their bond issues to be conservative or speculative investments?
   d. Why did they decide to purchase bonds instead of other investments, such as Guaranteed Investment Certificates, stocks, mutual funds, or real estate?

6. *Reading Financial Information in the Newspaper.* Using information from the local newspaper or *The Financial Post*, answer the following questions on the following bond issues: (Obj. 5)

   Newspaper _____ Date _____

	Current Yield	Volume	Close Price
AirCa 6.750l	_____	_____	_____
BCE 6.2	_____	_____	_____
Molson 5.4	_____	_____	_____

7. *Analyzing Yields.* In your own words, describe what affects the current yield and the yield to maturity for a bond. (Obj. 5)

8. *Evaluating a Bond Transaction.* Choose a corporate bond that you would consider purchasing. Then, using information obtained in the library or on the Internet, answer the questions on the evaluation form presented in the Financial Planning Calculations feature on page 373. On the basis of your research, would you still purchase this bond? Explain your answer. (Obj. 5)

LIFE SITUATION CASE

A Lesson from the Past

Back in 1990, Mary Goldberg, a 34-year-old divorcee, got a telephone call from a Bay Street account executive who said that one of his other clients had given him her name. Then, he told her his brokerage firm was selling a new corporate bond issue in New World Explorations, a company heavily engaged in oil exploration in western Canada. The bonds in this issue paid investors 13.2 percent a year. He then said that the minimum investment was $10,000 and that if she wanted to take advantage of this "once in a lifetime" opportunity, she had to move fast. To Mary, it was an opportunity that was too good to pass up, and she bit hook, line, and sinker. She sent the account executive a cheque—and never heard from him again. When she went to the library to research her bond investment, she found there was no such company as New World Explorations. She lost her $10,000 and quickly vowed she would never invest in bonds again. From now on, she would put her money in the bank, where it was guaranteed.

Over the years, she continued to deposit money in the bank and accumulated more than $90,000. Things seemed to be pretty much on track until one of her GICs matured. When she went to renew the GIC, the bank officer told her interest rates had fallen and current GIC interest rates ranged between $1\frac{1}{3}$ and $4\frac{1}{2}$ percent. To make matters worse, the banker told Mary that only the bank's three-year GIC offered the $4\frac{1}{2}$ percent interest rate. GICs with shorter maturities paid lower interest rates.

Faced with the prospects of lower interest rates, Mary decided to shop around for higher rates. She called several local banks and got pretty much the same answer. Then, a friend suggested that she talk to Peter, an account executive for TD Waterhouse. Peter told her there were conservative corporate bonds and quality stock issues that offered higher returns. But, he warned her, these investments were *not* guaranteed. If she wanted higher returns, she would have to take some risks.

While Mary wanted higher returns, she also remembered how she had lost $10,000 investing in corporate bonds. When she told Peter about her bond investment in the fictitious New World Exploration, he pointed out that she had made some pretty serious mistakes. For starters, she bought the bonds over the phone from someone she didn't know, and she bought them without doing any research. He assured her that the bonds and stocks he would recommend would be issued by real companies, and she would be able to find a lot of information on each of his recommendations at the library.

Questions

1. According to Mary Goldberg, the chance to invest in New World Explorations was "too good to pass up." Unfortunately, it was too good to be true, and she lost $10,000. Why do you think so many people are taken in by get-rich-quick schemes?
2. During the last part of the 1990s, investors were forced to look for ways to squeeze additional income from their investment portfolios. Do you think investing in corporate bonds or quality stocks is the best way to increase income? Give reasons for your answer.

CREATING A FINANCIAL PLAN

Investing in Bonds

Including bonds in an investment portfolio can be useful for achieving various financial goals when certain life situations, business conditions, and economic trends arise.

Web Sites for Investing in Bonds

- **www.bondcan.com**
- **www.webfin.com**
- **www.iemoney.com**
- **www.standardandpoors.com/canada/**
- **www.dbrs.com**
- **www.fin.gc.ca/secur/gocsec_e.html**
- **www.csb.gc.ca**
- **www.myfinancialsite.com**

(Note: Addresses and content of Web sites change, and new sites are created daily. Use search engines to update and locate Web sites for your current financial planning needs.)

Short-Term Financial Planning Activities

1. Assess various types of bond investments that might be appropriate for your various financial goals and life situation.
2. Compare the recent performance of various corporate bonds that could be appropriate investments for you.
3. Research the recent performance of federal government and municipal bonds. Determine how these might be used in your investment portfolio.

Long-Term Financial Planning Activities

1. Identify bond investing situations that could help minimize risk.
2. Develop a plan for selecting bond investments in the future.

13 Investing in Mutual Funds

A Fundamental Investment with Some Pizzazz!

In 1996, Bryan Nations was thinking about investing in the Mackenzie Universal Future mutual fund. After reading some research material published by *The Globe and Mail* in its Report on Mutual Funds, he decided to invest $5,000 in this fund. Then, he made a fatal mistake common to a lot of investors: He forgot about his investment and didn't even look at the statements he received from the investment company. Three years later, he was considering selling his shares in Mackenzie Universal, but he didn't even know the value of his investment.

Then, in his dentist's waiting room, Nations picked up a copy of the Fall 1999 *Mutual Fund Review*, and there it was—an article about the Mackenzie Universal Future mutual fund. The article touted the fund as a real high-flying investment with excellent returns: It had a one-year total return of 54.46 percent and a three-year annual return of 28.19 percent. So, in the three years since Nations purchased shares in Mackenzie Universal, he had doubled his original $5,000 investment. On the basis of this information alone, he decided to keep his investment. He also decided that he needed to do a better job of evaluating his investment on a regular basis.

He began his research by going to the Web site of Mackenzie Financial Corporation (www.mackenziefinancial.com), where he found his fund among all the mutual funds sponsored by the company. He learned that his fund had the following objective: "above-average long-term returns by investing in technologically advanced, often

export-oriented, Canadian companies. Approximately 50% of the portfolio emphasizes knowledge or technologically intensive industries. The balance of the portfolio comprises other companies in industries that provide a solid foundation for growth." There was also information on the fund's past performance, type, growth, retirement savings eligibility, and outlook. In addition, Nations was able to discover the proportional allocation of the fund, as well as extensive details about the portfolio manager.

Nations was surprised at how easy it was to find information on his investment. More importantly, the information he found on the Mackenzie Financial Web site supported the material reported in the *Mutual Fund Review* magazine. Those one-year and three-year returns were for real, and his investment really had doubled in value in just three years. After spending more than three hours on the Internet, he not only knew the value of his investment but also had a feeling that this mutual fund would continue to perform well in the future. According to Bryan Nations, this fund was a "keeper."

Recently, in the summer of 2002, Bryan Nations' shares of Mackenzie Universal Fund dropped from their high of fall 2000; however, Bryan Nation would still receive a very nice return if he were to sell his shares today. Compared with the three-year return of 28.19 percent he would have received in fall 1999, he would receive a return of approximately 52.8 percent if he were to sell his shares in summer 2002.

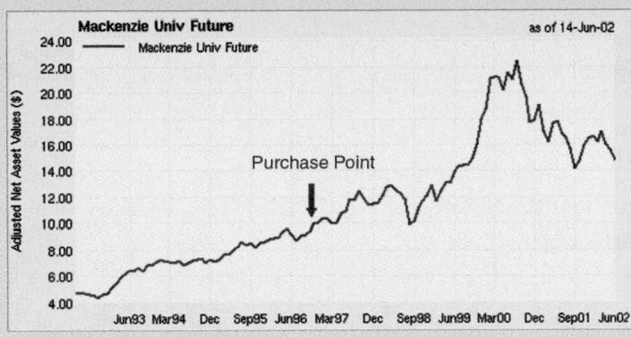

SOURCE: www.globefund.com Mackenzie Univ. Future as of Jun 14, 2002.

Calendar Year Returns		Calendar Year Returns	
2001	-7.6%	1996	16.3%
2000	-0.8%	1995	18.3%
1999	48.7%	1994	3.2%
1998	5.9%	1993	53.4%
1997	14.4%	1992	-4.1%

SOURCE: www.mackenziefinancial.com/

QUESTIONS

1 Although Bryan Nations doubled his original investment in three years, he now admits that he made mistakes during the first three years he owned shares in the Mackenzie Universal Future mutual fund. In your own words, what did he do wrong?

2 If you owned shares in the Mackenzie Universal Future mutual fund, would you use published materials available in the library or sources found on the Internet to monitor your investment? Explain your answer.

LEARNING OBJECTIVES

1 Describe the characteristics of mutual fund investments.

2 Classify mutual funds by investment objective.

3 Evaluate mutual funds for investment purposes.

4 Describe how and why mutual funds are bought and sold.

If you ever thought about buying stocks or bonds but decided not to, your reasons were probably like most other people's: You didn't know enough to make a good decision, and you lacked enough money to diversify your investments among several choices. These same two reasons explain why people invest in mutual funds. By pooling your money with money from other investors, a mutual fund can do for you what you can't do on your own. Specifically, a **mutual fund** is an investment chosen by people who pool their money to buy stocks, bonds, and other financial securities selected by professional managers who work for investment companies. Every person who invests in a mutual fund has the right to his or her proportional share of the assets of the fund and any income that the fund earns. Mutual funds are an excellent choice for many individuals. In many cases, they can also be used for retirement accounts.

Bryan Nations, the investor in the opening case, did his homework before purchasing shares in the Mackenzie Universal Future mutual fund. But like many investors, he just assumed his investment would increase in value. Thus, he made two critical mistakes. First, he didn't continue to monitor the value of his investment. Second, he didn't continue to evaluate his investment after his initial purchase. Fortunately for Nations, his mutual fund did earn exceptional returns over the first three years, and his investment doubled in value. While he was lucky, you

mutual fund An investment chosen by people who pool their money to buy stocks, bonds, and other financial securities selected by professional managers who work for an investment company.

may not be so fortunate. Make no mistake about this: *Good investors evaluate an investment before purchase. The best investors continue to evaluate their investments after the purchase.*

An investment in mutual funds is based on the concept of opportunity costs, which we have discussed throughout this text. Simply put, you have to be willing to take some chances if you want to get larger returns on your investments. Before deciding whether mutual funds are the right investment for you, read the material presented in the next section.

Why Investors Purchase Mutual Funds

Objective 1

Describe the characteristics of mutual fund investments.

Investors like—no, love—their mutual fund investments. The following statistics illustrate how important mutual fund investments are to both individuals and the nation's economy:

[1] Although the mutual fund concept originated in Europe and then spread to North America in the late 1800s, mutual funds didn't gain real popularity until the last 25 years.

[2] As of February 2002, the Investment Funds Institute of Canada (IFIC), the national trade association for the Canadian mutual fund industry, has a membership of 82 fund management companies sponsoring 1,864 mutual funds, 111 dealer firms selling mutual funds, and 65 affiliates. Its member funds manage nearly $427 billion in assets.

[3] The value of assets under management in the industry has increased from $3.5 billion in 1981 to nearly $427 billion—making mutual funds the fastest-growing sector of the Canadian financial services industry.

D I D   Y O U   K N O W ?

INDUSTRY STATISTICS

Net sales of all funds: $65.1 million

Net new sales (excl.reinv.distr.): $263 million

Reinvested Distributions: $197.5 million

Assets under administration: $436.3 billion

Unitholder accounts: 53.5 million

May 2002 Estimate Last updated:
June 4, 2002

SOURCE: http://www.ific.ca/

No doubt about it, the mutual fund industry is big business. And yet, you may be wondering why so many people invest in mutual funds.

The major reasons investors purchase mutual funds are *professional management* and *diversification*. Most investment companies do everything possible to convince you that they can do a better job of picking securities than you can. Sometimes, these claims are true, and sometimes, they are just so much hot air. Still, investment companies do have professional fund managers with years of experience who devote large amounts of time to picking just the "right" securities for their funds' portfolios. *Be warned:* Even the best portfolio managers make mistakes. So you, the investor, must be careful!

The diversification mutual funds offer spells safety because an occasional loss incurred with one investment contained in a mutual fund is usually offset by gains from other investments in the fund. For example, consider the diversification provided in the portfolio of the Royal Canadian Value Fund, shown in Exhibit 13–1. With more than $48 million in assets, this fund contains almost 45 different stock investments spread over 14 different industrial areas. Note that the information contained in Exhibit 13–1 is from the Royal Mutual Funds 2002 Annual Report. If you want more up-to-date information on the composition of investments within the fund or other information about the fund, visit the Royal Mutual Funds Web site at www.royalbank.com/rmf.

investment company
A firm that, for a management fee, invests the pooled funds of small investors in securities appropriate to its stated investment objectives.

CHARACTERISTICS OF MUTUAL FUNDS

An **investment company** is a firm that, for a management fee, invests the pooled funds of small investors in securities appropriate to its stated investment objectives. Today, mutual funds sponsored by investment companies may be classified as either closed-end funds or open-end mutual funds.

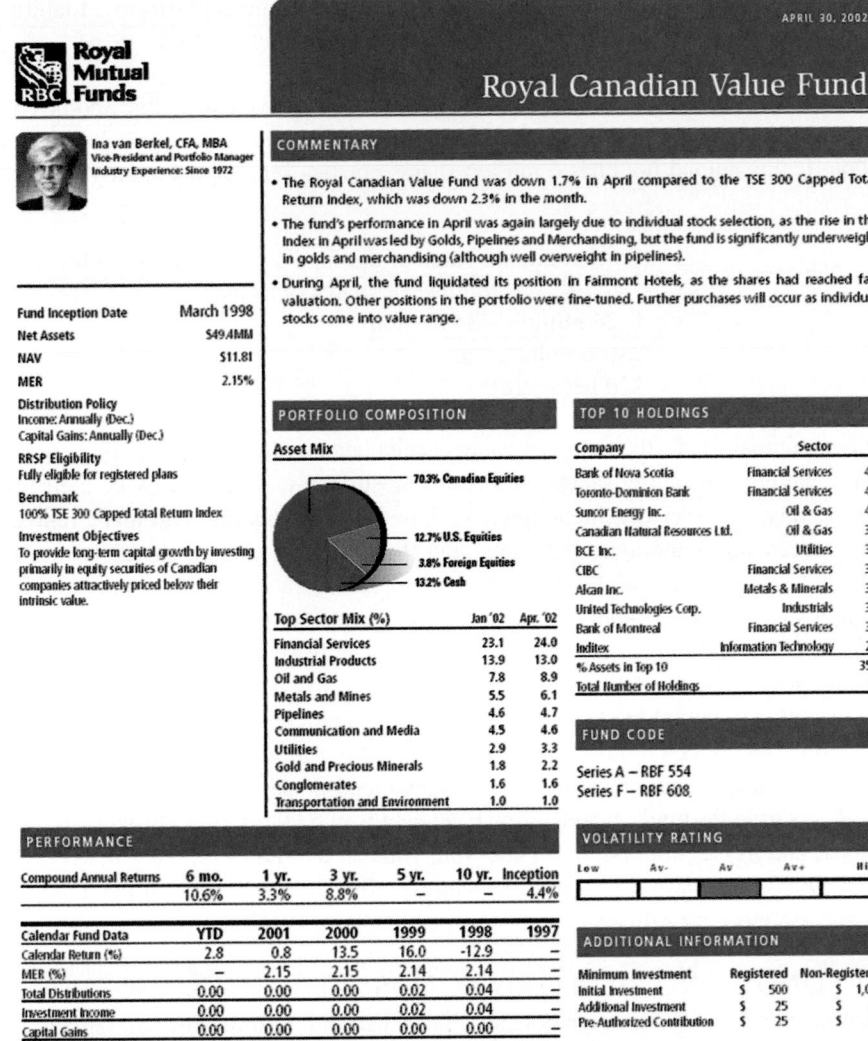

Exhibit 13–1

Types of Securities Included in the Portfolio of the Royal Canadian Value Fund

SOURCE: Royal Mutual Funds Report 2002, www.royalbank.com/rmf

CLOSED-END FUNDS OR OPEN-END MUTUAL FUNDS A **closed-end fund** is a fund of finite size. Its shares are issued by an investment company only when the fund is originally set up. Once that's done, the fund size remains more or less static. The fund neither issues nor redeems shares. Since a closed-end fund does not ever have to buy back shares from investors like an open-end mutual fund, it does not have to maintain a percentage of its asset in cash, therefore 100 percent of the fund's assets can be invested at all times. After all the shares originally issued have been sold, an investor can purchase shares only from another investor who is willing to sell. Shares of closed-end funds are traded on the floors of stock exchanges or in the over-the-counter market. Like the prices of stocks, the prices of shares for closed-end funds are determined by the factors of supply and demand, by the value of stocks and other investments contained in the fund's portfolio, and by investor expectations.

An **open-end fund** is a mutual fund whose shares are issued and redeemed by the investment company at the request of investors. Investors are free to buy and sell shares at the net asset value. The **net asset value (NAV)** per share is equal to the current market value of securities contained in the mutual fund's portfolio minus the mutual fund's liabilities divided by the number of shares outstanding:

closed-end fund A mutual fund whose shares are issued by an investment company only when the fund is originally set up.

open-end fund A mutual fund whose shares are issued and redeemed by the investment company at the request of investors.

net asset value (NAV) The current market value of the securities contained in the mutual fund's portfolio minus the mutual fund's liabilities divided by the number of shares outstanding.

$$\text{Net asset value per share} = \frac{\text{Current market value of the fund's portfolio} - \text{Liabilities}}{\text{Number of shares outstanding}}$$

For example, assume the portfolio of all investments contained in the Scotia Canadian Income Fund has a current market value of $124 million. The fund also has liabilities totalling $4 million. If this mutual fund has 6 million shares outstanding, the net asset value per share is $20:

$$\begin{aligned} \text{Net asset value} &= \frac{\text{Current market value of the fund's portfolio} - \text{Liabilities}}{\text{Number of shares outstanding}} \\ &= \frac{\$124 \text{ million} - \$4 \text{ million}}{6 \text{ million shares}} \\ &= \$20 \text{ per share} \end{aligned}$$

Visit the Web site

See Personal Financial Planning worksheets under Chapter 13 on the online learning centre at www.mcgrawhill.ca/college/kapoor.

For most mutual funds, the net asset value is calculated at the close of trading each day. In addition to buying and selling shares on request, most open-end funds provide their investors with a wide variety of services, including payroll deduction programs, automatic reinvestment programs, automatic withdrawal programs, and the option to change shares in one fund to another fund within the same fund family—all topics discussed later in this chapter. Two "new" types of funds have emerged in the last five years: exchange traded funds (ETFs) and index funds. ETFs and index funds are similar to conventional mutual funds in that they provide investors with an affordable way to invest in a diversified basket of securities. However, unlike conventional mutual funds, which can only be bought or sold at a fixed price at the end of each trading day, ETFs funds can be traded throughout the day at changing market prices on the stock exchange, and index funds are bought at end-of-day prices. The big banks are the main suppliers of index funds, whereas you have to buy an ETF through a broker, as you would buy a stock, and pay a commission. In addition, you can buy ETFs on margin, as well as sell them short. ETFs also have lower management expenses than their conventional mutual fund cousins and are more tax efficient.

LOAD FUNDS AND NO-LOAD FUNDS
Before investing in mutual funds, you should compare the cost of this type of investment with the cost of other investment alternatives, such as stocks or bonds. With regard to cost, mutual funds are classified as load funds or no-load funds. A **load fund** is a mutual fund in which investors pay a commission every time they buy (front-end load) or sell (back-end load) shares. The commission charge, sometimes referred to as the *sales fee*, may be as high as 8½ percent of the price for investments under $10,000. (Typically, this fee declines for investments over $10,000.)

load fund A mutual fund in which investors pay a commission (as high as 8½ percent) every time they purchase or sell shares.

While many exceptions exist, the average load charge for mutual funds is between 3 and 5 percent. Let's assume you decide to invest $10,000 in the Standard Life Growth Equity Fund. This fund charges a sales load of 5 percent that you must pay when you purchase shares. The dollar amount of the sales charge on your $10,000 investment is $500 ($10,000 × 5% = $500). After paying the $525, the amount available for investment is reduced to $9,500 ($10,000 − $500 = $9,500). The "stated" advantage of a load fund is that the fund's sales force (account executives, financial planners, or brokerage divisions of banks and other financial institutions) will explain the mutual fund to investors and offer advice as to when shares of the fund should be bought or sold.

no-load fund A mutual fund in which the individual investor pays no sales charge.

A **no-load fund** is a mutual fund in which the individual investor pays no sales charge. No-load funds don't charge commissions when you buy or sell shares because they have no salespeople. If you want to buy shares of a no-load fund, you must deal directly with the investment company. The usual means of contact is by telephone, the Internet, or mail. You can also purchase shares in a no-load fund from many discount brokers, such as TD Waterhouse.

As an investor, you must decide whether to invest in a load fund or a no-load fund. Some investment salespeople have claimed that load funds outperform no-load funds. But many

financial analysts suggest there is no significant difference between mutual funds that charge commissions and
those that do not. *Since no-load funds offer the same
investment opportunities load funds offer, you should
investigate them further before deciding which type of
mutual fund is best for you.* Although the sales commission should not be the decisive factor, the possibility of
saving an 8½-percent load charge is a factor to consider.
For example, suppose Marianne Lowen invests $10,000
in a mutual fund that charges an 8½ percent sales fee.
Since this fee is deducted in advance, her initial $10,000
investment is reduced by $850. Simply put, she now has
$9,150 that she can use to buy shares in this load fund. By
comparison, Jane Edwards decides to invest $10,000 in a
no-load mutual fund. Since there is no sales fee, she can
use the entire $10,000 to purchase shares in this no-load
fund. Depending on the load fund's performance, it may
take Marianne a year or more to "catch up" and cover the
cost of the sales fee.

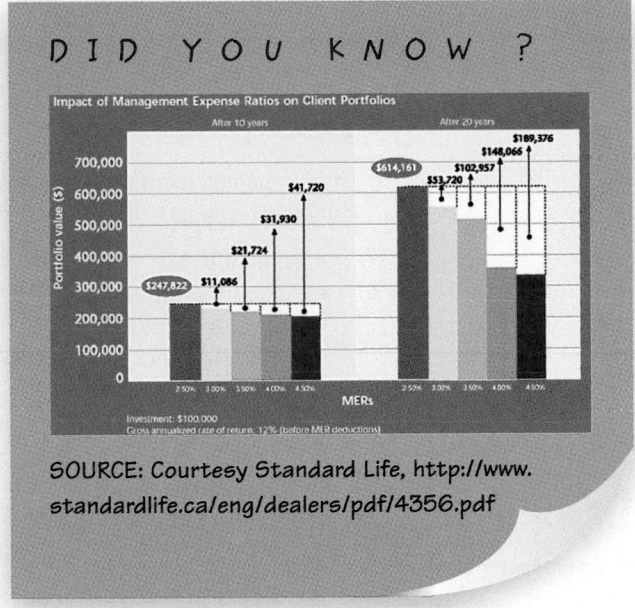

SOURCE: Courtesy Standard Life, http://www.
standardlife.ca/eng/dealers/pdf/4356.pdf

MANAGEMENT FEES AND OTHER CHARGES   In evaluating a specific
mutual fund, you should consider management fees and other charges. The investment companies that sponsor mutual funds charge management fees. This fee, which is disclosed in the
fund's prospectus, is a fixed percentage of the fund's asset value. Today, annual management
fees range between 0.5 and 4 percent of the fund's asset value. While fees vary considerably,
the average is one-half of 1 percent of the fund's assets.

Instead of charging investors a fee when they purchase shares in a mutual fund, some mutual funds charge a **contingent deferred sales load** (sometimes referred to as a *back-end load*).
These fees range from 1 to 6 percent, depending on how long you own the mutual fund before
making a withdrawal. For example, assume you withdraw $5,000 from shares that you own in
the Greenline Balanced Growth mutual fund within a year of your original purchase date. You
must pay a 5-percent contingent deferred sales fee. Your fee is $250 ($5,000 × 5% = $250).
After the fee is deducted from your $5,000 withdrawal, you will receive $4,750 ($5,000 – $250
= $4,750). Generally, the deferred charge declines until there is no withdrawal charge if you
own the shares in the fund for more than five to seven years. Unlike a front-end load, however, your entire $5,000 goes to work for you immediately. There is no deduction when you pur-
chase. Choosing the back-end load allows all of your investment dollars to go to work for you
immediately. Keep in mind, however, that although you don't pay a fee directly to your sales
representative at the time of purchase, the mutual fund company does. This, of course, increases its costs. As a result, you may be paying a higher MER. In addition, if the fund does not perform as well as expected, due to a change in management or other circumstances, you may be
reluctant to switch because of the high penalty. If all other factors are equal, a fund that does-
n't charge a contingent deferral sales load is superior to a fund that does.

**contingent deferred
sales load** A 1- to 6-
percent charge that
shareholders pay when
they withdraw their
investment from a
mutual fund.

Generally, all mutual funds have management expenses that are deducted from the fund.
The management fee pays for such things as the mutual fund company's investment management and marketing and administrative costs. Each fund also pays its own operating costs,
such as brokerage fees on securities trading, audit fees, and unitholder communications.

MANAGEMENT EXPENSE RATIO

The fund will report the management fee and direct costs it pays each year as a management
expense ratio (MER) that relates those costs to the fund's value. If a $100-million fund has $2
million in costs, its MER is 2 percent. The costs are deducted before the fund's performance

returns are calculated. If your fund made 13 percent and the MER was 2 percent, the reported return for the year would be 11 percent.

SPECIAL FEES

Unlike management expenses, which apply to all unitholders, special fees apply to individual situations. You pay them directly or through specific deductions. Some examples include:

- Annual RRSP, RRIF, or RESP trustee fee—this covers the cost of operating the plan.
- Account setup fee—some dealers levy a one-time charge for new clients.
- Short-term trading fee—mutual fund companies are allowed to deduct an amount, generally 2 percent from any redemption that occurs within 90 days of purchase; however, many don't.
- Transfer fee—at the discretion of the individual adviser, dealers can levy a charge of up to 2 percent when you switch among funds in the same family.
- Processing fees—your fund company may levy a fee if you require transactions that require special processing.

SERVICE FEES Also called *trailers*, these are ongoing commissions to pay advisers and dealers for ongoing service. The adviser or dealer gets a yearly amount that equals a certain percentage of your account's value. That's often about 1 percent on front-load accounts and $1/2$ percent on deferred sales load accounts. No-load companies may also pay trailers to dealers. You do not pay service fees directly. They're paid by the mutual fund company—in most cases, from its management fee. As with commissions, funds that carry low trailers or none at all may or may not have lower management expense ratios.

There are no easy answers, but your professional financial adviser or broker can help you determine which particular mutual fund best suits your financial needs. You can also do your own research to determine which fund is right for you. Factors to consider include whether you want to invest in a load fund or no-load fund, as well as the fund's management fees and expense ratios. As you will see later in this chapter, a number of sources of information can help you make your investment decisions.

The investment company's prospectus must provide all details relating to management fees, contingent deferred sales fees, and other expenses. Exhibit 13–2 shows a sample report on the AGF Canadian Growth Equity Fund, as presented by Yahoo mutual Fund Centre at http://mutualfunds.yahoo.ca. Here, you'll see a reported MER of 2.5 percent, the objective of the mutual fund, and the proportional investment by industry. It even provides information, on the NAVPS, or net asset value per share.

Exhibit 13–3 on page 388 summarizes load charges and no-load charges. In addition, it reports management fees, contingent deferred sales loads, and other charges.

DID YOU KNOW ?

Say, for example, you invest $1,000 in a fund with an MER of 2.5%. After 15 years, you would lose 32 percent of your contribution to fees and, after 25 years, you would lose 47 percent. But compare with a low MER of 0.5 percent. After 15 years, the fee costs you only 7 percent of your contribution. After 25 years, the amount is 12 percent.

SOURCE: "In tough times, fees matter more" by Carolyn Leitch, for *The Globe and Mail*, February 7, 2002, Section M.

CONCEPT CHECK 13-1

1. What type of information about a mutual fund can be found on the Internet?
2. What are two major reasons investors purchase mutual funds?
3. How do a closed-end fund and an open-end fund differ?
4. What are the typical fees charged for a load and no-load mutual fund?
5. What are the typical management fees, and front and back load fees?

Fund Background

Category	Canadian Small-Cap Equity
Fund Family	AGF Group of Funds
Total Assets in $millions (2002-05-31)	964.650
Year-to-Date Return	8.8800%
NAVPS (2002-06-14)	$ 35.6000
Daily Change	$ -0.2200
52 week high	$ 38.0600
52 week low	$ 28.5400

Objective

The fund's objective is to provide capital growth. It invests primarily in shares of small and medium Canadian companies that are expected to profit from future economic growth.

Strategy

Stock selection begins with an evaluation of companies that have demonstrated or have potential to achieve above-average growth in earnings and cash flow. Companies are evaluated through internal and street research. Interviews with corporate managers are crucial to determine their business plans and growth strategies. Successful investment candidates are then evaluated on the basis of a determination of a reasonable price to pay for that company's growth.

Fund Operations

Inception:	30-September-1994
Management Company:	AGF Funds Inc.
Managing Company since:	1-January-1972
Lead Manager:	Robert Farquharson
Manager Since:	30-September-1994
Manager Tenure:	7 years

Returns (%)

	3 mo	1 yr avg	3 yr avg	5 yr avg
AGC*GEQ.TO	4.0750	2.1800	11.1180	5.9170

Investment Information

New Investment	Open
Currency	CAD
Min Initial Investment	$ 1000
Min Subsequent Investment	$ 100
RRSP Eligible	Yes
RESP Eligible	Yes
Min. Initial Investment (RRSP)	$ 100
Min. Subsequent Investment (RRSP)	$ 25
Availability	AB,BC,MB,NB,NF,NU,NS,NT,ON,PE,PQ,SK,YT

Fees & Expenses

Management Fee	2.50%
Load or No-Load	Load
Choice of Front- or Back-End Load	Yes
Max Front-End Load	6.00%
Max Back-End Load	5.50%

Sector Weightings (%) 30-April-2002

Oil & Gas	19.02
Industrial/Capital Goods	12.87
Not Reported - Sector	8.97
Consumer Staples (Non Cyc)	7.32
Gold & Precious Metals	5.86
Pharmaceuticals & Biotechnology	5.27
Consumer Discretionary (Cyclical)	4.89
Financial	4.47
Merchandising	4.25
Commerical Services	3.82
Technology	2.91
Metals & Minerals	2.37
Health-Care Equipment & Services	2.30
Communications	2.20
Funds - Sector	1.80
Venture Capital	1.78
Transportation & Environment	1.64
Basic Materials	1.61
Software & Services	1.55
Real Estate - Sector	1.52
Paper & Forest Products	0.84
Utilities	0.65
Cash Equivalent - Sector	0.51
Energy	0.37
Insurance	0.33
Conglomerates	0.33
Supranational	0.25
Media	0.22
Index - Sector	0.08

Exhibit 13-2

Sample Mutual Fund Report on the AGF Growth Equity Fund, from Yahoo Mutual Fund Centre

SOURCE: Yahoo mutual fund centre at http://mutualfunds.yahoo.ca

Exhibit 13–3

Typical Fees Associated with Mutual Fund Investments

Type of Fee or Charge	Customary Amount
Load fund	Up to 8 ½ percent of the purchase
No-load fund	No sales charge
Management fee	0.25 to 3 percent per year of the fund's total assets
Contingent deferred sales load	1 to 6 percent of withdrawals, depending on how long you own the fund before making a withdrawal
Front-end loads	Most fund companies have lowered the maximum front-end load on their funds to around 6 percent.
Back-end loads	Generally, no commission if selling after a set number of years. If earlier, then the fee is usually on a sliding scale decreasing with time held. Fee is up to 0.5 percent higher than on front-loads.

Classifications of Mutual Funds

Objective 2

Classify mutual funds by investment objective.

The managers of mutual funds tailor their investment portfolios to the investment objectives of their customers. Usually, a fund's objectives are plainly disclosed in its prospectus. For example, the objectives of the Royal Balanced Growth Fund are as follows:

> "The Royal Balanced Growth Fund is considered a 'one-decision' fund, for growth-oriented investors investing in a diversified portfolio of Canadian, U.S., and International equities, and Canadian bonds, and short-term debt securities. The fund employs a more aggressive asset allocation strategy and invests in a more focused list of securities than the Royal Balanced Fund, in order to achieve the highest possible total return consistent with a moderate level of risk. The percentage of assets held in each asset class will vary according to the outlook for the economy and financial markets, and the fund intends to maximize its foreign content. The fund may also invest in derivative instruments."

While it may be helpful to categorize the 1,400-plus mutual funds into different categories, note that different sources of investment information may use different categories for the same mutual fund. In most cases, the name of the category gives a pretty good clue to the types of investments included within the category. The *major* fund categories are described as follows:

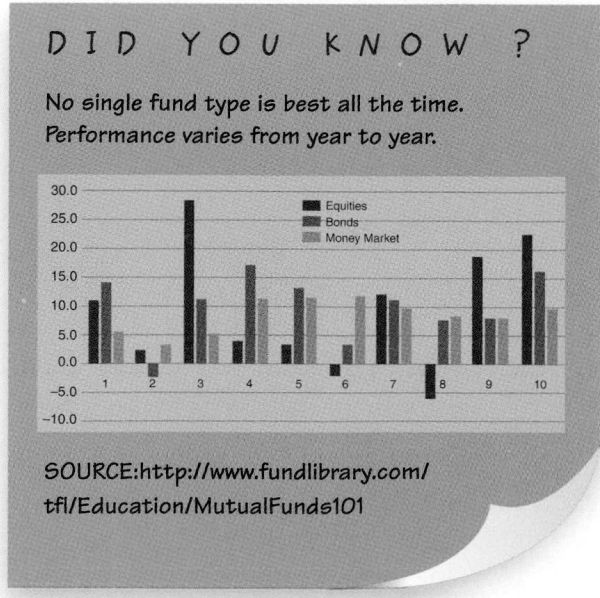

DID YOU KNOW ?

No single fund type is best all the time. Performance varies from year to year.

SOURCE:http://www.fundlibrary.com/ tfl/Education/MutualFunds101

- *Money market funds* seek to achieve a high level of income and liquidity through investment in short-term money market instruments, such as T-bills, commercial paper, and short-term government bonds. These are relatively low risk.
- *Mortgage funds* aim for income and safety. Investors in mortgage funds hold a group of mortgages, rather than a single property title. These have a lower risk than bond funds.
- *Bond funds* aim for safety of principal and income but are subject to capital gains and losses, which have tax implications. Bond funds are generally invested in good quality, high-yielding government and corporate debt securities. The risk here is related to changes in interest rates.
- *Dividend funds* aim for tax-advantaged income with some possibility of capital growth, and invest in preferred shares as well as high quality common shares that have a history of consistently paying dividends.

Advice from a Pro

WHY INVESTORS CHOOSE MUTUAL FUNDS

Mutual fund investing provides a good way to get started with small amounts of money, at the same time affording the investor professional management. By investing in mutual funds you can diversify your investments to fit your personal goals and objectives. However, the most important advantage is still the ability to get professional management.

When choosing a mutual fund, the pros recommend that investors rely on research. Research gives investors an understanding of the kind of investment they are making, whether or not they feel comfortable with the choice, and lets them know what the track record for a specific mutual fund is. While research may not be foolproof, it does provide a guide as to what can be expected of a particular fund in the future. Only after an investor has researched a potential investment is it possible to find a mutual fund that fits the investor's needs, had good management, and has a successful long-term track record.

According to a pro, many investors are always changing funds and chasing funds that were hot last year. Consequently, they incur more fees, sales charges, and so on. This can make mutual fund investing more expensive, and in most cases, investors end up with smaller total returns. This is not to say that changes cannot be made in the mutual funds an investor owns. However, it is best to give a well-managed fund time to work.

- *Balanced* and *asset allocation funds* are similar in that they both aim to provide a mixture of safety, income, and capital appreciation. Where they differ is in the fact that only balanced funds need respect a stated minimum investment in given classes of aggressive or defensive types of investments.
- *Equity* or *common stock funds* aim for capital gains and, as such, are invested almost entirely in common shares. These will tend to fluctuate in price much more than any of the previously listed funds.
- *Specialty funds* sacrifice diversification in an effort to build capital gains. They concentrate portfolio holdings on shares of a group of companies in one industry, geographical area, or segment of the capital market. They can be susceptible to fluctuations within industries and to currency value fluctuations as well.
- *International* or *global funds* are often considered a subset of specialty funds in that they are focused investments, with portfolios holding investments in the markets that offer the best prospects, regardless of location.
- *Real estate funds* aim for long-term growth through capital appreciation and the reinvestment of income by investing in income-producing real property. These are generally the least liquid of all the types of mutual funds.
- *Ethical funds* seek to make investment decisions that are guided by moral criteria that can vary from fund to fund. Each investment made is examined from the perspective of obeying certain requirements.
- *Segregated funds* are offered by insurance companies as an alternative to conventional mutual funds and offer a range of investment objectives and categories of securities. They are unique in that they guarantee that a portion (usually 75 percent or more) of your principal will be returned to you at maturity, regardless of the performance of the fund.
- *Labour-sponsored venture capital corporations (LSVCCs)* are sponsored by labour organizations, and their specific mandate is to invest in small to medium-sized businesses. LSVCCs have the advantage of being eligible for generous federal and provincial tax credits but entail higher risks.

family of funds A
group of mutual funds
managed by one
investment company.

A **family of funds** exists when one investment company manages a group of mutual funds. Each fund within the family has a different financial objective. For instance, one fund may be a government bond fund and another a growth fund. Most investment companies offer exchange privileges that enable shareholders to switch among the mutual funds in a fund family. For example, if you own shares in the Desjardins growth fund, you may, at your discretion, switch to the Desjardins ethical income fund. Generally, investors may give instructions to switch from one fund to another within the same family either in writing, over the telephone, or via the Internet. The family-of-funds concept makes it convenient for shareholders to switch their investments among funds as different funds offer more potential, financial reward, or security. Charges for exchanges, if any, generally are small for each transaction. For funds that do charge, the fee may be as low as $5 per transaction.

Many financial analysts suggest that the true mark of a quality mutual fund investment is the fund's ability to increase the investor's return during good times and maintain that return during bad times. To help accomplish this task, a large number of investors have turned to market timers. A **market timer** is an individual who helps investors decide when to switch their investments from one fund to another fund, usually within the same family of funds. Market timers usually charge an annual fee of $1\frac{1}{2}$ to 3 percent of the dollar value of the funds they manage. When evaluating market timers, keep in mind that the services they offer are a relatively recent innovation. Thus, it may be hard to judge their long-term track record accurately. Early research indicates that market timers must be evaluated on their individual investment philosophy and their past performance, and it is impossible to pass judgment on *all* market timers as a group.

market timer An
individual who helps
investors decide
when to switch their
investments from one
fund to another fund,
usually within the same
family of funds.

CONCEPT CHECK 13-2

1. How important is the investment objective as stated in a fund's prospectus?
2. Why do you think fund managers offer so many different kinds of funds?
3. What is a family of funds? How is it related to shareholder exchanges?
4. How does a market timer help people manage their mutual fund investments?

How to Make a Decision to Buy or Sell Mutual Funds

Objective 3

Evaluate mutual
funds for investment
purposes.

Often, the decision to buy or sell shares in mutual funds is "too easy" because investors assume they do not need to evaluate these investments. Why question what the professional portfolio managers decide to do? Yet, professionals do make mistakes. The responsibility for choosing the right mutual fund rests with *you*. After all, you are the only one who knows how much risk you are willing to assume and how a particular mutual fund can help you achieve your goals.

If you think there are mutual funds designed to meet just about any conceivable investment objective, you are probably right. Hundreds of mutual funds trade daily under the headings "aggressive growth," "small-cap," and "growth-income." Fortunately, a lot of information is available to help you evaluate a specific mutual fund. Unfortunately, you can get lost in all the facts and figures and forget your ultimate goal: to choose a mutual fund that will help you achieve your financial goals. To help you sort out all the research, statistics, and information about mutual funds and give you some direction as to what to do first, we have provided the checklist in Exhibit 13–4. The remainder of this section explains the types of information you can obtain from each source listed in the exhibit.

☐ **Step 1: Perform a financial checkup to make sure you are ready to invest.**
For more information, review the material presented in Chapter 10.

☐ **Step 2: Obtain the money you need to purchase mutual funds.**
Although the amount will vary, $250 to $2,500 is usually required to open an account with a brokerage firm or an investment company.

☐ **Step 3: Determine your investment objectives.**
For more information, review the material presented in Chapter 10.

☐ **Step 4: Find a fund with an objective that matches your objective.**
The Financial Post, The Globe and Mail's Report on Business, and *IE:Money* may help you identify funds with objectives that match your investment objectives. Also, you can contact the investment company and ask for a prospectus and an annual report for a specific mutual fund. Finally, you can use the Internet to screen mutual funds that are compatible with your investment objectives.

☐ **Step 5: Evaluate, evaluate, and evaluate any mutual fund before buying or selling.**
Complete the Evaluation of a Mutual Fund form on p. 397 before making a decision to buy or sell a mutual fund. Possible sources of information include newspapers, the fund's prospectus, the fund's annual report, financial publications, the Internet, and professional advisory services—all sources described in this chapter. Be sure to evaluate the fund manager's background and how long the manager has been managing the fund.

Exhibit 13–4

Common Steps Used by Investors to Evaluate Mutual Funds

HOW TO READ THE MUTUAL FUNDS SECTION OF THE NEWSPAPER

The Financial Post and *The Globe and Mail* provide information about mutual funds. Exhibit 13–5 is a guide to reading mutual fund tables as presented by *The Financial Post.* Other newspapers have similar reporting schemes, and in general, all provide the fund name, family, and current price. In addition, the 52-week highest and lowest paid prices will be shown, as well as the net asset value per share (NAVPS) and the percent change in price. Much of this same information is also available on the Internet.

The letters beside the name of a specific fund can be very informative. You can find out what they mean by looking at the footnotes that accompany the newspaper's mutual fund quotations. Generally, "N" means no-load, "U" means U.S. currency, "F" is front load or fee, and "B" signifies both front- and back-end fees.

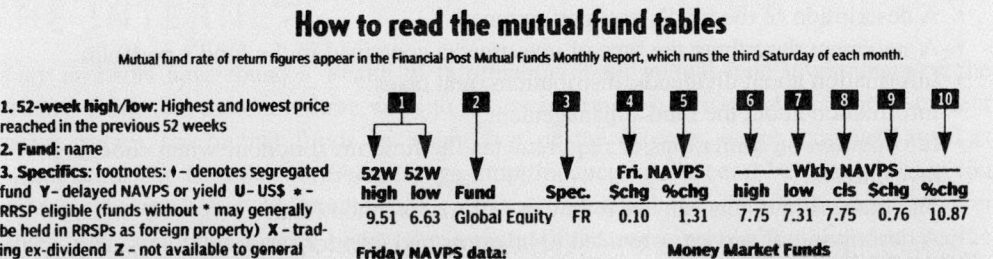

How to read the mutual fund tables

Mutual fund rate of return figures appear in the Financial Post Mutual Funds Monthly Report, which runs the third Saturday of each month.

1. 52-week high/low: Highest and lowest price reached in the previous 52 weeks
2. Fund: name
3. Specifics: footnotes: ◊ – denotes segregated fund **Y** – delayed NAVPS or yield **U** – US$ ∗ – RRSP eligible (funds without ∗ may generally be held in RRSPs as foreign property) **X** – trading ex-dividend **Z** – not available to general public **N** – no load fund **F** – front-end load or fee **D** – deferred declining redemption fee based on original capital invested **R** – deferred declining redemption fee based on market value **FD** – F or D at buyer's option **FR** – F or R at buyer's option **B** – both front- and back-end fee ... – data not available

52W high	52W low	Fund	Spec.	Fri. NAVPS $chg	%chg	Wkly NAVPS high	low	cls	$chg	%chg
9.51	6.63	Global Equity	FR	0.10	1.31	7.75	7.31	7.75	0.76	10.87

Friday NAVPS data:
4. **Dollar change:** from previous day
5. **% Change:** from previous day
Friday NAVPS data:
6. **High** on week
7. **Low** on week
8. **Close** on week
9. **$ Change** from previous week
10 **% Change** from previous week

Money Market Funds
Data for money market funds and segregated money market funds reflect current yields, not NAVPS. For example, under "dollar change" the figures would indicate the change in a fund's current yield in terms of percentage points. Pricing and yield data supplied by Fundata Canada Inc. is for information purposes only. Confirmation of price should be obtained from the fund sponsor.

Exhibit 13–5

Financial Information about Mutual Funds Available in the Mutual Funds Section of *The Financial Post*

SOURCE: *The Financial Post* (as part of *National Post*), Saturday, July 1 2000, p. C7.

Financial Planning for Life's Situations

A DREAM COME TRUE FOR THE ADAMSES

For Mike and Kathy Adams, both in their 30s, the last three years have been like a roller-coaster ride. In late 1996, they invested $11,500 in the Altamira Asia Pacific mutual fund. When they made their investment, just about everyone was talking about global investments. The fund seemed to be one of the best and was definitely a high flyer until October 1997. Then, the economies in Hong Kong, Indonesia, and other Pacific Rim countries began to experience financial troubles, and investors got scared. The Adamses' Altamira fund, like many other global investments in stocks and mutual funds, took a real hit. At that point, they considered selling their Altamira Asia Pacific shares, but they didn't want to lose some of their initial investment.

The Adamses had decided to purchase the fund on the basis of research they did in the library and on the Internet. Both admitted they were overwhelmed with the amount of information they found on mutual fund investments. Some of the more interesting articles stressed the need to diversify and place 10 to 30 percent of one's assets in global investments. According to another article, global investors enjoyed two major advantages. First, global investments provide investors with diversification. Second, economies in many nations around the globe are expanding faster than the Canadian economy.

On the basis of their research, the Adamses decided to go global, but then they had to decide if they wanted to invest in individual stocks issued by foreign companies or global mutual funds. Much of the research they read pointed out that purchasing individual, global stocks was a road full of potholes. For starters, evaluating foreign firms may be more difficult than evaluating Canadian firms because reliable accounting information is often scarce. It was easier to get reliable information about global mutual funds. By calling a toll-free phone number, they could obtain a prospectus, an annual report, and information about the fund manager. *Report on Business*, *Canadian Business*, *The Financial Post*, and other financial publications also provided information about global mutual fund investments. For these reasons, most financial planners recommended global mutual funds for people with less than $200,000 to invest.

Now, the Adamses are glad they didn't sell their shares in Altamira Asia Pacific. By the end of 1997, just a little over two months after the big downturn in October 1997, their fund had recovered and was worth more than they had paid for it. In late 1999, three years after their purchase of shares in Altamira Asia Pacific, they had averaged between 21 and 22 percent every year, and the value of their investment had increased to almost $20,000.

The Adamses continue to monitor their investment.

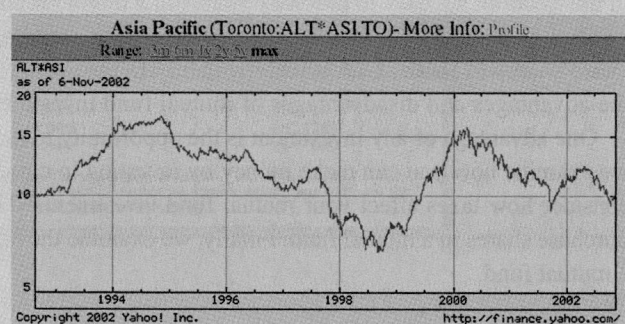

SOURCE: http://ca.finance.yahoo.com

---

income dividends The earnings a fund pays to shareholders after it has deducted expenses from its dividend and interest income.

capital gain distributions The payments made to a fund's shareholders that result from the sale of securities in the fund's portfolio.

RETURN ON INVESTMENT

As with other investments, the purpose of investing in a closed-end fund or an open-end fund is to earn a financial return. Shareholders in such funds can receive a return in one of three ways. First, both types of funds pay income dividends. **Income dividends** are the earnings a fund pays to shareholders after it has deducted expenses from its dividend and interest income. Mutual fund dividends are usually paid once or twice a year. Second, investors may receive capital gain distributions. **Capital gain distributions** are the payments made to a fund's shareholders that result from the sale of securities in the fund's portfolio. These amounts generally are paid once a year. Third, as with stock and bond investments, you can buy shares in both types of funds at a low price and then sell them after the price has increased. For example, assume you purchased shares in the Royal Dividend Mutual Fund at $22.50 per share and sold your shares two years later at $25 per share. In this case, you made $2.50 ($25 selling price

Financial Planning Calculations

EVALUATION OF A MUTUAL FUND

No checklist can serve as a foolproof guide for choosing a mutual fund. However, the following questions will help you evaluate a potential investment in such a fund.

CATEGORY 1: FUND CHARACTERISTICS

1. What is the value of the assets of this fund?
   _____
2. What is this fund's CBRS rating? _____
3. What is the minimum investment? _____
4. Does the fund allow telephone exchanges?
   ☐Yes ☐No
5. Is there a fee for telephone exchanges?
   ☐Yes ☐No

CATEGORY 2: COSTS

6. Is there a front-end load charge? If so, how much is it? _____
7. Is there a redemption fee? If so, how much is it?
   _____
8. How much is the annual management fee?
   _____
9. What is the fund's expense ratio? _____

CATEGORY 3: DIVERSIFICATION

10. What is the fund's objective? _____
11. What types of securities does the fund's portfolio include? _____
12. How many securities does the fund's portfolio include? _____
13. How many types of industries does the fund's portfolio include? _____

CATEGORY 4: FUND PERFORMANCE

14. How long has the fund manager been with the fund? _____
15. How would you describe the fund's performance over the past 12 months? _____
    _____
16. How would you describe the fund's performance over the past five years? _____
    _____
17. How would you describe the fund's performance over the past 10 years? _____
    _____

CATEGORY 5: CONCLUSION

18. On the basis of the above information, do you think an investment in this fund will help you achieve your investment goals?
    ☐Yes ☐No
19. Explain your answer to question 18.
    _____
    _____
    _____
    _____

A WORD OF CAUTION

When you use a checklist, there is always a danger of overlooking important relevant information. The above checklist is not a cure-all, but it does provide some very sound questions that you should answer before making a mutual fund investment decision. Quite simply, it is a place to start. If you need other information, *you* are responsible for obtaining it and for determining how it affects your potential investment.

---

minus $22.50 purchase price) per share. With this financial information and dollar amounts for income dividends and capital gain distributions, you can calculate a total return for your mutual fund investment. Before completing this section, you may want to examine the actual procedure used to calculate the dollar amount of total return and percentage of total return in the Financial Planning Calculations box on page 399.

When shares in a mutual fund are sold, the profit that results from an increase in value is referred to as a *capital gain*. Note the difference between a capital gain distribution and a capital gain. A capital gain distribution occurs when *the fund* distributes profits that result from *the fund* selling securities in the portfolio at a profit. On the other hand, a capital gain is the profit that results when *you* sell your shares in the mutual fund for more than you paid for them. Of course, if the price of a fund's shares goes down between the time of your purchase and the time of sale, you incur a loss.

TAXES AND MUTUAL FUNDS

Income dividends, capital gain distributions, and financial gains and losses from the sale of closed-end or open-end funds are subject to taxation. At the end of each year, investment companies are required to send each shareholder a statement specifying how much he or she received in dividends and capital gain distributions. Investment companies may provide this information as part of their year-end statement.

The following information provides general guidelines on how mutual fund transactions are taxed:

- When corporations pay dividends, they do so with after-tax income. To adjust for this, the dividend income you receive from them is taxed in a special way. You receive a dividend tax credit that is calculated by "grossing-up" or increasing the actual dividend by a certain percentage.
- Capital gains are now usually taxed as regular income, with only two exceptions. These exceptions are granted for capital gains on investment in specific small businesses and labour sponsored venture capital corporations.

Two specific problems develop with taxation of mutual funds. First, almost all investment companies allow you to reinvest income distributions and capital gain distributions from the fund in additional shares instead of receiving cash. Even though you didn't receive cash because you chose to reinvest such distributions, they are still taxable and must be reported on your federal tax return as current income. Second, when you purchase shares of stock, corporate bonds, or other investments and use the buy-and-hold technique described in Chapter 11, you decide when you sell. Thus, you can pick the tax year when you pay tax on capital gains or deduct capital losses. Mutual funds, on the other hand, buy and sell securities within the fund's portfolio on a regular basis during any 12-month period. At the end of the year, profits that result from the mutual fund's buying and selling activities are paid to shareholders in the form of capital gain distributions. Unlike with investments that you manage, you have no control over when the mutual fund sells securities and when you will be taxed on capital gain distributions.

To ensure having all of the documentation you need for tax reporting purposes, it is essential that *you* keep accurate records. The same records will help you monitor the value of your mutual fund investments and make more intelligent decisions with regard to buying and selling these investments.

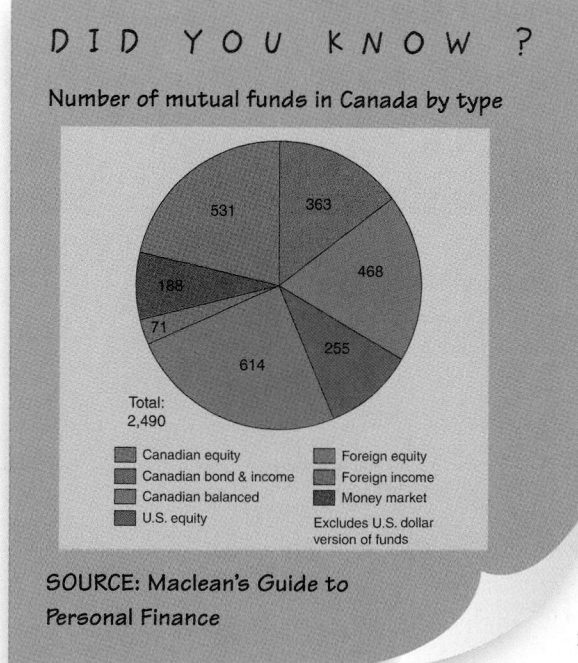

DID YOU KNOW ?

Number of mutual funds in Canada by type

Total: 2,490

- Canadian equity
- Canadian bond & income
- Canadian balanced
- U.S. equity
- Foreign equity
- Foreign income
- Money market

Excludes U.S. dollar version of funds

SOURCE: Maclean's Guide to Personal Finance

PURCHASE OPTIONS

You can buy shares of a closed-end fund through various stock exchanges or in the over-the-counter market. You can purchase shares of an open-end, no-load fund by contacting the investment company that sponsors the fund. You can purchase shares of an open-end, load fund through a salesperson who is authorized to sell them, through an account executive of a brokerage firm, or directly from the investment company that sponsors the fund.

You can also purchase both no-load and load funds from mutual fund supermarkets, available through discount brokerage firms. A mutual fund supermarket offers at least two advantages. First, instead of dealing with numerous investment companies that sponsor mutual funds, you can make one toll-free phone call to obtain information, purchase shares, and sell shares in a large number of mutual funds. Second, you receive one statement from the discount brokerage firm instead of receiving a statement from each investment company you deal with.

Financial Planning Calculations

CALCULATING TOTAL SHAREHOLDER RETURN FOR MUTUAL FUNDS

In Chapter 10, we defined total shareholder return (TSR) as a calculation that includes not only the yearly dollar amount of income but also any increase or decrease in market value from the original purchase price of an investment. For mutual funds, you can use the following calculation to determine the dollar amount of TSR:

> Income dividends
> + Capital gain distributions
> + Change in share market value
> _____
> Dollar amount of TSR

For example, assume you purchased 100 shares of BMO Bond Fund for $12.20 per share for a total investment of $1,220. During the next 12 months, you received income dividends of $0.45 a share and capital gain distributions of $0.90. Also, assume you sold your investment at the end of 12 months for $14.40 a share. As illustrated below, the dollar amount for TSR is $355:

Income dividends = 100 × $0.45 =	$ 45
Capital gain distributions = 100 × $0.90 =	+ 90
Change in share value = $14.40 – $12.20	
= $2.20 × 100 =	+ 220
Dollar amount of TSR	$ 355

To calculate the percentage of TSR, divide the dollar amount of TSR by the original cost of your mutual fund investment. The percentage of TSR for the above example is 29.1 percent, as follows:

$$\text{Percent of TSR} = \frac{\text{Dollar amount of TSR}}{\text{Original cost of your investment}}$$

$$= \frac{\$355}{\$1,220}$$

$$= 0.291, \text{ or } 29.1\%$$

One statement can be a real plus because it provides the information you need to monitor the value of your investments in one place and in the same format.

Because of the unique nature of open-end fund transactions, we will examine how investors buy and sell shares in this type of mutual fund from an investment company.

To purchase shares in an open-end mutual fund from an investment company, you may use four options: regular account transactions, voluntary savings plans, contractual savings plans, and reinvestment plans. The most popular and least complicated method of purchasing shares in an open-end fund is through a regular account transaction. When you use a regular account transaction, you decide how much money you want to invest and when you want to invest and simply buy as many shares as possible.

The chief advantage of the voluntary savings plan is that it allows you to make smaller purchases than the minimum purchases required by the regular account method described above. At the time of the initial purchase, you declare an intent to make regular minimum purchases of the fund's shares. Although there is no penalty for not making purchases, most investors feel an "obligation" to make purchases on a periodic basis, and, as noted throughout this text, small monthly investments are a great way to save for long-term objectives. For most voluntary savings plans, the minimum purchase ranges from $25 to $100 for each purchase after the initial investment. Funds try to make investing as easy as possible. Most offer payroll deduction plans, and many will deduct, upon proper shareholder authorization, a specified amount from a shareholder's bank account. Also, many investors can choose mutual funds as a vehicle to invest money that is contributed to an RRSP account. Chapter 14 provides more information on the tax advantages of different types of retirement accounts.

Contractual savings plans require you to make regular purchases over a specified period of time, usually 10 to 15 years. These plans are sometimes referred to as *front-end load funds* because almost all of the commissions are paid in the first few years of the contract period. You will incur penalties if you do not fulfill the purchase requirements. For example, if you drop out of a contractual savings plan before completing the purchase requirements, you sacrifice the prepaid commissions. Many financial experts and government regulatory agencies are critical of contractual savings plans.

You may also purchase shares in an open-end fund by using the fund's reinvestment plan. A **reinvestment plan** is a service provided by an investment company in which income dividends and capital gain distributions are automatically reinvested to purchase additional shares of the fund. Most reinvestment plans allow shareholders to use reinvested money to purchase shares without having to pay additional sales charges or commissions. *Reminder:* When your dividends or capital gain distributions are reinvested, you must still report these transactions as taxable income.

All four purchase options allow you to buy shares over a long period of time. As a result, you can use the principle of *dollar cost averaging*, which was introduced in Chapter 11. Dollar cost averaging allows you to average many individual purchase prices over a long period of time. This method helps you avoid the problem of buying high and selling low. With dollar cost averaging, you can make money if you sell your mutual fund shares at a price higher than their *average* purchase price.

reinvestment plan
A service provided by an investment company in which shareholder income dividends and capital gain distributions are automatically reinvested to purchase additional shares of the fund.

WITHDRAWAL OPTIONS

Because closed-end funds are listed on securities exchanges or traded in the over-the-counter market, it is possible to sell shares in such a fund to another investor. Shares in an open-end fund can be sold on any business day to the investment company that sponsors the fund. In this case, the shares are redeemed at their net asset value. All you have to do is give proper notification, and the fund will send you a cheque. With some funds, you can even write cheques to withdraw money from the fund.

In addition, most funds have provisions that allow investors with shares that have a minimum net asset value of at least $5,000 to use four options to systematically withdraw money. First, you may withdraw a specified, fixed dollar amount each investment period until your fund has been exhausted. Normally, an investment period is three months, and most funds require investors to withdraw a minimum amount, usually $50, each investment period.

A second option allows you to liquidate or "sell off" a certain number of shares each investment period. Since the net asset value of shares in a fund varies from one period to the next, the amount of money you receive will also vary. Once the specified number of shares has been sold, a cheque is mailed directly to you.

A third option allows you to withdraw a fixed percentage of asset growth. For example, assume you arrange to receive 60 percent of the asset growth of your investment, and the asset growth of your investment amounts to $800 in a particular investment period. For that period, you will receive a cheque for $480 ($800 × 60% = $480). If no asset growth occurs, no payment is made to you. Under this option, your principal remains untouched.

A final option allows you to withdraw all asset growth that results from income dividends and capital gains earned by the fund during an investment period. Under this option, your principal remains untouched.

Visit the Web site
See the Post-Test under Chapter 13 on the online learning centre at www.mcgrawhill.ca/ college/kapoor.

CONCEPT CHECK 13–4

1. How can you make money when investing in mutual funds?
2. What is the difference among income dividends, capital gain distributions, and capital gains?
3. How are income dividends, capital gain distributions, and capital gains reported on your federal tax return?
4. Whom would you contact to purchase a closed-end fund? An open-end fund?
5. What options can you use to purchase shares in a mutual fund from an investment company?
6. What options can you use to withdraw money from a mutual fund?

SUMMARY OF OBJECTIVES

Objective 1
Describe the characteristics of mutual fund investments.
The major reasons investors choose mutual funds are professional management and diversification. Mutual funds are also a convenient way to invest money. There are two types of mutual funds. A closed-end fund is a mutual fund whose shares are issued only when the fund is originally set up. An open-end fund is a mutual fund whose shares are sold and redeemed by the investment company at the net asset value (NAV) at the request of investors. Mutual funds are also classified as load or no-load funds. A load fund charges a commission every time you purchase shares. No commission is charged to purchase shares in a no-load fund. Mutual funds can also be front-end load or back-end load. Other possible fees include management fees and contingent deferred sales loads.

Objective 2
Classify mutual funds by investment objective.
The managers of mutual funds tailor their investment portfolios to the investment objectives of their customers. The major fund categories includes money market funds, mortgage funds, bond funds, dividend funds, balanced and asset allocation funds, equity or common stock funds, specialty funds, international or global funds, real estate funds, ethical funds, segregated funds, and labour-sponsored venture capital corporations (LSVCCs). Today, many investment companies use a family of funds concept, which allows shareholders to switch their investments among funds as different funds offer more potential, financial reward, or security.

Objective 3
Evaluate mutual funds for investment purposes.
The responsibility for choosing the "right" mutual fund rests with you, the investor. The information in newspapers, the financial objectives of the fund, the information in the prospectus and annual reports, financial publications, professional advisory services, and the Internet can all help you evaluate a mutual fund.

Objective 4
Describe how and why mutual funds are bought and sold.
The advantages and disadvantages of mutual funds have made mutual funds the investment of choice for many investors. For $250 to $2,500, you can open an account and begin investing. The shares of a closed-end fund are bought and sold on organized stock exchanges. The shares of an open-end fund may be purchased through a salesperson who is authorized to sell them, through an account executive of a brokerage firm, from a mutual fund supermarket, or from the investment company that sponsors the fund. The shares in an open-end fund can be sold to the investment company that sponsors the fund. Shareholders in mutual funds can receive a return in one of three ways: income dividends, capital gain distributions when the fund buys and sells securities in the fund's portfolio at a profit, and capital gains when shares in the mutual fund are sold at a higher price than the price paid. A number of purchase and withdrawal options are available.

KEY TERMS

capital gain distributions 396

closed-end fund 383

contingent deferred sales load 385

family of funds 390

income dividends 396

investment company 382

load fund 384

market timer 390

mutual fund 381

net asset value (NAV) 383

no-load fund 384

open-end fund 383

reinvestment plan 400

KEY FORMULAS

Page	Topic	Formula
384	Net asset value	$\text{Net asset value} = \dfrac{\text{Current market value of a funds portfolio} - \text{Liabilities}}{\text{Number of shares outstanding}}$
	Example:	$\text{Net asset value} = \dfrac{\$24,500,000 - \$2,000,000}{1,800,000}$
		$= \$12.50 \text{ per share}$

Page	Topic	Formula

| 399 | Total shareholder return | Income dividends
+ Capital gain distributions
+ Change in market value
──────────────────────
Dollar amount of TSR |
| | Example: | Dollar amount of $ 120
                 +   80
                 + 320
                 $ 520 |

| 399 | Percent of total shareholder return | $\text{Percent of TSR} = \dfrac{\text{Dollar amount of TSR}}{\text{Original cost of investment}}$ |
| | Example: | $\text{Percent of TSR} = \dfrac{\$\ 520}{\$4,500}$

$= 0.116\text{, or }11.6\%$ |

FINANCIAL PLANNING PROBLEMS

1. *Calculating Net Asset Value.* Given the following information, calculate the net asset value for the Altamira Bond mutual fund. (Obj. 1)

Total assets	$225,000,000
Total liabilities	$5,000,000
Total number of shares	4,400,000

2. *Calculating Net Asset Value.* Given the following information, calculate the net asset value for the New Empire small-cap mutual fund. (Obj. 1)

Total assets	$350,000,000
Total liabilities	$10,000,000
Total number of shares	17,000,000

3. *Calculating Sales Fees.* Jane Tong invested $15,000 in the ADA Diversified Futures Mutual Fund. The fund charges a 5.50 percent commission when shares are purchased. Calculate the amount of commission Jane must pay. (Obj. 1)

4. *Calculating Sales Fees.* Tony Matteo invested $9,800 in the CI Harbour Growth growth and income fund. The fund charges a 5.3 percent commission when shares are purchased. Calculate the amount of commission Tony must pay. (Obj. 1)

5. *Determining Management Fees.* Chris Lavigne invested a total of $8,500 in the AIC Diversified Canada Mutual Fund. The management fee for this particular fund is 2.38 percent of the total investment amount. Calculate the management fee Chris must pay this year. (Obj. 1)

6. *Calculating Contingent Deferred Sales Loads.* Mary Canfield purchased the All-Canadian Compound bond fund. While this fund doesn't charge a front-end load, it does charge a contingent deferred sales load of 4 percent for any withdrawals in the first five years. If Mary withdraws $6,000 during the second year, how much is the contingent deferred sales load? (Obj. 1)

7. *Matching Mutual Funds with Investor Needs.* This chapter classified mutual funds into different categories based on the nature of their investments. Using the following information, pick a mutual fund category that you consider suitable for each investor described and justify your choice. (Obj. 2)

   a. A 25-year-old single investor with a new job that pays $30,000 a year.
   Mutual fund category_____
   Why? _____

   b. A single parent with two children who has just received a $100,000 divorce settlement, has no job, and has not worked outside the home for the past five years.
   Mutual fund category _____
   Why? _____

   c. A husband and wife who are both in their early 60s and retired.
   Mutual fund category _____
   Why? _____

8. *Finding Total Return.* Assume that one year ago, you bought 100 shares of a mutual fund for $15 per share, you received a $.75-per-share capital gain distribution during the past 12 months, and the market value of the fund is now $18. Calculate the total return for this investment if you were to sell it now. (Obj. 3)

9. *Finding Percent of Total Shareholder Return.* Given the information in question 8, calculate the percent of TSR for your $1,500 investment. (Obj. 3)

10. *Using Dollar Cost Averaging.* Over a four-year period, Matt Ewing purchased shares in the Barreau du Quebec Canadian Equity Fund. Using the following information, answer the questions that follow. You may want to review the concept of dollar cost averaging in Chapter 11 before completing this problem. (Obj. 4)

Year	Investment Amount	Price per Share
1999	$3,000	$40 per share
2000	$3,000	$50 per share
2001	$3,000	$60 per share
2002	$3,000	$45 per share

a. At the end of four years, what is the total amount invested?

b. At the end of four years, what is the total number of mutual fund shares purchased?

c. At the end of four years, what is the average cost for each mutual fund share?

FINANCIAL PLANNING ACTIVITIES

1. *Deciding If Mutual Funds Are Right for You.* Assume you are 35, are divorced, and have just received a $120,000 legal settlement. Prepare a two-page report on the major reasons you want to invest in mutual funds. (Obj. 1)

2. *Applying Terms to Mutual Fund Investments.* Using recent newspapers, magazines, mutual fund reports, or the Internet, find examples of the following concepts: (Obj. 1)
   a. The net asset value for a mutual fund.
   b. An example of a load fund.
   c. An example of a no-load fund.
   d. The management fee for a specific mutual fund.
   e. A fund that charges a contingent deferred sales load.

3. *Understanding Fees Associated with Mutual Fund Investments.* Assume you are single, are 28 years old, and have decided to invest $8,000 in mutual funds. (Obj. 1)
   a. Prepare a chart that shows the typical charges for load funds, no-load funds, and management fees.
   b. Calculate the following fees for your $8,000 mutual fund investment: (1) a 5-percent load charge, and (2) an annual 0.50-percent management fee.

4. *Matching Mutual Funds with Investor Needs.* This chapter explored a number of different classifications of mutual funds. (Obj. 2)
   a. On the basis of your age and current financial situation, which type of mutual fund seems appropriate for your investment needs? Explain your answer.
   b. As people get closer to retirement, their investment goals often change. Assume you are now 45 and have accumulated $110,000 in a retirement account. In this situation, what type of mutual fund would you choose? Why?
   c. Assume you are now 60 years of age and have accumulated $400,000 in a retirement account. Also, assume you would like to retire when you are 65. What type of mutual funds would you choose to help you reach your investment goals? Why?

5. *Using Information to Evaluate Mutual Funds.* Obtain specific information on either the Fidelity Disciplined Equity Class mutual fund or the Fidelity Canadian Short Term Bond-A fund. Then, describe how each of the following sources of information could help you evaluate one of these mutual funds: (Obj. 3)
   a. Newspapers.
   b. The fund's investment objective.
   c. The fund's prospectus.
   d. The fund's annual report.
   e. Financial publications.
   f. The Internet.
   After researching one of the Fidelity funds, would you invest in the fund? Why or why not?

6. *Evaluating Mutual Funds.* Choose one of the following mutual funds and use information from newspapers, magazines, mutual fund reports, or the Internet to complete the mutual fund evaluation form presented in the Financial Planning Calculations feature on page 397. Then, answer the following questions: (Obj. 3)

Name of Fund	Type of Fund
AIM Canadian Premier	large-cap equity
Altamira Health Sciences	specialty
Dynamic APEX Balances	balanced
BMO Emerging Markets	emerging markets
AIC Diversified Canada	Canadian equity

   a. Which fund did you choose?
   b. Why did you choose this fund?
   c. Do you think this fund could help you achieve your investment objectives? Explain your answer.

7. *Applying the Concept of Dollar Cost Averaging.* In a one-page report, explain how the concept of dollar cost averaging applies to the options used to purchase mutual funds. (Obj. 4)

8. *Reading a Prospectus.* Obtain a mutual fund prospectus to determine the options you can use to purchase and redeem shares. Then, prepare a chart that illustrates which options can be used to purchase and redeem shares in the fund, and answer the following questions: (Obj. 4)
   a. Which purchase option would appeal to you?
   b. Assuming you are now of retirement age, which withdrawal option would appeal to you?

LIFE SITUATION CASE

The Wrong Mutual Fund?

According to Mike and Lorraine Racine, an Edmonton couple in their middle 30s, mutual funds were one of the biggest disappointments in their lives. In 1996, they invested $11,500 in the All-Canadian Resources mutual fund. Three years later, their original investment had lost over 20 percent, or about $2,500, during a period when most mutual funds were posting huge profits. What went wrong?

Three years after their investment, the Racines admitted they had invested money without researching the All-Canadian fund. They made their investment choice because Mike had heard a "high-powered" financial planner on a radio talk show raving about gold as the "ultimate" safe investment. Over the next two days, Mike had convinced Lorraine that gold was an investment that could be trusted. The Racines would have purchased the gold coins the talk show host was selling, but Mike lost the phone number. For lack of some other way to invest in gold, they decided to purchase shares in the All-Canadian Resources mutual fund. Besides, they reasoned, shares in a mutual fund would be a better investment than purchasing individual coins because mutual funds provided diversification and professional management. Both thought they were choosing the right investment. What could be better than a mutual fund that "specialized" in gold? Their investment would be a safe choice even if other investments went down in value.

The Racines also thought that since everybody was investing in mutual funds, they had to be the perfect investment. After all, there were thousands of different funds to choose from. Indeed, it seemed almost fashionable to invest in mutual funds. Because of professional management and diversification, there was no need to evaluate a mutual fund. Certainly, the fund manager knew more about picking the investments contained in the fund's portfolio than they did. It seemed mutual funds were almost guaranteed to increase in value. But after losing over 20 percent in three years, they realized that "almost guaranteed" was not the same thing as "guaranteed."

At the time of their investment, both had heard good things about All-Canadian mutual funds. A number of their friends had opened accounts with All-Canadian and had done well. And All-Canadian made it so easy! Just fill out an application, send the money, and let the professional managers make all the decisions. In fact, the Racines didn't realize that All-Canadian, the nation's largest mutual fund family, offered funds ranging from very conservative to very speculative investments. Simply put, they chose the wrong All-Canadian mutual fund.

Questions

1. Often, investors indicate that diversification and professional management are the two main reasons they choose mutual fund investments. How important do you consider these two factors? Why?
2. According to the Racines, everybody was investing in mutual funds—indeed, it seemed almost fashionable to invest in mutual funds. In your own words, what did the Racines do wrong?
3. Obtain information about a reputable mutual fund at the library or via the Internet. Then, complete a mutual fund evaluation form (see the Financial Planning Calculations feature on page 397) for this fund and answer the following questions:
   a. What sources of information did you use to evaluate the fund?
   b. What fees must investors pay to invest in the fund?
   c. What is the investment objective for the fund?
   d. How would you describe the fund's financial performance over the past 12 months? The past three years? The past five years?
   e. How would you rate the risk associated with the fund?
   f. Would you invest your money in this fund? Justify your answer.

CREATING A FINANCIAL PLAN

Investing in Mutual Funds

Diversification through the use of mutual funds provides investors with convenience and professional management. The variety of mutual funds contributes to your ability to achieve various financial goals.

Web Sites for Mutual Funds

- The Fund Library at **www.fundlibrary.com**
- Investor Canada at **www.canadian-investor.com**
- Webfin Money mutual funds at **www.webfin.com/en/funds/**
- Fundata Canada Inc. at **www.fundata.com**
- Fundwatch at **www.fundwatch.ca**

- GLOBEfund at **www.globefund.com**
- The Investment Funds Institute of Canada at **www.ific.ca**
- Canadian Mutual Fund **www.investcom.com/page/mutual.html**
- SEDAR at **www.sedar.com**
- Morningstar Canada at **www.morningstar.ca**
- The Canadian Financial Network at **www.canadianfinance.com**
- Yahoo mutual fund centre at **http://mutualfunds.yahoo.ca**
- Mutual funds investor centre at **www.mfea.com**

(Note: Addresses and content of Web sites change, and new sites are created daily. Use search engines to update and locate Web sites for your current financial planning needs.)

Short-Term Financial Planning Activities

1. Identify types of mutual funds that might be appropriate for your various financial goals and life situations.
2. Research the recent performance records and costs of various mutual funds that could be appropriate investments for you.

Long-Term Financial Planning Activities

1. Identify types of mutual funds that you might use for your long-term financial goals.
2. Develop a plan for selecting and monitoring your mutual fund portfolio.

CONTINUOUS CASE FOR PART 4

BUILDING AN INVESTMENT PROGRAM

Life Situation
Pamela, 43; Isaac, 45; three children, ages 16, 14, and 11

Financial Goals

• Evaluate current financial condition
• Build an investment portfolio that considers various risk factors

Financial Data

Monthly income	$ 4,900
Living expenses	4,450
Assets	262,700
Liabilities	84,600
Emergency fund	5,000

With approximately 20 years to retirement, Pamela and Isaac Mortimer want to establish a more aggressive investment program to accumulate funds for their long-term financial needs. Isaac does have a retirement program at work. This money, about $110,000, is invested in various conservative mutual funds. In addition, the Mortimers established their own investment program about four years ago, and today, they have about $36,000 invested in conservative stocks and mutual funds.

In addition to their investment program, the Mortimers have accumulated $11,000 to help pay for the children's education. Also, they have $5,000 tucked away in a savings account that serves as the family's emergency fund. Finally, both will qualify for the Canada Pension Plan when they reach retirement age.

Questions

1. How would you rate the Mortimers' financial condition at this stage in their lives?
2. Given the fact that Pamela is 43 and Isaac is 45 and they have three children who will soon begin their post-secondary education, what investment goals would be most appropriate for this middle-aged couple?
3. According to Pamela, "We both know we should have started our investment program sooner, but we always seemed to have 'emergencies' that took what extra money we had." Many investors feel the same way and, to compensate for a late start, often invest in highly speculative investments that promise large returns. Would you recommend such investments to a couple like the Mortimers? Explain your answer.
4. Describe the investment portfolio you would recommend for the Mortimers. Be sure to include *specific* types of investments (stocks, bonds, mutual funds, and so on), as well as information about the risk factor(s) associated with each investment alternative.

PART 5

CONTROLLING YOUR FINANCIAL FUTURE

CHAPTER **14**
Retirement Planning

CHAPTER **15**
Estate Planning

14 Retirement Planning

Scope Out Your Social Security Benefits

When Meg Hansen and her husband, Andrew Belanger, checked their CPP retirement benefits four years ago, they confirmed a nagging suspicion: They would have to play catchup to have a comfortable retirement. As a result, they closed their home renovation business in Red Deer, Alberta, and switched to careers that would provide steadier incomes. Hansen became a certified massage therapist, and Belanger returned to his previous occupation as a social worker.

The document that supplied the couple's wake-up call was the Canada Pension Plan (CPP) statement of contributions. This document provides you with a tally of your CPP contributions as well as estimates of the benefits you are eligible to receive. "When I got the statement, I realized I would get only about $300 a month in CPP benefits unless I did something about it," says Hanson, now 54. Belanger, now 65, would have been entitled to about $600, but his career switch enabled him to draw $763 in monthly benefits when he began collecting his CPP benefits.

When making retirement plans for clients, Marilyn, a personal finance adviser in Alberta, starts with the CPP personal contributor statement. She suggests that clients look at the benefit level and see if they can live on it. Often, they say they can't. "That serves as a motivator to make sure savings are moving in the right direction," she says.

The amount of the benefits you will receive is based on your earnings and your contributions to the plan. CPP covers virtually all working Canadians, except those who live in Quebec; Quebec workers come under the Quebec Pension Plan (QPP). These two plans are closely coordinated so that you are protected wherever you live in Canada. Whether in Canada or abroad at the time of retirement, you will receive your benefits in Canadian dollars.

Every year, if you are 30 years old or older, the CPP sends

you a statement of your contributions along with an estimate of the monthly benefit you can expect to receive when you retire at age 65. You may also apply for your personal statement of contributions once in any 12-month period.

It is important to check that the personal information that appears on your statement is accurate and complete. All Canada Pension Plan benefits you may be eligible for in the future will be based on this information. If your name, birthdate, social insurance number, or earnings and contributions information is incorrect or missing you should request that it be corrected.

Next, you need to determine whether you can live on your benefits. Keep in mind that the Canadian Pension Plan was designed to replace only 25 percent of the salary from which you made your CPP contributions. There are also restrictions regarding when you actually retire. For example, if you start your pension at age 60, your monthly payment will be 30 percent lower than if you wait to age 65, but by starting it sooner you are likely to get the pension for a longer period of time. If you start your pension at age 70, your monthly payment will be 30 percent higher than if you took it at age 65.

The CPP statement of contributions is an important personal finance tool. Make sure you carefully consider how the information it holds may affect your retirement plans and goals. It could be a real eye-opener.

QUESTIONS

1 What were Meg Hansen's and Andrew Belanger's concerns about retirement income?

2 Why did they close their home renovation business?

3 What document served as the couple's wake-up call?

4 How can the Internet assist you in retirement planning?

LEARNING OBJECTIVES

1   Recognize the importance of retirement planning.

2   Analyze your current assets and liabilities for retirement.

3   Estimate your retirement spending needs.

4   Identify your retirement housing needs.

5   Determine your planned retirement income.

6   Develop a balanced budget based on your retirement income.

Why Retirement Planning?

Retirement can be a rewarding phase of your life. However, a successful, happy retirement doesn't just happen; it takes planning and continual evaluation. Thinking about retirement in advance can help you anticipate future changes and gain a sense of control over the future.

The ground rules for retirement planning are changing rapidly. Re-examine your retirement plans if you hold any of these misconceptions:

- My expenses will drop when I retire.
- My retirement will last only 15 years.
- I can depend on the government and my company pension to pay for my basic living expenses.
- My pension benefits will increase to keep pace with inflation.
- My employer's health insurance plan and medicare will cover my medical expenses.
- There's plenty of time for me to start saving for retirement.
- Saving just a little bit won't help.

It is vital to engage in basic retirement planning activities throughout your working years and to update your retirement plans periodically. While it is never too late to begin sound financial planning, you can avoid many unnecessary and serious difficulties by starting this planning early. Saving now the future requires tackling the trade-offs between spending and saving, thus taking advantage of the time value of money.

TACKLING THE TRADE-OFFS

Although exceptions exist, the old adage "You can't have your cake and eat it, too" is particularly true in planning for retirement. For example, if you buy state-of-the-art home entertainment systems, drive expensive cars, and take extravagant vacations now, don't expect to retire with plenty of money.

Only by saving now and curtailing current spending can you ensure a comfortable retirement later. Yet, saving money doesn't come naturally to many young people. Ironically, although the time to begin saving is when you are young, the people who are in the best position to save are middle-aged.

THE IMPORTANCE OF STARTING EARLY

Consider this: If from age 25 to 65 you invest $300 per month and earn an average of 9 percent interest a year, you'll have $1.4 million in your retirement fund. Waiting just 10 years until

Objective 1

Recognize the importance of retirement planning.

Visit the Web site
See the Post-Test under Chapter 14 on the online learning centre at www.mcgrawhill.ca/ college/kapoor.

Many housing alternatives exist, several of which were discussed in Chapter 7. Staying in their present homes, whether a single-family dwelling, a condominium, or an apartment, is the alternative preferred by most people approaching retirement. That's what Mike and Abby Wootton decided to do after Mike took early retirement at age 47 from his job as a service manager of a Saskatoon Ford dealership in the late 1970s. Even though the couple had already paid off the mortgage on their small, three-bedroom ranch house and could have moved up into a bigger or fancier place, all Mike wanted to do was tinker in the garage and dabble in the stock market. A recent U.S. survey of over 5,000 men and women revealed that 92 percent wanted to own their homes in retirement.[1]

Diane Forrest of Grenville, Ontario, has seen the future, and she wants to be prepared. Diane, 69, has osteoporosis, just as her mother did. Although she's not having difficulty now, she knows the debilitating bone condition eventually could make it difficult, if not impossible, to navigate steep stairs, cramped bathrooms, and narrow doorways. So, two years ago, she and her husband Carl, a 72-year-old retired sales executive, moved into a novel type of home, one that can comfortably accommodate them no matter what disabilities old age may bring. Called a "universal design home," their residence is on the cutting edge of an architectural concept that an aging population may well embrace. The only house of its kind in the neighbourhood, it has wide doors, pull-out cabinet shelves, easy-to-reach electrical switches, and dozens of other features useful for elderly persons or those with disabilities. Yet, these features are incorporated into the design unobtrusively.

This new setup suits the Forrests just fine. Unlike their peers who are moving into continuing-care communities, they want to stay where they have always lived, near their three children and around people of all ages. They now have a home that can accommodate a wheelchair and even has a room for a nurse, if the need arises. "We hope to be able to live here for the rest of our lives," says Diane—in comfort and with all the touches they need to ease their daily tasks.

Whatever retirement housing alternative you choose, make sure you know what you are signing and understand what you are buying.

AVOIDING RETIREMENT HOUSING TRAPS

Too many people make the move without doing enough research, and invariably it's a mistake. How can retirees avoid being surprised by hidden tax and financial traps when they move?

Here are some tips from retirement specialists on how to uncover hidden taxes and other costs of a retirement area before moving:

- Write or call the local chamber of commerce to get an economic profile and details on area property taxes.
- Contact the province's tax department to find out provincial income, sales, and inheritance taxes and special exemptions for retirees. If your pension will be taxed by the province you're leaving, check whether the new province will give you credit for those taxes.
- Subscribe to the weekend edition of a local newspaper.
- Call a local accountant to find out which taxes are rising.
- Check with local utilities to estimate your energy costs. Visit the area in as many seasons as possible. Talk to retirees and other local residents about costs of health care, auto insurance, food, and clothing.
- Rent for a while instead of buying immediately.

Visit the Web site

See Personal Financial Planning worksheets under Chapter 14 on the online learning centre at www.mcgrawhill.ca/ college/kapoor.

CONCEPT CHECK 14–4

1. What are some housing options for retirees?
2. How can retirees avoid retirement housing traps?

---

[1] Jeanette A. Brandt, "Housing and Community Preferences: Will They Change in Retirement?" *Family Economics Review*, U.S. Department of Agriculture, May 1989, p.7.

Financial Planning Calculations

HOW MUCH INFLATION IS IN YOUR FUTURE?

Years to Retirement	3%	4%	5%	6%	7%	8%	9%	10%	11%	12%
5	1.2	1.2	1.3	1.3	1.4	1.5	1.5	1.6	1.7	1.8
8	1.3	1.4	1.5	1.6	1.7	1.8	2.0	2.1	2.3	2.5
10	1.4	1.5	1.6	1.8	2.0	2.2	2.4	2.6	2.8	3.1
12	1.5	1.6	1.8	2.0	2.3	2.5	2.8	3.1	3.5	3.9
15	1.6	1.8	2.1	2.4	2.8	3.2	3.6	4.2	4.8	5.5
18	1.8	2.0	2.4	2.8	3.4	4.0	4.7	5.6	6.5	7.7
20	2.0	2.2	2.7	3.2	3.9	4.7	5.6	6.7	8.1	9.6
25	2.1	2.7	3.4	4.3	5.4	6.8	8.6	10.8	13.6	17.0

ESTIMATED ANNUAL RATE OF INFLATION BETWEEN NOW AND RETIREMENT

1. Choose from the first column the approximate number of years until your retirement.
2. Choose an estimated annual rate of inflation. The rate of inflation cannot be predicted accurately and will vary from year to year.
3. Find the inflation factor corresponding to the number of years until your retirement and the estimated annual inflation rate. (Example: 10 years to retirement combined with a 4 percent estimated annual inflation rate yields a 1.5 inflation factor.)
4. Multiply the inflation factor by your estimated retirement income and your estimated retirement expenses. (Example: $6,000 × 1.5 = $9,000.)

Total annual inflated retirement income: $_____.
Total annual inflated retirement expenses: $_____.

SOURCES: The above figures are from a compound interest table showing the effective yield of lump-sum investments after inflation that appeared in Charles D. Hodgman, ed., *Mathematical Tables from the Handbook of Chemistry and Physics* (Cleveland: Chemical Rubber Publishing, 1959); *Citicorp Consumer Views*, July 1985, pp. 2–3, © Citicorp, 1985; *Financial Planning Tables*, A. G. Edwards, August 1991.

Planning Your Retirement Income

Once you have determined your approximate future expenses, you must evaluate the sources and amounts of your retirement income. Possible sources of income for many retirees are public pension plans, employer pension plans, and personal retirement plans.

Objective 5

Determine your planned retirement income.

PUBLIC PENSIONS

Public pensions have existed since 1927 and were initially paid only to those over the age of 70. Federal programs are the major source of public retirement pensions, but most provinces and the territories also provide income supplements for residents in financial need.

Canada's retirement income system has three levels; the Old Age Security (OAS) provides the first level, or foundation. If you meet certain residence requirements, you'll be entitled to a modest monthly pension once you reach the age of 65; The Canada Pension Plan (CPP), or Quebec Pension Plan (QPP), is the second level of the system. It provides you with a monthly retirement pension as early as 60, if you have paid into it. Also available is the Guaranteed Income Supplement (GIS) and Spouse's allowance (SPA). Public pensions are not intended to meet all your financial needs in retirement. Rather, they provide a modest base for you to build upon with additional, private savings. The third level of the retirement income system consists of private pensions and savings.

The various types of public pensions were and are tied to either residency requirements or income requirements, and could be contributory or non-contributory.

CANADA/QUEBEC PENSION PLAN (CPP/QPP)

The CPP dates to 1966, when the federal government started the program as a mandatory defined benefit indexed pension plan for all Canadians (besides residents of Quebec, who have a similar plan called the Quebec Pension Plan [QPP]). There are three kinds of Canada Pension Plan benefits: disability benefits (which include pensions for disabled contributors and benefits for their dependent children), retirement pension, and survivor benefits (which include the death benefit, the surviving spouse's pension, and the children's benefit).

CPP CONTRIBUTIONS
The contribution you are required to make is based on your salary. If you are self-employed, it is based on your net business income (after expenses). You do not contribute on any other source of income, such as investment earnings. If during a year, you contributed too much or earned less than a set minimum amount, you will receive a refund of contributions at income tax time. You pay contributions only on your annual earnings between the minimum and a set maximum level (these are called your "pensionable" earnings). Currently, the minimum level is frozen at $3,500. The maximum level is adjusted each January, based on increases in the average wage.

The amount you pay is based on the deduction rate, which was 3.9 percent for 2000, 4.3 percent for 2001, and 4.7 percent for 2002. See Exhibit 14-6 for deduction rate table. To calculate your required contribution amount for 2002, you would simply compute 4.7 percent of your earnings after the first $3,500, which is your year's basic exemption.

There is also a limit on the amount of your pensionable earnings that counted to calculate your CPP contribution. This is called the *year's maximum pensionable earnings*. In 2002, this figure was set at $39,100 a $800 increase over 2001. This means that the most you could be required to pay into the CPP in 2002 was $1,673.20 (that is, 4.7 percent of $39,100—$3,500). If you were self-employed, you would have been asked to pay double the amount— because employee CPP contributions are matched by the employer, and your payment would need to represent both employee and employer. This means that the maximum self-employed contribution you could be required to pay into the CPP in 2002 was $3,346.40 (that is, 9.4 percent of $39,100–$3,500).

BENEFITS
Both CPP and QPP benefits are payable at age 65, whether you continue to work or not. You can also start to receive your benefits as early as age 60 or as late as age 70. If you do so, however, the amount you receive will be reduced or increased by 0.5 percent for each month earlier or later than the month of your 65th birthday. The full CPP benefit is paid

Year	Employee/Employer Rate %	Combined/Self-employed Rate %
1998	3.2	6.4
1999	3.5	7.0
2000	3.9	7.8
2001	4.3	8.6
2002	4.7	9.4
2003	4.95	9.9
2004	4.95	9.9
2005	4.95	9.9
2006	4.95	9.9

Exhibit 14–6

Canada Pension Plan Contribution Rates

Employee contributions for earnings up to $37,400 (Employers pay equal amounts; self-employed persons pay twice these amounts.)

only when you retire at age 65. The full CPP benefit is based on 25 percent of your average monthly pensionable earnings adjusted for increases in each year's maximum pensionable earnings.

There are two clauses in the CPP/QPP regulations that favour a better benefit for you. The *dropout clause* allows you to leave the lowest 15 percent of your monthly contributions during your working years out of your calculations of contribution rates. The *child-rearing clause* allows up to seven years per child of not contributing. The overall objective of these clauses is to minimize the effect on your CPP benefits of financially adverse life events.

Review Exhibit 14–7 for the types of benefits available through the CPP, the average monthly benefit in 2002, and the maximum monthly benefit for 2002. You should also note that a portion of your CPP benefits can be assigned to your spouse or common-law partner, provided that he or she is at least 60 years old. This may give your family a tax advantage if your spouse is not in a position to receive CPP benefits.

OLD AGE SECURITY (OAS)
This public pension benefit was introduced in the Old Age Security Act, which came into effect in 1952. It is indexed to inflation on a quarterly basis. If you are over the age of 65 and have been a resident of Canada for at least 40 years since age 18, you qualify for full OAS benefits. With a minimum of 10 years of residency, you will receive 1/40 of the full benefit for each year you were a resident of Canada between the ages of 18 and 65.

Type of Benefit	Average Monthly Benefit (January 2002)	Maximun Monthly Benefit (2002)
Disability benefit	$720.08	$956.05
Retirement pension (at age 65)	$440.39	$788.75
Survivors benefit (under age 65)	$326.59	$437.99
Survivors benefit (age 65 and over)	$262.47	$473.25
Children of disabled contributors benefit	$183.73	$183.77
Children of deceased contributors benefit	$183.64	$183.77
Combined survivors & retirement benefit (pension at age 65)	$606.73	$788.75
Combined survivors & disability benefit	$870.54	$956.05
Death benefit (max lump sum)	$2,171.00	$2,500.00

Exhibit 14–7

Canada Pension Plan Payment Rates January–December 2002

Canada Pension Plan rates are adjusted every January if there are increases in the cost of living as measured by the Consumer Price Index. The table below lists the maximum and average monthly rates for Canada Pension Plan benefits for 2002.

SOURCE: Human Resources Development Canada, CPP Payments Rates Jan–Dec 2002. www.hrdc-drhc.gc. ca/isp/cpp/rates_e.shtml. Reproduced with permission of the Minister of Public Works and Government Series Canada, 2002.

The exact amount you receive will depend on your declared income for a given year and the benefit, if any, will be paid to you monthly. This benefit is taxed.

GUARANTEED INCOME SUPPLEMENT (GIS) Also introduced in the OAS Act of 1952, this pension is payable to low-income OAS recipients who are 65 and older. The amount you receive depends on your marital status as well as your income. As of 2002, the maximum monthly supplement for single individuals with no income was $526.08. For each $24 dollars of annual income reported by the individual, the monthly benefit is reduced by $1 ($12 per year). Thus, earned income essentially reduces benefits by 50 percent. This is not a tax, but rather an adjustment to benefits reported upon filing taxes. (Note: OAS benefits are not included as income for determining reductions to the GIS benefits. This benefit is not taxed.)

SPOUSE'S ALLOWANCE (SPA) Yet another pension introduced in the OAS Act of 1952 was the spouse's allowance. These benefits are payable to widows, widowers, and the spouses of OAS beneficiaries who are between 60 and 65 years old. Exhibit 14–8 summarizes the eligibility criteria for Canada's public pensions.

EMPLOYER PENSION PLANS

Another possible source of retirement income is the pension plan your company offers. With employer plans, your employer contributes to your retirement benefits, and sometimes you contribute, too. These plans are termed to be either *contributory* or *noncontributory*. Pension plans held by employers for their employees were formally called a *Registered Pension Plan*, or RPP.

Since private pension plans vary, you should find out (1) when you become eligible for pension benefits, and (2) what benefits you will be entitled to. Most employer plans are defined-contribution or defined-benefit plans.

DEFINED-CONTRIBUTION PLAN Over the last two decades, the defined-contribution plan has continued to grow rapidly, while the number of defined-benefit plans has generally dropped. A **defined-contribution plan** has an individual account for each employee; therefore, these plans are sometimes called *money purchase pension plans*. The plan document describes the amount the employee and/or employer will contribute, but it does not promise any particular benefit. When a plan participant retires or otherwise becomes eligible for benefits, the benefit is the total amount in the participant's account, including past investment earnings on amounts put into the account.

What happens to your benefits under an employer pension plan if you change jobs? One of the most important aspects of such plans is vesting. **Vesting** is your right to at least a portion of the benefits you have accrued given the employer's contributions to a pension plan, even if you leave the company before you retire. Typically, you become vested when you complete two years of continuous service with a participating employer, unless your employer established a vesting period of less than two years. If you leave your employer before your benefits are vested, you are entitled to a refund of your contributions, plus interest.

---

defined-contribution plan Also called a "money purchase pension plan," this plan specifies the contribution from the employee and/or employer but does not guarantee the pension benefit you will receive.

vesting An employee's right to at least a portion of the benefits accrued under an employer pension plan, even if the employee leaves the company before retiring.

Exhibit 14–8

Sources of Retirement Income

SOURCE: Ho & Robinson, *Personal Financial Planning* Third Edition (Captus Press, 2000, page 383).

Pensions	Non-Pension Savings
Old Age Security (OAS)	Registered Retirement Savings Plan (RRSP)
Guaranteed Income Supplement (GIS)	Deferred Profit Sharing Plan (DPSP)
Canada Pension Plan (CPP)	House (if you trade down)
Employer's Registered Pension Plan (RPP)	Vacation property (if you will sell)
	Tax shelters
	Reverse mortgage
	Unsheltered savings
	Locked-in funds

DEFINED-BENEFIT PLAN In a **defined-benefit plan**, the plan document specifies the benefits promised to the employee at the normal retirement age. The plan itself does not specify how much the employer must contribute annually. The plan's actuary determines the annual employer contribution required so that the plan fund will be sufficient to pay the promised benefits as each participant retires. If the fund is inadequate, the employer must make additional contributions. Because of their actuarial aspects, defined-benefit plans tend to be more complicated and more expensive to administer than defined-contribution plans. It is generally the employer's responsibility to ensure that sufficient funds are available to pay your pension when you retire. The employer assumes the risk of investing all contributions wisely to guarantee the future value of your pension.

> **defined-benefit plan** A plan that specifies the benefits the employee will receive at the normal retirement age.

Companies nationwide are switching their retirement plans to defined contributions from defined benefits. "Paternalistic employers are dying fast—if they're not already dead," says an actuary with an international consulting firm. The result is that "the shift to defined contributions has forced employees to take more responsibility for retirement. They have discretion as to how to invest the money and must make substantive decisions about their own financial futures."[2]

DEFERRED PROFIT SHARING PLAN (DPSP) Considered by some to be a company pension plan, a DPSP is a form of retirement saving set up for contributions from the employer only; these are tax-deductible for the company. The contribution is based on the company's net income according to an agreed-upon formula, and you will not be taxed on the DPSP holdings until you withdraw them.

One issue to consider is that the contribution made to a DPSP will be subtracted from your allowable RRSP contribution. This will reduce your tax savings if you might otherwise have made a larger contribution, and if the DPSP is not managed as well as your personal RRSP, it will reduce your potential return as well.

GROUP REGISTERED RETIREMENT SAVINGS PLAN This type of plan is an RRSP set up for a particular company's employees. The advantage this plan may have over a regular RPP relates to liquidity. Group RRSPs are the property of the employees, so they can take money out if they are in financial need (despite disincentives set up by the company to discourage this). Additionally, participation in a group RRSP by an employee may lower payroll tax withholding. The principal disadvantage to a group RRSP is that it may provide a smaller return than would a company pension plan.

PLAN PORTABILITY At one time, employees who changed jobs could not take their pension credits with them. Recent legislation enforcing *pension portability*, the right to transfer pension credits from one employer to another, changed that. Now, workers with vesting rights have three different options when they change jobs. They can leave their pension credits with their former employer and receive a pension on retirement, transfer their credits to their new employer if that firm's policy permits it, or transfer their benefits to a locked-in RRSP. In cases where the employee has not met the criteria allowing them vesting rights, changing companies will signify a total loss of their pension credits.

Use the checklist in Exhibit 14–9 to help you determine what your pension plan provides and requires.

PERSONAL RETIREMENT PLANS

In addition to the retirement plans offered by public pension plans and employer pension plans, many individuals have set up personal retirement plans.

The most popular personal retirement plan is an RRSP.

---

[2] Carol Kleinman, "Firms Shifting Retirement Planning, Risk to Workers," *Chicago Tribune*, January 19, 1992, sec. 8, p. 1.

Exhibit 14–9 Know Your Pension Plan Checklist

A. Plan Type Checklist

My plan is a:
- ☐ *Defined-benefit plan*
- ☐ *Defined-contribution plan*

B. Contributions Checklist

My pension plan is financed by:
- ☐ Employer contributions only.
- ☐ Employer and employee contributions.
- ☐ Union dues and assessments.

I contribute to my pension plan at the rate of
$_____ per I month I week I hour or
_____ percent of my compensation.

C. Vesting Checklist

My plan provides vesting after _____ years.

I need _____ more years of service to be fully vested.

D. Credited Service Checklist

I will have a year of service under my pension plan:
- ☐ If I work ____ hours in a 12-consecutive-month period.
- ☐ If I meet other requirements (specify).

The plan year (12-month period for which plan records are kept) ends on _____ of each year.

I will be credited for work performed:
- ☐ Before I became a participant in the plan.
- ☐ After the plan's normal retirement age.

As of now, _____ [date], I have earned _____ years of service toward my pension.

E. Retirement Benefit Checklist

I may begin to receive full normal retirement benefits at age _____.

Working beyond the normal retirement age ☐ will ☐ will not increase the pension paid to me when I retire.

I may retire at age _____ if I have completed _____ years of service. Apart from the age requirement, I need _____ more years of service to be eligible for early retirement benefits.

The amount of my normal retirement benefit is computed as follows: _____

The amount of my early retirement benefit is computed as follows: _____

My retirement benefit will be:
- ☐ Paid monthly for life.
- ☐ Paid to me in a lump sum.
- ☐ Adjusted to the cost of living.
- ☐ Paid to my survivor in the event of my death (see "Survivors' Benefit Checklist" below).

F. Disability Benefit Checklist

My plan ☐ does ☐ does not provide disability benefits.
My plan defines the term *disability* as follows: _____
_____

To be eligible for disability retirement benefits, I must be _____ years old and must have _____ years of service.

A determination as to whether my condition meets my plan's definition of disability is made by:
- ☐ A doctor chosen by me.
- ☐ A doctor designated by the plan administrator.
- ☐ Other.

I must send my application for disability retirement benefits to _____ within ____ months after I stop working.

If I qualify for disability benefits, I will continue to receive benefits:
- ☐ For life, if I remain disabled.
- ☐ Until I return to my former job.
- ☐ Other.

G. Survivors' Benefit Checklist

My pension plan ☐ provides ☐ does not provide a joint and survivor option or a similar provision for death benefits.

My spouse and I ☐ have ☐ have not rejected in writing the joint and survivor option.

Electing the joint and survivor option will reduce my pension benefit to _____.

My survivor will receive _____ per month for life if the following conditions are met (specify):
_____
_____.

H. Plan Termination Checklist

My benefits ☐ are ☐ are not insured.

I. Benefit Application Checklist

My employer ☐ will ☐ will not automatically submit my pension application for me.

I must apply for my pension benefits ☐ on a special form that I get from _____ within ____ months ☐ before ☐ after ☐ retire.

My application for pension benefits should be sent to
_____.

I must furnish the following documents when applying for my pension benefits:_____.

If my application for pension benefits is denied, I may appeal in writing to_____ within _____ days.

J. Suspension of Benefits Checklist

- ☐ I am covered by a single-employer plan or by a plan involving more than one employer.
- ☐ I am covered by a multi-employer plan.

SOURCE: Based on *Know Your Pension Plan* (Washington, DC: U.S. Department of Labor, 1992), pp. 5–10.

WHAT IS AN RRSP? An **RRSP** is an investment vehicle that allows you to shelter your savings from income taxes. Despite the common misconceptions, it is not a specific type of investment but a way to shelter your money in one or more of a variety of investment vehicles.

Legally, an RRSP is a trust, an arrangement in which certain property is given by a settlor to a trustee, an independent third party, who holds the property on behalf of the beneficiary (or beneficiaries) who will receive income and/or capital from the trust. As contributor to the plan you are the settlor, and more often than not the trustee is a bank, though it can also be a trust company, a brokerage firm, or a life insurance company. You are the beneficiary, unless you have designated the plan as a spousal RRSP, in which case your spouse is the beneficiary.

Perhaps the result of aggressive promotion in the personal finance industry, another common misconception about RRSPs is that everyone should have one. This is not correct. The principal motive behind RRSPs should be to allow you to defer taxation. The idea is to defer your income taxes to a time when your marginal rate of taxation will be less. Exhibit 14–10 shows the power of tax-deferred compounding of earnings. If your financial circumstances are already such that you pay little or no income tax, you likely don't need an RRSP or its restrictions—Canada's federal *Income Tax Act* allows you to register only certain specified investments as RRSPs. Other restrictions include contribution limits and early withdrawal penalties. These are discussed below.

> **Registered Retirement Savings Plan (RRSP)**
> An investment vehicle that allows you to shelter your savings from income taxes.

Eligible Investments

You can choose to register a number of investments, in combination or individually. Qualified investments include savings accounts, cash, Canada Savings Bonds and treasury bills, term deposits and GICs, corporate bonds (including stripped bonds), stocks, eligible mutual funds, and real estate. Qualified investments can be divided into three categories.

The first of the categories is *guaranteed funds*, such as savings accounts, term deposits, and GICs. These funds ensure the return of your principal plus a guaranteed rate of return, and are available from most financial institutions.

A second category of RRSP investments is *mutual funds*. These have no guarantee regarding rate of return or safety of your principal and are available from most financial institutions including investment dealers and life insurance companies. Mutual fund investments include equity funds, bond funds, balanced funds, and money market funds.

Finally, *life insurance and life annuity products*, sold by life insurance companies, may also qualify as RRSP investments. Be aware, however, that tying your life insurance to your RRSP may not be a sound financial plan, as doing so might require fixed annual payments that limit your annual contribution and your freedom to move your funds within the RRSP.

Types of RRSPs

The most commonly held RRSP, known as a "regular" RRSP, is the type that most Canadians have. A regular RRSP draws on the two first categories of investments only. They are a popular choice because fees are minimal and your investments require minimal management by you, but the return on investment is lower, given that your funds are invested in principally low-risk, low-return investments.

The second main type of RRSP, a self-directed RRSP, allows you greater scope and permits you to invest in all categories. Available from most financial institutions, including investment dealers, this type of RRSP allows you to invest in cash, treasury bills, bonds (including CSBs), mortgages, mutual funds, and stocks. The fees are higher than for regular RRSPs, and you need to pay closer attention, but many people find that the investment return and other advantages outweigh the disadvantages engendered by price and effort.

Another type of registered pension plan, is a spousal RRSP, which is also available to common-law couples. With this plan, you contribute to an RRSP in which your spouse is named as the beneficiary. This can be especially useful in cases where one spouse does not participate in the labour market, such as when young children must be cared for. Note that

Exhibit 14–10   Tackling the Trade-offs (saving now versus saving later)

Saver Abe				Saver Ben			
Age	Years	Contributions	Year-End Value	Age	Years	Contributions	Year-End Value
25	1	$ 2,000	$2,188	25	1	$ 0	$0
26	2	2,000	4,580	26	2	0	0
27	3	2,000	7,198	27	3	0	0
28	4	2,000	10,061	28	4	0	0
29	5	2,000	13,192	29	5	0	0
30	6	2,000	16,617	30	6	0	0
31	7	2,000	20,363	31	7	0	0
32	8	2,000	24,461	32	8	0	0
33	9	2,000	28,944	33	9	0	0
34	10	2,000	33,846	34	10	0	0
35	11	0	40,494	35	11	2,000	2,188
36	12	0	37,021	36	12	2,000	4,580
37	13	0	44,293	37	13	2,000	7,198
38	14	0	48,448	38	14	2,000	10,061
39	15	0	52,992	39	15	2,000	13,192
40	16	0	57,963	40	16	2,000	16,617
41	17	0	63,401	41	17	2,000	20,363
42	18	0	69,348	42	18	2,000	24,461
43	19	0	75,854	43	19	2,000	28,944
44	20	0	82,969	44	20	2,000	33,846
45	21	0	90,752	45	21	2,000	39,209
46	22	0	99,265	46	22	2,000	45,075
47	23	0	108,577	47	23	2,000	51,490
48	24	0	118,763	48	24	2,000	58,508
49	25	0	129,903	49	25	2,000	66,184
50	26	0	142,089	50	26	2,000	74,580
51	27	0	155,418	51	27	2,000	83,764
52	28	0	169,997	52	28	2,000	93,809
53	29	0	185,944	53	29	2,000	104,797
54	30	0	203,387	54	30	2,000	116,815
55	31	0	222,466	55	31	2,000	129,961
56	32	0	243,335	56	32	2,000	144,340
57	33	0	266,162	57	33	2,000	160,068
58	34	0	291,129	58	34	2,000	177,271
59	35	0	318,439	59	35	2,000	196,088
60	36	0	348,311	60	36	2,000	216,670
61	37	0	380,985	61	37	2,000	239,182
62	38	0	416,724	62	38	2,000	263,807
63	39	0	455,816	63	39	2,000	290,741
64	40	0	498,574	64	40	2,000	320,202
65	41	0	545,344	65	41	2,000	352,427
		$20,000				$62,000	

Saver Abe			Saver Ben		
Value at retirement*		$545,344	Value at retirement*		$352,427
Less total contributions	⟶	$ 20,000	Less total contributions	⟶	$ 62,000
Net earnings		$525,344	Net earnings		$290,427

*The table assumes a 9-percent fixed rate of return, compounded monthly, and no fluctuation of the principal. Distributions from an RRSP are subject to ordinary income taxes when withdrawn and may be subject to other limitations under RRSP rules.

SOURCE: *The Franklin Investor* (San Mateo, CA: Franklin Distributors, Inc., January 1989).

your contribution reduces your allowable contribution to your own plan, and you may not transfer funds from your own RRSP to your spouse's except in conditions where one spouse dies or under court order following a break-up. Further, if your spouse withdraws the funds sooner than two years plus the amount of time remaining in the year you make your contribution, the full amount of the funds will be taxed as though it were in your hands.

RRSP funds can also be used for a down payment on your first home under the Home Buyers' Plan. If you qualify as a first-time buyer you are allowed to withdraw up to $20,000 as a loan from your RRSP to buy or build a home, without counting the withdrawal as income. You must then repay the loan, without interest, over the next 15 years.

Generally, you will have to repay an amount to your RRSPs each year until you have repaid the entire amount you withdrew. If you do not repay the amount due for a year, it will be included in your income for that year.

RRSP funds can also be used to finance full-time training or education for you or your spouse or common-law partner under The Lifelong Learning Plan (LLP). LLP lets you withdraw up to $10,000 a year. You have to repay these withdrawals to your RRSPs over a period of no more than 10 years. Any amount that you do not repay when it is due will be included in your income for the year it was due. See how the Dlins used their RRSP in the Financial Planning for Life's Situations feature on page 428.

Contribution Limits If you have earned income (salary, wages, royalties, business income, rental income, or alimony) in a given year, you can contribute to your RRSP, but the amount allowable is subject to a maximum set by the government.

The amount of your maximum annual contribution depends on whether you also participate in an RPP, which has the effect of reducing your allowable contribution by a pension adjustment calculated by your employer and by the Canada Customs and Revenue Agency. The result of that calculation is sent to you late in each year and will differ for defined benefit plans and defined contribution plans.

If you don't participate in an RPP, you can contribute up to 18 percent of your earned income, or $13,500, whichever is less. Under the revisions put forth in the 1996 federal budget, that maximum will hold up to and including 2003. Following that year, the maximum will be $14,500 for 2004, $15,500 for 2005, and then indexed to inflation in 2006.

There are also other rules to consider. You are allowed to exceed your limit by $2,000 without incurring a penalty, but beyond this amount, you will be fined 1 percent per month. Further, in the event that you are unable to make your full contribution to the plan, you are allowed to "carry forward" the full amount of unpaid contribution to a later year. This means that if you for any reason have a year in which savings are minimal, you will be able to make up for your contribution shortfall by investing more in a year when you can put more aside.

On death, a taxpayer is normally taxed on the entire amount of any RRSP except where the funds are left to the taxpayer's spouse, in which case they are included in the spouse's income.

OPTIONS WHEN YOU DEREGISTER AN RRSP Your RRSP must be deregistered by the end of the year of your 69th birthday. At that point, you will have six choices as to what to do with your funds. The options available are to withdraw the funds and pay the income tax, purchase a single-payment life annuity, purchase a fixed-term annuity, set up a Registered Retirement Income Fund (RRIF), set up a Life Income Fund (LIF), or set up a segregated fund. Each option is discussed below.

Full Withdrawal The least favourable option when you deregister your RRSP is to simply withdraw the funds and pay the income tax on them, as doing so will negate the whole purpose of using this tax minimization tool. It is likely that your accumulated funds will be large enough to draw the highest marginal tax rate if you accept them as a lump sum. While you still benefit from the years of tax-free growth of your investments, that growth will be stifled by your high taxation rate. In addition, if you cash in your RRSP and do not convert it to a

Financial Planning for Life's Situations

BY CAMILLA CORNELL, *IE:MONEY*

For 29-year-old Rich Dlin, contributing to an RRSP was, he says, "part of my socialization. It's something you just do." Since he graduated from university with a joint math and teaching degree in 1999, and married Marla Nadler-Dlin, 28, the couple has managed to save an average of $5,000 a year between them—even without the benefit of a financial planner to lay down the law.

That money has given them options that aren't available to others in their age bracket. Instead of spending money on rent, the couple took advantage of the federal government's New Home Buyers' Plan to roll their RRSP money into a down payment on a condominium in 2000, without having to pay a tax penalty.

By the time their son Jonah was born two years later, the Dlins were able to trade the condo for a house. And, when Marla opted to give up her job as an accounts manager with a mid-sized company in favour of self-employment last year, they had enough money in RRSPs to provide a cushion should things not work out.

While retirement may be in the distant future for those under 35, Lenore Davis, a registered financial planner and senior partner with Dixon, Davis & Co. in Victoria, B.C., points out that having some assets can have implications for the present as well—as Rich and Marla's experience shows. "If you've got an asset base, you've got the freedom to pick and choose your jobs and your lifestyle," says Davis. "The people who don't have options are the people who have nothing to fall back on."

In addition, the couple is getting all the conventional benefits of an RRSP: namely, the investments are tax deductible, while the earnings accumulate tax free until you take them out, ostensibly at retirement—at which time, your income level and tax rate are both going to be lower. Rich, a self-employed computer consultant in the 26-percent tax bracket, figures it out this way: "If I contribute $100, that reduces my taxable income by $100, which reduces how much tax I'm going to pay by $26. That's $26 in my account, rather than Revenue Canada's." He admits he and Marla puzzled over whether to opt out of RRSP contributions for a few years and focus on paying down their mortgage. But they came to the conclusion that if they put money into an RRSP, they could use the tax refund to pay down their mortgage, getting maximum bang for their buck.

SOURCE: http://www.slam.ca/IEMoneyFeb99/ie_rrsps35. html,

---

further tax shelter, the financial institution is required to apply a withholding tax, which is a percentage of your RRSP. For example, withdraw less than $5,000, and there is a 10-percent withholding tax (outside Quebec); withdraw $5,001 to $15,000, and there is a 20-percent withholding tax; withdraw $15,001 plus, and there is a 30-percent withholding tax.

Annuities Annuities are an investment that usually pays a fixed level of payments on a regular basis (usually monthly or annually) for either a specified amount of time or until the death of the holder. They are meant to provide retirement income in much the same way as a salary provides regular income. If the annuity is bought with funds from a registered plan, then the purchase of the annuity is tax free, but the entire amount of each annuity payment is taxed. There are two main types of annuities: life annuities and fixed-term period annuities.

Following is a list of advantages and disadvantages that annuities have over other retirement income options:

Advantages
- Payment can continue until death, if it is a life annuity
- Level payments may suit your income needs better
- Simplicity—not having to worry about investments or withdrawals
- No heavy record-keeping requirements
- A legitimate tax shelter
- No investment limits
- Tax-free transfers between annuity companies

Disadvantages
- Less control over investments
- Less control over payout of income
- No protection from inflation, unless it is indexed
- No opportunity for retirement income to grow
- No opportunity for tax deferral
- Can't take out a lump sum for major purchases, unless cashable
- No protection for spouse, unless joint
- No estate planning benefits, unless joint

Make sure you take into consideration such fees as commission, underwriting, fund management, and penalties, when choosing your annuity provider.

Life Annuities If you purchase a single-payment life annuity, then the full amount of your RRSP funds will be transferred directly to the life insurance company from which you bought the annuity. The company will then convert those funds into a lifetime income payable to you, and your marginal rate of taxation will be based on your annual income rather than the whole of your funds. At any time, you have the option to cancel the annuity and take the commuted value of the remaining payments. Having done so, you can then either remove the funds from the tax shelter and pay the tax, or you can roll the funds over into an RRIF, discussed below. It must be noted that when the holder dies, any left over payments are not paid out to an estate or to beneficiaries. Life annuities are discussed in Chapter 9.

Fixed-Term Annuities Fixed-term annuities are available from both life insurance companies and trust companies. As with the life annuity above, this method allows you to convert your RRSP funds into income. The principal difference is that the benefit paid and cost of this type of annuity is not based upon your life expectancy, or on the pooling of your funds with those of others. Instead, your funds are simply converted into an income stream to be paid out for a fixed term. In the event that you die prior to the end of the term, the remaining unpaid funds will be paid to your estate or beneficiary, and your monthly income is based on the amount of your purchase, the term, and the current interest rates. As with the life annuity, you have the option to cancel at any time and either pay the taxes on the commuted value or roll it over to an RRIF.

Registered Retirement Income Funds (RRIFs) An RRIF is similar to a self-directed RRSP in that you can make your own investment decisions if you choose. Alternatively, you may also set one up so that little management is required. In either case, the Canada Customs and Revenue Agency will require that you withdraw a minimum amount from the plan until you reach the age of 71. The minimum withdrawal amount starts at 4.76 percent of the total value of the RRIF at age 69 and increases incrementally to 20 percent by age 94. You can adjust the amount and the frequency of the payments you receive. Monthly, quarterly, semi-annual, or annual payments are all options, as are lump-sum withdrawals. For example, if you have a RRIF worth $250, 000 and are aged 65 on January 1, in that year you will be required to withdraw at least $11, 900 (4.76 percent of $250,000) and will be accordingly taxed on that amount. Exhibit 14–11 shows a sample RRIF contract.

Life Income Funds (LIFs) Upon terminating your membership in your company RPP, or when you have transferred funds from a locked-in RRSP, you may elect to purchase an LIF. This income fund is available in all provinces, and the minimum deposit you must make to start one is $10,000. Similar to an RRIF, with an LIF you must withdraw a minimum amount every year, and the tax treatment is the same, but with this plan you are also subject to a maximum annual withdrawal amount based on interest rates and available investment returns. The balance of the funds in your LIF must be used to purchase a life annuity before December 31 of the year you turn 80. If you die before the end of the LIF term, the amount remaining in the fund will go to your designated beneficiary.

Exhibit 14–11

RRIF Minimum
Withdrawal
Amounts

SOURCE: www.canadian
moneysaver.ca

Age	Percentage
69	4.76
70	5.00
71	7.38
72	7.48
73	7.59
74	7.71
75	7.85
76	7.99
77	8.15
78	8.33
79	8.53
80	8.75

Age	Percentage
81	8.99
82	9.27
83	9.58
84	9.93
85	1.33
86	10.79
87	11.33
88	11.96
89	12.71
90	13.62
91	14.73
92	16.12

Segregated Funds Similar to mutual funds, but sold exclusively through life insurance companies, a segregated fund is essentially the purchase of units representing a share in a pool of assets supervised by a fund manager. The term "segregated" refers to the fact that the money in these funds is kept separate from the company's other assets. The principal advantages that segregated funds have over mutual funds are (1) that when you die, your fund's assets go directly to your beneficiary rather than to your estate, and (2) that a percentage of your capital is guaranteed no matter how poorly the fund performs. The percentage is generally around 75 percent but can go as high as 100 percent, in which case your only concern would be the depreciation of your money due to inflation.

WILL YOU HAVE ENOUGH MONEY DURING RETIREMENT?

Now that you have reviewed all the possible sources of your retirement income, estimate what your annual retirement income will be. Don't forget to inflate incomes or investments that increase with the cost of living (such as CPPbenefits) to what they will be when you retire. (Use the inflation factor table in the Financial Planning Calculations box on page 419.) Remember, inflation is a major uncontrollable variable for retirees.

Now, compare your total estimated retirement income with your total inflated retirement expenses. If your estimated income exceeds your estimated expenses and a large portion of your planned income will automatically increase with the cost of living during your retirement, you are in good shape. (You should evaluate your plans every few years between now and retirement to be sure your planned income is still adequate to meet your planned expenses.)

If, however, your planned retirement income is less than your estimated retirement expenses, now is the time to take action to increase your retirement income. Also, if a large portion of your retirement income is fixed and will not increase with inflation, you should make plans for a much larger retirement income to meet your rising expenses during retirement.

CONCEPT CHECK 14–5

1. What are possible sources of income for retirees?
2. How do defined-contribution plans differ from defined-benefit plans?
3. What options do you have for deregistering your retirement investments?

Financial Planning for Life's Situations

RRSP OR DOWN PAYMENT?

Miss White is 34 years old and is employed as a Senior Sales Representative for a small technology company in Montreal. Her gross annual salary is $30,000, and she has 31 years left to retirement. Miss White recently came into a $10,000 inheritance left to her by her grandmother. Should Miss White use the $10,000 to pay down her mortgage or contribute it to an RRSP? There are many factors to consider before we can make our decision. We are assuming the following:

- Marginal tax rate of approximately: 26% [1]
- RRSP annual compound rate: 8% [2]
- Whether or not she has achieved maximum contribution to her RRSP for current or previous years: No
- Amortization period: 25 years
- Frequency of payments: Monthly
- Mortgage term: Fixed rate 10 year closed at 8.15% [3], in the first year of payment.
- Down payment: $10,000 (High ratio mortgage)
- Mortgage amount: $79,000
- Total value of house and property: $89,000
- Prepayment penalties on mortgage: None, unless exceeding the 10-20% of the remaining capital. [4]

We are assuming that because of her young age, she will have plenty of time and money to pay off her mortgage and contribute to her RRSP. Given this factor, we are leaning towards the option of placing the $10,000 in her RRSP. In addition, we know that an RRSP contribution will reduce her taxable income and will most likely give her a tax refund, which she can then apply as a mortgage payment. Those closer to retirement may be tempted to pay down their mortgage and rightfully own their house sooner.

Miss White has placed a $10,000 down payment on her home and has foregone any contributions toward an RRSP. However, she can go back seven years and make payments of up to 18 percent or $13,500 (the lower dollar amount of the two options) of her income toward this RRSP. Therefore, she will be able to contribute $10,800 for the past two tax years (18% × $30,000 = $5,400, then $5,400 × 2 = $10,800). This guarantees that the option to contribute to her RRSP is open.

Financial advisers recommend that you pay down your mortgage in the earlier stages of its life span. Miss White is in the first year of mortgage payments; approximately 85 percent of her payment is still going towards the interest. Gaining equity in your home sounds like an attractive offer. Laws favour home ownership. "Once you build equity in your home, you'll never again pay the high non-deductible interest expense charged on credit cards, car loans, and other consumer debts. As a homeowner, you can obtain a low interest rate home equity loan (tax-deductible, no less) to cover your essential borrowing needs." [5]

The following numerical example evaluates the differences between applying a one-time lump sum against the principal of a mortgage versus an RRSP and the likely outcomes of both situations.

Scenario	Years to Pay off Mortgage	Mortgage Savings	Extra RRSP Savings	Total Benefit
#1: Apply lump sum to mortgage	17.8	$43,670	N/A	$43,670
#2: Invest lump sum in RRSP + apply tax savings to the next mortgage payment	22.7	$17,135	$70,143	$87,278

It is clear from our calculations, if she chose scenario #2, not only would Miss White reduce the life of her mortgage, but she would be able to build a nest egg. The total benefit in scenario 2 exceeds scenario 1 by an amazing amount of $43,608.

In conclusion, "Choosing between putting more money into your RRSP or paying down your mortgage involves a lot of serious number crunching, and the results depend on your mortgage rate, how many years you have left before your mortgage is paid off, as well as the return on your RRSP. Because of all the variables, some of which are hard to nail down, a good compromise is to maximize your RRSP contributions and to take the tax refund that the contributions earns you and put it down against your mortgage." [6] In other words, we are going to have our cake and eat it, too!

BIBLIOGRAPHY
1. http://www.hrblock.ca. From this site, we discovered how to determine the marginal tax rate, given our annual salary, and we used the Mortgage Calculator.
2. http://www.scotiabank.com/invest—RRSP rate of return.
3. http://www.bmo.com/mortgage—Terms of mortgage.
4. Buying and Selling a Home for Canadians for Dummies, by Tony Ioannou, Moira Bayne, Wendy Yano. CDG Books Canada Inc. Toronto, Ontario, 2000.
5. 106 Common Mistakes Home Owner's Make and How to Avoid Them, 3rd Edition. by Gary W. Eldred PhD., published by John Wiley & Sons Inc. New York, 2002.
6. Personal Finance for Canadians for Dummies, 3rd Edition, by Eric Tyson, Tony Martin. CDG Books Canada Inc. Toronto, Ontario, 2001.

SOURCE: Assignment by Alexandra Fuoco and Christina Fuoco for the Introductory Personal Finance Course Comm499F JMSB, Concordia University, Fall 2001.

Living on Your Retirement Income

Objective 6

Develop a balanced budget based on your retirement income.

As you planned retirement, you estimated a budget or spending plan, but you may find your actual expenses at retirement are higher than anticipated.

The first step in stretching your retirement income is to make sure you are receiving all of the income to which you are entitled. Examine the possible sources of retirement income mentioned earlier to see whether you could qualify for more programs or additional benefits. What assets or valuables could you use as a cash or income source?

To stay within your income, you may also need to make some changes in your spending plans. For example, you can use your skills and time instead of your money. There are probably many things you can do yourself instead of paying someone else to do them. Take advantage of free and low-cost recreation, such as walks, picnics, public parks, lectures, museums, libraries, art galleries, art fairs, gardening, and church and club programs.

TAX ADVANTAGES

Be sure to take full advantage of all the tax savings and benefits available to retirees. For more information, contact Human Resources and Development Canada (HRDC; www.hrdc-drhc. gc.ca). The HRDC provides a number of guides and publications available to help you understand your available options.

WORKING DURING RETIREMENT

You may want to work part time or start a new part-time career after you retire. Work can provide you with a greater sense of usefulness, involvement, and self-worth and may be the ideal way to add to your retirement income. You may want to pursue a personal interest or hobby, or you can contact your provincial or local agency on aging for information about employment opportunities for retirees.

Over 50 percent of recent retirees want to continue working part time or even full time after retirement, and only a small percentage are worried about outliving their financial resources. There is a rich talent pool of Canadians in the 55 to 75 age range, over 50 percent of whom are retired—and many of them are interested in continued employment. These individuals, with their proven skills and abilities, provide a flexible, cost-effective resource that can sustain our

Exhibit 14–12   Dipping into Your Nest Egg

Starting Amount of Nest Egg	You Can Reduce Your Nest Egg to Zero by Withdrawing This Much Each Month for the Stated Number of Years...					Or You Can Withdraw This Much Each Month and Leave Your Nest Egg Intact
	10 Years	15 Years	20 Years	25 Years	30 Years	
$ 10,000	$ 107	$ 81	$ 68	$ 61	$ 56	$ 46
15,000	161	121	102	91	84	69
20,000	215	162	136	121	112	92
25,000	269	202	170	152	140	115
30,000	322	243	204	182	168	138
40,000	430	323	272	243	224	184
50,000	537	404	340	304	281	230
60,000	645	485	408	364	337	276
80,000	859	647	544	486	449	368
100,000	1,074	808	680	607	561	460

Note: Based on an interest rate of 5.5 percent per year, compounded quarterly.
SOURCE: Select Committee on Aging, U.S. House of Representatives.

productivity gains and economic growth. What drives many of them is the desire to remain productively engaged in life.

If you decide to work part time after you retire, you should be aware of how your earnings will affect your public pension income. As long as you do not earn more than the annually exempt amount, your payments will not be affected. But if you earn more than the annual exempt amount, your payments will be reduced. Check with your Human Resources and Development Canada office for the latest information.

INVESTING FOR RETIREMENT

The guaranteed-income part of your retirement fund consists of money paid into lower-yield, very safe investments. To offset inflation, your retirement assets must earn enough to keep up with, and even exceed, the rate of inflation.

DIPPING INTO YOUR NEST EGG

When should you draw on your savings? The answer depends on your financial circumstances, your age, and how much you want to leave to your heirs. Your savings may be large enough to allow you to live comfortably on the interest alone. Or you may need to make regular withdrawals to help finance your retirement. Dipping into savings isn't wrong, but you must do so with caution.

How long would your savings last if you withdrew monthly income? If you have $10,000 in savings that earns 5.5 percent interest, compounded quarterly, you could take out $68 every month for 20 years before reducing this nest egg to zero. If you have $40,000, you could collect $224 every month for 30 years before exhausting your nest egg. For different possibilities, see Exhibit 14–12.

Exhibit 14–13   Major Sources of Retirement Income: Advantages and Disadvantages

Source	Advantages	Disadvantages
Public Pension Plans		
In planning	Forced savings Portable from job to job Cost shared with employer	Increasing economic pressure on the system as population ages
At retirement	Inflation-adjusted survivorship rights	Minimum retirement age specified Earned income may partially offset benefits
Employee Pension Plans		
In planning	Forced savings Cost shared or fully covered by employer	May not be portable No control over how funds are managed
At retirement	Survivorship rights	Cost-of-living increases may not be provided on a regular basis
Individual Saving and Investing (including housing, LIF, and RRSP plans)		
In planning	Current tax savings (e.g., RRSPs) Easily incorporated into family (i.e., housing) Portable Control over management of funds	Current needs compete with future needs Penalty for early withdrawal (RRSPs and LIF)
At retirement	Inflation resistant Can usually use as much of the funds as you wish, when you wish (within certain requirements)	Some sources taxable Mandatory minimum withdrawal restrictions (RRIF and LIF)
Post-retirement Employment		
In planning	Special earning skills can be used as they are developed	Technology and skills needed to keep up may change rapidly
At retirement	Inflation resistant	Ill health can mean loss of this income source

Financial Planning for Life's Situations

RETIREMENT CHECKLIST

As you approach retirement, assess your financial condition using the following checklist.

Don't wait too long, or you will miss one or more opportunities to maximize your future financial independence.

	Yes	No
1. Do you talk regularly and frankly to family members about finances and agree on your goals and the lifestyle you will prefer as you get older?	☐	☐
2. Do you know what your sources of income will be after retirement, how much to expect from each source, and when?	☐	☐
3. Do you save according to your plan, shifting from growth-producing to safe, income-producing investments?	☐	☐
4. Do you have your own credit history?	☐	☐
5. Do you have a current will or a living trust?	☐	☐
6. Do you know where you plan to live in retirement?	☐	☐
7. Do you anticipate the tax consequences of your retirement plans and of passing assets on to your heirs?	☐	☐
8. Do your children or other responsible family members know where your important documents are and whom to contact if questions arise?	☐	☐
9. Do you have legal documents, such as a living will or a power of attorney, specifying your instructions in the event of your death or incapacitating illness?	☐	☐

SOURCE: Adapted from *Staying Independent*, American Express Consumer Affairs Office and IDS Financial Services Inc.

Visit the Web site

See the Post-Test under Chapter 14 on the online learning centre at www.mcgrawhill.ca/college/kapoor.

Exhibit 14–13 on the previous page summarizes major sources of retirement income and their advantages and disadvantages. Finally, use the Financial Planning for Life's Situations box above to assess your financial condition as you approach retirement.

CONCEPT CHECK 14–6

1. What is the first step in stretching your retirement income?
2. How should you invest to obtain retirement income?

SUMMARY OF OBJECTIVES

Objective 1
Recognize the importance of retirement planning.
Retirement planning is important because you will probably spend many years in retirement; public pensions and a private pension may be insufficient to cover the cost of living; and inflation may erode the purchasing power of your retirement savings. Many young people are reluctant to think about retirement, but they should start retirement planning now, before they reach age 40.

Objective 2
Analyze your current assets and liabilities for retirement.
Analyze your current assets (everything you own) and your current liabilities (everything you owe). The difference between your assets and your liabilities is your net worth. Review your assets to ensure they are sufficient for retirement.

Objective 3
Estimate your retirement spending needs.
Since the spending patterns of retirees change, it is impossible to predict the exact amount of money you will need in retirement. However, you can estimate your expenses. Some of those expenses will increase; others will decrease. The expenses that are likely to be lower or eliminated are work-related expenses, clothing, housing expenses, federal income taxes, and commuting expenses.

Objective 4
Identify your retirement housing needs.
Where you live in retirement can influence your financial needs. You are the only one who can determine the location and housing that are best for you. Would you like to live in your present home or move to a new location? Consider the social aspects of moving.

Objective 5
Determine your planned retirement income.
Estimate your retirement expenses and adjust those expenses for inflation using the appropriate inflation factor. Your possible sources of income during retirement include the CPP, other public pension plans, employer pension plans, and personal retirement plans.

Objective 6
Develop a balanced budget based on your retirement income.
Compare your total estimated retirement income with your total inflated retirement expenses. If your income approximates your expenses, you are in good shape; if not, determine additional income needs and sources.

KEY TERMS

defined-benefit plan 423	**reverse annuity mortgage (RAM)**	**RRSP** 425
defined-contribution plan 422	412	**vesting** 422

FINANCIAL PLANNING PROBLEMS

1. *Preparing a Net Worth Statement.* Prepare your net worth statement using the guidelines presented in Exhibit 14–3. (Obj. 2)

2. *Comparing Spending Patterns during Retirement.* How will your spending patterns change during your retirement years? Compare your spending patterns with those shown in Exhibit 14–4. (Obj. 3)

3. *Calculating RRSP Contributions.* Gene and Dana Sladek both work. They have an adjusted gross income of $40,000, and they are filing a joint income tax return. What is the maximum RRSP contribution they can make? How much of that contribution is tax deductible? (Obj. 5)

4. *Calculating Net Pay and Spendable Income.* Assume your gross pay per pay period is $2,000 and you are in the 26-percent tax bracket (ignore provincial tax). Calculate your net pay and spendable income in the following situations: (Obj. 5)
   a. You save $200 per pay period after paying income tax on $2,000.
   b. You save $200 per pay period in an RPP.

5. *Calculating Monthly Withdrawals.* You have $50,000 in your retirement fund that is earning 5.5 percent per year, compounded quarterly. How many dollars in withdrawals per month would reduce this nest egg to zero in 20 years? How many dollars per month can you withdraw for as long as you live and still leave this nest egg intact? (Obj. 6)

FINANCIAL PLANNING ACTIVITIES

1. *Conducting Interviews.* Survey friends, relatives, and other people to get their views on retirement planning. Prepare a written report of your findings. (Obj. 1)

2. *Obtaining Information about Reverse Mortgages.* Obtain consumer information about reverse mortgages in the Royal Bank's *Your Money Matters*, available in all Royal Bank branches or online at www.royalbank.com. Evaluate the information. How might a reverse mortgage help you or a member of your family? (Obj. 2)

3. *Determining Expenses during Retirement.* Read newspaper or magazine articles to determine what expenses are likely to increase and decrease during retirement. How might this information affect your retirement-planning decisions? (Obj. 3)

4. *Evaluating Retirement Housing Options.* Which type of housing will best meet your retirement needs? Is such housing available in your community? Make a checklist of the advantages and disadvantages of your housing choice. (Obj. 4)

5. *Balancing a Retirement Budget.* Outline the steps you must take to live on your retirement income and balance your retirement budget. (Obj. 6)

LIFE SITUATION CASE

To Be Young, Thrifty, and in the Black: The Importance of Starting Early

Ann Farrell, a 28-year-old hydrogeologist, is one of the lucky ones. As a college senior in 1991, Farrell attended a seminar on investing early for retirement. "I remembered the figures if you started saving when you were young," she says. Indeed, the payoff is huge. Through compounding, 25-year-olds who invest $2,000 a year and stop at 34 will earn $142,000 more by the time they are 65 than someone who begins investing $2,000 at 35 and contributes $2,000 each year for the next 30 years.

Farrell already has $22,000 in her RRSP. That's a nice start compared with most of her peers. Research has found that nearly 70 percent of adults ages 22 to 32 have saved less than $10,000 for retirement.

When Farrell was a new employee in 1991 at an environmental consulting firm, she was barred for a year from the company's pension plan. Once eligible, she committed 8 percent of her paycheque in the two most aggressive stock funds offered (retirement growth and asset manager). The company matched 50 percent of her pre-tax contributions, up to 5 percent of her $28,000 salary.

Of course, it helped that her expenses were low. After graduation, Farrell—with only $500 to her name—moved back in with her parents, who charged her $200 a month for rent. She also travelled three out of every four weeks on work. "There is nowhere to spend money on the road," she claims. Still, she had to repay a $10,000 school loan and a $4,000 car loan. She also wanted to build an emergency fund. Once she began making headway on these goals, Farrell moved to her own place and gradually increased her pre-tax contribution to 10 percent. Last year, she upped it to 13 percent. The government allows employees to make a pre-tax contribution of up to $13,500 a year. Farrell is currently chipping in about $5,000 a year.

Oddly, the lack of growth in environmental consulting has worked to Farrell's benefit. While most Gen-Xers find themselves job hopping every two years or so to get ahead, Farrell stayed put because there wasn't much movement in her industry. So, she will become fully vested in her RPP this October, after five years in the plan.

Farrell has done a lot right, but she has a long road ahead of her. When she makes her next move—she may leave her company and go to business school—she needs to recognize the potholes that exist when protecting her retirement assets. For instance, if she decides to roll over her RPP, she'll have to examine all of the investment options and rollover requirements. If she doesn't, she could lose her head start on retirement savings.

Questions

1. What did Ann Farrell learn when she attended a seminar on retirement?

2. How much money did Farrell originally commit to her Company pension plan? In what funds did she invest her money?

3. What is the maximum contribution Farrell can make to her RRSP?

4. After how long and when did Farrell become fully vested in her RPP?

SOURCE: Adapted from Toddi Guttner, "To Be Young, Thrifty, and in the Black," *Business Week*, July 21, 1997, p. 76.

CREATING A FINANCIAL PLAN

Planning for Retirement

Long-term financial security is a common goal of most people. Retirement planning should consider both personal decisions (location, housing, activities) and financial factors (investments, pensions, living expenses).

Web Sites for Retirement Planning

- Revenue Canada, at **www.ccra-adrc.gc.ca**, provides important tax-related retirement information through its Forms and Publications link.
- RetireWeb, at **www.retireweb.com**, provides information on retirement planning and activities. A great site, it also provides annuity, life expectancy, RRIF, and other calculators.
- The Canadian Association for Retired People, at **www.carp.ca**, is a non-profit organization dedicated to 50+ lifestyles.
- Cannex, at **www.cannex.com**, is an online financial rate site providing up-to-date rates for annuities, GICs, RRSPs, mortgages, and other financial products. It is a great site to get information on the current market.
- Benefits Canada, at **www.benefitscanada.com**, is a magazine that claims to provide the most current pension and investment information available in Canada.

- Seniors Canada On-line, at **http://www.seniors.gc.ca/**, provides single-window access to Web-based information and services that are relevant to seniors 55+, their families, caregivers, and supporting service organizations.
- Human Resources Development Canada (HRDC), **http://www.hrdc-drhc.gc.ca/menu/seniors.shtml**, provides detailed information for seniors on retirement issues.

(Note: Addresses and content of Web Sites change, and new sites are created daily. Use search engines to update and locate Web sites for your current financial planning needs.)

Short-Term Financial Planning Activities

1. Identify personal and financial retirement needs for various stages of your life.
2. Compare the benefits and costs of an RRSP, an RPP, and other pension plans.

Long-Term Financial Planning Activities

1. Research costs and benefits of various housing alternatives.
2. Estimate future retirement income needs and identify appropriate investments to meet those needs.
3. Develop a plan for expanding personal interests and increasing contributions to retirement accounts.

15 Estate Planning

A Plan for the Endgame

Harry Frank talked to his lawyer about drafting a living will, but never completed one. Then, in 1995, he suffered severe brain damage in an automobile accident and spent three years in a persistent vegetative state. Last year, after his wife moved him to a nursing home to be close to his parents, she requested that his feeding tube be removed. Other family members objected. The device eventually was withdrawn, and Frank died—but only after an agonizing legal battle that tore his family apart.

Imagine suffering a stroke or being left in a coma as a result of an auto accident. Would you want to be kept on life support, fed through a tube, or given pain-controlling drugs, even if they hastened your death? You have the right to make these choices. You'll need two documents, called *advanced directives:* a living will that tells doctors and hospitals how you want to be cared for should you become terminally ill, and a health-care proxy who designates an advocate who can make sure your wishes are honoured.

Living wills do not give a hospital the right to "pull the plug" without consent of a patient's legal representative. If you want doctors to exhaust every effort to keep you alive, no matter what, you can also request that in a living will. You can say: "I don't want anything done," or you can say: "I want absolutely everything." Lawyers say it is important to be as specific as possible. If you want morphine or other pain medication in your last days, even if it is addictive or makes you drowsy, say so. If you want life support turned off if you are near death, write that down, too. Whatever its contents, a living will is one legal document that should not be kept in your safety deposit box. Give copies to your lawyer, your doctor, and your adult children, and take one to the hospital on your next visit.

Putting your wishes in writing does not guarantee that a hospital will honour them, however. To make sure it does, you'll need to appoint a legal representative, usually a relative or friend, who can handle your health-care decisions if you cannot. You make this choice by executing a designation of health-care proxy, health-care surrogate, or medical power of attorney. You might want to make your spouse your representative. But think about giving backup power to an adult child if you are not sure your spouse could handle such difficult decisions at a time of great stress.

QUESTIONS

1 How can you protect your wishes and your peace of mind with a living will?

2 Would you want to be kept on life support? Why, or why not?

3 In your opinion, who should have the right to make life-and-death decisions?

4 Should you keep your living will in a safety deposit box? Why, or why not?

LEARNING OBJECTIVES

1   Analyze the personal aspects of estate planning.

2   Assess the legal aspects of estate planning.

3   Distinguish among formats of wills.

4   Appraise various types of trusts and estates.

Why Estate Planning?

Your **estate** consists of everything you own. While you work, your objective is to accumulate funds for your future and for your dependants. As you grow older, your point of view will change. The emphasis in your financial planning will shift from accumulating assets to distributing them wisely. Your hard-earned wealth should go to those whom you wish to support and not to the various taxation agencies.

Contrary to widely held notions, estate planning, which includes wills and trusts, is useful not just to rich and elderly people. Trusts can be used for purposes other than tax advantages, such as choosing a guardian for children and avoiding family fights over personal belongings. Furthermore, most people can afford the expense of using them.

This chapter discusses a subject most people would rather avoid: death—your own or that of your spouse. Many people give little or no thought to setting their personal and financial affairs in order.

As you learned in Chapter 14, most people today live longer than those of previous generations and have ample time to think about and plan for the future. Yet, a large percentage of people do little or nothing to provide for those who will survive them.

Planning for your family's financial security in the event of your death or the death of your spouse is not easy. Therefore, the objective of this chapter is to help you initiate discussions about questions you should ask before that happens. Does your spouse, for instance, know what all of the family's resources and debts are? Does your family have enough insurance protection?

The question of whether your family can cope financially without your or your spouse's income and support is a difficult one. This chapter can't provide all of the answers, but it supplies a basis for sound estate planning for you and your family.

WHAT IS ESTATE PLANNING?

Estate planning is a definite plan for the administration and disposition of one's property during one's lifetime and at one's death. Thus, it involves both handling your property while you are alive and dealing with what happens to that property after your death.

Estate planning is an essential part of retirement planning and an integral part of financial planning. It has two components. The first consists of building your estate through savings, investments, and insurance. The second involves transferring your estate, at your death, in the manner you have specified. As this chapter explains, an estate plan is usually implemented by a will and one or more trust agreements.

Nearly every adult engages in financial decision making and must keep important records. Whatever your status—single or married, male or female, taxi driver or corporate executive—you must make financial decisions that are important to you. Those decisions may be even more important to others in your family. Knowledge in certain areas and good recordkeeping can simplify those decisions.

Objective 1

Analyze the personal aspects of estate planning.

estate Everything one owns.

Visit the Web site

See the Post-Test under Chapter 15 on the online learning centre at www.mcgrawhill.ca/college/kapoor.

estate planning A definite plan for the administration and disposition of one's property during one's lifetime and at one's death.

At first, planning for financial security and estate planning may seem complicated. Although many money matters require legal and technical advice, if you and your spouse learn the necessary skills, you will find yourselves managing your money affairs more efficiently and wisely. Begin by answering the questionnaire in the Financial Planning for Life's Situations box on page 441 to see how much you and your family know about your own money affairs. You and your family should be able to answer some of these questions. The questions can be bewildering if the subjects are unfamiliar to you, but after reading this chapter, you'll be able to answer most of them.

PROVINCIAL FAMILY LAW

Provincial family law can have a significant impact on your estate planning. Getting married, for example, will usually void a will made prior to the wedding. Equally, divorce and separation might also affect the validity of part or all of a will.

Provincial family law might also impact your capacity to order the disposition of your estate. If you wanted to disinherit your spouse or children, for example, they would be allowed to successfully contest your will if they could prove personal financial needs that had normally been provided for by you.

The particular nature and scope of the laws vary from province to province. The relevant provincial acts are as follows:

- *Family Relief Act*—Alberta and Newfoundland
- *Wills Variation Act*—British Columbia
- *Testator's Family Maintenance Act*—Manitoba, New Brunswick, and Nova Scotia
- *Succession Law Reform Act*—Ontario
- *Dependants of a Deceased Person Relief Act*—Prince Edward Island
- *Dependants Relief Act*—Saskatchewan, Yukon, and the Northwest Territories

The motive behind these laws is always the same. The idea is to protect those who have traditionally needed to depend on you and to ensure a just distribution of your estate.

Regardless of your familial situation, you should take the necessary steps to ensure that you clearly make your desires known regarding your estate. While these instructions might be constrained somewhat by your provincial laws, the alternative is to die *intestate* (without a will) and to have the whole of your estate distributed through an insensitive and not always apt legal system.

THE OPPORTUNITY COST OF RATIONALIZING

Daily living often gets in the way of thinking about death. You mean to organize things that others need to know in case you die, but you haven't done this yet. One of your rationalizations may be that you are not sure what information you need to provide.

Think about the outcome of your delay. Your beneficiary will meet people who offer specific types of assistance—morticians, clergy, lawyers, insurance agents, clerks of federal government agencies, and so on. These people will probably be strangers—sympathetic, courteous, and helpful, but disinterested. Also, your bereaved beneficiary may find it difficult to reveal confidences to them. Today, however, the information survivors need is as close as the Internet. Visit the Canadian Financial Publishing Group's Web site at www.cfpg.com/common/estate/index.htm for a comprehensive review of estate planning, as well as to link to its informative article "What to Do When a Family Member Dies."

The moral is to plan your estate while you are in good health and think through the provisions carefully. Last-minute "deathbed" estate planning may fail to carry out your wishes. Many

D I D   Y O U   K N O W ?

Forty percent of adults age 50 and older do not have a will.

SOURCE: www.metlife.com AARP Program Development and services, 4/00

Financial Planning for Life's Situations

ESTATE PLANNING CHECKLIST

Do you and your family members know the answers to the following questions?

1. Where are your previous years' income tax returns?
2. Where is your safety deposit box located? Where is the key to it kept?
3. What kinds and amounts of life insurance protection do you have?
4. Can you locate your insurance policies—life, health, property, casualty, and auto?
5. Who are the beneficiaries and contingent beneficiaries of your life insurance policies?
6. Do you and your spouse have current wills? Who drafted them? Where are they kept?
7. Do you have a separate record of the important papers you keep in your safety deposit box? Where is this record located?
8. Do you have a record of your spouse's and children's social insurance numbers?
9. Where is your marriage certificate and the birth certificates of all members of your family?
10. Do you know the name and address of your life insurance agent?
11. Do you know the principal financial resources and liabilities of your estate?
12. Are you knowledgeable about simple, daily, and compound interest rates? About retirement funds and property ownership?
13. Have you given any thought to funerals and burial arrangements?
14. What papers and records will be important to other people when you die?
15. Do you understand the functions of a bank trust department and the meaning of joint ownership?

SOURCE: *Planning with Your Beneficiaries* (Washington, DC: American Council of Life Insurance, Education, and Community Services, n.d.), p. 2.

Canadians are considering pre-planned funeral arrangements as part of their estate plan. Pre-planned funeral arrangements allow for family input, minimize the chances of additional costs, and ensure that your wishes are followed without burdening family members.

CONCEPT CHECK 15–1

1. If you needed information about estate planning, would you go to the library or the Internet? Why?
2. Why is estate planning an important component of financial planning?
3. Why is estate planning important for single as well as married individuals?

Legal Aspects of Estate Planning

When death occurs, proof of claims must be produced or the claims will not be processed. If no thought was given to gathering the necessary documents beforehand (with a sufficient number of copies), a period of financial hardship may follow until proof is obtained. If needed documentation cannot be located, irretrievable loss of funds may occur. Your heirs may experience emotionally painful delays until their rights have been established.

Important papers include the following:

[1] Birth certificates—yours, your spouse's, and your children's.
[2] Marriage certificates—always important, but especially important if you or your spouse were married previously—and divorce papers.

Objective 2

Assess the legal aspects of estate planning.

[3] Legal name changes—judgment of court documents pertaining to any legal changes in the names that appear on birth certificates (especially important to protect the adopted children of a previous marriage or children who have been adopted through adoption agencies).

[4] Military service records—or any other official statement of your military service details, if appropriate.

Here is a list of additional important documents :

- Government benefit documents.
- Veteran documents.
- Insurance policies.
- Transfer records of joint bank accounts.
- Safety deposit box records.
- Registration of automobiles.
- Title to stock and bond certificates.

You should have several copies of certain documents, because when you submit a claim the accompanying proof often becomes a permanent part of the claim file and is not returned. Remember too that in some circumstances, children may be required to furnish proof of their parents' birth, marriage, or divorce.

WILLS

will The legal declaration of a person's mind as to the disposition of his or her property after death.

intestate Without a valid will.

Visit the Web site
See Personal Financial Planning worksheets under Chapter 15 on the online learning centre at www.mcgrawhill.ca/ college/kapoor.

One of the most vital documents every adult should have is a written will. A **will** is the legal declaration of a person's mind as to the disposition of his or her property after death. Thus, a will is a way to transfer your property according to your wishes after you die (see Exhibit 15–1).

Whether you prepare a will before you die or neglect to take that sensible step, you still have a will. If you fail to prepare your own will, the province in which you legally reside steps in and controls the distribution of your estate without regard for wishes you may have had but failed to define in legal form. Thus, if you die **intestate**—without a valid will—the province's law of descent and distribution becomes your copy of the will (see Exhibit 15–2 on page 444).

THE EFFECT OF MARRIAGE OR DIVORCE ON YOUR WILL As mentioned above, changes to your marital status can affect the validity of your will. Even if does not, you may personally wish to make changes related to the changing role of a partner in your life. In the case of divorce, for example, the issue of ownership of familial debts and assets is often heatedly debated, and you should ensure that your will respects whatever agreement you come to.

If you marry after you have made a will, the will is revoked automatically unless certain conditions are met. For example, marriage does not revoke a will if

- The will indicates an intent that it not be revoked by a subsequent marriage.
- The will was drafted under circumstances indicating that it was in contemplation of marriage.

Because your existing will's legal status may be uncertain, you are better off drawing a new will to fit your new circumstances.

COST OF A WILL Legal fees for drafting a will vary with the complexities of your estate and family situation. A standard will costs between $200 and $350. The price varies from place to place, but generally the cost of writing a will is less than that for writing a living trust (to be discussed later in the chapter). Look for an attorney experienced in drafting wills and in estate planning.

Exhibit 15–1   What's in a Will

A will requires careful planning to ensure all aspects are covered. The chart below outlining the contents of a basic will clearly demonstrates this point.

Common Clause	Purpose of the Clause
Identification and Revocation Clause	Identifies you and your residence. Declares that this is your last will which revokes all prior wills.
Appointment of Executor(s)	Designates the individual or institution you appoint as your executor. May also designate alternative and successor executors if your original executor cannot act. The clause may provide for the payment of compensation to the executor for their services.
Payment of Debts	Directs your executor to pay all debts, such as mortgages, loans, and funeral and estate administration expenses.
Payment of Taxes and Fees	Authorizes your executor to pay income tax or probate fees that may be due.
Specific Bequests	Outlines the distribution of specific personal property, such as furniture, jewellery, cars. May also refer to your RRSPs, RRIFs, and pensions.
Legacies	Directs specific cash amounts to be paid.
Residual Estates	Outlines the distribution of your remaining property after all the specific bequests have been made.
Trusts	Sets out the terms of any trust created by your will.
Power Clauses	Enables your executor to exercise various powers in the management of your estate without the approval of the court.
Life Interest Clause	Used when you want to leave someone the income or the enjoyment of the asset, rather than the asset itself. Upon the life tenant's death, the asset would pass on to another beneficiary.
Encroachment Clause	Used in a trust when you want the trustee to be able to give the life tenant or a capital beneficiary additional funds for special circumstances or needs.
Common Disaster Clause	Outlines the distribution of your assets if an intended beneficiary dies at the same time as you.
Survival Clause	States that a beneficiary must survive you for a set period of time (often 30 days) before he or she can benefit from your estate.
Guardian Appointment	Names the individual(s) who would be appointed guardian of your minor children.
Testimonium and Attestation Clauses	These clauses are found at the end of your will. They ensure the legal requirements for a validly executed will are met.

SOURCE: Ho and Robinson, *Personal Financial Planning*, Third Edition (Captus Press, 2000, page 426).

CONCEPT CHECK 15–2

1. What are the legal aspects of estate planning?
2. What is a will? Why is it an important estate planning tool?
3. How does marriage or divorce affect a will?

EXHIBIT 15–2

Distribution of property when a person dies intestate (without a will)

Dies Leaving	Distribution
Spouse and no children	Entire estate to spouse
Spouse and one child (children of deceased child counted as one living child)	One-half to spouse and one half to child *per stirpes**
Spouse and more than one child (children of deceased child counted as one living child)	One-third to spouse and two-thirds to children *per stirpes*
Children (no spouse)	To children *per stirpes*
Father or mother, or both	Equally to parents or to surviving parent
Brothers and sisters only	Equally to brothers and sisters; if a brother or sister has died leaving a child or children, the child or children take his, her, or their parent's share by representation
Nephews and nieces only	Equally divided among nieces and nephews
Only other next-of-kin	Equally divided among next-of-kin of equal degree of consanguinity (half blood inherits equally with whole blood)

* *per stirpes* means that if the entitled person is deceased, his or her share of the inheritance will go to his or her children, equally.

SOURCE: Carr, Stevenson & Mackay, Barristers & Solicitors, http://www.csmlaw.com/estates.htm

Types and Formats of Wills

Objective 3

Distinguish among formats of wills.

holographic will A handwritten will.

formal will A will that is usually prepared with an attorney's assistance.

beneficiary A person who has been named to receive property under a will.

probate The legal procedure of proving a valid or invalid will.

Wills may be holographic or formal. A **holographic will** is a handwritten will that you prepare yourself. It should be written, dated, and signed entirely in your handwriting; no printed or typed information should be on its pages. Some provinces, however, may not recognize a holographic will.

A **formal will** is usually prepared with an attorney's assistance. It may be either typed or on a pre-printed form. You must sign the will and acknowledge it as your will in the presence of two witnesses, neither of whom is a **beneficiary** (a person you have named to receive property under the will). The witnesses must then sign the will in your presence.

WRITING YOUR WILL

The way to transfer your property according to your wishes is to write a will specifying those wishes. Joint ownership is no substitute for a will. Although jointly owned property passes directly to the joint owner and may be appropriate for some assets, such as your home, only a will allows you to distribute your property as a whole exactly as you wish. Select a person who will follow your instructions (your *executor*). By naming your own executor, you will eliminate the need for a court-appointed administrator, prevent unnecessary delay in the distribution of your property, and minimize settlement costs. See the Financial Planning for Life's Situations feature on the next page for guidance on important aspects of making a will.

An executor will have many important tasks. One of these is to obtain probate from court. **Probate** is the legal procedure of proving a valid or invalid will. It is the process by which an executor manages and distributes your property after you die according to your will's provisions. A probate court generally validates wills and makes sure debts are paid. You should

Financial Planning for Life's Situations

THE TEN COMMANDMENTS OF MAKING YOUR WILL

1. Work closely with your spouse as you prepare your will. Seek professional help so that your family objectives can be met, regardless of who dies first.

2. Write your will to conform with your current wishes. When your circumstances change (for example, when you retire or move to another province), review your will and, if appropriate, write a new one.

3. Do not choose a beneficiary as a witness. If such a person is called on to validate your will, he or she may not be able to collect an inheritance.

4. If you are remarrying, consider signing a pre-nuptial agreement to protect your children. If you sign such an agreement before the wedding, you and your intended spouse can legally agree that neither of you will make any claim on the other's estate. The agreement can be revoked later, if you both agree.

5. Consider using percentages, rather than dollar amounts, when you divide your estate. For example,

if you leave $15,000 to a friend and the rest to your spouse, your spouse will suffer if your estate shrinks to $17,000.

6. Both you and your spouse should have a will, and those wills should be separate documents.

7. Be flexible. Don't insist that your heirs keep stock or run a cattle ranch. If you do so, they may suffer if economic conditions change.

8. Sign the original copy of your will and keep it in a safe place; keep an unsigned copy at home for reference.

9. Alter your will by preparing a new will or adding a codicil. Don't change beneficiaries by writing on the will itself; this may invalidate the will.

10. Select an executor who is both willing and able to carry out the complicated tasks associated with the job.

---

avoid probate because it is expensive, lengthy, and public. As you'll read later, a living trust avoids probate and is less expensive, quicker, and more private.

SELECTING AN EXECUTOR Select an executor refered to as a liquidator in Quebec and a trustee in Ontario, who is both willing and able to carry out the complicated tasks associated with executing a will. These tasks are preparing an inventory of assets, collecting any money due, paying off any debts, preparing and filing all income and estate tax returns, liquidating and re-investing other assets to pay off debts and provide income for your family while the estate is being administered, distributing the estate, and making a final accounting to your beneficiaries and to the probate court.

Your executor can be a family member, a friend, an attorney, an accountant, or the trust department of a bank. Exhibit 15–3 summarizes typical duties of an executor.

SELECTING A GUARDIAN In addition to disposing of your estate, your will should name a guardian and/or trustee to care for minor children if both parents die at the same time, such as in an automobile accident or a plane crash. A **guardian** is a person who assumes the responsibilities of providing the children with personal care and of managing the estate for them. A **trustee**, on the other hand, is a person or an institution that holds or generally manages property for the benefit of someone else under a trust agreement.

You should take great care in selecting a guardian for your children. You want a guardian whose philosophy on raising children is similar to yours and who is willing to accept the responsibility.

Through your will, you may want to provide funds to raise your children. You could, for instance, leave a lump sum for an addition to the guardian's house and establish monthly payments to cover your children's living expenses.

guardian A person who assumes responsibility for providing children with personal care and managing the deceased's estate for them.

trustee A person or an institution that holds or manages property for the benefit of someone else under a trust agreement.

445

Exhibit 15–3

Major Responsibilities of an Executor

The complexity of the estates determines the duties to be performed and the sequence. Certain provincial statutes may vary these duties.

SOURCE: Adapted from Ho and Robinson, *Personal Financial Planning*, Third Edition, (Captus Press, 2000, pages 431 and 432).

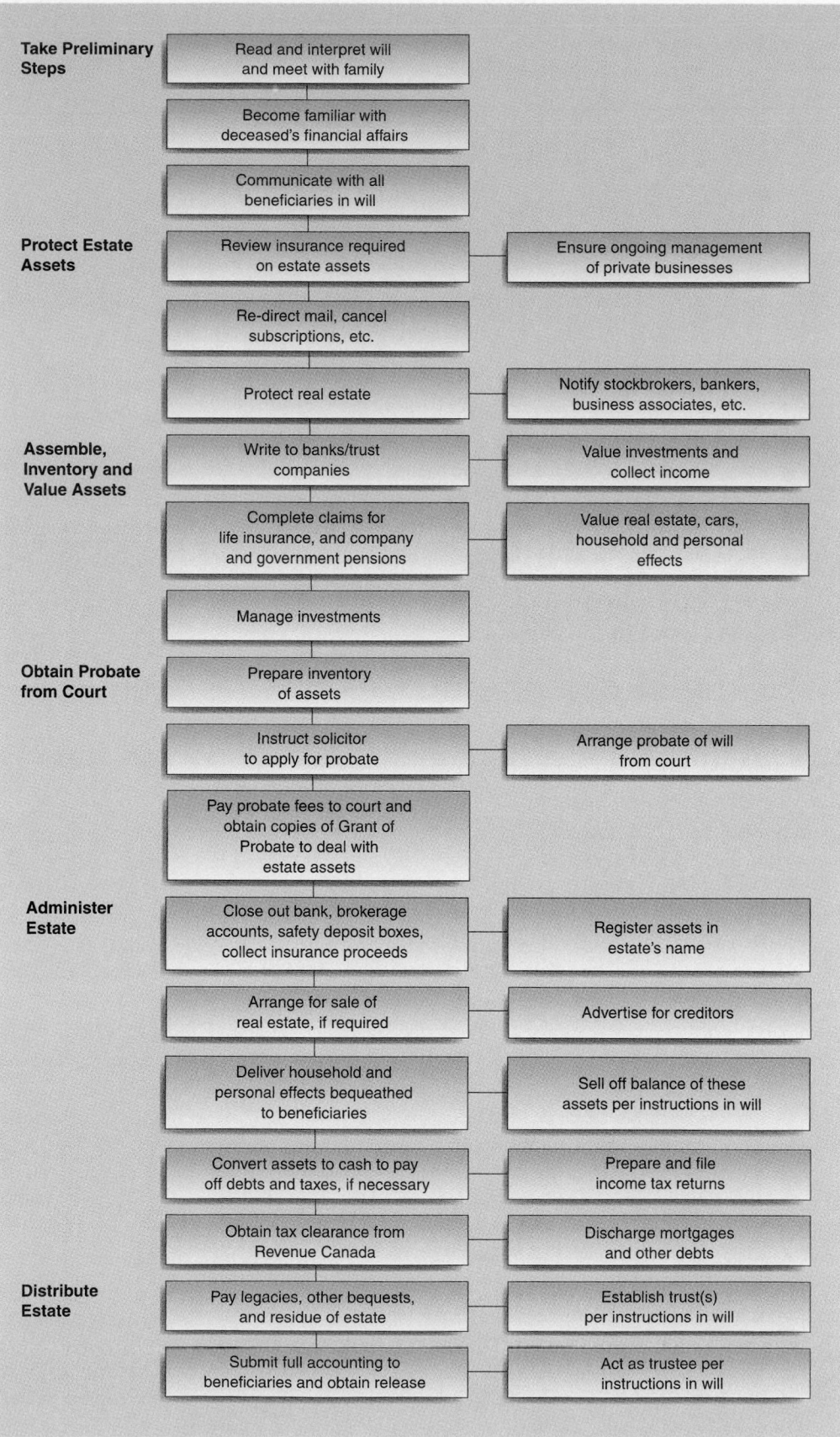

Take Preliminary Steps	Read and interpret will and meet with family
	Become familiar with deceased's financial affairs
	Communicate with all beneficiaries in will
Protect Estate Assets	Review insurance required on estate assets — Ensure ongoing management of private businesses
	Re-direct mail, cancel subscriptions, etc.
	Protect real estate — Notify stockbrokers, bankers, business associates, etc.
Assemble, Inventory and Value Assets	Write to banks/trust companies — Value investments and collect income
	Complete claims for life insurance, and company and government pensions — Value real estate, cars, household and personal effects
	Manage investments
Obtain Probate from Court	Prepare inventory of assets
	Instruct solicitor to apply for probate — Arrange probate of will from court
	Pay probate fees to court and obtain copies of Grant of Probate to deal with estate assets
Administer Estate	Close out bank, brokerage accounts, safety deposit boxes, collect insurance proceeds — Register assets in estate's name
	Arrange for sale of real estate, if required — Advertise for creditors
	Deliver household and personal effects bequeathed to beneficiaries — Sell off balance of these assets per instructions in will
	Convert assets to cash to pay off debts and taxes, if necessary — Prepare and file income tax returns
	Obtain tax clearance from Revenue Canada — Discharge mortgages and other debts
Distribute Estate	Pay legacies, other bequests, and residue of estate — Establish trust(s) per instructions in will
	Submit full accounting to beneficiaries and obtain release — Act as trustee per instructions in will

The guardian of the minor's estate manages the property you leave behind for your children. This guardian can be a person or the trust department of a financial institution, such as a bank. Property that you place in trust for your children can be managed by the trustee, rather than by the guardian of the minor's estate.

ALTERING OR REWRITING YOUR WILL

You should review your will if you move to a different province; if you have sold property mentioned in the will; if the size and composition of your estate have changed; if you have married, divorced, or remarried; or if potential heirs have died or been born.

Don't make any changes on the face of your will. Additions, deletions, or erasures on a will that has been signed and witnessed can invalidate the will.

If only a few changes are needed in your will, adding a codicil may be the best choice. A **codicil** is a document that explains, adds, or deletes provisions in your existing will. It identifies the will being amended and confirms the unchanged sections of the will. To be valid, it must conform to the legal requirements for a will.

codicil A document that modifies provisions in an existing will.

If you wish to make major changes in your will or if you have already added a codicil, preparing a new will is preferable to adding a new codicil. In the new will, include a clause revoking all earlier wills and codicils.

If you are rewriting a will because of a remarriage, consider drafting a **pre-nuptial agreement**. This is a documentary agreement between spouses before marriage. In such agreements, one or both parties often waive a right to receive property under the other's will or under provincial law. Be sure to consult an attorney in drafting a pre-nuptial agreement.

pre-nuptial agreement A documentary agreement between spouses before marriage.

Wills have existed for thousands of years; the oldest known will was written by the Egyptian pharaoh Uah in 2448 b.c. Recently a new type of will, called a *living will*, has emerged.

A LIVING WILL

A **living will** provides for your wishes to be followed if you become so physically or mentally disabled that you are unable to act on your own behalf. A living will is not a substitute for a traditional will. It enables an individual, while well, to express the intention that life be allowed to end if he or she becomes terminally ill. Exhibit 15–4 is an example of a typical living will.

living will A document that enables an individual, while well, to express the intention that life be allowed to end if he or she becomes terminally ill.

To ensure the effectiveness of a living will, discuss your intention of preparing such a will with the people closest to you. You should also discuss this with your family doctor. Sign and date your document before two witnesses. Witnessing shows that you signed of your own free will.

Give copies of your living will to those closest to you, and have your family doctor place a copy in your medical file. Keep the original document readily accessible, and look it over periodically—preferably once a year—to be sure your wishes have remained unchanged. To verify your intent, redate and initial each subsequent endorsement.

Working through end-of-life issues is difficult, but it can help avoid forcing your family to make a decision in a hospital waiting room—or worse, having your last wishes ignored.

A living will can become a problem. A once-healthy person may have a change of heart and prefer to remain alive even as death seems imminent. Living wills call for careful thought, but they do provide you with a choice as to the manner of your death.

> ### DID YOU KNOW ?
>
> Alberta, Manitoba, Newfoundland, Nova Scotia, Ontario, Quebec, and Saskatchewan have legalized the making of living wills. British Columbia and Prince Edward Island have also passed such laws, but they are not yet in force.
>
> SOURCE: The University of Toronto Joint Centre for Bioethics, http://www.utoronto.ca/jcb/

Exhibit 15–4

A Living Will: Example

SOURCE: *Don't Wait until Tomorrow* (Hartford, CT: Aetna Life and Casualty Company, n.d.), p. 11.

Living Will Declaration

Declaration made this _____ day of _____ (month, year)

I, _____, being of sound mind, willfully and voluntarily make known my desire that my dying shall not be artificially prolonged under the circumstances set forth below, do hereby declare

If at any time I should have an incurable injury, disease, or illness regarded as a terminal condition by my physician and if my physician has determined that the application of life-sustaining procedures would serve only to artificially prolong the dying process and that my death will occur whether or not life-sustaining procedures are utilized, I direct that such procedures be withheld or withdrawn and that I be permitted to die with only the administration of medication or the performance of any medical procedure deemed necessary to provide me with comfort care.

In the absence of my ability to give directions regarding the use of such life-sustaining procedures, it is my intention that this declaration shall be honoured by my family and physician as the final expression of my legal right to refuse medical or surgical treatment and accept the consequences from such refusal.

I understand the full import of this declaration, and I am emotionally and mentally competent to make this declaration.

Signed _____

City and Province of Residence _____

The declarant has been personally known to me, and I believe him or her to be of sound mind.

Witness _____

Witness _____

POWER OF ATTORNEY

power of attorney
A legal document authorizing someone to act on one's behalf.

Related to the concept of a living will is a **power of attorney**. A power of attorney is a legal document authorizing someone to act on your behalf. At some point in your life, you may become ill or incapacitated. You may then wish to have someone attend to your needs and your personal affairs. You can assign a power of attorney to anyone you choose.

The person you name can be given limited power or a great deal of power. The power given can be special—to carry out certain acts or transactions, or it can be general—to act completely for you. A conventional power of attorney is automatically revoked in a case of legal incapacity.

LETTER OF LAST INSTRUCTION

In addition to your will, you should prepare a *letter of last instruction*. This document, though not legally enforceable, can provide your heirs with important information. It should contain the details of your funeral arrangements. It should also contain the names of the people who are to be notified of your death and the locations of your bank accounts, safety deposit box, and other important items.

Types of Trusts and Estates

A trust is a property arrangement in which a trustee, such as a person or a bank trust department, holds title to, takes care of, and, in most cases, manages property for the benefit of someone else. The creator of the trust is called the **trustor** or grantor. A bank, as trustee, charges a modest fee for its services, generally based on the value of the trust assets. All trust assets added together are known as an *estate*.

It is a good idea to discuss with your attorney the possibility of establishing a trust as a means of managing your estate. Basically, a **trust** is a legal arrangement through which a trustee holds your assets for your benefit or that of your beneficiaries. "Trusts today are used for everything from protecting assets from creditors to managing property for young children or disabled elders,"[1] according to one tax attorney.

BENEFITS OF ESTABLISHING TRUSTS

Your individual circumstances dictate whether it makes sense to establish a trust. Here are some common reasons for setting up a trust. You can use a trust to

- Reduce or otherwise provide for payment of estate taxes.
- Avoid probate and transfer your assets immediately to your beneficiaries.
- Free yourself from management of your assets while you receive a regular income from the trust.
- Provide income for a surviving spouse or other beneficiaries.
- Ensure that your property serves a desired purpose after your death.

Trustee services are commonly provided by trust companies and, in some instances, by life insurance companies. An estate attorney can advise you about the right type of trust for you.

TYPES OF TRUSTS

There are three types of trusts. You can establish a living trust, a testamentary trust, or a spousal trust. Each of these types has particular advantages. Choose the type of trust that is most appropriate for your family situation.

LIVING OR INTER VIVOS TRUST A **living trust**, or *inter vivos trust*, is a property management arrangement that you establish while you are alive. Well-structured estate plans often start with a living trust that becomes irrevocable at death, changing itself into several other types of trusts.

TESTAMENTARY TRUST A **testamentary trust** is established by your will and becomes effective upon your death. Such a trust can be valuable if your beneficiaries are inexperienced in financial matters or if the potential estate tax is substantial. Like a living trust, a

Objective 4

Appraise various types of trusts and estates.

trustor The creator of a trust; also called the *grantor.*

trust A legal arrangement through which one's assets are held by a trustee.

living trust A trust that is created and provides benefits during the trustor's lifetime.

testamentary trust A trust established by the creator's will that becomes effective upon his or her death.

---

[1] Lynn Asinof, "Trust Funds Are Just for the Rich? Think Again," *The Wall Street Journal*, January 9, 1995, pp. C1, C10.

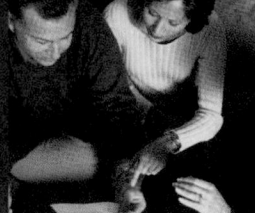

THE IMPORTANCE OF ESTATE PLANNING

Waiting too long can be very costly, say the pros. Too often people either don't want to think about death and incompetency or they do not have enough information to make informed decisions. Then a problem occurs, and by then many valuable planning opportunities have been lost. Anyone with a home, savings, or minor children should consult an experienced estate planning attorney.

The term *estate planning* generally refers to the legal issues involved in planning for death, incompetency, and reducing or avoiding estate taxes. The process for settling a deceased person's affairs is called *probate*. Probate is a court process with two primary goals: (1) to make sure all debts are paid, and (2) to distribute property to the proper recipients. A will is a set of your instructions to a probate court judge for settling your affairs. A will allows you to avoid some of the more expensive aspects of probate. If you have minor children, a will is an absolute necessity for naming guardians, who will raise your children if you and your spouse are deceased. If you don't have a will, your province will give you a will by statute. This is called *intestate probate*. Intestate probate usually takes much longer and is more expensive. Everyone should at least have a will or risk leaving the families with a lot of unnecessary cost and aggravation.

Planning for incompetency may be even more important than planning for death. What will happen if, because of age or illness, you are unable to make decisions for yourself? Everyone should have durable powers of attorney for health care and property management. A *durable power of attorney* is a document that authorizes the person you choose to make decisions for you if you cannot make decisions for yourself. A *living will* is a statement of intent that you do not want your life to be artificially prolonged by a life support system.

A *living trust* is a modern approach to solving many of the problems of basic estate planning. A properly established living trust avoids probate and guardianship and may reduce or eliminate estate taxes. When you create a living trust, you establish a new legal "person" that becomes the owner of your property. You do not give up any control of your affairs. Typically, you are the trustee (the manager of your property) and the beneficiary (the person entitled to the property). During your lifetime, there will be no effect on your day-to-day affairs. However, upon your death, because your trust—not you—is the legal owner of your property, there is no need for probate. Your designated successor trustee, typically your spouse or children, takes control of the trust and distributes your property according to your wishes without the cost and time of probate. If you become incompetent, a trust will empower your successor trustees to manage your affairs for you without the need for guardianship. A living trust can also be an invaluable tool to reduce or avoid estate taxes.

testamentary trust provides the benefits of asset management, financial bookkeeping, protection of the beneficiaries, and minimizing of estate taxes.

Newly acquired property can always be added to your trust. But what if you forget to change the title on some of your assets? A simple pourover will, written when the trust agreement is drafted, is the answer. A *pourover* will is a simple document stating that anything you may have neglected to place in your trust during your lifetime should be placed in it at your death. While assets passing under a pourover will are generally probated, a small amount may be excluded from probate.

SPOUSAL TRUST Subject to certain conditions, you can create a trust for your spouse (or common-law spouse). The principal conditions are that (1) all of the income of the trust must be paid to the spouse during the spouse's lifetime, and (2) that none of the capital can be distributed to anyone else during your spouse's lifetime. This trust can actually be classified as either an *inter vivos* trust or a *testamentary* trust. Capital gains on property are taxed only when the trust disposes of the property or when your spouse dies.

ESTATES

As mentioned earlier, your *estate* is everything you own. It includes all of your property—tangible and intangible, however acquired or owned, whether inside or outside the country. It may include jointly owned property, life insurance, and employee benefits. Thus, an important step in estate planning is taking inventory of everything you own, such as

[1] Cash, chequing accounts, savings accounts, GICs, and money market funds.

[2] Stocks, bonds (including provincial and Canada Savings Bonds), mutual funds, commodity futures, and tax shelters.

[3] Life insurance, employee benefits, and annuities.

[4] Your home and any other real estate, land and buildings, furniture, and fixtures.

[5] Farms, grain, livestock, machinery, and equipment.

[6] Proprietorship, partnership, and close corporation interests.

[7] Notes, accounts, and claims receivable.

[8] Interests in trusts and powers of appointment.

[9] Antiques, works of art, collectibles, cars, boats, planes, personal effects, and everything else.

ESTATE ASSETS NOT DISTRIBUTED BY A WILL

By law, there are two situations in which your assets will go directly to a beneficiary, independently of your will. The first is one in which your assets, such as life insurance, annuities, and RRSPs, already have a named beneficiary. Unless your beneficiary has pre-deceased you, these assets will be transferred directly without being subject to the process or expense of probate. In cases where the beneficiary has pre-deceased you, then the values will be transferred to your estate.

The second situation occurs when you have assets held in *joint tenancy*, which confers the right of survivorship. Note that this is not the same as *tenancy in common*, where the assets are owned in undivided shares. For example, if a couple owns a home in joint tenancy, then the ownership of that home will pass in its entirety to the spouse upon death of the other spouse. If the same couple owns their home as tenants in common, however, then one-half of the value of the home will count into the deceased spouse's estate.

LIFE INSURANCE AND EMPLOYEE BENEFITS Life insurance proceeds are free of income tax and excluded from probate. Assignment of ownership to your beneficiary or a trust removes a life insurance policy from your estate. Death benefits from qualified pension plans are excluded from your estate, unless they are payable to it.

LIFETIME GIFTS AND TRUSTS You can structure charitable gifts both during your lifetime and in your will to further your estate planning goals and make the most of available tax credits. There are a number of ways in which gifts of capital or property can be made with significant tax benefits. One example of this would be if you elected to make a charitable gift through your will. In this case, your taxable income in the year of your death would be deducted by the available tax credit for charitable donations; in 2001, this would have represented 29 percent of the donation above $200, up to 100 percent of your net income.

If you sit down with a qualified adviser and carefully map out a gifting strategy for your estate, it is possible to both fulfill your philanthropic desires and have your estate receive favourable tax treatment as well.

> **DID YOU KNOW?**
>
> Without an estate plan, the government may get up to 55 percent of your assets.
>
> SOURCE: www.metlife.com AARP Program Development and Services, 4/00.

Advice from a Pro

TAXES AT DEATH

The old saying that "there are only two certainties in life—death and taxes" holds true even at death. There is no escaping it, but there are ways to lessen the burden of this unanticipated beneficiary, called the government. While there are no true "estate taxes" in Canada, three potential taxes or pseudo-taxes may be incurred at death:

- Income tax due to the deemed disposition rules
- Provincial probate taxes
- U.S. Estate Tax on your U.S. assets

DEEMED DISPOSITION

In the year of death, a final (terminal) tax return must be filed by the estate's executor/liquidator that includes all income earned by the deceased up to the date of death. Also, included in income at death is the net capital gain recognized under the deemed disposition rules. The deemed disposition rules of the Income Tax Act treat all capital property owned by the deceased as if it was sold immediately prior to death. Thus, all unrecognized capital gains and losses are triggered at that point with the net capital gain (gains less losses) included in income. The Income Tax Act does contain provisions to defer the tax owing under the deemed disposition rules if the asset is left to a surviving spouse or to a special trust for a spouse (spousal trust) created by the deceased's will. This provision allows the spouse or the spousal trust to take ownership of the asset at the deceased's original cost. Hence, no tax is payable until either the spouse or the spousal trust sells the asset or until the surviving spouse dies. The tax is then payable on the basis of the asset's increase in value at that point in time.

RSPs AND RIFs

In addition to the potentially significant tax liability from recognized capital gains, it is also necessary to deregister (i.e., collapse) any registered assets, such as RSPs or RIFs, at the point of death. The full value of the RSP or RIF must be included on the deceased's final (terminal) tax return. There are exceptions to this deregistration requirement if the RSP or RIF is left to the surviving spouse, a common law spouse, and, in some cases, to a surviving child or grandchild. An RSP or RIF can be transferred tax free to a surviving spouse's own plan. Also, the RSP or RIF can be transferred tax-free to a financially dependent child or grandchild who is under age 18, or who is mentally or physically infirm, even if there is a surviving spouse. The registered funds must be used to purchase a term certain annuity with a term not exceeding the child's 18th year.

PROBATE TAXES

Upon death, the executor of your estate will typically be required to file for probate with the provincial court. The estate's executor must submit to the court the original will and an inventory of the deceased's assets. Upon acceptance of these documents by the court, letters (called "certificate of appointment of estate trustee with a will" in Ontario) are issued. This document serves to verify that the submitted will is a valid document and confirms the appointment of your executor. With the executor's submission to the court, he/she must also pay a probate tax. This tax is based on the total value of the assets that flow through the will. The rate charged varies between provinces with some provinces having a maximum fee. In situations where the estate is extremely simple and does not require any involvement with a third party, such as a financial institution, the will may not need to be probated. As well, probate taxes can be reduced by using previously discussed strategies, such as the naming of beneficiaries, Joint Tenancy with Right of Survivorship agreements, and the use of living trusts.

U.S. ESTATE TAX

In addition to the taxes payable in Canada, you may also be subject to a tax bill from the U.S. Government. Canadians who own U.S.-sourced assets, such as real estate, corporate stocks and certain bonds, and government debt are required to pay U.S. Estate Tax based on the market value of their U.S. assets at the time of death. For more information on U.S. Estate Tax, the Royal Bank of Canada offers a publication entitled, *Tax Implications of Investing in the United States.*

SOURCE: RBC Investments - Education Centre, http://www.rbcinvestments.com/ep_taxes.html

SETTLING YOUR ESTATE

If you have had a will drawn, you are *testate* in the eyes of the law, and an executor (named in your will) will carry out your wishes in due time. If you have not named an executor, the probate court (the court that supervises the distribution of estates) will appoint an administrator to carry out the instructions in your will.

PROBATE AND ADMINISTRATION COSTS Your estate administration costs will include fees for attorneys, accountants, appraisers, executors or administrators and trustees, court costs, bonding and surety costs, and miscellaneous expenses. These administration costs may run to 3 to 5 percent of your estate, depending on its size and complexity. While the percentage usually decreases as the size of the estate increases, it may be increased by additional complicating factors, such as handling a business interest. Inversely to administration costs, probate costs tend to rise with the size of the estate. The exact costs, payable to the court, are paid out of the proceeds of your estate and are set by the court.

If you don't have a will, you become *intestate* at your death. In that case, your estate is put under the control of a court-appointed administrator for distribution according to the laws of the province in which you reside.

Although the very process of estate planning is a trying one as it forces you to think about emotionally charged issues, such as what you leave behind and to whom, a will may be its most important feature. Remember the old adage that the act of not deciding is a decision in itself.

As we discuss earlier in this chapter, if you don't make a will or use some other legal method to transfer your property when you die, provincial law will determine what happens to your property. This process is called "intestate succession." Your property will be distributed to your spouse and children or, if you have neither, to the closest next of kin according to a statutory formula (usually in this order: parents; if neither is surviving, siblings; if none, nieces/nephews; if none, other next of kin). If no relatives can be found to inherit your property, it all goes to the government.

CONCEPT CHECK 15–4

1. Differentiate among the types of trusts.
2. What is included in an estate?
3. What are the two types of joint ownership?

SUMMARY OF OBJECTIVES

Objective 1
Analyze the personal aspects of estate planning.
Estate planning is an essential part of retirement planning and an integral part of financial planning. The first part of estate planning consists of building your estate; the second part consists of transferring your estate, at your death, in the manner you have specified. The personal aspects of estate planning depend on whether you are single or married. If you are married, your estate planning involves the interests of at least two people, and more if there are children. Never having been married does not eliminate the need to organize your financial affairs.

Objective 2
Assess the legal aspects of estate planning.
In the event of death, proof of claims must be produced or the claims will not be processed. Among the papers needed are birth certificates, marriage certificates, legal name changes, and military service records. Every adult should have a written will, which is the legal declaration of a person's wishes as to the disposition

of his or her property after death. Thus, a will is a way to transfer your property according to your wishes after you die.

Objective 3
Distinguish among formats of wills.
The two formats for wills are holographic and formal. A holographic will is handwritten and requires no witness but is a poor choice for most people and some provinces will not recognize it. A formal will is a typed document signed by you and witnessed by two individuals who must not be beneficiaries or the spouses of beneficiaries. A lawyer is usually employed to draft a formal will.

Objective 4
Appraise various types of trusts and estates.
Establishing a trust can be an excellent way to manage your estate. Popular forms of trusts include living trusts, spousal trusts, and testamentary trusts. An attorney's help is needed to establish a trust.

KEY TERMS

beneficiary 444

codicil 447

estate 439

estate planning 439

formal will 444

guardian 445

holographic will 444

intestate 442

living trust 449

living will 447

power of attorney 448

pre-nuptial agreement 447

probate 444

testamentary trust 449

trust 449

trustee 445

trustor 449

will 442

FINANCIAL PLANNING ACTIVITIES

1. *Preparing a Written Record of Personal Information.* Prepare a written record of personal information that would be helpful to you and your heirs. Make sure to include the location of family records, your military service file, and other important papers; medical records; bank accounts; charge accounts; the location of your safety deposit box; Canada Savings Bonds; stocks, bonds, and other securities; property owned; life insurance; annuities; and government benefits information. (Obj. 1)

2. *Developing Long-Term Estate Planning Goals.* Develop a list of specific long-term estate planning goals with your family. Discuss how those goals could be achieved even if you or your spouse died unexpectedly. (Obj. 1)

3. *Drafting a Simple Will.* Draft your will, using Exhibit 15–1 as a guideline. Who will you appoint as a trustee or guardian for your minor children? Why? (Obj. 2)

4. *Comparing Costs of Preparing a Will.* Contact several lawyers in your area to find out how much they would charge to prepare your simple will. Are their fees about the same? (Obj. 3)

5. *Using the Internet to Obtain Information about Wills.* Visit Metropolitan Life Insurance Company's Web page at www.lifeadvice.com. Using this information, prepare a report on the following: (a) Who needs a will? (b) What are the elements of a will (naming a guardian, naming an executor, preparing a will, updating a will, estate taxes, where to keep your will, living will, etc.)? (c) How is this report helpful in preparing your own will?

6. *Preparing the Letter of Last Instructions.* Prepare your own letter of last instructions. (Obj. 3)

7. *Determining Criteria in Choosing a Guardian.* Make a list of the criteria you will use in deciding who will be the guardian of your minor children if you and your spouse die at the same time. (Obj. 3)

8. *Establishing a Trust.* Discuss with your attorney the possibility of establishing a trust as a means of managing your estate. (Obj. 4)

LIFE SITUATION CASE

Don't Let Your Windfall Blow Away

Warren, a married entrepreneur who owns a successful promotions business, doesn't yet have kids, but he is already making plans. Last December, Warren received an unexpected inheritance of $1.4 million, after taxes, from his late grandfather. Instead of buying a Porsche or a new home, he did the right thing by his family-to-be and invested it all. "Warren is extremely fastidious," says Lesley Sommers, his financial planner.

Warren did what smart people do with sudden wealth: They decide not to blow it. A 1997 survey found that 59 percent of 1,000 respondents who received cash payouts of $20,000 or more had sought professional advice. An equal number had invested every dime. When Warren got his windfall, Sommers invested all but $100,000. Warren says, "She taught me that this

[windfall] should not change where I eat or go on vacation." So, if you win the lottery, don't blow it on houses, cars, vacations, and luxury items. Instead, pay off high-interest credit card and other debts that offer no tax deductions. Then, find a financial adviser. This professional can help you find a competent estate planner and create an investment plan.

Questions

1. What did Warren do with his $1.4 million inheritance?
2. What do smart people do with sudden wealth?

SOURCE: Adapted from Joan Oleck, "Don't Let Your Windfall Blow Away," *Business Week On-line*, December 1999, p. 116. Reprinted from the March 1, 1999 issue of *Business Week* by special permission. © 1999 McGraw-Hill Companies, Inc.

CREATING A FINANCIAL PLAN

Developing an Estate Plan

Most people do not think they have enough assets to do estate planning. However, the planned transfer of resources with the use of a will, trusts, and other legal vehicles is a necessary phase of your total financial plan.

Web Sites for Estate Planning

* Learn what's involved in developing an estate plan and how to take advantage of all your options at the TD Canada Trust site, **www.tdcanadatrust.com**
* The Canadian Financial Publishing Group, at **www.cfpg. com**, has articles on wills, probate, taxation, and other estate planning issues.
* The Royal Bank, at **www.royalbank.com**, has information on estate planning as part of its *Your Money Matters* series of guides.
* The Law Society of Upper Canada, at **www.lsuc.on.ca**, offers a guide for Ontario residents with regard to probating a will.
* The College Institute Educators' Association (CIEA) of BC,

at **www.ciea.bc.ca**, has a great retirement guide called "Planning for the Rest of Your Life."

(Note: Addresses and content of Web sites change, and new sites are created daily. Use search engines to update and locate Web sites for your current financial planning needs.)

Short-Term Financial Planning Activities

1. Investigate the cost of a will. Decide on the type of will and provisions appropriate for your life situation.
2. Using the Canada Customs and Revenue Agency and other Web sites, identify recent estate tax law changes that may affect your financial planning decisions.
3. Compare the benefits and costs of different trusts that might be appropriate for your life situation.

Long-Term Financial Planning Activities

1. Develop a plan for actions to be taken related to estate planning.
2. Identify saving and investing decisions that would minimize future estate taxes.

CONTINUOUS CASE FOR PART 5

PLANNING FOR TOMORROW

Life Situation
Pamela, 48; Isaac, 50; children, ages 21, 19, and 16

Financial Goals
* Replenish savings and investments used for college costs
* Plan for retirement in about 15 years
* Consider estate planning activities

Financial Data

Monthly income	$ 5,700
Living expenses	4,600
Assets	242,500
Liabilities	69,100

With two children in college, the Mortimers once again find their life situation changing. Compared with five years ago, their total assets have decreased from $262,700 to $242,500 due to college expenses. The Mortimers' oldest child will graduate next year, but the youngest will enter university in a couple of years. Therefore, the drain on the family's finances will continue.

The family's finances are adequate, but both Pamela and Isaac are beginning to worry about retirement. Over the years,

Isaac has taken advantage of different career opportunities. Today, his annual salary, $68,400, is higher than it has ever been. But his employment changes have resulted in a smaller pension fund than would be available had he remained with the same organization. The current value of his pension plan is just over $115,000. The investment program he and Pamela started almost 10 years ago is growing and is now worth about $62,000. But they still worry whether they will have enough money to finance their retirement dreams when Isaac retires in 15 years. According to Isaac, "If I retired today, we couldn't maintain our current lifestyle. In fact, we couldn't even exist."

Questions

1. How would you rate the Mortimers' financial condition at this stage in their lives?
2. Given that Pamela is 48 and Isaac is 50, what should be their major priorities as they continue planning for retirement?
3. What types of estate planning, if any, should the Mortimers consider at this time?

The Time Value of Money: Future Value and Present Value Computations

"If I deposit $10,000 today, how much will I have for a down payment on a house in five years?"

"Will $2,000 saved a year give me enough money when I retire?"

"How much must I save today to have enough for my children's college education?"

As introduced in Chapter 1 and used to measure financial opportunity costs in other chapters, the *time value of money*, more commonly referred to as *interest*, is the cost of money that is borrowed or lent. Interest can be compared to rent, the cost of using an apartment or other item. The time value of money is based on the fact that a dollar received today is worth more than a dollar that will be received one year from today because the dollar received today can be saved or invested and will be worth more than a dollar a year from today. Similarly, a dollar that will be received one year from today is currently worth less than a dollar today.

The time value of money has two major components: future value and present value. *Future value* computations, which are also referred to as *compounding*, yield the amount to which a current sum will increase based on a certain interest rate and period of time. *Present value*, which is calculated through a process called *discounting*, is the current value of a future sum based on a certain interest rate and period of time.

In future value problems, you are given an amount to save or invest and you calculate the amount that will be available at some future date. With present value problems, you are given the amount that will be available at some future date and you calculate the current value of that amount. Both future value and present value computations are based on basic interest rate calculations.

Future Value of a Single Amount

The future value of an amount consists of the original amount plus compound interest. This calculation involves the following elements:

$$FV = \text{Future value}$$
$$PV = \text{Present value}$$
$$i = \text{Interest rate}$$
$$n = \text{Number of time periods}$$

The formula for the future value of a single amount is

$$FV = PV(1 + i)^n$$

EXAMPLE A

The future value of $1 at 10 percent after three years is $1.33. This amount is calculated as follows:

$$\$1.33 = \$1.00 (1 + 0.10)^3$$

Future value tables are available to help you determine compounded interest amounts (see Exhibit A–1 on page 464). Looking at Exhibit A–1 for 10 percent and three years, you can see that $1 would be worth $1.33 at that time. For other amounts, multiply the table factor by the original amount.

This may be viewed as follows:

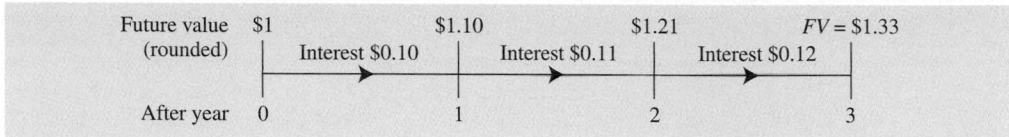

Using a financial calculator (BAII Plus Texas Instrument), you would solve the problem as shown below:

*Remember always clear the time value of money function before any calculation by pressing 2ND CLRTVM

3 N
10 I/Y
1 PV
0 PMT   (Optional, if registers are cleared)
CPT FV

The solution of –$1.33 is displayed. Remember from Chapter 1 that the BAII Plus displays the present value solution with a + and the future value solution with a – because it assumes one is an inflow and the other an outflow.

EXAMPLE B

If your savings of $400 earn 12 percent, compounded *monthly*, over a year and a half, use the table factor for 1 percent for 18 time periods. The future value of this amount is $478.40, calculated as follows:

$$\$478.40 = \$400 (1.196)$$

Using a financial calculator (BAII Plus Texas Instrument):

2ND CLRTVM
18 N   (There are 18 months in a year and a half)
1 I/Y   (I/Y = 12 % / 12 months = 1% a month)
400 PV
0 PMT   (Optional, if registers are cleared)
CPT FV

The solution of –$478.46 is displayed.

Sample Problem 1 What is the future value of $800 at 8 percent after six years?

Sample Problem 2 How much would you have in savings if you kept $200 on deposit for eight years at 8 percent, compounded *semi-annually*?

Future Value of a Series of Equal Amounts (An Annuity)

Future value may also be calculated for a situation in which regular additions are made to savings. The following formula is used to compute the future value annuity factor:

$$FV = \frac{[(1 + i)^n - 1]}{i}$$

This formula assumes that (1) each deposit is for the same amount, (2) the interest rate is the same for each time period, and (3) the deposits are made at the end of each time period.

EXAMPLE C

The future value of three $1 deposits made at the end of the next three years, earning 10 percent interest, is $3.31. This is calculated as follows:

$$\$3.31 = \$1 \times \frac{[(1 + 0.10)^3 - 1]}{0.10}$$

This may be viewed as follows:

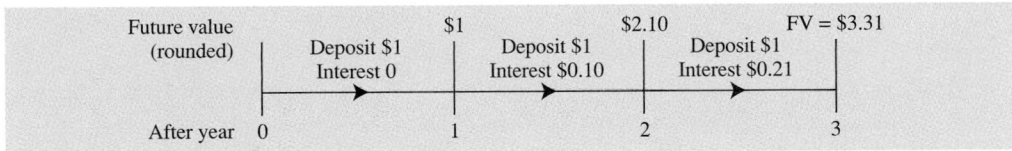

Using Exhibit A–2 on page 465, you can find this same amount for 10 percent for three time periods. To use the table for other amounts, multiply the table factors by the annual deposit.

Using a financial calculator (BAII Plus Texas Instrument):

2ND	CLRTVM
3	N
10	I/Y
0	PV
1	PMT (A deposit is an inflow)
CPT	FV

The solution of –$3.31 is displayed.

EXAMPLE D

If you plan to deposit $40 a year for 10 years, earning 8 percent compounded annually, use the table factor for 8 percent for 10 time periods. The future value of this amount is $579.48, calculated as follows:

$$\$579.48 = \$40(14.487)$$

Using a financial calculator (BAII Plus Texas Instrument):

2ND	CLRTVM
10	N
8	I/Y
0	PV
40	PMT (A deposit is an inflow)
CPT	FV

The solution of –$579.46 is displayed.

Sample Problem 3 What is the future value of an annual deposit of $230 earning 6 percent for 15 years?

Sample Problem 4 What amount would you have in a retirement account if you made annual deposits of $375 for 25 years earning 12 percent, compounded annually?

Present Value of a Single Amount

If you want to know how much you need to deposit now to receive a certain amount in the future, use the following formula:

$$PV = \frac{1}{(1+i)^n}$$

EXAMPLE E

The present value of $1 to be received three years from now based on a 10 percent interest rate is $0.75. This amount is calculated as follows:

$$\$0.75 = \frac{\$1}{(1+0.10)^3}$$

This may be viewed as follows:

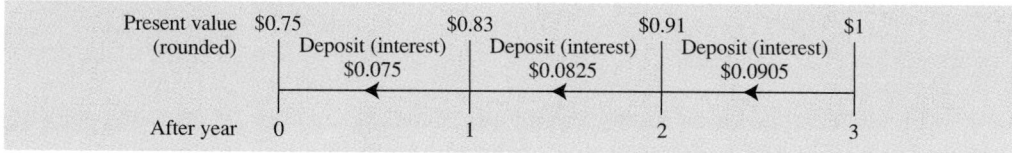

Present value tables are available to assist you in this process (see Exhibit A–3 on page 466). Note that $1 at 10 percent for three years has a present value of $0.75. For amounts other than $1, multiply the table factor by the amount involved.

Using a financial calculator (BAII Plus Texas Instrument):

2ND	CLRTVM
3	N
10	I/Y
1	FV
0	PMT	(Optional, if registers are cleared)
CPT	PV

The solution of $0.75 is displayed.

EXAMPLE F

If you want to have $300 seven years from now and your savings earn 10 percent, compounded *semi-annually*, use the table factor for 5 percent for 14 time periods. In this situation, the present value is $151.50, calculated as follows:

$$\$151.50 = \$300(0.505)$$

Using a financial calculator (BAII Plus Texas Instrument):

2ND	CLRTVM
14	N	(7 years × 2 periods per year (semi-annually) = 14 periods)
5	I/Y	(I/Y = 10 % / 2 periods (semi-annually) = 5% a period)

300	FV
0	PMT	(Optional, if registers are cleared)
CPT	PV

The solution of $151.52 is displayed.

Sample Problem 5 What is the present value of $2,200 earning 15 percent for eight years?

Sample Problem 6 To have $6,000 for a child's education in 10 years, what amount should a parent deposit in a savings account that earns 12 percent, compounded *quarterly*?

Present Value of a Series of Equal Amounts (An Annuity)

The final time value of money situation allows you to receive an amount at the end of each time period for a certain number of periods. The following formula is one to compute the present value annuity factor:

$$PV = \frac{1 - \dfrac{1}{(1 + i)^n}}{i}$$

EXAMPLE G

The present value of a $1 withdrawal at the end of the next three years would be $2.49, calculated as follows:

$$\$2.49 = \$1 \left[\frac{1 - \dfrac{1}{(1 + 0.10)^3}}{0.10} \right]$$

This may be viewed as follows:

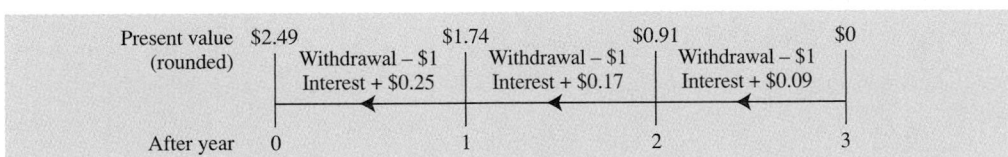

Present value (rounded)	$2.49	$1.74	$0.91	$0
	Withdrawal – $1	Withdrawal – $1	Withdrawal – $1	
	Interest + $0.25	Interest + $0.17	Interest + $0.09	
After year	0	1	2	3

This same amount appears in Exhibit A–4 on page 467 for 10 percent and three time periods. To use the table for other situations, multiply the table factor by the amount to be withdrawn each year.

Using a financial calculator (BAII Plus Texas Instrument):

2ND	CLRTVM
3	N
10	I/Y
0	FV
–1	PMT	(A withdrawal is an outflow)
CPT	PV

The solution of $2.49 is displayed.

EXAMPLE H

If you wish to withdraw $100 at the end of each year for 10 years from an account that earns 14 percent, compounded annually, what amount must you deposit now? Use the table factor for 14 percent for 10 time periods. In this situation, the present value is $521.60, calculated as follows:

$$\$521.60 = \$100(5.216)$$

Using a financial calculator (BAII Plus Texas Instrument):

2ND	CLRTVM	
10	N	
14	I/Y	
0	PV	
−100	PMT	(A withdrawal is an outflow)
CPT	PV	

The solution of $521.61 is displayed.

Sample Problem 7 What is the present value of a withdrawal of $200 at the end of each year for 14 years with an interest rate of 7 percent?

Sample Problem 8 How much would you have to deposit now to be able to withdraw $650 at the end of each year for 20 years from an account that earns 11 percent?

Using Present Value to Determine Loan Payments

Present value tables can also be used to determine amortized payments for a loan as follows:

$$\frac{\text{Amount borrowed}}{\text{Present value of a series table factor (Exhibit A–4)}} = \text{Loan payment}$$

EXAMPLE I

If you borrow $1,000 with a 6 percent interest rate to be repaid in three equal payments at the end of the next three years, the payments will be $374.11. This is calculated as follows:

$$\frac{\$1,000}{2,673} = \$374.11$$

Using a financial calculator (BAII Plus Texas Instrument):

2ND	CLRTVM	
3	N	
6	I/Y	
1000	PV	
0	FV	(A withdrawal is an outflow)
CPT	PMT	

The solution of $374.11 is displayed.

Sample Problem 9 What would be the annual payment amount for a $20,000, 10-year loan at 7 percent?

Answers to Sample Problems

[1] $800(1.587) = $1,269.60. (Use Exhibit A–1, 8%, 6 periods.)
[2] $200(1.873) = $374.60. (Use Exhibit A–1, 4%, 16 periods.)
[3] $230(23.276) = $5,353.48. (Use Exhibit A–2, 6%, 15 periods.)
[4] $375(133.33) = $49,998.75. (Use Exhibit A–2, 12%, 25 periods.)
[5] $2,200(0.327) = $719.40. (Use Exhibit A–3, 15%, 8 periods.)
[6] $6,000(0.307) = $1,842. (Use Exhibit A–3, 3%, 40 periods.)
[7] $200(8.745) = $1,749. (Use Exhibit A–4, 7%, 14 periods.)
[8] $650(7.963) = $5,175.95. (Use Exhibit A–4, 11%, 20 periods.)
[9] $20,000/7.024 = $2,847.38. (Use Exhibit A–4, 7%, 10 periods.)

Calculator Solutions

[1] Calculator : 2nd CLRTVM; 6 N; 8 I/Y; 800 PV; CPT FV; Solution $1,269.50
[2] Calculator : 2nd CLRTVM; 16 N; 4 I/Y; 200 PV; CPT FV; Solution $374.60
[3] Calculator : 2nd CLRTVM; 15 N; 6 I/Y; 230 PMT; CPT FV; Solution $5353.47
[4] Calculator : 2nd CLRTVM; 25 N; 12 I/Y; 375 PMT; CPT FV; Solution $50,000.20
[5] Calculator : 2nd CLRTVM; 8 N; 15 I/Y; 2,200 FV; CPT PV; Solution $719.18
[6] Calculator : 2nd CLRTVM; 40 N; 3 I/Y; 6,000 FV; CPT PV; Solution $1839.34
[7] Calculator : 2nd CLRTVM; 14 N; 7 I/Y; 200 PMT; CPT PV; Solution $1749.09
[8] Calculator : 2nd CLRTVM; 20 N; 11 I/Y; 650 PMT; CPT PV; Solution $5176.16
[9] Calculator : 2nd CLRTVM; 10 N; 7 I/Y; 20,000 PV; CPT PMT; Solution $2,847.55

Calculating the Effective Annual Rate (EAR) Using a Financial Calculator (BAll Plus Texas Instrument)

Example from Chapter 4 (page 111): How much is your nominal EAR on a $100 loan at 12 percent yearly, compounded monthly? (There are 12 compounding periods in a year.)

2ND	ICONV	↑	12 (Number of periods in a year)	ENTER
↓	12 (Rate of return for one period)	ENTER
↓	CPT

The effective rate of 12.68 percent is displayed on the screen.

EXAMPLE J

Assume your bank offers a 10-percent interest rate that is compounded every three months, while a competitor offers 10 percent compounded on a monthly basis. Which one offers a higher effective rate?

BANK (10% compounded every 3 months = 4 periods)

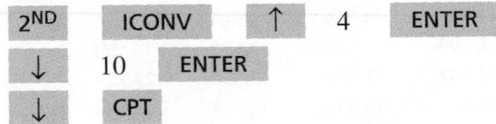

The effective rate is 10.38 percent.

COMPETITOR (10% compounded weekly = 52 periods)

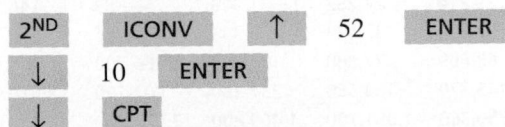

The effective rate is 10.51 percent.

As you can see, the competitor offers a higher return than your bank.

Exhibit A-1   Future Value (Compounded Sum) of $1 after a Given Number of Time Periods

$$FV = PV(1 + i)^n$$

Period	1%	2%	3%	4%	5%	6%	7%	8%	9%	10%	11%
1	1.010	1.020	1.030	1.040	1.050	1.060	1.070	1.080	1.090	1.100	1.110
2	1.020	1.040	1.061	1.082	1.103	1.124	1.145	1.166	1.188	1.210	1.232
3	1.030	1.061	1.093	1.125	1.158	1.191	1.225	1.260	1.295	1.331	1.368
4	1.041	1.082	1.126	1.170	1.216	1.262	1.311	1.360	1.412	1.464	1.518
5	1.051	1.104	1.159	1.217	1.276	1.338	1.403	1.469	1.539	1.611	1.685
6	1.062	1.126	1.194	1.265	1.340	1.419	1.501	1.587	1.677	1.772	1.870
7	1.072	1.149	1.230	1.316	1.407	1.504	1.606	1.714	1.828	1.949	2.076
8	1.083	1.172	1.267	1.369	1.477	1.594	1.718	1.851	1.993	2.144	2.305
9	1.094	1.195	1.305	1.423	1.551	1.689	1.838	1.999	2.172	2.358	2.558
10	1.105	1.219	1.344	1.480	1.629	1.791	1.967	2.159	2.367	2.594	2.839
11	1.116	1.243	1.384	1.539	1.710	1.898	2.105	2.332	2.580	2.853	3.152
12	1.127	1.268	1.426	1.601	1.796	2.012	2.252	2.518	2.813	3.138	3.498
13	1.138	1.294	1.469	1.665	1.886	2.133	2.410	2.720	3.066	3.452	3.883
14	1.149	1.319	1.513	1.732	1.980	2.261	2.579	2.937	3.342	3.797	4.310
15	1.161	1.346	1.558	1.801	2.079	2.397	2.759	3.172	3.642	4.177	4.785
16	1.173	1.373	1.605	1.873	2.183	2.540	2.952	3.426	3.970	4.595	5.311
17	1.184	1.400	1.653	1.948	2.292	2.693	3.159	3.700	4.328	5.054	5.895
18	1.196	1.428	1.702	2.026	2.407	2.854	3.380	3.996	4.717	5.560	6.544
19	1.208	1.457	1.754	2.107	2.527	3.026	3.617	4.316	5.142	6.116	7.263
20	1.220	1.486	1.806	2.191	2.653	3.207	3.870	4.661	5.604	6.727	8.062
25	1.282	1.641	2.094	2.666	3.386	4.292	5.427	6.848	8.623	10.835	13.585
30	1.348	1.811	2.427	3.243	4.322	5.743	7.612	10.063	13.268	17.449	22.892
40	1.489	2.208	3.262	4.801	7.040	10.286	14.974	21.725	31.409	45.259	65.001
50	1.645	2.692	4.384	7.107	11.467	18.420	29.457	46.902	74.358	117.390	184.570

Exhibit A-1 (Concluded)

Period	12%	13%	14%	15%	16%	17%	18%	19%	20%	25%	30%
1	1.120	1.130	1.140	1.150	1.160	1.170	1.180	1.190	1.200	1.250	1.300
2	1.254	1.277	1.300	1.323	1.346	1.369	1.392	1.416	1.440	1.563	1.690
3	1.405	1.443	1.482	1.521	1.561	1.602	1.643	1.685	1.728	1.953	2.197
4	1.574	1.630	1.689	1.749	1.811	1.874	1.939	2.005	2.074	2.441	2.856
5	1.762	1.842	1.925	2.011	2.100	2.192	2.288	2.386	2.488	3.052	3.713
6	1.974	2.082	2.195	2.313	2.436	2.565	2.700	2.840	2.986	3.815	4.827
7	2.211	2.353	2.502	2.660	2.826	3.001	3.185	3.379	3.583	4.768	6.276
8	2.476	2.658	2.853	3.059	3.278	3.511	3.759	4.021	4.300	5.960	8.157
9	2.773	3.004	3.252	3.518	3.803	4.108	4.435	4.785	5.160	7.451	10.604
10	3.106	3.395	3.707	4.046	4.411	4.807	5.234	5.696	6.192	9.313	13.786
11	3.479	3.836	4.226	4.652	5.117	5.624	6.176	6.777	7.430	11.642	17.922
12	3.896	4.335	4.818	5.350	5.936	6.580	7.288	8.064	8.916	14.552	23.298
13	4.363	4.898	5.492	6.153	6.886	7.699	8.599	9.596	10.699	18.190	30.288
14	4.887	5.535	6.261	7.076	7.988	9.007	10.147	11.420	12.839	22.737	39.374
15	5.474	6.254	7.138	8.137	9.266	10.539	11.974	13.590	15.407	28.422	51.186
16	6.130	7.067	8.137	9.358	10.748	12.330	14.129	16.172	18.488	35.527	66.542
17	6.866	7.986	9.276	10.761	12.468	14.426	16.672	19.244	22.186	44.409	86.504
18	7.690	9.024	10.575	12.375	14.463	16.879	19.673	22.091	26.623	55.511	112.460
19	8.613	10.197	12.056	14.232	16.777	19.748	23.214	27.252	31.948	69.389	146.190
20	9.646	11.523	13.743	16.367	19.461	23.106	27.393	32.429	38.338	86.736	190.050
25	17.000	21.231	26.462	32.919	40.874	50.658	62.669	77.388	95.396	264.700	705.640
30	29.960	39.116	50.950	66.212	85.850	111.070	143.370	184.680	237.380	807.790	2,620.000
40	93.051	132.780	188.880	267.860	378.720	533.870	750.380	1,051.700	1,469.800	7,523.200	36,119.000
50	289.000	450.740	700.230	1,083.700	1,670.700	2,566.200	3,927.400	5,988.900	9,100.400	70,065.000	497,929.000

Exhibit A-2   Future Value (Compounded Sum) of $1 Paid in at the End of Each Period for a Given Number of Time Periods (an Annuity) $FV = \dfrac{(1 + i)^n - 1}{i}$

Period	1%	2%	3%	4%	5%	6%	7%	8%	9%	10%	11%
1	1.000	1.000	1.000	1.000	1.000	1.000	1.000	1.000	1.000	1.000	1.000
2	2.010	2.020	2.030	2.040	2.050	2.060	2.070	2.080	2.090	2.100	2.110
3	3.030	3.060	3.091	3.122	3.153	3.184	3.215	3.246	3.278	3.310	3.342
4	4.060	4.122	4.184	4.246	4.310	4.375	4.440	4.506	4.573	4.641	4.710
5	5.101	5.204	5.309	5.416	5.526	5.637	5.751	5.867	5.985	6.105	6.228
6	6.152	6.308	6.468	6.633	6.802	6.975	7.153	7.336	7.523	7.716	7.913
7	7.214	7.434	7.662	7.898	8.142	8.394	8.654	8.923	9.200	9.487	9.783
8	8.286	8.583	8.892	9.214	9.549	9.897	10.260	10.637	11.028	11.436	11.859
9	9.369	9.755	10.159	10.583	11.027	11.491	11.978	12.488	13.021	13.579	14.164
10	10.462	10.950	11.464	12.006	12.578	13.181	13.816	14.487	15.193	15.937	16.722
11	11.567	12.169	12.808	13.486	14.207	14.972	15.784	16.645	17.560	18.531	19.561
12	12.683	13.412	14.192	15.026	15.917	16.870	17.888	18.977	20.141	21.384	22.713
13	13.809	14.680	15.618	16.627	17.713	18.882	20.141	21.495	22.953	24.523	26.212
14	14.947	15.974	17.086	18.292	19.599	21.015	22.550	24.215	26.019	27.975	30.095
15	16.097	17.293	18.599	20.024	21.579	23.276	25.129	27.152	29.361	31.772	34.405
16	17.258	18.639	20.157	21.825	23.657	25.673	27.888	30.324	33.003	35.950	39.190
17	18.430	20.012	21.762	23.698	25.840	20.213	30.840	33.750	36.974	40.545	44.501
18	19.615	21.412	23.414	25.645	28.132	30.906	33.999	37.450	41.301	45.599	50.396
19	20.811	22.841	25.117	27.671	30.539	33.760	37.379	41.446	46.018	51.159	56.939
20	22.019	24.297	26.870	29.778	33.066	36.786	40.995	45.762	51.160	57.275	64.203
25	28.243	32.030	36.459	41.646	47.727	54.865	63.249	73.106	84.701	98.347	114.410
30	34.785	40.588	47.575	56.085	66.439	79.058	94.461	113.280	136.310	164.490	199.020
40	48.886	60.402	75.401	95.026	120.800	154.760	199.640	259.060	337.890	442.590	581.830
50	64.463	84.579	112.800	152.670	209.350	290.340	406.530	573.770	815.080	1,163.900	1,668.800

Exhibit A-2 (Concluded)

Period	12%	13%	14%	15%	16%	17%	18%	19%	20%	25%	30%
1	1.000	1.000	1.000	1.000	1.000	1.000	1.000	1.000	1.000	1.000	1.000
2	2.120	2.130	2.140	2.150	2.160	2.170	2.180	2.190	2.200	2.250	2.300
3	3.374	3.407	3.440	3.473	3.506	3.539	3.572	3.606	3.640	3.813	3.990
4	4.779	4.850	4.921	4.993	5.066	5.141	5.215	5.291	5.368	5.766	6.187
5	6.353	6.480	6.610	6.742	6.877	7.014	7.154	7.297	7.442	8.207	9.043
6	8.115	8.323	8.536	8.754	8.977	9.207	9.442	9.683	9.930	11.259	12.756
7	10.089	10.405	10.730	11.067	11.414	11.772	12.142	12.523	12.916	15.073	17.583
8	12.300	12.757	13.233	13.727	14.240	14.773	15.327	15.902	16.499	19.842	23.858
9	14.776	15.416	16.085	16.786	17.519	18.285	19.086	19.923	20.799	25.802	32.015
10	17.549	18.420	19.337	20.304	21.321	22.393	23.521	24.701	25.959	33.253	42.619
11	20.655	21.814	23.045	24.349	25.733	27.200	28.755	30.404	32.150	42.566	56.405
12	24.133	25.650	27.271	29.002	30.850	32.824	34.931	37.180	39.581	54.208	74.327
13	28.029	29.985	32.089	34.352	36.786	39.404	42.219	45.244	48.497	68.760	97.625
14	32.393	34.883	37.581	40.505	43.672	47.103	50.818	54.841	59.196	86.949	127.910
15	37.280	40.417	43.842	47.580	51.660	56.110	60.965	66.261	72.035	109.690	167.290
16	42.753	46.672	50.980	55.717	60.925	66.649	72.939	79.850	87.442	138.110	218.470
17	48.884	53.739	59.118	65.075	71.673	78.979	87.068	96.022	105.930	173.640	285.010
18	55.750	61.725	68.394	75.836	84.141	93.406	103.740	115.270	128.120	218.050	371.520
19	63.440	70.749	78.969	88.212	98.603	110.290	123.410	138.170	154.740	273.560	483.970
20	72.052	80.947	91.025	102.440	115.380	130.030	146.630	165.420	186.690	342.950	630.170
25	133.330	155.620	181.870	212.790	249.210	292.110	342.600	402.040	471.980	1,054.800	2,348.800
30	241.330	293.200	356.790	434.750	530.310	647.440	790.950	966.700	1,181.900	3,227.200	8,730.000
40	767.090	1,013.700	1,342.000	1,779.100	2,360.800	3,134.500	4,163.210	5,529.800	7,343.900	30,089.000	120,393.000
50	2,400.000	3,459.500	4,994.500	7,217.700	10,436.000	15,090.000	21,813.000	31,515.000	45,497.000	80,256.000	165,976.000

Exhibit A–3   Present Value of $1 to Be Received at the End of a Given Number of Time Periods

$$PV = \frac{1}{(1 + i)^n}$$

Period	1%	2%	3%	4%	5%	6%	7%	8%	9%	10%	11%	12%
1	0.990	0.980	0.971	0.962	0.952	0.943	0.935	0.926	0.917	0.909	0.901	0.893
2	0.980	0.961	0.943	0.925	0.907	0.890	0.873	0.857	0.842	0.826	0.812	0.797
3	0.971	0.942	0.915	0.889	0.864	0.840	0.816	0.794	0.772	0.751	0.731	0.712
4	0.961	0.924	0.885	0.855	0.823	0.792	0.763	0.735	0.708	0.683	0.659	0.636
5	0.951	0.906	0.863	0.822	0.784	0.747	0.713	0.681	0.650	0.621	0.593	0.567
6	0.942	0.888	0.837	0.790	0.746	0.705	0.666	0.630	0.596	0.564	0.535	0.507
7	0.933	0.871	0.813	0.760	0.711	0.665	0.623	0.583	0.547	0.513	0.482	0.452
8	0.923	0.853	0.789	0.731	0.677	0.627	0.582	0.540	0.502	0.467	0.434	0.404
9	0.914	0.837	0.766	0.703	0.645	0.592	0.544	0.500	0.460	0.424	0.391	0.361
10	0.905	0.820	0.744	0.676	0.614	0.558	0.508	0.463	0.422	0.386	0.352	0.322
11	0.896	0.804	0.722	0.650	0.585	0.527	0.475	0.429	0.388	0.350	0.317	0.287
12	0.887	0.788	0.701	0.625	0.557	0.497	0.444	0.397	0.356	0.319	0.286	0.257
13	0.879	0.773	0.681	0.601	0.530	0.469	0.415	0.368	0.326	0.290	0.258	0.229
14	0.870	0.758	0.661	0.577	0.505	0.442	0.388	0.340	0.299	0.263	0.232	0.205
15	0.861	0.743	0.642	0.555	0.481	0.417	0.362	0.315	0.275	0.239	0.209	0.183
16	0.853	0.728	0.623	0.534	0.458	0.394	0.339	0.292	0.252	0.218	0.188	0.163
17	0.844	0.714	0.605	0.513	0.436	0.371	0.317	0.270	0.231	0.198	0.170	0.146
18	0.836	0.700	0.587	0.494	0.416	0.350	0.296	0.250	0.212	0.180	0.153	0.130
19	0.828	0.686	0.570	0.475	0.396	0.331	0.277	0.232	0.194	0.164	0.138	0.116
20	0.820	0.673	0.554	0.456	0.377	0.312	0.258	0.215	0.178	0.149	0.124	0.104
25	0.780	0.610	0.478	0.375	0.295	0.233	0.184	0.146	0.116	0.092	0.074	0.059
30	0.742	0.552	0.412	0.308	0.231	0.174	0.131	0.099	0.075	0.057	0.044	0.033
40	0.672	0.453	0.307	0.208	0.142	0.097	0.067	0.046	0.032	0.022	0.015	0.011
50	0.608	0.372	0.228	0.141	0.087	0.054	0.034	0.021	0.013	0.009	0.005	0.003

Exhibit A–3 (Concluded)

Period	13%	14%	15%	16%	17%	18%	19%	20%	25%	30%	35%	40%	50%
1	0.885	0.877	0.870	0.862	0.855	0.847	0.840	0.833	0.800	0.769	0.741	0.714	0.667
2	0.783	0.769	0.756	0.743	0.731	0.718	0.706	0.694	0.640	0.592	0.549	0.510	0.444
3	0.693	0.675	0.658	0.641	0.624	0.609	0.593	0.579	0.512	0.455	0.406	0.364	0.296
4	0.613	0.592	0.572	0.552	0.534	0.515	0.499	0.482	0.410	0.350	0.301	0.260	0.198
5	0.543	0.519	0.497	0.476	0.456	0.437	0.419	0.402	0.320	0.269	0.223	0.186	0.132
6	0.480	0.456	0.432	0.410	0.390	0.370	0.352	0.335	0.262	0.207	0.165	0.133	0.088
7	0.425	0.400	0.376	0.354	0.333	0.314	0.296	0.279	0.210	0.159	0.122	0.095	0.059
8	0.376	0.351	0.327	0.305	0.285	0.266	0.249	0.233	0.168	0.123	0.091	0.068	0.039
9	0.333	0.300	0.284	0.263	0.243	0.225	0.209	0.194	0.134	0.094	0.067	0.048	0.026
10	0.295	0.270	0.247	0.227	0.208	0.191	0.176	0.162	0.107	0.073	0.050	0.035	0.017
11	0.261	0.237	0.215	0.195	0.178	0.162	0.148	0.135	0.086	0.056	0.037	0.025	0.012
12	0.231	0.208	0.187	0.168	0.152	0.137	0.124	0.112	0.069	0.043	0.027	0.018	0.008
13	0.204	0.182	0.163	0.145	0.130	0.116	0.104	0.093	0.055	0.033	0.020	0.013	0.005
14	0.181	0.160	0.141	0.125	0.111	0.099	0.088	0.078	0.044	0.025	0.015	0.009	0.003
15	0.160	0.140	0.123	0.108	0.095	0.084	0.074	0.065	0.035	0.020	0.011	0.006	0.002
16	0.141	0.123	0.107	0.093	0.081	0.071	0.062	0.054	0.028	0.015	0.008	0.005	0.002
17	0.125	0.108	0.093	0.080	0.069	0.060	0.052	0.045	0.023	0.012	0.006	0.003	0.001
18	0.111	0.095	0.081	0.069	0.059	0.051	0.044	0.038	0.018	0.009	0.005	0.002	0.001
19	0.098	0.083	0.070	0.060	0.051	0.043	0.037	0.031	0.014	0.007	0.003	0.002	0
20	0.087	0.073	0.061	0.051	0.043	0.037	0.031	0.026	0.012	0.005	0.002	0.001	0
25	0.047	0.038	0.030	0.024	0.020	0.016	0.013	0.010	0.004	0.001	0.001	0	0
30	0.026	0.020	0.015	0.012	0.009	0.007	0.005	0.004	0.001	0	0	0	0
40	0.008	0.005	0.004	0.003	0.002	0.001	0.001	0.001	0	0	0	0	0
50	0.002	0.001	0.001	0.001	0	0	0	0	0	0	0	0	0

Exhibit A–4 Present Value of $1 Received at the End of Each Period for a Given Number of Time Periods (an Annuity)

$$PV = \frac{1 - \dfrac{1}{(1 + i)^n}}{1}$$

Period	1%	2%	3%	4%	5%	6%	7%	8%	9%	10%	11%	12%
1	0.990	0.980	0.971	0.962	0.952	0.943	0.935	0.926	0.917	0.909	0.901	0.893
2	1.970	1.942	1.913	1.886	1.859	1.833	1.808	1.783	1.759	1.736	1.713	1.690
3	2.941	2.884	2.829	2.775	2.723	2.673	2.624	2.577	2.531	2.487	2.444	2.402
4	3.902	3.808	3.717	3.630	3.546	3.465	3.387	3.312	3.240	3.170	3.102	3.037
5	4.853	4.713	4.580	4.452	4.329	4.212	4.100	3.993	3.890	3.791	3.696	3.605
6	5.795	5.601	5.417	5.242	5.076	4.917	4.767	4.623	4.486	4.355	4.231	4.111
7	6.728	6.472	6.230	6.002	5.786	5.582	5.389	5.206	5.033	4.868	4.712	4.564
8	7.652	7.325	7.020	6.733	6.463	6.210	5.971	5.747	5.535	5.335	5.146	4.968
9	8.566	8.162	7.786	7.435	7.108	6.802	6.515	6.247	5.995	5.759	5.537	5.328
10	9.471	8.983	8.530	8.111	7.722	7.360	7.024	6.710	6.418	6.145	5.889	5.650
11	10.368	9.787	9.253	8.760	8.306	7.887	7.499	7.139	6.805	6.495	6.207	5.938
12	11.255	10.575	9.954	9.385	8.863	8.384	7.943	7.536	7.161	6.814	6.492	6.194
13	12.134	11.348	10.635	9.986	9.394	8.853	8.358	7.904	7.487	7.103	6.750	6.424
14	13.004	12.106	11.296	10.563	9.899	9.295	8.745	8.244	7.786	7.367	6.982	6.628
15	13.865	12.849	11.939	11.118	10.380	9.712	9.108	8.559	8.061	7.606	7.191	6.811
16	14.718	13.578	12.561	11.652	10.838	10.106	9.447	8.851	8.313	7.824	7.379	6.974
17	15.562	14.292	13.166	12.166	11.274	10.477	9.763	9.122	8.544	8.022	7.549	7.102
18	16.398	14.992	13.754	12.659	11.690	10.828	10.059	9.372	8.756	8.201	7.702	7.250
19	17.226	15.678	14.324	13.134	12.085	11.158	10.336	9.604	8.950	8.365	7.839	7.366
20	18.046	16.351	14.877	13.590	12.462	11.470	10.594	9.818	9.129	8.514	7.963	7.469
25	22.023	19.523	17.413	15.622	14.094	12.783	11.654	10.675	9.823	9.077	8.422	7.843
30	25.808	22.396	19.600	17.292	15.372	13.765	12.409	11.258	10.274	9.427	8.694	8.055
40	32.835	27.355	23.115	19.793	17.159	15.046	13.332	11.925	10.757	9.779	8.951	8.244
50	39.196	31.424	25.730	21.482	18.256	15.762	13.801	12.233	10.962	9.915	9.042	8.304

Exhibit A–4 (Concluded)

Period	13%	14%	15%	16%	17%	18%	19%	20%	25%	30%	35%	40%	50%
1	0.885	0.877	0.870	0.862	0.855	0.847	0.840	0.833	0.800	0.769	0.741	0.714	0.667
2	1.668	1.647	1.626	1.605	1.585	1.566	1.547	1.528	1.440	1.361	1.289	1.224	1.111
3	2.361	2.322	2.283	2.246	2.210	2.174	2.140	2.106	1.952	1.816	1.696	1.589	1.407
4	2.974	2.914	2.855	2.798	2.743	2.690	2.639	2.589	2.362	2.166	1.997	1.849	1.605
5	3.517	3.433	3.352	3.274	3.199	3.127	3.058	2.991	2.689	2.436	2.220	2.035	1.737
6	3.998	3.889	3.784	3.685	3.589	3.498	3.410	3.326	2.951	2.643	2.385	2.168	1.824
7	4.423	4.288	4.160	4.039	3.922	3.812	3.706	3.605	3.161	2.802	2.508	2.263	1.883
8	4.799	4.639	4.487	4.344	4.207	4.078	3.954	3.837	3.329	2.925	2.598	2.331	1.922
9	5.132	4.946	4.772	4.607	4.451	4.303	4.163	4.031	3.463	3.019	2.665	2.379	1.948
10	5.426	5.216	5.019	4.833	4.659	4.494	4.339	4.192	3.571	3.092	2.715	2.414	1.965
11	5.687	5.453	5.234	5.029	4.836	4.656	4.486	4.327	3.656	3.147	2.752	2.438	1.977
12	5.918	5.660	5.421	5.197	4.988	4.793	4.611	4.439	3.725	3.190	2.779	2.456	1.985
13	6.122	5.842	5.583	5.342	5.118	4.910	4.715	4.533	3.780	3.223	2.799	2.469	1.990
14	6.302	6.002	5.724	5.468	5.229	5.008	4.802	4.611	3.824	3.249	2.814	2.478	1.993
15	6.462	6.142	5.847	5.575	5.324	5.092	4.876	4.675	3.859	3.268	2.825	2.484	1.995
16	6.604	6.265	5.954	5.668	5.405	5.162	4.938	4.730	3.887	3.283	2.834	2.489	1.997
17	6.729	6.373	6.047	5.749	5.475	5.222	4.988	4.775	3.910	3.295	2.840	2.492	1.998
18	6.840	6.467	6.128	5.818	5.534	5.273	5.033	4.812	3.928	3.304	2.844	2.494	1.999
19	6.938	6.550	6.198	5.877	5.584	5.316	5.070	4.843	3.942	3.311	2.848	2.496	1.999
20	7.025	6.623	6.259	5.929	5.628	5.353	5.101	4.870	3.954	3.316	2.850	2.497	1.999
25	7.330	6.873	6.464	6.097	5.766	5.467	5.195	4.948	3.985	3.329	2.856	2.499	2.000
30	7.496	7.003	6.566	6.177	5.829	5.517	5.235	4.979	3.995	3.332	2.857	2.500	2.000
40	7.634	7.105	6.642	6.233	5.871	5.548	5.258	4.997	3.999	3.333	2.857	2.500	2.000
50	7.675	7.133	6.661	6.246	5.880	5.554	5.262	4.999	4.000	3.333	2.857	2.500	2.000

Glossary

accident benefits Automobile insurance that covers medical expenses for people injured in one's car. 230

account executive A licensed individual who buys or sells securities for clients; also called a stockbroker. 337

actual cash value (ACV) A claim settlement method in which the insured receives payment based on the current replacement cost of a damaged or lost item, less depreciation. 227

adjusted balance method The assessment of finance charges after payments made during the billing period have been subtracted. 162

adult life cycle The stages in the family situation and financial needs of an adult. 10

all risk A policy in which any event that causes loss or damage to the insured property is covered unless it is specifically excluded. 224

amortization The reduction of a loan balance through payments made over a period of time. 198

annual percentage rate (APR) The percentage cost (or relative cost) of credit on a yearly basis. The APR yields a true rate of interest for comparisons with other sources of credit. 158

annualized holding period yield A yield calculation that takes into account the total return, the original investment, and the time the investment is held. 332

annuity A contract that provides pre-set installment payments for an agreed-upon period of time. 257

appraisal An estimate of the current value of a property. 204

assets Cash and other property with a monetary value. 39

automated teller machine (ATM) A computer terminal used to conduct banking transactions. 101

average daily balance method A method of computing finance charges that uses a weighted average of the account balance throughout the current billing period. 162

average tax rate Total tax due divided by gross income. 69

balance sheet A financial statement that reports what an individual or a family owns and owes; also called a *net worth statement*. 39

bank line of credit A pre-arranged loan from a bank for a specified amount. 130

bankruptcy A set of federal laws that allow you to either restructure your debts or remove certain debts. 21

bear market Occurs when investors are pessimistic about a nation's economy and sell stocks. 329

bearer bond A bond that is not registered in the investor's name. 361

beneficiary A person who has been named to receive property under a will. 444

beneficiary A person designated to receive something, such as life insurance proceeds, from the insured. 250

beta An index that compares the risk associated with a specific stock issue with the risk of the stock market in general. 333

blue-chip stock A safe investment that generally attracts conservative investors. 322

bodily injury liability Coverage for the risk of financial loss due to legal expenses, medical costs, lost wages, and other expenses associated with injuries caused by an automobile accident for which the insured was responsible. 230

bond indenture A legal document that details all of the conditions relating to a bond issue. 355

book value Determined by deducting all liabilities from the corporation's assets and dividing the remainder by the number of outstanding shares of common stock. 330

bull market Occurs when investors are optimistic about a nation's economy and buy stocks. 329

budget A specific plan for spending income. 45

budget variance The difference between the amount budgeted and the actual amount received or spent. 50

call feature A feature that allows the corporation to call in or buy outstanding bonds from current bondholders before the maturity date. 357

callable preferred stocks stocks that a corporation may exchange, at its option, for a specified amount of money. 320

capacity The borrower's financial ability to meet credit obligations. 146

capital The borrower's assets or net worth. 146

capital gain distributions The payments made to a fund's shareholders that result from the sale of securities in the fund's portfolio. 396

capital gains Profits from the sale of a capital asset, such as stocks, bonds, or real estate. 84

capitalization The total amount of securities—stocks and bonds—issued by a corporation. 322

cash flow The actual inflow and outflow of cash during a given time period. 41

cash flow statement A financial statement that summarizes cash receipts and payments for a given period. 42

cash value The amount received after giving up a life insurance policy. 246

character The borrower's attitude toward credit obligations. 146

chartered bank A financial institution that offers a full range of financial services to individuals, businesses, and government agencies. 105

churning The excessive buying and selling of securities to generate commissions. 338

closed-end credit One-time loans that the borrower pays back in a specified period of time and in payments of equal amounts. 129

closing costs Fees and charges paid when a real estate transaction is completed; also called *settlement costs*. 200

closed-end fund A mutual fund whose shares are issued by an investment company only when the fund is organized. 383

codicil A document that modifies provisions in an existing will. 447

co-insurance clause A policy provision that requires a homeowner to pay for part of the losses if the property is not insured for the specified percentage of the replacement value. 226

collateral A valuable asset that is pledged to ensure loan payments. 146

collision Automobile insurance that pays for damage to the insured's car when it is involved in an accident. 230

compounding A process that calculates interest based on previously earned interest. 17

comprehensive physical damage Automobile insurance that covers financial loss from damage to a vehicle caused by a risk other than a collision, such as fire, theft, glass breakage, hail, or vandalism. 230

conditions The general economic conditions that can affect a borrower's ability to repay a loan. 146

condominium An individually owned housing unit in a building with several such units. 191

consumer credit The use of credit for personal needs (except a home mortgage). 126

consumer proposal A maximum five-year plan for paying creditors all or a portion of a debt owed. 170

contingent deferred sales load A 1-to-6 percent charge that shareholders pay when they withdraw their investment from a mutual fund. 385

convertible bond A bond that can be exchanged, at the owner's option, for a specified number of shares of the corporation's common stocks. 357

co-operative housing A type of subsidized housing in which half of the units have geared-to-income rental prices. 191

co-payment A provision under which the insured pays a flat dollar amount each time a covered medical service is received after the deductible has been met. 269

corporate bond A corporation's written pledge to repay a specified amount of money with interest. 291, 354

credit An arrangement to receive cash, goods, or services now and pay for them in the future. 126

credit bureau A reporting agency that assembles credit and other information about consumers. 139

credit insurance Any type of insurance that ensures repayment of a loan in the event the borrower is unable to repay it. 170

credit reporting legislation
Credit Reporting Act—Applicable in British Columbia, Ontario, Nova Scotia, and Prince Edward Island
Credit Reporting Agencies Act—Applicable in Saskatchewan and Newfoundland
Personal Investigations Act—Applicable in Manitoba
Consumer Protection Act—Applicable in Quebec 143

credit union /caisse populaire A user-owned, nonprofit cooperative financial institution that is organized for the benefit of its members. 105

cumulative preferred stock stock with unpaid dividends that accumulate and must be paid before any cash dividend is paid to common shareholders. 320

current liabilities Debts that must be paid within a short time, usually less than a year. 41

current yield Determined by dividing the dollar amount of annual interest from an investment by its current market value. 372

current yield The yearly dollar amount of income generated by an investment divided by the investment's current market value. 331

cyclical stock A stock that follows the business cycle of advances and declines in the economy. 322

debenture A bond that is backed only by the reputation of the issuing corporation. 356

declining balance method A method of computing interest when more than one payment is made on a simple interest loan. 162

deductions Expenses that can be deducted from total income, such as certain medical expenses, child care expenses, union dues, attendant fees, investment counselling fees, and certain employment-related expenses. 63

deed or title A document that transfers ownership of property from one party to another. 201

defensive stock A stock that remains stable during declines in the economy. 322

deficit The amount by which actual spending exceeds planned spending. 50

defined-benefit plan A plan that specifies the benefits the employee will receive at the normal retirement age. 423

defined-contribution plan Also called a "money purchase pension plan," this plan specifies the contribution from the employee and/or employer but does not guarantee the pension benefit you will receive. 422

direct investment plan A plan that allows shareholders to purchase stock directly from a corporation without having to use an account executive or a brokerage firm. 343

disability income insurance Provides payments to replace income when an insured person is unable to work. 261

discretionary income Money left over after paying for housing, food, and other necessities. 44

discretionary order An order to buy or sell a security that lets the account executive decide when to execute the transaction and at what price. 340

diversification The process of spreading your assets among several types of investments to lessen risk. 294

dividend A distribution of money, stock, or other property that a corporation pays to shareholders. 291

dividend reinvestment plan A plan that allows current shareholders the option to reinvest or use their cash dividends to purchase stocks of the corporation. 343

dollar cost averaging A long-term technique used by investors who purchase an equal dollar amount of the same stock at equal intervals. 343

double indemnity A benefit under which the company pays twice the face value of the policy if the insured's death results from an accident. 253

driver classification A category based on the driver's age, gender, marital status, driving record, and driving habits; used to determine automobile insurance rates. 233

earnest money A portion of the price of a home that the buyer deposits as evidence of good faith to indicate a serious purchase offer.   194

earnings per share   A corporation's after-tax earnings divided by the number of outstanding shares of common stocks.   333

economics   The study of how wealth is created and distributed.   11

effective annual rate (EAR)   A formula that calculates the effective return, taking compounding into account.
EAR = (1 + km)m – 1
m   = number of periods in a year
km   = rate of return for one period.
111

efficient market theory   An investment theory based on the assumption that stock price movements are purely random; also called *the random walk theory*.   334

emergency fund   An amount of money you can obtain quickly in case of immediate need.   280

employment income   Money received for personal effort, such as wages, salary, commission, fees, tips, or bonuses.   62

equity capital   Money that a business obtains from its owners.   290

escrow account   Money, usually deposited with the lending institution, for the payment of property taxes and homeowner's insurance.   202

estate   Everything one owns.   439

estate planning   A definite plan for the administration and disposition of one's property during one's lifetime and at one's death.   439

excise tax   A tax imposed on specific goods and services, such as gasoline, cigarettes, alcoholic beverages, tires, and air travel.   60

exclusion   An amount not included in total income.   62

face value   The dollar amount the bondholder will receive at the bond's maturity.   354

family of funds   A group of mutual funds managed by one investment company.   390

finance charge   The total dollar amount paid to use credit.   158

financial plan   A formalized report that summarizes your current financial situation, analyzes your financial needs, and recommends future financial activities.   23

formal will   A will that is usually prepared with an attorney's assistance. 444

fundamental theory   An investment theory based on the assumption that a stock's intrinsic or real value is determined by the company's future earnings.   334

future value   The amount to which current savings will increase based on a certain interest rate and a certain time period; typically involves compounding.   17

government bond   The written pledge of a government or a municipality to repay a specified sum of money, along with interest.   291

growth stock   A stock issued by a corporation that has the potential to earn profits above the average profits of all firms in the economy.   322

Guaranteed Investment Certificates (GICs)   Term deposits made for a longer period, usually from one to five years. These are nonredeemable before maturity; the only way to retrieve funds prematurely is to sell the GIC to a broker at a discount. There is an active secondary market for GICs.   110

guardian   A person who assumes responsibility for providing children with personal care and managing the deceased's estate for them. 445

hazard   A factor that increases the likelihood of loss through some peril.   212

high-risk pool   Consists of people who are unable to obtain automobile insurance due to poor driving or accident records and must obtain coverage at high rates.   233

holographic will   A handwritten will. 444

home equity loan   A loan based on the current market value of a home less the amount still owed on the mortgage.   134

homeowner's insurance   Coverage for a place of residence and its associated financial risks.   220

household inventory   A list or other documentation of personal belongings, with purchase dates and cost information.   221

income   Inflows of cash to an individual or a household.   43

income dividends   The earnings a fund pays to shareholders after it has deducted expenses from its dividend and interest income.   396

income stock   A stock that pays higher-than-average dividends.   322

incontestability clause   A provision stating that the insurer cannot dispute the validity of a policy after a specified period.   252

index   A statistical measure of the changes in a portfolio of stocks representing a portion of the overall market.   313

inflation   A rise in the general level of prices.   13

initial public offering (IPO)   Occurs when a corporation sells stock to the general public for the first time. 336

insolvency   The inability to pay debts when they are due because liabilities far exceed the value of assets.   41

insurance   Protection against possible financial loss.   211

insurance company   A risk-sharing firm that assumes financial responsibility for losses that may result from an insured risk.   211

insured   A person covered by an insurance policy.   211

insurer   An insurance company.   211

interest   A periodic charge for the use of credit.   130

interest-adjusted index   A method of evaluating the cost of life insurance by taking into account the time value of money.   254

intestate   Without a valid will.   442

investment bank   A financial firm that assists corporations in raising funds, usually by helping to sell new security issues.   336

investment company   A firm that, for a management fee, invests the pooled funds of small investors in securities appropriate to its stated investment objectives.   382

investment income   Money received in the form of dividends, interest, capital gains, or rent from investments. Also called *portfolio income*.   62

large-cap stock   A stock issued by a large corporation that has a large amount of stock outstanding and a large amount of capitalization.   322

lease   A legal document that defines the conditions of a rental agreement. 188

liabilities   Amounts owed to others. 40

liability   Legal responsibility for the financial cost of another person's losses or injuries.   40, 218

limit order A request to buy or sell a stock at a specified price. 340

line of credit The dollar amount, which may or may not be borrowed, that a lender makes available to a borrower. 130

line of credit A short-term loan that is approved before the money is actually needed. 281

liquidity The ability to buy or sell an investment quickly without substantially affecting the investment's value. 290

liquidity The ability to readily convert financial resources into cash without a loss in value. 21

liquid assets Cash and items of value that can easily be converted to cash. 39

living trust A trust that is created and provides benefits during the trustor's lifetime. 449

living will A document that enables an individual, while well, to express the intention that life be allowed to end if he or she becomes terminally ill. 447

load fund A mutual fund in which investors pay a commission (as high as 8½ percent) every time they purchase shares. 384

long-term-care (LTC) Provides day-in, day-out care for long-term illness or disability. 266

long-term liabilities Debts that are not required to be paid in full until more than a year from now. 41

manufactured home A housing unit that is fully or partially assembed in a factory before being moved to the living site. 191

margin A speculative technique whereby an investor borrows part of the money needed to buy a particular stock. 344

marginal tax rate The rate of tax paid on the last (and next) dollar of taxable income. 69

market order A request to buy or sell a stock at the current market value. 339

market timer An individual who helps investors decide when to switch their investments from one fund to another fund, usually within the same family of funds. 390

maturity date For a corporate bond, the date on which the corporation is to repay the borrowed money. 354

money management Day-to-day financial activities necessary to manage current personal economic resources while working toward long-term financial security. 36

money market fund A savings–investment plan offered by investment companies, with earnings based on investments in various short-term financial instruments. 105

mortgage A long-term loan on a specific piece of property, such as a home or other real estate. 196

mortgage bond A corporate bond secured by various assets of the issuing firm. 357

mutual fund An investment chosen by people who pool their money to buy stocks, bonds, and other financial securities selected by professional managers who work for an investment company. 292, 381

named perils A policy in which only those perils that are specifically listed will be covered should a loss occur. 224

Nasdaq (pronounced "nazzdack") An electronic marketplace for over 6,000 stocks. 337

negligence Failure to take ordinary or reasonable care in a situation. 218

net asset value (NAV) The current market value of the securities contained in the mutual fund's portfolio minus the mutual fund's liabilities divided by the number of shares outstanding. 383

net income Total income reduced by certain adjustments, such as contributions to an RRSP or RPP. 63

net worth The difference between total assets and total liabilities. 41

no-fault insurance An automobile insurance program in which drivers involved in accidents collect medical expenses, lost wages, and related injury costs from their own insurance companies. 230

no-load fund A mutual fund in which the individual investor pays no sales charge. 384

nonforfeiture clause A provision that allows the insured not to forfeit all accrued benefits. 251

nonparticipating policy Life insurance that does not provide policy dividends. 248

nonprofit housing Rental housing owned by a community group, religious group, or nonprofit organization to provide affordable housing. 191

odd lot Fewer than 100 shares of a particular stock. 341

open-end credit A line of credit in which loans are made on a continuous basis and the borrower is billed periodically for at least partial payment. 129

open-end fund A mutual fund whose shares are issued and redeemed by the investment company at the request of investors. 383

opportunity cost What a person gives up by making a choice. 5

option The right to buy or sell a stock at a pre-determined price during a specified period of time. 346

overdraft protection An automatic loan made to chequing account customers to cover the amount of cheques written in excess of the available balance in the account. 114

over-the-counter (OTC) market a network of dealers who buy and sell the stocks of corporations that are not listed on a securities exchange. 337

par value An assigned (and often arbitrary) dollar value that is printed on a stock certificate. 319

participating policy Life insurance that provides policy dividends. 248

passive income Income resulting from business activities in which one does not actively participate. 62

penny stock A stock that typically sells for less than $1 per share. 323

peril The cause of a possible loss. 212

personal financial planning The process of managing your money to achieve personal economic satisfaction. 3

personal property floater Additional property insurance to cover the damage or loss of a specific item of high value. 221

policy A written contract for insurance. 211

policyholder A person who owns an insurance policy. 211

power of attorney A legal document authorizing someone to act on one's behalf. 448

pre-emptive right The right of current shareholders to purchase any new stocks the corporation issues before they are offered to the general public. 316

premium The amount of money a policyholder is charged for an insurance policy. 211

pre-nuptial agreement A documentary agreement between spouses before marriage. 447

present value The current value for a future amount based on a certain interest rate and a certain time period; also referred to as discounting. 17

previous balance method A method of computing finance charges that gives no credit for payments made during the billing period. 162

price–earnings ratio The price of a share of stock divided by the corporation's earnings per share of stocks outstanding over the last 12 months. 333

primary market A market in which an investor purchases financial securities, via an investment bank or other representative, from the issuer of those securities. 336

probate The legal procedure of proving a valid or invalid will. 444

proxy A legal form that lists the issues to be decided at a shareholders' meeting and requests that shareholders transfer their voting rights to some individual or individuals. 316

pure risk A risk in which there is only a chance of loss; also called *insurable risk*. 212

rate cap A limit on the increases and decreases in the interest rate charged on an adjustable-rate mortgage. 199

rate of return The percentage of increase in the value of savings as a result of interest earned; also called *yield*. 111

rating territory The place of residence used to determine a person's automobile insurance premium. 233

record date The date on which a shareholder must be registered on the corporation's books in order to receive dividend payments. 316

refinancing The process of obtaining a new mortgage on a home to get a lower interest rate. 200

registered bond A bond that is registered in the owner's name by the issuing company. 361

registered coupon bond A bond that is registered for principal only, and not for interest. 361

Registered Retirement Savings Plan (RRSP) An investment vehicle that allows you to shelter your savings from income taxes. 425

reinvestment plan A service provided by an investment company in which shareholder income dividends and capital gain distributions are automatically reinvested to purchase additional shares of the fund. 400

replacement value A claim settlement method in which the insured receives the full cost of repairing or replacing a damaged or lost item. 227

reverse annuity mortgage (RAM) A mortgage in which the lender uses the borrower's house as collateral to buy an annuity for the borrower from a life insurance company. 412

reverse mortgage A loan based on the equity in a home, which provides elderly homeowners with tax-free income and is paid back with interest when the home is sold or the homeowner dies. 200

rider A document attached to a policy that modifies its coverage. 223, 252

risk Chance or uncertainty of loss; may also mean "the insured." 212

round lot One hundred shares or multiples of 100 shares of a particular stock. 341

safety deposit box A private storage area at a financial institution with maximum security for valuables. 37

secondary market A market for existing financial securities that are currently traded among investors. 336

second mortgage A cash advance based on the paid-up value of a home; also called a *home equity loan*. 200

securities Investments, including stocks and bonds, mutual funds, options, and commodities, traded on securities exchanges or the over-the-counter markets. 314

securities exchange A marketplace where member brokers who represent investors meet to buy and sell securities. 337

self-insurance The process of establishing a monetary fund to cover the cost of a loss. 213

selling short Selling stocks that have been borrowed from a brokerage firm and must be replaced at a later date. 345

serial bonds Bonds of a single issue that mature on different dates. 358

simple interest Interest computed on the principal only and without compounding. 16

sinking fund A fund to which annual or semi-annual deposits are made for the purpose of redeeming a bond issue. 358

small-cap stock A stock issued by a company that has a capitalization of $150 million or less. 322

specialist An individual on the floor of the exchange who buys or sells a particular stock in an effort to maintain an orderly market. 339

speculative investment A high-risk investment made in the hope of earning a relatively large profit in a short time. 284

speculative risk A risk in which there is a chance of either loss or gain. 212

stock split A procedure in which the shares of common stocks owned by existing shareholders are divided into a larger number of shares. 317

stop order An order to sell a particular stock at the next available opportunity after its market price reaches a specified amount. 340

strict liability A situation in which a person is held responsible for intentional or unintentional actions. 219

subordinated debenture An unsecured bond that gives bondholders a claim secondary to that of other designated bondholders with respect to both interest payments and assets. 357

suicide clause A provision stating that if the insured dies by suicide during the first two years the policy is in force, the death benefit will equal the amount of the premium paid. 252

surplus The amount by which actual spending is less than planned spending. 50

take-home pay Earnings after deductions for taxes and other items; also called *disposable income*. 43

tax audit A detailed examination of your tax return by the Canada Customs and Revenue Agency. 90

tax credit An amount subtracted directly from the amount of taxes owing. 72

tax evasion The use of illegal actions to reduce one's taxes. 81

tax planning The use of legitimate methods to reduce one's taxes. 81

taxable income The net amount of income, after allowable deductions, on which income tax is computed. 62

tax-deferred income   Income that will be taxed at a later date.   62

tax shelter   An investment that provides immediate tax benefits and a reasonable expectation of a future profit.   62

technical theory   An investment theory based on the assumption that a stock's market value is determined by the forces of supply and demand in the stock market as a whole.   334

term deposits   A deposit that is made for a specified term in exchange for a higher rate of return. Can be redeemed before maturity by earning a reduced rate of interest (paying a penalty).   109

term insurance   Life insurance protection for a specified period of time; sometimes called temporary life insurance.   244

testamentary trust   A trust established by the creator's will that becomes effective upon his or her death.   449

time value of money   Increases in an amount of money as a result of interest earned.   16

title insurance   Insurance that, during the mortgage term, protects the owner or the lender against financial loss resulting from future defects in the title and from other unforeseen property claims not excluded by the policy.   200

total shareholder return (TSR)   A calculation that includes the yearly dollar amount of income as well as any increase or decrease in the original purchase price of the investment.   332

trust   A legal arrangement through which one's assets are held by a trustee.   449

trust   A legal agreement that provides for the management and control of assets by one party for the benefit of another.   100

trustee   A person or an institution that holds or manages property for the benefit of someone else under a trust agreement.   445

trustee   A financially independent firm that acts as the bondholders' representative.   356

trustor   The creator of a trust; also called the *grantor*.   449

umbrella policy   Supplementary personal liability coverage; also called a *personal catastrophe policy*.   223

uninsured motorist coverage   Automobile insurance coverage for the cost of injuries to a person and members of his or her family caused by a driver with inadequate insurance or by a hit-and-run driver.   230

universal life   A whole life policy that combines term insurance and investment elements.   248

values   Ideas and principles that a person considers correct, desirable, and important.   11

variable rate mortgage (VRM)   A home loan with an interest rate that can change during the mortgage term due to changes in market interest rates; also called a flexible-rate mortgage.   199

vesting   An employee's right to at least a portion of the benefits accrued under an employer pension plan, even if the employee leaves the company before retiring.   422

vicarious liability   A situation in which a person is held legally responsible for the actions of another person.   219

voluntary medical payments   Home insurance that pays the cost of minor accidental injuries on one's property.   223

whole life policy   An insurance plan in which the policyholder pays a specified premium each year for as long as he or she lives; also called a *straight life policy*, a *cash-value life policy*, or an *ordinary life policy*.   246

will   The legal declaration of a person's mind as to the disposition of his or her property after death.   442

yield   The rate of return earned by an investor who holds a bond for a stated period of time.   372

yield to maturity   A yield calculation that takes into account the relationships among a bond's maturity value, the time to maturity, the current price, and the dollar amount of interest.   374

zero-coupon bond   A bond that is sold at a price far below its face value, makes no annual or semi-annual interest payments, and is redeemed for its face value at maturity.   361

zoning laws   Restrictions on how the property in an area can be used.   192

Index

[A]

Accidental death benefit, 253
Accident benefits, 230
Accountants, 32
Account executives, 337–338, 364
Action plan
    creation and implementation, 6–7
    re-evaluation, 7–8
Activity accounts, 114
Actual cash value (ACV), 227
Adjustable life insurance, 249
Adjusted balance method, revolving
    credit, 162, 163
Adult life cycle, 10–11
Advanced directives, 438
    See also Living will
Affordable home purchase price, 196
Affordable monthly mortgage payment,
    196
Affordable mortgage amount, 196
Age, and credit, 147
All risk policies, 224, 225
Alternative courses
    evaluation, 5
    identifying, 4–5
Alternative minimum tax (AMT), 72
Amortization, 198
Annualized holding period yield,
    332–333
Annual meeting, stockholders, 316
Annual percentage rate (ARP), 158–159
Annual reports
    corporate, 329, 370
    mutual fund, 393
Annuities
    advantages and disadvantages, 258,
        428–429
    fixed-term annuities, 429
    guaranteed annuity, 259
    life annuities, 429
    present value, 461–462
    purpose, 257
    single-life annuity, 258–259
    tax considerations, 259
Antiques. *See* Collectibles
Appraisal, property, 193, 204
Asset allocation funds, 389
Assets, 39–40
Assumable mortgages, 199
Automated teller machines (ATMs),
    101, 102, 151
Automatic payments, 101

Automatic premium loans, 252
Automobile accidents, measures to take,
    in case of, 234
Automobile insurance
    accident benefits, 230
    adequate coverage, 231–232
    bodily injury coverages, 229–230
    bodily injury liability, 230
    collision insurance, 230
    comprehensive physical damage,
        230–231
    driver classification, 233
    high-risk-driver insurance, 233
    minimum coverage, 228–229
    no-fault insurance, 230
    premium factors, 232–233
    premium-reducing measures,
        233–234
    rating territory, 233
    towing and emergency coverage,
        231
    uninsured motorist coverage, 230
    waiver of depreciation coverage, 231
Automobile registrations, 442
Average daily balance method, revolv-
    ing credit, 162, 163
Average tax rate, 69

[B]

Back-end load, 384, 385
Balanced funds, 389
Balance sheet, 39–41, 45
Bank accounts
    cheque writing, 123
    chequing accounts, 113–115,
        122–124, 290
    deposits, 122
    federal deposit insurance, 112
    fees and charges, 112, 113, 114, 123
    individual account, 122
    joint account, 122, 442
    maintaining an account, 123–124
    opening an account, 122
    regular savings accounts, 109
Bank of Canada, 11–12, 375
Bankers, 32
Bank line of credit, 130
Bank reconciliation, 123–124
Bankruptcy, 169, 170–171
Bankruptcy and Insolvency Act, 170
Banks
    chartered banks, 105

    investment banks, 336
    schedule I banks, 105
    schedule II banks, 105
    Web-only banks, 109
Bank statement, 123
Bank statement balance, 124
Bearer bond, 361
Bear market, 329
Beneficiary, 250, 444
Beta, 333
Birth certificate, 441
Blank endorsement, 122
Bloomberg Professional services, 307
Blue-chip stocks, 322
Bodily injury liability, 230
Bond funds, 388
Bonds
    approximate market value, 361–362
    bond funds, 363
    bond indenture, 355
    bond yield calculations, 354,
        372–375
    call feature, 357–358
    certificates, 442
    commission, 364
    corporate, 291, 354–364
    debt instrument, 356, 363
    discount price, 361
    diversification strategy, 363, 367
    dollar amount of annual interest,
        354
    evaluation, 364, 370–375
    face value, 354
    interest income, 360–361
    interest rate risks, 287–288
    investments, 290, 291, 294–295
    maturity date, 354–355
    premium price, 358, 361
    ratings, 359, 371–372
    repayment at maturity, 362
    repayment provisions, 257–358
    total shareholder return, 363
    transactions, 362–364
    types, 110, 356–358, 365–369
    warrants, 369
    See also Government bonds
Book value, 330–331
British Columbia
    basic automobile insurance cover-
        age, 229
    Wills Variation Act, 440
Broadhead, Rick, 393
Brokerage firms, 338, 341

Budget
   defined, 45
   effective, 52
Budgeting
   emergency fund and savings, 47, 280
   estimating income, 46–47
   financial goals, 46
   fixed expenses, 47, 49
   phases in, 45–46
   process, 45–52
   recording spending amounts, 50
   reviewing spending and saving patterns, 50, 52
   successful, 52
   systems of, 53
   variable expenses, 49–50
Budget variance, 50
Bull market, 329
Bursaries, 62
Business 2.0, 305
Business failure risk, 288
Business Week, 305, 329
Buy-and-hold technique, 343

[C]

Caisses populaires. *See* Credit unions
Calculators, financial
   effective annual rate, 463
   time value of money functions, 19
   yield to maturity, 374
Callable bonds, 357–358
Callable preferred stocks, 320
Call options, 293, 346
Canada Deposit Insurance Corporation (CDIC), 112
Canada Mortgage and Housing Corporation (CMHC), 187, 195
Canada/Quebec Pension Plan (CPP/QPP), 420–421
Canada Savings Bonds, 110, 289, 366–368, 425
Canadian Association of Financial Planners (CAFP), 168, 300
Canadian Banker, 305, 329
Canadian Bond Rating Service (CBRS), 306, 358, 371, 372
Canadian Business, 305
Canadian Financial Publishing Group, 440
Canadian Institute of Financial Planning, 300
Canadian Life and Health Insurance

Association, 254
Canadian Loss Experience Automobile Rating (CLEAR), 232
Canadian MoneySaver, 305
Canadian Securities Administration (CSA), 33
Canadian Securities Institute (CSI), 300
Canoe Webfin, 168, 187
Capacity, to meet credit obligations, 146
Capital, 146
Capital dividends, 302
Capital gains, 65–66, 84, 334, 397, 398, 450
Capital gains distributions, 396–397
Capitalization, 322
Career, and lifestyle, 46
Carroll, Jim, 393
Cash dividends, 316
Cash flow statement
   analysis, 45
   cash inflows and outflows, 41–42
   expenses, 44
   income, 43–44
   net cash flow, 44
Cash management
   after-tax savings rate of return, 113
   ATM surcharges, 101
   automatic payments, 101
   cash advances, 130–131
   cash payment, 135
   chequing accounts, 113–115, 122–124
   common mistakes, 99
   interest rates, 102–103, 111–112
   minimum payment trap, 164
   online payments, 109
   opportunity costs of financial services, 102
   savings plans, 111–113
   uses and misuses of credit, 127, 156
Cash value, 246
Cash-value life policy. *See* Whole life policy
Certified cheques, 115
Character, borrower's, 146
Chequebook balance, 124
Cheque-cashing outlets, 106
Cheque writing, 123
Chequing accounts. *See* Bank accounts
CH.F.C. (Chartered Financial Consultant) designation, 254
Child care expenses, deductible expenses, 64

Churning, 338
Closed-end credit, 129–130
Closed-end funds
   features, 383
   purchase, 398
   return on investment, 396–397
   taxes, 398
Closed-end lease, 134-135
Closing costs, 200–202
CLU (Chartered Life Underwriter) designation, 254
Co-branding, 128, 131
Coins, 293
Co-insurance clause, 226, 270
Collateral, 146, 196
Collateral trust bonds, 368–369
Collectibles, 289, 290, 293
Collision insurance, 230
Commission charges, on stock transactions, 341–342
Commission-only planners, 32
Commodities, 293
Common stock funds, 389
Common stocks
   dividends, 291, 302, 315–317, 318–319
   dollar appreciation of stock value, 317
   equity financing, 315–316, 356, 369
   ex-dividend, 317
   record date, 316–317
   reverse split, 318
   stock split, 317–318
   voting rights, 316
   See also Stocks
Co-mortgagors, 195
Compounding, 17, 111
Compound interest bonds, 110, 366–367
Comprehensive physical damage, 230–231
Computer programs. *See* Software
Conditional sales contract, 134
Condominiums, 191
Consolidation loans, 170
Consumable-product goals, 9
Consumer price index, 14, 50
Consumer proposals, 170, 171
Consumer Reports, 329
Consumer spending, 13, 15
Contingent deferred sales load, 385
   See also Back-end load
Contractors, homebuilding, 191–192

Conventional mortgage, 195, 198–199
Conversion option, 245
Convertible bonds, 357
Convertible preferred stocks, 321
Co-operative housing, 191
Corporate notes, 369
Corporations
   capitalization, 322
   corporate reports, 305–306, 329
   debt financing, 356–358
   equity financing, 315–316, 356, 369
   public disclosure, 326, 327
   shareholders, 316
   sinking fund, 358
Co-signing, loans, 138–139, 195
Credit
   advantages, 127–128
   billing error, 150
   car loans, 134–135, 137, 157,
      165–166
   closed-end credit, 129–130, 132
   consumer credit, 126–127
   credit cards, 130–133, 135, 165, 168,
      225
   defined, 126
   disadvantages, 128–129
   float period, 128
   home equity loans, 134, 136
   insurance, 164
   interest, 130
   open-end credit, 130, 162–163
   security, 132–133, 150–151
Credit application
   borrower's rights, 146, 147, 148
   creditworthiness, 146, 149
Credit bureaus, 139–140
Credit capacity, 136–145
   debt-payments-to-income ratio, 138
   debt-to-equity ratio, 138
Credit costs
   adjusted balance method, 162, 163
   annual percentage rate (APR),
      158–159
   average daily balance method, 162,
      163
   declining balance, simple interest on,
      162
   expensive loans, 157
   fees and charges, 165
   finance charge, 158–159
   inexpensive loans, 157
   and inflation, 163–164
   lender risk vs. interest rate, 160
   medium-priced loans, 157
   minimum monthly payments, 164
   previous balance, 162, 163
   secured loan, 160

   shorter term, 160
   simple interest, 160–162
   term vs. interest costs, 159–160
   upfront cash, 160
   variable interest rate, 160
Credit counselling, 168
Credit counsellors, 32
Credit life insurance, 250
Credit rating
   access to credit reports, 143
   adverse data, 143
   credit file, 140–142
   incorrect information, 143–144
   mistakes, 148–149
   women, 148
Credit unions, 105
Critical illness
   benefits, 253
   insurance, 264, 271
Cumulative preferred stocks, 320
Current financial situation, analysis,
   3-4
Current liabilities, 41
Current ratio, 43
Current yield, 331–332, 372–374
Cyclical stocks, 322

[D]

Death benefits, 451
Debentures
   bondholders' rights, 356
   installment debentures, 368
   subordinated debenture, 357
   unsecured bonds, 356, 369
   warrants, 369
Debt management
   consolidation loans, 170
   consumer proposals, 170, 171
   counselling services, 168–169
   credit counselling, 168
   debt reduction, 14
   human costs of indebtedness, 167
   warning signs of debt problems,
      166–167
Debt-payments ratio, 43
Debt-payments-to-income ratio, 138
Debt ratio, 43
Debt-to-equity ratio, 138
Decreasing term insurance, 245–246
Deductibles, 226, 228, 232, 234
Deductions, 63–66, 72, 81
Deed, 200
Defensive stocks, 322
Deferred Profit Sharing Plans (DPSPs),
   423
   tax strategy, 86

Deficit, 50
Defined-benefit plan, 423
Defined-contribution plan, 422
Dental expense insurance, 266
*Dependants of a Deceased Person
   Relief Act*, 440
Dependants Relief Act, 440
Deposit form, 122
Derivatives, 293
Desk audit, 90
Desktop information services, 307
DINK method, of assessing life insur-
   ance coverage, 243
Direct deposit, 100-101
Direct deposit system, 53
Direct investment plan, 343
Disability
   definitions, 262
   risk management strategies, 214
Disability income insurance
   accident and sickness coverage, 262
   amount of benefits, 262
   assessing income requirements, 264
   consumer tips, 271
   duration of benefits, 262
   need for, 261–262
   noncancellable coverage, 262
   policy checklist, 265
   purpose, 261
   sources of income, 263–264
   waiting period, 262
Disabled people, deductible expenses,
   64
Disclosure, 342
Discount brokerage firms, 338, 341,
   342, 364, 384, 398–399
Discounting, 17
   See also Time value of money
Discretionary income, 44
Discretionary order, 340
Disposable income, 44
Diversification, 292, 294–295, 363, 367,
   382, 396
Dividend funds, 388
Dividend reinvestment plan, 343
Dividends, 291, 302, 315–317, 318–319
   capital dividends, 302
   income dividends, 396, 398
Dollar cost averaging, 343
Domestic bonds, 369
Dominion Bond Rating Service
   (DBRS), 358, 371, 372
Double indemnity, 253
Dow Jones Industrial Average, 314
Down payment, for home, 192, 195
Driver classification, 233
Dual agent, 193

Durable power of attorney, 450
Durable-product goals, 9

[E]

Earnest money, 194–195
Earnings per share, 333
Easy method, of assessing life insurance coverage, 242–243
Economic factors
consumer spending, 13, 15
economic conditions, 12–15, 146
financial institutions, 11–12
global influences, 11–12
interest rates, 12, 13, 15
market forces, 11
Economist, The, 305, 329
Effective annual rate (EAR), 111, 159, 463
Efficient market theory, 334
Electronic banking services, 100-102, 106, 109
Electronic cash, 102
Emergency fund, 47, 280
Employee benefits, death benefits, 451
Employment insurance, 263
Endorsement, 122
Endowment life insurance, 250
Enron, 331
Equifax Canada, 139, 145
Equity
equity capital, 290–291
equity financing, 315–316, 356
home ownership, 189
Equity funds, 389
Escrow account, 202
Estate planning
administration costs, 453
checklist, 441
estates, 451–453
letter of last instruction, 448
lifetime gifts and trusts, 451
power of attorney, 448
proof of claims, 441–442
purposes, 439–440
taxes, 452
trusts, 449–450
wills, 440, 442–447, 450
Estates, 439, 449
Ethical funds, 389
Eurobonds, 369
Exchange traded funds (ETFs), 384
Excise tax, 60
Exclusion, 62
Ex-dividend, 317
Executor, responsibilities, 444, 445, 446

[F]

Face value, 354
Factory financing, 134
Family of funds, 390
Family need method, of assessing life insurance coverage, 243–244
Family Relief Act, 440
Fee-and-commission planners, 32
Fee-only planners, 32
Field audit, 91
Finance charge, 158
FinanCenter, 168
Financial goals
analysis, 4, 14
in budgeting process, 45
goal setting guidelines, 9–10
key elements, 10
life situations and, 9
types, 8–9
Financial institutions, 11–12
compared, 106–108
deposit-type institutions, 104–105
electronic banking services, 100-102
nonbanks, 103
nondeposit institutions, 105–106
types of services, 100
Financial plan, 23
Financial planners
certification, 33–34, 300
compensation methods, 32, 300
evaluation, 33
role, 33, 299–300
specialists, 32
Financial planning
advantages, 3
components, 20–22
defined, 3
economic factors, 11–13
estate planning, 439
life situation, 10–11
personal values, 11
six-step process, 3–8
Financial Planning Proficiency Exam (FPPE), 33–34
Financing
debt, 356
equity financing, 315–316, 356
See also Credit
First mortgage bonds, 368
Fixed expenses, 44
budgeting, 47, 49
Foreign bonds, 369
Formal will, 444
Fortune, 305
Fraud
credit card, 131–134, 225

identity theft, 116, 150–151
Front-end load, 384, 399
Full-service brokerage firms, 338, 341, 364
Fundamental theory, 334
Fund Library, 306
Fund table, 391
Future value, 17
See also Time value of money

[G]

Gadsen, Stephen, 393
GE Capital Mortgage Insurance Company, 195
Gemstones, 289, 290, 293
Gifts, lifetime, 451
Global funds, 288, 389, 396
Global investments, 288–289
Globe and Mail, 305, 329
Goals. See Financial goals
Government benefit documents, 442
Government bonds, 290
Canada Savings Bonds, 110, 289, 366–368
marketable bonds, 356
municipal bonds, 368
provincial government securities, 368
treasury bills, 365–366
Government of Canada Real Return Bonds, 365
Grants. See Study grants
Gross Debt Service (GDS) ratio, 196
Gross domestic product (GDP), 13
Group insurance
health, 260–261
life, 250
Group registered retirement savings plan, 423
Growth stocks, 289–290, 322
GST
newly built homes, 201
and QST refunds, 79
Guaranteed annuities, 259
Guaranteed Income Supplement (GIS), 422
Guaranteed insurability option, 253
Guaranteed Investment Certificates (GICs), 108, 110, 112, 290
Guardian, 445, 447

[H]

Handyman's special, 192
Hazard, 212
Health insurance, 219
aggregate limits, 270

assigned benefits, 269
benefit limits, 269
cancellation and termination, 269
co-insurance, 270
consumer tips, 271
co-payment, 269
deductibles, 270
dental expense insurance, 266
eligibility, 269
exclusions and limitations provision, 269
group insurance, 260–261
guaranteed renewability, 269
indemnity policy, 269
individual insurance, 261
internal limits, 269–270
long-term-care insurance, 266-267
out-of-pocket limit, 270
policy checklist, 268
publicly financed health care, limits of, 259, 260
reimbursement policy, 269
supplemental coverage, 260–261, 266–270
trade-offs, 269–270
vision care insurance, 266
High-ratio mortgage, 195
High-risk pool, 233
Holographic will, 444
Home equity loans, 134, 136, 200
Home ownership
    benefits, 189–190
    capital gains, 84
    drawbacks, 190
    equity, 189, 431
    home-based business, 83
    home improvement, 192
    home insurance, 201
    maintenance costs, 190, 191, 203
    residence as tax shelter, 83
Homeowners insurance
    80-percent rule, 221–222
    actual cash value (ACV) method, 227
    additional living expense coverage, 220
    adequate coverage, 226–227
    basic personal liability coverage, 223
    cost factors, 227–228
    coverage checklist, 217
    credit card fraud coverage, 225
    deductibles, 226, 228
    dwelling and attached structures, 220
    fire department charges, 225
    personal property protection, 220–221, 223–225
    removal of damaged property, 225

replacement value of home, 221, 227
temporary repairs, 225
tenants, 223–224
types, 224–225
Home purchase
    closing, 200–202
    down payment, 192, 195
    financing, 195–202
    home buyers' plan, 83–84, 195
    home inspection, 193, 201
    housing market and purchase price, 194–195
    legal fees, 201
    location, 192
    offer to purchase, 194
    ownership needs, 189–190
    price and budget, 192
    process, 189–202
    property appraisal, 193
    property survey, 201
    purchase contract, 194–195
    real estate agents, 193
    service charges, 201
    warranties, 202
    See also Mortgages
Home sale, 204–205
Household expenditures, 415
Household inventory, 221
Housing
    housing market, 194
    lifestyle and, 183
    nonprofit, 191
    opportunity costs, 183–184
    renting-vs.-buying decision, 184–185
    retirement, 417–418
    types, 190–192
    See also Home ownership; Home purchase; Renting
Housing starts, 13
Human Resources and Development Canada (HRDC), 432

[I]

Identity theft, 116, 150–151
IE: Money, 169, 305, 329
Implied warranties, 202
Income
    defined, 43
    employment, 41–42, 62
    estimation, 46–47
    investment income, 62, 302–303
    passive income, 62
    sources, 43
Income dividends, 396
Income risk, 6

Income stocks, 322
Income tax
    "attribution rules," 85
    capital gains exemption, 65–66
    deadlines and penalties, 78–80
    deductions, 63–66, 72, 81
    dividends, 302, 398
    filing requirements, 61–62
    installment payments, 77–78
    interest, 302
    payments, 74–81
    Quebec tax return, 61–62, 67
    reassessment, 91
    reductions of source withholding, 77
    rental income, 303
    source withholding, 74, 76–77
    tax rates, 67–70
    terminal income tax return, 60, 452
    TONI system, 67–69
Income tax preparation, 62–74
    home filing system, 64–65
    net income, 63–65
    specialists, 90–91
    tax owing, 66–74
    total income, determining, 62–74
Incontestability clause, 252
Indexes. See Stock market indexes
Index funds, 384
Individual pension plan (IPP), tax strategy, 86
Industry Canada, 169
Inflation
    80-percent rule and, 222
    consumer price index, 14, 50
    cost of credit and, 163–164
    impact, 13–14
    and retirement, 410, 416, 419, 433
    and savings plans, 112
Inflation risk, 6, 287
Information sources
    bonds, 359–360, 370–371, 375
    business periodicals, 305, 329, 375
    corporate reports, 305–306, 326, 327, 374
    corporate Web sites, 323
    financial planning, 5, 6, 29–30, 304
    government publications, 305
    government reports, 275
    housing, 185
    investments, 303–307, 323–325, 329
    mutual funds, 390–395
    newspaper financial section, 304–305, 323, 391–392
    rental housing, 186
    stock advisory services, 325–326
    taxation, 87–89
    See also Online resources

ING Direct, 109
Initial public offerings (IPOs), 336
Insolvency, 41
Installment credit, 126
Installment debentures, 368
Institute of Canadian Bankers (ICB), 300
Insurance
    agents, 32, 233, 254
    annuities, 257–259
    automobile insurance, 228–234
    brokers, 254
    companies, 211, 254
    disability income insurance, 261–264
    exclusions, 225
    function, 211
    goals and needs, 215–216, 280
    health insurance, 219, 259–261, 266-270
    insurer, 211
    liability protection, 218–219, 223
    peril, 212
    policy, 211
    policyholder, 211
    premium, 211, 233–234
    program planning, 213–216
    riders, 223
    risks, 212–214
    third-party liability, 224
    worker's compensation coverage, 223
    See also Homeowners insurance; Life insurance
Insurance proceeds left with company, settlement option, 257
Intangible-product goals, 9
Interest-adjusted indexes, 254, 256
Interest-earning chequing accounts, 108, 114
Interest rate risk, 6, 287–288
Interest rates, 12, 13, 15
    5-yr mortgage rate, 104
    5-yr term deposit rate, 104
    30-yr T-bond rate, 104
    bank rate, 104, 161
    and bond value, 361
    credit card rates, 161
    and fixed-return investments, 287–288
    mortgages, 198
    nominal interest rate, 111–112
    prime rate, 104
    savings deposit rate, 104
    trends, 102–103
    variable-rate mortgages, 199
Intermediate goals, 8
International funds. *See* Global funds

Inter vivos trust. *See* Living trust
Intestate, 440, 444
Intestate probate, 450
Investing
    budgeting, 280, 297
    commitment to goals, 281
    diversification strategy, 292, 294–295, 296
    evaluating investments, 300
    financial checkup, 280–281
    goals, 279–280
    investment growth, 289–290
    investment income, 289
    investment liquidity, 290
    long-term investment strategies, 342–343
    long-term investors, 342
    mega trends, 347
    monitoring investments, 301
    personal plan, 295–298
    psychological aspects, 299
    recordkeeping, 301
    risk factors, 286–289
    risk tolerance, 285, 287
    safety and risk factors, 284–285
    saving strategies, 282, 297
    short-term investment strategies, 343–346
    sources of financing, 282
Investment assets, 40
Investment bank, 336
Investment companies, 105, 382
Investment income, 62, 289, 302–303
Investments
    global investments, 288–289
    monitoring, 301
    online scams, 327
    speculative investments, 284–285, 289, 290
    uninsured investments, 285
    See also under specific type of investment
Investment theories, 334

[J]

Joint, last to die life insurance, 253
Joint tenancy, assets held in, 451

[K]

Kirzner, Eric, 393

[L]

Labour-sponsored venture capital corporations, 389

Large-cap stocks, 322
Lawyers, 32
Leases
    closed-end lease, 134-135
    loan-vs.-lease decision, 137
    open-end lease, 135
Letter of last instruction, 448
Liabilities, 40–41
    defined, 218
    liability insurance, 218–219, 223
    liability risks, 212
    risk management strategies, 214
    third-party liability, 228, 229, 231
    voluntary medical payments, 223
Life Income Funds (LIFs), 429
Life income option, insurance, 257
Life insurance, 219
    application, 255
    automatic premium loans, 252
    beneficiary, 250
    buying, 253–257, 258
    concept, 239
    credit life insurance, 250
    critical illness benefits, 253
    endowment life insurance, 250
    estimating coverage requirements, 242–244
    "free look" period, 256
    grace period, 251
    group life insurance, 250
    guaranteed insurability option, 253
    incontestability clause, 252
    joint, last to die life insurance policy, 253
    life insurance companies, 105, 254
    misstatement of age provision, 252
    nonforfeiture clause, 251
    objectives, 242
    permanent life insurance, 246–249
    policy costs, 254, 256
    policy loan provision, 252
    policy reinstatement, 251
    principle, 240
    proceeds, 451
    purpose, 240
    retirement planning, 413
    riders, 252–253
    RRSP-eligible investment, 429
    settlement options, 256–257
    suicide clause, 252
    switching policies, 257
    term insurance, 244–246
    waiver of premium disability, 252
Lifelong Learning Plan (LLP), 427
Life situation
    budget allocations, 49
    and financial goals, 9

and housing, 183
  influence of, 10–11
Lifestyle
  family and, 46
  and housing, 183
  influences on, 46
Limited installment payment, insurance
  settlement, 257
Limited payment policy, 246, 248
Limit order, 340
Line of credit, 281
  bank, 130
  revolving, 134
Liquidity
  investment liquidity, 290
  and savings goals, 112
Liquidity ratio, 43
Liquidity risk, 6
Living trust, 449, 450
Living will, 447, 450
Load funds, 384
Loan companies. *See* Mortgage and
  loan companies
Loan-to-value ratio, 195
Long-term-care insurance, 266-267, 268
Long-term goals, 8
Long-term liabilities, 41
Lump-sum payment, insurance settle-
  ment option, 256

[M]

McDougall, Bruce, 393
Management expense ratio (MER),
  385–386
Manitoba
  basic automobile insurance cover-
    age, 229
  no-fault insurance, 230
  Testator's Family Maintenance Act,
    440
Manufactured homes, 191
Marginal tax, 69
Margin, buying stocks on, 343
Marketable bonds, 365
Market forces, 11
Market order, 339
Market risk, 288
Market timer, 390
Marriage certificate, 441
Maturity date, bonds, 354–355
Medical expense credit, 64
Medicare, 259
Mental budget, 53
Military service records, 442
Misstatement of age provision, 252
Mobile homes, 191

Money, 305
Money management
  15/15/70 rule, 297
  budgeting, 45–52
  financial statements, 41–45
  opportunity cost and, 36
  recordkeeping, 37–38
  saving, 52–55, 282
Money market accounts, 108
Money market funds, 105, 108, 388
Money orders, 115
MoneySaver, 305, 329
MoneySense, 329
Money supply, 12, 13
Monte Carlo method, 412
Moody's Investors Service, 324, 358
Mortality table, 241
Mortgage bonds, 368
Mortgage brokers, 196
Mortgage funds, 388
Mortgage and loan companies, 106, 193
Mortgages
  application process, 198
  assumable mortgage, 199
  conventional mortgage, 195,
    198–199
  defined, 196
  early loan retirement, 202, 431
  interest adjustment, 201
  loan qualification, 196–197
  mortgage insurance, 195, 201, 246
  multirate mortage, 199
  payment plan options, 199-200
  refinancing, 200
  reverse mortgage, 202
  second mortgage, 134, 136, 200
  variable-rate mortgages, 199
Moving expenses, 201
  tax deductible, 64
Multirate mortgage, 199
Mutual funds, 284, 289, 290
  advantages and disadvantages, 395
  back-end load, 384, 385
  capital gain distributions, 396–397
  classifications, 388–390
  closed-end fund, 383
  diversification, 382, 396
  evaluation, 391
  family of funds, 390
  fees and commissions, 384–388
  front-end load, 384, 399
  income dividends, 396
  investment company, 382
  investment goals and objectives, 392
  investments, 292, 381–382
  load funds, 384
  management expense ratio, 385–386

market timer, 390
mutual fund industry, 382
net asset value, 383
newspaper fund table, 391
no-load funds, 384–385
open-end fund, 383
professional management, 382
prospectus, 386, 392
purchase options, 398–400
reinvestment plan, 400
service fees, 386
special fees, 386
total shareholder return, 399
withdrawal options, 400
See also Registered Retirement
  Savings Plans

[N]

Name changes, legal, 442
Named perils policies, 224, 225
Nasdaq, 337
NASDAQ Composite Index, 314
National Foundation for Consumer
  Credit, 168
Negative amortization, 199
Negligence, 218
Net asset value (NAV), 383–384
Net cash flow, 44
Net income, 63
Net pay. *See* Take-home pay
Net worth, 41, 45, 411
Newsome, Mark, 393
Newsweek, 305, 329
No-fault insurance, 230
Nonbanks, 103
Nonparticipating policies, 248
Nonworking spouse method, of assess-
  ing life insurance coverage, 243
NYSE Composite Index, 314

[O]

Odd lots, 341
Offer to purchase, 194
Old Age Security (OAS), 421–422
Online banking. *See* Electronic banking
  services
Online brokerage firms, 341
Online resources
  automobile purchases, 7
  bonds, 370–371
  borrowing, 21
  credit cards, 168
  critical illness insurance, 271
  disability insurance, 271, 274–275
  estate planning, 22

financial planning, 4, 7, 21, 31, 168
financial privacy, 116
health insurance, 270, 274–275
home purchase, 187
investments, 7, 22
investments transactions, 7, 340–341
life insurance, 274
mortgage application, 7
mutual funds, 392, 393–395
online banking, 7
retirement planning, 7, 22, 411, 412, 432
saving, 21
search engines, 323–324
spending, 22
stock investments, 323–325
taxation, 7, 89
See also Information sources; Software
Online shopping, 132-133
Open-end credit, 130, 162–163
Open-end funds. See Mutual funds
Open-end lease, 135
Opportunity cost
of decisions, 5
financial, 16–19
housing choices, 183–184
and money management, 36
personal, 15
Options, 346
Ordinary life policy. See Whole life policy
Overdraft protection, 114–115
Over-the-counter market, 337, 364, 383, 398

[P]

Participating policies, 248
Participating preferred stocks, 320
Par value, 319
Passbook accounts, 108, 289, 290
Passive income, 62
Pawnshops, 106, 107
Payday loans, 107
Payroll deduction plan, 53, 77
Payroll Savings Program, 368
Pay-yourself-first saving strategy, 282, 297
Penny stock, 323
Pension plans
checklist, 424
disability income, 263–264
employer pension plans, 422–423
plan portability, 423
public pensions, 419–422
Peril, 212

Permanent life insurance
adjustable life insurance, 249
limited payment policy, 246, 248
nonparticipating policies, 248
participating policies, 248
universal life, 248
variable insurance, 248–249
whole life policy, 246, 251
Personal financial statements
balance sheet, 39–41
cash flow statement, 41–44
Personal income and expenditure statement. See Cash flow statement
Personal possessions, 39
Personal property floater, 221
Personal risk, 6, 212
Physical budget, 53
Point-of-sales transactions, 102
Policyholder, insurance, 211
Policy, insurance, 211, 442
loan provision, 252
reinstatement, 251
See also under specific type of insurance coverage
Political donations, 72
Pourover will, 450
Power of attorney, 448
Precious metals, 289, 290, 293
Pre-emptive right, 316
Preferred stocks, 287, 291
Pre-nuptial agreement, 445
Prepaid travel cards, 115
Pre-planned funeral arrangements, 441
Present value. See Time value of money
President's Choice Financial, 109
Previous balance method, revolving credit, 162, 163
Price-earnings (P/E) ratio, 333
Privacy, credit bureau regulation, 142–143
Private corporations, 315
Probate, 444–445, 450, 453
Probate taxes, 452
Professional dues, 64
Property insurance
personal property coverage, 221
potential losses, 217–218
See also Homeowners insurance
Property risks, 212
Property transfer, jointly owned property, 444
Prospectus, 306, 328, 329, 386, 392
Provincial securities regulations, 342
Proxy, 316
Public corporations, 315
Pure risk, 212
Put options, 293, 346

[Q]

QST. See GST, and QST refunds
Quebec
automobile insurance coverage, 229
no-fault insurance, 230
pension plan, 263–264, 421–422
Quicken Financial Network, 168

[R]

Random walk theory, 334
Rate of return, 111
See also Yield
Rating territory, 233
Real estate
agents, 32, 193, 204
assets, 39
investments, 284, 290, 292–293
real estate bonds, 369
rental property, 289, 303
Real estate funds, 389
Record date, 316–317
Recordkeeping
investments, 301
money management, 37–38
receipts, 64
tax records, 65
Registered bond, 361
Registered coupon bond, 361
Registered Education Savings Plans (RESPs), 84
Registered Financial Planners, 300
Registered Pension Plan (RPP), tax strategy, 85–86
Registered Retirement Income Funds (RRIFs), 429
Registered Retirement Savings Plans (RRSPs)
contribution limits, 427
deregistration options, 427–430
eligible investments, 425
home buyers' plan, 83–84, 195, 427, 428
investment vehicle, 425
Lifelong Learning Plan, 427
RRSP-vs.-down-payment decision, 431
tax strategy, 85
types, 425, 427
Regular chequing accounts, 114, 290
Regular interest bonds, 110, 366
Regular savings accounts, 108, 289, 290
Re-insuring, 213
Reinvestment plan, 400
Renewability option, 245

Renting
    advantages, 186–187
    costs, 189
    disadvantages, 187–189
    housing, 186
    tenants' rights, 189
Rent-to-own centres, 107
Replacement value, 221, 227
Restrictive endorsement, 122
Retained earnings, growth companies,
    289–290
Retirement
    budgeting, 432–434
    part-time work, 432–433
    risk management strategies, 214
    saving for, 14, 409–410, 417, 428
    tax planning, 85–86
    See also Pensions
Retirement planning
    assets, 412–413
    checklist, 434
    employer-sponsored programs,
        282
    housing, 417–418
    inflation, 410, 416, 419, 433
    living expenses, 414–416
    personal retirement plans, 423–430
    reasons for, 410
    software planning tools, 411, 412
    starting early, 409–410
    trade-offs, 409, 426
Reuters, 307
Reverse annuity mortgage (RAM),
    412–413
Reverse mortgages, 200
Reverse splits, 318
Revolving line of credit, 134
    See also Open-end credit
Riders, insurance, 223
Risk assumption, 213
Risk avoidance, 212–213
Risk reduction, 213
    investment, 299–303
Risks
    business failure risk, 288
    defined, 212
    evaluation, 5
    global investment risk, 288–289
    inflation risk, 287
    interest rate risk, 287–288
    market risk, 288
    and potential return, 285
    risk management, 212–213, 214
    types, 6, 212
Risk shifting, 213
Risk tolerance, 285, 286–287
Round lots, 341

[S]

S&P/TSX Composite Index, 313
Saskatchewan
    basic automobile insurance cover-
        age, 229
    Dependants Relief Act, 440
    no-fault insurance, 230
Saving, 52–55
    common reasons, 52
    emergency fund, 47, 280
    saving techniques, 52–54, 282
    target amounts, 54
    two-income households, 54–55
Savings ratio, 43
Scams, investment, 327
Schedule I banks, 105
Schedule II banks, 105
Scholarships, 62
Search engines, 31–32
Second mortgages. See Home equity
    loans
Secured loan, 160
Securities, 314
Securities exchanges, 337
Securities regulations, 342
SecurNat, 102
Segregated funds
    mutual funds, 389
    retirement investment, 430
Self-employment
    CPP contribution, 420
    tax planning, 84
Self-insurance, 213
Self-regulatory organizations (SROs),
    342
Selling short, 343
Serial bonds, 358
Sharpe, William F., 412
Short-term goals, 8
Simple interest, 160–162
Single-family dwellings, 190
Single-life annuity, 258–259
Sinking fund, 358
Small-cap stocks, 322
Smart cards, 102, 131
Software
    budgeting systems, 53
    cheque writing, 123
    integrated programs, 30–31
    investment analysis programs, 31
    spreadsheets, 30
    tax, 31
    tax preparation, 89
    See also Online resources
Special endorsement, 122
Speculative investments, 284–285, 289

Speculative risks, 212
Speculators, 342
Spending diary, 49
Spending plan. See Budget; Budgeting
Split mortgage, 199
Spousal RRSP, 425
Spousal trust, 450
Spouse's Allowance (SPA), 422
Spreadsheet software, 30
Stamps, 293
Standard & Poor's 500 Stock Index, 314
Standard & Poor's Financial
    Information Services, 324
Standard and Poor's Corporation, 358
Stockbrokers, 337–338
Stockhouse Canada, 306
Stock market indexes, 13, 313–314
Stocks
    annualized holding period yield,
        332–333
    beta, 333–334
    buy-and-hold technique, 343
    buying on margin, 343
    buying and selling stocks, 336–342
    classification, 322–323
    commission charges, 341–342
    common, 313–318
    common stocks, 291, 313–318
    direct investment plan, 343
    dividend reinvestment plan, 343
    dividends, 291, 302, 315–317,
        318–319
    dollar appreciation of stock value,
        317
    dollar cost averaging, 343
    evaluation of stock issue, 321–334
    ex-dividend, 317
    investments, 295, 334
    market value, 315, 329–330
    options, 346
    preferred stocks, 287
    price-earnings (P/E) ratio, 333
    primary market, 336–337
    record date, 316–317
    reverse splits, 318
    secondary market, 336, 337
    selling decision, 319
    selling short, 343
    stock certificates, 339–340, 442
    stock splits, 317–318
    total shareholder return, 332
    transactions, 339–341
    types, 291
    voting rights, 316
Stop order, 340
Stop-payment order, 123
Stored-value cards, 102

Straight life policy. *See* Whole life policy
Strict liability, 219
Strip bonds, 369
    See also Zero-coupon bonds
Students,
    health insurance, 260
    loans, 84
Study grants, 62
Subordinated debenture, 357
Subrogation, 230
Succession Law Reform Act, 440
Suicide clause, 252
Supplemental health insurance. *See* Health insurance
Surplus, 50
Survivor life, 253
Sweat equity, 192
System for Electronic Document Analysis and Retrieval (SEDAR), 306, 324, 375

[T]

Take-home pay, 44–45
Taxation
    annuities, 259
    capital gains, 65–66, 84, 334, 397, 398, 450
    compound interest bonds, 367
    earnings, 61
    electronic filing, 89
    excise tax, 60
    group health insurance, 260–261
    investment earnings, 302–303
    land transfer tax, 201
    mutual funds, 398
    property, 60, 190, 201
    purchases, 60
    purpose, 60
    wealth, 60
    See also Income tax; Income tax preparation
Tax audit
    audit rights, 91–92
    objections and appeals, 92
    types, 90–91
Tax Court of Canada, 92
Tax credit, 72–74, 84
Tax-deferred income, 62, 63
Tax-deferred investments, 84, 302
Tax evasion, 81
Tax-exempt income, 63, 302
Tax-exempt investments, 84
Tax planning
    accelerating deductions, 81
    accelerating receipt of income, 81

children's investments, 84–85
    delaying deductions, 81
    delaying receipt of income, 81
    divorced persons, 83
    employment-related expenses, 84
    home-based business, 83
    purchase of residence, 83–84
    purpose, 81
    residence as tax shelter, 83
    retired persons, 83
    self-employment, 84
    single parents, 83
    strategies, 81–86
    student loans, 84
    tax-deferred investments, 84
    tax-exempt investments, 84
Tax preparers, 32
Tax refund, 76
Tax shelters, 62
Technical theory, 334
Temporary life insurance. *See* Term life insurance
Tenancy in common, 451
Tenants insurance, 223–224
Term deposits, 109
Term life insurance
    consumer tips, 251
    conversion option, 245
    decreasing term, 240–246
    nature of, 244–245
    renewability option, 245
    term-to-100 policies, 246
Testamentary trust, 449–450
Testator's Family Maintenance Act, 440
Third-party liability, 224, 228, 229, 231
Ticker tape, 339
Time, 305
Times interest earned, 375
Time value of money
    compounding, 17
    financial calculators and, 19
    future value of a series of deposits, 17, 20, 459–460
    future value of a single amount, 17, 457–458
    future value tables, 464–465
    and investing for retirement, 283
    loan payments, 462
    long-term investment, 282–284
    opportunity cost, 16
    present value of a series of deposits, 18–19, 461–462
    present value of a series of equal amounts, 461–462
    present value of a single amount, 17–18, 24–25, 460–461

present value tables, 466–467
    simple interest, 16–17
Title insurance, 200
Title. *See* Deed
Total Debt Service (TDS) ratio, 196
Total shareholder return (TSR), 332, 363, 399
Towing coverage, 231
Townhouses, 191
Trade balance, 12, 13
Traders, 342
Trailers, 386
Trans Union of Canada, 139
Travel and entertainment cards, 132, 134, 156
Traveller's cheques, 115
Treasury bills (T-bills), 289, 356–366
Trust companies, 105
Trustee, 356
Trusts, 100, 449–450

[U]

Umbrella policy, 223
Underwriting fee, 195
Underwriting syndicate, 336
Unemployment, economic indicator, 13
Uninsured motorist coverage, 230
Union dues, 64
Units, securities bundle, 369
Universal life insurance, 248, 249

[V]

Value Line, 306
Values, 11, 46
    and lifestyle, 46
Variable expenses, 44
    budgeting, 49, 50
Variable life insurance, 248–249
Variable-rate mortgages, 199
Vehicle Information Centre of Canada (VICC), 232
Vesting, 422
Veterans documents, 442
Vicarious liability, 219
Vision care insurance, 266
Voluntary medical payments, 223
Vos, Wilfred, 393

[W]

Waiver of depreciation coverage, 231
Waiver of premium disability, 252
Walden, Gene, 393
Warrants, 369
Welfare, 264

Whole life policy, 246, 251
Williamson, Gordon, 393
Wills
    altering/rewriting, 447
    change in marital status and, 440,
        442
    contents, 443
    cost, 442
    executor, 445, 446
    guardian, 445, 447
    living will, 447, 450
    pourover will, 450

    purpose, 450
    will-making, 444–445
Wills Variation Act, 440
Worker's compensation, 264
Written budget, 53

[Y]

Yield
    annualized holding period yield,
        332–333

    bond investment, 372–375
    current yield, 372–374
    T-bills, 365–366
    yield to maturity, 374
    See also Rate of return
Yih, Jim, 393

[Z]

Zero-coupon bond, 361, 369
Zoning laws, 192

Frequently Used
Symbols and Formulas

A Key to the Icons Appearing in the Exercise Sets

↪ Concept reinforcement exercises, indicated by purple exercise numbers, provide basic practice with the new concepts and vocabulary.

1 Following most examples, students are directed to **TRY EXERCISES**. These selected exercises are identified with a color block around the exercise numbers.

Aha! Exercises labeled Aha! can often be solved quickly with the proper insight.

▦ Calculator exercises are designed to be worked using a scientific or graphing calculator.

〜 Graphing calculator exercises are designed to be worked using a graphing calculator and often provide practice for concepts discussed in the Technology Connections.

𝄞 Writing exercises are designed to be answered using one or more complete sentences.

Symbols

$=$	Is equal to
$\approx$	Is approximately equal to
$>$	Is greater than
$<$	Is less than
$\geq$	Is greater than or equal to
$\leq$	Is less than or equal to
$\in$	Is an element of
$\subseteq$	Is a subset of
$\lvert x \rvert$	The absolute value of x
$\{x \mid x \ldots\}$	The set of all x such that $x \ldots$
$-x$	The opposite of x
$\sqrt{x}$	The square root of x
$\sqrt[n]{x}$	The nth root of x
LCM	Least Common Multiple
LCD	Least Common Denominator
π	Pi
i	$\sqrt{-1}$
$f(x)$	f of x, or f at x
$f^{-1}(x)$	f inverse of x
$(f \circ g)(x)$	$f(g(x))$
e	Approximately 2.7
Σ	Summation
$n!$	Factorial notation

Formulas

$m = \dfrac{y_2 - y_1}{x_2 - x_1}$	Slope of a line
$y = mx + b$	Slope–intercept form of a linear equation
$y - y_1 = m(x - x_1)$	Point–slope form of a linear equation
$(A + B)(A - B) = A^2 - B^2$	Product of the sum and difference of the same two terms
$(A + B)^2 = A^2 + 2AB + B^2,$ $(A - B)^2 = A^2 - 2AB + B^2$	Square of a binomial
$d = rt$	Formula for distance traveled
$\dfrac{1}{a} \cdot t + \dfrac{1}{b} \cdot t = 1$	Work principle
$s = 16t^2$	Free-fall distance
$y = kx$	Direct variation
$y = \dfrac{k}{x}$	Inverse variation
$x = \dfrac{-b \pm \sqrt{b^2 - 4ac}}{2a}$	Quadratic formula
$P(t) = P_0 e^{kt}, k > 0$	Exponential growth
$P(t) = P_0 e^{-kt}, k > 0$	Exponential decay
$d = \sqrt{(x_2 - x_1)^2 + (y_2 - y_1)^2}$	Distance formula
$\binom{n}{r} = \dfrac{n!}{(n - r)! \, r!}$	$\binom{n}{r}$ notation

Resources Designed with You in Mind

This textbook was designed with features and applications to help make learning easier for you, but there's more than just the textbook if you want additional help. At www.mypearsonstore.com, you can check out these and other supplemental materials that can help you pass your math course.

Worksheets for Classroom or Lab Practice
(ISBN-10: 0-321-59933-0; ISBN-13: 978-0-321-59933-9)

Need more practice? Each worksheet provides key terms, fill-in-the-blank vocabulary practice, and exercises for each objective. There are two worksheets for every section of the text.

Videos on DVD
(ISBN-10: 0-321-59935-7; ISBN-13: 978-0-321-59935-3)

Miss a lecture? Need some extra help studying the night before an exam? Having a tough time with a certain topic? The Videos on DVD are here to help. Watch an experienced math instructor present important definitions, procedures, and concepts from each section of the book. The instructor will show you how to solve examples and exercises taken straight from the text.

Student's Solutions Manual
(ISBN-10: 0-321-58623-9; ISBN-13: 978-0-321-58623-0)

Looking for more than just the answer in the back of the book? The *Student's Solutions Manual* contains step-by-step solutions for all the odd-numbered exercises in the text as well as step-by-step solutions for Connecting the Concepts, Chapter Review Exercises, and Chapter Test exercises.

Elementary & Intermediate Algebra

Concepts & Applications

Marvin L. Bittinger, David J. Ellenbogen and Barbara L. Johnson

Volume 2
Custom Edition for Math 152, 152A, 152B and 153

Taken from:

Elementary & Intermediate Algebra: Concepts & Applications, Fifth Edition
by Marvin L. Bittinger, David J. Ellenbogen and Barbara L. Johnson

Custom Publishing

New York   Boston   San Francisco
London   Toronto   Sydney   Tokyo   Singapore   Madrid
Mexico City   Munich   Paris   Cape Town   Hong Kong   Montreal

Taken from:

Elementary & Intermediate Algebra: Concepts & Applications, Fifth Edition
by Marvin L. Bittinger, David J. Ellenbogen and Barbara L. Johnson
Copyright © 2010 by Pearson Education, Inc.
Published by Addison Wesley
Boston, Massachusetts 02116

This special edition published in cooperation with Pearson Custom Publishing.

Printed in the United States of America

10   9   8   7   6   5

2009360539

CG

**Pearson
Custom Publishing**
is a division of

www.pearsonhighered.com

ISBN 10: 0-558-35591-9
ISBN 13: 978-0-558-35591-3

Contents

7   Functions and Graphs   443

7.1   **Introduction to Functions**   444
Correspondences and Functions   •   Functions and Graphs   •
Function Notation and Equations   •   Applications

7.2   **Domain and Range**   455
Determining the Domain and the Range   •   Restrictions on Domain   •
Functions Defined Piecewise

7.3   **Graphs of Functions**   464
Linear Functions   •   Nonlinear Functions

   VISUALIZING FOR SUCCESS   469

   CONNECTING THE CONCEPTS   474

7.4   **The Algebra of Functions**   475
The Sum, Difference, Product, or Quotient of Two Functions   •
Domains and Graphs

7.5   **Formulas, Applications, and Variation**   484
Formulas   •   Direct Variation   •   Inverse Variation   •   Joint Variation
and Combined Variation

   STUDY SUMMARY   496
   REVIEW EXERCISES   498
   TEST   501

   CUMULATIVE REVIEWS: CHAPTERS 1–7   502

8   Systems of Linear Equations and Problem Solving   505

8.1   **Systems of Equations in Two Variables**   506
Translating   •   Identifying Solutions   •   Solving Systems Graphically

   VISUALIZING FOR SUCCESS   512

8.2   **Solving by Substitution or Elimination**   516
The Substitution Method   •   The Elimination Method

   CONNECTING THE CONCEPTS   523

8.3   **Solving Applications: Systems of Two Equations**   524
Total-Value and Mixture Problems   •   Motion Problems

8.4   **Systems of Equations in Three Variables**   537
Identifying Solutions   •   Solving Systems in Three Variables   •
Dependency, Inconsistency, and Geometric Considerations

8.5 **Solving Applications: Systems of Three Equations**   545
Applications of Three Equations in Three Unknowns

8.6 **Elimination Using Matrices**   552
Matrices and Systems   •   Row-Equivalent Operations

8.7 **Determinants and Cramer's Rule**   556
Determinants of 2×2 Matrices   •   Cramer's Rule: 2×2 Systems   •
Cramer's Rule: 3×3 Systems

8.8 **Business and Economics Applications**   561
Break-Even Analysis   •   Supply and Demand

STUDY SUMMARY   568
REVIEW EXERCISES   571
TEST   572
CUMULATIVE REVIEW: CHAPTERS 1–8   574

9   Inequalities and Problem Solving   577

9.1 **Inequalities and Domain**   578
Solving Inequalities Graphically   •   Domain   •   Problem Solving

9.2 **Intersections, Unions, and Compound Inequalities**   587
Intersections of Sets and Conjunctions of Sentences   •   Unions of Sets
and Disjunctions of Sentences   •   Interval Notation and Domains

9.3 **Absolute-Value Equations and Inequalities**   597
Equations with Absolute Value   •   Inequalities with Absolute Value

CONNECTING THE CONCEPTS   605

9.4 **Inequalities in Two Variables**   606
Graphs of Linear Inequalities   •   Systems of Linear Inequalities

VISUALIZING FOR SUCCESS   613

CONNECTING THE CONCEPTS   617

9.5 **Applications Using Linear Programming**   618
Objective Functions and Constraints   •   Linear Programming

STUDY SUMMARY   625
REVIEW EXERCISES   627
TEST   629
CUMULATIVE REVIEW: CHAPTERS 1–9   630

10   Exponents and Radicals   633

10.1 **Radical Expressions and Functions**   634
Square Roots and Square-Root Functions   •   Expressions of the Form $\sqrt{a^2}$ •
Cube Roots   •   Odd and Even nth Roots

VISUALIZING FOR SUCCESS   640

10.2 Rational Numbers as Exponents   643
Rational Exponents • Negative Rational Exponents •
Laws of Exponents • Simplifying Radical Expressions

10.3 Multiplying Radical Expressions   650
Multiplying Radical Expressions • Simplifying by Factoring •
Multiplying and Simplifying

10.4 Dividing Radical Expressions   656
Dividing and Simplifying • Rationalizing Denominators
or Numerators with One Term

10.5 Expressions Containing Several Radical Terms   662
Adding and Subtracting Radical Expressions • Products and Quotients of
Two or More Radical Terms • Rationalizing Denominators or Numerators
with Two Terms • Terms with Differing Indices

CONNECTING THE CONCEPTS   668

10.6 Solving Radical Equations   669
The Principle of Powers • Equations with Two Radical Terms

10.7 The Distance and Midpoint Formulas and Other
Applications   676
Using the Pythagorean Theorem • Two Special Triangles •
The Distance and Midpoint Formulas

10.8 The Complex Numbers   688
Imaginary and Complex Numbers • Addition and Subtraction •
Multiplication • Conjugates and Division • Powers of i

STUDY SUMMARY   695
REVIEW EXERCISES   698
TEST   700
CUMULATIVE REVIEW: CHAPTERS 1–10   701

11   Quadratic Functions and Equations   703

11.1 Quadratic Equations   704
The Principle of Square Roots • Completing the Square • Problem Solving

11.2 The Quadratic Formula   715
Solving Using the Quadratic Formula • Approximating Solutions

11.3 Studying Solutions of Quadratic Equations   720
The Discriminant • Writing Equations from Solutions

11.4 Applications Involving Quadratic Equations   725
Solving Problems • Solving Formulas

11.5 Equations Reducible to Quadratic   732
Recognizing Equations in Quadratic Form • Radical Equations
and Rational Equations

CONNECTING THE CONCEPTS   739

11.6 Quadratic Functions and Their Graphs   740
The Graph of $f(x) = ax^2$ • The Graph of $f(x) = a(x - h)^2$ •
The Graph of $f(x) = a(x - h)^2 - k$

11.7 More About Graphing Quadratic Functions   749
Completing the Square • Finding Intercepts

VISUALIZING FOR SUCCESS   753

11.8 Problem Solving and Quadratic Functions   756
Maximum and Minimum Problems • Fitting Quadratic Functions to Data

11.9 Polynomial and Rational Inequalities   766
Quadratic and Other Polynomial Inequalities • Rational Inequalities

STUDY SUMMARY   775
REVIEW EXERCISES   778
TEST   780

CUMULATIVE REVIEW: CHAPTERS 1–11   781

12   Exponential and Logarithmic Functions   783

12.1 Composite and Inverse Functions   784
Composite Functions • Inverses and One-to-One Functions •
Finding Formulas for Inverses • Graphing Functions and Their Inverses •
Inverse Functions and Composition

12.2 Exponential Functions   795
Graphing Exponential Functions • Equations with x and y Interchanged •
Applications of Exponential Functions

12.3 Logarithmic Functions   803
Graphs of Logarithmic Functions • Equivalent Equations •
Solving Certain Logarithmic Equations

12.4 Properties of Logarithmic Functions   810
Logarithms of Products • Logarithms of Powers • Logarithms
of Quotients • Using the Properties Together

12.5 Common and Natural Logarithms   817
Common Logarithms on a Calculator • The Base e and Natural
Logarithms on a Calculator • Changing Logarithmic Bases •
Graphs of Exponential and Logarithmic Functions, Base e

VISUALIZING FOR SUCCESS   822

CONNECTING THE CONCEPTS   824

12.6 Solving Exponential and Logarithmic Equations   825
Solving Exponential Equations • Solving Logarithmic Equations

12.7 Applications of Exponential and Logarithmic Functions   832
Applications of Logarithmic Functions • Applications of Exponential Functions

STUDY SUMMARY   845
REVIEW EXERCISES   847
TEST   849
CUMULATIVE REVIEW: CHAPTERS 1–12   850

13 Conic Sections 853

13.1 **Conic Sections: Parabolas and Circles** 854
Parabolas • Circles

13.2 **Conic Sections: Ellipses** 863
Ellipses Centered at $(0, 0)$ • Ellipses Centered at (h, k)

13.3 **Conic Sections: Hyperbolas** 870
Hyperbolas • Hyperbolas (Nonstandard Form) •
Classifying Graphs of Equations

CONNECTING THE CONCEPTS 878

13.4 **Nonlinear Systems of Equations** 879
Systems Involving One Nonlinear Equation •
Systems of Two Nonlinear Equations • Problem Solving

VISUALIZING FOR SUCCESS 885

STUDY SUMMARY 889
REVIEW EXERCISES 891
TEST 892

CUMULATIVE REVIEW: CHAPTERS 1–13 893

14 Sequences, Series, and the Binomial Theorem 895

14.1 **Sequences and Series** 896
Sequences • Finding the General Term • Sums and Series •
Sigma Notation

14.2 **Arithmetic Sequences and Series** 902
Arithmetic Sequences • Sum of the First n Terms of an Arithmetic Sequence •
Problem Solving

14.3 **Geometric Sequences and Series** 910
Geometric Sequences • Sum of the First n Terms of a Geometric Sequence •
Infinite Geometric Series • Problem Solving

CONNECTING THE CONCEPTS 920

14.4 **The Binomial Theorem** 921
Binomial Expansion Using Pascal's Triangle • Binomial Expansion Using
Factorial Notation

VISUALIZING FOR SUCCESS 928

STUDY SUMMARY 931
REVIEW EXERCISES 932
TEST 934

CUMULATIVE REVIEW/FINAL EXAM: CHAPTERS 1–14 935

R Elementary Algebra Review 939

R.1 **Introduction to Algebraic Expressions** 940
The Real Numbers • Operations on Real Numbers • Algebraic Expressions

R.2 Equations, Inequalities, and Problem Solving   947
Solving Equations and Formulas   •   Solving Inequalities   •   Problem Solving
R.3 Introduction to Graphing   955
Points and Ordered Pairs   •   Graphs and Slope   •   Linear Equations
R.4 Polynomials   962
Exponents   •   Polynomials   •   Addition and Subtraction of Polynomials   •
Multiplication of Polynomials   •   Division of Polynomials
R.5 Polynomials and Factoring   970
Common Factors and Factoring by Grouping   •   Factoring Trinomials   •
Factoring Special Forms   •   Solving Polynomial Equations by Factoring
R.6 Rational Expressions and Equations   979
Multiplication and Division of Rational Expressions   •   Addition and
Subtraction of Rational Expressions   •   Complex Rational Expressions   •
Solving Rational Equations

Appendixes   991

A   Mean, Median, and Mode   991
Mean   •   Median   •   Mode
B   Sets   994
Naming Sets   •   Membership   •   Subsets   •   Intersections   •   Unions
C   Synthetic Division   998
Streamlining Long Division   •   The Remainder Theorem

Tables   1003

1   Fraction and Decimal Equivalents   1003
2   Squares and Square Roots with Approximations to
     Three Decimal Places   1004

Answers   A-1

Glossary   G-1

Index   I-1

Index of Applications   I-10

Preface

It is with great pleasure that we introduce you to the fifth edition of *Elementary and Intermediate Algebra: Concepts and Applications*. Our goal, as always, is to present content that is easy to understand and has the depth required for success in this and future courses. In this edition, faculty will recognize features, applications, and explanations that they have come to rely on and expect. Students and faculty will also find many changes resulting from our own ideas for improvement as well as insights from faculty and students throughout North America. Thus this new edition contains exciting new features and applications, along with updates and refinements to those from previous editions.

Appropriate for a course, or courses, combining the study of elementary and intermediate algebra, this text covers both elementary and intermediate algebra topics without the repetition of instruction necessary in two separate texts. It is one of three texts in an algebra series that also includes *Elementary Algebra: Concepts and Applications*, Eighth Edition, by Bittinger/Ellenbogen, and *Intermediate Algebra: Concepts and Applications*, Eighth Edition, by Bittinger/Ellenbogen.

Approach

Our goal, quite simply, is to help today's students both learn and retain mathematical concepts. To achieve this goal, we feel that we must prepare developmental-mathematics students for the transition from "skills-oriented" elementary and intermediate algebra courses to more "concept-oriented" college-level mathematics courses. This requires that we teach these same students critical thinking skills: to reason mathematically, to communicate mathematically, and to identify and solve mathematical problems. Following are three aspects of our approach that we use to help meet the challenges we all face when teaching developmental mathematics.

Problem Solving

One distinguishing feature of our approach is our treatment of and emphasis on problem solving. We use problem solving and applications to motivate the material wherever possible, and we include real-life applications and problem-solving techniques throughout the text. Problem solving not only encourages students to think about how mathematics can be used, it helps to prepare them for more advanced material in future courses.

In Chapter 2, we introduce our five-step process for solving problems: (1) Familiarize, (2) Translate, (3) Carry out, (4) Check, and (5) State the answer. These steps are then used consistently throughout the text when encountering a problem-solving situation. Repeated use of this problem-solving strategy helps provide students with a starting point for any type of problem they encounter, and frees them to focus on the unique aspects of the particular problem situation. We often use estimation and carefully checked guesses to help with the *Familiarize* and *Check* steps (see pp. 110 and 422–423).

Applications

Interesting applications of mathematics help motivate both students and instructors. Solving applied problems gives students the opportunity to see their conceptual understanding put to use in a real way. In the fifth edition of *Elementary and Intermediate Algebra: Concepts and Applications*, we have increased the number of applications, the number of real-data problems, and the number of reference lines that specify the sources of the real-world data. As in the past, art is integrated into the applications and exercises to aid the student in visualizing the mathematics. (See pp. 111, 190, 260, 364.)

Pedagogy

New!

TRY EXERCISES

Try Exercises. This icon concludes nearly every example by pointing students to one or more parallel exercises from the corresponding exercise set so that they can immediately reinforce the concepts and skills presented in the examples. For easy identification in the exercise sets, the "Try" exercises have a shaded block on the exercise number. (See pp. 56, 256, 415.)

New!

Translating for Success and **Visualizing for Success.** These matching exercises help students learn to associate word problems (through translation) and graphs (through visualization) with their appropriate mathematical equations. (See pp. 134, 361 (Translating); pp. 212, 753 (Visualizing).) Each feature contains a corresponding activity in MyMathLab.

Revised!

Connecting the Concepts. Revised and expanded to include new Mixed Review exercises, this midchapter review helps students understand the big picture and prepare for chapter tests and cumulative reviews by relating the concept at hand to previously learned and upcoming concepts. (See pp. 206, 279, 739.)

Revised!

Study Summary. Found at the end of each chapter and now presented in a two-column format organized by section, this synopsis gives students a fast and effective review of key chapter terms and concepts paired with accompanying examples. (See pp. 139, 218, 367.)

Revised!

Cumulative Review. This review now appears after every chapter to help students retain and apply their knowledge from previous chapters. (See pp. 145, 300, 574.)

Algebraic–Graphical Connections. This feature provides students with a way to visualize concepts that might otherwise prove elusive. (See pp. 350, 416, 704.)

Study Skills. This feature in the margin provides tips for successful study habits that even experienced students will appreciate. Ranging from time management to test preparation, these study skills can be applied in any college course. (See pp. 86, 229, 597.)

Student Notes. These notes in the margin give students extra explanation of the mathematics appearing on that page. These comments are more casual in format than the typical exposition and range from suggestions for avoiding common mistakes to how to best read new notation. (See pp. 79, 312, 728.)

Technology Connection. These optional boxes in each chapter help students use a graphing calculator to better visualize a concept that they have just learned. To connect this optional instruction to the exercise sets, certain exercises are marked with a graphing calculator icon 📉 to indicate the optional use of technology. (See pp. 164, 351, 791.)

Revised!

Concept Reinforcement Exercises. Now with all answers listed in the answer section at the back of the book, these section and review exercises build students' confidence and comprehension through true/false, matching, and fill-in-the-blank exercises at the start of most exercise sets. To help further student understanding, emphasis is given to new vocabulary and notation developed in the section. (See pp. 10, 165, 760.)

Aha!

Aha! Exercises. These exercises are not more difficult than their neighboring exercises and can be solved quickly, without going through a lengthy computation, if the student has the proper insight. Designed to reward students who "look before they leap," the icon indicates the first time a new insight applies, and then it is up to the student to determine when to use the Aha! method on subsequent exercises. (See pp. 213, 285, 730.)

Revised!

Skill Review Exercises. These exercises, included in Section 1.2 and every section thereafter, review skills and concepts from preceding sections of the text. In most cases, these exercises prepare students for the next section. An introduction to each set directs students to the appropriate sections to review if necessary. On occasion, Skill Review exercises focus on a single topic in greater depth and from multiple perspectives. (See pp. 166, 243, 594.)

Synthesis Exercises. Synthesis exercises follow the Skill Review exercises at the end of each exercise set. Generally more challenging, these exercises synthesize skills and concepts from earlier sections with the present material, often providing students with deeper insight into the current topic. Aha! exercises are sometimes included as Synthesis exercises. (See pp. 99, 365, 714.)

Writing Exercises. These appear just before the Skill Review exercises (two basic writing exercises) and also in the Synthesis exercises (at least two more challenging exercises). Writing exercises aid student comprehension by requiring students to use critical thinking to provide explanations of concepts in one or more complete sentences. Because some instructors may collect answers to writing exercises and because more than one answer can be correct, only answers to writing exercises in the review section are included at the back of the text. (See pp. 58, 473, 686.)

Collaborative Corner. These optional activities for students to explore together usually appear two to three times per chapter at the end of an exercise set. Studies show that students who study in groups generally outperform those who do not, so these exercises are for students who want to solve mathematical problems together. Additional collaborative activities and suggestions for directing collaborative learning appear in the *Instructor and Adjunct Support Manual*. (See pp. 158, 537, 766.)

What's New in the Fifth Edition?

We have rewritten many key topics in response to user and reviewer feedback and have made significant improvements in design, art, pedagogy, and an expanded supplements package. Detailed information about the content changes is available in the form of a conversion guide. Please ask your local Pearson sales consultant for more information. Following is a list of the major changes in this edition.

NEW DESIGN

While incorporating a new layout, a fresh palette of colors, and new features, we have a larger page dimension for an open look and a typeface that is easy to read. As always, it is our goal to make the text look mature without being intimidating. In addition, we continue to pay close attention to the pedagogical use of color to make sure that it is used to present concepts in the clearest possible manner.

CONTENT CHANGES

A variety of content changes have been made throughout the text. Some of the more significant changes are listed below.

What's New in Combined

- Examples and exercises that use real data are updated or replaced with current applications.
- Over 35% of the exercises are new or updated.
- Quick-glance reminders for multistep process are included next to examples. These appear by one multistep example of each type. (See pp. 197, 333, 519.)
- Chapter 2 now includes increased practice of solving for y in a formula.
- Interval notation is introduced when students first solve inequalities in Section 2.6.
- Inequalities are now graphed on number lines using brackets and parentheses. Interval notation can thus be read directly from the graph of an inequality.
- Chapter 3 now gives increased emphasis to units when finding a rate of change.

- Discussion of negative exponents (Section 4.2) now immediately follows the introduction to the rules for manipulating exponents.
- Chapter 5 now makes greater use of prime factorizations as a tool for finding the largest common factor.
- Domains of radical functions are now discussed in Section 9.1, separately from domains of rational functions in Section 9.2.
- The distance formula is now presented in Section 10.7 as one application of the Pythagorean theorem.
- In Chapter 11, the discussion of the discriminant now directly follows the quadratic formula.

ANCILLARIES

The following ancillaries are available to help both instructors and students use this text more effectively.

STUDENT SUPPLEMENTS

New! Chapter Test Prep Video CD

- Watch instructors work through step-by-step solutions to all the chapter test exercises from the textbook. The Chapter Test Prep Video CD is included with each new student text.

New! Worksheets for Classroom or Lab Practice

by Carrie Green

These lab- and classroom-friendly workbooks offer the following resources for every section of the text:

- A list of learning objectives;
- Vocabulary practice problems;
- Extra practice exercises with ample work space.

ISBNs: 0-321-59933-0 and 978-0-321-59933-9

Student's Solutions Manual

by Christine S. Verity

- Contains completely worked-out solutions with step-by-step annotations for all the odd-numbered exercises in the text, with the exception of the writing exercises.
- New! Now contains all solutions to Chapter Review, Chapter Test, and Connecting the Concepts exercises.

ISBNs: 0-321-58623-9 and 978-0-321-58623-0

INSTRUCTOR SUPPLEMENTS

Annotated Instructor's Edition

- Provides answers to all text exercises in color next to the corresponding problems.
- Includes Teaching Tips.
- Icons identify writing ✍ and graphing calculator 📷 exercises.

ISBNs: 0-321-56726-9 and 978-0-321-56726-0

Instructor's Solutions Manual

by Christine S. Verity

- Contains fully worked-out solutions to the odd-numbered exercises and brief solutions to the even-numbered exercises in the exercise sets.
- Available for download at www.pearsonhighered.com

ISBNs: 0-321-58620-4 and 978-0-321-58620-9

Instructor and Adjunct Support Manual

- Includes resources designed to help both new and adjunct faculty with course preparation and classroom management.
- Offers helpful teaching tips correlated to the sections of the text.

ISBNs: 0-321-58624-7 and 978-0-321-58624-7

Videos on DVD

- A complete set of digitized videos on DVD for use at home or on campus.
- Includes a full lecture for each section of the text, many presented by author team members David J. Ellenbogen and Barbara Johnson.
- Optional subtitles in English are available.

ISBNs: 0-321-59935-7 and 978-0-321-59935-3

InterAct Math® Tutorial Website

www.interactmath.com

- Online practice and tutorial help.
- Retry an exercise with new values each time for unlimited practice and mastery.
- Every exercise is accompanied by an interactive guided solution that gives helpful feedback when an incorrect answer is entered.
- View the steps of a worked-out sample problem similar to those in the text.

Printable Test Bank

by Laurie Hurley

- Contains two multiple-choice tests per chapter, six free-response tests per chapter, and eight final exams.
- Available for download at www.pearsonhighered.com

PowerPoint® Lecture Slides

- Present key concepts and definitions from the text.
- Available for download at www.pearsonhighered.com

TestGen

www.pearsonhighered.com/testgen

- Enables instructors to build, edit, print, and administer tests using a computerized bank of questions developed to cover all text objectives.
- Algorithmically based, TestGen allows instructors to create multiple but equivalent versions of the same question or test with the click of a button.
- Instructors can also modify test bank questions or add new questions.
- Tests can be printed or administered online.

Pearson Math Adjunct Support Center

http://www.pearsontutorservices.com/math-adjunct.html

Staffed by qualified instructors with more than 50 years of combined experience at both the community college and university levels, this center provides assistance for faculty in the following areas:

- Suggested syllabus consultation;
- Tips on using materials packed with the text;
- Book-specific content assistance;
- Teaching suggestions, including advice on classroom strategies.

AVAILABLE FOR STUDENTS AND INSTRUCTORS

MyMathLab® Online Course (access code required)

MyMathLab is a series of text-specific, easily customizable online courses for Pearson Education's textbooks in mathematics and statistics. Powered by CourseCompass™ (our online teaching and learning environment) and MathXL® (our online homework, tutorial, and assessment system), MyMathLab gives you the tools you need to deliver all or a portion of your course online, whether your students are in a lab setting or working from home. MyMathLab provides a rich and flexible set of course materials, featuring free-response exercises that are algorithmically generated for unlimited practice and mastery. Students can also use online tools, such as video lectures, animations, and a multimedia textbook, to independently improve their understanding and performance. Instructors can use MyMathLab's homework and test managers to select and assign online exercises correlated directly to the textbook, and they can also create and assign their own online exercises and import TestGen tests for added flexibility. MyMathLab's online gradebook—designed specifically for mathematics and statistics—automatically tracks students' homework and test results and gives the instructor control over how to calculate final grades. Instructors can also add offline (paper-and-pencil) grades to the gradebook. MyMathLab also includes access to the **Pearson Tutor Center** (www.pearsontutorservices.com). The Tutor Center is staffed by qualified mathematics instructors who provide textbook-specific tutoring for students via toll-free phone, fax, e-mail, and interactive Web sessions. MyMathLab is available to qualified adopters. For more information, visit our website at www.mymathlab.com or contact your sales representative.

MathXL® Online Course (access code required)

MathXL® is a powerful online homework, tutorial, and assessment system that accompanies Pearson Education's textbooks in mathematics or statistics. With MathXL, instructors can create, edit, and assign online homework and tests using algorithmically generated exercises correlated at the objective level to the textbook. They can also create and assign their own online exercises and import TestGen tests for added flexibility. All student work is tracked in MathXL's online gradebook. Students can take chapter tests in MathXL and receive personalized study plans based on their test results. The study plan diagnoses weaknesses and links students directly to tutorial exercises for the objectives they need to study and retest. Students can also access supplemental animations and video clips directly from selected exercises. MathXL is available to qualified adopters. For more information, visit our website at www.mathxl.com, or contact your Pearson sales representative.

MathXL® Tutorials on CD

This interactive tutorial CD-ROM provides algorithmically generated practice exercises that are correlated at the objective level to the exercises in the textbook. Every practice exercise is accompanied by an example and a guided solution designed to involve students in the solution process. Selected exercises may also include a video clip to help students visualize concepts. The software provides helpful feedback for incorrect answers and can generate printed summaries of students' progress.

Acknowledgments

No book can be produced without a team of professionals who take pride in their work and are willing to put in long hours. Laurie Hurley, in particular, deserves extra thanks for her work as developmental editor. Rebecca Hubiak, Laurie Hurley, Holly Martinez, Ann Ostberg, and Christine Verity also deserve special thanks for their careful accuracy checks, well-thought-out suggestions, and uncanny eye for detail. Thanks to Carrie Green, Laurie Hurley, and Christine Verity for their outstanding work in preparing supplements.

We are also indebted to Chris Burditt and Jann MacInnes for their many fine ideas that appear in our Collaborative Corners and Vince McGarry and Janet Wyatt for their recommendations for Teaching Tips featured in the Annotated Instructor's Edition.

Geri Davis, of the Davis Group, Inc., performed superb work as designer, art editor, and photo researcher, and is always a pleasure to work with. Tracy Duff and her colleagues at Pre-Press PMG provided excellent composition and editorial support throughout the production process. Network Graphics generated the graphs, charts, and many of the illustrations. Not only are the people at Network reliable, but they clearly take pride in their work. The many illustrations appear thanks to Bill Melvin—an artist with insight and creativity.

Our team at Pearson deserves special thanks. Acquisitions Editor Randy Welch provided many fine suggestions, remaining involved and accessible throughout the project. Executive Project Manager Kari Heen carefully coordinated tasks and schedules, keeping a widely spread team working together. Associate Editor Joanna Doxey coordinated reviews and assisted in a variety of tasks with patience and creativity. Editorial Assistant Jonathan Wooding responded quickly to all requests, always in a pleasant manner. Production Manager Ron Hampton's attention to detail, willingness to listen, and creative responses helped result in a book that is beautiful to look at. Marketing Manager Marlana Voerster and Marketing Assistant Nathaniel Koven skillfully kept us in touch with the needs of faculty. Our Editor in Chief, Maureen O'Connor, and Editorial Director, Chris Hoag, deserve credit for assembling this fine team.

We also thank the students at Indiana University Purdue University Indianapolis and the Community College of Vermont and the following professors for their thoughtful reviews and insightful comments.

Elementary Algebra: Concepts and Applications, Eighth Edition

Roberta Abarca, *Centralia College*
Darla J. Aguilar, *Pima Community College, Desert Vista Campus*
Bonnie Alcorn, *Waubonsee College*
Eugene Alderman, *South University*
Joseph Berland, *Chabot College*
Paul Blankenship, *Lexington Community College*
Susan Caldiero, *Cosumnes River College*
David Casey, *Citrus College*
Emmett Dennis, *Southern Connecticut State University*
Henri Feiner, *Coastline Community College*
Gary Glaze, *Spokane Falls Community College*
Janet Hansen, *Dixie State College*
Elizabeth Hodes, *Santa Barbara City College*
Weilin Jang, *Austin Community College*
Paulette Kirkpatrick, *Wharton County Junior College*
Susan Knights, *Boise State University*
Jeff Koleno, *Lorain County Community College*
Julianne Labbiento, *Lehigh Carbon Community College*
Kathryn Lavelle, *Westchester Community College*
Amy Marolt, *Northeastern Mississippi Community College*
Rogers Martin, *Louisiana State University, Shreveport*
Ben Mayo, *Yakima Valley Community College*
Laurie McManus, *St. Louis Community College–Meramac*
Carol Metz, *Westchester Community College*
Anne Marie Mosher, *St. Louis Community College–Florissant Valley*
Pedro Mota, *Austin Community College, South Austin Campus*
Brenda M. Norman, *Tidewater Community College*
Kim Nunn, *Northeast State Technical College*
Michael Oppedisano, *Morrisville College SUNY*
Zaddock B. Reid, *San Bernardino Valley College*
Terry Reeves, *Red Rocks Community College*
Terri Seiver, *San Jacinto College–Central*
Timothy Thompson, *Oregon Institute of Technology*
Diane Trimble, *Tulsa Community College, West Campus*
Jennifer Vanden Eynden, *Grossmont College*
Beverly Vredevelt, *Spokane Falls Community College*
Michael Yarbrough, *Cosumnes River College*

Intermediate Algebra: Concepts and Applications, Eighth Edition

Marie Aratari, *Oakland Community College–Orange Ridge Campus*
Barbara Armenta, *Pima Community College*
Douglas Brozovic, *University of North Texas*
Barbara Burke, *Hawaii Pacific University*
Laura Burris, *Sam Houston State University*
Lisa Carnell, *High Point University*
Sharon Edgmon, *Bakersfield College*
Karen Ernst, *Hawkeye College*
Kathy Garrison, *Clayton College and State University*
Cynthia Harrison, *Baton Rouge Community College*
Tracey L. Johnson, *University of Georgia*
Joanne Kawczenski, *Luzerne County Community College*
Rachel Lamp, *North Iowa Area Community College*
Kevin J. Leith, *Central New Mexico Community College*
Stephanie Lochbaum, *Austin Community College*

Debi McCandrew, *Florence-Darlington Technical College*
Bob McCarthy, *Community College of Allegheny County—South Campus*
Doug Mace, *Kirtland Community College*
Timothy McKenna, *University of Michigan–Dearborn*
Rhea Meyerholtz, *Indiana State University*
Bronte Miller, *Patrick Henry Community College*
Kausha Miller, *Lexington Community College*
Rebecca Parrish, *Ohio University*
Kay Petrash, *Sam Houston State University*
Debra Pharo, *Northwestern Michigan College*
Terry Reeves, *Red Rocks Community College*
Kathy Rod, *Wharton County Junior College*
Nicole Saporito, *Luzerne Community College*
Elgin Schilhab, *Austin Community College*
M. Terry Simon, *University of Toledo*
Fran Smith, *Oakland Community College*
Donald Soloman, *University of Wisconsin–Milwaukee*

Elementary and Intermediate Algebra: Concepts and Applications, Fifth Edition

Michael Anzzolin, *Waubonsee Community College*
Jan Archibald, *Ventura College*
Don Brown, *Macon State College*
Gary Carpenter, *Pima Community College, Northwest Campus*
Tim Chappell, *Penn Valley Community College*
Ola Disu, *Tarrant County College*
Anissa Florence, *University of Louisville*
Sandy Gordon, *Central Carolina Technical College*
Sharon Hamsa, *Longview Community College*
Geoffrey Hirsch, *Ohlone College*
Pat Horacek, *Pensacola Junior College*
Sally Keely, *Clark College*
Ana Leon, *Louisville Community College*
Linda Lohman, *Jefferson Community College*
Bob Martin, *Tarrant County College*
Amy Petty, *South Suburban College*
Thomas Pulver, *Waubonsee Community College*
Angela Redmon, *Wenatchee Valley College*
Richard Rupp, *Del Mar College*
Mehdi Sadatmousavi, *Pima Community College*
Ann Thrower, *Kilgore College*

Finally, a special thank-you to all those who so generously agreed to discuss their professional use of mathematics in our chapter openers. These dedicated people all share a desire to make math more meaningful to students. We cannot imagine a finer set of role models.

M.L.B.
D.J.E.
B.L.J.

Functions and Graphs

CHAPTER

7

7.1
Introduction to Functions

7.2
Domain and Range

7.3
Graphs of Functions

CONNECTING THE CONCEPTS

7.4
The Algebra of Functions

7.5
Formulas, Applications, and Variation

STUDY SUMMARY
REVIEW EXERCISES
TEST
CUMULATIVE REVIEW

MELANIE CHAMBERS
MATH TEACHER/RECIPIENT OF
THE MILKEN FAMILY
FOUNDATION'S NATIONAL
EDUCATOR AWARD
Cedar Hill, Texas

Being proficient in math not only
has multiplied my career options
but also opens many doors for
those students who choose to
sharpen their math skills. As a
math instructor, I use math to
calculate students' performance
on assessments, disaggregate
data to differentiate instruction
to better meet student learning
needs, and demonstrate daily
how real-world problem solving
often entails mathematical
analysis.

AN APPLICATION

According to the National Assessment
of Educational Progress (NAEP), the
percentage of fourth-graders who are
proficient in math has grown from
21% in 1996 to 24% in 2000 and 39%
in 2007.

Estimate the percentage of fourth-
graders who showed proficiency in
2004 and predict the percentage who
will demonstrate proficiency in 2011.

Source: nationsreportcard.gov

This problem appears as Example 6 in
Section 7.1.

I n this chapter we introduce the concept of a *function*. As we will see, many functions are described using linear, polynomial, and rational expressions. Functions can also often be visualized graphically, as well as added, subtracted, multiplied, and divided. Near the end of the chapter, we solve formulas using equation-solving techniques studied earlier, and we use function notation when describing *direct* and *inverse variation*.

7.1   Introduction to Functions

Correspondences and Functions and Equations • Functions and Graphs • Function Notation • Applications

We now develop the idea of a *function*—one of the most important concepts in mathematics.

Correspondences and Functions

When forming ordered pairs to graph equations, we often say that the first coordinate of each ordered pair *corresponds* to the second coordinate. In much the same way, a function is a special kind of correspondence between two sets. For example,

To each person in a class	there corresponds	a date of birth.
To each bar code in a store	there corresponds	a price.
To each real number	there corresponds	the cube of that number.

In each example, the first set is called the **domain**. The second set is called the **range**. For any member of the domain, there is *exactly one* member of the range to which it corresponds. This kind of correspondence is called a **function**.

EXAMPLE   1

STUDENT NOTES ————

Note that not all correspondences are functions.

Determine whether each correspondence is a function.

a) *Domain*   *Range*

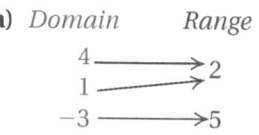

b) *Domain*   *Range*

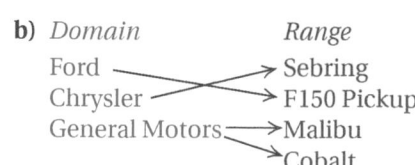

SOLUTION

a) The correspondence *is* a function because each member of the domain corresponds to *exactly one* member of the range.

b) The correspondence *is not* a function because a member of the domain (General Motors) corresponds to more than one member of the range.

TRY EXERCISE   9

> **Function**
>
> A *function* is a correspondence between a first set, called the *domain*, and a second set, called the *range*, such that each member of the domain corresponds to *exactly one* member of the range.

EXAMPLE 2   Determine whether each correspondence is a function.

Domain	*Correspondence*	*Range*
a) People in a doctor's waiting room	Each person's weight	A set of positive numbers
b) $\{-2, 0, 1, 2\}$	Each number's square	$\{0, 1, 4\}$
c) Authors of best-selling books	The titles of books written by each author	A set of book titles

SOLUTION

a) The correspondence *is* a function, because each person has *only one* weight.

b) The correspondence *is* a function, because every number has *only one* square.

c) The correspondence *is not* a function, because some authors have written *more than one* book.

> **TRY EXERCISE** 17

Although the correspondence in Example 2(c) is not a function, it is a *relation*.

> **Relation**
>
> A *relation* is a correspondence between a first set, called the *domain*, and a second set, called the *range*, such that each member of the domain corresponds to *at least one* member of the range.

Functions and Graphs

The functions in Examples 1(a) and 2(b) can be expressed as sets of ordered pairs. Example 1(a) can be written $\{(-3, 5), (1, 2), (4, 2)\}$ and Example 2(b) can be written $\{(-2, 4), (0, 0), (1, 1), (2, 4)\}$. We can graph these functions as follows.

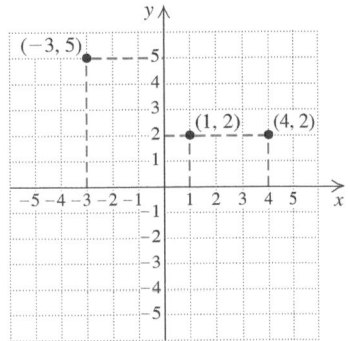

The function $\{(-3, 5), (1, 2), (4, 2)\}$
Domain is $\{-3, 1, 4\}$
Range is $\{5, 2\}$

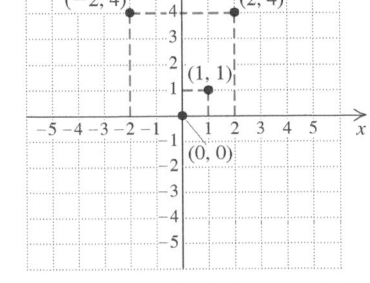

The function $\{(-2, 4), (0, 0), (1, 1), (2, 4)\}$
Domain is $\{-2, 0, 1, 2\}$
Range is $\{4, 0, 1\}$

We can find the domain and the range of a function directly from its graph. The domain is read from the horizontal axis and the range is read from the vertical axis. Note in the graphs above that if we move along the red dashed lines from the points to the horizontal axis, we find the members, or elements, of the domain. Similarly, if we move along the blue dashed lines from the points to the vertical axis, we find the elements of the range.

Functions are generally named using lowercase or uppercase letters. The function in the following example is named f.

EXAMPLE 3   For the function f represented below, determine each of the following.

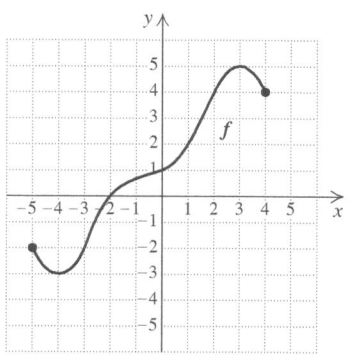

a) The member of the range that is paired with 2

b) The member of the domain that is paired with -3

SOLUTION

a) To determine what member of the range is paired with 2, first note that we are considering 2 in the domain. Thus we locate 2 on the horizontal axis. Next, we find the point directly above 2 on the graph of f. From that point, we can look to the vertical axis to find the corresponding y-coordinate, 4. Thus, 4 is the member of the range that is paired with 2.

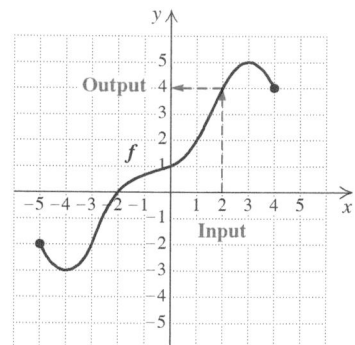

b) To determine what member of the domain is paired with -3, we note that we are considering -3 in the range. Thus we locate -3 on the vertical axis. From there we look at the graph of f to find any points for which -3 is the second coordinate. One such point exists, $(-4, -3)$. We observe that -4 is the only element of the domain paired with -3.

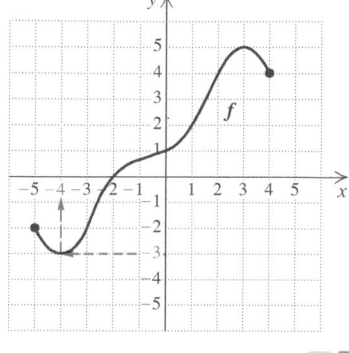

A closed dot on a graph, such as in Example 3, indicates that the point is part of the function. An open dot indicates that the point is *not* part of the function. (See Exercises 33 and 34 on p. 452.)

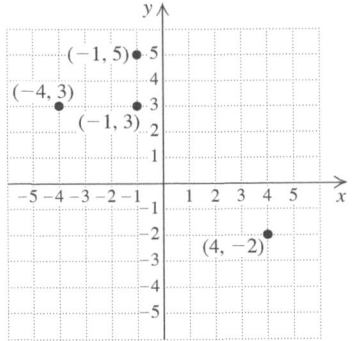

Recall that a function is a correspondence in which each member of the domain corresponds to *exactly* one member of the range. Thus the correspondence

$$\{(-1, 3), (4, -2), (-4, 3), (-1, 5)\}$$

is not a function because the member -1 of the domain corresponds to the members 3 and 5 of the range. Note on the graph at left that the point $(-1, 5)$ is directly above the point $(-1, 3)$.

Any time two points, such as $(-1, 3)$ and $(-1, 5)$, lie on the same vertical line, the graph containing those points cannot represent a function. This observation is the basis of the *vertical-line test*.

The Vertical-Line Test

If it is possible for a vertical line to cross a graph more than once, then the graph is not the graph of a function.

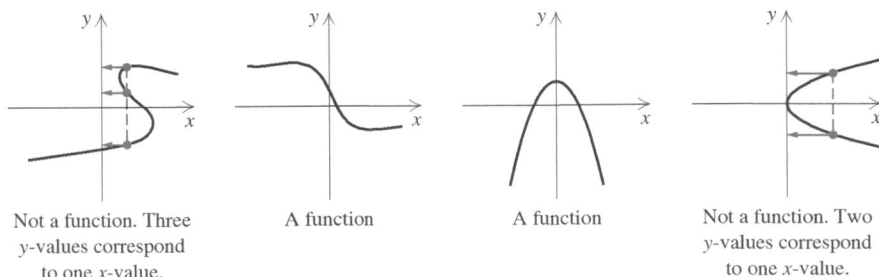

| Not a function. Three y-values correspond to one x-value. | A function | A function | Not a function. Two y-values correspond to one x-value. |

Function Notation and Equations

To understand function notation, it helps to imagine a "function machine." Think of putting a member of the domain (an *input*) into the machine. The machine is programmed to produce the appropriate member of the range (the *output*).

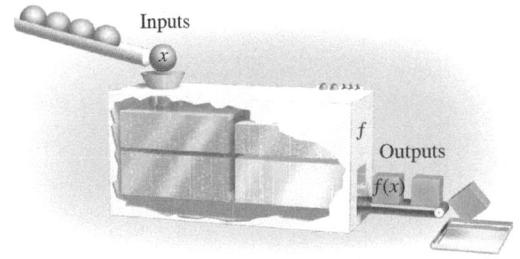

Inputs

Outputs

The function pictured has been named f. Here x represents an input, and $f(x)$ represents the corresponding output. In function notation, "$f(x)$" is read "f of x," or "f at x," or "the value of f at x." In Example 3(a), we showed that $f(2) = 4$, read "f of 2 equals 4."

CAUTION! $f(x)$ *does not* mean f times x.

Most functions are described by equations. For example, $f(x) = 2x + 3$ describes the function that takes an input x, multiplies it by 2, and then adds 3.

Input

$$f(x) \quad = \quad 2x \quad + 3$$

Double   Add 3

To calculate the output $f(4)$, we take the input 4, double it, and add 3 to get 11. That is, we substitute 4 into the formula for $f(x)$:

$$f(4) = 2 \cdot 4 + 3$$
$$= 11.$$

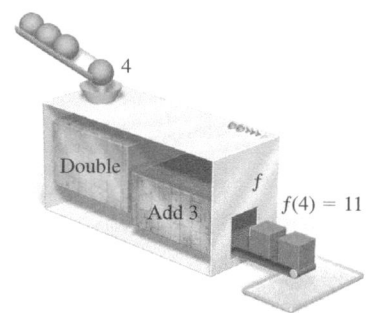

Sometimes, in place of $f(x) = 2x + 3$, we write $y = 2x + 3$, where it is understood that the value of y, the *dependent variable*, depends on our choice of x, the *independent variable*. To understand why $f(x)$ notation is so useful, consider two equivalent statements:

a) If $f(x) = 2x + 3$, then $f(4) = 11$.

b) If $y = 2x + 3$, then the value of y is 11 when x is 4.

The notation used in part (a) is far more concise and emphasizes that x is the independent variable.

EXAMPLE **4**   Find each indicated function value.

a) $f(5)$, for $f(x) = 3x + 2$ **b)** $g(-2)$, for $g(r) = 5r^2 + 3r$

c) $h(4)$, for $h(x) = 11$ **d)** $F(a) + 1$, for $F(x) = 2x - 7$

e) $F(a + 1)$, for $F(x) = 2x - 7$

SOLUTION   Finding function values is much like evaluating an algebraic expression.

a) $f(5) = 3(5) + 2 = 17$

b) $g(-2) = 5(-2)^2 + 3(-2)$
$$= 5 \cdot 4 - 6 = 14$$

c) For the function given by $h(x) = 11$, all inputs share the same output, 11. Therefore, $h(4) = 11$. The function h is an example of a *constant function*.

d) $F(a) + 1 = 2(a) - 7 + 1$ The input is a; $F(a) = 2a - 7$
$$= 2a - 6$$

e) $F(a + 1) = 2(a + 1) - 7$ The input is $a + 1$.
$$= 2a + 2 - 7 = 2a - 5$$

STUDENT NOTES ────────

In Example 4(e), it is important to note that the parentheses on the left are for function notation, whereas those on the right indicate multiplication.

TRY EXERCISE 41

Note that whether we write $f(x) = 3x + 2$, or $f(t) = 3t + 2$, or $f(\blacksquare) = 3\blacksquare + 2$, we still have $f(5) = 17$. The variable in the parentheses (the independent variable) is the variable in the algebraic expression. The letter chosen for the independent variable is not as important as the algebraic manipulations to which it is subjected.

Applications

Function notation is often used in formulas. For example, to emphasize that the area A of a circle is a function of its radius r, instead of

$$A = \pi r^2,$$

we can write

$$A(r) = \pi r^2.$$

EXAMPLE   5   A typical adult dosage of an antihistamine is 24 mg. Young's rule for determining the dosage size $c(a)$ for a typical child of age a is

$$c(a) = \frac{24a}{a + 12}.^*$$

What should the dosage be for a typical 8-yr-old child?

SOLUTION   We find $c(8)$:

$$c(8) = \frac{24(8)}{8 + 12} = \frac{192}{20} = 9.6.$$

The dosage for a typical 8-yr-old child is 9.6 mg.

▸ **TRY EXERCISE** 47

When a function is given as a graph, we can use the graph to estimate an unknown function value using known values.

EXAMPLE   6   *Elementary school math proficiency.*   According to the National Assessment of Educational Progress (NAEP), the percentage of fourth-graders who are proficient in math has grown from 21% in 1996 to 24% in 2000 and 39% in 2007. Estimate the percentage of fourth-graders who showed proficiency in 2004 and predict the percentage who will demonstrate proficiency in 2011.

Source: nationsreportcard.gov

SOLUTION

1., 2. Familiarize., Translate.   The given information enables us to plot and connect three points. We let the horizontal axis represent the year and the vertical axis the percentage of fourth-graders demonstrating mathematical proficiency. We label the function itself P.

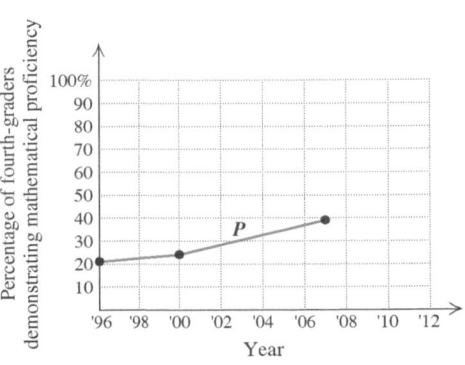

---

*Source: Olsen, June Looby, Leon J. Ablon, and Anthony Patrick Giangrasso, *Medical Dosage Calculations*, 6th ed.

3. Carry out. To estimate the percentage of fourth-graders showing mathematical proficiency in 2004, we locate the point directly above the year 2004. We then estimate its second coordinate by moving horizontally from that point to the *y*-axis. Although our result is not exact, we see that $P(2004) \approx 33$.

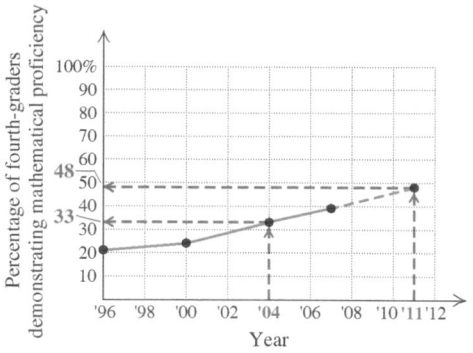

To predict the percentage of fourth-graders showing proficiency in 2011, we extend the graph and extrapolate. It appears that $P(2011) \approx 48$.

4. Check. A precise check requires consulting an outside information source. Since 33% is between 24% and 39% and 48% is greater than 39%, our estimates seem plausible.

5. State. In 2004, about 33% of all fourth-graders showed proficiency in math. By 2011, that figure is predicted to grow to 48%.

▶ **TRY EXERCISE** 59

7.1	**EXERCISE SET**	For Extra Help	MyMathLab	Math XL PRACTICE	WATCH	DOWNLOAD

↘ *Concept Reinforcement* *Complete each of the following sentences.*

1. A function is a special kind of _____ between two sets.

2. In any function, each member of the domain is paired with _____ one member of the range.

3. For any function, the set of all inputs, or first values, is called the _____.

4. For any function, the set of all outputs, or second values, is called the _____.

5. When a function is graphed, members of the domain are located on the _____ axis.

6. When a function is graphed, members of the range are located on the _____ axis.

7. The notation $f(3)$ is read _____.

8. The _____-line test can be used to determine whether or not a graph represents a function.

Determine whether each correspondence is a function.

9.
a ⟶ 2
b ↗
d ⟶ 3
g ⟶ 4
h ↗

10.
2 ⟶ a
↘ b
3 ⟶ d
4 ⟶ g
↘ h

11.
Girl's age (in months)	*Average daily weight gain (in grams)*
2	⟶ 21.8
9	⟶ 11.7
16	⟶ 8.5
23	⟶ 7.0

Source: *American Family Physician,* December 1993, p. 1435

12.

Boy's age (in months)	Average daily weight gain (in grams)

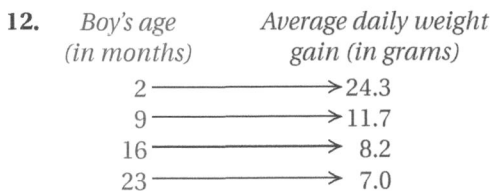

Source: *American Family Physician*, December 1993, p. 1435

13. *Birthday*   *Celebrity*

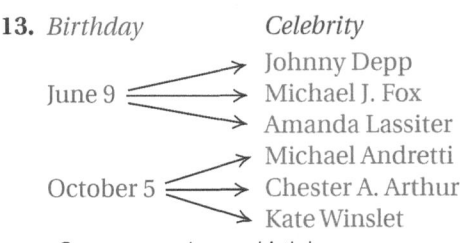

Source: www.leannesbirthdays.com

14. *Celebrity*   *Birthday*

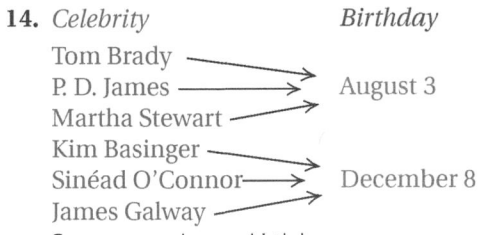

Source: www.leannesbirthdays.com

15. *Predator*   *Prey*

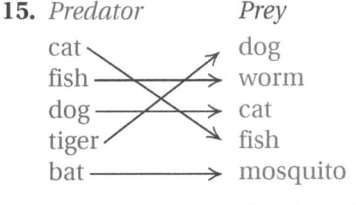

16. *State*   *Neighboring state*

Determine whether each of the following is a function. Identify any relations that are not functions.

Domain	Correspondence	Range
17. A pile of USB flash drives	The storage capacity of each flash drive	A set of storage capacities
18. The members of a rock band	An instrument the person can play	A set of instruments
19. The players on a team	The uniform number of each player	A set of numbers
20. A set of triangles	The area of each triangle	A set of numbers

For each graph of a function, determine (a) $f(1)$ and (b) any x-values for which $f(x) = 2$.

21.
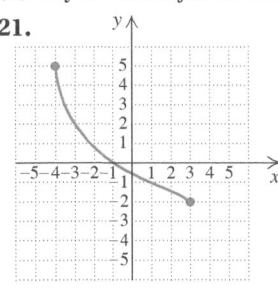

22.
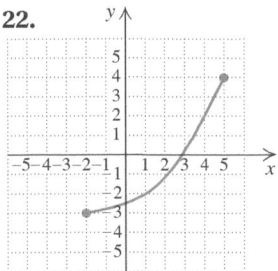

23.
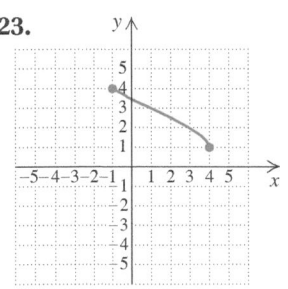

24.
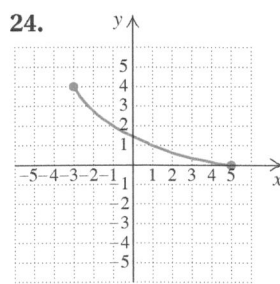

25.
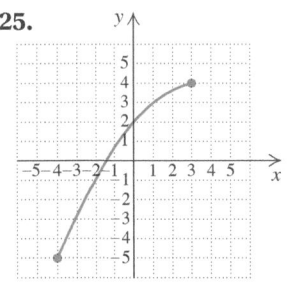

26.
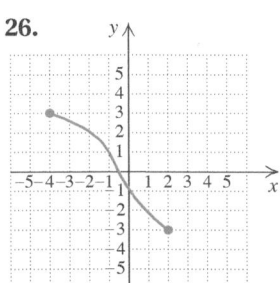

27.
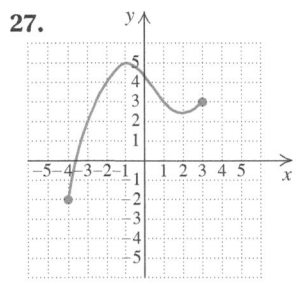

28.
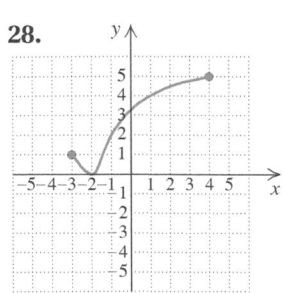

29.
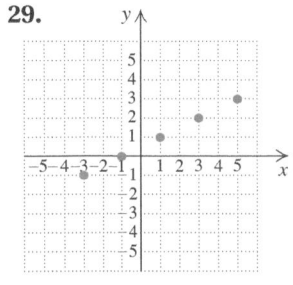

30.
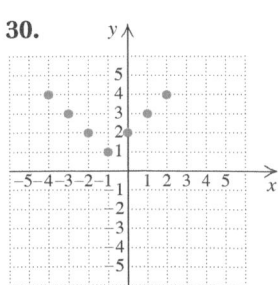

31.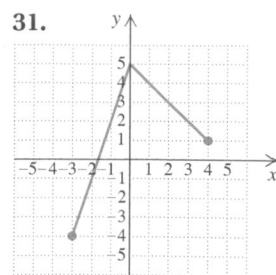

32.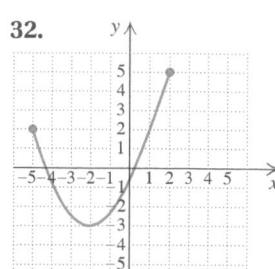

33.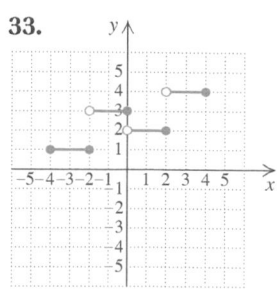

34.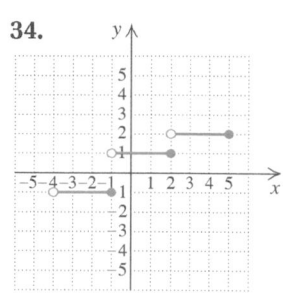

Determine whether each of the following is the graph of a function.

35.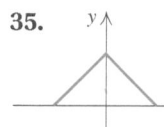

36.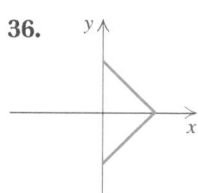

37.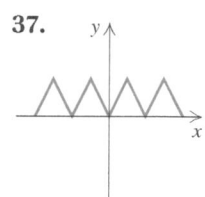

38.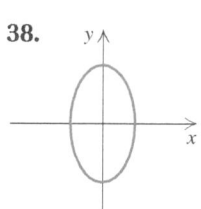

39.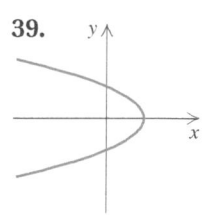

40.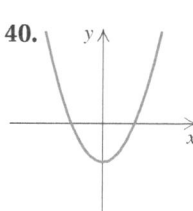

Find the function values.

41. $g(x) = 2x + 5$

   a) $g(0)$ **b)** $g(-4)$ **c)** $g(-7)$

   d) $g(8)$ **e)** $g(a + 2)$ **f)** $g(a) + 2$

42. $h(x) = 5x - 1$

   a) $h(4)$ **b)** $h(8)$ **c)** $h(-3)$

   d) $h(-4)$ **e)** $h(a - 1)$ **f)** $h(a) + 3$

43. $f(n) = 5n^2 + 4n$

   a) $f(0)$ **b)** $f(-1)$ **c)** $f(3)$

   d) $f(t)$ **e)** $f(2a)$ **f)** $f(3) - 9$

44. $g(n) = 3n^2 - 2n$

   a) $g(0)$ **b)** $g(-1)$ **c)** $g(3)$

   d) $g(t)$ **e)** $g(2a)$ **f)** $g(3) - 4$

45. $f(x) = \dfrac{x - 3}{2x - 5}$

   a) $f(0)$ **b)** $f(4)$ **c)** $f(-1)$

   d) $f(3)$ **e)** $f(x + 2)$ **f)** $f(a + h)$

46. $r(x) = \dfrac{3x - 4}{2x + 5}$

   a) $r(0)$ **b)** $r(2)$ **c)** $r\left(\frac{4}{3}\right)$

   d) $r(-1)$ **e)** $r(x + 3)$ **f)** $r(a + h)$

The function A described by $A(s) = s^2 \dfrac{\sqrt{3}}{4}$ gives the area of an equilateral triangle with side s.

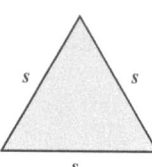

47. Find the area when a side measures 4 cm.

48. Find the area when a side measures 6 in.

The function V described by $V(r) = 4\pi r^2$ gives the surface area of a sphere with radius r.

49. Find the surface area when the radius is 3 in.

50. Find the surface area when the radius is 5 cm.

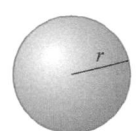

Archaeology.   *The function H described by*

$$H(x) = 2.75x + 71.48$$

can be used to predict the height, in centimeters, of a woman whose humerus (the bone from the elbow to the shoulder) is x cm long. Predict the height of a woman whose humerus is the length given.

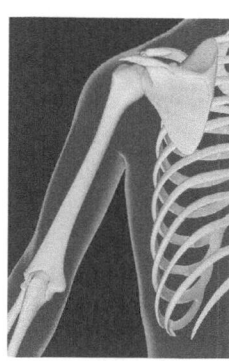

51. 34 cm   **52.** 31 cm

Chemistry.   *The function F described by*

$$F(C) = \tfrac{9}{5}C + 32$$

gives the Fahrenheit temperature corresponding to the Celsius temperature C.

53. Find the Fahrenheit temperature equivalent to −5° Celsius.

54. Find the Fahrenheit temperature equivalent to 10° Celsius.

Heart attacks and cholesterol.   *For Exercises 55 and 56, use the following graph, which shows the annual heart attack rate per 10,000 men as a function of blood cholesterol level.**

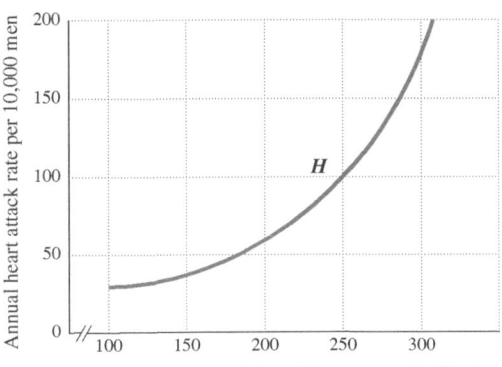

55. Approximate the annual heart attack rate for those men whose blood cholesterol level is 225 mg/dl. That is, find $H(225)$.

56. Approximate the annual heart attack rate for those men whose blood cholesterol level is 275 mg/dl. That is, find $H(275)$.

Films.   *For Exercises 57 and 58, use the following graph, which shows the number of movies released in the United States.*
Source: Nash Information Services

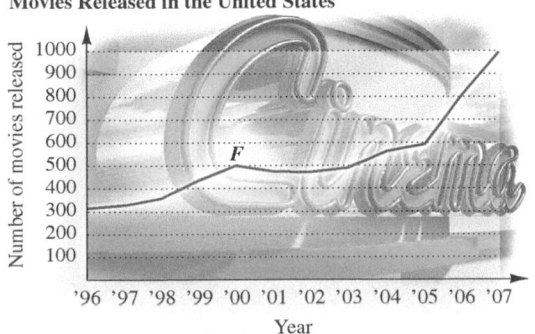

*Copyright 1989, CSPI. Adapted from *Nutrition Action Health-letter* (1875 Connecticut Avenue, N.W., Suite 300, Washington, DC 20009-5728. $24 for 10 issues).

57. Approximate the number of movies released in 2000. That is, find $F(2000)$.

58. Approximate the number of movies released in 2007. That is, find $F(2007)$.

Energy-saving lightbulbs.   *An energy bill signed into law in 2007 requires the United States to phase out standard incandescent lightbulbs. A more efficient replacement is the compact fluorescent (CFL) bulb. The table below lists incandescent wattage and the CFL wattage required to create the same amount of light.*
Source: U.S. Department of Energy

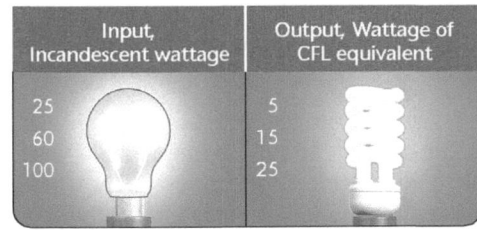

59. Use the data in the figure above to draw a graph. Estimate the wattage of a CFL bulb that creates light equivalent to a 75-watt incandescent bulb. Then predict the wattage of a CFL bulb that creates light equivalent to a 120-watt incandescent bulb.

60. Use the graph from Exercise 59 to estimate the wattage of a CFL bulb that creates light equivalent to a 40-watt incandescent bulb. Then predict the wattage of a CFL bulb that creates light equivalent to a 150-watt incandescent bulb.

Blood alcohol level.   *The following table can be used to predict the number of drinks required for a person of a specified weight to be considered legally intoxicated (blood alcohol level of 0.08 or above). One 12-oz glass of beer, a 5-oz glass of wine, or a cocktail containing 1 oz of a distilled liquor all count as one drink. Assume that all drinks are consumed within one hour.*

Input, Body Weight (in pounds)	Output, Number of Drinks
100	2.5
160	4
180	4.5
200	5

61. Use the data in the table above to draw a graph and to estimate the number of drinks that a 140-lb person would have to drink to be considered intoxicated. Then predict the number of drinks it would take for a 230-lb person to be considered intoxicated.

62. Use the graph from Exercise 61 to estimate the number of drinks that a 120-lb person would have to drink to be considered intoxicated. Then predict the number of drinks it would take for a 250-lb person to be considered intoxicated.

63. *Retailing.* Mountain View Gifts is experiencing constant growth. They recorded a total of $250,000 in sales in 2003 and $285,000 in 2008. Use a graph that displays the store's total sales as a function of time to estimate sales for 2004 and for 2011.

64. Use the graph in Exercise 63 to estimate sales for 2006 and for 2012.

Researchers at Yale University have suggested that the following graphs* may represent three different aspects of love.

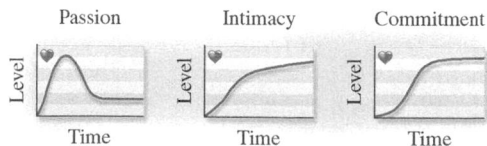

65. In what unit would you measure time if the horizontal length of each graph were ten units? Why?

66. Do you agree with the researchers that these graphs should be shaped as they are? Why or why not?

---

*From "A Triangular Theory of Love," by R. J. Sternberg, 1986, *Psychological Review*, **93**(2), 119–135. Copyright 1986 by the American Psychological Association, Inc. Reprinted by permission.

Skill Review

Review solving equations (Sections 2.2, 5.7, and 6.6).

Solve.

67. $2(x - 5) - 3 = 4 - (x - 1)$ [2.2]

68. $x^2 = 36$ [5.7]

69. $\dfrac{1}{x} = -2$ [6.6]

70. $\dfrac{1}{x} = x$ [6.6]

71. $(x - 2)(x + 3) = 6$ [5.7]

72. $\dfrac{1}{3}x + 2 = \dfrac{5}{4} + 3x$ [2.2]

73. $\dfrac{x + 1}{x} = 8$ [6.6]

74. $(x - 2)^2 = 36$ [5.7]

Synthesis

75. Jaylan is asked to write a function relating the number of fish in an aquarium to the amount of food needed for the fish. Which quantity should he choose as the independent variable? Why?

76. Explain in your own words why every function is a relation, but not every relation is a function.

For Exercises 77 and 78, let $f(x) = 3x^2 - 1$ and $g(x) = 2x + 5$.

77. Find $f(g(-4))$ and $g(f(-4))$.

78. Find $f(g(-1))$ and $g(f(-1))$.

79. If f represents the function in Exercise 15, find $f(f(f(f(\text{tiger}))))$.

Pregnancy. For Exercises 80–83, use the following graph of a woman's "stress test." This graph shows the size of a pregnant woman's contractions as a function of time.

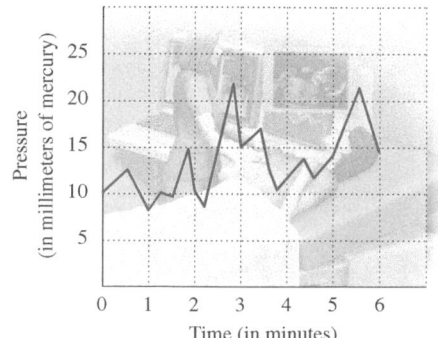

80. How large is the largest contraction that occurred during the test?

81. At what time during the test did the largest contraction occur?

82. On the basis of the information provided, how large a contraction would you expect 60 seconds after the end of the test? Why?

83. What is the frequency of the largest contraction?

84. Suppose that a function g is such that $g(-1) = -7$ and $g(3) = 8$. Find a formula for g if $g(x)$ is of the form $g(x) = mx + b$, where m and b are constants.

85. The *greatest integer function* $f(x) = [x]$ is defined as follows: $[x]$ is the greatest integer that is less than or equal to x. For example, if $x = 3.74$, then $[x] = 3$; and if $x = -0.98$, then $[x] = -1$. Graph the greatest integer function for $-5 \le x \le 5$. (The notation $f(x) = \text{INT}(x)$ is used in many graphing calculators and computer programs.)

86. *Energy expenditure.* On the basis of the information given below, what burns more energy: walking $4\frac{1}{2}$ mph for two hours or bicycling 14 mph for one hour?

Approximate Energy Expenditure by a 150-Pound Person in Various Activities

Activity	Calories per Hour
Walking, $2\frac{1}{2}$ mph	210
Bicycling, $5\frac{1}{2}$ mph	210
Walking, $3\frac{3}{4}$ mph	300
Bicycling, 13 mph	660

Source: Based on material prepared by Robert E. Johnson, M.D., Ph.D., and colleagues, University of Illinois.

7.2   Domain and Range

Determining the Domain and the Range • Restrictions on Domain • Functions Defined Piecewise

In Section 7.1, we saw that a function is a correspondence from a set called the *domain* to a set called the *range*. In this section, we look more closely at the concepts of domain and range.

Determining the Domain and the Range

When a function is given as a set of ordered pairs, the domain is the set of all first coordinates and the range is the set of all second coordinates.

EXAMPLE 1   Find the domain and the range for the function f given by

$$f = \{(2, 0), (-1, 5), (8, 0), (-3, 2)\}.$$

SOLUTION   The first coordinates are $2, -1, 8$, and -3. The second coordinates are $0, 5$, and 2. Thus we have

Domain of $f = \{2, -1, 8, -3\}$ and

Range of $f = \{0, 5, 2\}$.

TRY EXERCISE   7

We can also determine the domain and the range of a function from its graph.

EXAMPLE **2**   Find the domain and the range of the function *f* below.

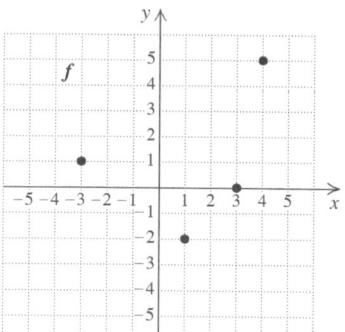

SOLUTION   Here *f* can be written $\{(-3, 1), (1, -2), (3, 0), (4, 5)\}$. The domain is the set of all first coordinates, $\{-3, 1, 3, 4\}$, and the range is the set of all second coordinates, $\{1, -2, 0, 5\}$.

> **TRY EXERCISE** 11

In Example 2, we could also have found the domain and the range directly, without first writing *f*, by observing the *x*- and *y*-values used in the graph.

EXAMPLE **3**   Find the domain and the range of the function *f* shown here.

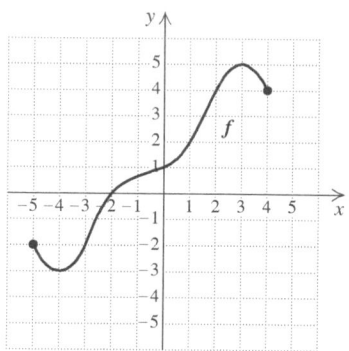

SOLUTION   The domain of the function is the set of all *x*-values that are used in the points on the curve. Because there are no breaks in the graph of *f*, these extend continuously from −5 to 4 and can be viewed as the curve's shadow, or *projection*, on the *x*-axis. Thus the domain is $\{x \mid -5 \le x \le 4\}$, or [−5, 4], shown below left.

The range of the function is the set of all *y*-values that are used in the points on the curve. These extend continuously from −3 to 5, and can be viewed as the curve's projection on the *y*-axis. Thus the range is $\{y \mid -3 \le y \le 5\}$, or [−3, 5], shown below right.

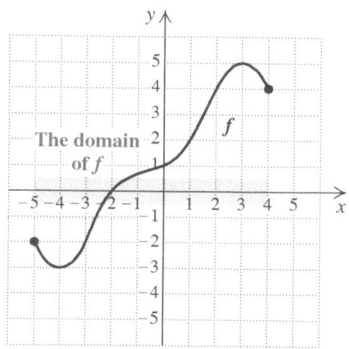

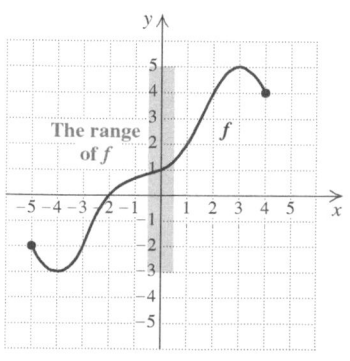

> **TRY EXERCISE** 15

In Example 3, the *endpoints* $(-5, -2)$ and $(4, 4)$ emphasize that the function is not defined for values of x less than -5 or greater than 4.

The graphs of some functions have no endpoints. Thus a function may have a domain and/or a range that extends without bound toward positive infinity or negative infinity.

EXAMPLE **4**   For the function g represented below, determine **(a)** the domain of g and **(b)** the range of g.

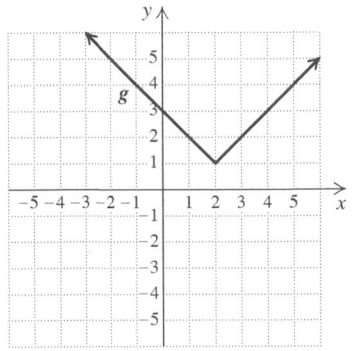

SOLUTION

a) The domain of g is the set of all x-values that are used in the points on the curve. The arrows on the ends of the graph indicate that it extends both left and right without end. Thus the shadow, or projection, of the graph on the x-axis is the entire x-axis. (See the graph on the left below.) The domain is $\{x \mid x$ is a real number$\}$, or $(-\infty, \infty)$.

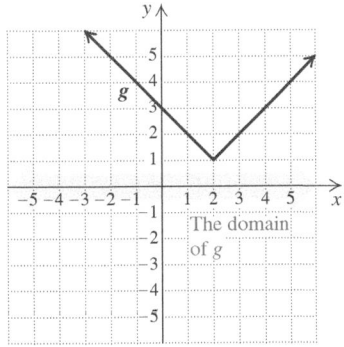
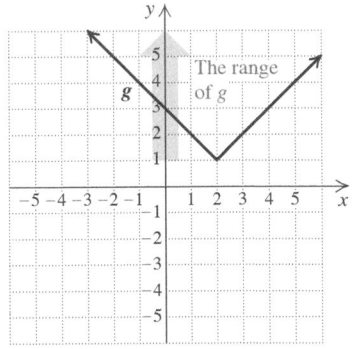

b) The range of g is the set of all y-values that are used in the points on the curve. The arrows on the ends of the graph indicate that it extends up without end. Thus the projection of the graph on the y-axis is the portion of the y-axis greater than or equal to 1. (See the graph on the right above.) The range is $\{y \mid y \geq 1\}$, or $[1, \infty)$.

TRY EXERCISE 25

The set of all real numbers is often abbreviated $\mathbb{R}$. Thus, in Example 4, we could write

Domain of $f = \mathbb{R}$.

EXAMPLE 5

Find the domain and the range of the function f shown here.

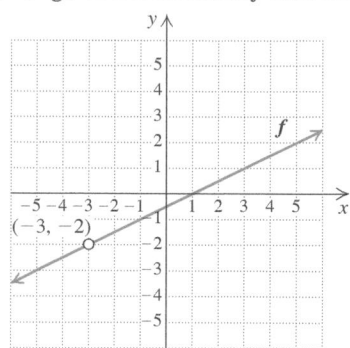

SOLUTION   The domain of f is the set of all x-values that are used in points on the curve. The open dot in the graph at $(-3, -2)$ indicates that there is no y-value that corresponds to $x = -3$; that is, the function is not defined for $x = -3$. Thus, -3 is not in the domain of the function, and

Domain of $f = \{x \mid x$ is a real number and $x \neq -3\}$.

There is no function value at $(-3, -2)$, so -2 is not in the range of the function. Thus we have

Range of $f = \{y \mid y$ is a real number and $y \neq -2\}$.   ▶ **TRY EXERCISE** ❯ 27

When a function is described by an equation, we assume that the domain is the set of all real numbers for which function values can be calculated. If an x-value is not in the domain of a function, the graph of the function will not include any point above or below that x-value.

EXAMPLE 6

For each equation, determine the domain of f.

a) $f(x) = |x|$ **b)** $f(x) = \dfrac{7}{2x - 6}$ **c)** $f(t) = \dfrac{t + 1}{t^2 - 4}$

SOLUTION

a) We ask ourselves, "Is there any number x for which we cannot compute $|x|$?" Since we can find the absolute value of *any* number, the answer is no. Thus the domain of f is $\mathbb{R}$, the set of all real numbers.

b) Is there any number x for which $\dfrac{7}{2x - 6}$ cannot be computed? Since $\dfrac{7}{2x - 6}$ cannot be computed when $2x - 6$ is 0, the answer is yes. To determine what x-value causes the denominator to be 0, we solve an equation:

$$2x - 6 = 0 \qquad \text{Setting the denominator equal to 0}$$
$$2x = 6 \qquad \text{Adding 6 to both sides}$$
$$x = 3. \qquad \text{Dividing both sides by 2}$$

Thus, 3 is *not* in the domain of f, whereas all other real numbers are. The domain of f is $\{x \mid x$ is a real number and $x \neq 3\}$.

c) The expression $\dfrac{t + 1}{t^2 - 4}$ is undefined when $t^2 - 4 = 0$:

$$t^2 - 4 = 0 \qquad \text{Setting the denominator equal to 0}$$
$$(t + 2)(t - 2) = 0 \qquad \text{Factoring}$$
$$t + 2 = 0 \quad or \quad t - 2 = 0 \qquad \text{Using the principle of zero products}$$
$$t = -2 \quad or \quad t = 2. \qquad \text{Solving; these are the values for which } (t + 1)/(t^2 - 4) \text{ is undefined.}$$

TECHNOLOGY CONNECTION

To visualize Example 6(a), note that the graph of $y_1 = |x|$ (which is entered $y_1 = \text{abs}(x)$, using the NUM option of the **MATH** menu) appears without interruption for any piece of the x-axis that we examine.

$y_1 = \text{abs}(x)$

In contrast, the graph of $y_2 = \dfrac{7}{2x - 6}$ in Example 6(b) has a break at $x = 3$.

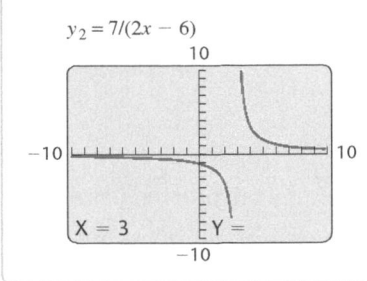

$y_2 = 7/(2x - 6)$

X = 3   Y =

Thus we have

Domain of $f = \{t \mid t$ is a real number *and* $t \neq -2$ *and* $t \neq 2\}$.

Note that when the numerator, $t + 1$, is zero, the function value is 0 and *is* defined.

> TRY EXERCISE 31

Restrictions on Domain

If a function is used as a model for an application, the problem situation may require restrictions on the domain; for example, length and time are generally nonnegative, and a person's age does not increase indefinitely.

EXAMPLE 7

Prize tee shirts. During intermission at sporting events, it has become common for team mascots to use a powerful slingshot to launch tightly rolled tee shirts into the stands. The height $h(t)$, in feet, of an airborne tee shirt t seconds after being launched can be approximated by

$$h(t) = -15t^2 + 70t + 25.$$

What is the domain of the function?

SOLUTION   The expression $-15t^2 + 70t + 25$ can be evaluated for any number t, so any restrictions on the domain will come from the problem situation.

First, we note that t cannot be negative, since it represents time from launch, so we have $t \geq 0$. If we make a drawing, we also note that the function will not be defined for values of t that make the height negative.

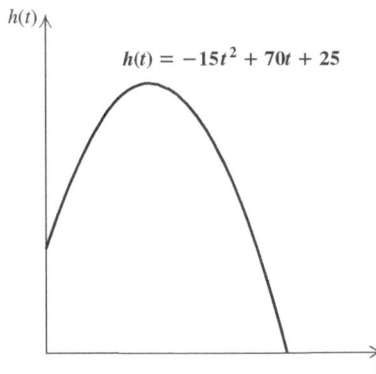

$h(t) = -15t^2 + 70t + 25$

Thus an upper limit for t will be the positive value of t for which $h(t) = 0$. Solving, we obtain

$$
\begin{aligned}
h(t) &= 0 \\
-15t^2 + 70t + 25 &= 0 && \text{Substituting} \\
\left.
\begin{aligned}
-5(3t^2 - 14t - 5) &= 0 \\
-5(3t + 1)(t - 5) &= 0
\end{aligned}
\right\} && \text{Factoring} \\
3t + 1 = 0 \quad or \quad t - 5 &= 0 && \text{Using the principle of zero products} \\
\left.
\begin{aligned}
3t = -1 \quad or \quad t &= 5 \\
t = -\tfrac{1}{3} \quad or \quad t &= 5.
\end{aligned}
\right\} && \text{Solving for } t
\end{aligned}
$$

We already know that $-\frac{1}{3}$ is not in the domain of the function because of the restriction $t \geq 0$ above.

The tee shirt will hit the ground after 5 sec, so we have $t \leq 5$. Putting the two restrictions together, we have $t \geq 0$ *and* $t \leq 5$, so the

Domain of $h = \{t \mid t$ is a real number *and* $0 \leq t \leq 5\}$, or $[0, 5]$.

> TRY EXERCISE 45

If the domain of a function is not specifically listed, it can be determined from a table, a graph, an equation, or an application.

> ### Domain of a Function
>
> The domain of a function $f(x)$ is the set of all inputs x.
>
> - If the correspondence is listed in a table or as a set of ordered pairs, the domain is the set of all first coordinates.
> - If the function is described by a graph, the domain is the set of all x-coordinates of the points on the graph.
> - If the function is described by an equation, the domain is the set of all numbers for which the value can be calculated.
> - If the function is used in an application, the domain is the set of all numbers that make sense in the problem.

Functions Defined Piecewise

Piecewise-defined functions are described by different equations for various parts of their domains. For example, the function $f(x) = |x|$ is described by

$$f(x) = \begin{cases} x, & \text{if } x \geq 0, \\ -x, & \text{if } x < 0. \end{cases}$$

To evaluate a piecewise-defined function for an input a, we first determine what part of the domain a belongs to. Then we use the formula corresponding to that part of the domain.

EXAMPLE **8** Find each function value for the function f given by

$$f(x) = |x| = \begin{cases} x, & \text{if } x \geq 0, \\ -x, & \text{if } x < 0. \end{cases}$$

a) $f(4)$ **b)** $f(-10)$

SOLUTION

a) Since $4 \geq 0$, we use the equation $f(x) = x$. Thus, $f(4) = 4$.

b) Since $-10 < 0$, we use the equation $f(x) = -x$. Thus, $f(-10) = -(-10) = 10$.

▶ **TRY EXERCISE** 53

EXAMPLE **9** Find each function value for the function g given by

$$g(x) = \begin{cases} x + 2, & \text{if } x \leq -2, \\ x^2, & \text{if } -2 < x \leq 5, \\ 3x, & \text{if } x > 5. \end{cases}$$

a) $g(-2)$ **b)** $g(3)$ **c)** $g(10)$

SOLUTION

a) Since $-2 \leq -2$, we use the first equation, $g(x) = x + 2$:

$$g(-2) = -2 + 2 = 0.$$

b) Since $-2 < 3 \leq 5$, we use the second equation, $g(x) = x^2$:

$$g(3) = 3^2 = 9.$$

c) Since $10 > 5$, we use the last equation, $g(x) = 3x$:

$$g(10) = 3 \cdot 10 = 30.$$

▶ **TRY EXERCISE** 55

7.2 **EXERCISE SET**

⤷ *Concept Reinforcement*   *For Exercises 1–6, use the function f given by*

$$f(x) = \begin{cases} x - 5, & \text{if } x < -6, \\ 2x^2, & \text{if } -6 \le x < -1, \\ |x|, & \text{if } -1 \le x < 10, \\ 3x + 1, & \text{if } x \ge 10. \end{cases}$$

Write the letter of the equation that should be used to find each function value. Letters may be used more than once or not at all.

1. ___ $f(0)$

2. ___ $f(15)$

3. ___ $f(10)$

4. ___ $f(-6)$

5. ___ $f(-1)$

6. ___ $f(-3)$

a) $f(x) = x - 5$

b) $f(x) = 2x^2$

c) $f(x) = |x|$

d) $f(x) = 3x + 1$

Find the domain and the range for each function given.

7. $f = \{(2, 8), (9, 3), (-2, 10), (-4, 4)\}$

8. $g = \{(1, 2), (2, 3), (3, 4), (4, 5)\}$

9. $g = \{(0, 0), (4, -2), (-5, 0), (-1, -2)\}$

10. $f = \{(3, 7), (2, 7), (1, 7), (0, 7)\}$

For each graph of a function f, determine the domain and the range of f.

11.
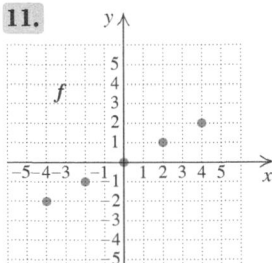

12.
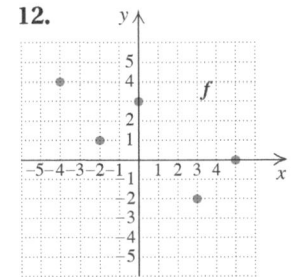

13.
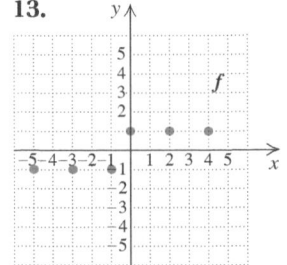

14.
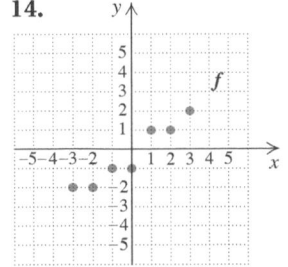

15.
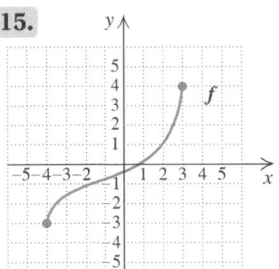

16.
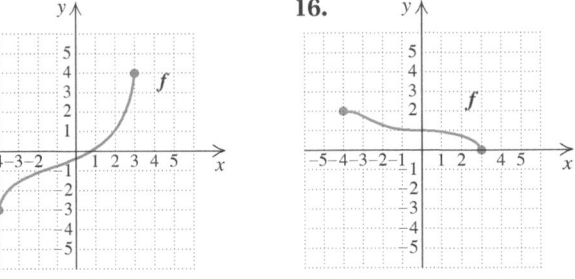

17.
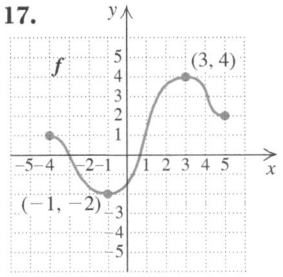

18.
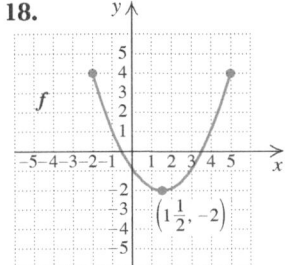

19.
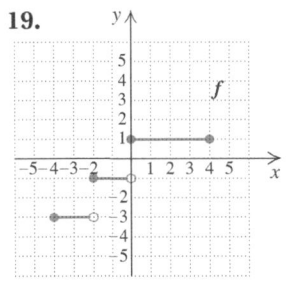

20.
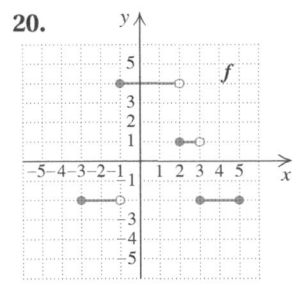

21.
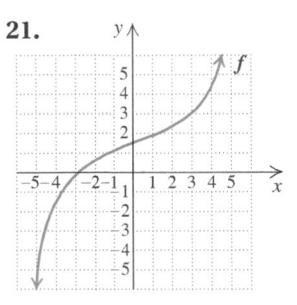

22.
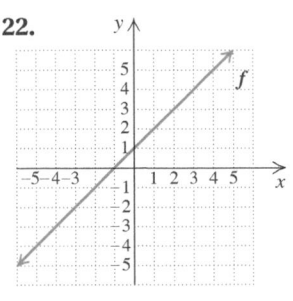

23.
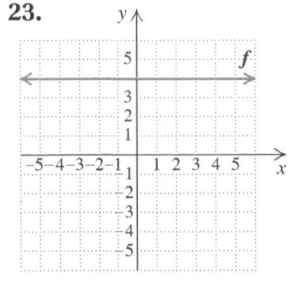

24.
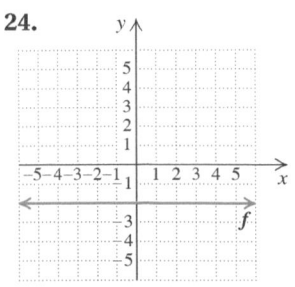

25.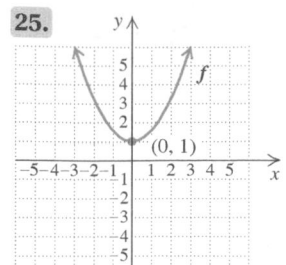

26.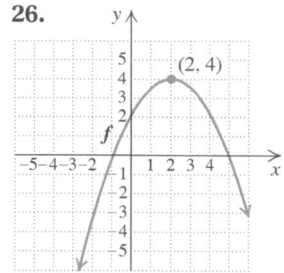

27.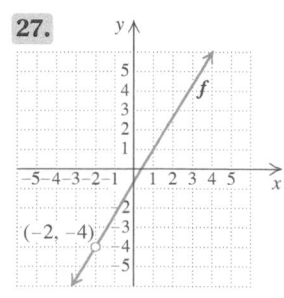

28.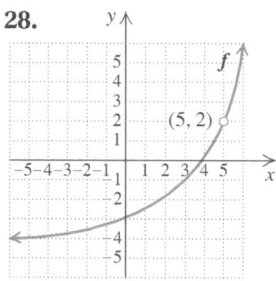

29.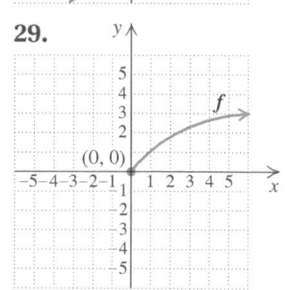

30.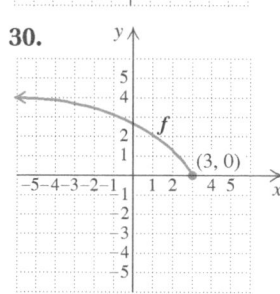

Find the domain of f.

31. $f(x) = \dfrac{5}{x - 3}$

32. $f(x) = \dfrac{7}{6 - x}$

33. $f(x) = \dfrac{x}{2x - 1}$

34. $f(x) = \dfrac{2x}{4x + 3}$

35. $f(x) = 2x + 1$

36. $f(x) = x^2 + 3$

37. $f(x) = |5 - x|$

38. $f(x) = |3x - 4|$

39. $f(x) = \dfrac{5}{x^2 - 9}$

40. $f(x) = \dfrac{x}{x^2 - 2x + 1}$

41. $f(x) = x^2 - 9$

42. $f(x) = x^2 - 2x + 1$

43. $f(x) = \dfrac{2x - 7}{x^2 + 8x + 7}$

44. $f(x) = \dfrac{x + 5}{2x^2 - x - 3}$

45. *Records in the 400-m run.* The record R for the 400-m run t years after 1930 is given by

$$R(t) = 46.8 - 0.075t.$$

What is the domain of the function?

46. *Records in the 1500-m run.* The record R for the 1500-m run t years after 1930 is given by

$$R(t) = 3.85 - 0.0075t.$$

What is the domain of the function?

47. *Consumer demand.* The amount A of coffee that consumers are willing to buy at price p is given by

$$A(p) = -2.5p + 26.5.$$

What is the domain of the function?

48. *Seller's supply.* The amount A of coffee that suppliers are willing to supply at price p is given by

$$A(p) = 2p - 11.$$

What is the domain of the function?

49. *Pressure at sea depth.* The pressure P, in atmospheres, at a depth d feet beneath the surface of the ocean is given by

$$P(d) = 0.03d + 1.$$

What is the domain of the function?

50. *Perimeter.* The perimeter P of an equilateral triangle with sides of length s is given by

$$P(s) = 3s.$$

What is the domain of the function?

51. *Fireworks displays.* The height h, in feet, of a "weeping willow" fireworks display, t seconds after having been launched from an 80-ft high rooftop, is given by

$$h(t) = -16t^2 + 64t + 80.$$

What is the domain of the function?

52. *Safety flares.* The height h, in feet, of a safety flare, t seconds after having been launched from a height of 224 ft, is given by

$$h(t) = -16t^2 + 80t + 224.$$

What is the domain of the function?

Find the indicated function values for each function.

53. $f(x) = \begin{cases} x, & \text{if } x < 0, \\ 2x + 1, & \text{if } x \geq 0 \end{cases}$

  a) $f(-5)$ **b)** $f(0)$ **c)** $f(10)$

54. $g(x) = \begin{cases} x - 5, & \text{if } x \leq 5, \\ 3x, & \text{if } x > 5 \end{cases}$

  a) $g(0)$ **b)** $g(5)$ **c)** $g(6)$

55. $G(x) = \begin{cases} x - 5, & \text{if } x < -1, \\ x, & \text{if } -1 \leq x \leq 2, \\ x + 2, & \text{if } x > 2 \end{cases}$

  a) $G(0)$ **b)** $G(2)$ **c)** $G(5)$

56. $F(x) = \begin{cases} 2x, & \text{if } x \leq 0, \\ x, & \text{if } 0 < x \leq 3, \\ -5x, & \text{if } x > 3 \end{cases}$

  a) $F(-1)$ **b)** $F(3)$ **c)** $F(10)$

57. $f(x) = \begin{cases} x^2 - 10, & \text{if } x < -10, \\ x^2, & \text{if } -10 \le x \le 10, \\ x^2 + 10, & \text{if } x > 10 \end{cases}$

a) $f(-10)$ b) $f(10)$ c) $f(11)$

58. $f(x) = \begin{cases} 2x^2 - 3, & \text{if } x < 2, \\ x^2, & \text{if } 2 \le x \le 4, \\ 5x - 7, & \text{if } x > 4 \end{cases}$

a) $f(0)$ b) $f(3)$ c) $f(6)$

59. Explain why the domain of the function given by $f(x) = \dfrac{x + 3}{2}$ is $\mathbb{R}$, but the domain of the function given by $g(x) = \dfrac{2}{x + 3}$ is not $\mathbb{R}$.

60. Chloe asserts that for a function described by a set of ordered pairs, the range of the function will always have the same number of elements as there are ordered pairs. Is she correct? Why or why not?

Skill Review

To prepare for Section 7.3, review graphs of linear equations (Section 3.6).

Graph. [3.6]

61. $y = 2x - 3$ **62.** $y = x + 5$

Find the slope and the y-intercept of each line. [3.6]

63. $y = \dfrac{2}{3}x - 4$ **64.** $y = -\dfrac{1}{4}x + 6$

65. $y = \dfrac{4}{3}x$ **66.** $y = -5x$

Synthesis

67. Ramiro states that $f(x) = \dfrac{x^2}{x}$ and $g(x) = x$ represent the same function. Is he correct? Why or why not?

68. Explain why the domain of a function can be viewed as the projection of its graph on the *x*-axis.

Sketch the graph of a function for which the domain and range are as given. Graphs may vary.

69. Domain: $\mathbb{R}$; range: $\mathbb{R}$

70. Domain: $\{3, 1, 4\}$; range: $\{0, 5\}$

71. Domain: $\{x \mid 1 \le x \le 5\}$; range: $\{y \mid 0 \le y \le 2\}$

72. Domain: $\{x \mid x \text{ is a real number } and \ x \ne 1\}$; range: $\{y \mid y \text{ is a real number } and \ y \ne -2\}$

For each graph of a function f, determine the domain and the range of f.

73.
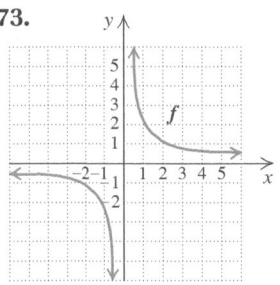

74.
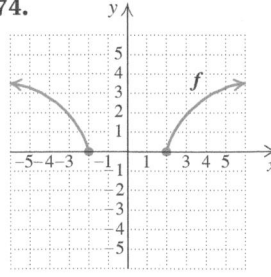

75.
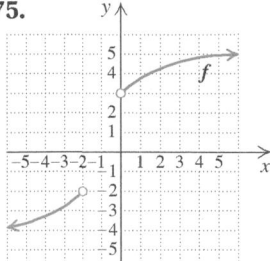

76.
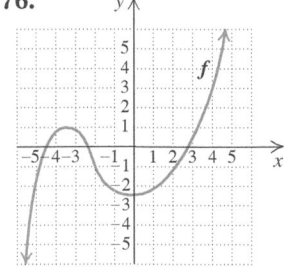

Graph each function on a graphing calculator and estimate its domain and range from the graph.

77. $f(x) = |x - 3|$ **78.** $f(x) = |x| - 3$

79. $f(x) = \dfrac{3}{x - 2}$ **80.** $f(x) = \dfrac{-1}{x + 3}$

81. Use a graphing calculator to estimate the range of the function in Exercise 51.

82. Use a graphing calculator to estimate the range of the function in Exercise 52.

83.–88. *For Exercises 83–88, graph the functions given in each of Exercises 53–58, respectively.*

89. A graphing calculator will interpret an expression like $x \ge 1$ as true or false, depending on the value of x. If the expression is true, the graphing calculator assigns a value of 1 to the expression. If the expression is false, the graphing calculator assigns a value of 0. To graph a piecewise-defined function using a graphing calculator, multiply each part of the definition by its domain, using the TEST menu to enter the inequality symbol. Thus the function in Exercise 53 is entered as $y_1 = x(x < 0) + (2x + 1)(x \ge 0)$. Use a graphing calculator in DOT mode to check your answers to Exercises 83–88.

7.3   Graphs of Functions

Linear Functions   ▪   Nonlinear Functions

A function can be classified both by the type of equation that is used and by the type of graph it represents. In this section, we will graph a variety of functions that are described by different equations.

Linear Functions

In Chapter 3, we graphed *linear equations*. Here we review such graphs and determine which types of linear graphs represent functions.

Any linear equation can be written in *standard form* $Ax + By = C$. If $B \neq 0$, the equation can also be written in *slope–intercept form*. The *point–slope form* is often used to write equations.

Equations of Lines

Standard form:	$Ax + By = C$
Slope–intercept form:	$y = mx + b$
Point–slope form:	$y - y_1 = m(x - x_1)$

Two points determine a line. If we know that an equation is linear, we can graph the equation by plotting two points that are on the line and drawing the line that goes through those points.

When an equation is written in slope–intercept form $y = mx + b$, the slope of the line is m and the y-intercept is $(0, b)$. Knowing the y-intercept gives us one point on the line, and we can use the slope to determine another point.

EXAMPLE 1   Graph: $4y = -3x + 8$.

SOLUTION   To graph $4y = -3x + 8$, we first rewrite it in slope–intercept form:

$$4y = -3x + 8$$
$$y = \tfrac{1}{4}(-3x + 8) \qquad \text{Multiplying both sides by } \tfrac{1}{4}$$
$$y = -\tfrac{3}{4}x + 2. \qquad \text{Using the distributive law}$$

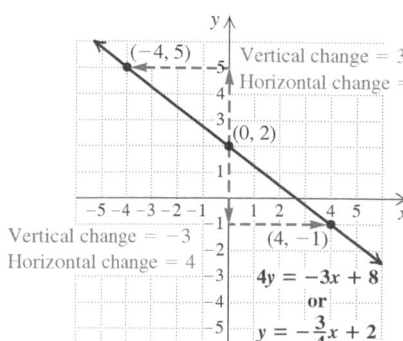

The slope is $-\tfrac{3}{4}$ and the y-intercept is $(0, 2)$. We plot $(0, 2)$ and think of the slope as either $\tfrac{-3}{4}$ or $\tfrac{3}{-4}$. Using the form $\tfrac{-3}{4}$, we start at $(0, 2)$ and move *down* 3 units (since the numerator is *negative*) and *to the right* 4 units (since the denominator is *positive*). We plot the new point, $(4, -1)$.

Alternatively, we can think of the slope as $\tfrac{3}{-4}$. Starting at $(0, 2)$, we move *up* 3 units (since the numerator is *positive*) and *to the left* 4 units (since the denominator is *negative*). This leads to another point on the graph, $(-4, 5)$. Using the points found, we draw and label the graph at left.

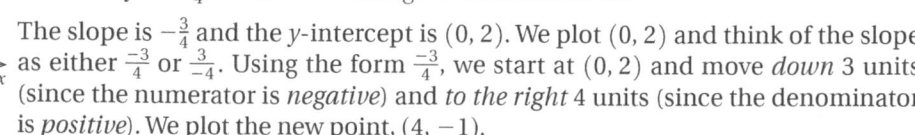
TRY EXERCISE   7

The graphs of equations of the form $y = b$ are horizontal lines with a slope of 0, and the graphs of equations of the form $x = a$ are vertical lines. The slope of a vertical line is undefined.

We can use the vertical-line test to determine which types of linear graphs represent functions. Consider the following graphs.

A function   A function   A function   Not a function

Any vertical line that passes through the graphs of $2x + 3y = 6$, $y = \frac{1}{2}x - 3$, and $y = 4$ will cross the graph only once. However, the vertical line through the point $(-2, 0)$ will cross the graph of $x = -2$ at *every* point. In general, *any* straight line that is not vertical is the graph of a function. A **linear function** is a function described by any linear equation whose graph is not vertical. A horizontal line represents a **constant function**.

> ### Linear Function
>
> A function described by an equation of the form $f(x) = mx + b$ is a *linear function*. Its graph is a straight line with slope m and y-intercept $(0, b)$.
>
> When $m = 0$, the function described by $f(x) = b$ is called a *constant function*. Its graph is a horizontal line through $(0, b)$.

EXAMPLE 2

Graph: $f(x) = 3x + 2$.

SOLUTION   The notations

$$f(x) = 3x + 2 \quad \text{and} \quad y = 3x + 2$$

are often used interchangeably. The function notation emphasizes that the second coordinate in each ordered pair is determined by the first coordinate of that pair.

We graph $f(x) = 3x + 2$ in the same way that we would graph $y = 3x + 2$. The vertical axis can be labeled y or $f(x)$. We could use a table of values or, since this is a linear function, use the slope and the y-intercept to graph the function.

Since $f(x) = 3x + 2$ is in the form $f(x) = mx + b$, we can tell from the equation that the slope is 3, or $\frac{3}{1}$, and the y-intercept is $(0, 2)$. We plot $(0, 2)$ and go *up* 3 units and *to the right* 1 unit to determine another point on the line, $(1, 5)$. After we have sketched the line, a third point can be calculated as a check.

TRY EXERCISE   19

EXAMPLE 3

Graph: $f(x) = -3$.

SOLUTION   This is a constant function. For every input x, the output is -3. The graph is a horizontal line.

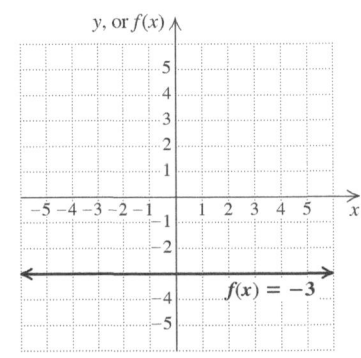

TRY EXERCISE   23

Linear functions are common in today's world.

EXAMPLE **4** *Cell-phone costs.* In 2008, an Apple iPhone cost $400. AT&T offered a plan including 450 daytime minutes a month for $60 per month. Formulate a mathematical model for the cost. Then use the model to estimate the number of months required for the total cost to reach $700.

Source: www.apple.com

SOLUTION

1. **Familiarize.** For this plan, a monthly fee is charged after an initial purchase has been made. After 1 month of service, the total cost will be $400 + $60 = $460. After 2 months, the total cost will be $400 + $60 · 2 = $520. We can write a general model if we let $C(t)$ represent the total cost, in dollars, for t months of service.

2. **Translate.** We reword and translate as follows:

Rewording: The total cost is the cost of the phone plus $60 per month.

Translating: $C(t)$ =   400   +   60 · t

where $t \geq 0$ (since there cannot be a negative number of months).

3. **Carry out.** To determine the time required for the total cost to reach $700, we substitute 700 for $C(t)$ and solve for t:

$$C(t) = 400 + 60t$$
$$700 = 400 + 60t \quad \text{Substituting}$$
$$300 = 60t \quad \text{Subtracting 400 from both sides}$$
$$5 = t. \quad \text{Dividing both sides by 60}$$

4. **Check.** We evaluate:

$$C(5) = 60 \cdot 5 + 400 = 300 + 400 = 700.$$

5. **State.** It takes 5 months for the total cost to reach $700. **TRY EXERCISE** 25

Since $f(x) = mx + b$ can be evaluated for any choice of x, the domain of all linear functions is $\mathbb{R}$, the set of all real numbers.

The second coordinate of every ordered pair in a constant function $f(x) = b$ is the number b. The range of a constant function thus consists of one number, b. For a nonconstant linear function, the graph extends indefinitely both up and down, so the range is the set of all real numbers, or $\mathbb{R}$.

> ### Domain and Range of a Linear Function
>
> The domain of any linear function $f(x) = mx + b$ is
>
> $$\{x \,|\, x \text{ is a real number}\}, \text{ or } \mathbb{R}.$$
>
> The range of any linear function $f(x) = mx + b, m \neq 0$, is
>
> $$\{y \,|\, y \text{ is a real number}\}, \text{ or } \mathbb{R}.$$
>
> The range of any constant function $f(x) = b$ is $\{b\}$.

EXAMPLE **5** Determine the domain and the range of each of the following functions.

a) f, where $f(x) = 2x - 10$ **b)** g, where $g(x) = 4$

SOLUTION

a) Since $f(x) = 2x - 10$ describes a linear function, but not a constant function,

Domain of $f = \mathbb{R}$ and
Range of $f = \mathbb{R}$.

b) The function described by $g(x) = 4$ is a constant function. Thus,

Domain of $g = \mathbb{R}$ and
Range of $g = \{4\}$.

> TRY EXERCISE 41

The graphs of nonlinear functions can get quite complex. We will now define several types of nonlinear functions and discuss some of their characteristics. The detailed study of their graphs appears later in this text or in other courses.

Nonlinear Functions

A function for which the graph is not a straight line is a **nonlinear function**. Some important types of nonlinear functions are listed below.

Type of function	*Example*
Absolute-value function	$f(x) = \lvert x \rvert$
Polynomial function	$p(x) = x^3 - 4x^2 + 1$
Quadratic function	$q(x) = x^2 + 5x + 2$
Rational function	$r(x) = \dfrac{x + 1}{x - 2}$

Note that linear and quadratic functions are special kinds of polynomial functions.

EXAMPLE **6**

State whether each equation describes a linear function, an absolute-value function, a general polynomial function, a quadratic function, or a rational function.

a) $f(x) = x^2 - 9$

b) $g(x) = \dfrac{3}{x}$

c) $h(x) = \dfrac{1}{4}x - 16$

d) $v(x) = 4x^4 - 13$

SOLUTION

a) Since f is described by a polynomial equation of degree 2, f is a *quadratic function*.

b) Since g is described by a rational equation, g is a *rational function*.

c) The function h is described by a linear equation, so h is a *linear function*. Note that although $\frac{1}{4}$ is a fraction, there are no variables in a denominator.

d) Since v is described by a polynomial equation, v is a *polynomial function*.

Since the graphs of nonlinear functions are not straight lines, we usually need to calculate more than two or three points to determine the shape of the graph.

EXAMPLE **7**

Graph the function given by $f(x) = \lvert x \rvert$, and determine the domain and the range of f.

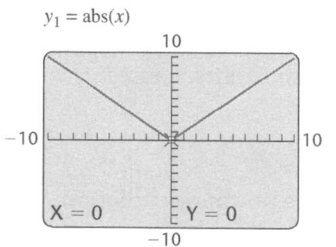
SOLUTION We calculate function values for several choices of x and list the results in a table.

$$f(0) = |0| = 0,$$
$$f(1) = |1| = 1,$$
$$f(2) = |2| = 2,$$
$$f(-1) = |-1| = 1,$$
$$f(-2) = |-2| = 2$$

x	$f(x) = |x|$	$(x, f(x))$
0	0	$(0, 0)$
1	1	$(1, 1)$
2	2	$(2, 2)$
-1	1	$(-1, 1)$
-2	2	$(-2, 2)$

When we plot these points, we observe a pattern. The value of the function is 0 when x is 0. Function values increase both as x increases from 0 and as x decreases from 0. The graph of f is V-shaped, with the "point" of the V at the origin.

Because we can find the absolute value of any real number, we have

Domain of $f = \mathbb{R}$, or $(-\infty, \infty)$.

Because the absolute value of a number is never negative, we have

Range of $f = \{y | y \geq 0\}$, or $[0, \infty)$.

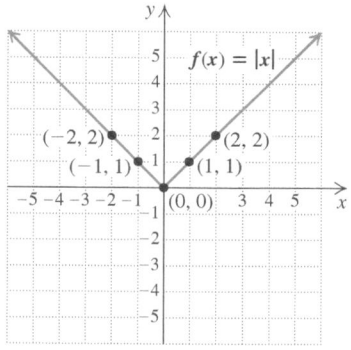

▶ **TRY EXERCISE** 65

Graphs of *polynomial functions* generally become more complex as the degree of the polynomial increases. In Chapter 11, we will study in greater detail the graphs of *quadratic functions*, or functions of the form

$$q(x) = ax^2 + bx + c, a \neq 0.$$

Since a polynomial can be evaluated for any real number, the domain of a polynomial is the set of all real numbers.

A *rational function* contains a variable in a denominator; thus its domain may be restricted. Division by zero is undefined, so any values of the variable that make a denominator 0 are not in the domain of the function.

EXAMPLE 8   Determine the domain of f.

a) $f(x) = x^3 + 5x^2 - 4x + 1$

b) $f(x) = \dfrac{x^2 - 4}{x + 2}$

SOLUTION

a) $f(x) = x^3 + 5x^2 - 4x + 1$ describes a polynomial function. The domain of any polynomial function is $\mathbb{R}$, so the domain of f is $\mathbb{R}$.

b) $f(x) = \dfrac{x^2 - 4}{x + 2}$ describes a rational function. Note that $f(x)$ is undefined for $x + 2 = 0$, or, equivalently, for $x = -2$. Thus the domain of $f = \{x | x$ is a real number and $x \neq -2\}$.

▶ **TRY EXERCISE** 43

Visualizing for Success

A
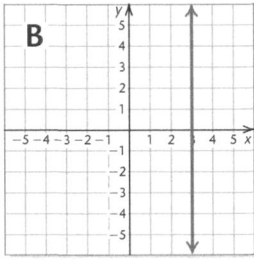

B
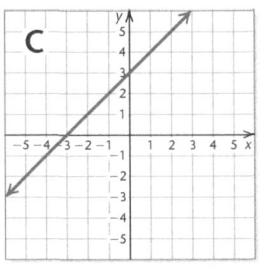

C
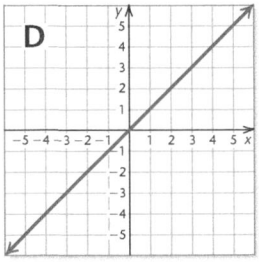

D
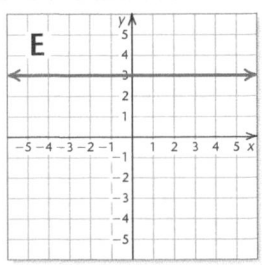

E

F
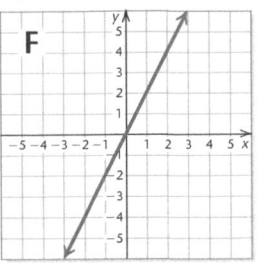

G
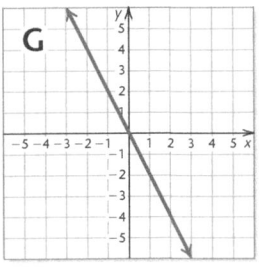

H
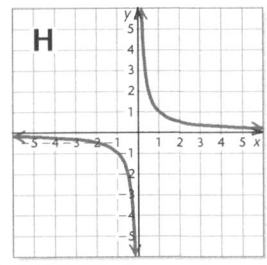

I
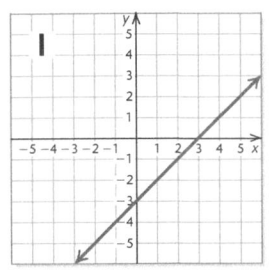

J
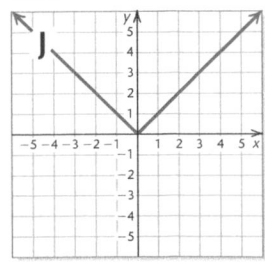

Match each equation or function with its graph.

1. $f(x) = x$

2. $f(x) = |x|$

3. $f(x) = x^2$

4. $f(x) = 3$

5. $x = 3$

6. $f(x) = x + 3$

7. $f(x) = x - 3$

8. $f(x) = 2x$

9. $f(x) = -2x$

10. $f(x) = \dfrac{1}{x}$

Answers on page A-28

An alternate, animated version of this activity appears in MyMathLab. To use MyMathLab, you need a course ID and a student access code. Contact your instructor for more information.

7.3   EXERCISE SET

For Extra Help      MathXL
MyMathLab   PRACTICE   WATCH   DOWNLOAD

🐍 *Concept Reinforcement*   *Answer true or false.*

1. The vertical-line test states that a graph is not that of a function if it contains a vertical line.

2. The graph of a constant function is a horizontal line.

3. The domain of a constant function consists of a single element.

4. The domain of a linear function is the set of all real numbers.

5. Linear functions are typically written in slope–intercept form.

6. Rational functions may have some restrictions on their domains.

Graph.

7. $y = 2x - 1$

8. $y = \frac{1}{3}x + 2$

9. $y = -\frac{2}{3}x + 3$

10. $y = -4x - 2$

11. $3y = 6 - 4x$

12. $5y = 2x - 15$

13. $x - y = 4$

14. $x + y = 3$

15. $y = -2$

16. $y = 3$

17. $x = 4$

18. $x = -1$

19. $f(x) = x + 3$

20. $f(x) = 2 - x$

21. $f(x) = \frac{3}{4}x + 1$

22. $f(x) = 3x + 2$

23. $g(x) = 4$

24. $g(x) = -5$

25. *Truck rentals.*   Titanium Trucks charges $30 for a one-day truck rental, plus $0.75 per mile. Formulate a linear function to model the cost $C(d)$ of a one-day rental driven d miles, and determine the number of miles driven if the total cost is $75.

26. *Taxis.*   A taxi ride in New York City costs $2.50 plus $2.00 per mile.* Formulate a linear function to model the cost $C(d)$ of a d-mile taxi ride, and determine the length of a ride that cost $23.50.

27. *Hair growth.*   Lauren had her hair cut to a length of 5 inches in order to donate the hair to Locks of Love. Her hair then grew at a rate of $\frac{1}{2}$ inch per month. Formulate a linear function to model the length $L(t)$

*Rates are higher between 4 P.M. and 8 P.M. (*Source:* Based on data from New York City Taxi and Limousine Commission, 2007)

of Lauren's hair t months after she had the haircut, and determine when her hair will be 15 inches long.

28. *Landscaping.*   On Saturday, Shelby Lawncare cut the lawn at Great Harrington Community College to a height of 2 in. Since then, the grass has grown at a rate of $\frac{1}{8}$ in. per day. Formulate a linear function to model the length $L(t)$ of the lawn t days after having been cut, and determine when the grass will be $3\frac{1}{2}$ in. high.

29. *Organic cotton.*   In 2006, 5960 acres in the U.S. were planted with organic cotton. This number is increasing by 849 acres each year. Formulate a linear function to model the number of acres of organic cotton $A(t)$ that is planted t years after 2006, and determine when 10,205 acres of organic cotton will be planted.
Source: Based on data from the Organic Trade Association

30. *Catering.*   Chrissie's Catering charges a setup fee of $75 plus $25 a person for catering a party. Formulate a linear function to model the cost $C(x)$ for a party for x people, and determine the number of people at a party if the cost was $775.

In Exercises 31–40, assume that a constant rate of change exists for each model formed.

31. *Automobile production.*   As demand has grown, worldwide production of small cars rose from 14.5 million in 2002 to 19 million in 2007. Let $a(t)$ represent the number of small cars produced t years after 2000.
Source: *The Wall Street Journal,* 10/22/07

a) Find a linear function that fits the data.

b) Use the function from part (a) to predict the number of small cars produced in 2013.

c) In what year will 25 million small cars be produced?

32. *Convention attendees.*   In recent years, Las Vegas has become a popular location for conventions. The number of convention attendees in Las Vegas rose from 4.6 million in 2002 to 6.1 million in 2006. Let $v(t)$ represent the number of convention attendees in Las Vegas t years after 2000.
Source: Las Vegas Convention and Visitors Authority

a) Find a linear function that fits the data.
b) Use the function from part (a) to predict the number of convention attendees in Las Vegas in 2011.
c) In what year will there be 8 million convention attendees in Las Vegas?

33. *Life expectancy of females in the United States.* In 1994, the life expectancy of females was 79.0 yr. In 2004, it was 80.4 yr. Let $E(t)$ represent life expectancy and t the number of years since 1990.
Source: *Statistical Abstract of the United States*, 2007

a) Find a linear function that fits the data.
Aha! **b)** Use the function of part (a) to predict the life expectancy of females in 2012.

34. *Life expectancy of males in the United States.*   In 1994, the life expectancy of males was 72.4 yr. In 2004, it was 75.2 yr. Let $E(t)$ represent life expectancy and t the number of years since 1990.
Source: *Statistical Abstract of the United States*, 2007

a) Find a linear function that fits the data.
b) Use the function of part (a) to predict the life expectancy of males in 2012.

35. *PAC contributions.*   In 2002, Political Action Committees (PACs) contributed $282 million to federal candidates. In 2006, the figure rose to $372.1 million. Let $A(t)$ represent the amount of PAC contributions, in millions, and t the number of years since 2000.
Source: Federal Election Commission

PAC contributions to federal candidates

2002 $282 million

2006 $372.1 million

a) Find a linear function that fits the data.
b) Use the function of part (a) to predict the amount of PAC contributions in 2010.

36. *Recycling.*   In 2000, Americans recycled 52.7 million tons of solid waste. In 2005, the figure grew to 58.4 million tons. Let $N(t)$ represent the number of tons recycled, in millions, and t the number of years since 2000.
Sources: U.S. EPA; Franklin Associates, Ltd.

a) Find a linear function that fits the data.
b) Use the function of part (a) to predict the amount recycled in 2012.

37. *Online banking.*   In 2000, about 16 million Americans conducted at least some of their banking online. By 2005, that number had risen to about 63 million. Let $N(t)$ represent the number of Americans using online banking, in millions, t years after 2000.

a) Find a linear function that fits the data.
Aha! **b)** Use the function of part (a) to predict the number of Americans who will use online banking in 2010.
c) In what year will 157 million Americans use online banking?

38. *Records in the 100-meter run.*   In 1999, the record for the 100-m run was 9.79 sec. In 2007, it was 9.77 sec. Let $R(t)$ represent the record in the 100-m run and t the number of years since 1999.
Sources: International Association of Athletics Federation; *Guinness World Records*

a) Find a linear function that fits the data.
b) Use the function of part (a) to predict the record in 2015 and in 2030.
c) When will the record be 9.6 sec?

39. *National Park land.*   In 1994, the National Park system consisted of about 74.9 million acres. By 2005, the figure had grown to 79 million acres. Let $A(t)$ represent the amount of land in the National Park system, in millions of acres, t years after 1990.
Source: *Statistical Abstract of the United States,* 2007

  a) Find a linear function that fits the data.
  b) Use the function of part (a) to predict the amount of land in the National Park system in 2010.

40. *Pressure at sea depth.*   The pressure 100 ft beneath the ocean's surface is approximately 4 atm (atmospheres), whereas at a depth of 200 ft, the pressure is about 7 atm.

  a) Find a linear function that expresses pressure as a function of depth.
  b) Use the function of part (a) to determine the pressure at a depth of 690 ft.

Classify each function as a linear function, an absolute-value function, a quadratic function, another polynomial function, or a rational function, and determine the domain of the function.

41. $f(x) = \dfrac{1}{3}x - 7$ **42.** $g(x) = \dfrac{x}{x + 1}$

43. $p(x) = x^2 + x + 1$ **44.** $t(x) = |x - 7|$

45. $f(t) = \dfrac{12}{3t + 4}$ **46.** $g(n) = 15 - 10n$

47. $f(x) = 0.02x^4 - 0.1x + 1.7$

48. $f(a) = 2|a + 3|$

49. $f(x) = \dfrac{x}{2x - 5}$ **50.** $g(x) = \dfrac{2x}{3x - 4}$

51. $f(n) = \dfrac{4n - 7}{n^2 + 3n + 2}$ **52.** $h(x) = \dfrac{x - 5}{2x^2 - 2}$

53. $f(n) = 200 - 0.1n$ **54.** $g(t) = \dfrac{t^2 - 3t + 7}{8}$

Given the graph of each function, determine the range of f.

55.

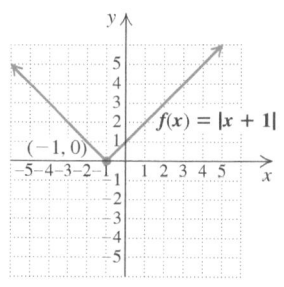

56.

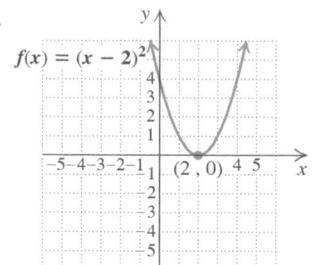

57.

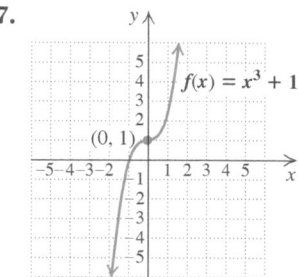

58.

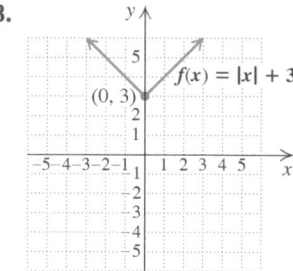

59.

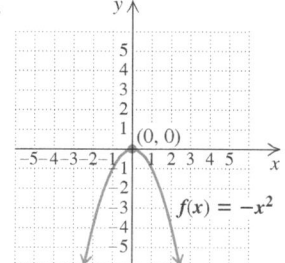

60.

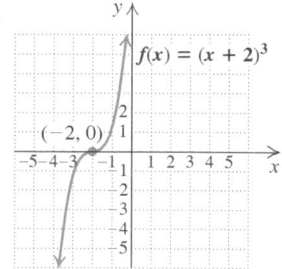

Graph each function and determine its domain and range.

61. $f(x) = x + 3$

62. $f(x) = 2x - 1$

63. $f(x) = -1$

64. $g(x) = 2$

65. $f(x) = |x| + 1$

66. $g(x) = |x - 3|$

67. $g(x) = x^2$

68. $f(x) = x^2 + 2$

69. Bob believes that the domain and range of all polynomial functions is $\mathbb{R}$. How could you convince him that he is mistaken?

70. Explain why the range of a constant function consists of only one number.

Skill Review

To prepare for Section 7.4, review polynomial operations (Sections 4.4 and 4.6).

Perform the indicated operations.

71. $(x^2 + 2x + 7) + (3x^2 - 8)$ [4.4]

72. $(3x^3 - x^2 + x) - (x^3 + 2x - 7)$ [4.4]

73. $(2x + 1)(x - 7)$ [4.6]

74. $(x - 3)(x + 4)$ [4.6]

75. $(x^3 + x^2 - 4x + 7) - (3x^2 - x + 2)$ [4.4]

76. $(2x^2 + x - 3) + (x^3 + 7)$ [4.4]

Synthesis

77. In 2004, Political Action Committees contributed $310.5 million to federal candidates. Does this information make your answer to Exercise 35(b) seem too low or too high? Why?

78. On the basis of your answers to Exercises 33 and 34, would you predict that at some point in the future the life expectancy of males will exceed that of females? Why or why not?

Given that $f(x) = mx + b$, classify each of the following as true or false.

79. $f(c + d) = f(c) + f(d)$

80. $f(cd) = f(c)f(d)$

81. $f(kx) = kf(x)$

82. $f(c - d) = f(c) - f(d)$

For Exercises 83–86, assume that a linear equation models each situation.

83. *Temperature conversion.* Water freezes at 32° Fahrenheit and at 0° Celsius. Water boils at 212°F and at 100°C. What Celsius temperature corresponds to a room temperature of 70°F?

84. *Depreciation of a computer.* After 6 mos of use, the value of Don's computer had dropped to $900. After 8 mos, the value had gone down to $750. How much did the computer cost originally?

85. *Cell-phone charges.* The total cost of Tam's cell phone was $410 after 5 mos of service and $690 after 9 mos. What costs had Tam already incurred when her service just began? Assume that Tam's monthly charge is constant.

86. *Operating expenses.* The total cost for operating Ming's Wings was $7500 after 4 mos and $9250 after 7 mos. Predict the total cost after 10 mos.

87. For a linear function g, $g(3) = -5$ and $g(7) = -1$.
   a) Find an equation for g.
   b) Find $g(-2)$.
   c) Find a such that $g(a) = 75$.

88. When several data points are available and they appear to be nearly collinear, a procedure known as *linear regression* can be used to find an equation for the line that most closely fits the data.

   a) Use a graphing calculator with a LINEAR REGRESSION option and the table that follows to find a linear function that predicts the wattage of a CFL (compact fluorescent) lightbulb as a function of the wattage of a standard incandescent bulb of equivalent brightness. Round coefficients to the nearest thousandth.

Energy Conservation

Incandescent Wattage	CFL Equivalent
25 W	5 W
50 W	9 W
60 W	15 W
100 W	25 W
120 W	28 W

Source: U.S. Department of Energy

   b) Use the function from part (a) to estimate the CFL wattage that is equivalent to a 75-watt incandescent bulb. Then compare your answer with the corresponding answer to Exercise 59 in Section 7.1. Which answer seems more reliable? Why?

CONNECTING the CONCEPTS

A function is a correspondence. This correspondence can be listed as a set of ordered pairs or described by an equation. The correspondence is between two sets, the domain and the range, and each member of the domain corresponds to exactly one member of the range.

For the function f: $\{(2, 3), (0, -4), (-8, 7)\}$:

The domain is $\{-8, 0, 2\}$.

The range is $\{-4, 3, 7\}$.

The input 2 corresponds to the output 3.

$f(2) = 3$

For the function given by $f(x) = x^2$:

The domain is $\mathbb{R}$.

The range is $[0, \infty)$.

The input -3 corresponds to the output 9.

$f(-3) = 9$

The independent variable is x.

MIXED REVIEW

Let $f = \{(3, 6), (4, 8), (-1, -2), (0, 0)\}$.

1. Find the domain of f.

2. Find the range of f.

3. Find $f(-1)$.

4. Graph f.

Let $g(x) = x - 1$ *and* $h(x) = \dfrac{2}{x}$.

5. Find the domain of g.

6. Find the domain of h.

7. Find $h(10)$.

8. Find $g(1) + h(1)$.

9. Find $(g \cdot h)(-2)$.

10. Find the domain of h/g.

11. Determine whether g is a linear function, a quadratic function, or a rational function.

12. Determine whether h is a linear function, a quadratic function, or a rational function.

13. Graph g and determine its range.

Use the following graph of F for Exercises 14–17.

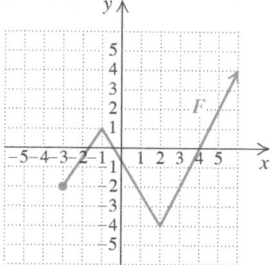

14. Determine from the graph whether F is a function.

15. Find $F(2)$.

16. Find the domain of F.

17. Find the range of F.

$$\text{Let } G(x) = \begin{cases} 1 - x, & \text{if } x < 1, \\ 10, & \text{if } x = 1, \\ x + 1, & \text{if } x > 1. \end{cases}$$

18. Find $G(3)$.

19. Find $G(1)$.

20. Find $G(-12)$.

7.4 | The Algebra of Functions

The Sum, Difference, Product, or Quotient of Two Functions   ■   Domains and Graphs

We now examine four ways in which functions can be combined.

The Sum, Difference, Product, or Quotient of Two Functions

Suppose that a is in the domain of two functions, f and g. The input a is paired with $f(a)$ by f and with $g(a)$ by g. The outputs can then be added to get $f(a) + g(a)$.

EXAMPLE   **1**   Let $f(x) = x + 4$ and $g(x) = x^2 + 1$. Find $f(2) + g(2)$.

SOLUTION   We visualize two function machines. Because 2 is in the domain of each function, we can compute $f(2)$ and $g(2)$.

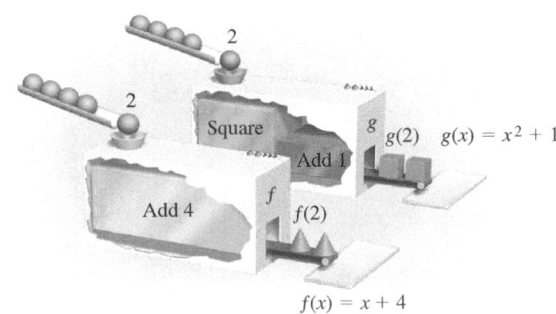

Since

$$f(2) = 2 + 4 = 6 \quad \text{and} \quad g(2) = 2^2 + 1 = 5,$$

we have

$$f(2) + g(2) = 6 + 5 = 11.$$

▸ TRY EXERCISE   7

In Example 1, suppose that we were to write $f(x) + g(x)$ as $(x + 4) + (x^2 + 1)$, or $f(x) + g(x) = x^2 + x + 5$. This could then be regarded as a "new" function. The notation $(f + g)(x)$ is generally used to denote a function formed in this manner. Similar notations exist for subtraction, multiplication, and division of functions.

The Algebra of Functions

If f and g are functions and x is in the domain of both functions, then:

1. $(f + g)(x) = f(x) + g(x)$;
2. $(f - g)(x) = f(x) - g(x)$;
3. $(f \cdot g)(x) = f(x) \cdot g(x)$;
4. $(f/g)(x) = f(x)/g(x)$, provided $g(x) \neq 0$.

EXAMPLE **2**   For $f(x) = x^2 - x$ and $g(x) = x + 2$, find the following.

a) $(f + g)(4)$ b) $(f - g)(x)$ and $(f - g)(-1)$
c) $(f/g)(x)$ and $(f/g)(-4)$ d) $(f \cdot g)(4)$

SOLUTION

a) Since $f(4) = 4^2 - 4 = 12$ and $g(4) = 4 + 2 = 6$, we have

$$(f + g)(4) = f(4) + g(4)$$
$$= 12 + 6 \quad \text{Substituting}$$
$$= 18.$$

Alternatively, we could first find $(f + g)(x)$:

$$(f + g)(x) = f(x) + g(x)$$
$$= x^2 - x + x + 2$$
$$= x^2 + 2. \quad \text{Combining like terms}$$

Thus,

$$(f + g)(4) = 4^2 + 2 = 18. \quad \text{Our results match.}$$

b) We have

$$(f - g)(x) = f(x) - g(x)$$
$$= x^2 - x - (x + 2) \quad \text{Substituting}$$
$$= x^2 - 2x - 2. \quad \begin{array}{l}\text{Removing parentheses and}\\\text{combining like terms}\end{array}$$

Thus,

$$(f - g)(-1) = (-1)^2 - 2(-1) - 2 \quad \begin{array}{l}\text{Using } (f - g)(x) \text{ is faster than}\\\text{using } f(x) - g(x).\end{array}$$
$$= 1. \quad \text{Simplifying}$$

c) We have

$$(f/g)(x) = f(x)/g(x)$$
$$= \frac{x^2 - x}{x + 2}. \quad \text{We assume that } x \neq -2.$$

Thus,

$$(f/g)(-4) = \frac{(-4)^2 - (-4)}{-4 + 2} \quad \text{Substituting}$$
$$= \frac{20}{-2} = -10.$$

d) Using our work in part (a), we have

$$(f \cdot g)(4) = f(4) \cdot g(4)$$
$$= 12 \cdot 6$$
$$= 72.$$

Alternatively, we could first find $(f \cdot g)(x)$:

$$(f \cdot g)(x) = f(x) \cdot g(x)$$
$$= (x^2 - x)(x + 2)$$
$$= x^3 + x^2 - 2x. \quad \text{Multiplying and combining like terms.}$$

Then

$$(f \cdot g)(4) = 4^3 + 4^2 - 2 \cdot 4$$
$$= 64 + 16 - 8$$
$$= 72.$$

TRY EXERCISE 17

Domains and Graphs

Although applications involving products and quotients of functions rarely appear in newspapers, situations involving sums or differences of functions often do appear in print. For example, the following graphs are similar to those published by the California Department of Education to promote breakfast programs in which students eat a balanced meal of fruit or juice, toast or cereal, and 2% or whole milk. The combination of carbohydrate, protein, and fat gives a sustained release of energy, delaying the onset of hunger for several hours.

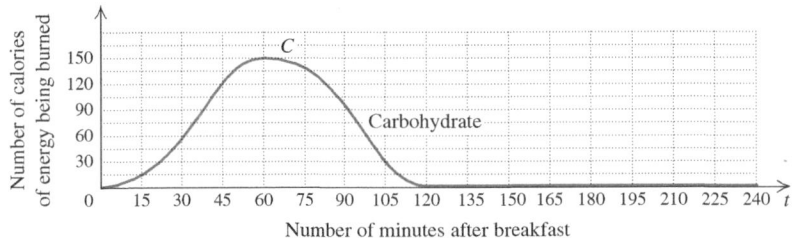

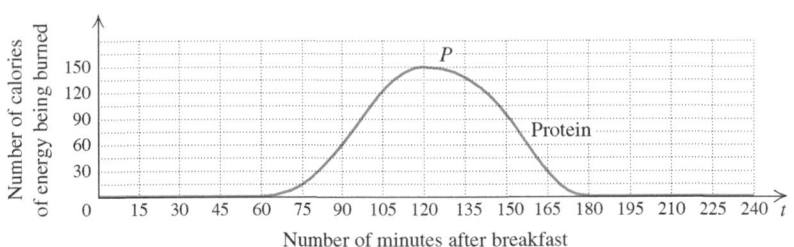

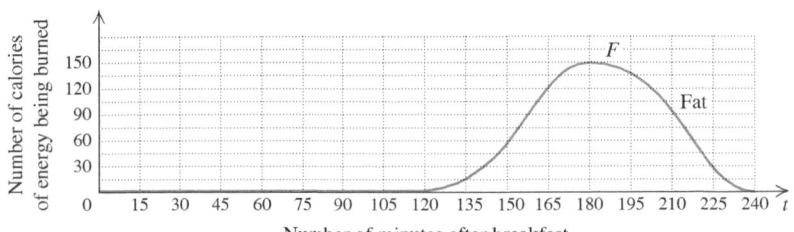

When the three graphs are superimposed, and the calorie expenditures added, it becomes clear that a balanced meal results in a steady, sustained supply of energy.

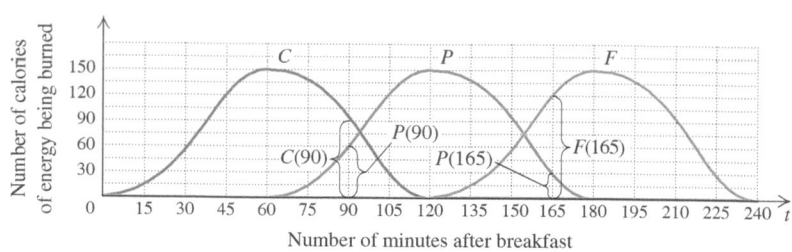

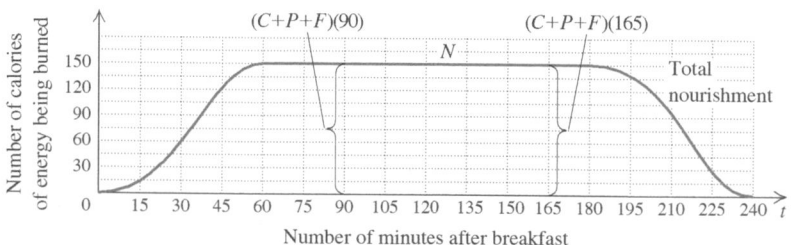

For any point $(t, N(t))$, we have

$$N(t) = (C + P + F)(t) = C(t) + P(t) + F(t).$$

To find $(f + g)(a), (f - g)(a), (f \cdot g)(a)$, or $(f/g)(a)$, we must know that $f(a)$ and $g(a)$ exist. This means a must be in the domain of both f and g.

EXAMPLE **3**   Let

$$f(x) = \frac{5}{x} \quad \text{and} \quad g(x) = \frac{2x - 6}{x + 1}.$$

Find the domain of $f + g$, the domain of $f - g$, and the domain of $f \cdot g$.

SOLUTION   Note that because division by 0 is undefined, we have

Domain of $f = \{x \,|\, x$ is a real number *and* $x \neq 0\}$

and

Domain of $g = \{x \,|\, x$ is a real number *and* $x \neq -1\}$.

In order to find $f(a) + g(a), f(a) - g(a)$, or $f(a) \cdot g(a)$, we must know that a is in *both* of the above domains. Thus,

Domain of $f + g$ = Domain of $f - g$ = Domain of $f \cdot g$

$$= \{x \,|\, x \text{ is a real number } and \ x \neq 0 \ and \ x \neq -1\}.$$

> **TRY EXERCISE** 43

Suppose that for $f(x) = x^2 - x$ and $g(x) = x + 2$, we want to find $(f/g)(-2)$. Finding $f(-2)$ and $g(-2)$ poses no problem:

$$f(-2) = 6 \quad \text{and} \quad g(-2) = 0;$$

but then

$$(f/g)(-2) = f(-2)/g(-2)$$
$$= 6/0. \quad \text{Division by 0 is undefined.}$$

Thus, although -2 is in the domain of both f and g, it is not in the domain of f/g.

We can also see this by writing $(f/g)(x)$:

$$(f/g)(x) = \frac{f(x)}{g(x)} = \frac{x^2 - x}{x + 2}.$$

Since $x + 2 = 0$ when $x = -2$, the domain of f/g must exclude -2.

Determining the Domain

The domain of $f + g$, $f - g$, or $f \cdot g$ is the set of all values common to the domains of f and g.

The domain of f/g is the set of all values common to the domains of f and g, excluding any values for which $g(x)$ is 0.

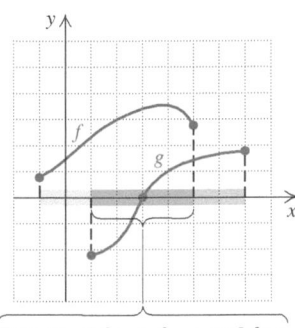

Domain of $f + g$, $f - g$, and $f \cdot g$

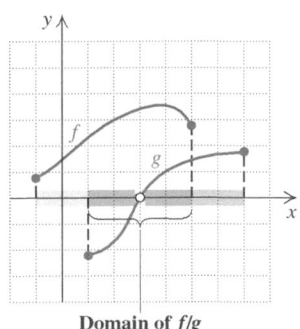

Domain of f/g

EXAMPLE 4   Given $f(x) = 1/x$ and $g(x) = 2x - 7$, find the domains of $f + g$, $f - g$, $f \cdot g$, and f/g.

SOLUTION   We first find the domain of f and the domain of g:

The domain of f is $\{x \mid x$ is a real number *and* $x \neq 0\}$.

The domain of g is $\mathbb{R}$.

STUDENT NOTES

The concern over a denominator being 0 arises throughout this course. Try to develop the habit of checking for any possible input values that would create a denominator of 0 whenever you work with functions.

The domains of $f + g$, $f - g$, and $f \cdot g$ are the set of all elements common to the domains of f and g. This consists of all real numbers except 0.

The domain of $f + g$ = the domain of $f - g$ = the domain of $f \cdot g$
$$= \{x \mid x \text{ is a real number } and \ x \neq 0\}.$$

Because we cannot divide by 0, the domain of f/g must also exclude any values of x for which $g(x)$ is 0. We determine those values by solving $g(x) = 0$:

$$g(x) = 0$$
$$2x - 7 = 0 \qquad \text{Replacing } g(x) \text{ with } 2x - 7$$
$$2x = 7$$
$$x = \tfrac{7}{2}.$$

The domain of f/g is the domain of the sum, difference, and product of f and g, found above, excluding $\tfrac{7}{2}$.

The domain of $f/g = \left\{x \mid x \text{ is a real number } and \ x \neq 0 \ and \ x \neq \tfrac{7}{2}\right\}$.

TRY EXERCISE   55

TECHNOLOGY CONNECTION

A partial check of Example 4 can be performed by setting up a table so the TBLSTART is 0 and the increment of change (ΔTbl) is 0.7. (Other choices, like 0.1, will also work.) Next, we let $y_1 = 1/x$ and $y_2 = 2x - 7$. Using Y-VARS to write $y_3 = y_1 + y_2$ and $y_4 = y_1/y_2$, we can create the table of values shown here. Note that when x is 3.5, a value for y_3 can be found, but y_4 is undefined. If we "de-select" y_1 and y_2 as we enter them, the columns for y_3 and y_4 appear without scrolling through the table.

X	Y3	Y4
0	ERROR	ERROR
.7	−4.171	−.2551
1.4	−3.486	−.1701
2.1	−2.324	−.1701
2.8	−1.043	−.2551
3.5	.28571	ERROR
4.2	1.6381	.17007

X = 0

Use a similar approach to partially check Example 3.

Division by 0 is not the only condition that can force restrictions on the domain of a function. In Chapter 10, we will examine functions similar to that given by $f(x) = \sqrt{x}$, for which the concern is taking the square root of a negative number.

7.4   EXERCISE SET

For Extra Help   MyMathLab   Math XL PRACTICE   WATCH   DOWNLOAD

Concept Reinforcement   Make each of the following sentences true by selecting the correct word for each blank.

1. If f and g are functions, then $(f + g)(x)$ is the _____ of the functions.
   sum/difference

2. One way to compute $(f - g)(2)$ is to _____ $g(2)$ from $f(2)$.
   erase/subtract

3. One way to compute $(f - g)(2)$ is to simplify $f(x) - g(x)$ and then _____ the result
   evaluate/substitute
   for $x = 2$.

4. The domain of $f + g$, $f - g$, and $f \cdot g$ is the set of all values common to the _____ of f and g.
   domains/ranges

5. The domain of f/g is the set of all values common to the domains of f and g, _____ any
   including/excluding
   values for which $g(x)$ is 0.

6. The height of $(f + g)(a)$ on a graph is the _____ of the heights of $f(a)$ and $g(a)$.
   product/sum

Let $f(x) = -2x + 3$ and $g(x) = x^2 - 5$. Find each of the following.

7. $f(3) + g(3)$

8. $f(4) + g(4)$

9. $f(1) - g(1)$

10. $f(2) - g(2)$

11. $f(-2) \cdot g(-2)$

12. $f(-1) \cdot g(-1)$

13. $f(-4)/g(-4)$

14. $f(3)/g(3)$

15. $g(1) - f(1)$

16. $g(-3)/f(-3)$

17. $(f + g)(x)$

18. $(g - f)(x)$

Let $F(x) = x^2 - 2$ and $G(x) = 5 - x$. Find each of the following.

19. $(F + G)(x)$

20. $(F + G)(a)$

21. $(F - G)(3)$

22. $(F - G)(2)$

23. $(F \cdot G)(a)$

24. $(G \cdot F)(x)$

25. $(F/G)(x)$

26. $(G - F)(x)$

27. $(G/F)(-2)$

28. $(F/G)(-1)$

29. $(F + F)(1)$

30. $(G \cdot G)(6)$

The following graph shows the number of births in the United States, in millions, from 1970–2004. Here $C(t)$ represents the number of Caesarean section births, $B(t)$ the number of non-Caesarean section births, and $N(t)$ the total number of births in year t.

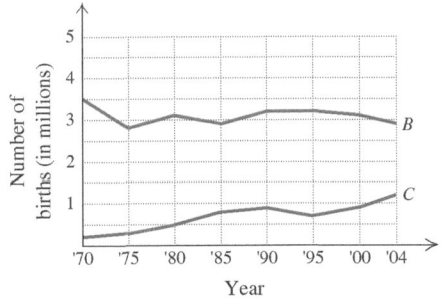

Source: National Center for Health Statistics

31. Use estimates of $C(2004)$ and $B(2004)$ to estimate $N(2004)$.

32. Use estimates of $C(1985)$ and $B(1985)$ to estimate $N(1985)$.

In 2004, a study comparing high doses of the cholesterol-lowering drugs Lipitor and Pravachol indicated that patients taking Lipitor were significantly less likely to have heart attacks or require angioplasty or surgery.

In the graph below, $L(t)$ is the percentage of patients on Lipitor (80 mg) and $P(t)$ is the percentage of patients on Pravachol (40 mg) who suffered heart problems or death t years after beginning to take the medication.
Source: New York Times, March 9, 2004

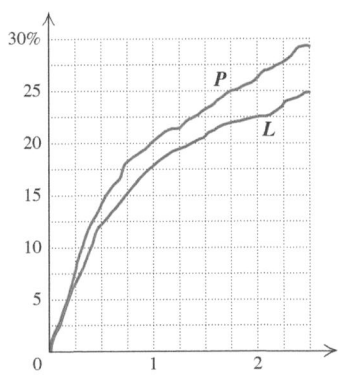

Years of follow-up of patients

Source: New England Journal of Medicine

33. Use estimates of $P(2)$ and $L(2)$ to estimate $(P - L)(2)$.

34. Use estimates of $P(1)$ and $L(1)$ to estimate $(P - L)(1)$.

Often function addition is represented by stacking the individual functions directly on top of each other. The graph below indicates how U.S. municipal solid waste has been managed. The braces indicate the values of the individual functions.

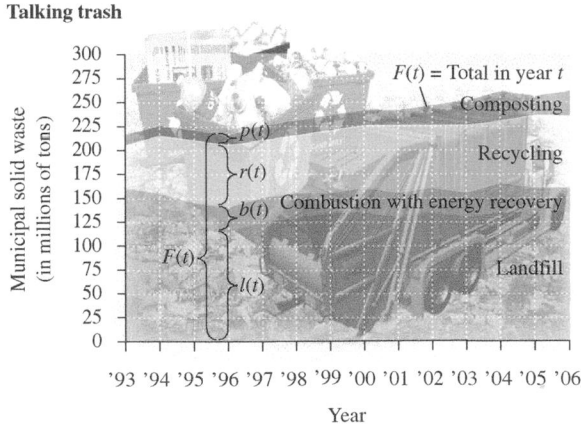

Source: Environmental Protection Agency

35. Estimate $(p + r)('05)$. What does it represent?

36. Estimate $(p + r + b)('05)$. What does it represent?

37. Estimate $F('96)$. What does it represent?

38. Estimate $F('06)$. What does it represent?

39. Estimate $(F - p)('04)$. What does it represent?

40. Estimate $(F - l)('03)$. What does it represent?

For each pair of functions f and g, determine the domain of the sum, difference, and product of the two functions.

41. $f(x) = x^2,$
  $g(x) = 7x - 4$

42. $f(x) = 5x - 1,$
  $g(x) = 2x^2$

43. $f(x) = \dfrac{1}{x + 5},$
  $g(x) = 4x^3$

44. $f(x) = 3x^2,$
  $g(x) = \dfrac{1}{x - 9}$

45. $f(x) = \dfrac{2}{x},$
  $g(x) = x^2 - 4$

46. $f(x) = x^3 + 1,$
  $g(x) = \dfrac{5}{x}$

47. $f(x) = x + \dfrac{2}{x - 1},$
  $g(x) = 3x^3$

48. $f(x) = 9 - x^2,$
  $g(x) = \dfrac{3}{x + 6} + 2x$

49. $f(x) = \dfrac{3}{2x + 9}$,

   $g(x) = \dfrac{5}{1 - x}$

50. $f(x) = \dfrac{5}{3 - x}$,

   $g(x) = \dfrac{1}{4x - 1}$

For each pair of functions f and g, determine the domain of f/g.

51. $f(x) = x^4$,
   $g(x) = x - 3$

52. $f(x) = 2x^3$,
   $g(x) = 5 - x$

53. $f(x) = 3x - 2$,
   $g(x) = 2x + 8$

54. $f(x) = 5 + x$,
   $g(x) = 6 - 2x$

55. $f(x) = \dfrac{3}{x - 4}$,
   $g(x) = 5 - x$

56. $f(x) = \dfrac{1}{2 - x}$,
   $g(x) = 7 + x$

57. $f(x) = \dfrac{2x}{x + 1}$,
   $g(x) = 2x + 5$

58. $f(x) = \dfrac{7x}{x - 2}$,
   $g(x) = 3x + 7$

For Exercises 59–66, consider the functions F and G as shown.

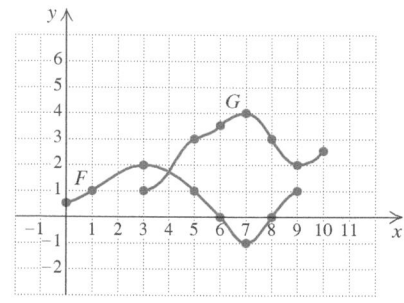

59. Determine $(F + G)(5)$ and $(F + G)(7)$.

60. Determine $(F \cdot G)(6)$ and $(F \cdot G)(9)$.

61. Determine $(G - F)(7)$ and $(G - F)(3)$.

62. Determine $(F/G)(3)$ and $(F/G)(7)$.

63. Find the domains of F, G, $F + G$, and F/G.

64. Find the domains of $F - G$, $F \cdot G$, and G/F.

65. Graph $F + G$.

66. Graph $G - F$.

In the following graph, S(t) represents the number of gallons of carbonated soft drinks consumed by the average American in year t, M(t) the number of gallons of milk, J(t) the number of gallons of fruit juice, and W(t) the number of gallons of bottled water.

Beverage consumption

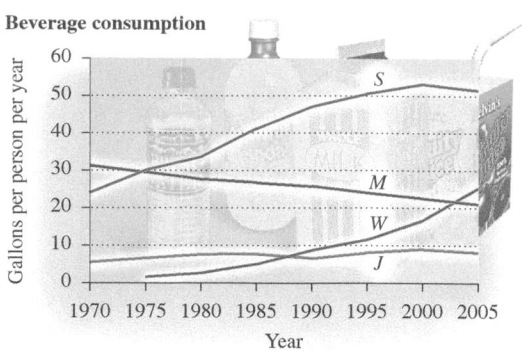

Source: Economic Research Service, U. S. Department of Agriculture

67. Between what years did the average American drink more soft drinks than juice, bottled water, and milk combined? Explain how you determined this.

68. Examine the graphs before Exercises 31 and 32. Did the total number of births increase or decrease from 1970 to 2004? Did the percent of births by Caesarean section increase or decrease from 1970 to 2004? Explain how you determined your answers.

Skill Review

To prepare for Section 7.5, review solving a formula for a variable (Section 2.3).

Solve. [2.3]

69. $ac = b$, for c

70. $x - wz = y$, for w

71. $pq - rq = st$, for q

72. $ab = d - cb$, for b

73. $ab - cd = 3b + d$, for b

74. $ab - cd = 3b + d$, for d

Synthesis

75. Examine the graphs following Example 2 and explain how they might be modified to represent the absorption of 200 mg of Advil® taken four times a day.

76. If $f(x) = c$, where c is some positive constant, describe how the graphs of $y = g(x)$ and $y = (f + g)(x)$ will differ.

77. Find the domain of F/G, if

$$F(x) = \dfrac{1}{x - 4} \quad \text{and} \quad G(x) = \dfrac{x^2 - 4}{x - 3}.$$

78. Find the domain of f/g, if

$$f(x) = \dfrac{3x}{2x + 5} \quad \text{and} \quad g(x) = \dfrac{x^4 - 1}{3x + 9}.$$

79. Sketch the graph of two functions f and g such that the domain of f/g is
$$\{x \mid -2 \le x \le 3 \ and \ x \ne 1\}.$$

80. Find the domains of $f + g, f - g, f \cdot g,$ and $f/g,$ if
$$f = \{(-2, 1), (-1, 2), (0, 3), (1, 4), (2, 5)\}$$
and
$$g = \{(-4, 4), (-3, 3), (-2, 4), (-1, 0), (0, 5), (1, 6)\}.$$

81. Find the domain of m/n, if
$$m(x) = 3x \quad for \ -1 < x < 5$$
and
$$n(x) = 2x - 3.$$

82. For f and g as defined in Exercise 80, find $(f + g)(-2), (f \cdot g)(0),$ and $(f/g)(1).$

83. Write equations for two functions f and g such that the domain of $f + g$ is
$$\{x \mid x \text{ is a real number } and \ x \ne -2 \ and \ x \ne 5\}.$$

84. Let $y_1 = 2.5x + 1.5, y_2 = x - 3,$ and $y_3 = y_1/y_2.$ Depending on whether the CONNECTED or DOT mode is used, the graph of y_3 appears as follows. Use algebra to determine which graph more accurately represents $y_3.$

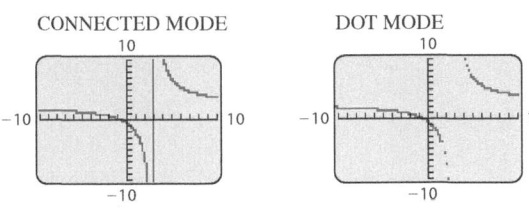

85. Using the window $[-5, 5, -1, 9]$, graph $y_1 = 5$, $y_2 = x + 2,$ and $y_3 = \sqrt{x}.$ Then predict what shape the graphs of $y_1 + y_2, y_1 + y_3,$ and $y_2 + y_3$ will take. Use a graphing calculator to check each prediction.

86. Use the TABLE feature on a graphing calculator to check your answers to Exercises 45, 47, 55, and 57. (See the Technology Connection on p. 480.)

COLLABORATIVE CORNER

Time On Your Hands

Focus: The algebra of functions

Time: 10–15 minutes

Group size: 2–3

The graph and the data at right chart the average retirement age $R(x)$ and life expectancy $E(x)$ of U.S. citizens in year x.

ACTIVITY

1. Working as a team, perform the appropriate calculations and then graph $E - R.$

2. What does $(E - R)(x)$ represent? In what fields of study or business might the function $E - R$ prove useful?

3. Should E and R really be calculated separately for men and women? Why or why not?

4. What advice would you give to someone considering early retirement?

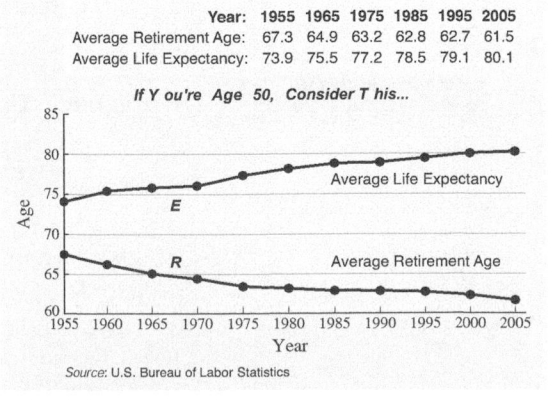

Year:	1955	1965	1975	1985	1995	2005
Average Retirement Age:	67.3	64.9	63.2	62.8	62.7	61.5
Average Life Expectancy:	73.9	75.5	77.2	78.5	79.1	80.1

Source: U.S. Bureau of Labor Statistics

7.5   Formulas, Applications, and Variation

Formulas • Direct Variation • Inverse Variation • Joint Variation and Combined Variation

Formulas

Formulas occur frequently as mathematical models. Many formulas contain rational expressions, and to solve such formulas for a specified letter, we proceed as when solving rational equations.

EXAMPLE 1   *Electronics.*   The formula

$$\frac{1}{R} = \frac{1}{r_1} + \frac{1}{r_2}$$

is used by electricians to determine the resistance R of two resistors r_1 and r_2 connected in parallel.* Solve for r_1.

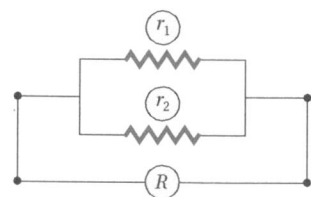

SOLUTION   We use the same approach as in Section 6.6:

$$Rr_1r_2 \cdot \frac{1}{R} = Rr_1r_2 \cdot \left(\frac{1}{r_1} + \frac{1}{r_2}\right)$$ Multiplying both sides by the LCD to clear fractions

$$Rr_1r_2 \cdot \frac{1}{R} = Rr_1r_2 \cdot \frac{1}{r_1} + Rr_1r_2 \cdot \frac{1}{r_2}$$ Multiplying to remove parentheses

$$r_1r_2 = Rr_2 + Rr_1.$$ Simplifying by removing factors equal to 1: $\frac{R}{R} = 1; \frac{r_1}{r_1} = 1; \frac{r_2}{r_2} = 1$

At this point it is tempting to multiply by $1/r_2$ to get r_1 alone on the left, *but* note that there is an r_1 on the right. We must get all the terms involving r_1 on the *same side* of the equation.

$$r_1r_2 - Rr_1 = Rr_2$$ Subtracting Rr_1 from both sides

$$r_1(r_2 - R) = Rr_2$$ Factoring out r_1 in order to combine like terms

$$r_1 = \frac{Rr_2}{r_2 - R}$$ Dividing both sides by $r_2 - R$ to get r_1 alone

This formula can be used to calculate r_1 whenever R and r_2 are known.

> TRY EXERCISE   17

EXAMPLE 2   *Astronomy.*   The formula

$$\frac{V^2}{R^2} = \frac{2g}{R + h}$$

is used to find a satellite's *escape velocity* V, where R is a planet's radius, h is the satellite's height above the planet, and g is the planet's gravitational constant. Solve for h.

---

*Recall that the subscripts 1 and 2 merely indicate that r_1 and r_2 are different variables representing similar quantities.

SOLUTION   We first multiply by the LCD, $R^2(R + h)$, to clear fractions:

$$\frac{V^2}{R^2} = \frac{2g}{R + h}$$

$$R^2(R + h)\frac{V^2}{R^2} = R^2(R + h)\frac{2g}{R + h} \qquad \text{Multiplying to clear fractions}$$

$$\frac{R^2(R + h)V^2}{R^2} = \frac{R^2(R + h)2g}{R + h}$$

$$(R + h)V^2 = R^2 \cdot 2g. \qquad \begin{array}{l}\text{Removing factors equal to 1:}\\[4pt] \frac{R^2}{R^2} = 1 \text{ and } \frac{R + h}{R + h} = 1\end{array}$$

Remember: We are solving for h. Although we *could* distribute V^2, since h appears only within the factor $R + h$, it is easier to divide both sides by V^2:

$$\frac{(R + h)V^2}{V^2} = \frac{2R^2g}{V^2} \qquad \text{Dividing both sides by } V^2$$

$$R + h = \frac{2R^2g}{V^2} \qquad \text{Removing a factor equal to 1: } \frac{V^2}{V^2} = 1$$

$$h = \frac{2R^2g}{V^2} - R. \qquad \text{Subtracting } R \text{ from both sides}$$

The last equation can be used to determine the height of a satellite above a planet when the planet's radius and gravitational constant, along with the satellite's escape velocity, are known.

▶ **TRY EXERCISE** ▶ 29

EXAMPLE 3

Acoustics (the Doppler Effect).   The formula

$$f = \frac{sg}{s + v}$$

is used to determine the frequency f of a sound that is moving at velocity v toward a listener who hears the sound as frequency g. Here s is the speed of sound in a particular medium. Solve for s.

STUDENT NOTES ————

The steps used to solve equations are precisely the same steps used to solve formulas. If you feel "rusty" in this regard, study the earlier section in which this type of equation first appeared. Then make sure that you can consistently solve those equations before returning to the work with formulas.

SOLUTION   We first clear fractions by multiplying by the LCD, $s + v$:

$$f \cdot (s + v) = \frac{sg}{s + v}(s + v)$$

$$fs + fv = sg. \qquad \begin{array}{l}\text{The variable for which we are solving, } s,\\ \text{appears on both sides, forcing us to}\\ \text{distribute on the left side.}\end{array}$$

Next, we must get all terms containing s on one side:

$$fv = sg - fs \qquad \text{Subtracting } fs \text{ from both sides}$$
$$fv = s(g - f) \qquad \text{Factoring out } s. \text{ This is like combining like terms.}$$
$$\frac{fv}{g - f} = s. \qquad \text{Dividing both sides by } g - f$$

Since s is isolated on one side, we have solved for s. This last equation can be used to determine the speed of sound whenever f, v, and g are known.

 TRY EXERCISE   19

To Solve a Rational Equation for a Specified Variable

1. Multiply both sides by the LCD to clear fractions, if necessary.
2. Multiply to remove parentheses, if necessary.
3. Get all terms with the specified variable alone on one side.
4. Factor out the specified variable if it is in more than one term.
5. Multiply or divide on both sides to isolate the specified variable.

Variation

To extend our study of formulas and functions, we now examine three real-world situations: direct variation, inverse variation, and combined variation.

DIRECT VARIATION

A computer technician earns $22 per hour. In 1 hr, $22 is earned. In 2 hr, $44 is earned. In 3 hr, $66 is earned, and so on. This gives rise to a set of ordered pairs:

$$(1, 22), (2, 44), (3, 66), (4, 88), \quad \text{and so on.}$$

Note that the ratio of earnings E to time t is $\frac{22}{1}$ in every case.

If a situation is modeled by pairs for which the ratio is constant, we say there is **direct variation**. Here earnings *vary directly* as the time:

We have $\dfrac{E}{t} = 22$, so $E = 22t$ or, using function notation, $E(t) = 22t$.

Direct Variation

When a situation is modeled by a linear function of the form $f(x) = kx$, or $y = kx$, where k is a nonzero constant, we say that there is *direct variation*, that y *varies directly* as x, or that y *is proportional to* x. The number k is called the *variation constant*, or *constant of proportionality*.

Note that for $k > 0$, any equation of the form $y = kx$ indicates that as x increases, y increases as well.

EXAMPLE 4

Find the variation constant and an equation of variation if y varies directly as x, and $y = 32$ when $x = 2$.

SOLUTION   We know that $(2, 32)$ is a solution of $y = kx$. Therefore,

$$32 = k \cdot 2 \qquad \text{Substituting}$$

$$\frac{32}{2} = k, \quad \text{or} \quad k = 16. \qquad \text{Solving for } k$$

The variation constant is 16. The equation of variation is $y = 16x$. The notation $y(x) = 16x$ or $f(x) = 16x$ is also used.   ▶ TRY EXERCISE ▶ 43

EXAMPLE 5

Ocean waves.   The speed v of a train of ocean waves varies directly as the swell period t, or time between successive waves. Waves with a swell period of 12 sec are traveling 21 mph. How fast are waves traveling that have a swell period of 20 sec?

Source: www.rodntube.com

SOLUTION

1. **Familiarize.** Because of the phrase "v . . . varies directly as . . . t," we express the speed of the wave v, in miles per hour, as a function of the swell period t, in seconds. Thus, $v(t) = kt$, where k is the variation constant. Because we are using ratios, we can use the units "seconds" and "miles per hour" without converting sec to hr or hr to sec. Knowing that waves with a swell period of 12 sec are traveling 21 mph, we have $v(12) = 21$.

2. **Translate.** We find the variation constant using the data and then use it to write the equation of variation:

$$v(t) = kt$$

$$v(12) = k \cdot 12 \qquad \text{Replacing } t \text{ with } 12$$

$$21 = k \cdot 12 \qquad \text{Replacing } v(12) \text{ with } 21$$

$$\frac{21}{12} = k \qquad \text{Solving for } k$$

$$1.75 = k. \qquad \text{This is the variation constant.}$$

The equation of variation is $v(t) = 1.75t$. This is the translation.

3. **Carry out.** To find the speed of waves with a swell period of 20 sec, we compute $v(20)$:

$$v(t) = 1.75t$$

$$v(20) = 1.75(20) \qquad \text{Substituting 20 for } t$$

$$= 35.$$

4. **Check.** To check, we could reexamine all our calculations. Note that our answer seems reasonable since the ratios $21/12$ and $35/20$ are both 1.75.

5. **State.** Waves with a swell period of 20 sec are traveling 35 mph.

▶ TRY EXERCISE ▶ 55

INVERSE VARIATION

Suppose a bus travels 20 mi. At 20 mph, the trip takes 1 hr. At 40 mph, it takes $\frac{1}{2}$ hr. At 60 mph, it takes $\frac{1}{3}$ hr, and so on. This gives pairs of numbers, all having the same product:

$$(20, 1), \left(40, \tfrac{1}{2}\right), \left(60, \tfrac{1}{3}\right), \left(80, \tfrac{1}{4}\right), \quad \text{and so on.}$$

Note that the product of each pair is 20. When a situation is modeled by pairs for which the product is constant, we say that there is **inverse variation**. Since $r \cdot t = 20$, we have

$$t = \frac{20}{r} \quad \text{or, using function notation,} \quad t(r) = \frac{20}{r}.$$

> ### Inverse Variation
>
> When a situation is modeled by a rational function of the form $f(x) = k/x$, or $y = k/x$, where k is a nonzero constant, we say that there is *inverse variation*, that *y varies inversely as x*, or that *y is inversely proportional to x*. The number k is called the *variation constant*, or *constant of proportionality*.

Note that for $k > 0$, any equation of the form $y = k/x$ indicates that as x increases, y decreases.

EXAMPLE **6**   Find the variation constant and an equation of variation if y varies inversely as x, and $y = 32$ when $x = 0.2$.

SOLUTION   We know that $(0.2, 32)$ is a solution of

$$y = \frac{k}{x}.$$

Therefore,

$$32 = \frac{k}{0.2} \quad \text{Substituting}$$
$$(0.2)32 = k$$
$$6.4 = k. \quad \text{Solving for } k$$

The variation constant is 6.4. The equation of variation is

$$y = \frac{6.4}{x}.$$

> TRY EXERCISE   49

There are many real-life quantities that vary inversely.

EXAMPLE **7**   *Movie downloads.*   The time t that it takes to download a movie file varies inversely as the transfer speed s of the Internet connection. A typical full-length movie file will transfer in 48 min at a transfer speed of 256 KB/s (kilobytes per second). How long will it take to transfer the same movie file at a transfer speed of 32 KB/s?

Source: www.xsvidmovies.com

SOLUTION

1. **Familiarize.** Because of the phrase ". . . varies inversely as the transfer speed," we express the download time t, in minutes, as a function of the transfer speed s, in kilobytes per second. Thus, $t(s) = k/s$.

2. **Translate.** We use the given information to solve for k. We will then use that result to write the equation of variation.

$$t(s) = \frac{k}{s}$$

$$t(256) = \frac{k}{256} \qquad \text{Replacing } s \text{ with } 256$$

$$48 = \frac{k}{256} \qquad \text{Replacing } t(256) \text{ with } 48$$

$$12{,}288 = k.$$

The equation of variation is $t(s) = 12{,}288/s$. This is the translation.

3. **Carry out.** To find the download time at a transfer speed of 32 KB/s, we calculate $t(32)$:

$$t(32) = \frac{12{,}288}{32} = 384.$$

4. **Check.** Note that, as expected, as the transfer speed goes *down*, the download time goes *up*. Also, the products $48 \cdot 256$ and $32 \cdot 384$ are both 12,288.

5. **State.** At a transfer speed of 32 KB/s, it will take 384 min, or 6 hr 24 min, to download the movie file.

> **TRY EXERCISE** 57

JOINT VARIATION AND COMBINED VARIATION

When a variable varies directly with more than one other variable, we say that there is *joint variation*. For example, in the formula for the volume of a right circular cylinder, $V = \pi r^2 h$, we say that V varies *jointly* as h and the square of r.

Joint Variation

y varies *jointly* as x and z if, for some nonzero constant k, $y = kxz$.

EXAMPLE   8

Find an equation of variation if y varies jointly as x and z, and $y = 30$ when $x = 2$ and $z = 3$.

SOLUTION   We have

$$y = kxz,$$

so

$$30 = k \cdot 2 \cdot 3$$
$$k = 5. \qquad \text{The variation constant is 5.}$$

The equation of variation is $y = 5xz$.

> **TRY EXERCISE** 73

Joint variation is one form of *combined variation*. In general, when a variable varies directly and/or inversely, at the same time, with more than one other variable, there is **combined variation**. Examples 8 and 9 are both examples of combined variation.

EXAMPLE **9** Find an equation of variation if y varies jointly as x and z and inversely as the square of w, and $y = 105$ when $x = 3$, $z = 20$, and $w = 2$.

SOLUTION   The equation of variation is of the form

$$y = k \cdot \frac{xz}{w^2},$$

so, substituting, we have

$$105 = k \cdot \frac{3 \cdot 20}{2^2}$$
$$105 = k \cdot 15$$
$$k = 7.$$

Thus,

$$y = 7 \cdot \frac{xz}{w^2}.$$

TRY EXERCISE ▶ 75

7.5   EXERCISE SET

For Extra Help
MyMathLab      PRACTICE   WATCH   DOWNLOAD

⤶ *Concept Reinforcement*   *Match each statement with the correct term that completes it from the list on the right.*

1. To clear fractions, we can multiply both sides of an equation by the ____.

2. With direct variation, pairs of numbers have a constant ____.

3. With inverse variation, pairs of numbers have a constant ____.

4. If $y = k/x$, then y varies ____ as x.

5. If $y = kx$, then y varies ____ as x.

6. If $y = kxz$, then y varies ____ as x and z.

a) Directly

b) Inversely

c) Jointly

d) LCD

e) Product

f) Ratio

Determine whether each situation represents direct variation or inverse variation.

7. Two painters can scrape a house in 9 hr, whereas three painters can scrape the house in 6 hr.

8. Andres planted 5 bulbs in 20 min and 7 bulbs in 28 min.

9. Salma swam 2 laps in 7 min and 6 laps in 21 min.

10. It took 2 band members 80 min to set up for a show; with 4 members working, it took 40 min.

11. It took 3 hr for 4 volunteers to wrap the campus' collection of Toys for Tots, but only 1.5 hr with 8 volunteers working.

12. Ayana's air conditioner cooled off 1000 ft^3 in 10 min and 3000 ft^3 in 30 min.

Solve each formula for the specified variable.

13. $f = \dfrac{L}{d}$; d

14. $\dfrac{W_1}{W_2} = \dfrac{d_1}{d_2}$; W_1

15. $s = \dfrac{(v_1 + v_2)t}{2}$; v_1

16. $s = \dfrac{(v_1 + v_2)t}{2}$; t

17. $\dfrac{t}{a} + \dfrac{t}{b} = 1$; b

18. $\dfrac{1}{R} = \dfrac{1}{r_1} + \dfrac{1}{r_2}$; R

19. $R = \dfrac{gs}{g + s}$; g

20. $K = \dfrac{rt}{r - t}$; t

21. $I = \dfrac{nE}{R + nr}$; n

22. $I = \dfrac{nE}{R + nr}$; r

23. $\dfrac{1}{p} + \dfrac{1}{q} = \dfrac{1}{f}$; q

24. $\dfrac{1}{p} + \dfrac{1}{q} = \dfrac{1}{f}$; p

25. $S = \dfrac{H}{m(t_1 - t_2)}$; t_1

26. $S = \dfrac{H}{m(t_1 - t_2)}$; H

27. $\dfrac{E}{e} = \dfrac{R + r}{r}$; r

28. $\dfrac{E}{e} = \dfrac{R + r}{R}$; R

29. $S = \dfrac{a}{1 - r}$; r

30. $S = \dfrac{a - ar^n}{1 - r}$; a

Aha! **31.** $c = \dfrac{f}{(a + b)c}$; $a + b$

32. $d = \dfrac{g}{d(c + f)}$; $c + f$

33. *Interest.*   The formula

$$P = \dfrac{A}{1 + r}$$

is used to determine what principal P should be invested for one year at $(100 \cdot r)\%$ simple interest in order to have A dollars after a year. Solve for r.

34. *Taxable interest.*   The formula

$$I_t = \dfrac{I_f}{1 - T}$$

gives the *taxable interest rate I_t* equivalent to the *tax-free interest rate I_f* for a person in the $(100 \cdot T)\%$ tax bracket. Solve for T.

35. *Average speed.*   The formula

$$v = \dfrac{d_2 - d_1}{t_2 - t_1}$$

gives an object's average speed v when that object has traveled d_1 miles in t_1 hours and d_2 miles in t_2 hours. Solve for t_1.

36. *Average acceleration.*   The formula

$$a = \dfrac{v_2 - v_1}{t_2 - t_1}$$

gives a vehicle's *average acceleration* when its velocity changes from v_1 at time t_1 to v_2 at time t_2. Solve for t_2.

37. *Work rate.*   The formula

$$\dfrac{1}{t} = \dfrac{1}{a} + \dfrac{1}{b}$$

gives the total time t required for two workers to complete a job, if the workers' individual times are a and b. Solve for t.

38. *Planetary orbits.*   The formula

$$\dfrac{x^2}{a^2} + \dfrac{y^2}{b^2} = 1$$

can be used to plot a planet's elliptical orbit of width $2a$ and length $2b$ (see p. 869 in Section 10.2). Solve for b^2.

39. *Semester average.*   The formula

$$A = \dfrac{2Tt + Qq}{2T + Q}$$

gives a student's average A after T tests and Q quizzes, where each test counts as 2 quizzes, t is the test average, and q is the quiz average. Solve for Q.

40. *Astronomy.*   The formula

$$L = \dfrac{dR}{D - d},$$

where D is the diameter of the sun, d is the diameter of the earth, R is the earth's distance from the sun, and L is some fixed distance, is used in calculating when lunar eclipses occur. Solve for D.

41. *Body-fat percentage.*   The YMCA calculates men's body-fat percentage p using the formula

$$p = \dfrac{-98.42 + 4.15c - 0.082w}{w},$$

where c is the waist measurement, in inches, and w is the weight, in pounds. Solve for w.
Source: YMCA guide to Physical Fitness Assessment

42. *Preferred viewing distance.*   Researchers model the distance D from which an observer prefers to watch television in "picture heights"—that is, multiples of the height of the viewing screen. The preferred viewing distance is given by

$$D = \frac{3.55H + 0.9}{H},$$

where D is in picture heights and H is in meters. Solve for H.

Source: www.tid.es, Telefonica Investigación y Desarrollo, S.A. Unipersonal

Find the variation constant and an equation of variation if y varies directly as x and the following conditions apply.

43. $y = 30$ when $x = 5$

44. $y = 80$ when $x = 16$

45. $y = 3.4$ when $x = 2$

46. $y = 2$ when $x = 5$

47. $y = 2$ when $x = \frac{1}{5}$

48. $y = 0.9$ when $x = 0.5$

Find the variation constant and an equation of variation in which y varies inversely as x, and the following conditions exist.

49. $y = 5$ when $x = 20$

50. $y = 40$ when $x = 8$

51. $y = 11$ when $x = 4$

52. $y = 9$ when $x = 10$

53. $y = 27$ when $x = \frac{1}{3}$

54. $y = 81$ when $x = \frac{1}{9}$

55. *Hooke's law.*   Hooke's law states that the distance d that a spring is stretched by a hanging object varies directly as the mass m of the object. If the distance is 20 cm when the mass is 3 kg, what is the distance when the mass is 5 kg?

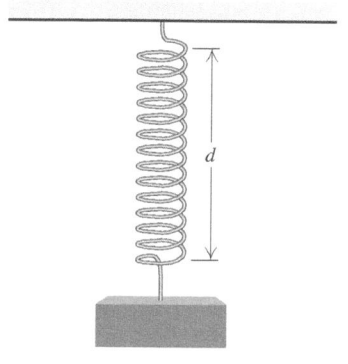

56. *Ohm's law.*   The electric current I, in amperes, in a circuit varies directly as the voltage V. When 15 volts are applied, the current is 5 amperes. What is the current when 18 volts are applied?

57. *Work rate.*   The time T required to do a job varies inversely as the number of people P working. It takes 5 hr for 7 volunteers to pick up rubbish from 1 mi of roadway. How long would it take 10 volunteers to complete the job?

58. *Pumping rate.*   The time t required to empty a tank varies inversely as the rate r of pumping. If a Briggs and Stratton pump can empty a tank in 45 min at the rate of 600 kL/min, how long will it take the pump to empty the tank at 1000 kL/min?

59. *Water from melting snow.*   The number of centimeters W of water produced from melting snow varies directly as the number of centimeters S of snow. Meteorologists know that under certain conditions, 150 cm of snow will melt to 16.8 cm of water. The average annual snowfall in Alta, Utah, is 500 in. Assuming the above conditions, how much water will replace the 500 in. of snow?

60. *Gardening.*   The number of calories burned by a gardener is directly proportional to the time spent gardening. It takes 30 min to burn 180 calories. How long would it take to burn 240 calories when gardening?

Source: www.healthstatus.com

Aha! **61.** *Mass of water in a human.*   The number of kilograms W of water in a human body varies directly as the mass of the body. A 96-kg person contains 64 kg of water. How many kilograms of water are in a 48-kg person?

62. *Weight on Mars.*   The weight M of an object on Mars varies directly as its weight E on Earth. A person who weighs 95 lb on Earth weighs 38 lb on Mars. How much would a 100-lb person weigh on Mars?

63. *String length and frequency.* The frequency of a string is inversely proportional to its length. A violin string that is 33 cm long vibrates with a frequency of 260 Hz. What is the frequency when the string is shortened to 30 cm?

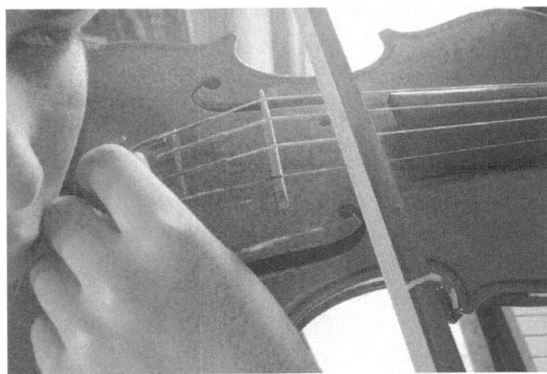

64. *Wavelength and frequency.* The wavelength W of a radio wave varies inversely as its frequency F. A wave with a frequency of 1200 kilohertz has a length of 300 meters. What is the length of a wave with a frequency of 800 kilohertz?

65. *Ultraviolet index.* At an ultraviolet, or UV, rating of 4, those people who are less sensitive to the sun will burn in 75 min. Given that the number of minutes it takes to burn, t, varies inversely with the UV rating, u, how long will it take less sensitive people to burn when the UV rating is 14?
Source: *The Electronic Textbook of Dermatology* at www.telemedicine.org

66. *Current and resistance.* The current I in an electrical conductor varies inversely as the resistance R of the conductor. If the current is $\frac{1}{2}$ ampere when the resistance is 240 ohms, what is the current when the resistance is 540 ohms?

67. *Air pollution.* The average U.S. household of 2.6 people released 0.94 ton of carbon monoxide into the environment in a recent year. How many tons were released nationally? Use 305,000,000 as the U.S. population.
Sources: Based on data from the U.S. Environmental Protection Agency and the U.S. Census Bureau

68. *Relative aperture.* The relative aperture, or f-stop, of a 23.5-mm lens is directly proportional to the focal length F of the lens. If a lens with a 150-mm focal length has an f-stop of 6.3, find the f-stop of a 23.5-mm lens with a focal length of 80 mm.

Find an equation of variation in which:

69. y varies directly as the square of x, and $y = 50$ when $x = 10$.

70. y varies directly as the square of x, and $y = 0.15$ when $x = 0.1$.

71. y varies inversely as the square of x, and $y = 50$ when $x = 10$.

72. y varies inversely as the square of x, and $y = 0.15$ when $x = 0.1$.

73. y varies jointly as x and z, and $y = 105$ when $x = 14$ and $z = 5$.

74. y varies jointly as x and z, and $y = \frac{3}{2}$ when $x = 2$ and $z = 10$.

75. y varies jointly as w and the square of x and inversely as z, and $y = 49$ when $w = 3$, $x = 7$, and $z = 12$.

76. y varies directly as x and inversely as w and the square of z, and $y = 4.5$ when $x = 15$, $w = 5$, and $z = 2$.

77. *Stopping distance of a car.* The stopping distance d of a car after the brakes have been applied varies directly as the square of the speed r. Once the brakes are applied, a car traveling 60 mph can stop in 138 ft. What stopping distance corresponds to a speed of 40 mph?
Source: Based on data from Edmunds.com

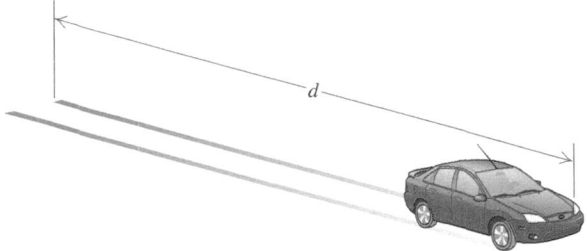

78. *Reverberation time.* A sound's reverberation time T is the time it takes for the sound level to decrease by 60 dB (decibels) after the sound has been turned off. Reverberation time varies directly as the volume V of a room and inversely as the sound absorption A of the room. A given sound has a reverberation time of 1.5 sec in a room with a volume of 90 m^3 and a sound absorption of 9.6. What is the reverberation time of the same sound in a room with a volume of 84 m^3 and a sound absorption of 10.5?
Source: www.isover.co.uk

79. *Volume of a gas.* The volume V of a given mass of a gas varies directly as the temperature T and inversely as the pressure P. If $V = 231$ cm^3 when $T = 300°$K (Kelvin) and $P = 20$ lb/cm^2, what is the volume when $T = 320°$K and $P = 16$ lb/cm^2?

80. *Intensity of a signal.* The intensity I of a television signal varies inversely as the square of the distance d from the transmitter. If the intensity is 25 W/m^2 at a distance of 2 km, what is the intensity 6.25 km from the transmitter?

81. *Atmospheric drag.* Wind resistance, or atmospheric drag, tends to slow down moving objects. Atmospheric drag W varies jointly as an object's surface area A and velocity v. If a car traveling at a speed of 40 mph with a surface area of 37.8 ft^2 experiences a drag of 222 N (Newtons), how fast must a car with 51 ft^2 of surface area travel in order to experience a drag force of 430 N?

82. *Drag force.* The drag force F on a boat varies jointly as the wetted surface area A and the square of the velocity of the boat. If a boat traveling 6.5 mph experiences a drag force of 86 N when the wetted surface area is 41.2 ft^2, find the wetted surface area of a boat traveling 8.2 mph with a drag force of 94 N.

83. If y varies directly as x, does doubling x cause y to be doubled as well? Why or why not?

84. Which exercise did you find easier to work: Exercise 15 or Exercise 19? Why?

Skill Review

To prepare for Chapter 8, review solving an equation for y and translating phrases to algebraic expressions (Sections 1.1 and 2.3).

Solve. [2.3]

85. $x - 6y = 3$, for y

86. $3x - 8y = 5$, for y

87. $5x + 2y = -3$, for y

88. $x + 8y = 4$, for y

Translate each of the following. Do not solve. [1.1]

89. Five more than twice a number is 49.

90. Three less than half of some number is 57.

91. The sum of two consecutive integers is 145.

92. The difference between a number and its opposite is 20.

Synthesis

93. Suppose that the number of customer complaints is inversely proportional to the number of employees hired. Will a firm reduce the number of complaints more by expanding from 5 to 10 employees, or from 20 to 25? Explain. Consider using a graph to help justify your answer.

94. Why do you think subscripts are used in Exercises 15 and 25 but not in Exercises 27 and 28?

95. *Escape velocity.* A satellite's escape velocity is 6.5 mi/sec, the radius of the earth is 3960 mi, and the earth's gravitational constant is 32.2 ft/sec^2. How far is the satellite from the surface of the earth? (See Example 2.)

96. The *harmonic mean* of two numbers a and b is a number M such that the reciprocal of M is the average of the reciprocals of a and b. Find a formula for the harmonic mean.

97. *Health-care.* Young's rule for determining the size of a particular child's medicine dosage c is

$$c = \frac{a}{a + 12} \cdot d,$$

where a is the child's age and d is the typical adult dosage. If a child's age is doubled, the dosage increases. Find the ratio of the larger dosage to the smaller dosage. By what percent does the dosage increase?

Source: Olsen, June Looby, Leon J. Ablon, and Anthony Patrick Giangrasso, *Medical Dosage Calculations*, 6th ed.

98. Solve for x:

$$x^2\left(1 - \frac{2pq}{x}\right) = \frac{2p^2q^3 - pq^2x}{-q}.$$

99. *Average acceleration.* The formula

$$a = \frac{\dfrac{d_4 - d_3}{t_4 - t_3} - \dfrac{d_2 - d_1}{t_2 - t_1}}{t_4 - t_2}$$

can be used to approximate average acceleration, where the d's are distances and the t's are the corresponding times. Solve for t_1.

100. If y varies inversely as the cube of x and x is multiplied by 0.5, what is the effect on y?

101. *Intensity of light.* The intensity I of light from a bulb varies directly as the wattage of the bulb and inversely as the square of the distance d from the bulb. If the wattage of a light source and its distance from reading matter are both doubled, how does the intensity change?

102. Describe in words the variation represented by $W = \dfrac{km_1 M_1}{d^2}$. Assume k is a constant.

103. *Tension of a musical string.* The tension T on a string in a musical instrument varies jointly as the string's mass per unit length m, the square of its length l, and the square of its fundamental frequency f. A 2-m long string of mass 5 gm/m with a fundamental frequency of 80 has a tension of 100 N (Newtons). How long should the same string be if its tension is going to be changed to 72 N?

104. *Volume and cost.* A peanut butter jar in the shape of a right circular cylinder is 4 in. high and 3 in. in diameter and sells for $1.20. If we assume that cost is proportional to volume, how much should a jar 6 in. high and 6 in. in diameter cost?

105. *Golf distance finder.* A device used in golf to estimate the distance d to a hole measures the size s that the 7-ft pin *appears* to be in a viewfinder. The viewfinder uses the principle, diagrammed here, that s gets bigger when d gets smaller. If $s = 0.56$ in. when $d = 50$ yd, find an equation of variation that expresses d as a function of s. What is d when $s = 0.40$ in.?

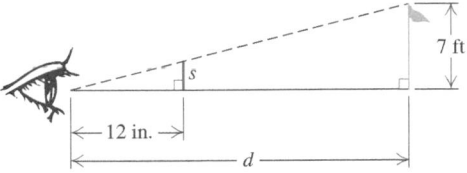

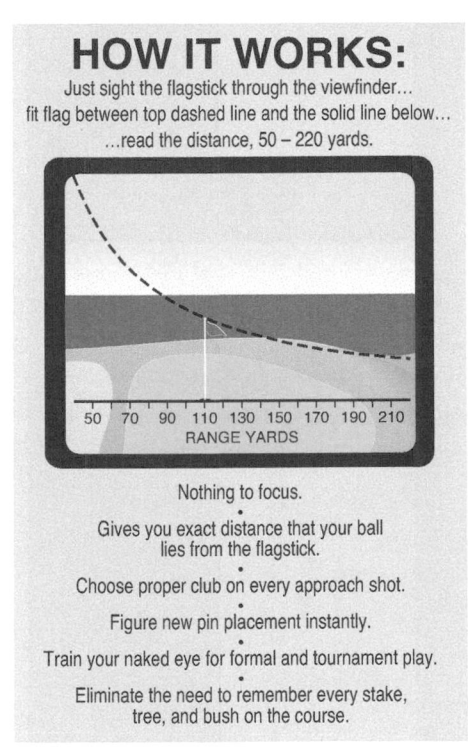

HOW IT WORKS:

Just sight the flagstick through the viewfinder...
fit flag between top dashed line and the solid line below...
...read the distance, 50 – 220 yards.

Nothing to focus.
·
Gives you exact distance that your ball
lies from the flagstick.
·
Choose proper club on every approach shot.
·
Figure new pin placement instantly.
·
Train your naked eye for formal and tournament play.
·
Eliminate the need to remember every stake,
tree, and bush on the course.

Study Summary

KEY TERMS AND CONCEPTS

EXAMPLES

A **function** is a correspondence between a first set, called the **domain**, and a second set, called the **range**, such that each member of the domain corresponds to *exactly one* member of the range.

The correspondence f: $\left\{\left(-1, \frac{1}{2}\right), (0, 1), (1, 2), (2, 4), (3, 8)\right\}$ is a function.

The domain of $f = \{-1, 0, 1, 2, 3\}$.

The range of $f = \left\{\frac{1}{2}, 1, 2, 4, 8\right\}$.

$f(-1) = \frac{1}{2}$

The input -1 corresponds to the output $\frac{1}{2}$.

The Vertical-Line Test

If it is possible for a vertical line to cross a graph more than once, then the graph is not the graph of a function.

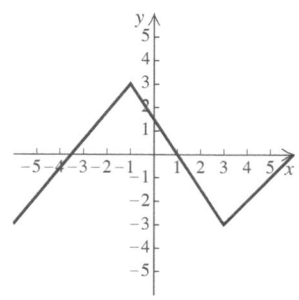

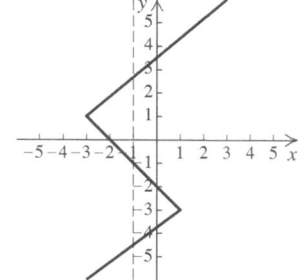

This *is* the graph of a function.   This *is not* the graph of a function.

The domain of a function is the set of all x-coordinates of the points on the graph.

The range of a function is the set of all y-coordinates of the points on the graph.

Consider the function given by $f(x) = |x| - 3$.

    The domain of the function is $\mathbb{R}$.

    The range of the function is $\{y | y \geq -3\}$, or $[-3, \infty)$.

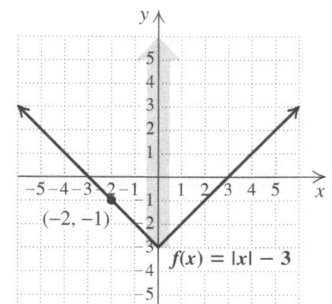

Unless otherwise stated, the domain of a function is the set of all numbers for which function values can be calculated.

Consider the function given by $f(x) = \dfrac{x + 2}{x - 7}$.

Function values cannot be calculated when the denominator is 0. Since $x - 7 = 0$ when $x = 7$, the domain of f is

$$\{x \mid x \text{ is a real number } and \ x \neq 7\}.$$

Linear Function

$$f(x) = mx + b$$

Constant Function

$$f(x) = b$$

Graph: $f(x) = \frac{1}{2}x - 3$.

We plot the y-intercept, $(0, -3)$. From there, we count off a slope of $\frac{1}{2}$: We go up 1 unit and to the right 2 units to the point $(2, -2)$. We then draw the graph.

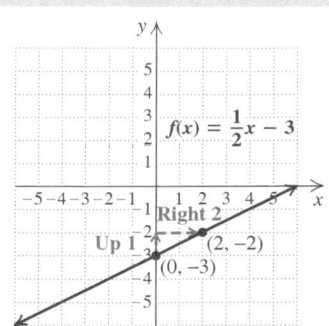

Graphs of nonlinear functions are not straight lines.

x	$f(x) = x^2 - 3$	$(x, f(x))$
0	-3	$(0, -3)$
-1	-2	$(-1, -2)$
1	-2	$(1, -2)$
-2	1	$(-2, 1)$
2	1	$(2, 1)$

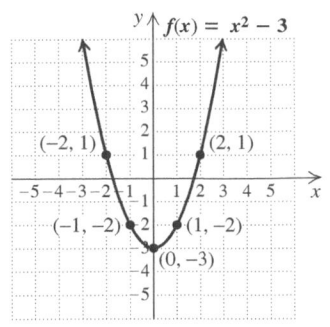

f is a quadratic function.

Domain of $f = \mathbb{R}$, or $(-\infty, \infty)$.

Range of $f = \{y | y \geq -3\}$, or $[-3, \infty)$.

SECTION 7.4: THE ALGEBRA OF FUNCTIONS

$(f + g)(x) = f(x) + g(x)$

$(f - g)(x) = f(x) - g(x)$

$(f \cdot g)(x) = f(x) \cdot g(x)$

$(f/g)(x) = f(x)/g(x)$, provided $g(x) \neq 0$

For $f(x) = x^2 + 3x$ and $g(x) = x - 5$:

$(f + g)(x) = f(x) + g(x)$
$\quad\quad\quad = x^2 + 3x + x - 5 = x^2 + 4x - 5;$

$(f - g)(x) = f(x) - g(x)$
$\quad\quad\quad = x^2 + 3x - (x - 5) = x^2 + 2x + 5;$

$(f \cdot g)(x) = f(x) \cdot g(x)$
$\quad\quad\quad = (x^2 + 3x)(x - 5) = x^3 - 2x^2 - 15x;$

$(f/g)(x) = f(x)/g(x)$, provided $g(x) \neq 0$
$\quad\quad\quad = \dfrac{x^2 + 3x}{x - 5}$, provided $x \neq 5$. $g(5) = 0$

SECTION 7.5: FORMULAS, APPLICATIONS, AND VARIATION

Direct Variation

$\quad y = kx$

If y varies directly as x and $y = 45$ when $x = 0.15$, find the equation of variation.

$$y = kx$$
$$45 = k(0.15)$$
$$300 = k$$

The equation of variation is $y = 300x$.

Inverse Variation

$\quad y = \dfrac{k}{x}$

If y varies inversely as x and $y = 45$ when $x = 0.15$, find the equation of variation.

$$y = \frac{k}{x}$$
$$45 = \frac{k}{0.15}$$
$$6.75 = k$$

The equation of variation is $y = \dfrac{6.75}{x}$.

Joint Variation	If y varies jointly as x and z and $y = 40$ when $x = 5$ and $z = 4$, find the equation of variation.
$y = kxz$	$$y = kxz$$ $$40 = k \cdot 5 \cdot 4$$ $$2 = k$$ The equation of variation is $y = 2xz$.

Review Exercises: Chapter 7

🔖 *Concept Reinforcement* *Classify each of the following as either true or false.*

1. Every function is a relation. [7.1]

2. When we are discussing functions, the notation $f(3)$ does not mean $f \cdot 3$. [7.1]

3. If a graph includes both $(9, 5)$ and $(7, 5)$, it cannot represent a function. [7.1]

4. The domain and the range of a function can be the same set of numbers. [7.2]

5. The horizontal-line test is a quick way to determine whether a graph represents a function. [7.1]

6. In a piecewise-defined function, the function values are determined using more than one rule. [7.2]

7. $(f + g)(x) = f(x) + g(x)$ is not an example of the distributive law when f and g are functions. [7.4]

8. In order for $(f/g)(a)$ to exist, we must have $g(a) \neq 0$. [7.4]

9. If x varies inversely as y, then there exists some constant k for which $x = k/y$. [7.5]

10. If 2 people can decorate for a party in 5 hr, and 10 people can decorate for the same party in 4 hr, the situation represents inverse variation. [7.5]

11. For the following graph of f, determine **(a)** $f(2)$; **(b)** the domain of f; **(c)** any x-values for which $f(x) = 2$; and **(d)** the range of f. [7.1], [7.2]

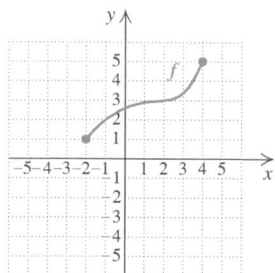

12. Find $g(-3)$ for $g(x) = \dfrac{x}{x + 1}$. [7.1]

13. Find $f(2a)$ for $f(x) = x^2 + 2x - 3$. [7.1]

14. The function $A(t) = 0.233t + 5.87$ can be used to estimate the median age of cars in the United States t years after 1990. (In this context, a median age of 3 yr means that half the cars are more than 3 yr old and half are less.) Predict the median age of cars in 2010; that is, find $A(20)$. [7.1]
Source: The Polk Co.

15. The following table shows the U.S. minimum hourly wage. Use the data in the table to draw a graph and to estimate the U.S. minimum hourly wage in 2012. [7.1]

Input, Year	Output, U.S. Minimum Hourly Wage
1997	$5.15
2007	5.85
2008	6.55
2009	7.25

For each of the graphs in Exercises 16–19, (a) determine whether the graph represents a function and (b) if so, determine the domain and the range of the function. [7.1], [7.2]

16.

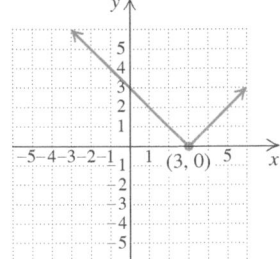

17.

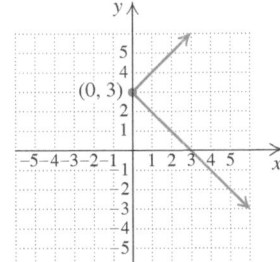

18.

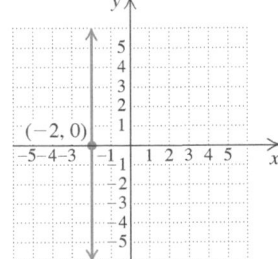

19.

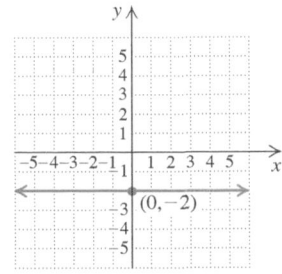

Find the domain of each function.

20. $f(x) = 3x^2 - 7$ [7.2]

21. $g(x) = \dfrac{x^2}{x - 1}$ [7.2]

22. $f(t) = \dfrac{1}{t^2 + 5t + 4}$ [7.2]

23. If a service agreement is cancelled, the amount that Vale Appliances will refund on the agreement is given by the function

$$r(t) = 900 - 15t,$$

where t is the number of weeks since the date of purchase. What is the domain of the function? [7.2]

24. For the function given by

$$f(x) = \begin{cases} 2 - x, & \text{if } x \leq -2, \\ x^2, & \text{if } -2 < x \leq 5, \\ x + 10, & \text{if } x > 5, \end{cases}$$

find **(a)** $f(-3)$; **(b)** $f(-2)$; **(c)** $f(4)$; and **(d)** $f(25)$. [7.2]

25. It costs $90 plus $30 a month to join the Family Fitness Center. Formulate a linear function to model the cost $C(t)$ for t months of membership, and determine the time required for the cost to reach $300. [7.3]

26. *Records in the 200-meter run.* In 1983, the record for the 200-m run was 19.75 sec. In 2007, it was 19.32 sec. Let $R(t)$ represent the record in the 200-m run and t the number of years since 1980. [7.3]

Source: International Association of Athletics Federation

a) Find a linear function that fits the data.
b) Use the function of part (a) to predict the record in 2013 and in 2020.

Classify each function as a linear function, an absolute-value function, a quadratic function, another polynomial function, or a rational function. [7.3]

27. $f(x) = |3x - 7|$

28. $g(x) = 4x^5 - 8x^3 + 7$

29. $p(x) = x^2 + x - 10$

30. $h(n) = 4n - 17$

31. $s(t) = \dfrac{t + 1}{t + 2}$

Graph each function and determine its domain and range. [7.3]

32. $f(x) = 3$

33. $f(x) = 2x + 1$

34. $g(x) = |x + 1|$

Let $g(x) = 3x - 6$ and $h(x) = x^2 + 1$. Find the following.

35. $(g \cdot h)(4)$ [7.4]

36. $(g - h)(-2)$ [7.4]

37. $(g/h)(-1)$ [7.4]

38. The domains of $g + h$ and $g \cdot h$ [7.4]

39. The domain of h/g [7.4]

Solve. [7.5]

40. $I = \dfrac{2V}{R + 2r}$, for r

41. $S = \dfrac{H}{m(t_1 - t_2)}$, for m

42. $\dfrac{1}{ac} = \dfrac{2}{ab} - \dfrac{3}{bc}$, for c

43. $T = \dfrac{A}{v(t_2 - t_1)}$, for t_1

44. Find an equation of variation in which y varies directly as x, and $y = 30$ when $x = 4$. [7.5]

45. Find an equation of variation in which y varies inversely as x, and $y = 3$ when $x = \frac{1}{4}$. [7.5]

46. Find an equation of variation in which y varies jointly as x and the square of w and inversely as z, and $y = 150$ when $x = 6$, $w = 10$, and $z = 2$. [7.5]

Solve. [7.5]

47. For those people with highly sensitive skin, an ultra-violet, or UV, rating of 6 will cause sunburn after 10 min. Given that the number of minutes it takes to burn t varies inversely as the UV rating u, how long will it take a highly sensitive person to burn on a day with a UV rating of 4?
Source: *The Electronic Textbook of Dermatology* found at www.telemedicine.org

48. The amount of waste generated by a family varies directly as the number of people in the family. The average U.S. family has 3.2 people and generates 14.4 lb of waste daily. How many pounds of waste would be generated daily by a family of 5?
Sources: Based on data from the U.S. Census Bureau and the U.S. Statistical Abstract 2007

49. *Electrical safety.* The amount of time t needed for an electrical shock to stop a 150-lb person's heart varies inversely as the square of the current flowing through the body. It is known that a 0.089-amp current is deadly to a 150-lb person after 3.4 sec. How long would it take a 0.096-amp current to be deadly?
Source: Safety Consulting Services

Synthesis

50. If two functions have the same domain and range, are the functions identical? Why or why not? [7.2]

51. Jenna believes that 0 is never in the domain of a rational function. Is she correct? Why or why not? [7.2]

52. Treasure Tea charges $7.99 for each package of loose tea. Shipping charges are $2.95 per package plus $20 per order for overnight delivery. Find a linear function for determining the cost of one order of x packages of tea, including shipping and overnight delivery. [7.3]

53. Determine the domain and the range of the function graphed below. [7.2]

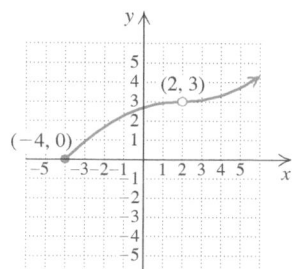

1. For the following graph of f, determine **(a)** $f(-2)$; **(b)** the domain of f; **(c)** any x-value for which $f(x) = \frac{1}{2}$; and **(d)** the range of f.

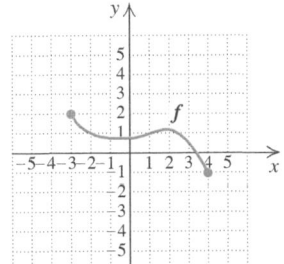

2. There were 41.9 million international visitors to the United States in 2002 and 51.0 million visitors in 2006. Draw a graph and estimate the number of international visitors in 2005.

   Sources: U.S. Department of Commerce, ITA, Office of Travel and Tourism Industries; Global Insight, Inc.

*For each of the following graphs, **(a)** determine whether the graph represents a function and **(b)** if so, determine the domain and the range of the function.*

3.

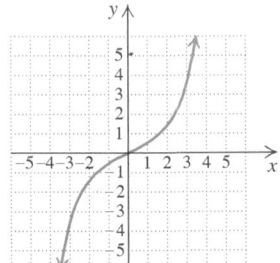

4.

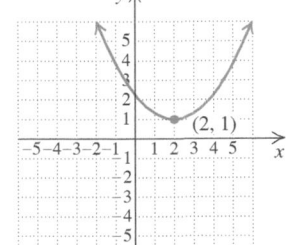

5.

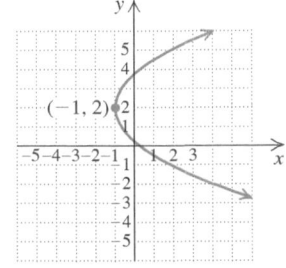

6. The distance d, in miles, that Kerry is from Chicago is given by the function $d(t) = 240 - 60t$, where t is the number of hours since he left Indianapolis. What is the domain of the function?

7. For the function given by

$$f(x) = \begin{cases} x^2, & \text{if } x < 0, \\ 3x - 5, & \text{if } 0 \le x \le 2, \\ x + 7, & \text{if } x > 2, \end{cases}$$

   find **(a)** $f(0)$; **(b)** $f(3)$.

8. Porter paid \$180 for his phone. His monthly service fee is \$55. Formulate a linear function to model the cost $C(t)$ for t months of service, and determine the amount of time required for the total cost to reach \$840.

9. If you rent a truck for one day and drive it 250 mi, the cost is \$100. If you rent it for one day and drive it 300 mi, the cost is \$115. Let $C(m)$ represent the cost, in dollars, of driving m miles.

   a) Find a linear function that fits the data.
   b) Use the function to determine how much it will cost to rent the truck for one day and drive it 500 mi.

Classify each function as a linear function, a quadratic function, another polynomial function, an absolute-value function, or a rational function. Then find the domain of each function.

10. $f(x) = \frac{1}{4}x + 7$

11. $g(x) = \dfrac{3}{x^2 - 16}$

12. $p(x) = 4x^2 + 7$

Graph each function and determine its domain and range.

13. $f(x) = \frac{1}{3}x - 2$ 14. $g(x) = x^2 - 1$

15. $h(x) = -\dfrac{1}{2}$

Find the following, given that $g(x) = \dfrac{1}{x}$ and $h(x) = 2x + 1$.

16. $g(-1)$ 17. $h(5a)$

18. $(g + h)(x)$

19. The domain of g

20. The domain of $g + h$

21. The domain of g/h

22. Solve $R = \dfrac{gs}{g + s}$ for s.

23. Find an equation of variation in which y varies directly as x, and $y = 10$ when $x = 20$.

24. The number of workers n needed to clean a stadium after a game varies inversely as the amount of time t allowed for the cleanup. If it takes 25 workers to clean the stadium when there are 6 hr allowed for the job, how many workers are needed if the stadium must be cleaned in 5 hr?

25. The surface area of a balloon varies directly as the square of its radius. The area is 325 in^2 when the radius is 5 in. What is the area when the radius is 7 in.?

Synthesis

26. The function $f(t) = 5 + 15t$ can be used to determine a bicycle racer's location, in miles from the starting line, measured t hours after passing the 5-mi mark.

a) How far from the start will the racer be 1 hr and 40 min after passing the 5-mi mark?

b) Assuming a constant rate, how fast is the racer traveling?

27. Given that $f(x) = 5x^2 + 1$ and $g(x) = 4x - 3$, find an expression for $h(x)$ so that the domain of $f/g/h$ is $\left\{x \mid x \text{ is a real number } and \ x \neq \frac{3}{4} \ and \ x \neq \frac{2}{7}\right\}$. Answers may vary.

Cumulative Review: Chapters 1–7

1. Evaluate
$$\frac{2x - y^2}{x + y}$$
for $x = 3$ and $y = -4$. [1.8]

2. Convert to scientific notation: 391,000,000. [4.2]

3. Determine the slope and the y-intercept for the line given by $7x - 4y = 12$. [3.6]

4. Find an equation for the line that passes through the points $(-1, 7)$ and $(4, -3)$. [3.7]

5. If
$$f(x) = \frac{x - 3}{x^2 - 11x + 30},$$
find **(a)** $f(3)$ and **(b)** the domain of f. [7.1], [7.2]

Graph on a plane.

6. $5x = y$ [3.2]

7. $8y + 2x = 16$ [3.3]

8. $f(x) = -4$ [7.2]

9. $y = \frac{1}{3}x - 2$ [3.6]

Perform the indicated operations and simplify.

10. $(8x^3y^2)(-3xy^2)$ [4.1]

11. $(5x^2 - 2x + 1)(3x^2 + x - 2)$ [4.5]

12. $(3x^2 + y)^2$ [4.6]

13. $(2x^2 - 9)(2x^2 + 9)$ [4.6]

14. $(-5m^3n^2 - 3mn^3) + (-4m^2n^2 + 4m^3n^2) - (2mn^3 - 3m^2n^2)$ [4.4]

15. $\dfrac{y^2 - 36}{2y + 8} \cdot \dfrac{y + 4}{y + 6}$ [6.2]

16. $\dfrac{x^4 - 1}{x^2 - x - 2} \div \dfrac{x^2 + 1}{x - 2}$ [6.2]

17. $\dfrac{5ab}{a^2 - b^2} + \dfrac{a + b}{a - b}$ [6.4]

18. $\dfrac{2}{m + 1} + \dfrac{3}{m - 5} - \dfrac{m^2 - 1}{m^2 - 4m - 5}$ [6.4]

19. $y - \dfrac{2}{3y}$ [6.4]

20. Simplify: $\dfrac{\dfrac{1}{x} - \dfrac{1}{y}}{x + y}$. [6.5]

Factor.

21. $4x^3 + 400x$ [5.1]

22. $x^2 + 8x - 84$ [5.2]

23. $16y^2 - 25$ [5.4]

24. $64x^3 + 8$ [5.5]

25. $t^2 - 16t + 64$ [5.4]

26. $x^6 - x^2$ [5.4]

27. $\frac{1}{8}b^3 - c^3$ [5.5]

28. $3t^2 + 17t - 28$ [5.3]

29. $x^5 - x^3y + x^2y - y^2$ [5.1]

Solve.

30. $8x = 1 + 16x^2$ [5.7]

31. $288 = 2y^2$ [5.7]

32. $\frac{1}{3}x - \frac{1}{5} \geq \frac{1}{5}x - \frac{1}{3}$ [2.6]

33. $5(x - 2) - (x - 3) = 7x - 2(5 - x)$ [2.2]

34. $\dfrac{6}{x - 5} = \dfrac{2}{2x}$ [6.6]

35. $\dfrac{3x}{x - 2} - \dfrac{6}{x + 2} = \dfrac{24}{x^2 - 4}$ [6.6]

36. $P = \dfrac{4a}{a + b}$, for a [7.5]

37. Find the slope of the line containing $(2, 5)$ and $(1, 10)$. [3.5]

38. Find the slope of the line given by $f(x) = 8x + 3$. [7.3]

39. Find the slope of the line given by $y + 6 = -4$. [3.5]

40. Find an equation of the line containing $(5, -2)$ and perpendicular to the line given by $x - y = 5$. [3.7]

Find the following, given that $f(x) = x + 5$ and $g(x) = x^2 - 1$.

41. $g(-10)$ [7.1]   **42.** $(g/f)(x)$ [7.4]

43. Find the domain of f if $f(x) = \dfrac{x}{x + 6}$. [7.2]

44. Determine the domain and the range of the function f represented below. [7.2]

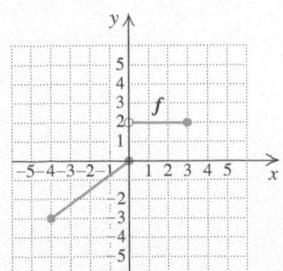

45. *Broadway revenue.* Gross revenue from Broadway shows has grown from $20 million in 1986–1987 to $939 million in 2006–2007. Let $r(t)$ represent gross revenue, in millions of dollars, from Broadway shows t seasons after the 1986–1987 season. [7.3]
Source: The League of American Theatres and Producers

   a) Find a linear function that fits the data.
   b) Use the function from part (a) to predict the gross revenue from Broadway shows in 2009–2010.
   c) In what season will the gross revenue from Broadway shows reach $1.4 billion?

46. *Broadway performances.* In January 2006, *The Phantom of the Opera* became the longest-running Broadway show with 7486 performances. By January 2008, the show had played 8302 times. Calculate the rate at which the number of performances was rising. [3.4]

47. *Quilting.* A rectangular quilted wall hanging is 4 in. longer than it is wide. The area of the quilt is 320 in². Find the perimeter of the quilt. [5.8]

48. *Hotel management.* The IQAir HealthPro Plus air purifier can clean the air in a 20-ft by 25-ft meeting room in 5 fewer minutes than it takes the Austin Healthmate HM400 to do the same job. Together the two machines can purify the air in the room in 6 min. How long would it take each machine, working alone, to purify the air in the room? [6.7]
Source: Manufacturers' and retailers' websites

49. *Driving delays.* According to the National Surface Transportation Policy and Revenue Study Commission, the best-case scenario for driving delays due to road work in 2055 will be 250% of the delays in 2005. If the commission predicts 30 billion hr of driving delays in 2055, how many hours of driving delays were there in 2005? [2.5]

50. *Driving time.*   The time t that it takes for Johann to drive to work varies inversely as his speed. On a day when Johann averages 45 mph, it takes him 20 min to drive to work. How long will it take him to drive to work when he averages only 40 mph? [7.5]

51. *Disaster relief.*   Six months after Hurricane Katrina struck the Gulf Coast in 2005, $2.18 billion of relief money had been distributed to disaster victims. This was $\frac{2}{3}$ of the amount raised by charity for disaster relief. How much money was still to be distributed? [2.5]
Source: www.washingtonpost.com

Synthesis

52. Multiply: $(x - 4)^3$. [4.5]

53. Find all roots for $f(x) = x^4 - 34x^2 + 225$. [5.6], [7.3]

Solve.

54. $\dfrac{18}{x - 9} + \dfrac{10}{x + 5} = \dfrac{28x}{x^2 - 4x - 45}$ [6.6]

55. $16x^3 = x$ [5.7]

56. *Photo books.*   An Everyday Photo Book costs $12 for the first 20 pages plus $0.75 for each additional page. Formulate a piecewise-defined function to model the cost $C(x)$ for a book with x pages. [7.2]
Source: snapfish.com

Systems of Linear Equations and Problem Solving

8.1
Systems of Equations in
Two Variables

8.2
Solving by Substitution
or Elimination

CONNECTING THE CONCEPTS

8.3
Solving Applications:
Systems of Two Equations

8.4
Systems of Equations in
Three Variables

8.5
Solving Applications:
Systems of Three
Equations

8.6
Elimination Using Matrices

8.7
Determinants and
Cramer's Rule

8.8
Business and Economics
Applications

STUDY SUMMARY
REVIEW EXERCISES
CHAPTER TEST
CUMULATIVE REVIEW

JUDITH L. BRONSTEIN
NATURALIST/ECOLOGIST
Tucson, Arizona

As an ecologist, I often use equations both to estimate numbers of organisms and to make predictions about how those numbers will change under different conditions. In this way, math helps us to answer questions like these: How quickly is the human population growing, and will food production be able to keep up? How many polar bears are left in the wild, how will their numbers be affected as the climate continues to change, and what approaches should be most successful for preserving them?

AN APPLICATION

The number of plant species listed as threatened or endangered has more than tripled in the past 20 years. In 2008, there were 746 species of plants in the United States that were considered threatened or endangered. The number of species considered threatened was 4 less than one-fourth of the number considered endangered. How many U.S. plant species were considered endangered and how many were considered threatened in 2008?

Source: U.S. Fish and Wildlife Service

This problem appears as Example 1 in Section 8.1 and as Example 1 in Section 8.3.

The most difficult part of problem solving is almost always translating the problem situation to mathematical language. In this chapter, we study *systems of equations* and how to solve them using graphing, substitution, elimination, and matrices. Systems of equations often provide the easiest way to model real-world situations in fields such as psychology, sociology, business, education, engineering, and science.

8.1   Systems of Equations in Two Variables

Translating   ▪   Identifying Solutions   ▪   Solving Systems Graphically

Translating

Problems involving two unknown quantities are often translated most easily using two equations in two unknowns. Together these equations form a **system of equations**. We look for a solution to the problem by attempting to find a pair of numbers for which *both* equations are true.

EXAMPLE   1   *Endangered species.*   The number of plant species listed as threatened (likely to become endangered) or endangered (in danger of becoming extinct) has more than tripled in the past 20 years. In 2008, there were 746 species of plants in the United States that were considered threatened or endangered. The number of species considered threatened was 4 less than one-fourth of the number considered endangered. How many U.S. plant species were considered endangered and how many were considered threatened in 2008?

Source: U.S. Fish and Wildlife Service

SOLUTION

1. **Familiarize.** Often statements of problems contain information that has no bearing on the question asked. In this case, the fact that the number of threatened or endangered species has tripled in the past 20 years does not help us solve the problem. Instead, we focus on the number of endangered species and the number of threatened species in 2008. We let t represent the number of threatened plant species and d represent the number of endangered plant species in 2008.

2. **Translate.** There are two statements to translate. First, we look at the total number of endangered or threatened species of plants:

   Rewording: The number of threatened species   plus   the number of endangered species   was   746.

   Translating: t $+$ d $=$ 746

   The second statement compares the two amounts, d and t:

   Rewording: The number of threatened species   was   4 less than one-fourth of the number of endangered species.

   Translating: t $=$ $\frac{1}{4}d - 4$

We have now translated the problem to a pair, or **system**, **of equations**:

$$t + d = 746,$$

$$t = \frac{1}{4}d - 4.$$

We complete the solution of this problem in Section 8.3.

TRY EXERCISE 41

System of Equations

A *system of equations* is a set of two or more equations, in two or more variables, for which a common solution is sought.

Problems like Example 1 *can* be solved using one variable; however, as problems become complicated, you will find that using more than one variable (and more than one equation) is often the preferable approach.

EXAMPLE 2

Jewelry design. A jewelry designer purchased 80 beads for a total of $39 (excluding tax) to make a necklace. Some of the beads were sterling silver beads that cost 40¢ each and the rest were gemstone beads that cost 65¢ each. How many of each type did the designer buy?

SOLUTION

1. **Familiarize.** To familiarize ourselves with this problem, let's guess that the designer bought 20 beads at 40¢ each and 60 beads at 65¢ each. The total cost would then be

$$20 \cdot 40¢ + 60 \cdot 65¢ = 800¢ + 3900¢, \quad \text{or} \quad 4700¢.$$

Since 4700¢ = $47 and $47 ≠ $39, our guess is incorrect. Rather than guess again, let's see how algebra can be used to translate the problem.

2. **Translate.** We let s = the number of silver beads and g = the number of gemstone beads. Since the cost of each bead is given in cents and the total cost is in dollars, we must choose one of the units to use throughout the problem. We choose to work in cents, so the total cost is 3900¢. The information can be organized in a table, which will help with the translating.

Type of Bead	Silver	Gemstone	Total	
Number Bought	s	g	80	→ $s + g = 80$
Price	40¢	65¢		
Amount	40s¢	65g¢	3900¢	→ $40s + 65g = 3900$

The first row of the table and the first sentence of the problem indicate that a total of 80 beads were bought:

$$s + g = 80.$$

Since each silver bead cost 40¢ and s beads were bought, 40s represents the amount paid, in cents, for the silver beads. Similarly, 65g represents the amount paid, in cents, for the gemstone beads. This leads to a second equation:

$$40s + 65g = 3900.$$

We now have the following system of equations as the translation:

$$s + g = 80,$$
$$40s + 65g = 3900.$$

We will complete the solution of this problem in Section 8.3.

TRY EXERCISE ▶ 49

Identifying Solutions

A *solution* of a system of two equations in two variables is an ordered pair of numbers that makes *both* equations true.

EXAMPLE 3   Determine whether $(-4, 7)$ is a solution of the system

$$x + y = 3,$$
$$5x - y = -27.$$

SOLUTION   As discussed in Chapter 3, unless stated otherwise, we use alphabetical order of the variables. Thus we replace x with -4 and y with 7:

> **CAUTION!** Be sure to check the ordered pair in *both* equations.

$$\frac{x + y = 3}{-4 + 7 \mid 3}$$
$$3 \overset{?}{=} 3 \quad \text{TRUE}$$

$$\frac{5x - y = -27}{5(-4) - 7 \mid -27}$$
$$-20 - 7 \mid$$
$$-27 \overset{?}{=} -27 \quad \text{TRUE}$$

The pair $(-4, 7)$ makes both equations true, so it is a solution of the system. We can also describe the solution by writing $x = -4$ and $y = 7$. Set notation can also be used to list the solution set $\{(-4, 7)\}$.

TRY EXERCISE ▶ 9

Solving Systems Graphically

Recall that the graph of an equation is a drawing that represents its solution set. If we graph the equations in Example 3, we find that $(-4, 7)$ is the only point common to both lines. Thus one way to solve a system of two equations is to graph both equations and identify any points of intersection. **The coordinates of each point of intersection represent a solution of that system.**

$$x + y = 3,$$
$$5x - y = -27$$

The point of intersection of the graphs is $(-4, 7)$.

The solution of the system is $(-4, 7)$.

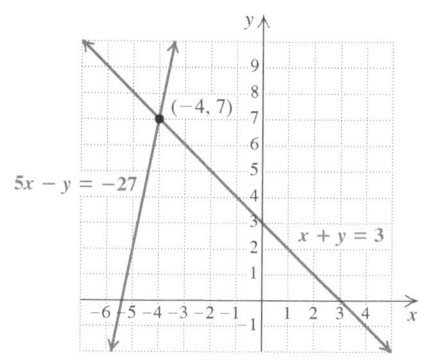

Most pairs of lines have exactly one point in common. We will soon see, however, that this is not always the case.

EXAMPLE 4   Solve each system graphically.

a) $y - x = 1,$
   $y + x = 3$

b) $y = -3x + 5,$
   $y = -3x - 2$

c) $3y - 2x = 6,$
   $-12y + 8x = -24$

SOLUTION

a) We graph each equation using any method studied in Chapter 3. All ordered pairs from line L_1 are solutions of the first equation. All ordered pairs from line L_2 are solutions of the second equation. The point of intersection has co-ordinates that make *both* equations true. Apparently, $(1, 2)$ is the solution. Graphs are not always accurate, so solving by graphing may yield approximate answers. Our check below shows that $(1, 2)$ is indeed the solution.

Graph both equations.

Look for any points in common.

$$y - x = 1,$$
$$y + x = 3$$

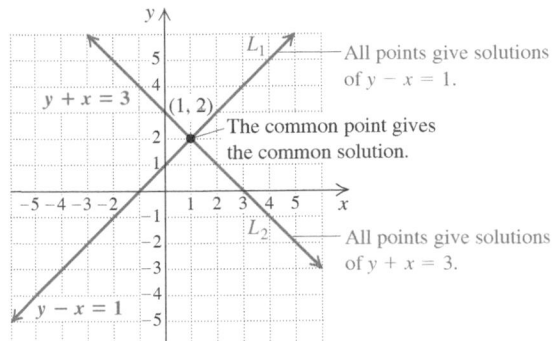

The common point gives the common solution.

All points give solutions of $y - x = 1$.

All points give solutions of $y + x = 3$.

Check.

Check:

$$\begin{array}{c|c} y - x = 1 \\ \hline 2 - 1 & 1 \\ 1 \overset{?}{=} 1 & \text{TRUE} \end{array}$$

$$\begin{array}{c|c} y + x = 3 \\ \hline 2 + 1 & 3 \\ 3 \overset{?}{=} 3 & \text{TRUE} \end{array}$$

b) We graph the equations. The lines have the same slope, -3, and different y-intercepts, so they are parallel. There is no point at which they cross, so the system has no solution.

$$y = -3x + 5,$$
$$y = -3x - 2$$

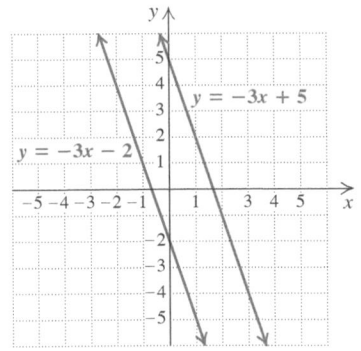

$y = -3x + 5$

$y = -3x - 2$

Although the system in Example 4(c) is true for an infinite number of ordered pairs, those pairs must be of a certain form. Only pairs that are solutions of $3y - 2x = 6$ or $-12y + 8x = -24$ are solutions of the system. It is incorrect to think that *all* ordered pairs are solutions.

c) We graph the equations and find that the same line is drawn twice. Thus any solution of one equation is a solution of the other. Each equation has an infinite number of solutions, so the system itself has an infinite number of solutions. We check one solution, $(0, 2)$, which is the y-intercept of each equation.

$$3y - 2x = 6,$$
$$-12y + 8x = -24$$

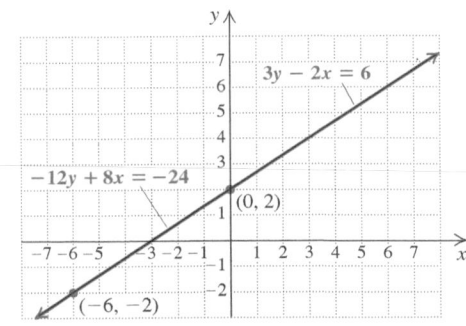

$3y - 2x = 6$

$-12y + 8x = -24$

$(0, 2)$

$(-6, -2)$

Check:

$$\begin{array}{c|c} 3y - 2x = 6 \\ \hline 3(2) - 2(0) & 6 \\ 6 - 0 & \\ & 6 \stackrel{?}{=} 6 \quad \text{TRUE} \end{array} \qquad \begin{array}{c|c} -12y + 8x = -24 \\ \hline -12(2) + 8(0) & -24 \\ -24 + 0 & \\ & -24 \stackrel{?}{=} -24 \quad \text{TRUE} \end{array}$$

You can check that $(-6, -2)$ is another solution of both equations. In fact, any pair that is a solution of one equation is a solution of the other equation as well. Thus the solution set is

$$\{(x, y) \mid 3y - 2x = 6\}$$

or, in words, "the set of all pairs (x, y) for which $3y - 2x = 6$." Since the two equations are equivalent, we could have written instead $\{(x, y) \mid -12y + 8x = -24\}$.

TRY EXERCISE ▶ 17

When we graph a system of two linear equations in two variables, one of the following three outcomes will occur.

1. The lines have one point in common, and that point is the only solution of the system (see Example 4a). Any system that has *at least one solution* is said to be **consistent**.

2. The lines are parallel, with no point in common, and the system has *no solution* (see Example 4b). This type of system is called **inconsistent**.

3. The lines coincide, sharing the same graph. Because every solution of one equation is a solution of the other, the system has an infinite number of solutions (see Example 4c). Since it has at least one solution, this type of system is also consistent.

TECHNOLOGY CONNECTION

On most graphing calculators, an INTERSECT option allows us to find the coordinates of the intersection directly.

To illustrate, consider the following system:

$$3.45x + 4.21y = 8.39,$$
$$7.12x - 5.43y = 6.18.$$

After solving for y in each equation, we obtain the graph below. Using INTERSECT, we see that, to the nearest hundredth, the coordinates of the intersection are $(1.47, 0.79)$.

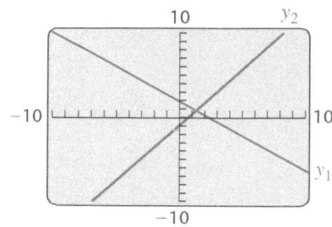

$y_1 = (8.39 - 3.45x)/4.21,$
$y_2 = (6.18 - 7.12x)/(-5.43)$

Use a graphing calculator to solve each of the following systems. Round all x- and y-coordinates to the nearest hundredth.

1. $y = -5.43x + 10.89,$
   $y = 6.29x - 7.04$
2. $y = 123.52x + 89.32,$
   $y = -89.22x + 33.76$
3. $2.18x + 7.81y = 13.78,$
   $5.79x - 3.45y = 8.94$
4. $-9.25x - 12.94y = -3.88,$
   $21.83x + 16.33y = 13.69$

When one equation in a system can be obtained by multiplying both sides of another equation by a constant, the two equations are said to be **dependent**. Thus the equations in Example 4(c) are dependent, but those in Examples 4(a) and 4(b) are **independent**. For systems of three or more equations, the definitions of dependent and independent will be slightly modified.

ALGEBRAIC–GRAPHICAL CONNECTION

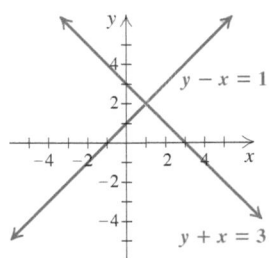

Graphs intersect at one point.

The system

$$y - x = 1,$$
$$y + x = 3$$

is *consistent* and has one solution. Since neither equation is a multiple of the other, the equations are *independent*.

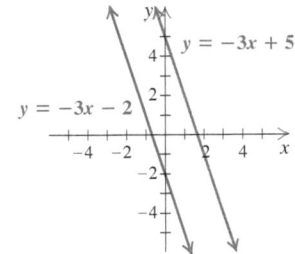

Graphs are parallel.

The system

$$y = -3x - 2,$$
$$y = -3x + 5$$

is *inconsistent* because there is no solution.

Since neither equation is a multiple of the other, the equations are *independent*.

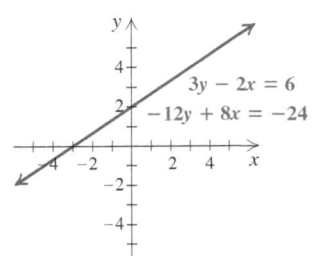

Equations have the same graph.

The system

$$3y - 2x = 6,$$
$$-12y + 8x = -24$$

is *consistent* and has an infinite number of solutions.

Since one equation is a multiple of the other, the equations are *dependent*.

Graphing is helpful when solving systems because it allows us to "see" the solution. It can also be used on systems of nonlinear equations, and in many applications, it provides a satisfactory answer. However, graphing often lacks precision, especially when fraction or decimal solutions are involved. In Section 8.2, we will develop two algebraic methods of solving systems. Both methods produce exact answers.

Visualizing for Success

A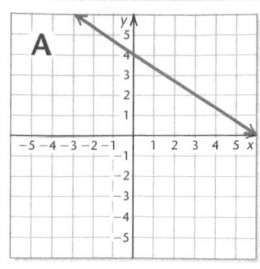

B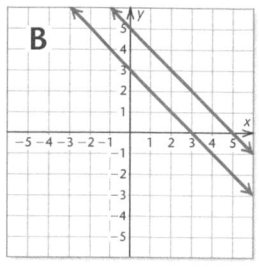

C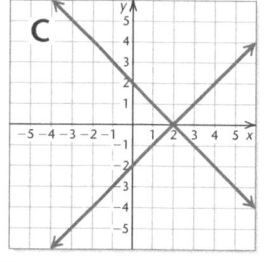

D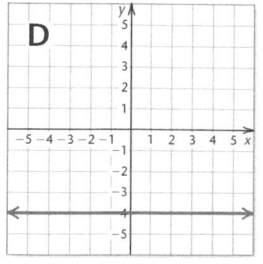

E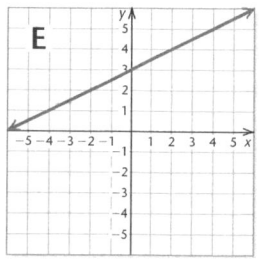

Match each equation or system of equations with its graph.

1. $x + y = 2,$
   $x - y = 2$

2. $y = \frac{1}{3}x - 5$

3. $4x - 2y = -8$

4. $2x + y = 1,$
   $x + 2y = 1$

5. $8y + 32 = 0$

6. $f(x) = -x + 4$

7. $\frac{2}{3}x + y = 4$

8. $x = 4,$
   $y = 3$

9. $y = \frac{1}{2}x + 3,$
   $2y - x = 6$

10. $y = -x + 5,$
    $y = 3 - x$

Answers on page A-32

An additional, animated version of this activity appears in MyMathLab. To use MyMathLab, you need a course ID and a student access code. Contact your instructor for more information.

F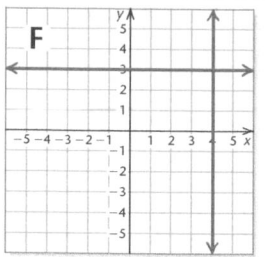

G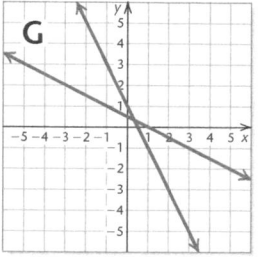

H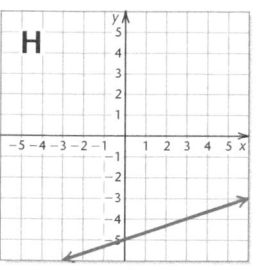

I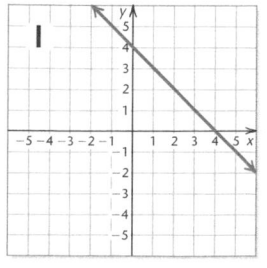

J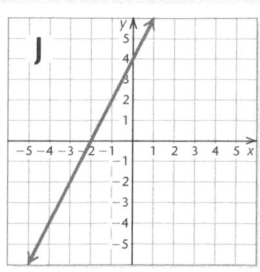

🐦 *Concept Reinforcement*   *Classify each statement as either true or false.*

1. Every system of equations has at least one solution.

2. It is possible for a system of equations to have an infinite number of solutions.

3. Every point of intersection of the graphs of the equations in a system corresponds to a solution of the system.

4. The graphs of the equations in a system of two equations may coincide.

5. The graphs of the equations in a system of two equations could be parallel lines.

6. Any system of equations that has at most one solution is said to be consistent.

7. Any system of equations that has more than one solution is said to be inconsistent.

8. The equations $x + y = 5$ and $2(x + y) = 2(5)$ are dependent.

Determine whether the ordered pair is a solution of the given system of equations. Remember to use alphabetical order of variables.

9. $(2, 3)$; $2x - y = 1$,
$\quad\quad\quad 5x - 3y = 1$

10. $(4, 0)$; $2x + 7y = 8$,
$\quad\quad\quad x - 9y = 4$

11. $(-5, 1)$; $x + 5y = 0$,
$\quad\quad\quad y = 2x + 9$

12. $(-1, -2)$; $x + 3y = -7$,
$\quad\quad\quad 3x - 2y = 12$

13. $(0, -5)$; $x - y = 5$,
$\quad\quad\quad y = 3x - 5$

14. $(5, 2)$; $a + b = 7$,
$\quad\quad\quad 2a - 8 = b$

Aha! 15. $(3, -1)$; $3x - 4y = 13$,
$\quad\quad\quad 6x - 8y = 26$

16. $(4, -2)$; $-3x - 2y = -8$,
$\quad\quad\quad 8 = 3x + 2y$

Solve each system graphically. Be sure to check your solution. If a system has an infinite number of solutions, use set-builder notation to write the solution set. If a system has no solution, state this.

17. $x - y = 1$,
$\quad x + y = 5$

18. $x + y = 6$,
$\quad x - y = 4$

19. $3x + y = 5$,
$\quad x - 2y = 4$

20. $2x - y = 4$,
$\quad 5x - y = 13$

21. $2y = 3x + 5$,
$\quad x = y - 3$

22. $4x - y = 9$,
$\quad x - 3y = 16$

23. $x = y - 1$,
$\quad 2x = 3y$

24. $a = 1 + b$,
$\quad b = 5 - 2a$

25. $y = -1$,
$\quad x = 3$

26. $y = 2$,
$\quad x = -4$

27. $t + 2s = -1$,
$\quad s = t + 10$

28. $b + 2a = 2$,
$\quad a = -3 - b$

29. $2b + a = 11$,
$\quad a - b = 5$

30. $y = -\frac{1}{3}x - 1$,
$\quad 4x - 3y = 18$

31. $y = -\frac{1}{4}x + 1$,
$\quad 2y = x - 4$

32. $6x - 2y = 2$,
$\quad 9x - 3y = 1$

33. $y - x = 5$,
$\quad 2x - 2y = 10$

34. $y = x + 2$,
$\quad 3y - 2x = 4$

35. $y = 3 - x$,
$\quad 2x + 2y = 6$

36. $2x - 3y = 6$,
$\quad 3y - 2x = -6$

37. For the systems in the odd-numbered exercises 17–35, which are consistent?

38. For the systems in the even-numbered exercises 18–36, which are consistent?

39. For the systems in the odd-numbered exercises 17–35, which contain dependent equations?

40. For the systems in the even-numbered exercises 18–36, which contain dependent equations?

Translate each problem situation to a system of equations. Do not attempt to solve, but save for later use.

41. The sum of two numbers is 10. The first number is $\frac{2}{3}$ of the second number. What are the numbers?

42. The sum of two numbers is 30. The first number is twice the second number. What are the numbers?

43. *e-mail usage.* In 2007, the average e-mail user sent 578 personal and business e-mails each week. The number of business e-mails was 30 more than the number of personal e-mails. How many of each type were sent each week?
Source: *JupiterResearch*

44. *Nontoxic furniture polish.* A nontoxic wood furniture polish can be made by mixing mineral (or olive) oil with vinegar. To make a 16-oz batch for a squirt bottle, Jazmun uses an amount of mineral oil that is 4 oz more than twice the amount of vinegar. How much of each ingredient is required?
Sources: Based on information from Chittenden Solid Waste District and *Clean House, Clean Planet* by Karen Logan

45. *Geometry.* Two angles are supplementary.* One angle is 3° less than twice the other. Find the measures of the angles.

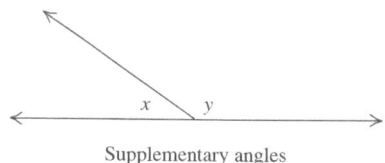

Supplementary angles

46. *Geometry.* Two angles are complementary.† The sum of the measures of the first angle and half the second angle is 64°. Find the measures of the angles.

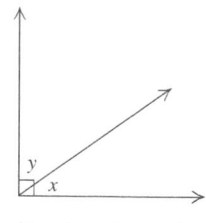

Complementary angles

47. *Basketball scoring.* Wilt Chamberlain once scored 100 points, setting a record for points scored in an NBA game. Chamberlain took only two-point shots and (one-point) foul shots and made a total of 64 shots. How many shots of each type did he make?

48. *Basketball scoring.* The Fenton College Cougars made 40 field goals in a recent basketball game, some 2-pointers and the rest 3-pointers. Altogether the 40 baskets counted for 89 points. How many of each type of field goal was made?

---

*The sum of the measures of two supplementary angles is 180°.
†The sum of the measures of two complementary angles is 90°.

49. *Retail sales.* Simply Souvenirs sold 45 hats and tee shirts. The hats sold for $14.50 each and the tee shirts for $19.50 each. In all, $697.50 was taken in for the souvenirs. How many of each type of souvenir were sold?

50. *Retail sales.* Cool Treats sold 60 ice cream cones. Single-dip cones sold for $2.50 each and double-dip cones for $4.15 each. In all, $179.70 was taken in for the cones. How many of each size cone were sold?

51. *Sales of pharmaceuticals.* In 2008, the Diabetic Express charged $83.29 for a 10-mL vial of Humalog insulin and $76.76 for a 10-mL vial of Lantus insulin. If a total of $3981.66 was collected for 50 vials of insulin, how many vials of each type were sold?

52. *Fundraising.* The Buck Creek Fire Department served 250 dinners. A child's plate cost $5.50 and an adult's plate cost $9.00. A total of $1935 was collected. How many of each type of plate was served?

53. *Lacrosse.* The perimeter of an NCAA men's lacrosse field is 340 yd. The length is 50 yd longer than the width. Find the dimensions.

$P = 340$ yd

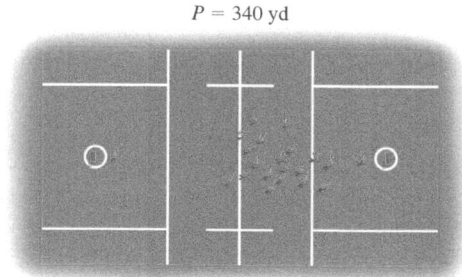

54. *Tennis.* The perimeter of a standard tennis court used for doubles is 228 ft. The width is 42 ft less than the length. Find the dimensions.

55. Write a problem for a classmate to solve that requires writing a system of two equations. Devise the problem so that the solution is "The Fever made 6 three-point baskets and 31 two-point baskets."

56. Write a problem for a classmate to solve that can be translated into a system of two equations. Devise the problem so that the solution is "In 2009, Diana took five 3-credit classes and two 4-credit classes."

Skill Review

To prepare for Section 8.2, review solving equations and formulas (Sections 2.2 and 2.3).

Solve. [2.2]

57. $3x + 2(5x - 1) = 6$

58. $4(3y + 2) - 7y = 3$

59. $9y = 5 - (y + 6)$

60. $2x - (x - 7) = 18$

Solve. [2.3]

61. $3x - y = 4$, for y

62. $5y - 2x = 7$, for x

Synthesis

Advertising media.   For Exercises 63 and 64, consider the following graph showing the U.S. market share for various advertising media.

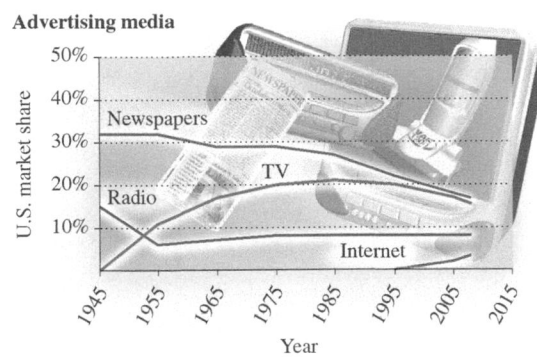

Advertising media

Source: *The Wall Street Journal*, 12/30/07

63. In what year did no one medium have a higher advertising market share than the others? Explain.

64. Will the Internet advertising market share ever exceed that of radio? TV? newspapers? If so, when? Explain your answers.

65. For each of the following conditions, write a system of equations.
a) $(5, 1)$ is a solution.
b) There is no solution.
c) There is an infinite number of solutions.

66. A system of linear equations has $(1, -1)$ and $(-2, 3)$ as solutions. Determine:
a) a third point that is a solution, and
b) how many solutions there are.

67. The solution of the following system is $(4, -5)$. Find A and B.

$$Ax - 6y = 13,$$
$$x - By = -8.$$

Translate to a system of equations. Do not solve.

68. *Ages.*   Tyler is twice as old as his son. Ten years ago, Tyler was three times as old as his son. How old are they now?

69. *Work experience.*   Dell and Juanita are mathematics professors at a state university. Together, they have 46 years of service. Two years ago, Dell had taught 2.5 times as many years as Juanita. How long has each taught at the university?

70. *Design.*   A piece of posterboard has a perimeter of 156 in. If you cut 6 in. off the width, the length becomes four times the width. What are the dimensions of the original piece of posterboard?

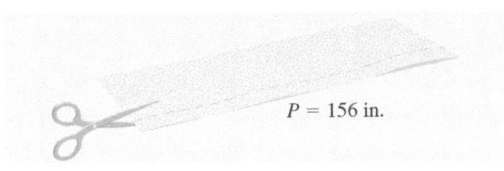

$P = 156$ in.

71. *Nontoxic scouring powder.*   A nontoxic scouring powder is made up of 4 parts baking soda and 1 part vinegar. How much of each ingredient is needed for a 16-oz mixture?

72. Solve Exercise 41 graphically.

73. Solve Exercise 44 graphically.

Solve graphically.

74. $y = |x|,$
         $3y - x = 8$

75. $x - y = 0,$
         $y = x^2$

In Exercises 76–79, use a graphing calculator to solve each system of linear equations for x and y. Round all coordinates to the nearest hundredth.

76. $y = 8.23x + 2.11,$
         $y = -9.11x - 4.66$

77. $y = -3.44x - 7.72,$
         $y = 4.19x - 8.22$

78. $14.12x + 7.32y = 2.98,$
         $21.88x - 6.45y = -7.22$

79. $5.22x - 8.21y = -10.21,$
         $-12.67x + 10.34y = 12.84$

8.2   Solving by Substitution or Elimination

The Substitution Method   •   The Elimination Method

The Substitution Method

Algebraic (nongraphical) methods for solving systems are often superior to graphing, especially when fractions are involved. One algebraic method, the *substitution method*, relies on having a variable isolated.

EXAMPLE 1

Solve the system

$$x + y = 4, \qquad (1)$$
$$x = y + 1. \qquad (2)$$

For easy reference, we have numbered the equations.

SOLUTION   Equation (2) says that x and $y + 1$ name the same number. Thus we can substitute $y + 1$ for x in equation (1):

$$x + y = 4 \qquad \text{Equation (1)}$$
$$(y + 1) + y = 4. \qquad \text{Substituting } y + 1 \text{ for } x$$

We solve this last equation, using methods learned earlier:

$$(y + 1) + y = 4$$
$$2y + 1 = 4 \qquad \text{Removing parentheses and combining like terms}$$
$$2y = 3 \qquad \text{Subtracting 1 from both sides}$$
$$y = \tfrac{3}{2}. \qquad \text{Dividing both sides by 2}$$

We now return to the original pair of equations and substitute $\tfrac{3}{2}$ for y in either equation so that we can solve for x. For this problem, calculations are slightly easier if we use equation (2):

$$x = y + 1 \qquad \text{Equation (2)}$$
$$= \tfrac{3}{2} + 1 \qquad \text{Substituting } \tfrac{3}{2} \text{ for } y$$
$$= \tfrac{3}{2} + \tfrac{2}{2} = \tfrac{5}{2}.$$

We obtain the ordered pair $\left(\tfrac{5}{2}, \tfrac{3}{2}\right)$. A check ensures that it is a solution.

Check:

$x + y = 4$		$x = y + 1$	
$\tfrac{5}{2} + \tfrac{3}{2}$	4	$\tfrac{5}{2}$	$\tfrac{3}{2} + 1$
$\tfrac{8}{2}$			$\tfrac{3}{2} + \tfrac{2}{2}$
$4 \overset{?}{=} 4$	TRUE	$\tfrac{5}{2} \overset{?}{=} \tfrac{5}{2}$	TRUE

Since $\left(\tfrac{5}{2}, \tfrac{3}{2}\right)$ checks, it is the solution.

> TRY EXERCISE   7

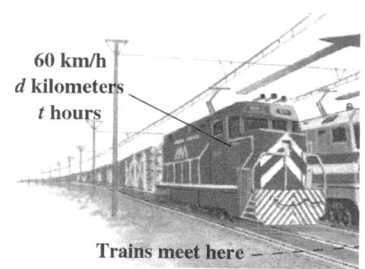

60 km/h
d kilometers
t hours

Trains meet here

A visualization of Example 1. Note that the coordinates of the intersection are not obvious.

The exact solution to Example 1 is difficult to find graphically because it involves fractions. The graph shown serves as a partial check and provides a visualization of the problem.

If neither equation in a system has a variable alone on one side, we first isolate a variable in one equation and then substitute.

EXAMPLE 2

Solve the system

$$2x + y = 6, \qquad (1)$$
$$3x + 4y = 4. \qquad (2)$$

SOLUTION   First, we select an equation and solve for one variable. We can isolate y by subtracting $2x$ from both sides of equation (1):

$$2x + y = 6 \qquad (1)$$
$$y = 6 - 2x. \qquad (3) \qquad \text{Subtracting } 2x \text{ from both sides}$$

Next, we proceed as in Example 1, by substituting:

$$3x + 4(6 - 2x) = 4 \qquad \text{Substituting } 6 - 2x \text{ for } y \text{ in equation (2).}$$
$$\text{Use parentheses!}$$
$$3x + 24 - 8x = 4 \qquad \text{Distributing to remove parentheses}$$
$$3x - 8x = 4 - 24 \qquad \text{Subtracting 24 from both sides}$$
$$-5x = -20$$
$$x = 4. \qquad \text{Dividing both sides by } -5$$

Next, we substitute 4 for x in either equation (1), (2), or (3). It is easiest to use equation (3) because it has already been solved for y:

$$y = 6 - 2x$$
$$= 6 - 2(4)$$
$$= 6 - 8 = -2.$$

The pair $(4, -2)$ appears to be the solution. We check in equations (1) and (2).

Check:

$$\begin{array}{c|c} 2x + y = 6 \\ \hline 2(4) + (-2) & 6 \\ 8 - 2 & \\ & 6 \overset{?}{=} 6 \quad \text{TRUE} \end{array} \qquad \begin{array}{c|c} 3x + 4y = 4 \\ \hline 3(4) + 4(-2) & 4 \\ 12 - 8 & \\ & 4 \overset{?}{=} 4 \quad \text{TRUE} \end{array}$$

Since $(4, -2)$ checks, it is the solution.   **TRY EXERCISE** ▸ 11

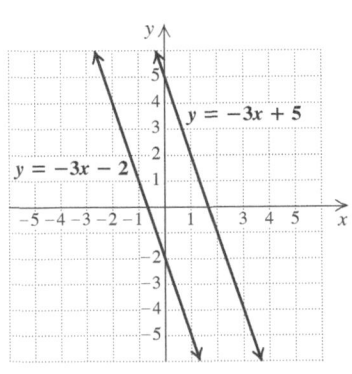

A visualization of Example 2

Some systems have no solution, as we saw graphically in Section 8.1. How do we recognize such systems if we are solving by an algebraic method?

EXAMPLE **3**   Solve the system

$$y = -3x + 5, \qquad (1)$$
$$y = -3x - 2. \qquad (2)$$

SOLUTION   We solved this system graphically in Example 4(b) of Section 8.1, and found that the lines are parallel and the system has no solution. Let's now try to solve the system by substitution. Proceeding as in Example 1, we substitute $-3x - 2$ for y in the first equation:

$$-3x - 2 = -3x + 5 \qquad \text{Substituting } -3x - 2 \text{ for } y \text{ in equation (1)}$$
$$-2 = 5. \qquad \text{Adding } 3x \text{ to both sides; } -2 = 5 \text{ is a contradiction. The equation is always false.}$$

Since there is no solution of $-2 = 5$, there is no solution of the system. We state that there is no solution.   **TRY EXERCISE** ▸ 21

A visualization of Example 3

When solving a system algebraically yields a contradiction, the system has no solution.

As we will see in Example 7, when solving a system of two equations algebraically yields an identity, the system has an infinite number of solutions.

The Elimination Method

The *elimination method* for solving systems of equations makes use of the *addition principle*: If $a = b$, then $a + c = b + c$. Consider the following system:

$$2x - 3y = 0,$$
$$-4x + 3y = -1.$$

Note that the $-3y$ in one equation and the $3y$ in the other are opposites. If we add all terms on the left side of the equations, the sum of $-3y$ and $3y$ is 0, so in effect, the variable y is "eliminated."

EXAMPLE 4   Solve the system

$$2x - 3y = 0, \qquad (1)$$
$$-4x + 3y = -1. \qquad (2)$$

SOLUTION   Note that according to equation (2), $-4x + 3y$ and -1 are the same number. Thus we can use the addition principle to work vertically and add $-4x + 3y$ to the left side of equation (1) and -1 to the right side:

$$2x - 3y = 0 \qquad (1)$$
$$\underline{-4x + 3y = -1} \qquad (2)$$
$$-2x + 0y = -1. \qquad \text{Adding}$$

This eliminates the variable y, and leaves an equation with just one variable, x, for which we solve:

$$-2x = -1$$
$$x = \tfrac{1}{2}.$$

Next, we substitute $\tfrac{1}{2}$ for x in equation (1) and solve for y:

$$2 \cdot \tfrac{1}{2} - 3y = 0 \qquad \text{Substituting. We also could have used equation (2).}$$
$$1 - 3y = 0$$
$$-3y = -1, \text{ so } y = \tfrac{1}{3}.$$

A visualization of Example 4

Check:

$$\begin{array}{c|c} 2x - 3y = 0 \\ \hline 2(\tfrac{1}{2}) - 3(\tfrac{1}{3}) & 0 \\ 1 - 1 & \\ 0 \stackrel{?}{=} 0 & \text{TRUE} \end{array} \qquad \begin{array}{c|c} -4x + 3y = -1 \\ \hline -4(\tfrac{1}{2}) + 3(\tfrac{1}{3}) & -1 \\ -2 + 1 & \\ -1 \stackrel{?}{=} -1 & \text{TRUE} \end{array}$$

Since $\left(\tfrac{1}{2}, \tfrac{1}{3}\right)$ checks, it is the solution. See also the graph at left.

▶ TRY EXERCISE   23

To eliminate a variable, we must sometimes multiply before adding.

EXAMPLE 5   Solve the system

$$5x + 4y = 22, \qquad (1)$$
$$-3x + 8y = 18. \qquad (2)$$

STUDENT NOTES

It is wise to double-check each step of your work as you go, rather than checking all steps at the end of a problem. Finding and correcting an error as it occurs saves you time in the long run. One common error is to forget to multiply *both* sides of the equation when you use the multiplication principle.

SOLUTION   If we add the left sides of the two equations, we will not eliminate a variable. However, if the $4y$ in equation (1) were changed to $-8y$, we would. To accomplish this change, we multiply both sides of equation (1) by -2:

$$
\begin{array}{ll}
-10x - 8y = -44 & \text{Multiplying both sides of equation (1) by } -2 \\
\underline{-3x + 8y = 18} & \\
-13x + 0 = -26 & \text{Adding} \\
x = 2. & \text{Solving for } x
\end{array}
$$

Then

$$
\begin{array}{ll}
-3 \cdot 2 + 8y = 18 & \text{Substituting 2 for } x \text{ in equation (2)} \\
-6 + 8y = 18 & \\
\left.\begin{array}{l} 8y = 24 \\ y = 3. \end{array}\right\} & \text{Solving for } y
\end{array}
$$

We obtain $(2, 3)$, or $x = 2$, $y = 3$. We leave it to the student to confirm that this checks and is the solution.

▶ **TRY EXERCISE** 29

Sometimes we must multiply twice in order to make two terms become opposites.

EXAMPLE **6**   Solve the system

$$
\begin{array}{ll}
2x + 3y = 17, & (1) \\
5x + 7y = 29. & (2)
\end{array}
$$

SOLUTION   We multiply so that the x-terms will be eliminated when we add.

Eliminate x.

Solve for y.

$$
\begin{array}{l}
2x + 3y = 17, \xrightarrow[\text{sides by 5}]{\text{Multiplying both}} \quad 10x + 15y = 85 \\
5x + 7y = 29 \xrightarrow[\text{sides by } -2]{\text{Multiplying both}} \quad \underline{-10x - 14y = -58} \\
 0 + y = 27 \quad \text{Adding} \\
 y = 27
\end{array}
$$

Next, we substitute to find x:

$$
\begin{array}{ll}
2x + 3 \cdot 27 = 17 & \text{Substituting 27 for } y \text{ in equation (1)} \\
2x + 81 = 17 & \\
\left.\begin{array}{l} 2x = -64 \\ x = -32. \end{array}\right\} & \text{Solving for } x
\end{array}
$$

Solve for x.

Check.

Check:

$$
\begin{array}{c|c}
\underline{2x + 3y = 17} & \underline{5x + 7y = 29} \\
2(-32) + 3(27) \;\big|\; 17 & 5(-32) + 7(27) \;\big|\; 29 \\
-64 + 81 \;\big| & -160 + 189 \;\big| \\
17 \overset{?}{=} 17 \;\; \text{\small TRUE} & 29 \overset{?}{=} 29 \;\; \text{\small TRUE}
\end{array}
$$

We obtain $(-32, 27)$, or $x = -32$, $y = 27$, as the solution.

▶ **TRY EXERCISE** 31

EXAMPLE 7

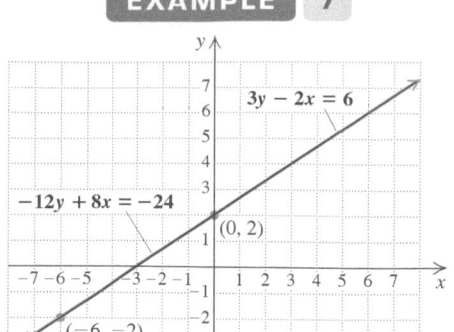

A visualization of Example 7

Solve the system

$$3y - 2x = 6, \qquad (1)$$
$$-12y + 8x = -24. \qquad (2)$$

SOLUTION We graphed this system in Example 4(c) of Section 8.1, and found that the lines coincide and the system has an infinite number of solutions. Suppose we were to solve this system using the elimination method:

$$12y - 8x = 24 \qquad \text{Multiplying both sides of equation (1) by 4}$$
$$\underline{-12y + 8x = -24}$$
$$0 = 0. \qquad \text{We obtain an identity; } 0 = 0 \text{ is always true.}$$

Note that both variables have been eliminated and what remains is an identity—that is, an equation that is always true. Any pair that is a solution of equation (1) is also a solution of equation (2). The equations are dependent and the solution set is infinite:

$$\{(x, y) \mid 3y - 2x = 6\}, \text{ or equivalently, } \{(x, y) \mid -12y + 8x = -24\}.$$

TRY EXERCISE 47

Example 3 and Example 7 illustrate how to tell algebraically whether a system of two equations is inconsistent or whether the equations are dependent.

Rules for Special Cases

When solving a system of two linear equations in two variables:

1. If we obtain an identity such as $0 = 0$, then the system has an infinite number of solutions. The equations are dependent and, since a solution exists, the system is consistent.*
2. If we obtain a contradiction such as $0 = 7$, then the system has no solution. The system is inconsistent.

Should decimals or fractions appear, it often helps to *clear* before solving.

EXAMPLE 8

Solve the system

$$0.2x + 0.3y = 1.7,$$
$$\tfrac{1}{7}x + \tfrac{1}{5}y = \tfrac{29}{35}.$$

SOLUTION We have

$$0.2x + 0.3y = 1.7, \longrightarrow \text{Multiplying both sides by } 10 \longrightarrow 2x + 3y = 17$$
$$\tfrac{1}{7}x + \tfrac{1}{5}y = \tfrac{29}{35} \longrightarrow \text{Multiplying both sides by } 35 \longrightarrow 5x + 7y = 29.$$

We multiplied both sides of the first equation by 10 to clear the decimals. Multiplication by 35, the least common denominator, clears the fractions in the second equation. The problem now happens to be identical to Example 6. The solution is $(-32, 27)$, or $x = -32, y = 27$.

TRY EXERCISE 35

The steps for each algebraic method for solving systems of two equations are given below. Note that in both methods, we find the value of one variable and then substitute to find the corresponding value of the other variable.

---

*Consistent systems and dependent equations are discussed in greater detail in Section 8.4.

To Solve a System Using Substitution

1. Isolate a variable in one of the equations (unless one is already isolated).
2. Substitute for that variable in the other equation, using parentheses.
3. Solve for the remaining variable.
4. Substitute the value of the second variable in any of the equations, and solve for the first variable.
5. Form an ordered pair and check in the original equations.

To Solve a System Using Elimination

1. Write both equations in standard form.
2. Multiply both sides of one or both equations by a constant, if necessary, so that the coefficients of one of the variables are opposites.
3. Add the left sides and the right sides of the resulting equations. One variable should be eliminated in the sum.
4. Solve for the remaining variable.
5. Substitute the value of the second variable in any of the equations, and solve for the first variable.
6. Form an ordered pair and check in the original equations.

8.2 EXERCISE SET

For Extra Help

Concept Reinforcement   In each of Exercises 1–6, match the system listed with the choice from the column on the right that would be a subsequent step in solving the system.

1. ____ $3x - 4y = 6,$
   $5x + 4y = 1$

2. ____ $2x - y = 8,$
   $y = 5x + 3$

3. ____ $x - 2y = 3,$
   $5x + 3y = 4$

4. ____ $8x + 6y = -15,$
   $5x - 3y = 8$

5. ____ $y = 4x - 7,$
   $6x + 3y = 19$

6. ____ $y = 4x - 1,$
   $y = -\frac{2}{3}x - 1$

a) $-5x + 10y = -15,$
   $5x + 3y = 4$

b) The lines intersect at $(0, -1)$.

c) $6x + 3(4x - 7) = 19$

d) $8x = 7$

e) $2x - (5x + 3) = 8$

f) $8x + 6y = -15,$
   $10x - 6y = 16$

For Exercises 7–54, if a system has an infinite number of solutions, use set-builder notation to write the solution set. If a system has no solution, state this.

Solve using the substitution method.

7. $y = 3 - 2x,$
   $3x + y = 5$

8. $3y + x = 4,$
   $x = 2y - 1$

9. $3x + 5y = 3,$
   $x = 8 - 4y$

10. $9x - 2y = 3,$
    $3x - 6 = y$

11. $3s - 4t = 14,$
    $5s + t = 8$

12. $m - 2n = 16,$
    $4m + n = 1$

13. $4x - 2y = 6,$
    $2x - 3 = y$

14. $t = 4 - 2s,$
    $t + 2s = 6$

15. $-5s + t = 11,$
    $4s + 12t = 4$

16. $5x + 6y = 14,$
    $-3y + x = 7$

17. $2x + 2y = 2,$
    $3x - y = 1$

18. $4p - 2q = 16,$
    $5p + 7q = 1$

19. $2a + 6b = 4,$
    $3a - b = 6$

20. $3x - 4y = 5,$
    $2x - y = 1$

21. $2x - 3 = y,$
    $y - 2x = 1$

22. $a - 2b = 3,$
    $3a = 6b + 9$

Solve using the elimination method.

23. $x + 3y = 7,$
    $-x + 4y = 7$

24. $2x + y = 6,$
    $x - y = 3$

25. $x - 2y = 11,$
    $3x + 2y = 17$

26. $5x - 3y = 8,$
    $-5x + y = 4$

27. $9x + 3y = -3,$
    $2x - 3y = -8$

28. $6x - 3y = 18,$
    $6x + 3y = -12$

29. $5x + 3y = 19,$
  $x - 6y = 11$

30. $3x + 2y = 3,$
  $9x - 8y = -2$

31. $5r - 3s = 24,$
  $3r + 5s = 28$

32. $5x - 7y = -16,$
  $2x + 8y = 26$

33. $6s + 9t = 12,$
  $4s + 6t = 5$

34. $10a + 6b = 8,$
  $5a + 3b = 2$

35. $\frac{1}{2}x - \frac{1}{6}y = 10,$
  $\frac{2}{5}x + \frac{1}{2}y = 8$

36. $\frac{1}{3}x + \frac{1}{5}y = 7,$
  $\frac{1}{6}x - \frac{2}{5}y = -4$

37. $\frac{x}{2} + \frac{y}{3} = \frac{7}{6},$
  $\frac{2x}{3} + \frac{3y}{4} = \frac{5}{4}$

38. $\frac{2x}{3} + \frac{3y}{4} = \frac{11}{12},$
  $\frac{x}{3} + \frac{7y}{18} = \frac{1}{2}$

Aha! **39.** $12x - 6y = -15,$
  $-4x + 2y = 5$

40. $8s + 12t = 16,$
  $6s + 9t = 12$

41. $0.3x + 0.2y = 0.3,$
  $0.5x + 0.4y = 0.4$

42. $0.3x + 0.2y = 5,$
  $0.5x + 0.4y = 11$

Solve using any appropriate method.

43. $a - 2b = 16,$
  $b + 3 = 3a$

44. $5x - 9y = 7,$
  $7y - 3x = -5$

45. $10x + y = 306,$
  $10y + x = 90$

46. $3(a - b) = 15,$
  $4a = b + 1$

47. $6x - 3y = 3,$
  $4x - 2y = 2$

48. $x + 2y = 8,$
  $x = 4 - 2y$

49. $3s - 7t = 5,$
  $7t - 3s = 8$

50. $2s - 13t = 120,$
  $-14s + 91t = -840$

51. $0.05x + 0.25y = 22,$
  $0.15x + 0.05y = 24$

52. $2.1x - 0.9y = 15,$
  $-1.4x + 0.6y = 10$

53. $13a - 7b = 9,$
  $2a - 8b = 6$

54. $3a - 12b = 9,$
  $4a - 5b = 3$

55. Describe a procedure that can be used to write an inconsistent system of equations.

56. Describe a procedure that can be used to write a system that has an infinite number of solutions.

Skill Review

To prepare for Section 8.3, review solving problems using the five-step problem-solving strategy (Section 2.5).

Solve. [2.5]

57. *Energy consumption.*   With average use, a toaster oven and a convection oven together consume 15 kilowatt hours (kWh) of electricity each month. A convection oven uses four times as much electricity as a toaster oven. How much does each use per month?
Source: Lee County Electric Cooperative

58. *Test scores.*   Ellia needs to average 80 on her tests in order to earn a B in her math class. Her average after 4 tests is 77.5. What score is needed on the fifth test in order to raise the average to 80?

59. *Real estate.*   After her house had been on the market for 6 months, Gina reduced the price to $94,500. This was $\frac{9}{10}$ of the original asking price. How much did Gina originally ask for her house?

60. *Car rentals.*   National Car Rental rents minivans to a university for $69 a day plus 30¢ per mile. An English professor rented a minivan for 2 days to take a group of students to a seminar. The bill was $225. How far did the professor drive the van?
Source: www.nationalcar.com

61. *Carpentry.*   Anazi cuts a 96-in. piece of wood trim into three pieces. The second piece is twice as long as the first. The third piece is one-tenth as long as the second. How long is each piece?

62. *Telephone calls.*   Terri's voice over the Internet (VoIP) phone service charges $0.36 for the first minute of each call and $0.06 for each additional $\frac{1}{2}$ minute. One month she was charged $28.20 for 35 calls. How many minutes did she use?

Synthesis

63. Some systems are more easily solved by substitution and some are more easily solved by elimination. What guidelines could be used to help someone determine which method to use?

64. Explain how it is possible to solve Exercise 39 mentally.

65. If $(1, 2)$ and $(-3, 4)$ are two solutions of $f(x) = mx + b,$ find m and b.

66. If $(0, -3)$ and $\left(-\frac{3}{2}, 6\right)$ are two solutions of $px - qy = -1,$ find p and q.

67. Determine a and b for which $(-4, -3)$ is a solution of the system

$$ax + by = -26,$$
$$bx - ay = 7.$$

68. Solve for x and y in terms of a and b:

$$5x + 2y = a,$$
$$x - y = b.$$

Solve.

69. $\dfrac{x + y}{2} - \dfrac{x - y}{5} = 1,$

$\dfrac{x - y}{2} + \dfrac{x + y}{6} = -2$

70. $3.5x - 2.1y = 106.2,$
$4.1x + 16.7y = -106.28$

Each of the following is a system of nonlinear equations. However, each is reducible to linear, since an appropriate substitution (say, u for 1/x and v for 1/y) yields a linear system. Make such a substitution, solve for the new variables, and then solve for the original variables.

71. $\dfrac{2}{x} + \dfrac{1}{y} = 0,$

$\dfrac{5}{x} + \dfrac{2}{y} = -5$

72. $\dfrac{1}{x} - \dfrac{3}{y} = 2,$

$\dfrac{6}{x} + \dfrac{5}{y} = -34$

73. A student solving the system

$$17x + 19y = 102,$$
$$136x + 152y = 826$$

graphs both equations on a graphing calculator and gets the following screen. The student then (incorrectly) concludes that the equations are dependent and the solution set is infinite. How can algebra be used to convince the student that a mistake has been made?

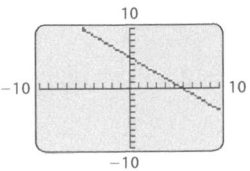

CONNECTING the CONCEPTS

We now have three different methods for solving systems of equations. Each method has certain strengths and weaknesses, as outlined below.

Method	Strengths	Weaknesses
Graphical	Solutions are displayed graphically. Can be used with any system that can be graphed.	For some systems, only approximate solutions can be found graphically. The graph drawn may not be large enough to show the solution.
Substitution	Yields exact solutions. Easy to use when a variable has a coefficient of 1.	Introduces extensive computations with fractions when solving more complicated systems. Solutions are not displayed graphically.
Elimination	Yields exact solutions. Easy to use when fractions or decimals appear in the system. The preferred method for systems of 3 or more equations in 3 or more variables (see Section 8.4).	Solutions are not displayed graphically.

(continued)

When selecting a method to use, consider the strengths and weaknesses listed above. If possible, begin solving the system mentally to help discover the method that seems best suited for that particular system.

MIXED REVIEW

Solve using the best method.

1. $x = y$,
$x + y = 2$

2. $x + y = 10$,
$x - y = 8$

3. $y = \frac{1}{2}x + 1$,
$y = 2x - 5$

4. $y = 2x - 3$,
$x + y = 12$

5. $x = 5$,
$y = 10$

6. $3x + 5y = 8$,
$3x - 5y = 4$

7. $2x - y = 1$,
$2y - 4x = 3$

8. $x = 2 - y$,
$3x + 3y = 6$

9. $x + 2y = 3$,
$3x = 4 - y$

10. $9x + 8y = 0$,
$11x - 7y = 0$

11. $10x + 20y = 40$,
$x - \quad y = 7$

12. $y = \frac{5}{3}x + 7$,
$y = \frac{5}{3}x - 8$

13. $2x - 5y = 1$,
$3x + 2y = 11$

14. $\dfrac{x}{2} + \dfrac{y}{3} = \dfrac{2}{3}$,
$\dfrac{x}{5} + \dfrac{5y}{2} = \dfrac{1}{4}$

15. $1.1x - 0.3y = 0.8$,
$2.3x + 0.3y = 2.6$

16. $y = -3$,
$x = 11$

17. $x - 2y = 5$,
$3x - 15 = 6y$

18. $12x - 19y = 13$,
$8x + 19y = 7$

19. $0.2x + 0.7y = 1.2$,
$0.3x - 0.1y = 2.7$

20. $\frac{1}{4}x = \frac{1}{3}y$,
$\frac{1}{2}x - \frac{1}{15}y = 2$

8.3   Solving Applications: Systems of Two Equations

Total-Value and Mixture Problems   ●   Motion Problems

You are in a much better position to solve problems now that you know how systems of equations can be used. Using systems often makes the translating step easier.

EXAMPLE **1**   *Endangered species.*   The number of plant species listed as threatened (likely to become endangered) or endangered (in danger of becoming extinct) has more than tripled in the past 20 years. In 2008, there were 746 species of plants in the United States that were considered threatened or endangered. The number considered threatened was 4 less than one-fourth of the number considered endangered. How many U.S. plant species were considered endangered and how many were considered threatened in 2008?

Source: U.S. Fish and Wildlife Service

Patch of Brighamia Insignis with flower

SOLUTION   The *Familiarize* and *Translate* steps were completed in Example 1 of Section 8.1. The resulting system of equations is

$$t + d = 746,$$
$$t = \tfrac{1}{4}d - 4,$$

where d is the number of endangered plant species and t is the number of threatened plant species in the United States in 2008.

3. **Carry out.** We solve the system of equations. Since one equation already has a variable isolated, let's use the substitution method:

$$t + d = 746$$
$$\tfrac{1}{4}d - 4 + d = 746 \qquad \text{Substituting } \tfrac{1}{4}d - 4 \text{ for } t$$
$$\tfrac{5}{4}d - 4 = 746 \qquad \text{Combining like terms}$$
$$\tfrac{5}{4}d = 750 \qquad \text{Adding 4 to both sides}$$
$$d = \tfrac{4}{5} \cdot 750 \qquad \text{Multiplying both sides by } \tfrac{4}{5} \colon \tfrac{4}{5} \cdot \tfrac{5}{4} = 1$$
$$d = 600. \qquad \text{Simplifying}$$

Next, using either of the original equations, we substitute and solve for t:

$$t = \tfrac{1}{4} \cdot 600 - 4 = 150 - 4 = 146.$$

4. **Check.** The sum of 600 and 146 is 746, so the total number of species is correct. Since 4 less than one-fourth of 600 is 150 − 4, or 146, the numbers check.

5. **State.** In 2008, there were 600 endangered plant species and 146 threatened plant species in the United States.

▶ TRY EXERCISE 45

Total-Value and Mixture Problems

Jewelry design.   In order to make a necklace, a jewelry designer purchased 80 beads for a total of $39 (excluding tax). Some of the beads were sterling silver beads that cost 40¢ each and the rest were gemstone beads that cost 65¢ each. How many of each type did the designer buy?

SOLUTION   The *Familiarize* and *Translate* steps were completed in Example 2 of Section 8.1.

3. **Carry out.** We are to solve the system of equations

$$s + g = 80, \qquad (1)$$
$$40s + 65g = 3900, \qquad (2) \qquad \text{Working in cents rather than dollars}$$

where s is the number of silver beads bought and g is the number of gemstone beads bought. Because both equations are in the form $Ax + By = C$, let's use the elimination method to solve the system. We can eliminate s by multiplying both sides of equation (1) by −40 and adding them to the corresponding sides of equation (2):

$$-40s - 40g = -3200 \qquad \text{Multiplying both sides of equation (1) by } -40$$
$$\underline{40s + 65g = 3900}$$
$$25g = 700 \qquad \text{Adding}$$
$$g = 28. \qquad \text{Solving for } g$$

To find s, we substitute 28 for g in equation (1) and then solve for s:

$$s + g = 80 \qquad \text{Equation (1)}$$
$$s + 28 = 80 \qquad \text{Substituting 28 for } g$$
$$s = 52. \qquad \text{Solving for } s$$

We obtain $(28, 52)$, or $g = 28$ and $s = 52$.

STUDENT NOTES

It is very important that you clearly label precisely what each variable represents. Not only will this assist you in writing equations, but it will help you to identify and state solutions.

EXAMPLE   2

4. **Check.** We check in the original problem. Recall that g is the number of gemstone beads and s the number of silver beads.

Number of beads:	$g + s = 28 + 52 = 80$
Cost of gemstone beads:	$65g = 65 \times 28 = 1820¢$
Cost of silver beads:	$40s = 40 \times 52 = \underline{2080¢}$
	Total $= 3900¢$

The numbers check.

5. **State.** The designer bought 28 gemstone beads and 52 silver beads.

TRY EXERCISE 15

Example 2 involved two types of items (silver beads and gemstone beads), the quantity of each type bought, and the total value of the items. We refer to this type of problem as a *total-value problem*.

EXAMPLE 3

Blending teas. Tea Pots n Treasures sells loose Oolong tea for $2.15 an ounce. Donna mixed Oolong tea with shaved almonds that sell for $0.95 an ounce to create the Market Street Oolong blend that sells for $1.85 an ounce. One week, she made 300 oz of Market Street Oolong. How much tea and how much shaved almonds did Donna use?

SOLUTION

1. **Familiarize.** This problem is similar to Example 2. Rather than silver beads and gemstone beads, we have ounces of tea and ounces of almonds. Instead of a different price for each type of bead, we have a different price per ounce for each ingredient. Finally, rather than knowing the total cost of the beads, we know the weight and the price per ounce of the mixture. Thus we can find the total value of the blend by multiplying 300 ounces times $1.85 per ounce. We let l = the number of ounces of Oolong tea and a = the number of ounces of shaved almonds.

2. **Translate.** Since a 300-oz batch was made, we must have

$$l + a = 300.$$

To find a second equation, note that the total value of the 300-oz blend must match the combined value of the separate ingredients:

Rewording: The value of the Oolong tea   plus   the value of the almonds   is   the value of the Market Street blend.

Translating: $l \cdot \$2.15$ + $a \cdot \$0.95$ = $300 \cdot \$1.85$

These equations can also be obtained from a table.

	Oolong Tea	Almonds	Market Street Blend	
Number of Ounces	l	a	300	→ $l + a = 300$
Price per Ounce	$2.15	$0.95	$1.85	
Value of Tea	$2.15l	$0.95a	$300 \cdot \$1.85$, or $555	→ $2.15l + 0.95a = 555$

Clearing decimals in the second equation, we have $215l + 95a = 55{,}500$. We have translated to a system of equations:

$$l + \quad a = 300, \qquad (1)$$
$$215l + 95a = 55{,}500. \qquad (2)$$

3. **Carry out.** We can solve using substitution. When equation (1) is solved for l, we have $l = 300 - a$. Substituting $300 - a$ for l in equation (2), we find a:

$215(300 - a) + 95a = 55{,}500$	Substituting
$64{,}500 - 215a + 95a = 55{,}500$	Using the distributive law
$-120a = -9000$	Combining like terms; subtracting 64,500 from both sides
$a = 75.$	Dividing both sides by -120

We have $a = 75$ and, from equation (1) above, $l + a = 300$. Thus, $l = 225$.

4. **Check.** Combining 225 oz of Oolong tea and 75 oz of almonds will give a 300-oz blend. The value of 225 oz of Oolong is $225(\$2.15)$, or $483.75. The value of 75 oz of almonds is $75(\$0.95)$, or $71.25. Thus the combined value of the blend is $483.75 + $71.25, or $555. A 300-oz blend priced at $1.85 an ounce would also be worth $555, so our answer checks.

5. **State.** The Market Street blend was made by combining 225 oz of Oolong tea and 75 oz of almonds.

TRY EXERCISE 23

EXAMPLE 4

Student loans. Rani's student loans totaled $9600. Part was a PLUS loan made at 8.5% interest and the rest was a Stafford loan made at 6.8% interest. After one year, Rani's loans accumulated $729.30 in interest. What was the original amount of each loan?

SOLUTION

1. **Familiarize.** We begin with a guess. If $3000 was borrowed at 8.5% and $6600 was borrowed at 6.8%, the two loans would total $9600. The interest would then be $0.085(\$3000)$, or $255, and $0.068(\$6600)$, or $448.80, for a total of only $703.80 in interest. Our guess was wrong, but checking the guess familiarized us with the problem. More than $3000 was borrowed at the higher rate.

2. **Translate.** We let $p =$ the amount of the PLUS loan and $s =$ the amount of the Stafford loan. Next, we organize a table in which the entries in each column come from the formula for simple interest:

$$Principal \cdot Rate \cdot Time = Interest.$$

	PLUS Loan	Stafford Loan	Total	
Principal	p	s	$9600	$\longrightarrow p + s = 9600$
Rate of Interest	8.5%	6.8%		
Time	1 yr	1 yr		
Interest	$0.085p$	$0.068s$	$729.30	$\longrightarrow 0.085p + 0.068s = 729.30$

The total amount borrowed is found in the first row of the table:

$$p + s = 9600.$$

A second equation, representing the accumulated interest, can be found in the last row:

$$0.085p + 0.068s = 729.30, \quad \text{or} \quad 85p + 68s = 729,300. \qquad \text{Clearing decimals}$$

3. **Carry out.** The system can be solved by elimination:

$$
\begin{array}{lll}
p + s = 9600, & \longrightarrow \text{Multiplying both} \longrightarrow & -85p - 85s = -816,000 \\
85p + 68s = 729,300. & \quad \text{sides by } -85 & \underline{85p + 68s = \;\;\; 729,300} \\
& & -17s = \;\; -86,700 \\
& p + s = 9600 \longleftarrow\! & s = 5100 \\
& p + 5100 = 9600 & \\
& p = 4500. &
\end{array}
$$

We find that $p = 4500$ and $s = 5100$.

4. **Check.** The total amount borrowed is $4500 + $5100, or $9600. The interest on $4500 at 8.5% for 1 yr is 0.085($4500), or $382.50. The interest on $5100 at 6.8% for 1 yr is 0.068($5100), or $346.80. The total amount of interest is $382.50 + $346.80, or $729.30, so the numbers check.

5. **State.** The PLUS loan was for $4500 and the Stafford loan was for $5100.

> TRY EXERCISE 29

Before proceeding to Example 5, briefly scan Examples 2–4 for similarities. Note that in each case, one of the equations in the system is a simple sum while the other equation represents a sum of products. Example 5 continues this pattern with what is commonly called a *mixture problem*.

Problem-Solving Tip

When solving a problem, see if it is patterned or modeled after a problem that you have already solved.

EXAMPLE 5   *Mixing fertilizers.*   Nature's Green Gardening, Inc., carries two brands of fertilizer containing nitrogen and water. "Gentle Grow" is 3% nitrogen and "Sun Saver" is 8% nitrogen. Nature's Green needs to combine the two types of solutions into a 90-L mixture that is 6% nitrogen. How much of each brand should be used?

SOLUTION

1. **Familiarize.** We make a drawing and note that we must consider not only the size of the mixture, but also its strength. Let's make a guess to gain familiarity with the problem.

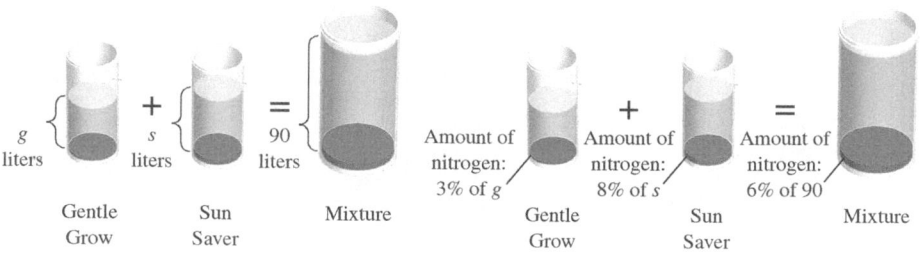

The total amount of the mixture must be 90 L.

The total amount of the nitrogen must be 6% of 90 L, or 5.4 L.

Suppose that 40 L of Gentle Grow and 50 L of Sun Saver are mixed. The resulting mixture will be the right size, 90 L, but will it be the right strength? To find out, note that 40 L of Gentle Grow would contribute $0.03(40) = 1.2$ L of nitrogen to the mixture while 50 L of Sun Saver would contribute $0.08(50) = 4$ L of nitrogen to the mixture. The total amount of nitrogen in the mixture would then be $1.2 + 4$, or 5.2 L. But we want 6% of 90, or 5.4 L, to be nitrogen. Our guess of 40 L and 50 L is close but incorrect. Checking our guess has familiarized us with the problem.

2. **Translate.** Let g = the number of liters of Gentle Grow and s = the number of liters of Sun Saver. The information can be organized in a table.

	Gentle Grow	Sun Saver	Mixture	
Number of Liters	g	s	90	$\longrightarrow$ $g + s = 90$
Percent of Nitrogen	3%	8%	6%	
Amount of Nitrogen	$0.03g$	$0.08s$	0.06×90, or 5.4 liters	$\longrightarrow$ $0.03g + 0.08s = 5.4$

If we add g and s in the first row, we get one equation. It represents the total amount of mixture: $g + s = 90$.

If we add the amounts of nitrogen listed in the third row, we get a second equation. This equation represents the amount of nitrogen in the mixture: $0.03g + 0.08s = 5.4$.

After clearing decimals, we have translated the problem to the system

$$g + s = 90, \quad (1)$$
$$3g + 8s = 540. \quad (2)$$

3. **Carry out.** We use the elimination method to solve the system:

$$-3g - 3s = -270 \qquad \text{Multiplying both sides of equation (1) by } -3$$

$$\underline{3g + 8s = 540}$$

$$5s = 270 \qquad \text{Adding}$$

$$s = 54; \qquad \text{Solving for } s$$

$$g + 54 = 90 \qquad \text{Substituting into equation (1)}$$

$$g = 36. \qquad \text{Solving for } g$$

4. **Check.** Remember, g is the number of liters of Gentle Grow and s is the number of liters of Sun Saver.

Total amount of mixture:	$g + s = 36 + 54 = 90$
Total amount of nitrogen:	3% of 36 + 8% of 54 = 1.08 + 4.32 = 5.4
Percentage of nitrogen in mixture:	$\dfrac{\text{Total amount of nitrogen}}{\text{Total amount of mixture}} = \dfrac{5.4}{90} = 6\%$

The numbers check in the original problem.

5. **State.** Nature's Green Gardening should mix 36 L of Gentle Grow with 54 L of Sun Saver.

TRY EXERCISE 25

Motion Problems

When a problem deals with distance, speed (rate), and time, recall the following.

Distance, Rate, and Time Equations

If r represents rate, t represents time, and d represents distance, then:

$$d = rt, \quad r = \frac{d}{t}, \quad \text{and} \quad t = \frac{d}{r}.$$

Be sure to remember at least one of these equations. The others can be obtained by multiplying or dividing on both sides as needed.

EXAMPLE 6   *Train travel.*   A Vermont Railways freight train, loaded with logs, leaves Boston, heading to Washington, D.C., at a speed of 60 km/h. Two hours later, an Amtrak® Metroliner leaves Boston, bound for Washington, D.C., on a parallel track at 90 km/h. At what point will the Metroliner catch up to the freight train?

SOLUTION

1. **Familiarize.** Let's make a guess and check to see if it is correct. Suppose the trains meet after traveling 180 km. We can then calculate the time for each train.

	Distance	*Rate*	*Time*
Freight Train	180 km	60 km/h	$\frac{180}{60} = 3$ hr
Metroliner	180 km	90 km/h	$\frac{180}{90} = 2$ hr

We see that the distance cannot be 180 km, since the difference in travel times for the trains is *not* 2 hr. Although our guess is wrong, we can use a similar chart to organize the information in this problem.

The distance at which the trains meet is unknown, but we do know that the trains will have traveled the same distance when they meet. We let $d =$ this distance.

The time that the trains are running is also unknown, but we do know that the freight train has a 2-hr head start. Thus if we let $t =$ the number of hours that the freight train is running before they meet, then $t - 2$ is the number of hours that the Metroliner runs before catching up to the freight train.

60 km/h
d kilometers
t hours

90 km/h
d kilometers
t − 2 hours

Trains meet here

2. **Translate.** We can organize the information in a chart. Each row is determined by the formula *Distance = Rate · Time*.

	Distance	Rate	Time	
Freight Train	d	60	t	$\longrightarrow\ d = 60t$
Metroliner	d	90	$t - 2$	$\longrightarrow\ d = 90(t - 2)$

Using *Distance = Rate · Time* twice, we get two equations:

$$d = 60t, \qquad (1)$$
$$d = 90(t - 2). \qquad (2)$$

3. **Carry out.** We solve the system using substitution:

$$60t = 90(t - 2) \qquad \text{Substituting } 60t \text{ for } d \text{ in equation (2)}$$
$$60t = 90t - 180$$
$$-30t = -180$$
$$t = 6.$$

STUDENT NOTES

Always be careful to answer the question asked in the problem. In Example 6, the problem asks for distance, not time. Answering "6 hr" would be incorrect.

The time for the freight train is 6 hr, which means that the time for the Metroliner is 6 − 2, or 4 hr. Remember that it is distance, not time, that the problem asked for. Thus for $t = 6$, we have $d = 60 \cdot 6 = 360$ km.

4. **Check.** At 60 km/h, the freight train will travel $60 \cdot 6$, or 360 km, in 6 hr. At 90 km/h, the Metroliner will travel $90 \cdot (6 - 2) = 360$ km in 4 hr. The numbers check.

5. **State.** The freight train will catch up to the Metroliner at a point 360 km from Boston.

> TRY EXERCISE 37

EXAMPLE 7

Jet travel. A Boeing 747-400 jet flies 4 hr west with a 60-mph tailwind. Returning *against* the wind takes 5 hr. Find the speed of the jet with no wind.

SOLUTION

1. **Familiarize.** We imagine the situation and make a drawing. Note that the wind *speeds up* the jet on the outbound flight but *slows down* the jet on the return flight.

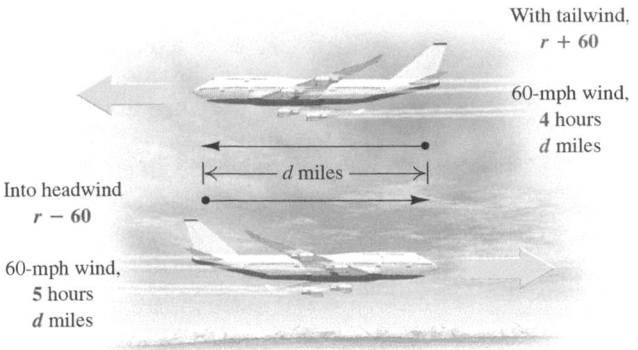

Let's make a guess of the jet's speed if there were no wind. Note that the distances traveled each way must be the same.

Speed with no wind:	400 mph
Speed with the wind:	$400 + 60 = 460$ mph
Speed against the wind:	$400 - 60 = 340$ mph
Distance with the wind:	$460 \cdot 4 = 1840$ mi
Distance against the wind:	$340 \cdot 5 = 1700$ mi

Since the distances are not the same, our guess of 400 mph is incorrect.

We let $r =$ the speed, in miles per hour, of the jet in still air. Then $r + 60 =$ the jet's speed with the wind and $r - 60 =$ the jet's speed against the wind. We also let $d =$ the distance traveled, in miles.

2. Translate. The information can be organized in a chart. The distances traveled are the same, so we use *Distance* = *Rate* (or *Speed*) · *Time*. Each row of the chart gives an equation.

	Distance	Rate	Time
With Wind	*d*	*r* + 60	4
Against Wind	*d*	*r* − 60	5

$\longrightarrow d = (r + 60)4$

$\longrightarrow d = (r - 60)5$

The two equations constitute a system:

$$d = (r + 60)4, \quad (1)$$
$$d = (r - 60)5. \quad (2)$$

3. Carry out. We solve the system using substitution:

$(r - 60)5 = (r + 60)4$ Substituting $(r - 60)5$ for *d* in equation (1)

$5r - 300 = 4r + 240$ Using the distributive law

$r = 540.$ Solving for *r*

4. Check. When $r = 540$, the speed with the wind is $540 + 60 = 600$ mph, and the speed against the wind is $540 - 60 = 480$ mph. The distance with the wind, $600 \cdot 4 = 2400$ mi, matches the distance into the wind, $480 \cdot 5 = 2400$ mi, so we have a check.

5. State. The speed of the jet with no wind is 540 mph.   `TRY EXERCISE 39`

Tips for Solving Motion Problems

1. Draw a diagram using an arrow or arrows to represent distance and the direction of each object in motion.
2. Organize the information in a chart.
3. Look for times, distances, or rates that are the same. These often can lead to an equation.
4. Translating to a system of equations allows for the use of two variables.
5. Always make sure that you have answered the question asked.

8.3   EXERCISE SET

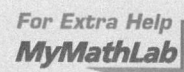

1.–14. For Exercises 1–14, solve Exercises 41–54 from pp. 513–514.

15. *Recycled paper.*   Staples® recently charged $3.79 per ream (package of 500 sheets) of regular paper and $5.49 per ream of paper made of recycled fibers. Last semester, Valley College spent $582.44 for 116 reams of paper. How many of each type were purchased?

16. *Photocopying.*   Quick Copy recently charged 49¢ per page for color copies and 7¢ per page for black-and-white copies. If Shirlee's bill for 90 copies was $11.34, how many copies of each type were made?

17. *Lighting.*   Lowe's Home Improvement recently sold 13-watt Feit Electric Ecobulbs® for $5 each and 18-watt Ecobulbs® for $6 each. If River County Hospital purchased 200 such bulbs for a total of $1140, how many of each type did they purchase?

18. *Office supplies.*   Staples® recently charged $17.99 per box of Pilot Precise® rollerball pens and $7.49 per box for Bic® Matic Grip mechanical pencils. If Kelling Community College purchased 120 such boxes for a total of $1234.80, how many boxes of each type did they purchase?

19. *Sales.*   Recently, officedepot.com sold a black HP C7115A Laser Jet print cartridge for $64.99 and a color Apple computer M3908GA ink cartridge for $58.99. During a promotion offering free shipping, a total of 450 of these cartridges was purchased for a total of $27,625.50. How many of each type were purchased?

20. *Sales.*   Office Max® recently advertised a three-subject notebook for $2.49 and a five-subject notebook for $3.79. At the start of a recent spring semester, a combination of 50 of these notebooks was sold for a total of $166.10. How many of each type were sold?

Aha! **21.** *Blending coffees.*   The Roasted Bean charges $13.00 per pound for Fair Trade Organic Mexican coffee and $11.00 per pound for Fair Trade Organic Peruvian coffee. How much of each type should be used to make a 28-lb blend that sells for $12.00 per pound?

22. *Mixed nuts.*   Oh Nuts! sells pistachio kernels for $6.50 per pound and almonds for $8.00 per pound. How much of each type should be used to make a 50-lb mixture that sells for $7.40 per pound?

23. *Event planning.*   As part of the refreshments for Yvette's 25th birthday party, Kim plans to provide a bowl of M&M candies. She wants to mix custom-printed M&Ms costing 60¢ per ounce with bulk M&Ms costing 25¢ per ounce to create 20 lb of a

mixture costing 32¢ per ounce. How much of each type of M&M should she use?
Source: www.mymms.com

24. *Blending spices.*   Spice of Life sells ground sumac for $1.35 an ounce and ground thyme for $1.85 an ounce. Aman wants to make a 20-oz Zahtar seasoning blend using the two spices that sells for $1.65 an ounce. How much of each spice should Aman use?

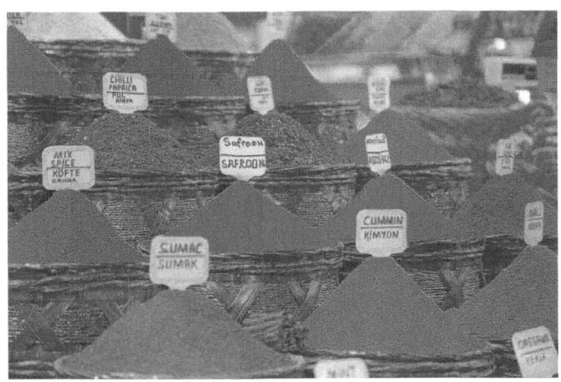

25. *Catering.*   Cati's Catering is planning an office reception. The office administrator has requested a candy mixture that is 25% chocolate. Cati has available mixtures that are either 50% chocolate or 10% chocolate. How much of each type should be mixed to get a 20-lb mixture that is 25% chocolate?

26. *Ink remover.*   Etch Clean Graphics uses one cleanser that is 25% acid and a second that is 50% acid. How many liters of each should be mixed to get 30 L of a solution that is 40% acid?

27. *Blending granola.*   Deep Thought Granola is 25% nuts and dried fruit. Oat Dream Granola is 10% nuts and dried fruit. How much of Deep Thought and how much of Oat Dream should be mixed to form a 20-lb batch of granola that is 19% nuts and dried fruit?

28. *Livestock feed.*   Soybean meal is 16% protein and corn meal is 9% protein. How many pounds of each should be mixed to get a 350-lb mixture that is 12% protein?

29. *Student loans.*   Stacey's two student loans totaled $12,000. One of her loans was at 6.5% simple interest and the other at 7.2%. After one year, Stacey owed $811.50 in interest. What was the amount of each loan?

30. *Investments.*   A self-employed contractor nearing retirement made two investments totaling $15,000. In one year, these investments yielded $1023 in simple interest. Part of the money was invested at 6% and the rest at 7.5%. How much was invested at each rate?

31. *Automotive maintenance.* "Steady State" antifreeze is 18% alcohol and "Even Flow" is 10% alcohol. How many liters of each should be mixed to get 20 L of a mixture that is 15% alcohol?

32. *Chemistry.* E-Chem Testing has a solution that is 80% base and another that is 30% base. A technician needs 150 L of a solution that is 62% base. The 150 L will be prepared by mixing the two solutions on hand. How much of each should be used?

33. *Octane ratings.* The octane rating of a gasoline is a measure of the amount of isooctane in the gas. Manufacturers recommend using 93-octane gasoline on retuned motors. How much 87-octane gas and 95-octane gas should Yousef mix in order to make 10 gal of 93-octane gas for his retuned Ford F-150?
Source: Champlain Electric and Petroleum Equipment

34. *Octane ratings.* The octane rating of a gasoline is a measure of the amount of isooctane in the gas. Subaru recommends 91-octane gasoline for the 2008 Legacy 3.0 R. How much 87-octane gas and 93-octane gas should Kelsey mix in order to make 12 gal of 91-octane gas for her Legacy?
Sources: Champlain Electric and Petroleum Equipment: Dean Team Ballwin

35. *Food science.* The following bar graph shows the milk fat percentages in three dairy products. How many pounds each of whole milk and cream should be mixed to form 200 lb of milk for cream cheese?

Milk fat

36. *Food science.* How much lowfat milk (1% fat) and how much whole milk (4% fat) should be mixed to make 5 gal of reduced fat milk (2% fat)?

37. *Train travel.* A train leaves Danville Union and travels north at a speed of 75 km/h. Two hours later, an express train leaves on a parallel track and travels north at 125 km/h. How far from the station will they meet?

38. *Car travel.* Two cars leave Salt Lake City, traveling in opposite directions. One car travels at a speed of 80 km/h and the other at 96 km/h. In how many hours will they be 528 km apart?

39. *Canoeing.* Kahla paddled for 4 hr with a 6-km/h current to reach a campsite. The return trip against the same current took 10 hr. Find the speed of Kahla's canoe in still water.

40. *Boating.* Cody's motorboat took 3 hr to make a trip downstream with a 6-mph current. The return trip against the same current took 5 hr. Find the speed of the boat in still water.

41. *Point of no return.* A plane flying the 3458-mi trip from New York City to London has a 50-mph tailwind. The flight's *point of no return* is the point at which the flight time required to return to New York is the same as the time required to continue to London. If the speed of the plane in still air is 360 mph, how far is New York from the point of no return?

42. *Point of no return.* A plane is flying the 2553-mi trip from Los Angeles to Honolulu into a 60-mph headwind. If the speed of the plane in still air is 310 mph, how far from Los Angeles is the plane's point of no return? (See Exercise 41.)

43. *Architecture.*   The rectangular ground floor of the John Hancock building has a perimeter of 860 ft. The length is 100 ft more than the width. Find the length and the width.

$x + 100$

x

44. *Real estate.*   The perimeter of a rectangular ocean-front lot is 190 m. The width is one-fourth of the length. Find the dimensions.

45. In 2007, Nintendo Co. sold three times as many Wii game machines in Japan as Sony Corp. sold PlayStation 3 consoles. Together, they sold 4.84 million game machines in Japan. How many of each were sold?
Source: Bloomberg.com

46. *Hockey rankings.*   Hockey teams receive 2 points for a win and 1 point for a tie. The Wildcats once won a championship with 60 points. They won 9 more games than they tied. How many wins and how many ties did the Wildcats have?

47. *Video rentals.*   At one time, Netflix offered an unlimited 1 DVD at-a-time rental plan for $8.99 per month and a rental plan with a limit of 2 DVDs per month for $4.99. During one week, 250 new subscribers paid $1975.50 for these plans. How many of each type of plan were purchased?

48. *Radio airplay.*   Roscoe must play 12 commercials during his 1-hr radio show. Each commercial is either 30 sec or 60 sec long. If the total commercial time during that hour is 10 min, how many commercials of each type does Roscoe play?

49. *Making change.*   Monica makes a $9.25 purchase at the bookstore with a $20 bill. The store has no bills and gives her the change in quarters and fifty-cent pieces. There are 30 coins in all. How many of each kind are there?

50. *Teller work.*   Sabina goes to a bank and gets change for a $50 bill consisting of all $5 bills and $1 bills. There are 22 bills in all. How many of each kind are there?

51. In what ways are Examples 3 and 4 similar? In what sense are their systems of equations similar?

52. Write at least three study tips of your own for someone beginning this exercise set.

Skill Review

To prepare for Section 8.4, review evaluating expressions with three variables (Sections 1.1, 1.3, and 1.8).

Evaluate.

53. $2x - 3y - z$, for $x = 5$, $y = 2$, and $z = 3$ [1.1]

54. $4x + y - 6z$, for $x = \frac{1}{2}$, $y = \frac{1}{2}$, and $z = \frac{1}{3}$ [1.3]

55. $x + y + 2z$, for $x = 1$, $y = -4$, and $z = -5$ [1.8]

56. $3a - b + 2c$, for $a = 1$, $b = -6$, and $c = 4$ [1.8]

57. $a - 2b - 3c$, for $a = -2$, $b = 3$, and $c = -5$ [1.8]

58. $2a - 5b - c$, for $a = \frac{1}{4}$, $b = -\frac{1}{4}$, and $c = -\frac{3}{2}$ [1.8]

Synthesis

59. Suppose that in Example 3 you are asked only for the amount of almonds needed for the Market Street blend. Would the method of solving the problem change? Why or why not?

60. Write a problem similar to Example 2 for a classmate to solve. Design the problem so that the solution is "The bakery sold 24 loaves of bread and 18 packages of sandwich rolls."

61. *Recycled paper.*   Unable to purchase 60 reams of paper that contains 20% post-consumer fiber, the Naylor School bought paper that was either 0% post-consumer fiber or 30% post-consumer fiber. How many reams of each should be purchased in order to use the same amount of post-consumer fiber as if the 20% post-consumer fiber paper were available?

62. *Automotive maintenance.*   The radiator in Natalie's car contains 6.3 L of antifreeze and water. This mixture is 30% antifreeze. How much of this mixture should she drain and replace with pure antifreeze so that there will be a mixture of 50% antifreeze?

63. *Metal alloys.*   In order for a metal to be labeled "sterling silver," the silver alloy must contain at least 92.5% pure silver. Nicole has 32 oz of coin silver, which is 90% pure silver. How much pure silver must she add to the coin silver in order to have a sterling-silver alloy?
Source: *The Jewelry Repair Manual*, R. Allen Hardy, Courier Dover Publications, 1996, p. 271.

64. *Exercise.*   Elyse jogs and walks to school each day. She averages 4 km/h walking and 8 km/h jogging. From home to school is 6 km and Elyse makes the trip in 1 hr. How far does she jog in a trip?

65. *Book sales.*   *American Economic History* can be purchased as a three-volume set for $88 or each volume can be purchased separately for $39. An economics class spent $1641 for 51 volumes. How many three-volume sets were ordered?
Source: National History Day, www.nhd.org

66. The tens digit of a two-digit positive integer is 2 more than three times the units digit. If the digits are interchanged, the new number is 13 less than half the given number. Find the given integer. (*Hint*: Let x = the tens-place digit and y = the units-place digit; then $10x + y$ is the number.)

67. *Wood stains.*   Williams' Custom Flooring has 0.5 gal of stain that is 20% brown and 80% neutral. A customer orders 1.5 gal of a stain that is 60% brown and 40% neutral. How much pure brown stain and how much neutral stain should be added to the original 0.5 gal in order to make up the order?*

68. *Train travel.*   A train leaves Union Station for Central Station, 216 km away, at 9 A.M. One hour later, a train leaves Central Station for Union Station. They meet at noon. If the second train had started at 9 A.M. and the first train at 10:30 A.M., they would still have met at noon. Find the speed of each train.

69. *Fuel economy.*   Grady's station wagon gets 18 miles per gallon (mpg) in city driving and 24 mpg in highway driving. The car is driven 465 mi on 23 gal of gasoline. How many miles were driven in the city and how many were driven on the highway?

70. *Biochemistry.*   Industrial biochemists routinely use a machine to mix a buffer of 10% acetone by adding 100% acetone to water. One day, instead of adding 5 L of acetone to create a vat of buffer, a machine added 10 L. How much additional water was needed to bring the concentration down to 10%?

71. See Exercise 67 above. Let x = the amount of pure brown stain added to the original 0.5 gal. Find a function $P(x)$ that can be used to determine the percentage of brown stain in the 1.5-gal mixture. On a graphing calculator, draw the graph of P and use INTERSECT to confirm the answer to Exercise 67.

72. *Gender.*   Phil and Phyllis are twins. Phyllis has twice as many brothers as she has sisters. Phil has the same number of brothers as sisters. How many girls and how many boys are in the family?

*This problem was suggested by Professor Chris Burditt of Yountville, California.

CORNER

How Many Two's? How Many Three's?

Focus: Systems of linear equations

Time: 20 minutes

Group size: 3

The box score at right, from the 2008 NBA All-Star game, contains information on how many field goals (worth either 2 or 3 points) and free throws (worth 1 point) each player attempted and made. For example, the line "Allen 10-14 3-5 28" means that the East's Ray Allen made 10 field goals out of 14 attempts and 3 free throws out of 5 attempts, for a total of 28 points.

ACTIVITY

1. Work as a group to develop a system of two equations in two unknowns that can be used to determine how many 2-pointers and how many 3-pointers were made by the West.

2. Each group member should solve the system from part (1) in a different way: one person algebraically, one person by making a table and methodically checking all combinations of 2- and 3-pointers, and one person by

guesswork. Compare answers when this has been completed.

3. Determine, as a group, how many 2- and 3-pointers the East made.

East (134)

James 12–22 1–1 27, Bosh 7–15 0–2 14, Howard 7–7 2–3 16, Wade 7–12 0–2 14, Kidd 1–2 0–0 2, Hamilton 4–9 0–0 9, Wallace 1–5 0–0 3, Billups 3–10 0–1 6, Jamison 1–3 0–0 2, Pierce 5–9 0–0 10, Johnson 1–2 0–0 3, Allen 10–14 3–5 28

Totals 59–110 6–14 134

West (128)

Anthony 8–17 2–3 18, Duncan 2–7 0–0 4, Ming 2–5 2–2 6, Bryant 0–0 0–0 0, Iverson 3–7 1–2 7, Nash 4–8 0–0 8, Stoudemire 8–11 1–3 18, Nowitzki 5–14 2–2 13, Paul 7–14 0–0 16, West 3–6 0–0 6, Roy 8–10 0–0 18, Boozer 7–15 0–2 14

Totals 57–114 8–14 128

| East | 34 | 40 | 32 | 28 | — | 134 |
| West | 28 | 37 | 28 | 35 | — | 128 |

8.4   Systems of Equations in Three Variables

Identifying Solutions   ▪   Solving Systems in Three Variables   ▪   Dependency, Inconsistency, and Geometric Considerations

Some problems translate directly to two equations. Others more naturally call for a translation to three or more equations. In this section, we learn how to solve systems of three linear equations. Later, we will use such systems in problem-solving situations.

Identifying Solutions

A **linear equation in three variables** is an equation equivalent to one in the form $Ax + By + Cz = D$, where $A, B, C,$ and D are real numbers. We refer to the form $Ax + By + Cz = D$ as *standard form* for a linear equation in three variables.

A solution of a system of three equations in three variables is an ordered triple (x, y, z) that makes *all three* equations true. The numbers in an ordered triple correspond to the variables in alphabetical order unless otherwise indicated.

EXAMPLE **1**   Determine whether $\left(\frac{3}{2}, -4, 3\right)$ is a solution of the system

$$4x - 2y - 3z = 5,$$
$$-8x - y + z = -5,$$
$$2x + y + 2z = 5.$$

SOLUTION   We substitute $\left(\frac{3}{2}, -4, 3\right)$ into the three equations, using alphabetical order:

$$\frac{4x - 2y - 3z = 5}{4 \cdot \frac{3}{2} - 2(-4) - 3 \cdot 3 \ \Big|\ 5}$$
$$6 + 8 - 9 \ \Big|$$
$$5 \overset{?}{=} 5 \quad \text{TRUE}$$

$$\frac{-8x - y + z = -5}{-8 \cdot \frac{3}{2} - (-4) + 3 \ \Big|\ -5}$$
$$-12 + 4 + 3 \ \Big|$$
$$-5 \overset{?}{=} -5 \quad \text{TRUE}$$

$$\frac{2x + y + 2z = 5}{2 \cdot \frac{3}{2} + (-4) + 2 \cdot 3 \ \Big|\ 5}$$
$$3 - 4 + 6 \ \Big|$$
$$5 \overset{?}{=} 5 \quad \text{TRUE}$$

The triple makes all three equations true, so it is a solution.

> **TRY EXERCISE** 7

Solving Systems in Three Variables

The graph of a linear equation in three variables is a plane. Because a three-dimensional coordinate system is required, solving systems in three variables graphically is difficult. The substitution method *can* be used but becomes cumbersome unless one or more of the equations has only two variables. Fortunately, the elimination method works well for a system of three equations in three variables. We first eliminate one variable to form a system of two equations in two variables. Once that simpler system has been solved, we substitute into one of the three original equations and solve for the third variable.

EXAMPLE **2**   Solve the following system of equations:

$$x + y + z = 4, \qquad (1)$$
$$x - 2y - z = 1, \qquad (2)$$
$$2x - y - 2z = -1. \qquad (3)$$

SOLUTION   We select *any* two of the three equations and work to get an equation in two variables. Let's add equations (1) and (2):

$$x + y + z = 4 \qquad (1)$$
$$\underline{x - 2y - z = 1} \qquad (2)$$
$$2x - y \qquad\quad = 5. \qquad (4) \qquad \text{Adding to eliminate } z$$

> **CAUTION!** Be sure to eliminate the same variable in both pairs of equations.

Next, we select a different pair of equations and eliminate the *same variable* that we did above. Let's use equations (1) and (3) to again eliminate z. Be careful! A common error is to eliminate a different variable in this step.

$$\begin{array}{l} x + y + z = 4, \\ 2x - y - 2z = -1 \end{array} \quad \xrightarrow[\text{of equation (1) by 2}]{\text{Multiplying both sides}} \quad \begin{array}{r} 2x + 2y + 2z = 8 \\ \underline{2x - y - 2z = -1} \\ 4x + y \qquad\quad = 7 \quad (5) \end{array}$$

Now we solve the resulting system of equations (4) and (5). That solution will give us two of the numbers in the solution of the original system.

$$2x - y = 5 \qquad (4)$$
$$\underline{4x + y = 7} \qquad (5)$$
$$6x \quad\;\; = 12 \qquad \text{Adding}$$
$$x = 2$$

Note that we now have two equations in two variables. Had we not eliminated the *same* variable in both of the above steps, this would not be the case.

We can use either equation (4) or (5) to find y. We choose equation (5):

$$4x + y = 7 \qquad (5)$$
$$4 \cdot 2 + y = 7 \qquad \text{Substituting 2 for } x \text{ in equation (5)}$$
$$8 + y = 7$$
$$y = -1.$$

We now have $x = 2$ and $y = -1$. To find the value for z, we use any of the original three equations and substitute to find the third number, z. Let's use equation (1) and substitute our two numbers in it:

$$x + y + z = 4 \qquad (1)$$
$$2 + (-1) + z = 4 \qquad \text{Substituting 2 for } x \text{ and } -1 \text{ for } y$$
$$1 + z = 4$$
$$z = 3.$$

We have obtained the triple $(2, -1, 3)$. It should check in *all three* equations:

$$\frac{x + y + z = 4}{2 + (-1) + 3 \;\vert\; 4} \qquad \frac{x - 2y - z = 1}{2 - 2(-1) - 3 \;\vert\; 1} \qquad \frac{2x - y - 2z = -1}{2 \cdot 2 - (-1) - 2 \cdot 3 \;\vert\; -1}$$
$$4 \overset{?}{=} 4 \quad \text{TRUE} \qquad\qquad 1 \overset{?}{=} 1 \quad \text{TRUE} \qquad\qquad -1 \overset{?}{=} -1 \quad \text{TRUE}$$

The solution is $(2, -1, 3)$.

TRY EXERCISE ▶ 9

Solving Systems of Three Linear Equations

To use the elimination method to solve systems of three linear equations:

1. Write all equations in the standard form $Ax + By + Cz = D$.
2. Clear any decimals or fractions.
3. Choose a variable to eliminate. Then select two of the three equations and work to get one equation in which the selected variable is eliminated.
4. Next, use a different pair of equations and eliminate the same variable that you did in step (3).
5. Solve the system of equations that resulted from steps (3) and (4).
6. Substitute the solution from step (5) into one of the original three equations and solve for the third variable. Then check.

EXAMPLE 3   Solve the system

$$4x - 2y - 3z = 5, \qquad (1)$$
$$-8x - y + z = -5, \qquad (2)$$
$$2x + y + 2z = 5. \qquad (3)$$

SOLUTION

> Write in standard form.

1., 2. The equations are already in standard form with no fractions or decimals.

3. Next, select a variable to eliminate. We decide on y because the y-terms are opposites of each other in equations (2) and (3). We add:

> Eliminate a variable. (We choose y.)

$$
\begin{array}{rl}
-8x - y + z = -5 & (2) \\
2x + y + 2z = 5 & (3) \\
\hline
-6x + 3z = 0. & (4) \qquad \text{Adding}
\end{array}
$$

4. We use another pair of equations to create a second equation in x and z. That is, we eliminate the same variable, y, as in step (3). We use equations (1) and (3):

> Eliminate the same variable using a different pair of equations.

$$
\begin{array}{l}
4x - 2y - 3z = 5, \\
2x + y + 2z = 5
\end{array}
\xrightarrow[\text{of equation (3) by 2}]{\text{Multiplying both sides}}
\begin{array}{rl}
4x - 2y - 3z = 5 \\
4x + 2y + 4z = 10 \\
\hline
8x + z = 15. & (5)
\end{array}
$$

5. Now we solve the resulting system of equations (4) and (5). That allows us to find two parts of the ordered triple.

> Solve the system of two equations in two variables.

$$
\begin{array}{l}
-6x + 3z = 0, \\
8x + z = 15
\end{array}
\xrightarrow[\text{of equation (5) by } -3]{\text{Multiplying both sides}}
\begin{array}{rl}
-6x + 3z = 0 \\
-24x - 3z = -45 \\
\hline
-30x = -45 \\
x = \frac{-45}{-30} = \frac{3}{2}
\end{array}
$$

We use equation (5) to find z:

$$
\begin{array}{ll}
8x + z = 15 & \\
8 \cdot \frac{3}{2} + z = 15 & \text{Substituting } \frac{3}{2} \text{ for } x \\
12 + z = 15 & \\
z = 3. &
\end{array}
$$

6. Finally, we use any of the original equations and substitute to find the third number, y. We choose equation (3):

> Solve for the remaining variable.

$$
\begin{array}{ll}
2x + y + 2z = 5 & (3) \\
2 \cdot \frac{3}{2} + y + 2 \cdot 3 = 5 & \text{Substituting } \frac{3}{2} \text{ for } x \text{ and 3 for } z \\
3 + y + 6 = 5 & \\
y + 9 = 5 & \\
y = -4. &
\end{array}
$$

> Check.

The solution is $\left(\frac{3}{2}, -4, 3\right)$. The check was performed as Example 1.

> **TRY EXERCISE** 23

Sometimes, certain variables are missing at the outset.

EXAMPLE 4   Solve the system

$$
\begin{array}{rl}
x + y + z = 180, & (1) \\
x - z = -70, & (2) \\
2y - z = 0. & (3)
\end{array}
$$

SOLUTION

1., 2. The equations appear in standard form with no fractions or decimals.

3., 4. Note that there is no y in equation (2). Thus, at the outset, we already have y eliminated from one equation. We need another equation with y eliminated, so we work with equations (1) and (3):

$$x + y + z = 180,$$
$$2y - z = 0$$

Multiplying both sides
of equation (1) by -2

$$-2x - 2y - 2z = -360$$
$$2y - z = 0$$
$$\overline{-2x \quad\quad - 3z = -360.} \quad (4)$$

5., 6. Now we solve the resulting system of equations (2) and (4):

$$x - z = -70,$$
$$-2x - 3z = -360$$

Multiplying both sides
of equation (2) by 2

$$2x - 2z = -140$$
$$-2x - 3z = -360$$
$$\overline{-5z = -500}$$
$$z = 100.$$

Continuing as in Examples 2 and 3, we get the solution $(30, 50, 100)$. The check is left to the student.

TRY EXERCISE 27

Dependency, Inconsistency, and Geometric Considerations

Each equation in Examples 2, 3, and 4 has a graph that is a plane in three dimensions. The solutions are points common to the planes of each system. Since three planes can have an infinite number of points in common or no points at all in common, we need to generalize the concept of *consistency*.

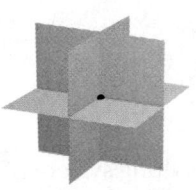  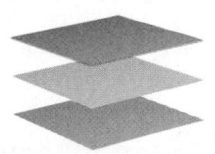 

Planes intersect at one point. System is *consistent* and has one solution.

Planes intersect along a common line. System is *consistent* and has an infinite number of solutions.

Three parallel planes. System is *inconsistent;* it has no solution.

Planes intersect two at a time, with no point common to all three. System is *inconsistent;* it has no solution.

Consistency

A system of equations that has at least one solution is said to be **consistent**.

A system of equations that has no solution is said to be **inconsistent**.

EXAMPLE 5   Solve:

$$y + 3z = 4, \quad (1)$$
$$-x - y + 2z = 0, \quad (2)$$
$$x + 2y + z = 1. \quad (3)$$

SOLUTION   The variable x is missing in equation (1). By adding equations (2) and (3), we can find a second equation in which x is missing:

$$-x - y + 2z = 0 \quad (2)$$
$$x + 2y + z = 1 \quad (3)$$
$$\overline{y + 3z = 1.} \quad (4) \quad \text{Adding}$$

Equations (1) and (4) form a system in y and z. We solve as before:

$$y + 3z = 4, \quad \xrightarrow[\text{of equation (1) by } -1]{\text{Multiplying both sides}} \quad \begin{array}{r} -y - 3z = -4 \\ y + 3z = 1 \end{array}$$
$$y + 3z = 1$$

This is a contradiction. $\longrightarrow 0 = -3.$ Adding

Since we end up with a *false* equation, or contradiction, we state that the system has no solution. It is *inconsistent*.

TRY EXERCISE 15

The notion of *dependency* from Section 8.1 can also be extended.

EXAMPLE 6   Solve:

$$\begin{array}{rcl} 2x + y + z &=& 3, \quad (1) \\ x - 2y - z &=& 1, \quad (2) \\ 3x + 4y + 3z &=& 5. \quad (3) \end{array}$$

SOLUTION   Our plan is to first use equations (1) and (2) to eliminate z. Then we will select another pair of equations and again eliminate z:

$$\begin{array}{r} 2x + y + z = 3 \\ x - 2y - z = 1 \\ \hline 3x - y = 4. \quad (4) \end{array}$$

Next, we use equations (2) and (3) to eliminate z again:

$$\begin{array}{l} x - 2y - z = 1, \\ 3x + 4y + 3z = 5 \end{array} \quad \xrightarrow[\text{of equation (2) by 3}]{\text{Multiplying both sides}} \quad \begin{array}{r} 3x - 6y - 3z = 3 \\ 3x + 4y + 3z = 5 \\ \hline 6x - 2y = 8. \quad (5) \end{array}$$

We now try to solve the resulting system of equations (4) and (5):

$$\begin{array}{l} 3x - y = 4, \\ 6x - 2y = 8 \end{array} \quad \xrightarrow[\text{of equation (4) by } -2]{\text{Multiplying both sides}} \quad \begin{array}{r} -6x + 2y = -8 \\ 6x - 2y = 8 \\ \hline 0 = 0. \quad (6) \end{array}$$

Equation (6), which is an identity, indicates that equations (1), (2), and (3) are *dependent*. This means that the original system of three equations is equivalent to a system of two equations. One way to see this is to observe that two times equation (1), minus equation (2), is equation (3). Thus removing equation (3) from the system does not affect the solution of the system.* In writing an answer to this problem, we simply state that "the equations are dependent."

TRY EXERCISE 21

Recall that when dependent equations appeared in Section 8.1, the solution sets were always infinite in size and were written in set-builder notation. There, all systems of dependent equations were *consistent*. This is not always the case for

---

*A set of equations is dependent if at least one equation can be expressed as a sum of multiples of other equations in that set.

systems of three or more equations. The following figures illustrate some possibilities geometrically.

The planes intersect along a common line. The equations are *dependent* and the system is *consistent*. There is an infinite number of solutions.

The planes coincide. The equations are *dependent* and the system is *consistent*. There is an infinite number of solutions.

Two planes coincide. The third plane is parallel. The equations are *dependent* and the system is *inconsistent*. There is no solution.

8.4 EXERCISE SET

Concept Reinforcement *Classify each statement as either true or false.*

1. $3x + 5y + 4z = 7$ is a linear equation in three variables.

2. Every system of three equations in three unknowns has at least one solution.

3. It is not difficult to solve a system of three equations in three unknowns by graphing.

4. If, when we are solving a system of three equations, a false equation results from adding a multiple of one equation to another, the system is inconsistent.

5. If, when we are solving a system of three equations, an identity results from adding a multiple of one equation to another, the equations are dependent.

6. Whenever a system of three equations contains dependent equations, there is an infinite number of solutions.

---

7. Determine whether $(2, -1, -2)$ is a solution of the system
$$x + y - 2z = 5,$$
$$2x - y - z = 7,$$
$$-x - 2y - 3z = 6.$$

8. Determine whether $(-1, -3, 2)$ is a solution of the system
$$x - y + z = 4,$$
$$x - 2y - z = 3,$$
$$3x + 2y - z = 1.$$

Solve each system. If a system's equations are dependent or if there is no solution, state this.

9. $x - y - z = 0,$
$2x - 3y + 2z = 7,$
$-x + 2y + z = 1$

10. $x + y - z = 0,$
$2x - y + z = 3,$
$-x + 5y - 3z = 2$

11. $x - y - z = 1,$
$2x + y + 2z = 4,$
$x + y + 3z = 5$

12. $x + y - 3z = 4,$
$2x + 3y + z = 6,$
$2x - y + z = -14$

13. $3x + 4y - 3z = 4,$
$5x - y + 2z = 3,$
$x + 2y - z = -2$

14. $2x - 3y + z = 5,$
$x + 3y + 8z = 22,$
$3x - y + 2z = 12$

15. $x + y + z = 0,$
$2x + 3y + 2z = -3,$
$-x - 2y - z = 1$

16. $3a - 2b + 7c = 13,$
$a + 8b - 6c = -47,$
$7a - 9b - 9c = -3$

17. $2x - 3y - z = -9,$
$2x + 5y + z = 1,$
$x - y + z = 3$

18. $4x + y + z = 17,$
$x - 3y + 2z = -8,$
$5x - 2y + 3z = 5$

Aha! **19.** $a + b + c = 5,$
$2a + 3b - c = 2,$
$2a + 3b - 2c = 4$

20. $u - v + 6w = 8,$
$3u - v + 6w = 14,$
$-u - 2v - 3w = 7$

21. $-2x + 8y + 2z = 4,$
$x + 6y + 3z = 4,$
$3x - 2y + z = 0$

22. $x - y + z = 4,$
$5x + 2y - 3z = 2,$
$4x + 3y - 4z = -2$

23. $2u - 4v - w = 8,$
$3u + 2v + w = 6,$
$5u - 2v + 3w = 2$

24. $4p + q + r = 3,$
$2p - q + r = 6,$
$2p + 2q - r = -9$

25. $r + \frac{3}{2}s + 6t = 2,$
$2r - 3s + 3t = 0.5,$
$r + s + t = 1$

26. $5x + 3y + \frac{1}{2}z = \frac{7}{2},$
$0.5x - 0.9y - 0.2z = 0.3,$
$3x - 2.4y + 0.4z = -1$

27. $4a + 9b = 8,$
$8a + 6c = -1,$
$6b + 6c = -1$

28. $3p + 2r = 11,$
$q - 7r = 4,$
$p - 6q = 1$

29. $x + y + z = 57,$
$-2x + y = 3,$
$x - z = 6$

30. $x + y + z = 105,$
$10y - z = 11,$
$2x - 3y = 7$

31. $a - 3c = 6,$
$b + 2c = 2,$
$7a - 3b - 5c = 14$

32. $2a - 3b = 2,$
$7a + 4c = \frac{3}{4},$
$2c - 3b = 1$

Aha! 33. $x + y + z = 83,$
$y = 2x + 3,$
$z = 40 + x$

34. $l + m = 7,$
$3m + 2n = 9,$
$4l + n = 5$

35. $x + z = 0,$
$x + y + 2z = 3,$
$y + z = 2$

36. $x + y = 0,$
$x + z = 1,$
$2x + y + z = 2$

37. $x + y + z = 1,$
$-x + 2y + z = 2,$
$2x - y = -1$

38. $y + z = 1,$
$x + y + z = 1,$
$x + 2y + 2z = 2$

39. Rondel always begins solving systems of three equations in three variables by using the first two equations to eliminate x. Is this a good approach? Why or why not?

40. Describe a method for writing an inconsistent system of three equations in three variables.

Skill Review

To prepare for Section 8.5, review translating sentences to equations (Section 1.1).

Translate each sentence to an equation. [1.1]

41. One number is half another.

42. The difference of two numbers is twice the first number.

43. The sum of three consecutive numbers is 100.

44. The sum of three numbers is 100.

45. The product of two numbers is five times a third number.

46. The product of two numbers is twice their sum.

Synthesis

47. Is it possible for a system of three linear equations to have exactly two ordered triples in its solution set? Why or why not?

48. Describe a procedure that could be used to solve a system of four equations in four variables.

Solve.

49. $\frac{x+2}{3} - \frac{y+4}{2} + \frac{z+1}{6} = 0,$
$\frac{x-4}{3} + \frac{y+1}{4} - \frac{z-2}{2} = -1,$
$\frac{x+1}{2} + \frac{y}{2} + \frac{z-1}{4} = \frac{3}{4}$

50. $w + x - y + z = 0,$
$w - 2x - 2y - z = -5,$
$w - 3x - y + z = 4,$
$2w - x - y + 3z = 7$

51. $w + x + y + z = 2,$
$w + 2x + 2y + 4z = 1,$
$w - x + y + z = 6,$
$w - 3x - y + z = 2$

For Exercises 52 and 53, let u represent $1/x$, v represent $1/y$, and w represent $1/z$. Solve for u, v, and w, and then solve for x, y, and z.

52. $\frac{2}{x} + \frac{2}{y} - \frac{3}{z} = 3,$
$\frac{1}{x} - \frac{2}{y} - \frac{3}{z} = 9,$
$\frac{7}{x} - \frac{2}{y} + \frac{9}{z} = -39$

53. $\frac{2}{x} - \frac{1}{y} - \frac{3}{z} = -1,$
$\frac{2}{x} - \frac{1}{y} + \frac{1}{z} = -9,$
$\frac{1}{x} + \frac{2}{y} - \frac{4}{z} = 17$

Determine k so that each system is dependent.

54. $x - 3y + 2z = 1,$
$2x + y - z = 3,$
$9x - 6y + 3z = k$

55. $5x - 6y + kz = -5,$
$x + 3y - 2z = 2,$
$2x - y + 4z = -1$

In each case, three solutions of an equation in x, y, and z are given. Find the equation.

56. $Ax + By + Cz = 12;$
$\left(1, \frac{3}{4}, 3\right), \left(\frac{4}{3}, 1, 2\right),$ and $(2, 1, 1)$

57. $z = b - mx - ny;$
$(1, 1, 2), (3, 2, -6),$ and $\left(\frac{3}{2}, 1, 1\right)$

58. Write an inconsistent system of equations that contains dependent equations.

59. Kadi and Ahmed both correctly solve the system
$$x + 2y - z = 1,$$
$$-x - 2y + z = 3,$$
$$2x + 4y - 2z = 2.$$

Kadi states "the equations are dependent" while Ahmed states "there is no solution." How did each person reach the conclusion?

CORNER

Finding the Preferred Approach

Focus: Systems of three linear equations

Time: 10–15 minutes

Group size: 3

Consider the six steps outlined on p. 539 along with the following system:

$$2x + 4y = 3 - 5z,$$
$$0.3x = 0.2y + 0.7z + 1.4,$$
$$0.04x + 0.03y = 0.07 + 0.04z.$$

ACTIVITY

1. Working independently, each group member should solve the system above. One person should begin by eliminating x, one should first eliminate y, and one should first eliminate z. Write neatly so that others can follow your steps.

2. Once all group members have solved the system, compare your answers. If the answers do not check, exchange notebooks and check each other's work. If a mistake is detected, allow the person who made the mistake to make the repair.

3. Decide as a group which of the three approaches above (if any) ranks as easiest and which (if any) ranks as most difficult. Then compare your rankings with the other groups in the class.

8.5   Solving Applications: Systems of Three Equations

Applications of Three Equations in Three Unknowns

Solving systems of three or more equations is important in many applications. Such systems arise in the natural and social sciences, business, and engineering. To begin, let's first look at a purely numerical application.

EXAMPLE 1   The sum of three numbers is 4. The first number minus twice the second, minus the third is 1. Twice the first number minus the second, minus twice the third is -1. Find the numbers.

SOLUTION

1. **Familiarize.** There are three statements involving the same three numbers. Let's label these numbers x, y, and z.

2. **Translate.** We can translate directly as follows.

The sum of the three numbers is 4.

$$x + y + z = 4$$

The first number minus twice the second minus the third is 1.

$$x - 2y - z = 1$$

Twice the first number minus the second minus twice the third is -1.

$$2x - y - 2z = -1$$

We now have a system of three equations:

$$x + y + z = 4,$$
$$x - 2y - z = 1,$$
$$2x - y - 2z = -1.$$

3. **Carry out.** We need to solve the system of equations. Note that we found the solution, $(2, -1, 3)$, in Example 2 of Section 8.4.

4. **Check.** The first statement of the problem says that the sum of the three numbers is 4. That checks, because $2 + (-1) + 3 = 4$. The second statement says that the first number minus twice the second, minus the third is 1: $2 - 2(-1) - 3 = 1$. That checks. The check of the third statement is left to the student.

5. **State.** The three numbers are 2, −1, and 3.

TRY EXERCISE   1

EXAMPLE   2   *Architecture.*   In a triangular cross section of a roof, the largest angle is 70° greater than the smallest angle. The largest angle is twice as large as the remaining angle. Find the measure of each angle.

SOLUTION

1. **Familiarize.** The first thing we do is make a drawing, or a sketch.

Since we don't know the size of any angle, we use x, y, and z to represent the three measures, from smallest to largest. Recall that the measures of the angles in any triangle add up to 180°.

2. **Translate.** This geometric fact about triangles gives us one equation:

$$x + y + z = 180.$$

Two of the statements can be translated almost directly.

The largest angle   is   70° greater than the smallest angle.

$$z \qquad = \qquad x + 70$$

The largest angle   is   twice as large as the remaining angle.

$$z \qquad = \qquad 2y$$

We now have a system of three equations:

$x + y + z = 180,$		$x + y + z = 180,$	
$x + 70 = z,$	or	$x \quad - z = -70,$	Rewriting in
$2y = z;$		$2y - z = 0.$	standard form

3. **Carry out.** The system was solved in Example 4 of Section 8.4. The solution is (30, 50, 100).

4. **Check.** The sum of the numbers is 180, so that checks. The measure of the largest angle, 100°, is 70° greater than the measure of the smallest angle, 30°, so that checks. The measure of the largest angle is also twice the measure of the remaining angle, 50°. Thus we have a check.

5. **State.** The angles in the triangle measure 30°, 50°, and 100°.

> TRY EXERCISE ▶ 5

EXAMPLE 3

Downloads. Kaya frequently downloads music, TV shows, and iPod games. In January, she downloaded 5 songs, 10 TV shows, and 3 games for a total of $40. In February, she spent a total of $135 for 25 songs, 25 TV shows, and 12 games. In March, she spent a total of $56 for 15 songs, 8 TV shows, and 5 games. Assuming each song is the same price, each TV show is the same price, and each iPod game is the same price, how much does each cost?

Source: www.iTunes.com

SOLUTION

1. **Familiarize.** We let s = the cost, in dollars, per song, t = the cost, in dollars, per TV show, and g = the cost, in dollars, per game. Then in January, Kaya spent $5 \cdot s$ for songs, $10 \cdot t$ for TV shows, and $3 \cdot g$ for iPod games. The sum of these amounts was $40. Each month's downloads will translate to an equation.

2. **Translate.** We can organize the information in a table.

	Cost of Songs	Cost of TV Shows	Cost of iPod Games	Total Cost	
January	$5s$	$10t$	$3g$	40	$\longrightarrow 5s + 10t + 3g = 40$
February	$25s$	$25t$	$12g$	135	$\longrightarrow 25s + 25t + 12g = 135$
March	$15s$	$8t$	$5g$	56	$\longrightarrow 15s + 8t + 5g = 56$

We now have a system of three equations:

$$5s + 10t + 3g = 40, \quad (1)$$
$$25s + 25t + 12g = 135, \quad (2)$$
$$15s + 8t + 5g = 56. \quad (3)$$

3. **Carry out.** We begin by using equations (1) and (2) to eliminate s.

$$\begin{array}{l} 5s + 10t + 3g = 40, \\ 25s + 25t + 12g = 135 \end{array} \xrightarrow[\text{of equation (1) by } -5]{\text{Multiplying both sides}} \begin{array}{r} -25s - 50t - 15g = -200 \\ \underline{25s + 25t + 12g = 135} \\ -25t - 3g = -65 \quad (4) \end{array}$$

We then use equations (1) and (3) to again eliminate s.

$$\begin{array}{l} 5s + 10t + 3g = 40, \\ 15s + 8t + 5g = 56 \end{array} \xrightarrow[\text{of equation (1) by } -3]{\text{Multiplying both sides}} \begin{array}{r} -15s - 30t - 9g = -120 \\ \underline{15s + 8t + 5g = 56} \\ -22t - 4g = -64 \quad (5) \end{array}$$

Now we solve the resulting system of equations (4) and (5).

$$-25t - 3g = -65 \xrightarrow{\text{Multiplying both sides of equation (4) by } -4} 100t + 12g = 260$$

$$-22t - 4g = -64 \xrightarrow{\text{Multiplying both sides of equation (5) by 3}} \begin{array}{r} -66t - 12g = -192 \\ \hline 34t = 68 \\ t = 2 \end{array}$$

To find g, we use equation (4):

$$-25t - 3g = -65$$
$$-25 \cdot 2 - 3g = -65 \qquad \text{Substituting 2 for } t$$
$$-50 - 3g = -65$$
$$-3g = -15$$
$$g = 5.$$

Finally, we use equation (1) to find s:

$$5s + 10t + 3g = 40$$
$$5s + 10 \cdot 2 + 3 \cdot 5 = 40 \qquad \text{Substituting 2 for } t \text{ and 5 for } g$$
$$5s + 20 + 15 = 40$$
$$5s + 35 = 40$$
$$5s = 5$$
$$s = 1.$$

4. **Check.** If a song costs \$1, a TV show costs \$2, and an iPod game costs \$5, then the total cost for each month's downloads is as follows:

January: $5 \cdot \$1 + 10 \cdot \$2 + 3 \cdot \$5 = \$5 + \$20 + \$15 = \$40$;

February: $25 \cdot \$1 + 25 \cdot \$2 + 12 \cdot \$5 = \$25 + \$50 + \$60 = \$135$;

March: $15 \cdot \$1 + 8 \cdot \$2 + 5 \cdot \$5 = \$15 + \$16 + \$25 = \$56$.

This checks with the information given in the problem.

5. **State.** A song costs \$1, a TV show costs \$2, and an iPod game costs \$5.

TRY EXERCISE 19

8.5 EXERCISE SET

For Extra Help
MyMathLab Math XP PRACTICE   WATCH    DOWNLOAD

Solve.

1. The sum of three numbers is 85. The second is 7 more than the first. The third is 2 more than four times the second. Find the numbers.

2. The sum of three numbers is 5. The first number minus the second plus the third is 1. The first minus the third is 3 more than the second. Find the numbers.

3. The sum of three numbers is 26. Twice the first minus the second is 2 less than the third. The third is the second minus three times the first. Find the numbers.

4. The sum of three numbers is 105. The third is 11 less than ten times the second. Twice the first is 7 more than three times the second. Find the numbers.

5. *Geometry.*   In triangle *ABC*, the measure of angle *B* is three times that of angle *A*. The measure of angle *C* is 20° more than that of angle *A*. Find the angle measures.

6. *Geometry.*   In triangle *ABC*, the measure of angle *B* is twice the measure of angle *A*. The measure of angle *C* is 80° more than that of angle *A*. Find the angle measures.

7. *Scholastic Aptitude Test.*   Many high-school students take the Scholastic Aptitude Test (SAT). Beginning in March 2005, students taking the SAT received three scores: a critical reading score, a mathematics score, and a writing score. The average total score of 2007 high-school seniors who took the SAT was 1511. The average mathematics score exceeded the reading score by 13 points and the average writing score was 8 points less than the reading score. What was the average score for each category?
Source: College Entrance Examination Board

8. *Advertising.*   In 2006, U.S. companies spent a total of $123.4 billion on newspaper, television, and magazine ads. The total amount spent on television ads was $7.4 billion more than the amount spent on newspaper and magazine ads together. The amount spent on magazine ads was $2 billion more than the amount spent on newspaper ads. How much was spent on each form of advertising?
Source: TNS Media Intelligence

9. *Nutrition.*   Most nutritionists now agree that a healthy adult diet includes 25–35 g of fiber each day. A breakfast of 2 bran muffins, 1 banana, and a 1-cup serving of Wheaties® contains 9 g of fiber; a breakfast of 1 bran muffin, 2 bananas, and a 1-cup serving of Wheaties® contains 10.5 g of fiber; and a breakfast of 2 bran muffins and a 1-cup serving of Wheaties® contains 6 g of fiber. How much fiber is in each of these foods?
Sources: usda.gov and InteliHealth.com

10. *Nutrition.*   Refer to Exercise 9. A breakfast consisting of 2 pancakes and a 1-cup serving of strawberries contains 4.5 g of fiber, whereas a breakfast of 2 pancakes and a 1-cup serving of Cheerios® contains 4 g of fiber. When a meal consists of 1 pancake, a 1-cup serving of Cheerios®, and a 1-cup serving of strawberries, it contains 7 g of fiber. How much fiber is in each of these foods?
Source: InteliHealth.com

Aha! **11.** *Automobile pricing.*   The basic model of a 2008 Jeep Grand Cherokee Rocky Mountain (2WD) with a tow package costs $30,815. When equipped with a tow package and a rear backup camera, the vehicle's price rose to $31,565. The cost of the basic model with a rear camera was $31,360. Find the basic price, the cost of a tow package, and the cost of a rear camera.
Source: www.jeep.com

12. *Telemarketing.*   Sven, Tina, and Laurie can process 740 telephone orders per day. Sven and Tina together can process 470 orders, while Tina and Laurie together can process 520 orders per day. How many orders can each person process alone?

13. *Coffee prices.*   Reba works at a Starbucks® coffee shop where a 12-oz cup of coffee costs $1.65, a 16-oz cup costs $1.85, and a 20-oz cup costs $1.95. During one busy period, Reba served 55 cups of coffee, emptying six 144-oz "brewers" while collecting a total of $99.65. How many cups of each size did Reba fill?

| 12 oz | 16 oz | 20 oz |
| $1.65 | $1.85 | $1.95 |

14. *Restaurant management.*   Chick-fil-A® recently sold small lemonades for $1.29, medium lemonades for $1.49, and large lemonades for $1.85. During a lunch-time rush, Chris sold 40 lemonades for a total of $59.40. The number of small and large drinks, combined, was 10 fewer than the number of medium drinks. How many drinks of each size were sold?

15. *Small-business loans.* Chelsea took out three loans for a total of $120,000 to start an organic orchard. Her bank loan was at an interest rate of 8%, the small-business loan was at an interest rate of 5%, and the mortgage on her house was at an interest rate of 4%. The total simple interest due on the loans in one year was $5750. The annual simple interest on the mortgage was $1600 more than the interest on the bank loan. How much did she borrow from each source?

16. *Investments.* A business class divided an imaginary investment of $80,000 among three mutual funds. The first fund grew by 10%, the second by 6%, and the third by 15%. Total earnings were $8850. The earnings from the first fund were $750 more than the earnings from the third. How much was invested in each fund?

17. *Gold alloys.* Gold used to make jewelry is often a blend of gold, silver, and copper. The relative amounts of the metals determine the color of the alloy. Red gold is 75% gold, 5% silver, and 20% copper. Yellow gold is 75% gold, 12.5% silver, and 12.5% copper. White gold is 37.5% gold and 62.5% silver. If 100 g of red gold costs $2265.40, 100 g of yellow gold costs $2287.75, and 100 g of white gold costs $1312.50, how much do gold, silver, and copper cost?
Source: World Gold Council

18. *Blending teas.* Verity has recently created three custom tea blends. A 5-oz package of Southern Sandalwood sells for $13.15 and contains 2 oz of Keemun tea, 2 oz of Assam tea, and 1 oz of a berry blend. A 4-oz package of Golden Sunshine sells for $12.50 and contains 3 oz of Assam tea and 1 oz of the berry blend. A 6-oz package of Mountain Morning sells for $12.50 and contains 2 oz of the berry blend, 3 oz of Keemun tea, and 1 oz of Assam tea. What is the price per ounce of Keemun tea, Assam tea, and the berry blend?

19. *Nutrition.* A dietician in a hospital prepares meals under the guidance of a physician. Suppose that for a particular patient a physician prescribes a meal to have 800 calories, 55 g of protein, and 220 mg of vitamin C. The dietician prepares a meal of roast beef, baked potatoes, and broccoli according to the data in the following table.

Serving Size	Calories	Protein (in grams)	Vitamin C (in milligrams)
Roast Beef, 3 oz	300	20	0
Baked Potato, 1	100	5	20
Broccoli, 156 g	50	5	100

How many servings of each food are needed in order to satisfy the doctor's orders?

20. *Nutrition.* Repeat Exercise 19 but replace the broccoli with asparagus, for which a 180-g serving contains 50 calories, 5 g of protein, and 44 mg of vitamin C. Which meal would you prefer eating?

21. Students in a Listening Responses class bought 40 tickets for a piano concert. The number of tickets purchased for seats in either the first mezzanine or the main floor was the same as the number purchased for seats in the second mezzanine. First mezzanine seats cost $52, main floor seats cost $38, and second mezzanine seats cost $28. The total cost of the tickets was $1432. How many of each type of ticket were purchased?

22. *Basketball scoring.*   The New York Knicks recently scored a total of 92 points on a combination of 2-point field goals, 3-point field goals, and 1-point foul shots. Altogether, the Knicks made 50 baskets and 19 more 2-pointers than foul shots. How many shots of each kind were made?

23. *World population growth.*   The world population is projected to be 9.4 billion in 2050. At that time, there is expected to be approximately 3.5 billion more people in Asia than in Africa. The population for the rest of the world will be approximately 0.3 billion less than two-fifths the population of Asia. Find the projected populations of Asia, Africa, and the rest of the world in 2050.
Source: U.S. Census Bureau

24. *History.*   Find the year in which the first U.S. transcontinental railroad was completed. The following are some facts about the number. The sum of the digits in the year is 24. The ones digit is 1 more than the hundreds digit. Both the tens and the ones digits are multiples of 3.

25. Problems like Exercises 13 and 14 could be classified as total-value problems. How do these problems differ from the total-value problems of Section 8.3?

26. Write a problem for a classmate to solve. Design the problem so that it translates to a system of three equations in three variables.

Skill Review

To prepare for Section 8.6, review simplifying expressions (Section 1.8).

Simplify. [1.8]

27. $-2(2x - 3y)$

28. $-(x - 6y)$

29. $-6(x - 2y) + (6x - 5y)$

30. $3(2a + 4b) + (5a - 12b)$

31. $-(2a - b - 6c)$

32. $-10(5a + 3b - c)$

33. $-2(3x - y + z) + 3(-2x + y - 2z)$

34. $(8x - 10y + 7z) + 5(3x + 2y - 4z)$

Synthesis

35. Consider Exercise 22. Suppose there were no foul shots made. Would there still be a solution? Why or why not?

36. Consider Exercise 13. Suppose Reba collected $50. Could the problem still be solved? Why or why not?

37. *Health insurance.*   In 2008, UniCare® health insurance for a 35-year-old and his or her spouse cost $174/month. That rate increased to $221/month if a child were included and $263/month if two children were included. The rate dropped to $134/month for just the applicant and one child. Find the separate costs for insuring the applicant, the spouse, the first child, and the second child.
Source: UniCare Life and Health Insurance Company® through www.ehealth.com

38. Find a three-digit positive integer such that the sum of all three digits is 14, the tens digit is 2 more than the ones digit, and if the digits are reversed, the number is unchanged.

39. *Ages.*   Tammy's age is the sum of the ages of Carmen and Dennis. Carmen's age is 2 more than the sum of the ages of Dennis and Mark. Dennis's age is four times Mark's age. The sum of all four ages is 42. How old is Tammy?

40. *Ticket revenue.*   A magic show's audience of 100 people consists of adults, students, and children. The ticket prices are $10 for adults, $3 for students, and 50¢ for children. The total amount of money taken in is $100. How many adults, students, and children are in attendance? Does there seem to be some information missing? Do some more careful reasoning.

41. *Sharing raffle tickets.*   Hal gives Tom as many raffle tickets as Tom first had and Gary as many as Gary first had. In like manner, Tom then gives Hal and Gary as many tickets as each then has. Similarly, Gary gives Hal and Tom as many tickets as each then has. If each finally has 40 tickets, with how many tickets does Tom begin?

42. Find the sum of the angle measures at the tips of the star in this figure.

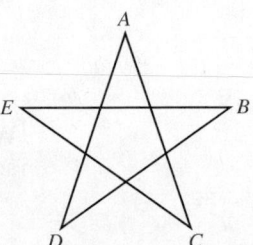

8.6   Elimination Using Matrices

Matrices and Systems   •   Row-Equivalent Operations

In solving systems of equations, we perform computations with the constants. If we agree to keep all like terms in the same column, we can simplify writing a system by omitting the variables. For example, the system

$$\begin{matrix} 3x + 4y = 5, \\ x - 2y = 1 \end{matrix} \quad \text{simplifies to} \quad \begin{matrix} 3 & 4 & 5 \\ 1 & -2 & 1 \end{matrix}$$

if we do not write the variables, the operation of addition, and the equals signs.

Matrices and Systems

In the example above, we have written a rectangular array of numbers. Such an array is called a **matrix** (plural, **matrices**). We ordinarily write brackets around matrices. The following are matrices:

$$\begin{bmatrix} -3 & 1 \\ 0 & 5 \end{bmatrix}, \quad \begin{bmatrix} 2 & 0 & -1 & 3 \\ -5 & 2 & 7 & -1 \\ 4 & 5 & 3 & 0 \end{bmatrix}, \quad \begin{bmatrix} 2 & 3 \\ 7 & 15 \\ -2 & 23 \\ 4 & 1 \end{bmatrix}$$ The individual numbers are called *elements* or *entries*.

The **rows** of a matrix are horizontal, and the **columns** are vertical.

$$\begin{bmatrix} 5 & -2 & 2 \\ 1 & 0 & 1 \\ 0 & 1 & 2 \end{bmatrix} \begin{matrix} \longrightarrow \text{row 1} \\ \longrightarrow \text{row 2} \\ \longrightarrow \text{row 3} \end{matrix}$$

column 1   column 2   column 3

Let's see how matrices can be used to solve a system.

EXAMPLE   1   Solve the system

$$\begin{matrix} 5x - 4y = -1, \\ -2x + 3y = 2. \end{matrix}$$

As an aid for understanding, we list the corresponding system in the margin.

$$\begin{matrix} 5x - 4y = -1, \\ -2x + 3y = 2 \end{matrix}$$

SOLUTION   We write a matrix using only coefficients and constants, listing *x*-coefficients in the first column and *y*-coefficients in the second. A dashed line separates the coefficients from the constants:

$$\begin{bmatrix} 5 & -4 & \vdots & -1 \\ -2 & 3 & \vdots & 2 \end{bmatrix}.$$ Consult the notes in the margin for further information.

Our goal is to transform

$$\begin{bmatrix} 5 & -4 & \vdots & -1 \\ -2 & 3 & \vdots & 2 \end{bmatrix} \quad \text{into the form} \quad \begin{bmatrix} a & b & \vdots & c \\ 0 & d & \vdots & e \end{bmatrix}.$$

We can then reinsert the variables *x* and *y*, form equations, and complete the solution.

Our calculations are similar to those that we would do if we wrote the entire equations. The first step is to multiply and/or interchange the rows so that each number in the first column below the first number is a multiple of that number. Here that means multiplying Row 2 by 5. This corresponds to multiplying both sides of the second equation by 5.

$5x - 4y = -1,$
$-10x + 15y = 10$

$$\begin{bmatrix} 5 & -4 & \vdots & -1 \\ -10 & 15 & \vdots & 10 \end{bmatrix}$$

New Row 2 = 5(Row 2 from the step above)
$= 5(-2 \quad 3 \quad \vdots \quad 2) = (-10 \quad 15 \quad \vdots \quad 10)$

Next, we multiply the first row by 2, add this to Row 2, and write that result as the "new" Row 2. This corresponds to multiplying the first equation by 2 and adding the result to the second equation in order to eliminate a variable. Write out these computations as necessary.

$5x - 4y = -1,$
$7y = 8$

$$\begin{bmatrix} 5 & -4 & \vdots & -1 \\ 0 & 7 & \vdots & 8 \end{bmatrix}$$

$2(\text{Row 1}) = 2(5 \quad -4 \quad \vdots \quad -1) = (10 \quad -8 \quad \vdots \quad -2)$
New Row 2 = $(10 \quad -8 \quad \vdots \quad -2) + (-10 \quad 15 \quad \vdots \quad 10)$
$= (0 \quad 7 \quad \vdots \quad 8)$

If we now reinsert the variables, we have

$$5x - 4y = -1, \qquad (1) \qquad \text{From Row 1}$$
$$7y = 8. \qquad (2) \qquad \text{From Row 2}$$

Solving equation (2) for y gives us

$$7y = 8 \qquad (2)$$
$$y = \tfrac{8}{7}.$$

Next, we substitute $\tfrac{8}{7}$ for y in equation (1):

$$5x - 4y = -1 \qquad (1)$$
$$5x - 4 \cdot \tfrac{8}{7} = -1 \qquad \text{Substituting } \tfrac{8}{7} \text{ for } y \text{ in equation (1)}$$
$$x = \tfrac{5}{7}. \qquad \text{Solving for } x$$

The solution is $\left(\tfrac{5}{7}, \tfrac{8}{7}\right)$. The check is left to the student.

TRY EXERCISE 7

EXAMPLE 2 Solve the system

$$2x - y + 4z = -3,$$
$$x \qquad - 4z = 5,$$
$$6x - y + 2z = 10.$$

SOLUTION We first write a matrix, using only the constants. Where there are missing terms, we must write 0's:

$2x - y + 4z = -3,$
$x \qquad - 4z = 5,$
$6x - y + 2z = 10$

$$\begin{bmatrix} 2 & -1 & 4 & \vdots & -3 \\ 1 & 0 & -4 & \vdots & 5 \\ 6 & -1 & 2 & \vdots & 10 \end{bmatrix}.$$

Our goal is to transform the matrix to one of the form

$ax + by + cz = d,$
$ey + fz = g,$
$hz = i$

$$\begin{bmatrix} a & b & c & \vdots & d \\ 0 & e & f & \vdots & g \\ 0 & 0 & h & \vdots & i \end{bmatrix}. \qquad \text{This matrix is in row-echelon form.}$$

A matrix of this form can be rewritten as a system of equations that is equivalent to the original system, and from which a solution can be easily found.

The first step is to multiply and/or interchange the rows so that each number in the first column is a multiple of the first number in the first row. In this case, we begin by interchanging Rows 1 and 2:

$$
\begin{array}{c}
x \qquad\;\; - 4z = 5, \\
2x - y + 4z = -3, \\
6x - y + 2z = 10
\end{array}
$$

$$
\left[\begin{array}{ccc|c}
1 & 0 & -4 & 5 \\
2 & -1 & 4 & -3 \\
6 & -1 & 2 & 10
\end{array}\right].
$$

This corresponds to interchanging the first two equations.

Next, we multiply the first row by -2, add it to the second row, and replace Row 2 with the result:

$$
\begin{array}{c}
x \qquad\;\; - 4z = 5, \\
-y + 12z = -13, \\
6x - y + 2z = 10
\end{array}
$$

$$
\left[\begin{array}{ccc|c}
1 & 0 & -4 & 5 \\
0 & -1 & 12 & -13 \\
6 & -1 & 2 & 10
\end{array}\right].
$$

$-2(1 \;\; 0 \;\; -4 \;\vdots\; 5) = (-2 \;\; 0 \;\; 8 \;\vdots\; -10)$ and
$(-2 \;\; 0 \;\; 8 \;\vdots\; -10) + (2 \;\; -1 \;\; 4 \;\vdots\; -3) =$
$(0 \;\; -1 \;\; 12 \;\vdots\; -13)$

Now we multiply the first row by -6, add it to the third row, and replace Row 3 with the result:

$$
\begin{array}{c}
x \qquad\;\; - 4z = 5, \\
-y + 12z = -13, \\
-y + 26z = -20
\end{array}
$$

$$
\left[\begin{array}{ccc|c}
1 & 0 & -4 & 5 \\
0 & -1 & 12 & -13 \\
0 & -1 & 26 & -20
\end{array}\right].
$$

$-6(1 \;\; 0 \;\; -4 \;\vdots\; 5) = (-6 \;\; 0 \;\; 24 \;\vdots\; -30)$ and
$(-6 \;\; 0 \;\; 24 \;\vdots\; -30) + (6 \;\; -1 \;\; 2 \;\vdots\; 10) =$
$(0 \;\; -1 \;\; 26 \;\vdots\; -20)$

Next, we multiply Row 2 by -1, add it to the third row, and replace Row 3 with the result:

$$
\begin{array}{c}
x \qquad\;\; - 4z = 5, \\
-y + 12z = -13, \\
14z = -7
\end{array}
$$

$$
\left[\begin{array}{ccc|c}
1 & 0 & -4 & 5 \\
0 & -1 & 12 & -13 \\
0 & 0 & 14 & -7
\end{array}\right].
$$

$-1(0 \;\; -1 \;\; 12 \;\vdots\; -13) = (0 \;\; 1 \;\; -12 \;\vdots\; 13)$ and
$(0 \;\; 1 \;\; -12 \;\vdots\; 13) + (0 \;\; -1 \;\; 26 \;\vdots\; -20) =$
$(0 \;\; 0 \;\; 14 \;\vdots\; -7)$

Reinserting the variables gives us

$$
\begin{aligned}
x \qquad -4z &= 5, \\
-y + 12z &= -13, \\
14z &= -7.
\end{aligned}
$$

We now solve this last equation for z and get $z = -\frac{1}{2}$. Next, we substitute $-\frac{1}{2}$ for z in the preceding equation and solve for y: $-y + 12\left(-\frac{1}{2}\right) = -13$, so $y = 7$. Since there is no y-term in the first equation of this last system, we need only substitute $-\frac{1}{2}$ for z to solve for x: $x - 4\left(-\frac{1}{2}\right) = 5$, so $x = 3$. The solution is $\left(3, 7, -\frac{1}{2}\right)$. The check is left to the student.

TRY EXERCISE 13

The operations used in the preceding example correspond to those used to produce equivalent systems of equations, that is, systems of equations that have the same solution. We call the matrices **row-equivalent** and the operations that produce them **row-equivalent operations.**

Row–Equivalent Operations

Row-Equivalent Operations

Each of the following row-equivalent operations produces a row-equivalent matrix:

a) Interchanging any two rows.
b) Multiplying all elements of a row by a nonzero constant.
c) Replacing a row with the sum of that row and a multiple of another row.

STUDENT NOTES

Note that row-equivalent matrices are not *equal*. It is the solutions of the corresponding systems that are the same.

The best overall method for solving systems of equations is by row-equivalent matrices; even computers are programmed to use them. Matrices are part of a branch of mathematics known as linear algebra. They are also studied in many courses in finite mathematics.

TECHNOLOGY CONNECTION

Row-equivalent operations can be performed on a graphing calculator. For example, to interchange the first and second rows of the matrix, as in step (1) of Example 2 above, we enter the matrix as matrix **A** and select "rowSwap" from the MATRIX MATH menu. Some graphing calculators will not automatically store the matrix produced using a row-equivalent operation, so when several operations are to be performed in succession, it is helpful to store the result of each operation as it is produced. In the window at right, we see both the matrix produced by the rowSwap operation and the indication that this matrix is stored, using (STO►), as matrix **B**.

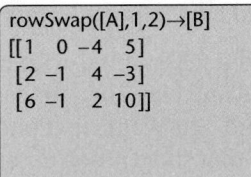
```
rowSwap([A],1,2)→[B]
[[1  0 -4   5]
 [2 -1   4 -3]
 [6 -1   2 10]]
```

1. Use a graphing calculator to proceed through all the steps in Example 2.

8.6 EXERCISE SET

For Extra Help
MyMathLab   Math XL PRACTICE   WATCH   DOWNLOAD

↪ *Concept Reinforcement* *Complete each of the following statements.*

1. A(n) _____ is a rectangular array of numbers.

2. The rows of a matrix are _____ and the _____ are vertical.

3. Each number in a matrix is called a(n) _____ or element.

4. The plural of the word matrix is _____.

5. As part of solving a system using matrices, we can interchange any two _____.

6. Before we reinsert the variables, the leftmost column in the matrix has zeros in all rows except the _____ one.

Solve using matrices.

7. $x + 2y = 11,$
$3x - y = 5$

8. $x + 3y = 16,$
$6x + y = 11$

9. $3x + y = -1,$
$6x + 5y = 13$

10. $2x - y = 6,$
$8x + 2y = 0$

11. $6x - 2y = 4,$
$7x + y = 13$

12. $3x + 4y = 7,$
$-5x + 2y = 10$

13. $3x + 2y + 2z = 3,$
$x + 2y - z = 5,$
$2x - 4y + z = 0$

14. $4x - y - 3z = 19,$
$8x + y - z = 11,$
$2x + y + 2z = -7$

15. $p - 2q - 3r = 3,$
$2p - q - 2r = 4,$
$4p + 5q + 6r = 4$

16. $x + 2y - 3z = 9,$
$2x - y + 2z = -8,$
$3x - y - 4z = 3$

17. $3p + 2r = 11,$
$q - 7r = 4,$
$p - 6q = 1$

18. $4a + 9b = 8,$
$8a + 6c = -1,$
$6b + 6c = -1$

19. $2x + 2y - 2z - 2w = -10,$
$w + y + z + x = -5,$
$x - y + 4z + 3w = -2,$
$w - 2y + 2z + 3x = -6$

20. $-w - 3y + z + 2x = -8,$
$\quad x + y - z - w = -4,$
$\quad w + y + z + x = 22,$
$\quad x - y - z - w = -14$

Solve using matrices.

21. *Coin value.* A collection of 42 coins consists of dimes and nickels. The total value is $3.00. How many dimes and how many nickels are there?

22. *Coin value.* A collection of 43 coins consists of dimes and quarters. The total value is $7.60. How many dimes and how many quarters are there?

23. *Snack mix.* Bree sells a dried-fruit mixture for $5.80 per pound and Hawaiian macadamia nuts for $14.75 per pound. She wants to blend the two to get a 15-lb mixture that she will sell for $9.38 per pound. How much of each should she use?

24. *Mixing paint.* Higher quality paint typically contains more solids. Alex has available paint that contains 45% solids and paint that contains 25% solids. How much of each should he use to create 20 gal of paint that contains 39% solids?

25. *Investments.* Elena receives $212 per year in simple interest from three investments totaling $2500. Part is invested at 7%, part at 8%, and part at 9%. There is $1100 more invested at 9% than at 8%. Find the amount invested at each rate.

26. *Investments.* Miguel receives $306 per year in simple interest from three investments totaling $3200. Part is invested at 8%, part at 9%, and part at 10%. There is $1900 more invested at 10% than at 9%. Find the amount invested at each rate.

27. Explain how you can recognize dependent equations when solving with matrices.

28. Explain how you can recognize an inconsistent system when solving with matrices.

Skill Review

To prepare for Section 8.7, review order of operations (Section 1.8).

Simplify. [1.8]

29. $3(-1) - (-4)(5)$

30. $7(-5) - 2(-8)$

31. $-2(5 \cdot 3 - 4 \cdot 6) - 3(2 \cdot 7 - 15) + 4(3 \cdot 8 - 5 \cdot 4)$

32. $6(2 \cdot 7 - 3(-4)) - 4(3(-8) - 10) + 5(4 \cdot 3 - (-2)7)$

Synthesis

33. If the matrices

$$\begin{bmatrix} a_1 & b_1 & \vdots & c_1 \\ d_1 & e_1 & \vdots & f_1 \end{bmatrix} \text{ and } \begin{bmatrix} a_2 & b_2 & \vdots & c_2 \\ d_2 & e_2 & \vdots & f_2 \end{bmatrix}$$

share the same solution, does it follow that the corresponding entries are all equal to each other $(a_1 = a_2, b_1 = b_2,$ etc.)? Why or why not?

34. Explain how the row-equivalent operations make use of the addition, multiplication, and distributive properties.

35. The sum of the digits in a four-digit number is 10. Twice the sum of the thousands digit and the tens digit is 1 less than the sum of the other two digits. The tens digit is twice the thousands digit. The ones digit equals the sum of the thousands digit and the hundreds digit. Find the four-digit number.

36. Solve for x and y:

$$ax + by = c,$$
$$dx + ey = f.$$

8.7 Determinants and Cramer's Rule

Determinants of 2 × 2 Matrices • Cramer's Rule: 2 × 2 Systems • Cramer's Rule: 3 × 3 Systems

Determinants of 2 × 2 Matrices

When a matrix has m rows and n columns, it is called an "m by n" matrix. Thus its *dimensions* are denoted by $m \times n$. If a matrix has the same number of rows and columns, it is called a **square matrix**. Associated with every square matrix is a number called its **determinant**, defined as follows for 2×2 matrices.

2 × 2 Determinants

The determinant of a two-by-two matrix $\begin{bmatrix} a & c \\ b & d \end{bmatrix}$ is denoted $\begin{vmatrix} a & c \\ b & d \end{vmatrix}$ and is defined as follows:

$$\begin{vmatrix} a & c \\ b & d \end{vmatrix} = ad - bc.$$

EXAMPLE **1**   Evaluate: $\begin{vmatrix} 2 & -5 \\ 6 & 7 \end{vmatrix}$.

SOLUTION   We multiply and subtract as follows:

$$\begin{vmatrix} 2 & -5 \\ 6 & 7 \end{vmatrix} = 2 \cdot 7 - 6 \cdot (-5) = 14 + 30 = 44.$$

TRY EXERCISE **7**

STUDY SKILLS

Find the Highlights

If you do not already own one, consider purchasing a highlighter to use as you read this text and work on the exercises. Often the best time to highlight an important sentence or step in an example is after you have read through the section the first time.

Cramer's Rule: 2 × 2 Systems

One of the many uses for determinants is in solving systems of linear equations in which the number of variables is the same as the number of equations and the constants are not all 0. Let's consider a system of two equations:

$$a_1 x + b_1 y = c_1,$$
$$a_2 x + b_2 y = c_2.$$

If we use the elimination method, a series of steps can show that

$$x = \frac{c_1 b_2 - c_2 b_1}{a_1 b_2 - a_2 b_1} \quad \text{and} \quad y = \frac{a_1 c_2 - a_2 c_1}{a_1 b_2 - a_2 b_1}.$$

These fractions can be rewritten using determinants.

Cramer's Rule: 2 × 2 Systems

The solution of the system

$$a_1 x + b_1 y = c_1,$$
$$a_2 x + b_2 y = c_2,$$

if it is unique, is given by

$$x = \frac{\begin{vmatrix} c_1 & b_1 \\ c_2 & b_2 \end{vmatrix}}{\begin{vmatrix} a_1 & b_1 \\ a_2 & b_2 \end{vmatrix}}, \quad y = \frac{\begin{vmatrix} a_1 & c_1 \\ a_2 & c_2 \end{vmatrix}}{\begin{vmatrix} a_1 & b_1 \\ a_2 & b_2 \end{vmatrix}}.$$

These formulas apply only if the denominator is not 0. If the denominator *is* 0, then one of two things happens:

1. If the denominator is 0 and the numerators are also 0, then the equations in the system are dependent.
2. If the denominator is 0 and at least one numerator is not 0, then the system is inconsistent.

To use Cramer's rule, we find the determinants and compute x and y as shown above. Note that the denominators are identical and the coefficients of x and y appear in the same position as in the original equations. In the numerator of x, the constants c_1 and c_2 replace a_1 and a_2. In the numerator of y, the constants c_1 and c_2 replace b_1 and b_2.

EXAMPLE **2**

Solve using Cramer's rule:

$$2x + 5y = 7,$$
$$5x - 2y = -3.$$

SOLUTION We have

$$x = \frac{\begin{vmatrix} 7 & 5 \\ -3 & -2 \end{vmatrix}}{\begin{vmatrix} 2 & 5 \\ 5 & -2 \end{vmatrix}}$$

$\leftarrow$ The constants $\begin{smallmatrix} 7 \\ -3 \end{smallmatrix}$ form the first column.

$\leftarrow$ The columns are the coefficients of the variables.

$$= \frac{7(-2) - (-3)5}{2(-2) - 5 \cdot 5} = \frac{1}{-29} = -\frac{1}{29}$$

and

$$y = \frac{\begin{vmatrix} 2 & 7 \\ 5 & -3 \end{vmatrix}}{\begin{vmatrix} 2 & 5 \\ 5 & -2 \end{vmatrix}}$$

$\leftarrow$ The constants $\begin{smallmatrix} 7 \\ -3 \end{smallmatrix}$ form the second column.

$\leftarrow$ The denominator is the same as in the expression for x.

$$= \frac{2(-3) - 5 \cdot 7}{-29} = \frac{-41}{-29} = \frac{41}{29}.$$

The solution is $\left(-\frac{1}{29}, \frac{41}{29}\right)$. The check is left to the student.

TRY EXERCISE 17

Cramer's Rule: 3 × 3 Systems

Cramer's rule can be extended for systems of three linear equations. However, before doing so, we must define what a 3 × 3 determinant is.

---

3 × 3 Determinants

The determinant of a three-by-three matrix can be defined as follows:

Subtract.   Add.

$$\begin{vmatrix} a_1 & b_1 & c_1 \\ a_2 & b_2 & c_2 \\ a_3 & b_3 & c_3 \end{vmatrix} = a_1 \begin{vmatrix} b_2 & c_2 \\ b_3 & c_3 \end{vmatrix} - a_2 \begin{vmatrix} b_1 & c_1 \\ b_3 & c_3 \end{vmatrix} + a_3 \begin{vmatrix} b_1 & c_1 \\ b_2 & c_2 \end{vmatrix}$$

STUDENT NOTES

Cramer's rule and the evaluation of determinants rely on patterns. Recognizing and remembering the patterns will help you understand and use the definitions.

Note that the a's come from the first column. Note too that the 2 × 2 determinants above can be obtained by crossing out the row and the column in which the a occurs.

For a_1:

$$\begin{vmatrix} a_1 & b_1 & c_1 \\ a_2 & b_2 & c_2 \\ a_3 & b_3 & c_3 \end{vmatrix}$$

For a_2:

$$\begin{vmatrix} a_1 & b_1 & c_1 \\ a_2 & b_2 & c_2 \\ a_3 & b_3 & c_3 \end{vmatrix}$$

For a_3:

$$\begin{vmatrix} a_1 & b_1 & c_1 \\ a_2 & b_2 & c_2 \\ a_3 & b_3 & c_3 \end{vmatrix}$$

EXAMPLE 3   Evaluate:

$$\begin{vmatrix} -1 & 0 & 1 \\ -5 & 1 & -1 \\ 4 & 8 & 1 \end{vmatrix}.$$

SOLUTION   We have

Subtract.   Add.

$$\begin{vmatrix} -1 & 0 & 1 \\ -5 & 1 & -1 \\ 4 & 8 & 1 \end{vmatrix} = -1\begin{vmatrix} 1 & -1 \\ 8 & 1 \end{vmatrix} - (-5)\begin{vmatrix} 0 & 1 \\ 8 & 1 \end{vmatrix} + 4\begin{vmatrix} 0 & 1 \\ 1 & -1 \end{vmatrix}$$

$$= -1(1 + 8) + 5(0 - 8) + 4(0 - 1) \qquad \text{Evaluating the three determinants}$$

$$= -9 - 40 - 4 = -53.$$

TRY EXERCISE 11

TECHNOLOGY CONNECTION

Determinants can be evaluated on most graphing calculators using **2ND** **MATRIX**. After entering a matrix, we select the determinant operation from the MATRIX MATH menu and enter the name of the matrix. The graphing calculator will return the value of the determinant of the matrix. For example, if

$$\mathbf{A} = \begin{bmatrix} 1 & 6 & -1 \\ -3 & -5 & 3 \\ 0 & 4 & 2 \end{bmatrix},$$

we have

det ([A])
26

1. Confirm the calculations in Example 4.

Cramer's Rule: 3 × 3 Systems

The solution of the system

$$a_1x + b_1y + c_1z = d_1,$$
$$a_2x + b_2y + c_2z = d_2,$$
$$a_3x + b_3y + c_3z = d_3$$

can be found using the following determinants:

$$D = \begin{vmatrix} a_1 & b_1 & c_1 \\ a_2 & b_2 & c_2 \\ a_3 & b_3 & c_3 \end{vmatrix}, \qquad D_x = \begin{vmatrix} d_1 & b_1 & c_1 \\ d_2 & b_2 & c_2 \\ d_3 & b_3 & c_3 \end{vmatrix},$$

D contains only coefficients. In D_x the d's replace the a's.

$$D_y = \begin{vmatrix} a_1 & d_1 & c_1 \\ a_2 & d_2 & c_2 \\ a_3 & d_3 & c_3 \end{vmatrix}, \qquad D_z = \begin{vmatrix} a_1 & b_1 & d_1 \\ a_2 & b_2 & d_2 \\ a_3 & b_3 & d_3 \end{vmatrix}.$$

In D_y, the d's replace the b's. In D_z, the d's replace the c's.

If a unique solution exists, it is given by

$$x = \frac{D_x}{D}, \qquad y = \frac{D_y}{D}, \qquad z = \frac{D_z}{D}.$$

EXAMPLE 4   Solve using Cramer's rule:

$$x - 3y + 7z = 13,$$
$$x + y + z = 1,$$
$$x - 2y + 3z = 4.$$

SOLUTION We compute D, D_x, D_y, and D_z:

$$D = \begin{vmatrix} 1 & -3 & 7 \\ 1 & 1 & 1 \\ 1 & -2 & 3 \end{vmatrix} = -10; \qquad D_x = \begin{vmatrix} 13 & -3 & 7 \\ 1 & 1 & 1 \\ 4 & -2 & 3 \end{vmatrix} = 20;$$

$$D_y = \begin{vmatrix} 1 & 13 & 7 \\ 1 & 1 & 1 \\ 1 & 4 & 3 \end{vmatrix} = -6; \qquad D_z = \begin{vmatrix} 1 & -3 & 13 \\ 1 & 1 & 1 \\ 1 & -2 & 4 \end{vmatrix} = -24.$$

Then

$$x = \frac{D_x}{D} = \frac{20}{-10} = -2;$$

$$y = \frac{D_y}{D} = \frac{-6}{-10} = \frac{3}{5};$$

$$z = \frac{D_z}{D} = \frac{-24}{-10} = \frac{12}{5}.$$

The solution is $\left(-2, \frac{3}{5}, \frac{12}{5}\right)$. The check is left to the student. **TRY EXERCISE** 21

In Example 4, we need not have evaluated D_z. Once x and y were found, we could have substituted them into one of the equations to find z.

To use Cramer's rule, we divide by D, provided $D \neq 0$. If $D = 0$ and at least one of the other determinants is not 0, then the system is inconsistent. If *all* the determinants are 0, then the equations in the system are dependent.

8.7 EXERCISE SET

 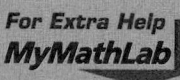  

Concept Reinforcement *Classify each statement as either true or false.*

1. A square matrix has the same number of rows and columns.

2. A 3 × 4 matrix has 3 rows and 4 columns.

3. A determinant is a number.

4. Cramer's rule exists only for 2 × 2 systems.

5. Whenever Cramer's rule yields a denominator that is 0, the system has no solution.

6. Whenever Cramer's rule yields a numerator that is 0, the equations are dependent.

Evaluate.

7. $\begin{vmatrix} 3 & 5 \\ 4 & 8 \end{vmatrix}$

8. $\begin{vmatrix} 3 & 2 \\ 2 & -3 \end{vmatrix}$

9. $\begin{vmatrix} 10 & 8 \\ -5 & -9 \end{vmatrix}$

10. $\begin{vmatrix} 3 & 2 \\ -7 & 11 \end{vmatrix}$

11. $\begin{vmatrix} 1 & 4 & 0 \\ 0 & -1 & 2 \\ 3 & -2 & 1 \end{vmatrix}$

12. $\begin{vmatrix} 2 & 4 & -2 \\ 1 & 0 & 2 \\ 0 & 1 & 3 \end{vmatrix}$

13. $\begin{vmatrix} -1 & -2 & -3 \\ 3 & 4 & 2 \\ 0 & 1 & 2 \end{vmatrix}$

14. $\begin{vmatrix} 5 & 2 & 2 \\ 0 & 1 & -1 \\ 3 & 3 & 1 \end{vmatrix}$

15. $\begin{vmatrix} -4 & -2 & 3 \\ -3 & 1 & 2 \\ 3 & 4 & -2 \end{vmatrix}$

16. $\begin{vmatrix} 2 & -1 & 1 \\ 1 & 2 & -1 \\ 3 & 4 & -3 \end{vmatrix}$

Solve using Cramer's rule.

17. $5x + 8y = 1,$
$3x + 7y = 5$

18. $3x - 4y = 6,$
$5x + 9y = 10$

19. $5x - 4y = -3,$
$7x + 2y = 6$

20. $-2x + 4y = 3,$
$3x - 7y = 1$

21. $3x - y + 2z = 1,$
$\quad x - y + 2z = 3,$
$\quad -2x + 3y + z = 1$

22. $3x + 2y - z = 4,$
$\quad 3x - 2y + z = 5,$
$\quad 4x - 5y - z = -1$

23. $2x - 3y + 5z = 27,$
$\quad x + 2y - z = -4,$
$\quad 5x - y + 4z = 27$

24. $\quad x - y + 2z = -3,$
$\quad x + 2y + 3z = 4,$
$\quad 2x + y + z = -3$

25. $\quad r - 2s + 3t = 6,$
$\quad 2r - s - t = -3,$
$\quad r + s + t = 6$

26. $a \quad\quad - 3c = 6,$
$\quad b + 2c = 2,$
$\quad 7a - 3b - 5c = 14$

27. Describe at least one of the patterns that you see in Cramer's rule.

28. Which version of Cramer's rule do you find more useful: the version for 2×2 systems or the version for 3×3 systems? Why?

Skill Review

To prepare for Section 8.8, review functions (Sections 7.1 and 7.4).

Find each of the following, given $f(x) = 80x + 2500$ and $g(x) = 150x$.

29. $f(90)$ [7.1]

30. $(g - f)(x)$ [7.4]

31. $(g - f)(10)$ [7.4]

32. $(g - f)(100)$ [7.4]

33. All values of x for which $f(x) = g(x)$ [7.1]

34. All values of x for which $(g - f)(x) = 0$ [7.4]

Synthesis

35. Cramer's rule states that if $a_1x + b_1y = c_1$ and $a_2x + b_2y = c_2$ are dependent, then
$$\begin{vmatrix} a_1 & b_1 \\ a_2 & b_2 \end{vmatrix} = 0.$$
Explain why this will always happen.

36. Under what conditions can a 3×3 system of linear equations be consistent but unable to be solved using Cramer's rule?

Solve.

37. $\begin{vmatrix} y & -2 \\ 4 & 3 \end{vmatrix} = 44$

38. $\begin{vmatrix} 2 & x & -1 \\ -1 & 3 & 2 \\ -2 & 1 & 1 \end{vmatrix} = -12$

39. $\begin{vmatrix} m+1 & -2 \\ m-2 & 1 \end{vmatrix} = 27$

40. Show that an equation of the line through (x_1, y_1) and (x_2, y_2) can be written
$$\begin{vmatrix} x & y & 1 \\ x_1 & y_1 & 1 \\ x_2 & y_2 & 1 \end{vmatrix} = 0.$$

8.8 Business and Economics Applications

Break-Even Analysis • Supply and Demand

Break–Even Analysis

The money that a business spends to manufacture a product is its *cost*. The **total cost** of production can be thought of as a function C, where $C(x)$ is the cost of producing x units. When the company sells the product, it takes in money. This is *revenue* and can be thought of as a function R, where $R(x)$ is the **total revenue** from the sale of x units. **Total profit** is the money taken in less the money spent, or total revenue minus total cost. Total profit from the production and sale of x units is a function P given by

$$\textbf{Profit = Revenue − Cost,} \quad \text{or} \quad P(x) = R(x) - C(x).$$

If $R(x)$ is greater than $C(x)$, there is a gain and $P(x)$ is positive. If $C(x)$ is greater than $R(x)$, there is a loss and $P(x)$ is negative. When $R(x) = C(x)$, the company breaks even.

There are two kinds of costs. First, there are costs like rent, insurance, machinery, and so on. These costs, which must be paid regardless of how many items are produced, are called *fixed costs*. Second, costs for labor, materials, marketing, and so on are called *variable costs*, because they vary according to the amount being produced. The sum of the fixed cost and the variable cost gives the **total cost**.

> **CAUTION!**   Do not confuse "cost" with "price." When we discuss the *cost* of an item, we are referring to what it costs to produce the item. The *price* of an item is what a consumer pays to purchase the item and is used when calculating revenue.

EXAMPLE **1**   *Manufacturing chairs.*   Renewable Designs is planning to make a new chair. Fixed costs will be $90,000, and it will cost $25 to produce each chair (variable costs). Each chair sells for $48.

a) Find the total cost $C(x)$ of producing x chairs.

b) Find the total revenue $R(x)$ from the sale of x chairs.

c) Find the total profit $P(x)$ from the production and sale of x chairs.

d) What profit will the company realize from the production and sale of 3000 chairs? of 8000 chairs?

e) Graph the total-cost, total-revenue, and total-profit functions using the same set of axes. Determine the break-even point.

SOLUTION

a) Total cost, in dollars, is given by

$$C(x) = \text{(Fixed costs) plus (Variable costs)},$$
$$\text{or}\quad C(x) = \quad 90{,}000 \quad + \quad 25x$$

where x is the number of chairs produced.

b) Total revenue, in dollars, is given by

$$R(x) = 48x. \qquad \text{\$48 times the number of chairs sold.}$$
We assume that every chair produced is sold.

c) Total profit, in dollars, is given by

$$P(x) = R(x) - C(x) \qquad \text{Profit is revenue minus cost.}$$
$$= 48x - (90{,}000 + 25x)$$
$$= 23x - 90{,}000.$$

d) Profits will be

$$P(3000) = 23 \cdot 3000 - 90{,}000 = -\$21{,}000$$

when 3000 chairs are produced and sold, and

$$P(8000) = 23 \cdot 8000 - 90{,}000 = \$94{,}000$$

when 8000 chairs are produced and sold. Thus the company loses money if only 3000 chairs are sold, but makes money if 8000 are sold.

e) The graphs of each of the three functions are shown below:

$$C(x) = 90{,}000 + 25x, \qquad \text{This represents the cost function.}$$
$$R(x) = 48x, \qquad \text{This represents the revenue function.}$$
$$P(x) = 23x - 90{,}000. \qquad \text{This represents the profit function.}$$

$C(x)$, $R(x)$, and $P(x)$ are all in dollars.

   The revenue function has a graph that goes through the origin and has a slope of 48. The cost function has an intercept on the $-axis of 90,000 and has a slope of 25. The profit function has an intercept on the $-axis of $-90{,}000$ and has a slope of 23. It is shown by the red and black dashed line. The red portion of the dashed line shows a "negative" profit, which is a loss. (That is what is known as "being in the red.") The black portion of the dashed line shows a "positive" profit, or gain. (That is what is known as "being in the black.")

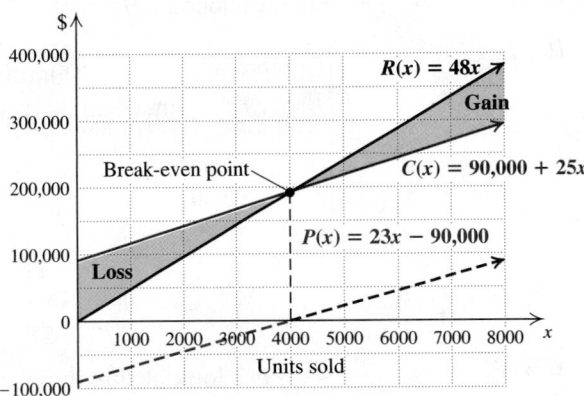

   Gains occur where revenue exceeds cost. Losses occur where revenue is less than cost. The **break-even point** occurs where the graphs of R and C cross. Thus to find the break-even point, we solve a system:

$$R(x) = 48x,$$
$$C(x) = 90{,}000 + 25x.$$

Since both revenue and cost are in *dollars* and they are equal at the break-even point, the system can be rewritten as

$$d = 48x, \qquad (1)$$
$$d = 90{,}000 + 25x \qquad (2)$$

and solved using substitution:

$$48x = 90{,}000 + 25x \qquad \text{Substituting } 48x \text{ for } d \text{ in equation (2)}$$
$$23x = 90{,}000$$
$$x \approx 3913.04.$$

   The firm will break even if it produces and sells about 3913 chairs (3913 will yield a tiny loss and 3914 a tiny gain), and takes in a total of $R(3913) = 48 \cdot 3913 = \$187{,}824$ in revenue. Note that the x-coordinate of the break-even point can also be found by solving $P(x) = 0$. The break-even point is (3913 chairs, $187,824).

▶ TRY EXERCISE 9

Supply and Demand

As the price of coffee varies, so too does the amount sold. The table and graph below show that *consumers will demand less as the price goes up.*

Demand Function, *D*

Price, *p*, per Kilogram	Quantity, *D(p)* (in millions of kilograms)
$ 8.00	25
9.00	20
10.00	15
11.00	10
12.00	5

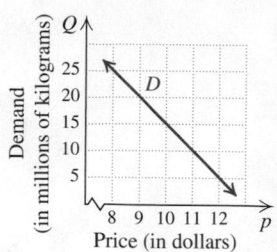

As the price of coffee varies, the amount made available varies as well. The table and graph below show that *sellers will supply more as the price goes up.*

Supply Function, *S*

Price, *p*, per Kilogram	Quantity, *S(p)* (in millions of kilograms)
$ 9.00	5
9.50	10
10.00	15
10.50	20
11.00	25

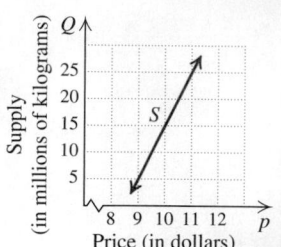

Let's look at the above graphs together. We see that as price increases, demand decreases. As price increases, supply increases. The point of intersection is called the **equilibrium point**. At that price, the amount that the seller will supply is the same amount that the consumer will buy. The situation is similar to a buyer and a seller negotiating the price of an item. The equilibrium point is the price and quantity that they finally agree on.

Any ordered pair of coordinates from the graph is (price, quantity), because the horizontal axis is the price axis and the vertical axis is the quantity axis. If *D* is a demand function and *S* is a supply function, then the equilibrium point is where demand equals supply:

$$D(p) = S(p).$$

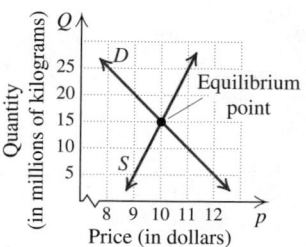

EXAMPLE 2   Find the equilibrium point for the demand and supply functions given:

$$D(p) = 1000 - 60p, \quad (1)$$
$$S(p) = 200 + 4p. \quad (2)$$

SOLUTION Since both demand and supply are *quantities* and they are equal at the equilibrium point, we rewrite the system as

$$q = 1000 - 60p, \quad (1)$$
$$q = 200 + 4p. \quad (2)$$

We substitute $200 + 4p$ for q in equation (1) and solve:

$$200 + 4p = 1000 - 60p \qquad \text{Substituting } 200 + 4p \text{ for } q \text{ in equation (1)}$$
$$200 + 64p = 1000 \qquad \text{Adding } 60p \text{ to both sides}$$
$$64p = 800 \qquad \text{Adding } -200 \text{ to both sides}$$
$$p = \tfrac{800}{64} = 12.5.$$

Thus the equilibrium price is $12.50 per unit.

To find the equilibrium quantity, we substitute $12.50 into either $D(p)$ or $S(p)$. We use $S(p)$:

$$S(12.5) = 200 + 4(12.5) = 200 + 50 = 250.$$

Therefore, the equilibrium quantity is 250 units, and the equilibrium point is ($12.50, 250).

TRY EXERCISE 19

8.8 EXERCISE SET

For Extra Help   MyMathLab   Math XP PRACTICE  WATCH DOWNLOAD

Concept Reinforcement *In each of Exercises 1–8, match the word or phrase with the most appropriate choice from the column on the right.*

1. ____ Total cost

2. ____ Fixed costs

3. ____ Variable costs

4. ____ Total revenue

5. ____ Total profit

6. ____ Price

7. ____ Break-even point

8. ____ Equilibrium point

a) The amount of money that a company takes in

b) The sum of fixed costs and variable costs

c) The point at which total revenue equals total cost

d) What consumers pay per item

e) The difference between total revenue and total cost

f) What companies spend whether or not a product is produced

g) The point at which supply equals demand

h) The costs that vary according to the number of items produced

---

For each of the following pairs of total-cost and total-revenue functions, find **(a)** *the total-profit function and* **(b)** *the break-even point.*

9. $C(x) = 35x + 200{,}000$,
 $R(x) = 55x$

10. $C(x) = 20x + 500{,}000$,
 $R(x) = 70x$

11. $C(x) = 15x + 3100$,
 $R(x) = 40x$

12. $C(x) = 30x + 49{,}500$,
 $R(x) = 85x$

13. $C(x) = 40x + 22{,}500$,
 $R(x) = 85x$

14. $C(x) = 20x + 10{,}000,$
$R(x) = 100x$

15. $C(x) = 24x + 50{,}000,$
$R(x) = 40x$

16. $C(x) = 40x + 8010,$
$R(x) = 58x$

Aha! **17.** $C(x) = 75x + 100{,}000,$
$R(x) = 125x$

18. $C(x) = 20x + 120{,}000,$
$R(x) = 50x$

Find the equilibrium point for each of the following pairs of demand and supply functions.

19. $D(p) = 2000 - 15p,$
$S(p) = 740 + 6p$

20. $D(p) = 1000 - 8p,$
$S(p) = 350 + 5p$

21. $D(p) = 760 - 13p,$
$S(p) = 430 + 2p$

22. $D(p) = 800 - 43p,$
$S(p) = 210 + 16p$

23. $D(p) = 7500 - 25p,$
$S(p) = 6000 + 5p$

24. $D(p) = 8800 - 30p,$
$S(p) = 7000 + 15p$

25. $D(p) = 1600 - 53p,$
$S(p) = 320 + 75p$

26. $D(p) = 5500 - 40p,$
$S(p) = 1000 + 85p$

Solve.

27. *Manufacturing MP3 players.*   SoundGen, Inc., is planning to manufacture a new type of MP3 player/cell phone. The fixed costs for production are $45,000. The variable costs for producing each unit are estimated to be $40. The revenue from each unit is to be $130. Find the following.

   a) The total cost $C(x)$ of producing x MP3/cell phones
   b) The total revenue $R(x)$ from the sale of x MP3/cell phones
   c) The total profit $P(x)$ from the production and sale of x MP3/cell phones
   d) The profit or loss from the production and sale of 3000 MP3/cell phones; of 400 MP3/cell phones
   e) The break-even point

28. *Computer manufacturing.*   Current Electronics is planning to introduce a new laptop computer. The fixed costs for production are $125,300. The variable costs for producing each computer are $450. The revenue from each computer is $800. Find the following.

   a) The total cost $C(x)$ of producing x computers
   b) The total revenue $R(x)$ from the sale of x computers

   c) The total profit $P(x)$ from the production and sale of x computers
   d) The profit or loss from the production and sale of 100 computers; of 400 computers
   e) The break-even point

29. *Pet safety.*   Ava designed and is now producing a pet car seat. The fixed costs for setting up production are $10,000. The variable costs for producing each seat are $30. The revenue from each seat is to be $80. Find the following.

   a) The total cost $C(x)$ of producing x seats
   b) The total revenue $R(x)$ from the sale of x seats
   c) The total profit $P(x)$ from the production and sale of x seats
   d) The profit or loss from the production and sale of 2000 seats; of 50 seats
   e) The break-even point

30. *Manufacturing caps.*   Martina's Custom Printing is planning on adding painter's caps to its product line. For the first year, the fixed costs for setting up production are $16,404. The variable costs for producing a dozen caps are $6.00. The revenue on each dozen caps will be $18.00. Find the following.

   a) The total cost $C(x)$ of producing x dozen caps
   b) The total revenue $R(x)$ from the sale of x dozen caps
   c) The total profit $P(x)$ from the production and sale of x dozen caps
   d) The profit or loss from the production and sale of 3000 dozen caps; of 1000 dozen caps
   e) The break-even point

31. In Example 1, the slope of the line representing Revenue is the sum of the slopes of the other two lines. This is not a coincidence. Explain why.

32. Variable costs and fixed costs are often compared to the slope and the *y*-intercept, respectively, of an equation for a line. Explain why you feel this analogy is or is not valid.

Skill Review

To prepare for Chapter 9, review solving equations using the addition and multiplication principles (Section 2.2).

Solve. [2.2]

33. $4x - 3 = 21$

34. $5 - x = 7$

35. $3x - 5 = 12x + 6$

36. $x - 4 = 9x - 10$

37. $3 - (x + 2) = 7$

38. $1 - 3(2x + 1) = 3 - 5x$

Synthesis

39. Rosie claims that since her fixed costs are $3000, she need sell only 10 custom birdbaths at $300 each in order to break even. Does this sound plausible? Why or why not?

40. In this section, we examined supply and demand functions for coffee. Does it seem realistic to you for the graph of *D* to have a constant slope? Why or why not?

41. *Yo-yo production.* Bing Boing Hobbies is willing to produce 100 yo-yo's at $2.00 each and 500 yo-yo's at $8.00 each. Research indicates that the public will buy 500 yo-yo's at $1.00 each and 100 yo-yo's at $9.00 each. Find the equilibrium point.

42. *Loudspeaker production.* Sonority Speakers, Inc., has fixed costs of $15,400 and variable costs of $100 for each pair of speakers produced. If the speakers sell for $250 per pair, how many pairs of speakers must be produced (and sold) in order to have enough profit to cover the fixed costs of two additional facilities? Assume that all fixed costs are identical.

Use a graphing calculator to solve.

43. *Dog food production.* Puppy Love, Inc., will soon begin producing a new line of puppy food. The marketing department predicts that the demand function will be $D(p) = -14.97p + 987.35$ and the supply function will be $S(p) = 98.55p - 5.13$.

  a) To the nearest cent, what price per unit should be charged in order to have equilibrium between supply and demand?

  b) The production of the puppy food involves $87,985 in fixed costs and $5.15 per unit in variable costs. If the price per unit is the value you found in part (a), how many units must be sold in order to break even?

44. *Computer production.* Brushstroke Computers, Inc., is planning a new line of computers, each of which will sell for $970. The fixed costs in setting up production are $1,235,580 and the variable costs for each computer are $697.

  a) What is the break-even point?

  b) The marketing department at Brushstroke is not sure that $970 is the best price. Their demand function for the new computers is given by $D(p) = -304.5p + 374,580$ and their supply function is given by $S(p) = 788.7p - 576,504$. To the nearest dollar, what price *p* would result in equilibrium between supply and demand?

  c) If the computers are sold for the equilibrium price found in part (b), what is the break-even point?

Study Summary

KEY TERMS AND CONCEPTS	EXAMPLES

SECTION 8.1: SYSTEMS OF EQUATIONS IN TWO VARIABLES

A **system of equations** is a set of two or more equations, in two or more variables. A solution of a system of equations must make all the equations true.

A system is **consistent** if it has at least one solution. Otherwise it is **inconsistent**.

The equations in a system are **dependent** if one of them can be written as a multiple and/or a sum of the other equation(s). Otherwise, they are **independent**.

Systems of two equations in two unknowns can be solved graphically.

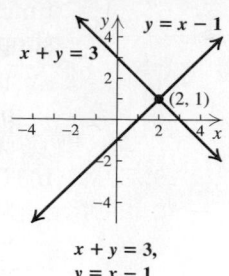

$x + y = 3$,
$y = x - 1$

The graphs intersect at (2, 1).
The solution is (2, 1).
The system is consistent.
The equations are independent.

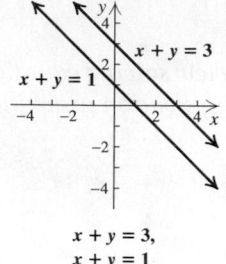

$x + y = 3$,
$x + y = 1$

The graphs do not intersect.
There is no solution.
The system is inconsistent.
The equations are independent.

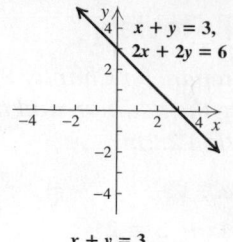

$x + y = 3$,
$2x + 2y = 6$

The graphs are the same.
The solution set is
$\{(x, y) \mid x + y = 3\}$.
The system is consistent.
The equations are dependent.

SECTION 8.2: SOLVING BY SUBSTITUTION OR ELIMINATION

Systems of equations can be solved using substitution.

Solve:

$2x + 3y = 8$,
$x = y + 1$.

Substitute and solve for y:

$2(y + 1) + 3y = 8$
$2y + 2 + 3y = 8$
$y = \frac{6}{5}$.

Substitute and solve for x:

$x = y + 1$
$x = \frac{6}{5} + 1$
$x = \frac{11}{5}$.

The solution is $\left(\frac{11}{5}, \frac{6}{5}\right)$.

Systems of equations can be solved using elimination.

Solve:

$4x - 2y = 6$,
$3x + y = 7$.

Eliminate y and solve for x:

$\begin{aligned} 4x - 2y &= 6 \\ 6x + 2y &= 14 \\ \hline 10x &= 20 \\ x &= 2. \end{aligned}$

Substitute and solve for y:

$3x + y = 7$
$3 \cdot 2 + y = 7$
$y = 1$.

The solution is (2, 1).

SECTION 8.3: SOLVING APPLICATIONS: SYSTEMS OF TWO EQUATIONS

Total-value, **mixture**, and **motion problems** often translate directly to systems of equations.

Total Value

A jewelry designer purchased 80 beads for a total of $39 to make a necklace. Some of the beads were sterling silver beads that cost 40¢ each and the rest were gemstone beads that cost 65¢ each. How many of each type were bought? (See Example 2 on pp. 525–526 for a solution.)

Mixture

Nature's Green Gardening, Inc., carries two brands of fertilizer containing nitrogen and water. "Gentle Grow" is 3% nitrogen and "Sun Saver" is 8% nitrogen. Nature's Green needs to combine the two types of solutions into a 90-L mixture that is 6% nitrogen. How much of each brand should be used? (See Example 5 on pp. 528–529 for a solution.)

Motion

A Boeing 747-400 jet flies 4 hr west with a 60-mph tailwind. Returning against the wind takes 5 hr. Find the speed of the jet with no wind. (See Example 7 on pp. 531–532 for a solution.)

SECTION 8.4: SYSTEMS OF EQUATIONS IN THREE VARIABLES

Systems of three equations in three variables are usually easiest to solve using elimination.

Solve:

$$x + y - z = 3, \quad (1)$$
$$-x + y + 2z = -5, \quad (2)$$
$$2x - y - 3z = 9 \quad (3)$$

Eliminate x using two equations:

$$x + y - z = 3 \quad (1)$$
$$\underline{-x + y + 2z = -5} \quad (2)$$
$$2y + z = -2.$$

Eliminate x again using two different equations:

$$-2x - 2y + 2z = -6 \quad (1)$$
$$\underline{2x - y - 3z = 9} \quad (3)$$
$$-3y - z = 3.$$

Solve the system of two equations for y and z:

$$2y + z = -2$$
$$\underline{-3y - z = 3}$$
$$-y = 1$$
$$y = -1$$

$$2(-1) + z = -2$$
$$z = 0.$$

Substitute and solve for x:

$$x + y - z = 3$$
$$x + (-1) - 0 = 3$$
$$x = 4.$$

The solution is $(4, -1, 0)$.

SECTION 8.5: SOLVING APPLICATIONS: SYSTEMS OF THREE EQUATIONS

Many problems with three unknowns can be solved after translating to a system of three equations.

In a triangular cross section of a roof, the largest angle is 70° greater than the smallest angle. The largest angle is twice as large as the remaining angle. Find the measure of each angle. (See Example 2 on pp. 546–547 for a solution.)

SECTION 8.6: ELIMINATION USING MATRICES

A **matrix** (plural, **matrices**) is a rectangular array of numbers. The individual numbers are called **entries** or **elements**.

$$\begin{bmatrix} 1 & 3 & -4 \\ -2 & 5 & 11 \end{bmatrix} \longrightarrow \text{row 1} \\ \longrightarrow \text{row 2}$$

column 1 column 2 column 3

The *dimensions* of this matrix are 2 × 3, read "two by three."

By using **row-equivalent** operations, we can solve systems of equations using matrices.

Solve: $x + 4y = 1,$
$2x - y = 3.$

Write as a matrix in row-echelon form:

$$\begin{bmatrix} 1 & 4 & \vdots & 1 \\ 2 & -1 & \vdots & 3 \end{bmatrix} \longrightarrow \begin{bmatrix} 1 & 4 & \vdots & 1 \\ 0 & -9 & \vdots & 1 \end{bmatrix}.$$

Rewrite as equations and solve:

$$-9y = 1 \longrightarrow x + 4\left(-\tfrac{1}{9}\right) = 1$$
$$y = -\tfrac{1}{9} \qquad\qquad x = \tfrac{13}{9}.$$

The solution is $\left(\tfrac{13}{9}, -\tfrac{1}{9}\right)$.

SECTION 8.7: DETERMINANTS AND CRAMER'S RULE

A **determinant** is a number associated with a square matrix.

Determinant of a 2 × 2 Matrix

$$\begin{vmatrix} a & c \\ b & d \end{vmatrix} = ad - bc$$

$$\begin{vmatrix} 2 & 3 \\ -1 & 5 \end{vmatrix} = 2 \cdot 5 - (-1)(3) = 13$$

Determinant of a 3 × 3 Matrix

$$\begin{vmatrix} a_1 & b_1 & c_1 \\ a_2 & b_2 & c_2 \\ a_3 & b_3 & c_3 \end{vmatrix} =$$

$$a_1 \begin{vmatrix} b_2 & c_2 \\ b_3 & c_3 \end{vmatrix} - a_2 \begin{vmatrix} b_1 & c_1 \\ b_3 & c_3 \end{vmatrix} + a_3 \begin{vmatrix} b_1 & c_1 \\ b_2 & c_2 \end{vmatrix}$$

$$\begin{vmatrix} 2 & 3 & 2 \\ 0 & 1 & 0 \\ -1 & 5 & -4 \end{vmatrix} = 2 \begin{vmatrix} 1 & 0 \\ 5 & -4 \end{vmatrix} - 0 \begin{vmatrix} 3 & 2 \\ 5 & -4 \end{vmatrix} + (-1) \begin{vmatrix} 3 & 2 \\ 1 & 0 \end{vmatrix}$$

$$= 2(-4 - 0) - 0 - 1(0 - 2)$$

$$= -8 + 2 = -6$$

We can use matrices and **Cramer's rule** to solve systems of equations.

Cramer's rule for 2 × 2 matrices is given on p. 557.

Cramer's rule for 3 × 3 matrices is given on p. 559.

Solve:

$$x - 3y = 7,$$
$$2x + 5y = 4.$$

$$x = \dfrac{\begin{vmatrix} 7 & -3 \\ 4 & 5 \end{vmatrix}}{\begin{vmatrix} 1 & -3 \\ 2 & 5 \end{vmatrix}}; \qquad y = \dfrac{\begin{vmatrix} 1 & 7 \\ 2 & 4 \end{vmatrix}}{\begin{vmatrix} 1 & -3 \\ 2 & 5 \end{vmatrix}}$$

$$x = \dfrac{47}{11} \qquad\qquad y = \dfrac{-10}{11}$$

The solution is $\left(\dfrac{47}{11}, -\dfrac{10}{11}\right)$.

SECTION 8.8: BUSINESS AND ECONOMICS APPLICATIONS

The **break-even point** occurs where the **revenue** equals the **cost**, or where **profit** is 0.

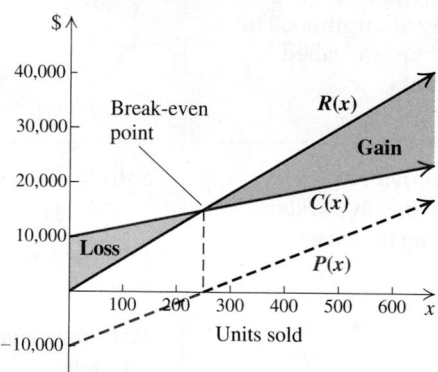

An **equilibrium point** occurs where the **supply** equals the **demand.**

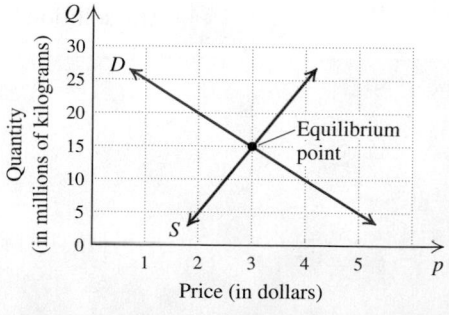

Review Exercises: Chapter 8

Concept Reinforcement *Complete each of the following sentences.*

1. The system

$$5x + 3y = 7,$$
$$y = 2x + 1$$

is most easily solved using the _____ method. [8.2]

2. The system

$$-2x + 3y = 8,$$
$$2x + 2y = 7$$

is most easily solved using the _____ method. [8.2]

3. Of the methods used to solve systems of equations, the _____ method may yield only approximate solutions. [8.1], [8.2]

4. When one equation in a system is a multiple of another equation in that system, the equations are said to be _____. [8.1]

5. A system for which there is no solution is said to be _____. [8.1]

6. When we are using an algebraic method to solve a system of equations, obtaining a _____ tells us that the system is inconsistent. [8.2]

7. When we are graphing to solve a system of two equations, if there is no solution, the lines will be _____. [8.1]

8. When a matrix has the same number of rows and columns, it is said to be _____. [8.7]

9. Cramer's rule is a formula in which the numerator and the denominator of each fraction is a(n) _____. [8.7]

10. At the break-even point, the value of the profit function is _____. [8.8]

For Exercises 11–19, if a system has an infinite number of solutions, use set-builder notation to write the solution set. If a system has no solution, state this.

Solve graphically. [8.1]

11. $y = x - 3,$
   $y = \frac{1}{4}x$

12. $2x - 3y = 12,$
   $4x + y = 10$

Solve using the substitution method. [8.2]

13. $5x - 2y = 4,$
   $x = y - 2$

14. $y = x + 2,$
   $y - x = 8$

15. $x - 3y = -2,$
   $7y - 4x = 6$

Solve using the elimination method. [8.2]

16. $2x + 5y = 8,$
   $6x - 5y = 10$

17. $4x - 7y = 18,$
   $9x + 14y = 40$

18. $3x - 5y = 9,$
   $5x - 3y = -1$

19. $1.5x - 3 = -2y,$
   $3x + 4y = 6$

Solve. [8.3]

20. Ana bought two melons and one pineapple for $8.96. If she had purchased one melon and two pineapples, she would have spent $1.49 more. What is the price of a melon? of a pineapple?

21. A freight train leaves Houston at midnight traveling north at a speed of 44 mph. One hour later, a passenger train, going 55 mph, travels north from Houston on a parallel track. How many hours will the passenger train travel before it overtakes the freight train?

22. D'Andre wants 14 L of fruit punch that is 10% juice. At the store, he finds only punch that is 15% juice or punch that is 8% juice. How much of each should he purchase?

Solve. If a system's equations are dependent or if there is no solution, state this. [8.4]

23. $x + 4y + 3z = 2,$
   $2x + y + z = 10,$
   $-x + y + 2z = 8$

24. $4x + 2y - 6z = 34,$
   $2x + y + 3z = 3,$
   $6x + 3y - 3z = 37$

25. $2x - 5y - 2z = -4,$
   $7x + 2y - 5z = -6,$
   $-2x + 3y + 2z = 4$

26. $3x + y = 2,$
   $x + 3y + z = 0,$
   $x + z = 2$

Solve.

27. In triangle ABC, the measure of angle A is four times the measure of angle C, and the measure of angle B is 45° more than the measure of angle C. What are the measures of the angles of the triangle? [8.5]

28. A nontoxic floor wax can be made from lemon juice and food-grade linseed oil. The amount of oil should be twice the amount of lemon juice. How much of each ingredient is needed to make 32 oz of floor wax? (The mix should be spread with a rag and buffed when dry.) [8.3]

29. The sum of the average number of times a man, a woman, and a one-year-old child cry each month is 56.7. A woman cries 3.9 more times than a man. The average number of times a one-year-old cries per month is 43.3 more than the average number of times combined that a man and a woman cry. What is the average number of times per month that each cries? [8.5]

Solve using matrices. Show your work. [8.6]

30. $3x + 4y = -13,$
$\quad 5x + 6y = 8$

31. $3x - y + z = -1,$
$\quad 2x + 3y + z = 4,$
$\quad 5x + 4y + 2z = 5$

Evaluate. [8.7]

32. $\begin{vmatrix} -2 & -5 \\ 3 & 10 \end{vmatrix}$

33. $\begin{vmatrix} 2 & 3 & 0 \\ 1 & 4 & -2 \\ 2 & -1 & 5 \end{vmatrix}$

Solve using Cramer's rule. Show your work. [8.7]

34. $2x + 3y = 6,$
$\quad x - 4y = 14$

35. $2x + y + z = -2,$
$\quad 2x - y + 3z = 6,$
$\quad 3x - 5y + 4z = 7$

36. Find the equilibrium point for the demand and supply functions

$$S(p) = 60 + 7p$$

and

$$D(p) = 120 - 13p. \quad [8.8]$$

37. Danae is beginning to produce organic honey. For the first year, the fixed costs for setting up production are $54,000. The variable costs for producing each pint of honey are $4.75. The revenue from each pint of honey is $9.25. Find the following. [8.8]

a) The total cost $C(x)$ of producing x pints of honey

b) The total revenue $R(x)$ from the sale of x pints of honey

c) The total profit $P(x)$ from the production and sale of x pints of honey

d) The profit or loss from the production and sale of 5000 pints of honey; of 15,000 pints of honey

e) The break-even point

Synthesis

38. How would you go about solving a problem that involves four variables? [8.5]

39. Explain how a system of equations can be both dependent and inconsistent. [8.4]

40. Danae is leaving a job that pays $36,000 a year to make honey (see Exercise 37). How many pints of honey must she produce and sell in order to make as much money as she earned at her previous job? [8.8]

41. Recently, Staples® charged $5.99 for a 2-count pack of Bic® Round Stic Grip mechanical pencils and $7.49 for a 12-count pack of Bic® Matic Grip mechanical pencils. Wiese Accounting purchased 138 of these two types of mechanical pencils for a total of $157.26. How many packs of each did they buy? [8.3]

42. Solve graphically:

$$y = x + 2,$$
$$y = x^2 + 2. \quad [8.1]$$

43. The graph of $f(x) = ax^2 + bx + c$ contains the points $(-2, 3)$, $(1, 1)$, and $(0, 3)$. Find a, b, and c and give a formula for the function. [8.5]

Test: Chapter 8

CHAPTER **Test Prep** VIDEO CD   *Step-by-step test solutions are found on the video CD in the front of this book.*

For Exercises 1–6, if a system has an infinite number of solutions, use set-builder notation to write the solution set. If a system has no solution, state this.

1. Solve graphically:

$$2x + y = 8,$$
$$y - x = 2.$$

Solve using the substitution method.

2. $x + 3y = -8,$
$\quad 4x - 3y = 23$

3. $2x - 4y = -6,$
$\quad x = 2y - 3$

Solve using the elimination method.

4. $3x - y = 7,$
$\quad x + y = 1$

5. $4y + 2x = 18,$
$\quad 3x + 6y = 26$

6. $4x - 6y = 3,$
$\quad 6x - 4y = -3$

7. The perimeter of a standard basketball court is 288 ft. The length is 44 ft longer than the width. Find the dimensions.

$P = 288$ ft

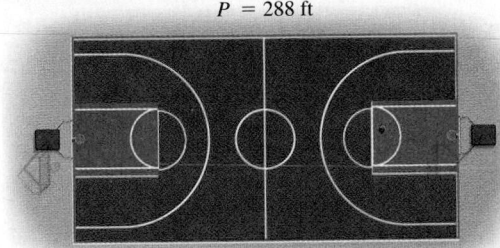

8. Pepperidge Farm® Goldfish is a snack food for which 40% of its calories come from fat. Rold Gold® Pretzels receive 9% of their calories from fat. How many grams of each would be needed to make 620 g of a snack mix for which 15% of the calories are from fat?

9. A truck leaves Gaston at noon traveling 55 mph. An hour later, a car leaves Gaston following the same route as the truck but traveling 65 mph. In how many hours will the car catch up to the truck?

Solve. If a system's equations are dependent or if there is no solution, state this.

10. $-3x + y - 2z = 8,$
$-x + 2y - z = 5,$
$2x + y + z = -3$

11. $6x + 2y - 4z = 15,$
$-3x - 4y + 2z = -6,$
$4x - 6y + 3z = 8$

12. $2x + 2y = 0,$
$4x + 4z = 4,$
$2x + y + z = 2$

13. $3x + 3z = 0,$
$2x + 2y = 2,$
$3y + 3z = 3$

Solve using matrices.

14. $4x + y = 12,$
$3x + 2y = 2$

15. $x + 3y - 3z = 12,$
$3x - y + 4z = 0,$
$-x + 2y - z = 1$

Evaluate.

16. $\begin{vmatrix} 4 & -2 \\ 3 & -5 \end{vmatrix}$

17. $\begin{vmatrix} 3 & 4 & 2 \\ -2 & -5 & 4 \\ 0 & 5 & -3 \end{vmatrix}$

18. Solve using Cramer's rule:
$3x + 4y = -1,$
$5x - 2y = 4.$

19. An electrician, a carpenter, and a plumber are hired to work on a house. The electrician earns $30 per hour, the carpenter $28.50 per hour, and the plumber $34 per hour. The first day on the job, they worked a total of 21.5 hr and earned a total of $673.00. If the plumber worked 2 more hours than the carpenter did, how many hours did each work?

20. Find the equilibrium point for the demand and supply functions

$$D(p) = 79 - 8p \quad \text{and} \quad S(p) = 37 + 6p,$$

where p is the price, in dollars, $D(p)$ is the number of units demanded, and $S(p)$ is the number of units supplied.

21. Kick Back, Inc., is producing a new hammock. For the first year, the fixed costs for setting up production are $44,000. The variable costs for producing each hammock are $25. The revenue from each hammock is $80. Find the following.

a) The total cost $C(x)$ of producing x hammocks

b) The total revenue $R(x)$ from the sale of x hammocks

c) The total profit $P(x)$ from the production and sale of x hammocks

d) The profit or loss from the production and sale of 300 hammocks; of 900 hammocks

e) The break-even point

Synthesis

22. The graph of the function $f(x) = mx + b$ contains the points $(-1, 3)$ and $(-2, -4)$. Find m and b.

23. Some of the world's best and most expensive coffee is Hawaii's Kona coffee. In order for coffee to be labeled "Kona Blend," it must contain at least 30% Kona beans. Bean Town Roasters has 40 lb of Mexican coffee. How much Kona coffee must they add if they wish to market it as Kona Blend?

Cumulative Review: Chapters 1–8

1. Evaluate $9t \div 6t^3$ for $t = -2$. [1.8]

2. Find the opposite of $-\frac{1}{10}$. [1.6]

3. Find the reciprocal of $-\frac{1}{10}$. [1.7]

4. Remove parentheses and simplify:
$$3x^2 - 2(-5x^2 + y) + y. \quad [1.8]$$

Simplify. Do not leave negative exponents in your answers.

5. $40 - 8^2 \div 4 \cdot 4$ [1.8]

6. $\dfrac{|-2 \cdot 5 - 3 \cdot 4|}{5^2 - 2 \cdot 7}$ [1.8]

7. $x^4 \cdot x^{-6} \cdot x^{13}$ [4.2]

8. $(6x^2y^3)^2(-2x^0y^4)^{-3}$ [4.2]

9. $\dfrac{-10a^7b^{-11}}{25a^{-4}b^{22}}$ [4.2]

10. $\left(\dfrac{3x^4y^{-2}}{4x^{-5}}\right)^4$ [4.2]

11. $(5.5 \times 10^{-3})(3.4 \times 10^8)$ [4.2]

12. $\dfrac{2.42 \times 10^5}{6.05 \times 10^{-2}}$ [4.2]

Solve.

13. $2x + 1 = 5(2 - x)$ [2.2]

14. $x^2 + 5x + 6 = 0$ [5.7]

15. $t + \dfrac{6}{t} = 5$ [6.6]

16. $\frac{1}{2}t + \frac{1}{6} = \frac{1}{3} - t$ [2.2]

17. $2y + 9 \le 5y + 11$ [2.6]

18. $n^2 = 100$ [5.7]

19. $3x + y = 5,$
    $y = x + 1$ [8.2]

20. $\dfrac{4}{x - 1} = \dfrac{3}{x + 2}$ [6.6]

21. $6x^2 = x + 2$ [5.7]

22. $x + y = 10,$
    $x - y = 4$ [8.2]

23. $x + y + z = -5,$
    $2x + 3y - 2z = 8,$
    $x - y + 4z = -21$ [8.4]

24. $2x + 5y - 3z = -11,$
    $-5x + 3y - 2z = -7,$
    $3x - 2y + 5z = 12$ [8.4]

Solve each formula. [2.3]

25. $t = \frac{1}{3}pq$, for p

26. $A = \dfrac{r + s}{2}$, for s

Add and, if possible, simplify.

27. $(8a^2 - 6a - 7) + (3a^3 + 6a - 7)$ [4.4]

28. $\dfrac{m + n}{2m + n} + \dfrac{n}{m - n}$ [6.4]

Subtract.

29. $(8a^2 - 6a - 7) - (3a^3 + 6a - 7)$ [4.4]

30. $\dfrac{x + 5}{x - 2} - \dfrac{x - 1}{2 - x}$ [6.4]

Multiply.

31. $(5a^2 + b)(5a^2 - b)$ [4.7]

32. $-3x^2(5x^3 - 6x^2 - 2x + 1)$ [4.5]

33. $(2n + 5)^2$ [4.6]

34. $(8t^2 + 5)(t^3 + 4)$ [4.6]

35. $\dfrac{x^2 - 2x + 1}{x^2 - 4} \cdot \dfrac{x^2 + 4x + 4}{x^2 - 3x + 2}$ [6.2]

Divide.

36. $(2x^2 - 5x - 3) \div (x - 3)$ [4.8]

37. $\dfrac{x^2 - x}{4x^2 + 8x} \div \dfrac{x^2 - 1}{2x}$ [6.2]

Factor completely.

38. $x^3 + x^2 + 2x + 2$ [5.1]

39. $m^4 - 1$ [5.4]

40. $2x^3 + 18x^2 + 40x$ [5.2]

41. $x^4 - 6x^2 + 9$ [5.4]

42. $4x^2 - 2x - 10$ [5.1]

43. $10x^2 - 29x + 10$ [5.3]

Graph.

44. $2x + y = 6$ [3.3]

45. $f(x) = -2x + 8$ [7.3]

46. $2x = 10$ [3.3]

47. $x = 2y$ [3.2]

48. Find the x-intercept and the y-intercept of the line given by $10x - 15y = 60$. [3.3]

49. Write the slope–intercept equation for the line with slope -2 and y-intercept $\left(0, \frac{4}{7}\right)$. [3.6]

50. Find an equation in slope–intercept form of the line containing the points $(-6, 3)$ and $(4, 2)$. [3.7]

51. Determine whether the lines given by the following equations are parallel, perpendicular, or neither:
$$2x = 4y + 7,$$
$$x - 2y = 5. \quad [3.6]$$

52. Find an equation of the line containing the point $(2, 1)$ and perpendicular to the line $x - 2y = 5$. [3.7]

53. For the graph of f shown, determine the domain, the range, $f(-3)$, and any value of x for which $f(x) = 5$. [7.2]

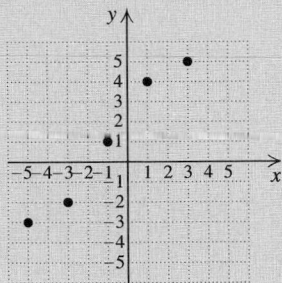

54. Determine the domain of the function given by

$$f(x) = \frac{7}{x + 10}. \quad [7.2]$$

Given $g(x) = 4x - 3$ *and* $h(x) = -2x^2 + 1$, *find the following function values.*

55. $h(4)$ [7.1]

56. $-g(0)$ [7.1]

57. $(g - h)(a)$ [7.4]

58. Evaluate: $\begin{vmatrix} 2 & -3 \\ 4 & 1 \end{vmatrix}$. [8.7]

Solve.

59. A library was mistakenly charged sales tax on an order of children's books. The invoice, including 5% sales tax, was for $1323. How much should the library have been charged? [2.4]

60. A snowmobile is traveling 40 mph faster than a dog sled. In the same time that the dog sled travels 24 mi, the snowmobile travels 104 mi. Find the speeds of the sled and the snowmobile. [6.7]

61. Each nurse practitioner at the Midway Clinic is required to see an average of at least 40 patients per day. During the first 4 workdays of one week, Michael saw 50, 35, 42, and 38 patients. How many patients must he see on the fifth day in order to meet his requirements? [2.7]

62. Tia and Avery live next door to each other on Meachin Street. Their house numbers are consecutive odd numbers, and the product of their house numbers is 143. Find the house numbers. [5.8]

63. Long-distance calls made using the "Ruby" prepaid calling card cost 1.4¢ per minute plus a maintenance fee of 99¢ per week. The "Sapphire" plan has a maintenance fee of only 69¢ per week, but calls cost 1.7¢ per minute. For what number of minutes per week will the two cards cost the same? [8.3]
Source: www.enjoyprepaid.com

64. The second angle of a triangle is twice as large as the first. The third angle is 15° less than the sum of the first two angles. Find the measure of each angle. [2.5]

65. A newspaper uses self-employed copywriters to write its advertising copy. If they use 12 copywriters, each person works 35 hr per week. How many hours per week would each person work if the newspaper uses 10 copywriters? [7.5]

Synthesis

66. Solve $t = px - qx$ for x. [2.3]

67. Write the slope–intercept equation of the line that contains the point $(-2, 3)$ and is parallel to the line $2x - y = 7$. [3.7]

68. Simplify: $\dfrac{t^2 - 9}{2t + 1} \div \dfrac{t^2 - 4t + 3}{6t^2 + 3t} \cdot \dfrac{2t^3 - t^2 + t}{4t + 12}$. [6.2]

69. Given that $f(x) = mx + b$ and that $f(5) = -3$ when $f(-4) = 2$, find m and b. [7.1], [8.3]

70. The maximum length of a postcard that can be mailed with one postcard stamp is $\frac{7}{4}$ in. longer than the maximum width. The maximum area is $\frac{51}{2}$ in^2. Find the maximum length and width of a postcard. [5.8]
Source: USPS

Inequalities and Problem Solving

9.1
Inequalities and Domain

9.2
Intersections, Unions, and
Compound Inequalities

9.3
Absolute-Value Equations
and Inequalities

CONNECTING THE CONCEPTS

9.4
Inequalities in
Two Variables

CONNECTING THE CONCEPTS

9.5
Applications Using
Linear Programming

STUDY SUMMARY
REVIEW EXERCISES
CHAPTER TEST
CUMULATIVE REVIEW

ANNE SAMUELS
REGISTERED NURSE/
NURSE MANAGEMENT
Springfield, Massachusetts

As a nurse, I use math every
day to calculate dosages of
medication. If an order prescribes
a dosage of 2.5 mg/kg twice a
day, I need to know the patient's
weight, change that weight from
pounds to kilograms, and then
calculate the dosage. As a nurse
manager, I use math to determine
the number of nurses needed
to care for patients and to work
out a budget for salaries
and equipment.

AN APPLICATION

The number of registered nurses $R(t)$
employed in the United States, in
millions, t years after 2000, can be
approximated by

$$R(t) = 0.05t + 2.2.$$

Determine (using an inequality) those
years for which more than 3 million
registered nurses will be employed in
the United States.

Source: Based on data from the U.S. Department
of Health and Human Services and the Bureau of
Labor Statistics

This problem appears as Example 5 in
Section 9.1.

I nequalities are mathematical sentences containing symbols such as < (is less than). In this chapter, we use the principles for solving inequalities developed in Chapter 2 to solve compound inequalities. We also combine our knowledge of inequalities and systems of equations to solve systems of inequalities.

9.1 Inequalities and Domain

Solving Inequalities Graphically   ▪   Domain   ▪   Problem Solving

Solving Inequalities Graphically

Recall from Chapter 1 that an **inequality** is any sentence containing $<, >, \leq, \geq$, or $\neq$ (see Section 1.4)—for example,

$$-2 < a, \quad x > 4, \quad x + 3 \leq 6, \quad 6 - 7y \geq 10y - 4, \quad \text{and} \quad 5x \neq 10.$$

Any replacement for the variable that makes an inequality true is called a **solution**. The set of all solutions is called the **solution set**. When all solutions of an inequality are found, we say that we have **solved** the inequality.

We can use two principles, developed in Chapter 2, to solve inequalities.

The Addition Principle for Inequalities

For any real numbers a, b, and c:

$$a < b \text{ is equivalent to } a + c < b + c;$$
$$a > b \text{ is equivalent to } a + c > b + c.$$

Similar statements hold for $\leq$ and $\geq$.

The Multiplication Principle for Inequalities

For any real numbers a and b, and for any *positive* number c,

$$a < b \text{ is equivalent to } ac < bc;$$
$$a > b \text{ is equivalent to } ac > bc.$$

For any real numbers a and b, and for any *negative* number c,

$$a < b \text{ is equivalent to } ac > bc;$$
$$a > b \text{ is equivalent to } ac < bc.$$

Similar statements hold for $\leq$ and $\geq$.

EXAMPLE **1**   Solve: $2x + 4 < -x + 1$.

SOLUTION

$$2x + 4 < -x + 1$$

$2x + 4 - 4 < -x + 1 - 4$ Subtracting 4 from both sides

$$2x < -x - 3$$

$2x + x < -x - 3 + x$ Adding x to both sides

$$3x < -3$$

$\dfrac{3x}{3} < \dfrac{-3}{3}$ Dividing both sides by 3. The $<$ symbol stays the same since 3 is positive.

$$x < -1$$

The solution set is $\{x \mid x < -1\}$, or $(-\infty, -1)$.

TRY EXERCISE 19

We now look at a graphical method for solving inequalities.

To solve the inequality in Example 1, $2x + 4 < -x + 1$, we let $f(x) = 2x + 4$ and $g(x) = -x + 1$. Consider the graphs of the functions $f(x) = 2x + 4$ and $g(x) = -x + 1$.

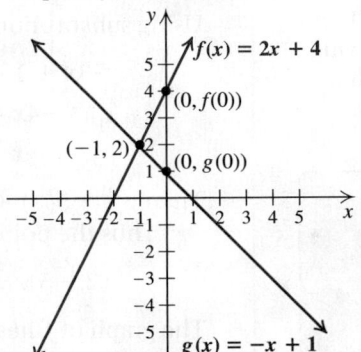

Graphs of $f(x)$ and $g(x)$

The graphs intersect at the point $(-1, 2)$. Thus, when $x = -1$, $f(x) = g(x)$. At all x-values except -1, either $f(x) > g(x)$ or $f(x) < g(x)$. Note from the graphs that $f(x) > g(x)$ when the graph of f lies above the graph of g. Also, $f(x) < g(x)$ when the graph of f lies below the graph of g.

Compare $f(0)$ and $g(0)$. Note from the graphs that $f(0)$ lies above $g(0)$. In fact, for all values of x greater than -1, $f(x) > g(x)$. For all values of x less than -1, $f(x) < g(x)$. In this way, the point of intersection of the graphs marks the endpoint of the solution set of an inequality.

Note that using the graphs of $f(x)$ and $g(x)$ to solve an inequality is not the same as graphing the solutions of the inequality.

For $f(x) = 2x + 4$ and $g(x) = -x + 1$, compare the following.

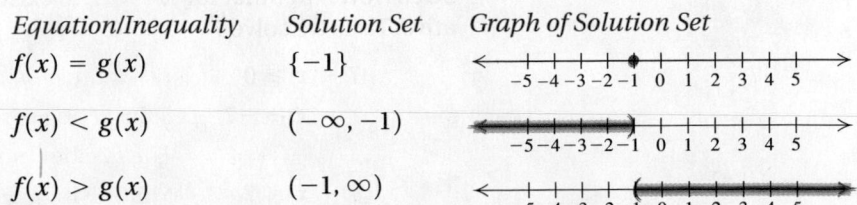

Equation/Inequality	Solution Set	Graph of Solution Set
$f(x) = g(x)$	$\{-1\}$	
$f(x) < g(x)$	$(-\infty, -1)$	
$f(x) > g(x)$	$(-1, \infty)$	

EXAMPLE 2

TECHNOLOGY CONNECTION

On most calculators, $4x - 1 \geq 5x - 2$ can be solved by graphing $y_1 = 4x - 1 \geq 5x - 2$ ($\geq$ is often found by pressing **2ND** **MATH**). The solution set is then displayed as an interval (shown by a horizontal line 1 unit above the x-axis).

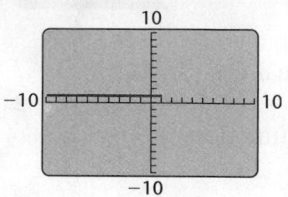

A check can also be made by graphing $y_1 = 4x - 1$ and $y_2 = 5x - 2$ and identifying those x-values for which $y_1 \geq y_2$.

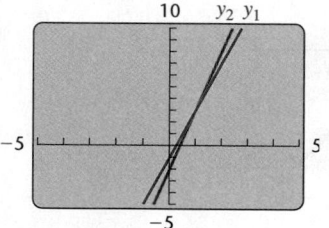

The INTERSECT option helps us find that $y_1 = y_2$ when $x = 1$. Note that $y_1 \geq y_2$ for x-values in the interval $(-\infty, 1]$.

Solve graphically: $-3x + 1 \geq x - 7$.

SOLUTION We let $f(x) = -3x + 1$ and $g(x) = x - 7$, and graph both functions. The solution set will consist of the interval for which the graph of f lies on or above the graph of g.

To find the point of intersection, we solve the system of equations

$$y = -3x + 1,$$
$$y = x - 7.$$

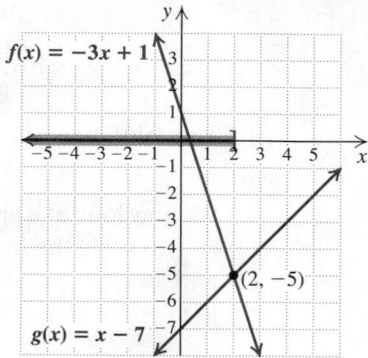

Using substitution, we have

$$-3x + 1 = x - 7$$
$$-4x = -8$$
$$x = 2.$$

Then $y = -3(2) + 1 = -5$.

Thus the point of intersection is

$$(2, -5).$$

The graph of f lies *on* the graph of g when $x = 2$. It lies *above* the graph of g when $x < 2$. Thus the solution of $-3x + 1 \geq x - 7$ is

$$\{x | x \leq 2\}, \quad \text{or} \quad (-\infty, 2].$$

This set is indicated by the purple shading on the x-axis.　**TRY EXERCISE** 33

Domain

Although radical notation is not discussed in detail until Chapter 10, we know that only nonnegative numbers have square roots that are real numbers. Thus finding the domain of a radical function often involves solving an inequality.

EXAMPLE 3

Find the domain of f if $f(x) = \sqrt{7 - x}$.

SOLUTION In order for $\sqrt{7 - x}$ to exist as a real number, $7 - x$ must be nonnegative. Thus we solve $7 - x \geq 0$:

$$7 - x \geq 0 \qquad \text{7 − x must be nonnegative.}$$
$$-x \geq -7 \qquad \text{Subtracting 7 from both sides}$$
$$\text{The symbol must be reversed.}$$
$$x \leq 7. \qquad \text{Multiplying both sides by −1}$$

When $x \leq 7$, the expression $7 - x$ is nonnegative. Thus the domain of f is $\{x | x \leq 7\}$, or $(-\infty, 7]$.　**TRY EXERCISE** 43

EXAMPLE 4   Find the domain of g if $g(x) = \sqrt{\frac{1}{2}x - 10}$.

SOLUTION   In order for $\sqrt{\frac{1}{2}x - 10}$ to exist as a real number, $\frac{1}{2}x - 10$ must be nonnegative. Thus we solve $\frac{1}{2}x - 10 \geq 0$:

$$\frac{1}{2}x - 10 \geq 0 \qquad \frac{1}{2}x - 10 \text{ must be nonnegative.}$$

$$\frac{1}{2}x \geq 10 \qquad \text{Adding 10 to both sides}$$

$$x \geq 20. \qquad \text{Multiplying both sides by 2.}$$
$$\text{The symbol } \geq \text{ remains the same.}$$

Thus the domain of g is $\{x \mid x \geq 20\}$, or $[20, \infty)$.

TRY EXERCISE 49

Problem Solving

Many problem-solving situations translate to inequalities.

EXAMPLE 5

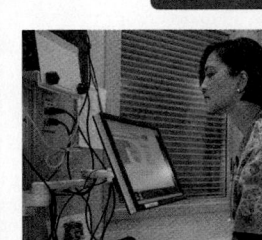

Registered nurses.   The number of registered nurses $R(t)$ employed in the United States, in millions, t years after 2000 can be approximated by

$$R(t) = 0.05t + 2.2.$$

Determine (using an inequality) those years for which more than 3 million registered nurses will be employed in the United States.

Source: Based on data from the U.S. Department of Health and Human Services and the Bureau of Labor Statistics

SOLUTION

1. **Familiarize.** We already have a formula. The number 0.05 tells us that employment of registered nurses is growing at a rate of 0.05 million (or 50,000) per year. The number 2.2 tells us that in 2000, there were approximately 2.2 million registered nurses employed in the United States.

2. **Translate.** We are asked to find the years for which *more than* 3 million registered nurses will be employed in the United States. Thus we have

   $$R(t) > 3$$
   $$0.05t + 2.2 > 3. \qquad \text{Substituting } 0.05t + 2.2 \text{ for } R(t)$$

3. **Carry out.** We solve the inequality:

   $$0.05t + 2.2 > 3$$
   $$0.05t > 0.8 \qquad \text{Subtracting 2.2 from both sides}$$
   $$t > 16. \qquad \text{Dividing both sides by 0.05}$$

   Note that this corresponds to years after 2016.

4. **Check.** We can partially check our answer by finding $R(t)$ for a value of t greater than 16. For example,

   $$R(20) = 0.05 \cdot 20 + 2.2 = 3.2, \text{ and } 3.2 > 3.$$

5. **State.** More than 3 million registered nurses will be employed in the United States for years after 2016.

TRY EXERCISE 57

EXAMPLE 6

Job offers.   After graduation, Rose had two job offers in sales:

Uptown Fashions: A salary of $600 per month, plus a commission of 4% of sales;

Ergo Designs: A salary of $800 per month, plus a commission of 6% of sales in excess of $10,000.

If sales always exceed $10,000, for what amount of sales would Uptown Fashions provide higher pay?

SOLUTION

1. **Familiarize.** Listing the given information in a table will be helpful.

Uptown Fashions Monthly Income	Ergo Designs Monthly Income
$600 salary 4% of sales *Total*: $600 + 4% of sales	$800 salary 6% of sales over $10,000 *Total*: $800 + 6% of sales over $10,000

Next, suppose that Rose sold a certain amount—say, $12,000—in one month. Which offer would be better? Working for Uptown, she would earn $600 plus 4% of $12,000, or $600 + 0.04(12,000) = \$1080$. Since with Ergo Designs commissions are paid only on sales in excess of $10,000, Rose would earn $800 plus 6% of ($12,000 − \$10,000), or $800 + 0.06(2000) = \$920$.

For monthly sales of $12,000, Uptown pays better. Similar calculations will show that for sales of $30,000 a month, Ergo pays better. To determine *all* values for which Uptown pays more money, we must solve an inequality that is based on the calculations above.

2. **Translate.** We let S = the amount of monthly sales, in dollars, and will assume $S > 10,000$ so that both plans will pay a commission. Examining the calculations in the *Familiarize* step, we see that monthly income from Uptown is $600 + 0.04S$ and from Ergo is $800 + 0.06(S − 10,000)$. We want to find all values of S for which

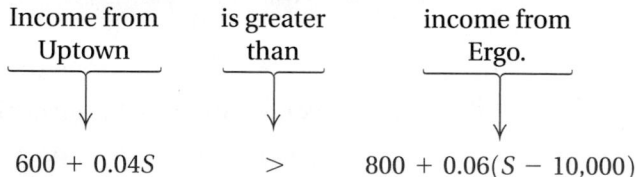

Income from Uptown	is greater than	income from Ergo.
$600 + 0.04S$	$>$	$800 + 0.06(S − 10,000)$

3. **Carry out.** We solve the inequality:

$$600 + 0.04S > 800 + 0.06(S − 10,000)$$

$600 + 0.04S > 800 + 0.06S − 600$	Using the distributive law
$600 + 0.04S > 200 + 0.06S$	Combining like terms
$400 > 0.02S$	Subtracting 200 and $0.04S$ from both sides
$20,000 > S$, or $S < 20,000.$	Dividing both sides by 0.02

4. **Check.** The above steps indicate that income from Uptown Fashions is higher than income from Ergo Designs for sales less than $20,000. In the *Familiarize* step, we saw that for sales of $12,000, Uptown pays more. Since $12,000 < 20,000$, this is a partial check.

5. **State.** When monthly sales are less than $20,000, Uptown Fashions provides the higher pay.

TRY EXERCISE 59

9.1 EXERCISE SET

🔖 **Concept Reinforcement** *Classify each of the following as equivalent inequalities, equivalent equations, equivalent expressions, or not equivalent.*

1. $5x + 7 = 6 - 3x$, $8x + 7 = 6$

2. $2(4x + 1)$, $8x + 2$

3. $x - 7 > -2$, $x > 5$

4. $t + 3 < 1$, $t < 2$

5. $-4t \leq 12$, $t \leq -3$

6. $\frac{3}{5}a + \frac{1}{5} = 2$, $3a + 1 = 10$

7. $6a + 9$, $3(2a + 3)$

8. $-4x \geq -8$, $x \geq 2$

9. $-\frac{1}{2}x < 7$, $x > 14$

10. $-\frac{1}{3}t \leq -5$, $t \geq 15$

Solve algebraically.

11. $3x + 1 < 7$

12. $2x - 5 \geq 9$

13. $3 - x \geq 12$

14. $8 - x < 15$

15. $\dfrac{2x + 7}{5} < -9$

16. $\dfrac{5y + 13}{4} > -2$

17. $\dfrac{3t - 7}{-4} \leq 5$

18. $\dfrac{2t - 9}{-3} \geq 7$

19. $3 - 8y \geq 9 - 4y$

20. $4m + 7 \geq 9m - 3$

21. $5(t - 3) + 4t < 2(7 + 2t)$

22. $2(4 + 2x) > 2x + 3(2 - 5x)$

23. $5[3m - (m + 4)] > -2(m - 4)$

24. $8x - 3(3x + 2) - 5 \geq 3(x + 4) - 2x$

Solve each inequality using the given graph.

25. $f(x) \geq g(x)$

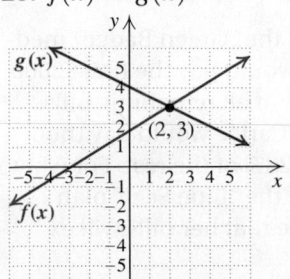

26. $f(x) < g(x)$

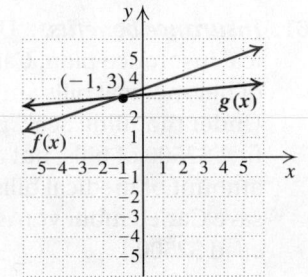

27. $f(x) < g(x)$

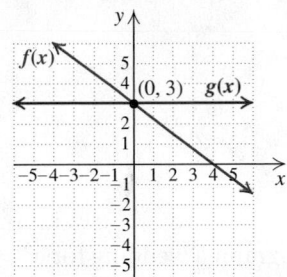

28. $f(x) \geq g(x)$

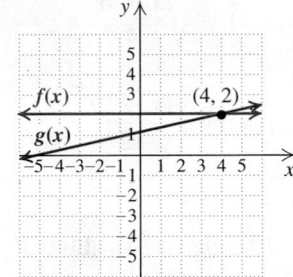

Solve graphically.

29. $x - 3 < 4$

30. $x + 4 \geq 6$

31. $2x - 3 \geq 1$

32. $3x + 1 < 1$

33. $x + 3 > 2x - 5$

34. $3x - 5 \leq 3 - x$

35. $\frac{1}{2}x - 2 \leq 1 - x$

36. $x + 5 > \frac{1}{3}x - 1$

37. Let $f(x) = 7 - 3x$ and $g(x) = 2x - 3$. Find all values of x for which $f(x) \leq g(x)$.

38. Let $f(x) = 8x - 9$ and $g(x) = 3x - 11$. Find all values of x for which $f(x) \leq g(x)$.

39. Let $y_1 = 2x - 7$ and $y_2 = 5x - 9$. Find all values of x for which $y_1 < y_2$.

40. Let $y_1 = 2x + 1$ and $y_2 = -\frac{1}{2}x + 6$. Find all values of x for which $y_1 < y_2$.

Find the domain of each function.

41. $f(x) = \sqrt{x - 10}$

42. $f(x) = \sqrt{x + 2}$

43. $f(x) = \sqrt{3 - x}$

44. $f(x) = \sqrt{11 - x}$

45. $f(x) = \sqrt{2x + 7}$

46. $f(x) = \sqrt{8 - 5x}$

47. $f(x) = \sqrt{8 - 2x}$

48. $f(x) = \sqrt{2x - 10}$

49. $f(x) = \sqrt{\frac{1}{3}x + 5}$

50. $f(x) = \sqrt{2x + \frac{1}{2}}$

51. $f(x) = \sqrt{\frac{x - 5}{4}}$

52. $f(x) = \sqrt{\frac{x + 7}{12}}$

Solve.

53. *Photography.*   Eli will photograph a wedding for a flat fee of $900 or for an hourly rate of $120. For what lengths of time would the hourly rate be less expensive?

54. *Truck rentals.*   Jenn can rent a moving truck for either $99 with unlimited mileage or $49 plus 80¢ per mile. For what mileages would the unlimited mileage plan save money?

55. *Exam scores.*   There are 80 questions on a college entrance examination. Two points are awarded for each correct answer, and one half point is deducted for each incorrect answer. How many questions does Tami need to answer correctly in order to score at least 100 on the test? Assume that Tami answers every question.

56. *Insurance claims.*   After a serious automobile accident, most insurance companies will replace the damaged car with a new one if repair costs exceed 80% of the NADA, or "blue-book," value of the car. Lorenzo's car recently sustained $9200 worth of damage but was not replaced. What was the blue-book value of his car?

57. *Crude-oil production.*   The yearly U.S. production of crude oil $C(t)$, in millions of barrels, t years after 2000 can be approximated by

$$C(t) = -40.5t + 2159.$$

Determine (using an inequality) those years for which domestic production will drop below 1750 million barrels.
Source: U.S. Energy Information Administration

58. *HDTVs.*   The percentage of U.S. households $p(t)$ with an HDTV t years after 2005 can be approximated by

$$p(t) = 8t + 12.5.$$

Determine (using an inequality) those years for which more than half of all U.S. households will have an HDTV.
Source: Based on data from Consumer Electronics Association

59. *Wages.*   Toni can be paid in one of two ways:

   Plan A: A salary of $400 per month, plus a commission of 8% of gross sales;

   Plan B: A salary of $610 per month, plus a commission of 5% of gross sales.

For what amount of gross sales should Toni select plan A?

60. *Wages.*   Eric can be paid for his masonry work in one of two ways:

   Plan A: $300 plus $9.00 per hour;

   Plan B: Straight $12.50 per hour.

Suppose that the job takes n hours. For what values of n is plan B better for Eric?

61. *Insurance benefits.*   Under the "Green Badge" medical insurance plan, Carlee would pay the first $2000 of her medical bills and 30% of all remaining bills. Under the "Blue Seal" plan, Carlee would pay the first $2500 of bills, but only 20% of the rest. For what amount of medical bills will the "Blue Seal" plan save Carlee money? (Assume that her bills will exceed $2500.)

62. *Checking accounts.* North Bank charges $10 per month for a student checking account. The first 8 checks are free, and each additional check costs $0.75. South Bank offers a student checking account with no monthly charge. The first 8 checks are free, and each additional check costs $3. For what numbers of checks is the South Bank plan more expensive? (Assume that the student will always write more than 8 checks.)

63. *Body fat percentage.* The function given by

$$F(d) = (4.95/d - 4.50) \times 100$$

can be used to estimate the body fat percentage $F(d)$ of a person with an average body density d, in kilograms per liter.

a) A man is considered obese if his body fat percentage is at least 25%. Find the body densities of an obese man.

b) A woman is considered obese if her body fat percentage is at least 32%. Find the body densities of an obese woman.

64. *Temperature conversion.* The function

$$C(F) = \tfrac{5}{9}(F - 32)$$

can be used to find the Celsius temperature $C(F)$ that corresponds to $F°$ Fahrenheit.

a) Gold is solid at Celsius temperatures less than 1063°C. Find the Fahrenheit temperatures for which gold is solid.

b) Silver is solid at Celsius temperatures less than 960.8°C. Find the Fahrenheit temperatures for which silver is solid.

65. *Manufacturing.* Bright Ideas is planning to make a new kind of lamp. Fixed costs will be $90,000, and variable costs will be $25 for the production of each lamp. The total-cost function for x lamps is

$$C(x) = 90{,}000 + 25x.$$

The company makes $48 in revenue for each lamp sold. The total-revenue function for x lamps is

$$R(x) = 48x.$$

(See Section 8.8.)

a) When $R(x) < C(x)$, the company loses money. Find the values of x for which the company loses money.

b) When $R(x) > C(x)$, the company makes a profit. Find the values of x for which the company makes a profit.

66. *Publishing.* The demand and supply functions for a locally produced poetry book are approximated by

$$D(p) = 2000 - 60p \quad \text{and}$$
$$S(p) = 460 + 94p,$$

where p is the price, in dollars (see Section 8.8).

a) Find those values of p for which demand exceeds supply.

b) Find those values of p for which demand is less than supply.

67. How is the solution of $x + 3 = 8$ related to the solution sets of

$$x + 3 > 8 \quad \text{and} \quad x + 3 < 8?$$

68. Can a negative number be in the domain of a radical function? Why or why not?

Skill Review

To prepare for Section 9.2, review finding domains of rational functions (Section 7.2).

Find the domain of f. [7.2]

69. $f(x) = \dfrac{5}{x}$

70. $f(x) = \dfrac{3}{x - 6}$

71. $f(x) = \dfrac{x - 2}{2x + 1}$

72. $f(x) = \dfrac{x + 3}{5x - 7}$

73. $f(x) = \dfrac{x + 10}{8}$

74. $f(x) = \dfrac{3}{x} + 5$

Synthesis

75. The percentage of the U.S. population that owns an HDTV cannot exceed 100%. How does this affect the answer to Exercise 58?

76. Explain how the addition principle can be used to avoid ever needing to multiply or divide both sides of an inequality by a negative number.

Solve for x and y. Assume that a, b, c, d, and m are positive constants.

77. $3ax + 2x \geq 5ax - 4$; assume $a > 1$

78. $6by - 4y \leq 7by + 10$

79. $a(by - 2) \geq b(2y + 5)$; assume $a > 2$

80. $c(6x - 4) < d(3 + 2x)$; assume $3c > d$

81. $c(2 - 5x) + dx > m(4 + 2x)$;
assume $5c + 2m < d$

82. $a(3 - 4x) + cx < d(5x + 2)$;
assume $c > 4a + 5d$

Determine whether each statement is true or false. If false, give an example that shows this.

83. For any real numbers a, b, c, and d, if $a < b$ and $c < d$, then $a - c < b - d$.

84. For all real numbers x and y, if $x < y$, then $x^2 < y^2$.

85. Are the inequalities

$$x < 3 \quad \text{and} \quad x + \frac{1}{x} < 3 + \frac{1}{x}$$

equivalent? Why or why not?

86. Are the inequalities

$$x < 3 \quad \text{and} \quad 0 \cdot x < 0 \cdot 3$$

equivalent? Why or why not?

Solve. Then graph.

87. $x + 5 \leq 5 + x$

88. $x + 8 < 3 + x$

89. $x^2 > 0$

90. $y_1 < y_2$

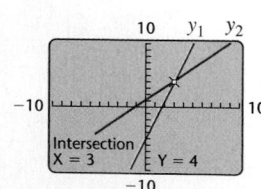

91. $y_1 \geq y_2$

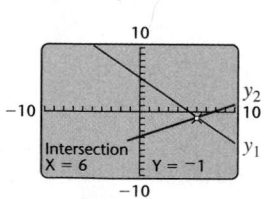

92. The graphs of $f(x) = 2x + 1$, $g(x) = -\frac{1}{2}x + 3$, and $h(x) = x - 1$ are as shown below. Solve each inequality, referring only to the figure.

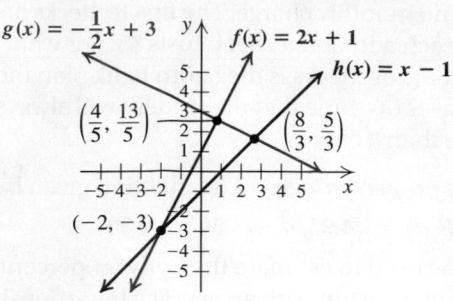

a) $2x + 1 \leq x - 1$
b) $x - 1 > -\frac{1}{2}x + 3$
c) $-\frac{1}{2}x + 3 < 2x + 1$

93. Assume that the graphs of $y_1 = -\frac{1}{2}x + 5$, $y_2 = x - 1$, and $y_3 = 2x - 3$ are as shown below. Solve each inequality, referring only to the figure.

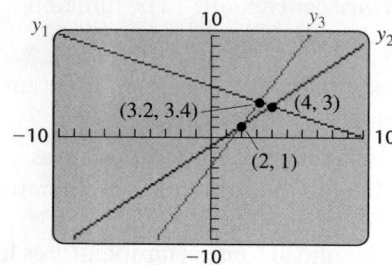

a) $-\frac{1}{2}x + 5 > x - 1$
b) $x - 1 \leq 2x - 3$
c) $2x - 3 \geq -\frac{1}{2}x + 5$

94. Using an approach similar to that in the Technology Connection on p. 580, use a graphing calculator to check your answers to Exercises 11, 37, and 40.

95. Use a graphing calculator to confirm the domains of the functions in Exercises 41, 43, and 47.

CORNER

Saving on Shipping Costs

Focus: Inequalities and problem solving

Time: 20–30 minutes

Group size: 2–3

For overnight delivery packages weighing up to 10 lb sent by Express Mail, the United States Postal Service charges (as of May 2008) $19.00 for up to one pound delivered to Zone 3 and, on average, $2.12 for each pound or part of a pound after the first. UPS Next Day Air charges $22.05 for a one-pound delivery to Zone 3 and each additional pound or part of a pound costs $1.45.*

ACTIVITY

1. One group member should determine the function p, where $p(x)$ represents the

cost, in dollars, of mailing x pounds using Express Mail.

2. One member should determine the function r, where $r(x)$ represents the cost, in dollars, of shipping x pounds using UPS Next Day Air.

3. A third member should graph p and r on the same set of axes.

4. Finally, working together, use the graph to determine those weights for which Express Mail is less expensive than UPS Next Day Air shipping. Express your answer in both set-builder notation and interval notation.

*This activity is based on an article by Michael Contino in *Mathematics Teacher*, May 1995.

9.2   Intersections, Unions, and Compound Inequalities

Intersections of Sets and Conjunctions of Sentences ▪ Unions of Sets and Disjunctions of Sentences ▪ Interval Notation and Domains

Two inequalities joined by the word "and" or the word "or" are called **compound inequalities**. Thus, "$x < -3 \ or \ x > 0$" and "$x < 5 \ and \ x > 3$" are two examples of compound inequalities. To discuss how to solve compound inequalities, we must first study ways in which sets can be combined.

Intersections of Sets and Conjunctions of Sentences

The **intersection** of two sets A and B is the set of all elements that are common to both A and B. We denote the intersection of sets A and B as

$$A \cap B.$$

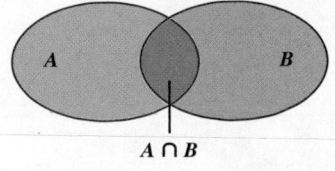

The intersection of two sets is represented by the purple region shown in the figure at left. For example, if $A = \{$all students who are taking a math class$\}$ and $B = \{$all students who are taking a history class$\}$, then $A \cap B = \{$all students who are taking a math class *and* a history class$\}$.

EXAMPLE 1

Find the intersection: $\{1, 2, 3, 4, 5\} \cap \{-2, -1, 0, 1, 2, 3\}$.

SOLUTION   The numbers 1, 2, and 3 are common to both sets, so the intersection is $\{1, 2, 3\}$.

TRY EXERCISE 11

When two or more sentences are joined by the word *and* to make a compound sentence, the new sentence is called a **conjunction** of the sentences. The following is a conjunction of inequalities:

$$-2 < x \quad and \quad x < 1.$$

A number is a solution of a conjunction if it is a solution of *both* of the separate parts. For example, -1 is a solution because it is a solution of $-2 < x$ as well as $x < 1$; that is, -1 is *both* greater than -2 *and* less than 1.

The solution set of a conjunction is the intersection of the solution sets of the individual sentences.

EXAMPLE 2

Graph and write interval notation for the conjunction

$$-2 < x \quad and \quad x < 1.$$

SOLUTION   We first graph $-2 < x$, then $x < 1$, and finally the conjunction $-2 < x$ and $x < 1$.

$\{x \mid -2 < x\}$ (number line) $(-2, \infty)$

$\{x \mid x < 1\}$ (number line) $(-\infty, 1)$

$\{x \mid -2 < x\} \cap \{x \mid x < 1\}$
$= \{x \mid -2 < x \text{ and } x < 1\}$ (number line) $(-2, 1)$

Because there are numbers that are both greater than -2 and less than 1, the solution set of the conjunction $-2 < x$ and $x < 1$ is the interval $(-2, 1)$. In set-builder notation, this is written $\{x \mid -2 < x < 1\}$, the set of all numbers that are *simultaneously* greater than -2 *and* less than 1.

TRY EXERCISE 33

For $a < b$,

$$a < x \quad and \quad x < b \quad \text{can be abbreviated} \quad a < x < b;$$

and, equivalently,

$$b > x \quad and \quad x > a \quad \text{can be abbreviated} \quad b > x > a.$$

Mathematical Use of the Word "and"

The word "and" corresponds to "intersection" and to the symbol "$\cap$". Any solution of a conjunction must make each part of the conjunction true.

EXAMPLE 3

Solve and graph: $-1 \leq 2x + 5 < 13$.

SOLUTION   This inequality is an abbreviation for the conjunction

$$-1 \leq 2x + 5 \quad and \quad 2x + 5 < 13.$$

The word *and* corresponds to set *intersection*. To solve the conjunction, we solve each of the two inequalities separately and then find the intersection of the solution sets:

$$-1 \leq 2x + 5 \quad and \quad 2x + 5 < 13$$
$$-6 \leq 2x \qquad and \qquad 2x < 8 \qquad \text{Subtracting 5 from both sides of each inequality}$$
$$-3 \leq x \qquad and \qquad x < 4. \qquad \text{Dividing both sides of each inequality by 2}$$

The solution of the conjunction is the intersection of the two separate solution sets.

$\{x \mid -3 \leq x\}$
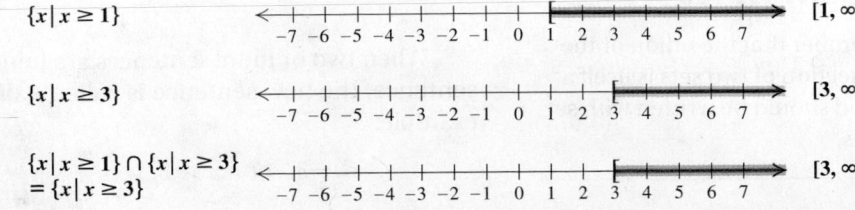
$[-3, \infty)$

$\{x \mid x < 4\}$
$(-\infty, 4)$

$\{x \mid -3 \leq x\} \cap \{x \mid x < 4\}$
$= \{x \mid -3 \leq x < 4\}$
$[-3, 4)$

We can abbreviate the answer as $-3 \leq x < 4$. The solution set is $\{x \mid -3 \leq x < 4\}$, or, in interval notation, $[-3, 4)$.

TRY EXERCISE 45

The steps in Example 3 are often combined as follows:

$$-1 \leq 2x + 5 < 13$$
$$-1 - 5 \leq 2x + 5 - 5 < 13 - 5 \qquad \text{Subtracting 5 from all three regions}$$
$$-6 \leq 2x < 8$$
$$-3 \leq x < 4. \qquad \text{Dividing by 2 in all three regions}$$

Such an approach saves some writing and will prove useful in Section 9.3.

> **CAUTION!**   The abbreviated form of a conjunction, like $-3 \leq x < 4$, can be written only if both inequality symbols point in the same direction. It is *not acceptable* to write a sentence like $-1 > x < 5$ since doing so does not indicate if *both* $-1 > x$ and $x < 5$ must be true or if it is enough for one of the separate inequalities to be true.

EXAMPLE 4

Solve and graph: $2x - 5 \geq -3 \ and \ 5x + 2 \geq 17$.

SOLUTION   We first solve each inequality, retaining the word *and*:

$$2x - 5 \geq -3 \quad and \quad 5x + 2 \geq 17$$
$$2x \geq 2 \qquad and \qquad 5x \geq 15$$
$$x \geq 1 \qquad and \qquad x \geq 3.$$

Keep the word "and."

Next, we find the intersection of the two separate solution sets.

$\{x \mid x \geq 1\}$
$[1, \infty)$

$\{x \mid x \geq 3\}$
$[3, \infty)$

$\{x \mid x \geq 1\} \cap \{x \mid x \geq 3\}$
$= \{x \mid x \geq 3\}$
$[3, \infty)$

The numbers common to both sets are those greater than or equal to 3. Thus the solution set is $\{x \mid x \geq 3\}$, or, in interval notation, $[3, \infty)$. You should check that any number in $[3, \infty)$ satisfies the conjunction whereas numbers outside $[3, \infty)$ do not.

TRY EXERCISE 67

Sometimes there is no way to solve both parts of a conjunction at once.

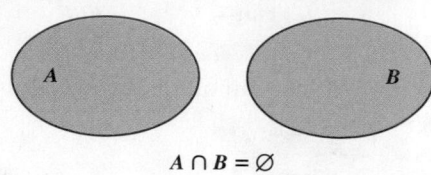

$A \cap B = \emptyset$

When $A \cap B = \emptyset$, A and B are said to be *disjoint*.

EXAMPLE 5

Solve and graph: $2x - 3 > 1$ *and* $3x - 1 < 2$.

SOLUTION   We solve each inequality separately:

$$2x - 3 > 1 \quad and \quad 3x - 1 < 2$$
$$2x > 4 \quad and \quad 3x < 3$$
$$x > 2 \quad and \quad x < 1.$$

The solution set is the intersection of the individual inequalities.

$\{x \mid x > 2\}$ (2, ∞)

$\{x \mid x < 1\}$ (−∞, 1)

$\{x \mid x > 2\} \cap \{x \mid x < 1\}$
$= \{x \mid x > 2 \ and \ x < 1\} = \emptyset$ ∅

Since no number is both greater than 2 and less than 1, the solution set is the empty set, $\emptyset$.

TRY EXERCISE 69

Unions of Sets and Disjunctions of Sentences

The **union** of two sets A and B is the collection of elements belonging to A and/or B. We denote the union of A and B by

$$A \cup B.$$

The union of two sets is often pictured as shown at left. For example, if $A = \{$all students who are taking a math class$\}$ and $B = \{$all students who are taking a history class$\}$, then $A \cup B = \{$all students who are taking a math class *or* a history class$\}$. Note that this set includes students who are taking a math class *and* a history class.

EXAMPLE 6

Find the union: $\{2, 3, 4\} \cup \{3, 5, 7\}$.

SOLUTION   The numbers in either or both sets are 2, 3, 4, 5, and 7, so the union is $\{2, 3, 4, 5, 7\}$.

TRY EXERCISE 13

STUDENT NOTES ———

Remember that the union or the intersection of two sets is itself a set and should be written with set braces.

When two or more sentences are joined by the word *or* to make a compound sentence, the new sentence is called a **disjunction** of the sentences. Here is an example:

$$x < -3 \quad or \quad x > 3.$$

A number is a solution of a disjunction if it is a solution of at least one of the separate parts. For example, -5 is a solution of this disjunction since -5 is a solution of $x < -3$.

> *The solution set of a disjunction is the union of the solution sets of the individual sentences.*

EXAMPLE   7   Graph and write interval notation for the disjunction

$$x < -3 \quad or \quad x > 3.$$

SOLUTION   We first graph $x < -3$, then $x > 3$, and finally the disjunction $x < -3 \, or \, x > 3$.

$\{x \mid x < -3\}$ 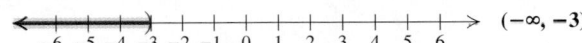 $(-\infty, -3)$

$\{x \mid x > 3\}$ $(3, \infty)$

$\{x \mid x < -3\} \cup \{x \mid x > 3\}$
$= \{x \mid x < -3 \, or \, x > 3\}$ $(-\infty, -3) \cup (3, \infty)$

The solution set of $x < -3 \, or \, x > 3$ is $\{x \mid x < -3 \, or \, x > 3\}$, or, in interval notation, $(-\infty, -3) \cup (3, \infty)$. There is no simpler way to write the solution.

TRY EXERCISE 27

Mathematical Use of the Word "or"

The word "or" corresponds to "union" and to the symbol "$\cup$". For a number to be a solution of a disjunction, it must be in *at least one* of the solution sets of the individual sentences.

EXAMPLE   8   Solve and graph: $7 + 2x < -1 \, or \, 13 - 5x \le 3$.

SOLUTION   We solve each inequality separately, retaining the word *or*:

$$7 + 2x < -1 \quad or \quad 13 - 5x \le 3$$
$$2x < -8 \quad or \quad -5x \le -10$$

Dividing by a negative and reversing the symbol

$$x < -4 \quad or \quad x \ge 2.$$

To find the solution set of the disjunction, we consider the individual graphs. We graph $x < -4$ and then $x \ge 2$. Then we take the union of the graphs.

$\{x \mid x < -4\}$ $(-\infty, -4)$

$\{x \mid x \ge 2\}$ $[2, \infty)$

$\{x \mid x < -4\} \cup \{x \mid x \ge 2\}$
$= \{x \mid x < -4 \, or \, x \ge 2\}$ $(-\infty, -4) \cup [2, \infty)$

The solution set is $\{x \mid x < -4 \, or \, x \ge 2\}$, or $(-\infty, -4) \cup [2, \infty)$.

TRY EXERCISE 63

> **CAUTION!**   A compound inequality like
>
> $$x < -4 \quad or \quad x \ge 2,$$
>
> as in Example 8, *cannot* be expressed as $2 \le x < -4$ because to do so would be to say that x is *simultaneously* less than -4 and greater than or equal to 2. No number is both less than -4 *and* greater than 2, but many are less than -4 *or* greater than 2.

EXAMPLE **9**   Solve: $-2x - 5 < -2 \ or \ x - 3 < -10$.

SOLUTION   We solve the individual inequalities, retaining the word *or*:

$$-2x - 5 < -2 \quad or \quad x - 3 < -10$$
$$-2x < 3 \quad or \quad x < -7$$

Dividing by a negative and reversing the symbol ———————— Keep the word "or."

$$x > -\tfrac{3}{2} \quad or \quad x < -7.$$

The solution set is $\left\{x \mid x < -7 \ or \ x > -\tfrac{3}{2}\right\}$, or $(-\infty, -7) \cup \left(-\tfrac{3}{2}, \infty\right)$.

TRY EXERCISE 65

EXAMPLE **10**   Solve: $3x - 11 < 4 \ or \ 4x + 9 \ge 1$.

SOLUTION   We solve the individual inequalities separately, retaining the word *or*:

$$3x - 11 < 4 \quad or \quad 4x + 9 \ge 1$$
$$3x < 15 \quad or \quad 4x \ge -8$$
$$x < 5 \quad or \quad x \ge -2.$$

Keep the word "or."

To find the solution set, we first look at the individual graphs.

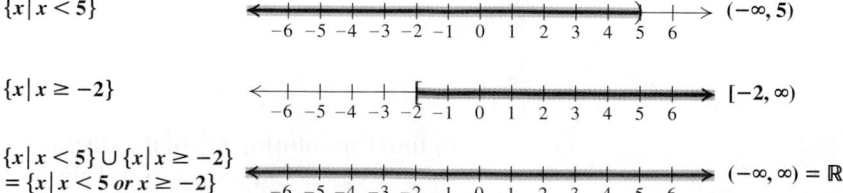

$\{x \mid x < 5\}$ $(-\infty, 5)$

$\{x \mid x \ge -2\}$ $[-2, \infty)$

$\{x \mid x < 5\} \cup \{x \mid x \ge -2\}$
$= \{x \mid x < 5 \ or \ x \ge -2\}$ $(-\infty, \infty) = \mathbb{R}$

Since *all* numbers are less than 5 or greater than or equal to -2, the two sets fill the entire number line. Thus the solution set is $\mathbb{R}$, the set of all real numbers.

TRY EXERCISE 51

Interval Notation and Domains

In Section 7.2, we saw that if $g(x) = \dfrac{5x - 2}{x - 3}$, then the number 3 is not in the domain of g. We can represent the domain of g using set-builder notation or interval notation.

EXAMPLE 11 Use interval notation to write the domain of g if $g(x) = \dfrac{5x-2}{x-3}$.

SOLUTION The expression $\dfrac{5x-2}{x-3}$ is not defined when the denominator is 0. We set $x - 3$ equal to 0 and solve:

$$x - 3 = 0$$
$$x = 3. \qquad \text{The number 3 is } not \text{ in the domain.}$$

We have the domain of $g = \{x \mid x \text{ is a real number } and \ x \neq 3\}$. If we graph this set, we see that the domain can be written as a union of two intervals.

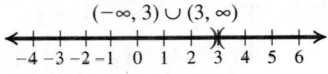

$$(-\infty, 3) \cup (3, \infty)$$

Thus the domain of $g = (-\infty, 3) \cup (3, \infty)$.

TRY EXERCISE 73

9.2 EXERCISE SET

For Extra Help MyMathLab MathXL PRACTICE WATCH DOWNLOAD

🖐 **Concept Reinforcement** *In each of Exercises 1–10, match the set with the most appropriate choice from the column on the right.*

1. ____ $\{x \mid x < -2 \text{ or } x > 2\}$

2. ____ $\{x \mid x < -2 \text{ and } x > 2\}$

3. ____ $\{x \mid x > -2\} \cap \{x \mid x < 2\}$

4. ____ $\{x \mid x \leq -2\} \cup \{x \mid x \geq 2\}$

5. ____ $\{x \mid x \leq -2\} \cup \{x \mid x \leq 2\}$

6. ____ $\{x \mid x \leq -2\} \cap \{x \mid x \leq 2\}$

7. ____ $\{x \mid x \geq -2\} \cap \{x \mid x \geq 2\}$

8. ____ $\{x \mid x \geq -2\} \cup \{x \mid x \geq 2\}$

9. ____ $\{x \mid x \leq 2\} \text{ and } \{x \mid x \geq -2\}$

10. ____ $\{x \mid x \leq 2\} \text{ or } \{x \mid x \geq -2\}$

a)

b)

c)

d)

e)

f)

g)

h)

i) $\mathbb{R}$

j) $\varnothing$

Find each indicated intersection or union.

11. $\{2, 4, 16\} \cap \{4, 16, 256\}$

12. $\{1, 2, 4\} \cup \{4, 6, 8\}$

13. $\{0, 5, 10, 15\} \cup \{5, 15, 20\}$

14. $\{2, 5, 9, 13\} \cap \{5, 8, 10\}$

15. $\{a, b, c, d, e, f\} \cap \{b, d, f\}$

16. $\{u, v, w\} \cup \{u, w\}$

17. $\{x, y, z\} \cup \{u, v, x, y, z\}$

18. $\{m, n, o, p\} \cap \{m, o, p\}$

19. $\{3, 6, 9, 12\} \cap \{5, 10, 15\}$

20. $\{1, 5, 9\} \cup \{4, 6, 8\}$

21. $\{1, 3, 5\} \cup \varnothing$

22. $\{1, 3, 5\} \cap \varnothing$

Graph and write interval notation for each compound inequality.

23. $1 < x < 3$

24. $0 \le y \le 5$

25. $-6 \le y \le 0$

26. $-8 < x \le -2$

27. $x \le -1 \, or \, x > 4$

28. $x < -5 \, or \, x > 1$

29. $x \le -2 \, or \, x > 1$

30. $x \le -5 \, or \, x > 2$

31. $-4 \le -x < 2$

32. $x > -7 \, and \, x < -2$

33. $x > -2 \, and \, x < 4$

34. $3 > -x \ge -1$

35. $5 > a \, or \, a > 7$

36. $t \ge 2 \, or \, -3 > t$

37. $x \ge 5 \, or \, -x \ge 4$

38. $-x < 3 \, or \, x < -6$

39. $7 > y \, and \, y \ge -3$

40. $6 > -x \ge 0$

41. $-x < 7 \, and \, -x \ge 0$

42. $x \ge -3 \, and \, x < 3$

Aha! **43.** $t < 2 \, or \, t < 5$

44. $t > 4 \, or \, t > -1$

Solve and graph each solution set.

45. $-3 \le x + 2 < 9$

46. $-1 < x - 3 < 5$

47. $0 < t - 4 \, and \, t - 1 \le 7$

48. $-6 \le t + 1 \, and \, t + 8 < 2$

49. $-7 \le 2a - 3 \, and \, 3a + 1 < 7$

50. $-4 \le 3n + 5 \, and \, 2n - 3 \le 7$

Aha! **51.** $x + 3 \le -1 \, or \, x + 3 > -2$

52. $x + 5 < -3 \, or \, x + 5 \ge 4$

53. $-10 \le 3x - 1 \le 5$

54. $-18 \le 4x + 2 \le 30$

55. $5 > \dfrac{x - 3}{4} > 1$

56. $3 \ge \dfrac{x - 1}{2} \ge -4$

57. $-2 \le \dfrac{x + 2}{-5} \le 6$

58. $-10 \le \dfrac{x + 6}{-3} \le -8$

59. $2 \le f(x) \le 8$, where $f(x) = 3x - 1$

60. $7 \ge g(x) \ge -2$, where $g(x) = 3x - 5$

61. $-21 \le f(x) < 0$, where $f(x) = -2x - 7$

62. $4 > g(t) \ge 2$, where $g(t) = -3t - 8$

63. $f(t) < 3 \, or \, f(t) > 8$, where $f(t) = 5t + 3$

64. $g(x) \le -2 \, or \, g(x) \ge 10$, where $g(x) = 3x - 5$

65. $6 > 2a - 1 \, or \, -4 \le -3a + 2$

66. $3a - 7 > -10 \, or \, 5a + 2 \le 22$

67. $a + 3 < -2 \, and \, 3a - 4 < 8$

68. $1 - a < -2 \, and \, 2a + 1 > 9$

69. $3x + 2 < 2 \, and \, 3 - x < 1$

70. $2x - 1 > 5 \, and \, 2 - 3x > 11$

71. $2t - 7 \le 5 \, or \, 5 - 2t > 3$

72. $5 - 3a \le 8 \, or \, 2a + 1 > 7$

For $f(x)$ as given, use interval notation to write the domain of f.

73. $f(x) = \dfrac{9}{x + 6}$

74. $f(x) = \dfrac{2}{x - 5}$

75. $f(x) = \dfrac{1}{x}$

76. $f(x) = -\dfrac{6}{x}$

77. $f(x) = \dfrac{x + 3}{2x - 8}$

78. $f(x) = \dfrac{x - 1}{3x + 6}$

79. Why can the conjunction $2 < x \, and \, x < 5$ be rewritten as $2 < x < 5$, but the disjunction $2 < x \, or \, x < 5$ cannot be rewritten as $2 < x < 5$?

80. Can the solution set of a disjunction be empty? Why or why not?

Skill Review

To prepare for Section 9.3, review graphing and solving equations by graphing (Sections 7.3 and 8.1).

Graph. [7.3]

81. $g(x) = 2x$

82. $f(x) = 4$

83. $g(x) = -3$

84. $f(x) = |x|$

Solve by graphing. [8.1]

85. $x + 4 = 3$

86. $x - 1 = -5$

Synthesis

87. What can you conclude about a, b, c, and d, if $[a, b] \cup [c, d] = [a, d]$? Why?

88. What can you conclude about a, b, c, and d, if $[a, b] \cap [c, d] = [a, b]$? Why?

89. Use the accompanying graph of $f(x) = 2x - 5$ to solve $-7 < 2x - 5 < 7$.

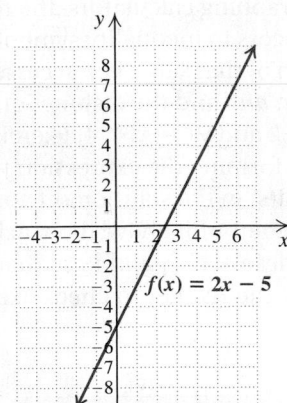

90. Use the accompanying graph of $g(x) = 4 - x$ to solve $4 - x < -2$ *or* $4 - x > 7$.

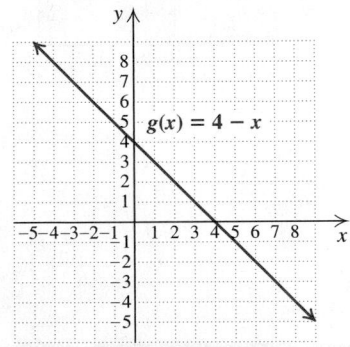

91. *Counseling.* The function given by

$$s(t) = 500t + 16,500$$

can be used to estimate the number of student visits to Cornell University's counseling center t years after 2000. For what years is the number of student visits between 18,000 and 21,000?
Source: Based on data from Cornell University

92. *Pressure at sea depth.* The function given by

$$P(d) = 1 + \frac{d}{33}$$

gives the pressure, in atmospheres (atm), at a depth of d feet in the sea. For what depths d is the pressure at least 1 atm and at most 7 atm?

93. *Converting dress sizes.* The function given by

$$f(x) = 2(x + 10)$$

can be used to convert dress sizes x in the United States to dress sizes $f(x)$ in Italy. For what dress sizes in the United States will dress sizes in Italy be between 32 and 46?

94. *Solid-waste generation.* The function given by

$$w(t) = 0.0125t + 4.525$$

can be used to estimate the number of pounds of solid waste, $w(t)$, produced daily, on average, by each person in the United States, t years after 2000. For what years will waste production range from 4.6 to 4.8 lb per person per day?

95. *Body fat percentage.* The function given by

$$F(d) = (4.95/d - 4.50) \times 100$$

can be used to estimate the body fat percentage $F(d)$ of a person with an average body density d, in kilograms per liter. A woman's body fat percentage is considered acceptable if $25 \le F(d) \le 31$. What body densities are considered acceptable for a woman?

96. *Temperatures of liquids.* The formula

$$C = \tfrac{5}{9}(F - 32)$$

can be used to convert Fahrenheit temperatures F to Celsius temperatures C.

a) Gold is liquid for Celsius temperatures C such that $1063° \le C < 2660°$. Find a comparable inequality for Fahrenheit temperatures.

b) Silver is liquid for Celsius temperatures C such that $960.8° \le C < 2180°$. Find a comparable inequality for Fahrenheit temperatures.

97. *Minimizing tolls.* A $6.00 toll is charged to cross the bridge to Sanibel Island from mainland Florida. A six-month reduced-fare pass costs $50 and reduces the toll to $2.00. A six-month unlimited-trip pass costs $300 and allows for free crossings. How many crossings in six months does it take for the reduced-fare pass to be the more economical choice?
Source: www.leewayinfo.com

Solve and graph.

98. $4a - 2 \le a + 1 \le 3a + 4$

99. $4m - 8 > 6m + 5$ *or* $5m - 8 < -2$

100. $x - 10 < 5x + 6 \le x + 10$

101. $3x < 4 - 5x < 5 + 3x$

Determine whether each sentence is true or false for all real numbers a, b, and c.

102. If $-b < -a$, then $a < b$.

103. If $a \le c$ and $c \le b$, then $b > a$.

104. If $a < c$ and $b < c$, then $a < b$.

105. If $-a < c$ and $-c > b$, then $a > b$.

For f(x) as given, use interval notation to write the domain of f.

106. $f(x) = \dfrac{\sqrt{5 + 2x}}{x - 1}$ **107.** $f(x) = \dfrac{\sqrt{3 - 4x}}{x + 7}$

108. For $f(x) = \sqrt{x - 5}$ and $g(x) = \sqrt{9 - x}$, use interval notation to write the domain of $f + g$.

109. Let $y_1 = -1$, $y_2 = 2x + 5$, and $y_3 = 13$. Then use the graphs of y_1, y_2, and y_3 to check the solution to Example 3.

110. Let $y_1 = -2x - 5$, $y_2 = -2$, $y_3 = x - 3$, and $y_4 = -10$. Then use the graphs of y_1, y_2, y_3, and y_4 to check the solution to Example 9.

111. Use a graphing calculator to check your answers to Exercises 45–48 and Exercises 63–66.

112. On many graphing calculators, the TEST key provides access to inequality symbols, while the LOGIC option of that same key accesses the conjunction *and* and the disjunction *or*. Thus, if $y_1 = x > -2$ and $y_2 = x < 4$, Exercise 33 can be checked by forming the expression $y_3 = y_1$ *and* y_2. The interval(s) in the solution set appears as a horizontal line 1 unit above the *x*-axis. (Be careful to "deselect" y_1 and y_2 so that only y_3 is drawn.) Use the TEST key to check Exercises 35, 39, 41, and 43.

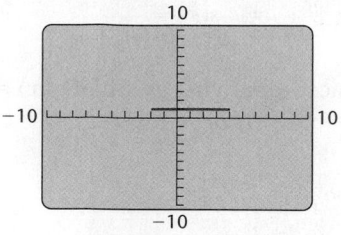

COLLABORATIVE CORNER

Reduce, Reuse, and Recycle

Focus: Compound inequalities

Time: 15–20 minutes

Group size: 2

In the United States, the amount of solid waste (rubbish) being recovered is slowly catching up to the amount being generated. In 2002, each person generated, on average, 4.55 lb of solid waste every day, of which 1.34 lb was recovered. In 2006, each person generated, on average, 4.60 lb of solid waste, of which 1.50 lb was recovered.

Source: U.S. Environmental Protection Agency

ACTIVITY

Assume that the amount of solid waste being generated and the amount being recovered are both increasing linearly. One group member should find a linear function w for which $w(t)$ represents the number of pounds of waste generated per person per day t years after 2000. The other group member should find a linear function r for which $r(t)$ represents the number of pounds recovered per person per day t years after 2000. Finally, working together, the group should determine those years for which the amount recovered will be more than $\frac{1}{3}$ of but less than $\frac{1}{2}$ of the amount generated.

9.3

Absolute-Value Equations and Inequalities

Equations with Absolute Value ■ Inequalities with Absolute Value

Equations with Absolute Value

Recall from Section 1.4 the definition of absolute value.

> ### Absolute Value
>
> The absolute value of x, denoted $|x|$, is defined as
>
> $$|x| = \begin{cases} x, & \text{if } x \geq 0, \\ -x, & \text{if } x < 0. \end{cases}$$
>
> (When x is nonnegative, the absolute value of x is x. When x is negative, the absolute value of x is the opposite of x.)

To better understand this definition, suppose x is -5. Then $|x| = |-5| = 5$, and 5 is the opposite of -5. This shows that when x represents a negative number, the absolute value of x is the opposite of x (which is positive).

Since distance is always nonnegative, we can think of a number's absolute value as its distance from zero on the number line.

EXAMPLE 1   Find the solution set: **(a)** $|x| = 4$; **(b)** $|x| = 0$; **(c)** $|x| = -7$.

SOLUTION

a) We interpret $|x| = 4$ to mean that the number x is 4 units from zero on the number line. There are two such numbers, 4 and -4. Thus the solution set is $\{-4, 4\}$.

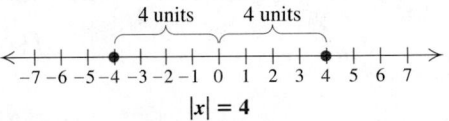

b) We interpret $|x| = 0$ to mean that x is 0 units from zero on the number line. The only number that satisfies this is 0 itself. Thus the solution set is $\{0\}$.

c) Since distance is always nonnegative, it doesn't make sense to talk about a number that is -7 units from zero. Remember: The absolute value of a number is nonnegative. Thus, $|x| = -7$ has no solution; the solution set is $\varnothing$.

TRY EXERCISE 15

Example 1 leads us to the following principle for solving equations.

> ### The Absolute-Value Principle for Equations
>
> For any positive number p and any algebraic expression X:
>
> **a)** The solutions of $|X| = p$ are those numbers that satisfy
>
> $$X = -p \quad \text{or} \quad X = p.$$
>
> **b)** The equation $|X| = 0$ is equivalent to the equation $X = 0$.
> **c)** The equation $|X| = -p$ has no solution.

EXAMPLE **2**   Find the solution set: **(a)** $|2x + 5| = 13$; **(b)** $|4 - 7x| = -8$.

SOLUTION

a) We use the absolute-value principle, knowing that $2x + 5$ must be either 13 or -13:

$$|X| = p$$
$$|2x + 5| = 13 \quad \text{Substituting}$$
$$2x + 5 = -13 \quad or \quad 2x + 5 = 13$$
$$2x = -18 \quad or \quad 2x = 8$$
$$x = -9 \quad or \quad x = 4.$$

Check: For -9:

$$\begin{array}{c|c} |2x + 5| = 13 & 13 \\ \hline |2(-9) + 5| & 13 \\ |-18 + 5| & \\ |-13| & \\ 13 \overset{?}{=} 13 & \text{TRUE} \end{array}$$

For 4:

$$\begin{array}{c|c} |2x + 5| = 13 & 13 \\ \hline |2 \cdot 4 + 5| & 13 \\ |8 + 5| & \\ |13| & \\ 13 \overset{?}{=} 13 & \text{TRUE} \end{array}$$

The number $2x + 5$ is 13 units from zero if x is replaced with -9 or 4. The solution set is $\{-9, 4\}$.

b) The absolute-value principle reminds us that absolute value is always nonnegative. The equation $|4 - 7x| = -8$ has no solution. The solution set is $\varnothing$.

TRY EXERCISE 21

To use the absolute-value principle, we must be sure that the absolute-value expression is alone on one side of the equation.

EXAMPLE **3**   Given that $f(x) = 2|x + 3| + 1$, find all x for which $f(x) = 15$.

SOLUTION   Since we are looking for $f(x) = 15$, we substitute:

$$f(x) = 15$$
$$2|x + 3| + 1 = 15 \quad \text{Replacing } f(x) \text{ with } 2|x + 3| + 1$$
$$2|x + 3| = 14 \quad \text{Subtracting 1 from both sides}$$
$$|x + 3| = 7 \quad \text{Dividing both sides by 2}$$
$$x + 3 = -7 \quad or \quad x + 3 = 7 \quad \begin{array}{l}\text{Using the absolute-value principle} \\ \text{for equations}\end{array}$$
$$x = -10 \quad or \quad x = 4.$$

The student should check that $f(-10) = f(4) = 15$. The solution set is $\{-10, 4\}$.

TRY EXERCISE 43

EXAMPLE **4**   Solve: $|x - 2| = 3$.

SOLUTION   Because this equation is of the form $|a - b| = c$, it can be solved in two different ways.

Method 1.   We interpret $|x - 2| = 3$ as stating that the number $x - 2$ is 3 units from zero. Using the absolute-value principle, we replace X with $x - 2$ and p with 3:

$$|X| = p$$
$$|x - 2| = 3$$
$$x - 2 = -3 \quad or \quad x - 2 = 3 \qquad \text{Using the absolute-value principle}$$
$$x = -1 \quad or \qquad x = 5.$$

> **CAUTION!**   There are two solutions of $|x - 2| = 3$. Simply solving $x - 2 = 3$ will yield only one of those solutions.

Method 2.   This approach is helpful in calculus. The expressions $|a - b|$ and $|b - a|$ can be used to represent the *distance between a and b* on the number line. For example, the distance between 7 and 8 is given by $|8 - 7|$ or $|7 - 8|$. From this viewpoint, the equation $|x - 2| = 3$ states that the distance between x and 2 is 3 units. We draw a number line and locate all numbers that are 3 units from 2.

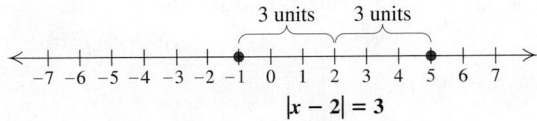

$$|x - 2| = 3$$

The solutions of $|x - 2| = 3$ are -1 and 5.

Check: The check consists of observing that both methods give the same solutions. The solution set is $\{-1, 5\}$.

▶ **TRY EXERCISE** 25

Sometimes an equation has two absolute-value expressions. Consider $|a| = |b|$. This means that a and b are the same distance from zero.

If a and b are the same distance from zero, then either they are the same number or they are opposites.

EXAMPLE 5   Solve: $|2x - 3| = |x + 5|$.

SOLUTION   The given equation tells us that $2x - 3$ and $x + 5$ are the same distance from zero. This means that they are either the same number or opposites:

This assumes the two numbers are the same.   This assumes the two numbers are opposites.

$$2x - 3 = x + 5 \quad or \quad 2x - 3 = -(x + 5)$$
$$x - 3 = 5 \quad or \quad 2x - 3 = -x - 5$$
$$x = 8 \quad or \quad 3x - 3 = -5$$
$$3x = -2$$
$$x = -\tfrac{2}{3}.$$

The check is left to the student. The solutions are 8 and $-\tfrac{2}{3}$ and the solution set is $\left\{-\tfrac{2}{3}, 8\right\}$.

▶ **TRY EXERCISE** 47

Inequalities with Absolute Value

Our methods for solving equations with absolute value can be adapted for solving inequalities. Inequalities of this sort arise regularly in more advanced courses.

EXAMPLE 6   Solve $|x| < 4$. Then graph.

SOLUTION   The solutions of $|x| < 4$ are all numbers whose *distance from zero is less than* 4. By substituting or by looking at the number line, we can see that numbers like $-3, -2, -1, -\frac{1}{2}, -\frac{1}{4}, 0, \frac{1}{4}, \frac{1}{2}, 1, 2$, and 3 are all solutions. In fact, the solutions are all the numbers between -4 and 4. The solution set is $\{x \mid -4 < x < 4\}$, or, in interval notation, $(-4, 4)$. The graph is as follows:

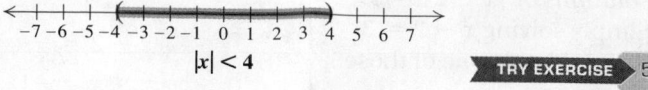

$$|x| < 4$$

TRY EXERCISE 57

EXAMPLE 7   Solve $|x| \geq 4$. Then graph.

SOLUTION   The solutions of $|x| \geq 4$ are all numbers that are at least 4 units from zero—in other words, those numbers x for which $x \leq -4$ *or* $4 \leq x$. The solution set is $\{x \mid x \leq -4 \text{ or } x \geq 4\}$. In interval notation, the solution set is $(-\infty, -4] \cup [4, \infty)$. We can check mentally with numbers like $-4.1, -5, 4.1$, and 5. The graph is as follows:

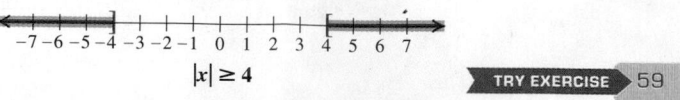

$$|x| \geq 4$$

TRY EXERCISE 59

Examples 1, 6, and 7 illustrate three types of problems in which absolute-value symbols appear. The general principle for solving such problems follows.

Principles for Solving Absolute-Value Problems

For any positive number p and any expression X:

a) The solutions of $|X| = p$ are those numbers that satisfy

$$X = -p \quad \text{or} \quad X = p.$$

b) The solutions of $|X| < p$ are those numbers that satisfy

$$-p < X < p.$$

c) The solutions of $|X| > p$ are those numbers that satisfy

$$X < -p \quad \text{or} \quad p < X.$$

The above principles are true for any positive number p.

If p is negative, any value of X will satisfy the inequality $|X| > p$ because absolute value is never negative. Thus, $|2x - 7| > -3$ is true for any real number x, and the solution set is $\mathbb{R}$.

If p is not positive, the inequality $|X| < p$ has no solution. Thus, $|2x - 7| < -3$ has no solution, and the solution set is $\varnothing$.

EXAMPLE **8**   Solve $|3x - 2| < 4$. Then graph.

SOLUTION   The number $3x - 2$ must be less than 4 units from zero. This is of the form $|X| < p$, so part (b) of the principles listed above applies:

$\lvert X \rvert < p$	This corresponds to $-p < X < p$.
$\lvert 3x - 2 \rvert < 4$	Replacing X with $3x - 2$ and p with 4
$-4 < 3x - 2 < 4$	The number $3x - 2$ must be within 4 units of zero.
$-2 < \quad 3x \quad < 6$	Adding 2
$-\frac{2}{3} < \quad x \quad < 2.$	Multiplying by $\frac{1}{3}$

The solution set is $\left\{ x \mid -\frac{2}{3} < x < 2 \right\}$. In interval notation, the solution is $\left(-\frac{2}{3}, 2 \right)$. The graph is as follows:

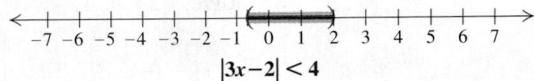

$|3x-2| < 4$

TRY EXERCISE   61

EXAMPLE **9**   Given that $f(x) = |4x + 2|$, find all x for which $f(x) \geq 6$.

SOLUTION   We have

$$f(x) \geq 6,$$

or $|4x + 2| \geq 6.$ Substituting

To solve, we use part (c) of the principles listed above. In this case, X is $4x + 2$ and p is 6:

$\lvert X \rvert \geq p$	This corresponds to $X < -p$ or $p < X$.
$\lvert 4x + 2 \rvert \geq 6$	Replacing X with $4x + 2$ and p with 6
$4x + 2 \leq -6 \quad or \quad 6 \leq 4x + 2$	The number $4x + 2$ must be at least 6 units from zero.
$4x \leq -8 \quad or \quad 4 \leq 4x$	Adding -2
$x \leq -2 \quad or \quad 1 \leq x.$	Multiplying by $\frac{1}{4}$

The solution set is $\{ x \mid x \leq -2 \ or \ x \geq 1 \}$. In interval notation, the solution is $(-\infty, -2] \cup [1, \infty)$. The graph is as follows:

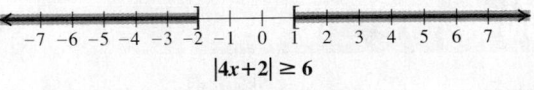

$|4x+2| \geq 6$

TRY EXERCISE   87

ALGEBRAIC–GRAPHICAL CONNECTION

We can visualize Examples 1(a), 6, and 7 by graphing $f(x) = |x|$ and $g(x) = 4$.

Solve: $|x| = 4$.

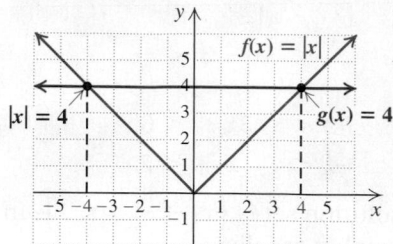

The graphs intersect at $(-4, 4)$ and $(4, 4)$.

$|x| = 4$ when $x = -4$ or $x = 4$.

The solution set of $|x| = 4$ is $\{-4, 4\}$.

Solve: $|x| < 4$.

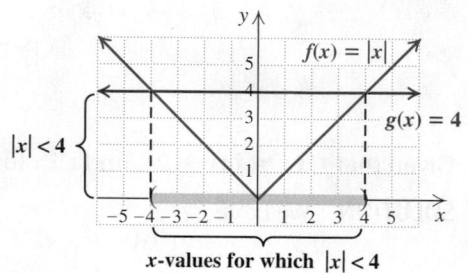

The graphs intersect at $(-4, 4)$ and $(4, 4)$.

$|x| < 4$ when $-4 < x < 4$.

The solution set of $|x| < 4$ is $(-4, 4)$.

Solve: $|x| \geq 4$.

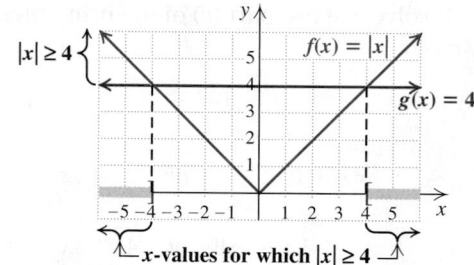

The graphs intersect at $(-4, 4)$ and $(4, 4)$.

$|x| \geq 4$ when $x \leq -4$ or $x \geq 4$.

The solution set of $|x| \geq 4$ is $(-\infty, -4] \cup [4, \infty)$.

TECHNOLOGY CONNECTION

To enter an absolute-value function on a graphing calculator, we press **MATH** and use the abs(option in the NUM menu. To solve $|4x + 2| = 6$, we graph $y_1 = \text{abs}(4x + 2)$ and $y_2 = 6$.

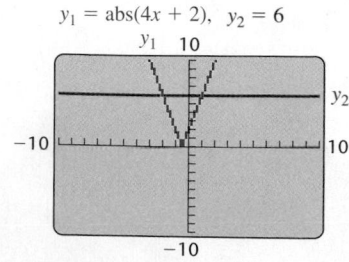

$y_1 = \text{abs}(4x + 2), \ y_2 = 6$

Using the INTERSECT option of the CALC menu, we find that the graphs intersect at $(-2, 6)$ and $(1, 6)$. The x-coordinates -2 and 1 are the solutions. To solve $|4x + 2| \geq 6$, note where the graph of y_1 is *on or above* the line $y = 6$. The corresponding x-values are the solutions of the inequality.

1. How can the same graph be used to solve $|4x + 2| < 6$?
2. Solve Example 8.
3. Use a graphing calculator to show that $|4x + 2| = -6$ has no solution.

9.3 EXERCISE SET

For Extra Help
MyMathLab
PRACTICE WATCH DOWNLOAD

Concept Reinforcement *Classify each statement as either true or false.*

1. $|x|$ is never negative.

2. $|x|$ is always positive.

3. If x is negative, then $|x| = -x$.

4. The number a is $|a|$ units from 0.

5. The distance between a and b can be expressed as $|a - b|$.

6. There are two solutions of $|3x - 8| = 17$.

7. There is no solution of $|4x + 9| > -5$.

8. All real numbers are solutions of $|2x - 7| < -3$.

Match each equation or inequality with an equivalent statement from the column on the right. Letters may be used more than once or not at all.

9. $|x - 3| = 5$ a) The solution set is $\varnothing$.

10. $|x - 3| < 5$ b) The solution set is $\mathbb{R}$.

11. $|x - 3| > 5$ c) $x - 3 > 5$

12. $|x - 3| < -5$ d) $x - 3 < -5 \ or \ x - 3 > 5$

13. $|x - 3| = -5$ e) $x - 3 = 5$

14. $|x - 3| > -5$ f) $x - 3 < 5$

         g) $x - 3 = -5 \ or \ x - 3 = 5$

         h) $-5 < x - 3 < 5$

Solve.

15. $|x| = 10$ 16. $|x| = 5$

Aha! 17. $|x| = -1$ 18. $|x| = -8$

19. $|p| = 0$ 20. $|y| = 7.3$

21. $|2x - 3| = 4$ 22. $|5x + 2| = 7$

23. $|3x + 5| = -8$ 24. $|7x - 2| = -9$

25. $|x - 2| = 6$ 26. $|x - 3| = 11$

27. $|x - 7| = 1$ 28. $|x - 4| = 5$

29. $|t| + 1.1 = 6.6$ 30. $|m| + 3 = 3$

31. $|5x| - 3 = 37$ 32. $|2y| - 5 = 13$

33. $7|q| + 2 = 9$ 34. $5|z| + 2 = 17$

35. $\left|\dfrac{2x - 1}{3}\right| = 4$ 36. $\left|\dfrac{4 - 5x}{6}\right| = 3$

37. $|5 - m| + 9 = 16$ 38. $|t - 7| + 1 = 4$

39. $5 - 2|3x - 4| = -5$

40. $3|2x - 5| - 7 = -1$

41. Let $f(x) = |2x + 6|$. Find all x for which $f(x) = 8$.

42. Let $f(x) = |2x - 4|$. Find all x for which $f(x) = 10$.

43. Let $f(x) = |x| - 3$. Find all x for which $f(x) = 5.7$.

44. Let $f(x) = |x| + 7$. Find all x for which $f(x) = 18$.

45. Let $f(x) = \left|\dfrac{1 - 2x}{5}\right|$. Find all x for which $f(x) = 2$.

46. Let $f(x) = \left|\dfrac{3x + 4}{3}\right|$. Find all x for which $f(x) = 1$.

Solve.

47. $|x - 7| = |2x + 1|$

48. $|3x + 2| = |x - 6|$

49. $|x + 4| = |x - 3|$

50. $|x - 9| = |x + 6|$

51. $|3a - 1| = |2a + 4|$

52. $|5t + 7| = |4t + 3|$

Aha! 53. $|n - 3| = |3 - n|$

54. $|y - 2| = |2 - y|$

55. $|7 - 4a| = |4a + 5|$

56. $|6 - 5t| = |5t + 8|$

Solve and graph.

57. $|a| \le 3$ 58. $|x| < 5$

59. $|t| > 0$ 60. $|t| \ge 1$

61. $|x - 1| < 4$ 62. $|x - 1| < 3$

63. $|n + 2| \le 6$ 64. $|a + 4| \le 0$

65. $|x - 3| + 2 > 7$ 66. $|x - 4| + 5 > 10$

Aha! 67. $|2y - 9| > -5$ 68. $|3y - 4| > -8$

69. $|3a + 4| + 2 \ge 8$ 70. $|2a + 5| + 1 \ge 9$

71. $|y - 3| < 12$ 72. $|p - 2| < 3$

73. $9 - |x + 4| \leq 5$

74. $12 - |x - 5| \leq 9$

75. $6 + |3 - 2x| > 10$

76. $|7 - 2y| < -8$

Aha! **77.** $|5 - 4x| < -6$

78. $7 + |4a - 5| \leq 26$

79. $\left| \dfrac{1 + 3x}{5} \right| > \dfrac{7}{8}$

80. $\left| \dfrac{2 - 5x}{4} \right| \geq \dfrac{2}{3}$

81. $|m + 3| + 8 \leq 14$

82. $|t - 7| + 3 \geq 4$

83. $25 - 2|a + 3| > 19$

84. $30 - 4|a + 2| > 12$

85. Let $f(x) = |2x - 3|$. Find all x for which $f(x) \leq 4$.

86. Let $f(x) = |5x + 2|$. Find all x for which $f(x) \leq 3$.

87. Let $f(x) = 5 + |3x - 4|$. Find all x for which $f(x) \geq 16$.

88. Let $f(x) = |2 - 9x|$. Find all x for which $f(x) \geq 25$.

89. Let $f(x) = 7 + |2x - 1|$. Find all x for which $f(x) < 16$.

90. Let $f(x) = 5 + |3x + 2|$. Find all x for which $f(x) < 19$.

91. Explain in your own words why -7 is not a solution of $|x| < 5$.

92. Explain in your own words why $[6, \infty)$ is only part of the solution of $|x| \geq 6$.

Skill Review

To prepare for Section 9.4, review graphing equations and solving systems of equations (Sections 3.3, 3.6, and 8.2).

Graph.

93. $3x - y = 6$ [3.3]

94. $y = \frac{1}{2}x - 1$ [3.6]

95. $x = -2$ [3.3]

96. $y = 4$ [3.3]

Solve using substitution or elimination. [8.2]

97. $x - 3y = 8,$
$2x + 3y = 4$

98. $x - 2y = 3,$
$x = y + 4$

99. $y = 1 - 5x,$
$2x - y = 4$

100. $3x - 2y = 4,$
$5x - 3y = 5$

Synthesis

101. Describe a procedure that could be used to solve any equation of the form $g(x) < c$ graphically.

102. Explain why the inequality $|x + 5| \geq 2$ can be interpreted as "the number x is at least 2 units from -5."

103. From the definition of absolute value, $|x| = x$ only when $x \geq 0$. Solve $|3t - 5| = 3t - 5$ using this same reasoning.

Solve.

104. $|3x - 5| = x$

105. $|x + 2| > x$

106. $2 \leq |x - 1| \leq 5$

107. $|5t - 3| = 2t + 4$

108. $t - 2 \leq |t - 3|$

Find an equivalent inequality with absolute value.

109. $-3 < x < 3$

110. $-5 \leq y \leq 5$

111. $x \leq -6 \ or \ 6 \leq x$

112. $x < -4 \ or \ 4 < x$

113. $x < -8 \ or \ 2 < x$

114. $-5 < x < 1$

115. x is less than 2 units from 7.

116. x is less than 1 unit from 5.

Write an absolute-value inequality for which the interval shown is the solution.

117.
```
<-+-+-+-+-+-+-+=========+->
 -7-6-5-4-3-2-1 0 1 2 3 4 5 6 7
```

118.
```
<-+=========+-+-+-+-+-+-+-+->
 -5-4-3-2-1 0 1 2 3 4 5 6 7 8 9
```

119.
```
<-=========+-+-+-+-+-+-+-+->
 -7-6-5-4-3-2-1 0 1 2 3 4 5 6 7
```

120.
```
<-+-+=========+-+-+->
 0 1 2 3 4 5 6 7 8 9 10 11 12 13 14
```

121. *Bungee jumping.*   A bungee jumper is bouncing up and down so that her distance d above a river satisfies the inequality $|d - 60 \text{ ft}| \leq 10 \text{ ft}$ (see the figure below). If the bridge from which she jumped is 150 ft above the river, how far is the bungee jumper from the bridge at any given time?

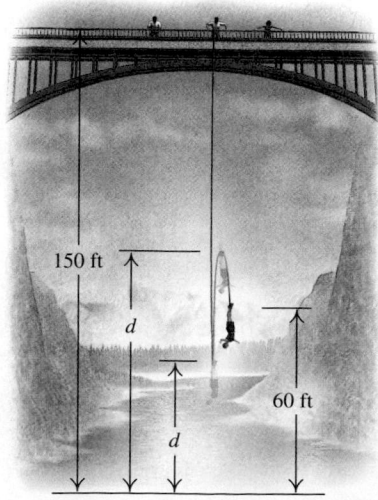

122. *Water level.* Depending on how dry or wet the weather has been, water in a well will rise and fall. The distance d, in feet, that a well's water level is below the ground satisfies the inequality $|d - 15| \leq 2.5$ (see the figure below).

a) Solve for d.

b) How tall a column of water is in the well at any given time?

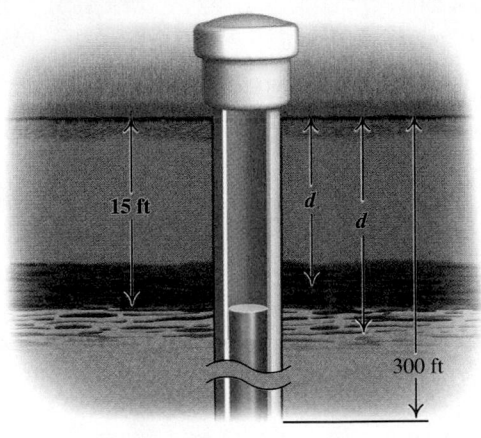

15 ft

d

d

300 ft

123. Use this graph of
$$f(x) = |2x - 6|$$
to solve
$$|2x - 6| \leq 4.$$

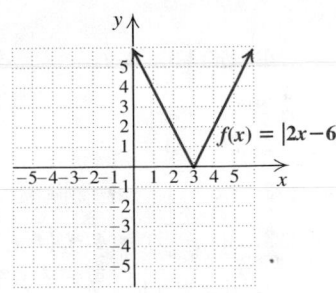

$f(x) = |2x - 6|$

124. Is it possible for an equation in x of the form $|ax + b| = c$ to have exactly one solution? Why or why not?

125. Isabel is using the following graph to solve $|x - 3| < 4$. How can you tell that a mistake has been made in entering $y = \text{abs}(x - 3)$?

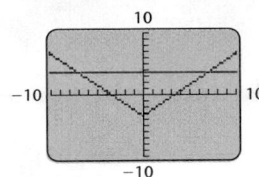

CONNECTING the CONCEPTS

In Chapters 1 and 4, we have learned to solve a variety of equations and inequalities. As we continue our study of algebra, we will learn to solve additional types of equations and inequalities, some of which will require new principles for solving. Following is a list of the principles we have used so far to solve equations and inequalities. Unless otherwise stated, a, b, and c can represent any real number.

The Addition and Multiplication Principles for Equations

$a = b$ is equivalent to $a + c = b + c$.

$a = b$ is equivalent to $ac = bc$, provided $c \neq 0$.

The Addition Principle for Inequalities

$a < b$ is equivalent to $a + c < b + c$.

$a > b$ is equivalent to $a + c > b + c$.

The Multiplication Principle for Inequalities

For any *positive* number c,

$a < b$ is equivalent to $ac < bc$;

$a > b$ is equivalent to $ac > bc$.

For any *negative* number c,

$a < b$ is equivalent to $ac > bc$;

$a > b$ is equivalent to $ac < bc$.

The Absolute-Value Principles for Equations and Inequalities

For any positive number p and any algebraic expression X:

The solutions of $|X| = p$ are those numbers that satisfy

$$X = -p \text{ or } X = p.$$

The solutions of $|X| < p$ are those numbers that satisfy

$$-p < X < p.$$

The solutions of $|X| > p$ are those numbers that satisfy

$$X < -p \text{ or } p < X.$$

MIXED REVIEW

Solve.

1. $2x + 3 = 7$

2. $3x - 1 > 8$

3. $3(t - 5) = 4 - (t + 1)$

4. $|2x + 1| = 7$

5. $-x \leq 6$

6. $5|t| < 20$

7. $2(3n + 6) - n = 4 - 3(n + 1)$

8. $3(2a + 9) = 5(3a - 7) - 6a$

9. $2 + |3x| = 10$

10. $|x - 3| \leq 10$

11. $\frac{1}{2}x - 7 = \frac{3}{4} + \frac{1}{4}x$

12. $|t| < 0$

13. $|2x + 5| + 1 \geq 13$

14. $2(x - 3) - x = 5x + 7 - 4x$

15. $|m + 6| - 8 < 10$

16. $\left|\dfrac{x + 2}{5}\right| = 8$

17. $4 - |7 - t| \leq 1$

18. $0.3x + 0.7 = 0.5x$

19. $8 - 5|a + 6| > 3$

20. $|5x + 7| + 9 \geq 4$

9.4   Inequalities in Two Variables

Graphs of Linear Inequalities • Systems of Linear Inequalities

In Section 2.6, we graphed inequalities in one variable on a number line. Now we graph inequalities in two variables on a plane.

Graphs of Linear Inequalities

When the equals sign in a linear equation is replaced with an inequality sign, a **linear inequality** is formed. Solutions of linear inequalities are ordered pairs.

EXAMPLE   **1**   Determine whether $(-3, 2)$ and $(6, -7)$ are solutions of $5x - 4y > 13$.

SOLUTION   Below, on the left, we replace x with -3 and y with 2. On the right, we replace x with 6 and y with -7.

$$\begin{array}{c|c} 5x - 4y > 13 \\ \hline 5(-3) - 4 \cdot 2 & 13 \\ -15 - 8 & \\ -23 \overset{?}{>} 13 & \text{FALSE} \end{array}$$

$$\begin{array}{c|c} 5x - 4y > 13 \\ \hline 5(6) - 4(-7) & 13 \\ 30 + 28 & \\ 58 \overset{?}{>} 13 & \text{TRUE} \end{array}$$

Since $-23 > 13$ is false, $(-3, 2)$ *is not* a solution.

Since $58 > 13$ is true, $(6, -7)$ *is* a solution.

TRY EXERCISE   7

The graph of a linear equation is a straight line. The graph of a linear inequality is a **half-plane**, with a **boundary** that is a straight line. To find the equation of the boundary, we replace the inequality sign with an equals sign.

EXAMPLE 2   Graph: $y \le x$.

SOLUTION   We first graph the equation of the boundary, $y = x$. Every solution of $y = x$ is an ordered pair, like $(3, 3)$, in which both coordinates are the same. The graph of $y = x$ is shown on the left below. Since the inequality symbol is $\le$, the line is drawn solid and is part of the graph of $y \le x$.

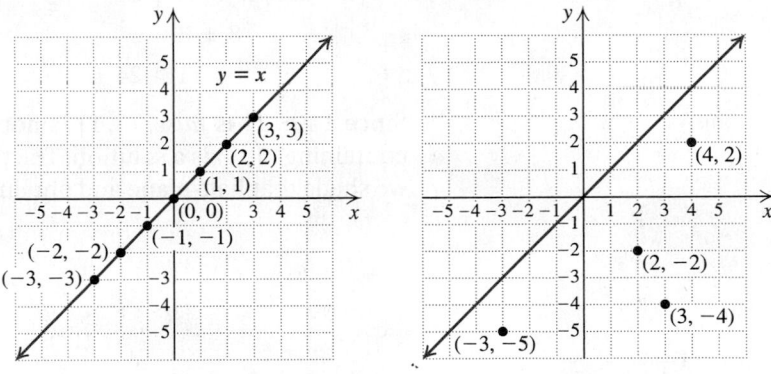

Note that in the graph on the right each ordered pair on the half-plane below $y = x$ contains a y-coordinate that is less than the x-coordinate. All these pairs represent solutions of $y \le x$. We check one pair, $(4, 2)$, as follows:

$$y \le x$$
$$2 \overset{?}{\le} 4 \quad \text{TRUE}$$

It turns out that *any* point on the same side of $y = x$ as $(4, 2)$ is also a solution. Thus, if one point in a half-plane is a solution, then *all* points in that half-plane are solutions.

We finish drawing the solution set by shading the half-plane below $y = x$. The complete solution set consists of the shaded half-plane as well as the boundary line itself.

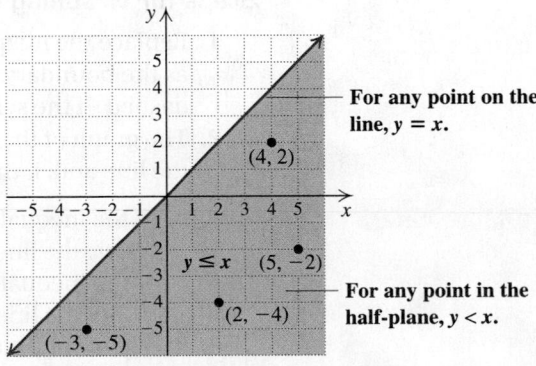

For any point on the line, $y = x$.

For any point in the half-plane, $y < x$.

TRY EXERCISE 11

From Example 2, we see that for any inequality of the form $y \le f(x)$ or $y < f(x)$, we shade *below* the graph of $y = f(x)$.

EXAMPLE   **3**   Graph: $8x + 3y > 24$.

SOLUTION   First, we sketch the graph of $8x + 3y = 24$. Since the inequality sign is $>$, points on this line do not represent solutions of the inequality, and the line is drawn dashed. Points representing solutions of $8x + 3y > 24$ are in either the half-plane above the line or the half-plane below the line. To determine which, we select a point that is not on the line and check whether it is a solution of $8x + 3y > 24$. Let's use $(1, 1)$ as this *test point*:

$$\begin{array}{c|c} \multicolumn{2}{c}{8x + 3y > 24} \\ \hline 8(1) + 3(1) & 24 \\ 8 + 3 & \\ 11 \overset{?}{>} 24 & \text{FALSE} \end{array}$$

Since $11 > 24$ is *false*, $(1, 1)$ is not a solution. Thus no point in the half-plane containing $(1, 1)$ is a solution. The points in the other half-plane *are* solutions, so we shade that half-plane and obtain the graph shown below.

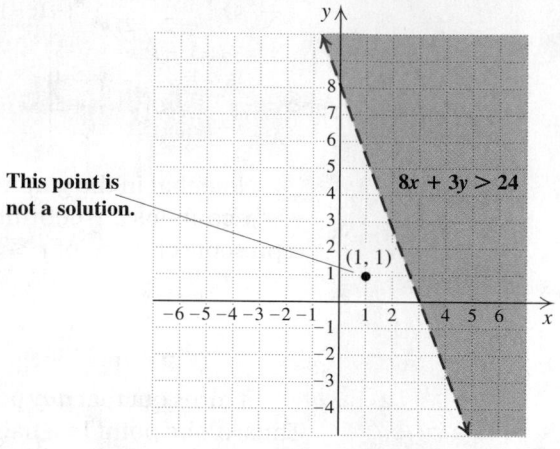

TRY EXERCISE   19

Steps for Graphing Linear Inequalities

1. Replace the inequality sign with an equals sign and graph this line as the boundary. If the inequality symbol is $<$ or $>$, draw the line dashed. If the symbol is $\leq$ or $\geq$, draw the line solid.

2. The graph of the inequality consists of a half-plane on one side of the line and, if the line is solid, the line as well.

   a) If the inequality is of the form $y < mx + b$ or $y \leq mx + b$, shade *below* the line.
   If the inequality is of the form $y > mx + b$ or $y \geq mx + b$, shade *above* the line.

   b) If y is not isolated, either solve for y and graph as in part (a) or simply graph the boundary and use a test point not on the line (as in Example 3). If the test point *is* a solution, shade the half-plane containing the point. If it is not a solution, shade the other half-plane.

EXAMPLE 4 Graph: $6x - 2y < 12$.

SOLUTION We could graph $6x - 2y = 12$ and use a test point, as in Example 3. Instead, let's solve $6x - 2y < 12$ for y:

$$6x - 2y < 12$$
$$-2y < -6x + 12 \quad \text{Adding } -6x \text{ to both sides}$$
$$y > 3x - 6. \quad \text{Dividing both sides by } -2 \text{ and reversing the } < \text{ symbol}$$

The graph consists of the half plane above the dashed boundary line $y = 3x - 6$ (see the graph below).

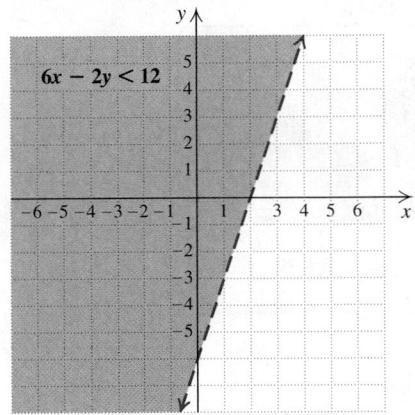

TRY EXERCISE 21

EXAMPLE 5 Graph $x > -3$ on a plane.

SOLUTION There is only one variable in this inequality. If we graph the inequality on a line, its graph is as follows:

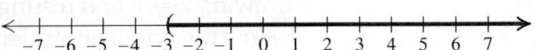

However, we can also write this inequality as $x + 0y > -3$ and graph it on a plane. We can use the same technique as in the examples above. First, we graph the boundary $x = -3$ in the plane, using a dashed line. Then we test some point, say, $(2, 5)$:

$$\frac{x + 0y > -3}{2 + 0 \cdot 5 \mid -3}$$
$$2 \overset{?}{>} -3 \quad \text{TRUE}$$

Since $(2, 5)$ is a solution, all points in the half-plane containing $(2, 5)$ are solutions. We shade that half-plane. Another approach is to simply note that the solutions of $x > -3$ are all pairs with first coordinates greater than -3.

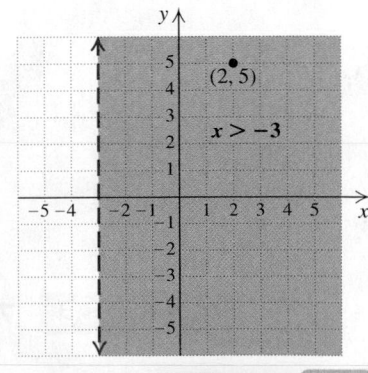

TRY EXERCISE 25

TECHNOLOGY CONNECTION

On most graphing calculators, an inequality like $y < \frac{6}{5}x + 3.49$ can be drawn by entering $(6/5)x + 3.49$ as y_1, moving the cursor to the GraphStyle icon just to the left of y_1, pressing **ENTER** until ◣ appears, and then pressing **GRAPH**.

Many calculators have an INEQUALZ program that is accessed using the **APPS** key. Running this program allows us to write inequalities at the **Y=** screen by pressing **ALPHA** and then one of the five keys just below the screen.

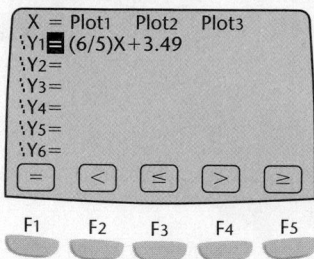

Although the graphs should be identical regardless of the method used, when we are using INEQUALZ, the boundary line appears dashed when $<$ or $>$ is selected.

$$y_1 < (6/5)x + 3.49, \text{ or}$$
$$◣ \, y_1 = (6/5)x + 3.49$$

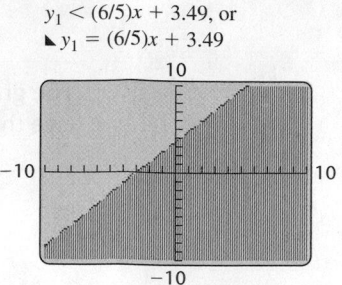

Graph each of the following. Solve for y first if necessary.

1. $y > x + 3.5$ **2.** $7y \le 2x + 5$
3. $8x - 2y < 11$ **4.** $11x + 13y + 4 \ge 0$

EXAMPLE **6**   Graph $y \le 4$ on a plane.

SOLUTION   The inequality is of the form $y \le mx + b$ (with $m = 0$), so we shade below the solid horizontal line representing $y = 4$.

This inequality can also be graphed by drawing $y = 4$ and testing a point above or below the line. The student should check that this results in a graph identical to the one at right.

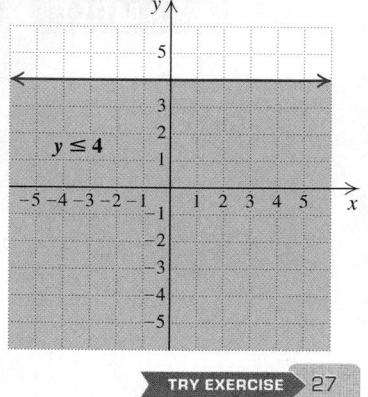

TRY EXERCISE 27

Systems of Linear Inequalities

To graph a system of equations, we graph the individual equations and then find the intersection of the graphs. We do the same thing for a system of inequalities: We graph each inequality and find the intersection of the graphs.

EXAMPLE **7**   Graph the system

$$x + y \le 4,$$
$$x - y < 4.$$

SOLUTION To graph $x + y \leq 4$, we graph $x + y = 4$ using a solid line. Since the test point $(0, 0)$ *is* a solution and $(0, 0)$ is below the line, we shade the half-plane below the graph red. The arrows near the ends of the line are another way of indicating the half-plane containing solutions.

Next, we graph $x - y < 4$. We graph $x - y = 4$ using a dashed line and consider $(0, 0)$ as a test point. Again, $(0, 0)$ is a solution, so we shade that side of the line blue. The solution set of the system is the region that is shaded purple (both red and blue) and part of the line $x + y = 4$.

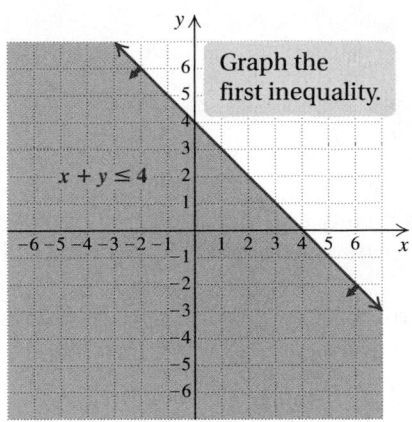
Graph the first inequality.
$x + y \leq 4$

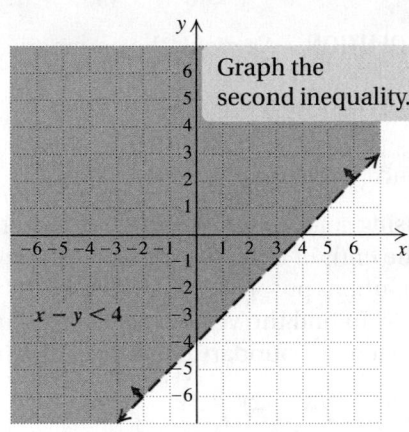
Graph the second inequality.
$x - y < 4$

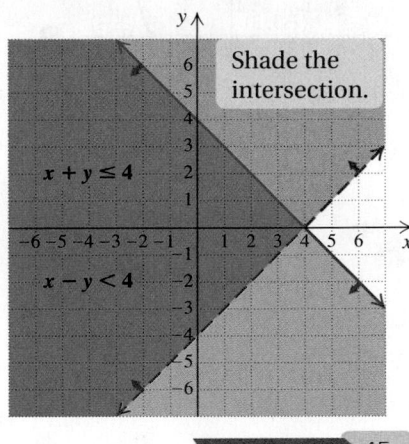
Shade the intersection.
$x + y \leq 4$
$x - y < 4$

TRY EXERCISE 45

EXAMPLE **8**

STUDENT NOTES ——————

If you don't use differently colored pencils or pens to shade different regions, consider using a pencil to make slashes that tilt in different directions in each region. You may also find it useful to attach arrows to the lines, as in the graphs shown.

Graph: $-2 < x \leq 3$.

SOLUTION This is a system of inequalities:

$$-2 < x,$$
$$x \leq 3.$$

We graph the equation $-2 = x$, and see that the graph of the first inequality is the half-plane to the right of the boundary $-2 = x$. It is shaded red.

We graph the second inequality, starting with the boundary line $x = 3$. The inequality's graph is the line and the half-plane to its left. It is shaded blue.

The solution set of the system is the region that is the intersection of the individual graphs. Since it is shaded both blue and red, it appears to be purple. All points in this region have x-coordinates that are greater than -2 but do not exceed 3.

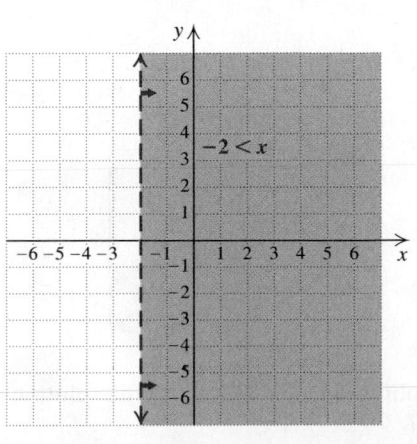
$-2 < x$

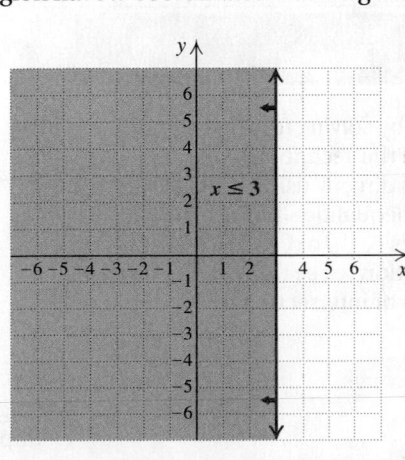
$x \leq 3$

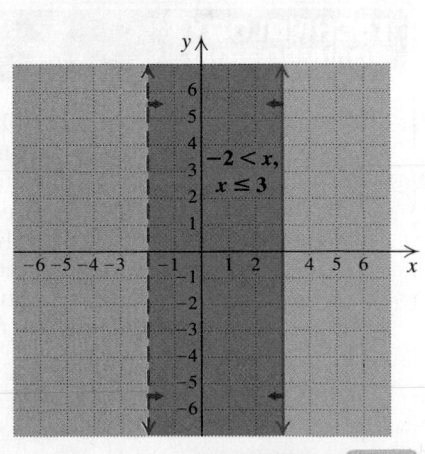
$-2 < x,$
$x \leq 3$

TRY EXERCISE 31

A system of inequalities may have a graph that consists of a polygon and its interior. In Section 9.5, we will have use for the corners, or *vertices* (singular, *vertex*), of such a graph.

EXAMPLE 9

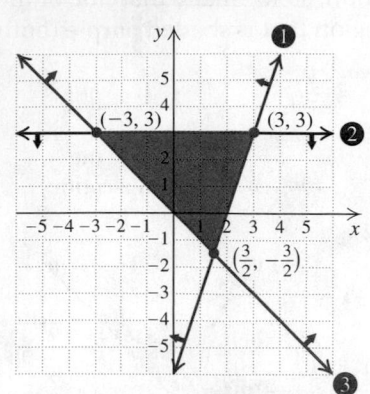

Graph the system of inequalities. Find the coordinates of any vertices formed.

$$6x - 2y \leq 12, \quad (1)$$
$$y - 3 \leq 0, \quad (2)$$
$$x + y \geq 0 \quad (3)$$

SOLUTION   We graph the boundaries

$$6x - 2y = 12,$$
$$y - 3 = 0,$$
and $\quad x + y = 0$

using solid lines. The regions for each inequality are indicated by the arrows near the ends of the lines. We note where the regions overlap and shade the region of solutions purple.

To find the vertices, we solve three different systems of two equations. The system of boundary equations from inequalities (1) and (2) is

$$6x - 2y = 12, \qquad \text{The student can use graphing, substitution, or}$$
$$y - 3 = 0. \qquad \text{elimination to solve these systems.}$$

Solving, we obtain the vertex $(3, 3)$.

The system of boundary equations from inequalities (1) and (3) is

$$6x - 2y = 12,$$
$$x + y = 0.$$

Solving, we obtain the vertex $\left(\frac{3}{2}, -\frac{3}{2}\right)$.

The system of boundary equations from inequalities (2) and (3) is

$$y - 3 = 0,$$
$$x + y = 0.$$

Solving, we obtain the vertex $(-3, 3)$.

TRY EXERCISE 49

TECHNOLOGY CONNECTION

Systems of inequalities can be graphed by solving for y and then graphing each inequality as in the Technology Connection on p. 610. To graph systems directly using the INEQUALZ application, enter the correct inequalities, press `GRAPH`, and then press `ALPHA` and Shades (`F1` or `F2`). At the SHADES menu, select Ineq Intersection to see the final graph. To find the vertices, or points of intersection, select PoI-Trace from the graph menu.

$$y_1 \geq 3x - 6, \quad y_2 \leq 3, \quad y_3 \geq -x$$

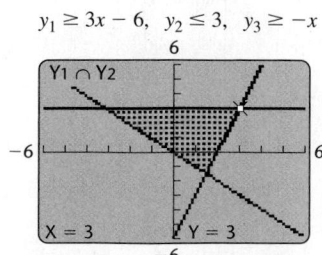

1. Use a graphing calculator to check the solution of Example 7.

A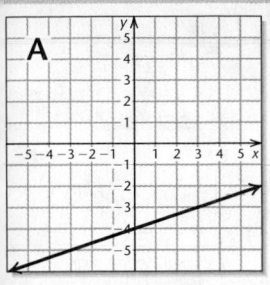

Visualizing for Success

F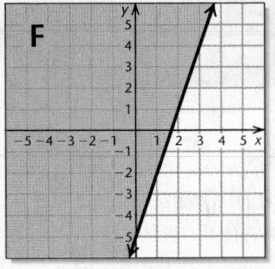

Match each equation, inequality, or system of equations or inequalities with its graph.

1. $x - y = 3,$
   $2x + y = 1$

2. $3x - y \leq 5$

3. $x > -3$

4. $y = \dfrac{1}{3}x - 4$

5. $y > \dfrac{1}{3}x - 4,$
   $y \leq x$

6. $x = y$

7. $y = 2x - 1,$
   $y = 2x - 3$

8. $2x - 5y = 10$

9. $x + y \leq 3,$
   $2y \leq x + 1$

10. $y = \dfrac{3}{2}$

Answers on page A-37

An additional, animated version of this activity appears in MyMathLab. To use MyMathLab, you need a course ID and a student access code. Contact your instructor for more information.

B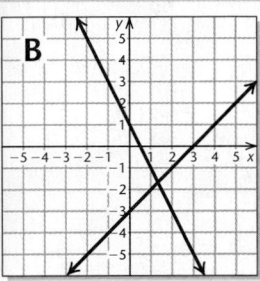

C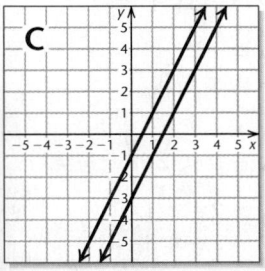

D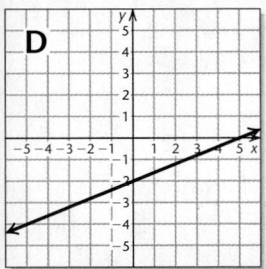

E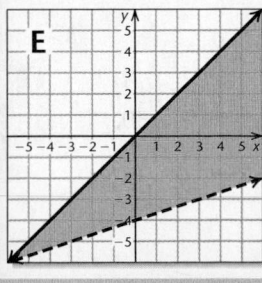

G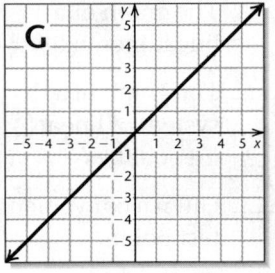

H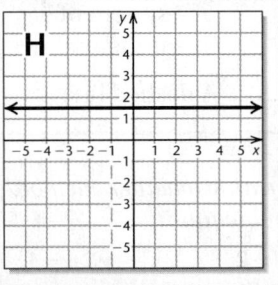

I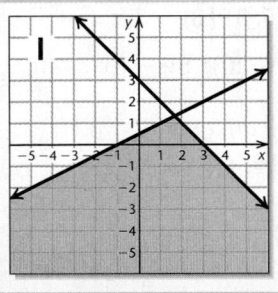

J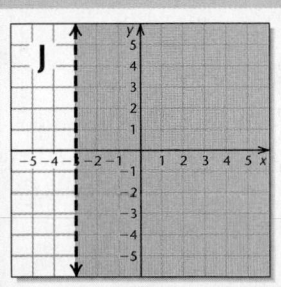

9.4 EXERCISE SET

 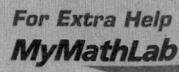  

🦢 **Concept Reinforcement** *In each of Exercises 1–6, match the phrase with the most appropriate choice from the column on the right.*

1. ____ A solution of a linear inequality

2. ____ The graph of a linear inequality

3. ____ The graph of a system of linear inequalities

4. ____ Often a convenient test point

5. ____ The name for the corners of a graph of a system of linear inequalities

6. ____ A dashed line

a) $(0, 0)$

b) Vertices

c) A half-plane

d) The intersection of two or more half-planes

e) An ordered pair that satisfies the inequality

f) Indicates the line is not part of the solution

Determine whether each ordered pair is a solution of the given inequality.

7. $(-2, 3)$; $2x - y > -4$

8. $(1, -6)$; $3x + y \geq -3$

9. $(5, 8)$; $3y - 5x \leq 0$

10. $(6, 20)$; $5y - 8x < 40$

Graph on a plane.

11. $y \geq \frac{1}{2}x$

12. $y \leq 3x$

13. $y > x - 3$

14. $y < x + 3$

15. $y \leq x + 2$

16. $y \geq x - 5$

17. $x - y \leq 4$

18. $x + y < 4$

19. $2x + 3y < 6$

20. $3x + 4y \leq 12$

21. $2y - x \leq 4$

22. $2y - 3x > 6$

23. $2x - 2y \geq 8 + 2y$

24. $3x - 2 \leq 5x + y$

25. $x > -2$

26. $x \geq 3$

27. $y \leq 6$

28. $y < -1$

29. $-2 < y < 7$

30. $-4 < y < -1$

31. $-5 \leq x < 4$

32. $-2 < y \leq 1$

33. $0 \leq y \leq 3$

34. $0 \leq x \leq 6$

Graph each system.

35. $y > x,$
$y < -x + 3$

36. $y < x,$
$y > -x + 1$

37. $y \leq x,$
$y \leq 2x - 5$

38. $y \geq x,$
$y \leq -x + 4$

39. $y \leq -3,$
$x \geq -1$

40. $y \geq -3,$
$x \geq 1$

41. $x > -4,$
$y < -2x + 3$

42. $x < 3,$
$y > -3x + 2$

43. $y \leq 5,$
$y \geq -x + 4$

44. $y \geq -2,$
$y \geq x + 3$

45. $x + y \leq 6,$
$x - y \leq 4$

46. $x + y < 1,$
$x - y < 2$

47. $y + 3x > 0,$
$y + 3x < 2$

48. $y - 2x \geq 1,$
$y - 2x \leq 3$

Graph each system of inequalities. Find the coordinates of any vertices formed.

49. $y \leq 2x - 3,$
$y \geq -2x + 1,$
$x \leq 5$

50. $2y - x \leq 2,$
$y - 3x \geq -4,$
$y \geq -1$

51. $x + 2y \leq 12,$
$2x + y \leq 12,$
$x \geq 0,$
$y \geq 0$

52. $x - y \leq 2,$
$x + 2y \geq 8,$
$y \leq 4$

53. $8x + 5y \leq 40,$
$x + 2y \leq 8,$
$x \geq 0,$
$y \geq 0$

54. $4y - 3x \geq -12,$
$4y + 3x \geq -36,$
$y \leq 0,$
$x \leq 0$

55. $y - x \geq 2,$
$y - x \leq 4,$
$2 \leq x \leq 5$

56. $3x + 4y \geq 12,$
$5x + 6y \leq 30,$
$1 \leq x \leq 3$

57. Explain in your own words why the boundary line is drawn dashed for the symbols < and > and why it is drawn solid for the symbols ≤ and ≥.

58. When graphing linear inequalities, Ron makes a habit of always shading above the line when the symbol ≥ is used. Is this wise? Why or why not?

Skill Review

To prepare for Section 9.5, review solving applications using the five-step problem-solving strategy (Sections 2.5 and 8.3).

Solve.

59. *Interest rate.* What rate of interest is required in order for a principal of $1560 to earn $25.35 in half a year? [2.5]

60. *Interest.* Luke invested $5000 in two accounts. He put $2200 in an account paying 4% simple interest and the rest in an account paying 5% simple interest. How much interest did he earn in one year from both accounts? [2.5]

61. *Investments.* Gina invested $10,000 in two accounts, one paying 3% simple interest and one paying 5% simple interest. After one year, she had earned $428 from both accounts. How much did she invest in each? [8.3]

62. *Catering.* Janice provided 20 lb of fresh vegetables for a reception. Carrots were $1.50 per pound and broccoli was $2.50 per pound. If she spent $38, how much of each vegetable did she buy? [8.3]

63. *Admissions.* There were 170 tickets sold for a high school basketball game. Tickets were $1 each for students and $3 each for adults. The total amount of money collected was $386. How many of each type of ticket were sold? [8.3]

64. *Agriculture.* Josh planted 400 acres in corn and soybeans. He planted 80 more acres in corn than he did in soybeans. How many acres of each did he plant? [8.3]

Synthesis

65. Explain how a system of linear inequalities could have a solution set containing exactly one pair.

66. In Example 7 on pp. 610–611, is the point (4, 0) part of the solution set? Why or why not?

Graph.

67. $x + y > 8,$
$x + y \le -2$

68. $x + y \ge 1,$
$-x + y \ge 2,$
$x \ge -2,$
$y \ge 2,$
$y \le 4,$
$x \le 2$

69. $x - 2y \le 0,$
$-2x + y \le 2,$
$x \le 2,$
$y \le 2,$
$x + y \le 4$

70. Write four systems of four inequalities that describe a 2-unit by 2-unit square that has (0, 0) as one of the vertices.

71. *Luggage size.* Unless an additional fee is paid, most major airlines will not check any luggage for which the sum of the item's length, width, and height exceeds 62 in. The U.S. Postal Service will ship a package only if the sum of the package's length and girth (distance around its midsection) does not exceed 130 in. Video Promotions is ordering several 30-in. long cases that will be both mailed and checked as luggage. Using w and h for width and height (in inches), respectively, write and graph an inequality that represents all acceptable combinations of width and height.
Sources: U.S. Postal Service; www.case2go.com

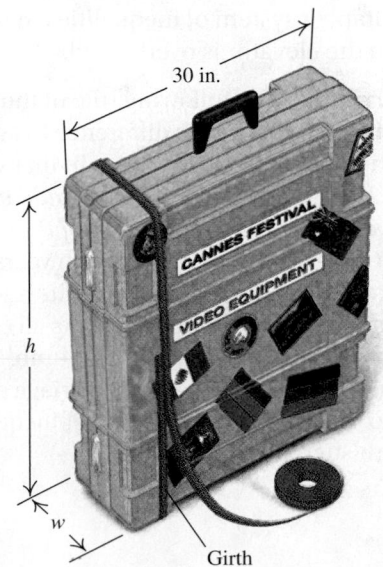
30 in.
h
w
Girth

72. *Hockey wins and losses.* The Skating Stars believe they need at least 60 points for the season in order to make the playoffs. A win is worth 2 points and a tie is worth 1 point. Graph a system of inequalities that describes the situation. (*Hint*: Let w = the number of wins and t = the number of ties.)

73. *Graduate-school admissions.* Students entering the Master of Science program in Computer Science and Engineering at University of Texas Arlington must meet minimum score requirements on the Graduate Records Examination (GRE). The GRE Quantitative score must be at least 700 and the GRE Verbal score must be at least 400. The sum of the GRE Quantitative and Verbal scores must be at least 1150. Both scores have a maximum of 800. Using q for the quantitative score and v for the verbal score, write and graph a system of inequalities that represents all combinations that meet the requirements for entrance into the program.
Source: University of Texas Arlington

74. *Widths of a basketball floor.* Sizes of basketball floors vary due to building sizes and other constraints such as cost. The length L is to be at most 94 ft and the width W is to be at most 50 ft. Graph a system of inequalities that describes the possible dimensions of a basketball floor.

75. *Elevators.* Many elevators have a capacity of 1 metric ton (1000 kg). Suppose that c children, each weighing 35 kg, and a adults, each 75 kg, are on an elevator. Graph a system of inequalities that indicates when the elevator is overloaded.

76. *Age of marriage.* The following rule of thumb for determining an appropriate difference in age between a bride and a groom appears in many Internet blogs: *The younger spouse's age should be at least seven more than half the age of the older spouse.* Let b = the age of the bride, in years, and g = the age of the groom, in years. Write and graph a system of inequalities that represents all combinations of ages that follow this rule of thumb. Should a minimum or maximum age for marriage exist? How would the graph of the system of inequalities change with such a requirement?

77. *Waterfalls.* In order for a waterfall to be classified as a classical waterfall, its height must be less than twice its crest width, and its crest width cannot exceed one-and-a-half times its height. The tallest waterfall in the world is about 3200 ft high. Let h represent a waterfall's height, in feet, and w the crest width, in feet. Write and graph a system of inequalities that represents all possible combinations of heights and crest widths of classical waterfalls.

78. Use a graphing calculator to check your answers to Exercises 35–48. Then use INTERSECT to determine any point(s) of intersection.

79. Use a graphing calculator to graph each inequality.
   a) $3x + 6y > 2$
   b) $x - 5y \le 10$
   c) $13x - 25y + 10 \le 0$
   d) $2x + 5y > 0$

CONNECTING the CONCEPTS

We have now solved a variety of equations, inequalities, systems of equations, and systems of inequalities. Below is a list of the different types of problems we have solved, illustrations of each type, and descriptions of the solutions. Note that a solution set may be empty.

Type	Example	Solution	Graph
Linear equations in one variable	$2x - 8 = 3(x + 5)$	A number	
Linear inequalities in one variable	$-3x + 5 > 2$	A set of numbers; an interval	
Linear equations in two variables	$2x + y = 7$	A set of ordered pairs; a line	
Linear inequalities in two variables	$x + y \geq 4$	A set of ordered pairs; a half-plane	
System of equations in two variables	$x + y = 3,$ $5x - y = -27$	An ordered pair or a set of ordered pairs	
System of inequalities in two variables	$6x - 2y \leq 12,$ $y - 3 \leq 0,$ $x + y \geq 0$	A set of ordered pairs; a region of a plane	

MIXED REVIEW

Graph each solution on a number line.

1. $x + 2 = 7$

2. $x + 2 > 7$

3. $x + 2 \leq 7$

4. $3(x - 7) - 2 = 5 - (2 - x)$

5. $6 - 2x \geq 8$

6. $7 > 5 - x$

Graph on a plane.

7. $x + y = 2$

8. $x + y < 2$

9. $x + y \geq 2$

10. $y = 3x - 3$

11. $x = 4$

12. $2x - 5y = -10$

13. $x + y = 1$,
$x - y = 1$

14. $y \geq 1 - x$,
$y \leq x - 3$,
$y \leq 2$

15. $2x + y < 6$

16. $x > 6y - 6$

17. $4x = 3y$

18. $y = 2x - 3$,
$y = -\frac{1}{2}x + 1$

19. $x - y \leq 3$,
$y \geq 2x$,
$2y - x \leq 2$

20. $3y = 8$

9.5 Applications Using Linear Programming

Objective Functions and Constraints • Linear Programming

There are many real-world situations in which we need to find a greatest value (a maximum) or a least value (a minimum). For example, most businesses like to know how to make the *most* profit with the *least* expense possible. Some such problems can be solved using systems of inequalities.

Objective Functions and Constraints

Often a quantity we wish to maximize depends on two or more other quantities. For example, a gardener's profits P might depend on the number of shrubs s and the number of trees t that are planted. If the gardener makes a $10 profit from each shrub and an $18 profit from each tree, the total profit, in dollars, is given by the **objective function**

$$P = 10s + 18t.$$

Thus the gardener might be tempted to simply plant lots of trees since they yield the greater profit. This would be a good idea were it not for the fact that the number of trees and shrubs planted—and thus the total profit—is subject to the demands, or **constraints**, of the situation. For example, to improve drainage, the gardener might be required to plant at least 3 shrubs. Thus the objective function would be subject to the *constraint*

$$s \geq 3.$$

Because of limited space, the gardener might also be required to plant no more than 10 plants. This would subject the objective function to a *second* constraint:

$$s + t \leq 10.$$

Finally, the gardener might be told to spend no more than $700 on the plants. If the shrubs cost $40 each and the trees cost $100 each, the objective function is subject to a *third* constraint:

The cost of the shrubs   plus   the cost of the trees   cannot exceed $700.

$$40s \qquad + \qquad 100t \qquad \leq \qquad 700$$

In short, the gardener wishes to maximize the objective function

$$P = 10s + 18t,$$

subject to the constraints

$$s \geq 3,$$
$$s + t \leq 10,$$
$$40s + 100t \leq 700,$$
$$\left. \begin{array}{l} s \geq 0, \\ t \geq 0. \end{array} \right\}$$ Because the number of trees and shrubs cannot be negative

These constraints form a system of linear inequalities that can be graphed.

Linear Programming

The gardener's problem is "How many shrubs and trees should be planted, subject to the constraints listed, in order to maximize profit?" To solve such a problem, we use a result from a branch of mathematics known as **linear programming**.

The Corner Principle

Suppose an objective function $F = ax + by + c$ depends on x and y (with a, b, and c constant). Suppose also that F is subject to constraints on x and y, which form a system of linear inequalities. If F has a minimum or a maximum value, then it can be found as follows:

1. Graph the system of inequalities and find the vertices.
2. Find the value of the objective function at each vertex. The greatest and the least of those values are the maximum and the minimum of the function, respectively.
3. The ordered pair at which the maximum or minimum occurs indicates the choice of (x, y) for which that maximum or minimum occurs.

This result was proven during World War II, when linear programming was developed to help allocate troops and supplies bound for Europe.

EXAMPLE   1   Solve the gardener's problem discussed above.

SOLUTION   We are asked to maximize $P = 10s + 18t$, subject to the constraints

$$s \geq 3,$$
$$s + t \leq 10,$$
$$40s + 100t \leq 700,$$
$$s \geq 0,$$
$$t \geq 0.$$

We graph the system, using the techniques of Section 9.4. The portion of the graph that is shaded represents all pairs that satisfy the constraints. It is sometimes called the *feasible region*.

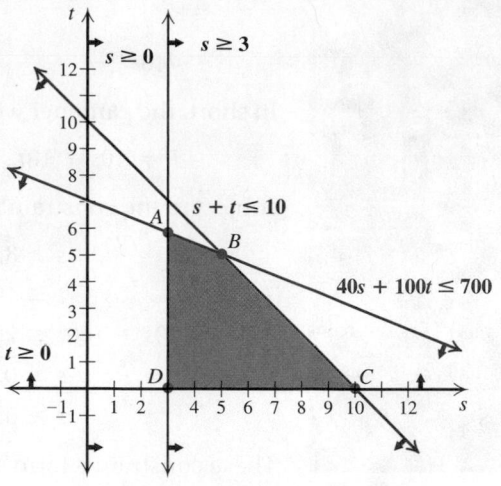

According to the corner principle, P is maximized at one of the vertices of the shaded region. To determine the coordinates of the vertices, we solve the following systems:

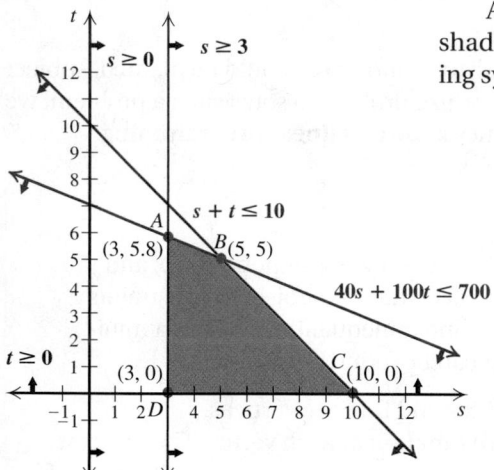

A: $\left.\begin{array}{r} 40s + 100t = 700, \\ s = 3; \end{array}\right\}$ The student can verify that the solution of this system is $(3, 5.8)$. The coordinates of point A are $(3, 5.8)$.

B: $\left.\begin{array}{r} s + t = 10, \\ 40s + 100t = 700; \end{array}\right\}$ The student can verify that the solution of this system is $(5, 5)$. The coordinates of point B are $(5, 5)$.

C: $\left.\begin{array}{r} s + t = 10, \\ t = 0; \end{array}\right\}$ The solution of this system is $(10, 0)$. The coordinates of point C are $(10, 0)$.

D: $\left.\begin{array}{r} t = 0, \\ s = 3. \end{array}\right\}$ The solution of this system is $(3, 0)$. The coordinates of point D are $(3, 0)$.

We now find the value of P at each vertex.

Vertex (s, t)	Profit $P = 10s + 18t$	
A $(3, 5.8)$	$10(3) + 18(5.8) = 134.4$	
B $(5, 5)$	$10(5) + 18(5) = 140$	⟵ Maximum
C $(10, 0)$	$10(10) + 18(0) = 100$	
D $(3, 0)$	$10(3) + 18(0) = 30$	⟵ Minimum

The greatest value of P occurs at $(5, 5)$. Thus profit is maximized at \$140 if the gardener plants 5 shrubs and 5 trees. Incidentally, we have also shown that profit is minimized at \$30 if 3 shrubs and 0 trees are planted.

▶ **TRY EXERCISE** 13

EXAMPLE **2**   *Grading.*   For his history grade, Cy can write book summaries for 70 points each or research papers for 80 points each. He estimates that each book summary will take 9 hr and each research paper will take 15 hr and that he will have at most 120 hr to spend. He may turn in a total of no more than 12 summaries or papers. How many of each should he write in order to receive the highest score?

SOLUTION

1. **Familiarize.** Since we are looking for the number of book summaries and the number of research papers, we let b = the number of book summaries and r = the number of research papers. Cy is limited by the number of hours he can spend and by the number of summaries and papers he can turn in. These two limits are the constraints.

2. **Translate.** We organize the information in a table.

Type	Number of Points for Each	Time Required for Each	Number Written	Total Time for Each Type	Total Points for Each Type
Book summary	70	9 hr	b	$9b$	$70b$
Research paper	80	15 hr	r	$15r$	$80r$
Total			$b + r \leq 12$	$9b + 15r \leq 120$	

↑ Because no more than 12 may be turned in

↑ Because the time cannot exceed 120 hr

↑ We wish to maximize the total score.

Let T represent the total score. We see from the table that

$$T = 70b + 80r.$$

We wish to maximize T subject to the number and time constraints:

$$b + r \leq 12,$$
$$9b + 15r \leq 120,$$
$$b \geq 0,\}$$
$$r \geq 0.\}$$

We include this because the number of summaries and papers cannot be negative.

3. **Carry out.** We graph the system and evaluate T at each vertex. The graph is as follows:

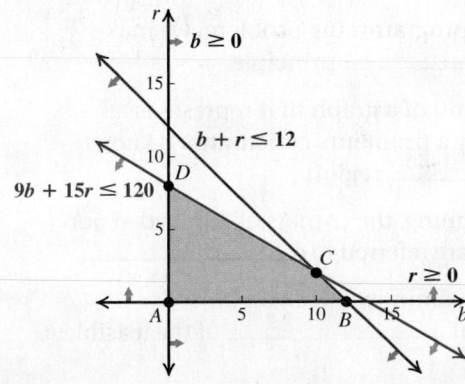

We find the coordinates of each vertex by solving a system of two linear equations. The coordinates of point A are obviously $(0, 0)$. To find the coordinates of point C, we solve the system

$$b + r = 12, \qquad (1)$$
$$9b + 15r = 120. \qquad (2)$$

We multiply both sides of equation (1) by -9 and add:

$$\begin{array}{r} -9b - 9r = -108 \\ \underline{9b + 15r = 120} \\ 6r = 12 \\ r = 2. \end{array}$$

Substituting, we find that $b = 10$. Thus the coordinates of C are $(10, 2)$. Point B is the intersection of $b + r = 12$ and $r = 0$, so B is $(12, 0)$. Point D is the intersection of $9b + 15r = 120$ and $b = 0$, so D is $(0, 8)$. Computing the score for each ordered pair, we obtain the table at left.

The greatest score in the table is 860, obtained when Cy writes 10 book summaries and 2 research papers.

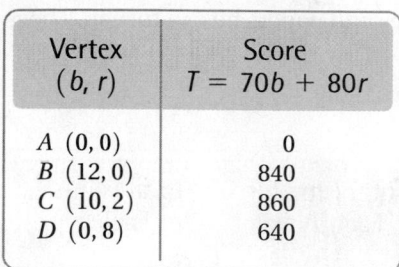

Vertex (b, r)	Score $T = 70b + 80r$
A $(0, 0)$	0
B $(12, 0)$	840
C $(10, 2)$	860
D $(0, 8)$	640

4. **Check.** We can check that $T \leq 860$ for any other pair in the shaded region. This is left to the student.

5. **State.** In order to maximize his score, Cy should write 10 book summaries and 2 research papers.

TRY EXERCISE 19

9.5 EXERCISE SET

For Extra Help

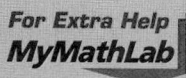  

↩ *Concept Reinforcement* *Complete each of the following sentences.*

1. In linear programming, the quantity we wish to maximize or minimize is given by the _____ function.

2. In linear programming, the demands arising from the given situation are known as _____.

3. To solve a linear programming problem, we make use of the _____ principle.

4. The shaded portion of a graph that represents all points that satisfy a problem's constraints is known as the _____ region.

5. In linear programming, the corners of the shaded portion of the graph are referred to as _____.

6. If it exists, the maximum value of an objective function occurs at a _____ of the feasible region.

Find the maximum and the minimum values of each objective function and the values of x and y at which they occur.

7. $F = 2x + 14y$,
   subject to
   $5x + 3y \leq 34$,
   $3x + 5y \leq 30$,
   $x \geq 0$,
   $y \geq 0$

8. $G = 7x + 8y$,
   subject to
   $3x + 2y \leq 12$,
   $2y - x \leq 4$,
   $x \geq 0$,
   $y \geq 0$

9. $P = 8x - y + 20$,
   subject to
   $6x + 8y \leq 48$,
   $0 \leq y \leq 4$,
   $0 \leq x \leq 7$

10. $Q = 24x - 3y + 52$,
    subject to
    $5x + 4y \leq 20$,
    $0 \leq y \leq 4$,
    $0 \leq x \leq 3$

11. $F = 2y - 3x$,
    subject to
    $y \leq 2x + 1$,
    $y \geq -2x + 3$,
    $x \leq 3$

12. $G = 5x + 2y + 4$,
    subject to
    $y \leq 2x + 1$,
    $y \geq -x + 3$,
    $x \leq 5$

13. *Lunch-time profits.* Art sells gumbo and sandwiches. To stay in business, Art must sell at least 10 orders of gumbo and 30 sandwiches each day. Because of limited space, no more than 40 orders of gumbo or 70 sandwiches can be made. The total number of orders cannot exceed 90. If profit is $1.65 per gumbo order and $1.05 per sandwich, how many of each item should Art sell in order to maximize profit?

14. *Gas mileage.* Caroline owns a car and a moped. She has at most 12 gal of gasoline to be used between the car and the moped. The car's tank holds at most 18 gal and the moped's 3 gal. The mileage for the car is 20 mpg and for the moped is 100 mpg. How many gallons of gasoline should each vehicle use if Caroline wants to travel as far as possible? What is the maximum number of miles?

15. *Photo albums.* Photo Perfect prints pages of photographs for albums. A page containing 4 photos costs $3 and a page containing 6 photos costs $5. Ann can spend no more than $90 for photo pages of her recent vacation, and can use no more than 20 pages in her album. What combination of 4-photo pages and 6-photo pages will maximize the number of photos she can display? What is the maximum number of photos that she can display?

16. *Milling.* Picture Rocks Lumber can convert logs into either lumber or plywood. In a given week, the mill can turn out 400 units of production, of which 100 units of lumber and 150 units of plywood are required by regular customers. The profit on a unit of lumber is $20 and on a unit of plywood is $30. How many units of each type should the mill produce in order to maximize profit?

17. *Investing.* Rosa is planning to invest up to $40,000 in corporate or municipal bonds, or both. She must invest from $6000 to $22,000 in corporate bonds, and she refuses to invest more than $30,000 in municipal bonds. The interest on corporate bonds is 8% and on municipal bonds is $7\frac{1}{2}$%. This is simple interest for one year. How much should Rosa invest in each type of bond in order to earn the most interest? What is the maximum interest?

18. *Investing.* Jamaal is planning to invest up to $22,000 in City Bank or the Southwick Credit Union, or both. He wants to invest at least $2000 but no more than $14,000 in City Bank. Because of insurance limitations, he will invest no more than $15,000 in the Southwick Credit Union. The interest in City Bank is 6% and in the credit union is $6\frac{1}{2}$%. This is simple interest for one year. How much should Jamaal invest in each bank in order to earn the most interest? What is the maximum interest?

19. *Test scores.* Corinna is taking a test in which short-answer questions are worth 10 points each and essay questions are worth 15 points each. She estimates that it will take 3 min to answer each short-answer question and 6 min to answer each essay question. The total time allowed is 60 min, and no more than 16 questions can be answered. Assuming that all her answers are correct, how many questions of each type should Corinna answer to get the best score?

20. *Test scores.* Edy is about to take a test that contains short-answer questions worth 4 points each and word problems worth 7 points each. Edy must do at least 5 short-answer questions, but time restricts doing more than 10. She must do at least 3 word problems, but time restricts doing more than 10. Edy can do no more than 18 questions in total. How many of each type of question must Edy do in order to maximize her score? What is this maximum score?

21. *Grape growing.* Auggie's vineyard consists of 240 acres upon which he wishes to plant Merlot and Cabernet grapes. Profit per acre of Merlot is $400 and profit per acre of Cabernet is $300. Furthermore, the total number of hours of labor available during the harvest season is 3200. Each acre of Merlot requires 20 hr of labor and each acre of Cabernet requires 10 hr of labor. Determine how the land should be divided between Merlot and Cabernet in order to maximize profit.

22. *Coffee blending.* The Coffee Peddler has 1440 lb of Sumatran coffee and 700 lb of Kona coffee. A batch of Hawaiian Blend requires 8 lb of Kona and 12 lb of Sumatran, and yields a profit of $90. A batch of Classic Blend requires 4 lb of Kona and 16 lb of Sumatran, and yields a $55 profit. How many batches of each kind should be made in order to maximize profit? What is the maximum profit? (*Hint:* Organize the information in a table.)

23. *Nutrition.* Becca is supposed to have at least 15 mg but no more than 45 mg of iron each day. She should also have at least 1500 mg but no more than 2500 mg of calcium per day. One serving of goat cheese contains 1 mg of iron, 500 mg of calcium, and 264 calories. One serving of hazelnuts contains 5 mg of iron, 100 mg of calcium, and 628 calories. How many servings of goat cheese and how many servings of hazelnuts should Becca eat in order to meet the daily requirements of iron and calcium but minimize the total number of calories?

24. *Textile production.* It takes Cosmic Stitching 2 hr of cutting and 4 hr of sewing to make a knit suit. To make a worsted suit, it takes 4 hr of cutting and 2 hr of sewing. At most 20 hr per day are available for cutting and at most 16 hr per day are available for sewing. The profit on a knit suit is $68 and on a worsted suit is $62. How many of each kind of suit should be made in order to maximize profit?

25. Before a student begins work in this section, what three sections of the text would you suggest he or she study? Why?

26. What does the use of the word "constraint" in this section have in common with the use of the word in everyday speech?

Skill Review

Review function notation and domains of functions (Sections 7.1 and 7.2).

27. If $f(x) = 4x - 7$, find $f(a) + h$. [7.1]

28. If $f(x) = 4x - 7$, find $f(a + h)$. [7.1]

Find the domain of f.

29. $f(x) = \dfrac{x - 5}{2x + 1}$ [7.2], [9.2]

30. $f(x) = \dfrac{3x}{x^2 + 1}$ [7.2]

31. $f(x) = \sqrt{2x + 8}$ [9.1]

32. $f(x) = \dfrac{3x}{x^2 - 1}$ [7.2], [9.2]

Synthesis

33. Explain how Exercises 17 and 18 can be answered by logical reasoning without linear programming.

34. Write a linear programming problem for a classmate to solve. Devise the problem so that profit must be maximized subject to at least two (nontrivial) constraints.

35. *Airplane production.* Alpha Tours has two types of airplanes, the T3 and the S5, and contracts requiring accommodations for a minimum of 2000 first-class, 1500 tourist-class, and 2400 economy-class passengers. The T3 costs $30 per mile to operate and can accommodate 40 first-class, 40 tourist-class, and 120 economy-class passengers, whereas the S5 costs $25 per mile to operate and can accommodate 80 first-class, 30 tourist-class, and 40 economy-class passengers. How many of each type of airplane should be used in order to minimize the operating cost?

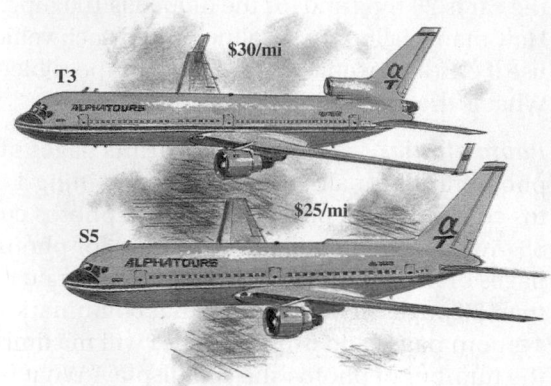

36. *Airplane production.* A new airplane, the T4, is now available, having an operating cost of $37.50 per mile and accommodating 40 first-class, 40 tourist-class, and 80 economy-class passengers. If the T3 of Exercise 35 were replaced with the T4, how many S5's and how many T4's would be needed in order to minimize the operating cost?

37. *Furniture production.* P. J. Edward Furniture Design produces chairs and sofas. The chairs require 20 ft of wood, 1 lb of foam rubber, and 2 sq yd of fabric. The sofas require 100 ft of wood, 50 lb of foam rubber, and 20 sq yd of fabric. The company has 1900 ft of wood, 500 lb of foam rubber, and 240 sq yd of fabric. The chairs can be sold for $80 each and the sofas for $1200 each. How many of each should be produced in order to maximize income?

Study Summary

KEY TERMS AND CONCEPTS	EXAMPLES

SECTION 9.1: INEQUALITIES AND DOMAIN

Inequalities can be solved graphically by determining the x-values for which one graph lies above or below another.

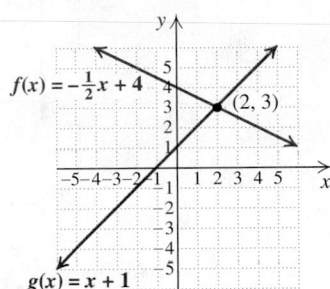

From the graph above, we can read the solution sets of the following inequalities.

Inequality	Solution Set
$f(x) < g(x)$	$\{x \mid x > 2\}$, or $(2, \infty)$
$f(x) \le g(x)$	$\{x \mid x \ge 2\}$, or $[2, \infty)$
$f(x) > g(x)$	$\{x \mid x < 2\}$, or $(-\infty, 2)$
$f(x) \ge g(x)$	$\{x \mid x \le 2\}$, or $(-\infty, 2]$

Only nonnegative numbers have square roots that are real numbers.

Find the domain of f if $f(x) = \sqrt{2x - 3}$.

$$2x - 3 \ge 0 \qquad 2x - 3 \text{ must be nonnegative}$$
$$2x \ge 3 \qquad \text{Adding 3 to both sides}$$
$$x \ge \frac{3}{2} \qquad \text{Dividing both sides by 2}$$

The domain of f is $\left\{x \mid x \ge \frac{3}{2}\right\}$, or $\left[\frac{3}{2}, \infty\right)$.

SECTION 9.2: INTERSECTIONS, UNIONS, AND COMPOUND INEQUALITIES

A **conjunction** consists of two or more sentences joined by the word *and*. The solution set of the conjunction is the **intersection** of the solution sets of the individual sentences.

$$-4 \le x - 1 \le 5$$

$$-4 \le x - 1 \quad and \quad x - 1 \le 5$$
$$-3 \le x \qquad and \qquad x \le 6$$

The solution set is $\{x \mid -3 \le x \le 6\}$, or $[-3, 6]$.

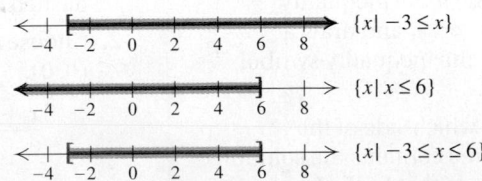

A **disjunction** consists of two or more sentences joined by the word *or*. The solution set of the disjunction is the **union** of the solution sets of the individual sentences.

$$2x + 9 < 1 \quad or \quad 5x - 2 \geq 3$$
$$2x < -8 \quad or \quad 5x \geq 5$$
$$x < -4 \quad or \quad x \geq 1$$

The solution set is $\{x \mid x < -4 \ or \ x \geq 1\}$, or $(-\infty, -4) \cup [1, \infty)$.

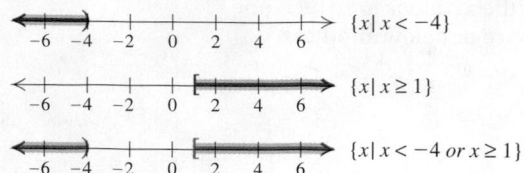

SECTION 9.3: ABSOLUTE-VALUE EQUATIONS AND INEQUALITIES

The Absolute-Value Principles for Equations and Inequalities

For any positive number p and any algebraic expression X:

a) The solutions of $|X| = p$ are those numbers that satisfy

$$X = -p \quad or \quad X = p.$$

b) The solutions of $|X| < p$ are those numbers that satisfy

$$-p < X < p.$$

c) The solutions of $|X| > p$ are those numbers that satisfy

$$X < -p \quad or \quad p < X.$$

If $|X| = 0$, then $X = 0$. If p is negative, then $|X| = p$ and $|X| < p$ have no solution, and any value of X will satisfy $|X| > p$.

$$|x + 3| = 4$$
$$x + 3 = 4 \quad or \quad x + 3 = -4 \qquad \text{Using part (a)}$$
$$x = 1 \quad or \qquad x = -7$$

The solution set is $\{-7, 1\}$.

$$|x + 3| < 4$$
$$-4 < x + 3 < 4 \qquad \text{Using part (b)}$$
$$-7 < x < 1$$

The solution set is $\{x \mid -7 < x < 1\}$, or $(-7, 1)$.

$$|x + 3| \geq 4$$
$$x + 3 \leq -4 \quad or \quad 4 \leq x + 3 \qquad \text{Using part (c)}$$
$$x \leq -7 \quad or \quad 1 \leq x$$

The solution set is $\{x \mid x \leq -7 \ or \ x \geq 1\}$, or $(-\infty, -7] \cup [1, \infty)$.

SECTION 9.4: INEQUALITIES IN TWO VARIABLES

To graph a linear inequality:

1. Graph the **boundary line**. Draw a dashed line if the inequality symbol is $<$ or $>$, and draw a solid line if the inequality symbol is $\leq$ or $\geq$.

2. Determine which side of the boundary line contains the solution set, and shade that **half-plane**.

Graph: $x + y < -1$.

1. Graph $x + y = -1$ using a dashed line.

2. Choose a test point not on the line: $(0, 0)$.

$$\frac{x + y < -1}{0 + 0 \ \underset{?}{\mid} \ -1}$$
$$0 \overset{?}{<} -1 \quad \text{FALSE}$$

Since $0 < -1$ is false, shade the half-plane that does *not* contain $(0, 0)$.

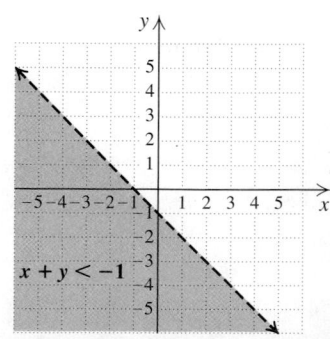

SECTION 9.5: APPLICATIONS USING LINEAR PROGRAMMING

The Corner Principle

The maximum or minimum value of an **objective function** over a *feasible region* is the maximum or minimum value of the function at a **vertex** of that region.

Maximize $F = x + 2y$ subject to

$$x + y \le 5,$$
$$x \ge 0,$$
$$y \ge 1.$$

1. Graph the feasible region.
2. Find the value of F at the vertices.

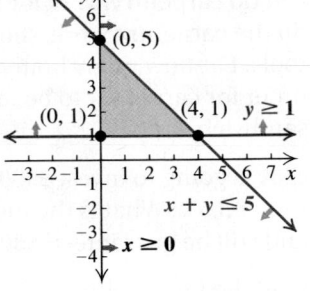

Vertex	$F = x + 2y$
$(0, 1)$	2
$(0, 5)$	10
$(4, 1)$	6

←—— The maximum value of F is 10.

Review Exercises: Chapter 9

🔖 *Concept Reinforcement*   *Classify each statement as either true or false.*

1. If x cannot exceed 10, then $x \le 10$. [9.1]

2. It is always true that if $a > b$, then $ac > bc$. [9.1]

3. The solution of $|3x - 5| \le 8$ is a closed interval. [9.3]

4. The inequality $2 < 5x + 1 < 9$ is equivalent to $2 < 5x + 1 \ or \ 5x + 1 < 9$. [9.2]

5. The solution set of a disjunction is the union of two solution sets. [9.2]

6. The equation $|x| = r$ has no solution when r is negative. [9.3]

7. $|f(x)| > 3$ is equivalent to $f(x) < -3 \ or \ f(x) > 3$. [9.3]

8. A test point is used to determine whether the line in a linear inequality is drawn solid or dashed. [9.4]

9. The graph of a system of linear inequalities is always a half-plane. [9.4]

10. The corner principle states that every objective function has a maximum or minimum value. [9.5]

Solve algebraically. [9.1]

11. $-6x - 5 < 4$

12. $-\dfrac{1}{2}x - \dfrac{1}{4} > \dfrac{1}{2} - \dfrac{1}{4}x$

13. $0.3y - 7 < 2.6y + 15$

14. $-2(x - 5) \ge 6(x + 7) - 12$

Solve graphically. [9.1]

15. $x - 2 < 3$

16. $4 - 3x > 1$

17. $x - 1 \le 2x + 3$

18. $\dfrac{1}{2}x \ge \dfrac{1}{3}x + 1$

19. Let $f(x) = 3x + 2$ and $g(x) = 10 - x$. Find all values of x for which $f(x) \le g(x)$. [9.1]

Solve. [9.1]

20. Mariah has two offers for a summer job. She can work in a sandwich shop for $8.40 an hour, or she can do carpentry work for $16 an hour. In order to do the carpentry work, she must spend $950 for tools. For how many hours must Mariah work in order for carpentry to be more profitable than the sandwich shop?

21. Clay is going to invest $9000, part at 3% and the rest at 3.5%. What is the most he can invest at 3% and still be guaranteed $300 in interest each year?

22. Find the intersection:
$$\{a, b, c, d\} \cap \{a, c, e, f, g\}. \quad [9.2]$$

23. Find the union:
$$\{a, b, c, d\} \cup \{a, c, e, f, g\}. \quad [9.2]$$

Graph and write interval notation. [9.2]

24. $x \le 2$ *and* $x > -3$

25. $x \le 3$ *or* $x > -5$

Solve and graph each solution set. [9.2]

26. $-3 < x + 5 \le 5$

27. $-15 < -4x - 5 < 0$

28. $3x < -9$ *or* $-5x < -5$

29. $2x + 5 < -17$ *or* $-4x + 10 \le 34$

30. $2x + 7 \le -5$ *or* $x + 7 \ge 15$

31. $f(x) < -5$ *or* $f(x) > 5$, where $f(x) = 3 - 5x$

For $f(x)$ as given, use interval notation to write the domain of f.

32. $f(x) = \dfrac{2x}{x + 3}$ [9.2]

33. $f(x) = \sqrt{5x - 10}$ [9.1]

34. $f(x) = \sqrt{1 - 4x}$ [9.1]

Solve. [9.3]

35. $|x| = 11$

36. $|t| \ge 21$

37. $|x - 8| = 3$

38. $|4a + 3| < 11$

39. $|3x - 4| \ge 15$

40. $|2x + 5| = |x - 9|$

41. $|5n + 6| = -11$

42. $\left|\dfrac{x + 4}{6}\right| \le 2$

43. $2|x - 5| - 7 > 3$ **44.** $19 - 3|x + 1| \ge 4$

45. Let $f(x) = |8x - 3|$. Find all x for which $f(x) < 0$. [9.3]

46. Graph $x - 2y \ge 6$ on a plane. [9.4]

Graph each system of inequalities. Find the coordinates of any vertices formed. [9.4]

47. $x + 3y > -1$,
  $x + 3y < 4$

48. $x - 3y \le 3$,
  $x + 3y \ge 9$,
  $y \le 6$

49. Find the maximum and the minimum values of
$$F = 3x + y + 4$$
subject to
$$y \le 2x + 1,$$
$$x \le 7,$$
$$y \ge 3. \qquad [9.5]$$

50. Custom Computers has two manufacturing plants. The Oregon plant cannot produce more than 60 computers per week, while the Ohio plant cannot produce more than 120 computers per week. The Electronics Outpost sells at least 160 Custom computers each week. It costs $40 to ship a computer to The Electronics Outpost from the Oregon plant and $25 to ship from the Ohio plant. How many computers should be shipped from each plant in order to minimize cost? [9.5]

Synthesis

51. Explain in your own words why $|X| = p$ has two solutions when p is positive and no solution when p is negative. [9.3]

52. Explain why the graph of the solution of a system of linear inequalities is the intersection, not the union, of the individual graphs. [9.4]

53. Solve: $|2x + 5| \le |x + 3|$. [9.3]

54. Classify as true or false: If $x < 3$, then $x^2 < 9$. If false, give an example showing why. [9.1]

55. Super Lock manufactures brass doorknobs with a 2.5-in. diameter and a ± 0.003-in. manufacturing tolerance, or allowable variation in diameter. Write the tolerance as an inequality with absolute value. [9.3]

Solve algebraically.

1. $-4y - 3 \geq 5$

2. $3(7 - x) < 2x + 5$

3. $-2(3x - 1) - 5 \geq 6x - 4(3 - x)$

Solve graphically.

4. $3 - x < 2$

5. $2x - 3 \geq x + 1$

6. Let $f(x) = -5x - 1$ and $g(x) = -9x + 3$. Find all values of x for which $f(x) > g(x)$.

7. Dani can rent a van for either $80 with unlimited mileage or $45 with 100 free miles and an extra charge of 40¢ for each mile over 100. For what numbers of miles traveled would the unlimited mileage plan save Dani money?

8. A refrigeration repair company charges $80 for the first half-hour of work and $60 for each additional hour. Blue Mountain Camp has budgeted $200 to repair its walk-in cooler. For what lengths of a service call will the budget not be exceeded?

9. Find the intersection:
   $$\{a, e, i, o, u\} \cap \{a, b, c, d, e\}.$$

10. Find the union:
    $$\{a, e, i, o, u\} \cup \{a, b, c, d, e\}.$$

For $f(x)$ as given, use interval notation to write the domain of f.

11. $f(x) = \sqrt{6 - 3x}$

12. $f(x) = \dfrac{x}{x - 7}$

Solve and graph each solution set.

13. $-5 < 4x + 1 \leq 3$

14. $3x - 2 < 7 \text{ or } x - 2 > 4$

15. $-3x > 12 \text{ or } 4x \geq -10$

16. $1 \leq 3 - 2x \leq 9$

17. $|n| = 15$

18. $|a| > 5$

19. $|3x - 1| < 7$

20. $|-5t - 3| \geq 10$

21. $|2 - 5x| = -12$

22. $g(x) < -3 \text{ or } g(x) > 3$, where $g(x) = 4 - 2x$

23. Let $f(x) = |2x - 1|$ and $g(x) = |2x + 7|$. Find all values of x for which $f(x) = g(x)$.

24. Graph $y \leq 2x + 1$ on a plane.

Graph the system of inequalities. Find the coordinates of any vertices formed.

25. $x + y \geq 3,$
    $x - y \geq 5$

26. $2y - x \geq -7,$
    $2y + 3x \leq 15,$
    $y \leq 0,$
    $x \leq 0$

27. Find the maximum and the minimum values of
    $$F = 5x + 3y$$
    subject to
    $$x + y \leq 15,$$
    $$1 \leq x \leq 6,$$
    $$0 \leq y \leq 12.$$

28. Swift Cuts makes $12 on each manicure and $18 on each haircut. A manicure takes 30 min and a haircut takes 50 min, and there are 5 stylists who each work 6 hr a day. If the salon can schedule 50 appointments a day, how many should be manicures and how many haircuts in order to maximize profit? What is the maximum profit?

Synthesis

Solve. Write the solution set using interval notation.

29. $|2x - 5| \leq 7 \text{ and } |x - 2| \geq 2$

30. $7x < 8 - 3x < 6 + 7x$

31. Write an absolute-value inequality for which the interval shown is the solution.

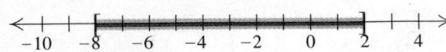

Cumulative Review: Chapters 1–9

Simplify. Do not leave negative exponents in your answers.

1. $3 + 24 \div 2^2 \cdot 3 - (6 - 7)$ [4.2]

2. $3c - [8 - 2(1 - c)]$ [4.2]

3. -10^{-2} [4.2]

4. $(3xy^{-4})(-2x^3y)$ [4.2]

5. $\left(\dfrac{18a^2b^{-1}}{12a^{-1}b}\right)^2$ [4.2]

6. $\dfrac{2x - 10}{x^3 - 125}$ [6.1]

Perform the indicated operations.

7. $(x - 5)(x + 5)$ [4.6]

8. $(3n - 2)(5n + 7)$ [4.6]

9. $\dfrac{1}{x + 5} - \dfrac{1}{x - 5}$ [6.4]

10. $\dfrac{x^2 - 3x}{2x^2 - x - 3} \div \dfrac{x^3}{x^2 - 2x - 3}$ [6.2]

Factor.

11. $25x^2 - 50x + 25$ [5.4]

12. $8mn + 14n - 12m - 21$ [5.1]

13. $8t^2 + 800$ [5.1]

Solve.

14. $3(x - 2) = 14 - x$ [2.2]

15. $x - 2 < 6 \text{ or } 2x + 1 > 5$ [9.2]

16. $x^2 - 2x - 3 = 5$ [5.7]

17. $\dfrac{3}{x + 1} = \dfrac{x}{4}$ [6.6]

18. $y = \frac{1}{2}x - 7,$
$2x - 4y = 3$ [8.2]

19. $x + 3y = 8,$
$2x - 3y = 7$ [8.2]

20. $|2x - 1| = 8$ [9.3]

21. $9(x - 3) - 4x < 2 - (3 - x)$ [2.6], [9.1]

22. $|4t| > 12$ [9.3]

23. $|3x - 2| \le 8$ [9.3]

Graph on a plane.

24. $y = \frac{2}{3}x - 4$ [3.6]

25. $x = -3$ [3.3]

26. $3x - y = 3$ [3.3]

27. $x + y \ge -2$ [9.4]

28. $f(x) = -x + 1$ [7.3]

29. $x - 2y > 4,$
$x + 2y \ge -2$ [9.4]

30. Find the slope and the y-intercept of the line given by $4x - 9y = 18$. [3.6]

31. Write a slope–intercept equation for the line with slope -7 and containing the point $(-3, -4)$. [3.7]

32. Find an equation of the line with y-intercept $(0, 4)$ and perpendicular to the line given by $3x + 2y = 1$. [3.6]

33. For the graph of f shown, determine the domain and the range of f. [7.2]

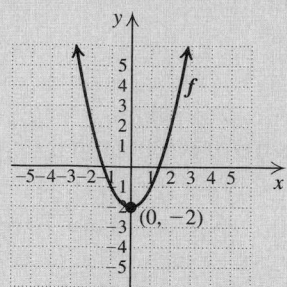

34. Determine the domain of the function given by
$f(x) = \dfrac{3}{2x + 5}$. [7.2], [9.2]

35. Find $g(-2)$ if $g(x) = 3x^2 - 5x$. [7.1]

36. Find $(f - g)(x)$ if $f(x) = x^2 + 3x$ and $g(x) = 9 - 3x$. [7.4]

37. Graph the solution set of $-3 \le f(x) \le 2$, where $f(x) = 1 - x$. [9.2]

38. Find the domain of h/g if $h(x) = \dfrac{1}{x}$ and

$g(x) = 3x - 1$. [7.4]

39. Solve for t: $at - dt = c$. [2.3]

40. The Baqueira, a resort in Spain, uses 549 snow cannons to make snow for its 4344 acres of ski runs. How many snow cannons should a resort containing 1448 acres of runs use in order to make a comparable amount of snow? [6.7]

Sources: www.bluebookski.com

41. *Water usage.* In dry climates, it takes about 11,600 gal of water to produce a pound of beef and a pound of wheat. The pound of beef requires 7000 more gallons of water than the pound of wheat. How much water does it take to produce each? [8.3]

Source: *The Wall Street Journal*, 1/28/08

42. *Book sales.* U.S. sales of books and maps were $34.6 billion in 2001 and $41.4 billion in 2004. Let $b(t)$ represent U.S. book sales t years after 2001. [7.3]

Source: Bureau of Economic Analysis

a) Find a linear function that fits the data.
b) Use the function from part (a) to predict U.S. book sales in 2010.
c) In what year will U.S. book sales be $50 billion?

43. *Fundraising.* Michelle is planning a fundraising dinner for Happy Hollow Children's Camp. The banquet facility charges a rental fee of $1500, but will waive the rental fee if more than $6000 is spent for catering. Michelle knows that 150 people will attend the dinner. [9.1]

a) How much should each dinner cost in order for the rental fee to be waived?
b) For what costs per person will the total cost (including the rental fee) exceed $6000?

44. *Perimeter of a rectangle.* The perimeter of a rectangle is 32 cm. If five times the width equals three times the length, what are the dimensions of the rectangle? [8.3]

45. *Utility bills.* One month Lori and Tony spent $920 for electricity, rent, and cell phone. The electric bill was $\frac{1}{4}$ of the rent, and the phone bill was $40 less than the electric bill. How much was the rent? [8.5]

46. *Banking.* Banks charge a fee to a customer whose checking account does not contain enough money to pay for a debit-card purchase or a written check. These insufficient-funds fees totaled $35 billion in the United States in a recent year. This was 70% of the total fee income of banks. What was the total fee income of banks in that year? [2.5]

47. *Catering.* Dan charges $35 per person for a vegetarian meal and $40 per person for a steak dinner. For one event, he served 28 dinners for a total cost of $1060. How many dinners were vegetarian and how many were steak? [8.3]

Synthesis

48. If $(2, 6)$ and $(-1, 5)$ are two solutions of $f(x) = mx + b$, find m and b. [8.2]

49. Find k such that the line containing $(-2, k)$ and $(3, 8)$ is parallel to the line containing $(1, 6)$ and $(4, -2)$. [3.6]

50. Use interval notation to write the domain of the function given by

$$f(x) = \frac{\sqrt{x+4}}{x}.\ [9.2]$$

51. Simplify: $\dfrac{2^{a-1} \cdot 2^{4a}}{2^{3(-2a+5)}}$. [4.2]

Exponents and Radicals

10.1
Radical Expressions
and Functions

10.2
Rational Numbers
as Exponents

10.3
Multiplying Radical
Expressions

10.4
Dividing Radical
Expressions

10.5
Expressions Containing
Several Radical Terms

CONNECTING THE CONCEPTS

10.6
Solving Radical Equations

10.7
The Distance and Midpoint
Formulas and Other
Applications

10.8
The Complex Numbers

STUDY SUMMARY
REVIEW EXERCISES
CHAPTER TEST
CUMULATIVE REVIEW

MICHAEL MANOLAKIS
FIREFIGHTER
Boston, Massachusetts

Firefighters use math every day. Hosing down a fire may seem simple, but there are considerations to take into account when getting water from its source to the end of the hose where the "pipeman" is attacking the fire. For example, the safest force or psi (pounds per square inch) needed at the tip of a hose is determined by its size. The safest force needed at the tip of a $1\frac{3}{4}$-in. line is 120 psi. To achieve this pressure, we must consider the distance and height of the hose line from the source of water. These two factors are necessary to accurately calculate and deliver the appropriate psi at the tip.

AN APPLICATION

The velocity of water flow, in feet per second, from a nozzle is given by

$$v(p) = 12.1\sqrt{p},$$

where p is the nozzle pressure, in pounds per square inch. Find the nozzle pressure if the water flow is 100 feet per second.

Source: Houston Fire Department Continuing Education

This problem appears as Exercise 65 in Section 10.6.

1 n this chapter, we learn about square roots, cube roots, fourth roots, and so on. These roots can be expressed in radical notation and appear in both radical expressions and radical equations. Exponents that are fractions are also studied and will ease some of our work with radicals. The chapter closes with an introduction to the complex-number system.

10.1   Radical Expressions and Functions

Square Roots and Square-Root Functions • Expressions of the Form $\sqrt{a^2}$ • Cube Roots • Odd and Even nth Roots

In this section, we consider roots, such as square roots and cube roots. We look at the symbolism that is used and ways in which symbols can be manipulated to get equivalent expressions. All of this will be important in problem solving.

Square Roots and Square-Root Functions

When a number is multiplied by itself, we say that the number is squared. Often we need to know what number was squared in order to produce some value a. If such a number can be found, we call that number a *square root* of a.

> **Square Root**
>
> The number c is a *square root* of a if $c^2 = a$.

For example,

    9 has -3 and 3 as square roots because $(-3)^2 = 9$ and $3^2 = 9$.

    25 has -5 and 5 as square roots because $(-5)^2 = 25$ and $5^2 = 25$.

    -4 does not have a real-number square root because there is no real number c for which $c^2 = -4$.

Note that every positive number has two square roots, whereas 0 has only itself as a square root. Negative numbers do not have real-number square roots, although later in this chapter we introduce the *complex-number* system in which such square roots do exist.

EXAMPLE   1

Find the two square roots of 36.

SOLUTION   The square roots are 6 and -6, because $6^2 = 36$ and $(-6)^2 = 36$.

> **TRY EXERCISE   9**

Whenever we refer to *the* square root of a number, we mean the nonnegative square root of that number. This is often referred to as the *principal square root* of the number.

> **Principal Square Root**
>
> The *principal square root* of a nonnegative number is its nonnegative square root. The symbol $\sqrt{}$ is called a *radical sign* and is used to indicate the principal square root of the number over which it appears.

STUDENT NOTES

It is important to remember the difference between *the* square root of 9 and *a* square root of 9. *A* square root of 9 means either 3 or -3, whereas *the* square root of 9, denoted $\sqrt{9}$, means the principal square root of 9, or 3.

EXAMPLE **2**   Simplify each of the following.

a) $\sqrt{25}$ b) $\sqrt{\dfrac{25}{64}}$ c) $-\sqrt{64}$ d) $\sqrt{0.0049}$

SOLUTION

a) $\sqrt{25} = 5$ $\sqrt{}$ indicates the principal square root. Note that $\sqrt{25} \neq -5$.

b) $\sqrt{\dfrac{25}{64}} = \dfrac{5}{8}$ Since $\left(\dfrac{5}{8}\right)^2 = \dfrac{25}{64}$

c) $-\sqrt{64} = -8$ Since $\sqrt{64} = 8$, $-\sqrt{64} = -8$.

d) $\sqrt{0.0049} = 0.07$ $(0.07)(0.07) = 0.0049$. Note too that
$$\sqrt{0.0049} = \sqrt{\dfrac{49}{10{,}000}} = \dfrac{7}{100}.$$

TRY EXERCISE 19

In addition to being read as "the principal square root of a," $\sqrt{a}$ is also read as "the square root of a," "root a," or "radical a." Any expression in which a radical sign appears is called a *radical expression*. The following are radical expressions:

$$\sqrt{5}, \quad \sqrt{a}, \quad -\sqrt{3x}, \quad \sqrt{\dfrac{y^2 + 7}{y}}, \quad \sqrt{x} + 8.$$

The expression under the radical sign is called the **radicand**. In the expressions above, the radicands are 5, a, $3x$, $(y^2 + 7)/y$, and x, respectively.

Values for square roots found on calculators are, for the most part, approximations. For example, a calculator will show a number like

2.23606798

for $\sqrt{5}$. The exact value of $\sqrt{5}$ is not given by any repeating or terminating decimal. In general, for any whole number a that is not a perfect square, $\sqrt{a}$ is a nonterminating, nonrepeating decimal or an *irrational number*.

The square-root function, given by

$$f(x) = \sqrt{x},$$

has $[0, \infty)$ as its domain and $[0, \infty)$ as its range. We can draw its graph by selecting convenient values for x and calculating the corresponding outputs. Once these ordered pairs have been graphed, a smooth curve can be drawn.

$f(x) = \sqrt{x}$

x	$\sqrt{x}$	$(x, f(x))$
0	0	$(0, 0)$
1	1	$(1, 1)$
4	2	$(4, 2)$
9	3	$(9, 3)$

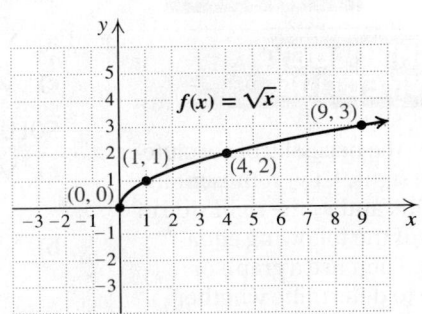

EXAMPLE **3**   For each function, find the indicated function value.

a) $f(x) = \sqrt{3x - 2}$; $f(1)$ b) $g(z) = -\sqrt{6z + 4}$; $g(3)$

SOLUTION

a) $f(1) = \sqrt{3 \cdot 1 - 2}$ Substituting
   $= \sqrt{1} = 1$ Simplifying

b) $g(3) = -\sqrt{6 \cdot 3 + 4}$ Substituting

$= -\sqrt{22}$ Simplifying. This answer is exact.

≈ -4.69041576 Using a calculator to write an approximation

▶ **TRY EXERCISE** ▸ 35

Expressions of the Form $\sqrt{a^2}$

As the next example shows, $\sqrt{a^2}$ does not always simplify to a.

EXAMPLE **4**   Evaluate $\sqrt{a^2}$ for the following values: **(a)** 5; **(b)** 0; **(c)** −5.

SOLUTION

a) $\sqrt{5^2} = \sqrt{25} = 5$ Same

b) $\sqrt{0^2} = \sqrt{0} = 0$ Same

c) $\sqrt{(-5)^2} = \sqrt{25} = 5$ Opposites   Note that $\sqrt{(-5)^2} \neq -5$.   ◼▪

You may have noticed that evaluating $\sqrt{a^2}$ is just like evaluating $|a|$.

> ## Simplifying $\sqrt{a^2}$
> For any real number a,
> $$\sqrt{a^2} = |a|.$$
> (The principal square root of a^2 is the absolute value of a.)

When a radicand is the square of a variable expression, like $(x + 5)^2$ or $36t^2$, absolute-value signs are needed when simplifying. We use absolute-value signs unless we know that the expression being squared is nonnegative. This ensures that our result is never negative.

EXAMPLE **5**   Simplify each expression. Assume that the variable can represent any real number.

a) $\sqrt{(x + 1)^2}$ **b)** $\sqrt{x^2 - 8x + 16}$

c) $\sqrt{a^8}$ **d)** $\sqrt{t^6}$

SOLUTION

a) $\sqrt{(x + 1)^2} = |x + 1|$ Since $x + 1$ can be negative (for example, if $x = -3$), absolute-value notation is required.

b) $\sqrt{x^2 - 8x + 16} = \sqrt{(x - 4)^2} = |x - 4|$ Since $x - 4$ can be negative, absolute-value notation is required.

c) Note that $(a^4)^2 = a^8$ and that a^4 is never negative. Thus,

$$\sqrt{a^8} = a^4.$$ Absolute-value notation is unnecessary here.

TECHNOLOGY CONNECTION

To see the necessity of absolute-value signs, let y_1 represent the left side and y_2 the right side of each of the following equations. Then use a graph or table to determine whether these equations are true.

1. $\sqrt{x^2} \stackrel{?}{=} x$

2. $\sqrt{x^2} \stackrel{?}{=} |x|$

3. $x \stackrel{?}{=} |x|$

d) Note that $(t^3)^2 = t^6$. Thus,

$$\sqrt{t^6} = |t^3|.$$ Since t^3 can be negative, absolute-value notation is required.

TRY EXERCISE 43

If we assume that the expression being squared is nonnegative, then absolute-value notation is not necessary.

EXAMPLE **6**   Simplify each expression. Assume that no radicands were formed by squaring negative quantities.

a) $\sqrt{y^2}$ **b)** $\sqrt{a^{10}}$ **c)** $\sqrt{9x^2 - 6x + 1}$

SOLUTION

a) $\sqrt{y^2} = y$ We assume that y is nonnegative, so no absolute-value notation is necessary. When y *is* negative, $\sqrt{y^2} \neq y$.

b) $\sqrt{a^{10}} = a^5$ Assuming that a^5 is nonnegative. Note that $(a^5)^2 = a^{10}$.

c) $\sqrt{9x^2 - 6x + 1} = \sqrt{(3x - 1)^2} = 3x - 1$ Assuming that $3x - 1$ is nonnegative

TRY EXERCISE 69

Cube Roots

We often need to know what number cubed produces a certain value. When such a number is found, we say that we have found a *cube root*. For example,

2 is the cube root of 8 because $2^3 = 2 \cdot 2 \cdot 2 = 8$;

-4 is the cube root of -64 because $(-4)^3 = (-4)(-4)(-4) = -64$.

> ### Cube Root
> The number c is the *cube root* of a if $c^3 = a$. In symbols, we write $\sqrt[3]{a}$ to denote the cube root of a.

Each real number has only one real-number cube root. The cube-root function, given by

$$f(x) = \sqrt[3]{x},$$

has $\mathbb{R}$ as its domain and $\mathbb{R}$ as its range. To draw its graph, we select convenient values for x and calculate the corresponding outputs. Once these ordered pairs have been graphed, a smooth curve is drawn. Note that the cube root of a positive number is positive, and the cube root of a negative number is negative.

$f(x) = \sqrt[3]{x}$

x	$\sqrt[3]{x}$	$(x, f(x))$
0	0	$(0, 0)$
1	1	$(1, 1)$
8	2	$(8, 2)$
-1	-1	$(-1, -1)$
-8	-2	$(-8, -2)$

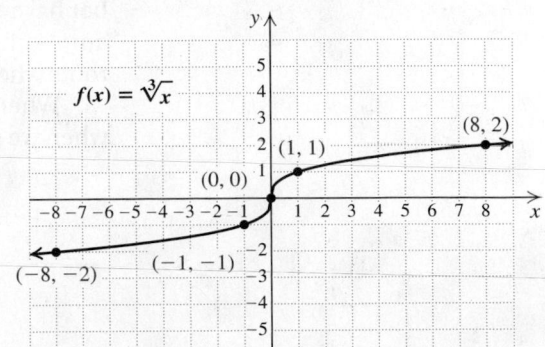

EXAMPLE **7** For each function, find the indicated function value.

a) $f(y) = \sqrt[3]{y}$; $f(125)$

b) $g(x) = \sqrt[3]{x - 1}$; $g(-26)$

SOLUTION

a) $f(125) = \sqrt[3]{125} = 5$ Since $5 \cdot 5 \cdot 5 = 125$

b) $g(-26) = \sqrt[3]{-26 - 1}$

$= \sqrt[3]{-27}$

$= -3$ Since $(-3)(-3)(-3) = -27$

> **TRY EXERCISE** 89

EXAMPLE **8** Simplify: $\sqrt[3]{-8y^3}$.

SOLUTION

$$\sqrt[3]{-8y^3} = -2y \quad \text{Since } (-2y)(-2y)(-2y) = -8y^3$$

> **TRY EXERCISE** 83

Odd and Even *n*th Roots

The 4th root of a number a is the number c for which $c^4 = a$. There are also 5th roots, 6th roots, and so on. We write $\sqrt[n]{a}$ for the principal *n*th root. The number n is called the *index* (plural, *indices*). When the index is 2, we do not write it.

When the index n is odd, we are taking an *odd root*. Note that every number has exactly one real root when n is odd. Odd roots of positive numbers are positive and odd roots of negative numbers are negative. Absolute-value signs are not used when finding odd roots.

EXAMPLE **9** Simplify each expression.

a) $\sqrt[5]{32}$ **b)** $\sqrt[5]{-32}$ **c)** $-\sqrt[5]{32}$

d) $-\sqrt[5]{-32}$ **e)** $\sqrt[7]{x^7}$ **f)** $\sqrt[9]{(t - 1)^9}$

SOLUTION

a) $\sqrt[5]{32} = 2$ Since $2^5 = 32$

b) $\sqrt[5]{-32} = -2$ Since $(-2)^5 = -32$

c) $-\sqrt[5]{32} = -2$ Taking the opposite of $\sqrt[5]{32}$

d) $-\sqrt[5]{-32} = -(-2) = 2$ Taking the opposite of $\sqrt[5]{-32}$

e) $\sqrt[7]{x^7} = x$ No absolute-value signs are needed.

f) $\sqrt[9]{(t - 1)^9} = t - 1$

> **TRY EXERCISE** 81

When the index n is even, we are taking an *even root*. Every positive real number has two real *n*th roots when n is even—one positive and one negative. For example, the fourth roots of 16 are -2 and 2. Negative numbers do not have real *n*th roots when n is even.

When n is even, the notation $\sqrt[n]{a}$ indicates the nonnegative *n*th root. Thus, when we simplify even *n*th roots, absolute-value signs are often required.

Compare the following.

Odd Root	Even Root
$\sqrt[3]{8} = 2$	$\sqrt[4]{16} = 2$
$\sqrt[3]{-8} = -2$	$\sqrt[4]{-16}$ is not a real number.
$\sqrt[3]{x^3} = x$	$\sqrt[4]{x^4} = |x|$

EXAMPLE 10   Simplify each expression, if possible. Assume that variables can represent any real number.

a) $\sqrt[4]{81}$ **b)** $-\sqrt[4]{81}$ **c)** $\sqrt[4]{-81}$

d) $\sqrt[4]{81x^4}$ **e)** $\sqrt[6]{(y + 7)^6}$

SOLUTION

a) $\sqrt[4]{81} = 3$ Since $3^4 = 81$

b) $-\sqrt[4]{81} = -3$ Taking the opposite of $\sqrt[4]{81}$

c) $\sqrt[4]{-81}$ cannot be simplified. $\sqrt[4]{-81}$ is not a real number.

d) $\sqrt[4]{81x^4} = |3x|$, or $3|x|$ Use absolute-value notation since x could represent a negative number.

e) $\sqrt[6]{(y + 7)^6} = |y + 7|$ Use absolute-value notation since $y + 7$ is negative for $y < -7$.

TRY EXERCISE 59

We summarize as follows.

Simplifying nth Roots

n	a	$\sqrt[n]{a}$	$\sqrt[n]{a^n}$
Even	Positive	Positive	$|a|$
	Negative	Not a real number	
Odd	Positive	Positive	a
	Negative	Negative	

EXAMPLE 11   Determine the domain of g if $g(x) = \sqrt[6]{7 - 3x}$.

SOLUTION   Since the index is even, the radicand, $7 - 3x$, must be nonnegative. We solve the inequality:

$7 - 3x \geq 0$ We cannot find the 6th root of a negative number.

$-3x \geq -7$

$x \leq \frac{7}{3}.$ Multiplying both sides by $-\frac{1}{3}$ and reversing the inequality

Thus,

Domain of $g = \left\{x \,|\, x \leq \frac{7}{3}\right\}$

$= \left(-\infty, \frac{7}{3}\right].$

TECHNOLOGY CONNECTION

To enter cube or higher roots on a graphing calculator, select options 4 or 5 of the **MATH** menu. The characters $6\sqrt[x]{}$ indicate the sixth root.

1. Use a **TABLE** or **GRAPH** and **TRACE** to check the solution of Example 11.

TRY EXERCISE 95

Visualizing for Success

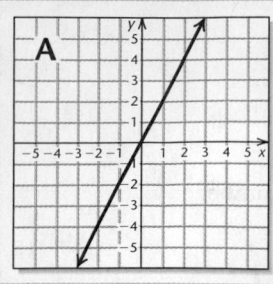

A

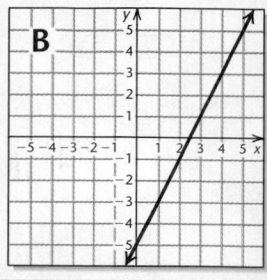

B

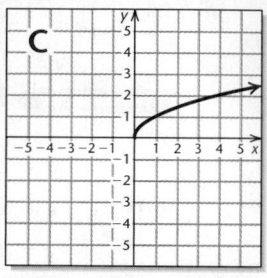

C

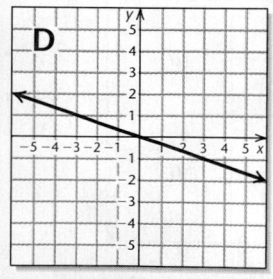

D

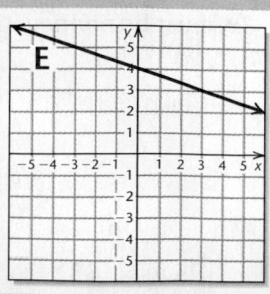

E

Match each function with its graph.

1. $f(x) = 2x - 5$

2. $f(x) = x^2 - 1$

3. $f(x) = \sqrt{x}$

4. $f(x) = x - 2$

5. $f(x) = -\frac{1}{3}x$

6. $f(x) = 2x$

7. $f(x) = 4 - x$

8. $f(x) = |2x - 5|$

9. $f(x) = -2$

10. $f(x) = -\frac{1}{3}x + 4$

Answers on page A-41

An additional, animated version of this activity appears in MyMathLab. To use MyMathLab, you need a course ID and a student access code. Consult your instructor for more information.

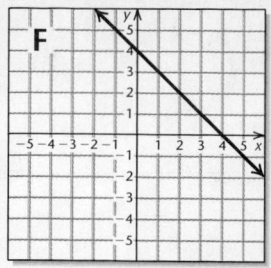

F

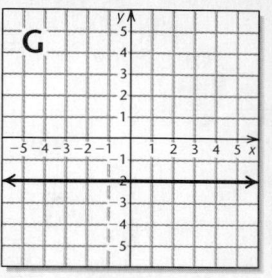

G

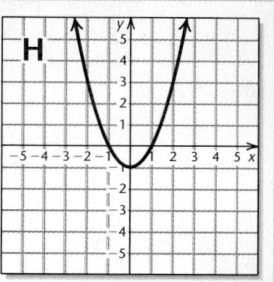

H

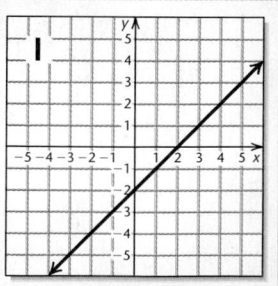

I

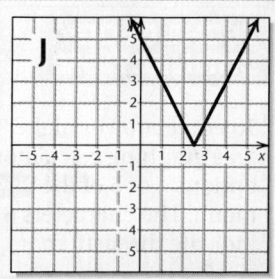

J

10.1 EXERCISE SET

For Extra Help    PRACTICE WATCH   DOWNLOAD

Concept Reinforcement *Select the appropriate word to complete each of the following.*

1. Every positive number has _____ square root(s).
   one/two

2. The principal square root is never _____.
   negative/positive

3. For any _____ number a, we have
   negative/positive
   $\sqrt{a^2} = a$.

4. For any _____ number a, we have
   negative/positive
   $\sqrt{a^2} = -a$.

5. If a is a whole number that is not a perfect square, then $\sqrt{a}$ is a(n) _____ number.
   irrational/rational

6. The domain of the function f given by $f(x) = \sqrt[3]{x}$ is all _____ numbers.
   whole/real/positive

7. If $\sqrt[4]{x}$ is a real number, then x must be _____.
   negative/positive/nonnegative.

8. If $\sqrt[3]{x}$ is negative, then x must be _____.
   negative/positive

For each number, find all of its square roots.

9. 64   10. 81

11. 100   12. 121

13. 400   14. 2500

15. 625   16. 225

Simplify.

17. $\sqrt{49}$ 18. $\sqrt{144}$

19. $-\sqrt{16}$ 20. $-\sqrt{100}$

21. $\sqrt{\dfrac{36}{49}}$ 22. $\sqrt{\dfrac{4}{9}}$

23. $-\sqrt{169}$ 24. $-\sqrt{196}$

25. $-\sqrt{\dfrac{16}{81}}$ 26. $-\sqrt{\dfrac{81}{144}}$

27. $\sqrt{0.04}$ 28. $\sqrt{0.36}$

29. $\sqrt{0.0081}$ 30. $\sqrt{0.0016}$

Identify the radicand and the index for each expression.

31. $5\sqrt{p^2 + 4}$ 32. $-7\sqrt{y^2 - 8}$

33. $x^2 y^3 \sqrt[5]{\dfrac{x}{y+4}}$ 34. $\dfrac{a^2}{b} \sqrt[6]{a(a+b)}$

For each function, find the specified function value, if it exists.

35. $f(t) = \sqrt{5t - 10};\ f(3), f(2), f(1), f(-1)$

36. $g(x) = \sqrt{x^2 - 25};\ g(-6), g(3), g(6), g(13)$

37. $t(x) = -\sqrt{2x^2 - 1};\ t(5), t(0), t(-1), t\left(-\tfrac{1}{2}\right)$

38. $p(z) = \sqrt{2z - 20};\ p(4), p(10), p(12), p(0)$

39. $f(t) = \sqrt{t^2 + 1};\ f(0), f(-1), f(-10)$

40. $g(x) = -\sqrt{(x+1)^2};\ g(-3), g(4), g(-5)$

Simplify. Remember to use absolute-value notation when necessary. If a root cannot be simplified, state this.

41. $\sqrt{100x^2}$ 42. $\sqrt{16t^2}$

43. $\sqrt{(8-t)^2}$ 44. $\sqrt{(a+3)^2}$

45. $\sqrt{y^2 + 16y + 64}$ 46. $\sqrt{x^2 - 4x + 4}$

47. $\sqrt{4x^2 + 28x + 49}$ 48. $\sqrt{9x^2 - 30x + 25}$

49. $-\sqrt[4]{256}$ 50. $-\sqrt[4]{625}$

51. $\sqrt[3]{-1}$ 52. $-\sqrt[3]{-1000}$

53. $-\sqrt[5]{-\dfrac{32}{243}}$ 54. $\sqrt[5]{-\dfrac{1}{32}}$

55. $\sqrt[6]{x^6}$ 56. $\sqrt[8]{y^8}$

57. $\sqrt[9]{t^9}$ 58. $\sqrt[5]{a^5}$

59. $\sqrt[4]{(6a)^4}$ 60. $\sqrt[4]{(7b)^4}$

61. $\sqrt[10]{(-6)^{10}}$ 62. $\sqrt[12]{(-10)^{12}}$

63. $\sqrt[414]{(a+b)^{414}}$ 64. $\sqrt[1976]{(2a+b)^{1976}}$

65. $\sqrt{a^{22}}$ 66. $\sqrt{x^{10}}$

67. $\sqrt{-25}$ 68. $\sqrt{-16}$

Simplify. Assume that no radicands were formed by raising negative quantities to even powers.

69. $\sqrt{16x^2}$ 70. $\sqrt{25t^2}$

71. $-\sqrt{(3t)^2}$ 72. $-\sqrt{(7c)^2}$

73. $\sqrt{(-5b)^2}$ 74. $\sqrt{(-10a)^2}$

75. $\sqrt{a^2 + 2a + 1}$ 76. $\sqrt{9 - 6y + y^2}$

77. $\sqrt[3]{27}$ 78. $-\sqrt[3]{64}$

79. $\sqrt[4]{16x^4}$ 80. $\sqrt[4]{81x^4}$

81. $\sqrt[5]{(x-1)^5}$

82. $-\sqrt[5]{(7y)^5}$

83. $-\sqrt[3]{-125y^3}$

84. $\sqrt[3]{-64x^3}$

85. $\sqrt{t^{18}}$

86. $\sqrt{a^{14}}$

87. $\sqrt{(x-2)^8}$

88. $\sqrt{(x+3)^{10}}$

For each function, find the specified function value, if it exists.

89. $f(x) = \sqrt[3]{x+1};\ f(7), f(26), f(-9), f(-65)$

90. $g(x) = -\sqrt[3]{2x-1};\ g(0), g(-62), g(-13), g(63)$

91. $g(t) = \sqrt[4]{t-3};\ g(19), g(-13), g(1), g(84)$

92. $f(t) = \sqrt[4]{t+1};\ f(0), f(15), f(-82), f(80)$

Determine the domain of each function described.

93. $f(x) = \sqrt{x-6}$

94. $g(x) = \sqrt{x+8}$

95. $g(t) = \sqrt[4]{t+8}$

96. $f(x) = \sqrt[4]{x-9}$

97. $g(x) = \sqrt[4]{10-2x}$

98. $g(t) = \sqrt[3]{2t-6}$

99. $f(t) = \sqrt[5]{2t+7}$

100. $f(t) = \sqrt[6]{4+3t}$

101. $h(z) = -\sqrt[6]{5z+2}$

102. $d(x) = -\sqrt[4]{5-7x}$

Aha! 103. $f(t) = 7 + \sqrt[8]{t^8}$

104. $g(t) = 9 + \sqrt[6]{t^6}$

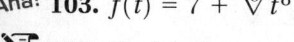 **105.** Explain how to write the negative square root of a number using radical notation.

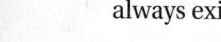 **106.** Does the square root of a number's absolute value always exist? Why or why not?

Skill Review

To prepare for Section 10.2, review exponents (Sections 4.1 and 4.2).

Simplify. Do not use negative exponents in your answer. [4.1], [4.2]

107. $(a^2b)(a^4b)$

108. $(3xy^8)(5x^2y)$

109. $(5x^2y^{-3})^3$

110. $(2a^{-1}b^2c)^{-3}$

111. $\left(\dfrac{10x^{-1}y^5}{5x^2y^{-1}}\right)^{-1}$

112. $\left(\dfrac{8x^3y^{-2}}{2xz^4}\right)^{-2}$

Synthesis

113. Under what conditions does the nth root of x^3 exist? Explain your reasoning.

114. Under what conditions does the nth root of x^2 exist? Explain your reasoning.

115. *Biology.* The number of species S of plants in Guyana in an area of A hectares can be estimated using the formula

$$S = 88.63\sqrt[4]{A}.$$

The Kaieteur National Park in Guyana has an area of 63,000 hectares. How many species of plants are in the park?
Source: Hans ter Steege, "A Perspective on Guyana and its Plant Richness," as found on www.bio.uu.nl

116. *Spaces in a parking lot.* A parking lot has attendants to park the cars. The number N of stalls needed for waiting cars before attendants can get to them is given by the formula $N = 2.5\sqrt{A}$, where A is the number of arrivals in peak hours. Find the number of spaces needed for the given number of arrivals in peak hours: **(a)** 25; **(b)** 36; **(c)** 49; **(d)** 64.

Determine the domain of each function described. Then draw the graph of each function.

117. $f(x) = \sqrt{x} + 5$

118. $g(x) = \sqrt{x+5}$

119. $g(x) = \sqrt{x} - 2$

120. $f(x) = \sqrt{x-2}$

121. Find the domain of f if

$$f(x) = \dfrac{\sqrt{x+3}}{\sqrt[4]{2-x}}.$$

122. Find the domain of g if

$$g(x) = \dfrac{\sqrt[4]{5-x}}{\sqrt[6]{x+4}}.$$

123. Find the domain of F if $F(x) = \dfrac{x}{\sqrt{x^2-5x-6}}$.

124. Use a graphing calculator to check your answers to Exercises 41, 45, and 59. On some graphing calculators, a MATH key is needed to enter higher roots.

125. Use a graphing calculator to check your answers to Exercises 117 and 118. (See Exercise 124.)

10.2   Rational Numbers as Exponents

Rational Exponents ▪ Negative Rational Exponents ▪ Laws of Exponents ▪
Simplifying Radical Expressions

We have already considered natural-number exponents and integer exponents. We now expand the study of exponents further to include all rational numbers. This will give meaning to expressions like $7^{1/3}$ and $(2x)^{-4/5}$. Such notation will help us simplify certain radical expressions.

Rational Exponents

When defining rational exponents, we want the rules for exponents to hold for rational exponents just as they do for integer exponents. In particular, we still want to add exponents when multiplying.

If $a^{1/2} \cdot a^{1/2} = a^{1/2+1/2} = a^1$,   then $a^{1/2}$ should mean $\sqrt{a}$.

If $a^{1/3} \cdot a^{1/3} \cdot a^{1/3} = a^{1/3+1/3+1/3} = a^1$, then $a^{1/3}$ should mean $\sqrt[3]{a}$.

$$a^{1/n} = \sqrt[n]{a}$$

$a^{1/n}$ means $\sqrt[n]{a}$. When a is nonnegative, n can be any natural number greater than 1. When a is negative, n can be any odd natural number greater than 1.

Thus, $a^{1/5} = \sqrt[5]{a}$ and $a^{1/10} = \sqrt[10]{a}$. Note that the denominator of the exponent becomes the index and the base becomes the radicand.

EXAMPLE **1**   Write an equivalent expression using radical notation and, if possible, simplify.

a) $16^{1/2}$ **b)** $(-8)^{1/3}$ **c)** $(abc)^{1/5}$ **d)** $(25x^{16})^{1/2}$

SOLUTION

a) $16^{1/2} = \sqrt{16} = 4$

b) $(-8)^{1/3} = \sqrt[3]{-8} = -2$

c) $(abc)^{1/5} = \sqrt[5]{abc}$

The denominator of the exponent becomes the index. The base becomes the radicand. Recall that for square roots, the index 2 is understood without being written.

d) $(25x^{16})^{1/2} = 25^{1/2}x^8 = \sqrt{25} \cdot x^8 = 5x^8$

TRY EXERCISE 11

EXAMPLE **2**   Write an equivalent expression using exponential notation.

a) $\sqrt[5]{9ab}$ **b)** $\sqrt[7]{\dfrac{x^3y}{4}}$ **c)** $\sqrt{5x}$

SOLUTION   Parentheses are required to indicate the base.

a) $\sqrt[5]{9ab} = (9ab)^{1/5}$

b) $\sqrt[7]{\dfrac{x^3y}{4}} = \left(\dfrac{x^3y}{4}\right)^{1/7}$

The index becomes the denominator of the exponent. The radicand becomes the base.

c) $\sqrt{5x} = (5x)^{1/2}$ The index 2 is understood without being written. We assume $x \geq 0$.

TRY EXERCISE 31

How shall we define $a^{2/3}$? If the property for multiplying exponents is to hold, we must have $a^{2/3} = (a^{1/3})^2$ and $a^{2/3} = (a^2)^{1/3}$. This would suggest that $a^{2/3} = \left(\sqrt[3]{a}\right)^2$ and $a^{2/3} = \sqrt[3]{a^2}$. We make our definition accordingly.

> ## Positive Rational Exponents
>
> For any natural numbers m and n ($n \neq 1$) and any real number a for which $\sqrt[n]{a}$ exists,
>
> $$a^{m/n} \quad \text{means} \quad \left(\sqrt[n]{a}\right)^m, \quad \text{or} \quad \sqrt[n]{a^m}.$$

EXAMPLE 3

Write an equivalent expression using radical notation and simplify.

a) $27^{2/3}$

b) $25^{3/2}$

SOLUTION

a) $27^{2/3}$ means $\left(\sqrt[3]{27}\right)^2$ or, equivalently, $\sqrt[3]{27^2}$. Let's see which is easier to simplify:

$$\left(\sqrt[3]{27}\right)^2 = 3^2 \qquad \sqrt[3]{27^2} = \sqrt[3]{729}$$
$$= 9; \qquad\qquad\quad = 9.$$

The simplification on the left is probably easier for most people.

b) $25^{3/2}$ means $\left(\sqrt[2]{25}\right)^3$ or, equivalently, $\sqrt[2]{25^3}$ (the index 2 is normally omitted). Since $\sqrt{25}$ is more commonly known than $\sqrt{25^3}$, we use that form:

$$25^{3/2} = \left(\sqrt{25}\right)^3 = 5^3 = 125.$$

TRY EXERCISE 23

STUDENT NOTES

It is important to remember both meanings of $a^{m/n}$. When the root of the base a is known, $\left(\sqrt[n]{a}\right)^m$ is generally easier to work with. When it is not known, $\sqrt[n]{a^m}$ is often more convenient.

EXAMPLE 4

Write an equivalent expression using exponential notation.

a) $\sqrt[3]{9^4}$

b) $\left(\sqrt[4]{7xy}\right)^5$

SOLUTION

a) $\sqrt[3]{9^4} = 9^{4/3}$ } The index becomes the denominator of the
b) $\left(\sqrt[4]{7xy}\right)^5 = (7xy)^{5/4}$ } fraction that is the exponent.

TRY EXERCISE 37

Negative Rational Exponents

Recall from Section 4.2 that $x^{-2} = 1/x^2$. Negative rational exponents behave similarly.

TECHNOLOGY CONNECTION

To approximate $7^{2/3}$, we enter 7 ⌃ (2/3).

1. Why are the parentheses needed above?
2. Compare the graphs of $y_1 = x^{1/2}$, $y_2 = x$, and $y_3 = x^{3/2}$ and determine those x-values for which $y_1 > y_3$.

> ## Negative Rational Exponents
>
> For any rational number m/n and any nonzero real number a for which $a^{m/n}$ exists,
>
> $$a^{-m/n} \quad \text{means} \quad \frac{1}{a^{m/n}}.$$

> *CAUTION!* A negative exponent does not indicate that the expression in which it appears is negative: $a^{-1} \neq -a$.

EXAMPLE **5**   Write an equivalent expression with positive exponents and, if possible, simplify.

a) $9^{-1/2}$

b) $(5xy)^{-4/5}$

c) $64^{-2/3}$

d) $4x^{-2/3}y^{1/5}$

e) $\left(\dfrac{3r}{7s}\right)^{-5/2}$

SOLUTION

a) $9^{-1/2} = \dfrac{1}{9^{1/2}}$ $9^{-1/2}$ is the reciprocal of $9^{1/2}$.

Since $9^{1/2} = \sqrt{9} = 3$, the answer simplifies to $\dfrac{1}{3}$.

b) $(5xy)^{-4/5} = \dfrac{1}{(5xy)^{4/5}}$ $(5xy)^{-4/5}$ is the reciprocal of $(5xy)^{4/5}$.

c) $64^{-2/3} = \dfrac{1}{64^{2/3}}$ $64^{-2/3}$ is the reciprocal of $64^{2/3}$.

Since $64^{2/3} = \left(\sqrt[3]{64}\right)^2 = 4^2 = 16$, the answer simplifies to $\dfrac{1}{16}$.

d) $4x^{-2/3}y^{1/5} = 4 \cdot \dfrac{1}{x^{2/3}} \cdot y^{1/5} = \dfrac{4y^{1/5}}{x^{2/3}}$

e) In Section 4.2, we found that $(a/b)^{-n} = (b/a)^n$. This property holds for *any* negative exponent:

$$\left(\dfrac{3r}{7s}\right)^{-5/2} = \left(\dfrac{7s}{3r}\right)^{5/2}.$$ Writing the reciprocal of the base and changing the sign of the exponent

▶ **TRY EXERCISE** ▸ 53

Laws of Exponents

The same laws hold for rational exponents as for integer exponents.

> ### Laws of Exponents
>
> For any real numbers a and b and any rational exponents m and n for which a^m, a^n, and b^m are defined:
>
> **1.** $a^m \cdot a^n = a^{m+n}$ When multiplying, add exponents if the bases are the same.
>
> **2.** $\dfrac{a^m}{a^n} = a^{m-n}$ When dividing, subtract exponents if the bases are the same. (Assume $a \neq 0$.)
>
> **3.** $(a^m)^n = a^{m \cdot n}$ To raise a power to a power, multiply the exponents.
>
> **4.** $(ab)^m = a^m b^m$ To raise a product to a power, raise each factor to the power and multiply.

EXAMPLE **6**   Use the laws of exponents to simplify.

a) $3^{1/5} \cdot 3^{3/5}$

b) $\dfrac{a^{1/4}}{a^{1/2}}$

c) $(7.2^{2/3})^{3/4}$

d) $(a^{-1/3}b^{2/5})^{1/2}$

SOLUTION

a) $3^{1/5} \cdot 3^{3/5} = 3^{1/5+3/5} = 3^{4/5}$ Adding exponents

b) $\dfrac{a^{1/4}}{a^{1/2}} = a^{1/4-1/2} = a^{1/4-2/4}$ Subtracting exponents after finding a common denominator

$$= a^{-1/4}, \text{ or } \dfrac{1}{a^{1/4}} \qquad a^{-1/4} \text{ is the reciprocal of } a^{1/4}.$$

c) $(7.2^{2/3})^{3/4} = 7.2^{(2/3)(3/4)} = 7.2^{6/12}$ Multiplying exponents

$$= 7.2^{1/2} \qquad \text{Using arithmetic to simplify the exponent}$$

d) $(a^{-1/3}b^{2/5})^{1/2} = a^{(-1/3)(1/2)} \cdot b^{(2/5)(1/2)}$ Raising a product to a power and multiplying exponents

$$= a^{-1/6}b^{1/5}, \text{ or } \dfrac{b^{1/5}}{a^{1/6}}$$

> **TRY EXERCISE** 69

Simplifying Radical Expressions

Many radical expressions contain radicands or factors of radicands that are powers. When these powers and the index share a common factor, rational exponents can be used to simplify the expression.

> ### To Simplify Radical Expressions
> 1. Convert radical expressions to exponential expressions.
> 2. Use arithmetic and the laws of exponents to simplify.
> 3. Convert back to radical notation as needed.

EXAMPLE 7   Use rational exponents to simplify. Do not use exponents that are fractions in the final answer.

a) $\sqrt[6]{(5x)^3}$ **b)** $\sqrt[5]{t^{20}}$

c) $\left(\sqrt[3]{ab^2c}\right)^{12}$ **d)** $\sqrt{\sqrt[3]{x}}$

SOLUTION

a) $\sqrt[6]{(5x)^3} = (5x)^{3/6}$ Converting to exponential notation

$$= (5x)^{1/2} \qquad \text{Simplifying the exponent}$$

$$= \sqrt{5x} \qquad \text{Returning to radical notation}$$

b) $\sqrt[5]{t^{20}} = t^{20/5}$ Converting to exponential notation

$$= t^4 \qquad \text{Simplifying the exponent}$$

c) $\left(\sqrt[3]{ab^2c}\right)^{12} = (ab^2c)^{12/3}$ Converting to exponential notation

$$= (ab^2c)^4 \qquad \text{Simplifying the exponent}$$

$$= a^4b^8c^4 \qquad \text{Using the laws of exponents}$$

d) $\sqrt{\sqrt[3]{x}} = \sqrt{x^{1/3}}$ Converting the radicand to exponential notation

$$= (x^{1/3})^{1/2} \qquad \text{Try to go directly to this step.}$$

$$= x^{1/6} \qquad \text{Using the laws of exponents}$$

$$= \sqrt[6]{x} \qquad \text{Returning to radical notation}$$

> **TRY EXERCISE** 87

TECHNOLOGY CONNECTION

One way to check Example 7(a) is to let $y_1 = (5x)^{3/6}$ and $y_2 = \sqrt{5x}$. Then use GRAPH or TABLE to see if $y_1 = y_2$. An alternative is to let $y_3 = y_2 - y_1$ and see if $y_3 = 0$. Check Example 7(a) using one of these two methods.

1. Why are rational exponents especially useful when working on a graphing calculator?

10.2   EXERCISE SET

Concept Reinforcement   *In each of Exercises 1–8, match the expression with the equivalent expression from the column on the right.*

1. ____ $x^{2/5}$

2. ____ $x^{5/2}$

3. ____ $x^{-5/2}$

4. ____ $x^{-2/5}$

5. ____ $x^{1/5} \cdot x^{2/5}$

6. ____ $(x^{1/5})^{5/2}$

7. ____ $\sqrt[5]{x^4}$

8. ____ $(\sqrt[4]{x})^5$

a) $x^{3/5}$

b) $(\sqrt[5]{x})^4$

c) $\sqrt{x^5}$

d) $x^{1/2}$

e) $\dfrac{1}{(\sqrt{x})^5}$

f) $\sqrt[4]{x^5}$

g) $\sqrt[5]{x^2}$

h) $\dfrac{1}{(\sqrt[5]{x})^2}$

Note: Assume for all exercises that all variables are nonnegative and that all denominators are nonzero.

Write an equivalent expression using radical notation and, if possible, simplify.

9. $y^{1/3}$

10. $t^{1/4}$

11. $36^{1/2}$

12. $125^{1/3}$

13. $32^{1/5}$

14. $81^{1/4}$

15. $64^{1/2}$

16. $100^{1/2}$

17. $(xyz)^{1/2}$

18. $(ab)^{1/4}$

19. $(a^2b^2)^{1/5}$

20. $(x^3y^3)^{1/4}$

21. $t^{5/6}$

22. $a^{3/2}$

23. $16^{3/4}$

24. $4^{7/2}$

25. $125^{4/3}$

26. $9^{5/2}$

27. $(81x)^{3/4}$

28. $(125a)^{2/3}$

29. $(25x^4)^{3/2}$

30. $(9y^6)^{3/2}$

Write an equivalent expression using exponential notation.

31. $\sqrt[3]{18}$

32. $\sqrt[4]{10}$

33. $\sqrt{30}$

34. $\sqrt{22}$

35. $\sqrt{x^7}$

36. $\sqrt{a^3}$

37. $\sqrt[5]{m^2}$

38. $\sqrt[5]{n^4}$

39. $\sqrt[4]{pq}$

40. $\sqrt[3]{cd}$

41. $\sqrt[5]{xy^2z}$

42. $\sqrt[7]{x^3y^2z^2}$

43. $(\sqrt{3mn})^3$

44. $(\sqrt[3]{7xy})^4$

45. $(\sqrt[7]{8x^2y})^5$

46. $(\sqrt[6]{2a^5b})^7$

47. $\dfrac{2x}{\sqrt[3]{z^2}}$

48. $\dfrac{3a}{\sqrt[5]{c^2}}$

Write an equivalent expression with positive exponents and, if possible, simplify.

49. $a^{-1/4}$

50. $m^{-1/3}$

51. $(2rs)^{-3/4}$

52. $(5xy)^{-5/6}$

53. $\left(\dfrac{1}{16}\right)^{-3/4}$

54. $\left(\dfrac{1}{8}\right)^{-2/3}$

55. $\dfrac{8c}{a^{-3/5}}$

56. $\dfrac{3b}{a^{-5/7}}$

57. $2a^{3/4}b^{-1/2}c^{2/3}$

58. $5x^{-2/3}y^{4/5}z$

59. $3^{-5/2}a^3b^{-7/3}$

60. $2^{-1/3}x^4y^{-2/7}$

61. $\left(\dfrac{2ab}{3c}\right)^{-5/6}$

62. $\left(\dfrac{7x}{8yz}\right)^{-3/5}$

63. $\dfrac{6a}{\sqrt[4]{b}}$

64. $\dfrac{5y}{\sqrt[3]{z}}$

Use the laws of exponents to simplify. Do not use negative exponents in any answers.

65. $11^{1/2} \cdot 11^{1/3}$

66. $5^{1/4} \cdot 5^{1/8}$

67. $\dfrac{3^{5/8}}{3^{-1/8}}$

68. $\dfrac{8^{7/11}}{8^{-2/11}}$

69. $\dfrac{4.3^{-1/5}}{4.3^{-7/10}}$

70. $\dfrac{2.7^{-11/12}}{2.7^{-1/6}}$

71. $(10^{3/5})^{2/5}$

72. $(5^{5/4})^{3/7}$

73. $a^{2/3} \cdot a^{5/4}$

74. $x^{3/4} \cdot x^{1/3}$

Aha! 75. $(64^{3/4})^{4/3}$

76. $(27^{-2/3})^{3/2}$

77. $(m^{2/3}n^{-1/4})^{1/2}$

78. $(x^{-1/3}y^{2/5})^{1/4}$

Use rational exponents to simplify. Do not use fraction exponents in the final answer.

79. $\sqrt[9]{x^3}$

80. $\sqrt[12]{a^3}$

81. $\sqrt[3]{y^{15}}$

82. $\sqrt[4]{y^{40}}$

83. $\sqrt[12]{a^6}$

84. $\sqrt[30]{x^5}$

85. $(\sqrt[7]{xy})^{14}$

86. $(\sqrt[3]{ab})^{15}$

87. $\sqrt[4]{(7a)^2}$

88. $\sqrt[8]{(3x)^2}$

89. $\left(\sqrt[8]{2x}\right)^6$

90. $\left(\sqrt[10]{3a}\right)^5$

91. $\sqrt{\sqrt[5]{m}}$

92. $\sqrt[6]{\sqrt{n}}$

93. $\sqrt[4]{(xy)^{12}}$

94. $\sqrt{(ab)^6}$

95. $\left(\sqrt[5]{a^2 b^4}\right)^{15}$

96. $\left(\sqrt[3]{x^2 y^5}\right)^{12}$

97. $\sqrt[3]{\sqrt[4]{xy}}$

98. $\sqrt[5]{\sqrt[3]{2a}}$

99. If $f(x) = (x + 5)^{1/2}(x + 7)^{-1/2}$, find the domain of f. Explain how you found your answer.

100. Let $f(x) = 5x^{-1/3}$. Under what condition will we have $f(x) > 0$? Why?

Skill Review

To prepare for Section 10.3, review multiplying and factoring polynomials (Sections 4.5 and 5.4).

Multiply. [4.5]

101. $(x + 5)(x - 5)$

102. $(x - 2)(x^2 + 2x + 4)$

Factor. [5.4]

103. $4x^2 + 20x + 25$

104. $9a^2 - 24a + 16$

105. $5t^2 - 10t + 5$

106. $3n^2 + 12n + 12$

Synthesis

107. Explain why $\sqrt[3]{x^6} = x^2$ for any value of x, whereas $\sqrt[2]{x^6} = x^3$ only when $x \ge 0$.

108. If $g(x) = x^{3/n}$, in what way does the domain of g depend on whether n is odd or even?

Use rational exponents to simplify.

109. $\sqrt{x\sqrt[3]{x^2}}$

110. $\sqrt[4]{\sqrt[3]{8x^3 y^6}}$

111. $\sqrt[14]{c^2 - 2cd + d^2}$

Music. *The function given by $f(x) = k2^{x/12}$ can be used to determine the frequency, in cycles per second, of a musical note that is x half-steps above a note with frequency k.* *

112. The frequency of concert A for a trumpet is 440 cycles per second. Find the frequency of the A that is two octaves (24 half-steps) above concert A (few trumpeters can reach this note.)

---

*This application was inspired by information provided by Dr. Homer B. Tilton of Pima Community College East.

113. Show that the G that is 7 half-steps (a "perfect fifth") above middle C (262 cycles per second) has a frequency that is about 1.5 times that of middle C.

114. Show that the C sharp that is 4 half-steps (a "major third") above concert A (see Exercise 112) has a frequency that is about 25% greater than that of concert A.

115. *Road pavement messages.* In a psychological study, it was determined that the proper length L of the letters of a word printed on pavement is given by

$$L = \frac{0.000169d^{2.27}}{h},$$

where d is the distance of a car from the lettering and h is the height of the eye above the surface of the road. All units are in meters. This formula says that from a vantage point h meters above the surface of the road, if a driver is to be able to recognize a message d meters away, that message will be the most recognizable if the length of the letters is L. Find L to the nearest tenth of a meter, given d and h.

a) $h = 1$ m, $d = 60$ m
b) $h = 0.9906$ m, $d = 75$ m
c) $h = 2.4$ m, $d = 80$ m
d) $h = 1.1$ m, $d = 100$ m

116. *Baseball.* The statistician Bill James has found that a baseball team's winning percentage P can be approximated by

$$P = \frac{r^{1.83}}{r^{1.83} + \sigma^{1.83}},$$

where r is the total number of runs scored by that team and σ (sigma) is the total number of runs scored by their opponents. During a recent season, the San Francisco Giants scored 799 runs and their opponents scored 749 runs. Use James's formula to predict the Giants' winning percentage (the team actually won 55.6% of their games).

Source: M. Bittinger, *One Man's Journey Through Mathematics.* Boston: Addison-Wesley, 2004

117. *Forestry.* The total wood volume T, in cubic feet, in a California black oak can be estimated using the formula

$$T = 0.936\, d^{1.97} h^{0.85},$$

where d is the diameter of the tree at breast height and h is the total height of the tree. How much wood is in a California black oak that is 3 ft in diameter at breast height and 80 ft high?

Source: Norman H. Pillsbury and Michael L. Kirkley, 1984. Equations for total, wood, and saw-log volume for thirteen California hardwoods, USDA Forest Service PNW Research Note No. 414: 52 p.

118. *Physics.* The equation $m = m_0(1 - v^2 c^{-2})^{-1/2}$, developed by Albert Einstein, is used to determine the mass m of an object that is moving v meters per second and has mass m_0 before the motion begins. The constant c is the speed of light, approximately 3×10^8 m/sec. Suppose that a particle with mass 8 mg is accelerated to a speed of $\frac{9}{5} \times 10^8$ m/sec. Without using a calculator, find the new mass of the particle.

119. Using a graphing calculator, select **MODE** SIMUL and the FORMAT EXPROFF. Then graph

$$y_1 = x^{1/2}, \qquad y_2 = 3x^{2/5},$$
$$y_3 = x^{4/7}, \quad \text{and} \quad y_4 = \tfrac{1}{5}x^{3/4}.$$

Looking only at coordinates, match each graph with its equation.

COLLABORATIVE CORNER

Are Equivalent Fractions Equivalent Exponents?

Focus: Functions and rational exponents

Time: 10–20 minutes

Group size: 3

Materials: Graph paper

In arithmetic, we have seen that $\frac{1}{3}, \frac{1}{6} \cdot 2$, and $2 \cdot \frac{1}{6}$ all represent the same number. Interestingly,

$$f(x) = x^{1/3},$$
$$g(x) = (x^{1/6})^2, \quad \text{and}$$
$$h(x) = (x^2)^{1/6}$$

represent three *different* functions.

ACTIVITY

1. Selecting a variety of values for x and using the definition of positive rational exponents, one group member should graph f, a second group member should graph g, and a third group member should graph h. Be sure to check whether negative x-values are in the domain of the function.

2. Compare the three graphs and check each other's work. How and why do the graphs differ?

3. Decide as a group which graph, if any, would best represent the graph of $k(x) = x^{2/6}$. Then be prepared to explain your reasoning to the entire class. (*Hint:* Study the definition of $a^{m/n}$ on p. 644 carefully.)

10.3 Multiplying Radical Expressions

Multiplying Radical Expressions • Simplifying by Factoring • Multiplying and Simplifying

Multiplying Radical Expressions

Note that $\sqrt{4}\sqrt{25} = 2 \cdot 5 = 10$. Also $\sqrt{4 \cdot 25} = \sqrt{100} = 10$. Likewise,

$$\sqrt[3]{27}\,\sqrt[3]{8} = 3 \cdot 2 = 6 \quad \text{and} \quad \sqrt[3]{27 \cdot 8} = \sqrt[3]{216} = 6.$$

These examples suggest the following.

The Product Rule for Radicals

For any real numbers $\sqrt[n]{a}$ and $\sqrt[n]{b}$,

$$\sqrt[n]{a} \cdot \sqrt[n]{b} = \sqrt[n]{a \cdot b}.$$

(The product of two *n*th roots is the *n*th root of the product of the two radicands.)

Rational exponents can be used to derive this rule:

$$\sqrt[n]{a} \cdot \sqrt[n]{b} = a^{1/n} \cdot b^{1/n} = (a \cdot b)^{1/n} = \sqrt[n]{a \cdot b}.$$

EXAMPLE 1 Multiply.

a) $\sqrt{2} \cdot \sqrt{7}$ b) $\sqrt{x + 3}\,\sqrt{x - 3}$

c) $\sqrt[3]{4} \cdot \sqrt[3]{5}$ d) $\sqrt[4]{\dfrac{y}{5}} \cdot \sqrt[4]{\dfrac{7}{x}}$

SOLUTION

a) When no index is written, roots are understood to be square roots with an unwritten index of two. We apply the product rule:

$$\sqrt{2} \cdot \sqrt{7} = \sqrt{2 \cdot 7}$$
$$= \sqrt{14}.$$

b) $\sqrt{x + 3}\,\sqrt{x - 3} = \sqrt{(x + 3)(x - 3)}$ The product of two square roots is
$$= \sqrt{x^2 - 9}$$ the square root of the product.

CAUTION! $\sqrt{x^2 - 9} \neq \sqrt{x^2} - \sqrt{9}.$
---

c) Both $\sqrt[3]{4}$ and $\sqrt[3]{5}$ have indices of three, so to multiply we can use the product rule:

$$\sqrt[3]{4} \cdot \sqrt[3]{5} = \sqrt[3]{4 \cdot 5} = \sqrt[3]{20}.$$

d) $\sqrt[4]{\dfrac{y}{5}} \cdot \sqrt[4]{\dfrac{7}{x}} = \sqrt[4]{\dfrac{y}{5} \cdot \dfrac{7}{x}} = \sqrt[4]{\dfrac{7y}{5x}}$ In Section 10.4, we discuss other ways to write answers like this.

TRY EXERCISE 7

To check Example 1(b), let
$y_1 = \sqrt{x + 3}\sqrt{x - 3}$ and
$y_2 = \sqrt{x^2 - 9}$ and compare:

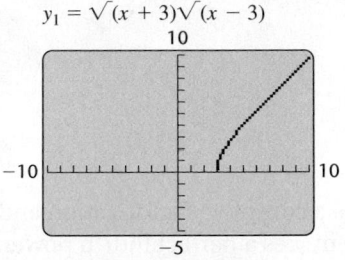

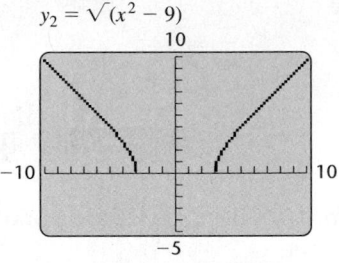

Because $y_1 = y_2$ for all
x-values that can be used in
both y_1 and y_2, Example 1(b)
is correct.

1. Why do the graphs above
differ in appearance?
(*Hint*: What are the
domains of the two
related functions?)

> **CAUTION!**   The product rule for radicals applies only when radicals have
> the same index:
> $$\sqrt[n]{a} \cdot \sqrt[m]{b} \neq \sqrt[nm]{a \cdot b}.$$

Simplifying by Factoring

The number p is a *perfect square* if there exists a rational number q for which
$q^2 = p$. We say that p is a *perfect cube* if $q^3 = p$ for some rational number q. In
general, p is a *perfect nth power* if $q^n = p$ for some rational number q. Thus, 16
and $\frac{1}{10,000}$ are both perfect 4th powers since $2^4 = 16$ and $\left(\frac{1}{10}\right)^4 = \frac{1}{10,000}$.
   The product rule allows us to simplify $\sqrt[n]{ab}$ whenever ab contains a factor
that is a perfect nth power.

> ### Using the Product Rule to Simplify
> $$\sqrt[n]{ab} = \sqrt[n]{a} \cdot \sqrt[n]{b}.$$
> $\left(\sqrt[n]{a} \text{ and } \sqrt[n]{b} \text{ must both be real numbers.}\right)$

To illustrate, suppose we wish to simplify $\sqrt{20}$. Since this is a *square* root, we
check to see if there is a factor of 20 that is a perfect square. There is one, 4, so we
express 20 as $4 \cdot 5$ and use the product rule:

$$\sqrt{20} = \sqrt{4 \cdot 5} \qquad \text{Factoring the radicand (4 is a perfect square)}$$
$$= \sqrt{4} \cdot \sqrt{5} \qquad \text{Factoring into two radicals}$$
$$= 2\sqrt{5}. \qquad \text{Finding the square root of 4}$$

> **To Simplify a Radical Expression with Index n by Factoring**
> **1.** Express the radicand as a product in which one factor is the largest
> perfect nth power possible.
> **2.** Rewrite the expression as the nth root of each factor.
> **3.** Simplify the expression containing the perfect nth power.
> **4.** Simplification is complete when no radicand has a factor that is a
> perfect nth power.

   **It is often safe to assume that a radicand does not represent a negative
number raised to an even power. We will henceforth make this assumption—
unless functions are involved—and discontinue use of absolute-value notation
when taking even roots.**

EXAMPLE **2**   Simplify by factoring: **(a)** $\sqrt{200}$; **(b)** $\sqrt{18x^2y}$; **(c)** $\sqrt[3]{-72}$; **(d)** $\sqrt[4]{162x^6}$.

SOLUTION

a) $\sqrt{200} = \sqrt{100 \cdot 2}$ 100 is the largest perfect-square factor of 200.
$$= \sqrt{100} \cdot \sqrt{2} = 10\sqrt{2}$$

Express the radicand as a product.   **b)** $\sqrt{18x^2y} = \sqrt{9 \cdot 2 \cdot x^2 \cdot y}$ $9x^2$ is the largest perfect-square factor of $18x^2y$.

     Rewrite as the *n*th root of each factor. $= \sqrt{9x^2} \cdot \sqrt{2y}$ Factoring into two radicals

         Simplify. $= 3x\sqrt{2y}$ Taking the square root of $9x^2$

c) $\sqrt[3]{-72} = \sqrt[3]{-8 \cdot 9}$ -8 is a perfect-cube (third-power) factor of -72.

       $= \sqrt[3]{-8} \cdot \sqrt[3]{9} = -2\sqrt[3]{9}$

d) $\sqrt[4]{162x^6} = \sqrt[4]{81 \cdot 2 \cdot x^4 \cdot x^2}$ $81 \cdot x^4$ is the largest perfect fourth-power factor of $162x^6$.

       $= \sqrt[4]{81x^4} \cdot \sqrt[4]{2x^2}$ Factoring into two radicals

       $= 3x\sqrt[4]{2x^2}$ Taking the fourth root of $81x^4$

Let's look at this example another way. We write a complete factorization and look for quadruples of factors. Each quadruple makes a perfect fourth power:

$$\sqrt[4]{162x^6} = \sqrt[4]{3 \cdot 3 \cdot 3 \cdot 3 \cdot 2 \cdot x \cdot x \cdot x \cdot x \cdot x \cdot x} \quad \begin{array}{l} 3 \cdot 3 \cdot 3 \cdot 3 = 3^4 \\ \text{and} \\ x \cdot x \cdot x \cdot x = x^4 \end{array}$$

$$= 3 \cdot x \cdot \sqrt[4]{2 \cdot x \cdot x}$$

$$= 3x\sqrt[4]{2x^2}.$$

> TRY EXERCISE 31

EXAMPLE 3   If $f(x) = \sqrt{3x^2 - 6x + 3}$, find a simplified form for $f(x)$. Because we are working with a function, assume that x can be any real number.

SOLUTION

$$f(x) = \sqrt{3x^2 - 6x + 3}$$

$$\left. \begin{array}{l} = \sqrt{3(x^2 - 2x + 1)} \\ = \sqrt{(x-1)^2 \cdot 3} \end{array} \right\} \quad \begin{array}{l} \text{Factoring the radicand; } x^2 - 2x + 1 \\ \text{is a perfect square.} \end{array}$$

$$= \sqrt{(x-1)^2} \cdot \sqrt{3} \quad \text{Factoring into two radicals}$$

$$= |x - 1|\sqrt{3} \quad \text{Finding the square root of } (x-1)^2$$

> TRY EXERCISE 43

TECHNOLOGY CONNECTION

To check Example 3, let $y_1 = \sqrt{(3x^2 - 6x + 3)}$, $y_2 = \text{abs}(x - 1)\sqrt{(3)}$, and $y_3 = (x - 1)\sqrt{(3)}$. Do the graphs all coincide? Why or why not?

EXAMPLE 4   Simplify: **(a)** $\sqrt{x^7y^{11}z^9}$; **(b)** $\sqrt[3]{16a^7b^{14}}$.

SOLUTION

a) There are many ways to factor $x^7y^{11}z^9$. Because of the square root (index of 2), we identify the largest exponents that are multiples of 2:

$$\sqrt{x^7y^{11}z^9} = \sqrt{x^6 \cdot x \cdot y^{10} \cdot y \cdot z^8 \cdot z} \quad \begin{array}{l} \text{The largest perfect-square} \\ \text{factor is } x^6y^{10}z^8. \end{array}$$

$$= \sqrt{x^6y^{10}z^8} \sqrt{xyz} \quad \text{Factoring into two radicals}$$

$$= x^{6/2}y^{10/2}z^{8/2}\sqrt{xyz} \quad \begin{array}{l} \text{Converting to rational expo-} \\ \text{nents. Try to do this mentally.} \end{array}$$

$$= x^3y^5z^4\sqrt{xyz}. \quad \text{Simplifying}$$

Check: $\left(x^3y^5z^4\sqrt{xyz} \right)^2 = (x^3)^2(y^5)^2(z^4)^2\left(\sqrt{xyz} \right)^2$

            $= x^6 \cdot y^{10} \cdot z^8 \cdot xyz = x^7y^{11}z^9.$

Our check shows that $x^3y^5z^4\sqrt{xyz}$ is the square root of $x^7y^{11}z^9$.

b) There are many ways to factor $16a^7b^{14}$. Because of the cube root (index of 3), we identify factors with the largest exponents that are multiples of 3:

$$\sqrt[3]{16a^7b^{14}} = \sqrt[3]{8 \cdot 2 \cdot a^6 \cdot a \cdot b^{12} \cdot b^2} \qquad \text{The largest perfect-cube factor is } 8a^6b^{12}.$$

$$= \sqrt[3]{8a^6b^{12}}\sqrt[3]{2ab^2} \qquad \text{Rewriting as a product of cube roots}$$

$$= 2a^2b^4\sqrt[3]{2ab^2}. \qquad \text{Simplifying the expression containing the perfect cube}$$

As a check, let's redo the problem using a complete factorization of the radicand:

$$\sqrt[3]{16a^7b^{14}} = \sqrt[3]{\boxed{2 \cdot 2 \cdot 2} \cdot 2 \cdot \boxed{a \cdot a \cdot a} \cdot \boxed{a \cdot a \cdot a} \cdot a \cdot \boxed{b \cdot b \cdot b} \cdot \boxed{b \cdot b \cdot b} \cdot \boxed{b \cdot b \cdot b} \cdot \boxed{b \cdot b \cdot b} \cdot b \cdot b}$$

Each triple of factors makes a cube.

$$= 2 \cdot a \cdot a \cdot b \cdot b \cdot b \cdot b \cdot \sqrt[3]{2 \cdot a \cdot b \cdot b}$$

$$= 2a^2b^4\sqrt[3]{2ab^2}. \qquad \text{Our answer checks.}$$

> **TRY EXERCISE** 51

> *Remember*: To simplify an nth root, identify factors in the radicand with exponents that are multiples of n.

Multiplying and Simplifying

We have used the product rule for radicals to find products and also to simplify radical expressions. For some radical expressions, it is possible to do both: First find a product and then simplify.

EXAMPLE 5   Multiply and simplify.

a) $\sqrt{15}\sqrt{6}$ **b)** $3\sqrt[3]{25} \cdot 2\sqrt[3]{5}$ **c)** $\sqrt[4]{8x^3y^5}\sqrt[4]{4x^2y^3}$

SOLUTION

a) $\sqrt{15}\sqrt{6} = \sqrt{15 \cdot 6} \qquad \text{Multiplying radicands}$

$$= \sqrt{90} = \sqrt{9}\sqrt{10} \qquad \text{9 is a perfect square.}$$

$$= 3\sqrt{10}$$

b) $3\sqrt[3]{25} \cdot 2\sqrt[3]{5} = 3 \cdot 2 \cdot \sqrt[3]{25 \cdot 5} \qquad \text{Using a commutative law; multiplying radicands}$

$$= 6 \cdot \sqrt[3]{125} \qquad \text{125 is a perfect cube.}$$

$$= 6 \cdot 5, \text{ or } 30$$

c) $\sqrt[4]{8x^3y^5}\sqrt[4]{4x^2y^3} = \sqrt[4]{32x^5y^8} \qquad \text{Multiplying radicands}$

$$= \sqrt[4]{16x^4y^8 \cdot 2x} \qquad \text{Identifying the largest perfect fourth-power factor}$$

$$= \sqrt[4]{16x^4y^8}\sqrt[4]{2x} \qquad \text{Factoring into radicals}$$

$$= 2xy^2\sqrt[4]{2x} \qquad \text{Finding the fourth root; assume } x \geq 0.$$

The checks are left to the student.

> **TRY EXERCISE** 65

10.3 EXERCISE SET

 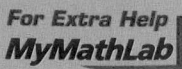  

Concept Reinforcement   *Classify each statement as either true or false.*

1. For any real numbers $\sqrt[n]{a}$ and $\sqrt[n]{b}$,
$\sqrt[n]{a} \cdot \sqrt[n]{b} = \sqrt[n]{ab}$.

2. For any real numbers $\sqrt[n]{a}$ and $\sqrt[n]{b}$,
$\sqrt[n]{a} + \sqrt[n]{b} = \sqrt[n]{a + b}$.

3. For any real numbers $\sqrt[n]{a}$ and $\sqrt[m]{b}$,
$\sqrt[n]{a} \cdot \sqrt[m]{b} = \sqrt[nm]{ab}$.

4. For $x > 0$, $\sqrt{x^2 - 9} = x - 3$.

5. The expression $\sqrt[3]{X}$ is not simplified if X contains a factor that is a perfect cube.

6. It is often possible to simplify $\sqrt{A \cdot B}$ even though $\sqrt{A}$ and $\sqrt{B}$ cannot be simplified.

Multiply.

7. $\sqrt{3}\,\sqrt{10}$

8. $\sqrt{6}\,\sqrt{5}$

9. $\sqrt[3]{7}\,\sqrt[3]{5}$

10. $\sqrt[3]{2}\,\sqrt[3]{3}$

11. $\sqrt[4]{6}\,\sqrt[4]{9}$

12. $\sqrt[4]{4}\,\sqrt[4]{10}$

13. $\sqrt{2x}\,\sqrt{13y}$

14. $\sqrt{5a}\,\sqrt{6b}$

15. $\sqrt[5]{8y^3}\,\sqrt[5]{10y}$

16. $\sqrt[5]{9t^2}\,\sqrt[5]{2t}$

17. $\sqrt{y - b}\,\sqrt{y + b}$

18. $\sqrt{x - a}\,\sqrt{x + a}$

19. $\sqrt[3]{0.7y}\,\sqrt[3]{0.3y}$

20. $\sqrt[3]{0.5x}\,\sqrt[3]{0.2x}$

21. $\sqrt[5]{x - 2}\,\sqrt[5]{(x - 2)^2}$

22. $\sqrt[4]{x - 1}\,\sqrt[4]{x^2 + x + 1}$

23. $\sqrt{\dfrac{2}{t}}\,\sqrt{\dfrac{3s}{11}}$

24. $\sqrt{\dfrac{7p}{6}}\,\sqrt{\dfrac{5}{q}}$

25. $\sqrt[7]{\dfrac{x - 3}{4}}\,\sqrt[7]{\dfrac{5}{x + 2}}$

26. $\sqrt[6]{\dfrac{a}{b - 2}}\,\sqrt[6]{\dfrac{3}{b + 2}}$

Simplify by factoring.

27. $\sqrt{12}$

28. $\sqrt{300}$

29. $\sqrt{45}$

30. $\sqrt{27}$

31. $\sqrt{8x^9}$

32. $\sqrt{75y^5}$

33. $\sqrt{120}$

34. $\sqrt{350}$

35. $\sqrt{36a^4b}$

36. $\sqrt{175y^8}$

37. $\sqrt[3]{8x^3y^2}$

38. $\sqrt[3]{27ab^6}$

39. $\sqrt[3]{-16x^6}$

40. $\sqrt[3]{-32a^6}$

Find a simplified form of $f(x)$. Assume that x can be any real number.

41. $f(x) = \sqrt[3]{40x^6}$

42. $f(x) = \sqrt[3]{27x^5}$

43. $f(x) = \sqrt{49(x - 3)^2}$

44. $f(x) = \sqrt{81(x - 1)^2}$

45. $f(x) = \sqrt{5x^2 - 10x + 5}$

46. $f(x) = \sqrt{2x^2 + 8x + 8}$

Simplify. Assume that no radicands were formed by raising negative numbers to even powers.

47. $\sqrt{a^{10}b^{11}}$

48. $\sqrt{x^8y^7}$

49. $\sqrt[3]{x^5y^6z^{10}}$

50. $\sqrt[3]{a^6b^7c^{13}}$

51. $\sqrt[4]{16x^5y^{11}}$

52. $\sqrt[5]{-32a^7b^{11}}$

53. $\sqrt[5]{x^{13}y^8z^{17}}$

54. $\sqrt[5]{a^6b^8c^9}$

55. $\sqrt[3]{-80a^{14}}$

56. $\sqrt[4]{810x^9}$

Multiply and simplify. Assume that no radicands were formed by raising negative numbers to even powers.

57. $\sqrt{5}\,\sqrt{10}$

58. $\sqrt{2}\,\sqrt{6}$

59. $\sqrt{6}\,\sqrt{33}$

60. $\sqrt{10}\,\sqrt{35}$

61. $\sqrt[3]{9}\,\sqrt[3]{3}$

62. $\sqrt[3]{2}\,\sqrt[3]{4}$

Aha! 63. $\sqrt{24y^5}\,\sqrt{24y^5}$

64. $\sqrt{120t^9}\,\sqrt{120t^9}$

65. $\sqrt[3]{5a^2}\,\sqrt[3]{2a}$

66. $\sqrt[3]{7x}\,\sqrt[3]{3x^2}$

67. $\sqrt{2x^5}\,\sqrt{10x^2}$

68. $\sqrt{5a^7}\,\sqrt{15a^3}$

69. $\sqrt[3]{s^2t^4}\,\sqrt[3]{s^4t^6}$

70. $\sqrt[3]{x^2y^4}\,\sqrt[3]{x^2y^6}$

71. $\sqrt[3]{(x - y)^2}\,\sqrt[3]{(x - y)^{10}}$

72. $\sqrt[3]{(t + 4)^5}\,\sqrt[3]{(t + 4)}$

73. $\sqrt[4]{20a^3b^7}\,\sqrt[4]{4a^2b^5}$

74. $\sqrt[4]{9x^7y^2}\,\sqrt[4]{9x^2y^9}$

75. $\sqrt[5]{x^3(y + z)^6}\,\sqrt[5]{x^3(y + z)^4}$

76. $\sqrt[5]{a^3(b - c)^4}\,\sqrt[5]{a^7(b - c)^4}$

77. Explain how you could convince a friend that
$\sqrt{x^2 - 16} \neq \sqrt{x^2} - \sqrt{16}$.

78. Why is it incorrect to say that, in general, $\sqrt{x^2} = x$?

Skill Review

Review simplifying rational expressions (Sections 6.1–6.5).

Perform the indicated operation and, if possible, simplify.

79. $\dfrac{15a^2x}{8b} \cdot \dfrac{24b^2x}{5a}$ [6.2]

80. $\dfrac{x^2 - 1}{x^2 - 4} \div \dfrac{x^2 - x - 2}{x^2 + x - 2}$ [6.2]

81. $\dfrac{x - 3}{2x - 10} - \dfrac{3x - 5}{x^2 - 25}$ [6.4]

82. $\dfrac{6x}{25y^2} + \dfrac{3y}{10x}$ [6.4]

83. $\dfrac{a^{-1} + b^{-1}}{ab}$ [6.5]

84. $\dfrac{\dfrac{1}{x + 1} - \dfrac{2}{x}}{\dfrac{3}{x} + \dfrac{1}{x + 1}}$ [6.5]

Synthesis

85. Explain why it is true that $\sqrt[n]{ab} = \sqrt[n]{a} \cdot \sqrt[n]{b}$ for any real numbers $\sqrt[n]{a}$ and $\sqrt[n]{b}$.

86. Is the equation $\sqrt{(2x + 3)^8} = (2x + 3)^4$ always, sometimes, or never true? Why?

87. *Radar range.* The function given by

$$R(x) = \frac{1}{2}\sqrt[4]{\frac{x \cdot 3.0 \times 10^6}{\pi^2}}$$

can be used to determine the maximum range $R(x)$, in miles, of an ARSR-3 surveillance radar with a peak power of x watts. Determine the maximum radar range when the peak power is 5×10^4 watts.
Source: Introduction to RADAR Techniques, Federal Aviation Administration, 1988

88. *Speed of a skidding car.* Police can estimate the speed at which a car was traveling by measuring its skid marks. The function given by

$$r(L) = 2\sqrt{5L}$$

can be used, where L is the length of a skid mark, in feet, and $r(L)$ is the speed, in miles per hour. Find

the exact speed and an estimate (to the nearest tenth mile per hour) for the speed of a car that left skid marks **(a)** 20 ft long; **(b)** 70 ft long; **(c)** 90 ft long. See also Exercise 102.

89. *Wind chill temperature.* When the temperature is T degrees Celsius and the wind speed is v meters per second, the *wind chill temperature*, T_w, is the temperature (with no wind) that it feels like. Here is a formula for finding wind chill temperature:

$$T_w = 33 - \frac{(10.45 + 10\sqrt{v} - v)(33 - T)}{22}.$$

Estimate the wind chill temperature (to the nearest tenth of a degree) for the given actual temperatures and wind speeds.

a) $T = 7°C,\ v = 8$ m/sec
b) $T = 0°C,\ v = 12$ m/sec
c) $T = -5°C,\ v = 14$ m/sec
d) $T = -23°C,\ v = 15$ m/sec

Simplify. Assume that all variables are nonnegative.

90. $\left(\sqrt{r^3t}\right)^7$

91. $\left(\sqrt[3]{25x^4}\right)^4$

92. $\left(\sqrt[3]{a^2b^4}\right)^5$

93. $\left(\sqrt{a^3b^5}\right)^7$

Draw and compare the graphs of each group of equations.

94. $f(x) = \sqrt{x^2 - 2x + 1}$,
$g(x) = x - 1$,
$h(x) = |x - 1|$

95. $f(x) = \sqrt{x^2 + 2x + 1}$,
$g(x) = x + 1$,
$h(x) = |x + 1|$

96. If $f(t) = \sqrt{t^2 - 3t - 4}$, what is the domain of f?

97. What is the domain of g, if $g(x) = \sqrt{x^2 - 6x + 8}$?

Solve.

98. $\sqrt[3]{5x^{k+1}} \ \sqrt[3]{25x^k} = 5x^7$, for k

99. $\sqrt[5]{4a^{3k+2}} \ \sqrt[5]{8a^{6-k}} = 2a^4$, for k

100. Use a graphing calculator to check your answers to Exercises 21 and 41.

101. Blair is puzzled. When he uses a graphing calculator to graph $y = \sqrt{x} \cdot \sqrt{x}$, he gets the following screen. Explain why Blair did not get the complete line $y = x$.

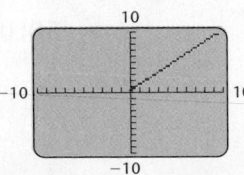

102. Does a car traveling twice as fast as another car leave a skid mark that is twice as long? (See Exercise 88.) Why or why not?

10.4 Dividing Radical Expressions

Dividing and Simplifying • Rationalizing Denominators or Numerators with One Term

Dividing and Simplifying

Just as the root of a product can be expressed as the product of two roots, the root of a quotient can be expressed as the quotient of two roots. For example,

$$\sqrt[3]{\frac{27}{8}} = \frac{3}{2} \quad \text{and} \quad \frac{\sqrt[3]{27}}{\sqrt[3]{8}} = \frac{3}{2}.$$

This example suggests the following.

> **The Quotient Rule for Radicals**
> For any real numbers $\sqrt[n]{a}$ and $\sqrt[n]{b}$, $b \neq 0$,
> $$\sqrt[n]{\frac{a}{b}} = \frac{\sqrt[n]{a}}{\sqrt[n]{b}}.$$

Remember that an nth root is simplified when its radicand has no factors that are perfect nth powers. Unless functions are involved, we assume that no radicands represent negative quantities raised to an even power.

EXAMPLE 1 Simplify by taking the roots of the numerator and the denominator.

a) $\sqrt[3]{\frac{27}{125}}$ **b)** $\sqrt{\frac{25}{y^2}}$

SOLUTION

a) $\sqrt[3]{\frac{27}{125}} = \frac{\sqrt[3]{27}}{\sqrt[3]{125}} = \frac{3}{5}$ Taking the cube roots of the numerator and the denominator

b) $\sqrt{\frac{25}{y^2}} = \frac{\sqrt{25}}{\sqrt{y^2}} = \frac{5}{y}$ Taking the square roots of the numerator and the denominator. Assume $y > 0$.

TRY EXERCISE 9

Any radical expressions appearing in the answers should be simplified as much as possible.

EXAMPLE 2 Simplify: **(a)** $\sqrt{\frac{16x^3}{y^8}}$; **(b)** $\sqrt[3]{\frac{27y^{14}}{8x^3}}$.

SOLUTION

a) $\sqrt{\frac{16x^3}{y^8}} = \frac{\sqrt{16x^3}}{\sqrt{y^8}}$

$$= \frac{\sqrt{16x^2 \cdot x}}{\sqrt{y^8}}$$

$$= \frac{4x\sqrt{x}}{y^4} \quad \text{Simplifying the numerator and the denominator}$$

b) $\sqrt[3]{\dfrac{27y^{14}}{8x^3}} = \dfrac{\sqrt[3]{27y^{14}}}{\sqrt[3]{8x^3}}$

$= \dfrac{\sqrt[3]{27y^{12}y^2}}{\sqrt[3]{8x^3}}$ y^{12} is the largest perfect-cube factor of y^{14}.

$= \dfrac{\sqrt[3]{27y^{12}}\,\sqrt[3]{y^2}}{\sqrt[3]{8x^3}}$

$= \dfrac{3y^4\sqrt[3]{y^2}}{2x}$ Simplifying the numerator and the denominator

TRY EXERCISE 17

If we read from right to left, the quotient rule tells us that to divide two radical expressions that have the same index, we can divide the radicands.

EXAMPLE 3

Divide and, if possible, simplify.

a) $\dfrac{\sqrt{80}}{\sqrt{5}}$

b) $\dfrac{5\sqrt[3]{32}}{\sqrt[3]{2}}$

c) $\dfrac{\sqrt{72xy}}{2\sqrt{2}}$

d) $\dfrac{\sqrt[4]{18a^9b^5}}{\sqrt[4]{3b}}$

SOLUTION

STUDENT NOTES

When writing radical signs, pay careful attention to what is included as the radicand. Each of the following represents a *different* number:

$\sqrt{\dfrac{5 \cdot 2}{3}},\quad \dfrac{\sqrt{5 \cdot 2}}{3},\quad \dfrac{\sqrt{5} \cdot 2}{3}.$

a) $\dfrac{\sqrt{80}}{\sqrt{5}} = \sqrt{\dfrac{80}{5}} = \sqrt{16} = 4$

> Because the indices match, we can divide the radicands.

b) $\dfrac{5\sqrt[3]{32}}{\sqrt[3]{2}} = 5\sqrt[3]{\dfrac{32}{2}} = 5\sqrt[3]{16}$

$= 5\sqrt[3]{8 \cdot 2}$ 8 is the largest perfect-cube factor of 16.

$= 5\sqrt[3]{8}\,\sqrt[3]{2} = 5 \cdot 2\sqrt[3]{2}$

$= 10\sqrt[3]{2}$

c) $\dfrac{\sqrt{72xy}}{2\sqrt{2}} = \dfrac{1}{2}\sqrt{\dfrac{72xy}{2}}$

> Because the indices match, we can divide the radicands.

$= \dfrac{1}{2}\sqrt{36xy} = \dfrac{1}{2} \cdot 6\sqrt{xy}$

$= 3\sqrt{xy}$

d) $\dfrac{\sqrt[4]{18a^9b^5}}{\sqrt[4]{3b}} = \sqrt[4]{\dfrac{18a^9b^5}{3b}}$

$= \sqrt[4]{6a^9b^4} = \sqrt[4]{a^8b^4}\,\sqrt[4]{6a}$ Note that 8 is the largest power less than 9 that is a multiple of the index 4.

$= a^2b\sqrt[4]{6a}$ *Partial check:* $(a^2b)^4 = a^8b^4$

TRY EXERCISE 27

Rationalizing Denominators or Numerators with One Term*

The expressions

$$\frac{1}{\sqrt{2}} \quad \text{and} \quad \frac{\sqrt{2}}{2}$$

are equivalent, but the second expression does not have a radical expression in the denominator.[†] We can **rationalize the denominator** of a radical expression if we multiply by 1 in either of two ways.

One way is to multiply by 1 *under* the radical to make the denominator of the radicand a perfect power.

EXAMPLE **4**

Rationalize each denominator.

a) $\sqrt{\dfrac{7}{3}}$ **b)** $\sqrt[3]{\dfrac{5}{16}}$

SOLUTION

a) We multiply by 1 under the radical, using $\frac{3}{3}$. We do this so that the denominator of the radicand will be a perfect square:

$$\sqrt{\frac{7}{3}} = \sqrt{\frac{7}{3} \cdot \frac{3}{3}} \qquad \text{Multiplying by 1 under the radical}$$

$$= \sqrt{\frac{21}{9}} \qquad \text{The denominator, 9, is now a perfect square.}$$

$$= \frac{\sqrt{21}}{\sqrt{9}} \qquad \text{Using the quotient rule for radicals}$$

$$= \frac{\sqrt{21}}{3}.$$

b) Note that $16 = 4^2$. Thus, to make the denominator a perfect cube, we multiply under the radical by $\frac{4}{4}$:

$$\sqrt[3]{\frac{5}{16}} = \sqrt[3]{\frac{5}{4 \cdot 4} \cdot \frac{4}{4}} \qquad \begin{array}{l}\text{Since the index is 3, we need 3 identical factors in} \\ \text{the denominator.}\end{array}$$

$$= \sqrt[3]{\frac{20}{4^3}} \qquad \text{The denominator is now a perfect cube.}$$

$$= \frac{\sqrt[3]{20}}{\sqrt[3]{4^3}}$$

$$= \frac{\sqrt[3]{20}}{4}.$$

> **TRY EXERCISE** 41

Another way to rationalize a denominator is to multiply by 1 *outside* the radical.

EXAMPLE **5**

Rationalize each denominator.

a) $\sqrt{\dfrac{4}{5b}}$ **b)** $\dfrac{\sqrt[3]{a}}{\sqrt[3]{25bc^5}}$ **c)** $\dfrac{3x}{\sqrt[5]{2x^2y^3}}$

---

*Denominators and numerators with two terms are rationalized in Section 10.5.
[†]See Exercise 73 on p. 661.

SOLUTION

a) We rewrite the expression as a quotient of two radicals. Then we simplify and multiply by 1:

$$\sqrt{\frac{4}{5b}} = \frac{\sqrt{4}}{\sqrt{5b}} = \frac{2}{\sqrt{5b}} \qquad \text{We assume } b > 0.$$

$$= \frac{2}{\sqrt{5b}} \cdot \frac{\sqrt{5b}}{\sqrt{5b}} \qquad \text{Multiplying by 1}$$

$$= \frac{2\sqrt{5b}}{\left(\sqrt{5b}\right)^2} \qquad \text{Try to do this step mentally.}$$

$$= \frac{2\sqrt{5b}}{5b}.$$

b) Note that the radicand $25bc^5$ is $5 \cdot 5 \cdot b \cdot c \cdot c \cdot c \cdot c \cdot c$. In order for this to be a cube, we need another factor of 5, two more factors of b, and one more factor of c. Thus we multiply by 1, using $\sqrt[3]{5b^2c}/\sqrt[3]{5b^2c}$:

$$\frac{\sqrt[3]{a}}{\sqrt[3]{25bc^5}} = \frac{\sqrt[3]{a}}{\sqrt[3]{25bc^5}} \cdot \frac{\sqrt[3]{5b^2c}}{\sqrt[3]{5b^2c}} \qquad \text{Multiplying by 1}$$

$$= \frac{\sqrt[3]{5ab^2c}}{\sqrt[3]{125b^3c^6}} \longleftarrow \text{This radicand is now a perfect cube.}$$

$$= \frac{\sqrt[3]{5ab^2c}}{5bc^2}.$$

c) To change the radicand $2x^2y^3$ into a perfect fifth power, we need four more factors of 2, three more factors of x, and two more factors of y. Thus we multiply by 1, using $\sqrt[5]{2^4x^3y^2}/\sqrt[5]{2^4x^3y^2}$, or $\sqrt[5]{16x^3y^2}/\sqrt[5]{16x^3y^2}$:

$$\frac{3x}{\sqrt[5]{2x^2y^3}} = \frac{3x}{\sqrt[5]{2x^2y^3}} \cdot \frac{\sqrt[5]{16x^3y^2}}{\sqrt[5]{16x^3y^2}} \qquad \text{Multiplying by 1}$$

$$= \frac{3x\sqrt[5]{16x^3y^2}}{\sqrt[5]{32x^5y^5}} \longleftarrow \begin{array}{l}\text{This radicand is now a}\\ \text{perfect fifth power.}\end{array}$$

$$= \frac{3x\sqrt[5]{16x^3y^2}}{2xy} = \frac{3\sqrt[5]{16x^3y^2}}{2y}. \qquad \text{Always simplify if possible.}$$

> **TRY EXERCISE** 47

Sometimes in calculus it is necessary to rationalize a numerator. To do so, we multiply by 1 to make the radicand in the *numerator* a perfect power.

EXAMPLE 6   Rationalize the numerator: $\dfrac{\sqrt[3]{4a^2}}{\sqrt[3]{5b}}$.

SOLUTION

$$\frac{\sqrt[3]{4a^2}}{\sqrt[3]{5b}} = \frac{\sqrt[3]{4a^2}}{\sqrt[3]{5b}} \cdot \frac{\sqrt[3]{2a}}{\sqrt[3]{2a}} \qquad \text{Multiplying by 1}$$

$$= \frac{\sqrt[3]{8a^3}}{\sqrt[3]{10ba}} \longleftarrow \text{This radicand is now a perfect cube.}$$

$$= \frac{2a}{\sqrt[3]{10ab}}$$

> **TRY EXERCISE** 59

In Section 10.5, we will discuss rationalizing denominators and numerators in which two terms appear.

10.4 EXERCISE SET

Concept Reinforcement *In each of Exercises 1–8, match the expression with an equivalent expression from the column on the right. Assume a, b > 0.*

1. ____ $\sqrt[4]{\dfrac{16a^6}{a^2}}$

2. ____ $\dfrac{\sqrt[3]{a^6}}{\sqrt[3]{b^9}}$

3. ____ $\sqrt[5]{\dfrac{a^6}{b^4}}$

4. ____ $\sqrt{\dfrac{a}{b^3}}$

5. ____ $\dfrac{\sqrt[5]{a^2}}{\sqrt[5]{b^2}}$

6. ____ $\dfrac{\sqrt{5a^4}}{\sqrt{5a^3}}$

7. ____ $\dfrac{\sqrt[5]{a^2}}{\sqrt[5]{b^3}}$

8. ____ $\sqrt[3]{\dfrac{a^2}{b^6}}$

a) $\dfrac{\sqrt[5]{a^2}\sqrt[5]{b^2}}{\sqrt[5]{b^5}}$

b) $\dfrac{a^2}{b^3}$

c) $\sqrt{\dfrac{a \cdot b}{b^3 \cdot b}}$

d) $\sqrt{a}$

e) $\dfrac{\sqrt[3]{a^2}}{b^2}$

f) $\sqrt[5]{\dfrac{a^6b}{b^4 \cdot b}}$

g) $2a$

h) $\dfrac{\sqrt[5]{a^2b^3}}{\sqrt[5]{b^5}}$

Divide and, if possible, simplify. Assume all variables represent positive numbers.

27. $\dfrac{\sqrt{18y}}{\sqrt{2y}}$

28. $\dfrac{\sqrt{700x}}{\sqrt{7x}}$

29. $\dfrac{\sqrt[3]{26}}{\sqrt[3]{13}}$

30. $\dfrac{\sqrt[3]{35}}{\sqrt[3]{5}}$

31. $\dfrac{\sqrt{40xy^3}}{\sqrt{8x}}$

32. $\dfrac{\sqrt{56ab^3}}{\sqrt{7a}}$

33. $\dfrac{\sqrt[3]{96a^4b^2}}{\sqrt[3]{12a^2b}}$

34. $\dfrac{\sqrt[3]{189x^5y^7}}{\sqrt[3]{7x^2y^2}}$

35. $\dfrac{\sqrt{100ab}}{5\sqrt{2}}$

36. $\dfrac{\sqrt{75ab}}{3\sqrt{3}}$

37. $\dfrac{\sqrt[4]{48x^9y^{13}}}{\sqrt[4]{3xy^{-2}}}$

38. $\dfrac{\sqrt[5]{64a^{11}b^{28}}}{\sqrt[5]{2ab^{-2}}}$

39. $\dfrac{\sqrt[3]{x^3 - y^3}}{\sqrt[3]{x - y}}$

40. $\dfrac{\sqrt[3]{r^3 + s^3}}{\sqrt[3]{r + s}}$

Hint: Factor and then simplify.

Simplify by taking the roots of the numerator and the denominator. Assume all variables represent positive numbers.

9. $\sqrt{\dfrac{49}{100}}$

10. $\sqrt{\dfrac{81}{25}}$

11. $\sqrt[3]{\dfrac{125}{8}}$

12. $\sqrt[3]{\dfrac{1000}{27}}$

13. $\sqrt{\dfrac{121}{t^2}}$

14. $\sqrt{\dfrac{144}{p^2}}$

15. $\sqrt{\dfrac{36y^3}{x^4}}$

16. $\sqrt{\dfrac{25a^5}{b^6}}$

17. $\sqrt[3]{\dfrac{27a^4}{8b^3}}$

18. $\sqrt[3]{\dfrac{64x^7}{216y^6}}$

19. $\sqrt[4]{\dfrac{32a^4}{2b^4c^8}}$

20. $\sqrt[4]{\dfrac{81x^4}{y^8z^4}}$

21. $\sqrt[4]{\dfrac{a^5b^8}{c^{10}}}$

22. $\sqrt[4]{\dfrac{x^9y^{12}}{z^6}}$

23. $\sqrt[5]{\dfrac{32x^6}{y^{11}}}$

24. $\sqrt[5]{\dfrac{243a^9}{b^{13}}}$

25. $\sqrt[6]{\dfrac{x^6y^8}{z^{15}}}$

26. $\sqrt[6]{\dfrac{a^9b^{12}}{c^{13}}}$

Rationalize each denominator. Assume all variables represent positive numbers.

41. $\sqrt{\dfrac{2}{5}}$

42. $\sqrt{\dfrac{7}{2}}$

43. $\dfrac{2\sqrt{5}}{7\sqrt{3}}$

44. $\dfrac{3\sqrt{5}}{2\sqrt{7}}$

45. $\sqrt[3]{\dfrac{5}{4}}$

46. $\sqrt[3]{\dfrac{2}{9}}$

47. $\dfrac{\sqrt[3]{3a}}{\sqrt[3]{5c}}$

48. $\dfrac{\sqrt[3]{7x}}{\sqrt[3]{3y}}$

49. $\dfrac{\sqrt[4]{5y^6}}{\sqrt[4]{9x}}$

50. $\dfrac{\sqrt[5]{3a^4}}{\sqrt[5]{2b^7}}$

51. $\sqrt[3]{\dfrac{2}{x^2y}}$

52. $\sqrt[3]{\dfrac{5}{ab^2}}$

53. $\sqrt{\dfrac{7a}{18}}$

54. $\sqrt{\dfrac{3x}{20}}$

55. $\sqrt[5]{\dfrac{9}{32x^5y}}$

56. $\sqrt[4]{\dfrac{7}{64a^2b^4}}$ **Aha!** 57. $\sqrt{\dfrac{10ab^2}{72a^3b}}$

58. $\sqrt{\dfrac{21x^2y}{75xy^5}}$

Rationalize each numerator. Assume all variables represent positive numbers.

59. $\sqrt{\dfrac{5}{11}}$

60. $\sqrt{\dfrac{2}{3}}$

61. $\dfrac{2\sqrt{6}}{5\sqrt{7}}$

62. $\dfrac{3\sqrt{10}}{2\sqrt{3}}$

63. $\dfrac{\sqrt{8}}{2\sqrt{3x}}$

64. $\dfrac{\sqrt{12}}{\sqrt{5y}}$

65. $\dfrac{\sqrt[3]{7}}{\sqrt[3]{2}}$

66. $\dfrac{\sqrt[3]{5}}{\sqrt[3]{4}}$

67. $\sqrt{\dfrac{7x}{3y}}$

68. $\sqrt{\dfrac{7a}{6b}}$

69. $\sqrt[3]{\dfrac{2a^5}{5b}}$

70. $\sqrt[3]{\dfrac{2a^4}{7b}}$

71. $\sqrt{\dfrac{x^3y}{2}}$

72. $\sqrt{\dfrac{ab^5}{3}}$

73. Explain why it is easier to approximate

$$\dfrac{\sqrt{2}}{2} \quad \text{than} \quad \dfrac{1}{\sqrt{2}}$$

if no calculator is available and $\sqrt{2} \approx 1.414213562$.

74. A student *incorrectly* claims that

$$\dfrac{5+\sqrt{2}}{\sqrt{18}} = \dfrac{5+\sqrt{1}}{\sqrt{9}} = \dfrac{5+1}{3}.$$

How could you convince the student that a mistake has been made? How would you explain the correct way of rationalizing the denominator?

Skill Review

To prepare for Section 10.5, review factoring expressions and multiplying polynomials (Sections 4.6 and 5.1).

Factor. [5.1]

75. $3x - 8xy + 2xz$

76. $4a^2c + 9ac - 3a^3c$

Multiply. [4.6]

77. $(a + b)(a - b)$

78. $(a^2 - 2y)(a^2 + 2y)$

79. $(8 + 3x)(7 - 4x)$

80. $(2y - x)(3a - c)$

Synthesis

81. Is the quotient of two irrational numbers always an irrational number? Why or why not?

82. Is it possible to understand how to rationalize a denominator without knowing how to multiply rational expressions? Why or why not?

83. *Pendulums.*   The *period* of a pendulum is the time it takes to complete one cycle, swinging to and fro. For a pendulum that is L centimeters long, the period T is given by the formula

$$T = 2\pi\sqrt{\dfrac{L}{980}},$$

where T is in seconds. Find, to the nearest hundredth of a second, the period of a pendulum of length **(a)** 65 cm; **(b)** 98 cm; **(c)** 120 cm. Use a calculator's $\boxed{\pi}$ key if possible.

Perform the indicated operations.

84. $\dfrac{7\sqrt{a^2b}\,\sqrt{25xy}}{5\sqrt{a^{-4}b^{-1}}\sqrt{49x^{-1}y^{-3}}}$

85. $\dfrac{\left(\sqrt[3]{81mn^2}\right)^2}{\left(\sqrt[3]{mn}\right)^2}$

86. $\dfrac{\sqrt{44x^2y^9z}\,\sqrt{22y^9z^6}}{\left(\sqrt{11xy^8z^2}\right)^2}$

87. $\sqrt{a^2 - 3} - \dfrac{a^2}{\sqrt{a^2 - 3}}$

88. $5\sqrt{\dfrac{x}{y}} + 4\sqrt{\dfrac{y}{x}} - \dfrac{3}{\sqrt{xy}}$

89. Provide a reason for each step in the following derivation of the quotient rule:

$$\sqrt[n]{\dfrac{a}{b}} = \left(\dfrac{a}{b}\right)^{1/n} \quad \underline{\hspace{2cm}}$$

$$= \dfrac{a^{1/n}}{b^{1/n}} \quad \underline{\hspace{2cm}}$$

$$= \dfrac{\sqrt[n]{a}}{\sqrt[n]{b}} \quad \underline{\hspace{2cm}}$$

90. Show that $\dfrac{\sqrt[n]{a}}{\sqrt[n]{b}}$ is the nth root of $\dfrac{a}{b}$ by raising it to the nth power and simplifying.

91. Let $f(x) = \sqrt{18x^3}$ and $g(x) = \sqrt{2x}$. Find $(f/g)(x)$ and specify the domain of f/g.

92. Let $f(t) = \sqrt{2t}$ and $g(t) = \sqrt{50t^3}$. Find $(f/g)(t)$ and specify the domain of f/g.

93. Let $f(x) = \sqrt{x^2 - 9}$ and $g(x) = \sqrt{x - 3}$. Find $(f/g)(x)$ and specify the domain of f/g.

10.5 Expressions Containing Several Radical Terms

Adding and Subtracting Radical Expressions ∎ Products and Quotients of Two or More Radical Terms ∎
Rationalizing Denominators or Numerators with Two Terms ∎ Terms with Differing Indices

Radical expressions like $6\sqrt{7} + 4\sqrt{7}$ or $(\sqrt{a} + \sqrt{b})(\sqrt{a} - \sqrt{b})$ contain more than one *radical term* and can sometimes be simplified.

Adding and Subtracting Radical Expressions

When two radical expressions have the same indices and radicands, they are said to be **like radicals**. Like radicals can be combined (added or subtracted) in much the same way that we combine like terms.

EXAMPLE **1**

Simplify by combining like radical terms.

a) $6\sqrt{7} + 4\sqrt{7}$ **b)** $\sqrt[3]{2} - 7x\sqrt[3]{2} + 5\sqrt[3]{2}$
c) $6\sqrt[5]{4x} + 3\sqrt[5]{4x} - \sqrt[3]{4x}$

STUDY SKILLS

*Review Material on
Your Own*

Never hesitate to review earlier material in which you feel a lack of confidence. For example, if you feel unsure about how to multiply with fraction notation, be sure to review that material before studying any new material that involves multiplication of fractions. Doing (and checking) some practice problems from that section is also a good way to sharpen any skills that you may not have used for a while.

SOLUTION

a) $6\sqrt{7} + 4\sqrt{7} = (6 + 4)\sqrt{7}$ Using the distributive law (factoring out $\sqrt{7}$)

     $= 10\sqrt{7}$ You can think: 6 square roots of 7 plus 4 square roots of 7 is 10 square roots of 7.

b) $\sqrt[3]{2} - 7x\sqrt[3]{2} + 5\sqrt[3]{2} = (1 - 7x + 5)\sqrt[3]{2}$ Factoring out $\sqrt[3]{2}$

     $= (6 - 7x)\sqrt[3]{2}$ These parentheses are important!

c) $6\sqrt[5]{4x} + 3\sqrt[5]{4x} - \sqrt[3]{4x} = (6 + 3)\sqrt[5]{4x} - \sqrt[3]{4x}$ Try to do this step mentally.

     $= 9\sqrt[5]{4x} - \sqrt[3]{4x}$ The indices are different. We cannot combine these terms.

> **TRY EXERCISE** 7

Our ability to simplify radical expressions can help us to find like radicals even when, at first, it may appear that there are none.

EXAMPLE **2**

Simplify by combining like radical terms, if possible.

a) $3\sqrt{8} - 5\sqrt{2}$
b) $9\sqrt{5} - 4\sqrt{3}$
c) $\sqrt[3]{2x^6y^4} + 7\sqrt[3]{2y}$

SOLUTION

a) $3\sqrt{8} - 5\sqrt{2} = 3\sqrt{4 \cdot 2} - 5\sqrt{2}$

     $= 3\sqrt{4} \cdot \sqrt{2} - 5\sqrt{2}$ Simplifying $\sqrt{8}$

     $= 3 \cdot 2 \cdot \sqrt{2} - 5\sqrt{2}$

     $= 6\sqrt{2} - 5\sqrt{2}$

     $= \sqrt{2}$ Combining like radicals

b) $9\sqrt{5} - 4\sqrt{3}$ cannot be simplified.   The radicands are different.

c) $\sqrt[3]{2x^6y^4} + 7\sqrt[3]{2y} = \sqrt[3]{x^6y^3 \cdot 2y} + 7\sqrt[3]{2y}$

$\qquad\qquad\qquad\quad = \sqrt[3]{x^6y^3} \cdot \sqrt[3]{2y} + 7\sqrt[3]{2y}$ Simplifying $\sqrt[3]{2x^6y^4}$

$\qquad\qquad\qquad\quad = x^2y \cdot \sqrt[3]{2y} + 7\sqrt[3]{2y}$

$\qquad\qquad\qquad\quad = (x^2y + 7)\sqrt[3]{2y}$ Factoring to combine like radical terms

> **TRY EXERCISE** 17

Products and Quotients of Two or More Radical Terms

Radical expressions often contain factors that have more than one term. Multiplying such expressions is similar to finding products of polynomials. Some products will yield like radical terms, which we can now combine.

EXAMPLE 3   Multiply.

a) $\sqrt{3}(x - \sqrt{5})$

b) $\sqrt[3]{y}\left(\sqrt[3]{y^2} + \sqrt[3]{2}\right)$

c) $(4\sqrt{3} + \sqrt{2})(\sqrt{3} - 5\sqrt{2})$

d) $(\sqrt{a} + \sqrt{b})(\sqrt{a} - \sqrt{b})$

SOLUTION

a) $\sqrt{3}(x - \sqrt{5}) = \sqrt{3} \cdot x - \sqrt{3} \cdot \sqrt{5}$ Using the distributive law

$\qquad\qquad\qquad = x\sqrt{3} - \sqrt{15}$ Multiplying radicals

b) $\sqrt[3]{y}\left(\sqrt[3]{y^2} + \sqrt[3]{2}\right) = \sqrt[3]{y} \cdot \sqrt[3]{y^2} + \sqrt[3]{y} \cdot \sqrt[3]{2}$ Using the distributive law

$\qquad\qquad\qquad\qquad = \sqrt[3]{y^3} + \sqrt[3]{2y}$ Multiplying radicals

$\qquad\qquad\qquad\qquad = y + \sqrt[3]{2y}$ Simplifying $\sqrt[3]{y^3}$

c) $(4\sqrt{3} + \sqrt{2})(\sqrt{3} - 5\sqrt{2}) = \overset{\text{F}}{4(\sqrt{3})^2} - \overset{\text{O}}{20\sqrt{3} \cdot \sqrt{2}} + \overset{\text{I}}{\sqrt{2} \cdot \sqrt{3}} - \overset{\text{L}}{5(\sqrt{2})^2}$

$\qquad\qquad\qquad\qquad\qquad = 4 \cdot 3 - 20\sqrt{6} + \sqrt{6} - 5 \cdot 2$ Multiplying radicals

$\qquad\qquad\qquad\qquad\qquad = 12 - 20\sqrt{6} + \sqrt{6} - 10$

$\qquad\qquad\qquad\qquad\qquad = 2 - 19\sqrt{6}$ Combining like terms

d) $(\sqrt{a} + \sqrt{b})(\sqrt{a} - \sqrt{b}) = (\sqrt{a})^2 - \sqrt{a}\sqrt{b} + \sqrt{a}\sqrt{b} - (\sqrt{b})^2$ Using FOIL

$\qquad\qquad\qquad\qquad\qquad = a - b$ Combining like terms

> **TRY EXERCISE** 41

   In Example 3(d) above, you may have noticed that since the outer and inner products in FOIL are opposites, the result, $a - b$, is not itself a radical expression. Pairs of radical expressions like $\sqrt{a} + \sqrt{b}$ and $\sqrt{a} - \sqrt{b}$ are called **conjugates**.

Rationalizing Denominators or Numerators with Two Terms

The use of conjugates allows us to rationalize denominators or numerators that contain two terms.

EXAMPLE 4   Rationalize each denominator: **(a)** $\dfrac{4}{\sqrt{3} + x}$; **(b)** $\dfrac{4 + \sqrt{2}}{\sqrt{5} - \sqrt{2}}$.

SOLUTION

a) $\dfrac{4}{\sqrt{3} + x} = \dfrac{4}{\sqrt{3} + x} \cdot \dfrac{\sqrt{3} - x}{\sqrt{3} - x}$ Multiplying by 1, using the conjugate of $\sqrt{3} + x$, which is $\sqrt{3} - x$

$= \dfrac{4(\sqrt{3} - x)}{(\sqrt{3} + x)(\sqrt{3} - x)}$ Multiplying numerators and denominators

$= \dfrac{4(\sqrt{3} - x)}{(\sqrt{3})^2 - x^2}$ Using FOIL in the denominator

$= \dfrac{4\sqrt{3} - 4x}{3 - x^2}$ Simplifying. No radicals remain in the denominator.

b) $\dfrac{4 + \sqrt{2}}{\sqrt{5} - \sqrt{2}} = \dfrac{4 + \sqrt{2}}{\sqrt{5} - \sqrt{2}} \cdot \dfrac{\sqrt{5} + \sqrt{2}}{\sqrt{5} + \sqrt{2}}$ Multiplying by 1, using the conjugate of $\sqrt{5} - \sqrt{2}$, which is $\sqrt{5} + \sqrt{2}$

$= \dfrac{(4 + \sqrt{2})(\sqrt{5} + \sqrt{2})}{(\sqrt{5} - \sqrt{2})(\sqrt{5} + \sqrt{2})}$ Multiplying numerators and denominators

$= \dfrac{4\sqrt{5} + 4\sqrt{2} + \sqrt{2}\sqrt{5} + (\sqrt{2})^2}{(\sqrt{5})^2 - (\sqrt{2})^2}$ Using FOIL

$= \dfrac{4\sqrt{5} + 4\sqrt{2} + \sqrt{10} + 2}{5 - 2}$ Squaring in the denominator and the numerator

$= \dfrac{4\sqrt{5} + 4\sqrt{2} + \sqrt{10} + 2}{3}$ No radicals remain in the denominator.

> **TRY EXERCISE** 61

To rationalize a numerator with two terms, we use the conjugate of the numerator.

EXAMPLE 5   Rationalize the numerator: $\dfrac{4 + \sqrt{2}}{\sqrt{5} - \sqrt{2}}$.

SOLUTION

$\dfrac{4 + \sqrt{2}}{\sqrt{5} - \sqrt{2}} = \dfrac{4 + \sqrt{2}}{\sqrt{5} - \sqrt{2}} \cdot \dfrac{4 - \sqrt{2}}{4 - \sqrt{2}}$ Multiplying by 1, using the conjugate of $4 + \sqrt{2}$, which is $4 - \sqrt{2}$

$= \dfrac{16 - (\sqrt{2})^2}{4\sqrt{5} - \sqrt{5}\sqrt{2} - 4\sqrt{2} + (\sqrt{2})^2}$

$= \dfrac{14}{4\sqrt{5} - \sqrt{10} - 4\sqrt{2} + 2}$

> **TRY EXERCISE** 71

Terms with Differing Indices

To multiply or divide radical terms with identical radicands but different indices, we can convert to exponential notation, use the rules for exponents, and then convert back to radical notation.

EXAMPLE 6

Divide and, if possible, simplify: $\dfrac{\sqrt[4]{(x + y)^3}}{\sqrt{x + y}}$.

STUDENT NOTES

Expressions similar to the one in Example 6 are most easily simplified by rewriting the expression using exponents in place of radicals. After simplifying, remember to write your final result in radical notation. In general, if a problem is presented in one form, it is expected that the final result be presented in the same form.

SOLUTION

$$\frac{\sqrt[4]{(x + y)^3}}{\sqrt{x + y}} = \frac{(x + y)^{3/4}}{(x + y)^{1/2}} \qquad \text{Converting to exponential notation}$$

$$= (x + y)^{3/4 - 1/2} \qquad \text{Since the bases are identical, we can subtract exponents:} \quad \tfrac{3}{4} - \tfrac{1}{2} = \tfrac{3}{4} - \tfrac{2}{4} = \tfrac{1}{4}.$$

$$\left. \begin{array}{l} = (x + y)^{1/4} \\ = \sqrt[4]{x + y} \end{array} \right\} \qquad \text{Converting back to radical notation}$$

> TRY EXERCISE 95

The steps used in Example 6 can be used in a variety of situations.

To Simplify Products or Quotients with Differing Indices

1. Convert all radical expressions to exponential notation.
2. When the bases are identical, subtract exponents to divide and add exponents to multiply. This may require finding a common denominator.
3. Convert back to radical notation and, if possible, simplify.

EXAMPLE 7

Multiply and simplify: $\sqrt{x^3}\sqrt[3]{x}$.

SOLUTION

$$\begin{array}{ll} \sqrt{x^3}\sqrt[3]{x} = x^{3/2} \cdot x^{1/3} & \text{Converting to exponential notation} \\ \quad = x^{11/6} & \text{Adding exponents: } \tfrac{3}{2} + \tfrac{1}{3} = \tfrac{9}{6} + \tfrac{2}{6} \\ \quad = \sqrt[6]{x^{11}} & \text{Converting back to radical notation} \\ \left. \begin{array}{l} = \sqrt[6]{x^6}\sqrt[6]{x^5} \\ = x\sqrt[6]{x^5} \end{array} \right\} & \text{Simplifying} \end{array}$$

> TRY EXERCISE 79

EXAMPLE 8

If $f(x) = \sqrt[3]{x^2}$ and $g(x) = \sqrt{x} + \sqrt[4]{x}$, find $(f \cdot g)(x)$.

SOLUTION   Recall from Section 7.4 that $(f \cdot g)(x) = f(x) \cdot g(x)$. Thus,

$$(f \cdot g)(x) = \sqrt[3]{x^2}\left(\sqrt{x} + \sqrt[4]{x}\right) \qquad \begin{array}{l} x \text{ is assumed to be} \\ \text{nonnegative.} \end{array}$$

$$= x^{2/3}(x^{1/2} + x^{1/4}) \qquad \begin{array}{l} \text{Converting to exponential} \\ \text{notation} \end{array}$$

$$= x^{2/3} \cdot x^{1/2} + x^{2/3} \cdot x^{1/4} \qquad \text{Using the distributive law}$$

$$= x^{2/3 + 1/2} + x^{2/3 + 1/4} \qquad \text{Adding exponents:}$$

$$= x^{7/6} + x^{11/12} \qquad \qquad \tfrac{2}{3} + \tfrac{1}{2} = \tfrac{4}{6} + \tfrac{3}{6}; \tfrac{2}{3} + \tfrac{1}{4} = \tfrac{8}{12} + \tfrac{3}{12}$$

$$= \sqrt[6]{x^7} + \sqrt[12]{x^{11}} \qquad \begin{array}{l} \text{Converting back to radical} \\ \text{notation} \end{array}$$

$$\left. \begin{array}{l} = \sqrt[6]{x^6}\sqrt[6]{x} + \sqrt[12]{x^{11}} \\ = x\sqrt[6]{x} + \sqrt[12]{x^{11}}. \end{array} \right\} \qquad \text{Simplifying}$$

> TRY EXERCISE 103

We often can write the final result as a single radical expression by finding a common denominator in the exponents.

EXAMPLE **9** Divide and, if possible, simplify: $\dfrac{\sqrt[3]{a^2b^4}}{\sqrt{ab}}$.

SOLUTION

$$\dfrac{\sqrt[3]{a^2b^4}}{\sqrt{ab}} = \dfrac{(a^2b^4)^{1/3}}{(ab)^{1/2}}$$ Converting to exponential notation

$$= \dfrac{a^{2/3}b^{4/3}}{a^{1/2}b^{1/2}}$$ Using the product and power rules

$$= a^{2/3-1/2}b^{4/3-1/2}$$ Subtracting exponents

$$= a^{1/6}b^{5/6}$$

$$= \sqrt[6]{a}\,\sqrt[6]{b^5}$$ Converting to radical notation

$$= \sqrt[6]{ab^5}$$ Using the product rule for radicals

TRY EXERCISE 91

10.5 EXERCISE SET

For Extra Help MyMathLab MathXL PRACTICE WATCH DOWNLOAD

🖐 *Concept Reinforcement* *For each of Exercises 1–6, fill in the blanks by selecting from the following words (which may be used more than once):*

radicand(s), indices, conjugate(s), base(s), denominator(s), numerator(s).

1. To add radical expressions, the _____ and the _____ must be the same.

2. To multiply radical expressions, the _____ must be the same.

3. To find a product by adding exponents, the _____ must be the same.

4. To add rational expressions, the _____ must be the same.

5. To rationalize the _____ of $\dfrac{\sqrt{c} - \sqrt{a}}{5}$, we multiply by a form of 1, using the _____ of $\sqrt{c} - \sqrt{a}$, or $\sqrt{c} + \sqrt{a}$, to write 1.

6. To find a quotient by subtracting exponents, the _____ must be the same.

Add or subtract. Simplify by combining like radical terms, if possible. Assume that all variables and radicands represent positive real numbers.

7. $4\sqrt{3} + 7\sqrt{3}$

8. $6\sqrt{5} + 2\sqrt{5}$

9. $7\sqrt[3]{4} - 5\sqrt[3]{4}$

10. $14\sqrt[5]{2} - 8\sqrt[5]{2}$

11. $\sqrt[3]{y} + 9\sqrt[3]{y}$

12. $4\sqrt[4]{t} - \sqrt[4]{t}$

13. $8\sqrt{2} - \sqrt{2} + 5\sqrt{2}$

14. $\sqrt{6} + 3\sqrt{6} - 8\sqrt{6}$

15. $9\sqrt[3]{7} - \sqrt{3} + 4\sqrt[3]{7} + 2\sqrt{3}$

16. $5\sqrt{7} - 8\sqrt[4]{11} + \sqrt{7} + 9\sqrt[4]{11}$

17. $4\sqrt{27} - 3\sqrt{3}$

18. $9\sqrt{50} - 4\sqrt{2}$

19. $3\sqrt{45} - 8\sqrt{20}$

20. $5\sqrt{12} + 16\sqrt{27}$

21. $3\sqrt[3]{16} + \sqrt[3]{54}$

22. $\sqrt[3]{27} - 5\sqrt[3]{8}$

23. $\sqrt{a} + 3\sqrt{16a^3}$

24. $2\sqrt{9x^3} - \sqrt{x}$

25. $\sqrt[3]{6x^4} - \sqrt[3]{48x}$

26. $\sqrt[3]{54x} - \sqrt[3]{2x^4}$

27. $\sqrt{4a - 4} + \sqrt{a - 1}$

28. $\sqrt{9y + 27} + \sqrt{y + 3}$

29. $\sqrt{x^3 - x^2} + \sqrt{9x - 9}$

30. $\sqrt{4x - 4} - \sqrt{x^3 - x^2}$

Multiply. Assume all variables represent nonnegative real numbers.

31. $\sqrt{2}(5 + \sqrt{2})$

32. $\sqrt{3}(6 - \sqrt{3})$

33. $3\sqrt{5}(\sqrt{6} - \sqrt{7})$

34. $4\sqrt{2}(\sqrt{3} + \sqrt{5})$

35. $\sqrt{2}(3\sqrt{10} - \sqrt{8})$

36. $\sqrt{3}(2\sqrt{15} - 3\sqrt{4})$

37. $\sqrt[3]{3}(\sqrt[3]{9} - 4\sqrt[3]{21})$

38. $\sqrt[3]{2}(\sqrt[3]{4} - 2\sqrt[3]{32})$

39. $\sqrt[3]{a}\left(\sqrt[3]{a^2} + \sqrt[3]{24a^2}\right)$

40. $\sqrt[3]{x}\left(\sqrt[3]{3x^2} - \sqrt[3]{81x^2}\right)$

41. $(2 + \sqrt{6})(5 - \sqrt{6})$

42. $(4 - \sqrt{5})(2 + \sqrt{5})$

43. $(\sqrt{2} + \sqrt{7})(\sqrt{3} - \sqrt{7})$

44. $(\sqrt{7} - \sqrt{2})(\sqrt{5} + \sqrt{2})$

45. $(2 - \sqrt{3})(2 + \sqrt{3})$

46. $(3 + \sqrt{11})(3 - \sqrt{11})$

47. $(\sqrt{10} - \sqrt{15})(\sqrt{10} + \sqrt{15})$

48. $(\sqrt{12} + \sqrt{5})(\sqrt{12} - \sqrt{5})$

49. $(3\sqrt{7} + 2\sqrt{5})(2\sqrt{7} - 4\sqrt{5})$

50. $(4\sqrt{5} - 3\sqrt{2})(2\sqrt{5} + 4\sqrt{2})$

51. $(4 + \sqrt{7})^2$ **52.** $(3 + \sqrt{10})^2$

53. $(\sqrt{3} - \sqrt{2})^2$ **54.** $(\sqrt{5} - \sqrt{3})^2$

55. $(\sqrt{2t} + \sqrt{5})^2$ **56.** $(\sqrt{3x} - \sqrt{2})^2$

57. $(3 - \sqrt{x + 5})^2$ **58.** $(4 + \sqrt{x - 3})^2$

59. $\left(2\sqrt[4]{7} - \sqrt[4]{6}\right)\left(3\sqrt[4]{9} + 2\sqrt[4]{5}\right)$

60. $\left(4\sqrt[3]{3} + \sqrt[3]{10}\right)\left(2\sqrt[3]{7} + 5\sqrt[3]{6}\right)$

Rationalize each denominator.

61. $\dfrac{6}{3 - \sqrt{2}}$ **62.** $\dfrac{5}{4 - \sqrt{5}}$

63. $\dfrac{2 + \sqrt{5}}{6 + \sqrt{3}}$ **64.** $\dfrac{1 + \sqrt{2}}{3 + \sqrt{5}}$

65. $\dfrac{\sqrt{a}}{\sqrt{a} + \sqrt{b}}$ **66.** $\dfrac{\sqrt{z}}{\sqrt{x} - \sqrt{z}}$

Aha! **67.** $\dfrac{\sqrt{7} - \sqrt{3}}{\sqrt{3} - \sqrt{7}}$ **68.** $\dfrac{\sqrt{7} + \sqrt{5}}{\sqrt{5} + \sqrt{2}}$

69. $\dfrac{3\sqrt{2} - \sqrt{7}}{4\sqrt{2} + 2\sqrt{5}}$ **70.** $\dfrac{5\sqrt{3} - \sqrt{11}}{2\sqrt{3} - 5\sqrt{2}}$

Rationalize each numerator. If possible, simplify your result.

71. $\dfrac{\sqrt{5} + 1}{4}$ **72.** $\dfrac{\sqrt{15} - 3}{6}$

73. $\dfrac{\sqrt{6} - 2}{\sqrt{3} + 7}$ **74.** $\dfrac{\sqrt{10} + 4}{\sqrt{2} - 3}$

75. $\dfrac{\sqrt{x} - \sqrt{y}}{\sqrt{x} + \sqrt{y}}$ **76.** $\dfrac{\sqrt{a} + \sqrt{b}}{\sqrt{a} - \sqrt{b}}$

77. $\dfrac{\sqrt{a + h} - \sqrt{a}}{h}$ **78.** $\dfrac{\sqrt{x - h} - \sqrt{x}}{h}$

Perform the indicated operation and simplify. Assume all variables represent positive real numbers.

79. $\sqrt[3]{a}\sqrt[6]{a}$ **80.** $\sqrt[10]{a}\sqrt[5]{a^2}$

81. $\sqrt{b^3}\sqrt[5]{b^4}$ **82.** $\sqrt[3]{b^4}\sqrt[4]{b^3}$

83. $\sqrt{xy^3}\sqrt[3]{x^2y}$ **84.** $\sqrt[5]{a^3b}\sqrt{ab}$

85. $\sqrt[4]{9ab^3}\sqrt{3a^4b}$ **86.** $\sqrt{2x^3y^3}\sqrt[3]{4xy^2}$

87. $\sqrt{a^4b^3c^4}\sqrt[3]{ab^2c}$ **88.** $\sqrt[3]{xy^2z}\sqrt{x^3yz^2}$

89. $\dfrac{\sqrt[3]{a^2}}{\sqrt[4]{a}}$ **90.** $\dfrac{\sqrt[3]{x^2}}{\sqrt[5]{x}}$

91. $\dfrac{\sqrt[4]{x^2y^3}}{\sqrt[3]{xy}}$ **92.** $\dfrac{\sqrt[5]{a^4b}}{\sqrt[3]{ab}}$

93. $\dfrac{\sqrt{ab^3}}{\sqrt[5]{a^2b^3}}$ **94.** $\dfrac{\sqrt[5]{x^3y^4}}{\sqrt{xy}}$

95. $\dfrac{\sqrt{(7 - y)^3}}{\sqrt[3]{(7 - y)^2}}$ **96.** $\dfrac{\sqrt[5]{(y - 9)^3}}{\sqrt{y - 9}}$

97. $\dfrac{\sqrt[4]{(5 + 3x)^3}}{\sqrt[3]{(5 + 3x)^2}}$ **98.** $\dfrac{\sqrt[3]{(2x + 1)^2}}{\sqrt[5]{(2x + 1)^2}}$

99. $\sqrt[3]{x^2y}\left(\sqrt{xy} - \sqrt[5]{xy^3}\right)$

100. $\sqrt[4]{a^2b}\left(\sqrt[3]{a^2b} - \sqrt[5]{a^2b^2}\right)$

101. $\left(m + \sqrt[3]{n^2}\right)\left(2m + \sqrt[4]{n}\right)$

102. $\left(r - \sqrt[4]{s^3}\right)\left(3r - \sqrt[5]{s}\right)$

In Exercises 103–106, f(x) and g(x) are as given. Find $(f \cdot g)(x)$. Assume all variables represent nonnegative real numbers.

103. $f(x) = \sqrt[4]{x}, \ g(x) = 2\sqrt{x} - \sqrt[3]{x^2}$

104. $f(x) = \sqrt[4]{2x} + 5\sqrt{2x}, \ g(x) = \sqrt[3]{2x}$

105. $f(x) = x + \sqrt{7}, \ g(x) = x - \sqrt{7}$

106. $f(x) = x - \sqrt{2}, \ g(x) = x + \sqrt{6}$

Let $f(x) = x^2$. Find each of the following.

107. $f(3 - \sqrt{2})$

108. $f(5 - \sqrt{3})$

109. $f(\sqrt{6} + \sqrt{21})$

110. $f(\sqrt{2} + \sqrt{10})$

111. In what way(s) is combining like radical terms similar to combining like terms that are monomials?

112. Why do we need to know how to multiply radical expressions before learning how to add them?

Skill Review

To prepare for Section 10.6, review solving equations (Sections 2.2, 5.7, and 6.6).

Solve.

113. $3x - 1 = 125$ [2.2]

114. $x + 5 - 2x = 3x + 6 - x$ [2.2]

115. $x^2 + 2x + 1 = 22 - 2x$ [5.7]

116. $9x^2 - 6x + 1 = 7 + 5x - x^2$ [5.7]

117. $\dfrac{1}{x} + \dfrac{1}{2} = \dfrac{1}{6}$ [6.6]

118. $\dfrac{x}{x - 4} + \dfrac{2}{x + 4} = \dfrac{x - 2}{x^2 - 16}$ [6.6]

Synthesis

119. Ramon *incorrectly* writes
$$\sqrt[5]{x^2} \cdot \sqrt{x^3} = x^{2/5} \cdot x^{3/2} = \sqrt[5]{x^3}.$$
What mistake do you suspect he is making?

120. After examining the expression $\sqrt[4]{25xy^3}\,\sqrt{5x^4y}$, Dyan (correctly) concludes that x and y are both nonnegative. Explain how she could reach this conclusion.

Find a simplified form for $f(x)$. Assume $x \geq 0$.

121. $f(x) = \sqrt{x^3 - x^2} + \sqrt{9x^3 - 9x^2} - \sqrt{4x^3 - 4x^2}$

122. $f(x) = \sqrt{20x^2 + 4x^3} - 3x\sqrt{45 + 9x} + \sqrt{5x^2 + x^3}$

123. $f(x) = \sqrt[4]{x^5 - x^4} + 3\sqrt[4]{x^9 - x^8}$

124. $f(x) = \sqrt[4]{16x^4 + 16x^5} - 2\sqrt[4]{x^8 + x^9}$

Simplify.

125. $7x\sqrt{(x + y)^3} - 5xy\sqrt{x + y} - 2y\sqrt{(x + y)^3}$

126. $\sqrt{27a^5(b + 1)}\,\sqrt[3]{81a(b + 1)^4}$

127. $\sqrt{8x(y + z)^5}\,\sqrt[3]{4x^2(y + z)^2}$

128. $\frac{1}{2}\sqrt{36a^5bc^4} - \frac{1}{2}\sqrt[3]{64a^4bc^6} + \frac{1}{6}\sqrt{144a^3bc^6}$

129. $\dfrac{\dfrac{1}{\sqrt{w}} - \sqrt{w}}{\dfrac{\sqrt{w} + 1}{\sqrt{w}}}$

130. $\dfrac{1}{4 + \sqrt{3}} + \dfrac{1}{\sqrt{3}} + \dfrac{1}{\sqrt{3} - 4}$

Express each of the following as the product of two radical expressions.

131. $x - 5$ 　　　　　　**132.** $y - 7$

133. $x - a$

Multiply.

134. $\sqrt{9 + 3\sqrt{5}}\,\sqrt{9 - 3\sqrt{5}}$

135. $(\sqrt{x + 2} - \sqrt{x - 2})^2$

136. Use a graphing calculator to check your answers to Exercises 25, 39, and 81.

CONNECTING the CONCEPTS

Many radical expressions can be simplified. It is important to know under which conditions radical expressions can be multiplied and divided and radical terms can be combined.

Multiplication and division: The indices must be the same.
$$\frac{\sqrt{50t^5}}{\sqrt{2t^{11}}} = \sqrt{\frac{50t^5}{2t^{11}}} = \sqrt{\frac{25}{t^6}} = \frac{5}{t^3}; \qquad \sqrt[4]{8x^3} \cdot \sqrt[4]{2x} = \sqrt[4]{16x^4} = 2x$$

Combining like terms: The indices and the radicands must both be the same.
$$\sqrt{75x} + \sqrt{12x} - \sqrt{3x} = 5\sqrt{3x} + 2\sqrt{3x} - \sqrt{3x} = 6\sqrt{3x}$$

Radical expressions with differing indices can sometimes be simplified using rational exponents.
$$\sqrt[3]{x^2}\sqrt{x} = x^{2/3}x^{1/2} = x^{4/6}x^{3/6} = x^{7/6} = \sqrt[6]{x^7} = x\sqrt[6]{x}$$

MIXED REVIEW

Simplify. Assume that all variables represent non-negative numbers. Thus no absolute-value signs are needed in an answer.

1. $\sqrt{(t + 5)^2}$

2. $\sqrt[3]{-27a^{12}}$

3. $\sqrt{6x}\sqrt{15x}$

4. $\dfrac{\sqrt{20y}}{\sqrt{45y}}$

5. $\sqrt{15t} + 4\sqrt{15t}$

6. $\sqrt[5]{a^5b^{10}c^{11}}$

7. $\sqrt{6}(\sqrt{10} - \sqrt{33})$

8. $\dfrac{-\sqrt[4]{80a^2b}}{\sqrt[4]{5a^{-1}b^{-6}}}$

9. $\dfrac{\sqrt{t}}{\sqrt[8]{t^3}}$

10. $\sqrt[5]{\dfrac{3a^{12}}{96a^2}}$

11. $2\sqrt{3} - 5\sqrt{12}$

12. $(\sqrt{5} + 3)(\sqrt{5} - 3)$

13. $(\sqrt{15} + \sqrt{10})^2$

14. $\sqrt{25x - 25} - \sqrt{9x - 9}$

15. $\sqrt{x^3y}\sqrt[5]{xy^4}$

16. $\sqrt[3]{5000} + \sqrt[3]{625}$

17. $\sqrt{\sqrt[5]{x^2}}$

18. $\sqrt{3x^2 + 6x + 3}$

19. $\left(\sqrt[4]{a^2b^3}\right)^2$

20. $\sqrt[3]{12x^2y^5}\sqrt[3]{18x^7y}$

10.6 Solving Radical Equations

The Principle of Powers • **Equations with Two Radical Terms**

In Sections 10.1–10.5, we learned how to manipulate radical expressions as well as expressions containing rational exponents. We performed this work to find *equivalent expressions*.

Now that we know how to work with radicals and rational exponents, we can learn how to solve a new type of equation.

The Principle of Powers

A **radical equation** is an equation in which the variable appears in a radicand. Examples are

$$\sqrt[3]{2x} + 1 = 5, \qquad \sqrt{a - 2} = 7, \qquad \text{and} \qquad 4 - \sqrt{3x + 1} = \sqrt{6 - x}.$$

To solve such equations, we need a new principle. Suppose $a = b$ is true. If we square both sides, we get another true equation: $a^2 = b^2$. This can be generalized.

> ### The Principle of Powers
>
> If $a = b$, then $a^n = b^n$ for any exponent n.

Note that the principle of powers is an "if–then" statement. The statement obtained by interchanging the two parts of the sentence—"if $a^n = b^n$ for some exponent n, then $a = b$"—*is not always true.* For example, "if $x = 3$, then $x^2 = 9$" is true, but the statement "if $x^2 = 9$, then $x = 3$" is *not* true when x is replaced with -3. For this reason, when both sides of an equation are raised to an even exponent, it is essential to check the answer(s) in the *original* equation.

EXAMPLE **1** Solve: $\sqrt{x} - 3 = 4$.

SOLUTION Before using the principle of powers, we need to isolate the radical term:

$$\sqrt{x} - 3 = 4$$
$$\sqrt{x} = 7 \qquad \text{Isolating the radical by adding 3 to both sides}$$
$$(\sqrt{x})^2 = 7^2 \qquad \text{Using the principle of powers}$$
$$x = 49.$$

Check:
$$\begin{array}{c|c} \sqrt{x} - 3 = 4 \\ \hline \sqrt{49} - 3 & 4 \\ 7 - 3 & \\ 4 \stackrel{?}{=} 4 & \text{TRUE} \end{array}$$

The solution is 49.

TRY EXERCISE 7

EXAMPLE **2** Solve: $\sqrt{x} + 5 = 3$.

SOLUTION

$$\sqrt{x} + 5 = 3$$
$$\sqrt{x} = -2 \qquad \text{Isolating the radical by adding } -5 \text{ to both sides}$$

The equation $\sqrt{x} = -2$ has no solution because the principal square root of a number is never negative. We continue as in Example 1 for comparison.

$$(\sqrt{x})^2 = (-2)^2 \qquad \text{Using the principle of powers}$$
$$x = 4$$

Check:
$$\begin{array}{c|c} \sqrt{x} + 5 = 3 \\ \hline \sqrt{4} + 5 & 3 \\ 2 + 5 & \\ 7 \stackrel{?}{=} 3 & \text{FALSE} \end{array}$$

The number 4 does not check. Thus, $\sqrt{x} + 5 = 3$ has no solution.

TRY EXERCISE 27

CAUTION! Raising both sides of an equation to an even power may not produce an equivalent equation. In this case, a check is essential.

Note in Example 2 that $x = 4$ has the solution 4, but $\sqrt{x} + 5 = 3$ has *no* solution. Thus the equations $x = 4$ and $\sqrt{x} + 5 = 3$ are *not* equivalent.

To Solve an Equation with a Radical Term
1. Isolate the radical term on one side of the equation.
2. Use the principle of powers and solve the resulting equation.
3. Check any possible solution in the original equation.

EXAMPLE 3   Solve: $x = \sqrt{x + 7} + 5$.

SOLUTION

$$x = \sqrt{x + 7} + 5$$

$$x - 5 = \sqrt{x + 7} \qquad \text{Isolating the radical by subtracting 5 from both sides}$$

$$(x - 5)^2 = (\sqrt{x + 7})^2 \left.\begin{array}{l}\\ \\ \end{array}\right\} \text{Using the principle of powers; squaring both sides}$$
$$x^2 - 10x + 25 = x + 7$$

$$x^2 - 11x + 18 = 0 \qquad \text{Adding } -x - 7 \text{ to both sides to write the quadratic equation in standard form}$$

$$(x - 9)(x - 2) = 0 \qquad \text{Factoring}$$

$$x = 9 \quad \text{or} \quad x = 2 \qquad \text{Using the principle of zero products}$$

The possible solutions are 9 and 2. Let's check.

Check: For 9:

$$\begin{array}{c|c} x = \sqrt{x + 7} + 5 \\ \hline 9 & \sqrt{9 + 7} + 5 \\ & 9 \overset{?}{=} 9 \qquad \text{TRUE} \end{array}$$

For 2:

$$\begin{array}{c|c} x = \sqrt{x + 7} + 5 \\ \hline 2 & \sqrt{2 + 7} + 5 \\ & 2 \overset{?}{=} 8 \qquad \text{FALSE} \end{array}$$

Since 9 checks but 2 does not, the solution is 9.

TRY EXERCISE 39

It is important to isolate a radical term before using the principle of powers. Suppose in Example 3 that both sides of the equation were squared *before* isolating the radical. We then would have had the expression $(\sqrt{x + 7} + 5)^2$ or $x + 7 + 10\sqrt{x + 7} + 25$ on the right side, and the radical would have remained in the problem.

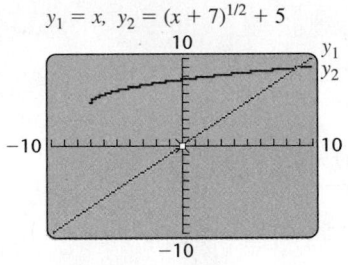
EXAMPLE 4   Solve: $(2x + 1)^{1/3} + 5 = 0$.

SOLUTION   We can use exponential notation to solve:

$$(2x + 1)^{1/3} + 5 = 0$$

$$(2x + 1)^{1/3} = -5 \qquad \text{Subtracting 5 from both sides}$$

$$[(2x + 1)^{1/3}]^3 = (-5)^3 \qquad \text{Cubing both sides}$$

$$(2x + 1)^1 = (-5)^3 \qquad \text{Multiplying exponents. Try to do this mentally.}$$

$$2x + 1 = -125$$

$$2x = -126 \qquad \text{Subtracting 1 from both sides}$$

$$x = -63.$$

Because both sides were raised to an *odd* power, a check is not *essential*. It is wise, however, for the student to confirm that -63 checks and is the solution.

TRY EXERCISE 25

Equations with Two Radical Terms

A strategy for solving equations with two or more radical terms is as follows.

To Solve an Equation with Two or More Radical Terms

1. Isolate one of the radical terms.
2. Use the principle of powers.
3. If a radical remains, perform steps (1) and (2) again.
4. Solve the resulting equation.
5. Check possible solutions in the original equation.

EXAMPLE 5   Solve: $\sqrt{2x - 5} = 1 + \sqrt{x - 3}$.

SOLUTION

$$\sqrt{2x - 5} = 1 + \sqrt{x - 3}$$
$$(\sqrt{2x - 5})^2 = (1 + \sqrt{x - 3})^2 \qquad \text{One radical is already isolated. We square both sides.}$$

This is like squaring a binomial. We square 1, then find twice the product of 1 and $\sqrt{x - 3}$, and finally square $\sqrt{x - 3}$. Study this carefully.

$$2x - 5 = 1 + 2\sqrt{x - 3} + (\sqrt{x - 3})^2$$
$$2x - 5 = 1 + 2\sqrt{x - 3} + (x - 3)$$
$$x - 3 = 2\sqrt{x - 3} \qquad \text{Isolating the remaining radical term}$$
$$(x - 3)^2 = (2\sqrt{x - 3})^2 \qquad \text{Squaring both sides}$$
$$x^2 - 6x + 9 = 4(x - 3) \qquad \text{Remember to square both the 2 and the } \sqrt{x - 3} \text{ on the right side.}$$
$$x^2 - 6x + 9 = 4x - 12$$
$$x^2 - 10x + 21 = 0$$
$$(x - 7)(x - 3) = 0 \qquad \text{Factoring}$$
$$x = 7 \quad or \quad x = 3 \qquad \text{Using the principle of zero products}$$

We leave it to the student to show that 7 and 3 both check and are the solutions.

TRY EXERCISE 41

CAUTION!   A common error in solving equations like

$$\sqrt{2x - 5} = 1 + \sqrt{x - 3}$$

is to obtain $1 + (x - 3)$ as the square of the right side. This is wrong because $(A + B)^2 \neq A^2 + B^2$. For example,

$$\left.\begin{array}{c} (1 + 2)^2 \neq 1^2 + 2^2 \\ 3^2 \neq 1 + 4 \\ 9 \neq 5. \end{array}\right\} \quad \begin{array}{l} \text{See Example 5 for the correct} \\ \text{expansion of } (1 + \sqrt{x - 3})^2. \end{array}$$

EXAMPLE **6** Let $f(x) = \sqrt{x+5} - \sqrt{x-7}$. Find all x-values for which $f(x) = 2$.

SOLUTION We must have $f(x) = 2$, or

$$\sqrt{x+5} - \sqrt{x-7} = 2.$$ Substituting for $f(x)$

To solve, we isolate one radical term and square both sides:

Isolate a radical term.

$$\sqrt{x+5} = 2 + \sqrt{x-7}$$ Adding $\sqrt{x-7}$ to both sides. This isolates one of the radical terms.

Raise both sides to the same power.

$$(\sqrt{x+5})^2 = (2 + \sqrt{x-7})^2$$ Using the principle of powers (squaring both sides)

$$x + 5 = 4 + 4\sqrt{x-7} + (x-7)$$ Using $(A+B)^2 = A^2 + 2AB + B^2$

$$5 = 4\sqrt{x-7} - 3$$ Adding $-x$ to both sides and combining like terms

Isolate a radical term.

$$8 = 4\sqrt{x-7}$$ Isolating the remaining radical term

$$2 = \sqrt{x-7}$$

Raise both sides to the same power.

$$2^2 = (\sqrt{x-7})^2$$ Squaring both sides

$$4 = x - 7$$

Solve.

$$11 = x.$$

Check.

Check: $f(11) = \sqrt{11+5} - \sqrt{11-7}$
$$= \sqrt{16} - \sqrt{4}$$
$$= 4 - 2 = 2.$$

We have $f(x) = 2$ when $x = 11$.

TRY EXERCISE ▸ 49

10.6 **EXERCISE SET**

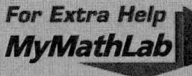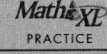

↪ **Concept Reinforcement** *Classify each statement as either true or false.*

1. If $x^2 = 25$, then $x = 5$.

2. If $t = 7$, then $t^2 = 49$.

3. If $\sqrt{x} = 3$, then $(\sqrt{x})^2 = 3^2$.

4. If $x^2 = 36$, then $x = 6$.

5. $\sqrt{x} - 8 = 7$ is equivalent to $\sqrt{x} = 15$.

6. $\sqrt{t} + 5 = 8$ is equivalent to $\sqrt{t} = 3$.

Solve.

7. $\sqrt{5x+1} = 4$

8. $\sqrt{7x-3} = 5$

9. $\sqrt{3x} + 1 = 5$

10. $\sqrt{2x} - 1 = 2$

11. $\sqrt{y+5} - 4 = 1$

12. $\sqrt{x-2} - 7 = -4$

13. $\sqrt{8-x} + 7 = 10$

14. $\sqrt{y+4} + 6 = 7$

15. $\sqrt[3]{y+3} = 2$

16. $\sqrt[3]{x-2} = 3$

17. $\sqrt[4]{t-10} = 3$

18. $\sqrt[4]{t+5} = 2$

19. $6\sqrt{x} = x$

20. $7\sqrt{y} = y$

21. $2y^{1/2} - 13 = 7$

22. $3x^{1/2} + 12 = 9$

23. $\sqrt[3]{x} = -5$

24. $\sqrt[3]{y} = -4$

25. $z^{1/4} + 8 = 10$

26. $x^{1/4} - 2 = 1$

Aha! **27.** $\sqrt{n} = -2$

28. $\sqrt{a} = -1$

29. $\sqrt[4]{3x+1} - 4 = -1$

30. $\sqrt[4]{2x+3} - 5 = -2$

31. $(21x + 55)^{1/3} = 10$

32. $(5y + 31)^{1/4} = 2$

33. $\sqrt[3]{3y + 6} + 7 = 8$

34. $\sqrt[3]{6x + 9} + 5 = 2$

35. $\sqrt{3t + 4} = \sqrt{4t + 3}$

36. $\sqrt{2t - 7} = \sqrt{3t - 12}$

37. $3(4 - t)^{1/4} = 6^{1/4}$

38. $2(1 - x)^{1/3} = 4^{1/3}$

39. $3 + \sqrt{5 - x} = x$

40. $x = \sqrt{x - 1} + 3$

41. $\sqrt{4x - 3} = 2 + \sqrt{2x - 5}$

42. $3 + \sqrt{z - 6} = \sqrt{z + 9}$

43. $\sqrt{20 - x} + 8 = \sqrt{9 - x} + 11$

44. $4 + \sqrt{10 - x} = 6 + \sqrt{4 - x}$

45. $\sqrt{x + 2} + \sqrt{3x + 4} = 2$

46. $\sqrt{6x + 7} - \sqrt{3x + 3} = 1$

47. If $f(x) = \sqrt{x} + \sqrt{x - 9}$, find any x for which $f(x) = 1$.

48. If $g(x) = \sqrt{x} + \sqrt{x - 5}$, find any x for which $g(x) = 5$.

49. If $f(t) = \sqrt{t - 2} - \sqrt{4t + 1}$, find any t for which $f(t) = -3$.

50. If $g(t) = \sqrt{2t + 7} - \sqrt{t + 15}$, find any t for which $g(t) = -1$.

51. If $f(x) = \sqrt{2x - 3}$ and $g(x) = \sqrt{x + 7} - 2$, find any x for which $f(x) = g(x)$.

52. If $f(x) = 2\sqrt{3x + 6}$ and $g(x) = 5 + \sqrt{4x + 9}$, find any x for which $f(x) = g(x)$.

53. If $f(t) = 4 - \sqrt{t - 3}$ and $g(t) = (t + 5)^{1/2}$, find any t for which $f(t) = g(t)$.

54. If $f(t) = 7 + \sqrt{2t - 5}$ and $g(t) = 3(t + 1)^{1/2}$, find any t for which $f(t) = g(t)$.

55. Explain in your own words why it is important to check your answers when using the principle of powers.

56. The principle of powers is an "if–then" statement that becomes false when the sentence parts are interchanged. Give an example of another such if–then statement from everyday life (answers will vary).

Skill Review

To prepare for Section 10.7, review finding dimensions of triangles and rectangles (Sections 2.5 and 5.8).

Solve.

57. *Sign dimensions.* The largest sign in the United States is a rectangle with a perimeter of 430 ft. The length of the rectangle is 5 ft longer than thirteen times the width. Find the dimensions of the sign. [2.5]
Source: Florida Center for Instructional Technology

58. *Sign dimensions.* The base of a triangular sign is 4 in. longer than twice the height. The area of the sign is 255 in². Find the dimensions of the sign. [5.8]

59. *Photograph dimensions.* A rectangular family photo is 4 in. longer than it is wide. The area of the photo is 140 in². Find the dimensions of the photograph. [5.8]

60. *Sidewalk length.* The length of a rectangular lawn between classroom buildings is 2 yd less than twice the width of the lawn. A path that is 34 yd long stretches diagonally across the area. What are the dimensions of the lawn? [5.8]

61. The sides of a right triangle are consecutive even integers. Find the length of each side. [5.8]

62. One leg of a right triangle is 5 cm long. The hypotenuse is 1 cm longer than the other leg. Find the length of the hypotenuse. [5.8]

Synthesis

63. Describe a procedure that could be used to create radical equations that have no solution.

64. Is checking essential when the principle of powers is used with an odd power n? Why or why not?

65. *Firefighting.* The velocity of water flow, in feet per second, from a nozzle is given by
$$v(p) = 12.1\sqrt{p},$$
where p is the nozzle pressure, in pounds per square inch (psi). Find the nozzle pressure if the water flow is 100 feet per second.
Source: Houston Fire Department Continuing Education

66. *Firefighting.* The velocity of water flow, in feet per second, from a water tank that is h feet high is given by
$$v(h) = 8\sqrt{h}.$$
Find the height of a water tank that provides a water flow of 60 feet per second.
Source: Houston Fire Department Continuing Education

67. *Music.* The frequency of a violin string varies directly with the square root of the tension on the string. A violin string vibrates with a frequency of 260 Hz when the tension on the string is 28 N. What is the frequency when the tension is 32 N?

68. *Music.* The frequency of a violin string varies inversely with the square root of the density of the string. A nylon violin string with a density of 1200 kg/m^3 vibrates with a frequency of 250 Hz. What is the frequency of a silk violin string with a density of 1300 kg/m^3?
Source: www.speech.kth.se

Steel manufacturing. *In the production of steel and other metals, the temperature of the molten metal is so great that conventional thermometers melt. Instead, sound is transmitted across the surface of the metal to a receiver on the far side and the speed of the sound is measured. The formula*

$$S(t) = 1087.7 \sqrt{\frac{9t + 2617}{2457}}$$

gives the speed of sound S(t), in feet per second, at a temperature of t degrees Celsius.

69. Find the temperature of a blast furnace where sound travels 1880 ft/sec.

70. Find the temperature of a blast furnace where sound travels 1502.3 ft/sec.

71. Solve the above equation for t.

Automotive repair. *For an engine with a displacement of 2.8 L, the function given by*

$$d(n) = 0.75\sqrt{2.8n}$$

can be used to determine the diameter size of the carburetor's opening, in millimeters. Here n is the number of rpm's at which the engine achieves peak performance.
Source: macdizzy.com

72. If the diameter of a carburetor's opening is 81 mm, for what number of rpm's will the engine produce peak power?

73. If a carburetor's opening is 84 mm, for what number of rpm's will the engine produce peak power?

Escape velocity. *A formula for the escape velocity v of a satellite is*

$$v = \sqrt{2gr}\sqrt{\frac{h}{r + h}},$$

where g is the force of gravity, r is the planet or star's radius, and h is the height of the satellite above the planet or star's surface.

74. Solve for h.

75. Solve for r.

Solve.

76. $\left(\dfrac{z}{4} - 5\right)^{2/3} = \dfrac{1}{25}$

77. $\dfrac{x + \sqrt{x + 1}}{x - \sqrt{x + 1}} = \dfrac{5}{11}$

78. $\sqrt{\sqrt{y} + 49} = 7$

79. $(z^2 + 17)^{3/4} = 27$

80. $x^2 - 5x - \sqrt{x^2 - 5x - 2} = 4$
(*Hint*: Let $u = x^2 - 5x - 2$.)

81. $\sqrt{8 - b} = b\sqrt{8 - b}$

Without graphing, determine the x-intercepts of the graphs given by each of the following.

82. $f(x) = \sqrt{x - 2} - \sqrt{x + 2} + 2$

83. $g(x) = 6x^{1/2} + 6x^{-1/2} - 37$

84. $f(x) = (x^2 + 30x)^{1/2} - x - (5x)^{1/2}$

85. Use a graphing calculator to check your answers to Exercises 9, 15, and 31.

86. Saul is trying to solve Exercise 73 using a graphing calculator. Without resorting to trial and error, how can he determine a suitable viewing window for finding the solution?

87. Use a graphing calculator to check your answers to Exercises 27, 35, and 41.

COLLABORATIVE CORNER

Tailgater Alert

Focus: Radical equations and problem solving
Time: 15–25 minutes
Group size: 2–3
Materials: Calculators or square-root tables

The faster a car is traveling, the more distance it needs to stop. Thus it is important for drivers to allow sufficient space between their vehicle and the vehicle in front of them. Police recommend that for each 10 mph of speed, a driver allow 1 car length. Thus a driver going 30 mph should have at least 3 car lengths between his or her vehicle and the one in front.

In Exercise Set 10.3, the function $r(L) = 2\sqrt{5L}$ was used to find the speed, in miles per hour, that a car was traveling when it left skid marks L feet long.

ACTIVITY

1. Each group member should estimate the length of a car in which he or she frequently travels. (Each should use a different length, if possible.)

2. Using a calculator as needed, each group member should complete the table below. Column 1 gives a car's speed s, and column 2 lists the minimum amount of space between cars traveling s miles per hour, as recommended by police. Column 3 is the speed that a vehicle *could* travel were it forced to stop in the distance listed in column 2, using the above function.

Column 1 s (in miles per hour)	Column 2 L(s) (in feet)	Column 3 r(L) (in miles per hour)
20		
30		
40		
50		
60		
70		

3. Determine whether there are any speeds at which the "1 car length per 10 mph" guideline might not suffice. On what reasoning do you base your answer? Compare tables to determine how car length affects the results. What recommendations would your group make to a new driver?

10.7 The Distance and Midpoint Formulas and Other Applications

Using the Pythagorean Theorem • Two Special Triangles • The Distance and Midpoint Formulas

Using the Pythagorean Theorem

There are many kinds of problems that involve powers and roots. Many also involve right triangles and the Pythagorean theorem, which we studied in Section 5.8 and restate here.

STUDY SKILLS

Making Sketches

One need not be an artist to make highly useful mathematical sketches. That said, it is important to make sure that your sketches are drawn accurately enough to represent the relative sizes within each shape. For example, if one side of a triangle is clearly the longest, make sure your drawing reflects this.

The Pythagorean Theorem*

In any right triangle, if a and b are the lengths of the legs and c is the length of the hypotenuse, then

$$a^2 + b^2 = c^2.$$

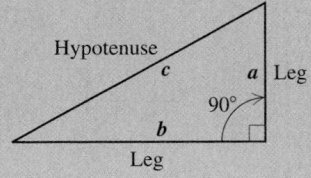

In using the Pythagorean theorem, we often make use of the following principle.

The Principle of Square Roots

For any nonnegative real number n,

$$\text{If} \quad x^2 = n, \quad \text{then} \quad x = \sqrt{n} \quad \text{or} \quad x = -\sqrt{n}.$$

For most real-world applications involving length or distance, $-\sqrt{n}$ is not needed.

EXAMPLE 1

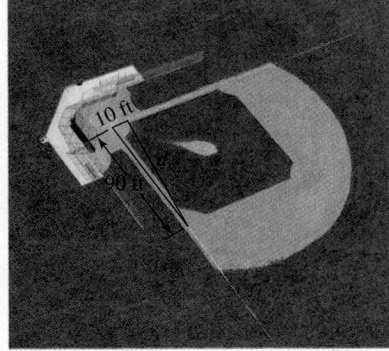

Baseball.   A baseball diamond is actually a square 90 ft on a side. Suppose a catcher fields a ball while standing on the third-base line 10 ft from home plate, as shown in the figure. How far is the catcher's throw to first base? Give an exact answer and an approximation to three decimal places.

SOLUTION   We make a drawing and let $d =$ the distance, in feet, to first base. Note that a right triangle is formed in which the leg from home plate to first base measures 90 ft and the leg from home plate to where the catcher fields the ball measures 10 ft.

We substitute these values into the Pythagorean theorem to find d:

$$d^2 = 90^2 + 10^2$$
$$d^2 = 8100 + 100$$
$$d^2 = 8200.$$

We now use the principle of square roots: If $d^2 = 8200$, then $d = \sqrt{8200}$ or $d = -\sqrt{8200}$. Since d represents a length, it follows that d is the positive square root of 8200:

$$d = \sqrt{8200} \text{ ft} \qquad \text{This is an exact answer.}$$
$$d \approx 90.554 \text{ ft.} \qquad \text{Using a calculator for an approximation}$$

TRY EXERCISE ▶ 19

---

*The converse of the Pythagorean theorem also holds. That is, if a, b, and c are the lengths of the sides of a triangle and $a^2 + b^2 = c^2$, then the triangle is a right triangle.

EXAMPLE **2**

Guy wires. The base of a 40-ft long guy wire is located 15 ft from the telephone pole that it is anchoring. How high up the pole does the guy wire reach? Give an exact answer and an approximation to three decimal places.

SOLUTION We make a drawing and let h = the height, in feet, to which the guy wire reaches. A right triangle is formed in which one leg measures 15 ft and the hypotenuse measures 40 ft. Using the Pythagorean theorem, we have

$$h^2 + 15^2 = 40^2$$
$$h^2 + 225 = 1600$$
$$h^2 = 1375$$
$$h = \sqrt{1375}.$$

Exact answer:

$\quad h = \sqrt{1375}\,\text{ft}$ Using the positive square root

Approximation:

$\quad h \approx 37.081\,\text{ft}$ Using a calculator

40 ft h

15 ft

> **TRY EXERCISE** 23

Two Special Triangles

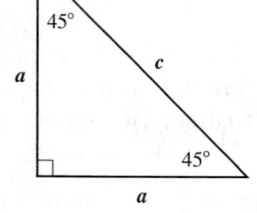

45°

a c

45°

a

When both legs of a right triangle are the same size, as shown at left, we call the triangle an *isosceles right triangle*. If one leg of an isosceles right triangle has length a, we can find a formula for the length of the hypotenuse as follows:

$$c^2 = a^2 + b^2$$
$$c^2 = a^2 + a^2 \qquad \text{Because the triangle is isosceles, both legs are the same size: } a = b.$$
$$c^2 = 2a^2. \qquad \text{Combining like terms}$$

Next, we use the principle of square roots. Because a, b, and c are lengths, there is no need to consider negative square roots or absolute values. Thus,

$$c = \sqrt{2a^2} \qquad \text{Using the principle of square roots}$$
$$c = \sqrt{a^2 \cdot 2} = a\sqrt{2}.$$

EXAMPLE **3**

One leg of an isosceles right triangle measures 7 cm. Find the length of the hypotenuse. Give an exact answer and an approximation to three decimal places.

SOLUTION We substitute:

$$c = a\sqrt{2} \qquad \text{This equation is worth remembering.}$$
$$c = 7\sqrt{2}.$$

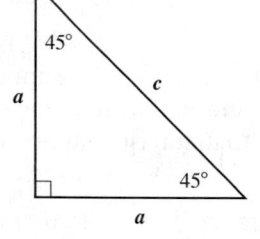

7   a

45°   45°

c

Exact answer: $c = 7\sqrt{2}\,\text{cm}$

Approximation: $c \approx 9.899\,\text{cm}$ Using a calculator

> **TRY EXERCISE** 29

When the hypotenuse of an isosceles right triangle is known, the lengths of the legs can be found.

EXAMPLE 4

The hypotenuse of an isosceles right triangle is 5 ft long. Find the length of a leg. Give an exact answer and an approximation to three decimal places.

SOLUTION   We replace c with 5 and solve for a:

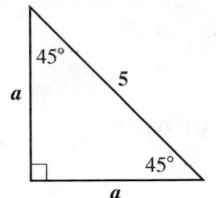

$$5 = a\sqrt{2} \qquad \text{Substituting 5 for } c \text{ in } c = a\sqrt{2}$$

$$\frac{5}{\sqrt{2}} = a \qquad \text{Dividing both sides by } \sqrt{2}$$

$$\frac{5\sqrt{2}}{2} = a. \qquad \text{Rationalize the denominator if desired.}$$

Exact answer: $a = \dfrac{5}{\sqrt{2}}$ ft, or $\dfrac{5\sqrt{2}}{2}$ ft

Approximation: $a \approx 3.536$ ft   Using a calculator

TRY EXERCISE 35

A second special triangle is known as a 30°–60°–90° triangle, so named because of the measures of its angles. Note that in an equilateral triangle, all sides have the same length and all angles are 60°. An altitude, drawn dashed in the figure, bisects, or splits in half, one angle and one side. Two 30°–60°–90° right triangles are thus formed.

If we let a represent the length of the shorter leg in a 30°–60°–90° triangle, then $2a$ represents the length of the hypotenuse. We have

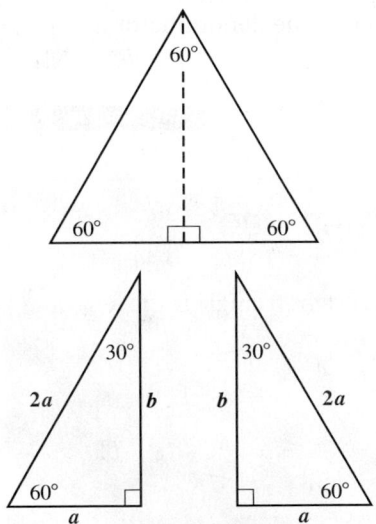

$$a^2 + b^2 = (2a)^2 \qquad \text{Using the Pythagorean theorem}$$

$$a^2 + b^2 = 4a^2$$

$$b^2 = 3a^2 \qquad \text{Subtracting } a^2 \text{ from both sides}$$

$$b = \sqrt{3a^2} \qquad \text{Considering only the positive square root}$$

$$b = \sqrt{a^2 \cdot 3}$$

$$b = a\sqrt{3}.$$

EXAMPLE 5

The shorter leg of a 30°–60°–90° triangle measures 8 in. Find the lengths of the other sides. Give exact answers and, where appropriate, an approximation to three decimal places.

SOLUTION   The hypotenuse is twice as long as the shorter leg, so we have

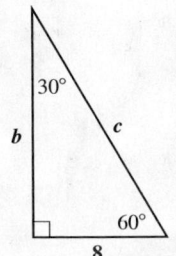

$$c = 2a \qquad \text{This relationship is worth remembering.}$$

$$= 2 \cdot 8 = 16 \text{ in.} \qquad \text{This is the length of the hypotenuse.}$$

The length of the longer leg is the length of the shorter leg times $\sqrt{3}$. This gives us

$$b = a\sqrt{3} \qquad \text{This is also worth remembering.}$$

$$= 8\sqrt{3} \text{ in.} \qquad \text{This is the length of the longer leg.}$$

Exact answer: $c = 16$ in., $b = 8\sqrt{3}$ in.

Approximation: $b \approx 13.856$ in.

TRY EXERCISE 37

EXAMPLE 6   The length of the longer leg of a 30°–60°–90° triangle is 14 cm. Find the length of the hypotenuse. Give an exact answer and an approximation to three decimal places.

SOLUTION   The length of the hypotenuse is twice the length of the shorter leg. We first find a, the length of the shorter leg, by using the length of the longer leg:

$$14 = a\sqrt{3} \qquad \text{Substituting 14 for } b \text{ in } b = a\sqrt{3}$$

$$\frac{14}{\sqrt{3}} = a. \qquad \text{Dividing by } \sqrt{3}$$

Since the hypotenuse is twice as long as the shorter leg, we have

$$c = 2a$$

$$= 2 \cdot \frac{14}{\sqrt{3}} \qquad \text{Substituting}$$

$$= \frac{28}{\sqrt{3}} \text{ cm.}$$

Exact answer: $c = \dfrac{28}{\sqrt{3}}$ cm, or $\dfrac{28\sqrt{3}}{3}$ cm if the denominator is rationalized.

Approximation: $c \approx 16.166$ cm

TRY EXERCISE 33

STUDENT NOTES

Perhaps the easiest way to remember the important results listed in the adjacent box is to write out, on your own, the derivations shown on pp. 678 and 679.

Lengths Within Isosceles and 30°–60°–90° Right Triangles

The length of the hypotenuse in an isosceles right triangle is the length of a leg times $\sqrt{2}$.

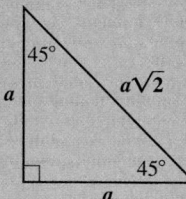

The length of the longer leg in a 30°–60°–90° right triangle is the length of the shorter leg times $\sqrt{3}$. The hypotenuse is twice as long as the shorter leg.

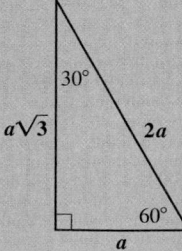

The Distance and Midpoint Formulas

We can use the Pythagorean theorem to find the distance between two points on a plane.

To find the distance between two points on the number line, we subtract. Depending on the order in which we subtract, the difference may be positive or negative. However, if we take the absolute value of the difference, we always obtain a positive value for the distance:

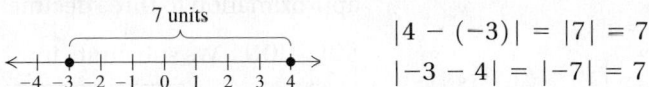

$$|4 - (-3)| = |7| = 7$$
$$|-3 - 4| = |-7| = 7$$

If two points are on a horizontal line, they have the same second coordinate. We can find the distance between them by subtracting their first coordinates and taking the absolute value of that difference.

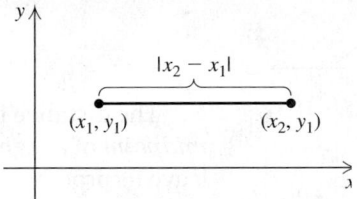

The distance between the points (x_1, y_1) and (x_2, y_1) on a horizontal line is thus $|x_2 - x_1|$. Similarly, the distance between the points (x_2, y_1) and (x_2, y_2) on a vertical line is $|y_2 - y_1|$.

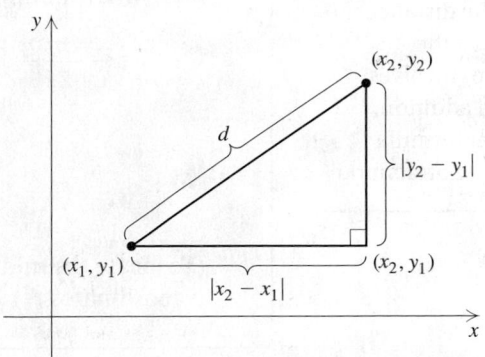

Now consider two points (x_1, y_1) and (x_2, y_2). If $x_1 \neq x_2$ and $y_1 \neq y_2$, these points, along with the point (x_2, y_1), describe a right triangle. The lengths of the legs are $|x_2 - x_1|$ and $|y_2 - y_1|$. We find d, the length of the hypotenuse, by using the Pythagorean theorem:

$$d^2 = |x_2 - x_1|^2 + |y_2 - y_1|^2.$$

Since the square of a number is the same as the square of its opposite, we can replace the absolute-value signs with parentheses:

$$d^2 = (x_2 - x_1)^2 + (y_2 - y_1)^2.$$

Taking the principal square root, we have a formula for distance.

> ### The Distance Formula
>
> The distance d between any two points (x_1, y_1) and (x_2, y_2) is given by
> $$d = \sqrt{(x_2 - x_1)^2 + (y_2 - y_1)^2}.$$

EXAMPLE 7   Find the distance between $(5, -1)$ and $(-4, 6)$. Find an exact answer and an approximation to three decimal places.

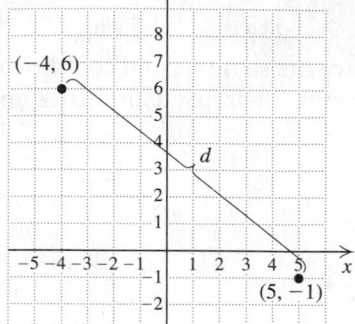

SOLUTION   We substitute into the distance formula:

$$d = \sqrt{(-4 - 5)^2 + [6 - (-1)]^2} \quad \text{Substituting. A drawing is optional.}$$
$$= \sqrt{(-9)^2 + 7^2}$$
$$= \sqrt{130} \quad \text{This is exact.}$$
$$\approx 11.402. \quad \text{Using a calculator for an approximation}$$

> **TRY EXERCISE** 51

   The distance formula is needed to verify a formula for the coordinates of the *midpoint* of a segment connecting two points. We state the midpoint formula and leave its proof to the exercises.

STUDENT NOTES

To help remember the formulas correctly, note that the distance formula (a variation on the Pythagorean theorem) involves both subtraction and addition, whereas the midpoint formula does not include any subtraction.

> ### The Midpoint Formula
>
> If the endpoints of a segment are (x_1, y_1) and (x_2, y_2), then the coordinates of the midpoint are
> $$\left(\frac{x_1 + x_2}{2}, \frac{y_1 + y_2}{2} \right).$$
>
>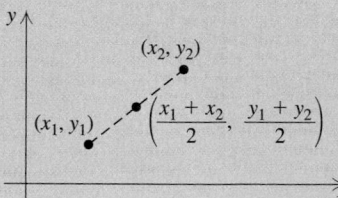
>
> (To locate the midpoint, average the x-coordinates and average the y-coordinates.)

EXAMPLE 8   Find the midpoint of the segment with endpoints $(-2, 3)$ and $(4, -6)$.

SOLUTION   Using the midpoint formula, we obtain

$$\left(\frac{-2 + 4}{2}, \frac{3 + (-6)}{2} \right), \quad \text{or} \quad \left(\frac{2}{2}, \frac{-3}{2} \right), \quad \text{or} \quad \left(1, -\frac{3}{2} \right).$$

> **TRY EXERCISE** 65

10.7 EXERCISE SET

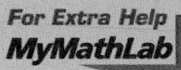

Concept Reinforcement *Complete each sentence with the best choice from the column on the right.*

1. In any _____ triangle, the square of the length of the hypotenuse is the sum of the squares of the lengths of the legs.

2. The shortest side of a right triangle is always one of the two _____.

3. The principle of _____ states that if $x^2 = n$, then $x = \sqrt{n}$ or $x = -\sqrt{n}$.

4. In a(n) _____ right triangle, both legs have the same length.

5. In a(n) _____ right triangle, the hypotenuse is twice as long as the shorter leg.

6. If both legs in a right triangle have measure a, then the _____ measures $a\sqrt{2}$.

a) Hypotenuse

b) Isosceles

c) Legs

d) Right

e) Square roots

f) 30°–60°–90°

In a right triangle, find the length of the side not given. Give an exact answer and, where appropriate, an approximation to three decimal places.

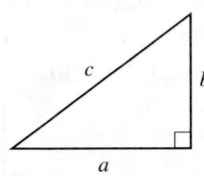

7. $a = 5, b = 3$

8. $a = 8, b = 10$

Aha! 9. $a = 9, b = 9$

10. $a = 10, b = 10$

11. $b = 15, c = 17$

12. $a = 7, c = 25$

In Exercises 13–18, give an exact answer and, where appropriate, an approximation to three decimal places.

13. A right triangle's hypotenuse is 8 m and one leg is $4\sqrt{3}$ m. Find the length of the other leg.

14. A right triangle's hypotenuse is 6 cm and one leg is $\sqrt{5}$ cm. Find the length of the other leg.

15. The hypotenuse of a right triangle is $\sqrt{20}$ in. and one leg measures 1 in. Find the length of the other leg.

16. The hypotenuse of a right triangle is $\sqrt{15}$ ft and one leg measures 2 ft. Find the length of the other leg.

Aha! 17. One leg in a right triangle is 1 m and the hypotenuse measures $\sqrt{2}$ m. Find the length of the other leg.

18. One leg of a right triangle is 1 yd and the hypotenuse measures 2 yd. Find the length of the other leg.

In Exercises 19–28, give an exact answer and, where appropriate, an approximation to three decimal places.

19. *Bicycling.* Clare routinely bicycles across a rectangular parking lot on her way to work. If the lot is 200 ft long and 150 ft wide, how far does Clare travel when she rides across the lot diagonally?

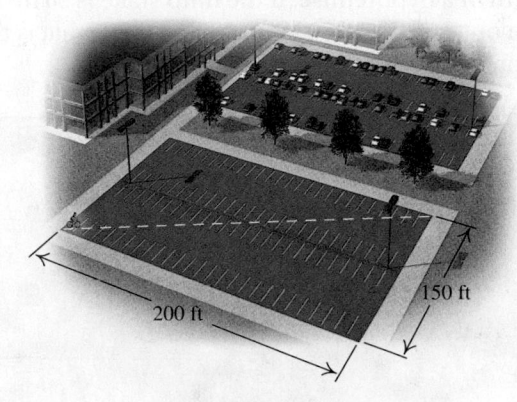

200 ft

150 ft

20. *Guy wire.* How long is a guy wire if it reaches from the top of a 15-ft pole to a point on the ground 10 ft from the pole?

21. *Softball.* A slow-pitch softball diamond is actually a square 65 ft on a side. How far is it from home plate to second base?

22. *Baseball.* Suppose the catcher in Example 1 makes a throw to second base from the same location. How far is that throw?

23. *Television sets.* What does it mean to refer to a 51-in. TV set? Such units refer to the diagonal of the screen. A 51-in. TV set has a width of 45 in. What is its height?

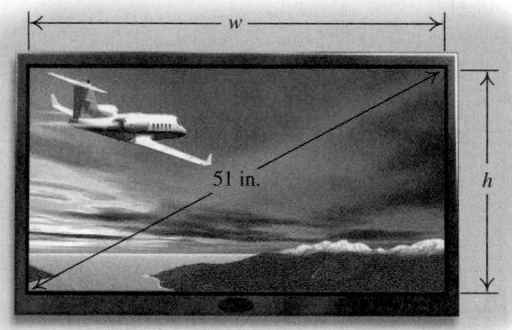

24. *Television sets.* A 53-in. TV set has a screen with a height of 28 in. What is its width? (See Exercise 23.)

25. *Speaker placement.* A stereo receiver is in a corner of a 12-ft by 14-ft room. Wire will run under a rug, diagonally, to a subwoofer in the far corner. If 4 ft of slack is required on each end, how long a piece of wire should be purchased?

26. *Distance over water.* To determine the width of a pond, a surveyor locates two stakes at either end of the pond and uses instrumentation to place a third stake so that the distance across the pond is the length of a hypotenuse. If the third stake is 90 m from one stake and 70 m from the other, what is the distance across the pond?

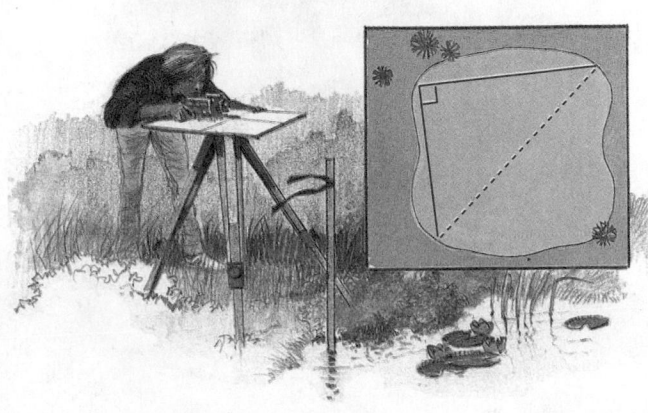

27. *Walking.* Students at Pohlman Community College have worn a path that cuts diagonally across the campus "quad." If the quad is actually a rectangle that Marissa measured to be 70 paces long and 40 paces wide, how many paces will Marissa save by using the diagonal path?

28. *Crosswalks.* The diagonal crosswalk at the intersection of State St. and Main St. is the hypotenuse of a triangle in which the crosswalks across State St. and Main St. are the legs. If State St. is 28 ft wide and Main St. is 40 ft wide, how much shorter is the distance traveled by pedestrians using the diagonal crosswalk?

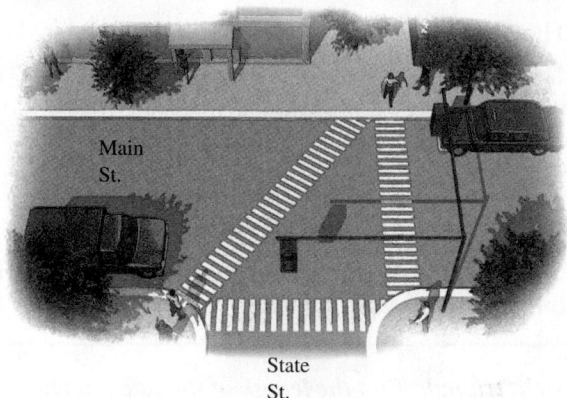

For each triangle, find the missing length(s). Give an exact answer and, where appropriate, an approximation to three decimal places.

29.

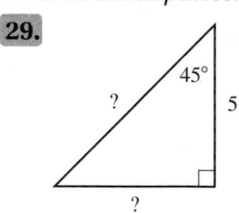

30.

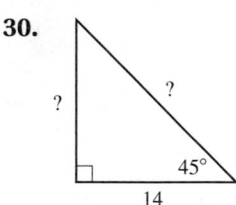

31.

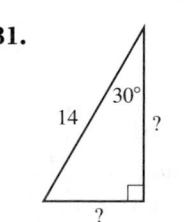

32.

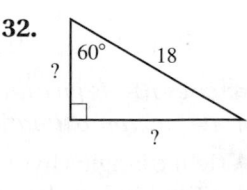

33.

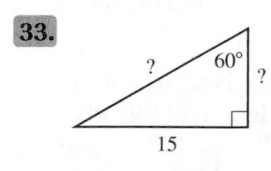

34.

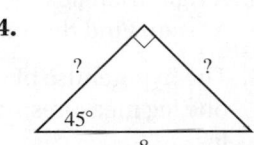

35.

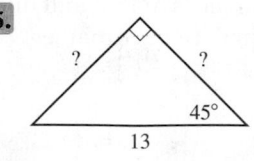

36.

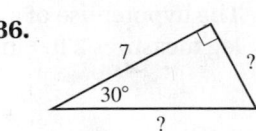

37.
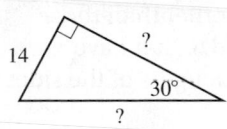

38.
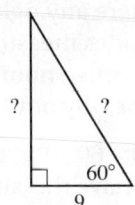

39.
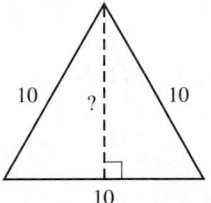

40.
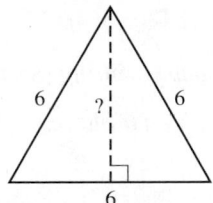

41.
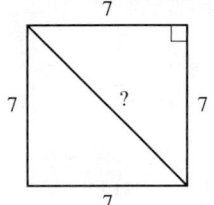

42.
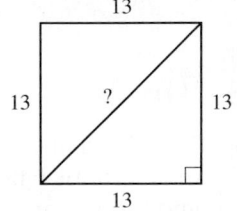

43.
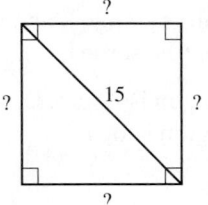

44.
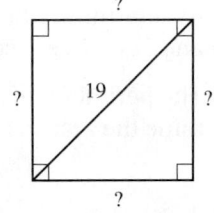

In Exercises 45–48, give an exact answer and, where appropriate, an approximation to three decimal places.

45. *Bridge expansion.*   During the summer heat, a 2-mi bridge expands 2 ft in length. If we assume that the bulge occurs straight up the middle, how high is the bulge? (The answer may surprise you. Most bridges have expansion spaces to avoid such buckling.)

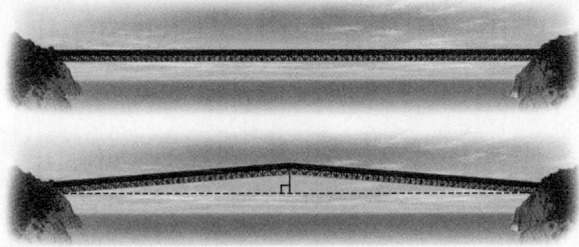

46. Triangle *ABC* has sides of lengths 25 ft, 25 ft, and 30 ft. Triangle *PQR* has sides of lengths 25 ft, 25 ft, and 40 ft. Which triangle, if either, has the greater area and by how much?

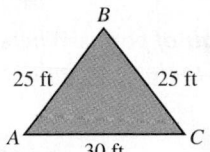
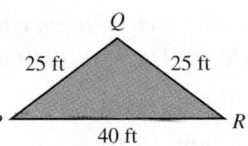

47. *Architecture.*   The Rushton Triangular Lodge in Northamptonshire, England, was designed and constructed by Sir Thomas Tresham between 1593 and 1597. The building is in the shape of an equilateral triangle with walls of length 33 ft. How many square feet of land is covered by the lodge?
Source: The Internet Encyclopedia of Science

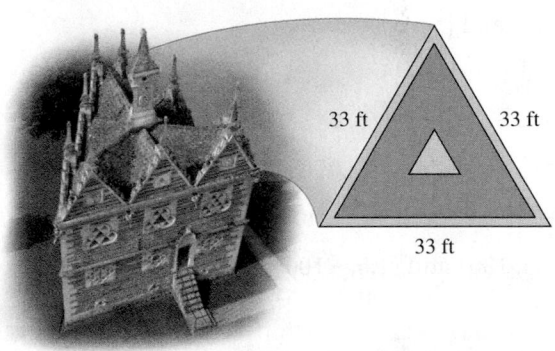

48. *Antenna length.*   As part of an emergency radio communication station, Rik sets up an "Inverted-V" antenna. He stretches a copper wire from one point on the ground to a point on a tree and then back down to the ground, forming two 30°–60°–90° triangles. If the wire is fastened to the tree 34 ft above the ground, how long is the copper wire?

49. Find all points on the *y*-axis of a Cartesian coordinate system that are 5 units from the point $(3, 0)$.

50. Find all points on the *x*-axis of a Cartesian coordinate system that are 5 units from the point $(0, 4)$.

Find the distance between each pair of points. Where appropriate, find an approximation to three decimal places.

51. $(4, 5)$ and $(7, 1)$

52. $(0, 8)$ and $(6, 0)$

53. $(0, -5)$ and $(1, -2)$

54. $(-1, -4)$ and $(-3, -5)$

55. $(-4, 4)$ and $(6, -6)$

56. $(5, 21)$ and $(-3, 1)$

Aha! **57.** $(8.6, -3.4)$ and $(-9.2, -3.4)$

58. $(5.9, 2)$ and $(3.7, -7.7)$

59. $\left(\frac{1}{2}, \frac{1}{3}\right)$ and $\left(\frac{5}{6}, -\frac{1}{6}\right)$

60. $\left(\frac{5}{7}, \frac{1}{14}\right)$ and $\left(\frac{1}{7}, \frac{11}{14}\right)$

61. $(-\sqrt{6}, \sqrt{6})$ and $(0, 0)$

62. $(\sqrt{5}, -\sqrt{3})$ and $(0, 0)$

63. $(-1, -30)$ and $(-2, -40)$

64. $(0.5, 100)$ and $(1.5, -100)$

Find the midpoint of each segment with the given endpoints.

65. $(-2, 5)$ and $(8, 3)$

66. $(1, 4)$ and $(9, -6)$

67. $(2, -1)$ and $(5, 8)$

68. $(-1, 2)$ and $(1, -3)$

69. $(-8, -5)$ and $(6, -1)$

70. $(8, -2)$ and $(-3, 4)$

71. $(-3.4, 8.1)$ and $(4.8, -8.1)$

72. $(4.1, 6.9)$ and $(5.2, -8.9)$

73. $\left(\frac{1}{6}, -\frac{3}{4}\right)$ and $\left(-\frac{1}{3}, \frac{5}{6}\right)$

74. $\left(-\frac{4}{5}, -\frac{2}{3}\right)$ and $\left(\frac{1}{8}, \frac{3}{4}\right)$

75. $(\sqrt{2}, -1)$ and $(\sqrt{3}, 4)$

76. $(9, 2\sqrt{3})$ and $(-4, 5\sqrt{3})$

77. Are there any right triangles, other than those with sides measuring 3, 4, and 5, that have consecutive numbers for the lengths of the sides? Why or why not?

78. If a 30°–60°–90° triangle and an isosceles right triangle have the same perimeter, which will have the greater area? Why?

Skill Review

Review graphing (Sections 3.2, 3.3, 3.6, and 9.4).

Graph on a plane.

79. $y = 2x - 3$ [3.6]

80. $y < x$ [9.4]

81. $8x - 4y = 8$ [3.3]

82. $2y - 1 = 7$ [3.3]

83. $x \geq 1$ [9.4]

84. $x - 5 = 6 - 2y$ [3.2]

Synthesis

85. Describe a procedure that uses the distance formula to determine whether three points, (x_1, y_1), (x_2, y_2), and (x_3, y_3), are vertices of a right triangle.

86. Outline a procedure that uses the distance formula to determine whether three points, (x_1, y_1), (x_2, y_2), and (x_3, y_3), are collinear (lie on the same line).

87. The perimeter of a regular hexagon is 72 cm. Determine the area of the shaded region shown.

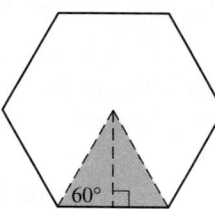

88. If the perimeter of a regular hexagon is 120 ft, what is its area? (*Hint*: See Exercise 87.)

89. Each side of a regular octagon has length *s*. Find a formula for the distance *d* between the parallel sides of the octagon.

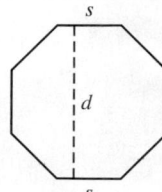

90. *Roofing.* Kit's home, which is 24 ft wide and 32 ft long, needs a new roof. By counting clapboards that are 4 in. apart, Kit determines that the peak of the roof is 6 ft higher than the sides. A packet of shingles covers 100 ft^2. How many packets will the job require?

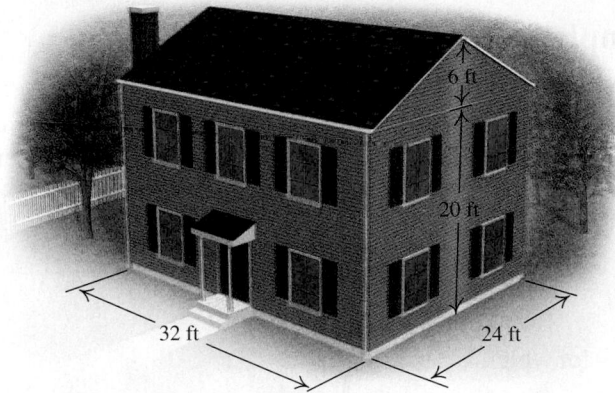

91. *Painting.* (Refer to Exercise 90.) A gallon of Benjamin Moore® exterior acrylic paint covers 450–500 ft^2. If Kit's house has dimensions as shown above, how many gallons of paint should be bought to paint the house? What assumption(s) is made in your answer?

92. *Contracting.* Oxford Builders has an extension cord on their generator that permits them to work, with electricity, anywhere in a circular area of 3850 ft^2. Find the dimensions of the largest square room they could work on without having to relocate the generator to reach each corner of the floor plan.

93. *Contracting.* Cleary Construction has a hose attached to their insulation blower that permits them to reach anywhere in a circular area of 6160 ft^2. Find the dimensions of the largest square room with 12-ft ceilings in which they could reach all corners with the hose while leaving the blower centrally located. Assume that the blower sits on the floor.

94. The length and the width of a rectangle are given by consecutive integers. The area of the rectangle is 90 cm^2. Find the length of a diagonal of the rectangle.

95. A cube measures 5 cm on each side. How long is the diagonal that connects two opposite corners of the cube? Give an exact answer.

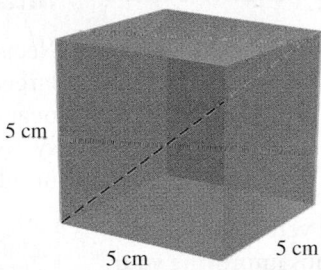

96. Prove the midpoint formula by showing that

  i) the distance from (x_1, y_1) to

$$\left(\frac{x_1 + x_2}{2}, \frac{y_1 + y_2}{2} \right)$$

  equals the distance from (x_2, y_2) to

$$\left(\frac{x_1 + x_2}{2}, \frac{y_1 + y_2}{2} \right);$$

  and

  ii) the points

$$(x_1, y_1), \left(\frac{x_1 + x_2}{2}, \frac{y_1 + y_2}{2} \right),$$

  and

$$(x_2, y_2)$$

  lie on the same line (see Exercise 86).

10.8 The Complex Numbers

Imaginary and Complex Numbers • Addition and Subtraction • Multiplication • Conjugates and Division • Powers of i

Imaginary and Complex Numbers

Negative numbers do not have square roots in the real-number system. However, a larger number system that contains the real-number system is designed so that negative numbers *do* have square roots. That system is called the **complex-number system**, and it will allow us to solve equations like $x^2 + 1 = 0$. The complex-number system makes use of i, a number that is, by definition, a square root of -1.

> **The Number i**
>
> i is the unique number for which $i = \sqrt{-1}$ and $i^2 = -1$.

We can now define the square root of a negative number as follows:

$$\sqrt{-p} = \sqrt{-1}\sqrt{p} = i\sqrt{p} \text{ or } \sqrt{p}i, \text{ for any positive number } p.$$

EXAMPLE 1 Express in terms of i: **(a)** $\sqrt{-7}$; **(b)** $\sqrt{-16}$; **(c)** $-\sqrt{-13}$; **(d)** $-\sqrt{-50}$.

SOLUTION

a) $\sqrt{-7} = \sqrt{-1 \cdot 7} = \sqrt{-1} \cdot \sqrt{7} = i\sqrt{7}$, or $\sqrt{7}i$ i is *not* under the radical.

b) $\sqrt{-16} = \sqrt{-1 \cdot 16} = \sqrt{-1} \cdot \sqrt{16} = i \cdot 4 = 4i$

c) $-\sqrt{-13} = -\sqrt{-1 \cdot 13} = -\sqrt{-1} \cdot \sqrt{13} = -i\sqrt{13}$, or $-\sqrt{13}i$

d) $-\sqrt{-50} = -\sqrt{-1} \cdot \sqrt{25} \cdot \sqrt{2} = -i \cdot 5 \cdot \sqrt{2} = -5i\sqrt{2}$, or $-5\sqrt{2}i$

TRY EXERCISE 9

> **Imaginary Numbers**
>
> An *imaginary number* is a number that can be written in the form $a + bi$, where a and b are real numbers and $b \neq 0$.

Don't let the name "imaginary" fool you. Imaginary numbers appear in fields such as engineering and the physical sciences. The following are examples of imaginary numbers:

$5 + 4i$,   Here $a = 5, b = 4$.

$\sqrt{3} - \pi i$,   Here $a = \sqrt{3}, b = -\pi$.

$\sqrt{7}i$ Here $a = 0, b = \sqrt{7}$.

The union of the set of all imaginary numbers and the set of all real numbers is the set of all **complex numbers**.

Complex Numbers

A *complex number* is any number that can be written in the form $a + bi$, where a and b are real numbers. (Note that a and b both can be 0.)

The following are examples of complex numbers:

$7 + 3i$ (here $a \neq 0$, $b \neq 0$); $4i$ (here $a = 0$, $b \neq 0$);

8 (here $a \neq 0$, $b = 0$); 0 (here $a = 0$, $b = 0$).

Complex numbers like $17i$ or $4i$, in which $a = 0$ and $b \neq 0$, are called *pure imaginary numbers*.

For $b = 0$, we have $a + 0i = a$, so every real number is a complex number. The relationships among various real and complex numbers are shown below.

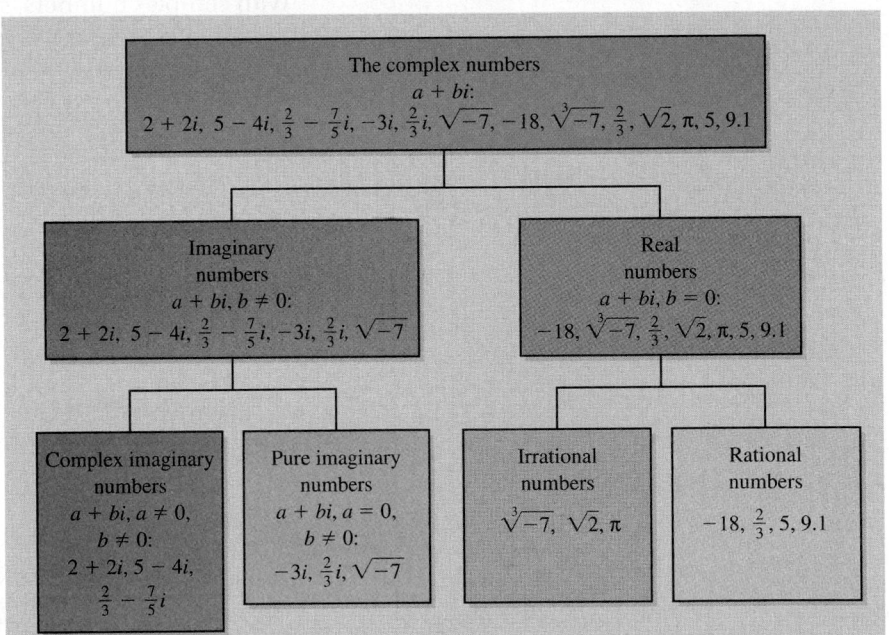

Note that although $\sqrt{-7}$ and $\sqrt[3]{-7}$ are both complex numbers, $\sqrt{-7}$ is imaginary whereas $\sqrt[3]{-7}$ is real.

Addition and Subtraction

The complex numbers obey the commutative, associative, and distributive laws. Thus we can add and subtract them as we do binomials.

EXAMPLE 2

Add or subtract and simplify.

a) $(8 + 6i) + (3 + 2i)$ **b)** $(4 + 5i) - (6 - 3i)$

SOLUTION

a) $(8 + 6i) + (3 + 2i) = (8 + 3) + (6i + 2i)$ Combining the real parts and the imaginary parts

$= 11 + (6 + 2)i = 11 + 8i$

b) $(4 + 5i) - (6 - 3i) = (4 - 6) + [5i - (-3i)]$ Note that the 6 and the $-3i$ are *both* being subtracted.

$$= -2 + 8i$$

TRY EXERCISE   27

Multiplication

To multiply square roots of negative real numbers, we first express them in terms of i. For example,

$$\sqrt{-2} \cdot \sqrt{-5} = \sqrt{-1} \cdot \sqrt{2} \cdot \sqrt{-1} \cdot \sqrt{5}$$
$$= i \cdot \sqrt{2} \cdot i \cdot \sqrt{5}$$
$$= i^2 \cdot \sqrt{10}$$
$$= -1\sqrt{10} = -\sqrt{10} \text{ is correct!}$$

> **CAUTION!** With complex numbers, simply multiplying radicands is *incorrect* when both radicands are negative: $\sqrt{-2} \cdot \sqrt{-5} \neq \sqrt{10}$.

With this in mind, we can now multiply complex numbers.

EXAMPLE 3   Multiply and simplify. When possible, write answers in the form $a + bi$.

a) $\sqrt{-4}\sqrt{-25}$ **b)** $\sqrt{-5} \cdot \sqrt{-7}$ **c)** $-3i \cdot 8i$

d) $-4i(3 - 5i)$ **e)** $(1 + 2i)(4 + 3i)$

SOLUTION

a) $\sqrt{-4}\sqrt{-25} = \sqrt{-1} \cdot \sqrt{4} \cdot \sqrt{-1} \cdot \sqrt{25}$
$$= i \cdot 2 \cdot i \cdot 5$$
$$= i^2 \cdot 10$$
$$= -1 \cdot 10 \qquad i^2 = -1$$
$$= -10$$

b) $\sqrt{-5} \cdot \sqrt{-7} = \sqrt{-1} \cdot \sqrt{5} \cdot \sqrt{-1} \cdot \sqrt{7}$ Try to do this step mentally.
$$= i \cdot \sqrt{5} \cdot i \cdot \sqrt{7}$$
$$= i^2 \cdot \sqrt{35}$$
$$= -1 \cdot \sqrt{35} \qquad i^2 = -1$$
$$= -\sqrt{35}$$

c) $-3i \cdot 8i = -24 \cdot i^2$
$$= -24 \cdot (-1) \qquad i^2 = -1$$
$$= 24$$

d) $-4i(3 - 5i) = -4i \cdot 3 + (-4i)(-5i)$ Using the distributive law
$$= -12i + 20i^2$$
$$= -12i - 20 \qquad i^2 = -1$$
$$= -20 - 12i \qquad \text{Writing in the form } a + bi$$

e) $(1 + 2i)(4 + 3i) = 4 + 3i + 8i + 6i^2$ Multiplying each term of $4 + 3i$ by each term of $1 + 2i$ (FOIL)

$$= 4 + 3i + 8i - 6 \qquad i^2 = -1$$
$$= -2 + 11i \qquad \text{Combining like terms}$$

TRY EXERCISES   35 and 49

Conjugates and Division

Recall that the conjugate of $4 + \sqrt{2}$ is $4 - \sqrt{2}$.

Conjugates of complex numbers are defined in a similar manner.

> ### Conjugate of a Complex Number
> The *conjugate* of a complex number $a + bi$ is $a - bi$, and the *conjugate* of $a - bi$ is $a + bi$.

EXAMPLE 4   Find the conjugate of each number.

a) $-3 - 7i$

b) $4i$

SOLUTION

a) $-3 - 7i$ The conjugate is $-3 + 7i$.

b) $4i$ The conjugate is $-4i$. Note that $4i = 0 + 4i$.

The product of a complex number and its conjugate is a real number.

EXAMPLE 5   Multiply: $(5 + 7i)(5 - 7i)$.

SOLUTION

$$
\begin{aligned}
(5 + 7i)(5 - 7i) &= 5^2 - (7i)^2 && \text{Using } (A + B)(A - B) = A^2 - B^2 \\
&= 25 - 49i^2 \\
&= 25 - 49(-1) && i^2 = -1 \\
&= 25 + 49 = 74
\end{aligned}
$$

TRY EXERCISE 55

Conjugates are used when dividing complex numbers. The procedure is much like that used to rationalize denominators in Section 10.5.

EXAMPLE 6   Divide and simplify to the form $a + bi$.

a) $\dfrac{-2 + 9i}{1 - 3i}$

b) $\dfrac{7 + 4i}{5i}$

SOLUTION

a) To divide and simplify $(-2 + 9i)/(1 - 3i)$, we multiply by 1, using the conjugate of the denominator to form 1:

$$
\begin{aligned}
\frac{-2 + 9i}{1 - 3i} &= \frac{-2 + 9i}{1 - 3i} \cdot \frac{1 + 3i}{1 + 3i} && \text{Multiplying by 1 using the conjugate of the denominator in the symbol for 1} \\[2mm]
&= \frac{(-2 + 9i)(1 + 3i)}{(1 - 3i)(1 + 3i)} && \text{Multiplying numerators; multiplying denominators} \\[2mm]
&= \frac{-2 - 6i + 9i + 27i^2}{1^2 - 9i^2} && \text{Using FOIL} \\[2mm]
&= \frac{-2 + 3i + (-27)}{1 - (-9)} && i^2 = -1 \\[2mm]
&= \frac{-29 + 3i}{10} && \text{Writing in the form } a + bi; \\[2mm]
&= -\frac{29}{10} + \frac{3}{10}i. && \text{note that } \frac{X + Y}{Z} = \frac{X}{Z} + \frac{Y}{Z}
\end{aligned}
$$

b) The conjugate of $5i$ is $-5i$, so we *could* multiply by $-5i/(-5i)$. However, when the denominator is a pure imaginary number, it is easiest if we multiply by i/i:

$$\frac{7 + 4i}{5i} = \frac{7 + 4i}{5i} \cdot \frac{i}{i} \qquad \text{Multiplying by 1 using } i/i. \text{ We can also use the}$$
$$\text{conjugate of } 5i \text{ to write } -5i/(-5i).$$

$$= \frac{7i + 4i^2}{5i^2} \qquad \text{Multiplying}$$

$$= \frac{7i + 4(-1)}{5(-1)} \qquad i^2 = -1$$

$$= \frac{7i - 4}{-5} = \frac{-4}{-5} + \frac{7}{-5}i, \text{ or } \frac{4}{5} - \frac{7}{5}i. \qquad \text{Writing in the form } a + bi$$

> **TRY EXERCISE** 73

Powers of i

Answers to problems involving complex numbers are generally written in the form $a + bi$. In the following discussion, we show why there is no need to use powers of i (other than 1) when writing answers.

Recall that -1 raised to an *even* power is 1, and -1 raised to an *odd* power is -1. Simplifying powers of i can then be done by using the fact that $i^2 = -1$ and expressing the given power of i in terms of i^2. Consider the following:

$$i^2 = -1,$$
$$i^3 = i^2 \cdot i = (-1)i = -i,$$
$$i^4 = (i^2)^2 = (-1)^2 = 1,$$
$$i^5 = i^4 \cdot i = (i^2)^2 \cdot i = (-1)^2 \cdot i = i,$$
$$i^6 = (i^2)^3 = (-1)^3 = -1. \longleftarrow \text{The pattern is now repeating.}$$

The powers of i cycle themselves through the values i, -1, $-i$, and 1. Even powers of i are -1 or 1 whereas odd powers of i are i or $-i$.

EXAMPLE 7   Simplify: **(a)** i^{18}; **(b)** i^{24}.

SOLUTION

a) $i^{18} = (i^2)^9$ Using the power rule

      $= (-1)^9 = -1$ Raising -1 to a power

b) $i^{24} = (i^2)^{12}$

      $= (-1)^{12} = 1$

> **TRY EXERCISE** 83

To simplify i^n when n is odd, we rewrite i^n as $i^{n-1} \cdot i$.

EXAMPLE 8   Simplify: **(a)** i^{29}; **(b)** i^{75}.

SOLUTION

a) $i^{29} = i^{28} i^1$ Using the product rule. This is a key step
                      when i is raised to an odd power.

      $= (i^2)^{14} i$ Using the power rule

      $= (-1)^{14} i$

      $= 1 \cdot i = i$

b) $i^{75} = i^{74} i^1$ Using the product rule

      $= (i^2)^{37} i$ Using the power rule

      $= (-1)^{37} i$

      $= -1 \cdot i = -i$

> **TRY EXERCISE** 85

10.8 EXERCISE SET

Concept Reinforcement *Classify each statement as either true or false.*

1. Imaginary numbers are so named because they have no real-world applications.

2. Every real number is imaginary, but not every imaginary number is real.

3. Every imaginary number is a complex number, but not every complex number is imaginary.

4. Every real number is a complex number, but not every complex number is real.

5. We add complex numbers by combining real parts and combining imaginary parts.

6. The product of a complex number and its conjugate is always a real number.

7. The square of a complex number is always a real number.

8. The quotient of two complex numbers is always a complex number.

Express in terms of i.

9. $\sqrt{-100}$

10. $\sqrt{-9}$

11. $\sqrt{-5}$

12. $\sqrt{-7}$

13. $\sqrt{-8}$

14. $\sqrt{-12}$

15. $-\sqrt{-11}$

16. $-\sqrt{-17}$

17. $-\sqrt{-49}$

18. $-\sqrt{-81}$

19. $-\sqrt{-300}$

20. $-\sqrt{-75}$

21. $6 - \sqrt{-84}$

22. $4 - \sqrt{-60}$

23. $-\sqrt{-76} + \sqrt{-125}$

24. $\sqrt{-4} + \sqrt{-12}$

25. $\sqrt{-18} - \sqrt{-64}$

26. $\sqrt{-72} - \sqrt{-25}$

Perform the indicated operation and simplify. Write each answer in the form a + bi.

27. $(3 + 4i) + (2 - 7i)$

28. $(5 - 6i) + (8 + 9i)$

29. $(9 + 5i) - (2 + 3i)$

30. $(8 + 7i) - (2 + 4i)$

31. $(7 - 4i) - (5 - 3i)$

32. $(5 - 3i) - (9 + 2i)$

33. $(-5 - i) - (7 + 4i)$

34. $(-2 + 6i) - (-7 + i)$

35. $5i \cdot 8i$

36. $3i \cdot 9i$

37. $(-4i)(-6i)$

38. $7i \cdot (-8i)$

39. $\sqrt{-36}\sqrt{-9}$

40. $\sqrt{-49}\sqrt{-16}$

41. $\sqrt{-3}\sqrt{-10}$

42. $\sqrt{-6}\sqrt{-7}$

43. $\sqrt{-6}\sqrt{-21}$

44. $\sqrt{-15}\sqrt{-10}$

45. $5i(2 + 6i)$

46. $2i(7 + 3i)$

47. $-7i(3 + 4i)$

48. $-4i(6 - 5i)$

49. $(1 + i)(3 + 2i)$

50. $(4 + i)(2 + 3i)$

51. $(6 - 5i)(3 + 4i)$

52. $(5 - 6i)(2 + 5i)$

53. $(7 - 2i)(2 - 6i)$

54. $(-4 + 5i)(3 - 4i)$

55. $(3 + 8i)(3 - 8i)$

56. $(1 + 2i)(1 - 2i)$

57. $(-7 + i)(-7 - i)$

58. $(-4 + 5i)(-4 - 5i)$

59. $(4 - 2i)^2$

60. $(1 - 2i)^2$

61. $(2 + 3i)^2$

62. $(3 + 2i)^2$

63. $(-2 + 3i)^2$

64. $(-5 - 2i)^2$

65. $\dfrac{10}{3 + i}$

66. $\dfrac{26}{5 + i}$

67. $\dfrac{2}{3 - 2i}$

68. $\dfrac{4}{2 - 3i}$

69. $\dfrac{2i}{5 + 3i}$

70. $\dfrac{3i}{4 + 2i}$

71. $\dfrac{5}{6i}$

72. $\dfrac{4}{7i}$

73. $\dfrac{5 - 3i}{4i}$

74. $\dfrac{2 + 7i}{5i}$

Aha! 75. $\dfrac{7i + 14}{7i}$

76. $\dfrac{6i + 3}{3i}$

77. $\dfrac{4 + 5i}{3 - 7i}$

78. $\dfrac{5 + 3i}{7 - 4i}$

79. $\dfrac{2 + 3i}{2 + 5i}$

80. $\dfrac{3 + 2i}{4 + 3i}$

81. $\dfrac{3 - 2i}{4 + 3i}$

82. $\dfrac{5 - 2i}{3 + 6i}$

Simplify.

83. i^{32}

84. i^{19}

85. i^{15}

86. i^{38}

87. i^{42}

88. i^{64}

89. i^9

90. $(-i)^{71}$

91. $(-i)^6$

92. $(-i)^4$

93. $(5i)^3$

94. $(-3i)^5$

95. $i^2 + i^4$

96. $5i^5 + 4i^3$

97. Is the product of two imaginary numbers always an imaginary number? Why or why not?

98. In what way(s) are conjugates of complex numbers similar to the conjugates used in Section 10.5?

Skill Review

To prepare for Section 11.1, review solving quadratic equations (Section 5.7).

Solve. [5.7]

99. $x^2 - x - 6 = 0$

100. $(x - 5)^2 = 0$

101. $t^2 = 100$

102. $2t^2 - 50 = 0$

103. $15x^2 = 14x + 8$

104. $6x^2 = 5x + 6$

Synthesis

105. Is the set of real numbers a subset of the set of complex numbers? Why or why not?

106. Is the union of the set of imaginary numbers and the set of real numbers the set of complex numbers? Why or why not?

Complex numbers are often graphed on a plane. The horizontal axis is the real axis and the vertical axis is the imaginary axis. A complex number such as $5 - 2i$ *then corresponds to 5 on the real axis and* -2 *on the imaginary axis.*

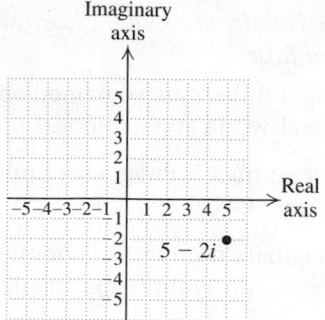

107. Graph each of the following.

   a) $3 + 2i$ **b)** $-1 + 4i$

   c) $3 - i$ **d)** $-5i$

108. Graph each of the following.

   a) $1 - 4i$ **b)** $-2 - 3i$

   c) i **d)** 4

The absolute value of a complex number $a + bi$ *is its distance from the origin. Using the distance formula, we have* $|a + bi| = \sqrt{a^2 + b^2}$. *Find the absolute value of each complex number.*

109. $|3 + 4i|$

110. $|8 - 6i|$

111. $|-1 + i|$

112. $|-3 - i|$

A function g is given by

$$g(z) = \frac{z^4 - z^2}{z - 1}.$$

113. Find $g(3i)$.

114. Find $g(1 + i)$.

115. Find $g(5i - 1)$.

116. Find $g(2 - 3i)$.

117. Evaluate

$$\frac{1}{w - w^2} \quad \text{for} \quad w = \frac{1 - i}{10}.$$

Simplify.

118. $\dfrac{i^5 + i^6 + i^7 + i^8}{(1 - i)^4}$

119. $(1 - i)^3(1 + i)^3$

120. $\dfrac{5 - \sqrt{5}i}{\sqrt{5}i}$

121. $\dfrac{6}{1 + \dfrac{3}{i}}$

122. $\left(\dfrac{1}{2} - \dfrac{1}{3}i\right)^2 - \left(\dfrac{1}{2} + \dfrac{1}{3}i\right)^2$

123. $\dfrac{i - i^{38}}{1 + i}$

Study Summary

KEY TERMS AND CONCEPTS	EXAMPLES

SECTION 10.1: RADICAL EXPRESSIONS AND FUNCTIONS

c is a **square root** of a if $c^2 = a$.

c is a **cube root** of a if $c^3 = a$.

$\sqrt{a}$ indicates the **principal** square root of a.

$\sqrt[n]{a}$ indicates the ***n*th root** of a.

index $\diagdown$

$\sqrt[n]{a}$ —— **radicand**

radical symbol $\diagup$

The square roots of 25 are -5 and 5.

The cube root of -8 is -2.

$\sqrt{25} = 5$

$\sqrt[3]{-8} = -2$

For all a,

$$\sqrt[n]{a^n} = |a| \text{ when } n \text{ is even;}$$

$$\sqrt[n]{a^n} = a \text{ when } n \text{ is odd.}$$

If a represents a nonnegative number,

$$\sqrt[n]{a^n} = a.$$

Assume that x can be any real number.

$$\sqrt{(3 + x)^2} = |3 + x|$$

Assume that x represents a nonnegative number.

$$\sqrt{(7x)^2} = 7x$$

SECTION 10.2: RATIONAL NUMBERS AS EXPONENTS

$a^{1/n}$ means $\sqrt[n]{a}$.

$a^{m/n}$ means $\left(\sqrt[n]{a}\right)^m$ or $\sqrt[n]{a^m}$.

$a^{-m/n}$ means $\dfrac{1}{a^{m/n}}$.

$64^{1/2} = \sqrt{64} = 8$

$125^{2/3} = \left(\sqrt[3]{125}\right)^2 = 5^2 = 25$

$8^{-1/3} = \dfrac{1}{8^{1/3}} = \dfrac{1}{2}$

SECTION 10.3: MULTIPLYING RADICAL EXPRESSIONS

The Product Rule for Radicals

For any real numbers $\sqrt[n]{a}$ and $\sqrt[n]{b}$,

$$\sqrt[n]{a} \cdot \sqrt[n]{b} = \sqrt[n]{a \cdot b}.$$

$$\sqrt[3]{4x} \cdot \sqrt[3]{5y} = \sqrt[3]{20xy}$$

Using the Product Rule to Simplify

For any real numbers $\sqrt[n]{a}$ and $\sqrt[n]{b}$,

$$\sqrt[n]{a \cdot b} = \sqrt[n]{a} \cdot \sqrt[n]{b}.$$

$$\begin{aligned}
\sqrt{75x^8y^{11}} &= \sqrt{25 \cdot x^8 \cdot y^{10} \cdot 3 \cdot y} \\
&= \sqrt{25} \cdot \sqrt{x^8} \cdot \sqrt{y^{10}} \cdot \sqrt{3y} \\
&= 5x^4y^5\sqrt{3y} \qquad \text{Assuming } y \text{ is nonnegative}
\end{aligned}$$

SECTION 10.4: DIVIDING RATIONAL EXPRESSIONS

The Quotient Rule for Radicals

For any real numbers $\sqrt[n]{a}$ and $\sqrt[n]{b}$, $b \neq 0$,

$$\sqrt[n]{\dfrac{a}{b}} = \dfrac{\sqrt[n]{a}}{\sqrt[n]{b}}.$$

$$\sqrt[3]{\dfrac{8y^4}{125}} = \dfrac{\sqrt[3]{8y^4}}{\sqrt[3]{125}} = \dfrac{2y\sqrt[3]{y}}{5}$$

$$\dfrac{\sqrt{18a^9}}{\sqrt{2a^3}} = \sqrt{\dfrac{18a^9}{2a^3}} = \sqrt{9a^6} = 3a^3 \qquad \text{Assuming } a \text{ is positive}$$

We can **rationalize a denominator** by multiplying by 1.

$$\frac{\sqrt[3]{5}}{\sqrt[3]{4y}} = \frac{\sqrt[3]{5}}{\sqrt[3]{4y}} \cdot \frac{\sqrt[3]{2y^2}}{\sqrt[3]{2y^2}} = \frac{\sqrt[3]{10y^2}}{\sqrt[3]{8y^3}} = \frac{\sqrt[3]{10y^2}}{2y}$$

SECTION 10.5: EXPRESSIONS CONTAINING SEVERAL RADICAL TERMS

Like radicals have the same indices and radicands and can be combined.

$$\sqrt{12} + 5\sqrt{3} = \sqrt{4 \cdot 3} + 5\sqrt{3} = 2\sqrt{3} + 5\sqrt{3} = 7\sqrt{3}$$

Radical expressions are multiplied in much the same way that polynomials are multiplied.

$$(1 + 5\sqrt{6})(4 - \sqrt{6}) = 1 \cdot 4 - 1\sqrt{6} + 4 \cdot 5\sqrt{6} - 5\sqrt{6} \cdot \sqrt{6}$$
$$= 4 - \sqrt{6} + 20\sqrt{6} - 5 \cdot 6$$
$$= -26 + 19\sqrt{6}$$

To rationalize a denominator containing two terms, we use the **conjugate** of the denominator to write a form of 1.

$$\frac{2}{1 - \sqrt{3}} = \frac{2}{1 - \sqrt{3}} \cdot \frac{1 + \sqrt{3}}{1 + \sqrt{3}} \qquad 1 + \sqrt{3} \text{ is the conjugate of } 1 - \sqrt{3}.$$
$$= \frac{2(1 + \sqrt{3})}{-2} = -1 - \sqrt{3}$$

When terms have different indices, we can often use rational exponents to simplify.

$$\sqrt[3]{p} \cdot \sqrt[4]{q^3} = p^{1/3} \cdot q^{3/4}$$
$$= p^{4/12} \cdot q^{9/12} \qquad \text{Finding a common denominator}$$
$$= \sqrt[12]{p^4 q^9}$$

SECTION 10.6: SOLVING RADICAL EQUATIONS

The Principle of Powers

If $a = b$, then $a^n = b^n$.

To solve a radical equation, use the principle of powers and the steps on pp. 670 and 672.

Solutions found using the principle of powers must be checked in the original equation.

$$x - 7 = \sqrt{x - 5}$$
$$(x - 7)^2 = (\sqrt{x - 5})^2$$
$$x^2 - 14x + 49 = x - 5$$
$$x^2 - 15x + 54 = 0$$
$$(x - 6)(x - 9) = 0$$
$$x = 6 \ \ or \ \ x = 9$$

Only 9 checks and is the solution.

$$2 + \sqrt{t} = \sqrt{t + 8}$$
$$(2 + \sqrt{t})^2 = (\sqrt{t + 8})^2$$
$$4 + 4\sqrt{t} + t = t + 8$$
$$4\sqrt{t} = 4$$
$$\sqrt{t} = 1$$
$$(\sqrt{t})^2 = (1)^2$$
$$t = 1$$

1 checks and is the solution.

SECTION 10.7: THE DISTANCE AND MIDPOINT FORMULAS AND OTHER APPLICATIONS

The Pythagorean Theorem

In any right triangle, if a and b are the lengths of the legs and c is the length of the hypotenuse, then

$$a^2 + b^2 = c^2.$$

Find the length of the hypotenuse of a right triangle with legs of lengths 4 and 7. Give an exact answer in radical notation, as well as a decimal approximation to three decimal places.

$$a^2 + b^2 = c^2$$
$$4^2 + 7^2 = c^2 \qquad \text{Substituting}$$
$$16 + 49 = c^2$$
$$65 = c^2$$
$$\sqrt{65} = c \qquad \text{This is exact.}$$
$$8.062 \approx c \qquad \text{This is approximate.}$$

Special Triangles

The length of the hypotenuse in an isosceles right triangle is the length of a leg times $\sqrt{2}$.

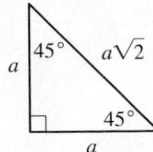

The length of the longer leg in a $30°$–$60°$–$90°$ triangle is the length of the shorter leg times $\sqrt{3}$. The hypotenuse is twice as long as the shorter leg.

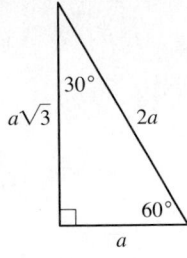

Find the missing lengths. Give an exact answer and, where appropriate, an approximation to three decimal places.

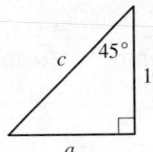

$$a = 10; \quad c = a\sqrt{2}$$
$$c = 10\sqrt{2}$$
$$c \approx 14.142$$

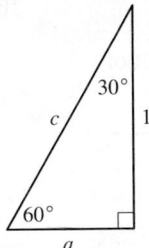

$$18 = a\sqrt{3} \qquad c = 2a$$
$$\frac{18}{\sqrt{3}} = a \qquad c = 2\left(\frac{18}{\sqrt{3}}\right)$$
$$10.392 \approx a; \qquad c = \frac{36}{\sqrt{3}}$$
$$c \approx 20.785$$

The Distance Formula

The distance d between any two points (x_1, y_1) and (x_2, y_2) is given by

$$d = \sqrt{(x_2 - x_1)^2 + (y_2 - y_1)^2}.$$

Find the distance between $(3, -5)$ and $(-1, -2)$.

$$d = \sqrt{(-1 - 3)^2 + (-2 - (-5))^2}$$
$$= \sqrt{(-4)^2 + (3)^2}$$
$$= \sqrt{16 + 9} = \sqrt{25} = 5$$

The Midpoint Formula

If the endpoints of a segment are (x_1, y_1) and (x_2, y_2), then the coordinates of the midpoint are

$$\left(\frac{x_1 + x_2}{2}, \frac{y_1 + y_2}{2}\right).$$

Find the midpoint of the segment with endpoints $(3, -5)$ and $(-1, -2)$.

$$\left(\frac{3 + (-1)}{2}, \frac{-5 + (-2)}{2}\right), \text{ or } \left(1, -\frac{7}{2}\right)$$

SECTION 10.8: THE COMPLEX NUMBERS

A **complex number** is any number that can be written in the form $a + bi$, where a and b are real numbers,

$$i = \sqrt{-1}, \quad \text{and} \quad i^2 = -1.$$

$$(3 + 2i) + (4 - 7i) = 7 - 5i$$

$$(8 + 6i) - (5 + 2i) = 3 + 4i$$

$$(2 + 3i)(4 - i) = 8 - 2i + 12i - 3i^2$$
$$= 8 + 10i - 3(-1) = 11 + 10i$$

$$\frac{1 - 4i}{3 - 2i} = \frac{1 - 4i}{3 - 2i} \cdot \frac{3 + 2i}{3 + 2i} \qquad \text{The conjugate of } 3 - 2i \text{ is } 3 + 2i.$$

$$= \frac{3 + 2i - 12i - 8i^2}{9 + 6i - 6i - 4i^2}$$

$$= \frac{3 - 10i - 8(-1)}{9 - 4(-1)} = \frac{11 - 10i}{13} = \frac{11}{13} - \frac{10}{13}i$$

Review Exercises: Chapter 10

Concept Reinforcement *Classify each statement as either true or false.*

1. $\sqrt{ab} = \sqrt{a} \cdot \sqrt{b}$ for any real numbers $\sqrt{a}$ and $\sqrt{b}$. [10.3]

2. $\sqrt{a + b} = \sqrt{a} + \sqrt{b}$ for any real numbers $\sqrt{a}$ and $\sqrt{b}$. [10.5]

3. $\sqrt{a^2} = a$, for any real number a. [10.1]

4. $\sqrt[3]{a^3} = a$, for any real number a. [10.1]

5. $x^{2/5}$ means $\sqrt[5]{x^2}$ and $\left(\sqrt[5]{x}\right)^2$. [10.2]

6. The hypotenuse of a right triangle is never shorter than either leg. [10.7]

7. Some radical equations have no solution. [10.6]

8. If $f(x) = \sqrt{x - 5}$, then the domain of f is the set of all nonnegative real numbers. [10.1]

Simplify. [10.1]

9. $\sqrt{\dfrac{100}{121}}$

10. $-\sqrt{0.36}$

Let $f(x) = \sqrt{x + 10}$. Find the following. [10.1]

11. $f(15)$

12. The domain of f

Simplify. Assume that each variable can represent any real number. [10.1]

13. $\sqrt{64t^2}$

14. $\sqrt{(c + 7)^2}$

15. $\sqrt{4x^2 + 4x + 1}$

16. $\sqrt[5]{-32}$

17. Write an equivalent expression using exponential notation: $\left(\sqrt[3]{5ab}\right)^4$. [10.2]

18. Write an equivalent expression using radical notation: $(16a^6)^{3/4}$. [10.2]

Use rational exponents to simplify. Assume $x, y \geq 0$. [10.2]

19. $\sqrt{x^6 y^{10}}$

20. $\left(\sqrt[6]{x^2 y}\right)^2$

Simplify. Do not use negative exponents in the answers. [10.2]

21. $(x^{-2/3})^{3/5}$

22. $\dfrac{7^{-1/3}}{7^{-1/2}}$

23. If $f(x) = \sqrt{25(x - 6)^2}$, find a simplified form for $f(x)$. [10.3]

Simplify. Write all answers using radical notation. Assume that all variables represent nonnegative numbers.

24. $\sqrt[4]{16x^{20}y^8}$ [10.3]

25. $\sqrt{250x^3y^2}$ [10.3]

26. $\sqrt{5a}\sqrt{7b}$ [10.3]

27. $\sqrt[3]{3x^4b}\sqrt[3]{9xb^2}$ [10.3]

28. $\sqrt[3]{-24x^{10}y^8}\ \sqrt[3]{18x^7y^4}$ [10.3]

29. $\sqrt[3]{-\dfrac{27y^{12}}{64}}$ [10.4]

30. $\dfrac{\sqrt[3]{60xy^3}}{\sqrt[3]{10x}}$ [10.4]

31. $\dfrac{\sqrt{75x}}{2\sqrt{3}}$ [10.4]

32. $\sqrt[4]{\dfrac{48a^{11}}{c^8}}$ [10.4]

33. $5\sqrt[3]{4y} + 2\sqrt[3]{4y}$ [10.5]

34. $2\sqrt{75} - 9\sqrt{3}$ [10.5]

35. $\sqrt[3]{8x^4} + \sqrt[3]{xy^6}$ [10.5]

36. $\sqrt{50} + 2\sqrt{18} + \sqrt{32}$ [10.5]

37. $(3 + \sqrt{10})(3 - \sqrt{10})$ [10.5]

38. $(\sqrt{3} - 3\sqrt{8})(\sqrt{5} + 2\sqrt{8})$ [10.5]

39. $\sqrt[4]{x}\ \sqrt{x}$ [10.5]

40. $\dfrac{\sqrt[3]{x^2}}{\sqrt[4]{x}}$ [10.5]

41. If $f(x) = x^2$, find $f(2 - \sqrt{a})$. [10.5]

42. Rationalize the denominator:
$$\dfrac{4\sqrt{5}}{\sqrt{2} + \sqrt{3}}.$$ [10.5]

43. Rationalize the numerator of the expression in Exercise 42. [10.5]

Solve. [10.6]

44. $\sqrt{y + 6} - 2 = 3$

45. $(x + 1)^{1/3} = -5$

46. $1 + \sqrt{x} = \sqrt{3x - 3}$

47. If $f(x) = \sqrt{x + 2} + x$, find a such that $f(a) = 4$.
[10.6]

Solve. Give an exact answer and, where appropriate, an approximation to three decimal places. [10.7]

48. The diagonal of a square has length 10 cm. Find the length of a side of the square.

49. A skate-park jump has a ramp that is 6 ft long and is 2 ft high. How long is its base?

6 ft   2 ft
?

50. Find the missing lengths. Give exact answers and, where appropriate, an approximation to three decimal places.

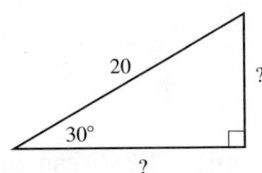

20

?

30°

?

51. Find the distance between $(-6, 4)$ and $(-1, 5)$. Give an exact answer and an approximation to three decimal places. [10.7]

52. Find the midpoint of the segment with endpoints $(-7, -2)$ and $(3, -1)$. [10.7]

53. Express in terms of i and simplify: $\sqrt{-45}$. [10.8]

54. Add: $(-4 + 3i) + (2 - 12i)$. [10.8]

55. Subtract: $(9 - 7i) - (3 - 8i)$. [10.8]

Simplify. [10.8]

56. $(2 + 5i)(2 - 5i)$

57. i^{34}

58. $(6 - 3i)(2 - i)$

59. Divide. Write the answer in the form $a + bi$.
$$\frac{7 - 2i}{3 + 4i}$$ [10.8]

Synthesis

60. What makes some complex numbers real and others imaginary? [10.8]

61. Explain why $\sqrt[n]{x^n} = |x|$ when n is even, but $\sqrt[n]{x^n} = x$ when n is odd. [10.1]

62. Write a quotient of two imaginary numbers that is a real number (answers may vary). [10.8]

63. Solve:
$$\sqrt{11x + \sqrt{6 + x}} = 6.$$ [10.6]

64. Simplify:
$$\frac{2}{1 - 3i} - \frac{3}{4 + 2i}.$$ [10.8]

65. Don's Discount Shoes has two locations. The sign at the original location is shaped like an isosceles right triangle. The sign at the newer location is shaped like a 30°–60°–90° triangle. The hypotenuse of each sign measures 6 ft. Which sign has the greater area and by how much? (Round to three decimal places.) [10.7]

Test: Chapter 10

Test Prep VIDEO CD — Step-by-step test solutions are found on the video CD in the front of this book.

Simplify. Assume that variables can represent any real number.

1. $\sqrt{50}$

2. $\sqrt[3]{-\dfrac{8}{x^6}}$

3. $\sqrt{81a^2}$

4. $\sqrt{x^2 - 8x + 16}$

5. Write an equivalent expression using exponential notation: $\sqrt{7xy}$.

6. Write an equivalent expression using radical notation: $(4a^3b)^{5/6}$.

7. If $f(x) = \sqrt{2x - 10}$, determine the domain of f.

8. If $f(x) = x^2$, find $f(5 + \sqrt{2})$.

Simplify. Write all answers using radical notation. Assume that all variables represent positive numbers.

9. $\sqrt[5]{32x^{16}y^{10}}$

10. $\sqrt[3]{4w}\sqrt[3]{4v^2}$

11. $\sqrt{\dfrac{100a^4}{9b^6}}$

12. $\dfrac{\sqrt[5]{48x^6y^{10}}}{\sqrt[5]{16x^2y^9}}$

13. $\sqrt[4]{x^3}\sqrt{x}$

14. $\dfrac{\sqrt{y}}{\sqrt[10]{y}}$

15. $8\sqrt{2} - 2\sqrt{2}$

16. $\sqrt{x^4y} + \sqrt{9y^3}$

17. $(7 + \sqrt{x})(2 - 3\sqrt{x})$

18. Rationalize the denominator:
$$\dfrac{\sqrt{3}}{5 + \sqrt{2}}.$$

Solve.

19. $6 = \sqrt{x - 3} + 5$

20. $x = \sqrt{3x + 3} - 1$

21. $\sqrt{2x} = \sqrt{x + 1} + 1$

Solve. For Exercises 22–24, give exact answers and approximations to three decimal places.

22. A referee jogs diagonally from one corner of a 50-ft by 90-ft basketball court to the far corner. How far does she jog?

23. The hypotenuse of a 30°–60°–90° triangle is 10 cm long. Find the lengths of the legs.

24. Find the distance between the points $(3, 7)$ and $(-1, 8)$.

25. Find the midpoint of the segment with endpoints $(2, -5)$ and $(1, -7)$.

26. Express in terms of i and simplify: $\sqrt{-50}$.

27. Subtract: $(9 + 8i) - (-3 + 6i)$.

28. Multiply. Write the answer in the form $a + bi$.
$$(4 - i)^2$$

29. Divide. Write the answer in the form $a + bi$.
$$\dfrac{-2 + i}{3 - 5i}$$

30. Simplify: i^{37}.

Synthesis

31. Solve:
$$\sqrt{2x - 2} + \sqrt{7x + 4} = \sqrt{13x + 10}.$$

32. Simplify:
$$\dfrac{1 - 4i}{4i(1 + 4i)^{-1}}.$$

33. The function $D(h) = 1.2\sqrt{h}$ can be used to approximate the distance D, in miles, that a person can see to the horizon from a height h, in feet. How far above sea level must a pilot fly in order to see a horizon that is 180 mi away?

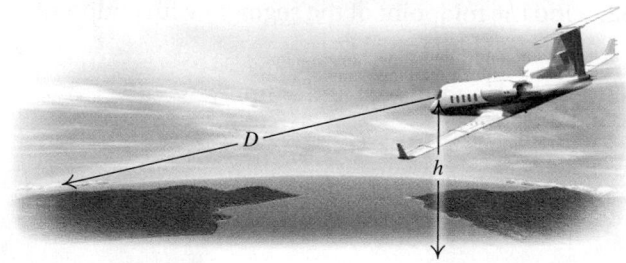

Cumulative Review: Chapters 1–10

Solve.

1. $2(x - 5) - 3 = 3(2x + 5)$ [2.2]

2. $x(x + 2) = 35$ [5.7]

3. $2y^2 = 50$ [5.7]

4. $\dfrac{1}{x} = \dfrac{2}{5}$ [6.6]

5. $\sqrt[3]{t} = -1$ [10.6]

6. $25x^2 - 10x + 1 = 0$ [5.7]

7. $|x - 2| \leq 5$ [9.3]

8. $2x + 5 > 6 \text{ or } x - 3 \leq 9$ [9.2]

9. $\dfrac{2x}{x - 1} + \dfrac{x}{x - 3} = 2$ [6.6]

10. $x = \sqrt{2x - 5} + 4$ [10.6]

11. $3x + y = 5,$
    $\quad x - y = -5$ [8.2]

12. $2x - y + z = 1,$
    $\quad x + 2y + z = -3,$
    $\quad 5x - y + 3z = 0$ [8.4]

Graph on a plane.

13. $3y = -6$ [3.3]

14. $y = -x + 5$ [3.6]

15. $x + y \leq 2$ [9.4]

16. $2x = y$ [3.2]

17. Determine the slope and the y-intercept of the line given by $y = -6 - x$. [3.6]

18. Find an equation for the line parallel to the line given by $y = 7x$ and passing through the point $(0, -11)$. [3.6]

Perform the indicated operations and, if possible, simplify. For radical expressions, assume that all variables represent positive numbers.

19. $18 \div 3 \cdot 2 - 6^2 \div (2 + 4)$ [1.8]

20. $(x^2y - 3x^2 - 4xy^2) - (x^2y - 3x^2 + 4xy^2)$ [4.4]

21. $(2a - 5b)^2$ [4.6]

22. $(c^2 - 3d)(c^2 + 3d)$ [4.6]

23. $\dfrac{1}{x} + \dfrac{1}{x + 1}$ [6.4]

24. $\dfrac{x + 3}{x - 2} - \dfrac{x + 5}{x + 1}$ [6.4]

25. $\dfrac{a^2 - a - 6}{a^2 - 1} \div \dfrac{a^2 - 6a + 9}{2a^2 + 3a + 1}$ [6.2]

26. $\dfrac{\dfrac{1}{x} + \dfrac{1}{x + 1}}{\dfrac{x}{x + 1}}$ [6.5]

27. $\sqrt{200} - 5\sqrt{8}$ [10.5]

28. $(1 + \sqrt{5})(4 - \sqrt{5})$ [10.5]

29. $\sqrt{10a^2b} \cdot \sqrt{15ab^3}$ [10.3]

30. $\sqrt[3]{y}\sqrt[5]{y}$ [10.5]

Factor.

31. $x^2 - 5x - 14$ [5.2]

32. $4y^8 - 4y^5$ [5.5]

33. $100c^2 - 25d^2$ [5.4]

34. $3t^2 - 5t - 8$ [5.3]

35. $3x^2 - 6x - 21$ [5.1]

36. $yt - xt - yz^2 + xz^2$ [5.1]

Find the domain of each function.

37. $f(x) = \dfrac{2x - 3}{x^2 - 6x + 9}$ [7.2]

38. $f(x) = \sqrt{2x - 11}$ [9.1]

Find each of the following, if $f(x) = \sqrt{2x - 3}$ and $g(x) = x^2$.

39. $f(14)$ [10.1]

40. $g(1 - \sqrt{5})$ [10.5]

41. $(f + g)(x)$ [7.4]

Solve.

42. *Flood rescue.* A flood rescue team uses a boat that travels 10 mph in still water. To reach a stranded family, they travel 7 mi against the current and return 7 mi with the current in a total time of $1\frac{2}{3}$ hr. What is the speed of the current? [6.7]

43. *Emergency shelter.* The entrance to a tent used by a rescue team is the shape of an equilateral triangle. If the base of the tent is 4 ft wide, how tall is the tent? Give an exact answer and an approximation to three decimal places. [10.7]

44. *Age at marriage.* The median age at first marriage for U.S. men has grown from 25.1 in 2001 to 25.5 in 2006. Let $m(t)$ represent the median age of men at first marriage t years after 2000. [7.3]
Source: U.S. Census Bureau

a) Find a linear function that fits the data.
b) Use the function from part (a) to predict the median age of men at first marriage in 2020.
c) In what year will the median age of men at first marriage be 28?

45. *Salary.* Neil's annual salary is $38,849. This includes a 6% superior performance raise. What would Neil's salary have been without the performance raise? [2.5]

46. *Food service.* Melted Goodness mixes Swiss chocolate and whipping cream to make a dessert fondue. Swiss chocolate costs $1.20 per ounce and whipping cream costs $0.30 per ounce. How much of each does Melted Goodness use to make 65 oz of fondue at a cost of $60.00? [8.3]

47. *Food cost.* The average cost of a Thanksgiving dinner in the United States rose from $34.56 in 2002 to $42.26 in 2007. What was the rate of increase? [3.4]
Sources: Purdue University; American Farm Bureau Federation

48. *Landscaping.* A rectangular parking lot is 80 ft by 100 ft. Part of the asphalt is removed in order to install a landscaped border of uniform width around it. The area of the new parking lot is 6300 ft^2. How wide is the landscaped border? [5.8]

Synthesis

49. Give an equation in standard form for the line whose x-intercept is $(-3, 0)$ and whose y-intercept is $(0, 5)$. [3.6]

50. Solve by graphing:
$$y = x - 1,$$
$$y = x^2 - 1. \quad [8.1]$$

Solve.

51. $\dfrac{\dfrac{1}{x} + \dfrac{1}{x+1}}{\dfrac{1}{x} - 1} = 1$ [6.4], [6.5]

52. $3\sqrt{2x - 11} = 2 + \sqrt{5x - 1}$ [10.6]

Quadratic Functions and Equations

11.1
Quadratic Equations

11.2
The Quadratic Formula

11.3
Studying Solutions of
Quadratic Equations

11.4
Applications Involving
Quadratic Equations

11.5
Equations Reducible
to Quadratic

CONNECTING THE CONCEPTS

11.6
Quadratic Functions and
Their Graphs

11.7
More About Graphing
Quadratic Functions

11.8
Problem Solving and
Quadratic Functions

11.9
Polynomial and Rational
Inequalities

STUDY SUMMARY
REVIEW EXERCISES
CHAPTER TEST
CUMULATIVE REVIEW

JANET FISHER
**MUSIC PUBLISHER AND
RECORD LABEL OWNER**
Los Angeles, California

As a music publisher and record label owner, I pay our songwriters and artists royalties based on sales and uses of their songs, both physical and digital. In the world of digital downloads, these royalties run from fractions of cents for a "streamed listen," to a set number of cents per download, depending on the site from which the purchase or stream is made. Varying advances are split between publishers and writers when a song is used in a film or TV show. When a writer has a combination of uses for his or her song, you can imagine how important math is in order to pay them properly.

AN APPLICATION

As more listeners download their music purchases, sales of compact discs are decreasing. According to Nielsen SoundScan, sales of music CDs increased from 500 million in 1997 to 700 million in 2001 and then decreased to 450 million in 2007. Find a quadratic function that fits the data, and use the function to estimate the sales of music CDs in 2009.

This problem appears as Example 3 in Section 11.8.

703

The mathematical translation of a problem is often a function or an equation containing a second-degree polynomial in one variable. Such functions or equations are said to be *quadratic*. In this chapter, we examine a variety of ways to solve quadratic equations and look at graphs and applications of quadratic functions.

11.1 Quadratic Equations

The Principle of Square Roots • Completing the Square • Problem Solving

The general form of a quadratic function is

$$f(x) = ax^2 + bx + c, \quad \text{with } a \neq 0.$$

The graph of a quadratic function is a *parabola*. Such graphs open up or down and can have 0, 1, or 2 x-intercepts. We learn to graph quadratic functions later in this chapter.

ALGEBRAIC–GRAPHICAL CONNECTION

The graphs of the quadratic function $f(x) = x^2 + 6x + 8$ and the linear function $g(x) = 0$ are shown below.

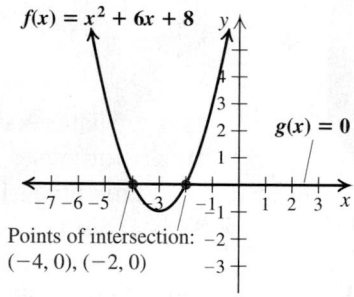

$f(x) = x^2 + 6x + 8$

$g(x) = 0$

Points of intersection: $(-4, 0), (-2, 0)$

Note that $(-4, 0)$ and $(-2, 0)$ are the points of intersection of the graphs of $f(x) = x^2 + 6x + 8$ and $g(x) = 0$ (the x-axis). In Sections 11.6 and 11.7, we will develop efficient ways to graph quadratic functions. For now, the graphs help us visualize solutions.

In Chapter 5, we solved equations like $x^2 + 6x + 8 = 0$ by factoring:

$$x^2 + 6x + 8 = 0$$
$$(x + 4)(x + 2) = 0 \qquad \text{Factoring}$$
$$x + 4 = 0 \quad or \quad x + 2 = 0 \qquad \begin{array}{l}\text{Using the principle} \\ \text{of zero products}\end{array}$$
$$x = -4 \quad or \qquad x = -2.$$

Note that -4 and -2 are the first coordinates of the points of intersection (or the x-intercepts) of the graph of $f(x)$ above.

In this section and the next, we develop algebraic methods for solving *any* quadratic equation, whether it is factorable or not.

EXAMPLE   1   Solve: $x^2 = 25$.

SOLUTION   We have

$$x^2 = 25$$
$$x^2 - 25 = 0 \qquad \text{Writing in standard form}$$
$$(x - 5)(x + 5) = 0 \qquad \text{Factoring}$$
$$x - 5 = 0 \quad or \quad x + 5 = 0 \qquad \text{Using the principle of zero products}$$
$$x = 5 \quad or \qquad x = -5.$$

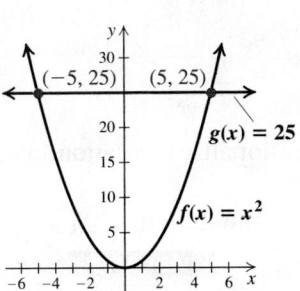

A visualization of Example 1

The solutions are 5 and −5. A graph in which $f(x) = x^2$ represents the left side of the original equation and $g(x) = 25$ represents the right side provides a check (see the figure at left). Of course, we can also check by substituting 5 and −5 into the original equation.

▶ **TRY EXERCISE**   7

The Principle of Square Roots

Let's reconsider $x^2 = 25$. We know from Chapter 10 that the number 25 has two real-number square roots, 5 and −5, the solutions of the equation in Example 1. Thus we see that square roots provide quick solutions for equations of the type $x^2 = k$.

> ### The Principle of Square Roots
> For any real number k, if $x^2 = k$, then
> $$x = \sqrt{k} \quad or \quad x = -\sqrt{k}.$$

EXAMPLE   2   Solve: $3x^2 = 6$. Give exact solutions and approximations to three decimal places.

SOLUTION   We have

$$3x^2 = 6$$
$$x^2 = 2 \qquad \text{Isolating } x^2$$
$$x = \sqrt{2} \quad or \quad x = -\sqrt{2}. \qquad \text{Using the principle of square roots}$$

We can use the symbol $\pm\sqrt{2}$ to represent both of the solutions.

> ***CAUTION!***   There are *two* solutions: $\sqrt{2}$ and $-\sqrt{2}$. Don't forget the second solution.

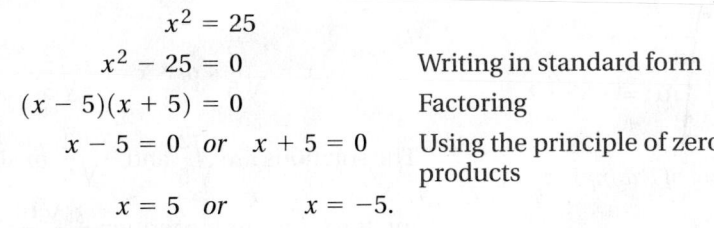

A visualization of Example 2

Check: For $\sqrt{2}$:

$$\begin{array}{c|c} 3x^2 = 6 \\ \hline 3(\sqrt{2})^2 & 6 \\ 3 \cdot 2 & \\ 6 \stackrel{?}{=} 6 & \text{TRUE} \end{array}$$

For $-\sqrt{2}$:

$$\begin{array}{c|c} 3x^2 = 6 \\ \hline 3(-\sqrt{2})^2 & 6 \\ 3 \cdot 2 & \\ 6 \stackrel{?}{=} 6 & \text{TRUE} \end{array}$$

The solutions are $\sqrt{2}$ and $-\sqrt{2}$, or $\pm\sqrt{2}$, which round to 1.414 and −1.414.

▶ **TRY EXERCISE**   11

EXAMPLE 3

Solve: $-5x^2 + 2 = 0$.

SOLUTION   We have

$$-5x^2 + 2 = 0$$

$$x^2 = \frac{2}{5} \qquad \text{Isolating } x^2$$

$$x = \sqrt{\frac{2}{5}} \quad or \quad x = -\sqrt{\frac{2}{5}}. \qquad \text{Using the principle of square roots}$$

The solutions are $\sqrt{\frac{2}{5}}$ and $-\sqrt{\frac{2}{5}}$, or simply $\pm\sqrt{\frac{2}{5}}$. If we rationalize the denominator, the solutions are written $\pm\frac{\sqrt{10}}{5}$. The checks are left to the student.

> **TRY EXERCISE** 15

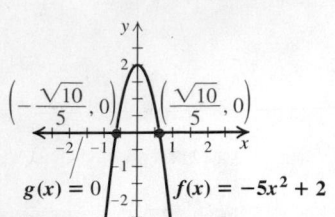

$\left(-\frac{\sqrt{10}}{5}, 0\right)$ $\left(\frac{\sqrt{10}}{5}, 0\right)$

$g(x) = 0$ $f(x) = -5x^2 + 2$

A visualization of Example 3

Sometimes we get solutions that are imaginary numbers.

EXAMPLE 4

Solve: $4x^2 + 9 = 0$.

SOLUTION   We have

$$4x^2 + 9 = 0$$

$$x^2 = -\frac{9}{4} \qquad \text{Isolating } x^2$$

$$x = \sqrt{-\frac{9}{4}} \quad or \quad x = -\sqrt{-\frac{9}{4}} \qquad \text{Using the principle of square roots}$$

$$x = \sqrt{\frac{9}{4}}\sqrt{-1} \quad or \quad x = -\sqrt{\frac{9}{4}}\sqrt{-1}$$

$$x = \frac{3}{2}i \quad\quad or \quad x = -\frac{3}{2}i. \qquad \text{Recall that } \sqrt{-1} = i.$$

Check: For $\frac{3}{2}i$:

$$\begin{array}{c|c} 4x^2 + 9 = 0 & \\ \hline 4\left(\frac{3}{2}i\right)^2 + 9 & 0 \\ 4 \cdot \frac{9}{4} \cdot i^2 + 9 & \\ 9(-1) + 9 & \\ & 0 \stackrel{?}{=} 0 \quad \text{TRUE} \end{array}$$

For $-\frac{3}{2}i$:

$$\begin{array}{c|c} 4x^2 + 9 = 0 & \\ \hline 4\left(-\frac{3}{2}i\right)^2 + 9 & 0 \\ 4 \cdot \frac{9}{4} \cdot i^2 + 9 & \\ 9(-1) + 9 & \\ & 0 \stackrel{?}{=} 0 \quad \text{TRUE} \end{array}$$

The solutions are $\frac{3}{2}i$ and $-\frac{3}{2}i$, or $\pm\frac{3}{2}i$. The graph at left confirms that there are no real-number solutions.

> **TRY EXERCISE** 19

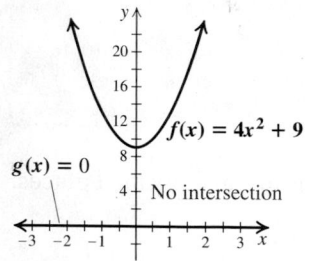

$f(x) = 4x^2 + 9$

$g(x) = 0$

No intersection

A visualization of Example 4

The principle of square roots can be restated in a more general form for any equation in which some algebraic expression squared equals a constant.

The Principle of Square Roots (Generalized Form)

For any real number k and any algebraic expression X:

$$\text{If } X^2 = k, \quad \text{then} \quad X = \sqrt{k} \quad or \quad X = -\sqrt{k}.$$

EXAMPLE 5

Let $f(x) = (x - 2)^2$. Find all x-values for which $f(x) = 7$.

SOLUTION   We are asked to find all x-values for which

$$f(x) = 7,$$

or

$$(x - 2)^2 = 7. \qquad \text{Substituting } (x - 2)^2 \text{ for } f(x)$$

The generalized principle of square roots gives us

$$x - 2 = \sqrt{7} \quad or \quad x - 2 = -\sqrt{7} \qquad \text{Using the principle of square roots}$$

$$x = 2 + \sqrt{7} \quad or \qquad x = 2 - \sqrt{7}.$$

Check: $f(2 + \sqrt{7}) = (2 + \sqrt{7} - 2)^2 = (\sqrt{7})^2 = 7.$

Similarly,

$$f(2 - \sqrt{7}) = (2 - \sqrt{7} - 2)^2 = (-\sqrt{7})^2 = 7.$$

The solutions are $2 + \sqrt{7}$ and $2 - \sqrt{7}$, or simply $2 \pm \sqrt{7}$.

 TRY EXERCISE ▸ 35

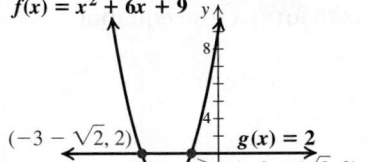

A visualization of Example 5

Example 5 is of the form $(x - a)^2 = c$, where a and c are constants. Sometimes we must factor in order to obtain this form.

EXAMPLE 6

Solve: $x^2 + 6x + 9 = 2$.

SOLUTION   We have

$$x^2 + 6x + 9 = 2 \qquad \text{The left side is the square of a binomial.}$$

$$(x + 3)^2 = 2 \qquad \text{Factoring}$$

$$x + 3 = \sqrt{2} \quad or \quad x + 3 = -\sqrt{2} \qquad \text{Using the principle of square roots}$$

$$x = -3 + \sqrt{2} \quad or \qquad x = -3 - \sqrt{2}. \qquad \text{Adding } -3 \text{ to both sides}$$

The solutions are $-3 + \sqrt{2}$ and $-3 - \sqrt{2}$, or $-3 \pm \sqrt{2}$. The checks are left to the student.

TRY EXERCISE ▸ 29

A visualization of Example 6

Completing the Square

Not all quadratic equations are in the form $X^2 = k$. By using a method called *completing the square*, we can use the principle of square roots to solve *any* quadratic equation by writing it in this form.

Suppose we want to solve the quadratic equation

$$x^2 + 6x + 4 = 0.$$

The trinomial $x^2 + 6x + 4$ is not a perfect square. We can, however, create an equivalent equation with a perfect-square trinomial on one side:

$$x^2 + 6x + 4 = 0$$

$$x^2 + 6x \qquad = -4 \qquad \text{Only variable terms are on the left side.}$$

$$x^2 + 6x + 9 = -4 + 9 \qquad \text{Adding 9 to both sides. We explain this shortly.}$$

$$(x + 3)^2 = 5. \qquad \text{We could now use the principle of square roots to solve.}$$

We chose to add 9 to both sides because it creates a perfect-square trinomial on the left side. The 9 was determined by taking half of the coefficient of x and squaring it—that is,

$$\left(\tfrac{1}{2} \cdot 6\right)^2 = 3^2, \quad or \quad 9.$$

To understand why this procedure works, examine the following drawings.

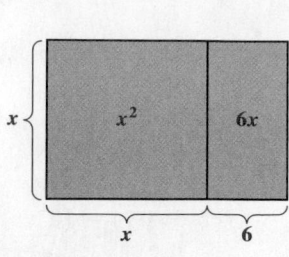 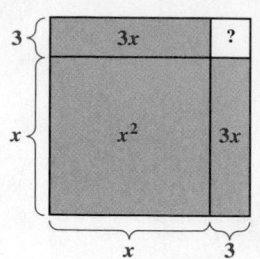

Note that the shaded areas in both figures represent the same area, $x^2 + 6x$. However, only the figure on the right, in which the $6x$ is halved, can be converted into a square with the addition of a constant term. The constant 9 is the "missing" piece that *completes* the square.

To complete the square for $x^2 + bx$, we add $(b/2)^2$.

Example 7, which follows, provides practice in finding numbers that complete the square. We will then use this skill to solve equations.

EXAMPLE **7**   Replace the blanks in each equation with constants to form a true equation.

a) $x^2 + 14x +$ _____ $= (x +$ _____ $)^2$
b) $x^2 - 5x +$ _____ $= (x -$ _____ $)^2$
c) $x^2 + \frac{3}{4}x +$ _____ $= (x +$ _____ $)^2$

SOLUTION   We take half of the coefficient of x and square it.

a) Half of 14 is 7, and $7^2 = 49$. Thus, $x^2 + 14x + 49$ is a perfect-square trinomial and is equivalent to $(x + 7)^2$. We have

$$x^2 + 14x + 49 = (x + 7)^2.$$

b) Half of -5 is $-\frac{5}{2}$, and $\left(-\frac{5}{2}\right)^2 = \frac{25}{4}$. Thus, $x^2 - 5x + \frac{25}{4}$ is a perfect-square trinomial and is equivalent to $\left(x - \frac{5}{2}\right)^2$. We have

$$x^2 - 5x + \frac{25}{4} = \left(x - \frac{5}{2}\right)^2.$$

c) Half of $\frac{3}{4}$ is $\frac{3}{8}$, and $\left(\frac{3}{8}\right)^2 = \frac{9}{64}$. Thus, $x^2 + \frac{3}{4}x + \frac{9}{64}$ is a perfect-square trinomial and is equivalent to $\left(x + \frac{3}{8}\right)^2$. We have

$$x^2 + \frac{3}{4}x + \frac{9}{64} = \left(x + \frac{3}{8}\right)^2.$$

 TRY EXERCISE 39

STUDENT NOTES

In problems like Examples 7(b) and (c), it is best to avoid decimal notation. Most students have an easier time recognizing $\frac{9}{64}$ as $\left(\frac{3}{8}\right)^2$ than seeing 0.140625 as 0.375^2.

We can now use the method of completing the square to solve equations.

EXAMPLE **8**   Solve: $x^2 - 8x - 7 = 0$.

SOLUTION   We begin by adding 7 to both sides:

$$x^2 - 8x - 7 = 0$$
$$x^2 - 8x \qquad = 7 \qquad\qquad \text{Adding 7 to both sides. We can now complete the square on the left side.}$$
$$x^2 - 8x + 16 = 7 + 16 \qquad \text{Adding 16 to both sides to complete the square: } \tfrac{1}{2}(-8) = -4, \text{ and } (-4)^2 = 16$$
$$(x - 4)^2 = 23 \qquad\qquad \text{Factoring and simplifying}$$
$$x - 4 = \pm\sqrt{23} \qquad\quad \text{Using the principle of square roots}$$
$$x = 4 \pm \sqrt{23}. \qquad \text{Adding 4 to both sides}$$

Check: For $4 + \sqrt{23}$:

$$\dfrac{x^2 - 8x - 7 = 0}{\begin{array}{c|c} (4 + \sqrt{23})^2 - 8(4 + \sqrt{23}) - 7 & 0 \\ 16 + 8\sqrt{23} + 23 - 32 - 8\sqrt{23} - 7 & \\ 16 + 23 - 32 - 7 + 8\sqrt{23} - 8\sqrt{23} & \\ & 0 \overset{?}{=} 0 \quad \text{TRUE} \end{array}}$$

For $4 - \sqrt{23}$:

$$\dfrac{x^2 - 8x - 7 = 0}{\begin{array}{c|c} (4 - \sqrt{23})^2 - 8(4 - \sqrt{23}) - 7 & 0 \\ 16 - 8\sqrt{23} + 23 - 32 + 8\sqrt{23} - 7 & \\ 16 + 23 - 32 - 7 - 8\sqrt{23} + 8\sqrt{23} & \\ & 0 \overset{?}{=} 0 \quad \text{TRUE} \end{array}}$$

The solutions are $4 + \sqrt{23}$ and $4 - \sqrt{23}$, or $4 \pm \sqrt{23}$.   **TRY EXERCISE** 53

Recall that the value of $f(x)$ must be 0 at any x-intercept of the graph of f. If $f(a) = 0$, then $(a, 0)$ is an x-intercept of the graph.

EXAMPLE 9   Find the x-intercepts of the graph of $f(x) = x^2 + 5x - 3$.

SOLUTION   We set $f(x)$ equal to 0 and solve:

$$f(x) = 0$$

$$x^2 + 5x - 3 = 0 \qquad \text{Substituting}$$

$$x^2 + 5x = 3 \qquad \text{Adding 3 to both sides}$$

$$x^2 + 5x + \frac{25}{4} = 3 + \frac{25}{4} \qquad \begin{array}{l}\text{Completing the square:} \\ \frac{1}{2} \cdot 5 = \frac{5}{2}, \text{ and } \left(\frac{5}{2}\right)^2 = \frac{25}{4}\end{array}$$

$$\left(x + \frac{5}{2}\right)^2 = \frac{37}{4} \qquad \text{Factoring and simplifying}$$

$$x + \frac{5}{2} = \pm\frac{\sqrt{37}}{2} \qquad \begin{array}{l}\text{Using the principle of square roots} \\ \text{and the quotient rule for radicals}\end{array}$$

$$x = -\frac{5}{2} \pm \frac{\sqrt{37}}{2}, \quad \text{or} \quad \frac{-5 \pm \sqrt{37}}{2}. \qquad \text{Adding } -\frac{5}{2} \text{ to both sides}$$

The x-intercepts are

$$\left(-\frac{5}{2} - \frac{\sqrt{37}}{2}, 0\right) \quad \text{and} \quad \left(-\frac{5}{2} + \frac{\sqrt{37}}{2}, 0\right), \quad \text{or}$$

$$\left(\frac{-5 - \sqrt{37}}{2}, 0\right) \quad \text{and} \quad \left(\frac{-5 + \sqrt{37}}{2}, 0\right).$$

The checks are left to the student.   **TRY EXERCISE** 59

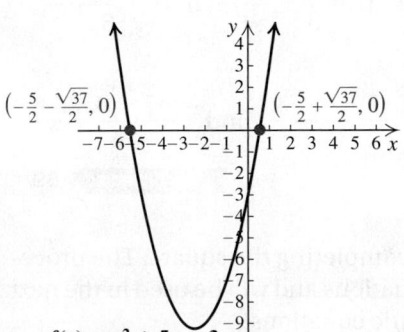

$\left(-\frac{5}{2} - \frac{\sqrt{37}}{2}, 0\right)$ $\left(-\frac{5}{2} + \frac{\sqrt{37}}{2}, 0\right)$

$f(x) = x^2 + 5x - 3$

A visualization of Example 9

Before we complete the square in a quadratic equation, the leading coefficient must be 1. When it is not 1, we divide both sides of the equation by whatever that coefficient may be.

> **To Solve a Quadratic Equation in x by Completing the Square**
>
> 1. Isolate the terms with variables on one side of the equation, and arrange them in descending order.
> 2. Divide both sides by the coefficient of x^2 if that coefficient is not 1.
> 3. Complete the square by taking half of the coefficient of x and adding its square to both sides.
> 4. Express the trinomial as the square of a binomial (factor the trinomial) and simplify the other side.
> 5. Use the principle of square roots (find the square roots of both sides).
> 6. Solve for x by adding or subtracting on both sides.

EXAMPLE 10   Solve: $3x^2 + 7x - 2 = 0$.

SOLUTION   We follow the steps listed above:

$$3x^2 + 7x - 2 = 0$$

Isolate the variable terms.

$$3x^2 + 7x = 2 \qquad \text{Adding 2 to both sides}$$

Divide both sides by the x^2-coefficient.

$$x^2 + \frac{7}{3}x = \frac{2}{3} \qquad \text{Dividing both sides by 3}$$

Complete the square.

$$x^2 + \frac{7}{3}x + \frac{49}{36} = \frac{2}{3} + \frac{49}{36} \qquad \begin{array}{l}\text{Completing the square:}\\ \left(\frac{1}{2} \cdot \frac{7}{3}\right)^2 = \frac{49}{36}\end{array}$$

Factor the trinomial.

$$\left(x + \frac{7}{6}\right)^2 = \frac{73}{36} \qquad \text{Factoring and simplifying}$$

Use the principle of square roots.

$$x + \frac{7}{6} = \pm\frac{\sqrt{73}}{6} \qquad \begin{array}{l}\text{Using the principle of square roots}\\ \text{and the quotient rule for radicals}\end{array}$$

Solve for x.

$$x = -\frac{7}{6} \pm \frac{\sqrt{73}}{6}, \quad \text{or} \quad \frac{-7 \pm \sqrt{73}}{6}. \qquad \text{Adding } -\tfrac{7}{6} \text{ to both sides}$$

The checks are left to the student. The solutions are $-\dfrac{7}{6} \pm \dfrac{\sqrt{73}}{6}$, or $\dfrac{-7 \pm \sqrt{73}}{6}$.

This can be written as

$$-\frac{7}{6} + \frac{\sqrt{73}}{6} \quad \text{and} \quad -\frac{7}{6} - \frac{\sqrt{73}}{6}, \quad \text{or} \quad \frac{-7 + \sqrt{73}}{6} \quad \text{and} \quad \frac{-7 - \sqrt{73}}{6}.$$

TRY EXERCISE 69

Any quadratic equation can be solved by completing the square. The procedure is also useful when graphing quadratic equations and will be used in the next section to develop a formula for solving quadratic equations.

Problem Solving

After one year, an amount of money P, invested at 4% per year, is worth 104% of P, or $P(1.04)$. If that amount continues to earn 4% interest per year, after the second year the investment will be worth 104% of $P(1.04)$, or $P(1.04)^2$. This is called **compounding interest** since after the first time period, interest is earned on both the initial investment *and* the interest from the first time period. Continuing the above pattern, we see that after the third year, the investment will be worth 104% of $P(1.04)^2$. Generalizing, we have the following.

> ### The Compound-Interest Formula
>
> If an amount of money P is invested at interest rate r, compounded annually, then in t years, it will grow to the amount A given by
>
> $$A = P(1 + r)^t. \qquad (r \text{ is written in decimal notation.})$$

We can use quadratic equations to solve certain interest problems.

EXAMPLE 11

Investment growth.   Katia invested $4000 at interest rate r, compounded annually. In 2 yr, it grew to $4410. What was the interest rate?

SOLUTION

1. **Familiarize.** We are already familiar with the compound-interest formula. If we were not, we would need to consult an outside source.
2. **Translate.** The translation consists of substituting into the formula:

   $$A = P(1 + r)^t$$
   $$4410 = 4000(1 + r)^2. \qquad \text{Substituting}$$

3. **Carry out.** We solve for r:

   $$4410 = 4000(1 + r)^2$$
   $$\tfrac{4410}{4000} = (1 + r)^2 \qquad \text{Dividing both sides by 4000}$$
   $$\tfrac{441}{400} = (1 + r)^2 \qquad \text{Simplifying}$$
   $$\pm\sqrt{\tfrac{441}{400}} = 1 + r \qquad \text{Using the principle of square roots}$$
   $$\pm\tfrac{21}{20} = 1 + r \qquad \text{Simplifying}$$
   $$-\tfrac{20}{20} \pm \tfrac{21}{20} = r \qquad \text{Adding } -1, \text{ or } -\tfrac{20}{20}, \text{ to both sides}$$
   $$\tfrac{1}{20} = r \quad \text{or} \quad -\tfrac{41}{20} = r.$$

4. **Check.** Since the interest rate cannot be negative, we need check only $\tfrac{1}{20}$, or 5%. If $4000 were invested at 5% interest, compounded annually, then in 2 yr it would grow to $4000(1.05)^2$, or $4410. The rate 5% checks.
5. **State.** The interest rate was 5%.

TRY EXERCISE 75

EXAMPLE 12

Free-falling objects.   The formula $s = 16t^2$ is used to approximate the distance s, in feet, that an object falls freely from rest in t seconds. The Grand Canyon Skywalk is 4000 ft above the Colorado River. How long will it take a stone to fall from the Skywalk to the river? Round to the nearest tenth of a second.

Source: www.grandcanyonskywalk.com

SOLUTION

1. **Familiarize.** We agree to disregard air resistance and use the given formula.
2. **Translate.** We substitute into the formula:

   $$s = 16t^2$$
   $$4000 = 16t^2.$$

3. **Carry out.** We solve for t:

$$4000 = 16t^2$$
$$250 = t^2$$
$$\sqrt{250} = t \quad$$ Using the principle of square roots; rejecting the negative square root since t cannot be negative in this problem
$$15.8 \approx t. \quad$$ Using a calculator and rounding to the nearest tenth

4. **Check.** Since $16(15.8)^2 = 3994.24 \approx 4000$, our answer checks.

5. **State.** It takes about 15.8 sec for a stone to fall freely from the Grand Canyon Skywalk to the river.

> **TRY EXERCISE** 79

TECHNOLOGY CONNECTION

As we saw in Section 5.7, a graphing calculator can be used to find approximate solutions of any quadratic equation that has real-number solutions.

To check Example 8, we graph $y = x^2 - 8x - 7$ and use the ZERO or ROOT option of the CALC menu. When asked for a Left and Right Bound, we enter cursor positions to the left of and to the right of the root. A Guess between the bounds is entered and a value for the root then appears.

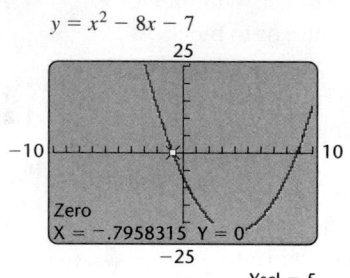

$y = x^2 - 8x - 7$

Zero
X = −.7958315 Y = 0

Yscl = 5

1. Use a graphing calculator to check the second solution of Example 8.
2. Use a graphing calculator to confirm the solutions in Example 9.
3. Can a graphing calculator be used to find *exact* solutions in Example 10? Why or why not?

4. Use a graphing calculator to confirm that there are no real-number solutions of $x^2 - 6x + 11 = 0$.

11.1   EXERCISE SET

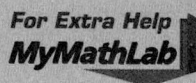 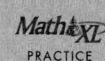 

For Extra Help
MyMathLab   MathXL   PRACTICE   WATCH   DOWNLOAD

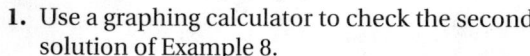 **Concept Reinforcement** *Complete each of the following to form true statements.*

1. The principle of square roots states that if $x^2 = k$, then $x =$ ____ or $x =$ ____.

2. If $(x + 5)^2 = 49$, then $x + 5 =$ ____ or $x + 5 =$ ____.

3. If $t^2 + 6t + 9 = 17$, then (____ $)^2 = 17$ and ____ $= \pm\sqrt{17}$.

4. The equations $x^2 + 8x +$ ____ $= 23$ and $x^2 + 8x = 7$ are equivalent.

5. The expressions $t^2 + 10t +$ ____ and $(t +$ ____ $)^2$ are equivalent.

6. The expressions $x^2 - 6x +$ ____ and $(x -$ ____ $)^2$ are equivalent.

Solve.

7. $x^2 = 100$

8. $t^2 = 144$

9. $p^2 - 50 = 0$

10. $c^2 - 8 = 0$

11. $5y^2 = 30$

12. $4y^2 = 12$

13. $9x^2 - 49 = 0$

14. $36a^2 - 25 = 0$

15. $6t^2 - 5 = 0$

16. $7x^2 - 5 = 0$

17. $a^2 + 1 = 0$

18. $t^2 + 4 = 0$

19. $4d^2 + 81 = 0$

20. $25y^2 + 16 = 0$

21. $(x - 3)^2 = 16$

22. $(x + 1)^2 = 100$

23. $(t + 5)^2 = 12$

24. $(y - 4)^2 = 18$

25. $(x + 1)^2 = -9$

26. $(x - 1)^2 = -49$

27. $\left(y + \frac{3}{4}\right)^2 = \frac{17}{16}$

28. $\left(t + \frac{3}{2}\right)^2 = \frac{7}{2}$

29. $x^2 - 10x + 25 = 64$ **30.** $x^2 - 6x + 9 = 100$

31. Let $f(x) = x^2$. Find x such that $f(x) = 19$.

32. Let $f(x) = x^2$. Find x such that $f(x) = 11$.

33. Let $f(x) = (x - 5)^2$. Find x such that $f(x) = 16$.

34. Let $g(x) = (x - 2)^2$. Find x such that $g(x) = 25$.

35. Let $F(t) = (t + 4)^2$. Find t such that $F(t) = 13$.

36. Let $f(t) = (t + 6)^2$. Find t such that $f(t) = 15$.

37. Let $g(x) = x^2 + 14x + 49$. Find x such that $g(x) = 49$.

38. Let $F(x) = x^2 + 8x + 16$. Find x such that $F(x) = 9$.

Replace the blanks in each equation with constants to complete the square and form a true equation.

39. $x^2 + 16x + \underline{\quad} = (x + \underline{\quad})^2$

40. $x^2 + 12x + \underline{\quad} = (x + \underline{\quad})^2$

41. $t^2 - 10t + \underline{\quad} = (t - \underline{\quad})^2$

42. $t^2 - 6t + \underline{\quad} = (t - \underline{\quad})^2$

43. $t^2 - 2t + \underline{\quad} = (t - \underline{\quad})^2$

44. $x^2 + 2x + \underline{\quad} = (x + \underline{\quad})^2$

45. $x^2 + 3x + \underline{\quad} = \left(x + \underline{\quad}\right)^2$

46. $t^2 - 9t + \underline{\quad} = \left(t - \underline{\quad}\right)^2$

47. $x^2 + \frac{2}{5}x + \underline{\quad} = \left(x + \underline{\quad}\right)^2$

48. $x^2 + \frac{2}{3}x + \underline{\quad} = \left(x + \underline{\quad}\right)^2$

49. $t^2 - \frac{5}{6}t + \underline{\quad} = \left(t - \underline{\quad}\right)^2$

50. $t^2 - \frac{5}{3}t + \underline{\quad} = \left(t - \underline{\quad}\right)^2$

Solve by completing the square. Show your work.

51. $x^2 + 6x = 7$

52. $x^2 + 8x = 9$

53. $t^2 - 10t = -23$

54. $t^2 - 4t = -1$

55. $x^2 + 12x + 32 = 0$

56. $x^2 + 16x + 15 = 0$

57. $t^2 + 8t - 3 = 0$

58. $t^2 + 6t - 5 = 0$

Complete the square to find the x-intercepts of each function given by the equation listed.

59. $f(x) = x^2 + 6x + 7$

60. $f(x) = x^2 + 10x - 2$

61. $g(x) = x^2 + 9x - 25$

62. $g(x) = x^2 + 5x + 2$

63. $f(x) = x^2 - 10x - 22$

64. $f(x) = x^2 - 8x - 10$

Solve by completing the square. Remember to first divide, as in Example 10, to make sure that the coefficient of x^2 is 1.

65. $9x^2 + 18x = -8$ **66.** $4x^2 + 8x = -3$

67. $3x^2 - 5x - 2 = 0$ **68.** $2x^2 - 5x - 3 = 0$

69. $5x^2 + 4x - 3 = 0$ **70.** $4x^2 + 3x - 5 = 0$

71. Find the x-intercepts of the function given by $f(x) = 4x^2 + 2x - 3$.

72. Find the x-intercepts of the function given by $f(x) = 3x^2 + x - 5$.

73. Find the x-intercepts of the function given by $g(x) = 2x^2 - 3x - 1$.

74. Find the x-intercepts of the function given by $g(x) = 3x^2 - 5x - 1$.

Interest.   *Use $A = P(1 + r)^t$ to find the interest rate in Exercises 75–78. Refer to Example 11.*

75. $2000 grows to $2420 in 2 yr

76. $1000 grows to $1440 in 2 yr

77. $6250 grows to $6760 in 2 yr

78. $6250 grows to $7290 in 2 yr

Free-falling objects.   *Use $s = 16t^2$ for Exercises 79–82. Refer to Example 12 and neglect air resistance.*

79. At a height of 290 ft, the Rainbow Bridge in Lake Powell National Monument, Utah, is the world's highest natural arch. How long would it take an object to fall freely from the bridge?
Source: *Guinness World Records* 2008

80. The Sears Tower in Chicago is 1454 ft tall. How long would it take an object to fall freely from the top?

81. At 2063 ft, the KVLY-TV tower in North Dakota is the tallest supported tower. How long would it take an object to fall freely from the top?
Source: North Dakota Tourism Division

82. El Capitan in Yosemite National Park is 3593 ft high. How long would it take a carabiner to fall freely from the top?
Source: *Guinness World Records* 2008

83. Explain in your own words a sequence of steps that can be used to solve any quadratic equation in the quickest way.

84. Write an interest-rate problem for a classmate to solve. Devise the problem so that the solution is "The loan was made at 7% interest."

Skill Review

To prepare for Section 11.2, review evaluating expressions and simplifying radical expressions (Sections 1.8, 10.3, and 10.8).

Evaluate. [1.8]

85. $b^2 - 4ac$, for $a = 3$, $b = 2$, and $c = -5$

86. $b^2 - 4ac$, for $a = 1$, $b = -1$, and $c = 4$

Simplify. [10.3], [10.8]

87. $\sqrt{200}$　　　　　　　　**88.** $\sqrt{96}$

89. $\sqrt{-4}$　　　　　　　　**90.** $\sqrt{-25}$

91. $\sqrt{-8}$　　　　　　　　**92.** $\sqrt{-24}$

Synthesis

93. What would be better: to receive 3% interest every 6 months, or to receive 6% interest every 12 months? Why?

94. Write a problem involving a free-falling object for a classmate to solve (see Example 12). Devise the problem so that the solution is "The object takes about 4.5 sec to fall freely from the top of the structure."

Find b such that each trinomial is a square.

95. $x^2 + bx + 81$　　　　　**96.** $x^2 + bx + 49$

97. If $f(x) = 2x^5 - 9x^4 - 66x^3 + 45x^2 + 280x$ and $x^2 - 5$ is a factor of $f(x)$, find all a for which $f(a) = 0$.

98. If $f(x) = \left(x - \frac{1}{3}\right)(x^2 + 6)$ and $g(x) = \left(x - \frac{1}{3}\right)\left(x^2 - \frac{2}{3}\right)$, find all a for which $(f + g)(a) = 0$.

99. *Boating.*　A barge and a fishing boat leave a dock at the same time, traveling at a right angle to each other. The barge travels 7 km/h slower than the fishing boat. After 4 hr, the boats are 68 km apart. Find the speed of each boat.

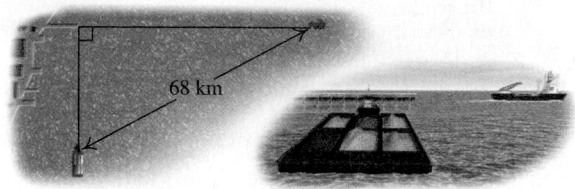

68 km

100. Find three consecutive integers such that the square of the first plus the product of the other two is 67.

101. Exercises 29, 33, and 53 can be solved on a graphing calculator without first rewriting in standard form. Simply let y_1 represent the left side of the equation and y_2 the right side. Then use a graphing calculator to determine the x-coordinate of any point of intersection. Use a graphing calculator to solve Exercises 29, 33, and 53 in this manner.

102. Use a graphing calculator to check your answers to Exercises 5, 13, 71, and 73.

103. Example 11 can be solved with a graphing calculator by graphing each side of

$$4410 = 4000(1 + r)^2.$$

How could you determine, from a reading of the problem, a suitable viewing window? What might that window be?

11.2   The Quadratic Formula

Solving Using the Quadratic Formula   ▪   Approximating Solutions

We can use the process of completing the square to develop a general formula for solving quadratic equations.

Solving Using the Quadratic Formula

Each time we solve by completing the square, the procedure is the same. When a procedure is repeated many times, we can often develop a formula to speed up our work.

We begin with a quadratic equation in standard form,

$$ax^2 + bx + c = 0,$$

with $a > 0$. For $a < 0$, a slightly different derivation is needed (see Exercise 60), but the result is the same. Let's solve by completing the square. As the steps are performed, compare them with Example 10 on p. 710.

$$ax^2 + bx = -c \qquad \text{Adding to both sides}$$

$$x^2 + \frac{b}{a}x = -\frac{c}{a} \qquad \text{Dividing both sides by } a$$

Half of $\frac{b}{a}$ is $\frac{b}{2a}$ and $\left(\frac{b}{2a}\right)^2$ is $\frac{b^2}{4a^2}$. We add $\frac{b^2}{4a^2}$ to both sides:

$$x^2 + \frac{b}{a}x + \frac{b^2}{4a^2} = -\frac{c}{a} + \frac{b^2}{4a^2} \qquad \text{Adding } \frac{b^2}{4a^2} \text{ to complete the square}$$

$$\left(x + \frac{b}{2a}\right)^2 = -\frac{4ac}{4a^2} + \frac{b^2}{4a^2} \qquad \text{Factoring on the left side; finding a common denominator on the right side}$$

$$\left(x + \frac{b}{2a}\right)^2 = \frac{b^2 - 4ac}{4a^2}$$

$$x + \frac{b}{2a} = \pm\frac{\sqrt{b^2 - 4ac}}{2a} \qquad \text{Using the principle of square roots and the quotient rule for radicals. Since } a > 0, \sqrt{4a^2} = 2a.$$

$$x = \frac{-b \pm \sqrt{b^2 - 4ac}}{2a}. \qquad \text{Adding } -\frac{b}{2a} \text{ to both sides}$$

It is important to remember the quadratic formula and know how to use it.

The Quadratic Formula

The solutions of $ax^2 + bx + c = 0$, $a \neq 0$, are given by

$$x = \frac{-b \pm \sqrt{b^2 - 4ac}}{2a}.$$

EXAMPLE **1**   Solve $5x^2 + 8x = -3$ using the quadratic formula.

SOLUTION   We first find standard form and determine a, b, and c:

$$5x^2 + 8x + 3 = 0; \qquad \text{Adding 3 to both sides to get 0 on one side}$$
$$a = 5, \quad b = 8, \quad c = 3.$$

Next, we use the quadratic formula:

$$x = \frac{-b \pm \sqrt{b^2 - 4ac}}{2a} \qquad \text{It is important to remember this formula.}$$

$$x = \frac{-8 \pm \sqrt{8^2 - 4 \cdot 5 \cdot 3}}{2 \cdot 5} \qquad \text{Substituting}$$

$$x = \frac{-8 \pm \sqrt{64 - 60}}{10} \qquad \boxed{\text{Be sure to write the fraction bar all the way across.}}$$

$$x = \frac{-8 \pm \sqrt{4}}{10} = \frac{-8 \pm 2}{10}$$

$$x = \frac{-8 + 2}{10} \quad or \quad x = \frac{-8 - 2}{10} \qquad \text{The symbol } \pm \text{ indicates two solutions.}$$

$$x = \frac{-6}{10} \quad or \quad x = \frac{-10}{10}$$

$$x = -\frac{3}{5} \quad or \quad x = -1.$$

The solutions are $-\frac{3}{5}$ and -1. The checks are left to the student.

▶ **TRY EXERCISE** 25

Because $5x^2 + 8x + 3$ can be factored, the quadratic formula may not have been the fastest way of solving Example 1. However, because the quadratic formula works for *any* quadratic equation, we need not spend too much time struggling to solve a quadratic equation by factoring.

STUDY SKILLS ————

Know It "By Heart"

When memorizing something like the quadratic formula, try to first understand and write out the derivation. Doing this two or three times will help you remember the formula.

———————————

> **To Solve a Quadratic Equation**
>   1. If the equation can be easily written in the form $ax^2 = p$ or $(x + k)^2 = d$, use the principle of square roots as in Section 11.1.
>   2. If step (1) does not apply, write the equation in the form $ax^2 + bx + c = 0$.
>   3. Try factoring and using the principle of zero products.
>   4. If factoring seems difficult or impossible, use the quadratic formula. Completing the square can also be used.
>
> The solutions of a quadratic equation can always be found using the quadratic formula. They cannot always be found by factoring.

Recall that a second-degree polynomial in one variable is said to be quadratic. Similarly, a second-degree polynomial function in one variable is said to be **a quadratic function**.

EXAMPLE 2   For the quadratic function given by $f(x) = 3x^2 - 6x - 4$, find all x for which $f(x) = 0$.

SOLUTION   We substitute and solve for x:

$$f(x) = 0$$
$$3x^2 - 6x - 4 = 0. \quad \text{Substituting}$$

Since $3x^2 - 6x - 4$ does not factor, we use the quadratic formula with $a = 3$, $b = -6$, and $c = -4$:

$$x = \frac{-(-6) \pm \sqrt{(-6)^2 - 4 \cdot 3 \cdot (-4)}}{2 \cdot 3}$$

$$= \frac{6 \pm \sqrt{36 + 48}}{6} \qquad (-6)^2 - 4 \cdot 3 \cdot (-4) = 36 - (-48) = 36 + 48$$

$$= \frac{6 \pm \sqrt{84}}{6} \qquad \text{Note that 4 is a perfect-square factor of 84.}$$

$$= \frac{6}{6} \pm \frac{\sqrt{84}}{6} \qquad \text{Writing as two fractions to simplify each separately}$$

$$= 1 \pm \frac{\sqrt{4}\sqrt{21}}{6} \qquad 84 = 4 \cdot 21$$

$$\left. \begin{array}{l} = 1 \pm \frac{2\sqrt{21}}{2 \cdot 3} \\[2mm] = 1 \pm \frac{\sqrt{21}}{3}. \end{array} \right\} \quad \text{Simplifying by removing a factor of 1: } \frac{2}{2} = 1$$

The solutions are $1 - \dfrac{\sqrt{21}}{3}$ and $1 + \dfrac{\sqrt{21}}{3}$. The checks are left to the student.

TRY EXERCISE 39

TECHNOLOGY CONNECTION

To check Example 2 by graphing $y_1 = 3x^2 - 6x - 4$, press TRACE and enter $1 + \sqrt{21}/3$. A rational approximation and the y-value 0 should appear.

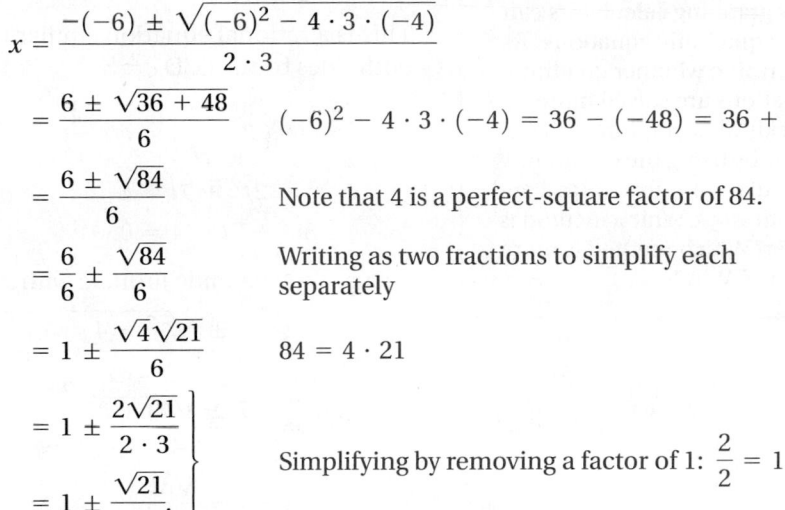

$y = 3x^2 - 6x - 4$

X = 2.5275252   Y = 0

Use this approach to check the other solution of Example 2.

Some quadratic equations have solutions that are imaginary numbers.

EXAMPLE 3   Solve: $x(x + 5) = 2(2x - 1)$.

SOLUTION   We first find standard form:

$$x^2 + 5x = 4x - 2 \qquad \text{Multiplying}$$
$$x^2 + x + 2 = 0. \qquad \text{Subtracting } 4x \text{ and adding 2 to both sides}$$

Since we cannot factor $x^2 + x + 2$, we use the quadratic formula with $a = 1$, $b = 1$, and $c = 2$:

$$x = \frac{-1 \pm \sqrt{1^2 - 4 \cdot 1 \cdot 2}}{2 \cdot 1} \qquad \text{Substituting}$$

$$= \frac{-1 \pm \sqrt{1 - 8}}{2}$$

$$= \frac{-1 \pm \sqrt{-7}}{2}$$

$$= \frac{-1 \pm i\sqrt{7}}{2}, \text{ or } -\frac{1}{2} \pm \frac{\sqrt{7}}{2} i.$$

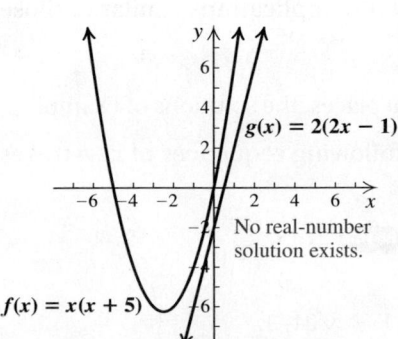

$g(x) = 2(2x - 1)$

No real-number solution exists.

$f(x) = x(x + 5)$

A visualization of Example 3

The solutions are $-\dfrac{1}{2} - \dfrac{\sqrt{7}}{2} i$ and $-\dfrac{1}{2} + \dfrac{\sqrt{7}}{2} i$. The checks are left to the student.

TRY EXERCISE 35

The quadratic formula can be used to solve certain rational equations.

EXAMPLE **4**

If $f(t) = 2 + \dfrac{7}{t}$ and $g(t) = \dfrac{4}{t^2}$, find all t for which $f(t) = g(t)$.

SOLUTION We set $f(t)$ equal to $g(t)$ and solve:

$$f(t) = g(t)$$

$$2 + \frac{7}{t} = \frac{4}{t^2}.\qquad \text{Substituting. Note that } t \ne 0.$$

This is a rational equation similar to those in Section 6.6. To solve, we multiply both sides by the LCD, t^2:

$$t^2\left(2 + \frac{7}{t}\right) = t^2 \cdot \frac{4}{t^2}$$

$$2t^2 + 7t = 4 \qquad \text{Simplifying}$$

$$2t^2 + 7t - 4 = 0. \qquad \text{Subtracting 4 from both sides}$$

We use the quadratic formula with $a = 2$, $b = 7$, and $c = -4$:

$$t = \frac{-7 \pm \sqrt{7^2 - 4 \cdot 2 \cdot (-4)}}{2 \cdot 2}$$

$$= \frac{-7 \pm \sqrt{49 + 32}}{4} \qquad 7^2 - 4 \cdot 2 \cdot (-4) = 49 - (-32) = 49 + 32$$

$$= \frac{-7 \pm \sqrt{81}}{4}$$

$$= \frac{-7 \pm 9}{4} \qquad \text{This means } \frac{-7 + 9}{4} \text{ or } \frac{-7 - 9}{4}.$$

$$t = \frac{2}{4} = \frac{1}{2} \quad or \quad t = \frac{-16}{4} = -4. \qquad \begin{array}{l}\text{Both answers should check}\\ \text{since } t \ne 0.\end{array}$$

You can confirm that $f\left(\tfrac{1}{2}\right) = g\left(\tfrac{1}{2}\right)$ and $f(-4) = g(-4)$. The solutions are $\tfrac{1}{2}$ and -4.

TRY EXERCISE 41

TECHNOLOGY CONNECTION

We saw in Sections 5.7 and 11.1 how graphing calculators can solve quadratic equations. To determine whether quadratic equations are solved more quickly on a graphing calculator or by using the quadratic formula, solve Examples 2 and 4 both ways. Which method is faster? Which method is more precise? Why?

Approximating Solutions

When the solution of an equation is irrational, a rational-number approximation is often useful. This is often the case in real-world applications similar to those found in Section 11.4.

EXAMPLE **5**

Use a calculator to approximate, to three decimal places, the solutions of Example 2.

SOLUTION On most calculators, one of the following sequences of keystrokes can be used to approximate $1 + \sqrt{21}/3$:

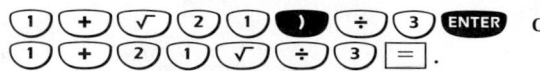

Similar keystrokes can be used to approximate $1 - \sqrt{21}/3$.

The solutions are approximately 2.527525232 and -0.5275252317. Rounded to three decimal places, the solutions are approximately 2.528 and -0.528.

TRY EXERCISE 45

STUDENT NOTES

It is important that you understand both the rules for order of operations *and* the manner in which your calculator applies those rules.

11.2 EXERCISE SET

🦢 **Concept Reinforcement**   *Classify each statement as either true or false.*

1. The quadratic formula can be used to solve *any* quadratic equation.

2. The steps used to derive the quadratic formula are the same as those used when solving by completing the square.

3. The quadratic formula does not work if solutions are imaginary numbers.

4. Solving by factoring is always slower than using the quadratic formula.

5. A quadratic equation can have as many as four solutions.

6. It is possible for a quadratic equation to have no real-number solutions.

Solve.

7. $2x^2 + 3x - 5 = 0$

8. $3x^2 - 7x + 2 = 0$

9. $u^2 + 2u - 4 = 0$

10. $u^2 - 2u - 2 = 0$

11. $t^2 + 3 = 6t$

12. $t^2 + 4t = 1$

13. $x^2 = 3x + 5$

14. $x^2 + 5x + 3 = 0$

15. $3t(t + 2) = 1$

16. $2t(t + 2) = 1$

17. $\dfrac{1}{x^2} - 3 = \dfrac{8}{x}$

18. $\dfrac{9}{x} - 2 = \dfrac{5}{x^2}$

19. $t^2 + 10 = 6t$

20. $t^2 + 10t + 26 = 0$

21. $p^2 - p + 1 = 0$

22. $p^2 + p + 4 = 0$

23. $x^2 + 4x + 6 = 0$

24. $x^2 + 11 = 6x$

25. $12t^2 + 17t = 40$

26. $15t^2 + 7t = 2$

27. $25x^2 - 20x + 4 = 0$

28. $36x^2 + 84x + 49 = 0$

29. $7x(x + 2) + 5 = 3x(x + 1)$

30. $5x(x - 1) - 7 = 4x(x - 2)$

31. $14(x - 4) - (x + 2) = (x + 2)(x - 4)$

32. $11(x - 2) + (x - 5) = (x + 2)(x - 6)$

33. $51p = 2p^2 + 72$

34. $72 = 3p^2 + 50p$

35. $x(x - 3) = x - 9$

36. $x(x - 1) = 2x - 7$

37. $x^3 - 8 = 0$ (*Hint*: Factor the difference of cubes. Then use the quadratic formula.)

38. $x^3 + 1 = 0$

39. Let $f(x) = 6x^2 - 7x - 20$. Find x such that $f(x) = 0$.

40. Let $g(x) = 4x^2 - 2x - 3$. Find x such that $g(x) = 0$.

41. Let
$$f(x) = \frac{7}{x} + \frac{7}{x + 4}.$$
Find all x for which $f(x) = 1$.

42. Let
$$g(x) = \frac{2}{x} + \frac{2}{x + 3}.$$
Find all x for which $g(x) = 1$.

43. Let
$$F(x) = \frac{3 - x}{4} \quad \text{and} \quad G(x) = \frac{1}{4x}.$$
Find all x for which $F(x) = G(x)$.

44. Let
$$f(x) = x + 5 \quad \text{and} \quad g(x) = \frac{3}{x - 5}.$$
Find all x for which $f(x) = g(x)$.

Solve using the quadratic formula. Then use a calculator to approximate, to three decimal places, the solutions as rational numbers.

45. $x^2 + 4x - 7 = 0$

46. $x^2 + 6x + 4 = 0$

Aha! **47.** $x^2 - 6x + 4 = 0$

48. $x^2 - 4x + 1 = 0$

49. $2x^2 - 3x - 7 = 0$

50. $3x^2 - 3x - 2 = 0$

📝 **51.** Are there any equations that can be solved by the quadratic formula but not by completing the square? Why or why not?

📝 **52.** Suppose you are solving a quadratic equation with no constant term ($c = 0$). Would you use factoring or the quadratic formula to solve? Why?

Skill Review

To prepare for Section 11.3, review multiplying and simplifying radical and complex-number expressions (Sections 10.5 and 10.8).

Multiply and simplify.

53. $(x - 2i)(x + 2i)$ [10.8]

54. $(x - 6\sqrt{5})(x + 6\sqrt{5})$ [10.5]

55. $(x - (2 - \sqrt{7}))(x - (2 + \sqrt{7}))$ [10.5]

56. $(x - (-3 + 5i))(x - (-3 - 5i))$ [10.8]

Simplify.

57. $\dfrac{-6 \pm \sqrt{(-4)^2 - 4(2)(2)}}{2(2)}$ [10.3]

58. $\dfrac{-(-1) \pm \sqrt{(6)^2 - 4(3)(5)}}{2(3)}$ [10.8]

Synthesis

59. Explain how you could use the quadratic formula to help factor a quadratic polynomial.

60. If $a < 0$ and $ax^2 + bx + c = 0$, then $-a$ is positive and the equivalent equation, $-ax^2 - bx - c = 0$, can be solved using the quadratic formula.
  a) Find this solution, replacing a, b, and c in the formula with $-a$, $-b$, and $-c$ from the equation.
  b) How does the result of part (a) indicate that the quadratic formula "works" regardless of the sign of a?

For Exercises 61–63, let

$$f(x) = \frac{x^2}{x - 2} + 1 \quad and \quad g(x) = \frac{4x - 2}{x - 2} + \frac{x + 4}{2}.$$

61. Find the x-intercepts of the graph of f.

62. Find the x-intercepts of the graph of g.

63. Find all x for which $f(x) = g(x)$.

Solve. Approximate the solutions to three decimal places.

64. $x^2 - 0.75x - 0.5 = 0$

65. $z^2 + 0.84z - 0.4 = 0$

Solve.

66. $(1 + \sqrt{3})x^2 - (3 + 2\sqrt{3})x + 3 = 0$

67. $\sqrt{2}x^2 + 5x + \sqrt{2} = 0$

68. $ix^2 - 2x + 1 = 0$

69. One solution of $kx^2 + 3x - k = 0$ is -2. Find the other.

70. Use a graphing calculator to solve Exercises 9, 27, and 43.

71. Use a graphing calculator to solve Exercises 11, 33, and 41. Use the method of graphing each side of the equation.

72. Can a graphing calculator be used to solve *any* quadratic equation? Why or why not?

11.3   Studying Solutions of Quadratic Equations

The Discriminant • Writing Equations from Solutions

The Discriminant

It is sometimes enough to know what *type* of number a solution will be, without actually solving the equation. Suppose we want to know if $4x^2 - 5x - 2 = 0$ has rational solutions (and thus can be solved by factoring). Using the quadratic formula, we would have

$$x = \frac{-b \pm \sqrt{b^2 - 4ac}}{2a}$$

$$= \frac{-(-5) \pm \sqrt{(-5)^2 - 4 \cdot 4(-2)}}{2 \cdot 4}.$$

Since $(-5)^2 - 4 \cdot 4 \cdot (-2) = 25 - 16(-2) = 25 + 32 = 57$ and since 57 is not a perfect square, the solutions of the equation are not rational numbers. This means that $4x^2 - 5x - 2 = 0$ *cannot* be solved by factoring. Note that the radicand, 57, determines what type of number the solutions will be.

The radicand $b^2 - 4ac$ is known as the **discriminant**. If a, b, and c are rational, then we have the following.

- When $b^2 - 4ac$ simplifies to 0, it doesn't matter if we use $+\sqrt{b^2 - 4ac}$ or $-\sqrt{b^2 - 4ac}$; we get the same solution twice. Thus, when the discriminant is 0, there is one *repeated* solution and it is rational.

  Example: $9x^2 + 6x + 1 = 0 \rightarrow b^2 - 4ac = 6^2 - 4 \cdot 9 \cdot 1 = 0$.
  Solving $9x^2 + 6x + 1 = 0$ gives the (repeated) solution $-\frac{1}{3}$.

- When $b^2 - 4ac$ is positive, there are two different real-number solutions: If $b^2 - 4ac$ is a perfect square, these solutions are rational numbers.

  Example: $6x^2 + 5x + 1 = 0 \rightarrow b^2 - 4ac = 5^2 - 4 \cdot 6 \cdot 1 = 1$.
  Solving $6x^2 + 5x + 1 = 0$ gives the solutions $-\frac{1}{3}$ and $-\frac{1}{2}$.

- When $b^2 - 4ac$ is positive but not a perfect square, there are two irrational solutions and they are conjugates of each other (see p. 663).

  Example: $x^2 + 4x + 2 = 0 \rightarrow b^2 - 4ac = 4^2 - 4 \cdot 1 \cdot 2 = 8$.
  Solving $x^2 + 4x + 2 = 0$ gives the solutions $-2 + \sqrt{2}$ and $-2 - \sqrt{2}$.

- When the discriminant is negative, there are two imaginary-number solutions and they are complex conjugates of each other.

  Example: $x^2 + 4x + 5 = 0 \rightarrow b^2 - 4ac = 4^2 - 4 \cdot 1 \cdot 5 = -4$.
  Solving $x^2 + 4x + 5 = 0$ gives the solutions $-2 + i$ and $-2 - i$.

Note that any equation for which $b^2 - 4ac$ is a perfect square can be solved by factoring.

Discriminant $b^2 - 4ac$	Nature of Solutions
0	One solution; a rational number

Positive
   Perfect square
   Not a perfect square
	Two different real-number solutions
	   Solutions are rational.
	   Solutions are irrational conjugates.

Negative	Two different imaginary-number solutions (complex conjugates)

EXAMPLE **1**

For each equation, determine what type of number the solutions are and how many solutions exist.

a) $9x^2 - 12x + 4 = 0$ **b)** $x^2 + 5x + 8 = 0$ **c)** $2x^2 + 7x - 3 = 0$

SOLUTION

a) For $9x^2 - 12x + 4 = 0$, we have

$$a = 9, \quad b = -12, \quad c = 4.$$

We substitute and compute the discriminant:

$$b^2 - 4ac = (-12)^2 - 4 \cdot 9 \cdot 4$$
$$= 144 - 144 = 0.$$

There is exactly one solution, and it is rational. This indicates that $9x^2 - 12x + 4 = 0$ can be solved by factoring.

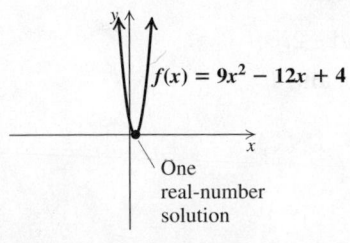

$f(x) = 9x^2 - 12x + 4$

One real-number solution

A visualization of part (a)

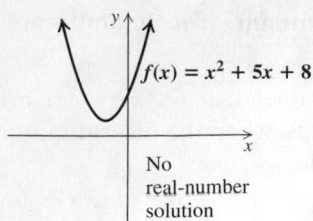

A visualization of part (b)

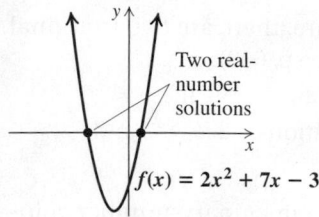

A visualization of part (c)

b) For $x^2 + 5x + 8 = 0$, we have

$$a = 1, \quad b = 5, \quad c = 8.$$

We substitute and compute the discriminant:

$$b^2 - 4ac = 5^2 - 4 \cdot 1 \cdot 8$$
$$= 25 - 32 = -7.$$

Since the discriminant is negative, there are two different imaginary-number solutions that are complex conjugates of each other.

c) For $2x^2 + 7x - 3 = 0$, we have

$$a = 2, \quad b = 7, \quad c = -3.$$

We substitute and compute the discriminant:

$$b^2 - 4ac = 7^2 - 4 \cdot 2(-3)$$
$$= 49 - (-24) = 73.$$

The discriminant is a positive number that is not a perfect square. Thus there are two different irrational solutions that are conjugates of each other.

> **TRY EXERCISE** 7

Discriminants can also be used to determine the number of x-intercepts of the graph of a quadratic function.

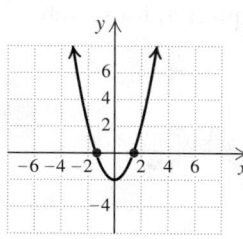

$y = ax^2 + bx + c$
$b^2 - 4ac > 0$
Two real solutions
of $ax^2 + bx + c = 0$
Two x-intercepts

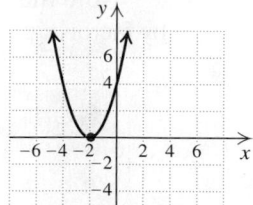

$y = ax^2 + bx + c$
$b^2 - 4ac = 0$
One real solution
of $ax^2 + bx + c = 0$
One x-intercept

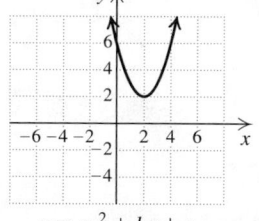

$y = ax^2 + bx + c$
$b^2 - 4ac < 0$
No real solutions
of $ax^2 + bx + c = 0$
No x-intercept

Writing Equations from Solutions

We know by the principle of zero products that $(x - 2)(x + 3) = 0$ has solutions 2 and -3. If we wish for two given numbers to be solutions of an equation, we can create such an equation, using the principle in reverse.

EXAMPLE 2   Find an equation for which the given numbers are solutions.

a) 3 and $-\frac{2}{5}$

b) $2i$ and $-2i$

c) $5\sqrt{7}$ and $-5\sqrt{7}$

d) $-4, 0,$ and 1

SOLUTION

a)
$$x = 3 \quad or \quad x = -\tfrac{2}{5}$$
$$x - 3 = 0 \quad or \quad x + \tfrac{2}{5} = 0 \qquad \text{Getting 0's on one side}$$
$$\left(x - 3\right)\left(x + \tfrac{2}{5}\right) = 0 \qquad \text{Using the principle of zero products (multiplying)}$$
$$x^2 + \tfrac{2}{5}x - 3x - 3 \cdot \tfrac{2}{5} = 0 \qquad \text{Multiplying}$$
$$x^2 - \tfrac{13}{5}x - \tfrac{6}{5} = 0 \qquad \text{Combining like terms}$$
$$5x^2 - 13x - 6 = 0 \qquad \text{Multiplying both sides by 5 to clear fractions}$$

Note that multiplying both sides by the LCD, 5, clears the equation of fractions. Had we preferred, we could have multiplied $x + \frac{2}{5} = 0$ by 5, thus clearing fractions *before* using the principle of zero products.

b)
$$x = 2i \quad or \quad x = -2i$$
$$x - 2i = 0 \quad or \quad x + 2i = 0 \qquad \text{Getting 0's on one side}$$
$$(x - 2i)(x + 2i) = 0 \qquad \text{Using the principle of zero products (multiplying)}$$
$$x^2 - (2i)^2 = 0 \qquad \text{Finding the product of a sum and a difference}$$
$$x^2 - 4i^2 = 0$$
$$x^2 + 4 = 0 \qquad i^2 = -1$$

c)
$$x = 5\sqrt{7} \quad or \quad x = -5\sqrt{7}$$
$$x - 5\sqrt{7} = 0 \quad or \quad x + 5\sqrt{7} = 0 \qquad \text{Getting 0's on one side}$$
$$(x - 5\sqrt{7})(x + 5\sqrt{7}) = 0 \qquad \text{Using the principle of zero products}$$
$$x^2 - (5\sqrt{7})^2 = 0 \qquad \text{Finding the product of a sum and a difference}$$
$$x^2 - 25 \cdot 7 = 0$$
$$x^2 - 175 = 0$$

d)
$$x = -4 \quad or \quad x = 0 \quad or \quad x = 1$$
$$x + 4 = 0 \quad or \quad x = 0 \quad or \quad x - 1 = 0 \qquad \text{Getting 0's on one side}$$
$$(x + 4)x(x - 1) = 0 \qquad \text{Using the principle of zero products}$$
$$x(x^2 + 3x - 4) = 0 \qquad \text{Multiplying}$$
$$x^3 + 3x^2 - 4x = 0$$

TRY EXERCISE 29

To check any of these equations, we can simply substitute one or more of the given solutions. For example, in Example 2(d) above,
$$(-4)^3 + 3(-4)^2 - 4(-4) = -64 + 3 \cdot 16 + 16$$
$$= -64 + 48 + 16 = 0.$$

The other checks are left to the student.

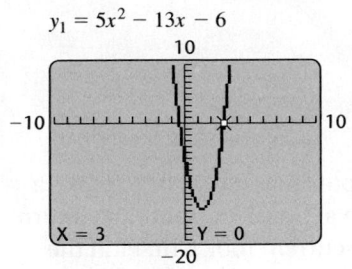

11.3 EXERCISE SET

 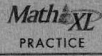

↪ *Concept Reinforcement Match the nature of the solution(s) with each discriminant. Answers may be used more than once.*

1. ____ $b^2 - 4ac = 9$
2. ____ $b^2 - 4ac = 0$
3. ____ $b^2 - 4ac = -1$
4. ____ $b^2 - 4ac = 1$
5. ____ $b^2 - 4ac = 8$
6. ____ $b^2 - 4ac = 12$

a) One rational solution
b) Two different rational solutions
c) Two different irrational solutions
d) Two different imaginary-number solutions

For each equation, determine what type of number the solutions are and how many solutions exist.

7. $x^2 - 7x + 5 = 0$
8. $x^2 - 5x + 3 = 0$
9. $x^2 + 11 = 0$
10. $x^2 + 7 = 0$
11. $x^2 - 11 = 0$
12. $x^2 - 7 = 0$
13. $4x^2 + 8x - 5 = 0$
14. $4x^2 - 12x + 9 = 0$
15. $x^2 + 4x + 6 = 0$
16. $x^2 - 2x + 4 = 0$
17. $9t^2 - 48t + 64 = 0$
18. $10t^2 - t - 2 = 0$
Aha! 19. $9t^2 + 3t = 0$
20. $4m^2 + 7m = 0$

21. $x^2 + 4x = 8$ **22.** $x^2 + 5x = 9$

23. $2a^2 - 3a = -5$ **24.** $3a^2 + 5 = -7a$

25. $7x^2 = 19x$ **26.** $5x^2 = 48x$

27. $y^2 + \frac{9}{4} = 4y$ **28.** $x^2 = \frac{1}{2}x - \frac{3}{5}$

Write a quadratic equation having the given numbers as solutions.

29. $-5, 4$

30. $-2, 8$

31. 3, only solution (*Hint*: It must be a repeated solution.)

32. -5, only solution

33. $-1, -3$

34. $-2, -5$

35. $5, \frac{3}{4}$

36. $4, \frac{2}{3}$

37. $-\frac{1}{4}, -\frac{1}{2}$

38. $\frac{1}{2}, \frac{1}{3}$

39. $2.4, -0.4$

40. $-0.6, 1.4$

41. $-\sqrt{3}, \sqrt{3}$

42. $-\sqrt{7}, \sqrt{7}$

43. $2\sqrt{5}, -2\sqrt{5}$

44. $3\sqrt{2}, -3\sqrt{2}$

45. $4i, -4i$

46. $3i, -3i$

47. $2 - 7i, 2 + 7i$

48. $5 - 2i, 5 + 2i$

49. $3 - \sqrt{14}, 3 + \sqrt{14}$

50. $2 - \sqrt{10}, 2 + \sqrt{10}$

51. $1 - \dfrac{\sqrt{21}}{3}, 1 + \dfrac{\sqrt{21}}{3}$

52. $\dfrac{5}{4} - \dfrac{\sqrt{33}}{4}, \dfrac{5}{4} + \dfrac{\sqrt{33}}{4}$

Write a third-degree equation having the given numbers as solutions.

53. $-2, 1, 5$ **54.** $-5, 0, 2$

55. $-1, 0, 3$ **56.** $-2, 2, 3$

57. Explain why there are not two different solutions when the discriminant is 0.

58. Describe a procedure that could be used to write an equation having the first 7 natural numbers as solutions.

Skill Review

To prepare for Section 11.4, review solving formulas and solving motion problems (Sections 6.7, 7.5, and 8.3).

Solve each formula for the specified variable. [7.5]

59. $\dfrac{c}{d} = c + d$, for c

60. $\dfrac{p}{q} = \dfrac{a + b}{b}$, for b

61. $x = \dfrac{3}{1 - y}$, for y

Solve.

62. *Boating.* Kiara's motorboat took 4 hr to make a trip downstream with a 2-mph current. The return trip against the same current took 6 hr. Find the speed of the boat in still water. [8.3]

63. *Walking.* Jamal walks 1.5 mph faster than Kade. In the time it takes Jamal to walk 7 mi, Kade walks 4 mi. Find the speed of each person. [6.7]

64. *Aviation.* Taryn's Cessna travels 120 mph in still air. She flies 140 mi into the wind and 140 mi with the wind in a total of 2.4 hr. Find the wind speed. [6.7]

Synthesis

65. If we assume that a quadratic equation has integers for coefficients, will the product of the solutions always be a real number? Why or why not?

66. Can a fourth-degree equation with rational coefficients have exactly three irrational solutions? Why or why not?

67. The graph of an equation of the form

$$y = ax^2 + bx + c$$

is a curve similar to the one shown below. Determine a, b, and c from the information given.

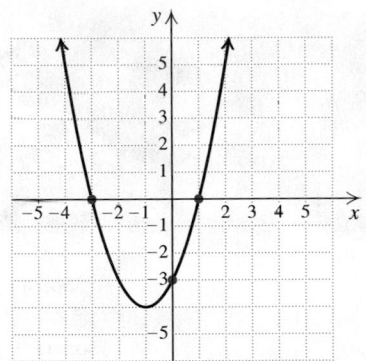

68. Show that the product of the solutions of $ax^2 + bx + c = 0$ is c/a.

For each equation under the given condition, (a) find k and (b) find the other solution.

69. $kx^2 - 2x + k = 0$; one solution is -3

70. $x^2 - kx + 2 = 0$; one solution is $1 + i$

71. $x^2 - (6 + 3i)x + k = 0$; one solution is 3

72. Show that the sum of the solutions of $ax^2 + bx + c = 0$ is $-b/a$.

73. Show that whenever there is just one solution of $ax^2 + bx + c = 0$, that solution is of the form $-b/(2a)$.

74. Find h and k, where $3x^2 - hx + 4k = 0$, the sum of the solutions is -12, and the product of the solutions is 20. (*Hint*: See Exercises 68 and 72.)

75. Suppose that $f(x) = ax^2 + bx + c$, with $f(-3) = 0$, $f\left(\frac{1}{2}\right) = 0$, and $f(0) = -12$. Find a, b, and c.

76. Find an equation for which $2 - \sqrt{3}$, $2 + \sqrt{3}$, $5 - 2i$, and $5 + 2i$ are solutions.

Aha! **77.** Write a quadratic equation with integer coefficients for which $-\sqrt{2}$ is one solution.

78. Write a quadratic equation with integer coefficients for which $10i$ is one solution.

79. Find an equation with integer coefficients for which $1 - \sqrt{5}$ and $3 + 2i$ are two of the solutions.

80. A discriminant that is a perfect square indicates that factoring can be used to solve the quadratic equation. Why?

81. While solving a quadratic equation of the form $ax^2 + bx + c = 0$ with a graphing calculator, Keisha gets the following screen. How could the sign of the discriminant help her check the graph?

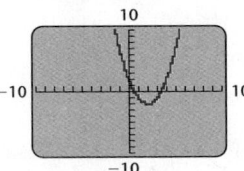

11.4   Applications Involving Quadratic Equations

Solving Problems   •   Solving Formulas

Solving Problems

As we found in Section 6.7, some problems translate to rational equations. The solution of such rational equations can involve quadratic equations.

EXAMPLE   1   *Motorcycle travel.*   Fiona rode her motorcycle 300 mi at a certain average speed. Had she traveled 10 mph faster, the trip would have taken 1 hr less. Find Fiona's average speed.

SOLUTION

1. **Familiarize.** We make a drawing, labeling it with the information provided. As in Section 6.7, we can create a table. We let r represent the rate, in miles per hour, and t the time, in hours, for Fiona's trip.

Time t 300 miles   Speed r

Time $t - 1$ 300 miles   Speed $r + 10$

Distance	Speed	Time
300	r	t	$\longrightarrow r = \dfrac{300}{t}$
300	$r + 10$	$t - 1$	$\longrightarrow r + 10 = \dfrac{300}{t - 1}$

Recall that the definition of speed, $r = d/t$, relates the three quantities.

2. **Translate.** From the table, we obtain

$$r = \frac{300}{t} \quad \text{and} \quad r + 10 = \frac{300}{t - 1}.$$

3. **Carry out.** A system of equations has been formed. We substitute for r from the first equation into the second and solve the resulting equation:

$$\frac{300}{t} + 10 = \frac{300}{t - 1}$$
Substituting $300/t$ for r

$$t(t - 1) \cdot \left[\frac{300}{t} + 10\right] = t(t - 1) \cdot \frac{300}{t - 1}$$
Multiplying by the LCD to clear fractions

$$t(t - 1) \cdot \frac{300}{t} + t(t - 1) \cdot 10 = t(t - 1) \cdot \frac{300}{t - 1}$$
Using the distributive law

$$\frac{\cancel{t}(t - 1)}{1} \cdot \frac{300}{\cancel{t}} + t(t - 1) \cdot 10 = \frac{t\cancel{(t - 1)}}{1} \cdot \frac{300}{\cancel{t - 1}}$$
Removing factors that equal 1: $t/t = 1$ and $(t - 1)/(t$

$$\left.\begin{aligned} 300(t - 1) + 10(t^2 - t) &= 300t \\ 300t - 300 + 10t^2 - 10t &= 300t \\ 10t^2 - 10t - 300 &= 0 \end{aligned}\right\}$$
Rewriting in standard form

$$t^2 - t - 30 = 0$$
Multiplying by $\frac{1}{10}$ or dividing by 10

$$(t - 6)(t + 5) = 0$$
Factoring

$$t = 6 \quad \text{or} \quad t = -5.$$
Principle of zero products

4. **Check.** Note that we have solved for t, not r as required. Since negative time has no meaning here, we disregard the -5 and use 6 hr to find r :

$$r = \frac{300 \text{ mi}}{6 \text{ hr}} = 50 \text{ mph}.$$

> **CAUTION!** Always make sure that you find the quantity asked for in the problem.

To see if 50 mph checks, we increase the speed 10 mph to 60 mph and see how long the trip would have taken at that speed:

$$t = \frac{d}{r} = \frac{300 \text{ mi}}{60 \text{ mph}} = 5 \text{ hr}.$$ Note that mi/mph = mi $\div \dfrac{\text{mi}}{\text{hr}} =$

$$\cancel{\text{mi}} \cdot \frac{\text{hr}}{\cancel{\text{mi}}} = \text{hr}.$$

This is 1 hr less than the trip actually took, so the answer checks.

5. **State.** Fiona traveled at an average speed of 50 mph.   > TRY EXERCISE 1

Solving Formulas

Recall that to solve a formula for a certain letter, we use the principles for solving equations to get that letter alone on one side.

> EXAMPLE 2

Period of a pendulum.   The time T required for a pendulum of length l to swing back and forth (complete one period) is given by the formula $T = 2\pi\sqrt{l/g}$, where g is the earth's gravitational constant. Solve for l.

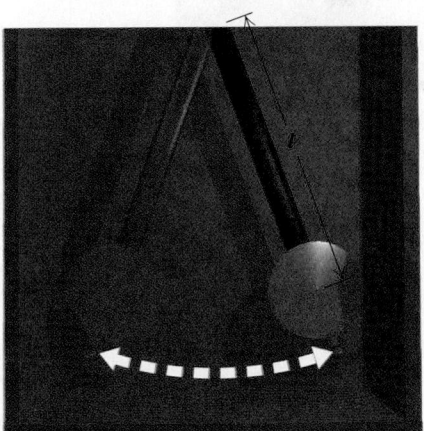

SOLUTION   We have

$$T = 2\pi\sqrt{\frac{l}{g}}$$ This is a radical equation (see Section 10.6).

$$T^2 = \left(2\pi\sqrt{\frac{l}{g}}\right)^2$$ Squaring both sides

$$T^2 = 2^2\pi^2\frac{l}{g}$$

$$gT^2 = 4\pi^2 l$$ Multiplying both sides by g to clear fractions

$$\frac{gT^2}{4\pi^2} = l.$$ Dividing both sides by $4\pi^2$

We now have l alone on one side and l does not appear on the other side, so the formula is solved for l.   > TRY EXERCISE 21

In formulas for which variables represent only nonnegative numbers, there is no need for absolute-value signs when taking square roots.

EXAMPLE 3

Hang time.* An athlete's *hang time* is the amount of time that the athlete can remain airborne when jumping. A formula relating an athlete's vertical leap V, in inches, to hang tIme T, in seconds, is $V = 48T^2$. Solve for T.

SOLUTION We have

$$48T^2 = V$$

$$T^2 = \frac{V}{48} \qquad \text{Dividing by 48 to isolate } T^2$$

$$T = \frac{\sqrt{V}}{\sqrt{48}} \qquad \begin{array}{l}\text{Using the principle of square roots}\\ \text{and the quotient rule for radicals.}\\ \text{We assume } V, T \geq 0.\end{array}$$

$$= \frac{\sqrt{V}}{\sqrt{16}\sqrt{3}}$$

$$= \frac{\sqrt{V}}{4\sqrt{3}}$$

$$\left.\begin{array}{l} = \dfrac{\sqrt{V}}{4\sqrt{3}} \cdot \dfrac{\sqrt{3}}{\sqrt{3}} \\[2ex] = \dfrac{\sqrt{3V}}{12}. \end{array}\right\} \quad \text{Rationalizing the denominator}$$

TRY EXERCISE 15

EXAMPLE 4

Falling distance. An object tossed downward with an initial speed (velocity) of v_0 will travel a distance of s meters, where $s = 4.9t^2 + v_0 t$ and t is measured in seconds. Solve for t.

SOLUTION Since t is squared in one term and raised to the first power in the other term, the equation is quadratic in t.

$$4.9t^2 + v_0 t = s$$

$$4.9t^2 + v_0 t - s = 0 \qquad \text{Writing standard form}$$

$$a = 4.9, \quad b = v_0, \quad c = -s$$

$$t = \frac{-v_0 \pm \sqrt{(v_0)^2 - 4(4.9)(-s)}}{2(4.9)} \qquad \text{Using the quadratic formula}$$

Since the negative square root would yield a negative value for t, we use only the positive root:

$$t = \frac{-v_0 + \sqrt{(v_0)^2 + 19.6s}}{9.8}.$$

TRY EXERCISE 25

STUDENT NOTES ———

After identifying which numbers to use as a, b, and c, be careful to replace only the *letters* in the quadratic formula.

---

*This formula is taken from an article by Peter Brancazio, "The Mechanics of a Slam Dunk," *Popular Mechanics,* November 1991. Courtesy of Professor Peter Brancazio, Brooklyn College.

The following list of steps should help you when solving formulas for a given letter. Try to remember that when solving a formula, you use the same approach that you would to solve an equation.

To Solve a Formula for a Letter—Say, *h*

1. Clear fractions and use the principle of powers, as needed. Perform these steps until radicals containing *h* are gone and *h* is not in any denominator.
2. Combine all like terms.
3. If the only power of *h* is h^1, the equation can be solved as in Sections 2.3 and 7.5. (See Example 2.)
4. If h^2 appears but *h* does not, solve for h^2 and use the principle of square roots to solve for *h*. (See Example 3.)
5. If there are terms containing both *h* and h^2, put the equation in standard form and use the quadratic formula. (See Example 4.)

11.4   EXERCISE SET

 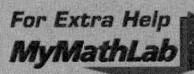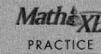

Solve.

1. *Car trips.* During the first part of a trip, Tara's Honda traveled 120 mi at a certain speed. Tara then drove another 100 mi at a speed that was 10 mph slower. If the total time of Tara's trip was 4 hr, what was her speed on each part of the trip?

2. *Canoeing.* During the first part of a canoe trip, Ken covered 60 km at a certain speed. He then traveled 24 km at a speed that was 4 km/h slower. If the total time for the trip was 8 hr, what was the speed on each part of the trip?

3. *Car trips.* Diane's Dodge travels 200 mi averaging a certain speed. If the car had gone 10 mph faster, the trip would have taken 1 hr less. Find Diane's average speed.

4. *Car trips.* Stuart's Subaru travels 280 mi averaging a certain speed. If the car had gone 5 mph faster, the trip would have taken 1 hr less. Find Stuart's average speed.

5. *Air travel.* A Cessna flies 600 mi at a certain speed. A Beechcraft flies 1000 mi at a speed that is 50 mph faster, but takes 1 hr longer. Find the speed of each plane.

6. *Air travel.* A turbo-jet flies 50 mph faster than a super-prop plane. If a turbo-jet goes 2000 mi in 3 hr less time than it takes the super-prop to go 2800 mi, find the speed of each plane.

7. *Bicycling.* Naoki bikes the 36 mi to Hillsboro averaging a certain speed. The return trip is made at a speed 3 mph slower. Total time for the round trip is 7 hr. Find Naoki's average speed on each part of the trip.

8. *Car speed.* On a sales trip, Mark drives the 600 mi to Richmond averaging a certain speed. The return trip is made at an average speed that is 10 mph slower. Total time for the round trip is 22 hr. Find Mark's average speed on each part of the trip.

9. *Navigation.* The Hudson River flows at a rate of 3 mph. A patrol boat travels 60 mi upriver and returns in a total time of 9 hr. What is the speed of the boat in still water?

■ **10.** *Navigation.* The current in a typical Mississippi River shipping route flows at a rate of 4 mph. In order for a barge to travel 24 mi upriver and then return in a total of 5 hr, approximately how fast must the barge be able to travel in still water?

11. *Filling a pool.* A well and a spring are filling a swimming pool. Together, they can fill the pool in 3 hr. The well, working alone, can fill the pool in 8 hr less time than the spring. How long would the spring take, working alone, to fill the pool?

12. *Filling a tank.* Two pipes are connected to the same tank. Working together, they can fill the tank in 4 hr. The larger pipe, working alone, can fill the tank in 6 hr less time than the smaller one. How long would the smaller one take, working alone, to fill the tank?

■ **13.** *Paddleboats.* Kofi paddles 1 mi upstream and 1 mi back in a total time of 1 hr. The speed of the river is 2 mph. Find the speed of Kofi's paddleboat in still water.

■ **14.** *Rowing.* Abby rows 10 km upstream and 10 km back in a total time of 3 hr. The speed of the river is 5 km/h. Find Abby's speed in still water.

Solve each formula for the indicated letter. Assume that all variables represent nonnegative numbers.

15. $A = 4\pi r^2$, for r
(Surface area of a sphere of radius r)

16. $A = 6s^2$, for s
(Surface area of a cube with sides of length s)

17. $A = 2\pi r^2 + 2\pi rh$, for r
(Surface area of a right cylindrical solid with radius r and height h)

18. $N = \dfrac{k^2 - 3k}{2}$, for k
(Number of diagonals of a polygon with k sides)

19. $F = \dfrac{Gm_1 m_2}{r^2}$, for r
(Law of gravity)

20. $N = \dfrac{kQ_1 Q_2}{s^2}$, for s
(Number of phone calls between two cities)

21. $c = \sqrt{gH}$, for H
(Velocity of ocean wave)

22. $V = 3.5\sqrt{h}$, for h
(Distance to horizon from a height)

23. $a^2 + b^2 = c^2$, for b
(Pythagorean formula in two dimensions)

24. $a^2 + b^2 + c^2 = d^2$, for c
(Pythagorean formula in three dimensions)

25. $s = v_0 t + \dfrac{gt^2}{2}$, for t
(A motion formula)

26. $A = \pi r^2 + \pi rs$, for r
(Surface area of a cone)

27. $N = \frac{1}{2}(n^2 - n)$, for n
(Number of games if n teams play each other once)

28. $A = A_0(1 - r)^2$, for r
(A business formula)

29. $T = 2\pi\sqrt{\dfrac{l}{g}}$, for g
(A pendulum formula)

30. $W = \sqrt{\dfrac{1}{LC}}$, for L
(An electricity formula)

Aha! **31.** $at^2 + bt + c = 0$, for t
(An algebraic formula)

32. $A = P_1(1 + r)^2 + P_2(1 + r)$, for r
(Amount in an account when P_1 is invested for 2 yr and P_2 for 1 yr at interest rate r)

Solve.

33. *Falling distance.* (Use $4.9t^2 + v_0 t = s$.)
   a) A bolt falls off an airplane at an altitude of 500 m. Approximately how long does it take the bolt to reach the ground?
   b) A ball is thrown downward at a speed of 30 m/sec from an altitude of 500 m. Approximately how long does it take the ball to reach the ground?
   c) Approximately how far will an object fall in 5 sec, when thrown downward at an initial velocity of 30 m/sec from a plane?

34. *Falling distance.* (Use $4.9t^2 + v_0 t = s$.)
   a) A ring is dropped from a helicopter at an altitude of 75 m. Approximately how long does it take the ring to reach the ground?
   b) A coin is tossed downward with an initial velocity of 30 m/sec from an altitude of 75 m. Approximately how long does it take the coin to reach the ground?
   c) Approximately how far will an object fall in 2 sec, if thrown downward at an initial velocity of 20 m/sec from a helicopter?

35. *Bungee jumping.* Chad is tied to one end of a 40-m elasticized (bungee) cord. The other end of the cord is tied to the middle of a bridge. If Chad jumps off the bridge, for how long will he fall before the cord begins to stretch? (Use $4.9t^2 = s$.)

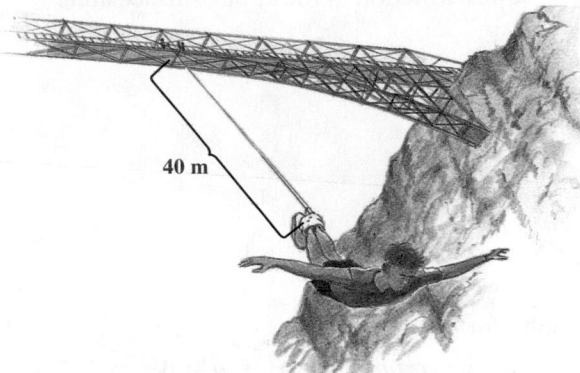

40 m

36. *Bungee jumping.* Chika is tied to a bungee cord (see Exercise 35) and falls for 2.5 sec before her cord begins to stretch. How long is the bungee cord?

37. *Hang time.* The NBA's Dwight Howard has a vertical leap of 38 in. What is his hang time? (Use $V = 48T^2$.)
Source: www.dwighthoward.com

38. *League schedules.* In a bowling league, each team plays each of the other teams once. If a total of 66 games is played, how many teams are in the league? (See Exercise 27.)

For Exercises 39 and 40, use $4.9t^2 + v_0t = s$.

39. *Downward speed.* A stone thrown downward from a 100-m cliff travels 51.6 m in 3 sec. What was the initial velocity of the object?

40. *Downward speed.* A pebble thrown downward from a 200-m cliff travels 91.2 m in 4 sec. What was the initial velocity of the object?

For Exercises 41 and 42, use $A = P_1(1 + r)^2 + P_2(1 + r)$. (See Exercise 32.)

41. *Compound interest.* A firm invests $3200 in a savings account for 2 yr. At the beginning of the second

year, an additional $1800 is invested. If a total of $5375.48 is in the account at the end of the second year, what is the annual interest rate?

42. *Compound interest.* A business invests $10,000 in a savings account for 2 yr. At the beginning of the second year, an additional $3500 is invested. If a total of $14,822.75 is in the account at the end of the second year, what is the annual interest rate?

43. Marti is tied to a bungee cord that is twice as long as the cord tied to Rafe's. Will Marti's fall take twice as long as Rafe's before their cords begin to stretch? Why or why not? (See Exercises 35 and 36.)

44. Under what circumstances would a negative value for t, time, have meaning?

Skill Review

To prepare for Section 11.5, review raising a power to a power and solving rational equations and radical equations (Sections 4.1, 6.6, and 10.6).

Simplify.

45. $(m^{-1})^2$ [4.2]

46. $(t^{1/3})^2$ [10.2]

47. $(y^{1/6})^2$ [10.2]

48. $(z^{1/4})^2$ [10.2]

Solve.

49. $t^{-1} = \dfrac{1}{2}$ [6.6], [10.6]

50. $x^{1/4} = 3$ [10.6]

Synthesis

51. Write a problem for a classmate to solve. Devise the problem so that (a) the solution is found after solving a rational equation and (b) the solution is "The express train travels 90 mph."

52. In what ways do the motion problems of this section (like Example 1) differ from the motion problems in Section 6.7?

53. *Biochemistry.* The equation

$$A = 6.5 - \frac{20.4t}{t^2 + 36}$$

is used to calculate the acid level A in a person's blood t minutes after sugar is consumed. Solve for t.

54. *Special relativity.* Einstein found that an object with initial mass m_0 and traveling velocity v has mass

$$m = \frac{m_0}{\sqrt{1 - \dfrac{v^2}{c^2}}},$$

where c is the speed of light. Solve the formula for c.

55. Find a number for which the reciprocal of 1 less than the number is the same as 1 more than the number.

56. *Purchasing.* A discount store bought a quantity of potted plants for $250 and sold all but 15 at a profit of $3.50 per plant. With the total amount received, the manager could buy 4 more than twice as many as were bought before. Find the cost per plant.

57. *Art and aesthetics.* For over 2000 yr, artists, sculptors, and architects have regarded the proportions of a "golden" rectangle as visually appealing. A rectangle of width w and length l is considered "golden" if

$$\frac{w}{l} = \frac{l}{w + l}.$$

Solve for l.

58. *Diagonal of a cube.* Find a formula that expresses the length of the three-dimensional diagonal of a cube as a function of the cube's surface area.

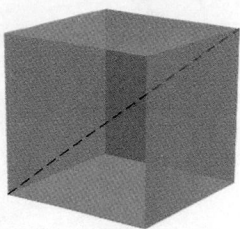

59. Solve for n:
$$mn^4 - r^2pm^3 - r^2n^2 + p = 0.$$

60. *Surface area.* Find a formula that expresses the diameter of a right cylindrical solid as a function of its surface area and its height. (See Exercise 17.)

61. A sphere is inscribed in a cube as shown in the figure below. Express the surface area of the sphere as a function of the surface area S of the cube. (See Exercise 15.)

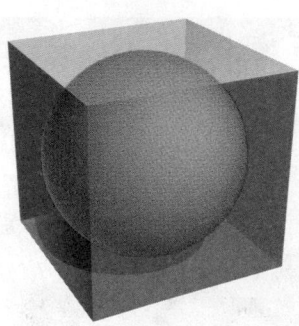

11.5 Equations Reducible to Quadratic

Recognizing Equations in Quadratic Form ▪ Radical Equations and Rational Equations

Recognizing Equations in Quadratic Form

Certain equations that are not really quadratic can be thought of in such a way that they can be solved as quadratic. For example, because the square of x^2 is x^4, the equation $x^4 - 9x^2 + 8 = 0$ is said to be "quadratic in x^2":

$$x^4 - 9x^2 + 8 = 0$$
$$\downarrow \quad\quad \downarrow \quad\quad \downarrow \quad \downarrow$$
$$(x^2)^2 - 9(x^2) + 8 = 0 \quad \text{Thinking of } x^4 \text{ as } (x^2)^2$$
$$\downarrow \quad\quad \downarrow \quad\quad \downarrow \quad \downarrow$$
$$u^2 - 9u + 8 = 0. \quad \text{To make this clearer, write } u \text{ instead of } x^2.$$

The equation $u^2 - 9u + 8 = 0$ can be solved for u by factoring or by the quadratic formula. Then, remembering that $u = x^2$, we can solve for x. Equations that can be solved like this are *reducible to quadratic* and are said to be *in quadratic form.*

EXAMPLE   **1**

Solve: $x^4 - 9x^2 + 8 = 0$.

SOLUTION   We begin by letting $u = x^2$ and finding u^2:

$$u = x^2$$
$$u^2 = (x^2)^2 = x^4.$$

Then we solve by substituting u^2 for x^4 and u for x^2:

$$u^2 - 9u + 8 = 0$$
$$(u - 8)(u - 1) = 0 \qquad \text{Factoring}$$
$$u - 8 = 0 \quad or \quad u - 1 = 0 \qquad \text{Principle of zero products}$$
$$u = 8 \quad or \qquad u = 1.$$

STUDENT NOTES

To identify an equation in quadratic form, look for two variable expressions in the equation. The exponent in one expression is twice the exponent in the other expression.

We replace u with x^2 and solve these equations:

$$x^2 = 8 \qquad or \quad x^2 = 1$$
$$x = \pm\sqrt{8} \quad or \quad x = \pm 1 \qquad \boxed{\text{We are solving for } x.}$$
$$x = \pm 2\sqrt{2} \quad or \quad x = \pm 1.$$

To check, note that for both $x = 2\sqrt{2}$ and $-2\sqrt{2}$, we have $x^2 = 8$ and $x^4 = 64$. Similarly, for both $x = 1$ and -1, we have $x^2 = 1$ and $x^4 = 1$. Thus instead of making four checks, we need make only two.

Check: For $\pm 2\sqrt{2}$:

$$\begin{array}{c|c} x^4 - 9x^2 + 8 = 0 & \\ \hline (\pm 2\sqrt{2})^4 - 9(\pm 2\sqrt{2})^2 + 8 & 0 \\ 64 - 9 \cdot 8 + 8 & \\ & 0 \overset{?}{=} 0 \quad \text{TRUE} \end{array}$$

For ± 1:

$$\begin{array}{c|c} x^4 - 9x^2 + 8 = 0 & \\ \hline (\pm 1)^4 - 9(\pm 1)^2 + 8 & 0 \\ 1 - 9 + 8 & \\ & 0 \overset{?}{=} 0 \quad \text{TRUE} \end{array}$$

The solutions are $1, -1, 2\sqrt{2}$, and $-2\sqrt{2}$.

TRY EXERCISE   17

CAUTION!   A common error when working on problems like Example 1 is to solve for u but forget to solve for x. Remember to solve for the *original* variable!

Equations like those in Example 1 can be solved directly by factoring:

$$x^4 - 9x^2 + 8 = 0$$
$$(x^2 - 1)(x^2 - 8) = 0$$
$$x^2 - 1 = 0 \quad or \quad x^2 - 8 = 0$$
$$x^2 = 1 \quad or \qquad x^2 = 8$$
$$x = \pm 1 \quad or \qquad x = \pm 2\sqrt{2}.$$

However, it often becomes difficult to solve the equation without first making a substitution.

To recognize an equation in quadratic form, inspect all the variable expressions in the equation. For an equation to be written in the form $au^2 + bu + c = 0$, it is necessary to identify one variable expression as u and a second variable expression as u^2.

EXAMPLE 2   Find the x-intercepts of the graph of $f(x) = (x^2 - 1)^2 - (x^2 - 1) - 2$.

SOLUTION   The x-intercepts occur where $f(x) = 0$ so we must have

$$(x^2 - 1)^2 - (x^2 - 1) - 2 = 0. \quad \text{Setting } f(x) \text{ equal to 0}$$

If we identify $x^2 - 1$ as u, the equation can be written in quadratic form:

$$u = x^2 - 1$$
$$u^2 = (x^2 - 1)^2.$$

Substituting, we have

$$u^2 - u - 2 = 0 \qquad \text{Substituting in}$$
$$\qquad\qquad\qquad\qquad (x^2 - 1)^2 - (x^2 - 1) - 2 = 0$$
$$(u - 2)(u + 1) = 0$$
$$u = 2 \quad or \quad u = -1. \quad \text{Using the principle of}$$
$$\qquad\qquad\qquad\qquad\qquad \text{zero products}$$

Next, we replace u with $x^2 - 1$ and solve these equations:

$$x^2 - 1 = 2 \qquad or \quad x^2 - 1 = -1$$
$$x^2 = 3 \qquad or \qquad x^2 = 0 \qquad \text{Adding 1 to both sides}$$
$$x = \pm\sqrt{3} \quad or \qquad x = 0. \qquad \text{Using the principle of}$$
$$\qquad\qquad\qquad\qquad\qquad\qquad \text{square roots}$$

The x-intercepts occur at $(-\sqrt{3}, 0)$, $(0, 0)$, and $(\sqrt{3}, 0)$.   ▶ TRY EXERCISE ▶ 49

Radical Equations and Rational Equations

Sometimes rational equations, radical equations, or equations containing exponents that are fractions are reducible to quadratic. It is especially important that answers to these equations be checked in the original equation.

EXAMPLE 3   Solve: $x - 3\sqrt{x} - 4 = 0$.

SOLUTION   This radical equation could be solved using the method discussed in Section 10.6. However, if we note that the square of $\sqrt{x}$ is x, we can regard the equation as "quadratic in $\sqrt{x}$."
We determine u and u^2:

$$u = \sqrt{x}$$
$$u^2 = x.$$

Substituting, we have

$$x - 3\sqrt{x} - 4 = 0$$
$$u^2 - 3u - 4 = 0$$
$$(u - 4)(u + 1) = 0$$
$$u = 4 \quad or \quad u = -1. \quad \text{Using the principle of}$$
$$\qquad\qquad\qquad\qquad\qquad \text{zero products}$$

Next, we replace u with $\sqrt{x}$ and solve these equations:

$$\sqrt{x} = 4 \quad or \quad \sqrt{x} = -1.$$

Squaring gives us $x = 16$ or $x = 1$ and also makes checking essential.

Check: For 16:

$$
\begin{array}{c|c}
x - 3\sqrt{x} - 4 = 0 & \\
\hline
16 - 3\sqrt{16} - 4 & 0 \\
16 - 3 \cdot 4 - 4 & \\
& 0 \overset{?}{=} 0 \quad \text{TRUE}
\end{array}
$$

For 1:

$$
\begin{array}{c|c}
x - 3\sqrt{x} - 4 = 0 & \\
\hline
1 - 3\sqrt{1} - 4 & 0 \\
1 - 3 \cdot 1 - 4 & \\
& -6 \overset{?}{=} 0 \quad \text{FALSE}
\end{array}
$$

The number 16 checks, but 1 does not. Had we noticed that $\sqrt{x} = -1$ has no solution (since principal square roots are never negative), we could have solved only the equation $\sqrt{x} = 4$. The solution is 16.   **TRY EXERCISE** 21

The following tips may prove useful.

To Solve an Equation That Is Reducible to Quadratic

1. Look for two variable expressions in the equation. One expression should be the square of the other.
2. Write down any substitutions that you are making.
3. Remember to solve for the variable that is used in the original equation.
4. Check possible answers in the original equation.

EXAMPLE 4   Solve: $2m^{-2} + m^{-1} - 15 = 0$.

SOLUTION   Note that the square of m^{-1} is $(m^{-1})^2$, or m^{-2}. We let $u = m^{-1}$:

Determine u and u^2.

$$u = m^{-1}$$
$$u^2 = m^{-2}.$$

Substituting, we have

Substitute.

$$2u^2 + u - 15 = 0 \qquad \text{Substituting in } 2m^{-2} + m^{-1} - 15 = 0$$

$$(2u - 5)(u + 3) = 0$$

$$2u - 5 = 0 \quad or \quad u + 3 = 0 \qquad \text{Using the principle of zero products}$$

$$2u = 5 \quad or \qquad u = -3$$

Solve for u.

$$u = \frac{5}{2} \quad or \qquad u = -3.$$

Now we replace u with m^{-1} and solve:

$$m^{-1} = \frac{5}{2} \qquad or \quad m^{-1} = -3$$

$$\frac{1}{m} = \frac{5}{2} \qquad or \quad \frac{1}{m} = -3 \qquad \text{Recall that } m^{-1} = \frac{1}{m}.$$

$$1 = \frac{5}{2}m \quad or \qquad 1 = -3m \qquad \text{Multiplying both sides by } m$$

Solve for the original variable.

$$\frac{2}{5} = m \quad or \qquad -\frac{1}{3} = m. \qquad \text{Solving for } m$$

Check.

Check:

For $\frac{2}{5}$:

$$\frac{2m^{-2} + m^{-1} - 15 = 0}{}$$

$2\left(\frac{2}{5}\right)^{-2} + \left(\frac{2}{5}\right)^{-1} - 15$	0
$2\left(\frac{5}{2}\right)^2 + \left(\frac{5}{2}\right) - 15$	
$2\left(\frac{25}{4}\right) + \frac{5}{2} - 15$	
$\frac{25}{2} + \frac{5}{2} - 15$	
$\frac{30}{2} - 15$	

$$0 \overset{?}{=} 0 \quad \text{TRUE}$$

For $-\frac{1}{3}$:

$$\frac{2m^{-2} + m^{-1} - 15 = 0}{}$$

$2\left(-\frac{1}{3}\right)^{-2} + \left(-\frac{1}{3}\right)^{-1} - 15$	0
$2\left(-\frac{3}{1}\right)^2 + \left(-\frac{3}{1}\right) - 15$	
$2(9) + (-3) - 15$	
$18 - 3 - 15$	

$$0 \overset{?}{=} 0 \quad \text{TRUE}$$

Both numbers check. The solutions are $-\frac{1}{3}$ and $\frac{2}{5}$.

TRY EXERCISE 29

Note that Example 4 can also be written

$$\frac{2}{m^2} + \frac{1}{m} - 15 = 0.$$

It can then be solved by letting $u = 1/m$ and $u^2 = 1/m^2$ or by clearing fractions as in Section 6.6.

EXAMPLE 5

Solve: $t^{2/5} - t^{1/5} - 2 = 0$.

SOLUTION Note that the square of $t^{1/5}$ is $(t^{1/5})^2$, or $t^{2/5}$. The equation is therefore quadratic in $t^{1/5}$, so we let $u = t^{1/5}$:

$$u = t^{1/5}$$
$$u^2 = t^{2/5}.$$

Substituting, we have

$$u^2 - u - 2 = 0 \qquad \text{Substituting in } t^{2/5} - t^{1/5} - 2 = 0$$
$$(u - 2)(u + 1) = 0$$
$$u = 2 \quad or \quad u = -1. \qquad \text{Using the principle of zero products}$$

Now we replace u with $t^{1/5}$ and solve:

$$t^{1/5} = 2 \quad or \quad t^{1/5} = -1$$
$$t = 32 \quad or \qquad t = -1. \qquad \text{Principle of powers; raising both sides to the 5th power}$$

Check:

For 32:

$$\frac{t^{2/5} - t^{1/5} - 2 = 0}{}$$

$32^{2/5} - 32^{1/5} - 2$	0
$(32^{1/5})^2 - 32^{1/5} - 2$	
$2^2 - 2 - 2$	

$$0 \overset{?}{=} 0 \quad \text{TRUE}$$

For -1:

$$\frac{t^{2/5} - t^{1/5} - 2 = 0}{}$$

$(-1)^{2/5} - (-1)^{1/5} - 2$	0
$[(-1)^{1/5}]^2 - (-1)^{1/5} - 2$	
$(-1)^2 - (-1) - 2$	

$$0 \overset{?}{=} 0 \quad \text{TRUE}$$

Both numbers check. The solutions are 32 and -1.

TRY EXERCISE 33

EXAMPLE 6   Solve: $(5 + \sqrt{r})^2 + 6(5 + \sqrt{r}) + 2 = 0$.

SOLUTION   We determine u and u^2:

$$u = 5 + \sqrt{r}$$
$$u^2 = (5 + \sqrt{r})^2.$$

Substituting, we have

$$u^2 + 6u + 2 = 0$$

$$u = \frac{-6 \pm \sqrt{6^2 - 4 \cdot 1 \cdot 2}}{2 \cdot 1} \qquad \text{Using the quadratic formula}$$

$$= \frac{-6 \pm \sqrt{28}}{2}$$

$$\left.\begin{array}{l} = \dfrac{-6}{2} \pm \dfrac{2\sqrt{7}}{2} \\[2mm] = -3 \pm \sqrt{7}. \end{array}\right\} \quad \text{Simplifying; } \sqrt{28} = \sqrt{4}\sqrt{7}$$

Now we replace u with $5 + \sqrt{r}$ and solve for r:

$$\begin{array}{lll} 5 + \sqrt{r} = -3 + \sqrt{7} & \text{or} \quad 5 + \sqrt{r} = -3 - \sqrt{7} & u = -3 + \sqrt{7} \\ \sqrt{r} = -8 + \sqrt{7} & \text{or} \qquad \sqrt{r} = -8 - \sqrt{7}. & \text{or } u = -3 - \sqrt{7} \end{array}$$

We could now solve for r and check possible solutions, but first let's examine $-8 + \sqrt{7}$ and $-8 - \sqrt{7}$. Since $\sqrt{7} \approx 2.6$, both $-8 + \sqrt{7}$ and $-8 - \sqrt{7}$ are negative. Since the principal square root of r is never negative, both values of $\sqrt{r}$ must be rejected. Note too that in the original equation, $(5 + \sqrt{r})^2$, $6(5 + \sqrt{r})$, and 2 are all positive. Thus it is impossible for their sum to be 0.

The original equation has no solution.

TRY EXERCISE 25

11.5 EXERCISE SET

For Extra Help
MyMathLab   Math XL PRACTICE   WATCH   DOWNLOAD

🔖 ***Concept Reinforcement***   *In each of Exercises 1–8, match the equation with a substitution from the column on the right that could be used to reduce the equation to quadratic form.*

1. ____ $4x^6 - 2x^3 + 1 = 0$
2. ____ $3x^4 + 4x^2 - 7 = 0$
3. ____ $5x^8 + 2x^4 - 3 = 0$
4. ____ $2x^{2/3} - 5x^{1/3} + 4 = 0$
5. ____ $3x^{4/3} + 4x^{2/3} - 7 = 0$
6. ____ $2x^{-2/3} + x^{-1/3} + 6 = 0$
7. ____ $4x^{-4/3} - 2x^{-2/3} + 3 = 0$
8. ____ $3x^{-4} + 4x^{-2} - 2 = 0$

a) $u = x^{-1/3}$
b) $u = x^{1/3}$
c) $u = x^{-2}$
d) $u = x^2$
e) $u = x^{-2/3}$
f) $u = x^3$
g) $u = x^{2/3}$
h) $u = x^4$

Write the substitution that could be used to make each equation quadratic in u.

9. For $3p - 4\sqrt{p} + 6 = 0$, use $u = $ _____.

10. For $x^{1/2} - x^{1/4} - 2 = 0$, use $u = $ _____.

11. For $(x^2 + 3)^2 + (x^2 + 3) - 7 = 0$, use $u = $ _____.

12. For $t^{-6} + 5t^{-3} - 6 = 0$, use $u = $ _____.

13. For $(1 + t)^4 + (1 + t)^2 + 4 = 0$, use $u = $ _____.

14. For $w^{1/3} - 3w^{1/6} + 8 = 0$, use $w = $ _____.

Solve.

15. $x^4 - 13x^2 + 36 = 0$

16. $x^4 - 17x^2 + 16 = 0$

17. $t^4 - 7t^2 + 12 = 0$

18. $t^4 - 11t^2 + 18 = 0$

19. $4x^4 - 9x^2 + 5 = 0$

20. $9x^4 - 38x^2 + 8 = 0$

21. $w + 4\sqrt{w} - 12 = 0$

22. $s + 3\sqrt{s} - 40 = 0$

23. $(x^2 - 7)^2 - 3(x^2 - 7) + 2 = 0$

24. $(x^2 - 2)^2 - 12(x^2 - 2) + 20 = 0$

25. $r - 2\sqrt{r} - 6 = 0$

26. $s - 4\sqrt{s} - 1 = 0$

27. $(1 + \sqrt{x})^2 + 5(1 + \sqrt{x}) + 6 = 0$

28. $(3 + \sqrt{x})^2 + 3(3 + \sqrt{x}) - 10 = 0$

29. $x^{-2} - x^{-1} - 6 = 0$

30. $2x^{-2} - x^{-1} - 1 = 0$

31. $4t^{-2} - 3t^{-1} - 1 = 0$

32. $2m^{-2} + 7m^{-1} - 15 = 0$

33. $t^{2/3} + t^{1/3} - 6 = 0$

34. $w^{2/3} - 2w^{1/3} - 8 = 0$

35. $y^{1/3} - y^{1/6} - 6 = 0$

36. $t^{1/2} + 3t^{1/4} + 2 = 0$

37. $t^{1/3} + 2t^{1/6} = 3$

38. $m^{1/2} + 6 = 5m^{1/4}$

39. $(3 - \sqrt{x})^2 - 10(3 - \sqrt{x}) + 23 = 0$

40. $(5 + \sqrt{x})^2 - 12(5 + \sqrt{x}) + 33 = 0$

41. $16\left(\dfrac{x-1}{x-8}\right)^2 + 8\left(\dfrac{x-1}{x-8}\right) + 1 = 0$

42. $9\left(\dfrac{x+2}{x+3}\right)^2 - 6\left(\dfrac{x+2}{x+3}\right) + 1 = 0$

43. $x^4 + 5x^2 - 36 = 0$

44. $x^4 + 5x^2 + 4 = 0$

45. $(n^2 + 6)^2 - 7(n^2 + 6) + 10 = 0$

46. $(m^2 + 7)^2 - 6(m^2 + 7) - 16 = 0$

Find all x-intercepts of the given function f. If none exists, state this.

47. $f(x) = 5x + 13\sqrt{x} - 6$

48. $f(x) = 3x + 10\sqrt{x} - 8$

49. $f(x) = (x^2 - 3x)^2 - 10(x^2 - 3x) + 24$

50. $f(x) = (x^2 - 6x)^2 - 2(x^2 - 6x) - 35$

51. $f(x) = x^{2/5} + x^{1/5} - 6$

52. $f(x) = x^{1/2} - x^{1/4} - 6$

Aha! **53.** $f(x) = \left(\dfrac{x^2 + 2}{x}\right)^4 + 7\left(\dfrac{x^2 + 2}{x}\right)^2 + 5$

54. $f(x) = \left(\dfrac{x^2 + 1}{x}\right)^4 + 4\left(\dfrac{x^2 + 1}{x}\right)^2 + 12$

55. To solve $25x^6 - 10x^3 + 1 = 0$, Jose lets $u = 5x^3$ and Robin lets $u = x^3$. Can they both be correct? Why or why not?

56. Jenn writes that the solutions of $x^4 - 5x^2 + 6 = 0$ are 2 and 3. What mistake is she making?

Skill Review

To prepare for Section 11.6, review graphing functions (Section 7.3).

Graph. [7.3]

57. $f(x) = x$

58. $g(x) = x + 2$

59. $h(x) = x - 2$

60. $f(x) = x^2$

61. $g(x) = x^2 + 2$

62. $h(x) = x^2 - 2$

Synthesis

63. Describe a procedure that could be used to solve any equation of the form $ax^4 + bx^2 + c = 0$.

64. Describe a procedure that could be used to write an equation that is quadratic in $3x^2 - 1$. Then explain how the procedure could be adjusted to write equations that are quadratic in $3x^2 - 1$ and have no real-number solution.

Solve.

65. $3x^4 + 5x^2 - 1 = 0$

66. $5x^4 - 7x^2 + 1 = 0$

67. $(x^2 - 5x - 1)^2 - 18(x^2 - 5x - 1) + 65 = 0$

68. $(x^2 - 4x - 2)^2 - 13(x^2 - 4x - 2) + 30 = 0$

69. $\dfrac{x}{x-1} - 6\sqrt{\dfrac{x}{x-1}} - 40 = 0$

70. $\left(\sqrt{\dfrac{x}{x-3}}\right)^2 - 24 = 10\sqrt{\dfrac{x}{x-3}}$

71. $a^5(a^2 - 25) + 13a^3(25 - a^2) + 36a(a^2 - 25) = 0$

72. $a^3 - 26a^{3/2} - 27 = 0$

73. $x^6 - 28x^3 + 27 = 0$

74. $x^6 + 7x^3 - 8 = 0$

75. Use a graphing calculator to check your answers to Exercises 15, 17, 41, and 53.

76. Use a graphing calculator to solve
$$x^4 - x^3 - 13x^2 + x + 12 = 0.$$

77. While trying to solve $0.05x^4 - 0.8 = 0$ with a graphing calculator, Salam gets the screen at right. Can Salam solve this equation with a graphing calculator? Why or why not?

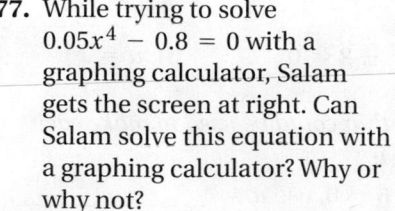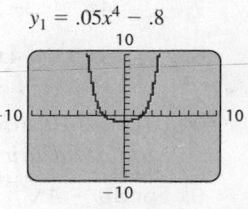

CONNECTING the CONCEPTS

We have studied four different ways of solving quadratic equations. Each method has advantages and disadvantages, as outlined below. Note that although the quadratic formula can be used to solve *any* quadratic equation, the other methods are sometimes faster and easier to use. Also note that any of these methods can be used when solving equations that are reducible to quadratic.

Method	Advantages	Disadvantages	Example
Factoring	Can be very fast.	Can be used only on certain equations. Many equations are difficult or impossible to solve by factoring.	$x^2 - x - 6 = 0$ $(x - 3)(x + 2) = 0$ $x = 3 \quad or \quad x = -2$
The principle of square roots	Fastest way to solve equations of the form $X^2 = k$. Can be used to solve *any* quadratic equation.	Can be slow when original equation is not written in the form $X^2 = k$.	$(x - 5)^2 = 2$ $x - 5 = \pm\sqrt{2}$ $x = 5 \pm \sqrt{2}$
Completing the square	Works well on equations of the form $x^2 + bx = -c$, when b is even. Can be used to solve *any* quadratic equation.	Can be complicated when $a \neq 1$ or when b is not even in $x^2 + bx = -c$.	$x^2 + 14x = -2$ $x^2 + 14x + 49 = -2 + 49$ $(x + 7)^2 = 47$ $x + 7 = \pm\sqrt{47}$ $x = -7 \pm \sqrt{47}$
The quadratic formula	Can be used to solve *any* quadratic equation.	Can be slower than factoring or the principle of square roots for certain equations.	$x^2 - 2x - 5 = 0$ $x = \dfrac{-(-2) \pm \sqrt{(-2)^2 - 4(1)(-5)}}{2 \cdot 1}$ $= \dfrac{2 \pm \sqrt{24}}{2}$ $= \dfrac{2}{2} \pm \dfrac{2\sqrt{6}}{2} = 1 \pm \sqrt{6}$

MIXED REVIEW

Solve. Examine each exercise carefully, and try to solve using the easiest method.

1. $x^2 - 3x - 10 = 0$

2. $x^2 = 121$

3. $x^2 + 6x = 10$

4. $x^2 + x - 3 = 0$

5. $(x + 1)^2 = 2$

6. $x^2 - 10x + 25 = 0$

7. $x^2 - x - 1 = 0$

8. $x^2 - 2x = 6$

9. $4t^2 = 11$

(continued)

10. $2t^2 + 1 = 3t$

11. $c^2 + c + 1 = 0$

12. $16c^2 = 7c$

13. $6y^2 - 7y - 10 = 0$

14. $y^2 - 2y + 8 = 0$

15. $x^4 - 10x^2 + 9 = 0$

16. $x^4 - 8x^2 - 9 = 0$

17. $t(t - 3) = 2t(t + 1)$

18. $(t + 4)(t - 3) = 18$

19. $(m^2 + 3)^2 - 4(m^2 + 3) - 5 = 0$

20. $m^{-4} - 5m^{-2} + 6 = 0$

11.6 Quadratic Functions and Their Graphs

The Graph of $f(x) = ax^2$ • The Graph of $f(x) = a(x - h)^2$ • The Graph of $f(x) = a(x - h)^2 + k$

We have seen that the graph of any linear function $f(x) = mx + b$ is a straight line. In this section and the next, we will see that the graph of any quadratic function $f(x) = ax^2 + bx + c$ is a *parabola*. We examine the shape of such graphs by first looking at quadratic functions with $b = 0$ and $c = 0$.

The Graph of $f(x) = ax^2$

The most basic quadratic function is $f(x) = x^2$.

EXAMPLE **1**

Graph: $f(x) = x^2$.

SOLUTION We choose some values for x and compute $f(x)$ for each. Then we plot the ordered pairs and connect them with a smooth curve.

x	$f(x) = x^2$	$(x, f(x))$
-3	9	$(-3, 9)$
-2	4	$(-2, 4)$
-1	1	$(-1, 1)$
0	0	$(0, 0)$
1	1	$(1, 1)$
2	4	$(2, 4)$
3	9	$(3, 9)$

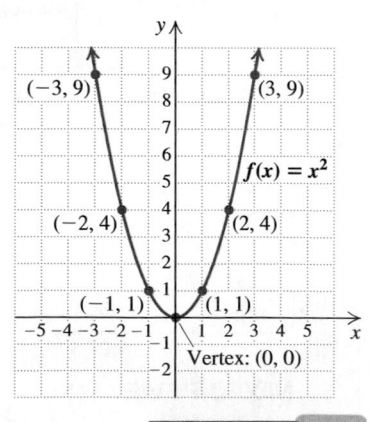

TRY EXERCISE 11

All quadratic functions have graphs similar to the one in Example 1. Such curves are called **parabolas**. They are U-shaped and can open upward, as in Example 1, or downward. The "turning point" of the graph is called the **vertex** of the parabola. The vertex of the graph in Example 1 is (0, 0).

A parabola is symmetric with respect to a line that goes through the center of the parabola and the vertex. This line is known as the parabola's **axis of symmetry**. In Example 1, the y-axis (the vertical line $x = 0$) is the axis of symmetry. Were the paper folded on this line, the two halves of the curve would match.

STUDENT NOTES

By paying attention to the symmetry of each parabola and the location of the vertex, you save yourself considerable work. Note too that when we are graphing ax^2, the x-values 1 unit to the right or left of the vertex are paired with the y-value a units above the vertex. Thus the graph of $y = \frac{3}{2}x^2$ includes the points $\left(-1, \frac{3}{2}\right)$ and $\left(1, \frac{3}{2}\right)$.

TECHNOLOGY CONNECTION

To explore the effect of a on the graph of $y = ax^2$, let $y_1 = x^2$, $y_2 = 3x^2$, and $y_3 = \frac{1}{3}x^2$. Graph the equations and use ⟨TRACE⟩ to see how the y-values compare, using ⌢ or ⌣ to hop the cursor from one curve to the next.

Many graphing calculators include a Transfrm application. If you run that application and let $y_1 = Ax^2$, the graph becomes interactive. A value for A can be entered while viewing the graph, or the values can be stepped up or down by pressing ⟨ or ⟩.

1. Compare the graphs of $y_1 = \frac{1}{5}x^2$, $y_2 = x^2$, $y_3 = \frac{5}{2}x^2$, $y_4 = -\frac{1}{5}x^2$, $y_5 = -x^2$, and $y_6 = -\frac{5}{2}x^2$.
2. Describe the effect that A has on each graph.

The graph of any function of the form $y = ax^2$ has a vertex of $(0, 0)$ and an axis of symmetry $x = 0$. By plotting points, we can compare the graphs of $g(x) = \frac{1}{2}x^2$ and $h(x) = 2x^2$ with the graph of $f(x) = x^2$.

x	$g(x) = \frac{1}{2}x^2$
-3	$\frac{9}{2}$
-2	2
-1	$\frac{1}{2}$
0	0
1	$\frac{1}{2}$
2	2
3	$\frac{9}{2}$

x	$h(x) = 2x^2$
-3	18
-2	8
-1	2
0	0
1	2
2	8
3	18

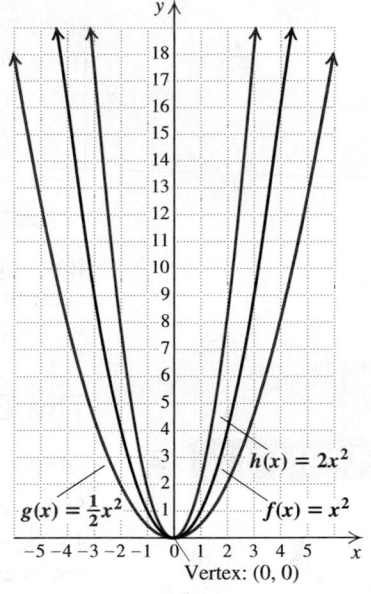

Vertex: $(0, 0)$

Note that the graph of $g(x) = \frac{1}{2}x^2$ is "wider" than the graph of $f(x) = x^2$, and the graph of $h(x) = 2x^2$ is "narrower." The vertex and the axis of symmetry, however, remain $(0, 0)$ and the line $x = 0$, respectively.

When we consider the graph of $k(x) = -\frac{1}{2}x^2$, we see that the parabola is the same shape as the graph of $g(x) = \frac{1}{2}x^2$, but opens downward. We say that the graphs of k and g are *reflections* of each other across the x-axis.

x	$k(x) = -\frac{1}{2}x^2$
-3	$-\frac{9}{2}$
-2	-2
-1	$-\frac{1}{2}$
0	0
1	$-\frac{1}{2}$
2	-2
3	$-\frac{9}{2}$

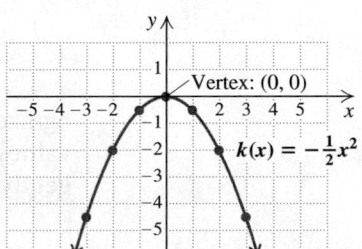

Vertex: $(0, 0)$

Graphing $f(x) = ax^2$

The graph of $f(x) = ax^2$ is a parabola with $x = 0$ as its axis of symmetry. Its vertex is the origin.

For $a > 0$, the parabola opens upward. For $a < 0$, the parabola opens downward.

If $|a|$ is greater than 1, the parabola is narrower than $y = x^2$.

If $|a|$ is between 0 and 1, the parabola is wider than $y = x^2$.

The width of a parabola and whether it opens upward or downward are determined by the coefficient a in $f(x) = ax^2 + bx + c$. In the remainder of this section, we graph quadratic functions that are written in a form from which the vertex can be read directly.

The Graph of $f(x) = a(x - h)^2$

EXAMPLE 2

Graph: $f(x) = (x - 3)^2$.

SOLUTION   We choose some values for x and compute $f(x)$. Since $(x - 3)^2 = 1 \cdot (x - 3)^2$, $a = 1$, and the graph opens upward. It is important to note that when an input here is 3 more than an input for Example 1, the outputs match. We plot the points and draw the curve.

x	$f(x) = (x - 3)^2$
-1	16
0	9
1	4
2	1
3	0
4	1
5	4
6	9

← Vertex

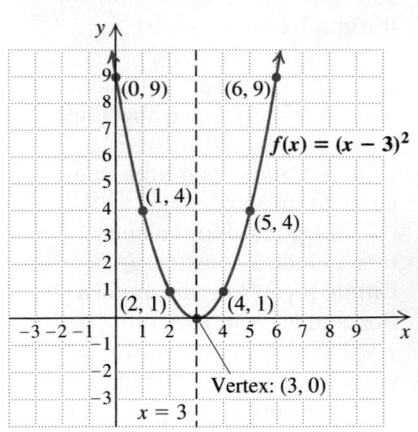

Note that $f(x)$ is smallest when $x - 3$ is 0, that is, for $x = 3$. Thus the line $x = 3$ is now the axis of symmetry and the point $(3, 0)$ is the vertex. Had we recognized earlier that $x = 3$ is the axis of symmetry, we could have computed some values on one side, such as $(4, 1)$, $(5, 4)$, and $(6, 9)$, and then used symmetry to get their mirror images $(2, 1)$, $(1, 4)$, and $(0, 9)$ without further computation.

TRY EXERCISE 19

The result of Example 2 can be generalized:

The vertex of the graph of $f(x) = a(x - h)^2$ is $(h, 0)$.

EXAMPLE 3

Graph: $g(x) = -2(x + 4)^2$.

SOLUTION   We choose some values for x and compute $g(x)$. Since $a = -2$, the graph will open downward. Note that $g(x)$ is greatest when $x + 4$ is 0, that is, for $x = -4$. Thus the line given by $x = -4$ is the axis of symmetry and the point $(-4, 0)$ is the vertex. We plot some points and draw the curve.

To explore the effect of h on the graph of $f(x) = a(x - h)^2$, let $y_1 = 7x^2$ and $y_2 = 7(x - 1)^2$. Graph both y_1 and y_2 and compare y-values, beginning at $x = 1$ and increasing x by one unit at a time. The G-T or HORIZ **MODE** can be used to view a split screen showing both the graph and a table.

Next, let $y_3 = 7(x - 2)^2$ and compare its graph and y-values with those of y_1 and y_2. Then let $y_4 = 7(x + 1)^2$ and $y_5 = 7(x + 2)^2$.

1. Compare graphs and y-values and describe the effect of h on the graph of $f(x) = a(x - h)^2$.
2. If the Transfrm application is available, let $y_1 = A(x - B)^2$ and describe the effect that A and B have on each graph.

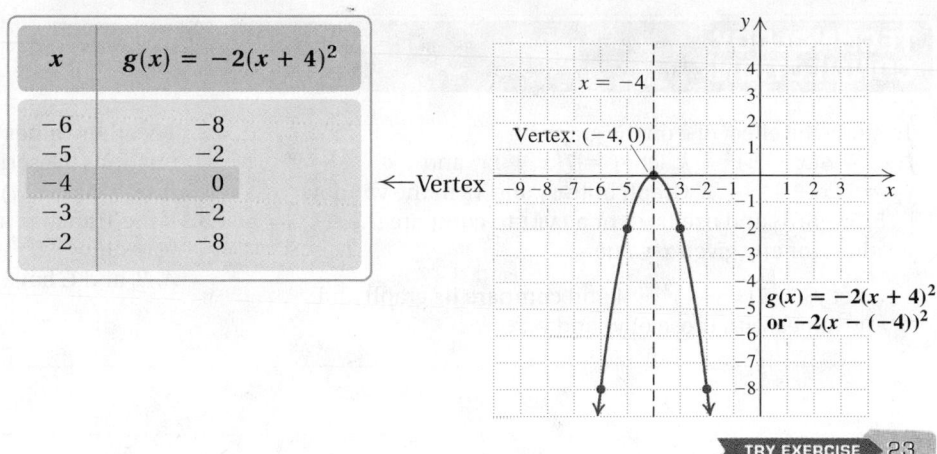

x	$g(x) = -2(x + 4)^2$
-6	-8
-5	-2
-4	0
-3	-2
-2	-8

←Vertex

$x = -4$

Vertex: $(-4, 0)$

$g(x) = -2(x + 4)^2$
or $-2(x - (-4))^2$

TRY EXERCISE 23

In Example 2, the graph of $f(x) = (x - 3)^2$ looks just like the graph of $y = x^2$, except that it is moved, or *translated*, 3 units to the right. In Example 3, the graph of $g(x) = -2(x + 4)^2$ looks like the graph of $y = -2x^2$, except that it is shifted 4 units to the left. These results are generalized as follows.

Graphing $f(x) = a(x - h)^2$

The graph of $f(x) = a(x - h)^2$ has the same shape as the graph of $y = ax^2$.

- If h is positive, the graph of $y = ax^2$ is shifted h units to the right.
- If h is negative, the graph of $y = ax^2$ is shifted $|h|$ units to the left.
- The vertex is $(h, 0)$ and the axis of symmetry is $x = h$.

The Graph of $f(x) = a(x - h)^2 + k$

Given a graph of $f(x) = a(x - h)^2$, what happens if we add a constant k? Suppose that we add 2. This increases $f(x)$ by 2, so the curve is moved up. If k is negative, the curve is moved down. The axis of symmetry for the parabola remains $x = h$, but the vertex will be at (h, k), or, equivalently, $(h, f(h))$.

Because of the shape of their graphs, quadratic functions have either a *minimum* value or a *maximum* value. Many real-world applications involve finding that value. For example, a business owner is concerned with minimizing cost and maximizing profit. If a parabola opens upward $(a > 0)$, the function value, or y-value, at the vertex is a least, or minimum, value. That is, it is less than the y-value at any other point on the graph. If the parabola opens downward $(a < 0)$, the function value at the vertex is a greatest, or maximum, value.

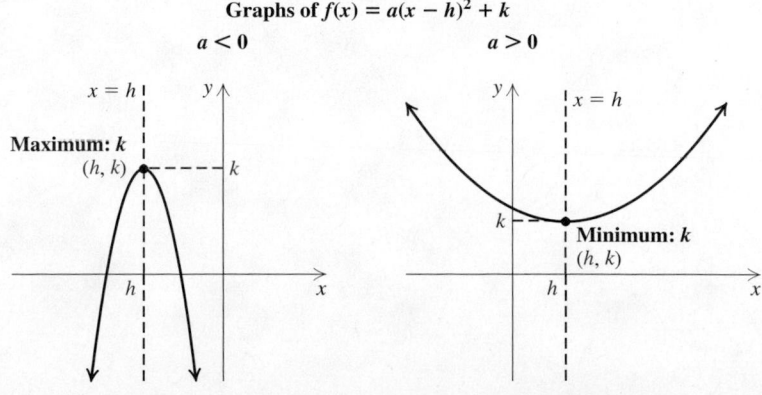

Graphs of $f(x) = a(x - h)^2 + k$

$a < 0$ $a > 0$

$x = h$ Maximum: k (h, k) k h

$x = h$ k Minimum: k (h, k) h

TECHNOLOGY CONNECTION

To study the effect of k on the graph of $f(x) = a(x - h)^2 + k$, let $y_1 = 7(x - 1)^2$ and $y_2 = 7(x - 1)^2 + 2$. Graph both y_1 and y_2 in the window $[-5, 5, -5, 5]$ and use TRACE or a TABLE to compare the y-values for any given x-value.

1. Let $y_3 = 7(x - 1)^2 - 4$ and compare its graph and y-values with those of y_1 and y_2.

2. Try other values of k, including decimals and fractions. Describe the effect of k on the graph of $f(x) = a(x - h)^2$.

3. If the Transfrm application is available, let $y_1 = A(x - B)^2 + C$ and describe the effect that A, B, and C have on each graph.

Graphing $f(x) = a(x - h)^2 + k$

The graph of $f(x) = a(x - h)^2 + k$ has the same shape as the graph of $y = a(x - h)^2$.

- If k is positive, the graph of $y = a(x - h)^2$ is shifted k units up.
- If k is negative, the graph of $y = a(x - h)^2$ is shifted $|k|$ units down.
- The vertex is (h, k), and the axis of symmetry is $x = h$.
- For $a > 0$, the minimum function value is k. For $a < 0$, the maximum function value is k.

EXAMPLE **4**   Graph $g(x) = (x - 3)^2 - 5$, and find the minimum function value.

SOLUTION   The graph will look like that of $f(x) = (x - 3)^2$ (see Example 2) but shifted 5 units down. You can confirm this by plotting some points. For instance, $g(4) = (4 - 3)^2 - 5 = -4$, whereas in Example 2, $f(4) = (4 - 3)^2 = 1$.

The vertex is now $(3, -5)$, and the minimum function value is -5.

x	$g(x) = (x - 3)^2 - 5$
0	4
1	−1
2	−4
3	−5
4	−4
5	−1
6	4

← Vertex

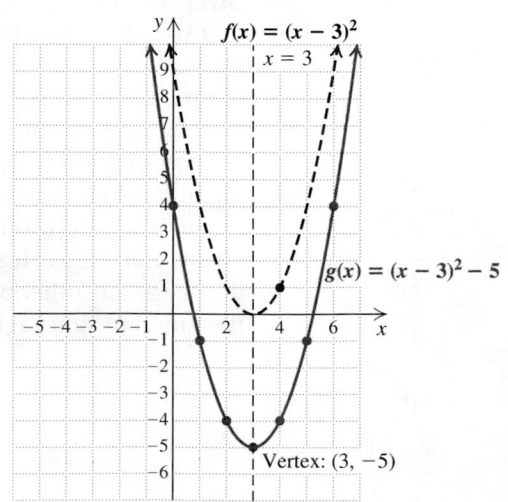

TRY EXERCISE 39

EXAMPLE **5** Graph $h(x) = \frac{1}{2}(x - 3)^2 + 6$, and find the minimum function value.

SOLUTION The graph looks just like that of $f(x) = \frac{1}{2}x^2$ but moved 3 units to the right and 6 units up. The vertex is $(3, 6)$, and the axis of symmetry is $x = 3$. We draw $f(x) = \frac{1}{2}x^2$ and then shift the curve over and up. The minimum function value is 6. By plotting some points, we have a check.

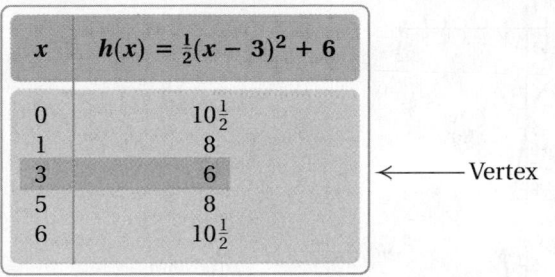

x	$h(x) = \frac{1}{2}(x - 3)^2 + 6$
0	$10\frac{1}{2}$
1	8
3	6
5	8
6	$10\frac{1}{2}$

←——— Vertex

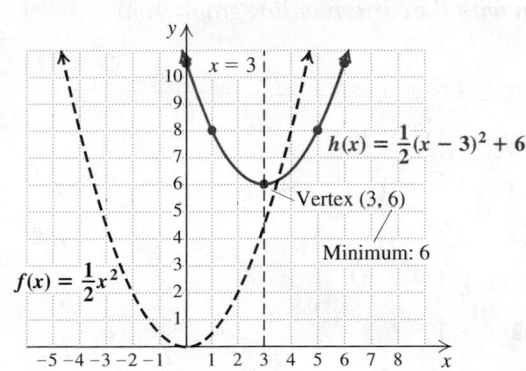

TRY EXERCISE ▶ 43

EXAMPLE **6** Graph $y = -2(x + 3)^2 + 5$. Find the vertex, the axis of symmetry, and the maximum or minimum value.

SOLUTION We first express the equation in the equivalent form

$$y = -2[x - (-3)]^2 + 5.$$ This is in the form $y = a(x - h)^2 + k$.

The graph looks like that of $y = -2x^2$ translated 3 units to the left and 5 units up. The vertex is $(-3, 5)$, and the axis of symmetry is $x = -3$. Since -2 is negative, the graph opens downward, and we know that 5, the second coordinate of the vertex, is the maximum y-value.

We compute a few points as needed, selecting convenient x-values on either side of the vertex. The graph is shown here.

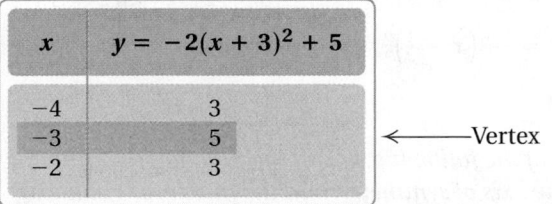

x	$y = -2(x + 3)^2 + 5$
-4	3
-3	5
-2	3

←———Vertex

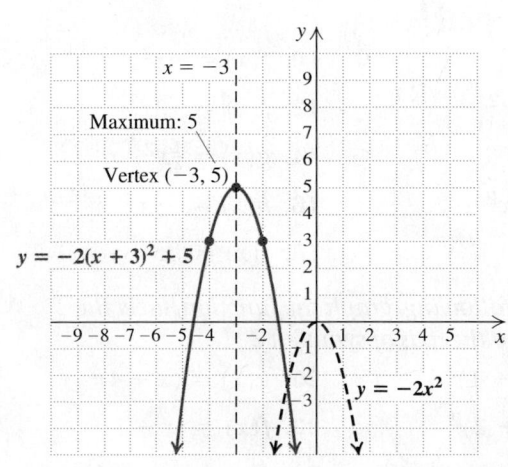

TRY EXERCISE ▶ 45

11.6 EXERCISE SET

Concept Reinforcement   *In each of Exercises 1–8, match the equation with the corresponding graph from those shown.*

1. ____ $f(x) = 2(x - 1)^2 + 3$

2. ____ $f(x) = -2(x - 1)^2 + 3$

3. ____ $f(x) = 2(x + 1)^2 + 3$

4. ____ $f(x) = 2(x - 1)^2 - 3$

5. ____ $f(x) = -2(x + 1)^2 + 3$

6. ____ $f(x) = -2(x + 1)^2 - 3$

7. ____ $f(x) = 2(x + 1)^2 - 3$

8. ____ $f(x) = -2(x - 1)^2 - 3$

c)
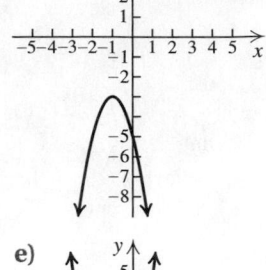

d)
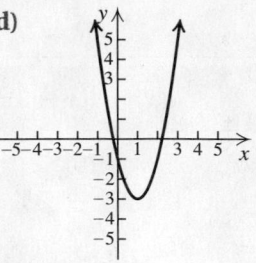

e)
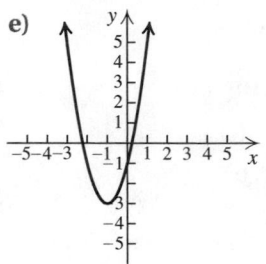

f)
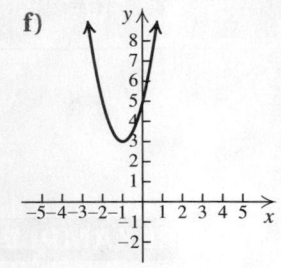

a)   b)
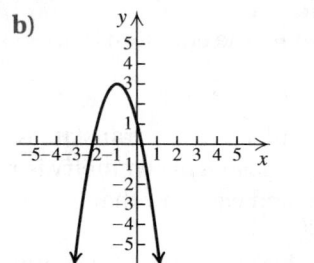

g)
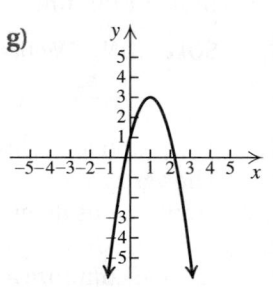

h)
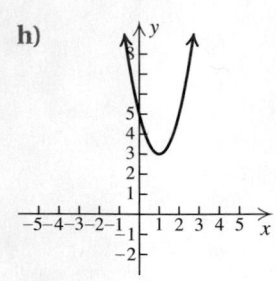

Graph.

9. $f(x) = x^2$

10. $f(x) = -x^2$

11. $f(x) = -2x^2$

12. $f(x) = -3x^2$

13. $g(x) = \frac{1}{3}x^2$

14. $g(x) = \frac{1}{4}x^2$

Aha! 15. $h(x) = -\frac{1}{3}x^2$

16. $h(x) = -\frac{1}{4}x^2$

17. $f(x) = \frac{5}{2}x^2$

18. $f(x) = \frac{3}{2}x^2$

For each of the following, graph the function, label the vertex, and draw the axis of symmetry.

19. $g(x) = (x + 1)^2$

20. $g(x) = (x + 4)^2$

21. $f(x) = (x - 2)^2$

22. $f(x) = (x - 1)^2$

23. $f(x) = -(x + 1)^2$

24. $f(x) = -(x - 1)^2$

25. $g(x) = -(x - 2)^2$

26. $g(x) = -(x + 4)^2$

27. $f(x) = 2(x + 1)^2$

28. $f(x) = 2(x + 4)^2$

29. $g(x) = 3(x - 4)^2$

30. $g(x) = 3(x - 5)^2$

31. $h(x) = -\frac{1}{2}(x - 4)^2$

32. $h(x) = -\frac{3}{2}(x - 2)^2$

33. $f(x) = \frac{1}{2}(x - 1)^2$

34. $f(x) = \frac{1}{3}(x + 2)^2$

35. $f(x) = -2(x + 5)^2$

36. $f(x) = -3(x + 7)^2$

37. $h(x) = -3\left(x - \frac{1}{2}\right)^2$

38. $h(x) = -2\left(x + \frac{1}{2}\right)^2$

For each of the following, graph the function and find the vertex, the axis of symmetry, and the maximum value or the minimum value.

39. $f(x) = (x - 5)^2 + 2$

40. $f(x) = (x + 3)^2 - 2$

41. $f(x) = (x + 1)^2 - 3$

42. $f(x) = (x - 1)^2 + 2$

43. $g(x) = \frac{1}{2}(x + 4)^2 + 1$

44. $g(x) = -(x - 2)^2 - 4$

45. $h(x) = -2(x - 1)^2 - 3$

46. $h(x) = -2(x + 1)^2 + 4$

47. $f(x) = 2(x + 3)^2 + 1$

48. $f(x) = 2(x - 5)^2 - 3$

49. $g(x) = -\frac{3}{2}(x - 2)^2 + 4$

50. $g(x) = \frac{3}{2}(x + 2)^2 - 1$

Without graphing, find the vertex, the axis of symmetry, and the maximum value or the minimum value.

51. $f(x) = 5(x - 3)^2 + 9$

52. $f(x) = 2(x - 1)^2 - 10$

53. $f(x) = -\frac{3}{7}(x + 8)^2 + 2$

54. $f(x) = -\frac{1}{4}(x + 4)^2 - 12$

55. $f(x) = \left(x - \frac{7}{2}\right)^2 - \frac{29}{4}$

56. $f(x) = -\left(x + \frac{3}{4}\right)^2 + \frac{17}{16}$

57. $f(x) = -\sqrt{2}(x + 2.25)^2 - \pi$

58. $f(x) = 2\pi(x - 0.01)^2 + \sqrt{15}$

59. Explain, without plotting points, why the graph of $y = x^2 - 4$ looks like the graph of $y = x^2$ translated 4 units down.

60. Explain, without plotting points, why the graph of $y = (x + 2)^2$ looks like the graph of $y = x^2$ translated 2 units to the left.

Skill Review

To prepare for Section 11.7, review finding intercepts and completing the square (Sections 3.3, 5.7, and 11.1).

Find the x-intercept and the y-intercept. [3.3]

61. $8x - 6y = 24$

62. $3x + 4y = 8$

Find the x-intercepts. [5.7]

63. $y = x^2 + 8x + 15$

64. $y = 2x^2 - x - 3$

Replace the blanks with constants to form a true equation. [11.1]

65. $x^2 - 14x + \underline{\quad} = (x - \underline{\quad})^2$

66. $x^2 + 7x + \underline{\quad} = \left(x + \underline{\quad}\right)^2$

Synthesis

67. Before graphing a quadratic function, Martha always plots five points. First, she calculates and plots the coordinates of the vertex. Then she plots *four* more points after calculating *two* more ordered pairs. How is this possible?

68. If the graphs of $f(x) = a_1(x - h_1)^2 + k_1$ and $g(x) = a_2(x - h_2)^2 + k_2$ have the same shape, what, if anything, can you conclude about the a's, the h's, and the k's? Why?

Write an equation for a function having a graph with the same shape as the graph of $f(x) = \frac{3}{5}x^2$, but with the given point as the vertex.

69. $(1, 3)$

70. $(2, 8)$

71. $(4, -7)$

72. $(9, -6)$

73. $(-2, -5)$

74. $(-4, -2)$

For each of the following, write the equation of the parabola that has the shape of $f(x) = 2x^2$ or $g(x) = -2x^2$ and has a maximum value or a minimum value at the specified point.

75. Minimum: $(2, 0)$

76. Minimum: $(-4, 0)$

77. Maximum: $(0, -5)$

78. Maximum: $(3, 8)$

Use the following graph of $f(x) = a(x - h)^2 + k$ for Exercises 79–82.

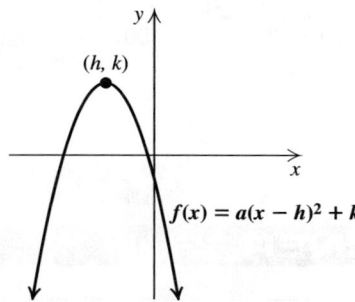

79. Describe what will happen to the graph if h is increased.

80. Describe what will happen to the graph if k is decreased.

81. Describe what will happen to the graph if a is replaced with $-a$.

82. Describe what will happen to the graph if $(x - h)$ is replaced with $(x + h)$.

Find an equation for the quadratic function F that satisfies the following conditions.

83. The graph of F is the same shape as the graph of f, where $f(x) = 3(x + 2)^2 + 7$, and $F(x)$ is a minimum at the same point that $g(x) = -2(x - 5)^2 + 1$ is a maximum.

84. The graph of F is the same shape as the graph of f, where $f(x) = -\frac{1}{3}(x - 2)^2 + 7$, and $F(x)$ is a maximum at the same point that $g(x) = 2(x + 4)^2 - 6$ is a minimum.

Functions other than parabolas can be translated. When calculating $f(x)$, if we replace x with $x - h$, where h is a constant, the graph will be moved horizontally. If we replace $f(x)$ with $f(x) + k$, the graph will be moved vertically. Use the graph below for Exercises 85–90.

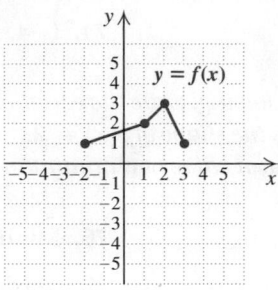

Draw a graph of each of the following.

85. $y = f(x - 1)$

86. $y = f(x + 2)$

87. $y = f(x) + 2$

88. $y = f(x) - 3$

89. $y = f(x + 3) - 2$

90. $y = f(x - 3) + 1$

91. Use the TRACE and/or TABLE features of a graphing calculator to confirm the maximum and minimum values given as answers to Exercises 51, 53, and 55. Be sure to adjust the window appropriately. On many graphing calculators, a maximum or minimum option may be available by using a CALC key.

92. Use a graphing calculator to check your graphs for Exercises 18, 28, and 48.

93. While trying to graph $y = -\frac{1}{2}x^2 + 3x + 1$, Yusef gets the following screen. How can Yusef tell at a glance that a mistake has been made?

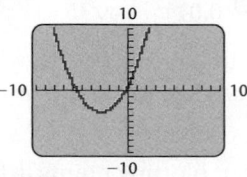

CORNER

(COLLABORATIVE)

Match the Graph

Focus: Graphing quadratic functions

Time: 15–20 minutes

Group size: 6

Materials: Index cards

ACTIVITY

1. On each of six index cards, write one of the following equations:

$$y = \tfrac{1}{2}(x - 3)^2 + 1; \qquad y = \tfrac{1}{2}(x - 1)^2 + 3;$$
$$y = \tfrac{1}{2}(x + 1)^2 - 3; \qquad y = \tfrac{1}{2}(x + 3)^2 + 1;$$
$$y = \tfrac{1}{2}(x + 3)^2 - 1; \qquad y = \tfrac{1}{2}(x + 1)^2 + 3.$$

2. Fold each index card and mix up the six cards in a hat or bag. Then, one by one, each group member should select one of the equations. Do not let anyone see your equation.

3. Each group member should carefully graph the equation selected. Make the graph large enough so that when it is finished, it can be easily viewed by the rest of the group. Be sure to scale the axes and label the vertex, but **do not label the graph with the equation used**.

4. When all group members have drawn a graph, place the graphs in a pile. The group should then match and agree on the correct equation for each graph *with no help from the person who drew the graph*. If a mistake has been made and a graph has no match, determine what its equation *should* be.

5. Compare your group's labeled graphs with those of other groups to reach consensus within the class on the correct label for each graph.

11.7   More About Graphing Quadratic Functions

Completing the Square   •   Finding Intercepts

Completing the Square

By *completing the square* (see Section 11.1), we can rewrite any polynomial $ax^2 + bx + c$ in the form $a(x - h)^2 + k$. Once that has been done, the procedures discussed in Section 11.6 will enable us to graph any quadratic function.

EXAMPLE 1

Graph: $g(x) = x^2 - 6x + 4$. Label the vertex and the axis of symmetry.

SOLUTION   We have

$$g(x) = x^2 - 6x + 4$$
$$= (x^2 - 6x) + 4.$$

To complete the square inside the parentheses, we take half the x-coefficient, $\frac{1}{2} \cdot (-6) = -3$, and square it to get $(-3)^2 = 9$. Then we add $9 - 9$ inside the parentheses:

$$g(x) = (x^2 - 6x + 9 - 9) + 4 \qquad \text{The effect is of adding 0.}$$
$$= (x^2 - 6x + 9) + (-9 + 4) \qquad \text{Using the associative law of addition to regroup}$$
$$= (x - 3)^2 - 5. \qquad \text{Factoring and simplifying}$$

This equation appeared as Example 4 of Section 11.6. The graph is that of $f(x) = x^2$ translated 3 units right and 5 units down. The vertex is $(3, -5)$, and the axis of symmetry is $x = 3$.

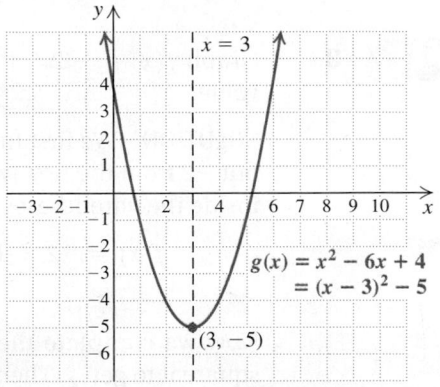

TRY EXERCISE   19

When the leading coefficient is not 1, we factor out that number from the first two terms. Then we complete the square and use the distributive law.

EXAMPLE 2

Graph: $f(x) = 3x^2 + 12x + 13$. Label the vertex and the axis of symmetry.

SOLUTION   Since the coefficient of x^2 is not 1, we need to factor out that number—in this case, 3—from the first two terms. Remember that we want the form $f(x) = a(x - h)^2 + k$:

$$f(x) = 3x^2 + 12x + 13$$
$$= 3(x^2 + 4x) + 13.$$

STUDY SKILLS

Use What You Know

An excellent and common strategy for solving any new type of problem is to rewrite the problem in an equivalent form that we already know how to solve. Although this is not always feasible, when it is—as in most of the problems in this section—it can make a new topic much easier to learn.

STUDENT NOTES

In this section, we add and subtract the same number when completing the square instead of adding the same number to both sides of the equation. We do this because we are using function notation. The effect is the same with both approaches: An equivalent equation is formed.

Now we complete the square as before. We take half of the x-coefficient, $\frac{1}{2} \cdot 4 = 2$, and square it: $2^2 = 4$. Then we add $4 - 4$ inside the parentheses:

$$f(x) = 3(x^2 + 4x + 4 - 4) + 13. \qquad \text{Adding } 4 - 4, \text{ or } 0, \text{ inside the parentheses}$$

The distributive law allows us to separate the -4 from the perfect-square trinomial so long as it is multiplied by 3. *This step is critical*:

$$f(x) = 3(x^2 + 4x + 4) + 3(-4) + 13 \qquad \text{This leaves a perfect-square trinomial inside the parentheses.}$$

$$= 3(x + 2)^2 + 1. \qquad \text{Factoring and simplifying}$$

The vertex is $(-2, 1)$, and the axis of symmetry is $x = -2$. The coefficient of x^2 is 3, so the graph is narrow and opens upward. We choose a few x-values on either side of the vertex, compute y-values, and then graph the parabola.

x	$f(x) = 3(x + 2)^2 + 1$
-2	1
-3	4
-1	4

$\longleftarrow$ Vertex

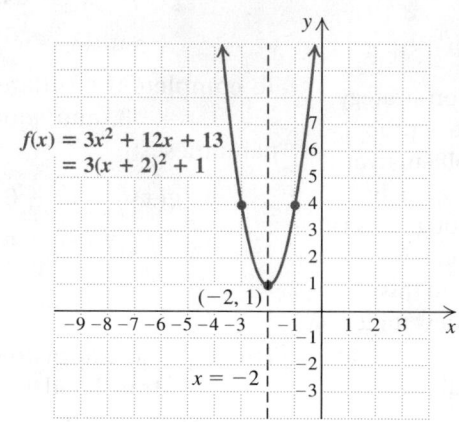

$f(x) = 3x^2 + 12x + 13$
$= 3(x + 2)^2 + 1$

$(-2, 1)$

$x = -2$

TRY EXERCISE 23

EXAMPLE **3**   Graph $f(x) = -2x^2 + 10x - 7$, and find the maximum or minimum function value.

SOLUTION   We first find the vertex by completing the square. To do so, we factor out -2 from the first two terms of the expression. This makes the coefficient of x^2 inside the parentheses 1:

$$f(x) = -2x^2 + 10x - 7$$
$$= -2(x^2 - 5x) - 7.$$

Now we complete the square as before. We take half of the x-coefficient and square it to get $\frac{25}{4}$. Then we add $\frac{25}{4} - \frac{25}{4}$ inside the parentheses:

$$f(x) = -2\left(x^2 - 5x + \tfrac{25}{4} - \tfrac{25}{4}\right) - 7$$
$$= -2\left(x^2 - 5x + \tfrac{25}{4}\right) + (-2)\left(-\tfrac{25}{4}\right) - 7 \qquad \text{Multiplying by } -2, \text{ using the distributive law, and regrouping}$$
$$= -2\left(x - \tfrac{5}{2}\right)^2 + \tfrac{11}{2}. \qquad \text{Factoring and simplifying}$$

The vertex is $\left(\frac{5}{2}, \frac{11}{2}\right)$, and the axis of symmetry is $x = \frac{5}{2}$. The coefficient of x^2, -2, is negative, so the graph opens downward and the second coordinate of the vertex, $\frac{11}{2}$, is the maximum function value.

We plot a few points on either side of the vertex, including the y-intercept, $f(0)$, and graph the parabola.

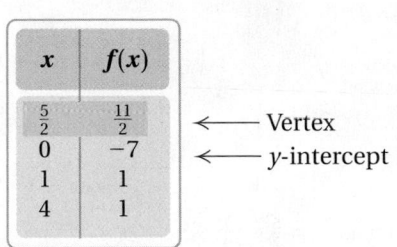

x	$f(x)$	
$\frac{5}{2}$	$\frac{11}{2}$	← Vertex
0	-7	← y-intercept
1	1	
4	1	

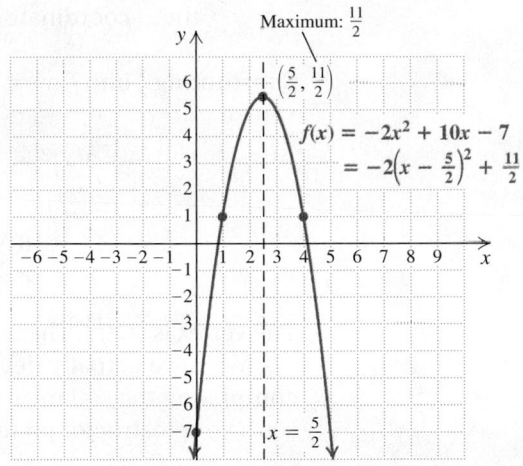

TRY EXERCISE ▸ 39

The method used in Examples 1–3 can be generalized to find a formula for locating the vertex. We complete the square as follows:

$$f(x) = ax^2 + bx + c$$

$$= a\left(x^2 + \frac{b}{a}x\right) + c. \qquad \text{Factoring } a \text{ out of the first two terms.} \\ \text{Check by multiplying.}$$

Half of the x-coefficient, $\frac{b}{a}$, is $\frac{b}{2a}$. We square it to get $\frac{b^2}{4a^2}$ and add $\frac{b^2}{4a^2} - \frac{b^2}{4a^2}$ inside the parentheses. Then we distribute the a and regroup terms:

$$f(x) = a\left(x^2 + \frac{b}{a}x + \frac{b^2}{4a^2} - \frac{b^2}{4a^2}\right) + c$$

$$= a\left(x^2 + \frac{b}{a}x + \frac{b^2}{4a^2}\right) + a\left(-\frac{b^2}{4a^2}\right) + c \qquad \text{Using the distributive law}$$

$$= a\left(x + \frac{b}{2a}\right)^2 + \frac{-b^2}{4a} + \frac{4ac}{4a} \qquad \text{Factoring and finding a common denominator}$$

$$= a\left[x - \left(-\frac{b}{2a}\right)\right]^2 + \frac{4ac - b^2}{4a}.$$

Thus we have the following.

The Vertex of a Parabola

The vertex of the parabola given by $f(x) = ax^2 + bx + c$ is

$$\left(-\frac{b}{2a}, f\left(-\frac{b}{2a}\right)\right), \quad \text{or} \quad \left(-\frac{b}{2a}, \frac{4ac - b^2}{4a}\right).$$

- The x-coordinate of the vertex is $-b/(2a)$.
- The axis of symmetry is $x = -b/(2a)$.
- The second coordinate of the vertex is most commonly found by computing $f\left(-\frac{b}{2a}\right)$.

Let's reexamine Example 3 to see how we could have found the vertex directly. From the formula above,

$$\text{the } x\text{-coordinate of the vertex is } -\frac{b}{2a} = -\frac{10}{2(-2)} = \frac{5}{2}.$$

Substituting $\frac{5}{2}$ into $f(x) = -2x^2 + 10x - 7$, we find the second coordinate of the vertex:

$$\begin{aligned}
f\left(\tfrac{5}{2}\right) &= -2\left(\tfrac{5}{2}\right)^2 + 10\left(\tfrac{5}{2}\right) - 7 \\
&= -2\left(\tfrac{25}{4}\right) + 25 - 7 \\
&= -\tfrac{25}{2} + 18 \\
&= -\tfrac{25}{2} + \tfrac{36}{2} = \tfrac{11}{2}.
\end{aligned}$$

The vertex is $\left(\frac{5}{2}, \frac{11}{2}\right)$. The axis of symmetry is $x = \frac{5}{2}$.

We have actually developed two methods for finding the vertex. One is by completing the square and the other is by using a formula. You should check to see if your instructor prefers one method over the other or wants you to use both.

Finding Intercepts

All quadratic functions have a y-intercept and 0, 1, or 2 x-intercepts. For $f(x) = ax^2 + bx + c$, the y-intercept is $(0, f(0))$, or $(0, c)$. To find x-intercepts, if any exist, we look for points where $y = 0$ or $f(x) = 0$. Thus, for $f(x) = ax^2 + bx + c$, the x-intercepts occur at those x-values for which

$$ax^2 + bx + c = 0.$$

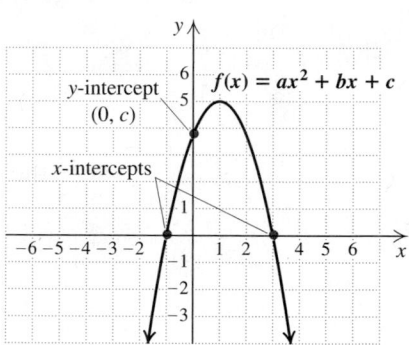

EXAMPLE 4   Find any x-intercepts and the y-intercept of the graph of $f(x) = x^2 - 2x - 2$.

SOLUTION   The y-intercept is simply $(0, f(0))$, or $(0, -2)$. To find any x-intercepts, we solve

$$0 = x^2 - 2x - 2.$$

We are unable to factor $x^2 - 2x - 2$, so we use the quadratic formula and get $x = 1 \pm \sqrt{3}$. Thus the x-intercepts are $(1 - \sqrt{3}, 0)$ and $(1 + \sqrt{3}, 0)$.

If graphing, we would approximate, to get $(-0.7, 0)$ and $(2.7, 0)$.

TRY EXERCISE ▶ 43

If the solutions of $f(x) = 0$ are imaginary, the graph of f has no x-intercepts.

A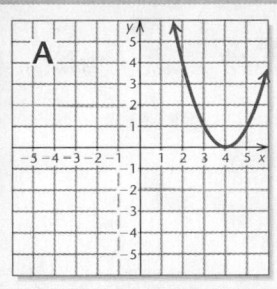

B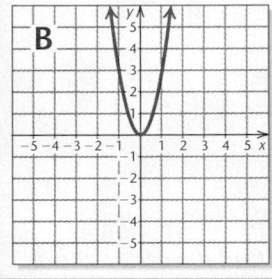

C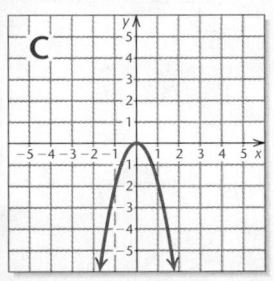

D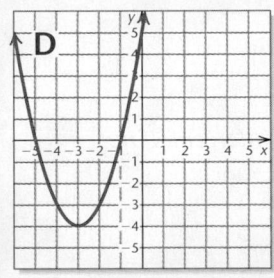

E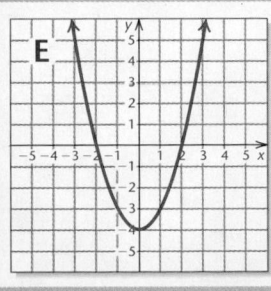

Match each function with its graph.

1. $f(x) = 3x^2$

2. $f(x) = x^2 - 4$

3. $f(x) = (x - 4)^2$

4. $f(x) = x - 4$

5. $f(x) = -2x^2$

6. $f(x) = x + 3$

7. $f(x) = |x + 3|$

8. $f(x) = (x + 3)^2$

9. $f(x) = \sqrt{x + 3}$

10. $f(x) = (x + 3)^2 - 4$

Answers on page A-48.

An additional, animated version of this activity appears in MyMathLab. To use MyMathLab, you need a course ID and a student access code. Contact your instructor for more information.

F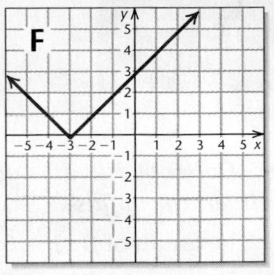

G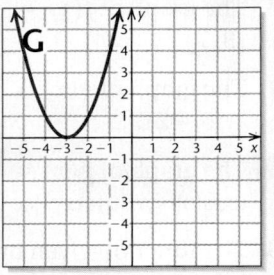

H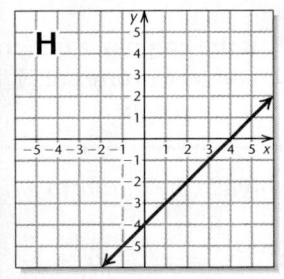

I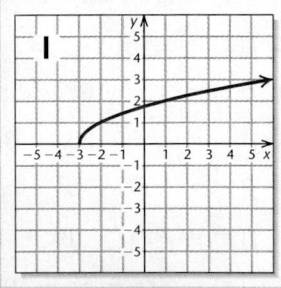

J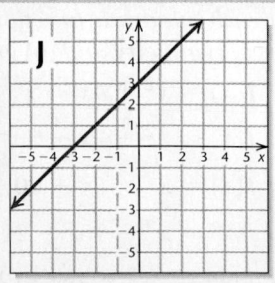

11.7   **EXERCISE SET**

✎ **Concept Reinforcement**   *Classify each statement as either true or false.*

1. The graph of $f(x) = 3x^2 - x + 6$ opens upward.

2. The function given by $g(x) = -x^2 + 3x + 1$ has a minimum value.

3. The graph of $f(x) = -2(x - 3)^2 + 7$ has its vertex at $(3, 7)$.

4. The graph of $g(x) = 4(x + 6)^2 - 2$ has its vertex at $(-6, -2)$.

5. The graph of $g(x) = \frac{1}{2}\left(x - \frac{3}{2}\right)^2 + \frac{1}{4}$ has $x = \frac{1}{4}$ as its axis of symmetry.

6. The function given by $f(x) = (x - 2)^2 - 5$ has a minimum value of -5.

7. The y-intercept of the graph of $f(x) = 2x^2 - 6x + 7$ is $(7, 0)$.

8. If the graph of a quadratic function f opens upward and has a vertex of $(1, 5)$, then the graph has no x-intercepts.

Complete the square to write each function in the form $f(x) = a(x - h)^2 + k$.

9. $f(x) = x^2 - 8x + 2$

10. $f(x) = x^2 - 6x - 1$

11. $f(x) = x^2 + 3x - 5$

12. $f(x) = x^2 + 5x + 3$

13. $f(x) = 3x^2 + 6x - 2$

14. $f(x) = 2x^2 - 20x - 3$

15. $f(x) = -x^2 - 4x - 7$

16. $f(x) = -2x^2 - 8x + 4$

17. $f(x) = 2x^2 - 5x + 10$

18. $f(x) = 3x^2 + 7x - 3$

For each quadratic function, (a) find the vertex and the axis of symmetry and (b) graph the function.

19. $f(x) = x^2 + 4x + 5$

20. $f(x) = x^2 + 2x - 5$

21. $f(x) = x^2 + 8x + 20$

22. $f(x) = x^2 - 10x + 21$

23. $h(x) = 2x^2 - 16x + 25$

24. $h(x) = 2x^2 + 16x + 23$

25. $f(x) = -x^2 + 2x + 5$

26. $f(x) = -x^2 - 2x + 7$

27. $g(x) = x^2 + 3x - 10$

28. $g(x) = x^2 + 5x + 4$

29. $h(x) = x^2 + 7x$

30. $h(x) = x^2 - 5x$

31. $f(x) = -2x^2 - 4x - 6$

32. $f(x) = -3x^2 + 6x + 2$

For each quadratic function, (a) find the vertex, the axis of symmetry, and the maximum or minimum function value and (b) graph the function.

33. $g(x) = x^2 - 6x + 13$

34. $g(x) = x^2 - 4x + 5$

35. $g(x) = 2x^2 - 8x + 3$

36. $g(x) = 2x^2 + 5x - 1$

37. $f(x) = 3x^2 - 24x + 50$

38. $f(x) = 4x^2 + 16x + 13$

39. $f(x) = -3x^2 + 5x - 2$

40. $f(x) = -3x^2 - 7x + 2$

41. $h(x) = \frac{1}{2}x^2 + 4x + \frac{19}{3}$

42. $h(x) = \frac{1}{2}x^2 - 3x + 2$

Find any x-intercepts and the y-intercept. If no x-intercepts exist, state this.

43. $f(x) = x^2 - 6x + 3$

44. $f(x) = x^2 + 5x + 4$

45. $g(x) = -x^2 + 2x + 3$

46. $g(x) = x^2 - 6x + 9$

Aha! 47. $f(x) = x^2 - 9x$

48. $f(x) = x^2 - 7x$

49. $h(x) = -x^2 + 4x - 4$

50. $h(x) = -2x^2 - 20x - 50$

51. $g(x) = x^2 + x - 5$

52. $g(x) = 2x^2 + 3x - 1$

53. $f(x) = 2x^2 - 4x + 6$

54. $f(x) = x^2 - x + 2$

55. The graph of a quadratic function f opens downward and has no x-intercepts. In what quadrant(s) must the vertex lie? Explain your reasoning.

56. Is it possible for the graph of a quadratic function to have only one x-intercept if the vertex is off the x-axis? Why or why not?

Skill Review

To prepare for Section 11.8, review solving systems of three equations in three unknowns (Section 8.4).

Solve. [8.4]

57. $x + y + z = 3,$
   $x - y + z = 1,$
   $-x - y + z = -1$

58. $x - y + z = -6,$
   $2x + y + z = 2,$
   $3x + y + z = 0$

59. $z = 8,$
   $x + y + z = 23,$
   $2x + y - z = 17$

60. $z = -5,$
   $2x - y + 3z = -27,$
   $x + 2y + 7z = -26$

61. $1.5 = c,$
   $52.5 = 25a + 5b + c,$
   $7.5 = 4a + 2b + c$

62. $\frac{1}{2} = c,$
   $5 = 9a + 6b + 2c,$
   $29 = 81a + 9b + c$

Synthesis

63. If the graphs of two quadratic functions have the same x-intercepts, will they also have the same vertex? Why or why not?

64. Suppose that the graph of $f(x) = ax^2 + bx + c$ has $(x_1, 0)$ and $(x_2, 0)$ as x-intercepts. Explain why the graph of $g(x) = -ax^2 - bx - c$ will also have $(x_1, 0)$ and $(x_2, 0)$ as x-intercepts.

For each quadratic function, find **(a)** *the maximum or minimum value and* **(b)** *any x-intercepts and the y-intercept.*

65. $f(x) = 2.31x^2 - 3.135x - 5.89$

66. $f(x) = -18.8x^2 + 7.92x + 6.18$

67. Graph the function
$$f(x) = x^2 - x - 6.$$
Then use the graph to approximate solutions to each of the following equations.

a) $x^2 - x - 6 = 2$
b) $x^2 - x - 6 = -3$

68. Graph the function
$$f(x) = \frac{x^2}{2} + x - \frac{3}{2}.$$
Then use the graph to approximate solutions to each of the following equations.

a) $\dfrac{x^2}{2} + x - \dfrac{3}{2} = 0$

b) $\dfrac{x^2}{2} + x - \dfrac{3}{2} = 1$

c) $\dfrac{x^2}{2} + x - \dfrac{3}{2} = 2$

Find an equivalent equation of the type
$$f(x) = a(x - h)^2 + k.$$

69. $f(x) = mx^2 - nx + p$

70. $f(x) = 3x^2 + mx + m^2$

71. A quadratic function has $(-1, 0)$ as one of its intercepts and $(3, -5)$ as its vertex. Find an equation for the function.

72. A quadratic function has $(4, 0)$ as one of its intercepts and $(-1, 7)$ as its vertex. Find an equation for the function.

Graph.

73. $f(x) = |x^2 - 1|$

74. $f(x) = |x^2 - 3x - 4|$

75. $f(x) = |2(x - 3)^2 - 5|$

76. Use a graphing calculator to check your answers to Exercises 25, 41, 53, 65, and 67.

11.8 Problem Solving and Quadratic Functions

Maximum and Minimum Problems ▪ Fitting Quadratic Functions to Data

Let's look now at some of the many situations in which quadratic functions are used for problem solving.

Maximum and Minimum Problems

We have seen that for any quadratic function f, the value of $f(x)$ at the vertex is either a maximum or a minimum. Thus problems in which a quantity must be maximized or minimized can be solved by finding the coordinates of a vertex, assuming the problem can be modeled with a quadratic function.

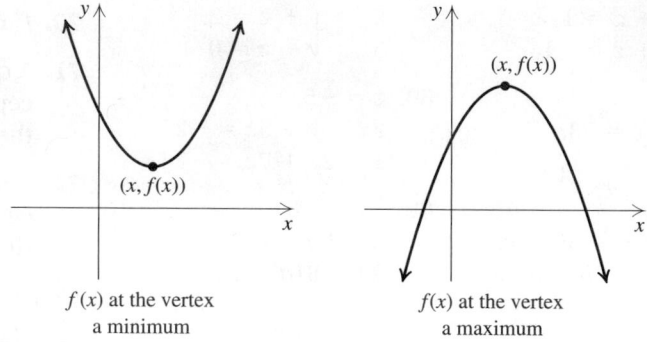

$f(x)$ at the vertex a minimum $f(x)$ at the vertex a maximum

EXAMPLE 1

Museum attendance. After the admission fee was dropped, attendance at the Indianapolis Museum of Art began to rise after several years of decline. The number of museum admissions, in thousands, t years after 2000 can be approximated by $m(t)$, where $m(t) = 32t^2 - 320t + 975$. In what year was the museum attendance the lowest, and how many people went to the museum that year?

Source: Based on information in the *Indianapolis Star*, 9/9/07

SOLUTION

1., 2. Familiarize and **Translate.** We are given the function for museum attendance. Note that it is a quadratic function of the number of years since 2000. The coefficient of the squared term is positive, so the graph opens upward and there is a minimum value. The calculator-generated graph at left confirms this.

3. Carry out. We can either complete the square or use the formula for the vertex. Completing the square, we have

$$m(t) = 32t^2 - 320t + 975$$
$$= 32(t^2 - 10t) + 975$$
$$= 32(t^2 - 10t + 25 - 25) + 975 \qquad \text{Completing the square}$$
$$= 32(t^2 - 10t + 25) - (32)(25) + 975$$
$$= 32(t - 5)^2 + 175. \qquad \text{Factoring and simplifying}$$

There is a minimum value of 175 when $t = 5$.

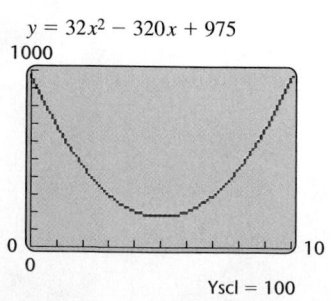

$y = 32x^2 - 320x + 975$

Yscl = 100

A visualization for Example 1

4. **Check.** Using the formula, we have $-b/(2a) = -(-320)/64 = 5$. Then

$$m(5) = 32(5)^2 - 320(5) + 975 = 175.$$

Both approaches give the same minimum, and that minimum is also confirmed by the graph. The answer checks.

5. **State.** The minimum attendance was 175,000. It occurred 5 yr after 2000, or in 2005.

> TRY EXERCISE ▶ 7

EXAMPLE 2

Swimming area.   A lifeguard has 100 m of roped-together flotation devices with which to cordon off a rectangular swimming area at North Beach. If the shoreline forms one side of the rectangle, what dimensions will maximize the size of the area for swimming?

SOLUTION

1. **Familiarize.** We make a drawing and label it, letting w = the width of the rectangle, in meters, and l = the length of the rectangle, in meters.

   Recall that Area = $l \cdot w$ and Perimeter = $2w + 2l$. Since the beach forms one length of the rectangle, the flotation devices comprise three sides. Thus

   $$2w + l = 100.$$

   To get a better feel for the problem, we can look at some possible dimensions for a rectangular area that can be enclosed with 100 m of flotation devices. All possibilities are chosen so that $2w + l = 100$.

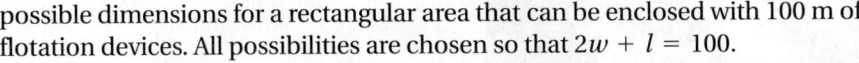

l	w	Rope Length	Area	
40 m	30 m	100 m	1200 m^2	What choice of l and
30 m	35 m	100 m	1050 m^2	w will maximize A?
20 m	40 m	100 m	800 m^2	
⋮	⋮	⋮	⋮	

2. **Translate.** We have two equations: One guarantees that all 100 m of flotation devices are used; the other expresses area in terms of length and width.

$$2w + l = 100,$$
$$A = l \cdot w$$

3. **Carry out.** We need to express A as a function of l or w but not both. To do so, we solve for l in the first equation to obtain $l = 100 - 2w$. Substituting for l in the second equation, we get a quadratic function:

$$A = (100 - 2w)w \quad \text{Substituting for } l$$
$$= 100w - 2w^2. \quad \text{This represents a parabola opening downward, so a maximum exists.}$$

Factoring and completing the square, we get

$$A = -2(w^2 - 50w + 625 - 625) \quad \text{We could also use the vertex formula.}$$
$$= -2(w - 25)^2 + 1250.$$

There is a maximum value of 1250 when $w = 25$.

TECHNOLOGY CONNECTION

To generate a table of values for Example 2, let x represent the width of the swimming area, in meters. If l represents the length, in meters, we must have $100 = 2x + l$. Next, solve for l and use that expression for y_1. Then let $y_2 = x \cdot y_1$ (to enter y_1, press **VARS** and select Y-VARS and then FUNCTION and then 1) so that y_2 represents the area. Scroll through the resulting table, adjusting the settings as needed, to determine at what point the area is maximized.

4. **Check.** If $w = 25$ m, then $l = 100 - 2 \cdot 25 = 50$ m. These dimensions give an area of 1250 m². Note that 1250 m² is greater than any of the values for A found in the *Familiarize* step. To be more certain, we could check values other than those used in that step. For example, if $w = 26$ m, then $l = 48$ m, and $A = 26 \cdot 48 = 1248$ m². Since 1250 m² is greater than 1248 m², it appears that we have a maximum.

5. **State.** The largest rectangular area for swimming that can be enclosed is 25 m by 50 m.

> TRY EXERCISE ▶ 11

Fitting Quadratic Functions to Data

Whenever a certain quadratic function fits a situation, that function can be determined if three inputs and their outputs are known. Each of the given ordered pairs is called a *data point*.

EXAMPLE 3

Music CDs. As more listeners download their music purchases, sales of compact discs are decreasing. According to Nielsen SoundScan, sales of music CDs increased from 500 million in 1997 to 700 million in 2001 and then decreased to 450 million in 2007. As the graph suggests, sales of music CDs can be modeled by a quadratic function.

Years After 1997	Number of Music CDs Sold in the United States (in millions)
0	500
4	700
10	450

Source: Nielsen SoundScan

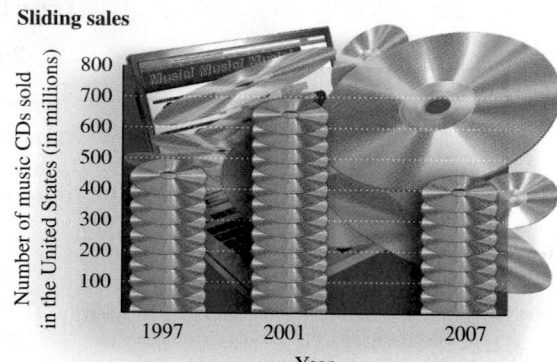

Sliding sales

a) Let t represent the number of years since 1997 and $S(t)$ the total number of CDs sold, in millions. Use the data points $(0, 500)$, $(4, 700)$, and $(10, 450)$ to find a quadratic function that fits the data.

b) Use the function from part (a) to estimate the sales of music CDs in 2009.

SOLUTION

a) We are looking for a function of the form $S(t) = at^2 + bt + c$ given that $S(0) = 500$, $S(4) = 700$, and $S(10) = 450$. Thus,

$$500 = a \cdot 0^2 + b \cdot 0 + c, \qquad \text{Using the data point } (0, 500)$$
$$700 = a \cdot 4^2 + b \cdot 4 + c, \qquad \text{Using the data point } (4, 700)$$
$$450 = a \cdot 10^2 + b \cdot 10 + c. \qquad \text{Using the data point } (10, 450)$$

After simplifying, we see that we need to solve the system

$$500 = c, \qquad\qquad\qquad (1)$$
$$700 = 16a + 4b + c, \qquad (2)$$
$$450 = 100a + 10b + c. \quad (3)$$

STUDENT NOTES ———

Try to keep the "big picture" in mind on problems like Example 3. Solving a system of three equations is but one part of the solution.

To use a graphing calculator to fit a quadratic function to the data in Example 3, we first select EDIT in the **STAT** menu and enter the given data.

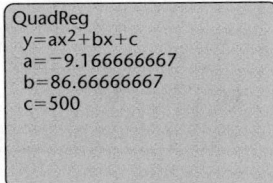

To fit a quadratic function to the data, we press **STAT** **▷** **5** **VARS** **▷** **1** **1** **ENTER**. The first three keystrokes select QuadReg from the STAT CALC menu. The keystrokes **VARS** **▷** **1** **1** copy the regression equation to the equation-editor screen as y_1.

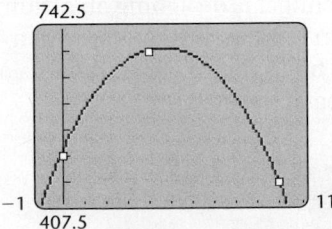

We see that the regression equation is $y = -9.166666667x^2 + 86.66666667x + 500$. We press **Y=** **∧** **ENTER** to turn on the PLOT feature and **ZOOM** **9** to see the regression equation graphed with the data points.

To check Example 3(b), we set Indpnt to Ask in the Table Setup and enter $X = 12$ in the table. A Y_1-value of 220 confirms our answer.

1. Use the above approach to estimate the sales of music CDs in 2005.

We know from equation (1) that $c = 500$. Substituting that value into equations (2) and (3), we have

$$700 = 16a + 4b + 500,$$
$$450 = 100a + 10b + 500.$$

Subtracting 500 from both sides of each equation, we have

$$200 = 16a + 4b, \qquad \textbf{(4)}$$
$$-50 = 100a + 10b. \qquad \textbf{(5)}$$

To solve, we multiply equation (4) by 5 and equation (5) by -2. We then add to eliminate b:

$$\begin{aligned} 1000 &= 80a + 20b \\ 100 &= -200a - 20b \\ \hline 1100 &= -120a \end{aligned}$$

$$-\frac{1100}{120} = a, \quad \text{or} \quad a = -\frac{55}{6}. \qquad \text{Simplifying}$$

Next, we solve for b, using equation (5) above:

$$-50 = 100\left(-\frac{55}{6}\right) + 10b$$

$$-50 = -\frac{2750}{3} + 10b$$

$$\frac{2600}{3} = 10b \qquad \text{Adding } \tfrac{2750}{3} \text{ to both sides and simplifying}$$

$$\frac{2600}{30} = b, \quad \text{or} \quad b = \frac{260}{3}. \qquad \text{Dividing both sides by 10 and simplifying}$$

We can now write $S(t) = at^2 + bt + c$ as

$$S(t) = -\frac{55}{6}t^2 + \frac{260}{3}t + 500.$$

b) To find the sales of CDs in 2009, we evaluate the function. Note that 2009 is 12 yr after 1997. Thus,

$$S(12) = -\frac{55}{6} \cdot 12^2 + \frac{260}{3} \cdot 12 + 500$$

$$= 220.$$

In 2009, an estimated 220 million music CDs will be sold.

TRY EXERCISE 35

11.8 EXERCISE SET

For Extra Help
MyMathLab   MathXL PRACTICE   WATCH   DOWNLOAD

Concept Reinforcement   *In each of Exercises 1–6, match the description with the graph that displays that characteristic.*

1. ____ A minimum value of $f(x)$ exists.

2. ____ A maximum value of $f(x)$ exists.

3. ____ No maximum or minimum value of $f(x)$ exists.

4. ____ The data points appear to suggest a linear model for g.

5. ____ The data points appear to suggest that g is a quadratic function with a maximum.

6. ____ The data points appear to suggest that g is a quadratic function with a minimum.

a)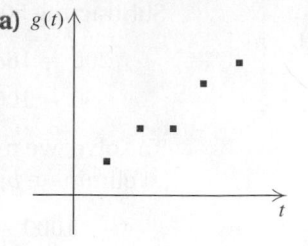

b)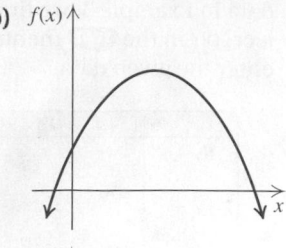

c)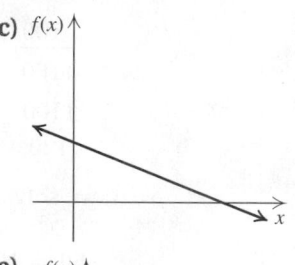

d)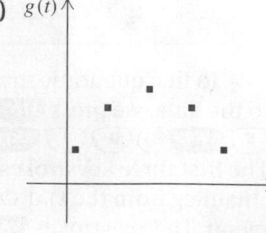

e)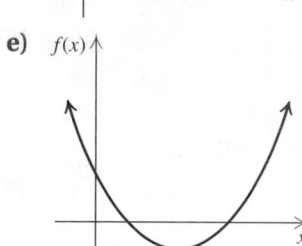

f)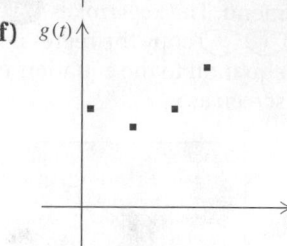

Solve.

7. Newborn calves.   The number of pounds of milk per day recommended for a calf that is x weeks old can be approximated by $p(x)$, where

$$p(x) = -0.2x^2 + 1.3x + 6.2.$$

When is a calf's milk consumption greatest and how much milk does it consume at that time?
Source: C. Chaloux, University of Vermont, 1998

8. Stock prices.   The value of a share of I. J. Solar can be represented by $V(x) = x^2 - 6x + 13$, where x is the number of months after January 2009. What is the lowest value $V(x)$ will reach, and when did that occur?

9. Minimizing cost.   Sweet Harmony Crafts has determined that when x hundred dulcimers are built, the average cost per dulcimer can be estimated by

$$C(x) = 0.1x^2 - 0.7x + 2.425,$$

where $C(x)$ is in hundreds of dollars. What is the minimum average cost per dulcimer and how many dulcimers should be built in order to achieve that minimum?

10. Maximizing profit.   Recall that total profit P is the difference between total revenue R and total cost C. Given $R(x) = 1000x - x^2$ and $C(x) = 3000 + 20x$, find the total profit, the maximum value of the total profit, and the value of x at which it occurs.

11. Architecture.   An architect is designing an atrium for a hotel. The atrium is to be rectangular with a perimeter of 720 ft of brass piping. What dimensions will maximize the area of the atrium?

12. *Furniture design.*   A furniture builder is designing a rectangular end table with a perimeter of 128 in. What dimensions will yield the maximum area?

13. *Patio design.*   A stone mason has enough stones to enclose a rectangular patio with 60 ft of perimeter, assuming that the attached house forms one side of the rectangle. What is the maximum area that the mason can enclose? What should the dimensions of the patio be in order to yield this area?

14. *Garden design.*   Ginger is fencing in a rectangular garden, using the side of her house as one side of the rectangle. What is the maximum area that she can enclose with 40 ft of fence? What should the dimensions of the garden be in order to yield this area?

15. *Molding plastics.*   Economite Plastics plans to produce a one-compartment vertical file by bending the long side of an 8-in. by 14-in. sheet of plastic along two lines to form a U shape. How tall should the file be in order to maximize the volume that the file can hold?

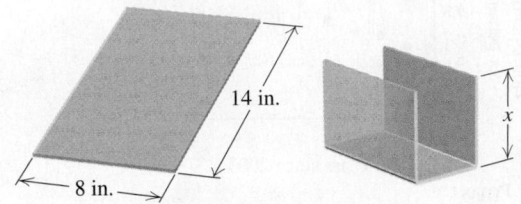

16. *Composting.*   A rectangular compost container is to be formed in a corner of a fenced yard, with 8 ft of chicken wire completing the other two sides of the rectangle. If the chicken wire is 3 ft high, what dimensions of the base will maximize the container's volume?

17.   What is the maximum product of two numbers that add to 18? What numbers yield this product?

18.   What is the maximum product of two numbers that add to 26? What numbers yield this product?

19.   What is the minimum product of two numbers that differ by 8? What are the numbers?

20.   What is the minimum product of two numbers that differ by 7? What are the numbers?

Aha! **21.**   What is the maximum product of two numbers that add to −10? What numbers yield this product?

22.   What is the maximum product of two numbers that add to −12? What numbers yield this product?

Choosing models.   *For the scatterplots and graphs in Exercises 23–34, determine which, if any, of the following functions might be used as a model for the data: Linear, with $f(x) = mx + b$; quadratic, with $f(x) = ax^2 + bx + c$, $a > 0$; quadratic, with $f(x) = ax^2 + bx + c$, $a < 0$; neither quadratic nor linear.*

23.   **Sonoma Sunshine**

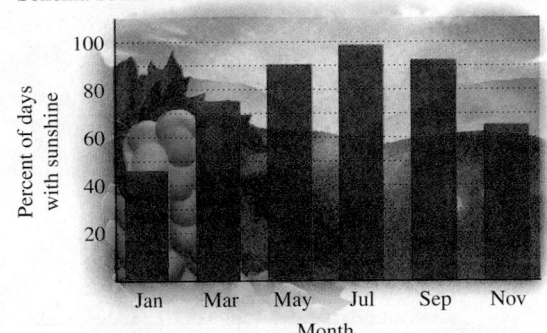

Source: www.city-data.com

24.   **Sonoma Precipitation**

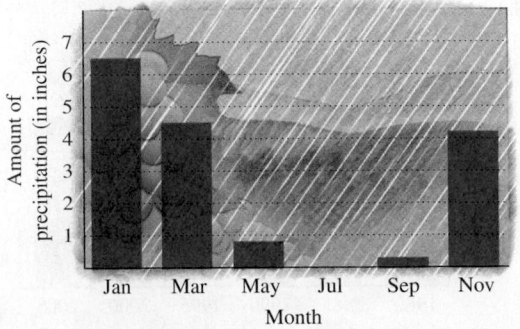

Source: www.city-data.com

25. **Safe sight distance to the left**

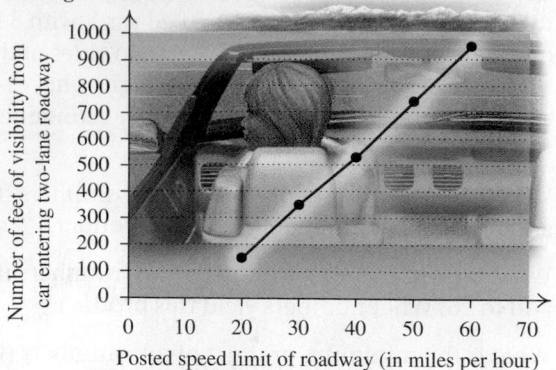

Source: Institute of Traffic Engineers

26. **Safe sight distance to the right**

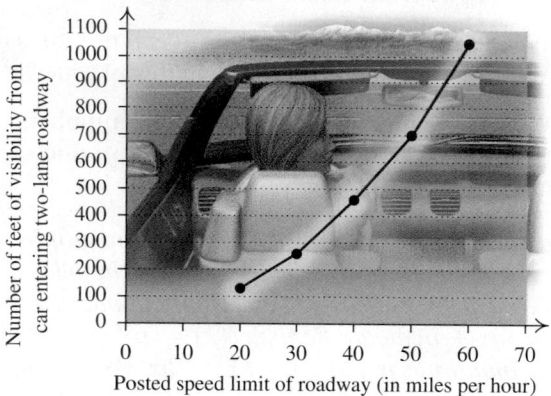

Source: Institute of Traffic Engineers

27. **Winter Olympic volunteers**

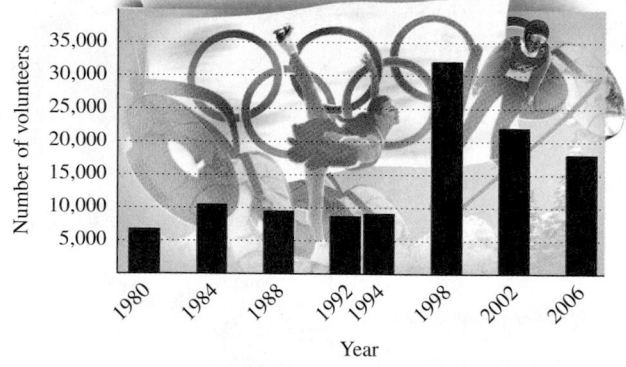

28. **U.S. senior population**

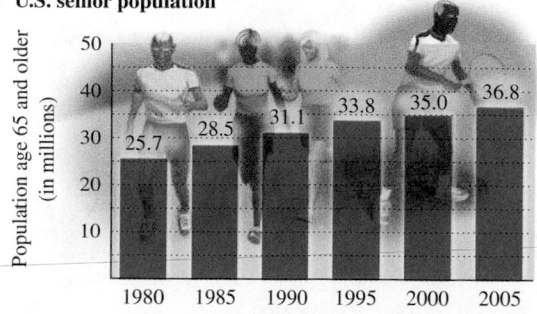

Source: U.S. Bureau of Labor Statistics

29. **Changing work force**

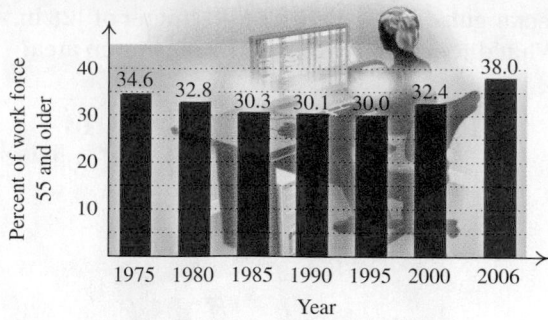

Source: U.S. Department of Labor, Bureau of Labor Statistics

30. **Airline bumping rate**

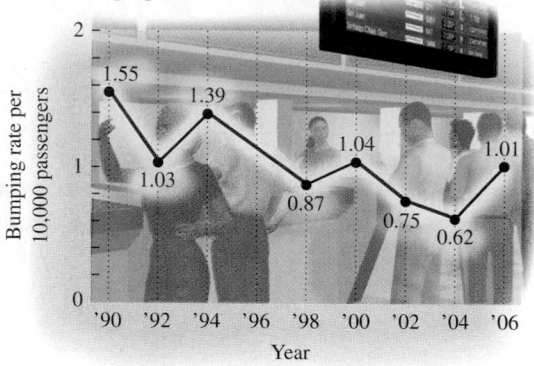

Source: U.S. Department of Transportation

31. **Hybrid vehicles**

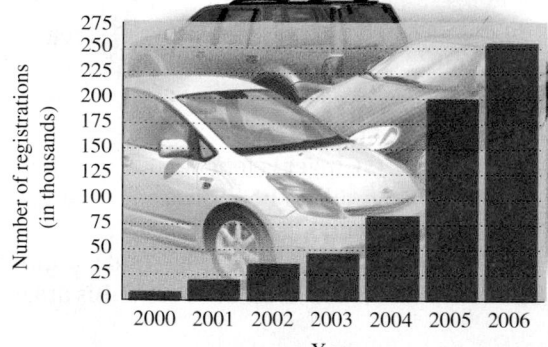

Source: R.L. Polk & Co.

32.

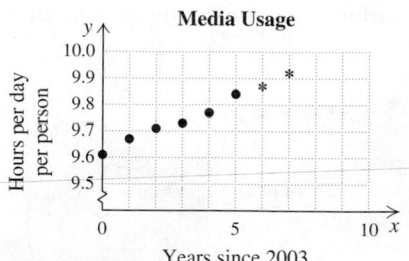

* Projected

Source: Statistical Abstract of the United States

33. Employee contribution to health insurance premium

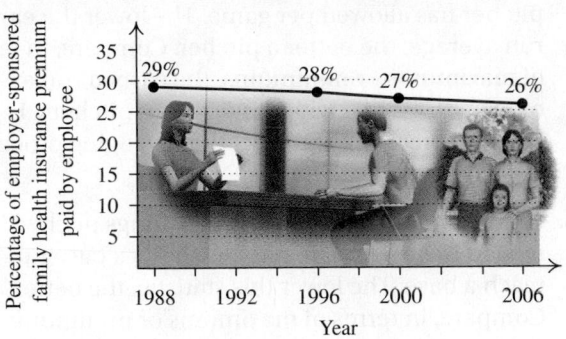

Source: Based on data from Kaiser

34. Average number of live births per 1000 women, 2005

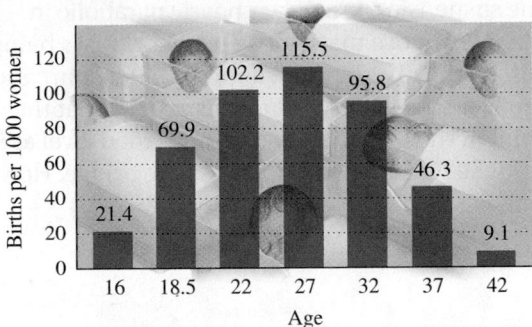

Source: U.S. Centers for Disease Control

Find a quadratic function that fits the set of data points.

35. $(1, 4), (-1, -2), (2, 13)$

36. $(1, 4), (-1, 6), (-2, 16)$

37. $(2, 0), (4, 3), (12, -5)$

38. $(-3, -30), (3, 0), (6, 6)$

39. a) Find a quadratic function that fits the following data.

Travel Speed (in kilometers per hour)	Number of Nighttime Accidents (for every 200 million kilometers driven)
60	400
80	250
100	250

b) Use the function to estimate the number of nighttime accidents that occur at 50 km/h.

40. a) Find a quadratic function that fits the following data.

Travel Speed (in kilometers per hour)	Number of Daytime Accidents (for every 200 million kilometers driven)
60	100
80	130
100	200

b) Use the function to estimate the number of daytime accidents that occur at 50 km/h.

41. *Archery.* The Olympic flame tower at the 1992 Summer Olympics was lit at a height of about 27 m by a flaming arrow that was launched about 63 m from the base of the tower. If the arrow landed about 63 m beyond the tower, find a quadratic function that expresses the height h of the arrow as a function of the distance d that it traveled horizontally.

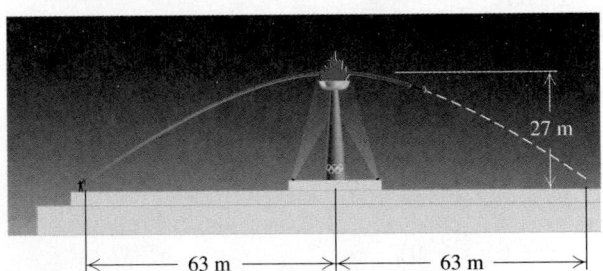

42. *Outsourcing.* The revenue, in billions of dollars, from India's outsourcing industry is shown in the following table.

Year	Outsourcing Revenue (in billions of dollars)
2001	$12
2004	21
2007	48

Source: Nasscom

a) Let t represent the number of years since 2000 and $r(t)$ the revenue, in billions of dollars. Find a quadratic function that fits the data.

b) Use the function to estimate India's outsourcing revenue in 2012.

43. Does every nonlinear function have a minimum or a maximum value? Why or why not?

44. Explain how the leading coefficient of a quadratic function can be used to determine if a maximum or a minimum function value exists.

Skill Review

To prepare for Section 11.9, review solving inequalities and rational expressions and equations (Chapters 6 and 9).

Solve.

45. $2x - 3 > 5$ [9.1]

46. $4 - x \le 7$ [9.1]

47. $|9 - x| \ge 2$ [9.3]

48. $|4x + 1| < 11$ [9.3]

Subtract. [6.4]

49. $\dfrac{x - 3}{x + 4} - 5$

50. $\dfrac{x}{x - 1} - 1$

Solve. [6.6]

51. $\dfrac{x - 3}{x + 4} = 5$

52. $\dfrac{x}{x - 1} = 1$

53. $\dfrac{x}{(x - 3)(x + 7)} = 0$

54. $\dfrac{(x + 6)(x - 9)}{x + 5} = 0$

Synthesis

The following graphs can be used to compare the baseball statistics of pitcher Roger Clemens with the 31 other pitchers since 1968 who started at least 10 games in at least 15 seasons and pitched at least 3000 innings. Use the graphs to answer questions 55 and 56.

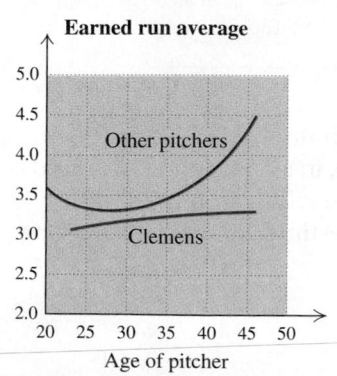

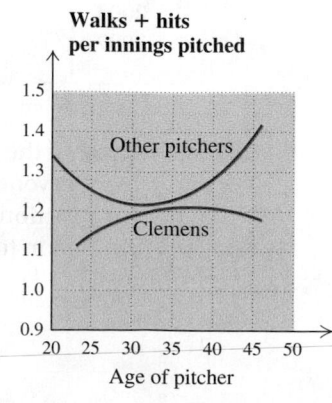

Source: The New York Times, February 10, 2008;
Eric Bradlow, Shane Jensen, Justin Wolfers and Adi Wyner

55. The earned run average describes how many runs a pitcher has allowed per game. The lower the earned run average, the better a pitcher. Compare, in terms of maximums or minimums, the earned run average of Roger Clemens with that of other pitchers. Is there any reason to suspect that the aging process was unusual for Clemens? Explain.

56. The statistic "Walks + hits per innings pitched" is related to how often a pitcher allows a batter to reach a base. The lower this statistic, the better. Compare, in terms of maximums or minimums, the "walks + hits" statistic of Roger Clemens with that of other pitchers.

57. *Bridge design.* The cables supporting a straight-line suspension bridge are nearly parabolic in shape. Suppose that a suspension bridge is being designed with concrete supports 160 ft apart and with vertical cables 30 ft above road level at the mid-point of the bridge and 80 ft above road level at a point 50 ft from the midpoint of the bridge. How long are the longest vertical cables?

58. *Trajectory of a launched object.* The height above the ground of a launched object is a quadratic function of the time that it is in the air. Suppose that a flare is launched from a cliff 64 ft above sea level. If 3 sec after being launched the flare is again level with the cliff, and if 2 sec after that it lands in the sea, what is the maximum height that the flare will reach?

59. *Cover charges.* When the owner of Sweet Sounds charges a $10 cover charge, an average of 80 people will attend a show. For each 25¢ increase in admission price, the average number attending decreases by 1. What should the owner charge in order to make the most money?

60. *Crop yield.* An orange grower finds that she gets an average yield of 40 bushels (bu) per tree when she plants 20 trees on an acre of ground. Each time she adds one tree per acre, the yield per tree decreases by 1 bu, due to congestion. How many trees per acre should she plant for maximum yield?

61. *Norman window.*   A *Norman window* is a rectangle with a semicircle on top. Big Sky Windows is designing a Norman window that will require 24 ft of trim. What dimensions will allow the maximum amount of light to enter a house?

62. *Minimizing area.*   A 36-in. piece of string is cut into two pieces. One piece is used to form a circle while the other is used to form a square. How should the string be cut so that the sum of the areas is a minimum?

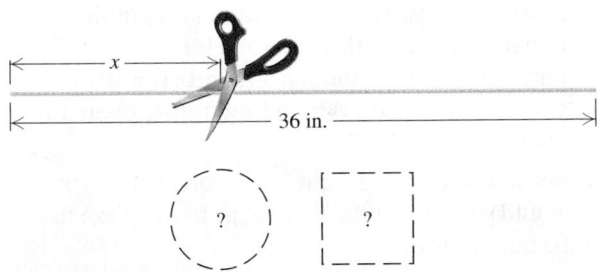

Regression can be used to find the "best"-fitting quadratic function when more than three data points are provided. In Exercises 63 and 64, six data points are given, but the approach used in the Technology Connection on p. 759 still applies.

63. *Hybrid vehicles.*   The number of hybrid vehicles in the United States during several years is shown in the table below.

Year	Number of Vehicles
2001	19,963
2002	35,934
2003	45,943
2004	83,153
2005	199,148
2006	254,545

Source: R. L. Polk & Co.

a) Use regression to find a quadratic function that can be used to estimate the number of hybrid vehicles $h(x)$ in the United States x years after 2000.

b) Use the function found in part (a) to predict the number of hybrid vehicles in the United States in 2010.

64. *Hydrology.*   The drawing below shows the cross section of a river. Typically rivers are deepest in the middle, with the depth decreasing to 0 at the edges. A hydrologist measures the depths D, in feet, of a river at distances x, in feet, from one bank. The results are listed in the table below.

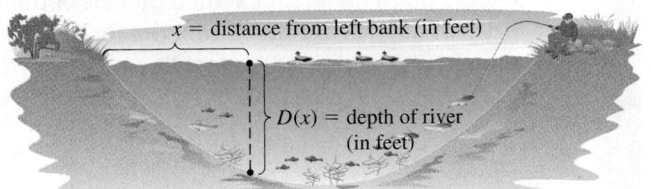

Distance x, from the Left Bank (in feet)	Depth, D, of the River (in feet)
0	0
15	10.2
25	17
50	20
90	7.2
100	0

a) Use regression to find a quadratic function that fits the data.

b) Use the function to estimate the depth of the river 70 ft from the left bank.

COLLABORATIVE CORNER

Parabolic Pizza

Focus: Modeling
Time: 20–30 minutes
Group size: 3
Materials: Graphing calculators are optional.

College Pizza on Chestnut Street in Philadelphia, PA, sells a 10-in.–diameter cheese pizza for $5.00, a 14-in. cheese pizza for $7.50, and an 18-in. cheese pizza for $11.00. Which models better the price of the pizza: a linear function or a quadratic function of the diameter?

Source: Campusfood.com

ACTIVITY

1. As a group, carefully graph the ordered pairs from the data above in the form (diameter, price). Do the data appear to be quadratic or linear?

2. Each group member should choose one of the following to fit a model to the data, where $p(x)$ is the price, in dollars, of an x-inch–diameter pizza. Then, using a different color for each graph, that member should graph the function on the same graph as the ordered pairs.

a) Linear function $p(x) = mx + b$, using the points (10, 5) and (14, 7.5)
b) Linear function $p(x) = mx + b$, using the points (10, 5) and (18, 11)
c) Quadratic function $p(x) = ax^2 + bx + c$, using all three points

3. As a group, determine which function from part (1) appears to be the best fit.

4. One way to tell whether a function is a good fit is to see how well it predicts another known value. College Pizza also sells a 16-in. cheese pizza for $9.00. Each group member should use the function from part (2) to predict the price of a 16-in. cheese pizza. Which function came the closest to predicting the actual value?

5. If a graphing calculator is available, use the LINREG and QUADREG options to fit and graph linear and quadratic functions for the four data points (three pairs from part (1) and one pair from part (4)). Which function appears to give the best fit?

6. Because the area of a circle is given by $A = \pi r^2$, would you expect the price of a cheese pizza to be quadratic or linear?

11.9   Polynomial and Rational Inequalities

Quadratic and Other Polynomial Inequalities • Rational Inequalities

Quadratic and Other Polynomial Inequalities

Inequalities like the following are called *polynomial inequalities*:

$$x^3 - 5x > x^2 + 7, \qquad 4x - 3 < 9, \qquad 5x^2 - 3x + 2 \geq 0.$$

Second-degree polynomial inequalities in one variable are called *quadratic inequalities*. To solve polynomial inequalities, we often focus attention on where the outputs of a polynomial function are positive and where they are negative.

EXAMPLE 1   Solve: $x^2 + 3x - 10 > 0$.

SOLUTION   Consider the "related" function $f(x) = x^2 + 3x - 10$. We are looking for those x-values for which $f(x) > 0$. Graphically, function values are positive when the graph is above the x-axis.

The graph of f opens upward since the leading coefficient is positive. Thus y-values are positive *outside* the interval formed by the x-intercepts. To find the intercepts, we set the polynomial equal to 0 and solve:

$$x^2 + 3x - 10 = 0$$
$$(x + 5)(x - 2) = 0$$
$$x + 5 = 0 \quad \text{or} \quad x - 2 = 0$$
$$x = -5 \quad \text{or} \quad x = 2. \qquad \text{The } x\text{-intercepts are } (-5, 0) \text{ and } (2, 0).$$

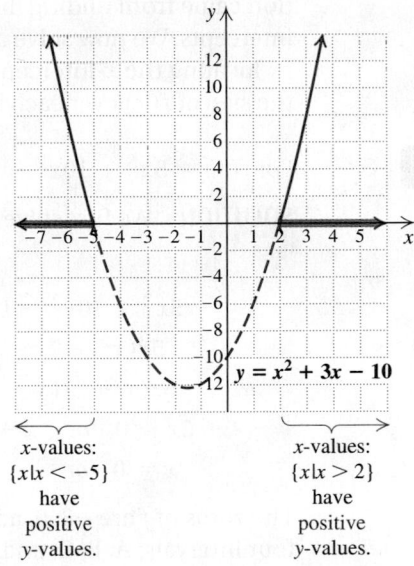

x-values: $\{x | x < -5\}$ have positive y-values.

x-values: $\{x | x > 2\}$ have positive y-values.

Thus the solution set of the inequality is

$$(-\infty, -5) \cup (2, \infty), \text{ or } \{x | x < -5 \text{ or } x > 2\}.$$

TRY EXERCISE 13

Any inequality with 0 on one side can be solved by considering a graph of the related function and finding intercepts as in Example 1. Sometimes the quadratic formula is needed to find the intercepts.

EXAMPLE 2

Solve: $x^2 - 2x \le 2$.

SOLUTION   We first write the quadratic inequality in standard form, with 0 on one side:

$$x^2 - 2x - 2 \le 0. \qquad \text{This is equivalent to the original inequality.}$$

The graph of $f(x) = x^2 - 2x - 2$ is a parabola opening upward. Values of $f(x)$ are negative for x-values between the x-intercepts. We find the x-intercepts by solving $f(x) = 0$:

$$x = \frac{-b \pm \sqrt{b^2 - 4ac}}{2a}$$
$$= \frac{-(-2) \pm \sqrt{(-2)^2 - 4 \cdot 1(-2)}}{2 \cdot 1}$$
$$= \frac{2 \pm \sqrt{12}}{2} = \frac{2}{2} \pm \frac{2\sqrt{3}}{2} = 1 \pm \sqrt{3}.$$

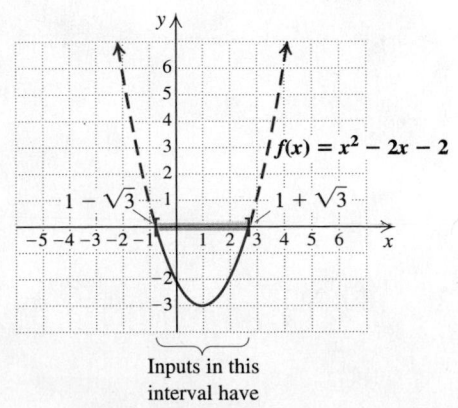

Inputs in this interval have negative or 0 outputs.

At the x-intercepts, $1 - \sqrt{3}$ and $1 + \sqrt{3}$, the value of $f(x)$ is 0. Since the inequality symbol is $\leq$, the solution set will include all values of x for which $f(x)$ is negative *or* $f(x)$ is 0. Thus the solution set of the inequality is

$$[1 - \sqrt{3}, 1 + \sqrt{3}], \quad \text{or} \quad \{x \mid 1 - \sqrt{3} \leq x \leq 1 + \sqrt{3}\}.$$

TRY EXERCISE ▶ 21

In Example 2, it was not essential to draw the graph. The important information came from finding the x-intercepts and the sign of $f(x)$ on each side of those intercepts. We now solve a third-degree polynomial inequality, without graphing, by locating the x-intercepts, or **zeros**, of f and then using *test points* to determine the sign of $f(x)$ over each interval of the x-axis.

EXAMPLE 3

For $f(x) = 5x^3 + 10x^2 - 15x$, find all x-values for which $f(x) > 0$.

SOLUTION   We first solve the related equation:

$$f(x) = 0$$
$$5x^3 + 10x^2 - 15x = 0 \qquad \text{Substituting}$$
$$5x(x^2 + 2x - 3) = 0$$
$$5x(x + 3)(x - 1) = 0$$
$$5x = 0 \quad or \quad x + 3 = 0 \quad or \quad x - 1 = 0$$
$$x = 0 \quad or \qquad x = -3 \quad or \qquad x = 1.$$

The zeros of f are -3, 0, and 1. These zeros divide the number line, or x-axis, into four intervals: A, B, C, and D.

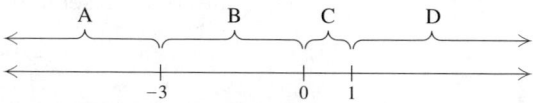

Next, selecting one convenient test value from each interval, we determine the sign of $f(x)$ for that interval. We know that, within each interval, the sign of $f(x)$ cannot change. If it did, there would need to be another zero in that interval. Using the factored form of $f(x)$ eases the computations:

$$f(x) = 5x(x + 3)(x - 1).$$

STUDENT NOTES

When we are evaluating test values, there is often no need to do lengthy computations since all we need to determine is the sign of the result.

For interval A,

$$f(-4) = \underbrace{5(-4)}\,\underbrace{((-4) + 3)}\,\underbrace{((-4) - 1)}$$

$$\underbrace{\text{Negative} \,\cdot\, \text{Negative} \,\cdot\, \text{Negative}}_{\text{Negative}}$$

-4 is a convenient value in interval A.

Only the sign is important. The product of three negative numbers is negative, so $f(-4)$ is negative.

For interval B,

$$f(-1) = \underbrace{5(-1)}\,\underbrace{((-1) + 3)}\,\underbrace{((-1) - 1)}$$

$$\underbrace{\text{Negative} \,\cdot\, \text{Positive} \,\cdot\, \text{Negative}}_{\text{Positive}}$$

-1 is a convenient value in interval B.

$f(-1)$ is positive.

y↑

$f(x) > 0$

$f(x) > 0$

$f(x) < 0$

$f(x) < 0$

$f(x) = 5x(x + 3)(x - 1)$

A visualization of Example 3

For interval C,

$$f\left(\tfrac{1}{2}\right) = \underbrace{5 \cdot \tfrac{1}{2}} \cdot \underbrace{\left(\tfrac{1}{2} + 3\right)} \cdot \underbrace{\left(\tfrac{1}{2} - 1\right)}.$$ $\tfrac{1}{2}$ is a convenient value in interval C.

$$\underbrace{\text{Positive} \cdot \text{Positive} \cdot \text{Negative}}$$

$$\text{Negative}$$ $f\left(\tfrac{1}{2}\right)$ is negative.

For interval D,

$$f(2) = \underbrace{5 \cdot 2} \cdot \underbrace{(2 + 3)} \cdot \underbrace{(2 - 1)}.$$ 2 is a convenient value in interval D.

$$\text{Positive} \cdot \text{Positive} \cdot \text{Positive}$$ $f(2)$ is positive.

Recall that we are looking for all x for which $5x^3 + 10x^2 - 15x > 0$. The calculations above indicate that $f(x)$ is positive for any number in intervals B and D. The solution set of the original inequality is

$$(-3, 0) \cup (1, \infty), \quad \text{or} \quad \{x | -3 < x < 0 \text{ or } x > 1\}.$$

TRY EXERCISE ▸ 29

The calculations in Example 3 were made simpler by using a factored form of the polynomial and by focusing on only the *sign* of $f(x)$. By looking at how many positive or negative factors are multiplied, we are able to determine the sign of the polynomial function.

To Solve a Polynomial Inequality Using Factors

1. Add or subtract to get 0 on one side and solve the related polynomial equation by factoring.
2. Use the numbers found in step (1) to divide the number line into intervals.
3. Using a test value from each interval, determine the sign of the function over each interval. First find the sign of each factor, and then determine the sign of the product of the factors. Remember that the product of an odd number of negative numbers is negative.
4. Select the interval(s) for which the inequality is satisfied and write interval notation or set-builder notation for the solution set. Include endpoints of intervals when $\leq$ or $\geq$ is used.

EXAMPLE **4**

For $f(x) = 4x^3 - 4x$, find all x-values for which $f(x) \leq 0$.

SOLUTION   We first solve the related equation:

Solve $f(x) = 0$.

$$f(x) = 0$$
$$4x^3 - 4x = 0$$
$$4x(x^2 - 1) = 0$$
$$4x(x + 1)(x - 1) = 0$$
$$4x = 0 \quad or \quad x + 1 = 0 \quad or \quad x - 1 = 0$$
$$x = 0 \quad or \qquad x = -1 \quad or \qquad x = 1.$$

Divide the number line into intervals.

The function f has zeros at $-1, 0,$ and 1, so we divide the number line into four intervals:

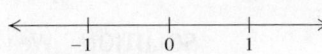

The product $4x(x + 1)(x - 1)$ is positive or negative, depending on the signs of $4x$, $x + 1$, and $x - 1$. This can be determined by making a chart.

Interval:	$(-\infty, -1)$	$(-1, 0)$	$(0, 1)$	$(1, \infty)$
Sign of $4x$:	−	−	+	+
Sign of $x + 1$:	−	+	+	+
Sign of $x - 1$:	−	−	−	+
Sign of product $4x(x + 1)(x - 1)$:	−	+	−	+

Determine the sign of the function over each interval.

A product is negative when it has an odd number of negative factors. Since the $\leq$ sign allows for equality, the endpoints -1, 0, and 1 are solutions. From the chart, we see that the solution set is

Select the interval(s) for which the inequality is satisfied.

$$(-\infty, -1] \cup [0, 1], \quad \text{or} \quad \{x \mid x \leq -1 \text{ or } 0 \leq x \leq 1\}.$$

TRY EXERCISE 31

TECHNOLOGY CONNECTION

To solve $2.3x^2 \leq 9.11 - 2.94x$, we write the inequality in the form $2.3x^2 + 2.94x - 9.11 \leq 0$ and graph the function $f(x) = 2.3x^2 + 2.94x - 9.11$.

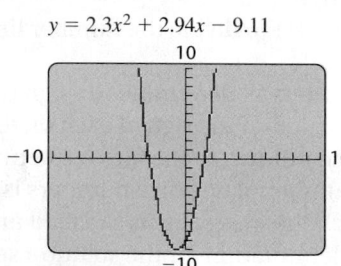

$y = 2.3x^2 + 2.94x - 9.11$

The region in which the graph lies *on or below* the x-axis begins somewhere between -3 and -2, and

continues to somewhere between 1 and 2. Using the ZERO option of CALC and rounding, we find that the endpoints are -2.73 and 1.45. The solution set is approximately $\{x \mid -2.73 \leq x \leq 1.45\}$.

Had the inequality been $2.3x^2 > 9.11 - 2.94x$, we would look for portions of the graph that lie *above* the x-axis. An approximate solution set of this inequality is $\{x \mid x < -2.73 \text{ or } x > 1.45\}$.

Use a graphing calculator to solve each inequality. Round the values of the endpoints to the nearest hundredth.

1. $4.32x^2 - 3.54x - 5.34 \leq 0$
2. $7.34x^2 - 16.55x - 3.89 \geq 0$
3. $10.85x^2 + 4.28x + 4.44$
   $> 7.91x^2 + 7.43x + 13.03$
4. $5.79x^3 - 5.68x^2 + 10.68x$
   $> 2.11x^3 + 16.90x - 11.69$

Rational Inequalities

Inequalities involving rational expressions are called **rational inequalities**. Like polynomial inequalities, rational inequalities can be solved using test values. Unlike polynomials, however, rational expressions often have values for which the expression is undefined. These values must be used when dividing the number line into intervals.

EXAMPLE 5   Solve: $\dfrac{x - 3}{x + 4} \geq 2$.

SOLUTION   We write the related equation by changing the $\geq$ symbol to $=$:

$$\frac{x - 3}{x + 4} = 2. \quad \text{Note that } x \neq -4.$$

Next, we solve this related equation:

$$(x + 4) \cdot \frac{x - 3}{x + 4} = (x + 4) \cdot 2 \qquad \text{Multiplying both sides by the LCD, } x + 4$$

$$x - 3 = 2x + 8$$

$$-11 = x. \qquad \text{Solving for } x$$

Since -11 is a solution of the related equation, we use -11 when dividing the number line into intervals. Since the rational expression is undefined for $x = -4$, we also use -4:

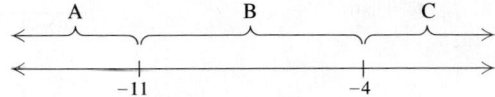

We test a number from each interval to see where the original inequality is satisfied:

$$\frac{x - 3}{x + 4} \geq 2.$$

For Interval A,

$$\text{Test } -15, \quad \frac{-15 - 3}{-15 + 4} = \frac{-18}{-11}$$

$$= \frac{18}{11} \not\geq 2. \qquad \begin{array}{l} -15 \text{ } \textit{is not} \text{ a solution, so interval A is} \\ \text{not part of the solution set.} \end{array}$$

For Interval B,

$$\text{Test } -8, \quad \frac{-8 - 3}{-8 + 4} = \frac{-11}{-4}$$

$$= \frac{11}{4} \geq 2. \qquad \begin{array}{l} -8 \text{ } \textit{is} \text{ a solution, so interval B is part of} \\ \text{the solution set.} \end{array}$$

For Interval C,

$$\text{Test } 1, \quad \frac{1 - 3}{1 + 4} = \frac{-2}{5}$$

$$= -\frac{2}{5} \not\geq 2. \qquad \begin{array}{l} 1 \text{ } \textit{is not} \text{ a solution, so interval C is not} \\ \text{part of the solution set.} \end{array}$$

The solution set includes interval B. The endpoint -11 is included because the inequality symbol is $\geq$ and -11 is a solution of the related equation. The number -4 is *not* included because $(x - 3)/(x + 4)$ is undefined for $x = -4$. Thus the solution set of the original inequality is

$$[-11, -4), \quad \text{or} \quad \{x \mid -11 \leq x < -4\}.$$

TRY EXERCISE 37

ALGEBRAIC–GRAPHICAL CONNECTION

To compare the algebraic solution of Example 5 with a graphical solution, we graph $f(x) = (x - 3)/(x + 4)$ and the line $y = 2$. The solutions of $(x - 3)/(x + 4) \geq 2$ are found by locating all x-values for which $f(x) \geq 2$.

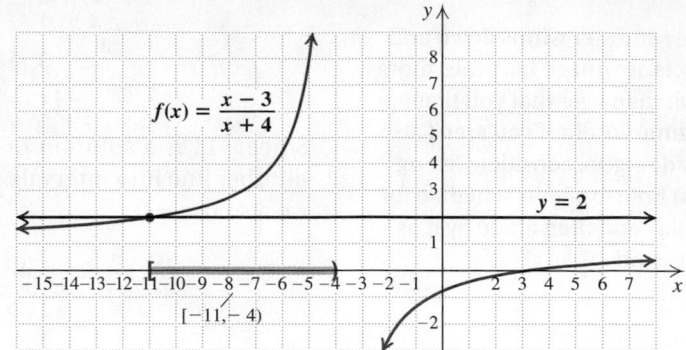

To Solve a Rational Inequality

1. Find any replacements for which any rational expression is undefined.
2. Change the inequality symbol to an equals sign and solve the related equation.
3. Use the numbers found in steps (1) and (2) to divide the number line into intervals.
4. Substitute a test value from each interval into the inequality. If the number is a solution, then the interval to which it belongs is part of the solution set.
5. Select the interval(s) and any endpoints for which the inequality is satisfied and use interval notation or set-builder notation for the solution set. If the inequality symbol is $\leq$ or $\geq$, then the solutions from step (2) are also included in the solution set. All numbers found in step (1) must be excluded from the solution set, even if they are solutions from step (2).

11.9   EXERCISE SET

For Extra Help 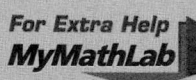  PRACTICE WATCH DOWNLOAD

Concept Reinforcement *Classify each statement as either true or false.*

1. The solution of $(x - 3)(x + 2) \leq 0$ is $[-2, 3]$.

2. The solution of $(x + 5)(x - 4) \geq 0$ is $[-5, 4]$.

3. The solution of $(x - 1)(x - 6) > 0$ is $\{x | x < 1 \ or \ x > 6\}$.

4. The solution of $(x + 4)(x + 2) < 0$ is $(-4, -2)$.

5. To solve $\dfrac{x + 2}{x - 3} < 0$ using intervals, we divide the number line into the intervals $(-\infty, -2)$ and $(-2, \infty)$.

6. To solve $\dfrac{x - 5}{x + 4} \geq 0$ using intervals, we divide the number line into the intervals $(-\infty, -4), (-4, 5)$, and $(5, \infty)$.

Solve each inequality using the graph provided.

7. $p(x) \leq 0$

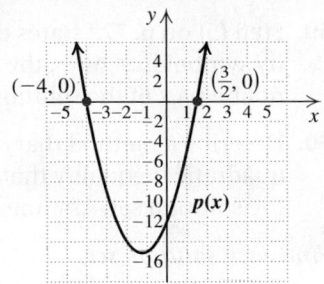

8. $p(x) < 0$

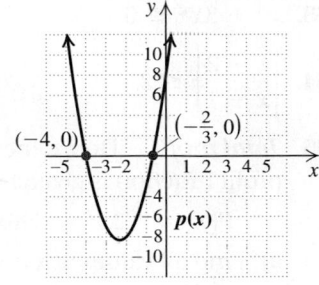

9. $x^4 + 12x > 3x^3 + 4x^2$

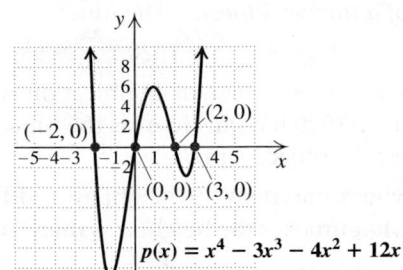

10. $x^4 + x^3 \geq 6x^2$

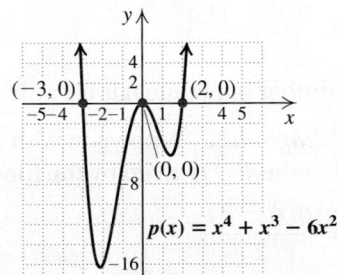

11. $\dfrac{x-1}{x+2} < 3$

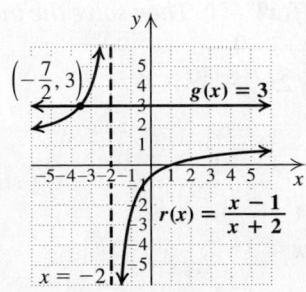

12. $\dfrac{2x-1}{x-5} \geq 1$

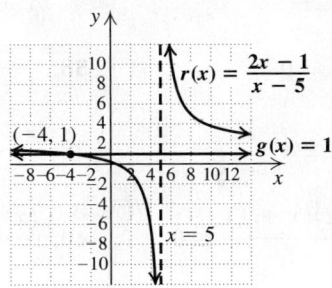

Solve.

13. $(x-6)(x-5) < 0$

14. $(x+8)(x+10) > 0$

15. $(x+7)(x-2) \geq 0$

16. $(x-1)(x+4) \leq 0$

17. $x^2 - x - 2 > 0$

18. $x^2 + x - 2 < 0$

Aha! **19.** $x^2 + 4x + 4 < 0$

20. $x^2 + 6x + 9 < 0$

21. $x^2 - 4x \leq 3$

22. $x^2 + 6x \geq 2$

23. $3x(x+2)(x-2) < 0$

24. $5x(x+1)(x-1) > 0$

25. $(x-1)(x+2)(x-4) \geq 0$

26. $(x+3)(x+2)(x-1) < 0$

27. For $f(x) = 7 - x^2$, find all x-values for which $f(x) \geq 3$.

28. For $f(x) = 14 - x^2$, find all x-values for which $f(x) > 5$.

29. For $g(x) = (x-2)(x-3)(x+1)$, find all x-values for which $g(x) > 0$.

30. For $g(x) = (x+3)(x-2)(x+1)$, find all x-values for which $g(x) < 0$.

31. For $F(x) = x^3 - 7x^2 + 10x$, find all x-values for which $F(x) \leq 0$.

32. For $G(x) = x^3 - 8x^2 + 12x$, find all x-values for which $G(x) \geq 0$.

Solve.

33. $\dfrac{1}{x-5} < 0$

34. $\dfrac{1}{x+4} > 0$

35. $\dfrac{x+1}{x-3} \geq 0$

36. $\dfrac{x-2}{x+4} \leq 0$

37. $\dfrac{x+1}{x+6} \geq 1$

38. $\dfrac{x-1}{x-2} \leq 1$

39. $\dfrac{(x-2)(x+1)}{x-5} \leq 0$

40. $\dfrac{(x+4)(x-1)}{x+3} \geq 0$

41. $\dfrac{x}{x+3} \geq 0$

42. $\dfrac{x-2}{x} \leq 0$

43. $\dfrac{x-5}{x} < 1$

44. $\dfrac{x}{x-1} > 2$

45. $\dfrac{x-1}{(x-3)(x+4)} \leq 0$

46. $\dfrac{x+2}{(x-2)(x+7)} \geq 0$

47. For $f(x) = \dfrac{5-2x}{4x+3}$, find all x-values for which $f(x) \geq 0$.

48. For $g(x) = \dfrac{2+3x}{2x-4}$, find all x-values for which $g(x) \geq 0$.

49. For $G(x) = \dfrac{1}{x-2}$, find all x-values for which $G(x) \leq 1$.

50. For $F(x) = \dfrac{1}{x-3}$, find all x-values for which $F(x) \leq 2$.

51. Explain how any quadratic inequality can be solved by examining a parabola.

52. Describe a method for creating a quadratic inequality for which there is no solution.

Skill Review

To prepare for Section 12.1, review function notation (Chapter 7).

Graph each function. [7.3]

53. $f(x) = x^3 - 2$

54. $g(x) = \dfrac{2}{x}$

55. If $f(x) = x + 7$, find $f\left(\dfrac{1}{a^2}\right)$. [7.1]

56. If $g(x) = x^2 - 3$, find $g(\sqrt{a-5})$. [7.1], [10.1]

57. If $g(x) = x^2 + 2$, find $g(2a+5)$. [7.1]

58. If $f(x) = \sqrt{4x+1}$, find $g(3a-5)$. [7.1]

Synthesis

59. Step (5) on p. 772 states that even when the inequality symbol is $\leq$ or $\geq$, the solutions from step (2) may not be part of the solution set. Why?

60. Describe a method that could be used to create a quadratic inequality that has $(-\infty, a] \cup [b, \infty)$ as the solution set. Assume $a < b$.

Find each solution set.

61. $x^2 + 2x < 5$

62. $x^4 + 2x^2 \geq 0$

63. $x^4 + 3x^2 \leq 0$

64. $\left|\dfrac{x+2}{x-1}\right| \leq 3$

65. *Total profit.* Derex, Inc., determines that its total-profit function is given by
$$P(x) = -3x^2 + 630x - 6000.$$
a) Find all values of x for which Derex makes a profit.
b) Find all values of x for which Derex loses money.

66. *Height of a thrown object.* The function
$$S(t) = -16t^2 + 32t + 1920$$
gives the height S, in feet, of an object thrown from a cliff that is 1920 ft high. Here t is the time, in seconds, that the object is in the air.
a) For what times does the height exceed 1920 ft?
b) For what times is the height less than 640 ft?

67. *Number of handshakes.* There are n people in a room. The number N of possible handshakes by the people is given by the function
$$N(n) = \dfrac{n(n-1)}{2}.$$
For what number of people n is $66 \leq N \leq 300$?

68. *Number of diagonals.* A polygon with n sides has D diagonals, where D is given by the function
$$D(n) = \dfrac{n(n-3)}{2}.$$
Find the number of sides n if
$$27 \leq D \leq 230.$$

Use a graphing calculator to graph each function and find solutions of $f(x) = 0$. Then solve the inequalities $f(x) < 0$ and $f(x) > 0$.

69. $f(x) = x^3 - 2x^2 - 5x + 6$

70. $f(x) = \dfrac{1}{3}x^3 - x + \dfrac{2}{3}$

71. $f(x) = x + \dfrac{1}{x}$

72. $f(x) = x - \sqrt{x}, x \geq 0$

73. $f(x) = \dfrac{x^3 - x^2 - 2x}{x^2 + x - 6}$

74. $f(x) = x^4 - 4x^3 - x^2 + 16x - 12$

Find the domain of each function

75. $f(x) = \sqrt{x^2 - 4x - 45}$

76. $f(x) = \sqrt{9 - x^2}$

77. $f(x) = \sqrt{x^2 + 8x}$

78. $f(x) = \sqrt{x^2 + 2x + 1}$

79. Describe a method that could be used to create a rational inequality that has $(-\infty, a] \cup (b, \infty)$ as the solution set. Assume $a < b$.

80. Use a graphing calculator to solve Exercises 43 and 49 by drawing two curves, one for each side of the inequality.

Study Summary

KEY TERMS AND CONCEPTS	EXAMPLES
SECTION 11.1: QUADRATIC EQUATIONS	

A **quadratic equation in standard form** is written $ax^2 + bx + c = 0$, with a, b, and c constant and $a \neq 0$. Some quadratic equations can be solved by factoring.	$x^2 - 3x - 10 = 0$ $(x + 2)(x - 5) = 0$ $x + 2 = 0 \quad or \quad x - 5 = 0$ $x = -2 \quad or \qquad x = 5$
The Principle of Square Roots For any real number k, if $X^2 = k$, then $X = \sqrt{k} \quad or \quad X = -\sqrt{k}$.	$x^2 - 8x + 16 = 25$ $(x - 4)^2 = 25$ $x - 4 = -5 \quad or \quad x - 4 = 5$ $x = -1 \quad or \qquad x = 9$
Any quadratic equation can be solved by **completing the square**.	$x^2 + 6x = 1$ $x^2 + 6x + \left(\frac{6}{2}\right)^2 = 1 + \left(\frac{6}{2}\right)^2$ $x^2 + 6x + 9 = 1 + 9$ $(x + 3)^2 = 10$ $x + 3 = \pm\sqrt{10}$ $x = -3 \pm \sqrt{10}$

SECTION 11.2: THE QUADRATIC FORMULA

The Quadratic Formula

The solutions of $ax^2 + bx + c = 0$ are given by

$$x = \frac{-b \pm \sqrt{b^2 - 4ac}}{2a}.$$

$3x^2 - 2x - 5 = 0 \qquad a = 3, b = -2, c = -5$

$$x = \frac{-(-2) \pm \sqrt{(-2)^2 - 4 \cdot 3(-5)}}{2 \cdot 3}$$

$$x = \frac{2 \pm \sqrt{4 + 60}}{6}$$

$$x = \frac{2 \pm \sqrt{64}}{6}$$

$$x = \frac{2 \pm 8}{6}$$

$$x = \frac{10}{6} = \frac{5}{3} \quad or \quad x = \frac{-6}{6} = -1$$

SECTION 11.3: STUDYING SOLUTIONS OF QUADRATIC EQUATIONS

The **discriminant** of the quadratic formula is $b^2 - 4ac$.

$b^2 - 4ac = 0 \rightarrow$ One solution; a rational number

$b^2 - 4ac > 0 \rightarrow$ Two real solutions; both are rational if $b^2 - 4ac$ is a perfect square.

$b^2 - 4ac < 0 \rightarrow$ Two imaginary-number solutions

For $4x^2 - 12x + 9 = 0$, $b^2 - 4ac = (-12)^2 - 4(4)(9)$

$\qquad\qquad = 144 - 144 = 0.$ The discriminant is zero.

Thus, $4x^2 - 12x + 9 = 0$ has one rational solution.

For $x^2 + 6x - 2 = 0$, $b^2 - 4ac = (6)^2 - 4(1)(-2)$

$\qquad\qquad = 36 + 8 = 44.$ The discriminant is not a perfect square.

Thus, $x^2 + 6x - 2 = 0$ has two irrational real-number solutions.

For $2x^2 - 3x + 5 = 0$, $b^2 - 4ac = (-3)^2 - 4(2)(5)$

$\qquad\qquad = 9 - 40 = -31.$ The discriminant is negative.

Thus, $2x^2 - 3x + 5 = 0$ has two imaginary-number solutions.

SECTION 11.4: APPLICATIONS INVOLVING QUADRATIC EQUATIONS

To solve a formula for a letter, use the same principles used to solve equations.

Solve $y = pn^2 + dn$ *for* n.

$pn^2 + dn - y = 0$ Writing standard form of a quadratic equation

$$n = \frac{-d \pm \sqrt{d^2 - 4p(-y)}}{2 \cdot p}$$ Using the quadratic formula; $a = p, b = d, c = -y$

$$n = \frac{-d \pm \sqrt{d^2 + 4py}}{2p}$$

SECTION 11.5: EQUATIONS REDUCIBLE TO QUADRATIC

Equations that are **reducible to quadratic** or in **quadratic form** can be solved by making an appropriate substitution.

$x^4 - 10x^2 + 9 = 0$ Let $u = x^2$. Then $u^2 = x^4$.

$u^2 - 10u + 9 = 0$ Substituting

$(u - 9)(u - 1) = 0$

$u - 9 = 0 \quad or \quad u - 1 = 0$

$u = 9 \quad or \qquad u = 1$ Solving for u

$x^2 = 9 \quad or \qquad x^2 = 1$

$x = \pm 3 \quad or \qquad x = \pm 1$ Solving for x

SECTION 11.6: QUADRATIC FUNCTIONS AND THEIR GRAPHS
SECTION 11.7: MORE ABOUT GRAPHING QUADRATIC FUNCTIONS

The graph of a quadratic function

$$f(x) = ax^2 + bx + c = a(x - h)^2 + k$$

is a **parabola**. The graph opens upward for $a > 0$ and downward for $a < 0$.

The **vertex** is (h, k) and the **axis of symmetry** is $x = h$.

If $a > 0$, the function has a **minimum** value of k, and if $a < 0$, the function has a **maximum** value of k.

The vertex and the axis of symmetry occur at $x = -\dfrac{b}{2a}$.

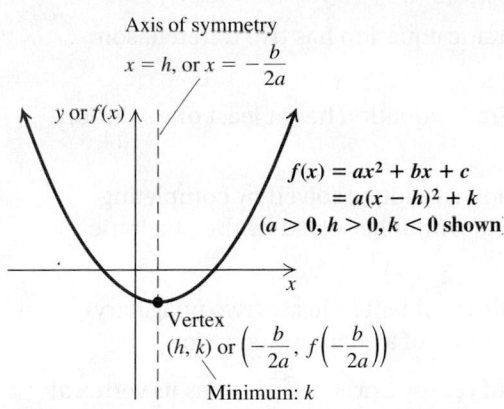

Axis of symmetry
$x = h$, or $x = -\dfrac{b}{2a}$

y or $f(x)$

$f(x) = ax^2 + bx + c$
$= a(x - h)^2 + k$
$(a > 0, h > 0, k < 0$ shown$)$

Vertex
(h, k) or $\left(-\dfrac{b}{2a}, f\left(-\dfrac{b}{2a}\right)\right)$

Minimum: k

SECTION 11.8: PROBLEM SOLVING AND QUADRATIC FUNCTIONS

Some problem situations can be **modeled** using quadratic functions. For those problems, a quantity can often be **maximized** or **minimized** by finding the coordinates of a vertex.

A lifeguard has 100 m of roped-together flotation devices with which to cordon off a rectangular swimming area at North Beach. If the shoreline forms one side of the rectangle, what dimensions will maximize the size of the area for swimming?

This problem and its solution appear as Example 2 on pp. 757–758.

SECTION 11.9: POLYNOMIAL AND RATIONAL INEQUALITIES

The x-intercepts, or **zeros**, of a function are used to divide the x-axis into intervals when solving a **polynomial inequality**. (See p. 769.)

Solve: $x^2 - 2x - 15 > 0$.

$$x^2 - 2x - 15 = 0 \qquad \text{Solving the related equation}$$
$$(x - 5)(x + 3) = 0$$
$$x = 5 \quad or \quad x = -3 \qquad \text{-3 and 5 divide the number line into three intervals.}$$

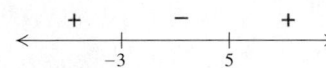

$$\begin{array}{c c c}+ & - & + \\ \hline & \quad & \\ -3 & & 5\end{array}$$

The solutions of a rational equation and any replacements that make a denominator zero are both used to divide the x-axis into intervals when solving a **rational inequality**. (See p. 772.)

Since $f(x) = x^2 - 2x - 15 = (x - 5)(x + 3)$,

$f(x)$ is positive for $x < -3$;
$f(x)$ is negative for $-3 < x < 5$;
$f(x)$ is positive for $x > 5$.

Thus, $x^2 - 2x - 15 > 0$ for $(-\infty, -3) \cup (5, \infty)$, or $\{x \mid x < -3 \ or \ x > 5\}$.

Concept Reinforcement *Classify each statement as either true or false.*

1. Every quadratic equation has two different solutions. [11.3]

2. Every quadratic equation has at least one solution. [11.3]

3. If an equation cannot be solved by completing the square, it cannot be solved by the quadratic formula. [11.2]

4. A negative discriminant indicates two imaginary-number solutions of a quadratic equation. [11.3]

5. The graph of $f(x) = 2(x + 3)^2 - 4$ has its vertex at $(3, -4)$. [11.6]

6. The graph of $g(x) = 5x^2$ has $x = 0$ as its axis of symmetry. [11.6]

7. The graph of $f(x) = -2x^2 + 1$ has no minimum value. [11.6]

8. The zeros of $g(x) = x^2 - 9$ are -3 and 3. [11.6]

9. If a quadratic function has two different imaginary-number zeros, the graph of the function has two x-intercepts. [11.7]

10. To solve a polynomial inequality, we often must solve a polynomial equation. [11.9]

Solve.

11. $9x^2 - 2 = 0$ [11.1]

12. $8x^2 + 6x = 0$ [11.1]

13. $x^2 - 12x + 36 = 9$ [11.1]

14. $x^2 - 4x + 8 = 0$ [11.2]

15. $x(3x + 4) = 4x(x - 1) + 15$ [11.2]

16. $x^2 + 9x = 1$ [11.2]

17. $x^2 - 5x - 2 = 0$. Use a calculator to approximate, to three decimal places, the solutions with rational numbers. [11.2]

18. Let $f(x) = 4x^2 - 3x - 1$. Find x such that $f(x) = 0$. [11.2]

Replace the blanks with constants to form a true equation. [11.1]

19. $x^2 - 18x + \underline{\quad} = (x - \underline{\quad})^2$

20. $x^2 + \frac{3}{5}x + \underline{\quad} = (x + \underline{\quad})^2$

21. Solve by completing the square. Show your work.
$$x^2 - 6x + 1 = 0 \quad [11.1]$$

22. \$2500 grows to \$2704 in 2 yr. Use the formula $A = P(1 + r)^t$ to find the interest rate. [11.1]

23. The U.S. Bank Tower in Los Angeles, California, is 1018 ft tall. Use $s = 16t^2$ to approximate how long it would take an object to fall from the top. [11.1]

For each equation, determine whether the solutions are real or imaginary. If they are real, specify whether they are rational or irrational. [11.3]

24. $x^2 + 3x - 6 = 0$

25. $x^2 + 2x + 5 = 0$

26. Write a quadratic equation having the solutions $3i$ and $-3i$. [11.3]

27. Write a quadratic equation having -5 as its only solution. [11.3]

Solve. [11.4]

28. Horizons has a manufacturing plant located 300 mi from company headquarters. Their corporate pilot must fly from headquarters to the plant and back in 4 hr. If there is a 20-mph headwind going and a 20-mph tailwind returning, how fast must the plane be able to travel in still air?

29. Working together, Dani and Cheri can reply to a day's worth of customer-service e-mails in 4 hr. Working alone, Dani takes 6 hr longer than Cheri. How long would it take Cheri to reply to the e-mails alone?

30. Find all x-intercepts of the graph of $f(x) = x^4 - 13x^2 + 36$. [11.5]

Solve. [11.5]

31. $15x^{-2} - 2x^{-1} - 1 = 0$

32. $(x^2 - 4)^2 - (x^2 - 4) - 6 = 0$

33. a) Graph: $f(x) = -3(x + 2)^2 + 4$. [11.6]
    b) Label the vertex.
    c) Draw the axis of symmetry.
    d) Find the maximum or the minimum value.

34. For the function given by $f(x) = 2x^2 - 12x + 23$: [11.7]
    a) find the vertex and the axis of symmetry;
    b) graph the function.

35. Find any x-intercepts and the y-intercept of the graph of
$$f(x) = x^2 - 9x + 14. \quad [11.7]$$

36. Solve $N = 3\pi\sqrt{\dfrac{1}{p}}$ for p. [11.4]

37. Solve $2A + T = 3T^2$ for T. [11.4]

State whether each graph appears to represent a quadratic function or a linear function. [11.8]

38. **Increase in health insurance premiums**

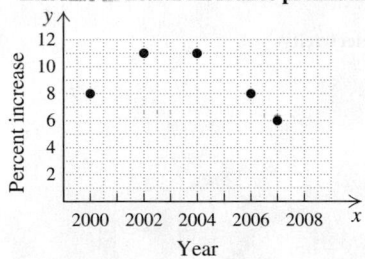

Source: Kaiser/HRET

39. **Health benefits in small firms**

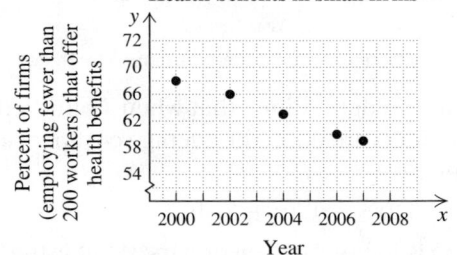

Source: Kaiser/HRET

40. Eastgate Consignments wants to build a rectangular area in a corner for children to play in while their parents shop. They have 30 ft of low fencing. What is the maximum area they can enclose? What dimensions will yield this area? [11.8]

41. The following table lists the percent increase in health insurance premiums x years after 2000. (See Exercise 38.) [11.8]

Years Since 2000	Percent Increase in Health Insurance Premiums
0	8
2	11
6	8

a) Find the quadratic function that fits the data.
b) Use the function to estimate the percent increase in health insurance premiums in 2005.

Solve. [11.9]

42. $x^3 - 3x > 2x^2$

43. $\dfrac{x-5}{x+3} \le 0$

Synthesis

44. Explain how the x-intercepts of a quadratic function can be used to help find the maximum or minimum value of the function. [11.7], [11.8]

45. Suppose that the quadratic formula is used to solve a quadratic equation. If the discriminant is a perfect square, could factoring have been used to solve the equation? Why or why not? [11.2], [11.3]

46. What is the greatest number of solutions that an equation of the form $ax^4 + bx^2 + c = 0$ can have? Why? [11.5]

47. Discuss two ways in which completing the square was used in this chapter. [11.1], [11.2], [11.7]

48. A quadratic function has x-intercepts at -3 and 5. If the y-intercept is at -7, find an equation for the function. [11.7]

49. Find h and k if, for $3x^2 - hx + 4k = 0$, the sum of the solutions is 20 and the product of the solutions is 80. [11.3]

50. The average of two positive integers is 171. One of the numbers is the square root of the other. Find the integers. [11.5]

Solve.

1. $25x^2 - 7 = 0$

2. $4x(x - 2) - 3x(x + 1) = -18$

3. $x^2 + 2x + 3 = 0$

4. $2x + 5 = x^2$

5. $x^{-2} - x^{-1} = \frac{3}{4}$

6. $x^2 + 3x = 5$. Use a calculator to approximate, to three decimal places, the solutions with rational numbers.

7. Let $f(x) = 12x^2 - 19x - 21$. Find x such that $f(x) = 0$.

Replace the blanks with constants to form a true equation.

8. $x^2 - 20x +$ ____ $= (x -$ ____ $)^2$

9. $x^2 + \frac{2}{7}x +$ ____ $= (x +$ ____ $)^2$

10. Solve by completing the square. Show your work.
$$x^2 + 10x + 15 = 0$$

11. Determine the type of number that the solutions of $x^2 + 2x + 5 = 0$ will be.

12. Write a quadratic equation having solutions $\sqrt{11}$ and $-\sqrt{11}$.

Solve.

13. The Connecticut River flows at a rate of 4 km/h for the length of a popular scenic route. In order for a cruiser to travel 60 km upriver and then return in a total of 8 hr, how fast must the boat be able to travel in still water?

14. Dal and Kim can assemble a swing set in $1\frac{1}{2}$ hr. Working alone, it takes Kim 4 hr longer than Dal to assemble the swing set. How long would it take Dal, working alone, to assemble the swing set?

15. Find all x-intercepts of the graph of
$$f(x) = x^4 - 15x^2 - 16.$$

16. a) Graph: $f(x) = 4(x - 3)^2 + 5$.
   b) Label the vertex.
   c) Draw the axis of symmetry.
   d) Find the maximum or the minimum function value.

17. For the function $f(x) = 2x^2 + 4x - 6$:
   a) find the vertex and the axis of symmetry;
   b) graph the function.

18. Find the x- and y-intercepts of
$$f(x) = x^2 - x - 6.$$

19. Solve $V = \frac{1}{3}\pi(R^2 + r^2)$ for r. Assume all variables are positive.

20. State whether the graph appears to represent a linear function, a quadratic function, or neither.

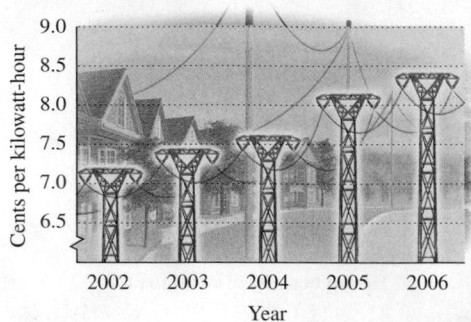

Average price of electricity

Source: Energy Information Administration, U.S. Department of Energy

21. Jay's Metals has determined that when x hundred storage cabinets are built, the average cost per cabinet is given by
$$C(x) = 0.2x^2 - 1.3x + 3.4025,$$
where $C(x)$ is in hundreds of dollars. What is the minimum cost per cabinet and how many cabinets should be built to achieve that minimum?

22. Find the quadratic function that fits the data points $(0, 0)$, $(3, 0)$, and $(5, 2)$.

Solve.

23. $x^2 + 5x < 6$

24. $x - \dfrac{1}{x} \geq 0$

Synthesis

25. One solution of $kx^2 + 3x - k = 0$ is -2. Find the other solution.

26. Find a fourth-degree polynomial equation, with integer coefficients, for which $-\sqrt{3}$ and $2i$ are solutions.

27. Solve: $x^4 - 4x^2 - 1 = 0$.

Cumulative Review: Chapters 1–11

Simplify.

1. $-3 \cdot 8 \div (-2)^3 \cdot 4 - 6(5 - 7)$ [1.8]

2. $\dfrac{18a^5bc^{10}}{24a^{-5}bc^3}$ [4.2]

3. $(5x^2y - 8xy - 6xy^2) - (2xy - 9x^2y + 3xy^2)$ [4.7]

4. $(9p^2q + 8t)(9p^2q - 8t)$ [4.7]

5. $\dfrac{t^2 - 25}{9t^2 + 24t + 16} \div \dfrac{3t^2 - 11t - 20}{t^2 + t}$ [6.2]

6. $\dfrac{1}{4 - x} + \dfrac{8}{x^2 - 16} - \dfrac{2}{x + 4}$ [6.4]

7. $\sqrt[3]{18x^4y} \cdot \sqrt[3]{6x^2y}$ [10.3]

8. $(3\sqrt{2} + i)(2\sqrt{2} - i)$ [10.8]

Factor.

9. $12x^4 - 75y^4$ [5.4]

10. $x^3 - 24x^2 + 80x$ [5.2]

11. $100m^6 - 100$ [5.5]

12. $6t^2 + 35t + 36$ [5.3]

Solve.

13. $2(5x - 3) - 8x = 4 - (3 - x)$ [2.2]

14. $2(5x - 3) - 8x < 4 - (3 - x)$ [2.6]

15. $\begin{aligned} 2x - 6y &= 3, \\ -3x + 8y &= -5 \end{aligned}$ [8.2]

16. $x(x - 5) = 66$ [5.7]

17. $\dfrac{2}{t} + \dfrac{1}{t - 1} = 2$ [6.6]

18. $\sqrt{x} = 1 + \sqrt{2x - 7}$ [10.6]

19. $m^2 + 10m + 25 = 2$ [11.1]

20. $3x^2 + 1 = x$ [11.2]

Graph.

21. $9x - 2y = 18$ [3.3]

22. $x < \frac{1}{2}y$ [9.4]

23. $y = 2(x - 3)^2 + 1$ [11.6]

24. $f(x) = x^2 + 4x + 3$ [11.7]

25. Find an equation in slope–intercept form whose graph has slope -5 and y-intercept $\left(0, \frac{1}{2}\right)$. [3.6]

26. Find the slope of the line containing $(8, 3)$ and $(-2, 10)$. [3.5]

27. For the function described by $f(x) = 3x^2 - 8x - 7$, find $f(-2)$. [7.1]

Find the domain of each function.

28. $f(x) = \sqrt{10 - x}$ [9.1]

29. $f(x) = \dfrac{x + 3}{x - 4}$ [9.2]

Solve each formula for the specified letter.

30. $b = \dfrac{a + c}{2a}$, for a [7.5]

31. $p = 2\sqrt{\dfrac{r}{3t}}$, for t [11.4]

Solve.

32. *Mobile ad spending.*   The amount spent worldwide in advertising on mobile devices can be estimated by $f(x) = 0.4x^2 + 0.01x + 0.9$, where x is the number of years after 2005 and $f(x)$ is in billions of dollars.
Source: Based on data from eMarketer

   a) How much was spent worldwide for mobile ads in 2008? [7.1]

   b) When will worldwide mobile ad spending reach $41 billion? [11.4]

33. *Wi-fi hotspots.*   The number of Wi-fi hotspots worldwide grew from 19,000 in 2002 to 118,000 in 2005. Let $h(t)$ represent the number of hotspots, in thousands, t years after 2000. [7.1]
Source: IDC

   a) Find a linear function that fits the data.
   b) Use the function from part (a) to predict the number of Wi-fi hotspots in 2010.
   c) In what year will there be 500,000 Wi-fi hotspots?

34. *Gold prices.* Annette is selling some of her gold jewelry. She has 4 bracelets and 1 necklace that weigh a total of 3 oz. [2.5]

   a) Annette's jewelry is 58% gold. How many ounces of gold does her jewelry contain?

   b) A gold dealer offers Annette $1044 for the jewelry. How much per ounce of gold was she offered?

   c) The price of gold at the time of Annette's sale was $800 an ounce. What percent of the gold price was she offered for her jewelry?

35. *Education.* Sven ordered number tiles at $9 per set and alphabet tiles at $15 per set for his classroom. He ordered a total of 36 sets for $384. How many sets of each did he order? [8.3]

36. *Minimizing cost.* Dormitory Furnishings has determined that when x bunk beds are built, the average cost, in dollars, per bunk bed can be estimated by $c(x) = 0.004375x^2 - 3.5x + 825$. What is the minimum average cost per bunk bed and how many bunk beds should be built to achieve that minimum? [11.8]

37. *Volunteer work.* It takes Deanna twice as long to set up a fundraising auction as it takes Donna. Together they can set up for the auction in 4 hr. How long would it take each of them to do the job alone? [6.7]

38. *Canoeing.* Kent paddled for 2 hr with a 5-km/h current to reach a campsite. The return trip against the same current took 7 hr. Find the speed of Kent's canoe in still water. [8.3]

39. *Truck rentals.* Josh and Lindsay plan to rent a moving truck. The truck costs $70 plus 40¢ per mile. They have budgeted $90 for the truck rental. For what mileages will they not exceed their budget? [2.7]

Synthesis

Solve.

40. $\dfrac{\dfrac{1}{x}}{2 + \dfrac{1}{x-1}} = 3$ [6.5], [11.2]

41. $x^4 + 5x^2 \leq 0$ [11.9]

42. The graph of the function $f(x) = mx + b$ contains the point $(2, 3)$ and is perpendicular to the line containing the points $(-1, 4)$ and $(-2, 5)$. Find the equation of the function. [3.7]

43. Find the points of intersection of the graphs of $f(x) = x^2 + 8x + 1$ and $g(x) = 10x + 6$. [11.2]

Exponential and Logarithmic Functions

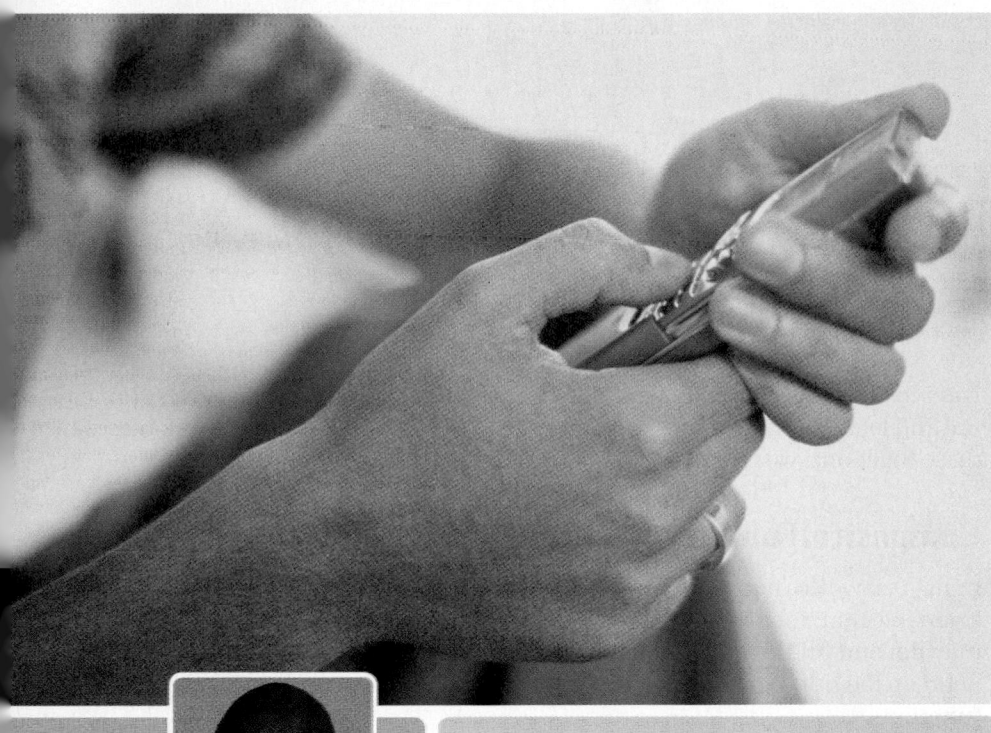

12.1
Composite and Inverse
Functions

12.2
Exponential Functions

12.3
Logarithmic Functions

12.4
Properties of Logarithmic
Functions

12.5
Common and Natural
Logarithms

CONNECTING THE CONCEPTS

12.6
Solving Exponential and
Logarithmic Equations

12.7
Applications of
Exponential and
Logarithmic Functions

STUDY SUMMARY
REVIEW EXERCISES
CHAPTER TEST
CUMULATIVE REVIEW

PAUL WILLIAMS
DATA SYSTEMS SPECIALIST
Indianapolis, Indiana

Because I work with computers
and networking every day,
everything around me is based
on math. Computers and their
algorithms are based in the
binary number system. We use
mathematical tools such as
statistics and graphs to study
network bottlenecks in computers
and transmission pipes and to
detect network saturation points.

AN APPLICATION

In 2000, there were approximately
12 million text messages sent each
month in the United States. This
number has increased exponentially at
an average rate of 108% per year. Find
the exponential growth function that
models the data, and estimate the
number of text messages sent each
month in 2009.

Source: Based on information from
www.cellulist.com

This problem appears as Example 4 in
Section 12.7.

The functions that we consider in this chapter have rich applications in many fields, such as epidemiology (the study of the spread of disease), population growth, and marketing.

The theory centers on functions with variable exponents (*exponential functions*). Results follow from those functions, their properties, and properties of their closely related *inverse* functions.

12.1 Composite and Inverse Functions

Composite Functions • Inverses and One-to-One Functions • Finding Formulas for Inverses •
Graphing Functions and Their Inverses • Inverse Functions and Composition

Later in this chapter, we introduce two closely related types of functions: exponential and logarithmic functions. In order to properly understand the link between these functions, we must first understand composite and inverse functions.

Composite Functions

In the real world, functions frequently occur in which some quantity depends on a variable that, in turn, depends on another variable. For instance, a firm's profits may depend on the number of items the firm produces, which may in turn depend on the number of employees hired. Functions like this are called **composite functions**.

For example, the function g that gives a correspondence between women's shoe sizes in the United States and those in Britain is given by $g(x) = x - 2$, where x is the U.S. size and $g(x)$ is the British size. Thus a U.S. size 4 corresponds to a shoe size of $g(4) = 4 - 2$, or 2, in Britain.

A second function converts women's shoe sizes in Britain to those in Italy. This particular function is given by $f(x) = 2x + 28$, where x is the British size and $f(x)$ is the corresponding Italian size. Thus a British size 2 corresponds to an Italian size $f(2) = 2 \cdot 2 + 28$, or 32.

It is correct to conclude that a U.S. size 4 corresponds to an Italian size 32 and that some function h describes this correspondence.

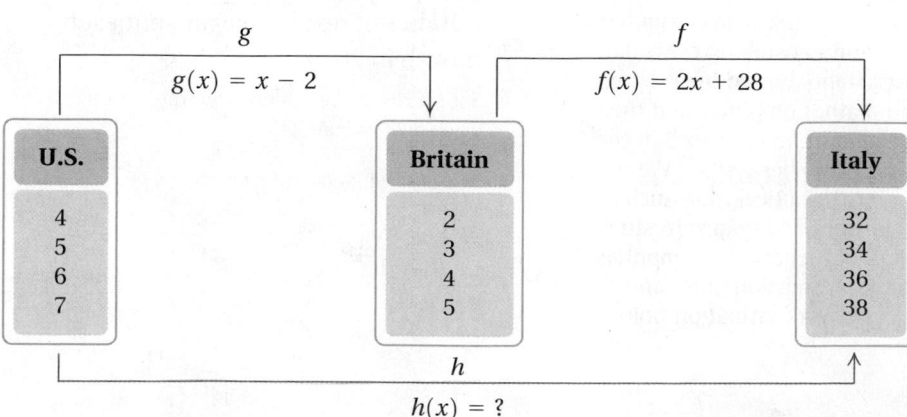

STUDENT NOTES

Throughout this chapter, keep in mind that equations such as $g(x) = x - 2$ and $g(t) = t - 2$ describe the same function g. Both equations tell us to find a function value by subtracting 2 from the input.

Size x shoes in the United States correspond to size $g(x)$ shoes in Britain, where

$$g(x) = x - 2.$$

Size n shoes in Britain correspond to size $f(n)$ shoes in Italy. Similarly, size $g(x)$ shoes in Britain correspond to size $f(g(x))$ shoes in Italy. Since the x in the expression $f(g(x))$ represents a U.S. shoe size, we can find the Italian shoe size that corresponds to a U.S. size x as follows:

$$f(g(x)) = f(x - 2) = 2(x - 2) + 28 \quad \text{Using } g(x) \text{ as an input}$$
$$= 2x - 4 + 28 = 2x + 24.$$

This gives a formula for h: $h(x) = 2x + 24$. Thus U.S. size 4 corresponds to Italian size $h(4) = 2(4) + 24$, or 32. We call h the *composition* of f and g and denote it by $f \circ g$ (read "the composition of f and g," "f composed with g," or "f circle g").

> ### Composition of Functions
> The *composite function* $f \circ g$, the *composition* of f and g, is defined as
> $$(f \circ g)(x) = f(g(x)).$$

We can visualize the composition of functions as follows.

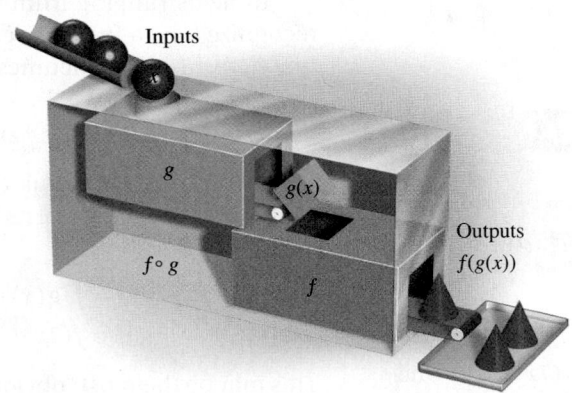

EXAMPLE **1**   Given $f(x) = 3x$ and $g(x) = 1 + x^2$:

a) Find $(f \circ g)(5)$ and $(g \circ f)(5)$.   **b)** Find $(f \circ g)(x)$ and $(g \circ f)(x)$.

SOLUTION   Consider each function separately:

$$f(x) = 3x \qquad \text{This function multiplies each input by 3.}$$

and

$$g(x) = 1 + x^2. \qquad \text{This function adds 1 to the square of each input.}$$

a) To find $(f \circ g)(5)$, we find $g(5)$ and then use that as an input for f:

$$(f \circ g)(5) = f(g(5)) = f(1 + 5^2) \qquad \text{Using } g(x) = 1 + x^2$$
$$= f(26) = 3 \cdot 26 = 78. \qquad \text{Using } f(x) = 3x$$

To find $(g \circ f)(5)$, we find $f(5)$ and then use that as an input for g:

$$(g \circ f)(5) = g(f(5)) = g(3 \cdot 5) \qquad \text{Note that } f(5) = 3 \cdot 5 = 15.$$
$$= g(15) = 1 + 15^2 = 1 + 225 = 226.$$

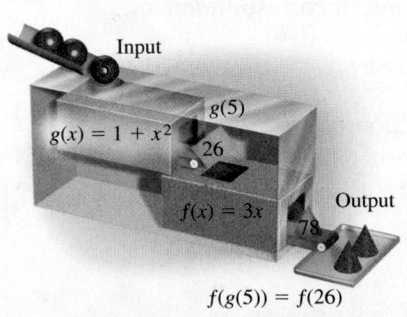

A composition machine for Example 1

b) We find $(f \circ g)(x)$ by substituting $g(x)$ for x in the equation for $f(x)$:

$$(f \circ g)(x) = f(g(x)) = f(1 + x^2) \qquad \text{Using } g(x) = 1 + x^2$$
$$= 3 \cdot (1 + x^2) = 3 + 3x^2. \qquad \text{Using } f(x) = 3x$$

To find $(g \circ f)(x)$, we substitute $f(x)$ for x in the equation for $g(x)$:

$$(g \circ f)(x) = g(f(x)) = g(3x) \qquad \text{Substituting } 3x \text{ for } f(x)$$
$$= 1 + (3x)^2 = 1 + 9x^2.$$

We can now find the function values of part (a) using the functions of part (b):

$$(f \circ g)(5) = 3 + 3(5)^2 = 3 + 3 \cdot 25 = 78;$$
$$(g \circ f)(5) = 1 + 9(5)^2 = 1 + 9 \cdot 25 = 226. \qquad \text{TRY EXERCISE} \quad 9$$

Example 1 shows that, in general, $(f \circ g)(x) \neq (g \circ f)(x)$.

EXAMPLE **2**   Given $f(x) = \sqrt{x}$ and $g(x) = x - 1$, find $(f \circ g)(x)$ and $(g \circ f)(x)$.

SOLUTION

$$(f \circ g)(x) = f(g(x)) = f(x - 1) = \sqrt{x - 1}; \qquad \text{Using } g(x) = x - 1$$
$$(g \circ f)(x) = g(f(x)) = g(\sqrt{x}) = \sqrt{x} - 1 \qquad \text{Using } f(x) = \sqrt{x}$$

TRY EXERCISE 15

In fields ranging from chemistry to geology and economics, one needs to recognize how a function can be regarded as the composition of two "simpler" functions. This is sometimes called *de*composition.

EXAMPLE **3**   If $h(x) = (7x + 3)^2$, find f and g such that $h(x) = (f \circ g)(x)$.

SOLUTION   We can think of $h(x)$ as the result of first finding $7x + 3$ and then squaring that. This suggests that $g(x) = 7x + 3$ and $f(x) = x^2$. We check by forming the composition:

$$(f \circ g)(x) = f(g(x))$$
$$= f(7x + 3) = (7x + 3)^2 = h(x), \text{ as desired.}$$

This may be the most "obvious" solution, but there are other less obvious answers. For example, if $f(x) = (x - 1)^2$ and $g(x) = 7x + 4$, then

$$(f \circ g)(x) = f(g(x)) = f(7x + 4)$$
$$= (7x + 4 - 1)^2 = (7x + 3)^2 = h(x). \qquad \text{TRY EXERCISE} \quad 21$$

TECHNOLOGY CONNECTION

In Example 3, we see that if $g(x) = 7x + 3$ and $f(x) = x^2$, then $f(g(x)) = (7x + 3)^2$. One way to show this is to let $y_1 = 7x + 3$ and $y_2 = x^2$. If we let $y_3 = (7x + 3)^2$ and $y_4 = y_2(y_1)$, we can use graphs or a table to show that $y_3 = y_4$.

1. Check Example 2 by using the above approach.

Inverses and One-to-One Functions

Let's view the following two functions as relations, or correspondences.

Countries and Their Capitals

Domain (Set of Inputs)	Range (Set of Outputs)
Australia	Canberra
China	Beijing
Germany	Berlin
Madagascar	Antananaviro
Turkey	Ankara
United States	Washington, D.C.

Phone Keys

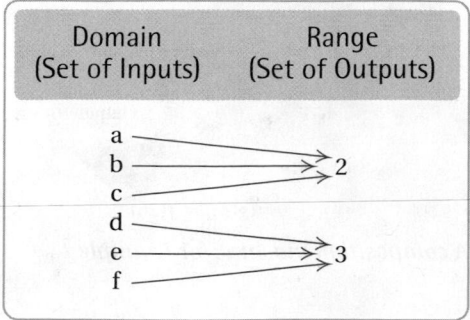

Suppose we reverse the arrows. We obtain what is called the **inverse relation**. Are these inverse relations functions?

Countries and Their Capitals

Range (Set of Outputs)	Domain (Set of Inputs)
Australia ←	Canberra
China ←	Beijing
Germany ←	Berlin
Madagascar ←	Antananaviro
Turkey ←	Ankara
United States ←	Washington, D.C.

Phone Keys

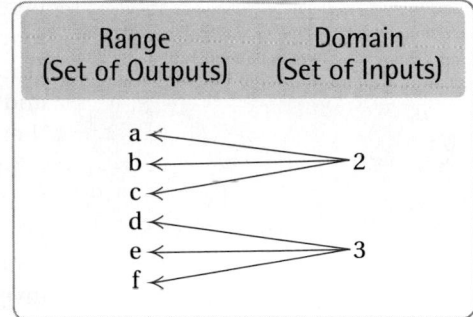

Recall that for each input, a function has exactly one output. However, it is possible for different inputs to correspond to the same output. Only when this possibility is *excluded* will the inverse be a function. For the functions listed above, this means the inverse of the "Capitals" correspondence is a function, but the inverse of the "Phone Keys" correspondence is not.

In the Capitals function, each input has its own output, so it is a **one-to-one-function**. In the Phone Keys function, a and b are both paired with 2. Thus the Phone Keys function is not a one-to-one function.

One-To-One Function

A function f is *one-to-one* if different inputs have different outputs. That is, if for a and b in the domain of f with $a \neq b$, we have $f(a) \neq f(b)$, then f is one-to-one. If a function is one-to-one, then its inverse correspondence is also a function.

How can we tell graphically whether a function is one-to-one?

EXAMPLE   4

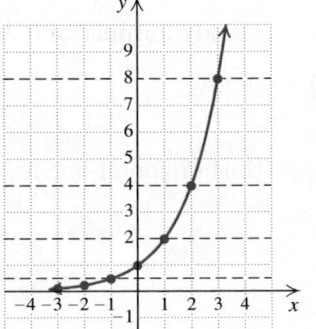

At left is the graph of a function similar to those we will study in Section 12.2. Determine whether the function is one-to-one and thus has an inverse that is a function.

SOLUTION   A function is one-to-one if different inputs have different outputs—that is, if no two x-values have the same y-value. For this function, we cannot find two x-values that have the same y-value. Note that this means that no horizontal line can be drawn so that it crosses the graph more than once. The function is one-to-one so its inverse is a function.

▶ TRY EXERCISE   31

The graph of every function must pass the vertical-line test. In order for a function to have an inverse that is a function, it must pass the *horizontal-line test* as well.

The Horizontal-Line Test

If it is impossible to draw a horizontal line that intersects a function's graph more than once, then the function is one-to-one. For every one-to-one function, an inverse function exists.

EXAMPLE 5

Determine whether the function $f(x) = x^2$ is one-to-one and thus has an inverse that is a function.

SOLUTION   The graph of $f(x) = x^2$ is shown here. Many horizontal lines cross the graph more than once. For example, the line $y = 4$ crosses where the first coordinates are -2 and 2. Although these are different inputs, they have the same output. That is, $-2 \neq 2$, but

$$f(-2) = (-2)^2 = 4 = 2^2 = f(2).$$

Thus the function is not one-to-one and no inverse function exists.

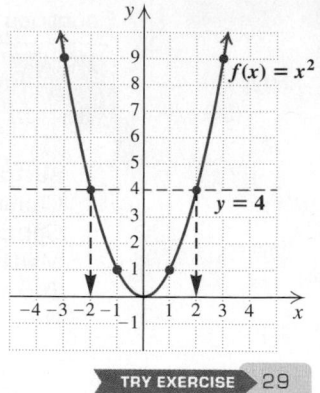

TRY EXERCISE ▸ 29

Finding Formulas for Inverses

When the inverse of f is also a function, it is denoted f^{-1} (read "f-inverse").

> **CAUTION!**   The -1 in f^{-1} is *not* an exponent!

Suppose a function is described by a formula. If its inverse is a function, how do we find a formula for that inverse? For any equation in two variables, if we interchange the variables, we form an equation of the inverse correspondence. If it is a function, we proceed as follows to find a formula for f^{-1}.

> **To Find a Formula for f^{-1}**
>
> First make sure that f is one-to-one. Then:
>
> 1. Replace $f(x)$ with y.
> 2. Interchange x and y. (This gives the inverse function.)
> 3. Solve for y.
> 4. Replace y with $f^{-1}(x)$. (This is inverse function notation.)

EXAMPLE 6

Determine whether each function is one-to-one and if it is, find a formula for $f^{-1}(x)$.

a) $f(x) = x + 2$

b) $f(x) = 2x - 3$

SOLUTION

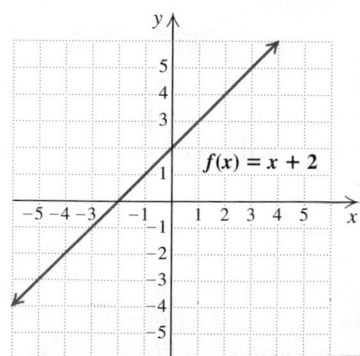

a) The graph of $f(x) = x + 2$ is shown at left. It passes the horizontal-line test, so it is one-to-one. Thus its inverse is a function.

1. Replace $f(x)$ with y: $y = x + 2$.
2. Interchange x and y: $x = y + 2$.   This gives the inverse function.
3. Solve for y: $x - 2 = y$.
4. Replace y with $f^{-1}(x)$: $f^{-1}(x) = x - 2$.   We also "reversed" the equation.

In this case, the function f adds 2 to all inputs. Thus, to "undo" f, the function f^{-1} must subtract 2 from its inputs.

b) The function $f(x) = 2x - 3$ is also linear. Any linear function that is not constant will pass the horizontal-line test. Thus, f is one-to-one.

  1. Replace $f(x)$ with y: $y = 2x - 3$.
  2. Interchange x and y: $x = 2y - 3$.
  3. Solve for y: $x + 3 = 2y$

$$\frac{x + 3}{2} = y.$$

  4. Replace y with $f^{-1}(x)$: $f^{-1}(x) = \dfrac{x + 3}{2}.$

In this case, the function f doubles all inputs and then subtracts 3. Thus, to "undo" f, the function f^{-1} adds 3 to each input and then divides by 2.

TRY EXERCISE 35

Graphing Functions and Their Inverses

How do the graphs of a function and its inverse compare?

EXAMPLE 7

Graph $f(x) = 2x - 3$ and $f^{-1}(x) = (x + 3)/2$ on the same set of axes. Then compare.

SOLUTION   The graph of each function follows. Note that the graph of f^{-1} can be drawn by reflecting the graph of f across the line $y = x$. That is, if we graph $f(x) = 2x - 3$ in wet ink and fold the paper along the line $y = x$, the graph of $f^{-1}(x) = (x + 3)/2$ will appear as the impression made by f.

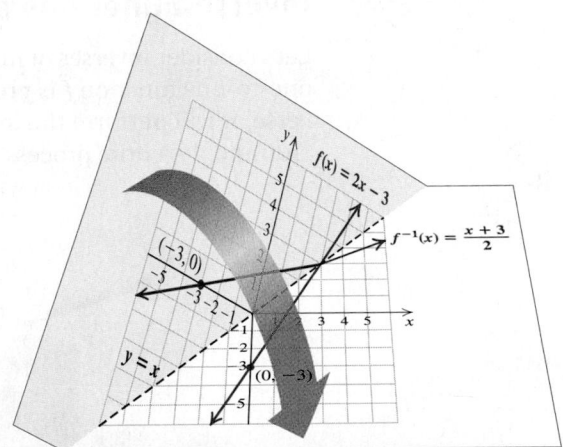

When x and y are interchanged to find a formula for the inverse, we are, in effect, reflecting or flipping the graph of $f(x) = 2x - 3$ across the line $y = x$. For example, when $(0, -3)$, the coordinates of the y-intercept of the graph of f, are reversed, we get $(-3, 0)$, the x-intercept of the graph of f^{-1}.

TRY EXERCISE 59

Visualizing Inverses
The graph of f^{-1} is a reflection of the graph of f across the line $y = x$.

EXAMPLE   8   Consider $g(x) = x^3 + 2$.

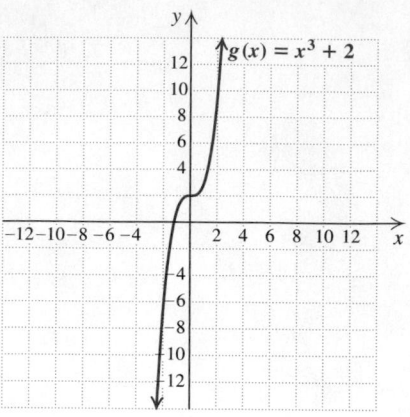

a) Determine whether the function is one-to-one.

b) If it is one-to-one, find a formula for its inverse.

c) Graph the inverse, if it exists.

SOLUTION

a) The graph of $g(x) = x^3 + 2$ is shown at right. It passes the horizontal-line test and thus is one-to-one and has an inverse that is a function.

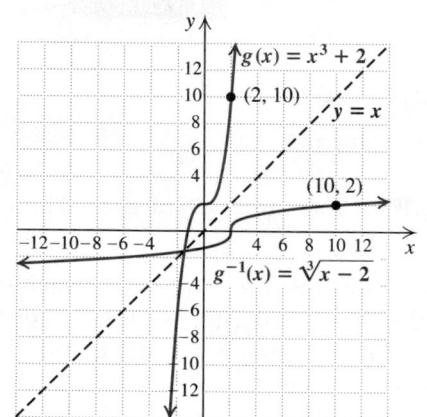

b) 1. Replace $g(x)$ with y: $y = x^3 + 2$.   Using $g(x) = x^3 + 2$

   2. Interchange x and y: $x = y^3 + 2$.

   3. Solve for y: $x - 2 = y^3$

   $\sqrt[3]{x - 2} = y$.   Each real number has only one cube root, so we can solve for y.

   4. Replace y with $g^{-1}(x)$: $g^{-1}(x) = \sqrt[3]{x - 2}$.

c) To graph g^{-1}, we can reflect the graph of $g(x) = x^3 + 2$ across the line $y = x$, as we did in Example 7. We also could graph $g^{-1}(x) = \sqrt[3]{x - 2}$ by plotting points. Note that $(2, 10)$ is on the graph of g, whereas $(10, 2)$ is on the graph of g^{-1}. The graphs of g and g^{-1} are shown at left.   **TRY EXERCISE** 61

Inverse Functions and Composition

Let's consider inverses of functions in terms of function machines. Suppose that a one-to-one function f is programmed into a machine. If the machine is run in reverse, it will perform the inverse function f^{-1}. Inputs then enter at the opposite end, and the entire process is reversed.

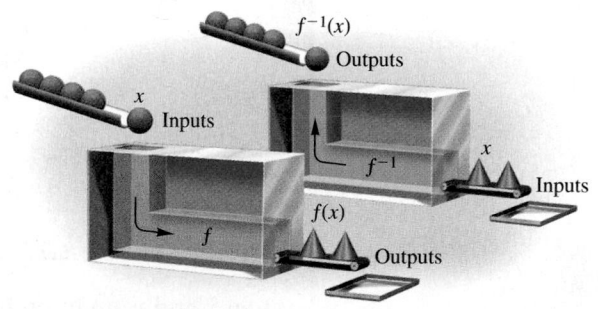

Consider $f(x) = x^3 + 2$ and $f^{-1}(x) = \sqrt[3]{x - 2}$ from Example 8. For the input 3,

$$f(3) = 3^3 + 2 = 27 + 2 = 29.$$

The output is 29. Let's now use 29 for the input in the inverse:

$$f^{-1}(29) = \sqrt[3]{29 - 2} = \sqrt[3]{27} = 3.$$

The function f takes 3 to 29. The inverse function f^{-1} takes the number 29 back to 3.

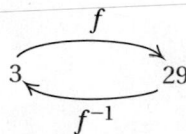

In general, if f is one-to-one, then f^{-1} takes the output $f(x)$ back to x. Similarly, f takes the output $f^{-1}(x)$ back to x.

> ## Composition and Inverses
> If a function f is one-to-one, then f^{-1} is the unique function for which
> $$(f^{-1} \circ f)(x) = f^{-1}(f(x)) = x \quad \text{and} \quad (f \circ f^{-1})(x) = f(f^{-1}(x)) = x.$$

EXAMPLE **9**

Let $f(x) = 2x + 1$. Show that

$$f^{-1}(x) = \frac{x - 1}{2}.$$

SOLUTION We find $(f^{-1} \circ f)(x)$ and $(f \circ f^{-1})(x)$ and check to see that each is x.

$$(f^{-1} \circ f)(x) = f^{-1}(f(x)) = f^{-1}(2x + 1)$$

$$= \frac{(2x + 1) - 1}{2}$$

$$= \frac{2x}{2} = x \qquad \text{Thus, } (f^{-1} \circ f)(x) = x.$$

$$(f \circ f^{-1})(x) = f(f^{-1}(x)) = f\left(\frac{x - 1}{2}\right)$$

$$= 2 \cdot \frac{x - 1}{2} + 1$$

$$= x - 1 + 1 = x \qquad \text{Thus, } (f \circ f^{-1})(x) = x.$$

TRY EXERCISE 69

TECHNOLOGY CONNECTION

To determine whether $y_1 = 2x + 6$ and $y_2 = \frac{1}{2}x - 3$ are inverses of each other, we can graph both functions, along with the line $y = x$, on a "squared" set of axes. It *appears* that y_1 and y_2 are inverses of each other. A more precise check is achieved by selecting the DRAWINV option of the (DRAW) menu. The resulting graph of the inverse of y_1 should coincide with y_2.

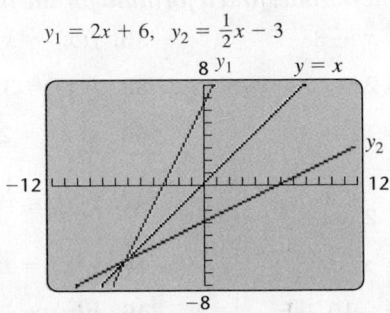

$y_1 = 2x + 6, \quad y_2 = \frac{1}{2}x - 3$

For a more dependable check, examine a TABLE in which $y_1 = 2x + 6$ and $y_2 = \frac{1}{2} \cdot y_1 - 3$. Note that y_2 "undoes" what y_1 does.

TBLSTART $= -3$ ΔTBL $= 1$ $y_2 = \frac{1}{2}y_1 - 3$

X	Y1	Y2
−3	0	−3
−2	2	−2
−1	4	−1
0	6	0
1	8	1
2	10	2
3	12	3

X = 3

1. Use a graphing calculator to check Examples 7, 8, and 9.
2. Will DRAWINV work for *any* choice of y_1? Why or why not?

12.1 EXERCISE SET

For Extra Help
MyMathLab
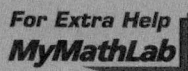
Math XL
PRACTICE
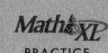
WATCH

DOWNLOAD

Concept Reinforcement *Classify each statement as either true or false.*

1. The composition of two functions f and g is written $f \circ g$.

2. The notation $(f \circ g)(x)$ means $f(g(x))$.

3. If $f(x) = x^2$ and $g(x) = x + 3$, then $(g \circ f)(x) = (x + 3)^2$.

4. For any function h, there is only one way to decompose the function as $h = f \circ g$.

5. The function f is one-to-one if $f(1) = 1$.

6. The -1 in f^{-1} is an exponent.

7. The function f is the inverse of f^{-1}.

8. If g and h are inverses of each other, then $(g \circ h)(x) = x$.

For each pair of functions, find **(a)** $(f \circ g)(1)$; **(b)** $(g \circ f)(1)$; **(c)** $(f \circ g)(x)$; **(d)** $(g \circ f)(x)$.

9. $f(x) = x^2 + 1$; $g(x) = x - 3$

10. $f(x) = x + 4$; $g(x) = x^2 - 5$

11. $f(x) = 5x + 1$; $g(x) = 2x^2 - 7$

12. $f(x) = 3x^2 + 4$; $g(x) = 4x - 1$

13. $f(x) = x + 7$; $g(x) = 1/x^2$

14. $f(x) = 1/x^2$; $g(x) = x + 2$

15. $f(x) = \sqrt{x}$; $g(x) = x + 3$

16. $f(x) = 10 - x$; $g(x) = \sqrt{x}$

17. $f(x) = \sqrt{4x}$; $g(x) = 1/x$

18. $f(x) = \sqrt{x + 3}$; $g(x) = 13/x$

19. $f(x) = x^2 + 4$; $g(x) = \sqrt{x - 1}$

20. $f(x) = x^2 + 8$; $g(x) = \sqrt{x + 17}$

Find $f(x)$ and $g(x)$ such that $h(x) = (f \circ g)(x)$. Answers may vary.

21. $h(x) = (3x - 5)^4$

22. $h(x) = (2x + 7)^3$

23. $h(x) = \sqrt{9x + 1}$

24. $h(x) = \sqrt[3]{4x - 5}$

25. $h(x) = \dfrac{6}{5x - 2}$

26. $h(x) = \dfrac{3}{x} + 4$

Determine whether each function is one-to-one.

27. $f(x) = -x$

28. $f(x) = x + 5$

Aha! **29.** $f(x) = x^2 + 3$

30. $f(x) = 3 - x^2$

31.
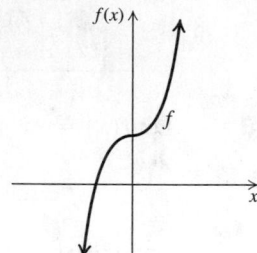

32.
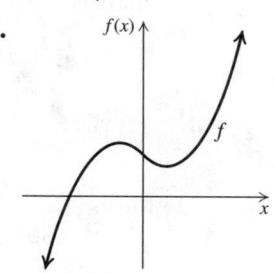

33.
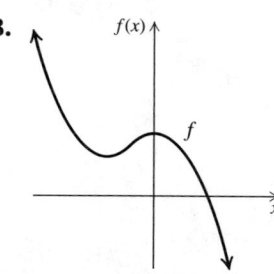

34.
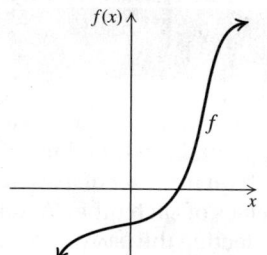

For each function, **(a)** *determine whether it is one-to-one;* **(b)** *if it is one-to-one, find a formula for the inverse.*

35. $f(x) = x + 3$

36. $f(x) = x + 2$

37. $f(x) = 2x$

38. $f(x) = 3x$

39. $g(x) = 3x - 1$

40. $g(x) = 2x - 3$

41. $f(x) = \dfrac{1}{2}x + 1$

42. $f(x) = \dfrac{1}{3}x + 2$

43. $g(x) = x^2 + 5$

44. $g(x) = x^2 - 4$

45. $h(x) = -10 - x$

46. $h(x) = 7 - x$

Aha! **47.** $f(x) = \dfrac{1}{x}$

48. $f(x) = \dfrac{3}{x}$

49. $g(x) = 1$

50. $h(x) = 8$

51. $f(x) = \dfrac{2x + 1}{3}$

52. $f(x) = \dfrac{3x + 2}{5}$

53. $f(x) = x^3 + 5$

54. $f(x) = x^3 - 4$

55. $g(x) = (x - 2)^3$

56. $g(x) = (x + 7)^3$

57. $f(x) = \sqrt{x}$

58. $f(x) = \sqrt{x - 1}$

Graph each function and its inverse using the same set of axes.

59. $f(x) = \dfrac{2}{3}x + 4$

60. $g(x) = \dfrac{1}{4}x + 2$

61. $f(x) = x^3 + 1$

62. $f(x) = x^3 - 1$

63. $g(x) = \dfrac{1}{2}x^3$

64. $g(x) = \dfrac{1}{3}x^3$

65. $F(x) = -\sqrt{x}$

66. $f(x) = \sqrt{x}$

67. $f(x) = -x^2, x \geq 0$

68. $f(x) = x^2 - 1, x \leq 0$

69. Let $f(x) = \sqrt[3]{x - 4}$. Show that
$$f^{-1}(x) = x^3 + 4.$$

70. Let $f(x) = 3/(x + 2)$. Show that
$$f^{-1}(x) = \dfrac{3}{x} - 2.$$

71. Let $f(x) = (1 - x)/x$. Show that
$$f^{-1}(x) = \dfrac{1}{x + 1}.$$

72. Let $f(x) = x^3 - 5$. Show that
$$f^{-1}(x) = \sqrt[3]{x + 5}.$$

73. **Dress sizes in the United States and Italy.** A size-6 dress in the United States is size 36 in Italy. A function that converts dress sizes in the United States to those in Italy is
$$f(x) = 2(x + 12).$$
   a) Find the dress sizes in Italy that correspond to sizes 8, 10, 14, and 18 in the United States.
   b) Determine whether f has an inverse that is a function. If so, find a formula for the inverse.

c) Use the inverse function to find dress sizes in the United States that correspond to sizes 40, 44, 52, and 60 in Italy.

74. **Dress sizes in the United States and France.** A size-6 dress in the United States is size 38 in France. A function that converts dress sizes in the United States to those in France is
$$f(x) = x + 32.$$
   a) Find the dress sizes in France that correspond to sizes 8, 10, 14, and 18 in the United States.
   b) Determine whether f has an inverse that is a function. If so, find a formula for the inverse.
   c) Use the inverse function to find dress sizes in the United States that correspond to sizes 40, 42, 46, and 50 in France.

75. Is there a one-to-one relationship between items in a store and the price of each of those items? Why or why not?

76. Mathematicians usually try to select "logical" words when forming definitions. Does the term "one-to-one" seem logical? Why or why not?

Skill Review

To prepare for Section 12.2, review simplifying exponential expressions and graphing equations (Sections 4.2, 7.3, and 10.2).

Simplify.

77. 2^{-3} [4.2]

78. $5^{(1-3)}$ [4.2]

79. $4^{5/2}$ [10.2]

80. $3^{7/10}$ [10.2]

Graph. [7.3]

81. $y = x^3$

82. $x = y^3$

Synthesis

83. The function $V(t) = 750(1.2)^t$ is used to predict the value $V(t)$ of a certain rare stamp t years from 2008. Do not calculate $V^{-1}(t)$, but explain how V^{-1} could be used.

84. An organization determines that the cost per person $C(x)$, in dollars, of chartering a bus with x passengers is given by

$$C(x) = \frac{100 + 5x}{x}.$$

Determine $C^{-1}(x)$ and explain how this inverse function could be used.

For Exercises 85 and 86, graph the inverse of f.

85.

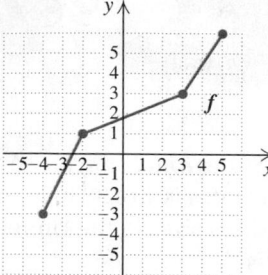

86.

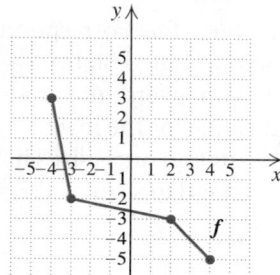

87. *Dress sizes in France and Italy.* Use the information in Exercises 73 and 74 to find a function for the French dress size that corresponds to a size x dress in Italy.

88. *Dress sizes in Italy and France.* Use the information in Exercises 73 and 74 to find a function for the Italian dress size that corresponds to a size x dress in France.

89. What relationship exists between the answers to Exercises 87 and 88? Explain how you determined this.

90. Show that function composition is associative by showing that $((f \circ g) \circ h)(x) = (f \circ (g \circ h))(x)$.

91. Show that if $h(x) = (f \circ g)(x)$, then $h^{-1}(x) = (g^{-1} \circ f^{-1})(x)$. (*Hint*: Use Exercise 90.)

Determine whether or not the given pairs of functions are inverses of each other.

92. $f(x) = 0.75x^2 + 2$; $g(x) = \sqrt{\dfrac{4(x - 2)}{3}}$

93. $f(x) = 1.4x^3 + 3.2$; $g(x) = \sqrt[3]{\dfrac{x - 3.2}{1.4}}$

94. $f(x) = \sqrt{2.5x + 9.25}$;
$g(x) = 0.4x^2 - 3.7, x \geq 0$

95. $f(x) = 0.8x^{1/2} + 5.23$;
$g(x) = 1.25(x^2 - 5.23), x \geq 0$

96. $f(x) = 2.5(x^3 - 7.1)$;
$g(x) = \sqrt[3]{0.4x + 7.1}$

97. Match each function in Column A with its inverse from Column B.

Column A

(1) $y = 5x^3 + 10$

(2) $y = (5x + 10)^3$

(3) $y = 5(x + 10)^3$

(4) $y = (5x)^3 + 10$

Column B

A. $y = \dfrac{\sqrt[3]{x} - 10}{5}$

B. $y = \sqrt[3]{\dfrac{x}{5}} - 10$

C. $y = \sqrt[3]{\dfrac{x - 10}{5}}$

D. $y = \dfrac{\sqrt[3]{x - 10}}{5}$

98. Examine the following table. Is it possible that f and g are inverses of each other? Why or why not?

x	$f(x)$	$g(x)$
6	6	6
7	6.5	8
8	7	10
9	7.5	12
10	8	14
11	8.5	16
12	9	18

99. The following window appears on a graphing calculator.

X	Y1	Y2
0	1	−2
1	1.5	0
2	2	2
3	2.5	4
4	3	6
5	3.5	8
6	4	10

X = 0

a) What evidence is there that the functions Y1 and Y2 are inverses of each other?

b) Find equations for Y1 and Y2, assuming that both are linear functions.

c) On the basis of your answer to part (b), are Y1 and Y2 inverses of each other?

12.2 Exponential Functions

Graphing Exponential Functions ▪ Equations with *x* and *y* Interchanged ▪
Applications of Exponential Functions

In this section, we introduce a new type of function, the *exponential function*. These functions and their inverses, called *logarithmic functions*, have applications in many fields.

Consider the graph below. The rapidly rising curve approximates the graph of an *exponential function*.

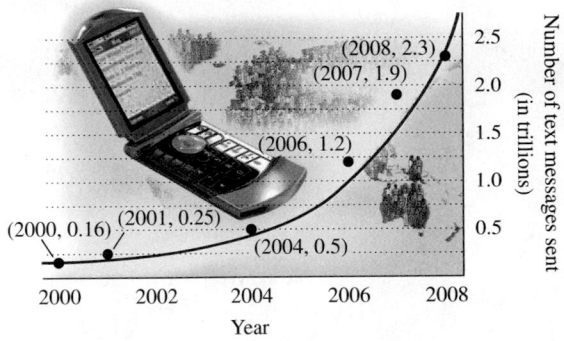

Worldwide text messaging

(2008, 2.3)
(2007, 1.9)
(2006, 1.2)
(2000, 0.16) (2001, 0.25)
(2004, 0.5)

Number of text messages sent (in trillions)

Year

Source: Mobile SMS Marketing, Gartner

Graphing Exponential Functions

In Chapter 10, we studied exponential expressions with rational-number exponents, such as

$$5^{1/4}, \quad 3^{-3/4}, \quad 7^{2.34}, \quad 5^{1.73}.$$

For example, $5^{1.73}$, or $5^{173/100}$, represents the 100th root of 5 raised to the 173rd power. What about expressions with irrational exponents, such as $5^{\sqrt{3}}$ or $7^{-\pi}$? To attach meaning to $5^{\sqrt{3}}$, consider a rational approximation, r, of $\sqrt{3}$. As r gets closer to $\sqrt{3}$, the value of 5^r gets closer to some real number p.

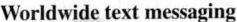

r closes in on $\sqrt{3}$.	5^r closes in on some real number p.
$1.7 < r < 1.8$	$15.426 \approx 5^{1.7} < p < 5^{1.8} \approx 18.119$
$1.73 < r < 1.74$	$16.189 \approx 5^{1.73} < p < 5^{1.74} \approx 16.452$
$1.732 < r < 1.733$	$16.241 \approx 5^{1.732} < p < 5^{1.733} \approx 16.267$

We define $5^{\sqrt{3}}$ to be the number p. To eight decimal places,

$$5^{\sqrt{3}} \approx 16.24245082.$$

Any positive irrational exponent can be interpreted in a similar way. Negative irrational exponents are then defined using reciprocals. Thus, so long as a is positive, a^x has meaning for *any* real number x. All of the laws of exponents still hold, but we will not prove that here. We can now define an *exponential function*.

Exponential Function

The function $f(x) = a^x$, where a is a positive constant, $a \neq 1$, and x is any real number, is called the *exponential function*, base a.

We require the base a to be positive to avoid imaginary numbers that would result from taking even roots of negative numbers. The restriction $a \neq 1$ is made to exclude the constant function $f(x) = 1^x$, or $f(x) = 1$.

The following are examples of exponential functions:

$$f(x) = 2^x, \qquad f(x) = \left(\tfrac{1}{3}\right)^x, \qquad f(x) = 5^{-3x}. \qquad \text{Note that } 5^{-3x} = (5^{-3})^x.$$

Like polynomial functions, the domain of an exponential function is the set of all real numbers. Unlike polynomial functions, exponential functions have a variable exponent. Because of this, graphs of exponential functions either rise or fall dramatically.

EXAMPLE 1

Graph the exponential function given by $y = f(x) = 2^x$.

SOLUTION   We compute some function values, thinking of y as $f(x)$, and list the results in a table. It is a good idea to start by letting $x = 0$.

$$f(0) = 2^0 = 1; \qquad\qquad f(-1) = 2^{-1} = \frac{1}{2^1} = \frac{1}{2};$$
$$f(1) = 2^1 = 2;$$
$$f(2) = 2^2 = 4; \qquad\qquad f(-2) = 2^{-2} = \frac{1}{2^2} = \frac{1}{4};$$
$$f(3) = 2^3 = 8;$$
$$f(-3) = 2^{-3} = \frac{1}{2^3} = \frac{1}{8}$$

x	y, or $f(x)$
0	1
1	2
2	4
3	8
-1	$\frac{1}{2}$
-2	$\frac{1}{4}$
-3	$\frac{1}{8}$

Next, we plot these points and connect them with a smooth curve.

The curve comes very close to the x-axis, but does not touch or cross it.

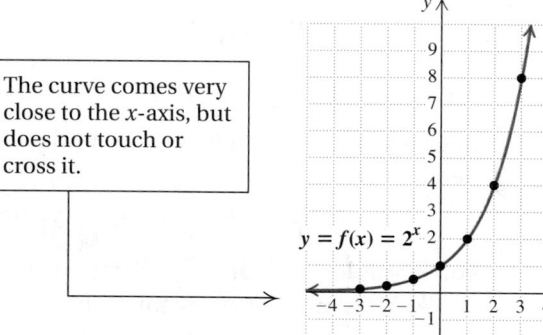

$y = f(x) = 2^x$

Be sure to plot enough points to determine how steeply the curve rises.

Note that as x increases, the function values increase without bound. As x decreases, the function values decrease, getting closer to 0. The x-axis, or the line $y = 0$, is a horizontal *asymptote*, meaning that the curve gets closer and closer to this line the further we move to the left.

TRY EXERCISE   7

EXAMPLE 2

Graph: $y = f(x) = \left(\tfrac{1}{2}\right)^x$.

SOLUTION   We compute some function values, thinking of y as $f(x)$, and list the results in a table. Before we do this, note that

$$y = f(x) = \left(\tfrac{1}{2}\right)^x = (2^{-1})^x = 2^{-x}.$$

Then we have

$$f(0) = 2^{-0} = 1; \qquad\qquad f(3) = 2^{-3} = \frac{1}{2^3} = \frac{1}{8};$$
$$f(1) = 2^{-1} = \frac{1}{2^1} = \frac{1}{2}; \qquad f(-1) = 2^{-(-1)} = 2^1 = 2;$$
$$f(-2) = 2^{-(-2)} = 2^2 = 4;$$
$$f(2) = 2^{-2} = \frac{1}{2^2} = \frac{1}{4}; \qquad f(-3) = 2^{-(-3)} = 2^3 = 8.$$

x	y, or $f(x)$
0	1
1	$\frac{1}{2}$
2	$\frac{1}{4}$
3	$\frac{1}{8}$
-1	2
-2	4
-3	8

Graphing calculators are helpful when graphing equations like $y = 5000(1.075)^x$. To choose a window, we note that y-values are positive and increase rapidly. One suitable window is $[-10, 10, 0, 15000]$, with a y-scale of 1000.

$$y = 5000(1.075)^x$$

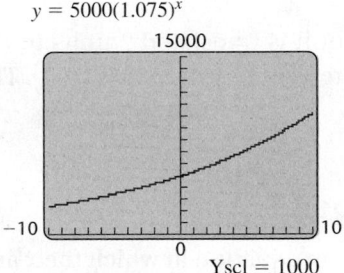

Graph each pair of functions. Select an appropriate window and scale.

1. $y_1 = \left(\frac{5}{2}\right)^x$ and $y_2 = \left(\frac{2}{5}\right)^x$
2. $y_1 = 3.2^x$ and $y_2 = 3.2^{-x}$
3. $y_1 = \left(\frac{3}{7}\right)^x$ and $y_2 = \left(\frac{7}{3}\right)^x$
4. $y_1 = 5000(1.08)^x$ and $y_2 = 5000(1.08)^{x-3}$

Next, we plot these points and connect them with a smooth curve. This curve is a mirror image, or *reflection*, of the graph of $y = 2^x$ (see Example 1) across the y-axis. The line $y = 0$ is again the horizontal asymptote.

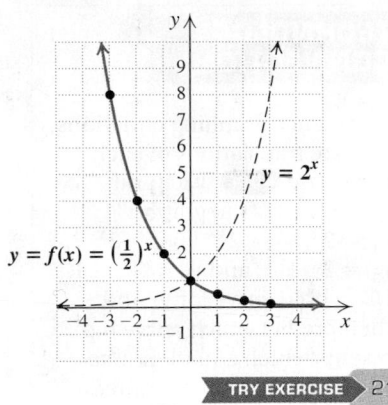

TRY EXERCISE 21

From Examples 1 and 2, we can make the following observations.

- For $a > 1$, the graph of $f(x) = a^x$ increases from left to right. The greater the value of a, the steeper the curve. (See the figure on the left below.)

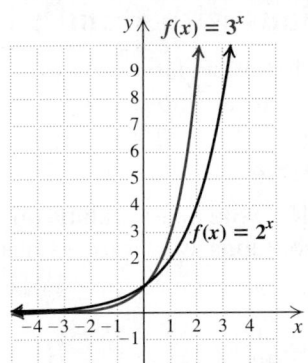

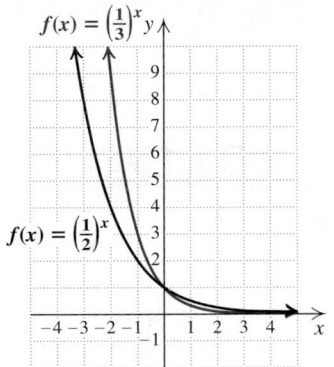

- For $0 < a < 1$, the graph of $f(x) = a^x$ decreases from left to right. For smaller values of a, the curve is steeper. (See the figure on the right above.)
- All graphs of $f(x) = a^x$ go through the y-intercept $(0, 1)$.
- All graphs of $f(x) = a^x$ have the x-axis as the horizontal asymptote.
- If $f(x) = a^x$, with $a > 0$, $a \neq 1$, the domain of f is all real numbers, and the range of f is all positive real numbers.
- For $a > 0$, $a \neq 1$, the function given by $f(x) = a^x$ is one-to-one. Its graph passes the horizontal-line test.

EXAMPLE 3

STUDENT NOTES

When using translations, make sure that you are shifting in the correct direction. When in doubt, substitute a value for x and make some calculations.

Graph: $y = f(x) = 2^{x-2}$.

SOLUTION We construct a table of values. Then we plot the points and connect them with a smooth curve. Here $x - 2$ is the *exponent*.

$f(0) = 2^{0-2} = 2^{-2} = \frac{1}{4}$;
$f(1) = 2^{1-2} = 2^{-1} = \frac{1}{2}$;
$f(2) = 2^{2-2} = 2^0 = 1$;
$f(3) = 2^{3-2} = 2^1 = 2$;
$f(4) = 2^{4-2} = 2^2 = 4$;
$f(-1) = 2^{-1-2} = 2^{-3} = \frac{1}{8}$;
$f(-2) = 2^{-2-2} = 2^{-4} = \frac{1}{16}$

x	y, or $f(x)$
0	$\frac{1}{4}$
1	$\frac{1}{2}$
2	1
3	2
4	4
-1	$\frac{1}{8}$
-2	$\frac{1}{16}$

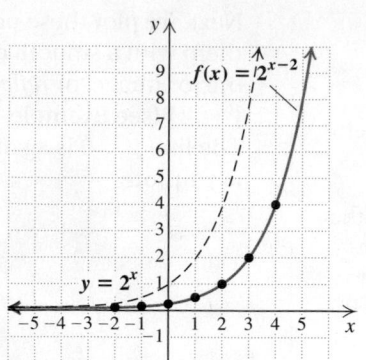

The graph looks just like the graph of $y = 2^x$, but it is translated 2 units to the right. The y-intercept of $y = 2^x$ is $(0, 1)$. The y-intercept of $y = 2^{x-2}$ is $\left(0, \frac{1}{4}\right)$. The line $y = 0$ is again the horizontal asymptote.

TRY EXERCISE 17

Equations with x and y Interchanged

It will be helpful in later work to be able to graph an equation in which the x and the y in $y = a^x$ are interchanged.

EXAMPLE **4**

Graph: $x = 2^y$.

SOLUTION Note that x is alone on one side of the equation. To find ordered pairs that are solutions, we choose values for y and then compute values for x.

For $y = 0$, $x = 2^0 = 1$.
For $y = 1$, $x = 2^1 = 2$.
For $y = 2$, $x = 2^2 = 4$.
For $y = 3$, $x = 2^3 = 8$.
For $y = -1$, $x = 2^{-1} = \frac{1}{2}$.
For $y = -2$, $x = 2^{-2} = \frac{1}{4}$.
For $y = -3$, $x = 2^{-3} = \frac{1}{8}$.

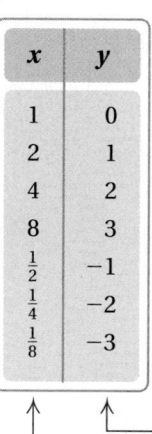

x	y
1	0
2	1
4	2
8	3
$\frac{1}{2}$	−1
$\frac{1}{4}$	−2
$\frac{1}{8}$	−3

(1) Choose values for y.
(2) Compute values for x.

We plot the points and connect them with a smooth curve.

This curve does not touch or cross the y-axis, which serves as a vertical asymptote.

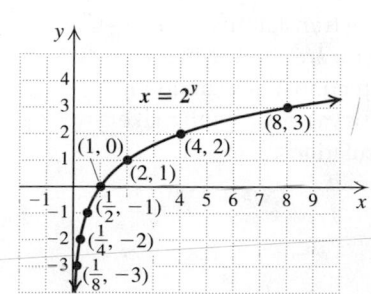

Note too that this curve looks just like the graph of $y = 2^x$, except that it is reflected across the line $y = x$, as shown here.

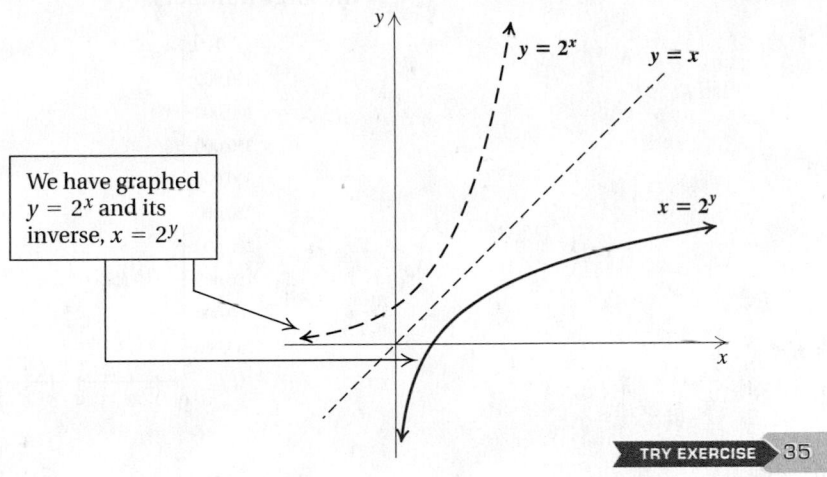

We have graphed $y = 2^x$ and its inverse, $x = 2^y$.

TRY EXERCISE 35

Applications of Exponential Functions

EXAMPLE 5

Interest compounded annually. The amount of money A that a principal P will be worth after t years at interest rate i, compounded annually, is given by the formula

$$A = P(1 + i)^t.$$ You might review Example 11 in Section 11.1.

Suppose that $100,000 is invested at 8% interest, compounded annually.

a) Find a function for the amount in the account after t years.

b) Find the amount of money in the account at $t = 0$, $t = 4$, $t = 8$, and $t = 10$.

c) Graph the function.

SOLUTION

a) If $P = \$100,000$ and $i = 8\% = 0.08$, we can substitute these values and form the following function:

$$A(t) = \$100,000(1 + 0.08)^t \qquad \text{Using } A = P(1 + i)^t$$
$$= \$100,000(1.08)^t.$$

b) To find the function values, a calculator with a power key is helpful.

$$A(0) = \$100,000(1.08)^0 \qquad\qquad A(8) = \$100,000(1.08)^8$$
$$= \$100,000(1) \qquad\qquad\qquad \approx \$100,000(1.85093021)$$
$$= \$100,000 \qquad\qquad\qquad\quad \approx \$185,093.02$$

$$A(4) = \$100,000(1.08)^4 \qquad\qquad A(10) = \$100,000(1.08)^{10}$$
$$= \$100,000(1.36048896) \qquad\quad \approx \$100,000(2.158924997)$$
$$\approx \$136,048.90 \qquad\qquad\qquad \approx \$215,892.50$$

TECHNOLOGY CONNECTION

Graphing calculators can quickly find many function values. Let $y_1 = 100,000(1.08)^x$. Then use the TABLE feature with INDPNT set to ASK to check Example 5(b).

c) We use the function values computed in part (b), and others if we wish, to draw the graph as follows. Note that the axes are scaled differently because of the large numbers.

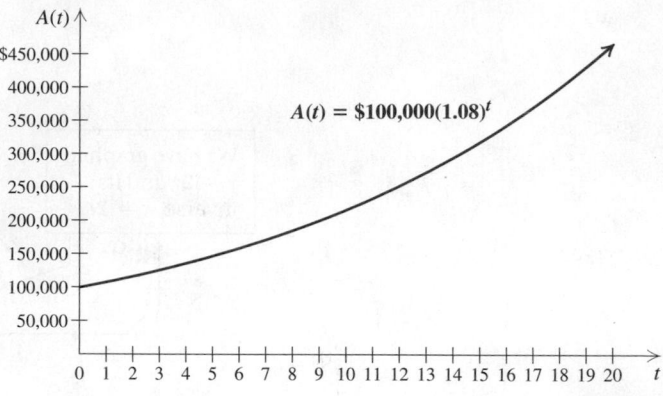

$$A(t) = \$100,000(1.08)^t$$

TRY EXERCISE ▶ 39

12.2 EXERCISE SET

 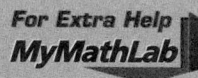 
↪ **Concept Reinforcement** *Classify each statement as either true or false.*

1. The graph of $f(x) = a^x$ always passes through the point $(0, 1)$.

2. The graph of $g(x) = \left(\frac{1}{2}\right)^x$ gets closer and closer to the x-axis as x gets larger and larger.

3. The graph of $f(x) = 2^{x-3}$ looks just like the graph of $y = 2^x$, but it is translated 3 units to the right.

4. The graph of $g(x) = 2^x - 3$ looks just like the graph of $y = 2^x$, but it is translated 3 units up.

5. The graph of $y = 3^x$ gets close to, but never touches, the y-axis.

6. The graph of $x = 3^y$ gets close to, but never touches, the y-axis.

Graph.

7. $y = f(x) = 3^x$

8. $y = f(x) = 4^x$

9. $y = 6^x$

10. $y = 5^x$

11. $y = 2^x + 1$

12. $y = 2^x + 3$

13. $y = 3^x - 2$

14. $y = 3^x - 1$

15. $y = 2^x - 5$

16. $y = 2^x - 4$

17. $y = 2^{x-3}$

18. $y = 2^{x-1}$

19. $y = 2^{x+1}$

20. $y = 2^{x+3}$

21. $y = \left(\frac{1}{4}\right)^x$

22. $y = \left(\frac{1}{5}\right)^x$

23. $y = \left(\frac{1}{3}\right)^x$

24. $y = \left(\frac{1}{10}\right)^x$

25. $y = 2^{x+1} - 3$

26. $y = 2^{x-3} - 1$

27. $x = 6^y$

28. $x = 3^y$

29. $x = 3^{-y}$

30. $x = 2^{-y}$

31. $x = 4^y$

32. $x = 5^y$

33. $x = \left(\frac{4}{3}\right)^y$

34. $x = \left(\frac{3}{2}\right)^y$

Graph each pair of equations on the same set of axes.

35. $y = 3^x, \ x = 3^y$

36. $y = 2^x, \ x = 2^y$

37. $y = \left(\frac{1}{2}\right)^x, \ x = \left(\frac{1}{2}\right)^y$

38. $y = \left(\frac{1}{4}\right)^x, \ x = \left(\frac{1}{4}\right)^y$

Solve.

39. *Music downloads.* The number $M(t)$ of single tracks downloaded, in billions, t years after 2003 can be approximated by

$$M(t) = 0.353\,(1.244)^t.$$

Source: International Federation of the Phonographic Industry

a) Estimate the number of single tracks downloaded in 2006, in 2008, and in 2012.

b) Graph the function.

40. *Growth of bacteria.* The bacteria *Escherichia coli* are commonly found in the human bladder. Suppose that 3000 of the bacteria are present at time $t = 0$. Then t minutes later, the number of bacteria present can be approximated by

$$N(t) = 3000(2)^{t/20}.$$

a) How many bacteria will be present after 10 min? 20 min? 30 min? 40 min? 60 min?

b) Graph the function.

41. *Smoking cessation.*   The percentage of smokers P who receive telephone counseling to quit smoking and are still successful t months later can be approximated by

$$P(t) = 21.4(0.914)^t.$$

Sources: *New England Journal of Medicine;* data from California's Smokers' Hotline

a) Estimate the percentage of smokers receiving telephone counseling who are successful in quitting for 1 month, 3 months, and 1 year.

b) Graph the function.

42. *Smoking cessation.*   The percentage of smokers P who, without telephone counseling, have successfully quit smoking for t months (see Exercise 41) can be approximated by

$$P(t) = 9.02(0.93)^t.$$

Sources: *New England Journal of Medicine;* data from California's Smokers' Hotline

a) Estimate the percentage of smokers not receiving telephone counseling who are successful in quitting for 1 month, 3 months, and 1 year.

b) Graph the function.

43. *Marine biology.*   Due to excessive whaling prior to the mid 1970s, the humpback whale is considered an endangered species. The worldwide population of humpbacks, $P(t)$, in thousands, t years after 1900 $(t < 70)$ can be approximated by*

$$P(t) = 150(0.960)^t.$$

a) How many humpback whales were alive in 1930? in 1960?

b) Graph the function.

44. *Salvage value.*   A laser printer is purchased for $1200. Its value each year is about 80% of the value of the preceding year. Its value, in dollars, after t years is given by the exponential function

$$V(t) = 1200(0.8)^t.$$

a) Find the value of the printer after 0 yr, 1 yr, 2 yr, 5 yr, and 10 yr.

b) Graph the function.

45. *Marine biology.*   As a result of preservation efforts in most countries in which whaling was common, the humpback whale population has grown since the 1970s. The worldwide population of hump-

backs, $P(t)$, in thousands, t years after 1982 can be approximated by*

$$P(t) = 5.5(1.047)^t.$$

a) How many humpback whales were alive in 1992? in 2004?

b) Graph the function.

46. *Recycling aluminum cans.*   It is estimated that $\frac{1}{2}$ of all aluminum cans distributed will be recycled each year. A beverage company distributes 250,000 cans. The number still in use after time t, in years, is given by the exponential function

$$N(t) = 250{,}000\left(\tfrac{1}{2}\right)^t.$$

Source: The Aluminum Association, Inc., 2005

a) How many cans are still in use after 0 yr? 1 yr? 4 yr? 10 yr?

b) Graph the function.

47. *Spread of zebra mussels.*   Beginning in 1988, infestations of zebra mussels started spreading throughout North American waters.[†] These mussels spread with such speed that water treatment facilities, power plants, and entire ecosystems can become threatened. The function

$$A(t) = 10 \cdot 34^t$$

can be used to estimate the number of square centimeters of lake bottom that will be covered with mussels t years after an infestation covering 10 cm² first occurs.

a) How many square centimeters of lake bottom will be covered with mussels 5 yr after an infestation covering 10 cm² first appears? 7 yr after the infestation first appears?

b) Graph the function.

---

*Based on information from the American Cetacean Society, 2001, and the ASK Archive, 1998.
[†]Many thanks to Dr. Gerald Mackie of the Department of Zoology at the University of Guelph in Ontario for the background information for this exercise.

48. *Cell phones.* The number of cell phones in use in the United States is increasing exponentially. The number N, in millions, in use can be estimated by

$$N(t) = 7.12(1.3)^t,$$

where t is the number of years after 1990.
Source: Based on data from CTIA-The Wireless Association

a) Estimate the number of cell phones in use in 1995, in 2005, and in 2010.

b) Graph the function.

49. Without using a calculator, explain why 2^π must be greater than 8 but less than 16.

50. Suppose that $1000 is invested for 5 yr at 7% interest, compounded annually. In what year will the most interest be earned? Why?

Skill Review

Review factoring polynomials (Sections 5.1–5.6).

Factor.

51. $3x^2 - 48$ [5.4]

52. $x^2 - 20x + 100$ [5.4]

53. $6x^2 + x - 12$ [5.3]

54. $8x^6 - 64y^6$ [5.5]

55. $6y^2 + 36y - 240$ [5.2]

56. $5x^4 - 10x^3 - 3x^2 + 6x$ [5.1]

Synthesis

57. Examine Exercise 48. Do you believe that the equation for the number of cell phones in use in the United States will be accurate 20 yr from now? Why or why not?

58. Explain why the graph of $x = 2^y$ is the graph of $y = 2^x$ reflected across the line $y = x$.

Determine which of the two numbers is larger. Do not use a calculator.

59. $\pi^{1.3}$ or $\pi^{2.4}$

60. $\sqrt{8^3}$ or $8^{\sqrt{3}}$

Graph.

61. $f(x) = 2.5^x$

62. $f(x) = 0.5^x$

63. $y = 2^x + 2^{-x}$

64. $y = \left|\left(\frac{1}{2}\right)^x - 1\right|$

65. $y = |2^x - 2|$

66. $y = 2^{-(x-1)^2}$

67. $y = |2^{x^2} - 1|$

68. $y = 3^x + 3^{-x}$

Graph both equations using the same set of axes.

69. $y = 3^{-(x-1)}, \ x = 3^{-(y-1)}$

70. $y = 1^x, \ x = 1^y$

71. *Navigational devices.* The number of GPS navigational devices in use in the United States has grown from 0.5 million in 2000 to 4 million in 2004 to 50 million in 2008. After pressing **STAT** and entering the data, use the ExpReg option in the STAT CALC menu to find an exponential function that models the number of navigational devices in use t years after 2000. Then use that function to predict the total number of devices in use in 2012.
Source: Telematics Research Group

72. *Keyboarding speed.* Trey is studying keyboarding. After he has studied for t hours, Trey's speed, in words per minute, is given by the exponential function

$$S(t) = 200[1 - (0.99)^t].$$

Use a graph and/or table of values to predict Trey's speed after studying for 10 hr, 40 hr, and 80 hr.

73. The following graph shows growth in the height of ocean waves over time, assuming a steady surface wind.
Source: magicseaweed.com

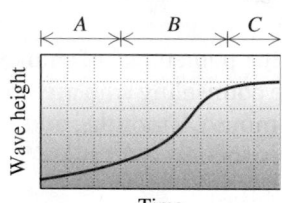

Source: magicseaweed.com

a) Consider the portions of the graph marked A, B, and C. Suppose that each portion can be labeled Exponential Growth, Linear Growth, or Saturation. How would you label each portion?

b) Small vertical movements in wind, surface roughness of water, and gravity are three forces that create waves. How might these forces be related to the shape of the wave-height graph?

74. Consider any exponential function of the form $f(x) = a^x$ with $a > 1$. Will it always follow that $f(3) - f(2) > f(2) - f(1)$, and, in general, $f(n + 2) - f(n + 1) > f(n + 1) - f(n)$? Why or why not? (*Hint*: Think graphically.)

75. On many graphing calculators, it is possible to enter and graph $y_1 = A \wedge (X - B) + C$ after first pressing **APPS** Transfrm. Use this application to graph $f(x) = 2.5^{x-3} + 2, g(x) = 2.5^{x+3} + 2,$ $h(x) = 2.5^{x-3} - 2,$ and $k(x) = 2.5^{x+3} - 2.$

COLLABORATIVE

CORNER

The True Cost of a New Car

Focus: Car loans and exponential functions

Time: 30 minutes

Group size: 2

Materials: Calculators with exponentiation keys

The formula

$$M = \frac{Pr}{1 - (1 + r)^{-n}}$$

is used to determine the payment size, *M*, when a loan of *P* dollars is to be repaid in *n* equally sized monthly payments. Here *r* represents the monthly interest rate. Loans repaid in this fashion are said to be *amortized* (spread out equally) over a period of *n* months.

ACTIVITY

1. Suppose one group member is selling the other a car for $2600, financed at 1% interest per month for 24 months. What should be the size of each monthly payment?

2. Suppose both group members are shopping for the same model new car. To save time, each group member visits a different dealer. One dealer offers the car for $13,000 at 10.5% interest (0.00875 monthly interest) for 60 months (no down payment). The other dealer offers the same car for $12,000, but at 12% interest (0.01 monthly interest) for 48 months (no down payment).

   a) Determine the monthly payment size for each offer. Then determine the total amount paid for the car under each offer. How much of each total is interest?

   b) Work together to find the annual interest rate for which the total cost of 60 monthly payments for the $13,000 car would equal the total amount paid for the $12,000 car (as found in part a above).

12.3   Logarithmic Functions

Graphs of Logarithmic Functions ▪ Equivalent Equations ▪ Solving Certain Logarithmic Equations

We are now ready to study inverses of exponential functions. These functions have many applications and are called *logarithm,* or *logarithmic, functions.*

Graphs of Logarithmic Functions

Consider the exponential function $f(x) = 2^x$. Like all exponential functions, *f* is one-to-one. Can a formula for f^{-1} be found? To answer this, we use the method of Section 12.1:

1. Replace $f(x)$ with y: $y = 2^x$.
2. Interchange *x* and *y*: $x = 2^y$.

3. Solve for y: $y =$ the exponent to which we raise 2 to get x.

4. Replace y with $f^{-1}(x)$: $f^{-1}(x) =$ the exponent to which we raise 2 to get x.

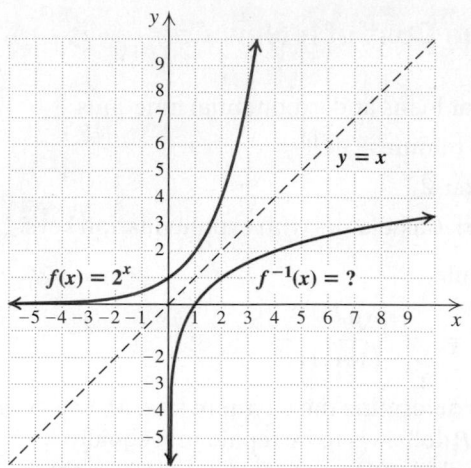

We now define a new symbol to replace the words "the exponent to which we raise 2 to get x":

$\log_2 x$, read "the logarithm, base 2, of x," or "log, base 2, of x," means "the exponent to which we raise 2 to get x."

Thus if $f(x) = 2^x$, then $f^{-1}(x) = \log_2 x$. Note that $f^{-1}(8) = \log_2 8 = 3$, because 3 is *the exponent to which we raise* 2 *to get* 8.

EXAMPLE   **1**   Simplify: **(a)** $\log_2 32$; **(b)** $\log_2 1$; **(c)** $\log_2 \frac{1}{8}$.

SOLUTION

a) Think of $\log_2 32$ as the exponent to which we raise 2 to get 32. That exponent is 5. Therefore, $\log_2 32 = 5$.

b) We ask ourselves: "To what exponent do we raise 2 in order to get 1?" That exponent is 0 (recall that $2^0 = 1$). Thus, $\log_2 1 = 0$.

c) To what exponent do we raise 2 in order to get $\frac{1}{8}$? Since $2^{-3} = \frac{1}{8}$, we have $\log_2 \frac{1}{8} = -3$.

         TRY EXERCISE   9

Although numbers like $\log_2 13$ can be only approximated, we must remember that $\log_2 13$ represents *the exponent to which we raise* 2 *to get* 13. That is, $2^{\log_2 13} = 13$. A calculator indicates that $\log_2 13 \approx 3.7$ and $2^{3.7} \approx 13$.

For any exponential function $f(x) = a^x$, the inverse is called a **logarithmic function, base a**. The graph of the inverse can be drawn by reflecting the graph of $f(x) = a^x$ across the line $y = x$. It will be helpful to remember that the inverse of $f(x) = a^x$ is given by $f^{-1}(x) = \log_a x$.

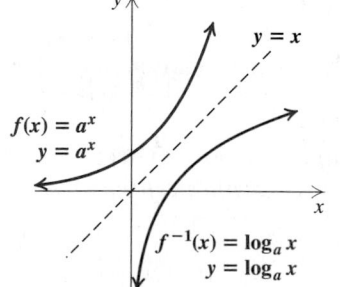

The Meaning of $\log_a x$

For $x > 0$ and a a positive constant other than 1, $\log_a x$ is the exponent to which a must be raised in order to get x. Thus,

$$\log_a x = m \quad \text{means} \quad a^m = x$$

or equivalently,

$$\log_a x \text{ is that unique exponent for which } a^{\log_a x} = x.$$

It is important to remember that *a logarithm is an exponent*. It might help to verbalize: "The logarithm, base *a*, of a number *x* is the exponent to which *a* must be raised in order to get *x*."

EXAMPLE 2

Simplify: $7^{\log_7 85}$.

SOLUTION   Remember that $\log_7 85$ is the exponent to which 7 is raised to get 85. Raising 7 to that exponent, we have

$$7^{\log_7 85} = 85.$$

> **TRY EXERCISE** 35

Because logarithmic and exponential functions are inverses of each other, the result in Example 2 should come as no surprise: If $f(x) = \log_7 x$, then

for $\quad f(x) = \log_7 x$, we have $f^{-1}(x) = 7^x$

and $\quad f^{-1}(f(x)) = f^{-1}(\log_7 x) = 7^{\log_7 x} = x.$

Thus, $f^{-1}(f(85)) = 7^{\log_7 85} = 85.$

The following is a comparison of exponential and logarithmic functions.

Exponential Function	Logarithmic Function
$y = a^x$	$x = a^y$
$f(x) = a^x$	$g(x) = \log_a x$
$a > 0, a \neq 1$	$a > 0, a \neq 1$
The domain is $\mathbb{R}$.	The range is $\mathbb{R}$.
$y > 0$ (Outputs are positive.)	$x > 0$ (Inputs are positive.)
$f^{-1}(x) = \log_a x$	$g^{-1}(x) = a^x$

EXAMPLE 3

Graph: $y = f(x) = \log_5 x$.

SOLUTION   If $y = \log_5 x$, then $5^y = x$. We can find ordered pairs that are solutions by choosing values for y and computing the x-values.

For $y = 0, x = 5^0 = 1.$
For $y = 1, x = 5^1 = 5.$
For $y = 2, x = 5^2 = 25.$
For $y = -1, x = 5^{-1} = \frac{1}{5}.$
For $y = -2, x = 5^{-2} = \frac{1}{25}.$

(1) Select y. ⎯⎯⎯⎯
(2) Compute x. ⎯⎯⎯

This table shows the following:

$\left. \begin{array}{l} \log_5 1 = 0; \\[4pt] \log_5 5 = 1; \\[4pt] \log_5 25 = 2; \\[4pt] \log_5 \frac{1}{5} = -1; \\[4pt] \log_5 \frac{1}{25} = -2. \end{array} \right\}$

These can all be checked using the equations above.

x, or 5^y	y
1	0
5	1
25	2
$\frac{1}{5}$	-1
$\frac{1}{25}$	-2

TECHNOLOGY CONNECTION

To see that $f(x) = 10^x$ and $g(x) = \log_{10} x$ are inverses of each other, let $y_1 = 10^x$ and $y_2 = \log_{10} x = \log x$. Then, using a squared window, compare both graphs. If possible, select DrawInv from the (DRAW) menu and then press (VARS) (▷) (1) (1) (ENTER) to see another representation of f^{-1}. Finally, let $y_3 = y_1(y_2)$ and $y_4 = y_2(y_1)$ to show, using a table or graphs, that, for $x > 0$, $y_3 = y_4 = x$.

We plot the set of ordered pairs and connect the points with a smooth curve. The graphs of $y = 5^x$ and $y = x$ are shown only for reference.

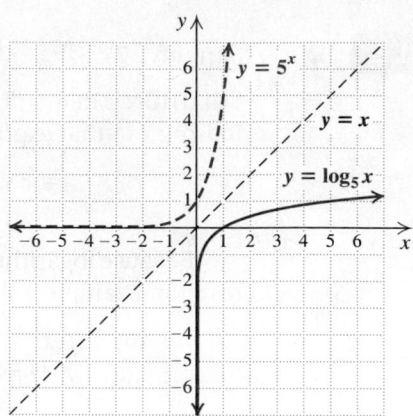

TRY EXERCISE 37

Equivalent Equations

We use the definition of logarithm to rewrite a *logarithmic equation* as an equivalent *exponential equation* or the other way around:

$$m = \log_a x \quad \text{is equivalent to} \quad a^m = x.$$

> *CAUTION!* **Do not forget this relationship!** It is probably the most important definition in the chapter. Many times this definition will be used to justify a property we are considering.

EXAMPLE 4 Rewrite each as an equivalent exponential equation: **(a)** $y = \log_3 5$; **(b)** $-2 = \log_a 7$; **(c)** $a = \log_b d$.

SOLUTION

a) $y = \log_3 5$ is equivalent to $3^y = 5$ The logarithm is the exponent.

The base remains the base.

b) $-2 = \log_a 7$ is equivalent to $a^{-2} = 7$

c) $a = \log_b d$ is equivalent to $b^a = d$ TRY EXERCISE 47

We also use the definition of logarithm to rewrite an exponential equation as an equivalent logarithmic equation.

EXAMPLE 5 Rewrite each as an equivalent logarithmic equation: **(a)** $8 = 2^x$; **(b)** $y^{-1} = 4$; **(c)** $a^b = c$.

SOLUTION

a) $8 = 2^x$ is equivalent to $x = \log_2 8$ The exponent is the logarithm.

The base remains the base.

b) $y^{-1} = 4$ is equivalent to $-1 = \log_y 4$

c) $a^b = c$ is equivalent to $b = \log_a c$ TRY EXERCISE 63

Solving Certain Logarithmic Equations

Many logarithmic equations can be solved by rewriting them as equivalent exponential equations.

EXAMPLE   6   Solve: **(a)** $\log_2 x = -3$; **(b)** $\log_x 16 = 2$.

SOLUTION

a) $\log_2 x = -3$

$\quad\quad 2^{-3} = x \quad\quad$ Rewriting as an exponential equation

$\quad\quad \frac{1}{8} = x \quad\quad$ Computing 2^{-3}

Check: $\log_2 \frac{1}{8}$ is the exponent to which 2 is raised to get $\frac{1}{8}$. Since that exponent is -3, we have a check. The solution is $\frac{1}{8}$.

b) $\log_x 16 = 2$

$\quad\quad x^2 = 16 \quad\quad\quad\quad$ Rewriting as an exponential equation

$\quad x = 4 \quad or \quad x = -4 \quad$ Principle of square roots

Check: $\log_4 16 = 2$ because $4^2 = 16$. Thus, 4 is a solution of $\log_x 16 = 2$. Because all logarithmic bases must be positive, -4 cannot be a solution. Logarithmic bases must be positive because logarithms are defined using exponential functions that require positive bases. The solution is 4.

TRY EXERCISE   79

One method for solving certain logarithmic and exponential equations relies on the following property, which results from the fact that exponential functions are one-to-one.

The Principle of Exponential Equality

For any real number b, where $b \neq -1, 0,$ or 1,

$$b^{x_1} = b^{x_2} \quad \text{is equivalent to} \quad x_1 = x_2.$$

(Powers of the same base are equal if and only if the exponents are equal.)

EXAMPLE   7   Solve: **(a)** $\log_{10} 1000 = x$; **(b)** $\log_4 1 = t$.

SOLUTION

a) We rewrite $\log_{10} 1000 = x$ in exponential form and solve:

$\quad\quad 10^x = 1000 \quad\quad$ Rewriting as an exponential equation

$\quad\quad 10^x = 10^3 \quad\quad$ Writing 1000 as a power of 10

$\quad\quad\quad x = 3. \quad\quad\quad$ Equating exponents

Check: This equation can also be solved directly by determining the exponent to which we raise 10 in order to get 1000. In both cases we find that $\log_{10} 1000 = 3$, so we have a check. The solution is 3.

b) We rewrite $\log_4 1 = t$ in exponential form and solve:

$$4^t = 1 \qquad \text{Rewriting as an exponential equation}$$
$$4^t = 4^0 \qquad \text{Writing 1 as a power of 4. This can be done mentally.}$$
$$t = 0. \qquad \text{Equating exponents}$$

Check: As in part (a), this equation can be solved directly by determining the exponent to which we raise 4 in order to get 1. In both cases we find that $\log_4 1 = 0$, so we have a check. The solution is 0.

TRY EXERCISE 81

Example 7 illustrates an important property of logarithms.

> **$\log_a 1$**
>
> The logarithm, base a, of 1 is always 0: $\log_a 1 = 0$.

This follows from the fact that $a^0 = 1$ is equivalent to the logarithmic equation $\log_a 1 = 0$. Thus, $\log_{10} 1 = 0$, $\log_7 1 = 0$, and so on.

Another property results from the fact that $a^1 = a$. This is equivalent to the logarithmic equation $\log_a a = 1$.

> **$\log_a a$**
>
> The logarithm, base a, of a is always 1: $\log_a a = 1$.

Thus, $\log_{10} 10 = 1$, $\log_8 8 = 1$, and so on.

12.3   EXERCISE SET

For Extra Help
MyMathLab   Math_XP
PRACTICE   WATCH   DOWNLOAD

Concept Reinforcement   *In each of Exercises 1–8, match the expression or equation with an equivalent expression or equation from the column on the right.*

1. _____ $\log_5 25$

2. _____ $2^5 = x$

3. _____ $\log_5 5$

4. _____ $\log_2 1$

5. _____ $\log_5 5^x$

6. _____ $\log_x 27 = 5$

7. _____ $5 = 2^x$

8. _____ $x^{-2} = 5$

a) 1

b) x

c) $x^5 = 27$

d) $\log_2 x = 5$

e) $\log_2 5 = x$

f) $\log_x 5 = -2$

g) 2

h) 0

Simplify.

9. $\log_{10} 1000$

10. $\log_{10} 100$

11. $\log_7 49$

12. $\log_2 8$

13. $\log_3 81$

14. $\log_3 9$

15. $\log_5 \frac{1}{25}$

16. $\log_5 \frac{1}{5}$

17. $\log_8 \frac{1}{8}$

18. $\log_8 \frac{1}{64}$

19. $\log_5 625$

20. $\log_5 125$

21. $\log_7 7$

22. $\log_9 1$

23. $\log_3 1$

24. $\log_3 3$

Aha! 25. $\log_6 6^5$

26. $\log_6 6^9$

27. $\log_{10} 0.01$

28. $\log_{10} 0.1$

29. $\log_{16} 4$

30. $\log_{100} 10$

31. $\log_9 27$

32. $\log_4 32$

33. $\log_{1000} 100$

34. $\log_{16} 8$

35. $3^{\log_3 29}$

36. $6^{\log_6 13}$

Graph.

37. $y = \log_{10} x$

38. $y = \log_2 x$

39. $y = \log_3 x$

40. $y = \log_7 x$

41. $f(x) = \log_6 x$

42. $f(x) = \log_4 x$

43. $f(x) = \log_{2.5} x$

44. $f(x) = \log_{1/2} x$

Graph both functions using the same set of axes.

45. $f(x) = 3^x, \ f^{-1}(x) = \log_3 x$

46. $f(x) = 4^x, \ f^{-1}(x) = \log_4 x$

Rewrite each of the following as an equivalent exponential equation. Do not solve.

47. $x = \log_{10} 8$

48. $y = \log_8 10$

49. $\log_9 9 = 1$

50. $\log_6 36 = 2$

51. $\log_{10} 0.1 = -1$

52. $\log_{10} 0.01 = -2$

53. $\log_{10} 7 = 0.845$

54. $\log_{10} 3 = 0.4771$

55. $\log_c m = 8$

56. $\log_b n = 23$

57. $\log_r C = t$

58. $\log_m P = a$

59. $\log_e 0.25 = -1.3863$

60. $\log_e 0.989 = -0.0111$

61. $\log_r T = -x$

62. $\log_c M = -w$

Rewrite each of the following as an equivalent logarithmic equation. Do not solve.

63. $10^2 = 100$

64. $10^4 = 10,000$

65. $5^{-3} = \frac{1}{125}$

66. $2^{-5} = \frac{1}{32}$

67. $16^{1/4} = 2$

68. $8^{1/3} = 2$

69. $10^{0.4771} = 3$

70. $10^{0.3010} = 2$

71. $z^m = 6$

72. $m^n = r$

73. $p^t = q$

74. $y^t = x$

75. $e^3 = 20.0855$

76. $e^2 = 7.3891$

77. $e^{-4} = 0.0183$

78. $e^{-2} = 0.1353$

Solve.

79. $\log_6 x = 2$

80. $\log_4 x = 3$

81. $\log_2 32 = x$

82. $\log_5 25 = x$

83. $\log_x 9 = 1$

84. $\log_x 12 = 1$

85. $\log_x 7 = \frac{1}{2}$

86. $\log_x 9 = \frac{1}{2}$

87. $\log_3 x = -2$

88. $\log_2 x = -1$

89. $\log_{32} x = \frac{2}{5}$

90. $\log_8 x = \frac{2}{3}$

91. In what way is a logarithm an exponent?

92. Is it easier to find x given $x = \log_9 \frac{1}{3}$ or given $9^x = \frac{1}{3}$? Explain your reasoning.

Skill Review

Review simplifying rational and radical expressions (Chapters 6 and 10).

Simplify.

93. $\sqrt{18a^3b} \sqrt{50ab^7}$ [10.3]

94. $(2\sqrt{3} + \sqrt{5})(2\sqrt{3} - \sqrt{10})$ [10.5]

95. $\sqrt{192x} - \sqrt{75x}$ [10.5]

96. $\sqrt[4]{\sqrt[3]{x}}$ [10.2]

97. $\dfrac{\dfrac{3}{x} - \dfrac{2}{xy}}{\dfrac{2}{x^2} + \dfrac{1}{xy}}$ [6.5]

98. $\dfrac{\dfrac{4+x}{x^2 + 2x + 1}}{\dfrac{3}{x+1} - \dfrac{2}{x+2}}$ [6.5]

Synthesis

99. Would a manufacturer be pleased or unhappy if sales of a product grew logarithmically? Why?

100. Explain why the number $\log_2 13$ must be between 3 and 4.

101. Graph both equations using the same set of axes:
$$y = \left(\tfrac{3}{2}\right)^x, \qquad y = \log_{3/2} x.$$

Graph.

102. $y = \log_2 (x - 1)$

103. $y = \log_3 |x + 1|$

Solve.

104. $|\log_3 x| = 2$

105. $\log_4 (3x - 2) = 2$

106. $\log_8 (2x + 1) = -1$

107. $\log_{10} (x^2 + 21x) = 2$

Simplify.

108. $\log_{1/4} \frac{1}{64}$

109. $\log_{1/5} 25$

110. $\log_{81} 3 \cdot \log_3 81$

111. $\log_{10} (\log_4 (\log_3 81))$

112. $\log_2 (\log_2 (\log_4 256))$

113. Show that $b^{x_1} = b^{x_2}$ is *not* equivalent to $x_1 = x_2$ for $b = 0$ or $b = 1$.

114. If $\log_b a = x$, does it follow that $\log_a b = 1/x$? Why or why not?

12.4 Properties of Logarithmic Functions

Logarithms of Products • Logarithms of Powers • Logarithms of Quotients •
Using the Properties Together

Logarithmic functions are important in many applications and in more advanced mathematics. We now establish some basic properties that are useful in manipulating expressions involving logarithms. As their proofs reveal, the properties of logarithms are related to the properties of exponents.

Logarithms of Products

The first property we discuss is related to the product rule for exponents: $a^m \cdot a^n = a^{m+n}$. Its proof appears immediately after Example 2.

> ### The Product Rule for Logarithms
> For any positive numbers M, N, and a ($a \neq 1$),
> $$\log_a (MN) = \log_a M + \log_a N.$$
> (The logarithm of a product is the sum of the logarithms of the factors.)

EXAMPLE **1**

Express as an equivalent expression that is a sum of logarithms: $\log_2 (4 \cdot 16)$.

SOLUTION We have

$$\log_2 (4 \cdot 16) = \log_2 4 + \log_2 16. \qquad \text{Using the product rule for logarithms}$$

As a check, note that

$$\log_2 (4 \cdot 16) = \log_2 64 = 6 \qquad 2^6 = 64$$

and that

$$\log_2 4 + \log_2 16 = 2 + 4 = 6. \qquad 2^2 = 4 \text{ and } 2^4 = 16$$

> TRY EXERCISE 7

EXAMPLE **2**

Express as an equivalent expression that is a single logarithm: $\log_b 7 + \log_b 5$.

SOLUTION We have

$$\log_b 7 + \log_b 5 = \log_b (7 \cdot 5) \qquad \text{Using the product rule for logarithms}$$
$$= \log_b 35.$$

> TRY EXERCISE 13

A Proof of the Product Rule. Let $\log_a M = x$ and $\log_a N = y$. Converting to exponential equations, we have $a^x = M$ and $a^y = N$.

Now we multiply the left side of the first exponential equation by the left side of the second equation and similarly multiply the right sides to obtain

$$MN = a^x \cdot a^y, \quad \text{or} \quad MN = a^{x+y}.$$

Converting back to a logarithmic equation, we get

$$\log_a (MN) = x + y.$$

Recalling what x and y represent, we have

$$\log_a(MN) = \log_a M + \log_a N.$$

Logarithms of Powers

The second basic property is related to the power rule for exponents: $(a^m)^n = a^{mn}$. Its proof follows Example 3.

> ### The Power Rule for Logarithms
> For any positive numbers M and a ($a \neq 1$), and any real number p,
>
> $$\log_a M^p = p \cdot \log_a M.$$
>
> (The logarithm of a power of M is the exponent times the logarithm of M.)

To better understand the power rule, note that

$$\log_a M^3 = \log_a(M \cdot M \cdot M) = \log_a M + \log_a M + \log_a M = 3\log_a M.$$

EXAMPLE 3   Use the power rule for logarithms to write an equivalent expression that is a product: **(a)** $\log_a 9^{-5}$; **(b)** $\log_7 \sqrt[3]{x}$.

SOLUTION

a) $\log_a 9^{-5} = -5\log_a 9$ Using the power rule for logarithms

b) $\log_7 \sqrt[3]{x} = \log_7 x^{1/3}$ Writing exponential notation

$\phantom{\log_7 \sqrt[3]{x}} = \frac{1}{3}\log_7 x$ Using the power rule for logarithms

TRY EXERCISE 17

A Proof of the Power Rule.   Let $x = \log_a M$. We then write the equivalent exponential equation, $a^x = M$. Raising both sides to the pth power, we get

$$(a^x)^p = M^p, \quad \text{or} \quad a^{xp} = M^p. \qquad \text{Multiplying exponents}$$

Converting back to a logarithmic equation gives us

$$\log_a M^p = xp.$$

But $x = \log_a M$, so substituting, we have

$$\log_a M^p = (\log_a M)p = p \cdot \log_a M.$$

STUDENT NOTES

Without understanding and *remembering* the rules of this section, it will be extremely difficult to solve the equations of Section 12.6.

Logarithms of Quotients

The third property that we study is similar to the quotient rule for exponents: $a^m/a^n = a^{m-n}$. Its proof follows Example 5.

> ### The Quotient Rule for Logarithms
> For any positive numbers M, N, and a ($a \neq 1$),
>
> $$\log_a \frac{M}{N} = \log_a M - \log_a N.$$
>
> (The logarithm of a quotient is the logarithm of the dividend minus the logarithm of the divisor.)

To better understand the quotient rule, note that

$$\log_2 \tfrac{8}{32} = \log_2 \tfrac{1}{4} = -2$$

and $\log_2 8 - \log_2 32 = 3 - 5 = -2.$

EXAMPLE 4   Express as an equivalent expression that is a difference of logarithms: $\log_t (6/U)$.

SOLUTION

$$\log_t \frac{6}{U} = \log_t 6 - \log_t U \qquad \text{Using the quotient rule for logarithms}$$

> **TRY EXERCISE** 23

EXAMPLE 5   Express as an equivalent expression that is a single logarithm:

$$\log_b 17 - \log_b 27.$$

SOLUTION

$$\log_b 17 - \log_b 27 = \log_b \frac{17}{27} \qquad \begin{array}{l}\text{Using the quotient rule for}\\ \text{logarithms "in reverse"}\end{array}$$

> **TRY EXERCISE** 27

A Proof of the Quotient Rule.   Our proof uses both the product rule and the power rule:

$$
\begin{aligned}
\log_a \frac{M}{N} &= \log_a (MN^{-1}) && \text{Rewriting } \frac{M}{N} \text{ as } MN^{-1}\\
&= \log_a M + \log_a N^{-1} && \text{Using the product rule for logarithms}\\
&= \log_a M + (-1)\log_a N && \text{Using the power rule for logarithms}\\
&= \log_a M - \log_a N.
\end{aligned}
$$

Using the Properties Together

EXAMPLE 6   Express as an equivalent expression, using the individual logarithms of x, y, and z.

a) $\log_b \dfrac{x^3}{yz}$ **b)** $\log_a \sqrt[4]{\dfrac{xy}{z^3}}$

SOLUTION

a) $\log_b \dfrac{x^3}{yz} = \log_b x^3 - \log_b yz$ Using the quotient rule for logarithms

$\qquad\qquad = 3\log_b x - \log_b yz$ Using the power rule for logarithms

$\qquad\qquad = 3\log_b x - (\log_b y + \log_b z)$ Using the product rule for logarithms. Because of the subtraction, parentheses are essential.

$\qquad\qquad = 3\log_b x - \log_b y - \log_b z$ Using the distributive law

b) $\log_a \sqrt[4]{\dfrac{xy}{z^3}} = \log_a \left(\dfrac{xy}{z^3}\right)^{1/4}$ Writing exponential notation

$\qquad = \dfrac{1}{4} \cdot \log_a \dfrac{xy}{z^3}$ Using the power rule for logarithms

$\qquad = \dfrac{1}{4} (\log_a xy - \log_a z^3)$ Using the quotient rule for logarithms. Parentheses are important.

$\qquad = \dfrac{1}{4} (\log_a x + \log_a y - 3 \log_a z)$ Using the product rule and the power rule for logarithms

> TRY EXERCISE   37

CAUTION! Because the product and quotient rules replace one term with two, it is often essential to apply the rules within parentheses, as in Example 6.

EXAMPLE 7

Express as an equivalent expression that is a single logarithm.

a) $\dfrac{1}{2} \log_a x - 7 \log_a y + \log_a z$ **b)** $\log_a \dfrac{b}{\sqrt{x}} + \log_a \sqrt{bx}$

SOLUTION

a) $\dfrac{1}{2} \log_a x - 7 \log_a y + \log_a z$

$\qquad = \log_a x^{1/2} - \log_a y^7 + \log_a z$ Using the power rule for logarithms

$\qquad = \left(\log_a \sqrt{x} - \log_a y^7\right) + \log_a z$ Using parentheses to emphasize the order of operations; $x^{1/2} = \sqrt{x}$

$\qquad = \log_a \dfrac{\sqrt{x}}{y^7} + \log_a z$ Using the quotient rule for logarithms. Note that all terms have the same base.

$\qquad = \log_a \dfrac{z\sqrt{x}}{y^7}$ Using the product rule for logarithms

b) $\log_a \dfrac{b}{\sqrt{x}} + \log_a \sqrt{bx} = \log_a \dfrac{b \cdot \sqrt{bx}}{\sqrt{x}}$ Using the product rule for logarithms

$\qquad = \log_a b\sqrt{b}$ Removing a factor equal to 1: $\dfrac{\sqrt{x}}{\sqrt{x}} = 1$

$\qquad = \log_a b^{3/2}$, or $\dfrac{3}{2} \log_a b$ Since $b\sqrt{b} = b^1 \cdot b^{1/2}$

> TRY EXERCISE   49

If we know the logarithms of two different numbers (with the same base), the properties allow us to calculate other logarithms.

EXAMPLE 8

Given $\log_a 2 = 0.431$ and $\log_a 3 = 0.683$, use the properties of logarithms to calculate a value for each of the following. If this is not possible, state so.

a) $\log_a 6$ **b)** $\log_a \frac{2}{3}$ **c)** $\log_a 81$

d) $\log_a \frac{1}{3}$ **e)** $\log_a (2a)$ **f)** $\log_a 5$

SOLUTION

a) $\log_a 6 = \log_a(2 \cdot 3) = \log_a 2 + \log_a 3$ Using the product rule for logarithms

$$= 0.431 + 0.683 = 1.114$$

Check: $a^{1.114} = a^{0.431} \cdot a^{0.683} = 2 \cdot 3 = 6$

b) $\log_a \frac{2}{3} = \log_a 2 - \log_a 3$ Using the quotient rule for logarithms

$$= 0.431 - 0.683 = -0.252$$

c) $\log_a 81 = \log_a 3^4 = 4 \log_a 3$ Using the power rule for logarithms

$$= 4(0.683) = 2.732$$

d) $\log_a \frac{1}{3} = \log_a 1 - \log_a 3$ Using the quotient rule for logarithms

$$= 0 - 0.683 = -0.683$$

e) $\log_a (2a) = \log_a 2 + \log_a a$ Using the product rule for logarithms

$$= 0.431 + 1 = 1.431$$

f) $\log_a 5$ *cannot be found using these properties.* $(\log_a 5 \neq \log_a 2 + \log_a 3)$

TRY EXERCISE 55

A final property follows from the product rule: Since $\log_a a^k = k \log_a a$, and $\log_a a = 1$, we have $\log_a a^k = k$.

The Logarithm of the Base to an Exponent

For any base a,

$$\log_a a^k = k.$$

(The logarithm, base a, of a to an exponent is the exponent.)

This property also follows from the definition of logarithm: k is the exponent to which you raise a in order to get a^k.

EXAMPLE 9   Simplify: **(a)** $\log_3 3^7$; **(b)** $\log_{10} 10^{-5.2}$.

SOLUTION

a) $\log_3 3^7 = 7$ 7 is the exponent to which you raise 3 in order to get 3^7.

b) $\log_{10} 10^{-5.2} = -5.2$ **TRY EXERCISE** 65

We summarize the properties of logarithms as follows.

For any positive numbers M, N, and a $(a \neq 1)$:

$$\log_a (MN) = \log_a M + \log_a N; \qquad \log_a M^p = p \cdot \log_a M;$$

$$\log_a \frac{M}{N} = \log_a M - \log_a N; \qquad \log_a a^k = k.$$

> **CAUTION!** Keep in mind that, in general,
>
> $\log_a (M + N) \neq \log_a M + \log_a N,$ $\log_a (MN) \neq (\log_a M)(\log_a N),$
>
> $\log_a (M - N) \neq \log_a M - \log_a N,$ $\log_a \dfrac{M}{N} \neq \dfrac{\log_a M}{\log_a N}.$

12.4 EXERCISE SET

➤ **Concept Reinforcement** *In each of Exercises 1–6, match the expression with an equivalent expression from the column on the right.*

1. ____ $\log_7 20$
2. ____ $\log_7 5^4$
3. ____ $\log_7 \frac{5}{4}$
4. ____ $\log_7 7$
5. ____ $\log_7 1$
6. ____ $\log_7 5 + \log_7 6$

a) $\log_7 5 - \log_7 4$
b) 1
c) 0
d) $\log_7 30$
e) $\log_7 5 + \log_7 4$
f) $4 \log_7 5$

Express as an equivalent expression that is a sum of logarithms.

7. $\log_3 (81 \cdot 27)$
8. $\log_2 (16 \cdot 32)$
9. $\log_4 (64 \cdot 16)$
10. $\log_5 (25 \cdot 125)$
11. $\log_c (rst)$
12. $\log_t (3ab)$

Express as an equivalent expression that is a single logarithm.

13. $\log_a 2 + \log_a 10$
14. $\log_b 5 + \log_b 9$
15. $\log_c t + \log_c y$
16. $\log_t H + \log_t M$

Express as an equivalent expression that is a product.

17. $\log_a r^8$
18. $\log_b t^5$
19. $\log_2 y^{1/3}$
20. $\log_{10} y^{1/2}$
21. $\log_b C^{-3}$
22. $\log_c M^{-5}$

Express as an equivalent expression that is a difference of two logarithms.

23. $\log_2 \frac{5}{11}$
24. $\log_3 \frac{29}{13}$
25. $\log_b \dfrac{m}{n}$
26. $\log_a \dfrac{y}{x}$

Express as an equivalent expression that is a single logarithm.

27. $\log_a 19 - \log_a 2$
28. $\log_b 3 - \log_b 32$
29. $\log_b 36 - \log_b 4$
30. $\log_a 26 - \log_a 2$
31. $\log_a x - \log_a y$
32. $\log_b c - \log_b d$

Express as an equivalent expression, using the individual logarithms of w, x, y, and z.

33. $\log_a (xyz)$
34. $\log_a (wxy)$
35. $\log_a (x^3 z^4)$
36. $\log_a (x^2 y^5)$
37. $\log_a (w^2 x^{-2} y)$
38. $\log_a (xy^2 z^{-3})$
39. $\log_a \dfrac{x^5}{y^3 z}$
40. $\log_a \dfrac{x^4}{yz^2}$
41. $\log_b \dfrac{xy^2}{wz^3}$
42. $\log_b \dfrac{w^2 x}{y^3 z}$
43. $\log_a \sqrt{\dfrac{x^7}{y^5 z^8}}$
44. $\log_c \sqrt{\dfrac{x^4}{y^3 z^2}}$
45. $\log_a \sqrt[3]{\dfrac{x^6 y^3}{a^2 z^7}}$
46. $\log_a \sqrt[4]{\dfrac{x^8 y^{12}}{a^3 z^5}}$

Express as an equivalent expression that is a single logarithm and, if possible, simplify.

47. $8 \log_a x + 3 \log_a z$
48. $2 \log_b m + \frac{1}{2} \log_b n$
49. $\log_a x^2 - 2 \log_a \sqrt{x}$
50. $\log_a \dfrac{a}{\sqrt{x}} - \log_a \sqrt{ax}$
51. $\frac{1}{2} \log_a x + 5 \log_a y - 2 \log_a x$
52. $\log_a 2x + 3(\log_a x - \log_a y)$
53. $\log_a (x^2 - 9) - \log_a (x + 3)$
54. $\log_a (2x + 10) - \log_a (x^2 - 25)$

Given $\log_b 3 = 0.792$ *and* $\log_b 5 = 1.161$. *If possible, use the properties of logarithms to calculate values for each of the following.*

55. $\log_b 15$

56. $\log_b \frac{5}{3}$

57. $\log_b \frac{3}{5}$

58. $\log_b \frac{1}{3}$

59. $\log_b \frac{1}{5}$

60. $\log_b \sqrt{b}$

61. $\log_b \sqrt{b^3}$

62. $\log_b 3b$

63. $\log_b 8$

64. $\log_b 45$

Simplify.

Aha! 65. $\log_t t^{10}$

66. $\log_p p^{-5}$

67. $\log_e e^m$

68. $\log_Q Q^t$

69. Explain the difference between the phrases "the logarithm of a quotient" and "a quotient of logarithms."

70. How could you convince someone that
$$\log_a c \neq \log_c a?$$

Skill Review

To prepare for Section 12.5, review graphing functions and finding domains of functions.

Graph.

71. $f(x) = \sqrt{x} - 3$ [10.1]

72. $g(x) = \sqrt[3]{x} + 1$ [10.1]

73. $g(x) = x^3 + 2$ [7.3]

74. $f(x) = 1 - x^2$ [11.7]

Find the domain of each function.

75. $f(x) = \dfrac{x - 3}{x + 7}$ [9.1]

76. $f(x) = \dfrac{x}{(x - 2)(x + 3)}$ [9.1]

77. $g(x) = \sqrt{10 - x}$ [10.1]

78. $g(x) = |x^2 - 6x + 7|$ [7.2]

Synthesis

79. A student *incorrectly* reasons that
$$\log_b \frac{1}{x} = \log_b \frac{x}{xx}$$
$$= \log_b x - \log_b x + \log_b x = \log_b x.$$
What mistake has the student made?

80. Why are properties of logarithms related to properties of exponents?

Express as an equivalent expression that is a single logarithm and, if possible, simplify.

81. $\log_a (x^8 - y^8) - \log_a (x^2 + y^2)$

82. $\log_a (x + y) + \log_a (x^2 - xy + y^2)$

Express as an equivalent expression that is a sum or a difference of logarithms and, if possible, simplify.

83. $\log_a \sqrt{1 - s^2}$

84. $\log_a \dfrac{c - d}{\sqrt{c^2 - d^2}}$

85. If $\log_a x = 2$, $\log_a y = 3$, and $\log_a z = 4$, what is
$$\log_a \frac{\sqrt[3]{x^2 z}}{\sqrt[3]{y^2 z^{-2}}}?$$

86. If $\log_a x = 2$, what is $\log_a (1/x)$?

87. If $\log_a x = 2$, what is $\log_{1/a} x$?

Solve.

88. $\log_{10} 2000 - \log_{10} x = 3$

89. $\log_2 80 + \log_2 x = 5$

Classify each of the following as true or false. Assume a, x, P, and $Q > 0$, $a \neq 1$.

90. $\log_a \left(\dfrac{P}{Q}\right)^x = x \log_a P - \log_a Q$

91. $\log_a (Q + Q^2) = \log_a Q + \log_a (Q + 1)$

92. Use graphs to show that
$$\log x^2 \neq \log x \cdot \log x.$$
(*Note:* log means $\log_{10}$.)

12.5

12.5   Common and Natural Logarithms

Common Logarithms on a Calculator   ■   The Base e and Natural Logarithms on a Calculator   ■
Changing Logarithmic Bases   ■   Graphs of Exponential and Logarithmic Functions, Base e

Any positive number other than 1 can serve as the base of a logarithmic function. However, some numbers are easier to use than others, and there are logarithmic bases that fit into certain applications more naturally than others.

Base-10 logarithms, called **common logarithms**, are useful because they have the same base as our "commonly" used decimal system. Before calculators became widely available, common logarithms helped with tedious calculations. In fact, that is why logarithms were devised.

The logarithmic base most widely used today is an irrational number named e. We will consider e and base e, or *natural*, logarithms later in this section. First we examine common logarithms.

Common Logarithms on a Calculator

Before the advent of scientific calculators, printed tables listed common logarithms. Today we find common logarithms using calculators.

Here, and in most books, the abbreviation **log**, with no base written, is understood to mean logarithm base 10, that is, a common logarithm. Thus,

$$\log 17 \quad \text{means} \quad \log_{10} 17. \qquad \begin{array}{l}\text{It is important to remember}\\\text{this abbreviation.}\end{array}$$

The key for common logarithms is usually marked **LOG**. To find the common logarithm of a number, we key in that number and press **LOG**. With most graphing calculators, we press **LOG**, the number, and then **ENTER**.

EXAMPLE   **1**   Use a calculator to approximate each number to four decimal places.

a) $\log 5312$ **b)** $\dfrac{\log 6500}{\log 0.007}$

SOLUTION

a) We enter 5312 and then press **LOG**. On most graphing calculators, we press **LOG**, followed by 5312 and **ENTER**. We find that

$$\log 5312 \approx 3.7253. \qquad \text{Rounded to four decimal places}$$

b) We enter 6500 and then press **LOG**. Next, we press **÷**, enter 0.007, and then press **LOG** **=**. On most graphing calculators, we press **LOG**, key in 6500, press **)** **÷** **LOG**, key in 0.007, and then press **)** **ENTER**. Be careful not to round until the end:

$$\frac{\log 6500}{\log 0.007} \approx -1.7694. \qquad \text{Rounded to four decimal places}$$

TRY EXERCISE   11

The inverse of a logarithmic function is an exponential function. Because of this, on many calculators the **LOG** key doubles as the $\boxed{10^x}$ key after a **2ND** or $\boxed{\text{SHIFT}}$ key is pressed. Calculators lacking a $\boxed{10^x}$ key may have a key labeled $\boxed{x^y}$, $\boxed{a^x}$, or **^**. Such a key can raise any positive real number to any real-numbered exponent.

STUDY SKILLS

Is Your Answer Reasonable?

It is always a good idea—especially when using a calculator—to check that your answer is reasonable. It is easy for an incorrect calculation or keystroke to result in an answer that is clearly too big or too small.

TECHNOLOGY CONNECTION

To find log 6500/log 0.007 on a graphing calculator, we must use parentheses with care.

1. What keystrokes are needed to create the following?

     log(7)/log(3)
                 1.771243749

EXAMPLE **2** Use a calculator to approximate $10^{3.417}$ to four decimal places.

SOLUTION We enter 3.417 and then press (10ˣ). On most graphing calculators, (10ˣ) is pressed first, followed by 3.417 and **ENTER**. Rounding to four decimal places, we have

$$10^{3.417} \approx 2612.1614.$$

 **TRY EXERCISE** 21

The Base e and Natural Logarithms on a Calculator

When interest is compounded n times a year, the compound interest formula is

$$A = P\left(1 + \frac{r}{n}\right)^{nt},$$

where A is the amount that an initial investment P is worth after t years at interest rate r. Suppose that \$1 is invested at 100% interest for 1 year (no bank would pay this). The preceding formula becomes a function A defined in terms of the number of compounding periods n:

$$A(n) = \left(1 + \frac{1}{n}\right)^n.$$

Let's find some function values. We use a calculator and round to six decimal places.

n	$A(n) = \left(1 + \dfrac{1}{n}\right)^n$
1 (compounded annually)	\$2.00
2 (compounded semiannually)	2.25
3	2.370370
4 (compounded quarterly)	2.441406
12 (compounded monthly)	2.613035
100	2.704814
365 (compounded daily)	2.714567
8760 (compounded hourly)	2.718127

The numbers in this table approach a very important number in mathematics, called e. Because e is irrational, its decimal representation does not terminate or repeat.

The Number e

$$e \approx 2.7182818284\ldots$$

Logarithms base e are called **natural logarithms**, or **Napierian logarithms**, in honor of John Napier (1550–1617), the "inventor" of logarithms.

The abbreviation "ln" is generally used with natural logarithms. Thus,

$\ln 53$ means $\log_e 53$. It is important to remember this abbreviation.

On most calculators, the key for natural logarithms is marked **LN**.

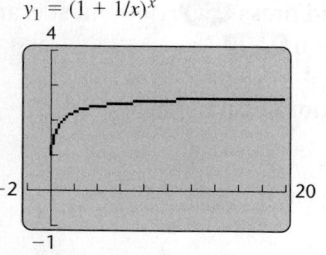

TECHNOLOGY CONNECTION

To visualize the number e, let $y_1 = (1 + 1/x)^x$.

$y_1 = (1 + 1/x)^x$

1. Use (TRACE) or (TABLE) to confirm that as x gets larger, the number e is more closely approximated.
2. Graph $y_2 = e$ and compare y_1 and y_2 for large values of x.
3. Confirm that 0 is not in the domain of this function. Why?

EXAMPLE 3   Use a calculator to approximate ln 4568 to four decimal places.

SOLUTION   We enter 4568 and then press **LN**. On most graphing calculators, we press **LN** first, followed by 4568 and **ENTER**. We find that

$$\ln 4568 \approx 8.4268. \qquad \text{Rounded to four decimal places}$$

> **TRY EXERCISE** 25

On many calculators, the **LN** key doubles as the **eˣ** key after a **2ND** or **SHIFT** key has been pressed.

EXAMPLE 4   Use a calculator to approximate $e^{-1.524}$ to four decimal places.

SOLUTION   We enter -1.524 and then press **eˣ**. On most graphing calculators, **eˣ** is pressed first, followed by -1.524 and **ENTER**. Since $e^{-1.524}$ is irrational, our answer is approximate:

$$e^{-1.524} \approx 0.2178. \qquad \text{Rounded to four decimal places}$$

> **TRY EXERCISE** 31

Changing Logarithmic Bases

Most calculators can find both common and natural logarithms. To find a logarithm with some other base, a conversion formula is often used.

> ### The Change-of-Base Formula
>
> For any logarithmic bases a and b, and any positive number M,
>
> $$\log_b M = \frac{\log_a M}{\log_a b}.$$
>
> (To find the log, base b, of M, we typically compute $\log M / \log b$ or $\ln M / \ln b$.)

Proof.   Let $x = \log_b M$. Then,

$$b^x = M \qquad \log_b M = x \text{ is equivalent to } b^x = M.$$

$$\log_a b^x = \log_a M \qquad \text{Taking the logarithm, base } a, \text{ on both sides}$$

$$x \log_a b = \log_a M \qquad \text{Using the power rule for logarithms}$$

$$x = \frac{\log_a M}{\log_a b}. \qquad \text{Dividing both sides by } \log_a b$$

But at the outset we stated that $x = \log_b M$. Thus, by substitution, we have

$$\log_b M = \frac{\log_a M}{\log_a b}. \qquad \text{This is the change-of-base formula.}$$

EXAMPLE   5

Find $\log_5 8$ using the change-of-base formula.

SOLUTION   We use the change-of-base formula with $a = 10$, $b = 5$, and $M = 8$:

$$\log_5 8 = \frac{\log_{10} 8}{\log_{10} 5}$$ Substituting into $\log_b M = \dfrac{\log_a M}{\log_a b}$

$$\approx \frac{0.903089987}{0.6989700043}$$ Using **LOG** twice

$$\approx 1.2920.$$ When using a calculator, it is best not to round until the end.

To check, note that $\ln 8 / \ln 5 \approx 1.2920$. We can also use a calculator to verify that $5^{1.2920} \approx 8$.

TRY EXERCISE ▶ 35

EXAMPLE   6

Find $\log_4 31$.

SOLUTION   As shown in the check of Example 5, base e can also be used.

$$\log_4 31 = \frac{\log_e 31}{\log_e 4}$$ Substituting into $\log_b M = \dfrac{\log_a M}{\log_a b}$

STUDENT NOTES

The choice of the logarithm base a in the change-of-base formula should be either 10 or e so that the logarithms can be found using a calculator. Either choice will yield the same end result.

$$= \frac{\ln 31}{\ln 4} \approx \frac{3.433987204}{1.386294361}$$ Using **LN** twice

$$\approx 2.4771.$$ *Check*: $4^{2.4771} \approx 31$

TRY EXERCISE ▶ 41

Graphs of Exponential and Logarithmic Functions, Base e

EXAMPLE   7

Graph $f(x) = e^x$ and $g(x) = e^{-x}$ and state the domain and the range of f and g.

SOLUTION   We use a calculator with an $\boxed{e^x}$ key to find approximate values of e^x and e^{-x}. Using these values, we can graph the functions.

x	e^x	e^{-x}
0	1	1
1	2.7	0.4
2	7.4	0.1
−1	0.4	2.7
−2	0.1	7.4

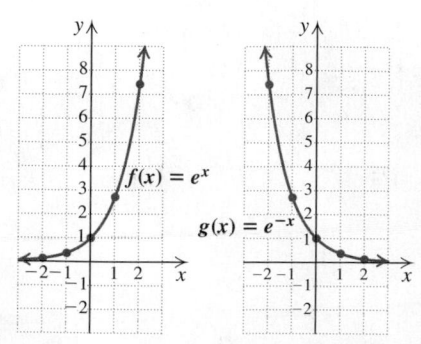

The domain of each function is $\mathbb{R}$ and the range of each function is $(0, \infty)$.

TRY EXERCISE ▶ 61

EXAMPLE 8   Graph $f(x) = e^{-x} + 2$ and state the domain and the range of f.

SOLUTION   We find some solutions with a calculator, plot them, and then draw the graph. For example, $f(2) = e^{-2} + 2 \approx 0.1 + 2 \approx 2.1$. The graph is exactly like the graph of $g(x) = e^{-x}$, but is translated up 2 units.

x	$e^{-x} + 2$
0	3
1	2.4
2	2.1
-1	4.7
-2	9.4

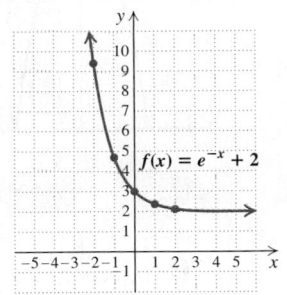

The domain of f is $\mathbb{R}$ and the range is $(2, \infty)$.

TRY EXERCISE 49

EXAMPLE 9   Graph and state the domain and the range of each function.

a) $g(x) = \ln x$

b) $f(x) = \ln (x + 3)$

SOLUTION

a) We find some solutions with a calculator and then draw the graph. As expected, the graph is a reflection across the line $y = x$ of the graph of $y = e^x$.

x	$\ln x$
1	0
4	1.4
7	1.9
0.5	-0.7

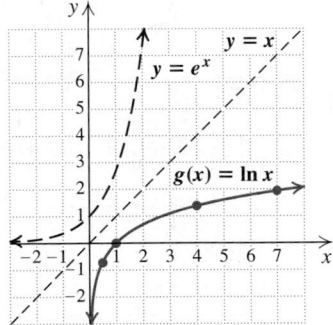

TECHNOLOGY CONNECTION

Logarithmic functions with bases other than 10 or e can be drawn using the change-of-base formula. For example, $y = \log_5 x$ can be written $y = \ln x/\ln 5$.

1. Graph $y = \log_7 x$.
2. Graph $y = \log_5 (x + 2)$.
3. Graph $y = \log_7 x + 2$.

The domain of g is $(0, \infty)$ and the range is $\mathbb{R}$.

b) We find some solutions with a calculator, plot them, and draw the graph.

x	$\ln (x + 3)$
0	1.1
1	1.4
2	1.6
3	1.8
4	1.9
-1	0.7
-2	0
-2.5	-0.7

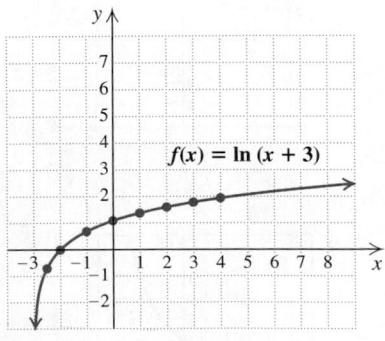

The graph of $y = \ln (x + 3)$ is the graph of $y = \ln x$ translated 3 units to the left. Since $x + 3$ must be positive, the domain is $(-3, \infty)$ and the range is $\mathbb{R}$.

TRY EXERCISE 63

Visualizing for Success

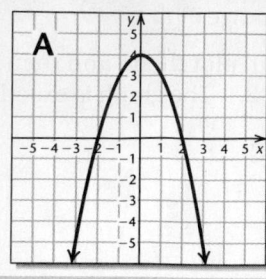

A

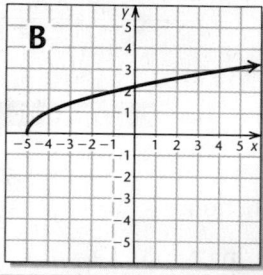

B

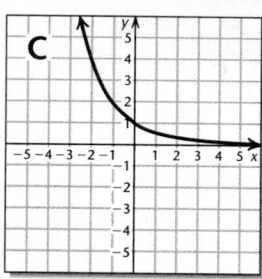

C

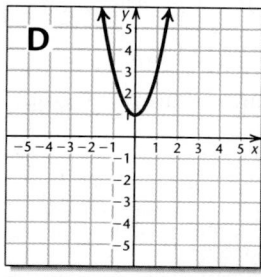

D

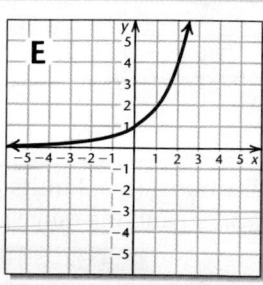

E

Match each function with its graph.

1. $f(x) = 2x - 3$

2. $f(x) = 2x^2 + 1$

3. $f(x) = \sqrt{x} + 5$

4. $f(x) = |x - 4|$

5. $f(x) = \ln x$

6. $f(x) = 2^{-x}$

7. $f(x) = -4$

8. $f(x) = \log x + 3$

9. $f(x) = 2^x$

10. $f(x) = 4 - x^2$

Answers on page A-56

An additional, animated version of this activity appears in MyMathLab. To use MyMathLab, you need a course ID and a student access code. Contact your instructor for more information.

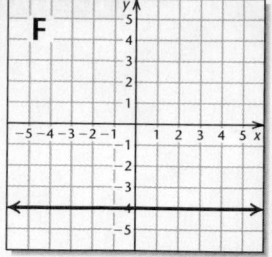

F

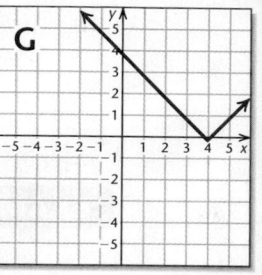

G

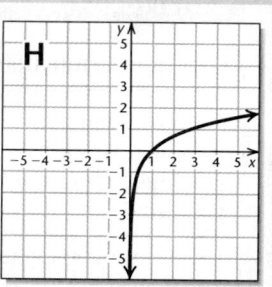

H

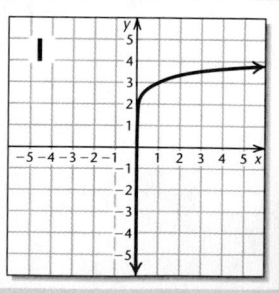

I

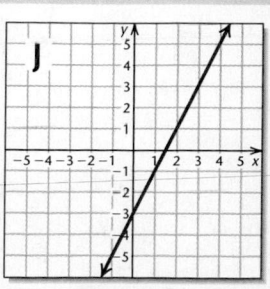

J

12.5 EXERCISE SET

 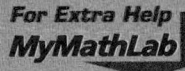

🦢 **Concept Reinforcement** *Classify each statement as either true or false.*

1. The expression log 23 means $\log_{10} 23$.

2. The expression ln 7 means $\log_e 7$.

3. The number e is approximately 2.7.

4. The expressions log 9 and log 18/log 2 are equivalent.

5. The expressions log 9 and log 18 − log 2 are equivalent.

6. The expressions $\log_2 9$ and ln 9/ln 2 are equivalent.

7. The expressions ln 81 and 2 ln 9 are equivalent.

8. The domain of the function given by $f(x) = \ln(x + 2)$ is $(-2, \infty)$.

9. The range of the function given by $g(x) = e^x$ is $(0, \infty)$.

10. The range of the function given by $f(x) = \ln x$ is $(-\infty, \infty)$.

▦ *Use a calculator to find each of the following to four decimal places.*

11. log 7

12. log 2

13. log 13.7

14. log 98.3   Aha!   15. log 1000

16. log 100

17. log 0.75

18. log 0.25

19. $\dfrac{\log 8200}{\log 2}$

20. $\dfrac{\log 5700}{\log 5}$

21. $10^{1.7}$

22. $10^{0.59}$

23. $10^{-2.9523}$

24. $10^{-3.2046}$

25. ln 9

26. ln 13

27. ln 0.0062

28. ln 0.00073

29. $\dfrac{\ln 2300}{0.08}$

30. $\dfrac{\ln 1900}{0.07}$

31. $e^{2.71}$

32. $e^{3.06}$

33. $e^{-3.49}$

34. $e^{-2.64}$

▦ *Find each of the following logarithms using the change-of-base formula. Round answers to four decimal places.*

35. $\log_3 28$

36. $\log_6 37$

37. $\log_2 100$

38. $\log_7 100$

39. $\log_4 5$

40. $\log_8 7$

41. $\log_{0.1} 2$

42. $\log_{0.25} 25$

43. $\log_2 0.1$

44. $\log_{25} 0.25$

45. $\log_\pi 10$

46. $\log_\pi 100$

▦ *Graph and state the domain and the range of each function.*

47. $f(x) = e^x$

48. $f(x) = e^{-x}$

49. $f(x) = e^x + 3$

50. $f(x) = e^x + 2$

51. $f(x) = e^x - 2$

52. $f(x) = e^x - 3$

53. $f(x) = 0.5e^x$

54. $f(x) = 2e^x$

55. $f(x) = 0.5e^{2x}$

56. $f(x) = 2e^{-0.5x}$

57. $f(x) = e^{x-3}$

58. $f(x) = e^{x-2}$

59. $f(x) = e^{x+2}$

60. $f(x) = e^{x+3}$

61. $f(x) = -e^x$

62. $f(x) = -e^{-x}$

63. $g(x) = \ln x + 1$

64. $g(x) = \ln x + 3$

65. $g(x) = \ln x - 2$

66. $g(x) = \ln x - 1$

67. $g(x) = 2 \ln x$

68. $g(x) = 3 \ln x$

69. $g(x) = -2 \ln x$

70. $g(x) = -\ln x$

71. $g(x) = \ln(x + 2)$

72. $g(x) = \ln(x + 1)$

73. $g(x) = \ln(x - 1)$

74. $g(x) = \ln(x - 3)$

75. Using a calculator, Adan gives an *incorrect* approximation for log 79 that is between 4 and 5. How could you convince him, without using a calculator, that he is mistaken?

76. Examine Exercise 75. What mistake do you believe Adan made?

Skill Review

To prepare for Section 12.6, review solving equations.

Solve.

77. $x^2 - 3x - 28 = 0$ [5.7]   **78.** $5x^2 - 7x = 0$ [5.7]

79. $17x - 15 = 0$ [2.2]   **80.** $\frac{5}{3} = 2t$ [2.2]

81. $(x - 5) \cdot 9 = 11$ [2.2]   **82.** $\frac{x + 3}{x - 3} = 7$ [6.6]

83. $x^{1/2} - 6x^{1/4} + 8 = 0$ [11.5]

84. $2y - 7\sqrt{y} + 3 = 0$ [11.5]

Synthesis

85. Explain how the graph of $f(x) = e^x$ could be used to graph the function given by $g(x) = 1 + \ln x$.

86. How would you explain to a classmate why $\log_2 5 = \log 5/\log 2$ *and* $\log_2 5 = \ln 5/\ln 2$?

Knowing only that $\log 2 \approx 0.301$ *and* $\log 3 \approx 0.477$, *approximate each of the following to three decimal places.*

87. $\log_6 81$ **88.** $\log_9 16$ **89.** $\log_{12} 36$

90. Find a formula for converting common logarithms to natural logarithms.

91. Find a formula for converting natural logarithms to common logarithms.

Solve for x. Give an approximation to four decimal places.

92. $\log (275x^2) = 38$ **93.** $\log (492x) = 5.728$

94. $\frac{3.01}{\ln x} = \frac{28}{4.31}$

95. $\log 692 + \log x = \log 3450$

For each function given below, (a) determine the domain and the range, (b) set an appropriate window, and (c) draw the graph. Graphs may vary, depending on the scale used.

96. $f(x) = 7.4e^x \ln x$

97. $f(x) = 3.4 \ln x - 0.25e^x$

98. $f(x) = x \ln (x - 2.1)$

99. $f(x) = 2x^3 \ln x$

100. Use a graphing calculator to check your answers to Exercises 49, 57, and 71.

101. Use a graphing calculator to check your answers to Exercises 48, 54, and 64.

102. In an attempt to solve $\ln x = 1.5$, Emma gets the following graph. How can Emma tell at a glance that she has made a mistake?

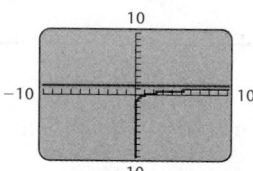

CONNECTING the CONCEPTS

It is important to distinguish between *simplifying* an exponential or logarithmic *expression* and *solving* an exponential or logarithmic *equation*. We use the following properties to simplify expressions and to rewrite equivalent logarithmic and exponential equations.

$\log_a x = m$ means $x = a^m$.	$\log_a a^k = k$
$\log_a (MN) = \log_a M + \log_a N$	$\log_a a = 1$
$\log_a \dfrac{M}{N} = \log_a M - \log_a N$	$\log_a 1 = 0$
$\log_a M^p = p \cdot \log_a M$	$\log x = \log_{10} x$
$\log_b M = \dfrac{\log_a M}{\log_a b}$	$\ln x = \log_e x$

MIXED REVIEW

Simplify.

1. $\log_4 16$

2. $\log_5 \frac{1}{5}$

3. $\log_{100} 10$

4. $\log_{10} 100$

5. $\log 10$

6. $\ln 1$

7. $\log 10^4$

8. $\ln e^8$

9. $e^{\ln 7}$

10. $10^{\log 3}$

Rewrite each of the following as an equivalent exponential equation.

11. $\log_x 3 = m$

12. $\log_2 1024 = 10$

Rewrite each of the following as an equivalent logarithmic equation.

13. $e^t = x$

14. $64^{2/3} = 16$

Solve.

15. $\log_x 64 = 3$

16. $\log_3 x = -1$

17. Express as an equivalent expression using $\log x$, $\log y$, and $\log z$:

$$\log \sqrt{\frac{x^2}{yz^3}}.$$

18. Express as an equivalent expression that is a single logarithm: $\log a - 2\log b - \log c$.

Find each of the following logarithms using the change-of-base formula. Round answers to four decimal places where appropriate.

19. $\log_4 8$

20. $\log_5 100$

12.6 Solving Exponential and Logarithmic Equations

Solving Exponential Equations • Solving Logarithmic Equations

Solving Exponential Equations

Equations with variables in exponents, such as $5^x = 12$ and $2^{7x} = 64$, are called **exponential equations**. In Section 12.3, we solved certain exponential equations by using the principle of exponential equality. We restate that principle below.

The Principle of Exponential Equality

For any real number b, where $b \neq -1$, 0, or 1,

$$b^x = b^y \quad \text{is equivalent to} \quad x = y.$$

(Powers of the same base are equal if and only if the exponents are equal.)

EXAMPLE 1   Solve: $4^{3x} = 16$.

SOLUTION   Note that $16 = 4^2$. Thus we can write each side as a power of the same base:

$$4^{3x} = 4^2 \qquad \text{Rewriting 16 as a power of 4}$$
$$3x = 2 \qquad \text{Since the base on each side is 4, the exponents are equal.}$$
$$x = \tfrac{2}{3}. \qquad \text{Solving for } x$$

Since $4^{3x} = 4^{3(2/3)} = 4^2 = 16$, the answer checks. The solution is $\tfrac{2}{3}$.

TRY EXERCISE   9

In Example 1, we wrote both sides of the equation as powers of 4. When it seems impossible to write both sides of an equation as powers of the same base, we use the following principle and write an equivalent logarithmic equation.

The Principle of Logarithmic Equality

For any logarithmic base a, and for $x, y > 0$,

$$x = y \quad \text{is equivalent to} \quad \log_a x = \log_a y.$$

(Two expressions are equal if and only if the logarithms of those expressions are equal.)

The principle of logarithmic equality, used together with the power rule for logarithms, allows us to solve equations in which the variable is an exponent.

EXAMPLE 2   Solve: $7^{x-2} = 60$.

SOLUTION   We have

Take the logarithm of both sides.

$$7^{x-2} = 60$$
$$\log 7^{x-2} = \log 60 \qquad \text{Using the principle of logarithmic equality to take the common logarithm on both sides. Natural logarithms also would work.}$$

Use the power rule for logarithms.

$$(x - 2)\log 7 = \log 60 \qquad \text{Using the power rule for logarithms}$$
$$x - 2 = \frac{\log 60}{\log 7} \quad \longleftarrow \boxed{\textit{CAUTION!} \text{ This is } not \log 60 - \log 7.}$$

$$x = \frac{\log 60}{\log 7} + 2 \qquad \text{Adding 2 to both sides}$$

Solve for x.

$$x \approx 4.1041. \qquad \text{Using a calculator and rounding to four decimal places}$$

Check.   Since $7^{4.1041-2} \approx 60.0027$, we have a check. We can also note that since $7^{4-2} = 49$, we expect a solution greater than 4. The solution is $\dfrac{\log 60}{\log 7} + 2$, or approximately 4.1041.

TRY EXERCISE   17

ALGEBRAIC–GRAPHICAL CONNECTION

The solution of $4^x = 16$ can be visualized by graphing $y = 4^x$ and $y = 16$ on the same set of axes. The y-values for both equations are the same where the graphs intersect. The x-value at that point is the solution of the equation. That x-value appears to be 2. Since $4^2 = 16$, we see that this is indeed the case.

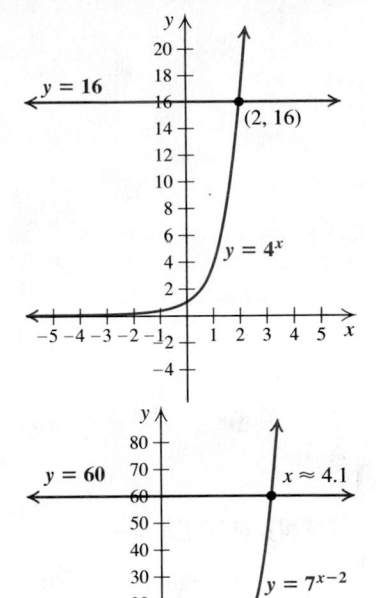

Similarly, the solution of Example 2 can be visualized by graphing $y = 7^{x-2}$ and $y = 60$ and identifying the x-value at the point of intersection. As expected, this value appears to be approximately 4.1.

EXAMPLE 3   Solve: $e^{0.06t} = 1500$.

SOLUTION Since one side is a power of e, it is easiest to take the *natural logarithm* on both sides:

$$\ln e^{0.06t} = \ln 1500 \qquad \text{Taking the natural logarithm on both sides}$$

$$0.06t = \ln 1500 \qquad \begin{array}{l}\text{Finding the logarithm of the base to a power:}\\ \log_a a^k = k. \text{ Logarithmic and exponential}\\ \text{functions are inverses of each other.}\end{array}$$

$$t = \frac{\ln 1500}{0.06} \qquad \text{Dividing both sides by 0.06}$$

$$\approx 121.887. \qquad \begin{array}{l}\text{Using a calculator and rounding to three}\\ \text{decimal places}\end{array}$$

TRY EXERCISE 21

To Solve an Equation of the Form $a^t = b$ for t

1. Take the logarithm (either natural or common) of both sides.
2. Use the power rule for logarithms so that the variable is no longer written as an exponent.
3. Divide both sides by the coefficient of the variable to isolate the variable.
4. If appropriate, use a calculator to find an approximate solution.

Solving Logarithmic Equations

Recall from Section 12.3 that certain logarithmic equations can be solved by writing an equivalent exponential equation.

EXAMPLE 4   Solve: **(a)** $\log_4 (8x - 6) = 3$; **(b)** $\ln (5x) = 27$.

SOLUTION

a) $\log_4 (8x - 6) = 3$

$\qquad\qquad 4^3 = 8x - 6$.   Writing the equivalent exponential equation

$\qquad\qquad 64 = 8x - 6$

$\qquad\qquad 70 = 8x$ Adding 6 to both sides

$\qquad\qquad x = \frac{70}{8}$, or $\frac{35}{4}$.

Check:

$$\log_4 (8x - 6) = 3$$

$$\begin{array}{c|c} \log_4 (8 \cdot \frac{35}{4} - 6) & 3 \\ \log_4 (2 \cdot 35 - 6) & \\ \log_4 64 & \\ 3 \overset{?}{=} 3 & \text{TRUE} \end{array}$$

The solution is $\frac{35}{4}$.

b) $\ln (5x) = 27$ Remember: $\ln (5x)$ means $\log_e (5x)$.

$\quad e^{27} = 5x$ Writing the equivalent exponential equation

$\quad \dfrac{e^{27}}{5} = x$ This is a very large number.

The solution is $\dfrac{e^{27}}{5}$. The check is left to the student.   **TRY EXERCISE** 45

Often the properties for logarithms are needed in order to solve a logarithmic equation. The goal is to first write an equivalent equation in which the variable appears in just one logarithmic expression. We then isolate that expression and solve as in Example 4.

EXAMPLE 5   Solve.

a) $\log x + \log (x - 3) = 1$

b) $\log_2 (x + 7) - \log_2 (x - 7) = 3$

c) $\log_7 (x + 1) + \log_7 (x - 1) = \log_7 8$

SOLUTION

a) To increase understanding, we write in the base, 10.

Find a single logarithm.

$\qquad \log_{10} x + \log_{10} (x - 3) = 1$

$\qquad\quad \log_{10} [x(x - 3)] = 1$ Using the product rule for logarithms to obtain a single logarithm

Write an equivalent exponential equation.

$\qquad\qquad x(x - 3) = 10^1$ Writing an equivalent exponential equation

$\qquad\qquad x^2 - 3x = 10$

$\qquad\qquad x^2 - 3x - 10 = 0$

$\qquad\qquad (x + 2)(x - 5) = 0$ Factoring

$\qquad x + 2 = 0 \quad or \quad x - 5 = 0$ Using the principle of zero products

Solve.

$\qquad\quad x = -2 \quad or \qquad x = 5$

Check.

Check:

For −2:

$$\frac{\log x + \log (x - 3) = 1}{\log (-2) + \log (-2 - 3) \overset{?}{=} 1}$$ FALSE

For 5:

$$\begin{array}{c|c} \log x + \log (x - 3) = 1 & \\ \hline \log 5 + \log (5 - 3) & 1 \\ \log 5 + \log 2 & \\ \log 10 & \\ & 1 \overset{?}{=} 1 \quad \text{TRUE} \end{array}$$

The number −2 *does not check* because the logarithm of a negative number is undefined. The solution is 5.

b) We have

$$\log_2 (x + 7) - \log_2 (x - 7) = 3$$

$$\log_2 \frac{x + 7}{x - 7} = 3$$ Using the quotient rule for logarithms to obtain a single logarithm

$$\frac{x + 7}{x - 7} = 2^3$$ Writing an equivalent exponential equation

$$\frac{x + 7}{x - 7} = 8$$

$$x + 7 = 8(x - 7)$$ Multiplying by the LCD, $x - 7$

$$x + 7 = 8x - 56$$ Using the distributive law

$$63 = 7x$$

$$9 = x.$$ Dividing by 7

Check:

$$\begin{array}{c|c} \log_2 (x + 7) - \log_2 (x - 7) = 3 & \\ \hline \log_2 (9 + 7) - \log_2 (9 - 7) & 3 \\ \log_2 16 - \log_2 2 & \\ 4 - 1 & \\ & 3 \overset{?}{=} 3 \quad \text{TRUE} \end{array}$$

The solution is 9.

c) We have

$$\log_7 (x + 1) + \log_7 (x - 1) = \log_7 8$$

$$\log_7 [(x + 1)(x - 1)] = \log_7 8$$ Using the product rule for logarithms

$$\log_7 (x^2 - 1) = \log_7 8$$ Multiplying. Note that both sides are base-7 logarithms.

$$x^2 - 1 = 8$$ Using the principle of logarithmic equality. Study this step carefully.

$$x^2 - 9 = 0$$

$$(x - 3)(x + 3) = 0$$ Solving the quadratic equation

$$x = 3 \quad or \quad x = -3.$$

We leave it to the student to show that 3 checks but −3 does not. The solution is 3.

TRY EXERCISE 55

TECHNOLOGY CONNECTION

To solve exponential and logarithmic equations, we can use the INTERSECT option of the CALC menu to determine the x-coordinate at each intersection.

   For example, to solve $e^{0.5x} - 7 = 2x + 6$, we graph $y_1 = e^{0.5x} - 7$ and $y_2 = 2x + 6$ as shown. Using INTERSECT twice, we find that the x-coordinates at the intersections are approximately −6.48 and 6.52.

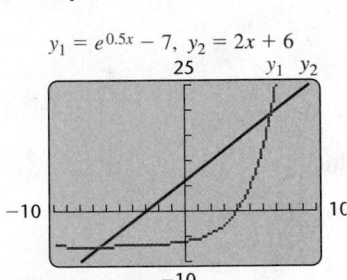

$y_1 = e^{0.5x} - 7, \ y_2 = 2x + 6$

Yscl = 5

   Use a graphing calculator to solve each equation to the nearest hundredth.

1. $e^{7x} = 14$
2. $8e^{0.5x} = 3$
3. $xe^{3x-1} = 5$
4. $4 \ln (x + 3.4) = 2.5$
5. $\ln 3x = 0.5x - 1$
6. $\ln x^2 = -x^2$

12.6   EXERCISE SET

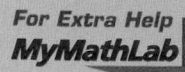
Concept Reinforcement   *In each of Exercises 1–8, match the equation with an equivalent equation from the column on the right that could be the next step in the solution process.*

1. _____ $5^x = 3$

2. _____ $e^{5x} = 3$

3. _____ $\ln x = 3$

4. _____ $\log_x 5 = 3$

5. _____ $\log_5 x + \log_5 (x - 2) = 3$

6. _____ $\log_5 x - \log_5 (x - 2) = 3$

7. _____ $\ln x - \ln (x - 2) = 3$

8. _____ $\log x + \log (x - 2) = 3$

a) $\ln e^{5x} = \ln 3$

b) $\log_5 (x^2 - 2x) = 3$

c) $\log (x^2 - 2x) = 3$

d) $\log_5 \dfrac{x}{x - 2} = 3$

e) $\log 5^x = \log 3$

f) $e^3 = x$

g) $\ln \dfrac{x}{x - 2} = 3$

h) $x^3 = 5$

Solve. Where appropriate, include approximations to three decimal places.

9. $3^{2x} = 81$

10. $2^{3x} = 64$

11. $4^x = 32$

12. $9^x = 27$

13. $2^x = 10$

14. $2^x = 24$

15. $2^{x+5} = 16$

16. $2^{x-1} = 8$

17. $8^{x-3} = 19$

18. $5^{x+2} = 15$

19. $e^t = 50$

20. $e^t = 20$

21. $e^{-0.02t} = 8$

22. $e^{-0.01t} = 100$

23. $4.9^x - 87 = 0$

24. $7.2^x - 65 = 0$

25. $19 = 2e^{4x}$

26. $29 = 3e^{2x}$

27. $7 + 3e^{-x} = 13$

28. $4 + 5e^{-x} = 9$

Aha! 29. $\log_3 x = 4$

30. $\log_2 x = 6$

31. $\log_4 x = -2$

32. $\log_5 x = -3$

33. $\ln x = 5$

34. $\ln x = 4$

35. $\ln (4x) = 3$

36. $\ln (3x) = 2$

37. $\log x = 1.2$

38. $\log x = 0.6$

39. $\ln (2x + 1) = 4$

40. $\ln (4x - 2) = 3$

Aha! 41. $\ln x = 1$

42. $\log x = 1$

43. $5 \ln x = -15$

44. $3 \ln x = -3$

45. $\log_2 (8 - 6x) = 5$

46. $\log_5 (7 - 2x) = 3$

47. $\log (x - 9) + \log x = 1$

48. $\log (x + 9) + \log x = 1$

49. $\log x - \log (x + 3) = 1$

50. $\log x - \log (x + 7) = -1$

Aha! 51. $\log (2x + 1) = \log 5$

52. $\log (x + 1) - \log x = 0$

53. $\log_4 (x + 3) = 2 + \log_4 (x - 5)$

54. $\log_2 (x + 3) = 4 + \log_2 (x - 3)$

55. $\log_7 (x + 1) + \log_7 (x + 2) = \log_7 6$

56. $\log_6 (x + 3) + \log_6 (x + 2) = \log_6 20$

57. $\log_5 (x + 4) + \log_5 (x - 4) = \log_5 20$

58. $\log_4 (x + 2) + \log_4 (x - 7) = \log_4 10$

59. $\ln (x + 5) + \ln (x + 1) = \ln 12$

60. $\ln (x - 6) + \ln (x + 3) = \ln 22$

61. $\log_2 (x - 3) + \log_2 (x + 3) = 4$

62. $\log_3 (x - 4) + \log_3 (x + 4) = 2$

63. $\log_{12} (x + 5) - \log_{12} (x - 4) = \log_{12} 3$

64. $\log_6 (x + 7) - \log_6 (x - 2) = \log_6 5$

65. $\log_2 (x - 2) + \log_2 x = 3$

66. $\log_4 (x + 6) - \log_4 x = 2$

67. Madison finds that the solution of $\log_3 (x + 4) = 1$ is -1, but rejects -1 as an answer. What mistake do you suspect she is making?

68. Could Example 2 have been solved by taking the natural logarithm on both sides? Why or why not?

Skill Review

To prepare for Section 12.7, review using the five-step problem-solving strategy.

Solve.

69. A rectangle is 6 ft longer than it is wide. Its perimeter is 26 ft. Find the length and the width. [2.5]

70. Under one health insurance plan offered in California, the maximum co-pay for an individual is $3000 per calendar year. The co-pay for each visit to a specialist is $40, and the co-pay for a hospitalization is $1000. With hospitalizations and specialist visits, Marguerite reached the maximum co-pay in 2008. If she was hospitalized twice, how many visits to specialists did she make? [9.1]
Source: ehealthinsurance.com

71. Joanna wants to mix Golden Days bird seed containing 25% sunflower seeds with Snowy Friends bird seed containing 40% sunflower seeds. She wants 50 lb of a mixture containing 33% sunflower seeds. How much of each type should she use? [8.3]

72. The outside edge of a picture frame measures 12 cm by 19 cm, and 144 cm^2 of picture shows. Find the width of the frame. [5.8]

73. Max can key in a musical score in 2 hr. Miles takes 3 hr to key in the same score. How long would it take them, working together, to key in the score? [6.7]

74. A sign is in the shape of a right triangle. The hypotenuse is 3 ft long, and the base and the height of the triangle are equal. Find the length of the base and the height. Round to the nearest tenth of a foot. [10.7]

Synthesis

75. Can the principle of logarithmic equality be expanded to include all functions? That is, is the statement "$m = n$ is equivalent to $f(m) = f(n)$" true for any function f? Why or why not?

76. Explain how Exercises 37 and 38 could be solved using the graph of $f(x) = \log x$.

Solve. If no solution exists, state this.

77. $8^x = 16^{3x+9}$

78. $27^x = 81^{2x-3}$

79. $\log_6 (\log_2 x) = 0$

80. $\log_x (\log_3 27) = 3$

81. $\log_5 \sqrt{x^2 - 9} = 1$

82. $x \log \frac{1}{8} = \log 8$

83. $2^{x^2+4x} = \frac{1}{8}$

84. $\log (\log x) = 5$

85. $\log_5 |x| = 4$

86. $\log x^2 = (\log x)^2$

87. $\log \sqrt{2x} = \sqrt{\log 2x}$

88. $1000^{2x+1} = 100^{3x}$

89. $3^{x^2} \cdot 3^{4x} = \frac{1}{27}$

90. $3^{3x} \cdot 3^{x^2} = 81$

91. $\log x^{\log x} = 25$

92. $3^{2x} - 8 \cdot 3^x + 15 = 0$

93. $(81^{x-2})(27^{x+1}) = 9^{2x-3}$

94. $3^{2x} - 3^{2x-1} = 18$

95. Given that $2^y = 16^{x-3}$ and $3^{y+2} = 27^x$, find the value of $x + y$.

96. If $x = (\log_{125} 5)^{\log_5 125}$, what is the value of $\log_3 x$?

97. Find the value of x for which the natural logarithm is the same as the common logarithm.

98. Use a graphing calculator to check your answers to Exercises 11, 31, 41, and 59.

12.7   Applications of Exponential and Logarithmic Functions

Applications of Logarithmic Functions   •   Applications of Exponential Functions

We now consider applications of exponential and logarithmic functions.

Applications of Logarithmic Functions

EXAMPLE   1

Sound levels.   To measure the volume, or "loudness," of a sound, the *decibel* scale is used. The loudness L, in decibels (dB), of a sound is given by

$$L = 10 \cdot \log \frac{I}{I_0},$$

where I is the intensity of the sound, in watts per square meter (W/m^2), and $I_0 = 10^{-12}$ W/m^2. (I_0 is approximately the intensity of the softest sound that can be heard by the human ear.)

a) The average maximum intensity of sound in a New York subway car is about 3.2×10^{-3} W/m^2. How loud, in decibels, is the sound level?

Source: Columbia University Mailman School of Public Health

b) The Occupational Safety and Health Administration (OSHA) considers sustained sound levels of 90 dB and above unsafe. What is the intensity of such sounds?

SOLUTION

a) To find the loudness, in decibels, we use the above formula:

$$
\begin{aligned}
L &= 10 \cdot \log \frac{I}{I_0} \\
&= 10 \cdot \log \frac{3.2 \times 10^{-3}}{10^{-12}} & \text{Substituting} \\
&= 10 \cdot \log \left(3.2 \times 10^9\right) & \text{Subtracting exponents} \\
&= 10 \left(\log 3.2 + \log 10^9\right) & \log MN = \log M + \log N \\
&= 10 \left(\log 3.2 + 9\right) & \log_{10} 10^9 = 9 \\
&\approx 10 \left(0.5051 + 9\right) & \text{Approximating } \log 3.2 \\
&= 10 \left(9.5051\right) & \text{Adding within the parentheses} \\
&\approx 95. & \text{Multiplying and rounding}
\end{aligned}
$$

The volume of the sound in a subway car is about 95 decibels.

b) We substitute and solve for I:

$$L = 10 \cdot \log \frac{I}{I_0}$$

$$90 = 10 \cdot \log \frac{I}{10^{-12}} \qquad \text{Substituting}$$

$$9 = \log \frac{I}{10^{-12}} \qquad \text{Dividing both sides by 10}$$

$$9 = \log I - \log 10^{-12} \qquad \text{Using the quotient rule for logarithms}$$

$$9 = \log I - (-12) \qquad \log 10^a = a$$

$$-3 = \log I \qquad \text{Adding } -12 \text{ to both sides}$$

$$10^{-3} = I. \qquad \text{Converting to an exponential equation}$$

Sustained sounds with intensities exceeding 10^{-3} W/m^2 are considered unsafe.

> **TRY EXERCISE** 15

EXAMPLE **2**

Chemistry: pH of liquids. In chemistry, the pH of a liquid is a measure of its acidity. We calculate pH as follows:

$$\text{pH} = -\log [\text{H}^+],$$

where $[\text{H}^+]$ is the hydrogen ion concentration in moles per liter.

a) The hydrogen ion concentration of human blood is normally about 3.98×10^{-8} moles per liter. Find the pH.

Source: www.merck.com

b) The average pH of seawater is about 8.2. Find the hydrogen ion concentration.

Source: www.seafriends.org.nz

SOLUTION

a) To find the pH of blood, we use the above formula:

$$\text{pH} = -\log [\text{H}^+]$$

$$= -\log [3.98 \times 10^{-8}]$$

$$\approx -(-7.400117) \qquad \text{Using a calculator}$$

$$\approx 7.4.$$

The pH of human blood is normally about 7.4.

b) We substitute and solve for $[\text{H}^+]$:

$$8.2 = -\log [\text{H}^+] \qquad \text{Using pH} = -\log [\text{H}^+]$$

$$-8.2 = \log [\text{H}^+] \qquad \text{Dividing both sides by } -1$$

$$10^{-8.2} = [\text{H}^+] \qquad \text{Converting to an exponential equation}$$

$$6.31 \times 10^{-9} \approx [\text{H}^+]. \qquad \text{Using a calculator; writing scientific notation}$$

The hydrogen ion concentration of seawater is about 6.31×10^{-9} moles per liter.

> **TRY EXERCISE** 11

Applications of Exponential Functions

EXAMPLE **3**

Interest compounded annually.   Suppose that $25,000 is invested at 4% interest, compounded annually. In t years, it will grow to the amount A given by

$$A(t) = 25{,}000(1.04)^t.$$

(See Example 5 in Section 12.2.)

a) How long will it take to accumulate $80,000 in the account?

b) Find the amount of time it takes for the $25,000 to double itself.

SOLUTION

a) We set $A(t) = 80{,}000$ and solve for t:

$$80{,}000 = 25{,}000(1.04)^t$$

$$\frac{80{,}000}{25{,}000} = 1.04^t \qquad \text{Dividing both sides by 25,000}$$

$$3.2 = 1.04^t$$

$$\log 3.2 = \log 1.04^t \qquad \text{Taking the common logarithm on both sides}$$

$$\log 3.2 = t \log 1.04 \qquad \text{Using the power rule for logarithms}$$

$$\frac{\log 3.2}{\log 1.04} = t \qquad \text{Dividing both sides by log 1.04}$$

$$29.7 \approx t. \qquad \text{Using a calculator}$$

Remember that when doing a calculation like this on a calculator, it is best to wait until the end to round. At an interest rate of 4% per year, it will take about 29.7 yr for $25,000 to grow to $80,000.

STUDENT NOTES

Study the different steps in the solution of Example 3(b). Note that if 50,000 and 25,000 are replaced with 6000 and 3000, the doubling time is unchanged.

b) To find the *doubling time*, we replace $A(t)$ with 50,000 and solve for t:

$$50{,}000 = 25{,}000(1.04)^t$$

$$2 = (1.04)^t \qquad \text{Dividing both sides by 25,000}$$

$$\log 2 = \log (1.04)^t \qquad \text{Taking the common logarithm on both sides}$$

$$\log 2 = t \log 1.04 \qquad \text{Using the power rule for logarithms}$$

$$t = \frac{\log 2}{\log 1.04} \approx 17.7. \qquad \text{Dividing both sides by log 1.04 and using a calculator}$$

At an interest rate of 4% per year, the doubling time is about 17.7 yr.

TRY EXERCISE 21

Like investments, populations often grow exponentially.

Exponential Growth

An **exponential growth model** is a function of the form

$$P(t) = P_0 e^{kt}, \quad k > 0,$$

where P_0 is the population at time 0, $P(t)$ is the population at time t, and k is the **exponential growth rate** for the situation. The **doubling time** is the amount of time necessary for the population to double in size.

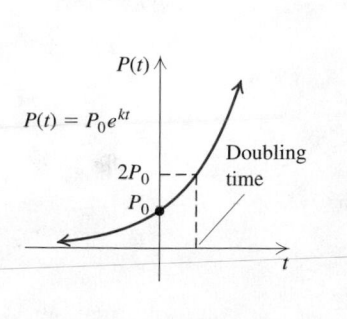

The exponential growth rate is the rate of growth of a population or other quantity at any *instant* in time. Since the population is continually growing, the percent of total growth after one year will exceed the exponential growth rate.

EXAMPLE 4

Text messaging.   In 2000, there were approximately 12 million text messages sent each month in the United States. This number has increased exponentially at an average rate of 108% per year.

Source: Based on information from www.cellulist.com

a) Find the exponential growth function that models the data.

b) Estimate the number of text messages sent each month in 2009.

SOLUTION

a) In 2000, at $t = 0$, the number of messages was 12 million per month. We substitute 12 for P_0 and 108%, or 1.08, for k. This gives the exponential growth function

$$P(t) = 12e^{1.08t}.$$

b) In 2009, we have $t = 9$ (since 9 yr have passed since 2000). To determine the number of messages in 2009, we compute $P(9)$:

$$P(9) = 12e^{1.08(9)} \qquad \text{Using } P(t) = 12e^{1.08t} \text{ from part (a)}$$
$$= 12e^{9.72} \approx 200,000. \qquad \text{Using a calculator}$$

In 2009, the number of text messages sent in the United States each month will reach approximately 200,000 million, or 200 billion.

> **TRY EXERCISE** 23

EXAMPLE 5

Cruise ship passengers.   In 1970, cruise lines carried approximately 500,000 passengers. This number has increased exponentially to 12.1 million in 2006.

Source: Cruise Lines International Association

a) Find the exponential growth rate and the exponential growth function.

b) Estimate the year in which cruise lines will carry 20 million passengers.

SOLUTION

a) We use $S(t) = S_0 e^{kt}$, where t is the number of years since 1970 and $S(t)$ is the number of passengers, in millions. Since 500,000 is half a million, we substitute 0.5 for S_0:

$$S(t) = 0.5e^{kt}.$$

To find the exponential growth rate k, note that after 36 yr (2006 − 1970 = 36), there were 12.1 million passengers:

$$S(36) = 0.5e^{k \cdot 36}$$
$$12.1 = 0.5e^{36k} \qquad \text{Substituting}$$
$$24.2 = e^{36k} \qquad \text{Dividing both sides by 0.5}$$
$$\ln 24.2 = \ln e^{36k} \qquad \text{Taking the natural logarithm on both sides}$$
$$\ln 24.2 = 36k \qquad \ln e^{36k} = \log_e e^{36k} = 36k$$
$$\frac{\ln 24.2}{36} = k \qquad \text{Dividing both sides by 36}$$
$$0.089 \approx k. \qquad \text{Using a calculator and rounding}$$

The exponential growth rate is 8.9% and the exponential growth function is given by $S(t) = 0.5e^{0.089t}$.

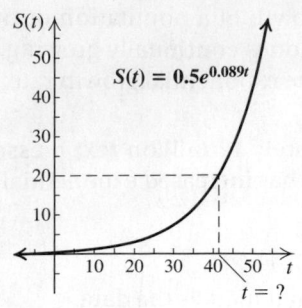

A visualization of Example 5

b) To estimate the year in which cruise lines will carry 20 million passengers, we replace $S(t)$ with 20 and solve for t:

$$20 = 0.5e^{0.089t}$$

$$40 = e^{0.089t} \qquad \text{Dividing both sides by 0.5}$$

$$\ln 40 = \ln e^{0.089t} \qquad \text{Taking the natural logarithm on both sides}$$

$$\ln 40 = 0.089t \qquad \ln e^a = a$$

$$\frac{\ln 40}{0.089} = t \qquad \text{Dividing both sides by 0.089}$$

$$41.4 \approx t. \qquad \text{Using a calculator}$$

Rounding to 41, we see that, according to this model, cruise lines will carry 20 million passengers 41 yr after 1970, or in 2011. **TRY EXERCISE 31**

EXAMPLE 6

Interest compounded continuously. When an amount of money P_0 is invested at interest rate k, compounded *continuously*, interest is computed every "instant" and added to the original amount. The balance $P(t)$, after t years, is given by the exponential growth model

$$P(t) = P_0 e^{kt}.$$

a) Suppose that \$30,000 is invested and grows to \$44,754.75 in 5 yr. Find the exponential growth function.

b) What is the doubling time?

SOLUTION

a) We have $P(0) = 30{,}000$. Thus the exponential growth function is

$$P(t) = 30{,}000e^{kt}, \quad \text{where } k \text{ must still be determined.}$$

Knowing that for $t = 5$ we have $P(5) = 44{,}754.75$, it is possible to solve for k:

$$44{,}754.75 = 30{,}000e^{k(5)}$$

$$44{,}754.75 = 30{,}000e^{5k}$$

$$\frac{44{,}754.75}{30{,}000} = e^{5k} \qquad \text{Dividing both sides by 30,000}$$

$$1.491825 = e^{5k}$$

$$\ln 1.491825 = \ln e^{5k} \qquad \text{Taking the natural logarithm on both sides}$$

$$\ln 1.491825 = 5k \qquad \ln e^a = a$$

$$\frac{\ln 1.491825}{5} = k \qquad \text{Dividing both sides by 5}$$

$$0.08 \approx k. \qquad \text{Using a calculator and rounding}$$

The interest rate is about 0.08, or 8%, compounded continuously. Because interest is being compounded continuously, the yearly interest rate is a bit more than 8%. The exponential growth function is

$$P(t) = 30{,}000e^{0.08t}.$$

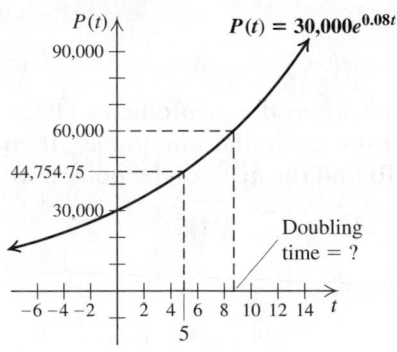

$P(t) = 30,000e^{0.08t}$

A visualization of Example 6

b) To find the doubling time T, we replace $P(T)$ with 60,000 and solve for T:

$$60{,}000 = 30{,}000e^{0.08T}$$

$$2 = e^{0.08T} \qquad \text{Dividing both sides by 30,000}$$

$$\ln 2 = \ln e^{0.08T} \qquad \text{Taking the natural logarithm on both sides}$$

$$\ln 2 = 0.08T \qquad \ln e^a = a$$

$$\frac{\ln 2}{0.08} = T \qquad \text{Dividing both sides by 0.08}$$

$$8.7 \approx T. \qquad \text{Using a calculator and rounding}$$

Thus the original investment of \$30,000 will double in about 8.7 yr.

TRY EXERCISE 41

For any specified interest rate, continuous compounding gives the highest yield and the shortest doubling time.

In some real-life situations, a quantity or population is *decreasing* or *decaying* exponentially.

Exponential Decay

An **exponential decay model** is a function of the form

$$P(t) = P_0e^{-kt}, \quad k > 0,$$

where P_0 is the quantity present at time 0, $P(t)$ is the amount present at time t, and k is the **decay rate**. The **half-life** is the amount of time necessary for half of the quantity to decay.

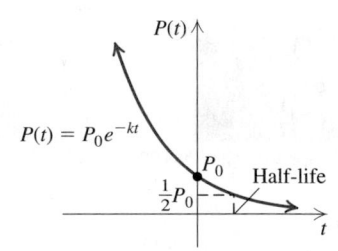

$P(t) = P_0e^{-kt}$

Half-life

EXAMPLE 7

Chaco Canyon, New Mexico

Carbon dating.   The radioactive element carbon-14 has a half-life of 5750 yr. The percentage of carbon-14 in the remains of organic matter can be used to determine the age of that material. Recently, while digging in Chaco Canyon, New Mexico, archaeologists found corn pollen that had lost 38.1% of its carbon-14. The age of this corn pollen was evidence that Indians had been cultivating crops in the Southwest centuries earlier than scientists had thought. What was the age of the pollen?

Source: *American Anthropologist*

SOLUTION   We first find k. To do so, we use the concept of half-life. When $t = 5750$ (the half-life), $P(t)$ is half of P_0. Then

$$0.5P_0 = P_0e^{-k(5750)} \qquad \text{Substituting in } P(t) = P_0e^{-kt}$$

$$0.5 = e^{-5750k} \qquad \text{Dividing both sides by } P_0$$

$$\ln 0.5 = \ln e^{-5750k} \qquad \text{Taking the natural logarithm on both sides}$$

$$\ln 0.5 = -5750k \qquad \ln e^a = a$$

$$\frac{\ln 0.5}{-5750} = k \qquad \text{Dividing}$$

$$0.00012 \approx k. \qquad \text{Using a calculator and rounding}$$

Now we have a function for the decay of carbon-14:

$$P(t) = P_0 e^{-0.00012t}.$$ This completes the first part of our solution.

(*Note*: This equation can be used for subsequent carbon-dating problems.) If the corn pollen has lost 38.1% of its carbon-14 from an initial amount P_0, then $100\% - 38.1\%$, or 61.9%, of P_0 is still present. To find the age t of the pollen, we solve this equation for t:

$$0.619P_0 = P_0 e^{-0.00012t} \qquad \text{We want to find } t \text{ for which } P(t) = 0.619P_0.$$

$$0.619 = e^{-0.00012t} \qquad \text{Dividing both sides by } P_0$$

$$\ln 0.619 = \ln e^{-0.00012t} \qquad \text{Taking the natural logarithm on both sides}$$

$$\ln 0.619 = -0.00012t \qquad \ln e^a = a$$

$$\frac{\ln 0.619}{-0.00012} = t \qquad \text{Dividing both sides by } -0.00012$$

$$4000 \approx t. \qquad \text{Using a calculator}$$

The pollen is about 4000 yr old.

TRY EXERCISE ▸ 35

12.7 EXERCISE SET

 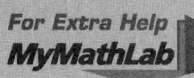 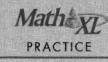 
⌨ *Solve.*

1. Asteroids. The total number $A(t)$ of known asteroids t years after 1990 can be estimated by

$$A(t) = 77(1.283)^t.$$

Source: Based on data from NASA

a) Determine the year in which the number of known asteroids first reached 4000.

b) What is the doubling time for the number of known asteroids?

2. Social networking. The number of unique (different) visitors per month to Facebook t months after April 2006 can be estimated by

$$F(t) = 11.755(1.109)^t,$$

where $F(t)$ is in millions.

Source: Based on data from comScore World Metrix

a) In what month will the number of Facebook visitors first reach 1 billion?

b) What is the doubling time for the number of unique Facebook visitors per month?

3. Health. The rate of number of deaths due to stroke in the United States can be estimated by

$$S(t) = 180(0.97)^t,$$

where $S(t)$ is the number of deaths per 100,000 people and t is the number of years since 1960.

Source: Based on data from Centers for Disease Control and Prevention

a) In what year was the death rate due to stroke 100 per 100,000 people?

b) In what year will the death rate due to stroke be 25 per 100,000 people?

4. Alternative fuels. The number of gallons of ethanol produced in the United States can be estimated by

$$E(t) = 0.18(1.137)^t,$$

where $E(t)$ is the annual production, in billions of gallons, t years after 1980.

a) In what year did the United States produce 5 billion gal of ethanol?

b) In what year will the United States produce 25 billion gal of ethanol?

5. Student loan repayment. A college loan of $29,000 is made at 3% interest, compounded annually. After t years, the amount due, A, is given by the function

$$A(t) = 29{,}000(1.03)^t.$$

a) After what amount of time will the amount due reach $35,000?

b) Find the doubling time.

6. Spread of a rumor. The number of people who have heard a rumor increases exponentially. If all who hear a rumor repeat it to two people a day, and if 20 people start the rumor, the number of people N who have heard the rumor after t days is given by

$$N(t) = 20(3)^t.$$

a) After what amount of time will 1000 people have heard the rumor?

b) What is the doubling time for the number of people who have heard the rumor?

7. *Health insurance.* The percentage of workers covered by a conventional health plan is decreasing exponentially. The percentage of covered workers $W(t)$ enrolled in conventional plans t years after 1988 can be estimated by

$$W(t) = 89(0.837)^t.$$

Sources: Based on data from Kaiser and HRET

a) According to this model, in what year did the percentage of covered workers enrolled in conventional plans drop below 50%?

b) In what year will the percentage of covered workers enrolled in conventional plans drop below 1%?

8. *Smoking.* The percentage of smokers who received telephone counseling and had successfully quit smoking for t months is given by

$$P(t) = 21.4(0.914)^t.$$

Sources: *New England Journal of Medicine*: data from California's Smoker's Hotline

a) In what month will 15% of those who quit and used telephone counseling still be smoke-free?

b) In what month will 5% of those who quit and used telephone counseling still be smoke-free?

9. *Marine biology.* As a result of preservation efforts in countries in which whaling was once common, the humpback whale population has grown since the 1970s. The worldwide population $P(t)$, in thousands, t years after 1982 can be estimated by

$$P(t) = 5.5(1.047)^t.$$

a) In what year will the humpback whale population reach 30,000?

b) Find the doubling time.

10. *World population.* The world population $P(t)$, in billions, t years after 2000 can be approximated by

$$P(t) = 4.553(1.014)^t.$$

Sources: Based on data from U.S. Census Bureau; International Data Base

a) In what year will the world population reach 10 billion?

b) Find the doubling time.

Use the pH formula given in Example 2 for Exercises 11–14.

11. *Chemistry.* The hydrogen ion concentration of fresh-brewed coffee is about 1.3×10^{-5} moles per liter. Find the pH.

12. *Chemistry.* The hydrogen ion concentration of milk is about 1.6×10^{-7} moles per liter. Find the pH.

13. *Medicine.* When the pH of a patient's blood drops below 7.4, a condition called *acidosis* sets in. Acidosis can be deadly when the patient's pH reaches 7.0. What would the hydrogen ion concentration of the patient's blood be at that point?

14. *Medicine.* When the pH of a patient's blood rises above 7.4, a condition called *alkalosis* sets in. Alkalosis can be deadly when the patient's pH reaches 7.8. What would the hydrogen ion concentration of the patient's blood be at that point?

Use the formula in Example 1 for Exercises 15–18.

15. *Racing.* The intensity of sound from a race car in full throttle is about $10\ \text{W/m}^2$. How loud in decibels is this sound level?

Source: nascar.about.com

16. *Audiology.* The intensity of sound in normal conversation is about $3.2 \times 10^{-6}\ \text{W/m}^2$. How loud in decibels is this sound level?

17. Concerts. The crowd at a Hearsay concert at Wembley Arena in London cheered at a sound level of 128.8 dB. What is the intensity of such a sound?
Source: www.peterborough.gov.uk

18. City ordinances. In Albuquerque, New Mexico, the maximum allowable sound level from a car's exhaust is 96 dB. What is the intensity of such a sound?
Source: www.cabq.gov

19. E-mail volume. The SenderBase® Security Network ranks e-mail volume using a logarithmic scale. The magnitude M of a network's daily e-mail volume is given by

$$M = \log \frac{v}{1.34},$$

where v is the number of e-mail messages sent each day. How many e-mail messages are sent each day by a network that has a magnitude of 7.5?
Source: forum.spamcop.net

20. Richter scale. The Richter scale, developed in 1935, has been used for years to measure earthquake magnitude. The Richter magnitude m of an earthquake is given by the formula

$$m = \log \frac{A}{A_0},$$

where A is the maximum amplitude of the earthquake and A_0 is a constant. What is the magnitude on the Richter scale of an earthquake with an amplitude that is a million times A_0?

Use the compound-interest formula in Example 6 for Exercises 21 and 22.

21. Interest compounded continuously. Suppose that P_0 is invested in a savings account where interest is compounded continuously at 2.5% per year.
   a) Express $P(t)$ in terms of P_0 and 0.025.
   b) Suppose that $5000 is invested. What is the balance after 1 yr? after 2 yr?
   c) When will an investment of $5000 double itself?

22. Interest compounded continuously. Suppose that P_0 is invested in a savings account where interest is compounded continuously at 3.1% per year.
   a) Express $P(t)$ in terms of P_0 and 0.031.
   b) Suppose that $1000 is invested. What is the balance after 1 yr? after 2 yr?
   c) When will an investment of $1000 double itself?

23. Population growth. In 2008, the population of the United States was 304 million and the exponential growth rate was 0.9% per year.
Source: U.S. Census Bureau
   a) Find the exponential growth function.
   b) Predict the U.S. population in 2012.
   c) When will the U.S. population reach 325 million?

24. World population growth. In 2008, the world population was 6.7 billion and the exponential growth rate was 1.14% per year.
Source: U.S. Census Bureau
   a) Find the exponential growth function.
   b) Predict the world population in 2014.
   c) When will the world population be 8.0 billion?

25. Zebra mussels. The number of zebra mussels in a river grows at an exponential growth rate of 340% per year. What is the doubling time for zebra mussels?

26. Population growth. The exponential growth rate of the population of United Arab Emirates is 4.4% per year (one of the highest in the world). What is the doubling time?
Sources: Based on data from U.S. Census Bureau; International Data Base 2007

27. World population. The function

$$Y(x) = 71.41 \ln \frac{x}{4.6}$$

can be used to estimate the number of years $Y(x)$ after 2000 required for the world population to reach x billion people.
Sources: Based on data from U.S. Census Bureau; International Data Base
   a) In what year will the world population reach 10 billion?
   b) In what year will the world population reach 12 billion?
   c) Graph the function.

28. Marine biology. The function

$$Y(x) = 21.77 \ln \frac{x}{5.5}$$

can be used to estimate the number of years $Y(x)$ after 1982 required for the world's humpback whale population to reach x thousand whales.
   a) In what year will the whale population reach 15,000?
   b) In what year will the whale population reach 25,000?
   c) Graph the function.

29. Forgetting. Students in an English class took a final exam. They took equivalent forms of the exam at monthly intervals thereafter. The average score $S(t)$, in percent, after t months was found to be given by

$$S(t) = 68 - 20 \log (t + 1), \quad t \geq 0.$$

a) What was the average score when they initially took the test, $t = 0$?

b) What was the average score after 4 months? after 24 months?

c) Graph the function.

d) After what time t was the average score 50%?

30. Health insurance. The amount spent each year by the U.S. government for health insurance for low-income children can be estimated by

$$h(t) = 2.6 \ln t,$$

where $h(t)$ is in billions of dollars and t is the number of years after 1998.

Source: Based on data from the Congressional Budget Office

a) How much was spent on health insurance for low-income children in 2007?

b) Graph the function.

c) In what year will $7 billion be spent on health insurance for low-income children?

31. Wind power. U.S. wind-power capacity has grown exponentially from about 2000 megawatts in 1990 to 17,000 megawatts in 2007.

Source: American Wind Energy Association.

a) Find the exponential growth rate k and write an equation for an exponential function that can be used to predict U.S. wind-power capacity t years after 1990.

b) Estimate the year in which wind-power capacity will reach 50,000 megawatts.

32. Spread of a computer virus. The number of computers infected by a virus t hours after it first appears usually increases exponentially. In 2004, the "MyDoom" worm spread from 100 computers to about 100,000 computers in 24 hr.

Source: Based on data from IDG News Service

a) Find the exponential growth rate k and write an equation for an exponential function that can be used to predict the number of computers infected t hours after the virus first appeared in 100 computers.

b) Assuming exponential growth, estimate how long it took the MyDoom worm to infect 9000 computers.

33. Cable costs. In 1997, the cost to construct communication cables under the ocean was approximately $8200 per gigabit per second per mile. This cost for subsea cables dropped exponentially to $500 by 2007.

Source: Based on information from TeleGeography

a) Find the exponential growth rate k, and write an equation for an exponential function that can be used to predict the cost of subsea cables t years after 1997.

b) Estimate the cost of subsea cables in 2010.

c) In what year (theoretically) will it cost only $1 per gigabit per second per mile to construct subsea cables?

34. Decline in farmland. The number of acres of farmland in the United States has decreased from 945 million acres in 2000 to 932 million acres in 2006. Assume the number of acres of farmland is decreasing exponentially.

Source: Statistical Abstract of the United States

a) Find the value k, and write an equation for an exponential function that can predict the number of acres of U.S. farmland t years after 2000.

b) Predict the number of acres of farmland in 2015.

c) In what year (theoretically) will there be only 800 million acres of U.S. farmland remaining?

35. Archaeology. A date palm seedling is growing in Kibbutz Ketura, Israel, from a seed found in King Herod's palace at Masada. The seed had lost 21% of its carbon-14. How old was the seed? (See Example 7.)

Source: Based on information from www.sfgate.com

36. Archaeology. Soil from beneath the Kish Church in Azerbaijan was found to have lost 12% of its carbon-14. How old was the soil? (See Example 7.)

Source: Based on information from www.azer.com

37. Chemistry. The exponential decay rate of iodine-131 is 9.6% per day. What is its half-life?

38. Chemistry. The decay rate of krypton-85 is 6.3% per year. What is its half-life?

39. Caffeine. The half-life of caffeine in the human body for a healthy adult is approximately 5 hr.

a) What is the exponential decay rate?

b) How long will it take 95% of the caffeine consumed to leave the body?

40. Home construction. The chemical urea formaldehyde was found in some insulation used in houses built during the mid to late 1960s. Unknown at the time was the fact that urea formaldehyde emitted toxic fumes as it decayed. The half-life of urea formaldehyde is 1 yr.

a) What is its decay rate?

b) How long will it take 95% of the urea formaldehyde present to decay?

41. *Value of a sports card.* Legend has it that because he objected to teenagers smoking, and because his first baseball card was issued in cigarette packs, the great shortstop Honus Wagner halted production of his card before many were produced. One of these cards was purchased in 1991 by hockey great Wayne Gretzky (and a partner) for $451,000. The same card was sold in 2007 for $2.8 million. For the following questions, assume that the card's value increases exponentially, as it has for many years.

WAGNER, PITTSBURG

a) Find the exponential growth rate k, and determine an exponential function that can be used to estimate the dollar value, $V(t)$, of the card t years after 1991.
b) Predict the value of the card in 2012.
c) What is the doubling time for the value of the card?
d) In what year will the value of the card first exceed $4,000,000?

42. *Art masterpieces.* As of April 2008, the highest auction price for a contemporary painting was $72.8 million, paid in 2007 for Rothko's *White Center (Yellow, Pink and Lavender on Rose).* The same painting sold for about $10,000 in 1960.

a) Find the exponential growth rate k, and determine the exponential growth function that can be used to estimate $V(t)$, the painting's value, in millions of dollars, t years after 1960.
b) Estimate the value of the painting in 2012.
c) What is the doubling time for the value of the painting?
d) How long after 1960 will the value of the painting be $1 billion?

43. Write a problem for a classmate to solve in which information is provided and the classmate is asked to find an exponential growth function. Make the problem as realistic as possible.

44. Examine the restriction on t in Exercise 29.

a) What upper limit might be placed on t?
b) In practice, would this upper limit ever be enforced? Why or why not?

Skill Review

To prepare for Section 13.1, review the distance and midpoint formulas, completing the square, and graphing parabolas (Sections 10.7, 11.1, and 11.7).

Find the distance between each pair of points. [10.7]

45. $(-3, 7)$ and $(-2, 6)$ **46.** $(1, 5)$ and $(4, 1)$

Find the coordinates of the midpoint of the segment connecting each pair of points. [10.7]

47. $(3, -8)$ and $(5, -6)$

48. $(2, -11)$ and $(-9, -8)$

Solve by completing the square. [11.1]

49. $x^2 + 8x = 1$

50. $x^2 - 10x = 15$

Graph. [11.7]

51. $y = x^2 - 5x - 6$

52. $g(x) = 2x^2 - 6x + 3$

Synthesis

53. Will the model used in Example 4 to predict the number of text messages still be realistic in 2030? Why or why not?

54. *Atmospheric pressure.* Atmospheric pressure P at an elevation of a feet above sea level is given by

$$P = P_0 e^{-0.00004a},$$

where P_0 is the pressure at sea level, which is approximately 29.9 in inches of mercury (Hg). Explain how a barometer, or some other device for measuring atmospheric pressure, can be used to find the height of a skyscraper.

55. *Sports salaries.* As of April 2008, Alex Rodriguez of the New York Yankees had the largest contract in sports history. As part of the 10-year $275-million deal, he will receive $20 million in 2016. How much money would need to be invested in 2008, at 4% interest compounded continuously, in order to have $20 million for Rodriguez in 2016? (This is much like determining what $20 million in 2016 is worth in 2008 dollars.)
Source: *The San Francisco Chronicle*

56. *Supply and demand.* The supply and demand for the sale of stereos by Sound Ideas are given by

$$S(x) = e^x \quad \text{and} \quad D(x) = 162{,}755e^{-x},$$

where $S(x)$ is the price at which the company is willing to supply x stereos and $D(x)$ is the demand price for a quantity of x stereos. Find the equilibrium point. (For reference, see Section 8.8.)

57. *Stellar magnitude.* The apparent stellar magnitude m of a star with received intensity I is given by

$$m(I) = -(19 + 2.5 \cdot \log I),$$

where I is in watts per square meter (W/m^2). The smaller the apparent stellar magnitude, the brighter the star appears.
Source: The Columbus Optical SETI Observatory

a) The intensity of light received from the sun is 1390 W/m^2. What is the apparent stellar magnitude of the sun?
b) The 5-m diameter Hale telescope on Mt. Palomar can detect a star with magnitude +23. What is the received intensity of light from such a star?

58. *Growth of bacteria.* The bacteria *Escherichia coli* (*E. coli*) are commonly found in the human bladder. Suppose that 3000 of the bacteria are present at time $t = 0$. Then t minutes later, the number of bacteria present is

$$N(t) = 3000(2)^{t/20}.$$

If 100,000,000 bacteria accumulate, a bladder infection can occur. If, at 11:00 A.M., a patient's bladder contains 25,000 *E. coli* bacteria, at what time can infection occur?

59. Show that for exponential growth at rate k, the doubling time T is given by $T = \dfrac{\ln 2}{k}$.

60. Show that for exponential decay at rate k, the half-life T is given by $T = \dfrac{\ln 2}{k}$.

61. *Generic drugs.* Largely because of budget constraints, the Food and Drug Administration (FDA) cannot keep up with the rapidly increasing number of applications for approval of generic drugs. The following table shows the number of applications and the number of approvals for generic drugs for recent years.

Year	Number of New Applications for Generic Drugs	Number of Approvals of Generic Drugs
2001	300	310
2002	361	364
2003	449	373
2004	563	413
2005	766	467
2006	810	525

Source: U.S. Food and Drug Administration

a) Graph the data for applications submitted to the FDA, and determine which would be a better fit for the data: an exponential function or a linear function. Explain your reasoning.
b) Graph the data for approvals from the FDA, and determine which would be a better fit for the data: an exponential function or a linear function. Explain your reasoning.
c) Use regression to fit a function to each set of data.
d) If the trends continue, in what year will there be only half as many approvals as applications?

COLLABORATIVE CORNER

Safe Listening

Focus: Logarithmic models

Time: 30 minutes

Group size: 2–4

Materials: MP3 players (one per group) with music

The *decibel* scale is used to measure the volume, or "loudness," of a sound. Listening to music at a high volume can lead to damaged hearing, because the power required to produce louder volumes increases exponentially.

ACTIVITY

1. Group members should work together to answer the following questions.

   a) The volume V, in decibels (dB), of sound on an MP3 player is given by

   $$V = 10 \cdot \log \frac{P}{P_0},$$

   where P is the power needed to produce the sound, in milliwatts (mW), and $P_0 = 0.1$ mW is the power needed to produce the lowest volume that registers on the MP3 player. Find V_0, the volume when the lowest power setting is used $(P = P_0)$.

   b) On a typical MP3 player, each time the volume is stepped up by pressing the volume button, the volume increases by 1.5 decibels (dB). If the volume is stepped up 20 times from V_0, by how many decibels does the volume increase?

   c) If the volume is stepped up 20 times from V_0, how much power is required to produce the sound?

   d) By how much does the power level increase every time the volume is stepped up?

   e) Solve the formula for P. What type of function is this?

2. One group member should begin listening to a song on the MP3 player. If possible, the song should be recent and downloaded from a music site.

   a) Most MP3 songs are designed to play at 100 dB. Beyond this volume, the music begins to sound distorted. Starting at the minimum volume level, the listener should increase the volume until the music begins to sound distorted. Calculate the approximate decibel increase per step for this MP3 player by dividing 100 by the number of times the volume was stepped up. How much power would be needed to produce this volume?

   b) The Occupational Safety and Health Administration (OSHA) considers sustained sound levels of 90 dB and above unsafe. Using the decibel increase per step from part 2(a), calculate the number of steps needed to increase the volume from the minimum volume level to 90 dB.

   c) Starting again at the minimum volume level, the listener should increase the volume the calculated number of steps until the volume reaches approximately 90 dB. How much power is required to produce this volume?

   d) How many times as much power is used to produce 100 dB as to produce 90 dB?

Thanks to Greg Massey, Embedded Software Engineer, for suggesting this application.

Study Summary

KEY TERMS AND CONCEPTS	EXAMPLES

SECTION 12.1: COMPOSITE AND INVERSE FUNCTIONS

The **composition** of f and g is defined as
$$(f \circ g)(x) = f(g(x)).$$

If $f(x) = \sqrt{x}$ and $g(x) = 2x - 5$, then
$$(f \circ g)(x) = f(g(x)) = f(2x - 5)$$
$$= \sqrt{2x - 5}.$$

A function f is **one-to-one** if different inputs have different outputs. The graph of a one-to-one function passes the **horizontal-line test**.

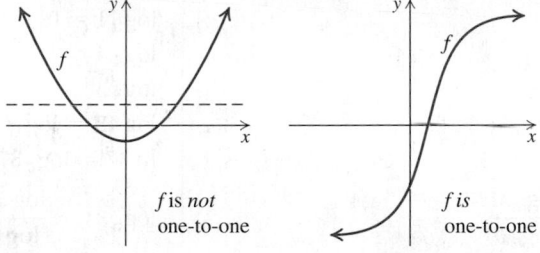

f is *not* one-to-one

f is one-to-one

If f is one-to-one, it is possible to find its inverse:

1. Replace $f(x)$ with y.
2. Interchange x and y.
3. Solve for y.

4. Replace y with $f^{-1}(x)$.

If $f(x) = 2x - 3$, find $f^{-1}(x)$.

1. $y = 2x - 3$
2. $x = 2y - 3$
3. $x + 3 = 2y$
   $$\frac{x + 3}{2} = y$$
4. $\dfrac{x + 3}{2} = f^{-1}(x)$

SECTION 12.2: EXPONENTIAL FUNCTIONS
SECTION 12.3: LOGARITHMIC FUNCTIONS

For an **exponential function** f:
$f(x) = a^x$;
$a > 0,\ a \neq 1$;
Domain: $\mathbb{R}$;
$f^{-1}(x) = \log_a x$.

For a **logarithmic function** g:
$g(x) = \log_a x$;
$a > 0,\ a \neq 1$;
Domain: $(0, \infty)$;
$g^{-1}(x) = a^x$.

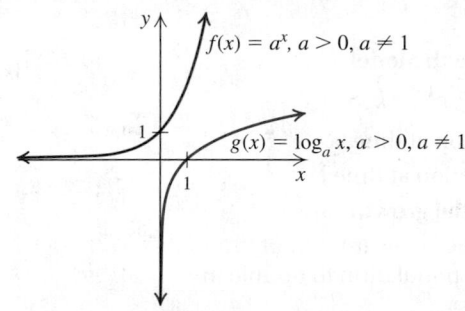

$\log_a x = m$ means $a^m = x$.

$\log_8 x = 2$
$\ \ \ 8^2 = x$ Rewriting as an exponential equation
$\ \ 64 = x$

SECTION 12.4: PROPERTIES OF LOGARITHMIC FUNCTIONS
SECTION 12.5: COMMON AND NATURAL LOGARITHMS

Properties of Logarithms

$\log_a (MN) = \log_a M + \log_a N$

$\log_a \dfrac{M}{N} = \log_a M - \log_a N$

$\log_a M^p = p \cdot \log_a M$

$\log_a 1 = 0$

$\log_a a = 1$

$\log_a a^k = k$

$\log M = \log_{10} M$

$\ln M = \log_e M$

$\log_b M = \dfrac{\log_a M}{\log_a b}$

$\log_7 10 = \log_7 5 + \log_7 2$

$\log_5 \dfrac{14}{3} = \log_5 14 - \log_5 3$

$\log_8 5^{12} = 12 \log_8 5$

$\log_9 1 = 0$

$\log_4 4 = 1$

$\log_3 3^8 = 8$

$\log 43 = \log_{10} 43$

$\ln 37 = \log_e 37$

$\log_6 31 = \dfrac{\log 31}{\log 6} = \dfrac{\ln 31}{\ln 6}$

SECTION 12.6: SOLVING EXPONENTIAL AND LOGARITHMIC EQUATIONS

The Principle of Exponential Equality

For any real number b, $b \neq -1, 0,$ or 1:

$\qquad b^x = b^y$ is equivalent to $x = y$.

$25 = 5^x$

$5^2 = 5^x$

$\ \ 2 = x$

The Principle of Logarithmic Equality

For any logarithm base a, and for $x, y > 0$:

$x = y$ is equivalent to $\log_a x = \log_a y$.

$\ \ \ 83 = 7^x$

$\log 83 = \log 7^x$

$\log 83 = x \log 7$

$\dfrac{\log 83}{\log 7} = x$

SECTION 12.7: APPLICATIONS OF EXPONENTIAL AND LOGARITHMIC FUNCTIONS

Exponential Growth Model

$\qquad P(t) = P_0 e^{kt}, \quad k > 0$

P_0 is the population at time 0.

$P(t)$ is the population at time t.

k is the **exponential growth rate**.

The **doubling time** is the amount of time necessary for the population to double in size.

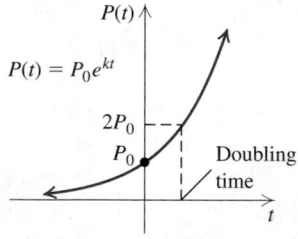

Exponential Decay Model

$\qquad P(t) = P_0 e^{-kt}, \quad k > 0$

P_0 is the quantity present at time 0.

$P(t)$ is the amount present at time t.

k is the **exponential decay rate**.

The **half-life** is the amount of time necessary for half of the quantity to decay.

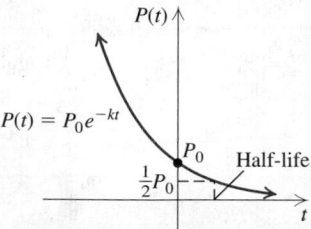

Review Exercises: Chapter 12

Concept Reinforcement *In each of Exercises 1–10, classify the statement as either true or false.*

1. The functions given by $f(x) = 3^x$ and $g(x) = \log_3 x$ are inverses of each other. [12.3]

2. A function's doubling time is the amount of time t for which $f(t) = 2 \cdot f(0)$. [12.7]

3. A radioactive isotope's half-life is the amount of time t for which $f(t) = \frac{1}{2} \cdot f(0)$. [12.7]

4. $\ln(ab) = \ln a - \ln b$ [12.4]

5. $\log x^a = x \ln a$ [12.4]

6. $\log_a \frac{m}{n} = \log_a m - \log_a n$ [12.4]

7. For $f(x) = 3^x$, the domain of f is $[0, \infty)$. [12.2]

8. For $g(x) = \log_2 x$, the domain of g is $[0, \infty)$. [12.3]

9. The function F is not one-to-one if $F(-2) = F(5)$. [12.1]

10. The function g is one-to-one if it passes the vertical-line test. [12.1]

---

11. Find $(f \circ g)(x)$ and $(g \circ f)(x)$ if $f(x) = x^2 + 1$ and $g(x) = 2x - 3$. [12.1]

12. If $h(x) = \sqrt{3 - x}$, find $f(x)$ and $g(x)$ such that $h(x) = (f \circ g)(x)$. Answers may vary. [12.1]

13. Determine whether $f(x) = 4 - x^2$ is one-to-one. [12.1]

Find a formula for the inverse of each function. [12.1]

14. $f(x) = x - 10$

15. $g(x) = \dfrac{3x + 1}{2}$

16. $f(x) = 27x^3$

Graph.

17. $f(x) = 3^x + 1$ [12.2]   18. $x = \left(\frac{1}{4}\right)^y$ [12.2]

19. $y = \log_5 x$ [12.3]

Simplify. [12.3]

20. $\log_9 81$ 21. $\log_3 \frac{1}{9}$

22. $\log_2 2^{11}$ 23. $\log_{16} 4$

Rewrite as an equivalent logarithmic equation. [12.3]

24. $2^{-3} = \frac{1}{8}$ 25. $25^{1/2} = 5$

Rewrite as an equivalent exponential equation. [12.3]

26. $\log_4 16 = x$ 27. $\log_8 1 = 0$

Express as an equivalent expression using the individual logarithms of x, y, and z. [12.4]

28. $\log_a x^4 y^2 z^3$

29. $\log_a \dfrac{x^5}{yz^2}$

30. $\log \sqrt[4]{\dfrac{z^2}{x^3 y}}$

Express as an equivalent expression that is a single logarithm and, if possible, simplify. [12.4]

31. $\log_a 5 + \log_a 8$

32. $\log_a 48 - \log_a 12$

33. $\frac{1}{2} \log a - \log b - 2 \log c$

34. $\frac{1}{3}[\log_a x - 2 \log_a y]$

Simplify. [12.4]

35. $\log_m m$ 36. $\log_m 1$

37. $\log_m m^{17}$

Given $\log_a 2 = 1.8301$ and $\log_a 7 = 5.0999$, find each of the following. [12.4]

38. $\log_a 14$ 39. $\log_a \frac{2}{7}$

40. $\log_a 28$ 41. $\log_a 3.5$

42. $\log_a \sqrt{7}$ 43. $\log_a \frac{1}{4}$

Use a calculator to find each of the following to four decimal places. [12.5]

44. $\log 75$ 45. $10^{1.789}$

46. $\ln 0.3$ 47. $e^{-0.98}$

Find each of the following logarithms using the change-of-base formula. Round answers to four decimal places. [12.5]

48. $\log_5 50$ 49. $\log_6 5$

Graph and state the domain and the range of each function. [12.5]

50. $f(x) = e^x - 1$ 51. $g(x) = 0.6 \ln x$

Solve. Where appropriate, include approximations to four decimal places. [12.6]

52. $5^x = 125$

53. $3^{2x} = \frac{1}{9}$

54. $\log_3 x = -4$

55. $\log_x 16 = 4$

56. $\log x = -3$

57. $6 \ln x = 18$

58. $4^{2x-5} = 19$

59. $2^x = 12$

60. $e^{-0.1t} = 0.03$

61. $2 \ln x = -6$

62. $\log (2x - 5) = 1$

63. $\log_4 x - \log_4 (x - 15) = 2$

64. $\log_3 (x - 4) = 2 - \log_3 (x + 4)$

65. In a business class, students were tested at the end of the course with a final exam. They were then tested again 6 months later. The forgetting formula was determined to be

$$S(t) = 82 - 18 \log (t + 1),$$

where $S(t)$ was the average student grade t months after taking the final exam. [12.7]

   a) Determine the average score when they first took the exam (when $t = 0$).

   b) What was the average score after 6 months?

   c) After what time was the average score 54?

66. A laptop computer is purchased for $1500. Its value each year is about 80% of its value in the preceding year. Its value in dollars after t years is given by the exponential function

$$V(t) = 1500(0.8)^t. \quad [12.7]$$

   a) After what amount of time will the computer's value be $900?

   b) After what amount of time will the computer's value be half the original value?

67. U.S. companies spent $885 million in e-mail marketing in 2005. This amount was predicted to grow exponentially to $1.1 billion in 2010. [12.7]
Source: Jupiter Research

   a) Find the exponential growth rate k, and write a function that describes the amount $A(t)$, in millions of dollars, spent on e-mail marketing t years after 2005.

   b) Estimate the amount spent on e-mail marketing in 2008.

   c) In what year will U.S. companies spend $2 billion on e-mail marketing?

   d) Find the doubling time.

68. In 2005, consumers received, on average, 3253 spam messages. The volume of spam messages per consumer is decreasing exponentially with an exponential decay rate of 13.7% per year. [12.7]

   a) Find the exponential decay function that can be used to predict the average number of spam messages, $M(t)$, t years after 2005.

   b) Predict the number of spam messages received per consumer in 2010.

   c) In what year, theoretically, will the average consumer receive 100 spam messages?

69. The value of Aret's stock market portfolio doubled in 6 yr. What was the exponential growth rate? [12.7]

70. How long will it take $7600 to double if it is invested at 4.2%, compounded continuously? [12.7]

71. How old is a skull that has lost 34% of its carbon-14? (Use $P(t) = P_0 e^{-0.00012t}$.) [12.7]

72. What is the pH of coffee if its hydrogen ion concentration is 7.9×10^{-6} moles per liter? (Use $\text{pH} = -\log [\text{H}^+].$) [12.7]

73. The roar of a lion can reach a sound intensity of 2.5×10^{-1} W/m². How loud in decibels is this sound level? $\left(\text{Use } L = 10 \cdot \log \dfrac{I}{10^{-12}\,\text{W/m}^2}. \right)$ [12.7]

Source: en.allexperts.com

Synthesis

74. Explain why negative numbers do not have logarithms. [12.3]

75. Explain why $f(x) = e^x$ and $g(x) = \ln x$ are inverse functions. [12.5]

Solve. [12.6]

76. $\ln (\ln x) = 3$

77. $2^{x^2+4x} = \frac{1}{8}$

78. Solve the system:

$$5^{x+y} = 25,$$
$$2^{2x-y} = 64. \quad [12.6]$$

Test: Chapter 12

 **CHAPTER Test Prep VIDEO CD** *Step-by-step test solutions are found on the video CD in the back of this book.*

1. Find $(f \circ g)(x)$ and $(g \circ f)(x)$ if $f(x) = x + x^2$ and $g(x) = 2x + 1$.

2. If
$$h(x) = \frac{1}{2x^2 + 1},$$
find $f(x)$ and $g(x)$ such that $h(x) = (f \circ g)(x)$. Answers may vary.

3. Determine whether $f(x) = x^2 + 3$ is one-to-one.

Find a formula for the inverse of each function.

4. $f(x) = 3x + 4$

5. $g(x) = (x + 1)^3$

Graph.

6. $f(x) = 2^x - 3$

7. $g(x) = \log_7 x$

Simplify.

8. $\log_5 125$

9. $\log_{100} 10$

10. $3^{\log_3 18}$

11. $\log_n n$

12. $\log_c 1$

13. $\log_a a^{19}$

14. Rewrite as an equivalent logarithmic equation: $5^{-4} = \frac{1}{625}$.

15. Rewrite as an equivalent exponential equation: $m = \log_2 \frac{1}{2}$.

16. Express as an equivalent expression using the individual logarithms of a, b, and c:
$$\log \frac{a^3 b^{1/2}}{c^2}.$$

17. Express as an equivalent expression that is a single logarithm:
$$\tfrac{1}{3} \log_a x + 2 \log_a z.$$

Given $\log_a 2 = 0.301$, $\log_a 6 = 0.778$, and $\log_a 7 = 0.845$, find each of the following.

18. $\log_a 14$

19. $\log_a 3$

20. $\log_a 16$

Use a calculator to find each of the following to four decimal places.

21. $\log 25$

22. $10^{-0.8}$

23. $\ln 0.4$

24. $e^{4.8}$

25. Find $\log_3 14$ using the change-of-base formula. Round to four decimal places.

Graph and state the domain and the range of each function.

26. $f(x) = e^x + 3$

27. $g(x) = \ln(x - 4)$

Solve. Where appropriate, include approximations to four decimal places.

28. $2^x = \frac{1}{32}$

29. $\log_4 x = \frac{1}{2}$

30. $\log x = -2$

31. $5^{4-3x} = 87$

32. $7^x = 1.2$

33. $\ln x = 3$

34. $\log(x - 3) + \log(x + 1) = \log 5$

35. The average walking speed R of people living in a city of population P is given by $R = 0.37 \ln P + 0.05$, where R is in feet per second and P is in thousands.

   a) The population of Tulsa, Oklahoma, is 383,000. Find the average walking speed.
   b) San Diego, California, has an average walking speed of about 3 ft/sec. Find the population.

36. The population of Nigeria was about 140 million in 2008 and the exponential growth rate was 2.4% per year.

   a) Write an exponential function describing the population of Nigeria.
   b) What will the population be in 2012? in 2016?
   c) When will the population be 200 million?
   d) What is the doubling time?

37. The average cost of a year at a private four-year college grew exponentially from $21,855 in 2001 to $27,317 in 2006.
   Source: National Center for Education Statistics

   a) Find the exponential growth rate k, and write a function that approximates the cost $C(t)$ of a year of college t years after 2001.
   b) Predict the cost of a year of college in 2012.
   c) In what year will the average cost of college be $50,000?

38. An investment with interest compounded continuously doubled itself in 16 yr. What is the interest rate?

39. How old is an animal bone that has lost 43% of its carbon-14? (Use $P(t) = P_0 e^{-0.00012t}$.)

40. Blue whales and fin whales are the loudest animals, with sound levels up to 188 dB. What is the intensity of such a sound? $\left(\text{Use } L = 10 \cdot \log \dfrac{I}{10^{-12} \text{ W/m}^2}. \right)$
   Source: *Guinness World Records*

41. The hydrogen ion concentration of water is 1.0×10^{-7} moles per liter. What is the pH? (Use $\text{pH} = -\log[\text{H}^+]$.)

Synthesis

42. Solve: $\log_5 |2x - 7| = 4$.

43. If $\log_a x = 2$, $\log_a y = 3$, and $\log_a z = 4$, find
$$\log_a \frac{\sqrt[3]{x^2 z}}{\sqrt[3]{y^2 z^{-1}}}.$$

1. Evaluate $\dfrac{x^0 + y}{-z}$ for $x = 6$, $y = 9$, and $z = -5$.

[1.8], [4.1]

Simplify.

2. $(-2x^2y^{-3})^{-4}$ [4.2]

3. $(-5x^4y^{-3}z^2)(-4x^2y^2)$ [4.2]

4. $\dfrac{3x^4y^6z^{-2}}{-9x^4y^2z^3}$ [4.2]

5. $(1.5 \times 10^{-3})(4.2 \times 10^{-12})$ [4.2]

6. $3^3 + 2^2 - (32 \div 4 - 16 \div 8)$ [1.8]

Solve.

7. $3(2x - 3) = 9 - 5(2 - x)$ [2.2]

8. $4x - 3y = 15$,
   $3x + 5y = 4$ [8.2]

9. $\begin{aligned} x + y - 3z &= -1, \\ 2x - y + z &= 4, \\ -x - y + z &= 1 \end{aligned}$ [8.4]

10. $x(x - 3) = 70$ [5.7]

11. $\dfrac{7}{x^2 - 5x} - \dfrac{2}{x - 5} = \dfrac{4}{x}$ [6.6]

12. $\sqrt{4 - 5x} = 2x - 1$ [10.6]

13. $\sqrt[3]{2x} = 1$ [10.6]

14. $3x^2 + 48 = 0$ [11.1]

15. $x^4 - 13x^2 + 36 = 0$ [11.5]

16. $\log_x 81 = 2$ [12.3]

17. $3^{5x} = 7$ [12.6]

18. $\ln x - \ln(x - 8) = 1$ [12.6]

19. $x^2 + 4x > 5$ [11.9]

20. If $f(x) = x^2 + 6x$, find a such that $f(a) = 11$. [11.2]

21. If $f(x) = |2x - 3|$, find all x for which $f(x) \geq 7$. [9.3]

Solve.

22. $D = \dfrac{ab}{b + a}$, for a [7.5]

23. $d = ax^2 + vx$, for x [11.4]

24. Find the domain of the function f given by

$$f(x) = \dfrac{x + 4}{3x^2 - 5x - 2}.$$ [9.2]

Perform the indicated operations and simplify.

25. $(5p^2q^3 + 6pq - p^2 + p) - (2p^2q^3 + p^2 - 5pq - 9)$ [4.7]

26. $(3x^2 - z^3)^2$ [4.7]

27. $\dfrac{1 + \dfrac{3}{x}}{x - 1 - \dfrac{12}{x}}$ [6.5]

28. $\dfrac{a^2 - a - 6}{a^3 - 27} \cdot \dfrac{a^2 + 3a + 9}{6}$ [6.2]

29. $\dfrac{3}{x + 6} - \dfrac{2}{x^2 - 36} + \dfrac{4}{x - 6}$ [6.4]

30. $\dfrac{\sqrt[3]{24xy^8}}{\sqrt[3]{3xy}}$ [10.4]

31. $\sqrt{x + 5}\,\sqrt[5]{x + 5}$ [10.5]

32. $(2 - i\sqrt{3})(6 + i\sqrt{3})$ [10.8]

33. $(x^4 - 8x^3 + 15x^2 + x - 3) \div (x - 3)$ [4.8]

Factor.

34. $27 + 64n^3$ [5.5]

35. $6x^2 + 8xy - 8y^2$ [5.3]

36. $x^4 - 4x^3 + 7x - 28$ [5.1]

37. $2m^2 + 12mn + 18n^2$ [5.4]

38. $x^4 - 16y^4$ [5.4]

39. Rationalize the denominator:

$$\dfrac{3 - \sqrt{y}}{2 - \sqrt{y}}.$$ [10.5]

40. Find the inverse of f if $f(x) = 9 - 2x$. [12.1]

41. Find a linear function with a graph that contains the points $(0, -8)$ and $(-1, 2)$. [7.3]

42. Find an equation of the line whose graph has a y-intercept of $(0, 5)$ and is perpendicular to the line given $2x + y = 6$. [3.6]

Graph.

43. $5x = 15 + 3y$ [3.3]

44. $y = \log_3 x$ [12.3]

45. $-2x - 3y \leq 12$ [9.4]

46. Graph: $f(x) = 2x^2 + 12x + 19$. [11.7]
    a) Label the vertex.
    b) Draw the axis of symmetry.
    c) Find the maximum or minimum value.

47. Graph $f(x) = 2e^x$ and determine the domain and the range. [12.5]

48. Express as a single logarithm:

$$3 \log x - \tfrac{1}{2} \log y - 2 \log z. \quad [12.4]$$

Solve.

49. *Colorado River.* The Colorado River delivers 1.5 million acre-feet of water to Mexico each year. This is only 10% of the volume of the river; the remainder is diverted at an earlier time for agricultural use. How much water is diverted each year from the Colorado River? [2.5]
Source: www.sierraclub.org

50. *Desalination.* More cities are supplying some of their fresh water through desalination, the process of removing the salt from ocean water. The worldwide desalination capacity has grown exponentially from 15 million m³ per day in 1990 to 55 million m³ per day in 2007. [12.7]
Source: Global Water Intelligence

a) Find the exponential growth rate k, and write an equation for an exponential function that can be used to predict the worldwide desalination capacity $D(t)$, in millions of cubic meters per day, t years after 1990.

b) Predict the worldwide desalination capacity in 2012.

c) In what year will the worldwide desalination capacity reach 100 million m³ per day?

51. *Gasoline consumption.* The number of barrels of gasoline consumed per day in the United States has increased from 8.5 million in 2000 to 9.3 million in 2006.
Source: U.S. Department of Energy, Energy Information Administration

a) At what rate did gasoline consumption increase from 2000 to 2006? [3.4]

b) Find a linear function g that fits the data. Let t represent the number of years since 2000. [7.3]

c) Find an exponential function G that fits the data. Let t represent the number of years since 2000. [12.7]

52. Good's Candies of Indiana makes all their chocolates by hand. It takes Anne 10 min to coat a tray of candies in chocolate. It takes Clay 12 min to coat a tray of candies. How long would it take Anne and Clay, working together, to coat the candies? [6.7]

53. Joe's Thick and Tasty salad dressing gets 45% of its calories from fat. The Light and Lean dressing gets 20% of its calories from fat. How many ounces of each should be mixed in order to get 15 oz of dressing that gets 30% of its calories from fat? [8.3]

54. A fishing boat with a trolling motor can move at a speed of 5 km/h in still water. The boat travels 42 km downriver in the same time that it takes to travel 12 km upriver. What is the speed of the river? [6.7]

55. What is the minimum product of two numbers whose difference is 14? What are the numbers that yield this product? [11.8]

56. Students in a biology class just took a final exam. A formula for predicting the average exam grade on a similar test t months later is

$$S(t) = 78 - 15 \log (t + 1).$$

a) Find the students' average score when they first took the final exam. [12.7]

b) What would the expected average score be on a retest after 4 months? [12.7]

Synthesis

Solve.

57. $\dfrac{5}{3x - 3} + \dfrac{10}{3x + 6} = \dfrac{5x}{x^2 + x - 2}$ [6.6]

58. $\log \sqrt{3x} = \sqrt{\log 3x}$ [12.6]

59. The Danville Express travels 280 mi at a certain speed. If the speed had been increased by 5 mph, the trip could have been made in 1 hr less time. Find the actual speed. [11.4]

Conic Sections

CHAPTER

13

13.1
Conic Sections: Parabolas and Circles

13.2
Conic Sections: Ellipses

13.3
Conic Sections: Hyperbolas

CONNECTING THE CONCEPTS

13.4
Nonlinear Systems of Equations

STUDY SUMMARY
REVIEW EXERCISES
CHAPTER TEST
CUMULATIVE REVIEW

RAGHVENDRA SAHAI
ASTRONOMER
Pasadena, California

As an astronomer, I study stars and interstellar matter, that is, the gas and dust that lie in the vastness of space between the stars in our galaxy. My research includes obtaining images of the clouds of gas and dust ejected by dying sun-like stars. Calculus allows me to solve the equations governing these processes, and thus understand the physical properties of the dust and gas. Trigonometry helps me in figuring out the complex motions and velocities of the ejected matter.

AN APPLICATION

The maximum distance of the planet Mars from the sun is 2.48×10^8 mi. The minimum distance is 3.46×10^7 mi. The sun is at one focus of the elliptical orbit. Find the distance from the sun to the other focus.

This problem appears as Exercise 49 in Section 13.2.

The ellipse described on the preceding page is one example of a *conic section*, meaning that it can be regarded as a cross section of a cone. This chapter presents a variety of applications and equations with graphs that are conic sections. We have already worked with two conic sections, *lines* and *parabolas*, in Chapters 3 and 11.

13.1   Conic Sections: Parabolas and Circles

Parabolas ■ Circles

This section and the next two examine curves formed by cross sections of cones. These curves are all graphs of $Ax^2 + By^2 + Cxy + Dx + Ey + F = 0$. The constants $A, B, C, D, E,$ and F determine which of the following shapes will serve as the graph.

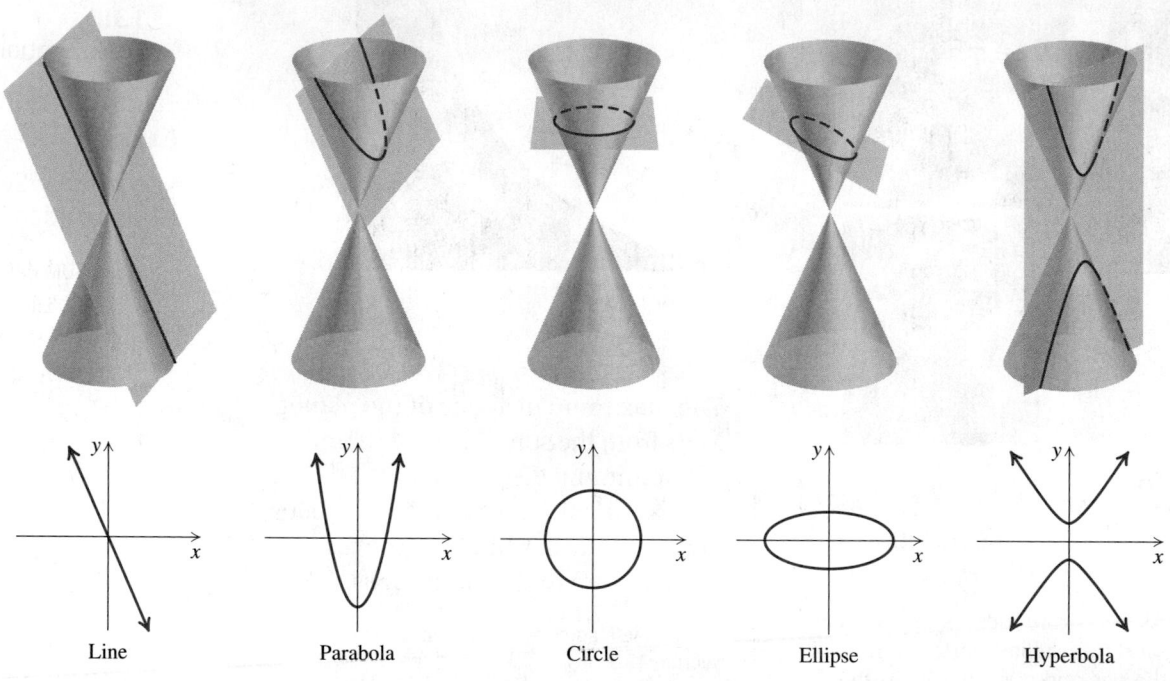

Line   Parabola   Circle   Ellipse   Hyperbola

Parabolas

When a cone is cut as shown in the second figure above, the conic section formed is a **parabola**. Parabolas have many applications in electricity, mechanics, and optics. A cross section of a contact lens or a satellite dish is a parabola, and arches that support certain bridges are parabolas.

> ### Equation of a Parabola
>
> A parabola with a vertical axis of symmetry opens upward or downward and has an equation that can be written in the form
>
> $$y = ax^2 + bx + c.$$
>
> A parabola with a horizontal axis of symmetry opens to the right or to the left and has an equation that can be written in the form
>
> $$x = ay^2 + by + c.$$

Parabolas with equations of the form $f(x) = ax^2 + bx + c$ were graphed in Chapter 11.

EXAMPLE **1**

Graph: $y = x^2 - 4x + 9$.

SOLUTION   To locate the vertex, we can use either of two approaches. One way is to complete the square:

$y = (x^2 - 4x) + 9$	Note that half of -4 is -2, and $(-2)^2 = 4$.
$= (x^2 - 4x + 4 - 4) + 9$	Adding and subtracting 4
$= (x^2 - 4x + 4) + (-4 + 9)$	Regrouping
$= (x - 2)^2 + 5.$	Factoring and simplifying

The vertex is $(2, 5)$.

A second way to find the vertex is to recall that the x-coordinate of the vertex of the parabola given by $y = ax^2 + bx + c$ is $-b/(2a)$:

$$x = -\frac{b}{2a} = -\frac{-4}{2(1)} = 2.$$

To find the y-coordinate of the vertex, we substitute 2 for x:

$$y = x^2 - 4x + 9 = 2^2 - 4(2) + 9 = 5.$$

Either way, the vertex is $(2, 5)$. Next, we calculate and plot some points on each side of the vertex. As expected for a positive coefficient of x^2, the graph opens upward.

x	y	
2	5	←Vertex
0	9	←y-intercept
1	6	
3	6	
4	9	

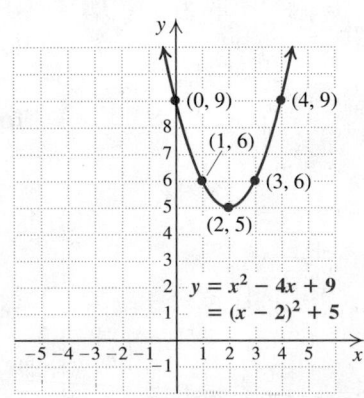

TRY EXERCISE 11

> **To Graph an Equation of the Form $y = ax^2 + bx + c$**
>
> 1. Find the vertex (h, k) either by completing the square to find an equivalent equation
>
> $$y = a(x - h)^2 + k,$$
>
>   or by using $-b/(2a)$ to find the x-coordinate and substituting to find the y-coordinate.
> 2. Choose other values for x on each side of the vertex, and compute the corresponding y-values.
> 3. The graph opens upward for $a > 0$ and downward for $a < 0$.

Any equation of the form $x = ay^2 + by + c$ represents a horizontal parabola that opens to the right for $a > 0$, opens to the left for $a < 0$, and has an axis of symmetry parallel to the x-axis.

EXAMPLE 2   Graph: $x = y^2 - 4y + 9$.

SOLUTION   This equation is like that in Example 1 but with x and y interchanged. The vertex is $(5, 2)$ instead of $(2, 5)$. To find ordered pairs, we choose values for y on each side of the vertex. Then we compute values for x. Note that the x- and y-values of the table in Example 1 are now switched. You should confirm that, by completing the square, we get $x = (y - 2)^2 + 5$.

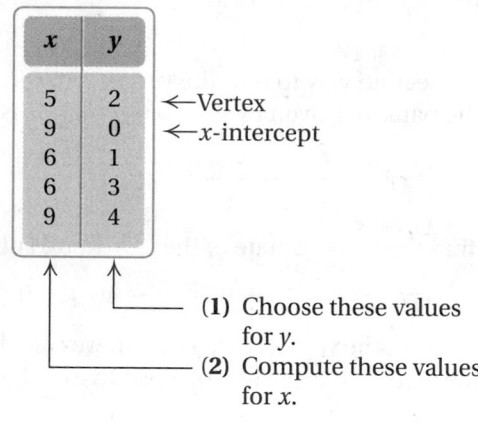

x	y
5	2	←Vertex
9	0	←x-intercept
6	1	
6	3	
9	4	

(1) Choose these values for y.
(2) Compute these values for x.

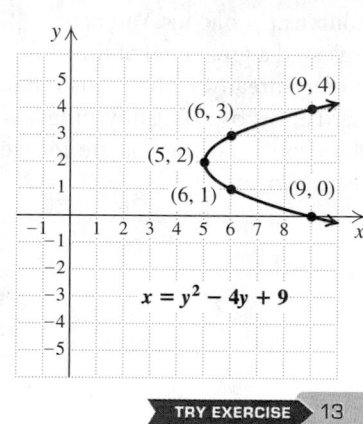

$$x = y^2 - 4y + 9$$

TRY EXERCISE 13

> **To Graph an Equation of the Form $x = ay^2 + by + c$**
>
> 1. Find the vertex (h, k) either by completing the square to find an equivalent equation
>
> $$x = a(y - k)^2 + h,$$
>
>   or by using $-b/(2a)$ to find the y-coordinate and substituting to find the x-coordinate.
> 2. Choose other values for y that are on either side of k and compute the corresponding x-values.
> 3. The graph opens to the right if $a > 0$ and to the left if $a < 0$.

EXAMPLE   3   Graph: $x = -2y^2 + 10y - 7$.

SOLUTION   We find the vertex by completing the square:

$$x = -2y^2 + 10y - 7$$
$$= -2(y^2 - 5y \quad\;\;) - 7$$
$$= -2\left(y^2 - 5y + \tfrac{25}{4}\right) - 7 - (-2)\tfrac{25}{4} \qquad \tfrac{1}{2}(-5) = \tfrac{-5}{2}; \left(\tfrac{-5}{2}\right)^2 = \tfrac{25}{4}; \text{ we}$$
$$\qquad\qquad\qquad\qquad\qquad\qquad\qquad\qquad\qquad \text{add and subtract } (-2)\tfrac{25}{4}.$$
$$= -2\left(y - \tfrac{5}{2}\right)^2 + \tfrac{11}{2}. \qquad\qquad \text{Factoring and simplifying}$$

The vertex is $\left(\tfrac{11}{2}, \tfrac{5}{2}\right)$.

For practice, we also find the vertex by first computing its y-coordinate, $-b/(2a)$, and then substituting to find the x-coordinate:

$$y = -\frac{b}{2a} = -\frac{10}{2(-2)} = \frac{5}{2}$$
$$x = -2y^2 + 10y - 7 = -2\left(\tfrac{5}{2}\right)^2 + 10\left(\tfrac{5}{2}\right) - 7$$
$$= \tfrac{11}{2}.$$

To find ordered pairs, we choose values for y on each side of the vertex and then compute values for x. A table is shown below, together with the graph. The graph opens to the left because the y^2-coefficient, -2, is negative.

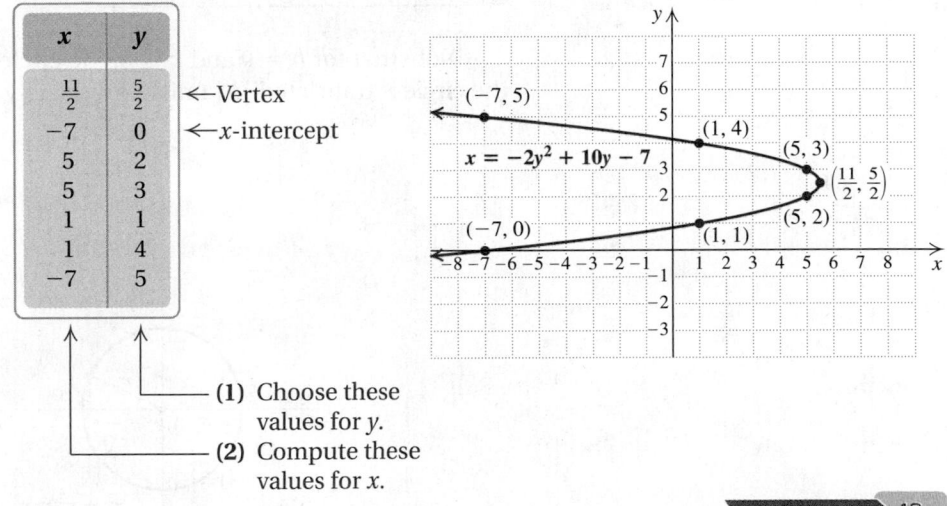

x	y	
$\tfrac{11}{2}$	$\tfrac{5}{2}$	←Vertex
-7	0	←x-intercept
5	2	
5	3	
1	1	
1	4	
-7	5	

(1) Choose these values for y.
(2) Compute these values for x.

TRY EXERCISE   19

Circles

Another conic section, the **circle**, is the set of points in a plane that are a fixed distance r, called the **radius** (plural, **radii**), from a fixed point (h, k), called the **center**. Note that the word radius can mean either any segment connecting a point on a circle to the center or the length of such a segment. Using the idea of a fixed distance r and the distance formula,

$$d = \sqrt{(x_2 - x_1)^2 + (y_2 - y_1)^2},$$

we can find the equation of a circle.

If (x, y) is on a circle of radius r, centered at (h, k), then by the definition of a circle and the distance formula, it follows that

$$r = \sqrt{(x - h)^2 + (y - k)^2}.$$

Squaring both sides gives the equation of a circle in standard form.

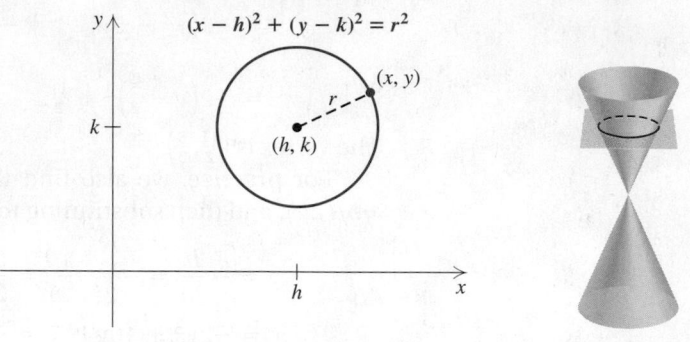

Equation of a Circle (Standard Form)

The equation of a circle, centered at (h, k), with radius r, is given by

$$(x - h)^2 + (y - k)^2 = r^2.$$

Note that for $h = 0$ and $k = 0$, the circle is centered at the origin. Otherwise, the circle is translated $|h|$ units horizontally and $|k|$ units vertically.

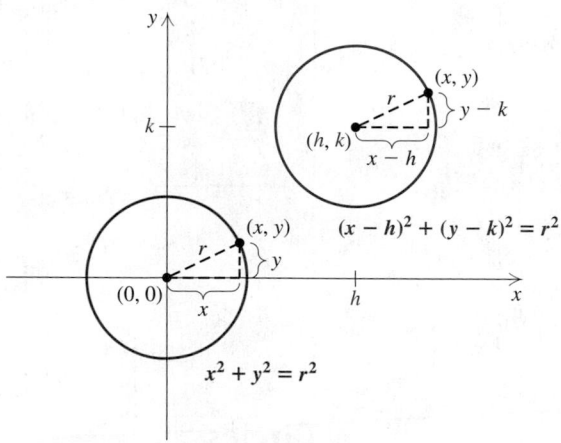

EXAMPLE 4   Find an equation of the circle centered at $(4, -5)$ with radius 6.

SOLUTION   Using the standard form, we obtain

$$(x - 4)^2 + (y - (-5))^2 = 6^2, \quad \text{Using } (x - h)^2 + (y - k)^2 = r^2$$

or

$$(x - 4)^2 + (y + 5)^2 = 36.$$

> **TRY EXERCISE** ▸ 31

EXAMPLE 5   Find the center and the radius and then graph each circle.

a) $(x - 2)^2 + (y + 3)^2 = 4^2$

b) $x^2 + y^2 + 8x - 2y + 15 = 0$

SOLUTION

a) We write standard form:

$$(x - 2)^2 + [y - (-3)]^2 = 4^2.$$

The center is $(2, -3)$ and the radius is 4. To graph, we plot the points $(2, 1)$, $(2, -7)$, $(-2, -3)$, and $(6, -3)$, which are, respectively, 4 units above, below, left, and right of $(2, -3)$. We then either sketch a circle by hand or use a compass.

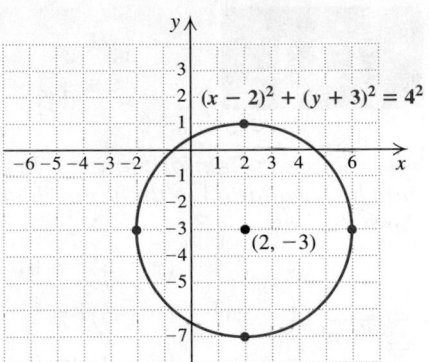

b) To write the equation $x^2 + y^2 + 8x - 2y + 15 = 0$ in standard form, we complete the square twice, once with $x^2 + 8x$ and once with $y^2 - 2y$:

$$x^2 + y^2 + 8x - 2y + 15 = 0$$
$$x^2 + 8x \quad\quad + y^2 - 2y \quad\quad = -15 \qquad \text{Grouping the } x\text{-terms and the } y\text{-terms; subtracting 15 from both sides}$$

$$x^2 + 8x + 16 + y^2 - 2y + 1 = -15 + 16 + 1 \qquad \text{Adding } \left(\tfrac{8}{2}\right)^2, \text{ or 16, and } \left(-\tfrac{2}{2}\right)^2, \text{ or 1, to both sides to get standard form}$$

$$(x + 4)^2 + (y - 1)^2 = 2 \qquad \text{Factoring}$$
$$[x - (-4)]^2 + (y - 1)^2 = (\sqrt{2})^2. \qquad \text{Writing standard form}$$

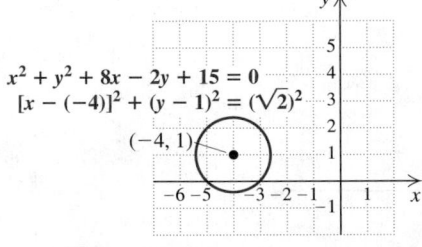

The center is $(-4, 1)$ and the radius is $\sqrt{2}$.

TRY EXERCISE 51

TECHNOLOGY CONNECTION

Most graphing calculators graph only functions, so graphing the equation of a circle usually requires two steps:

1. Solve the equation for y. The result will include a $\pm$ sign in front of a radical.
2. Graph two functions, one for the + sign and the other for the − sign, on the same set of axes.

For example, to graph $(x - 3)^2 + (y + 1)^2 = 16$, solve for $y + 1$ and then y:

$$(y + 1)^2 = 16 - (x - 3)^2$$
$$y + 1 = \pm\sqrt{16 - (x - 3)^2}$$
$$y = -1 \pm \sqrt{16 - (x - 3)^2},$$

or

$$y_1 = -1 + \sqrt{16 - (x - 3)^2}$$

and

$$y_2 = -1 - \sqrt{16 - (x - 3)^2}.$$

When both functions are graphed (in a "squared" window to eliminate distortion), the result is as follows.

$$y_1 = -1 + \sqrt{16 - (x - 3)^2},$$
$$y_2 = -1 - \sqrt{16 - (x - 3)^2}$$

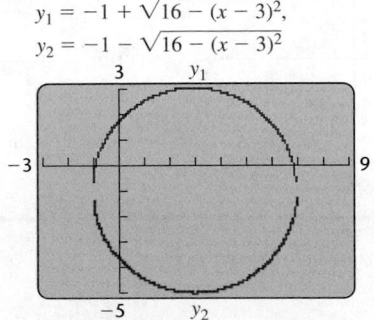

On many calculators, pressing **APPS** and selecting Conics and then Circle accesses a program in which equations in standard form can be graphed directly and then Traced.

Graph each of the following equations.

1. $x^2 + y^2 - 16 = 0$
2. $(x - 1)^2 + (y - 2)^2 = 25$
3. $(x + 3)^2 + (y - 5)^2 = 16$
4. $(x - 5)^2 + (y + 6)^2 = 49$

13.1   EXERCISE SET

 Concept Reinforcement   In each of Exercises 1–8, match the equation with the graph of that equation from those shown.

1. ____ $(x - 2)^2 + (y + 5)^2 = 9$

2. ____ $(x + 2)^2 + (y - 5)^2 = 9$

3. ____ $(x - 5)^2 + (y + 2)^2 = 9$

4. ____ $(x + 5)^2 + (y - 2)^2 = 9$

5. ____ $y = (x - 2)^2 - 5$

6. ____ $y = (x - 5)^2 - 2$

7. ____ $x = (y - 2)^2 - 5$

8. ____ $x = (y - 5)^2 - 2$

a)

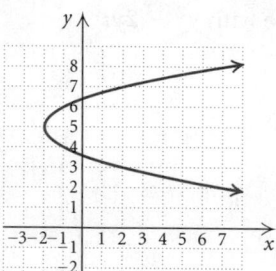

b)

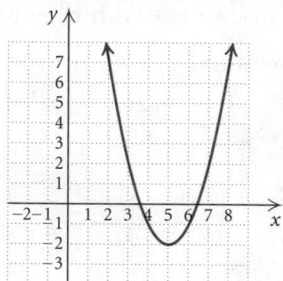

c)

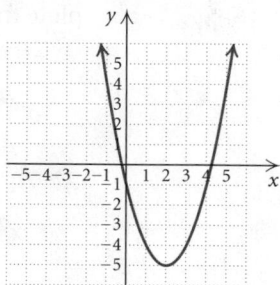

d)

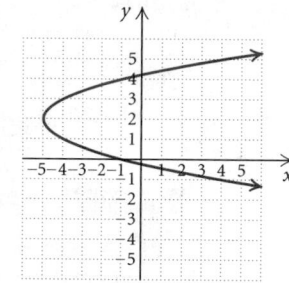

e)

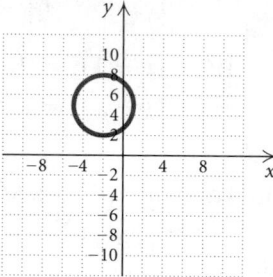

f)

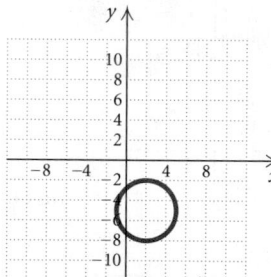

g)

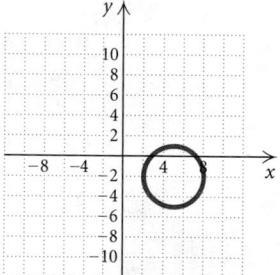

h)

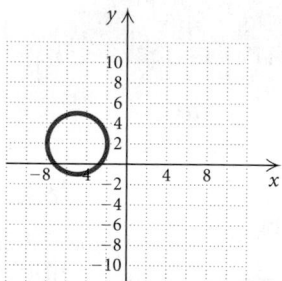

Graph. Be sure to label each vertex.

9. $y = -x^2$

10. $y = 2x^2$

11. $y = -x^2 + 4x - 5$

12. $x = 4 - 3y - y^2$

13. $x = y^2 - 4y + 2$

14. $y = x^2 + 2x + 3$

15. $x = y^2 + 3$

16. $x = -y^2$

17. $x = 2y^2$

18. $x = y^2 - 1$

19. $x = -y^2 - 4y$

20. $x = y^2 + 3y$

21. $y = x^2 - 2x + 1$

22. $y = x^2 + 2x + 1$

23. $x = -\frac{1}{2}y^2$

24. $y = -\frac{1}{2}x^2$

25. $x = -y^2 + 2y - 1$

26. $x = -y^2 - 2y + 3$

27. $x = -2y^2 - 4y + 1$

28. $x = 2y^2 + 4y - 1$

Find an equation of the circle satisfying the given conditions.

29. Center $(0, 0)$, radius 8

30. Center $(0, 0)$, radius 11

31. Center $(7, 3)$, radius $\sqrt{6}$

32. Center $(5, 6)$, radius $\sqrt{11}$

33. Center $(-4, 3)$, radius $3\sqrt{2}$

34. Center $(-2, 7)$, radius $2\sqrt{5}$

35. Center $(-5, -8)$, radius $10\sqrt{3}$

36. Center $(-7, -2)$, radius $5\sqrt{2}$

Aha! **37.** Center $(0, 0)$, passing through $(-3, 4)$

38. Center $(0, 0)$, passing through $(11, -10)$

39. Center $(-4, 1)$, passing through $(-2, 5)$

40. Center $(-1, -3)$, passing through $(-4, 2)$

Find the center and the radius of each circle. Then graph the circle.

41. $x^2 + y^2 = 1$

42. $x^2 + y^2 = 25$

43. $(x + 1)^2 + (y + 3)^2 = 49$

44. $(x - 2)^2 + (y + 3)^2 = 100$

45. $(x - 4)^2 + (y + 3)^2 = 10$

46. $(x + 5)^2 + (y - 1)^2 = 15$

47. $x^2 + y^2 = 8$

48. $x^2 + y^2 = 20$

49. $(x - 5)^2 + y^2 = \frac{1}{4}$

50. $x^2 + (y - 1)^2 = \frac{1}{25}$

51. $x^2 + y^2 + 8x - 6y - 15 = 0$

52. $x^2 + y^2 + 6x - 4y - 15 = 0$

53. $x^2 + y^2 - 8x + 2y + 13 = 0$

54. $x^2 + y^2 + 6x + 4y + 12 = 0$

55. $x^2 + y^2 + 10y - 75 = 0$

56. $x^2 + y^2 - 8x - 84 = 0$

57. $x^2 + y^2 + 7x - 3y - 10 = 0$

58. $x^2 + y^2 - 21x - 33y + 17 = 0$

59. $36x^2 + 36y^2 = 1$

60. $4x^2 + 4y^2 = 1$

61. Does the graph of an equation of a circle include the point that is the center? Why or why not?

62. Is a point a conic section? Why or why not?

Skill Review

To prepare for Section 13.2, review solving quadratic equations (Section 11.1).

Solve. [11.1]

63. $\dfrac{y^2}{16} = 1$

64. $\dfrac{x^2}{a^2} = 1$

65. $\dfrac{(x - 1)^2}{25} = 1$

66. $\dfrac{(y + 5)^2}{12} = 1$

67. $\dfrac{1}{4} + \dfrac{(y + 3)^2}{36} = 1$

68. $\dfrac{1}{9} + \dfrac{(x - 2)^2}{4} = 1$

Synthesis

69. On a piece of graph paper, draw a line and a point not on the line. Then plot several points that are the same distance from the point and from the line. What shape do the points appear to form? How is this set of points different from a circle?

70. If an equation has two terms with the same degree, can its graph be a parabola? Why or why not?

Find an equation of a circle satisfying the given conditions.

71. Center $(3, -5)$ and tangent to (touching at one point) the y-axis

72. Center $(-7, -4)$ and tangent to the x-axis

73. The endpoints of a diameter are $(7, 3)$ and $(-1, -3)$.

74. Center $(-3, 5)$ with a circumference of 8π units

75. Find the point on the y-axis that is equidistant from $(2, 10)$ and $(6, 2)$.

76. Find the point on the x-axis that is equidistant from $(-1, 3)$ and $(-8, -4)$.

77. *Wrestling.* The equation $x^2 + y^2 = \frac{81}{4}$, where x and y represent the number of meters from the center, can be used to draw the outer circle on a wrestling mat used in International, Olympic, and World Championship wrestling. The equation $x^2 + y^2 = 16$ can be used to draw the inner edge of the red zone. Find the area of the red zone.

Source: Based on data from the Government of Western Australia

78. *Snowboarding.* Each side edge of the Burton X8 155 snowboard is an arc of a circle with a "running length" of 1180 mm and a "sidecut depth" of 23 mm (see the figure below).
Source: evogear.com

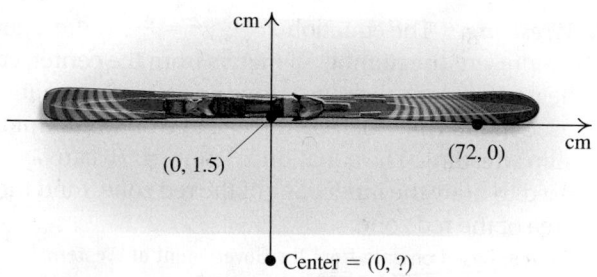

a) Using the coordinates shown, locate the center of the circle. (*Hint*: Equate distances.)
b) What radius is used for the edge of the board?

79. *Snowboarding.* The Never Summer Infinity 149 snowboard has a running length of 1160 mm and a sidecut depth of 23.5 mm (see Exercise 78). What radius is used for the edge of this snowboard?
Source: neversummer.com

80. *Skiing.* The Rossignol Blast ski, when lying flat and viewed from above, has edges that are arcs of a circle. (Actually, each edge is made of two arcs of slightly different radii. The arc for the rear half of the ski edge has a slightly larger radius.)
Source: evogear.com

a) Using the coordinates shown, locate the center of the circle. (*Hint*: Equate distances.)
b) What radius is used for the arc passing through $(0, 1.5)$ and $(72, 0)$?

81. *Doorway construction.* Engle Carpentry needs to cut an arch for the top of an entranceway. The arch needs to be 8 ft wide and 2 ft high. To draw the arch, the carpenters will use as a compass a stretched string with chalk attached at an end.

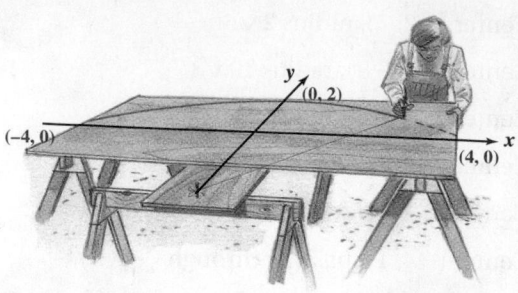

a) Using a coordinate system, locate the center of the circle.
b) What radius should the carpenters use to draw the arch?

82. *Archaeology.* During an archaeological dig, Estella finds the bowl fragment shown below. What was the original diameter of the bowl?

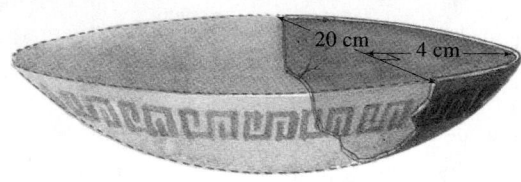

83. *Ferris wheel design.* A ferris wheel has a radius of 24.3 ft. Assuming that the center is 30.6 ft off the ground and that the origin is below the center, as in the following figure, find an equation of the circle.

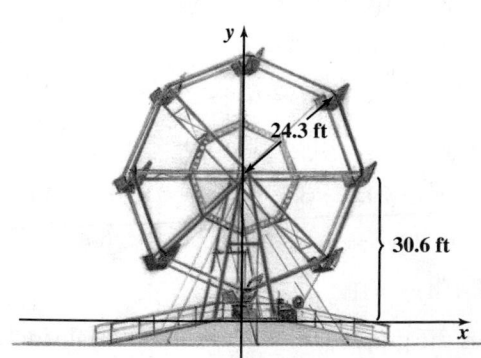

84. Use a graph of the equation $x = y^2 - y - 6$ to approximate to the nearest tenth the solutions of each of the following equations.
a) $y^2 - y - 6 = 2$
b) $y^2 - y - 6 = -3$

85. *Power of a motor.* The horsepower of a certain kind of engine is given by the formula

$$H = \frac{D^2 N}{2.5},$$

where N is the number of cylinders and D is the diameter, in inches, of each piston. Graph this equation, assuming that $N = 6$ (a six-cylinder engine). Let D run from 2.5 to 8. Then use the graph to estimate the diameter of each piston in a six-cylinder 120-horsepower engine.

86. If the equation $x^2 + y^2 - 6x + 2y - 6 = 0$ is written as $y^2 + 2y + (x^2 - 6x - 6) = 0$, it can be regarded as quadratic in y.

a) Use the quadratic formula to solve for y.

b) Show that the graph of your answer to part (a) coincides with the graph in the Technology Connection on p. 859.

87. How could a graphing calculator best be used to help you sketch the graph of an equation of the form $x = ay^2 + by + c$?

88. Why should a graphing calculator's window be "squared" before graphing a circle?

13.2   Conic Sections: Ellipses

Ellipses Centered at $(0, 0)$ •   Ellipses Centered at (h, k)

When a cone is cut at an angle, as shown below, the conic section formed is an *ellipse*. To draw an ellipse, stick two tacks in a piece of cardboard. Then tie a loose string to the tacks, place a pencil as shown, and draw an oval by moving the pencil while stretching the string tight.

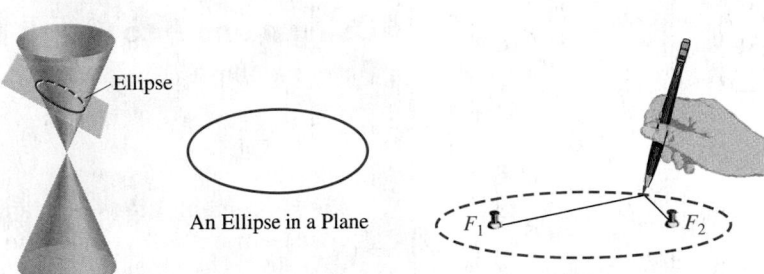

An Ellipse in a Plane

Ellipses Centered at $(0, 0)$

An **ellipse** is defined as the set of all points in a plane for which the sum of the distances from two fixed points F_1 and F_2 is constant. The points F_1 and F_2 are called **foci** (pronounced fō-sī), the plural of focus. In the figure above, the tacks are at the foci and the length of the string is the constant sum of the distances from the tacks to the pencil. The midpoint of the segment F_1F_2 is the **center**. The equation of an ellipse follows. Its derivation is outlined in Exercise 51.

Equation of an Ellipse Centered at the Origin

The equation of an ellipse centered at the origin and symmetric with respect to both axes is

$$\frac{x^2}{a^2} + \frac{y^2}{b^2} = 1, \quad a, b > 0. \qquad \text{(Standard form)}$$

To graph an ellipse centered at the origin, it helps to first find the intercepts. If we replace x with 0, we can find the y-intercepts:

$$\frac{0^2}{a^2} + \frac{y^2}{b^2} = 1$$

$$\frac{y^2}{b^2} = 1$$

$$y^2 = b^2 \quad \text{or} \quad y = \pm b.$$

Thus the y-intercepts are $(0, b)$ and $(0, -b)$. Similarly, the x-intercepts are $(a, 0)$ and $(-a, 0)$. If $a > b$, the ellipse is said to be horizontal and $(-a, 0)$ and $(a, 0)$ are referred to as the **vertices** (singular, **vertex**). If $b > a$, the ellipse is said to be vertical and $(0, -b)$ and $(0, b)$ are then the vertices.

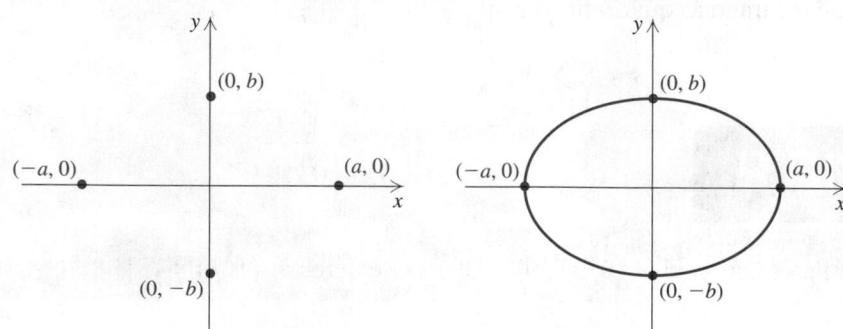

Plotting these four points and drawing an oval-shaped curve, we graph the ellipse. If a more precise graph is desired, we can plot more points.

Using a and b to Graph an Ellipse

For the ellipse

$$\frac{x^2}{a^2} + \frac{y^2}{b^2} = 1,$$

the x-intercepts are $(-a, 0)$ and $(a, 0)$. The y-intercepts are $(0, -b)$ and $(0, b)$. For $a^2 > b^2$, the ellipse is horizontal. For $b^2 > a^2$, the ellipse is vertical.

EXAMPLE 1   Graph the ellipse

$$\frac{x^2}{4} + \frac{y^2}{9} = 1.$$

SOLUTION   Note that

$$\frac{x^2}{4} + \frac{y^2}{9} = \frac{x^2}{2^2} + \frac{y^2}{3^2}.$$ Identifying a and b. Since $b^2 > a^2$, the ellipse is vertical.

Since $a = 2$ and $b = 3$, the x-intercepts are $(-2, 0)$ and $(2, 0)$, and the y-intercepts are $(0, -3)$ and $(0, 3)$. We plot these points and connect them with an oval-shaped curve. To plot two other points, we let $x = 1$ and solve for y:

$$\frac{1^2}{4} + \frac{y^2}{9} = 1$$

$$36\left(\frac{1}{4} + \frac{y^2}{9}\right) = 36 \cdot 1$$

$$36 \cdot \frac{1}{4} + 36 \cdot \frac{y^2}{9} = 36$$

$$9 + 4y^2 = 36$$

$$4y^2 = 27$$

$$y^2 = \frac{27}{4}$$

$$y = \pm\sqrt{\frac{27}{4}}$$

$$y \approx \pm 2.6.$$

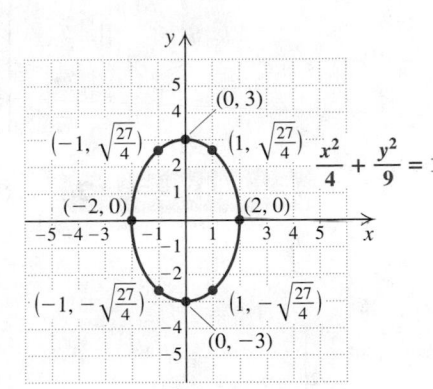

Thus, $(1, 2.6)$ and $(1, -2.6)$ can also be used to draw the graph. Similarly, the points $(-1, 2.6)$ and $(-1, -2.6)$ should appear on the graph.

TRY EXERCISE ▶ 9

EXAMPLE   2

Graph: $4x^2 + 25y^2 = 100$.

SOLUTION   To write the equation in standard form, we divide both sides by 100 to get 1 on the right side:

$$\frac{4x^2 + 25y^2}{100} = \frac{100}{100} \qquad \text{Dividing by 100 to get 1 on the right side}$$

$$\left.\begin{array}{c}\dfrac{4x^2}{100} + \dfrac{25y^2}{100} = 1 \\[2ex] \dfrac{x^2}{25} + \dfrac{y^2}{4} = 1\end{array}\right\} \qquad \text{Simplifying}$$

$$\frac{x^2}{5^2} + \frac{y^2}{2^2} = 1. \qquad a = 5, b = 2$$

STUDENT NOTES

Note that any equation of the form $Ax^2 + By^2 = C$ (with $A \neq B$ and $A, B > 0$) can be rewritten as an equivalent equation in standard form. The graph is an ellipse.

The x-intercepts are $(-5, 0)$ and $(5, 0)$, and the y-intercepts are $(0, -2)$ and $(0, 2)$. We plot the intercepts and connect them with an oval-shaped curve. Other points can also be computed and plotted.

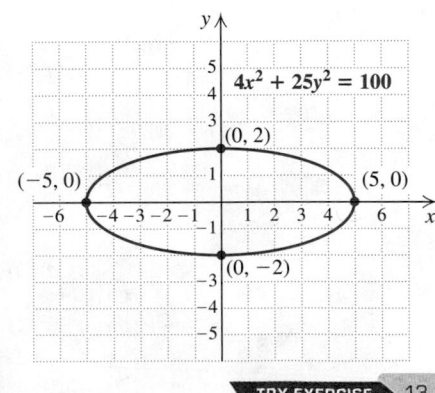

TRY EXERCISE ▶ 13

Ellipses Centered at (h, k)

Horizontal and vertical translations, similar to those used in Chapter 11, can be used to graph ellipses that are not centered at the origin.

Equation of an Ellipse Centered at (h, k)

The standard form of a horizontal or vertical ellipse centered at (h, k) is

$$\frac{(x - h)^2}{a^2} + \frac{(y - k)^2}{b^2} = 1.$$

The vertices are $(h + a, k)$ and $(h - a, k)$ if horizontal; $(h, k + b)$ and $(h, k - b)$ if vertical.

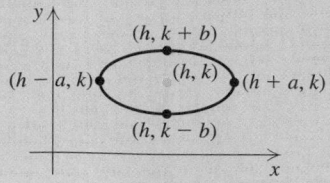

EXAMPLE **3**

Graph the ellipse

$$\frac{(x - 1)^2}{4} + \frac{(y + 5)^2}{9} = 1.$$

SOLUTION Note that

$$\frac{(x - 1)^2}{4} + \frac{(y + 5)^2}{9} = \frac{(x - 1)^2}{2^2} + \frac{(y + 5)^2}{3^2}.$$

Thus, $a = 2$ and $b = 3$. To determine the center of the ellipse, (h, k), note that

$$\frac{(x - 1)^2}{2^2} + \frac{(y + 5)^2}{3^2} = \frac{(x - 1)^2}{2^2} + \frac{(y - (-5))^2}{3^2}.$$

Thus the center is $(1, -5)$. We plot points 2 units to the left and right of center, as well as 3 units above and below center. These are the points $(3, -5)$, $(-1, -5)$, $(1, -2)$, and $(1, -8)$. The graph of the ellipse is shown at left.

Note that this ellipse is the same as the ellipse in Example 1 but translated 1 unit to the right and 5 units down.

TRY EXERCISE **27**

Ellipses have many applications. Communications satellites move in elliptical orbits with the earth as a focus while the earth itself follows an elliptical path around the sun. A medical instrument, the lithotripter, uses shock waves originating at one focus to crush a kidney stone located at the other focus.

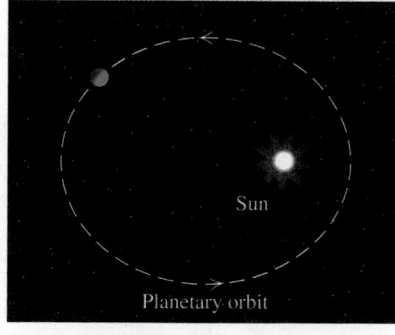

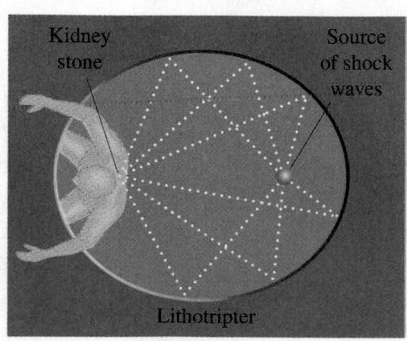

In some buildings, an ellipsoidal ceiling creates a "whispering gallery" in which a person at one focus can whisper and still be heard clearly at the other focus. This happens because sound waves coming from one focus are all reflected to the other focus. Similarly, light waves bouncing off an ellipsoidal mirror are used in a dentist's or surgeon's reflector light. The light source is located at one focus while the patient's mouth or surgical field is at the other.

TECHNOLOGY CONNECTION

To graph an ellipse on a graphing calculator, we solve for y and graph two functions.

To illustrate, let's check Example 2:

$$4x^2 + 25y^2 = 100$$
$$25y^2 = 100 - 4x^2$$
$$y^2 = 4 - \frac{4}{25}x^2$$
$$y = \pm\sqrt{4 - \frac{4}{25}x^2}.$$

Using a squared window, we have our check:

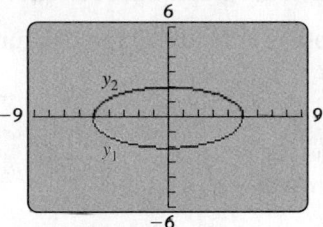

$$y_1 = -\sqrt{4 - \frac{4}{25}x^2}, \quad y_2 = \sqrt{4 - \frac{4}{25}x^2}$$

On many calculators, pressing (APPS) and selecting Conics and then Ellipse accesses a program in which equations in Standard Form can be graphed directly.

13.2   EXERCISE SET

 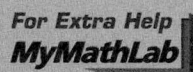

↩ **Concept Reinforcement** *Classify each statement as either true or false.*

1. The graph of $\dfrac{x^2}{25} + \dfrac{y^2}{50} = 1$ is a vertical ellipse.

2. The graph of $\dfrac{x^2}{30} + \dfrac{y^2}{20} = 1$ is a vertical ellipse.

3. The graph of $\dfrac{x^2}{25} - \dfrac{y^2}{9} = 1$ is a horizontal ellipse.

4. The graph of $\dfrac{-x^2}{20} + \dfrac{y^2}{16} = 1$ is a horizontal ellipse.

5. The graph of $\dfrac{x^2}{9} + \dfrac{y^2}{25} = 1$ includes the points $(-3, 0)$ and $(3, 0)$.

6. The graph of $\dfrac{x^2}{36} + \dfrac{y^2}{25} = 1$ includes the points $(0, -5)$ and $(0, 5)$.

7. The graph of $\dfrac{(x + 3)^2}{25} + \dfrac{(y - 2)^2}{36} = 1$ is an ellipse centered at $(-3, 2)$.

8. The graph of $\dfrac{(x - 2)^2}{49} + \dfrac{(y + 5)^2}{9} = 1$ is an ellipse centered at $(2, -5)$.

Graph each of the following equations.

9. $\dfrac{x^2}{1} + \dfrac{y^2}{4} = 1$

10. $\dfrac{x^2}{4} + \dfrac{y^2}{1} = 1$

11. $\dfrac{x^2}{25} + \dfrac{y^2}{9} = 1$

12. $\dfrac{x^2}{16} + \dfrac{y^2}{25} = 1$

13. $4x^2 + 9y^2 = 36$

14. $9x^2 + 4y^2 = 36$

15. $16x^2 + 9y^2 = 144$

16. $9x^2 + 16y^2 = 144$

17. $2x^2 + 3y^2 = 6$

18. $5x^2 + 7y^2 = 35$

Aha! 19. $5x^2 + 5y^2 = 125$

20. $8x^2 + 5y^2 = 80$

21. $3x^2 + 7y^2 - 63 = 0$

22. $3x^2 + 3y^2 - 48 = 0$

23. $16x^2 = 16 - y^2$

24. $9y^2 = 9 - x^2$

25. $16x^2 + 25y^2 = 1$

26. $9x^2 + 4y^2 = 1$

27. $\dfrac{(x - 3)^2}{9} + \dfrac{(y - 2)^2}{25} = 1$

28. $\dfrac{(x - 2)^2}{25} + \dfrac{(y - 4)^2}{9} = 1$

29. $\dfrac{(x + 4)^2}{16} + \dfrac{(y - 3)^2}{49} = 1$

30. $\dfrac{(x + 5)^2}{4} + \dfrac{(y - 2)^2}{36} = 1$

31. $12(x - 1)^2 + 3(y + 4)^2 = 48$
 (*Hint*: Divide both sides by 48.)

32. $4(x - 6)^2 + 9(y + 2)^2 = 36$

Aha! **33.** $4(x + 3)^2 + 4(y + 1)^2 - 10 = 90$

34. $9(x + 6)^2 + (y + 2)^2 - 20 = 61$

35. Explain how you can tell from the equation of an ellipse whether the graph will be horizontal or vertical.

36. Can an ellipse ever be the graph of a function? Why or why not?

Skill Review

Review solving equations.

Solve.

37. $x^2 - 5x + 3 = 0$ [11.2]   **38.** $\log_x 81 = 4$ [12.6]

39. $\dfrac{4}{x + 2} + \dfrac{3}{2x - 1} = 2$ [6.6]

40. $3 - \sqrt{2x - 1} = 1$ [10.6]

41. $x^2 = 11$ [11.1]   **42.** $x^2 + 4x = 60$ [5.7]

Synthesis

43. Explain how it is possible to recognize that the graph of $9x^2 + 18x + y^2 - 4y + 4 = 0$ is an ellipse.

44. As the foci get closer to the center of an ellipse, what shape does the graph begin to resemble? Explain why this happens.

Find an equation of an ellipse that contains the following points.

45. $(-9, 0), (9, 0), (0, -11)$, and $(0, 11)$

46. $(-7, 0), (7, 0), (0, -10)$, and $(0, 10)$

47. $(-2, -1), (6, -1), (2, -4)$, and $(2, 2)$

48. $(4, 3), (-6, 3), (-1, -1)$, and $(-1, 7)$

49. *Astronomy.* The maximum distance of the planet Mars from the sun is 2.48×10^8 mi. The minimum distance is 3.46×10^7 mi. The sun is at one focus of the elliptical orbit. Find the distance from the sun to the other focus.

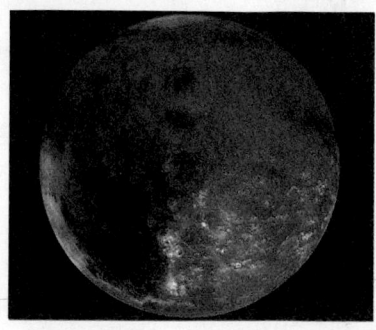

50. *Theatrical lighting.* The spotlight on a violin soloist casts an ellipse of light on the floor below her that is 6 ft wide and 10 ft long. Find an equation of that ellipse if the performer is in its center, x is the distance from the performer to the side of the ellipse, and y is the distance from the performer to the top of the ellipse.

51. Let $(-c, 0)$ and $(c, 0)$ be the foci of an ellipse. Any point $P(x, y)$ is on the ellipse if the sum of the distances from the foci to P is some constant. Use $2a$ to represent this constant.

a) Show that an equation for the ellipse is given by

$$\frac{x^2}{a^2} + \frac{y^2}{a^2 - c^2} = 1.$$

b) Substitute b^2 for $a^2 - c^2$ to get standard form.

52. *President's office.* The Oval Office of the President of the United States is an ellipse 31 ft wide and 38 ft long. Show in a sketch precisely where the President and an adviser could sit to best hear each other using the room's acoustics. (*Hint:* See Exercise 51(b) and the discussion following Example 3.)

53. *Dentistry.* The light source in some dental lamps shines against a reflector that is shaped like a portion of an ellipse in which the light source is

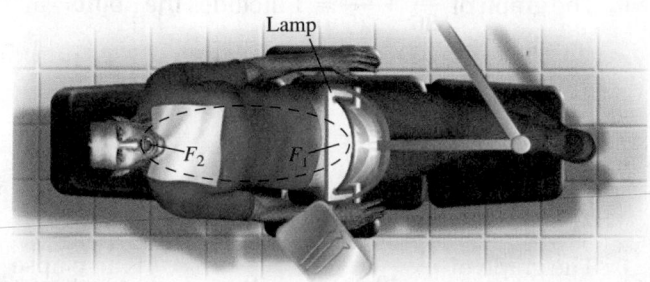

one focus of the ellipse. Reflected light enters a patient's mouth at the other focus of the ellipse. If the ellipse from which the reflector was formed is 2 ft wide and 6 ft long, how far should the patient's mouth be from the light source? (*Hint*: See Exercise 51(b).)

54. *Firefighting.*   The size and shape of certain forest fires can be approximated as the union of two "half-ellipses." For the blaze modeled below, the equation of the smaller ellipse—the part of the fire moving *into* the wind—is

$$\frac{x^2}{40{,}000} + \frac{y^2}{10{,}000} = 1.$$

The equation of the other ellipse—the part moving *with* the wind—is

$$\frac{x^2}{250{,}000} + \frac{y^2}{10{,}000} = 1.$$

Determine the width and the length of the fire.

Source for figure: "Predicting Wind-Driven Wild Land Fire Size and Shape," Hal E. Anderson, Research Paper INT-305, U.S. Department of Agriculture, Forest Service, February 1983

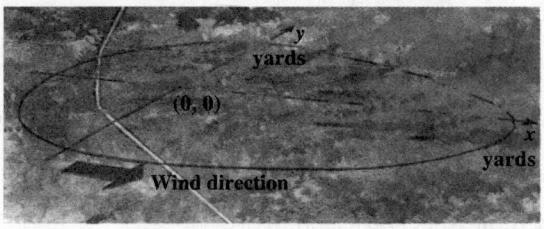

For each of the following equations, complete the square as needed and find an equivalent equation in standard form. Then graph the ellipse.

55. $x^2 - 4x + 4y^2 + 8y - 8 = 0$

56. $4x^2 + 24x + y^2 - 2y - 63 = 0$

57. Use a graphing calculator to check your answers to Exercises 11, 25, 29, and 33.

COLLABORATIVE CORNER

A Cosmic Path

Focus: Ellipses

Time: 20–30 minutes

Group size: 2

Materials: Scientific calculators

On May 4, 2007, Comet 17P/Holmes was at the point closest to the sun in its orbit. Comet 17P is traveling in an elliptical orbit with the sun as one focus, and one orbit takes about 6.88 yr. One astronomical unit (AU) is 93,000,000 mi. One group member should do the following calculations in AU and the other in millions of miles.

Source: Harvard-Smithsonian Center for Astrophysics

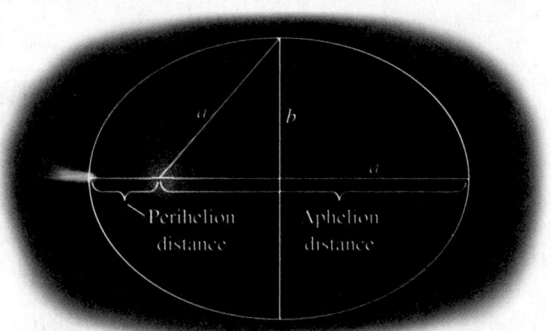

ACTIVITY

1. At its *perihelion*, a comet with an elliptical orbit is at the point in its orbit closest to the sun. At its *aphelion*, the comet is at the point farthest from the sun. The perihelion distance for Comet 17P is 2.053218 AU, and the aphelion distance is 5.183610 AU. Use these distances to find *a*. (See the following diagram.)

2. Using the figure above, express b^2 as a function of *a*. Then find *b* using the value found for *a* in part (1).

3. One formula for approximating the perimeter of an ellipse is

$$P = \pi\left(3a + 3b - \sqrt{(3a + b)(a + 3b)}\right),$$

developed by the Indian mathematician S. Ramanujan in 1914. How far does Comet 17P travel in one orbit?

4. What is the speed of the comet? Find the answer in AU per year and in miles per hour.

13.3 Conic Sections: Hyperbolas

Hyperbolas ▪ Hyperbolas (Nonstandard Form) ▪ Classifying Graphs of Equations

Hyperbolas

A **hyperbola** looks like a pair of parabolas, but the shapes are not quite parabolic. A hyperbola has two **vertices** and the line through the vertices is known as the **axis**. The point halfway between the vertices is called the **center**. The two curves that comprise a hyperbola are called **branches**.

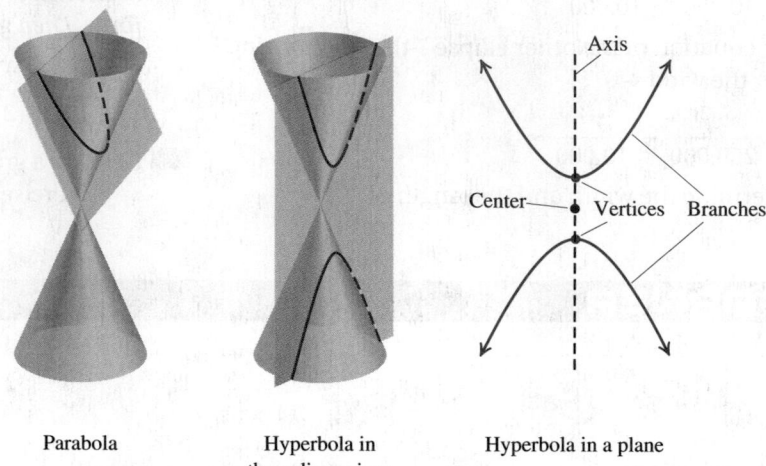

Parabola Hyperbola in three dimensions Hyperbola in a plane

Equation of a Hyperbola Centered at the Origin

A hyperbola with its center at the origin* has its equation as follows:

$$\frac{x^2}{a^2} - \frac{y^2}{b^2} = 1 \qquad \text{(Horizontal axis)};$$

$$\frac{y^2}{b^2} - \frac{x^2}{a^2} = 1 \qquad \text{(Vertical axis)}.$$

Note that both equations have 1 on the right-hand side and subtraction between the terms. For the discussion that follows, we assume $a, b > 0$.

To graph a hyperbola, it helps to begin by graphing two lines called **asymptotes**. Although the asymptotes themselves are not part of the graph, they serve as guidelines for an accurate sketch.

As a hyperbola gets farther away from the origin, it gets closer and closer to its asymptotes. The larger $|x|$ gets, the closer the graph gets to an asymptote. The asymptotes act to "constrain" the graph of a hyperbola. Parabolas are *not* constrained by any asymptotes.

───────────

*Hyperbolas with horizontal or vertical axes and centers *not* at the origin are discussed in Exercises 59–64.

Asymptotes of a Hyperbola

For hyperbolas with equations as shown below, the asymptotes are the lines

$$y = \frac{b}{a}x \quad \text{and} \quad y = -\frac{b}{a}x.$$

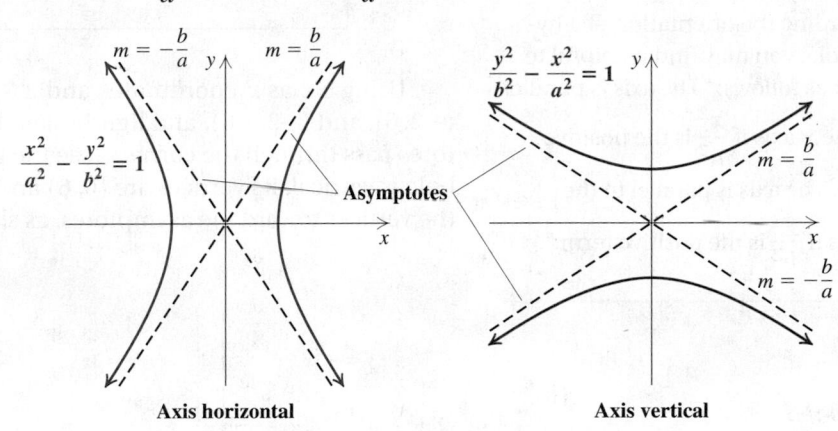

Axis horizontal   Axis vertical

In Section 13.2, we used a and b to determine the width and the length of an ellipse. For hyperbolas, a and b are used to determine the base and the height of a rectangle that can be used as an aid in sketching asymptotes and locating vertices. This is illustrated in the following example.

EXAMPLE **1**   Graph: $\dfrac{x^2}{4} - \dfrac{y^2}{9} = 1$.

SOLUTION   Note that

$$\frac{x^2}{4} - \frac{y^2}{9} = \frac{x^2}{2^2} - \frac{y^2}{3^2}, \qquad \text{Identifying } a \text{ and } b$$

so $a = 2$ and $b = 3$. The asymptotes are thus

$$y = \frac{3}{2}x \quad \text{and} \quad y = -\frac{3}{2}x.$$

To help us sketch asymptotes and locate vertices, we use a and b—in this case, 2 and 3—to form the pairs $(-2, 3)$, $(2, 3)$, $(2, -3)$, and $(-2, -3)$. We plot these pairs and lightly sketch a rectangle. The asymptotes pass through the corners and, since this is a horizontal hyperbola, the vertices are where the rectangle intersects the x-axis. Finally, we draw the hyperbola, as shown below.

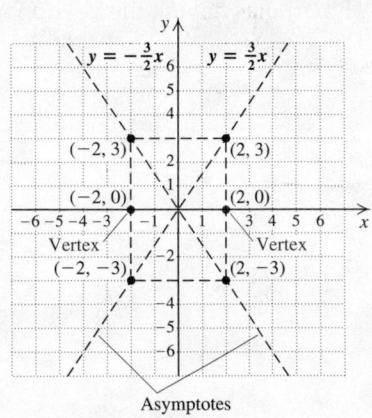

Asymptotes

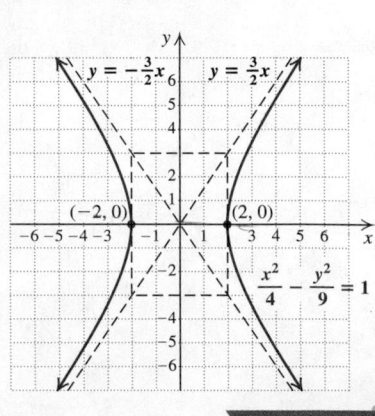

TRY EXERCISE 11

EXAMPLE 2

Graph: $\dfrac{y^2}{36} - \dfrac{x^2}{4} = 1$.

SOLUTION   Note that

$$\dfrac{y^2}{36} - \dfrac{x^2}{4} = \dfrac{y^2}{6^2} - \dfrac{x^2}{2^2} = 1.$$

> Whether the hyperbola is horizontal or vertical is determined by which term is nonnegative. Here the y^2-term is nonnegative, so the hyperbola is vertical.

Using ± 2 as x-coordinates and ± 6 as y-coordinates, we plot $(2, 6)$, $(2, -6)$, $(-2, 6)$, and $(-2, -6)$, and lightly sketch a rectangle through them. The asymptotes pass through the corners (see the figure on the left below). Since the hyperbola is vertical, its vertices are $(0, 6)$ and $(0, -6)$. Finally, we draw curves through the vertices toward the asymptotes, as shown below.

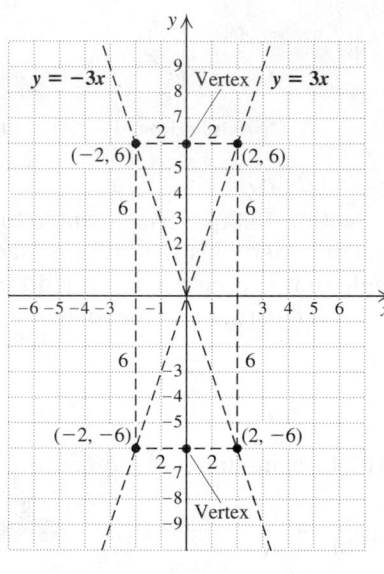
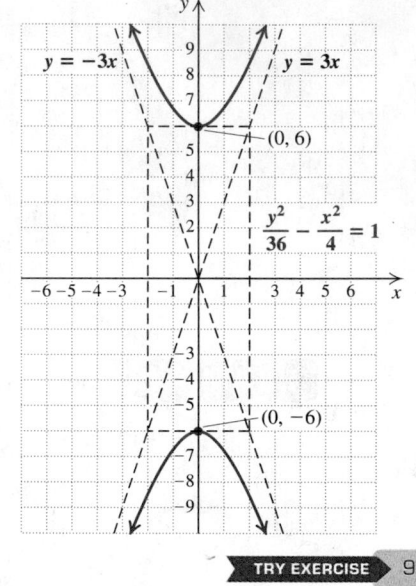

TRY EXERCISE ▶ 9

Hyperbolas (Nonstandard Form)

The equations for hyperbolas just examined are the standard ones, but there are other hyperbolas. We consider some of them.

> ### Equation of a Hyperbola in Nonstandard Form
>
> Hyperbolas having the x- and y-axes as asymptotes have equations as follows:
>
> $$xy = c, \quad \text{where } c \text{ is a nonzero constant.}$$

EXAMPLE 3   Graph: $xy = -8$.

SOLUTION   We first solve for y:

$$y = -\frac{8}{x}.$$ Dividing both sides by x. Note that $x \neq 0$.

Next, we find some solutions and form a table. Note that x cannot be 0 and that for large values of $|x|$, the value of y is close to 0. Thus the x- and y-axes serve as asymptotes. We plot the points and draw two curves.

x	y
2	-4
-2	4
4	-2
-4	2
1	-8
-1	8
8	-1
-8	1

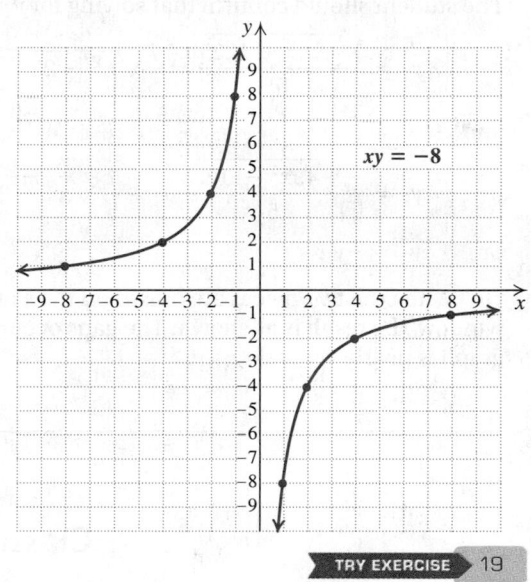

$xy = -8$

TRY EXERCISE 19

Hyperbolas have many applications. A jet breaking the sound barrier creates a sonic boom with a wave front the shape of a cone. The intersection of the cone with the ground is one branch of a hyperbola. Some comets travel in hyperbolic orbits, and a cross section of many lenses is hyperbolic in shape.

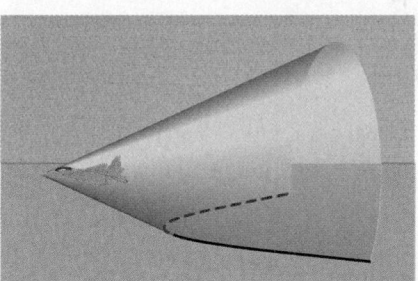

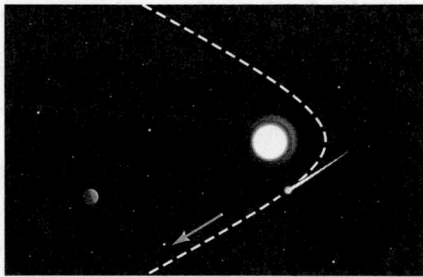

TECHNOLOGY CONNECTION

The procedure used to graph a hyperbola in standard form is similar to that used to draw a circle or an ellipse. Consider the graph of

$$\frac{x^2}{25} - \frac{y^2}{49} = 1.$$

The student should confirm that solving for y yields

$$y_1 = \frac{\sqrt{49x^2 - 1225}}{5} = \frac{7}{5}\sqrt{x^2 - 25}$$

and

$$y_2 = \frac{-\sqrt{49x^2 - 1225}}{5} = -\frac{7}{5}\sqrt{x^2 - 25},$$

or $y_2 = -y_1.$

When the two pieces are drawn on the same squared window, the result is as shown. The gaps occur where the graph is nearly vertical.

$$y_1 = \frac{7}{5}\sqrt{x^2 - 25},$$
$$y_2 = -\frac{7}{5}\sqrt{x^2 - 25}$$

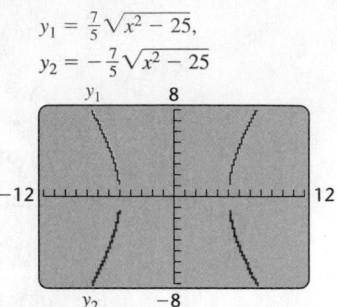

On many calculators, pressing **APPS** and selecting Conics and then Hyperbola accesses a program in which hyperbolas in standard form can be graphed directly. Graph each of the following.

1. $\dfrac{x^2}{16} - \dfrac{y^2}{60} = 1$ **2.** $16x^2 - 3y^2 = 64$

3. $\dfrac{y^2}{20} - \dfrac{x^2}{64} = 1$ **4.** $45y^2 - 9x^2 = 441$

Classifying Graphs of Equations

By writing an equation of a conic section in a standard form, we can classify its graph as a parabola, a circle, an ellipse, or a hyperbola. Every conic section can also be represented by an equation of the form

$$Ax^2 + By^2 + Cxy + Dx + Ey + F = 0.$$

We can also classify graphs using values of A and B.

Graph	Standard Form		$Ax^2 + By^2 + Cxy + Dx + Ey + F = 0$
Parabola	$y = ax^2 + bx + c$;	Vertical parabola	Either $A = 0$ or $B = 0$, but not both.
	$x = ay^2 + by + c$	Horizontal parabola	
Circle	$x^2 + y^2 = r^2$;	Center at the origin	$A = B$
	$(x - h)^2 + (y - k)^2 = r^2$	Center at (h, k)	
Ellipse	$\dfrac{x^2}{a^2} + \dfrac{y^2}{b^2} = 1$;	Center at the origin	$A \neq B$, and A and B have the same sign.
	$\dfrac{(x - h)^2}{a^2} + \dfrac{(y - k)^2}{b^2} = 1$	Center at (h, k)	
Hyperbola	$\dfrac{x^2}{a^2} - \dfrac{y^2}{b^2} = 1$;	Horizontal hyperbola	A and B have opposite signs.
	$\dfrac{y^2}{b^2} - \dfrac{x^2}{a^2} = 1$	Vertical hyperbola	
	$xy = c$	Asymptotes are axes	Only C and F are nonzero.

Algebraic manipulations may be needed to express an equation in one of the preceding forms.

EXAMPLE 4   Classify the graph of each equation as a circle, an ellipse, a parabola, or a hyperbola. Refer to the above table as needed.

a) $5x^2 = 20 - 5y^2$ **b)** $x + 3 + 8y = y^2$

c) $x^2 = y^2 + 4$ **d)** $x^2 = 16 - 4y^2$

SOLUTION

a) We get the terms with variables on one side by adding $5y^2$ to both sides:

$$5x^2 + 5y^2 = 20.$$

Since x and y are *both* squared, we do not have a parabola. The fact that the squared terms are *added* tells us that we do not have a hyperbola. Do we have a circle? We factor the 5 out of both terms on the left and then divide by 5:

$$5(x^2 + y^2) = 20 \qquad \text{Factoring out 5}$$
$$x^2 + y^2 = 4 \qquad \text{Dividing both sides by 5}$$
$$x^2 + y^2 = 2^2. \qquad \text{This is an equation for a circle.}$$

We see that the graph is a circle centered at the origin with radius 2.

We can also write the equation in the form

$$5x^2 + 5y^2 - 20 = 0. \qquad A = 5, B = 5$$

Since $A = B$, the graph is a circle.

b) The equation $x + 3 + 8y = y^2$ has only one variable that is squared, so we solve for the other variable:

$$x = y^2 - 8y - 3. \qquad \text{This is an equation for a parabola.}$$

The graph is a horizontal parabola that opens to the right.

We can also write the equation in the form

$$y^2 - x - 8y - 3 = 0. \qquad A = 0, B = 1$$

Since $A = 0$ and $B \neq 0$, the graph is a parabola.

c) In $x^2 = y^2 + 4$, both variables are squared, so the graph is not a parabola. We subtract y^2 on both sides and divide by 4 to obtain

$$\frac{x^2}{2^2} - \frac{y^2}{2^2} = 1. \qquad \text{This is an equation for a hyperbola.}$$

The minus sign here indicates that the graph is a hyperbola. Because it is the x^2-term that is nonnegative, the hyperbola is horizontal.

We can also write the equation in the form

$$x^2 - y^2 - 4 = 0. \qquad A = 1, B = -1$$

Since A and B have opposite signs, the graph is a hyperbola.

d) In $x^2 = 16 - 4y^2$, both variables are squared, so the graph cannot be a parabola. We obtain the following equivalent equation:

$$x^2 + 4y^2 = 16. \qquad \text{Adding } 4y^2 \text{ to both sides}$$

If the coefficients of the terms were the same, we would have the graph of a circle, as in part (a), but they are not. Dividing both sides by 16 yields

$$\frac{x^2}{16} + \frac{y^2}{4} = 1.$$ This is an equation for an ellipse.

The graph of this equation is a horizontal ellipse.
We can also write the equation in the form

$$x^2 + 4y^2 - 16 = 0.$$ $A = 1, B = 4$

Since $A \neq B$ and both A and B are positive, the graph is an ellipse.

TRY EXERCISES ▶ 27 and 29

13.3   EXERCISE SET

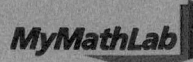   

🖐 **Concept Reinforcement**   *In each of Exercises 1–8, match the conic section with the equation in the column on the right that represents that type of conic section.*

1. ____ A hyperbola with a horizontal axis

2. ____ A hyperbola with a vertical axis

3. ____ An ellipse with its center not at the origin

4. ____ An ellipse with its center at the origin

5. ____ A circle with its center at the origin

6. ____ A circle with its center not at the origin

7. ____ A parabola opening upward or downward

8. ____ A parabola opening to the right or left

a) $\dfrac{x^2}{10} + \dfrac{y^2}{12} = 1$

b) $(x + 1)^2 + (y - 3)^2 = 30$

c) $y - x^2 = 5$

d) $\dfrac{x^2}{9} - \dfrac{y^2}{10} = 1$

e) $x - 2y^2 = 3$

f) $\dfrac{y^2}{20} - \dfrac{x^2}{35} = 1$

g) $3x^2 + 3y^2 = 75$

h) $\dfrac{(x - 1)^2}{10} + \dfrac{(y - 4)^2}{8} = 1$

Graph each hyperbola. Label all vertices and sketch all asymptotes.

9. $\dfrac{y^2}{16} - \dfrac{x^2}{16} = 1$ **10.** $\dfrac{x^2}{9} - \dfrac{y^2}{9} = 1$

11. $\dfrac{x^2}{4} - \dfrac{y^2}{25} = 1$ **12.** $\dfrac{y^2}{16} - \dfrac{x^2}{9} = 1$

13. $\dfrac{y^2}{36} - \dfrac{x^2}{9} = 1$ **14.** $\dfrac{x^2}{25} - \dfrac{y^2}{36} = 1$

15. $y^2 - x^2 = 25$ **16.** $x^2 - y^2 = 4$

17. $25x^2 - 16y^2 = 400$ **18.** $4y^2 - 9x^2 = 36$

Graph.

19. $xy = -6$ **20.** $xy = 8$

21. $xy = 4$ **22.** $xy = -9$

23. $xy = -2$ **24.** $xy = -1$

25. $xy = 1$ **26.** $xy = 2$

Classify each of the following as the equation of a circle, an ellipse, a parabola, or a hyperbola.

27. $x^2 + y^2 - 6x + 10y - 40 = 0$

28. $y - 4 = 2x^2$

29. $9x^2 + 4y^2 - 36 = 0$

30. $x + 3y = 2y^2 - 1$

31. $4x^2 - 9y^2 - 72 = 0$

32. $y^2 + x^2 = 8$

33. $y^2 = 20 - x^2$

34. $2y + 13 + x^2 = 8x - y^2$

35. $x - 10 = y^2 - 6y$

36. $y = \dfrac{5}{x}$

37. $x - \dfrac{3}{y} = 0$

38. $9x^2 = 9 - y^2$

39. $y + 6x = x^2 + 5$

40. $x^2 = 49 + y^2$

41. $25y^2 = 100 + 4x^2$

42. $3x^2 + 5y^2 + x^2 = y^2 + 49$

43. $3x^2 + y^2 - x = 2x^2 - 9x + 10y + 40$

44. $4y^2 + 20x^2 + 1 = 8y - 5x^2$

45. $16x^2 + 5y^2 - 12x^2 + 8y^2 - 3x + 4y = 568$

46. $56x^2 - 17y^2 = 234 - 13x^2 - 38y^2$

47. Explain how the equation of a hyperbola differs from the equation of an ellipse.

48. Is it possible for a hyperbola to represent the graph of a function? Why or why not?

Skill Review

To prepare for Section 13.4, review solving systems of equations and solving quadratic equations (Sections 8.2 and 11.2).

Solve.

49. $5x + 2y = -3,$
  $2x + 3y = 12$ [8.2]

50. $4x - 2y = 5,$
  $3x + 5y = -6$ [8.2]

51. $\frac{3}{4}x^2 + x^2 = 7$ [11.2]

52. $3x^2 + 10x - 8 = 0$ [11.2]

53. $x^2 - 3x - 1 = 0$ [11.2]

54. $x^2 + \dfrac{25}{x^2} = 26$ [11.5]

Synthesis

55. What is it in the equation of a hyperbola that controls how wide open the branches are? Explain your reasoning.

56. If, in
$$\frac{x^2}{a^2} - \frac{y^2}{b^2} = 1,$$
$a = b$, what are the asymptotes of the graph? Why?

Find an equation of a hyperbola satisfying the given conditions.

57. Having intercepts $(0, 6)$ and $(0, -6)$ and asymptotes $y = 3x$ and $y = -3x$

58. Having intercepts $(8, 0)$ and $(-8, 0)$ and asymptotes $y = 4x$ and $y = -4x$

The standard form for equations of horizontal or vertical hyperbolas centered at (h, k) are as follows:

$$\frac{(x - h)^2}{a^2} - \frac{(y - k)^2}{b^2} = 1$$

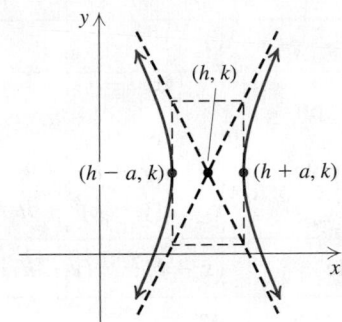

$$\frac{(y - k)^2}{b^2} - \frac{(x - h)^2}{a^2} = 1$$

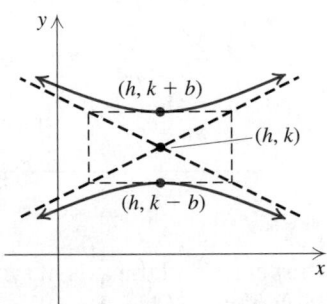

The vertices are as labeled and the asymptotes are

$$y - k = \frac{b}{a}(x - h) \quad \text{and} \quad y - k = -\frac{b}{a}(x - h).$$

For each of the following equations of hyperbolas, complete the square, if necessary, and write in standard form. Find the center, the vertices, and the asymptotes. Then graph the hyperbola.

59. $\dfrac{(x - 5)^2}{36} - \dfrac{(y - 2)^2}{25} = 1$

60. $\dfrac{(x - 2)^2}{9} - \dfrac{(y - 1)^2}{4} = 1$

61. $8(y + 3)^2 - 2(x - 4)^2 = 32$

62. $25(x - 4)^2 - 4(y + 5)^2 = 100$

63. $4x^2 - y^2 + 24x + 4y + 28 = 0$

64. $4y^2 - 25x^2 - 8y - 100x - 196 = 0$

65. Use a graphing calculator to check your answers to Exercises 13, 25, 31, and 59.

CONNECTING the CONCEPTS

When graphing equations of conic sections, it is usually helpful to first determine what type of graph the equation represents. We then find the coordinates of key points and equations of lines that determine the shape and the location of the graph.

Graph	Equation	Key Points	Equations of Lines
Parabola	$y = a(x - h)^2 + k$ $x = a(y - k)^2 + h$	Vertex: (h, k) Vertex: (h, k)	Axis of symmetry: $x = h$ Axis of symmetry: $y = k$
Circle	$(x - h)^2 + (y - k)^2 = r^2$	Center: (h, k)	
Ellipse	$\dfrac{x^2}{a^2} + \dfrac{y^2}{b^2} = 1$	x-intercepts: $(-a, 0), (a, 0)$; y-intercepts: $(0, -b), (0, b)$	
Hyperbola	$\dfrac{x^2}{a^2} - \dfrac{y^2}{b^2} = 1$ $\dfrac{y^2}{b^2} - \dfrac{x^2}{a^2} = 1$	Vertices: $(-a, 0), (a, 0)$ Vertices: $(0, -b), (0, b)$	Asymptotes (for both equations): $y = \dfrac{b}{a}x, y = -\dfrac{b}{a}x$
	$xy = c$		Asymptotes: $x = 0, y = 0$

MIXED REVIEW

1. Find the vertex and the axis of symmetry of the graph of $y = 3(x - 4)^2 + 1$.

2. Find the vertex and the axis of symmetry of the graph of $x = y^2 + 2y + 3$.

3. Find the center of the graph of $(x - 3)^2 + (y - 2)^2 = 5$.

4. Find the center of the graph of $x^2 + 6x + y^2 + 10y = 12$.

5. Find the x-intercepts and the y-intercepts of the graph of $\dfrac{x^2}{144} + \dfrac{y^2}{81} = 1$.

6. Find the vertices of the graph of $\dfrac{x^2}{9} - \dfrac{y^2}{121} = 1$.

7. Find the vertices of the graph of $4y^2 - x^2 = 4$.

8. Find the asymptotes of the graph of $\dfrac{y^2}{9} - \dfrac{x^2}{4} = 1$.

Classify each of the following as the graph of a parabola, a circle, an ellipse, or a hyperbola. Then graph.

9. $x^2 + y^2 = 36$

10. $y = x^2 - 5$

11. $\dfrac{x^2}{25} + \dfrac{y^2}{49} = 1$

12. $\dfrac{x^2}{25} - \dfrac{y^2}{49} = 1$

13. $x = (y + 3)^2 + 2$

14. $4x^2 + 9y^2 = 36$

15. $xy = -4$

16. $(x + 2)^2 + (y - 3)^2 = 1$

17. $x^2 + y^2 - 8y - 20 = 0$

18. $x = y^2 + 2y$

19. $16y^2 - x^2 = 16$

20. $x = \dfrac{9}{y}$

13.4	**Nonlinear Systems of Equations**

Systems Involving One Nonlinear Equation ▪ Systems of Two Nonlinear Equations ▪ Problem Solving

The equations appearing in systems of two equations have thus far in our discussion always been linear. We now consider systems of two equations in which at least one equation is nonlinear.

Systems Involving One Nonlinear Equation

Suppose that a system consists of an equation of a circle and an equation of a line. In what ways can the circle and the line intersect? The figures below represent three ways in which the situation can occur. We see that such a system will have 0, 1, or 2 real solutions.

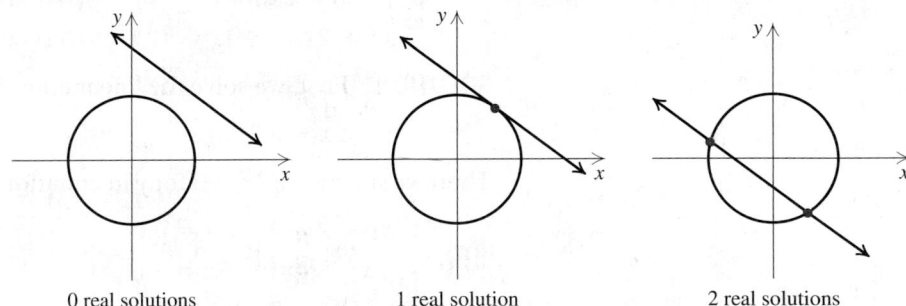

0 real solutions	1 real solution	2 real solutions

Recall that graphing, *elimination*, and *substitution* were all used to solve systems of linear equations. To solve systems in which one equation is of first degree and one is of second degree, it is preferable to use the *substitution* method.

EXAMPLE **1**

Solve the system

$$x^2 + y^2 = 25, \quad (1) \qquad \text{(The graph is a circle.)}$$
$$3x - 4y = 0. \quad (2) \qquad \text{(The graph is a line.)}$$

SOLUTION   First, we solve the linear equation, (2), for x:

$$x = \tfrac{4}{3}y. \quad (3) \qquad \text{We could have solved for } y \text{ instead.}$$

Then we substitute $\tfrac{4}{3}y$ for x in equation (1) and solve for y:

$$\left(\tfrac{4}{3}y\right)^2 + y^2 = 25$$
$$\tfrac{16}{9}y^2 + y^2 = 25$$
$$\tfrac{25}{9}y^2 = 25$$
$$y^2 = 9 \qquad \text{Multiplying both sides by } \tfrac{9}{25}$$
$$y = \pm 3. \qquad \text{Using the principle of square roots}$$

Now we substitute these numbers for y in equation (3) and solve for x:

for $y = 3$, $x = \tfrac{4}{3}(3) = 4$;   The ordered pair is $(4, 3)$.
for $y = -3$, $x = \tfrac{4}{3}(-3) = -4$.   The ordered pair is $(-4, -3)$.

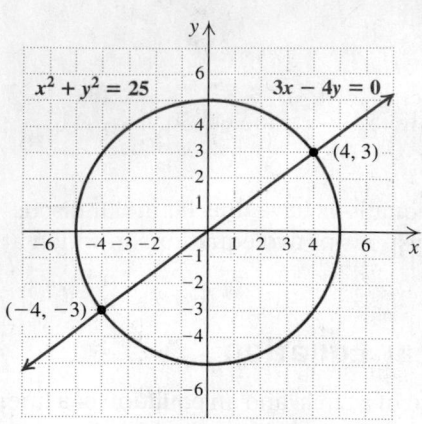

$x^2 + y^2 = 25$ $3x - 4y = 0$

$(4, 3)$

$(-4, -3)$

Check: For $(4, 3)$:

$$\begin{array}{c|c} x^2 + y^2 = 25 \\ \hline 4^2 + 3^2 & 25 \\ 16 + 9 & \\ 25 \stackrel{?}{=} 25 & \text{TRUE} \end{array} \qquad \begin{array}{c|c} 3x - 4y = 0 \\ \hline 3(4) - 4(3) & 0 \\ 12 - 12 & \\ 0 \stackrel{?}{=} 0 & \text{TRUE} \end{array}$$

It is left to the student to confirm that $(-4, -3)$ also checks in both equations. The pairs $(4, 3)$ and $(-4, -3)$ check, so they are solutions. The graph at left serves as a check. Intersections occur at $(4, 3)$ and $(-4, -3)$.

TRY EXERCISE 7

Even if we do not know what the graph of each equation in a system looks like, the algebraic approach of Example 1 can still be used.

EXAMPLE 2   Solve the system

$$\begin{array}{ll} y + 3 = 2x, & (1) \quad \text{(A first-degree equation)} \\ x^2 + 2xy = -1. & (2) \quad \text{(A second-degree equation)} \end{array}$$

SOLUTION   First, we solve the linear equation (1) for y:

$$y = 2x - 3. \quad (3)$$

Then we substitute $2x - 3$ for y in equation (2) and solve for x:

$$\begin{aligned} x^2 + 2x(2x - 3) &= -1 \\ x^2 + 4x^2 - 6x &= -1 \\ 5x^2 - 6x + 1 &= 0 \\ (5x - 1)(x - 1) &= 0 \qquad \text{Factoring} \\ 5x - 1 = 0 \quad &or \quad x - 1 = 0 \qquad \begin{array}{l} \text{Using the principle of} \\ \text{zero products} \end{array} \\ x = \tfrac{1}{5} \quad &or \qquad x = 1. \end{aligned}$$

Now we substitute these numbers for x in equation (3) and solve for y:

for $x = \tfrac{1}{5}$, $y = 2\left(\tfrac{1}{5}\right) - 3 = -\tfrac{13}{5}$;   The ordered pair is $\left(\tfrac{1}{5}, -\tfrac{13}{5}\right)$.

for $x = 1$, $y = 2(1) - 3 = -1$.   The ordered pair is $(1, -1)$.

You can confirm that $\left(\tfrac{1}{5}, -\tfrac{13}{5}\right)$ and $(1, -1)$ check, so they are both solutions.

TRY EXERCISE 13

EXAMPLE 3   Solve the system

$$\begin{array}{ll} x + y = 5, & (1) \quad \text{(The graph is a line.)} \\ y = 3 - x^2. & (2) \quad \text{(The graph is a parabola.)} \end{array}$$

SOLUTION   We substitute $3 - x^2$ for y in the first equation:

$$\begin{aligned} x + 3 - x^2 &= 5 \\ -x^2 + x - 2 &= 0 \qquad \text{Adding } -5 \text{ to both sides and rearranging} \\ x^2 - x + 2 &= 0. \qquad \text{Multiplying both sides by } -1 \end{aligned}$$

Real-number solutions of systems of equations can be found using the INTERSECT option of CALC.

To solve Example 2,

$$y + 3 = 2x,$$
$$x^2 + 2xy = -1,$$

we solve each equation for y and then graph:

$$\left. \begin{array}{l} y_1 = 2x - 3, \\ y_2 = \dfrac{-1 - x^2}{2x}. \end{array} \right\} \quad \begin{array}{l} \text{Note that} \\ x, y \neq 0. \end{array}$$

$y_1 = 2x - 3, \quad y_2 = \dfrac{-1 - x^2}{2x}$

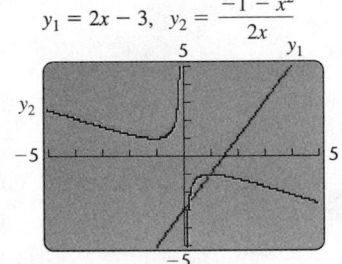

Using INTERSECT, we find the solutions to be $(0.2, -2.6)$ and $(1, -1)$.

Solve each system. Round all values to two decimal places.

1. $\quad 4xy - 7 = 0,$
   $\quad x - 3y - 2 = 0$
2. $\quad x^2 + y^2 = 14,$
   $\quad 16x + 7y^2 = 0$

Since $x^2 - x + 2$ does not factor, we need the quadratic formula:

$$x = \frac{-b \pm \sqrt{b^2 - 4ac}}{2a}$$

$$= \frac{-(-1) \pm \sqrt{(-1)^2 - 4 \cdot 1 \cdot 2}}{2(1)} \quad \text{Substituting}$$

$$= \frac{1 \pm \sqrt{1 - 8}}{2} = \frac{1 \pm \sqrt{-7}}{2} = \frac{1}{2} \pm \frac{\sqrt{7}}{2}i.$$

Solving equation (1) for y gives us $y = 5 - x$. Substituting values for x gives

$$y = 5 - \left(\frac{1}{2} + \frac{\sqrt{7}}{2}i \right) = \frac{9}{2} - \frac{\sqrt{7}}{2}i \quad \text{and}$$

$$y = 5 - \left(\frac{1}{2} - \frac{\sqrt{7}}{2}i \right) = \frac{9}{2} + \frac{\sqrt{7}}{2}i.$$

The solutions are

$$\left(\frac{1}{2} + \frac{\sqrt{7}}{2}i, \frac{9}{2} - \frac{\sqrt{7}}{2}i \right) \quad \text{and} \quad \left(\frac{1}{2} - \frac{\sqrt{7}}{2}i, \frac{9}{2} + \frac{\sqrt{7}}{2}i \right).$$

There are no real-number solutions. Note in the figure at right that the graphs do not intersect. Getting only nonreal solutions tells us that the graphs do not intersect.

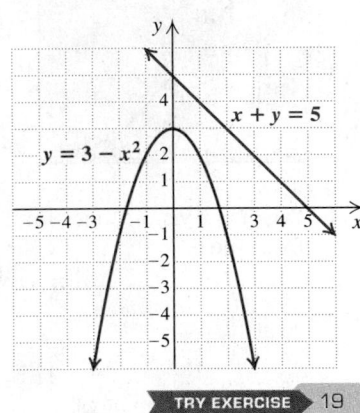

TRY EXERCISE 19

Systems of Two Nonlinear Equations

We now consider systems of two second-degree equations. Graphs of such systems can involve any two conic sections. The following figure shows some ways in which a circle and a hyperbola can intersect.

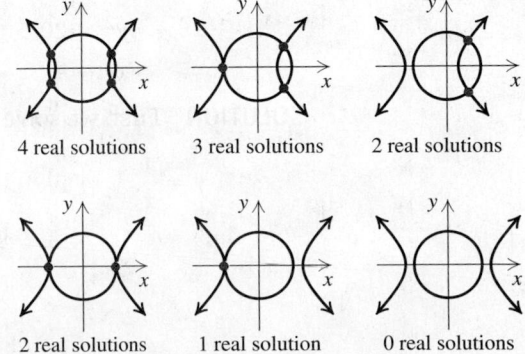

To solve systems of two second-degree equations, we either substitute or eliminate. The elimination method is generally better when both equations are of the form $Ax^2 + By^2 = C$. Then we can eliminate an x^2-term or a y^2-term in a manner similar to the procedure used in Chapter 8.

EXAMPLE 4

Solve the system

$$2x^2 + 5y^2 = 22, \quad (1) \quad \text{(The graph is an ellipse.)}$$
$$3x^2 - y^2 = -1. \quad (2) \quad \text{(The graph is a hyperbola.)}$$

SOLUTION Here we multiply equation (2) by 5 and then add:

$$
\begin{array}{ll}
2x^2 + 5y^2 = 22 & \\
\underline{15x^2 - 5y^2 = -5} & \text{Multiplying both sides of equation (2) by 5} \\
17x^2 \quad\quad = 17 & \text{Adding} \\
\quad\quad x^2 = 1 & \\
\quad\quad x = \pm 1. &
\end{array}
$$

There is no x-term, and whether x is -1 or 1, we have $x^2 = 1$. Thus we can simultaneously substitute 1 and -1 for x in equation (2):

$$
\left.
\begin{array}{l}
3 \cdot (\pm 1)^2 - y^2 = -1 \\
3 - y^2 = -1 \\
-y^2 = -4 \\
\end{array}
\right\}
\quad
\begin{array}{l}
\text{Since } (-1)^2 = 1^2, \text{ we can evaluate for} \\
x = -1 \text{ and } x = 1 \text{ simultaneously.}
\end{array}
$$

$$y^2 = 4 \quad \text{or} \quad y = \pm 2.$$

Thus, if $x = 1$, then $y = 2$ or $y = -2$; and if $x = -1$, then $y = 2$ or $y = -2$. The four possible solutions are $(1, 2)$, $(1, -2)$, $(-1, 2)$, and $(-1, -2)$.

Check: Since $(2)^2 = (-2)^2$ and $(1)^2 = (-1)^2$, we can check all four pairs at once.

$$
\begin{array}{c|c}
\multicolumn{2}{c}{2x^2 + 5y^2 = 22} \\
\hline
2(\pm 1)^2 + 5(\pm 2)^2 & 22 \\
2 + 20 & \\
22 \overset{?}{=} 22 & \text{TRUE}
\end{array}
\qquad
\begin{array}{c|c}
\multicolumn{2}{c}{3x^2 - y^2 = -1} \\
\hline
3(\pm 1)^2 - (\pm 2)^2 & -1 \\
3 - 4 & \\
-1 \overset{?}{=} -1 & \text{TRUE}
\end{array}
$$

The solutions are $(1, 2)$, $(1, -2)$, $(-1, 2)$, and $(-1, -2)$. **TRY EXERCISE** ▶ 29

When a product of variables is in one equation and the other equation is of the form $Ax^2 + By^2 = C$, we often solve for a variable in the equation with the product and then use substitution.

EXAMPLE 5

Solve the system

$$x^2 + 4y^2 = 20, \quad (1) \quad \text{(The graph is an ellipse.)}$$
$$xy = 4. \quad (2) \quad \text{(The graph is a hyperbola.)}$$

SOLUTION First, we solve equation (2) for y:

$$y = \frac{4}{x}. \quad \text{Dividing both sides by } x. \text{ Note that } x \neq 0.$$

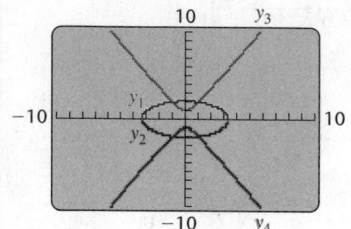

Then we substitute $4/x$ for y in equation (1) and solve for x:

$$x^2 + 4\left(\frac{4}{x}\right)^2 = 20$$

$$x^2 + \frac{64}{x^2} = 20$$

$$x^4 + 64 = 20x^2 \qquad \text{Multiplying by } x^2$$

$$x^4 - 20x^2 + 64 = 0 \qquad \text{Obtaining standard form. This equation is reducible to quadratic.}$$

$$(x^2 - 4)(x^2 - 16) = 0 \qquad \text{Factoring. If you prefer, let } u = x^2 \text{ and substitute.}$$

$$(x - 2)(x + 2)(x - 4)(x + 4) = 0 \qquad \text{Factoring again}$$

$$x = 2 \quad or \quad x = -2 \quad or \quad x = 4 \quad or \quad x = -4. \qquad \text{Using the principle of zero products}$$

Since $y = 4/x$, for $x = 2$, we have $y = 4/2$, or 2. Thus, $(2, 2)$ is a solution. Similarly, $(-2, -2)$, $(4, 1)$, and $(-4, -1)$ are solutions. You can show that all four pairs check.

TRY EXERCISE 37

Problem Solving

We now consider applications that can be modeled by a system of equations in which at least one equation is not linear.

EXAMPLE 6

Architecture.   For a college fitness center, an architect wants to lay out a rectangular piece of land that has a perimeter of 204 m and an area of 2565 m². Find the dimensions of the piece of land.

SOLUTION

1. **Familiarize.** We draw and label a sketch, letting $l =$ the length and $w =$ the width, both in meters.

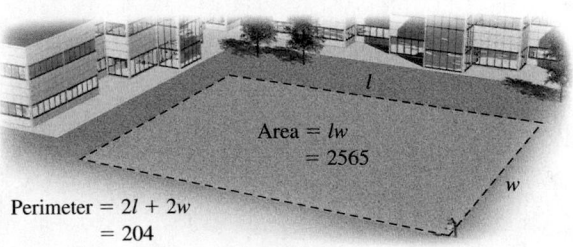

Area = lw
= 2565

Perimeter = $2l + 2w$
= 204

2. **Translate.** We then have the following translation:

Perimeter: $2w + 2l = 204$;

Area: $lw = 2565$.

3. **Carry out.** We solve the system

$$2w + 2l = 204,$$

$$lw = 2565.$$

Solving the second equation for l gives us $l = 2565/w$. Then we substitute $2565/w$ for l in the first equation and solve for w:

$$2w + 2\left(\frac{2565}{w}\right) = 204$$

$$2w^2 + 2(2565) = 204w \qquad \text{Multiplying both sides by } w$$

$$2w^2 - 204w + 2(2565) = 0 \qquad \text{Standard form}$$

$$w^2 - 102w + 2565 = 0 \qquad \text{Multiplying by } \tfrac{1}{2}$$

> Factoring could be used instead of the quadratic formula, but the numbers are quite large.

$$w = \frac{-(-102) \pm \sqrt{(-102)^2 - 4 \cdot 1 \cdot 2565}}{2 \cdot 1}$$

$$w = \frac{102 \pm \sqrt{144}}{2} = \frac{102 \pm 12}{2}$$

$$w = 57 \quad or \quad w = 45.$$

If $w = 57$, then $l = 2565/w = 2565/57 = 45$. If $w = 45$, then $l = 2565/w = 2565/45 = 57$. Since length is usually considered to be longer than width, we have the solution $l = 57$ and $w = 45$, or $(57, 45)$.

4. **Check.** If $l = 57$ and $w = 45$, the perimeter is $2 \cdot 57 + 2 \cdot 45$, or 204. The area is $57 \cdot 45$, or 2565. The numbers check.

5. **State.** The length is 57 m and the width is 45 m.

▶ **TRY EXERCISE** ▸ 47

EXAMPLE 7   *Laptop dimensions.*   The screen on Tara's new laptop has an area of 90 in^2 and a $\sqrt{200.25}$-in. diagonal. Find the width and the length of the screen.

SOLUTION

1. **Familiarize.** We make a drawing and label it. Note that the width, the length, and the diagonal form a right triangle. We let $l =$ the length and $w =$ the width, both in inches.

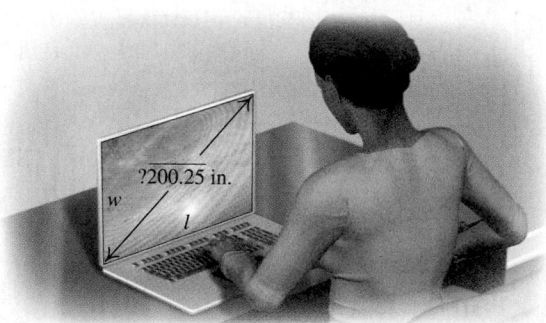

2. **Translate.** We translate to a system of equations:

$$l^2 + w^2 = (\sqrt{200.25})^2, \qquad \text{Using the Pythagorean theorem}$$

$$lw = 90. \qquad \text{Using the formula for the area of a rectangle}$$

3. **Carry out.** We solve the system

$$\left.\begin{array}{l} l^2 + w^2 = (\sqrt{200.25})^2, \\ lw = 90. \end{array}\right\} \quad \begin{array}{l} \text{You should complete the solution of} \\ \text{this system.} \end{array}$$

We get $(12, 7.5)$, $(7.5, 12)$, $(-12, -7.5)$, and $(-7.5, -12)$.

4. **Check.** Since measurements must be positive and length is usually greater than width, we check only $(12, 7.5)$. In the right triangle, $12^2 + 7.5^2 = 144 + 56.25 = 200.25$. The area is $12(7.5) = 90$, so our answer checks.

5. **State.** The length is 12 in. and the width is 7.5 in.

▶ **TRY EXERCISE** ▸ 51

Visualizing for Success

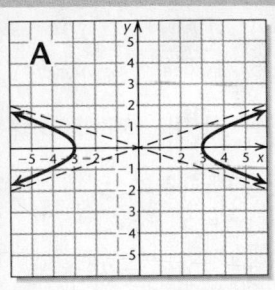

A

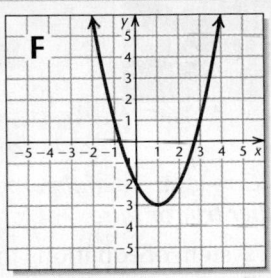

F

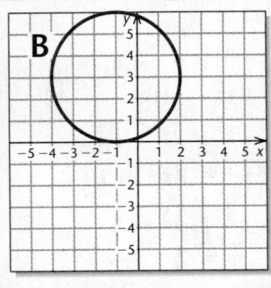

B

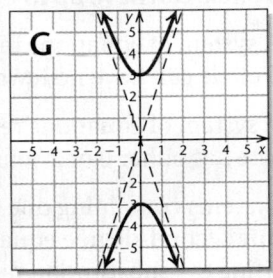

G

Match each equation with its graph

1. $(x - 1)^2 + (y + 3)^2 = 9$

2. $\dfrac{x^2}{9} - \dfrac{y^2}{1} = 1$

3. $y = (x - 1)^2 - 3$

4. $(x + 1)^2 + (y - 3)^2 = 9$

5. $x = (y - 1)^2 - 3$

6. $\dfrac{(x + 1)^2}{9} + \dfrac{(y - 3)^2}{1} = 1$

7. $xy = 3$

8. $y = -(x + 1)^2 + 3$

9. $\dfrac{y^2}{9} - \dfrac{x^2}{1} = 1$

10. $\dfrac{(x - 1)^2}{1} + \dfrac{(y + 3)^2}{9} = 1$

Answers on page A-64

An additional, animated version of this activity appears in MyMathLab. To use MyMathLab, you need a course ID and a student access code. Contact your instructor for more information.

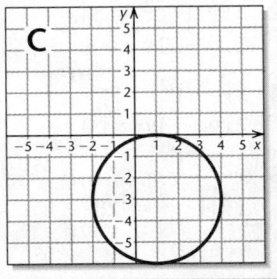

C

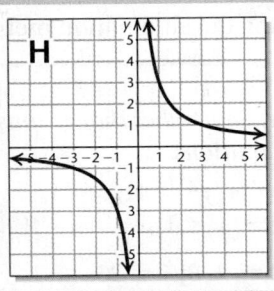

H

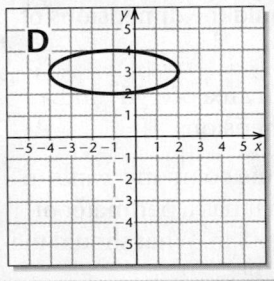

D

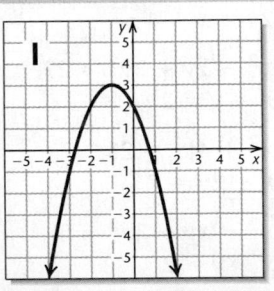

I

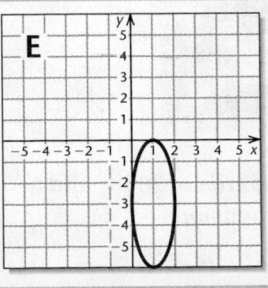

E

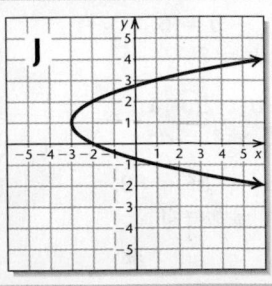

J

13.4 EXERCISE SET

 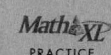
⤵ *Concept Reinforcement* *Classify each statement as either true or false.*

1. A system of equations that represent a line and an ellipse can have 0, 1, or 2 solutions.

2. A system of equations that represent a parabola and a circle can have up to 4 solutions.

3. A system of equations representing a hyperbola and a circle can have no fewer than 2 solutions.

4. A system of equations representing an ellipse and a line has either 0 or 2 solutions.

5. Systems containing one first-degree equation and one second-degree equation are most easily solved using the substitution method.

6. Systems containing two second-degree equations of the form $Ax^2 + By^2 = C$ are most easily solved using the elimination method.

Solve. Remember that graphs can be used to confirm all real solutions.

7. $x^2 + y^2 = 41$,
$y - x = 1$

8. $x^2 + y^2 = 45$,
$y - x = 3$

9. $4x^2 + 9y^2 = 36$,
$3y + 2x = 6$

10. $9x^2 + 4y^2 = 36$,
$3x + 2y = 6$

11. $y^2 = x + 3$,
$2y = x + 4$

12. $y = x^2$,
$3x = y + 2$

13. $x^2 - xy + 3y^2 = 27$,
$x - y = 2$

14. $2y^2 + xy + x^2 = 7$,
$x - 2y = 5$

15. $x^2 + 4y^2 = 25$,
$x + 2y = 7$

16. $x^2 - y^2 = 16$,
$x - 2y = 1$

17. $x^2 - xy + 3y^2 = 5$,
$x - y = 2$

18. $m^2 + 3n^2 = 10$,
$m - n = 2$

19. $3x + y = 7$,
$4x^2 + 5y = 24$

20. $2y^2 + xy = 5$,
$4y + x = 7$

21. $a + b = 6$,
$ab = 8$

22. $p + q = -1$,
$pq = -12$

23. $2a + b = 1$,
$b = 4 - a^2$

24. $4x^2 + 9y^2 = 36$,
$x + 3y = 3$

25. $a^2 + b^2 = 89$,
$a - b = 3$

26. $xy = 10$,
$x + y = 7$

27. $y = x^2$,
$x = y^2$

28. $x^2 + y^2 = 25$,
$y^2 = x + 5$

Aha! 29. $x^2 + y^2 = 16$,
$x^2 - y^2 = 16$

30. $y^2 - 4x^2 = 25$,
$4x^2 + y^2 = 25$

31. $x^2 + y^2 = 25$,
$xy = 12$

32. $x^2 - y^2 = 16$,
$x + y^2 = 4$

33. $x^2 + y^2 = 9$,
$25x^2 + 16y^2 = 400$

34. $x^2 + y^2 = 4$,
$9x^2 + 16y^2 = 144$

35. $x^2 + y^2 = 14$,
$x^2 - y^2 = 4$

36. $x^2 + y^2 = 16$,
$y^2 - 2x^2 = 10$

37. $x^2 + y^2 = 10$,
$xy = 3$

38. $x^2 + y^2 = 5$,
$xy = 2$

39. $x^2 + 4y^2 = 20$,
$xy = 4$

40. $x^2 + y^2 = 13$,
$xy = 6$

41. $2xy + 3y^2 = 7$,
$3xy - 2y^2 = 4$

42. $3xy + x^2 = 34$,
$2xy - 3x^2 = 8$

43. $4a^2 - 25b^2 = 0$,
$2a^2 - 10b^2 = 3b + 4$

44. $xy - y^2 = 2$,
$2xy - 3y^2 = 0$

45. $ab - b^2 = -4$,
$ab - 2b^2 = -6$

46. $x^2 - y = 5$,
$x^2 + y^2 = 25$

Solve.

47. *Art.* Elliot is designing a rectangular stained glass miniature that has a perimeter of 28 cm and a diagonal of length 10 cm. What should the dimensions of the glass be?

48. *Geometry.* A rectangle has an area of 2 yd² and a perimeter of 6 yd. Find its dimensions.

49. *Tile design.* The Clay Works tile company wants to make a new rectangular tile that has a perimeter of 6 in. and a diagonal of length $\sqrt{5}$ in. What should the dimensions of the tile be?

?5 in.

50. *Geometry.* A rectangle has an area of 20 in² and a perimeter of 18 in. Find its dimensions.

51. *Design of a van.* The cargo area of a delivery van must be 60 ft², and the length of a diagonal must accommodate a 13-ft board. Find the dimensions of the cargo area.

52. *Dimensions of a rug.* The diagonal of a Persian rug is 25 ft. The area of the rug is 300 ft². Find the length and the width of the rug.

53. The product of two numbers is 90. The sum of their squares is 261. Find the numbers.

54. *Investments.* A certain amount of money saved for 1 yr at a certain interest rate yielded $125 in simple interest. If $625 more had been invested and the rate had been 1% less, the interest would have been the same. Find the principal and the rate.

55. *Garden design.* A garden contains two square flower beds. Find the length of each bed if the sum of their areas is 832 ft² and the difference of their areas is 320 ft².

56. *TV dimensions.* The Kaplans' new LCD screen has an area of 1100 in² and has a $\sqrt{2561}$-in. diagonal. Find the width and the length of the screen.

57. The area of a rectangle is $\sqrt{3}$ m², and the length of a diagonal is 2 m. Find the dimensions.

58. The area of a rectangle is $\sqrt{2}$ m², and the length of a diagonal is $\sqrt{3}$ m. Find the dimensions.

59. How can an understanding of conic sections be helpful when a system of nonlinear equations is being solved algebraically?

60. Suppose a system of equations is comprised of one linear equation and one nonlinear equation. Is it possible for such a system to have three solutions? Why or why not?

Skill Review

To prepare for Section 14.1, review evaluating expressions (Section 1.8).

Simplify. [1.8]

61. $(-1)^9(-3)^2$

62. $(-1)^{10}(-3)^3$

Evaluate each of the following. [1.8]

63. $\dfrac{(-1)^k}{k-6}$, for $k = 7$

64. $\dfrac{(-1)^k}{k-5}$, for $k = 10$

65. $\dfrac{n}{2}(3 + n)$, for $n = 11$

66. $\dfrac{7(1 - r^2)}{1 - r}$, for $r = \frac{1}{2}$

Synthesis

67. Write a problem that translates to a system of two equations. Design the problem so that at least one equation is nonlinear and so that no real solution exists.

68. Write a problem for a classmate to solve. Devise the problem so that a system of two nonlinear equations with exactly one real solution is solved.

69. Find the equation of a circle that passes through $(-2, 3)$ and $(-4, 1)$ and whose center is on the line $5x + 8y = -2$.

70. Find the equation of an ellipse centered at the origin that passes through the points $(2, -3)$ and $(1, \sqrt{13})$.

Solve.

71. $p^2 + q^2 = 13,$
$\dfrac{1}{pq} = -\dfrac{1}{6}$

72. $a + b = \dfrac{5}{6},$
$\dfrac{a}{b} + \dfrac{b}{a} = \dfrac{13}{6}$

73. *Fence design.* A roll of chain-link fencing contains 100 ft of fence. The fencing is bent at a 90° angle to enclose a rectangular work area of 2475 ft², as shown. Determine the length and the width of the rectangle.

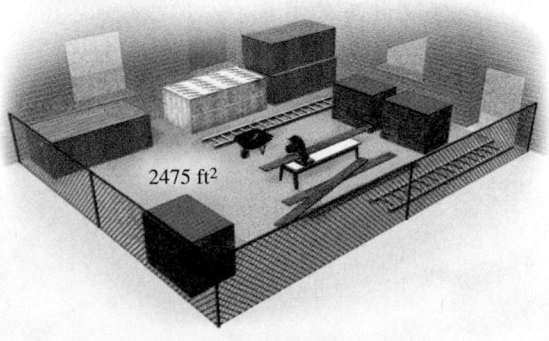

2475 ft²

74. A piece of wire 100 cm long is to be cut into two pieces and those pieces are each to be bent to make a square. The area of one square is to be 144 cm^2 greater than that of the other. How should the wire be cut?

75. *Box design.* Four squares with sides 5 in. long are cut from the corners of a rectangular metal sheet that has an area of 340 in^2. The edges are bent up to form an open box with a volume of 350 in^3. Find the dimensions of the box.

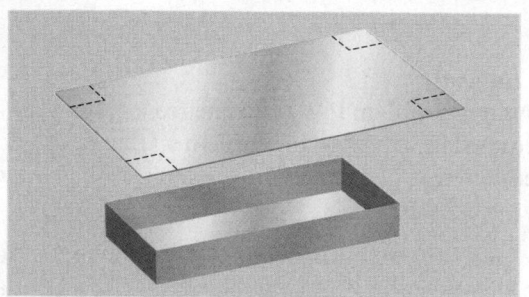

76. *Computer screens.* The ratio of the length to the height of the screen on a computer monitor is 4 to 3. A Dell Inspiron notebook has a 15-in. diagonal screen. Find the dimensions of the screen.

77. *HDTV screens.* The ratio of the length to the height of an HDTV screen is 16 to 9. The Sollar Lounge has an HDTV screen with a 73-in. diagonal screen. Find the dimensions of the screen.

78. *Railing sales.* Fireside Castings finds that the total revenue R from the sale of x units of railing is given by

$$R = 100x + x^2.$$

Fireside also finds that the total cost C of producing x units of the same product is given by

$$C = 80x + 1500.$$

A break-even point is a value of x for which total revenue is the same as total cost; that is, $R = C$. How many units must be sold to break even?

79. Use a graphing calculator to check your answers to Exercises 13, 25, and 47.

Study Summary

KEY TERMS AND CONCEPTS	EXAMPLES

SECTION 13.1: CONIC SECTIONS: PARABOLAS AND CIRCLES

Parabola

$y = ax^2 + bx + c$ Opens upward ($a > 0$) or downward ($a < 0$)

$\quad = a(x - h)^2 + k;$ Vertex: (h, k)

$x = ay^2 + by + c$ Opens right ($a > 0$) or left ($a < 0$)

$\quad = a(y - k)^2 + h$ Vertex: (h, k)

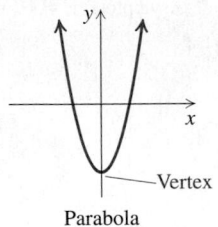

Parabola

$x = -y^2 + 4y - 1$

$\quad = -(y^2 - 4y \quad) - 1$

$\quad = -(y^2 - 4y + 4) - 1 - (-1)(4)$

$\quad = -(y - 2)^2 + 3 \qquad a = -1;$ parabola opens left

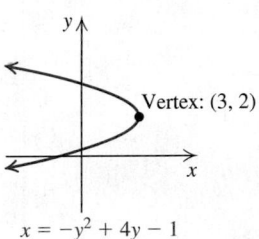

Vertex: $(3, 2)$

$x = -y^2 + 4y - 1$

Circle

$x^2 + y^2 = r^2;$ Radius: r Center: $(0, 0)$

$(x - h)^2 + (y - k)^2 = r^2$ Radius: r Center: (h, k)

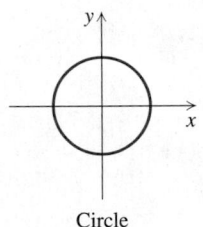

Circle

$x^2 + y^2 + 2x - 6y + 6 = 0$

$x^2 + 2x + \quad y^2 - 6y \quad = -6$

$x^2 + 2x + 1 + y^2 - 6y + 9 = -6 + 1 + 9$

$(x + 1)^2 + (y - 3)^2 = 4$

$[x - (-1)]^2 + (y - 3)^2 = 2^2$ Radius: 2   Center: $(-1, 3)$

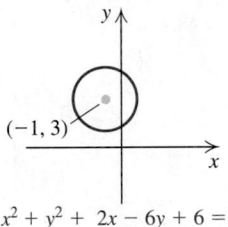

$(-1, 3)$

$x^2 + y^2 + 2x - 6y + 6 = 0$

SECTION 13.2: CONIC SECTIONS: ELLIPSES

Ellipse

$\dfrac{x^2}{a^2} + \dfrac{y^2}{b^2} = 1;$ Center: $(0, 0)$

$\dfrac{(x - h)^2}{a^2} + \dfrac{(y - k)^2}{b^2} = 1$ Center: (h, k)

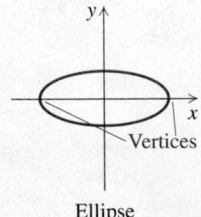

Vertices

Ellipse

$\dfrac{(x - 4)^2}{4} + \dfrac{(y + 1)^2}{9} = 1$

$\dfrac{(x - 4)^2}{2^2} + \dfrac{[y - (-1)]^2}{3^2} = 1$ $3 > 2$; ellipse is vertical   Center: $(4, -1)$

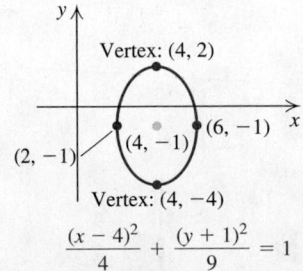

Vertex: $(4, 2)$

$(2, -1)$ $(4, -1)$ $(6, -1)$

Vertex: $(4, -4)$

$\dfrac{(x - 4)^2}{4} + \dfrac{(y + 1)^2}{9} = 1$

SECTION 13.3: CONIC SECTIONS: HYPERBOLAS

Hyperbola

$\dfrac{x^2}{a^2} - \dfrac{y^2}{b^2} = 1;$ Two branches opening right and left

$\dfrac{y^2}{b^2} - \dfrac{x^2}{a^2} = 1$ Two branches opening upward and downward

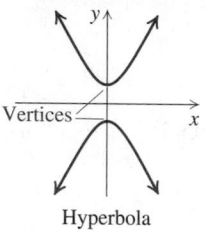

Hyperbola

$\dfrac{x^2}{4} - \dfrac{y^2}{1} = 1$

$\dfrac{x^2}{2^2} - \dfrac{y^2}{1^2} = 1$ Opens right and left

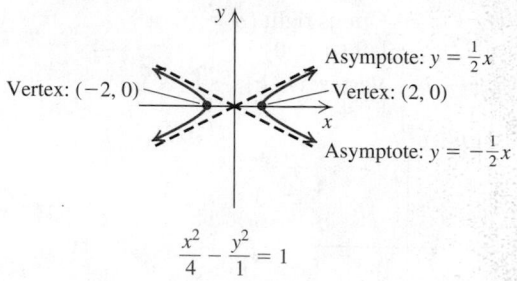

$\dfrac{x^2}{4} - \dfrac{y^2}{1} = 1$

SECTION 13.4: NONLINEAR SYSTEMS OF EQUATIONS

We can solve a system containing at least one nonlinear equation using substitution or elimination.

Solve:

$x^2 - y = -1,$ (1)   (The graph is a parabola.)

$x + 2y = 3.$ (2)   (The graph is a line.)

$x = 3 - 2y$ Solving for x in equation (2)

$(3 - 2y)^2 - y = -1$ Substituting for x in equation (1)

$9 - 12y + 4y^2 - y = -1$

$4y^2 - 13y + 10 = 0$

$(4y - 5)(y - 2) = 0$

$4y - 5 = 0$ *or* $y - 2 = 0$

$y = \frac{5}{4}$ *or* $y = 2$ Solving for y

If $y = \frac{5}{4}$, then $x = 3 - 2\left(\frac{5}{4}\right) = \frac{1}{2}$. $\left(\frac{1}{2}, \frac{5}{4}\right)$ is a solution.

If $y = 2$, then $x = 3 - 2(2) = -1$. $(-1, 2)$ is a solution.

The solutions are $\left(\frac{1}{2}, \frac{5}{4}\right)$ and $(-1, 2)$.

Review Exercises: Chapter 13

Concept Reinforcement *Classify each statement as either true or false.*

1. Every parabola that opens upward or downward can represent the graph of a function. [13.1]

2. The center of a circle is part of the circle itself. [13.1]

3. The foci of an ellipse are part of the ellipse itself. [13.2]

4. It is possible for a hyperbola to represent the graph of a function. [13.3]

5. If an equation of a conic section has only one term of degree 2, its graph cannot be a circle, an ellipse, or a hyperbola. [13.3]

6. Two nonlinear graphs can intersect in more than one point. [13.4]

7. Every system of nonlinear equations has at least one real solution. [13.4]

8. Both substitution and elimination can be used as methods for solving a system of nonlinear equations. [13.4]

Find the center and the radius of each circle. [13.1]

9. $(x + 3)^2 + (y - 2)^2 = 16$

10. $(x - 5)^2 + y^2 = 11$

11. $x^2 + y^2 - 6x - 2y + 1 = 0$

12. $x^2 + y^2 + 8x - 6y = 20$

13. Find an equation of the circle with center $(-4, 3)$ and radius 4. [13.1]

14. Find an equation of the circle with center $(7, -2)$ and radius $2\sqrt{5}$. [13.1]

Classify each equation as a circle, an ellipse, a parabola, or a hyperbola. Then graph.

15. $5x^2 + 5y^2 = 80$ [13.1], [13.3]

16. $9x^2 + 2y^2 = 18$ [13.2], [13.3]

17. $y = -x^2 + 2x - 3$ [13.1], [13.3]

18. $\dfrac{y^2}{9} - \dfrac{x^2}{4} = 1$ [13.3]

19. $xy = 9$ [13.3]

20. $x = y^2 + 2y - 2$ [13.1], [13.3]

21. $\dfrac{(x + 1)^2}{3} + (y - 3)^2 = 1$ [13.2], [13.3]

22. $x^2 + y^2 + 6x - 8y - 39 = 0$ [13.1], [13.3]

Solve. [13.4]

23. $x^2 - y^2 = 21,$
    $x + y = 3$

24. $x^2 - 2x + 2y^2 = 8,$
    $2x + y = 6$

25. $x^2 - y = 5,$
    $2x - y = 5$

26. $x^2 + y^2 = 25,$
    $x^2 - y^2 = 7$

27. $x^2 - y^2 = 3,$
    $y = x^2 - 3$

28. $x^2 + y^2 = 18,$
    $2x + y = 3$

29. $x^2 + y^2 = 100,$
    $2x^2 - 3y^2 = -120$

30. $x^2 + 2y^2 = 12,$
    $xy = 4$

31. A rectangular bandstand has a perimeter of 38 m and an area of 84 m². What are the dimensions of the bandstand? [13.4]

32. One type of carton used by tableproducts.com exactly fits both a rectangular plate of area 108 in² and chopsticks of length 15 in., laid diagonally on top of the plate. Find the length and the width of the carton. [13.4]

33. The perimeter of a square mirror is 12 cm more than the perimeter of another square mirror. Its area exceeds the area of the other by 39 cm². Find the perimeter of each mirror. [13.4]

34. The sum of the areas of two circles is 130π ft². The difference of the circumferences is 16π ft. Find the radius of each circle. [13.4]

Synthesis

35. How does the graph of a hyperbola differ from the graph of a parabola? [13.1], [13.3]

36. Explain why function notation rarely appears in this chapter, and list the graphs discussed for which function notation could be used. [13.1], [13.2], [13.3]

37. Solve: [13.4]
$$4x^2 - x - 3y^2 = 9,$$
$$-x^2 + x + y^2 = 2.$$

38. Find the points whose distance from $(8, 0)$ and from $(-8, 0)$ is 10. [13.1]

39. Find an equation of the circle that passes through $(-2, -4)$, $(5, -5)$, and $(6, 2)$. [13.1], [13.4]

40. Find an equation of the ellipse with the following intercepts: $(-10, 0)$, $(10, 0)$, $(0, -1)$, and $(0, 1)$. [13.2]

41. Find the point on the *x*-axis that is equidistant from $(-3, 4)$ and $(5, 6)$. [13.1]

Test: Chapter 13

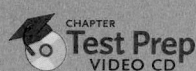

CHAPTER
Test Prep
VIDEO CD

Step-by-step test solutions are found on the video CD in the back of this book.

1. Find an equation of the circle with center $(3, -4)$ and radius $2\sqrt{3}$.

Find the center and the radius of each circle.

2. $(x - 4)^2 + (y + 1)^2 = 5$

3. $x^2 + y^2 + 4x - 6y + 4 = 0$

Classify the equation as a circle, an ellipse, a parabola, or a hyperbola. Then graph.

4. $y = x^2 - 4x - 1$

5. $x^2 + y^2 + 2x + 6y + 6 = 0$

6. $\dfrac{x^2}{16} - \dfrac{y^2}{9} = 1$

7. $16x^2 + 4y^2 = 64$

8. $xy = -5$

9. $x = -y^2 + 4y$

Solve.

10. $x^2 + y^2 = 36,$
$3x + 4y = 24$

11. $x^2 - y = 3,$
$2x + y = 5$

12. $x^2 - 2y^2 = 1,$
$xy = 6$

13. $x^2 + y^2 = 10,$
$x^2 = y^2 + 2$

14. A rectangular bookmark with diagonal of length $5\sqrt{5}$ has an area of 22. Find the dimensions of the bookmark.

15. Two squares are such that the sum of their areas is $8\ m^2$ and the difference of their areas is $2\ m^2$. Find the length of a side of each square.

16. A rectangular dance floor has a diagonal of length 40 ft and a perimeter of 112 ft. Find the dimensions of the dance floor.

17. Brett invested a certain amount of money for 1 yr and earned $72 in interest. Erin invested $240 more than Brett at an interest rate that was $\frac{5}{6}$ of the rate given to Brett, but she earned the same amount of interest. Find the principal and the interest rate for Brett's investment.

Synthesis

18. Find an equation of the ellipse passing through $(6, 0)$ and $(6, 6)$ with vertices at $(1, 3)$ and $(11, 3)$.

19. Find the point on the *y*-axis that is equidistant from $(-3, -5)$ and $(4, -7)$.

20. The sum of two numbers is 36, and the product is 4. Find the sum of the reciprocals of the numbers.

21. *Theatrical production.* An E.T.C. spotlight for a college's production of *Hamlet* projects an ellipse of light on a stage that is 8 ft wide and 14 ft long. Find an equation of that ellipse if an actor is in its center and *x* represents the number of feet, horizontally, from the actor to the edge of the ellipse and *y* represents the number of feet, vertically, from the actor to the edge of the ellipse.

Simplify.

1. $(4t^2 - 5s)^2$ [4.7]

2. $\dfrac{1}{3t} + \dfrac{1}{t-3}$ [6.4]

3. $\dfrac{x - \dfrac{1}{a}}{a - \dfrac{1}{x}}$ [6.5]

4. $\sqrt{6t}\,\sqrt{15t^3 w}$ [10.3]

5. $(81a^{2/3}b^{1/4})^{3/4}$ [10.2]

6. $\log_2 \dfrac{1}{16}$ [12.3]

7. $(4 + 3i)(4 - 3i)$ [10.8]

8. $\log_m 1$ [12.4]

9. -8^{-2} [4.2]

10. $\sqrt{8} - 2\sqrt{2} + \sqrt{12}$ [10.5]

Factor.

11. $100x^2 - 60xy + 9y^2$ [5.4]

12. $3m^6 - 24$ [5.5]

13. $ax + by - ay - bx$ [5.1]

14. $32x^2 - 20x - 3$ [5.3]

Solve. Where appropriate, give an approximation to four decimal places.

15. $3(x - 5) - 4x \geq 2(x + 5)$ [9.1]

16. $16x^2 - 18x = 0$ [5.7]

17. $\dfrac{2}{x} + \dfrac{1}{x-2} = 1$ [6.6]

18. $5x^2 + 5 = 0$ [11.2]

19. $\log_x 64 = 3$ [12.6]

20. $3^x = 1.5$ [12.6]

21. $x = \sqrt{2x - 5} + 4$ [10.6]

22. $x^2 + 2y^2 = 5,$
$2x^2 + y^2 = 7$ [13.4]

Graph.

23. $3x - y = 9$ [3.3]

24. $y = \log_5 x$ [12.3]

25. $\dfrac{x^2}{25} + \dfrac{y^2}{1} = 1$ [13.2]

26. $f(x) = 2^{x-1}$ [12.2]

27. $x^2 + (y - 3)^2 = 4$ [13.1]

28. $x < 2y + 1$ [9.4]

29. Graph: $f(x) = -(x + 2)^2 + 3$. [11.7]

    a) Label the vertex.
    b) Draw the axis of symmetry.
    c) Find the maximum or minimum value.

30. Find the domain of the function given by
$$f(x) = \sqrt{5 - 3x}. \quad [9.1]$$

31. Solve $t = \dfrac{ab}{c^2}$ for c. [11.4]

32. Find the slope–intercept equation of the line containing the points $(-3, 6)$ and $(1, 2)$. [3.7]

33. Write a quadratic equation having the solutions $\sqrt{3}$ and $-\sqrt{3}$. Answers may vary. [11.3]

34. Write an equivalent exponential equation:
$$\log_t 16 = m. \quad [12.4]$$

Solve.

35. *Aviation.* BlueAir owns two types of airplanes. One type flies 60 mph faster than the other. Laura often rents a plane from BlueAir to visit her parents. The flight takes 4 hr with the faster plane and 4 hr 24 min with the slower plane. What distance does she fly? [8.3]

36. *Aviation.* It takes Greg 21 hr longer than it takes Kyle to service a Cessna 350. Together they can service the plane in 10 hr. How long would it take each of them, working alone, to service the plane? [6.7]

37. *Employment.*   The average supermarket employee worked 32.3 hr per week in 2003. This number fell to 29.5 hr per week in 2007. [7.3]
Source: *The Wall Street Journal, 3/8/08*

    a) Find a linear function that fits the data. Let *t* represent the number of years since 2003.

    b) Use the function from part (a) to predict the number of hours the average supermarket employee will work in 2010.

    c) Assuming the trend continues, in what year will the average supermarket employee work 20 hr per week?

38. *Picture frames.*   The outside edge of a rectangular picture frame measures 18 in. by 11 in., and 120 in^2 of picture shows. How wide is the frame? [5.8]

39. *Population.*   The population of Latvia was 2.26 million in 2007 and was decreasing exponentially at a rate of 0.95% per year. [12.7]
Source: Based on information from *CIA World Factbook*

    a) Write an exponential function describing the population of Latvia *t* years after 2007.

    b) Predict what the population will be in 2025.

    c) What is the half life of the population?

40. *Geometry.*   In triangle *ABC*, the measure of angle *B* is three times the measure of angle *A*. The measure of angle *C* is 105° greater than the measure of angle *A*. Find the angle measures. [2.5]

41. *Art.*   Elyse is designing a rectangular tray. She wants to put a row of beads around the tray, and has enough beads to make an edge that is 32 in. long. What dimensions of the tray will give it the greatest area? [11.8]

42. *Geometry.*   In right triangle *ABC*, the hypotenuse is 8 cm long and one leg is 3 cm long. Find the length of the other leg. Give an exact answer and an approximation to three decimal places. [10.7]

Synthesis

43. Find *a* and *b* if the graph of

$$ax - 6y = 3x + by + 2$$

is a vertical line passing through $(-1, 0)$. [3.3]

44. Solve:

$$\begin{aligned} w - x + 3y - z &= -1, \\ 2w + x + y + 2z &= 8, \\ -w - 2x + 5y - z &= -1, \\ 2w + 3x - 4y + z &= 0. \end{aligned}$$ [8.4]

45. If *y* varies inversely as the square root of *x* and *x* is multiplied by 100, what is the effect on *y*? [7.5], [10.1]

46. For $f(x) = x - \dfrac{1}{x^2}$, find all *x*-values for which $f(x) \le 0$. [11.9]

Sequences, Series, and the Binomial Theorem

CHAPTER

14

14.1
Sequences and Series

14.2
Arithmetic Sequences and Series

14.3
Geometric Sequences and Series

CONNECTING THE CONCEPTS

14.4
The Binomial Theorem

STUDY SUMMARY
REVIEW EXERCISES
CHAPTER TEST
CUMULATIVE REVIEW

**ALEXIS SPENCER-BYERS;
LEE HARPER**
COFFEE SHOP OWNERS
Jackson, Mississippi

At our coffee house, we make many different beverages. To satisfy our customers, each beverage must include the properly measured and combined ingredients to obtain the desired flavor, look, and aroma. Meanwhile, as owners, we need to know exactly how much it costs us to make each item in order to determine our prices. Behind each tasty treat is a series of calculations for determining recipes, managing cash flow, and evaluating profit margins.

AN APPLICATION

Approximately 17 billion espresso-based coffees were sold in the United States in 2007. This number is expected to grow by 4% each year. How many espresso-based coffees will be sold from 2007 through 2015?

Source: Based on data in the *Indianapolis Star,* 11/22/07

This problem appears as Exercise 65 in Exercise Set 14.3.

The first three sections of this chapter are devoted to *sequences* and *series*. A sequence is simply an ordered list. For example, when a baseball coach writes a batting order, a sequence is being formed. When the members of a sequence are numbers, they can be added. Such a sum is called a *series*. Section 14.4 presents the *binomial theorem*, which is used to expand expressions of the form $(a + b)^n$. Such an expansion is itself a series.

14.1 Sequences and Series

Sequences ▪ Finding the General Term ▪ Sums and Series ▪ Sigma Notation

Sequences

Suppose that $10,000 is invested at 5%, compounded annually. The value of the account at the start of years 1, 2, 3, 4, and so on, is

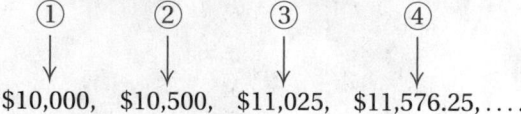

$10,000, $10,500, $11,025, $11,576.25, ...

We can regard this as a function that pairs 1 with $10,000, 2 with $10,500, 3 with $11,025, and so on. This is an example of a **sequence** (or **progression**). The domain of a sequence is a set of consecutive positive integers beginning with 1, and the range varies from sequence to sequence.

If we stop after a certain number of years, we obtain a **finite sequence**:

$10,000, $10,500, $11,025, $11,576.25.

If we continue listing the amounts in the account, we obtain an **infinite sequence**:

$10,000, $10,500, $11,025, $11,576.25, $12,155.06, ...

The three dots near the end indicate that the sequence goes on without stopping.

Sequences

An *infinite sequence* is a function having for its domain the set of natural numbers: $\{1, 2, 3, 4, 5, \ldots\}$.

A *finite sequence* is a function having for its domain a set of natural numbers: $\{1, 2, 3, 4, 5, \ldots, n\}$, for some natural number n.

As another example, consider the sequence given by

$$a(n) = 2^n, \quad \text{or} \quad a_n = 2^n.$$

The notation a_n means $a(n)$ but is used more commonly with sequences. Some function values (also called *terms* of the sequence) follow:

$$a_1 = 2^1 = 2,$$
$$a_2 = 2^2 = 4,$$
$$a_3 = 2^3 = 8,$$
$$a_6 = 2^6 = 64.$$

The first term of the sequence is a_1, the fifth term is a_5, and the nth term, or **general term**, is a_n. This sequence can also be denoted in the following ways:

$$2, 4, 8, \ldots;$$

or $2, 4, 8, \ldots, 2^n, \ldots.$ The 2^n emphasizes that the nth term of this sequence is found by raising 2 to the nth power.

EXAMPLE 1   Find the first four terms and the 57th term of the sequence for which the general term is given by $a_n = (-1)^n/(n + 1)$.

SOLUTION   We have

$$a_1 = \frac{(-1)^1}{1 + 1} = -\frac{1}{2}, \quad \text{Substituting in } a_n = \frac{(-1)^n}{n + 1}$$

$$a_2 = \frac{(-1)^2}{2 + 1} = \frac{1}{3},$$

$$a_3 = \frac{(-1)^3}{3 + 1} = -\frac{1}{4},$$

$$a_4 = \frac{(-1)^4}{4 + 1} = \frac{1}{5},$$

$$a_{57} = \frac{(-1)^{57}}{57 + 1} = -\frac{1}{58}.$$

Note that the expression $(-1)^n$ causes the signs of the terms to alternate between positive and negative, depending on whether n is even or odd.

> TRY EXERCISE 17

Finding the General Term

By looking for a pattern, we can often write an expression for the general term of a sequence. When only a few terms are given, more than one pattern may fit.

EXAMPLE 2   For each sequence, predict the general term.

a) $1, 4, 9, 16, 25, \ldots$

b) $2, 4, 8, \ldots$

c) $-1, 2, -4, 8, -16, \ldots$

TECHNOLOGY CONNECTION

Sequences are entered and graphed much like functions. The difference is that the SEQUENCE MODE must be selected. You can then enter U_n or V_n using n as the variable. Use this approach to check Example 1 with a table of values for the sequence.

SOLUTION

a) $1, 4, 9, 16, 25 \ldots$

These are squares of consecutive positive integers, so the general term could be n^2.

b) $2, 4, 8, \ldots$

We regard the pattern as powers of 2, in which case 16 would be the next term and 2^n the general term. The sequence could then be written with more terms as

$$2, 4, 8, 16, 32, 64, 128, \ldots.$$

c) $-1, 2, -4, 8, -16, \ldots$

These are powers of 2 with alternating signs, so the general term may be

$$\overset{\text{Making sure the signs}}{(-1)^n[2^{n-1}].}$$

Making sure the signs of the terms alternate

Raising 2 to a power that is 1 less than the term's position

To check, note that -4 is the third term, and $(-1)^3[2^{3-1}] = -1 \cdot 2^2 = -4$.

 **TRY EXERCISE** 29

In part (b) above, suppose that the second term is found by adding 2, the third term by adding 4, the next term by adding 6, and so on. In this case, 14 would be the next term and the sequence would be

$$2, 4, 8, 14, 22, 32, 44, 58, \ldots.$$

This illustrates that the fewer terms we are given, the greater the uncertainty about determining the nth term.

Sums and Series

Series

Given the infinite sequence

$$a_1, a_2, a_3, a_4, \ldots, a_n, \ldots,$$

the sum of the terms

$$a_1 + a_2 + a_3 + \cdots + a_n + \cdots$$

is called an *infinite series* and is denoted S_∞. A *partial sum* is the sum of the first n terms:

$$a_1 + a_2 + a_3 + \cdots + a_n.$$

A partial sum is also called a *finite series* and is denoted S_n.

EXAMPLE 3   For the sequence $-2, 4, -6, 8, -10, 12, -14$, find: **(a)** S_2; **(b)** S_3; **(c)** S_7.

SOLUTION

a) $S_2 = -2 + 4 = 2$ This is the sum of the first 2 terms.

b) $S_3 = -2 + 4 + (-6) = -4$ This is the sum of the first 3 terms.

c) $S_7 = -2 + 4 + (-6) + 8 + (-10) + 12 + (-14) = -8$ This is the sum of the first 7 terms.

TRY EXERCISE 45

Sigma Notation

When the general term of a sequence is known, the Greek letter Σ (uppercase sigma) can be used to write a series. For example, the sum of the first four terms of the sequence $3, 5, 7, 9, 11, \ldots, 2k + 1, \ldots$ can be named as follows, using *sigma notation*, or *summation notation*:

$$\sum_{k=1}^{4} (2k + 1). \quad \begin{array}{l}\text{This represents} \\ (2 \cdot 1 + 1) + (2 \cdot 2 + 1) + (2 \cdot 3 + 1) + (2 \cdot 4 + 1).\end{array}$$

This is read "the sum as k goes from 1 to 4 of $(2k + 1)$." The letter k is called the *index of summation*. The index need not always start at 1.

EXAMPLE 4

Write out and evaluate each sum.

a) $\displaystyle\sum_{k=1}^{5} k^2$ b) $\displaystyle\sum_{k=4}^{6} (-1)^k (2k)$ c) $\displaystyle\sum_{k=0}^{3} (2^k + 5)$

STUDENT NOTES

A great deal of information is condensed into sigma notation. Be careful to pay attention to what values the index of summation will take on. Evaluate the expression following sigma, the general term, for each value and then add the results.

SOLUTION

a) $\displaystyle\sum_{k=1}^{5} k^2 = 1^2 + 2^2 + 3^2 + 4^2 + 5^2 = 1 + 4 + 9 + 16 + 25 = 55$

Evaluate k^2 for all integers from 1 through 5. Then add.

b) $\displaystyle\sum_{k=4}^{6} (-1)^k (2k) = (-1)^4 (2 \cdot 4) + (-1)^5 (2 \cdot 5) + (-1)^6 (2 \cdot 6)$

$= 8 - 10 + 12 = 10$

c) $\displaystyle\sum_{k=0}^{3} (2^k + 5) = (2^0 + 5) + (2^1 + 5) + (2^2 + 5) + (2^3 + 5)$

$= 6 + 7 + 9 + 13 = 35$

TRY EXERCISE 49

EXAMPLE 5

Write sigma notation for each sum.

a) $1 + 4 + 9 + 16 + 25$
b) $3 + 9 + 27 + 81 + \cdots$
c) $-1 + 3 - 5 + 7$

SOLUTION

a) $1 + 4 + 9 + 16 + 25$

Note that this is a sum of squares, $1^2 + 2^2 + 3^2 + 4^2 + 5^2$, so the general term is k^2. Sigma notation is

$$\sum_{k=1}^{5} k^2. \quad \text{The sum starts with } 1^2 \text{ and ends with } 5^2.$$

Answers can vary here. For example, another—perhaps less obvious—way of writing $1 + 4 + 9 + 16 + 25$ is

$$\sum_{k=2}^{6} (k - 1)^2.$$

b) $3 + 9 + 27 + 81 + \cdots$

This is a sum of powers of 3, and it is also an infinite series. We use the symbol ∞ for infinity and write the series using sigma notation:

$$\sum_{k=1}^{\infty} 3^k.$$

c) $-1 + 3 - 5 + 7$

Except for the alternating signs, this is the sum of the first four positive odd numbers. It is useful to remember that $2k - 1$ is a formula for the kth positive odd number. It is also important to remember that the factor $(-1)^k$ can be used to create the alternating signs. The general term is thus $(-1)^k(2k - 1)$, beginning with $k = 1$. Sigma notation is

$$\sum_{k=1}^{4} (-1)^k(2k - 1).$$

To check, we can evaluate $(-1)^k(2k - 1)$ using $1, 2, 3$, and 4. Then we can write the sum of the four terms. We leave this to the student.

TRY EXERCISE 61

14.1   EXERCISE SET

For Extra Help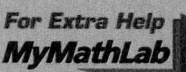

↪ **Concept Reinforcement**   *In each of Exercises 1–6, match the expression with the most appropriate expression from the column on the right.*

1. ____ $\displaystyle\sum_{k=1}^{4} k^2$

2. ____ $\displaystyle\sum_{k=3}^{6} (-1)^k$

3. ____ $5 + 10 + 15 + 20$

4. ____ $a_n = 5^n$

5. ____ $a_n = 3n + 2$

6. ____ $a_1 + a_2 + a_3$

a) $-1 + 1 + (-1) + 1$

b) $a_2 = 25$

c) $a_2 = 8$

d) $\displaystyle\sum_{k=1}^{4} 5k$

e) S_3

f) $1 + 4 + 9 + 16$

Find the indicated term of each sequence.

7. $a_n = 5n + 3$; a_8

8. $a_n = 3n - 4$; a_8

9. $a_n = (3n + 1)(2n - 5)$; a_9

10. $a_n = (3n + 2)^2$; a_6

11. $a_n = (-1)^{n-1}(3.4n - 17.3)$; a_{12}

12. $a_n = (-2)^{n-2}(45.68 - 1.2n)$; a_{23}

13. $a_n = 3n^2(9n - 100)$; a_{11}

14. $a_n = 4n^2(2n - 39)$; a_{22}

15. $a_n = \left(1 + \dfrac{1}{n}\right)^2$; a_{20}

16. $a_n = \left(1 - \dfrac{1}{n}\right)^3$; a_{15}

In each of the following, the nth term of a sequence is given. Find the first 4 terms; the 10th term, a_{10}; and the 15th term, a_{15}, of the sequence.

17. $a_n = 3n - 1$

18. $a_n = 2n + 1$

19. $a_n = n^2 + 2$

20. $a_n = n^2 - 2n$

21. $a_n = \dfrac{n}{n + 1}$

22. $a_n = \dfrac{n^2 - 1}{n^2 + 1}$

23. $a_n = \left(-\dfrac{1}{2}\right)^{n-1}$

24. $a_n = (-2)^{n+1}$

25. $a_n = (-1)^n/n$

26. $a_n = (-1)^n n^2$

27. $a_n = (-1)^n(n^3 - 1)$

28. $a_n = (-1)^{n+1}(3n - 5)$

Look for a pattern and then write an expression for the general term, or nth term, a_n, of each sequence. Answers may vary.

29. 2, 4, 6, 8, 10, ...

30. 1, 3, 5, 7, ...

31. −1, 1, −1, 1, ...

32. 1, −1, 1, −1, ...

33. 1, −2, 3, −4, ...

34. −1, 2, −3, 4, ...

35. 3, 5, 7, 9, ...

36. 4, 6, 8, 10, ...

37. 0, 3, 8, 15, 24, ...

38. 2, 6, 12, 20, 30, ...

39. $\frac{1}{2}, \frac{2}{3}, \frac{3}{4}, \frac{4}{5}, \frac{5}{6}, \ldots$

40. $1 \cdot 3, 2 \cdot 4, 3 \cdot 5, 4 \cdot 6, \ldots$

41. 0.1, 0.01, 0.001, 0.0001, ...

42. $\frac{1}{2}, \frac{1}{4}, \frac{1}{8}, \frac{1}{16}, \ldots$

43. −1, 4, −9, 16, ...

44. 1, −4, 9, −16, ...

Find the indicated partial sum for each sequence.

45. −1, 2, −3, 4, −5, 6, ...; S_{10}

46. 2, −4, 6, −8, 10, −12, ...; S_{10}

47. 1, $\frac{1}{10}$, $\frac{1}{100}$, $\frac{1}{1000}$, ...; S_6

48. 3, 6, 9, 12, 15, ...; S_6

Write out and evaluate each sum.

49. $\sum\limits_{k=1}^{5} \frac{1}{2k}$

50. $\sum\limits_{k=1}^{6} \frac{1}{2k-1}$

51. $\sum\limits_{k=0}^{4} 10^k$

52. $\sum\limits_{k=2}^{6} \sqrt{5k-1}$

53. $\sum\limits_{k=2}^{8} \frac{k}{k-1}$

54. $\sum\limits_{k=2}^{5} \frac{k-1}{k+1}$

55. $\sum\limits_{k=1}^{8} (-1)^{k+1} 2^k$

56. $\sum\limits_{k=1}^{7} (-1)^k 4^{k+1}$

57. $\sum\limits_{k=0}^{5} (k^2 - 2k + 3)$

58. $\sum\limits_{k=0}^{5} (k^2 - 3k + 4)$

59. $\sum\limits_{k=3}^{5} \frac{(-1)^k}{k(k+1)}$

60. $\sum\limits_{k=3}^{7} \frac{k}{2^k}$

Rewrite each sum using sigma notation. Answers may vary.

61. $\frac{2}{3} + \frac{3}{4} + \frac{4}{5} + \frac{5}{6} + \frac{6}{7}$

62. $\frac{1}{1^2} + \frac{1}{2^2} + \frac{1}{3^2} + \frac{1}{4^2} + \frac{1}{5^2}$

63. $1 + 4 + 9 + 16 + 25 + 36$

64. $1 + \sqrt{2} + \sqrt{3} + 2 + \sqrt{5} + \sqrt{6}$

65. $4 - 9 + 16 - 25 + \cdots + (-1)^n n^2$

66. $9 - 16 + 25 + \cdots + (-1)^{n+1} n^2$

67. $6 + 12 + 18 + 24 + \cdots$

68. $11 + 22 + 33 + 44 + \cdots$

69. $\frac{1}{1 \cdot 2} + \frac{1}{2 \cdot 3} + \frac{1}{3 \cdot 4} + \frac{1}{4 \cdot 5} + \cdots$

70. $\frac{1}{1 \cdot 2^2} + \frac{1}{2 \cdot 3^2} + \frac{1}{3 \cdot 4^2} + \frac{1}{4 \cdot 5^2} + \cdots$

71. The sequence 1, 4, 9, 16, ... can be written as $f(x) = x^2$ with the domain the set of all positive integers. Explain how the graph of f would compare with the graph of $y = x^2$.

72. Consider the sums

$$\sum_{k=1}^{5} 3k^2 \quad \text{and} \quad 3 \sum_{k=1}^{5} k^2.$$

a) Which is easier to evaluate and why?

b) Is it true that

$$\sum_{k=1}^{n} ca_k = c \sum_{k=1}^{n} a_k?$$

Why or why not?

Skill Review

To prepare for Section 14.2, review evaluating expressions and simplifying expressions (Section 1.8).

Evaluate. [1.8]

73. $\frac{7}{2}(a_1 + a_7)$, for $a_1 = 8$ and $a_7 = 20$

74. $a_1 + (n-1)d$, for $a_1 = 3$, $n = 10$, and $d = -2$

Simplify. [1.8]

75. $(a_1 + 3d) + d$

76. $(a_1 + 5d) + (a_n - 5d)$

77. $(a_1 + a_n) + (a_1 + a_n) + (a_1 + a_n)$

78. $(a_1 + 8d) - (a_1 + 7d)$

Synthesis

79. Explain why the equation

$$\sum_{k=1}^{n} (a_k + b_k) = \sum_{k=1}^{n} a_k + \sum_{k=1}^{n} b_k$$

is true for any positive integer n. What laws are used to justify this result?

80. Can a finite series be formed from an infinite sequence? Can an infinite series be formed from a finite sequence? Why or why not?

Some sequences are given by a recursive *definition. The value of the first term, a_1, is given, and then we are told how to find any subsequent term from the term preceding it. Find the first six terms of each of the following recursively defined sequences.*

81. $a_1 = 1, a_{n+1} = 5a_n - 2$

82. $a_1 = 0, a_{n+1} = (a_n)^2 + 3$

83. *Value of a projector.* The value of an LCD projector is \$2500. Its scrap value each year is 80% of its value the year before. Write a sequence listing the scrap value of the machine at the start of each year for a 10-yr period.

84. *Cell biology.* A single cell of bacterium divides into two every 15 min. Suppose that the same rate of division is maintained for 4 hr. Write a sequence listing the number of cells after successive 15-min periods.

85. Find S_{100} and S_{101} for the sequence in which $a_n = (-1)^n$.

Find the first five terms of each sequence; then find S_5.

86. $a_n = \dfrac{1}{2^n} \log 1000^n$

87. $a_n = i^n, i = \sqrt{-1}$

88. Find all values for x that solve the following:

$$\sum_{k=1}^{x} i^k = -1.$$

89. The nth term of a sequence is given by

$$a_n = n^5 - 14n^4 + 6n^3 + 416n^2 - 655n - 1050.$$

Use a graphing calculator with a TABLE feature to determine which term in the sequence is 6144.

90. To define a sequence recursively on a graphing calculator (see Exercises 81 and 82), we use the SEQ MODE. The general term U_n or V_n can often be expressed in terms of U_{n-1} or V_{n-1} by pressing **2ND** **7** or **2ND** **8**. The starting values of U_n, V_n, and n are set as one of the WINDOW variables.

Use recursion to determine how many different handshakes occur when 50 people shake hands with one another. To develop the recursion formula, begin with a group of 2 and determine how many additional handshakes occur with the arrival of each new person.

14.2 Arithmetic Sequences and Series

Arithmetic Sequences • Sum of the First *n* Terms of an Arithmetic Sequence • Problem Solving

In this section, we concentrate on sequences and series that are said to be arithmetic (pronounced ar-ith-MET-ik).

Arithmetic Sequences

In an **arithmetic sequence** (or **progression**), adding the same number to any term gives the next term in the sequence. For example, the sequence 2, 5, 8, 11, 14, 17, ... is arithmetic because adding 3 to any term produces the next term.

> ### Arithmetic Sequence
> A sequence is *arithmetic* if there exists a number d, called the *common difference*, such that $a_{n+1} = a_n + d$ for any integer $n \geq 1$.

EXAMPLE 1 For each arithmetic sequence, identify the first term, a_1, and the common difference, d.

a) 4, 9, 14, 19, 24, ...   **b)** 27, 20, 13, 6, −1, −8, ...

SOLUTION   To find a_1, we simply use the first term listed. To find d, we choose any term other than a_1 and subtract the preceding term from it.

Sequence	First Term, a_1	Common Difference, d
a) 4, 9, 14, 19, 24, ...	4	$5 \leftarrow 9 - 4 = 5$
b) 27, 20, 13, 6, −1, −8, ...	27	$-7 \leftarrow 20 - 27 = -7$

To find the common difference, we subtracted a_1 from a_2. Had we subtracted a_2 from a_3 or a_3 from a_4, we would have found the same values for d.

Check: As a check, note that when d is added to each term, the result is the next term in the sequence.

TRY EXERCISE 11

To develop a formula for the general, nth, term of any arithmetic sequence, we denote the common difference by d and write out the first few terms:

$a_1,$
$a_2 = a_1 + d,$
$a_3 = a_2 + d = (a_1 + d) + d = a_1 + 2d,$ Substituting $a_1 + d$ for a_2
$a_4 = a_3 + d = (a_1 + 2d) + d = a_1 + 3d.$ Substituting $a_1 + 2d$ for a_3

Note that the coefficient of d in each case is 1 less than the subscript.

Generalizing, we obtain the following formula.

> ### To Find a_n for an Arithmetic Sequence
> The nth term of an arithmetic sequence with common difference d is
> $$a_n = a_1 + (n - 1)d, \quad \text{for any integer } n \geq 1.$$

EXAMPLE 2 Find the 14th term of the arithmetic sequence 6, 9, 12, 15, ...

SOLUTION   First we note that $a_1 = 6$, $d = 3$, and $n = 14$. Using the formula for the nth term of an arithmetic sequence, we have

$$a_n = a_1 + (n - 1)d$$
$$a_{14} = 6 + (14 - 1) \cdot 3 = 6 + 13 \cdot 3 = 6 + 39 = 45.$$

The 14th term is 45.

TRY EXERCISE 17

EXAMPLE **3**

For the sequence in Example 2, which term is 300? That is, find n if $a_n = 300$.

SOLUTION We substitute into the formula for the nth term of an arithmetic sequence and solve for n:

$$a_n = a_1 + (n - 1)d$$
$$300 = 6 + (n - 1) \cdot 3$$
$$300 = 6 + 3n - 3$$
$$297 = 3n$$
$$99 = n.$$

The term 300 is the 99th term of the sequence.

TRY EXERCISE 23

Given two terms and their places in an arithmetic sequence, we can construct the sequence.

EXAMPLE **4**

The 3rd term of an arithmetic sequence is 14, and the 16th term is 79. Find a_1 and d and construct the sequence.

SOLUTION We know that $a_3 = 14$ and $a_{16} = 79$. Thus we would have to add d a total of 13 times to get from 14 to 79. That is,

$$14 + 13d = 79. \qquad a_3 \text{ and } a_{16} \text{ are 13 terms apart; } 16 - 3 = 13$$

Solving $14 + 13d = 79$, we obtain

$$13d = 65 \qquad \text{Subtracting 14 from both sides}$$
$$d = 5. \qquad \text{Dividing both sides by 13}$$

We subtract d twice from a_3 to get to a_1. Thus,

$$a_1 = 14 - 2 \cdot 5 = 4. \qquad a_1 \text{ and } a_3 \text{ are 2 terms apart; } 3 - 1 = 2$$

The sequence is 4, 9, 14, 19, ... Note that we could have subtracted d a total of 15 times from a_{16} in order to find a_1.

TRY EXERCISE 33

In general, d should be subtracted $(n - 1)$ times from a_n in order to find a_1.

Sum of the First n Terms of an Arithmetic Sequence

When the terms of an arithmetic sequence are added, an **arithmetic series** is formed. To develop a formula for computing S_n when the series is arithmetic, we list the first n terms of the sequence as follows:

This is the next-to-last term. If you add d to this term, the result is a_n.

$$a_1, (a_1 + d), (a_1 + 2d), \ldots, (a_n - 2d), (a_n - d), a_n$$

This term is two terms back from the end. If you add d to this term, you get the next-to-last term, $a_n - d$.

Thus, S_n is given by

$$S_n = a_1 + (a_1 + d) + (a_1 + 2d) + \cdots + (a_n - 2d) + (a_n - d) + a_n.$$

Using a commutative law, we have a second equation:

$$S_n = a_n + (a_n - d) + (a_n - 2d) + \cdots + (a_1 + 2d) + (a_1 + d) + a_1.$$

Adding corresponding terms on each side of the two equations above, we get

$$2S_n = [a_1 + a_n] + [(a_1 + d) + (a_n - d)] + [(a_1 + 2d) + (a_n - 2d)]$$
$$+ \cdots + [(a_n - 2d) + (a_1 + 2d)] + [(a_n - d) + (a_1 + d)] + [a_n + a_1].$$

This simplifies to

$$2S_n = [a_1 + a_n] + [a_1 + a_n] + [a_1 + a_n]$$
$$+ \cdots + [a_n + a_1] + [a_n + a_1] + [a_n + a_1].$$

There are n bracketed sums.

Since $[a_1 + a_n]$ is being added n times, it follows that

$$2S_n = n[a_1 + a_n].$$

Dividing both sides by 2 leads to the following formula.

STUDENT NOTES

The formula for the sum of an arithmetic sequence is very useful, but remember that it does not work for sequences that are not arithmetic.

> **To Find S_n for an Arithmetic Sequence**
>
> The sum of the first n terms of an arithmetic sequence is given by
>
> $$S_n = \frac{n}{2}(a_1 + a_n).$$

EXAMPLE 5   Find the sum of the first 100 positive even numbers.

SOLUTION   The sum is

$$2 + 4 + 6 + \cdots + 198 + 200.$$

This is the sum of the first 100 terms of the arithmetic sequence for which

$$a_1 = 2, \quad n = 100, \quad \text{and} \quad a_n = 200.$$

Substituting in the formula

$$S_n = \frac{n}{2}(a_1 + a_n),$$

we get

$$S_{100} = \frac{100}{2}(2 + 200) = 50(202) = 10{,}100.$$

TRY EXERCISE ▸ 39

The above formula is useful when we know the first and last terms, a_1 and a_n. To find S_n when a_n is unknown, but a_1, n, and d are known, we can use $a_n = a_1 + (n - 1)d$ to calculate a_n and then proceed as in Example 5.

EXAMPLE 6   Find the sum of the first 15 terms of the arithmetic sequence 4, 7, 10, 13, ...

SOLUTION   Note that

$$a_1 = 4, \quad n = 15, \quad \text{and} \quad d = 3.$$

Before using the formula for S_n, we find a_{15}:

$$a_{15} = 4 + (15 - 1)3 \qquad \text{Substituting into the formula for } a_n$$
$$= 4 + 14 \cdot 3 = 46.$$

Thus, knowing that $a_{15} = 46$, we have

$$S_{15} = \tfrac{15}{2}(4 + 46) \qquad \text{Using the formula for } S_n$$
$$= \tfrac{15}{2}(50) = 375.$$

TRY EXERCISE ▸ 37

Problem Solving

In problem-solving situations, translation may involve sequences or series. As always, there is often a variety of ways in which a problem can be solved. You should use the approach that is best or easiest for you. In this chapter, however, we will try to emphasize sequences and series and their related formulas.

EXAMPLE 7

Hourly wages. Chris accepts a job managing a music store, starting with an hourly wage of $14.60, and is promised a raise of 25¢ per hour every 2 months for 5 years. After 5 years of work, what will be Chris's hourly wage?

SOLUTION

1. **Familiarize.** It helps to write down the hourly wage for several two-month time periods.

   Beginning: 14.60,

   After two months: 14.85,

   After four months: 15.10,

   and so on.

   What appears is a sequence of numbers: $14.60, 14.85, 15.10, \ldots$. Since the same amount is added each time, the sequence is arithmetic.

   We list what we know about arithmetic sequences. The pertinent formulas are

   $$a_n = a_1 + (n - 1)d$$

   and

   $$S_n = \frac{n}{2}(a_1 + a_n).$$

   In this case, we are not looking for a sum, so it is probably the first formula that will give us our answer. We want to determine the last term in a sequence. To do so, we need to know a_1, n, and d. From our list above, we see that

   $$a_1 = 14.60 \quad \text{and} \quad d = 0.25.$$

   What is n? That is, how many terms are in the sequence? After 1 year, there have been 6 raises, since Chris gets a raise every 2 months. There are 5 years, so the total number of raises will be $5 \cdot 6$, or 30. Altogether, there will be 31 terms: the original wage and 30 increased rates.

2. **Translate.** We want to find a_n for the arithmetic sequence in which $a_1 = 14.60$, $n = 31$, and $d = 0.25$.

3. **Carry out.** Substituting in the formula for a_n gives us

   $$a_{31} = 14.60 + (31 - 1) \cdot 0.25$$
   $$= 22.10.$$

4. **Check.** We can check by redoing the calculations or we can calculate in a slightly different way for another check. For example, at the end of a year, there will be 6 raises, for a total raise of $1.50. At the end of 5 years, the total raise will be $5 \times \$1.50$, or $7.50. If we add that to the original wage of $14.60, we obtain $22.10. The answer checks.

5. **State.** After 5 years, Chris's hourly wage will be $22.10.

TRY EXERCISE 47

EXAMPLE **8**   *Telephone pole storage.*   A stack of telephone poles has 30 poles in the bottom row. There are 29 poles in the second row, 28 in the next row, and so on. How many poles are in the stack if there are 5 poles in the top row?

SOLUTION

1. **Familiarize.**   The following figure shows the ends of the poles. There are 30 poles on the bottom and one fewer in each successive row. How many rows will there be?

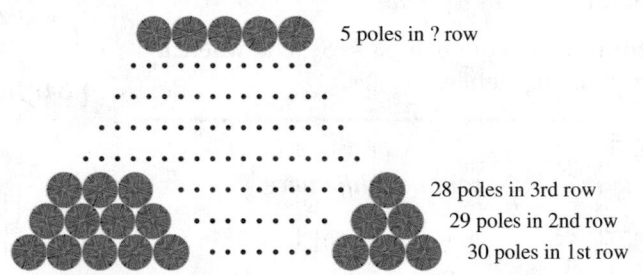

5 poles in ? row

28 poles in 3rd row
29 poles in 2nd row
30 poles in 1st row

Note that there are $30 - 1 = 29$ poles in the 2nd row, $30 - 2 = 28$ poles in the 3rd row, $30 - 3 = 27$ poles in the 4th row, and so on. The pattern leads to $30 - 25 = 5$ poles in the 26th row.

The situation is represented by the equation

$30 + 29 + 28 + \cdots + 5.$ There are 26 terms in this series.

Thus we have an arithmetic series. We recall the formula

$$S_n = \frac{n}{2}(a_1 + a_n).$$

2. **Translate.**   We want to find the sum of the first 26 terms of an arithmetic sequence in which $a_1 = 30$ and $a_{26} = 5$.

3. **Carry out.**   Substituting into the above formula gives us

$S_{26} = \frac{26}{2}(30 + 5)$

$= 13 \cdot 35 = 455.$

4. **Check.**   In this case, we can check the calculations by doing them again. A longer, more difficult way would be to do the entire addition:

$30 + 29 + 28 + \cdots + 5.$

5. **State.**   There are 455 poles in the stack.

TRY EXERCISE 49

 **14.2**   **EXERCISE SET**

 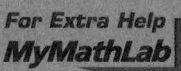 

⤴ **Concept Reinforcement**   *Classify each statement as either true or false.*

1. In an arithmetic sequence, the difference between any two consecutive terms is always the same.

2. In an arithmetic sequence, if $a_9 - a_8 = 4$, then $a_{13} - a_{12} = 4$ as well.

3. In an arithmetic sequence containing 17 terms, the common difference is $a_{17} - a_1$.

4. To find a_{20} in an arithmetic sequence, add the common difference to a_1 a total of 20 times.

5. The sum of the first 20 terms of an arithmetic sequence can be found by knowing just a_1 and a_{20}

6. The sum of the first 30 terms of an arithmetic sequence can be found by knowing just a_1 and d, the common difference.

7. The notation S_5 means $a_1 + a_5$.

8. For any arithmetic sequence, $S_9 = S_8 + d$, where d is the common difference.

Find the first term and the common difference.

9. 8, 13, 18, 23, . . .

10. 2.5, 3, 3.5, 4, . . .

11. 7, 3, −1, −5, . . .

12. −8, −5, −2, 1, . . .

13. $\frac{3}{2}, \frac{9}{4}, 3, \frac{15}{4}, \ldots$

14. $\frac{3}{5}, \frac{1}{10}, -\frac{2}{5}, \ldots$

15. $8.16, $8.46, $8.76, $9.06, . . .

16. $825, $804, $783, $762, . . .

17. Find the 19th term of the arithmetic sequence 10, 18, 26, ...

18. Find the 23rd term of the arithmetic sequence 10, 16, 22, ...

19. Find the 18th term of the arithmetic sequence 8, 2, −4, ...

20. Find the 14th term of the arithmetic sequence $3, \frac{7}{3}, \frac{5}{3}, \ldots$.

21. Find the 13th term of the arithmetic sequence $1200, $964.32, $728.64, ...

22. Find the 10th term of the arithmetic sequence $2345.78, $2967.54, $3589.30, ...

23. In the sequence of Exercise 17, what term is 210?

24. In the sequence of Exercise 18, what term is 208?

25. In the sequence of Exercise 19, what term is −328?

26. In the sequence of Exercise 20, what term is −27?

27. Find a_{18} when $a_1 = 8$ and $d = 10$.

28. Find a_{20} when $a_1 = 12$ and $d = -5$.

29. Find a_1 when $d = 4$ and $a_8 = 33$.

30. Find a_1 when $d = 8$ and $a_{11} = 26$.

31. Find n when $a_1 = 5$, $d = -3$, and $a_n = -76$.

32. Find n when $a_1 = 25$, $d = -14$, and $a_n = -507$.

33. For an arithmetic sequence in which $a_{17} = -40$ and $a_{28} = -73$, find a_1 and d. Write the first five terms of the sequence.

34. In an arithmetic sequence, $a_{17} = \frac{25}{3}$ and $a_{32} = \frac{95}{6}$. Find a_1 and d. Write the first five terms of the sequence.

Aha! 35. Find a_1 and d if $a_{13} = 13$ and $a_{54} = 54$.

36. Find a_1 and d if $a_{12} = 24$ and $a_{25} = 50$.

37. Find the sum of the first 20 terms of the arithmetic series $1 + 5 + 9 + 13 + \cdots$.

38. Find the sum of the first 14 terms of the arithmetic series $11 + 7 + 3 + \cdots$.

39. Find the sum of the first 250 natural numbers.

40. Find the sum of the first 400 natural numbers.

41. Find the sum of the even numbers from 2 to 100, inclusive.

42. Find the sum of the odd numbers from 1 to 99, inclusive.

43. Find the sum of all multiples of 6 from 6 to 102, inclusive.

44. Find the sum of all multiples of 4 that are between 15 and 521.

45. An arithmetic series has $a_1 = 4$ and $d = 5$. Find S_{20}.

46. An arithmetic series has $a_1 = 9$ and $d = -3$. Find S_{32}.

Solve.

47. *Band formations.*   The South Brighton Drum and Bugle Corps has 7 musicians in the front row, 9 in the second row, 11 in the third row, and so on, for 15 rows. How many musicians are in the last row? How many musicians are there altogether?

48. *Gardening.*   A gardener is planting tulip bulbs at the entrance to a college. She puts 50 bulbs in the first row, 46 in the second row, 42 in the third row, and so on, for 13 rows. How many bulbs will be in the last row? How many bulbs will she plant altogether?

49. *Archaeology.*   Many ancient Mayan pyramids were constructed over a span of several generations. Each layer of the pyramid has a stone perimeter, enclosing a layer of dirt or debris on which a structure once stood. One drawing of such a pyramid indicates that the perimeter of the bottom layer contains 36 stones, the next level up contains 32 stones, and so on, up to the top row, which contains 4 stones. How many stones are in the pyramid?

50. *Telephone pole piles.*   How many poles will be in a pile of telephone poles if there are 50 in the first layer, 49 in the second, and so on, until there are 6 in the top layer?

51. *Accumulated savings.*   If 10¢ is saved on October 1, another 20¢ on October 2, another 30¢ on October 3, and so on, how much is saved during October? (October has 31 days.)

52. *Accumulated savings.*   Carrie saves money in an arithmetic sequence: $700 for the first year, another $850 the second, and so on, for 20 yr. How much does she save in all (disregarding interest)?

53. *Auditorium design.*   Theaters are often built with more seats per row as the rows move toward the back. The Community Theater has 20 seats in the first row, 22 in the second, 24 in the third, and so on, for 16 rows. How many seats are in the theater?

54. *Accumulated savings.*   Shirley sets up an investment so that it yields $5000 the first year, $6125 the second year, $7250 the third year, and so on, for 25 yr. What is the total yield from the investment?

55. It is said that as a young child, the mathematician Karl F. Gauss (1777–1855) was able to compute the sum $1 + 2 + 3 + \cdots + 100$ very quickly in his head. Explain how Gauss might have done this and present a formula for the sum of the first n natural numbers. (*Hint:* $1 + 99 = 100$.)

56. Write a problem for a classmate to solve. Devise the problem so that its solution requires computing S_{17} for an arithmetic sequence.

Skill Review

Review finding equations.

Find an equation of the line satisfying the given conditions.

57. Slope $\frac{1}{3}$, *y*-intercept $(0, 10)$ [3.6]

58. Containing the points $(2, 3)$ and $(4, -5)$ [3.7]

59. Containing the point $(5, 0)$ and parallel to the line given by $2x + y = 8$ [3.7]

60. Containing the point $(-1, -4)$ and perpendicular to the line given by $3x - 4y = 7$ [3.7]

Find an equation of the circle satisfying the given conditions. [13.1]

61. Center $(0, 0)$, radius 4

62. Center $(-2, 1)$, radius $2\sqrt{5}$

Synthesis

63. When every term in an arithmetic sequence is an integer, S_n must also be an integer. Given that n, a_1, and a_n may each, at times, be even or odd, explain why $\frac{n}{2}(a_1 + a_n)$ is always an integer.

64. The sum of the first n terms of an arithmetic sequence is also given by

$$S_n = \frac{n}{2}\big[2a_1 + (n - 1)d\big].$$

Use the earlier formulas for a_n and S_n to explain how this equation was developed.

65. A frog is at the bottom of a 100-ft well. With each jump, the frog climbs 4 ft, but then slips back 1 ft. How many jumps does it take for the frog to reach the top of the hole?

66. Find a formula for the sum of the first n consecutive odd numbers starting with 1:

$$1 + 3 + 5 + \cdots + (2n - 1).$$

67. Prove that if p, m, and q are consecutive terms in an arithmetic sequence, then

$$m = \frac{p + q}{2}.$$

68. *Straight-line depreciation.*   A company buys a color laser printer for $5200 on January 1 of a given year. The machine is expected to last for 8 yr, at the end of which time its *trade-in*, or *salvage*, *value* will be $1100. If the company figures the decline in value to be the same each year, then the trade-in values, after t years, $0 \le t \le 8$, form an arithmetic sequence given by

$$a_t = C - t\left(\frac{C - S}{N}\right),$$

where C is the original cost of the item, N the years of expected life, and S the salvage value.

a) Find the formula for a_t for the straight-line depreciation of the printer.
b) Find the trade-in value after 0 yr, 1 yr, 2 yr, 3 yr, 4 yr, 7 yr, and 8 yr.
c) Find a formula that expresses a_t recursively.

69. Use your answer to Exercise 39 to find the sum of all integers from 501 through 750.

14.3   Geometric Sequences and Series

Geometric Sequences • Sum of the First n Terms of a Geometric Sequence •
Infinite Geometric Series • Problem Solving

In an arithmetic sequence, a certain number is added to each term to get the next term. When each term in a sequence is *multiplied* by a certain fixed number to get the next term, the sequence is **geometric**. In this section, we examine both geometric sequences (or progressions) and geometric series.

Geometric Sequences

Consider the sequence

$$2, 6, 18, 54, 162, \ldots$$

If we multiply each term by 3, we obtain the next term. The multiplier is called the *common ratio* because it is found by dividing any term by the preceding term.

> ## Geometric Sequence
> A sequence is *geometric* if there exists a number r, called the *common ratio*, for which
> $$\frac{a_{n+1}}{a_n} = r, \quad \text{or} \quad a_{n+1} = a_n \cdot r \quad \text{for any integer } n \geq 1.$$

EXAMPLE 1 For each geometric sequence, find the common ratio.

a) $4, 20, 100, 500, 2500, \ldots$

b) $3, -6, 12, -24, 48, -96, \ldots$

c) $\$5200, \$3900, \$2925, \$2193.75, \ldots$

SOLUTION

Sequence	*Common Ratio*	
a) $4, 20, 100, 500, 2500, \ldots$	5	$\frac{20}{4} = 5, \frac{100}{20} = 5$, and so on
b) $3, -6, 12, -24, 48, -96, \ldots$	-2	$\frac{-6}{3} = -2, \frac{12}{-6} = -2$, and so on
c) $\$5200, \$3900, \$2925, \$2193.75, \ldots$	0.75	$\dfrac{\$3900}{\$5200} = 0.75, \dfrac{\$2925}{\$3900} = 0.75$

TRY EXERCISE 11

Note that when the signs of the terms alternate, the common ratio is negative.

To develop a formula for the general, or *n*th, term of a geometric sequence, let a_1 be the first term and let r be the common ratio. We write out the first few terms as follows:

$$a_1,$$
$$a_2 = a_1 r,$$
$$a_3 = a_2 r = (a_1 r)r = a_1 r^2, \qquad \text{Substituting } a_1 r \text{ for } a_2$$
$$a_4 = a_3 r = (a_1 r^2)r = a_1 r^3. \qquad \text{Substituting } a_1 r^2 \text{ for } a_3$$

Note that the exponent is 1 less than the subscript.

Generalizing, we obtain the following.

> ## To Find a_n for a Geometric Sequence
> The *n*th term of a geometric sequence with common ratio r is given by
> $$a_n = a_1 r^{n-1}, \quad \text{for any integer } n \geq 1.$$

EXAMPLE 2 Find the 7th term of the geometric sequence $4, 20, 100, \ldots$.

SOLUTION First, we note that

$$a_1 = 4 \quad \text{and} \quad n = 7.$$

To find the common ratio, we can divide any term (other than the first) by the term preceding it. Since the second term is 20 and the first is 4,

$$r = \frac{20}{4}, \quad \text{or } 5.$$

The formula

$$a_n = a_1 r^{n-1}$$

gives us

$$a_7 = 4 \cdot 5^{7-1} = 4 \cdot 5^6 = 4 \cdot 15{,}625 = 62{,}500.$$

> **TRY EXERCISE** 19

EXAMPLE 3 Find the 10th term of the geometric sequence

$$64, -32, 16, -8, \ldots.$$

SOLUTION First, we note that

$$a_1 = 64, \quad n = 10, \quad \text{and} \quad r = \frac{-32}{64} = -\frac{1}{2}.$$

Then, using the formula for the nth term of a geometric sequence, we have

$$a_{10} = 64 \cdot \left(-\frac{1}{2}\right)^{10-1} = 64 \cdot \left(-\frac{1}{2}\right)^9 = 2^6 \cdot \left(-\frac{1}{2^9}\right) = -\frac{1}{2^3} = -\frac{1}{8}.$$

The 10th term is $-\frac{1}{8}$.

> **TRY EXERCISE** 23

Sum of the First n Terms of a Geometric Sequence

We next develop a formula for S_n when a sequence is geometric:

$$a_1, \ a_1 r, \ a_1 r^2, \ a_1 r^3, \ldots, a_1 r^{n-1}, \ldots.$$

The **geometric series** S_n is given by

$$S_n = a_1 + a_1 r + a_1 r^2 + \cdots + a_1 r^{n-2} + a_1 r^{n-1}. \tag{1}$$

Multiplying both sides by r gives us

$$r S_n = a_1 r + a_1 r^2 + a_1 r^3 + \cdots + a_1 r^{n-1} + a_1 r^n. \tag{2}$$

When we subtract corresponding sides of equation (2) from equation (1), the color terms drop out, leaving

$$S_n - r S_n = a_1 - a_1 r^n$$
$$S_n(1 - r) = a_1(1 - r^n), \quad \text{Factoring}$$

or

$$S_n = \frac{a_1(1 - r^n)}{1 - r}. \quad \text{Dividing both sides by } 1 - r$$

To Find S_n for a Geometric Sequence

The sum of the first n terms of a geometric sequence with common ratio r is given by

$$S_n = \frac{a_1(1 - r^n)}{1 - r}, \quad \text{for any } r \neq 1.$$

EXAMPLE 4 Find the sum of the first 7 terms of the geometric sequence $3, 15, 75, 375, \ldots.$

SOLUTION First, we note that

$$a_1 = 3, \quad n = 7, \quad \text{and} \quad r = \frac{15}{3} = 5.$$

Then, substituting in the formula $S_n = \dfrac{a_1(1 - r^n)}{1 - r}$, we have

$$S_7 = \frac{3(1 - 5^7)}{1 - 5} = \frac{3(1 - 78{,}125)}{-4}$$

$$= \frac{3(-78{,}124)}{-4}$$

$$= 58{,}593.$$

> **TRY EXERCISE** 33

Infinite Geometric Series

Suppose we consider the sum of the terms of an infinite geometric sequence, such as 3, 6, 12, 24, 48, ... We get what is called an **infinite geometric series**:

$$3 + 6 + 12 + 24 + 48 + \cdots.$$

Here, as n increases, the sum of the first n terms, S_n, increases without bound. There are also infinite series that get closer and closer to some specific number. Here is an example:

$$\frac{1}{2} + \frac{1}{4} + \frac{1}{8} + \frac{1}{16} + \cdots + \frac{1}{2^n} + \cdots.$$

Let's consider S_n for the first four values of n:

$$
\begin{aligned}
S_1 &= \tfrac{1}{2} & &= \tfrac{1}{2} = 0.5, \\
S_2 &= \tfrac{1}{2} + \tfrac{1}{4} & &= \tfrac{3}{4} = 0.75, \\
S_3 &= \tfrac{1}{2} + \tfrac{1}{4} + \tfrac{1}{8} & &= \tfrac{7}{8} = 0.875, \\
S_4 &= \tfrac{1}{2} + \tfrac{1}{4} + \tfrac{1}{8} + \tfrac{1}{16} & &= \tfrac{15}{16} = 0.9375.
\end{aligned}
$$

> The denominator of each sum is 2^n, where n is the subscript of S. The numerator is $2^n - 1$.

Thus, for this particular series, we have

$$S_n = \frac{2^n - 1}{2^n} = \frac{2^n}{2^n} - \frac{1}{2^n} = 1 - \frac{1}{2^n}.$$

Note that the value of S_n is less than 1 for any value of n, but as n gets larger and larger, the value of $1/2^n$ gets closer to 0 and the value of S_n gets closer to 1. We can visualize S_n by considering a square with area 1. For S_1, we shade half the square. For S_2, we shade half the square plus half the remaining part, or $\tfrac{1}{4}$. For S_3, we shade the parts shaded in S_2 plus half the remaining part. Again we see that the values of S_n will continue to get close to 1 (shading the complete square).

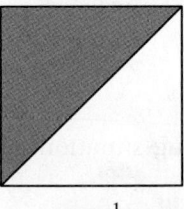

$$S_1 = \frac{1}{2}$$

$$S_2 = \frac{3}{4}$$

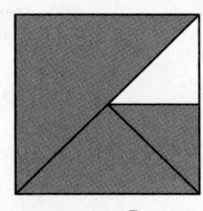

$$S_3 = \frac{7}{8}$$

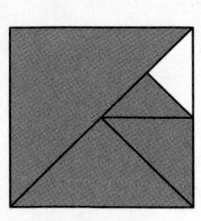

$$S_4 = \frac{15}{16}$$

We say that 1 is the **limit** of S_n and that 1 is the sum of this infinite geometric series. An infinite geometric series is denoted S_∞. It can be shown (but we will not do so here) that the sum of the terms of an infinite geometric sequence exists if and only if $|r| < 1$ (that is, the common ratio's absolute value is less than 1).

To find a formula for the sum of an infinite geometric series, we first consider the sum of the first n terms:

$$S_n = \frac{a_1(1 - r^n)}{1 - r} = \frac{a_1 - a_1 r^n}{1 - r}. \qquad \text{Using the distributive law}$$

For $|r| < 1$, it follows that the value of r^n gets closer to 0 as n gets larger. (Check this by selecting a number between -1 and 1 and finding larger and larger powers on a calculator.) As r^n gets closer to 0, so too does $a_1 r^n$. Thus, S_n gets closer to $a_1/(1 - r)$.

The Limit of an Infinite Geometric Series

For $|r| < 1$, the limit of an infinite geometric series is given by

$$S_\infty = \frac{a_1}{1 - r}. \qquad \text{(For } |r| \geq 1\text{, no limit exists.)}$$

EXAMPLE **5** Determine whether each series has a limit. If a limit exists, find it.

a) $1 + 3 + 9 + 27 + \cdots$ **b)** $-35 + 7 - \frac{7}{5} + \frac{7}{25} + \cdots$

SOLUTION

a) Here $r = 3$, so $|r| = |3| = 3$. Since $|r| \not< 1$, the series does *not* have a limit.

b) Here $r = -\frac{1}{5}$, so $|r| = |-\frac{1}{5}| = \frac{1}{5}$. Since $|r| < 1$, the series *does* have a limit. We find the limit by substituting into the formula for S_∞:

$$S_\infty = \frac{-35}{1 - \left(-\frac{1}{5}\right)} = \frac{-35}{\frac{6}{5}} = -35 \cdot \frac{5}{6} = \frac{-175}{6} = -29\frac{1}{6}.$$

TRY EXERCISE 41

EXAMPLE **6** Find fraction notation for $0.63636363\ldots$.

SOLUTION We can express this as

$$0.63 + 0.0063 + 0.000063 + \cdots.$$

This is an infinite geometric series, where $a_1 = 0.63$ and $r = 0.01$. Since $|r| < 1$, this series has a limit:

$$S_\infty = \frac{a_1}{1 - r} = \frac{0.63}{1 - 0.01} = \frac{0.63}{0.99} = \frac{63}{99}.$$

Thus fraction notation for $0.63636363\ldots$ is $\frac{63}{99}$, or $\frac{7}{11}$.

TRY EXERCISE 53

Problem Solving

For some problem-solving situations, the translation may involve geometric sequences or series.

EXAMPLE   7

Daily wages.   Suppose you were offered a job for the month of September (30 days) under the following conditions. You will be paid $0.01 for the first day, $0.02 for the second, $0.04 for the third, and so on, doubling your previous day's salary each day. How much would you earn? (Would you take the job? Make a guess before reading further.)

SOLUTION

1. **Familiarize.**   You earn $0.01 the first day, $0.01(2) the second day, $0.01(2)(2) the third day, and so on. Since each day's wages are a constant multiple of the previous day's wages, a geometric sequence is formed.

2. **Translate.**   The amount earned is the geometric series

$$\$0.01 + \$0.01(2) + \$0.01(2^2) + \$0.01(2^3) + \cdots + \$0.01(2^{29}),$$

where $a_1 = \$0.01$, $n = 30$, and $r = 2$.

3. **Carry out.**   Using the formula

$$S_n = \frac{a_1(1 - r^n)}{1 - r},$$

we have

$$S_{30} = \frac{\$0.01(1 - 2^{30})}{1 - 2}$$

$$= \frac{\$0.01(-1{,}073{,}741{,}823)}{-1} \qquad \text{Using a calculator}$$

$$= \$10{,}737{,}418.23.$$

4. **Check.**   The calculations can be repeated as a check.

5. **State.**   The pay exceeds $10.7 million for the month. Most people would probably take the job!

TRY EXERCISE ▶ 69

EXAMPLE   8

Loan repayment.   Francine's student loan is in the amount of $6000. Interest is 9% compounded annually, and the entire amount is to be paid after 10 yr. How much is to be paid back?

SOLUTION

1. **Familiarize.**   Suppose we let P represent any principal amount. At the end of one year, the amount owed will be $P + 0.09P$, or $1.09P$. That amount will be the principal for the second year. The amount owed at the end of the second year will be $1.09 \times \text{New principal} = 1.09(1.09P)$, or 1.09^2P. Thus the amount owed at the beginning of successive years is as follows:

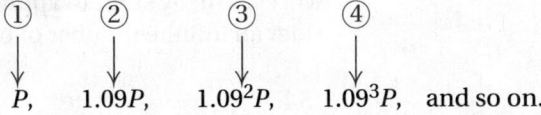

$$P, \qquad 1.09P, \qquad 1.09^2P, \qquad 1.09^3P, \quad \text{and so on.}$$

We have a geometric sequence. The amount owed at the beginning of the 11th year will be the amount owed at the end of the 10th year.

2. **Translate.**   We have a geometric sequence with $a_1 = 6000$, $r = 1.09$, and $n = 11$. The appropriate formula is

$$a_n = a_1 r^{n-1}.$$

3. Carry out. We substitute and calculate:

$$a_{11} = \$6000(1.09)^{11-1} = \$6000(1.09)^{10}$$

$$\approx \$14{,}204.18. \quad \text{Using a calculator and rounding to the nearest hundredth}$$

4. Check. A check, by repeating the calculations, is left to the student.

5. State. Francine will owe \$14,204.18 at the end of 10 yr.

> TRY EXERCISE ▶ 61

> **EXAMPLE** **9**

Bungee jumping. A bungee jumper rebounds 60% of the height jumped. Clyde's bungee jump is made using a cord that stretches to 200 ft.

a) After jumping and then rebounding 9 times, how far has Clyde traveled upward (the total rebound distance)?

b) Theoretically, how far will Clyde travel upward (bounce) before coming to rest?

SOLUTION

1. Familiarize. Let's do some calculations and look for a pattern.

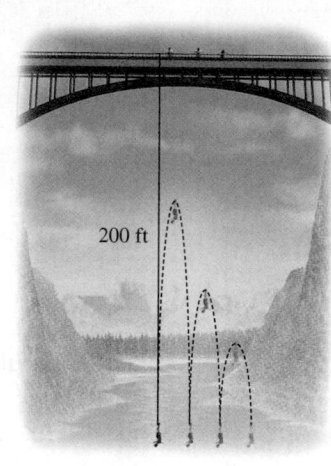

200 ft

First fall:	200 ft
First rebound:	0.6×200, or 120 ft
Second fall:	120 ft, or 0.6×200
Second rebound:	0.6×120, or $0.6(0.6 \times 200)$, which is 72 ft
Third fall:	72 ft, or $0.6(0.6 \times 200)$
Third rebound:	0.6×72, or $0.6(0.6(0.6 \times 200))$, which is 43.2 ft

The rebound distances form a geometric sequence:

① ② ③ ④

$$120, \quad 0.6 \times 120, \quad 0.6^2 \times 120, \quad 0.6^3 \times 120, \ldots.$$

2. Translate.

a) The total rebound distance after 9 bounces is the sum of a geometric sequence. The first term is 120 and the common ratio is 0.6. There will be 9 terms, so we can use the formula

$$S_n = \frac{a_1(1 - r^n)}{1 - r}.$$

b) Theoretically, Clyde will never stop bouncing. Realistically, the bouncing will eventually stop. To approximate the actual distance bounced, we consider an infinite number of bounces and use the formula

$$S_\infty = \frac{a_1}{1 - r}. \quad \text{Since } r = 0.6 \text{ and } |0.6| < 1, \text{ we know that } S_\infty \text{ exists.}$$

3. Carry out.

a) We substitute into the formula and calculate:

$$S_9 = \frac{120[1 - (0.6)^9]}{1 - 0.6} \approx 297. \quad \text{Using a calculator}$$

b) We substitute and calculate:

$$S_\infty = \frac{120}{1 - 0.6} = 300.$$

4. **Check.** We can do the calculations again.

5. **State.**

a) In 9 bounces, Clyde will have traveled upward a total distance of about 297 ft.

b) Theoretically, Clyde will travel upward a total of 300 ft before coming to rest.

TRY EXERCISE ▸ 67

14.3 EXERCISE SET

🢒 **Concept Reinforcement** *Classify each of the following as an arithmetic sequence, a geometric sequence, an arithmetic series, a geometric series, or none of these.*

1. $3, 6, 12, 24, \ldots$

2. $-2, 3, 8, 13, \ldots$

3. $10, 7, 4, 1, -2, \ldots$

4. $1000, 500, 250, 125, \ldots$

5. $4 + 20 + 100 + 500 + 2500 + 12{,}500$

6. $10 + 12 + 14 + 16 + 18 + 20$

7. $3 - \frac{3}{2} + \frac{3}{4} - \frac{3}{8} + \frac{3}{16} - \cdots$

8. $1 + \frac{1}{2} + \frac{1}{3} + \frac{1}{4} + \frac{1}{5} + \frac{1}{6} + \cdots$

Find the common ratio for each geometric sequence.

9. $10, 20, 40, 80, \ldots$

10. $5, 20, 80, 320, \ldots$

11. $6, -0.6, 0.06, -0.006, \ldots$

12. $-5, -0.5, -0.05, -0.005, \ldots$

13. $\frac{1}{2}, -\frac{1}{4}, \frac{1}{8}, -\frac{1}{16}, \ldots$

14. $\frac{2}{3}, -\frac{4}{3}, \frac{8}{3}, -\frac{16}{3}, \ldots$

15. $75, 15, 3, \frac{3}{5}, \ldots$

16. $12, -4, \frac{4}{3}, -\frac{4}{9}, \ldots$

17. $\dfrac{1}{m}, \dfrac{6}{m^2}, \dfrac{36}{m^3}, \dfrac{216}{m^4}, \ldots$

18. $4, \dfrac{4m}{5}, \dfrac{4m^2}{25}, \dfrac{4m^3}{125}, \ldots$

Find the indicated term for each geometric sequence.

19. $2, 6, 18, \ldots$; the 7th term

20. $2, 8, 32, \ldots$; the 9th term

21. $\sqrt{3}, 3, 3\sqrt{3}, \ldots$; the 10th term

22. $2, 2\sqrt{2}, 4, \ldots$; the 8th term

23. $-\frac{8}{243}, \frac{8}{81}, -\frac{8}{27}, \ldots$; the 14th term

24. $\frac{7}{625}, \frac{-7}{125}, \frac{7}{25}, \ldots$; the 13th term

25. $\$1000, \$1040, \$1081.60, \ldots$; the 10th term

26. $\$1000, \$1050, \$1102.50, \ldots$; the 12th term

Find the nth, or general, term for each geometric sequence.

27. $1, 5, 25, 125, \ldots$

28. $2, 4, 8, \ldots$

29. $1, -1, 1, -1, \ldots$

30. $\frac{1}{4}, \frac{1}{16}, \frac{1}{64}, \ldots$

31. $\dfrac{1}{x}, \dfrac{1}{x^2}, \dfrac{1}{x^3}, \ldots$

32. $5, \dfrac{5m}{2}, \dfrac{5m^2}{4}, \ldots$

For Exercises 33–40, use the formula for S_n to find the indicated sum for each geometric series.

33. S_9 for $6 + 12 + 24 + \cdots$

34. S_6 for $16 - 8 + 4 - \cdots$

35. S_7 for $\frac{1}{18} - \frac{1}{6} + \frac{1}{2} - \cdots$

Aha! **36.** S_5 for $7 + 0.7 + 0.07 + \cdots$

37. S_8 for $1 + x + x^2 + x^3 + \cdots$

38. S_{10} for $1 + x^2 + x^4 + x^6 + \cdots$

39. S_{16} for $\$200 + \$200(1.06) + \$200(1.06)^2 + \cdots$

40. S_{23} for $\$1000 + \$1000(1.08) + \$1000(1.08)^2 + \cdots$

Determine whether each infinite geometric series has a limit. If a limit exists, find it.

41. $18 + 6 + 2 + \cdots$

42. $80 + 20 + 5 + \cdots$

43. $7 + 3 + \frac{9}{7} + \cdots$

44. $12 + 9 + \frac{27}{4} + \cdots$

45. $3 + 15 + 75 + \cdots$

46. $2 + 3 + \frac{9}{2} + \cdots$

47. $4 - 6 + 9 - \frac{27}{2} + \cdots$

48. $-6 + 3 - \frac{3}{2} + \frac{3}{4} - \cdots$

49. $0.43 + 0.0043 + 0.000043 + \cdots$

50. $0.37 + 0.0037 + 0.000037 + \cdots$

51. $\$500(1.02)^{-1} + \$500(1.02)^{-2} + \$500(1.02)^{-3} + \cdots$

52. $\$1000(1.08)^{-1} + \$1000(1.08)^{-2} + \$1000(1.08)^{-3} + \cdots$

Find fraction notation for each repeating decimal.

53. $0.5555\ldots$

54. $0.8888\ldots$

55. $3.4646\ldots$

56. $1.2323\ldots$

57. $0.15151515\ldots$

58. $0.12121212\ldots$

📱 *Solve. Use a calculator as needed for evaluating formulas.*

59. *Rebound distance.* A ping-pong ball is dropped from a height of 20 ft and always rebounds one-fourth of the distance fallen. How high does it rebound the 6th time?

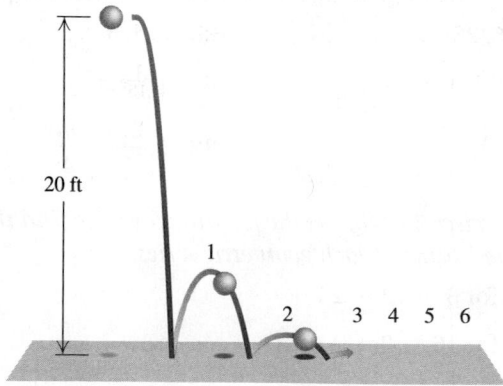

20 ft

1 2 3 4 5 6

60. *Rebound distance.* Approximate the total of the rebound heights of the ball in Exercise 59.

61. *Population growth.* Yorktown has a current population of 100,000, and the population is increasing by 3% each year. What will the population be in 15 yr?

62. *Amount owed.* Gilberto borrows $15,000. The loan is to be repaid in 13 yr at 5.5% interest, compounded annually. How much will be repaid at the end of 13 yr?

63. *Shrinking population.* A population of 5000 fruit flies is dying off at a rate of 4% per minute. How many flies will be alive after 15 min?

64. *Shrinking population.* For the population of fruit flies in Exercise 63, how long will it take for only 1800 fruit flies to remain alive? (*Hint:* Use logarithms.) Round to the nearest minute.

65. *Food service.* Approximately 17 billion espresso-based coffees were sold in the United States in 2007. This number is expected to grow by 4% each year. How many espresso-based coffees will be sold from 2007 through 2015?
Source: Based on data in the *Indianapolis Star*, 11/22/07

66. *Text messaging.* Approximately 160 billion text messages were sent worldwide in 2000. Since then, the number of text messages sent each year has grown by about 140% per year. How many text messages were sent worldwide from 2000 through 2010?
Source: Based on data from mobilesmsmarketing.com

67. *Rebound distance.* A superball dropped from the top of the Washington Monument (556 ft high) rebounds three-fourths of the distance fallen. How far (up and down) will the ball have traveled when it hits the ground for the 6th time?

68. *Rebound distance.* Approximate the total distance that the ball of Exercise 67 will have traveled when it comes to rest.

69. *Stacking paper.* Construction paper is about 0.02 in. thick. Beginning with just one piece, a stack is doubled again and again 10 times. Find the height of the final stack.

70. *Monthly earnings.*   Suppose you accepted a job for the month of February (28 days) under the following conditions. You will be paid $0.01 the first day, $0.02 the second, $0.04 the third, and so on, doubling your previous day's salary each day. How much would you earn?

71. Under what circumstances is it possible for the 5th term of a geometric sequence to be greater than the 4th term but less than the 7th term?

72. When r is negative, a series is said to be *alternating*. Why do you suppose this terminology is used?

Skill Review

To prepare for Section 14.4, review products of binomials (Section 4.5).

Multiply. [4.5]

73. $(x + y)^2$

74. $(x + y)^3$

75. $(x - y)^3$

76. $(x - y)^4$

77. $(2x + y)^3$

78. $(2x - y)^3$

Synthesis

79. Write a problem for a classmate to solve. Devise the problem so that a geometric series is involved and the solution is "The total amount in the bank is $900(1.08)^{40}$, or about $19,550."

80. The infinite series

$$S_\infty = 2 + \frac{1}{2} + \frac{1}{2 \cdot 3} + \frac{1}{2 \cdot 3 \cdot 4} + \frac{1}{2 \cdot 3 \cdot 4 \cdot 5}$$
$$+ \frac{1}{2 \cdot 3 \cdot 4 \cdot 5 \cdot 6} + \cdots$$

is not geometric, but it does have a sum. Using $S_1, S_2, S_3, S_4, S_5,$ and S_6, make a conjecture about the value of S_∞ and explain your reasoning.

Calculate each of the following sums.

81. $\displaystyle\sum_{k=1}^{\infty} 6(0.9)^k$

82. $\displaystyle\sum_{k=1}^{\infty} 5(-0.7)^k$

83. Find the sum of the first n terms of
$$x^2 - x^3 + x^4 - x^5 + \cdots.$$

84. Find the sum of the first n terms of
$$1 + x + x^2 + x^3 + \cdots.$$

85. The sides of a square are each 16 cm long. A second square is inscribed by joining the midpoints of the sides, successively. In the second square we repeat the process, inscribing a third square. If this process is continued indefinitely, what is the sum of all of the areas of all the squares? (*Hint*: Use an infinite geometric series.)

86. Show that $0.999\ldots$ is 1.

87. Using Example 5 and Exercises 41–52, explain how the graph of a geometric sequence can be used to determine whether a geometric series has a limit.

88. To compare the *graphs* of an arithmetic and a geometric sequence, we plot n on the horizontal axis and a_n on the vertical axis. Graph Example 1(a) of Section 14.2 and Example 1(a) of Section 14.3 on the same set of axes. How do the graphs of geometric sequences differ from the graphs of arithmetic sequences?

CONNECTING the CONCEPTS

A *sequence* is simply an ordered list. A *series* is a sum of consecutive terms in a sequence. Some sequences of numbers have patterns and a formula can be found for a general term. If each pair of consecutive terms has a common difference, the sequence is *arithmetic*. If each pair of consecutive terms has a common ratio, the sequence is *geometric*. Arithmetic and geometric sequences have formulas for general terms and for sums.

Arithmetic Sequences	Geometric Sequences
$a_n = a_1 + (n-1)d$	$a_n = a_1 r^{n-1}$
$S_n = \dfrac{n}{2}(a_1 + a_n)$	$S_n = \dfrac{a_1(1-r^n)}{1-r};$ $S_\infty = \dfrac{a_1}{1-r},\ |r| < 1$

MIXED REVIEW

1. Find a_{20} if $a_n = n^2 - 5n$.

2. Write an expression for the general term a_n of the sequence $\frac{1}{2}, \frac{1}{3}, \frac{1}{4}, \frac{1}{5}, \ldots$.

3. Find S_{12} for the sequence $1, 2, 3, 4, \ldots$.

4. Write out and evaluate the sum
   $$\sum_{k=2}^{5} k^2.$$

5. Rewrite using sigma notation:
   $1 - 2 + 3 - 4 + 5 - 6$.

6. Find the common difference for the arithmetic sequence $115, 112, 109, 106, \ldots$.

7. Find the 21st term of the arithmetic sequence $10, 15, 20, 25, \ldots$.

8. Which term is 22 in the arithmetic sequence $10, 10.2, 10.4, 10.6, \ldots$?

9. For an arithmetic sequence, find a_{25} when $a_1 = 9$ and $d = -2$.

10. For an arithmetic sequence, find a_1 when $d = 11$ and $a_5 = 65$.

11. For an arithmetic sequence, find n when $a_1 = 5$, $d = -\frac{1}{2}$, and $a_n = 0$.

12. Find S_{30} for the arithmetic series
    $2 + 12 + 22 + 32 + \cdots$.

13. Find the common ratio for the geometric sequence $\frac{1}{3}, -\frac{1}{6}, \frac{1}{12}, -\frac{1}{24}, \ldots$.

14. Find the 8th term of the geometric sequence $5, 10, 20, 40, \ldots$.

15. Find the nth, or general, term for the geometric sequence $2, -2, 2, -2, \ldots$.

16. Find S_{10} for the geometric series
    $\$100 + \$100(1.03) + \$100(1.03)^2 + \cdots$.

17. Determine whether the infinite geometric series $0.9 + 0.09 + 0.009 + \cdots$ has a limit. If a limit exists, find it.

18. Determine whether the infinite geometric series $0.9 + 9 + 90 + \cdots$ has a limit. If a limit exists, find it.

19. Renata earns \$1 on June 1, another \$2 on June 2, another \$3 on June 3, another \$4 on June 4, and so on. How much does she earn during the 30 days of June?

20. Dwight earns \$1 on June 1, another \$2 on June 2, another \$4 on June 3, another \$8 on June 4, and so on. How much does he earn during the 30 days of June?

CORNER

Bargaining for a Used Car

Focus: Geometric series

Time: 30 minutes

Group size: 2

Materials: Graphing calculators are optional.

ACTIVITY*

1. One group member ("the seller") has a car for sale and is asking $3500. The second ("the buyer") offers $1500. The seller splits the difference ($3500 − $1500 = $2000, and $2000 ÷ 2 = $1000) and lowers the price to $2500. The buyer then splits the difference again ($2500 − $1500 = $1000, and $1000 ÷ 2 = $500) and counters with $2000. Continue in this manner and stop when you are able to agree on the car's selling price to the nearest penny.

2. What should the buyer's initial offer be in order to achieve a purchase price of $2000 or less? (Check several guesses to find the appropriate initial offer.)

---

*This activity is based on the article "Bargaining Theory, or Zeno's Used Cars," by James C. Kirby, *The College Mathematics Journal*, **27**(4), September 1996.

3. The seller's price in the bargaining above can be modeled recursively (see Exercises 81, 82, and 90 in Section 14.1) by the sequence

$$a_1 = 3500, \qquad a_n = a_{n-1} - \frac{d}{2^{2n-3}},$$

where d is the difference between the initial price and the first offer. Use this recursively defined sequence to solve parts (1) and (2) above either manually or by using the SEQ MODE and the TABLE feature of a graphing calculator.

4. The first four terms in the sequence in part (3) can be written as

$$a_1, \quad a_1 - \frac{d}{2}, \quad a_1 - \frac{d}{2} - \frac{d}{8},$$

$$a_1 - \frac{d}{2} - \frac{d}{8} - \frac{d}{32}.$$

Use the formula for the limit of an infinite geometric series to find a simple algebraic formula for the eventual sale price, P, when the bargaining process from above is followed. Verify the formula by using it to solve parts (1) and (2) above.

14.4 | The Binomial Theorem

Binomial Expansion Using Pascal's Triangle   ■   Binomial Expansion Using Factorial Notation

The expression $(x + y)^2$ may be regarded as a series: $x^2 + 2xy + y^2$. This sum of terms is the *expansion* of $(x + y)^2$. For powers greater than 2, finding the expansion of $(x + y)^n$ can be time-consuming. In this section, we look at two methods of streamlining binomial expansion.

Binomial Expansion Using Pascal's Triangle

Consider the following expanded powers of $(a + b)^n$.

$$(a + b)^0 = \qquad\qquad 1$$
$$(a + b)^1 = \qquad\qquad a + b$$
$$(a + b)^2 = \qquad\qquad a^2 + 2a^1b^1 + b^2$$
$$(a + b)^3 = \qquad a^3 + 3a^2b^1 + 3a^1b^2 + b^3$$
$$(a + b)^4 = \quad a^4 + 4a^3b^1 + 6a^2b^2 + 4a^1b^3 + b^4$$
$$(a + b)^5 = a^5 + 5a^4b^1 + 10a^3b^2 + 10a^2b^3 + 5a^1b^4 + b^5$$

Each expansion is a polynomial. There are some patterns worth noting:

1. There is one more term than the power of the binomial, n. That is, there are $n + 1$ terms in the expansion of $(a + b)^n$.

2. In each term, the sum of the exponents is the power to which the binomial is raised.

3. The exponents of a start with n, the power of the binomial, and decrease to 0 (since $a^0 = 1$, the last term has no factor of a). The first term has no factor of b, so powers of b start with 0 and increase to n.

4. The coefficients start at 1, increase through certain values, and then decrease through these same values back to 1.

Let's study the coefficients further. Suppose we wish to expand $(a + b)^8$. The patterns we noticed above indicate 9 terms in the expansion:

$$a^8 + c_1a^7b + c_2a^6b^2 + c_3a^5b^3 + c_4a^4b^4 + c_5a^3b^5 + c_6a^2b^6 + c_7ab^7 + b^8.$$

How can we determine the values for the c's? One method seems very simple, but it has some drawbacks. It involves writing down the coefficients in a triangular array as follows. We form what is known as **Pascal's triangle**:

$(a + b)^0$:					1				
$(a + b)^1$:				1		1			
$(a + b)^2$:			1		2		1		
$(a + b)^3$:		1		3		3		1	
$(a + b)^4$:	1		4		6		4		1
$(a + b)^5$: 1		5		10		10		5		1

There are many patterns in the triangle. Find as many as you can.

Perhaps you discovered a way to write the next row of numbers, given the numbers in the row above it. There are always 1's on the outside. Each remaining number is the sum of the two numbers above:

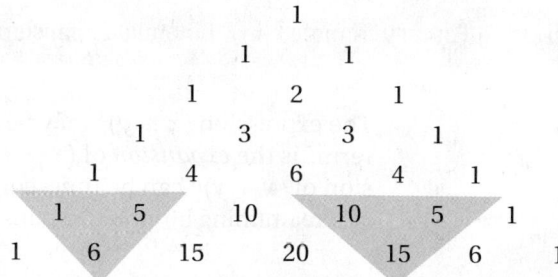

We see that in the bottom (seventh) row

the 1st and last numbers are 1;

the 2nd number is $1 + 5$, or 6;

the 3rd number is $5 + 10$, or 15;

the 4th number is $10 + 10$, or 20;

the 5th number is $10 + 5$, or 15; and

the 6th number is $5 + 1$, or 6.

Thus the expansion of $(a + b)^6$ is

$$(a + b)^6 = 1a^6 + 6a^5b + 15a^4b^2 + 20a^3b^3 + 15a^2b^4 + 6ab^5 + 1b^6.$$

To expand $(a + b)^8$, we complete two more rows of Pascal's triangle:

```
                     1
                  1     1
               1     2     1
            1     3     3     1
         1     4     6     4     1
      1     5    10    10     5     1
   1     6    15    20    15     6     1
 1    7    21    35    35    21    7    1
1   8   28   56   70   56   28   8   1
```

The expansion of $(a + b)^8$ has coefficients found in the 9th row above:

$$(a + b)^8 = 1a^8 + 8a^7b + 28a^6b^2 + 56a^5b^3 + 70a^4b^4 + 56a^3b^5 + 28a^2b^6 + 8ab^7 + 1b^8.$$

We can generalize our results as follows:

The Binomial Theorem (Form 1)

For any binomial $a + b$ and any natural number n,

$$(a + b)^n = c_0a^nb^0 + c_1a^{n-1}b^1 + c_2a^{n-2}b^2$$
$$+ \cdots + c_{n-1}a^1b^{n-1} + c_na^0b^n,$$

where the numbers $c_0, c_1, c_2, \ldots, c_n$ are from the $(n + 1)$st row of Pascal's triangle.

A proof of the binomial theorem is beyond the scope of this text.

EXAMPLE **1**   Expand: $(u - v)^5$.

SOLUTION   Using the binomial theorem, we have $a = u$, $b = -v$, and $n = 5$. We use the 6th row of Pascal's triangle: 1   5   10   10   5   1. Thus,

$$(u - v)^5 = [u + (-v)]^5 \quad \text{Rewriting } u - v \text{ as a sum}$$
$$= 1(u)^5 + 5(u)^4(-v)^1 + 10(u)^3(-v)^2 + 10(u)^2(-v)^3$$
$$+ 5(u)^1(-v)^4 + 1(-v)^5$$
$$= u^5 - 5u^4v + 10u^3v^2 - 10u^2v^3 + 5uv^4 - v^5.$$

Note that the signs of the terms alternate between $+$ and $-$. When $-v$ is raised to an odd power, the sign is $-$; when the power is even, the sign is $+$.

EXAMPLE **2**   Expand: $\left(2t + \dfrac{3}{t}\right)^6$.

SOLUTION   Note that $a = 2t$, $b = 3/t$, and $n = 6$. We use the 7th row of Pascal's triangle: 1 6 15 20 15 6 1. Thus,

$$\left(2t + \frac{3}{t}\right)^6 = 1(2t)^6 + 6(2t)^5\left(\frac{3}{t}\right)^1 + 15(2t)^4\left(\frac{3}{t}\right)^2 + 20(2t)^3\left(\frac{3}{t}\right)^3$$

$$+ 15(2t)^2\left(\frac{3}{t}\right)^4 + 6(2t)^1\left(\frac{3}{t}\right)^5 + 1\left(\frac{3}{t}\right)^6$$

$$= 64t^6 + 6\left(32t^5\right)\left(\frac{3}{t}\right) + 15(16t^4)\left(\frac{9}{t^2}\right) + 20(8t^3)\left(\frac{27}{t^3}\right)$$

$$+ 15(4t^2)\left(\frac{81}{t^4}\right) + 6(2t)\left(\frac{243}{t^5}\right) + \frac{729}{t^6}$$

$$= 64t^6 + 576t^4 + 2160t^2 + 4320 + 4860t^{-2} + 2916t^{-4} + 729t^{-6}.$$

Binomial Expansion Using Factorial Notation

The drawback to using Pascal's triangle is that we must compute all the preceding rows in the table to obtain the row we need. The following method avoids this difficulty. It will also enable us to find a specific term—say, the 8th term—without computing all the other terms in the expansion. This method is useful in such courses as finite mathematics, calculus, and statistics.

To develop the method, we need some new notation. Products of successive natural numbers, such as $6 \cdot 5 \cdot 4 \cdot 3 \cdot 2 \cdot 1$ and $8 \cdot 7 \cdot 6 \cdot 5 \cdot 4 \cdot 3 \cdot 2 \cdot 1$, have a special notation. For the product $6 \cdot 5 \cdot 4 \cdot 3 \cdot 2 \cdot 1$, we write 6!, read "6 factorial."

Factorial Notation

For any natural number n,

$$n! = n(n - 1)(n - 2)\cdots(3)(2)(1).$$

Here are some examples:

$$6! = 6 \cdot 5 \cdot 4 \cdot 3 \cdot 2 \cdot 1 = 720,$$
$$5! =\quad\; 5 \cdot 4 \cdot 3 \cdot 2 \cdot 1 = 120,$$
$$4! =\quad\quad\; 4 \cdot 3 \cdot 2 \cdot 1 = \;24,$$
$$3! =\quad\quad\quad\; 3 \cdot 2 \cdot 1 = \quad6,$$
$$2! =\quad\quad\quad\quad\; 2 \cdot 1 = \quad2,$$
$$1! =\quad\quad\quad\quad\quad\; 1 = \quad1.$$

We also define 0! to be 1 for reasons explained shortly.

To simplify expressions like

$$\frac{8!}{5!\,3!},$$

note that

$$8! = 8 \cdot 7 \cdot 6 \cdot 5 \cdot 4 \cdot 3 \cdot 2 \cdot 1 = 8 \cdot 7! = 8 \cdot 7 \cdot 6! = 8 \cdot 7 \cdot 6 \cdot 5!$$

and so on.

> **CAUTION!** $\dfrac{6!}{3!} \neq 2!$ To see this, note that
>
> $$\dfrac{6!}{3!} = \dfrac{6 \cdot 5 \cdot 4 \cdot \cancel{3} \cdot \cancel{2} \cdot \cancel{1}}{\cancel{3} \cdot \cancel{2} \cdot \cancel{1}} = 6 \cdot 5 \cdot 4.$$

EXAMPLE 3   Simplify: $\dfrac{8!}{5!3!}$.

SOLUTION

$$\dfrac{8!}{5!3!} = \dfrac{8 \cdot 7 \cdot 6 \cdot 5!}{5! \cdot 3 \cdot 2 \cdot 1} = 8 \cdot 7 \qquad \text{Removing a factor equal to 1: } \dfrac{6 \cdot 5!}{5! \cdot 3 \cdot 2} = 1$$

$$= 56$$

▶ **TRY EXERCISE** 15

STUDENT NOTES

It is important to recognize factorial notation as representing a product with descending factors. Thus, $7!$, $7 \cdot 6!$, and $7 \cdot 6 \cdot 5!$ all represent the same product.

The following notation is used in our second formulation of the binomial theorem.

$\dbinom{n}{r}$ **Notation**

For n and r nonnegative integers with $n \geq r$,

$$\dbinom{n}{r}, \quad \text{read "} n \text{ choose } r \text{,"} \quad \text{means} \quad \dfrac{n!}{(n-r)!\,r!}.^*$$

EXAMPLE 4   Simplify: **(a)** $\dbinom{7}{2}$; **(b)** $\dbinom{9}{6}$; **(c)** $\dbinom{6}{6}$.

SOLUTION

a) $\dbinom{7}{2} = \dfrac{7!}{(7-2)!\,2!}$

$$= \dfrac{7!}{5!\,2!} = \dfrac{7 \cdot 6 \cdot 5!}{5! \cdot 2 \cdot 1} = \dfrac{7 \cdot 6}{2} \qquad \text{We can write } 7! \text{ as } 7 \cdot 6 \cdot 5! \text{ to aid our simplification.}$$

$$= 7 \cdot 3$$

$$= 21$$

TECHNOLOGY CONNECTION

The PRB option of the MATH menu provides access to both factorial calculations and NCR. In both cases, a number must be entered first. To find $\dbinom{7}{2}$, we press ⑦ **MATH**, select PRB and NCR, and press ② **ENTER**.

```
7 nCr 2
                          21
```

1. Find $12!$.
2. Find $\dbinom{8}{3}$ and $\dbinom{12}{5}$.

---

*In many books and for many calculators, the notation $_nC_r$ is used instead of $\dbinom{n}{r}$.

b) $\begin{pmatrix} 9 \\ 6 \end{pmatrix} = \dfrac{9!}{3!6!}$

$= \dfrac{9 \cdot 8 \cdot 7 \cdot 6!}{3 \cdot 2 \cdot 1 \cdot 6!} = \dfrac{9 \cdot 8 \cdot 7}{3 \cdot 2}$ Writing 9! as $9 \cdot 8 \cdot 7 \cdot 6!$ to help with simplification

$= 3 \cdot 4 \cdot 7$

$= 84$

c) $\begin{pmatrix} 6 \\ 6 \end{pmatrix} = \dfrac{6!}{0!6!} = \dfrac{6!}{1 \cdot 6!}$ Since $0! = 1$

$= \dfrac{6!}{6!}$

$= 1$

TRY EXERCISE 17

Now we can restate the binomial theorem using our new notation.

The Binomial Theorem (Form 2)

For any binomial $a + b$ and any natural number n,

$$(a + b)^n = \begin{pmatrix} n \\ 0 \end{pmatrix} a^n + \begin{pmatrix} n \\ 1 \end{pmatrix} a^{n-1}b + \begin{pmatrix} n \\ 2 \end{pmatrix} a^{n-2}b^2 + \cdots + \begin{pmatrix} n \\ n \end{pmatrix} b^n.$$

EXAMPLE 5   Expand: $(3x + y)^4$.

SOLUTION   We use the binomial theorem (Form 2) with $a = 3x$, $b = y$, and $n = 4$:

$(3x + y)^4 = \begin{pmatrix} 4 \\ 0 \end{pmatrix}(3x)^4 + \begin{pmatrix} 4 \\ 1 \end{pmatrix}(3x)^3 y + \begin{pmatrix} 4 \\ 2 \end{pmatrix}(3x)^2 y^2 + \begin{pmatrix} 4 \\ 3 \end{pmatrix}(3x)y^3 + \begin{pmatrix} 4 \\ 4 \end{pmatrix} y^4$

$= \dfrac{4!}{4!0!} 3^4 x^4 + \dfrac{4!}{3!1!} 3^3 x^3 y + \dfrac{4!}{2!2!} 3^2 x^2 y^2 + \dfrac{4!}{1!3!} 3xy^3 + \dfrac{4!}{0!4!} y^4$

$= 1 \cdot 81x^4 + 4 \cdot 27x^3 y + 6 \cdot 9x^2 y^2 + 4 \cdot 3xy^3 + y^4$

$= 81x^4 + 108x^3 y + 54x^2 y^2 + 12xy^3 + y^4.$ Simplifying

TRY EXERCISE 29

EXAMPLE 6   Expand: $(x^2 - 2y)^{5}$.

SOLUTION   In this case, $a = x^2$, $b = -2y$, and $n = 5$:

$(x^2 - 2y)^5 = \begin{pmatrix} 5 \\ 0 \end{pmatrix}(x^2)^5 + \begin{pmatrix} 5 \\ 1 \end{pmatrix}(x^2)^4 (-2y) + \begin{pmatrix} 5 \\ 2 \end{pmatrix}(x^2)^3 (-2y)^2$

$\qquad + \begin{pmatrix} 5 \\ 3 \end{pmatrix}(x^2)^2 (-2y)^3 + \begin{pmatrix} 5 \\ 4 \end{pmatrix}(x^2)(-2y)^4 + \begin{pmatrix} 5 \\ 5 \end{pmatrix}(-2y)^5$

$\qquad = \dfrac{5!}{5!0} x^{10} + \dfrac{5!}{4!1!} x^8 (-2y) + \dfrac{5!}{3!2!} x^6 (-2y)^2$

$\qquad + \dfrac{5!}{2!3!} x^4 (-2y)^3 + \dfrac{5!}{1!4!} x^2 (-2y)^4 + \dfrac{5!}{0!5!} (-2y)^5$

$\qquad = x^{10} - 10x^8 y + 40x^6 y^2 - 80x^4 y^3 + 80x^2 y^4 - 32y^5.$

TRY EXERCISE 35

Note that in the binomial theorem (Form 2), $\binom{n}{0}a^n b^0$ gives us the first term, $\binom{n}{1}a^{n-1}b^1$ gives us the second term, $\binom{n}{2}a^{n-2}b^2$ gives us the third term, and so on. This can be generalized to give a method for finding a specific term without writing the entire expansion.

Finding a Specific Term

When $(a + b)^n$ is expanded and written in descending powers of a, the $(r + 1)$st term is

$$\binom{n}{r}a^{n-r}b^r.$$

EXAMPLE 7

Find the 5th term in the expansion of $(2x - 3y)^7$.

SOLUTION To find the 5th term, we note that $5 = 4 + 1$. Thus, $r = 4$, $a = 2x$, $b = -3y$, and $n = 7$. Using the above formula, we have

$$\binom{n}{r}a^{n-r}b^r = \binom{7}{4}(2x)^{7-4}(-3y)^4, \text{ or } \frac{7!}{3!\,4!}(2x)^3(-3y)^4, \text{ or } 22{,}680x^3y^4.$$

TRY EXERCISE 45

It is because of the binomial theorem that $\binom{n}{r}$ is called a *binomial coefficient*. We can now explain why 0! is defined to be 1. In the binomial theorem,

$\binom{n}{0}$ must equal 1 when using the definition $\binom{n}{r} = \dfrac{n!}{(n - r)!\,r!}$.

Thus we must have

$$\binom{n}{0} = \frac{n!}{(n - 0)!\,0!} = \frac{n!}{n!\,0!} = 1.$$

This is satisfied only if 0! is defined to be 1.

Visualizing for Success

A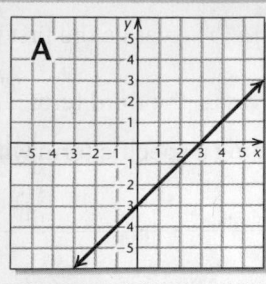

B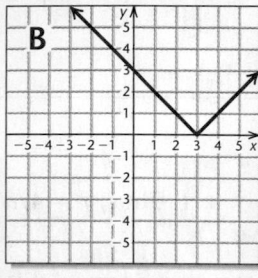

C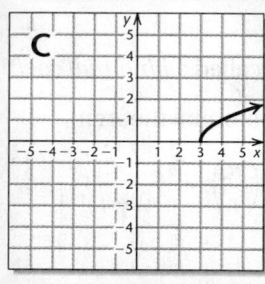

D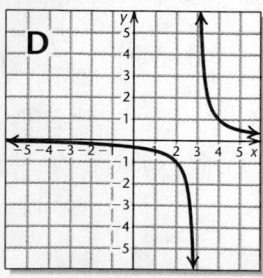

E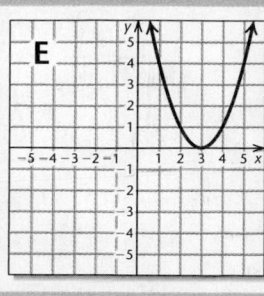

F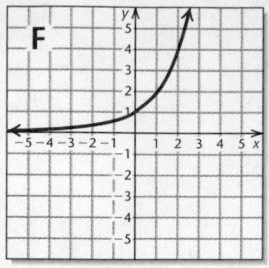

G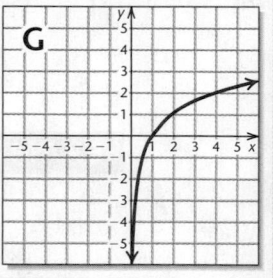

H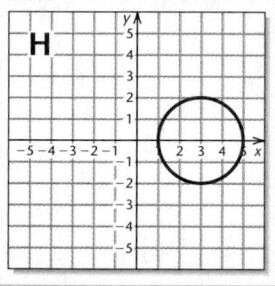

I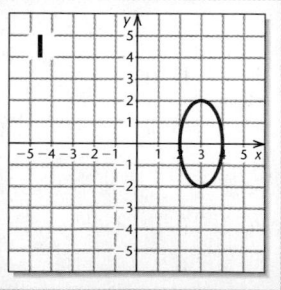

J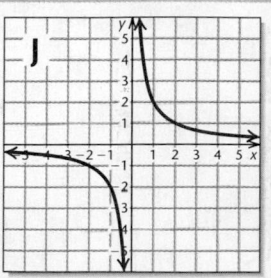

Match each equation with its graph.

1. $xy = 2$

2. $y = \log_2 x$

3. $y = x - 3$

4. $(x - 3)^2 + y^2 = 4$

5. $\dfrac{(x - 3)^2}{1} + \dfrac{y^2}{4} = 1$

6. $y = |x - 3|$

7. $y = (x - 3)^2$

8. $y = \dfrac{1}{x - 3}$

9. $y = 2^x$

10. $y = \sqrt{x - 3}$

Answers on page A-67

An additional, animated version of this activity appears in MyMathLab. To use MyMathLab, you need a course ID and a student access code. Contact your instructor for more information.

14.4 EXERCISE SET

 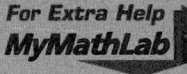

Concept Reinforcement *Complete each of the following.*

1. The last term in the expansion of $(x + 2)^5$ is _____.

2. The expansion of $(x + y)^7$, when simplified, contains a total of _____ terms.

3. In the expansion of $(a + b)^9$, the exponents in each term add to _____.

4. The expression _____ represents $4 \cdot 3 \cdot 2 \cdot 1$.

5. The expression _____ represents $\dfrac{8!}{3! \, 5!}$.

6. In the expansion of $(a + b)^{10}$, the coefficient of $a^8 b^2$ is the same as the coefficient of _____.

7. In the expansion of $(x + y)^9$, the coefficient of y^9 is _____.

8. The notation $\begin{pmatrix} 9 \\ 5 \end{pmatrix}$ is read _____.

Simplify.

9. $4!$

10. $9!$

11. $10!$

12. $12!$

13. $\dfrac{10!}{8!}$

14. $\dfrac{12!}{10!}$

15. $\dfrac{9!}{4! \, 5!}$

16. $\dfrac{10!}{6! \, 4!}$

17. $\begin{pmatrix} 10 \\ 4 \end{pmatrix}$

18. $\begin{pmatrix} 8 \\ 5 \end{pmatrix}$

Aha! 19. $\begin{pmatrix} 9 \\ 9 \end{pmatrix}$

20. $\begin{pmatrix} 7 \\ 7 \end{pmatrix}$

21. $\begin{pmatrix} 30 \\ 2 \end{pmatrix}$

22. $\begin{pmatrix} 51 \\ 49 \end{pmatrix}$

23. $\begin{pmatrix} 40 \\ 38 \end{pmatrix}$

24. $\begin{pmatrix} 35 \\ 2 \end{pmatrix}$

Expand. Use both of the methods shown in this section.

25. $(a - b)^4$

26. $(m + n)^5$

27. $(p + q)^7$

28. $(x - y)^6$

29. $(3c - d)^7$

30. $(x^2 - 3y)^5$

31. $(t^{-2} + 2)^6$

32. $(3c - d)^6$

33. $(x - y)^5$

34. $(x - y)^3$

35. $\left(3s + \dfrac{1}{t} \right)^9$

36. $\left(x + \dfrac{2}{y} \right)^9$

37. $(x^3 - 2y)^5$

38. $(a^2 - b^3)^5$

39. $(\sqrt{5} + t)^6$

40. $(\sqrt{3} - t)^4$

41. $\left(\dfrac{1}{\sqrt{x}} - \sqrt{x} \right)^6$

42. $(x^{-2} + x^2)^4$

Find the indicated term for each binomial expression.

43. 3rd, $(a + b)^6$

44. 6th, $(x + y)^7$

45. 12th, $(a - 3)^{14}$

46. 11th, $(x - 2)^{12}$

47. 5th, $(2x^3 + \sqrt{y})^8$

48. 4th, $\left(\dfrac{1}{b^2} + c \right)^7$

49. Middle, $(2u + 3v^2)^{10}$

50. Middle two, $(\sqrt{x} + \sqrt{3})^5$

Aha! 51. 9th, $(x - y)^8$

52. 13th, $(a - \sqrt{b})^{12}$

53. Maya claims that she can calculate mentally the first two and the last two terms of the expansion of $(a + b)^n$ for any whole number n. How do you think she does this?

54. Without performing any calculations, explain why the expansions of $(x - y)^8$ and $(y - x)^8$ must be equal.

Skill Review

Review graphing equations and inequalities.

Graph.

55. $y = x^2 - 5$ [11.7]

56. $y = x - 5$ [3.6]

57. $y \geq x - 5$ [9.4]

58. $y = 5^x$ [12.2]

59. $f(x) = \log_5 x$ [12.3]

60. $x^2 + y^2 = 5$ [13.1]

Synthesis

61. Explain how someone can determine the x^2-term of the expansion of $\left(x - \dfrac{3}{x} \right)^{10}$ without calculating any other terms.

62. Devise two problems requiring the use of the binomial theorem. Design the problems so that one is solved more easily using Form 1 and the other is solved more easily using Form 2. Then explain what makes one form easier to use than the other in each case.

63. Show that there are exactly $\begin{pmatrix} 5 \\ 3 \end{pmatrix}$ ways of choosing a subset of size 3 from $\{a, b, c, d, e\}$.

64. *Baseball.* During the 2007 season, Matt Holliday of the Colorado Rockies had a batting average of 0.340. In that season, if someone were to randomly select 5 of his "at-bats," the probability of Holliday getting exactly 3 hits would be the 3rd term of the binomial expansion of $(0.340 + 0.660)^5$. Find that term and use a calculator to estimate the probability.
Source: www.mlb.com

65. *Widows or divorcees.* The probability that a woman will be either widowed or divorced is 85%. If 8 women are randomly selected, the probability that exactly 5 of them will be either widowed or divorced is the 6th term of the binomial expansion of $(0.15 + 0.85)^8$. Use a calculator to estimate that probability.

66. *Baseball.* In reference to Exercise 64, the probability that Holliday will get *at most* 3 hits is found by adding the last 4 terms of the binomial expansion of $(0.340 + 0.660)^5$. Find these terms and use a calculator to estimate the probability.

67. *Widows or divorcees.* In reference to Exercise 65, the probability that *at least* 6 of the women will be widowed or divorced is found by adding the last three terms of the binomial expansion of $(0.15 + 0.85)^8$. Find these terms and use a calculator to estimate the probability.

68. Find the term of
$$\left(\dfrac{3x^2}{2} - \dfrac{1}{3x} \right)^{12}$$
that does not contain x.

69. Prove that
$$\begin{pmatrix} n \\ r \end{pmatrix} = \begin{pmatrix} n \\ n - r \end{pmatrix}$$
for any whole numbers n and r. Assume $r \le n$.

70. Find the middle term of $(x^2 - 6y^{3/2})^6$.

71. Find the ratio of the 4th term of
$$\left(p^2 - \dfrac{1}{2} p \sqrt[3]{q} \right)^5$$
to the 3rd term.

72. Find the term containing $\dfrac{1}{x^{1/6}}$ of
$$\left(\sqrt[3]{x} - \dfrac{1}{\sqrt{x}} \right)^7.$$

Aha! **73.** Multiply: $(x^2 + 2xy + y^2)(x^2 + 2xy + y^2)^2(x + y)$.

74. What is the degree of $(x^3 + 2)^4$?

Study Summary

KEY TERMS AND CONCEPTS	EXAMPLES

SECTION 14.1: SEQUENCES AND SERIES

An ordered list of numbers that ends is a **finite sequence**.

An ordered list of numbers that does not end is an **infinite sequence**.

A **series** is a sum of terms of a sequence.

$5, 7, 8, 11, 17$ is a finite sequence.

$6, 9, 12, 15, \ldots$ is an infinite sequence.

$6 + 9 + 12 + 15 + \cdots$ is an infinite series.

Sigma or **Summation Notation**

$$\sum_{k=1}^{n} a_k$$

k is the **index of summation**

$$\sum_{k=3}^{5} (-1)^k (k^2) = (-1)^3 (3^2) + (-1)^4 (4^2) + (-1)^5 (5^2)$$
$$= -1 \cdot 9 + 1 \cdot 16 + (-1) \cdot 25$$
$$= -9 + 16 - 25 = -18$$

SECTION 14.2: ARITHMETIC SEQUENCES AND SERIES

Arithmetic Sequences and Series

$a_{n+1} = a_n + d$ — d is the **common difference**.

$a_n = a_1 + (n-1)d$ — The nth term

$S_n = \dfrac{n}{2}(a_1 + a_n)$ — The sum of the first n terms

For the arithmetic sequence $10, 7, 4, 1, \ldots$:

$d = -3$;

$a_7 = 10 + (7-1)(-3) = 10 - 18 = -8$;

$S_7 = \dfrac{7}{2}(10 + (-8)) = \dfrac{7}{2}(2) = 7.$

SECTION 14.3: GEOMETRIC SEQUENCES AND SERIES

Geometric Sequences and Series

$a_{n+1} = a_n \cdot r$ — r is the **common ratio**.

$a_n = a_1 r^{n-1}$ — The nth term

$S_n = \dfrac{a_1(1 - r^n)}{1 - r}, r \neq 1$ — The sum of the first n terms

$S_\infty = \dfrac{a_1}{1 - r}, |r| < 1$ — Limit of an infinite geometric series

For the geometric sequence $25, -5, 1, -\frac{1}{5}, \ldots$:

$r = -\dfrac{1}{5}$;

$a_7 = 25\left(-\dfrac{1}{5}\right)^{7-1} = 5^2 \cdot \dfrac{1}{5^6} = \dfrac{1}{625}$;

$S_7 = \dfrac{25\left(1 - \left(-\frac{1}{5}\right)^7\right)}{1 - \left(-\frac{1}{5}\right)} = \dfrac{5^2\left(\frac{78,126}{5^7}\right)}{\frac{6}{5}} = \dfrac{13,021}{625}$;

$S_\infty = \dfrac{25}{1 - \left(-\frac{1}{5}\right)} = \dfrac{125}{6}.$

SECTION 14.4: THE BINOMIAL THEOREM

Factorial Notation

$n! = n(n-1)(n-2) \cdots 3 \cdot 2 \cdot 1$

$7! = 7 \cdot 6 \cdot 5 \cdot 4 \cdot 3 \cdot 2 \cdot 1 = 5040$

Binomial Coefficient

$\dbinom{n}{r} = {}_nC_r = \dfrac{n!}{(n-r)!\, r!}$

$\dbinom{10}{3} = {}_{10}C_3 = \dfrac{10!}{7!\, 3!} = \dfrac{10 \cdot 9 \cdot 8 \cdot 7!}{7! \cdot 3 \cdot 2 \cdot 1} = 120$

Binomial Theorem

$$(a + b)^n = \binom{n}{0}a^n + \binom{n}{1}a^{n-1}b + \cdots + \binom{n}{n}b^n$$

$$(r + 1)\text{st term of } (a + b)^n: \binom{n}{r}a^{n-r}b^r$$

$$(1 - 2x)^3 = \binom{3}{0}1^3 + \binom{3}{1}1^2(-2x)$$

$$+ \binom{3}{2}1(-2x)^2 + \binom{3}{3}(-2x)^3$$

$$= 1 \cdot 1 + 3 \cdot 1(-2x) + 3 \cdot 1 \cdot (4x^2) + 1 \cdot (-8x^3)$$

$$= 1 - 6x + 12x^2 - 8x^3$$

$$3\text{rd term of } (1 - 2x)^3: \binom{3}{2}(1)^1(-2x)^2 = 12x^2 \qquad r = 2$$

Review Exercises: Chapter 14

👈 **Concept Reinforcement**   *Classify each statement as either true or false.*

1. The next term in the arithmetic sequence $10, 15, 20, \ldots$ is 35. [14.2]

2. The next term in the geometric sequence $2, 6, 18, 54, \ldots$ is 162. [14.3]

3. $\displaystyle\sum_{k=1}^{3} k^2$ means $1^2 + 2^2 + 3^3$. [14.1]

4. If $a_n = 3n - 1$, then $a_{17} = 19$. [14.1]

5. A geometric sequence has a common difference. [14.3]

6. The infinite geometric series $10 - 5 + \frac{5}{2} - \cdots$ has a limit. [14.3]

7. For any natural number $n, n! = n(n - 1)$. [14.4]

8. When simplified, the expansion of $(x + y)^{17}$ has 19 terms. [14.4]

Find the first four terms; the 8th term, a_8; and the 12th term, a_{12}. [14.1]

9. $a_n = 10n - 9$

10. $a_n = \dfrac{n - 1}{n^2 + 1}$

Write an expression for the general term of each sequence. Answers may vary. [14.1]

11. $-5, -10, -15, -20, \ldots$

12. $-1, 3, -5, 7, -9, \ldots$

Write out and evaluate each sum. [14.1]

13. $\displaystyle\sum_{k=1}^{5} (-2)^k$

14. $\displaystyle\sum_{k=2}^{7} (1 - 2k)$

Rewrite using sigma notation. [14.1]

15. $7 + 14 + 21 + 28 + 35 + 42$

16. $\dfrac{-1}{2} + \dfrac{1}{4} + \dfrac{-1}{8} + \dfrac{1}{16} + \dfrac{-1}{32}$

17. Find the 14th term of the arithmetic sequence $-3, -7, -11, \ldots$. [14.2]

18. An arithmetic sequence has $a_1 = 11$ and $a_{16} = 14$. Find the common difference, d. [14.2]

19. An arithmetic sequence has $a_8 = 20$ and $a_{24} = 100$. Find the first term, a_1, and the common difference, d. [14.2]

20. Find the sum of the first 17 terms of the arithmetic series $-8 + (-11) + (-14) + \cdots$. [14.2]

21. Find the sum of all the multiples of 5 from 5 to 500, inclusive. [14.2]

22. Find the 20th term of the geometric sequence $2, 2\sqrt{2}, 4, \ldots$. [14.3]

23. Find the common ratio of the geometric sequence $40, 30, \frac{45}{2}, \ldots$. [14.3]

24. Find the nth term of the geometric sequence $-2, 2, -2, \ldots$. [14.3]

25. Find the nth term of the geometric sequence $3, \frac{3}{4}x, \frac{3}{16}x^2, \ldots$ [14.3]

26. Find S_6 for the geometric series

$$3 + 15 + 75 + \cdots.$$

[14.3]

27. Find S_{12} for the geometric series

$$3x - 6x + 12x - \cdots. \quad [14.3]$$

Determine whether each infinite geometric series has a limit. If a limit exists, find it. [14.3]

28. $6 + 3 + 1.5 + 0.75 + \cdots$

29. $7 - 4 + \frac{16}{7} - \cdots$

30. $-\dfrac{1}{2} + \dfrac{1}{2} + \left(-\dfrac{1}{2}\right) + \dfrac{1}{2} + \cdots$

31. $0.04 + 0.08 + 0.16 + 0.32 + \cdots$

32. $\$2000 + \$1900 + \$1805 + \$1714.75 + \cdots$

33. Find fraction notation for $0.555555\ldots$ [14.3]

34. Find fraction notation for $1.454545\ldots$ [14.3]

35. Tyrone took a job working in a convenience store starting with an hourly wage of $11.50. He was promised a raise of 40¢ per hour every 3 mos for 8 yr. After 8 yr, what will be his hourly wage? [14.2]

36. A stack of poles has 42 poles in the bottom row. There are 41 poles in the second row, 40 poles in the third row, and so on, ending with 1 pole in the top row. How many poles are in the stack? [14.2]

37. Janine's student loan is for $12,000 at 4%, compounded annually. The total amount is to be paid off in 7 yr. How much will she then owe? [14.3]

38. Find the total rebound distance of a ball, given that it is dropped from a height of 12 m and each rebound is one-third of the preceding one. [14.3]

Simplify. [14.4]

39. 7!

40. $\dbinom{10}{3}$

41. Find the 3rd term of $(a + b)^{20}$. [14.4]

42. Expand: $(x - 2y)^4$. [14.4]

Synthesis

43. What happens to a_n in a geometric sequence with $|r| < 1$, as n gets larger? Why? [14.3]

44. Compare the two forms of the binomial theorem given in the text. Under what circumstances would one be more useful than the other? [14.4]

45. Find the sum of the first n terms of the geometric series $1 - x + x^2 - x^3 + \cdots$. [14.3]

46. Expand: $(x^{-3} + x^3)^5$. [14.4]

Test: Chapter 14

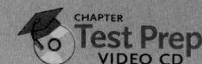

1. Find the first five terms and the 12th term of a sequence with general term $a_n = \dfrac{1}{n^2 + 1}$.

2. Write an expression for the general term of the sequence $\frac{4}{3}, \frac{4}{9}, \frac{4}{27}, \ldots$.

3. Write out and evaluate:
$$\sum_{k=2}^{5} (1 - 2^k).$$

4. Rewrite using sigma notation:
$$1 + (-8) + 27 + (-64) + 125.$$

5. Find the 13th term, a_{13}, of the arithmetic sequence $\frac{1}{2}, 1, \frac{3}{2}, 2, \ldots$.

6. Find the common difference d of an arithmetic sequence when $a_1 = 7$ and $a_7 = -11$.

7. Find a_1 and d of an arithmetic sequence when $a_5 = 16$ and $a_{10} = -3$.

8. Find the sum of all the multiples of 12 from 24 to 240, inclusive.

9. Find the 10th term of the geometric sequence $-3, 6, -12, \ldots$.

10. Find the common ratio of the geometric sequence $22\frac{1}{2}, 15, 10, \ldots$.

11. Find the nth term of the geometric sequence $3, 9, 27, \ldots$.

12. Find S_9 for the geometric series
$$11 + 22 + 44 + \cdots.$$

Determine whether each infinite geometric series has a limit. If a limit exists, find it.

13. $0.5 + 0.25 + 0.125 + \cdots$

14. $0.5 + 1 + 2 + 4 + \cdots$

15. $\$1000 + \$80 + \$6.40 + \cdots$

16. Find fraction notation for $0.85858585\ldots$.

17. An auditorium has 31 seats in the first row, 33 seats in the second row, 35 seats in the third row, and so on, for 18 rows. How many seats are in the 17th row?

18. Alyssa's uncle Ken gave her \$100 for her first birthday, \$200 for her second birthday, \$300 for her third birthday, and so on, until her eighteenth birthday. How much did he give her in all?

19. Each week the price of a \$10,000 boat will be reduced 5% of the previous week's price. If we assume that it is not sold, what will be the price after 10 weeks?

20. Find the total rebound distance of a ball that is dropped from a height of 18 m, with each rebound two-thirds of the preceding one.

21. Simplify: $\dbinom{12}{9}$.

22. Expand: $(x - 3y)^5$.

23. Find the 4th term in the expansion of $(a + x)^{12}$.

Synthesis

24. Find a formula for the sum of the first n even natural numbers:
$$2 + 4 + 6 + \cdots + 2n.$$

25. Find the sum of the first n terms of
$$1 + \frac{1}{x} + \frac{1}{x^2} + \frac{1}{x^3} + \cdots.$$

Simplify.

1. $\left| -\dfrac{2}{3} + \dfrac{1}{5} \right|$ [1.8]

2. $y - [3 - 4(5 - 2y) - 3y]$ [14.3]

3. $(10 \cdot 8 - 9 \cdot 7)^2 - 54 \div 9 - 3$ [1.8]

4. $(2.7 \times 10^{-24})(3.1 \times 10^9)$ [4.2]

5. Evaluate
$$\dfrac{ab - ac}{bc}$$
for $a = -2$, $b = 3$, and $c = -4$. [1.8]

Perform the indicated operations to create an equivalent expression. Be sure to simplify your result if possible.

6. $(5a^2 - 3ab - 7b^2) - (2a^2 + 5ab + 8b^2)$ [4.7]

7. $(2a - 1)(2a + 1)$ [4.6]

8. $(3a^2 - 5y)^2$ [4.7]

9. $\dfrac{1}{x - 2} - \dfrac{4}{x^2 - 4} + \dfrac{3}{x + 2}$ [6.4]

10. $\dfrac{x^2 - 6x + 8}{4x + 12} \cdot \dfrac{x + 3}{x^2 - 4}$ [6.2]

11. $\dfrac{3x + 3y}{5x - 5y} \div \dfrac{3x^2 + 3y^2}{5x^3 - 5y^3}$ [6.2]

12. $\dfrac{x - \dfrac{a^2}{x}}{1 + \dfrac{a}{x}}$ [6.5]

13. $\sqrt{12a}\,\sqrt{12a^3b}$ [10.3]

14. $(-9x^2y^5)(3x^8y^{-7})$ [4.2]

15. $(125x^6y^{1/2})^{2/3}$ [10.2]

16. $\dfrac{\sqrt[3]{x^2y^5}}{\sqrt[4]{xy^2}}$ [10.5]

17. $(4 + 6i)(2 - i)$, where $i = \sqrt{-1}$ [10.8]

Factor, if possible, to form an equivalent expression.

18. $4x^2 - 12x + 9$ [5.4]

19. $27a^3 - 8$ [5.5]

20. $12s^4 - 48t^2$ [5.4]

21. $15y^4 + 33y^2 - 36$ [5.3]

22. Divide:
$$(7x^4 - 5x^3 + x^2 - 4) \div (x - 2).\ [4.8]$$

23. For the function described by
$$f(x) = 3x^2 - 4x,$$
find $f(-2)$. [7.1]

Find the domain of each function.

24. $f(x) = \sqrt{2x - 8}$ [10.1]

25. $g(x) = \dfrac{x - 4}{x^2 - 10x + 25}$ [9.2]

26. Write an equivalent expression by rationalizing the denominator:
$$\dfrac{1 - \sqrt{x}}{1 + \sqrt{x}}.\ [10.5]$$

27. Find a linear equation whose graph has a y-intercept of $(0, -8)$ and is parallel to the line whose equation is $3x - y = 6$. [3.6]

28. Write a quadratic equation whose solutions are $5\sqrt{2}$ and $-5\sqrt{2}$. [11.3]

29. Find the center and the radius of the circle given by
$$x^2 + y^2 - 4x + 6y - 23 = 0.\ [13.1]$$

30. Write an equivalent expression that is a single logarithm:
$$\tfrac{2}{3}\log_a x - \tfrac{1}{2}\log_a y + 5\log_a z.\ [12.4]$$

31. Write an equivalent exponential equation:
$$\log_a c = 5.\ [12.3]$$

Use a calculator to find each of the following. Round to four decimal places. [12.5]

32. $\log 120$

33. $\log_5 3$

34. Find the distance between the points $(-1, -5)$ and $(2, -1)$. [10.7]

35. Find the 21st term of the arithmetic sequence $19, 12, 5, \ldots$. [14.2]

36. Find the sum of the first 25 terms of the arithmetic series $-1 + 2 + 5 + \cdots$. [14.2]

37. Write an expression for the general term of the geometric sequence $16, 4, 1, \ldots$. [14.3]

38. Find the 7th term of $(a - 2b)^{10}$. [14.4]

39. Find the sum of the first nine terms of the geometric series $4 + 6 + 9 + \cdots$. [14.3]

Solve.

40. $8(x - 1) - 3(x - 2) = 1$ [2.2]

41. $\dfrac{6}{x} + \dfrac{6}{x + 2} = \dfrac{5}{2}$ [6.6]

42. $2x + 1 > 5 \; or \; x - 7 \le 3$ [9.2]

43. $5x + 6y = -2,$
$3x + 10y = 2$ [8.2]

44. $x + y - z = 0,$
$3x + y + z = 6,$
$x - y + 2z = 5$ [8.4]

45. $3\sqrt{x - 1} = 5 - x$ [10.6]

46. $x^4 - 29x^2 + 100 = 0$ [11.5]

47. $x^2 + y^2 = 8,$
$x^2 - y^2 = 2$ [13.4]

48. $4^x = 12$ [12.6]

49. $\log(x^2 - 25) - \log(x + 5) = 3$ [12.6]

50. $\log_5 x = -2$ [12.6]

51. $7^{2x+3} = 49$ [12.6]

52. $|2x - 1| \le 5$ [9.3]

53. $15x^2 + 45 = 0$ [11.1]

54. $x^2 + 4x = 3$ [11.2]

55. $y^2 + 3y > 10$ [11.9]

56. Let $f(x) = x^2 - 2x$. Find a such that $f(a) = 80$. [11.1]

57. If $f(x) = \sqrt{-x + 4} + 3$ and $g(x) = \sqrt{x - 2} + 3$, find a such that $f(a) = g(a)$. [10.6]

58. Solve $V = P - Prt$ for r. [2.3]

59. Solve $I = \dfrac{R}{R + r}$ for R. [7.5]

Graph.

60. $3x - y = 7$ [3.6]

61. $x^2 + y^2 = 100$ [13.1]

62. $\dfrac{x^2}{36} - \dfrac{y^2}{9} = 1$ [13.3]

63. $y = \log_2 x$ [12.3]

64. $f(x) = 2^x - 3$ [12.2]

65. $2x - 3y < -6$ [9.4]

66. Graph: $f(x) = -2(x - 3)^2 + 1$. [11.7]

    a) Label the vertex.
    b) Draw the axis of symmetry.
    c) Find the maximum or minimum value.

Solve.

67. The Brighton recreation department plans to fence in a rectangular park next to a river. (Note that no fence will be needed along the river.) What is the area of the largest region that can be fenced in with 200 ft of fencing? [11.8]

68. The perimeter of a rectangular sign is 34 ft. The length of a diagonal is 13 ft. Find the dimensions of the sign. [13.4]

69. A movie club offers two types of membership. Limited members pay a fee of $40 a year and can rent movies for $2.45 each. Preferred members pay $60 a year and can rent movies for $1.65 each. For what numbers of annual movie rentals would it be less expensive to be a preferred member? [9.1]

70. Find three consecutive odd integers whose sum is 177. [2.5]

71. Cosmos Tastes mixes herbs that cost $2.68 an ounce with herbs that cost $4.60 an ounce to create a seasoning that costs $3.80 an ounce. How many ounces of each herb should be mixed together to make 24 oz of the seasoning? [8.3]

72. An airplane can fly 190 mi with the wind in the same time it takes to fly 160 mi against the wind. The speed of the wind is 30 mph. How fast can the plane fly in still air? [6.7]

73. Jared can tap the sugar maple trees in Southway Farm in 21 hr. Delia can tap the trees in 14 hr. How long would it take them, working together, to tap the trees? [6.7]

74. The centripetal force F of an object moving in a circle varies directly as the square of the velocity v and inversely as the radius r of the circle. If $F = 8$ when $v = 1$ and $r = 10$, what is F when $v = 2$ and $r = 16$? [7.5]

75. *Mortgages.*   The loan-to-value ratio of a mortgage is the ratio of the amount owed on the loan to the value of the home. In 2002, the average homeowner owed 80% of the value of the home. By 2007, largely due to falling home prices, this amount had risen to 87%.
Source: UBS Mortgage Strategy Group

a) What was the average rate of change? [3.4]
b) Find a linear function that fits the data. Let t represent the number of years since 2000. [7.3]
c) Use the function from part (b) to predict the average loan-to-value ratio in 2010. [7.3]
d) Assuming the trend continues, in what year will the average U.S. homeowner owe 95% of the value of the home? [7.3]

76. *Mortgages.*   In a reverse mortgage, the lender makes payments to the borrower and the borrower keeps control of the house. The loan is repaid when the house is sold. The number of reverse mortgages in the United States has increased exponentially from approximately 160 in 1990 to 108,000 in 2007. [12.7]
Source: U.S. Department of Housing and Urban Development

a) Find the exponential growth rate k, and write an equation for an exponential function that can be used to predict the number of reverse mortgages t years after 1990.
b) Predict the number of reverse mortgages in 2012.
c) In what year will there be 1 million reverse mortgages?

77. *Retirement.*   Sarita invested $2000 in a retirement account on her 22nd birthday. If the account earns 5% interest, compounded annually, how much will this investment be worth on her 62nd birthday? [14.3]

Synthesis

Solve.

78. $\dfrac{9}{x} - \dfrac{9}{x + 12} = \dfrac{108}{x^2 + 12x}$ [6.6]

79. $\log_2(\log_3 x) = 2$ [12.6]

80. y varies directly as the cube of x and x is multiplied by 0.5. What is the effect on y? [7.5]

81. Diaphantos, a famous mathematician, spent $\frac{1}{6}$ of his life as a child, $\frac{1}{12}$ as an adolescent, and $\frac{1}{7}$ as a bachelor. Five years after he was married, he had a son who died 4 years before his father at half his father's final age. How long did Diaphantos live? [8.5]

Elementary Algebra Review

BEN GIVENS
WIND FARM OPERATIONS
MANAGER
Trent, Texas

The operations and maintenance of a wind farm depend heavily on data. We use many complicated mathematical algorithms to analyze the performance of the turbines. Production data are used to determine royalty payments and revenue for the project on a monthly basis. Without math, there would be no way to perform these tasks.

AN APPLICATION

The number of watts of power P generated by a particular turbine at a wind speed of x miles per hour can be approximated by the polynomial

$$P = 0.0157x^3 + 0.1163x^2 - 1.3396x + 3.7063.$$

Estimate the power generated by a 10-mph wind.

Source: Based on data from *QST*, November 2006

This exercise appears as Exercise 47 in Section R.4.

R.1
Introduction to Algebraic Expressions

A Review of Chapter 1

R.2
Equations, Inequalities, and Problem Solving

A Review of Chapter 2

R.3
Introduction to Graphing

A Review of Chapter 3

R.4
Polynomials

A Review of Chapter 4

R.5
Polynomials and Factoring

A Review of Chapter 5

R.6
Rational Expressions and Equations

A Review of Chapter 6

T his chapter is a review of the first six chapters of this text. Each section corresponds to a chapter of the text. For further explanation of the topics in this chapter, refer to the section or pages referenced in the margin.

R.1   Introduction to Algebraic Expressions

The Real Numbers   •   Operations on Real Numbers   •   Algebraic Expressions

The Real Numbers

Sets of real numbers (Section 1.4)

> ### Sets of Numbers
> *Natural numbers:* $\{1, 2, 3, \dots\}$
> *Whole numbers:* $\{0, 1, 2, 3, \dots\}$
> *Integers:* $\{\dots, -3, -2, -1, 0, 1, 2, 3, \dots\}$
> *Rational numbers:* $\left\{ \dfrac{a}{b} \,\middle|\, a \text{ and } b \text{ are integers and } b \neq 0 \right\}$

Terminating decimals (p. 32)

Repeating decimals (p. 32)

Irrational numbers (p. 32)

Real numbers (p. 33)

Rational numbers can always be written as **terminating** or **repeating** decimals. **Irrational numbers,** like $\sqrt{2}$ or π, can be thought of as nonterminating and nonrepeating decimals. The set of **real numbers** consists of all rational and irrational numbers, taken together.

Real numbers can be represented by points on a number line.

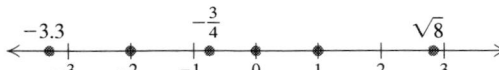

Order (p. 34)

Equation (p. 6)

Inequality (p. 34)

We can compare, or **order,** real numbers by their graphs on the number line. For any two numbers, the one to the left is less than the one to the right.

Sentences like $\frac{1}{4} = 0.25$, containing an equals sign, are called **equations**. An **inequality** is a sentence containing $>$ (is greater than), $<$ (is less than), $\geq$ (is greater than or equal to), or $\leq$ (is less than or equal to). Equations and inequalities can be true or false.

EXAMPLE **1**   Write true or false for each equation or inequality.

a) $-2\frac{1}{3} = -\frac{7}{3}$ **b)** $1 = -1$ **c)** $-5 < -2$

d) $-3 \geq 2$ **e)** $1.1 \leq 1.1$

SOLUTION

a) $-2\frac{1}{3} = -\frac{7}{3}$ is *true* because $-2\frac{1}{3}$ and $-\frac{7}{3}$ represent the same number.

b) $1 = -1$ is a *false* equation.

c) $-5 < -2$ is *true* because -5 is to the left of -2 on the number line.

d) $-3 \geq 2$ is *false* because neither $-3 > 2$ nor $-3 = 2$ is true.

e) $1.1 \leq 1.1$ is *true* because $1.1 = 1.1$ is true.

TRY EXERCISE   1

Absolute value (p. 35)

The distance of a number from 0 is called the **absolute value** of the number. The notation $|-4|$ represents the absolute value of -4. The absolute value of a number is never negative.

EXAMPLE 2

Find the absolute value: **(a)** $|-4|$; **(b)** $\left|\frac{11}{3}\right|$; **(c)** $|0|$.

SOLUTION

a) $|-4| = 4$ since -4 is 4 units from 0.

b) $\left|\frac{11}{3}\right| = \frac{11}{3}$ since $\frac{11}{3}$ is $\frac{11}{3}$ units from 0.

c) $|0| = 0$ since 0 is 0 units from itself.

TRY EXERCISE   7

Operations on Real Numbers

Addition (Section 1.5)

Rules for Addition of Real Numbers

1. *Positive numbers*: Add as usual. The answer is positive.
2. *Negative numbers*: Add absolute values and make the answer negative.
3. *A positive and a negative number*: Subtract the smaller absolute value from the greater absolute value. Then:
   a) If the positive number has the greater absolute value, the answer is positive.
   b) If the negative number has the greater absolute value, the answer is negative.
   c) If the numbers have the same absolute value, the answer is 0.
4. *One number is zero*: The sum is the other number.

Opposite (p. 44)

Every real number has an **opposite**. The opposite of -6 is 6, the opposite of 3.7 is -3.7, and the opposite of 0 is itself. When opposites are added, the result is 0. Finding the opposite of a number is often called "changing its sign."

Subtraction of real numbers is defined in terms of addition and opposites.

Subtraction (Section 1.6)

Subtraction of Real Numbers

To subtract, add the opposite of the number being subtracted.

The rules for multiplication of real numbers can be stated together.

Multiplication and division (Section 1.7)

Rules for Multiplication and Division

To multiply or divide two nonzero real numbers:

1. Using the absolute values, multiply or divide, as indicated.
2. If the signs are the same, the answer is positive.
3. If the signs are different, the answer is negative.

EXAMPLE 3

Perform the indicated operations: **(a)** $-13 + (-9)$; **(b)** $-\frac{4}{5} + \frac{1}{10}$; **(c)** $-6 - (-7.3)$; **(d)** $3(-1.5)$; **(e)** $\left(-\frac{4}{9}\right) \div \left(-\frac{2}{5}\right)$.

SOLUTION

a) $-13 + (-9) = -22$

Two negatives. *Think:* Add the absolute values, 13 and 9, to get 22. Make the answer *negative,* -22.

b) $-\frac{4}{5} + \frac{1}{10} = -\frac{8}{10} + \frac{1}{10} = -\frac{7}{10}$

A negative and a positive. *Think:* The difference of absolute values is $\frac{8}{10} - \frac{1}{10}$, or $\frac{7}{10}$. The negative number has the larger absolute value, so the answer is *negative,* $-\frac{7}{10}$.

c) $-6 - (-7.3) = -6 + 7.3 = 1.3$

Change the subtraction to addition and add the opposite.

d) $3(-1.5) = -4.5$

Think: $3(1.5) = 4.5$. The signs are different, so the answer is negative.

e) $\left(-\frac{4}{9}\right) \div \left(-\frac{2}{5}\right) = \left(-\frac{4}{9}\right) \cdot \left(-\frac{5}{2}\right)$

Multiplying by the reciprocal. The answer is positive.

$= \frac{20}{18} = \frac{10}{9} \cdot \frac{2}{2} = \frac{10}{9}$

TRY EXERCISE 11

Division by 0 (p. 55)

Exponential notation (p. 60)

Addition, subtraction, and multiplication are defined for all real numbers, but we cannot **divide by 0**. For example, $\frac{0}{3} = 0 \div 3 = 0$, but $\frac{3}{0} = 3 \div 0$ is **undefined**.

A product like $2 \cdot 2 \cdot 2 \cdot 2$, in which the factors are the same, is called a **power**. Powers are often written using **exponential notation**:

$2 \cdot 2 \cdot 2 \cdot 2 = 2^4.$ ← There are 4 factors; 4 is the *exponent*.

⌐— 2 is the *base*.

A number raised to the power of 1 is the number itself; for example, $3^1 = 3$.

An expression containing a series of operations is not necessarily evaluated from left to right. Instead, we perform the operations according to the following rules.

Rules for Order of Operations

1. Calculate within the innermost grouping symbols, $(\ )$, $[\ ]$, $\{\ \}$, $|\ |$, and above or below fraction bars.
2. Simplify all exponential expressions.
3. Perform all multiplications and divisions, working from left to right.
4. Perform all additions and subtractions, working from left to right.

EXAMPLE 4

Simplify: $3 - [(4 \times 5) + 12 \div 2^3 \times 6] + 5$.

SOLUTION

$3 - [(4 \times 5) + 12 \div 2^3 \times 6] + 5$

$= 3 - [20 + 12 \div 2^3 \times 6] + 5$ Doing the calculations in the innermost parentheses first

$= 3 - [20 + 12 \div 8 \times 6] + 5$ Working inside the brackets; evaluating 2^3

$= 3 - [20 + 1.5 \times 6] + 5$ $12 \div 8$ is the first multiplication or division working from left to right.

$$= 3 - [20 + 9] + 5 \qquad \text{Multiplying}$$

$$= 3 - 29 + 5 \qquad \begin{array}{l}\text{Completing the calculations}\\\text{within the brackets}\end{array}$$

$$\left.\begin{array}{l}= -26 + 5\\= -21\end{array}\right\} \qquad \begin{array}{l}\text{Adding and subtracting from}\\\text{left to right}\end{array}$$

> TRY EXERCISE 45

Algebraic expression (p. 3)

Constant (p. 2)

Variable (p. 2)

Evaluate (p. 3)

Substitute (p. 3)

Algebraic Expressions

In an **algebraic expression** like $2xt^3$, the number 2 is a **constant** and x and t are **variables**. Algebraic expressions containing variables can be **evaluated** by **substituting** a number for each variable in the expression and following the rules for order of operations.

EXAMPLE   5

The perimeter P of a rectangle of length l and width w is given by the formula $P = 2l + 2w$. Find the perimeter when l is 16 in. and w is 7.5 in.

SOLUTION   We evaluate, substituting 16 in. for l and 7.5 in. for w and carrying out the operations:

$$P = 2l + 2w$$

Substitute. $= 2 \cdot 16 + 2 \cdot 7.5$

Carry out the operations. $= 32 + 15$

$= 47$ in.

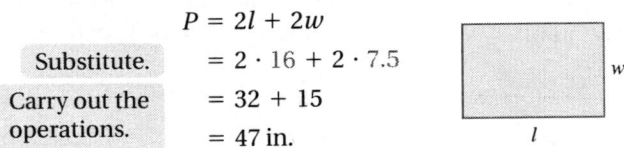

> TRY EXERCISE 59

Expressions that represent the same number are said to be **equivalent**. The laws that follow provide methods for writing equivalent expressions.

Laws and Properties of Real Numbers

Commutative laws:	$a + b = b + a; \ ab = ba$
Associative laws:	$a + (b + c) = (a + b) + c;$ $a(bc) = (ab)c$
Distributive law:	$a(b + c) = ab + ac$
Identity property of 1:	$1 \cdot a = a \cdot 1 = a$
Identity property of 0:	$a + 0 = 0 + a = a$
Law of opposites:	$a + (-a) = 0$
Multiplicative property of 0:	$0 \cdot a = a \cdot 0 = 0$
Property of -1:	$-1 \cdot a = -a$
Opposite of a sum:	$-(a + b) = -a + (-b)$
$\dfrac{-a}{b} = \dfrac{a}{-b} = -\dfrac{a}{b},$	$\dfrac{-a}{-b} = \dfrac{a}{b}$

Factor (p. 17)

The distributive law can be used to multiply and to **factor** expressions. We factor an expression when we write an equivalent expression that is a product.

EXAMPLE **6**   Write an equivalent expression as indicated.

a) Multiply: $-2(5x - 3)$.   **b)** Factor: $5x + 10y + 5$.

SOLUTION

a) $-2(5x - 3) = -2(5x + (-3))$ Adding the opposite

$\qquad = -2 \cdot 5x + (-2) \cdot (-3)$ Using the distributive law

$\qquad = (-2 \cdot 5)x + 6$ Using the associative law for
    multiplication

$\qquad = -10x + 6$

b) $5x + 10y + 5 = 5 \cdot x + 5 \cdot 2y + 5 \cdot 1$ The common factor is 5.

$\qquad = 5(x + 2y + 1)$ Using the distributive law

Factoring can be checked by multiplying:

$$5(x + 2y + 1) = 5 \cdot x + 5 \cdot 2y + 5 \cdot 1 = 5x + 10y + 5.$$

TRY EXERCISES ▸ 61 and 69

Terms (p. 17)

Combine like terms (p. 41)

The **terms** of an algebraic expression are separated by plus signs. When two terms have variable factors that are exactly the same, the terms are called **like**, or **similar**, **terms**. The distributive law enables us to **combine**, or **collect**, **like terms**.

EXAMPLE **7**   Combine like terms: $-5m + 3n - 4n + 10m$.

SOLUTION

$-5m + 3n - 4n + 10m$

$= -5m + 3n + (-4n) + 10m$ Rewriting as addition

$= -5m + 10m + 3n + (-4n)$ Using the commutative law
    of addition

$= (-5 + 10)m + (3 + (-4))n$ Using the distributive law

$= 5m + (-n)$

$= 5m - n$ Rewriting as subtraction

TRY EXERCISE ▸ 75

We can also use the distributive law to help simplify algebraic expressions containing parentheses.

EXAMPLE **8**   Simplify: **(a)** $4x - (y - 2x)$; **(b)** $3(t + 2) - 6(t - 1)$.

SOLUTION

a) $4x - (y - 2x) = 4x - y + 2x$ Removing parentheses and changing the
    sign of every term

$\qquad = 6x - y$ Combining like terms

b) $3(t + 2) - 6(t - 1) = 3t + 6 - 6t + 6$ Multiplying each term of $t + 2$ by
    3 and each term of $t - 1$ by -6

$\qquad = -3t + 12$ Combining like terms

TRY EXERCISE ▸ 81

Value (p. 3)
Solution (p. 6)

If the expressions on each side of an equation have the same **value** for a given number, then that number is a **solution** of the equation.

EXAMPLE **9**   Determine whether each number is a solution of $x - 2 = -5$.

a) 3   **b)** -3

SOLUTION

a) We have:

$$x - 2 = -5 \quad \text{Writing the equation}$$
$$3 - 2 \mid -5 \quad \text{Substituting 3 for } x$$
$$1 \overset{?}{=} -5 \quad 1 = -5 \text{ is FALSE}$$

Since $3 - 2 = -5$ is false, 3 is not a solution of $x - 2 = -5$.

b) We have

$$x - 2 = -5$$
$$-3 - 2 \mid -5$$
$$-5 \overset{?}{=} -5 \quad \text{TRUE}$$

Since $-3 - 2 = -5$ is true, -3 is a solution of $x - 2 = -5$.

TRY EXERCISE 89

**Translating to algebraic
expressions** (p. 4)

Translating to equations (p. 6)

Certain word phrases can be translated to algebraic expressions. These in turn can often be used to translate problems to equations.

EXAMPLE **10**   *Energy Use.*   Translate the following problem to an equation. Do not solve.

On average, a home spa costs about $192 a year to operate. This is 16 times as much as the average annual operating cost of a home computer. How much does it cost to operate a home computer for a year?

Source: U.S. Department of Energy

SOLUTION   We let c represent the annual cost of operating a home computer. We then reword the problem to make the translation more direct.

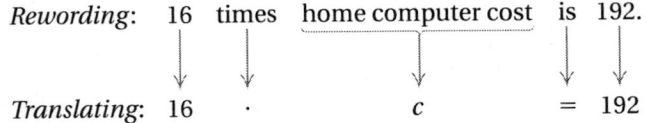

Rewording: 16   times   home computer cost   is   192.

Translating: 16   · c =   192

TRY EXERCISE 95

R.1   **EXERCISE SET**

Classify each equation or inequality as true or false.

1. $1.4 = 1.41$

2. $-3 \geq -3$

3. $-8 < -7$

4. $0 \leq -1$

5. $0 > -5$

6. $\frac{1}{10} = 0.1$

Find each absolute value.

7. $|22|$

8. $\left|\frac{11}{4}\right|$

9. $|-1.3|$

10. $|-105|$

Simplify.

11. $(-14) + (-11)$

12. $3 - (-2)$

13. $-\frac{1}{3} - \frac{2}{5}$

14. $\frac{3}{8} \div \frac{3}{5}$

15. $4.2 - 10.7$

16. $(-1.3)(2.8)$

17. $-9 + 0$

18. $\left(-\frac{1}{2}\right) + \frac{1}{8}$

19. $0 \div (-10)$

20. $0 - 32$

21. $\left(-\frac{3}{10}\right) + \left(-\frac{1}{5}\right)$

22. $\left(-\frac{4}{7}\right)\left(\frac{7}{4}\right)$

23. $-3.8 + 9.6$

24. $-0.01 + 1$

25. $(-12) \div 4$

26. $(-87)(0)$

27. $32 - (-7)$

28. $-100 + 35$

29. $(-10)(-17.5)$

30. $-10 - 2.68$

31. $(-68) + 36$

32. $175 \div (-25)$

33. $2 + (-3) + 7 + 10$

34. $-5 + (-15) + 13 + (-1)$

35. $3 \cdot (-2) \cdot (-1) \cdot (-1)$

36. $(-6) \cdot (-5) \cdot (-4) \cdot (-3) \cdot (-2) \cdot (-1)$

37. $(-1)^4 + 2^3$

38. $(-1)^5 + 2^4$

39. $2 \times 6 - 3 \times 5$

40. $12 \div 4 + 15 \div 3$

41. $3 - (11 + 2 \cdot 4)$

42. $3 - 11 + 2 \cdot 4$

43. $4 \cdot 5^2$

44. $7 \cdot 2^3$

45. $25 - 8 \times 3 + 1$

46. $12 - 16 \times 5 + 4$

47. $2 - (3^3 + 16 \div (-2)^3)$

48. $-7 - (8 + 10 \cdot 2^2)$

49. $|6(-3)| + |(-2)(-9)|$

50. $3 - |2 - 7 + 4|$

51. $\dfrac{7000 + (-10)^3}{10^2 \times (2 + 4)}$

52. $\dfrac{3 - 2 \times 6 - 5}{2(3 + 7)^2}$

53. $2 + 8 \div 2 \times 2$

54. $2 + 8 \div (2 \times 2)$

Evaluate.

55. $y - x$, for $x = 10$ and $y = 3$

56. $n - 2m$, for $m = 6$ and $n = 11$

57. $-3 - x^2 + 12x$, for $x = 5$

58. $14 + (y - 5)^2 - 12 \div y$, for $y = -2$

59. The area of a parallelogram with base b and height h is bh. Find the area of the parallelogram when the height is 3.5 cm and the base is 8 cm.

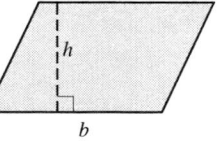

60. The area of a triangle with base b and height h is $\frac{1}{2}bh$. Find the area of the triangle when the height is 2 in. and the base is 6.2 in.

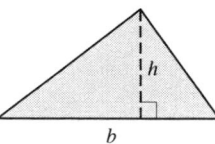

Multiply.

61. $4(2x + 7)$

62. $3(5y + 1)$

63. $-2(15 - 3x)$

64. $-7(3x - 5)$

65. $2(4a + 6b - 3c)$

66. $5(8p + q - 5r)$

67. $-3(2x - y + z)$

68. $-10(-6 - y - z)$

Factor.

69. $8x + 6y$

70. $7p + 14q$

71. $3 + 3w$

72. $4x + 4y$

73. $10x + 50y + 100$

74. $81p + 27q + 9$

Combine like terms.

75. $3p - 2p$

76. $4x + 3x$

77. $4m + 10 - 5m + 12$

78. $3a - 4b - b - 6a$

79. $-6x + 7 + x$

80. $16r + (-7r) + 3s$

Remove parentheses and simplify.

81. $2p - (7 - 4p)$

82. $4r - (3r + 5)$

83. $6x + 5y - 7(x - y)$

84. $14m - 6(2n - 3m) + n$

85. $6[2a + 4(a - 2b)]$

86. $2[2a + 1 - (3a - 6)]$

87. $3 - 2[5(x - 10y) - (3 + 2y)]$

88. $7 - 4[2(3 - 2x) - 5(4x - 3)]$

Determine whether the given number is a solution of the given equation.

89. $4; 3x - 2 = 10$

90. $12; 100 = 4x + 50$

91. $-3; 4 - x = 1$

92. $-1; 2 = 5 + 3x$

93. $4.6; \dfrac{x}{2} = 2.3$

94. $144; \dfrac{x}{9} = 16$

Translate each problem to an equation. Do not solve.

95. Three times what number is 348?

96. What number added to 256 is 113?

97. *Fast-food calories.* A McDonald's Big Mac® contains 500 calories. This is 69 more calories than a Taco Bell Beef Burrito® provides. How many calories are in a Taco Bell Beef Burrito?

98. *Coca-Cola® consumption.* The average U.S. citizen consumes 296 servings of Coca-Cola each year. This is 7.4 times the international average. What is the international average per capita consumption of Coke?

99. *Vegetable production.* It takes 42 gal of water to produce 1 lb of broccoli. This is twice the amount of water used to produce 1 lb of lettuce. How many gallons of water does it take to produce 1 lb of lettuce?

100. *Sports costs.* The average annual cost for scuba diving is $470. This is $458 more than the average annual cost to play badminton. What is the average annual cost to play badminton?

<table>
<tr><td>**R.2**</td><td># Equations, Inequalities, and Problem Solving</td></tr>
</table>

Solving Equations and Formulas   ■   Solving Inequalities   ■   Problem Solving

Solving Equations and Formulas

Any replacement for the variable in an equation that makes the equation true is called a *solution* of the equation. To **solve** an equation means to find all of its solutions.

Equivalent equations (p. 79)

We use the following principles to write **equivalent equations**, or equations with the same solutions.

The Addition and Multiplication Principles for Equations

The addition principle (p. 79)

The Addition Principle

For any real numbers a, b, and c,

$$a = b \quad \text{is equivalent to} \quad a + c = b + c.$$

The multiplication principle (p. 81)

The Multiplication Principle

For any real numbers a, b, and c, with $c \neq 0$,

$$a = b \quad \text{is equivalent to} \quad a \cdot c = b \cdot c.$$

To solve $x + a = b$ for x, we add $-a$ to (or subtract a from) both sides. To solve $ax = b$ for x, we multiply both sides by $\frac{1}{a}$ (or divide both sides by a).

To solve an equation like $-3x - 10 = 14$, we first isolate the variable term, $-3x$, using the addition principle. Then we use the multiplication principle to get the variable by itself.

EXAMPLE 1   Solve: $-3x - 10 = 14$.

SOLUTION

$$-3x - 10 = 14$$

$$-3x - 10 + 10 = 14 + 10 \qquad \text{Using the addition principle: Adding 10 to both sides}$$

Isolate the x-term. $\quad -3x = 24 \qquad \text{Simplifying}$

$$\frac{-3x}{-3} = \frac{24}{-3} \qquad \text{Dividing both sides by } -3$$

Isolate x. $\quad x = -8 \qquad \text{Simplifying}$

Check:
$$\begin{array}{c|c} -3x - 10 = 14 \\ \hline -3(-8) - 10 & 14 \\ 24 - 10 & \\ 14 \overset{?}{=} 14 & \text{TRUE} \end{array}$$

The solution is -8.

TRY EXERCISE   13

Clearing fractions (p. 88)

Equations are generally easier to solve when they do not contain fractions. The easiest way to clear an equation of fractions is to multiply *every term on both sides* of the equation by the least common denominator.

EXAMPLE 2

Solve: $\frac{5}{2} - \frac{1}{6}t = \frac{2}{3}$.

SOLUTION The number 6 is the least common denominator, so we multiply both sides by 6.

$$\frac{5}{2} - \frac{1}{6}t = \frac{2}{3}$$

$$6\left(\frac{5}{2} - \frac{1}{6}t\right) = 6 \cdot \frac{2}{3} \qquad \text{Multiplying both sides by 6}$$

$$6 \cdot \frac{5}{2} - 6 \cdot \frac{1}{6}t = 6 \cdot \frac{2}{3} \qquad \text{Using the distributive law. Be sure to multiply every term by 6.}$$

$$15 - t = 4 \qquad \text{The fractions are cleared.}$$

$$15 - t - 15 = 4 - 15 \qquad \text{Subtracting 15 from both sides}$$

$$-t = -11 \qquad \begin{aligned}15 - t - 15 &= 15 + (-t) + (-15)\\ &= -t + 15 + (-15) = -t\end{aligned}$$

$$(-1)(-t) = (-1)(-11) \qquad \text{Multiplying both sides by } -1 \text{ to change the sign}$$

$$t = 11$$

Check:

$$\frac{5}{2} - \frac{1}{6}t = \frac{2}{3}$$

$$\begin{array}{c|c}
\frac{5}{2} - \frac{1}{6}(11) & \frac{2}{3} \\
\frac{5}{2} - \frac{11}{6} & \\
\frac{15}{6} - \frac{11}{6} & \\
\frac{2}{3} \overset{?}{=} \frac{2}{3} & \text{TRUE}
\end{array}$$

The solution is 11.

TRY EXERCISE 19

To solve equations that contain parentheses, we can use the distributive law to first remove the parentheses. If like terms appear in an equation, we combine them and then solve.

EXAMPLE 3

Solve: $1 - 3(4 - x) = 2(x + 5) - 3x$.

SOLUTION

$$1 - 3(4 - x) = 2(x + 5) - 3x$$

$$1 - 12 + 3x = 2x + 10 - 3x \qquad \text{Using the distributive law}$$

$$-11 + 3x = -x + 10 \qquad \text{Combining like terms; } 1 - 12 = -11 \text{ and } 2x - 3x = -x$$

$$-11 + 3x + x = 10 \qquad \text{Adding } x \text{ to both sides to get all } x\text{-terms on one side}$$

$$-11 + 4x = 10 \qquad \text{Combining like terms}$$

$$4x = 10 + 11 \qquad \text{Adding 11 to both sides to isolate the } x\text{-term}$$

$$4x = 21 \qquad \text{Simplifying}$$

$$x = \frac{21}{4} \qquad \text{Dividing both sides by 4}$$

Check:

$$\begin{array}{c|c}
1 - 3(4 - x) = 2(x + 5) - 3x \\
\hline
1 - 3\left(4 - \frac{21}{4}\right) & 2\left(\frac{21}{4} + 5\right) - 3\left(\frac{21}{4}\right) \\
1 - 3\left(-\frac{5}{4}\right) & 2\left(\frac{41}{4}\right) - \frac{63}{4} \\
1 + \frac{15}{4} & \frac{82}{4} - \frac{63}{4} \\
\frac{19}{4} \stackrel{?}{=} \frac{19}{4} & \text{TRUE}
\end{array}$$

The solution is $\frac{21}{4}$.

> **TRY EXERCISE** 25

Conditional equation (p. 90)
Identity (p. 90)
Contradiction (p. 90)

Formulas (Section 2.3)

The equations in Examples 1–3 are **conditional**—that is, they are true for some values of x and false for other values of x. An **identity** is an equation like $x + 1 = x + 1$ that is true for all values of x. A **contradiction** is an equation like $x + 1 = x + 2$ that is never true.

A **formula** is an equation using two or more letters that represents a relationship between two or more quantities. A formula can be solved for a specified letter using the principles for solving equations.

EXAMPLE 4

The formula

$$A = \frac{a + b + c + d}{4}$$

gives the average A of four test scores a, b, c, and d. Solve for d.

SOLUTION   We have

$$A = \frac{a + b + c + d}{4}$$ We want the letter d alone.

$$4A = a + b + c + d$$ Multiplying by 4 to clear the fraction

$$4A - a - b - c = d.$$ Subtracting $a + b + c$ from (or adding $-a - b - c$ to) both sides. The letter d is now isolated.

We can also write this as $d = 4A - a - b - c$. This formula can be used to determine the test score needed to obtain a specified average if three tests have already been taken.

> **TRY EXERCISE** 33

Solving Inequalities

Solutions of inequalities (p. 121)
Graphs of inequalities (p. 122)

A **solution of an inequality** is a replacement of the variable that makes the inequality true. The solutions of an inequality in one variable can be **graphed**, or represented by a drawing, on the number line. All points that are solutions are shaded. A parenthesis indicates an endpoint that is not a solution and a bracket indicates an endpoint that is a solution.

EXAMPLE 5

Graph each inequality: **(a)** $m \le 2$; **(b)** $-1 \le x < 4$.

SOLUTION

a) The solutions of $m \le 2$ are shown on the number line by shading points to the left of 2 as well as the point at 2. The bracket at 2 indicates that 2 is a part of the graph (that is, it is a solution of $m \le 2$).

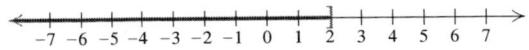

b) In order to be a solution of the inequality $-1 \leq x < 4$, a number must be a solution of both $-1 \leq x$ and $x < 4$. The solutions are shaded on the number line, with a parenthesis indicating that 4 is not a solution and a bracket indicating that -1 is a solution.

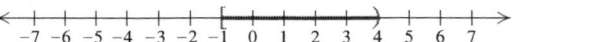

Set-builder notation (p. 123)
Interval notation (p. 123)

In Example 5, note that $m \leq 2$ and $-1 \leq x < 4$ are inequalities that describe a solution set. Since it is impossible to list all the solutions, we use **set-builder notation** or **interval notation** to write such sets.

Using set-builder notation, we write the solution set of Example 5(a) as

$$\{m \mid m \leq 2\},$$

read

"the set of all m such that m is less than or equal to 2."

Interval notation uses parentheses, ( ), and brackets, [ ], to describe a set of real numbers.

Interval Notation	Set-builder Notation	Graph
(a, b) open interval	$\{x \mid a < x < b\}$	(a, b)
$[a, b]$ closed interval	$\{x \mid a \leq x \leq b\}$	$[a, b]$
$(a, b]$ half-open interval	$\{x \mid a < x \leq b\}$	$(a, b]$
$[a, b)$ half-open interval	$\{x \mid a \leq x < b\}$	$[a, b)$
(a, ∞)	$\{x \mid x > a\}$	
$[a, \infty)$	$\{x \mid x \geq a\}$	
$(-\infty, a)$	$\{x \mid x < a\}$	
$(-\infty, a]$	$\{x \mid x \leq a\}$	

Thus, for example, the solution set of Example 5(a), in interval notation, is $(-\infty, 2]$.

Equivalent inequalities (p. 124)

As with equations, our goal when solving inequalities is to isolate the variable on one side. We use principles that enable us to write **equivalent inequalities**—inequalities having the same solution set. The addition principle is similar to the addition principle for equations; the multiplication principle contains an important difference.

The addition principle for inequalities (p. 124)

The multiplication principle for inequalities (p. 126)

> ## The Addition and Multiplication Principles for Inequalities
>
> ### The Addition Principle
>
> For any real numbers a, b, and c,
>
> $$a < b \quad \text{is equivalent to} \quad a + c < b + c, \quad \text{and}$$
> $$a > b \quad \text{is equivalent to} \quad a + c > b + c.$$
>
> ### The Multiplication Principle
>
> For any real numbers a and b, and for any *positive* number c,
>
> $$a < b \quad \text{is equivalent to} \quad ac < bc, \quad \text{and}$$
> $$a > b \quad \text{is equivalent to} \quad ac > bc.$$
>
> For any real numbers a and b, and for any *negative* number c,
>
> $$a < b \quad \text{is equivalent to} \quad ac > bc, \quad \text{and}$$
> $$a > b \quad \text{is equivalent to} \quad ac < bc.$$
>
> Similar statements hold for $\leq$ and $\geq$.

Note that when we multiply both sides of an inequality by a negative number, we must reverse the direction of the inequality symbol in order to have an equivalent inequality.

EXAMPLE 6   Solve $-2x \geq 5$ and then graph the solution.

SOLUTION   We have

$$-2x \geq 5$$

$$\frac{-2x}{-2} \leq \frac{5}{-2} \qquad \text{Multiplying by } -\frac{1}{2} \text{ or dividing by } -2$$

The symbol must be reversed!

$$x \leq -\frac{5}{2}.$$

Any number less than or equal to $-\frac{5}{2}$ is a solution. The graph is as follows:

$-\frac{5}{2}$

-7 -6 -5 -4 -3 -2 -1 0 1 2 3 4 5 6 7

The solution set is $\left\{ x \mid x \leq -\frac{5}{2} \right\}$, or $\left(-\infty, -\frac{5}{2} \right]$.   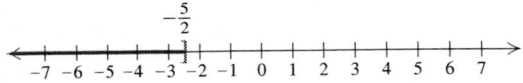 **TRY EXERCISE** 47

We can use the addition and multiplication principles together to solve inequalities. We can also combine like terms, remove parentheses, and clear fractions and decimals.

EXAMPLE   7   Solve: $2 - 3(x + 5) > 4 - 6(x - 1)$.

SOLUTION   We have

$$2 - 3(x + 5) > 4 - 6(x - 1)$$

$$2 - 3x - 15 > 4 - 6x + 6 \qquad \text{Using the distributive law to remove parentheses}$$

$$-3x - 13 > -6x + 10 \qquad \text{Simplifying}$$

$$-3x + 6x > 10 + 13 \qquad \text{Adding } 6x \text{ and also 13, to get all } x\text{-terms on one side and all other terms on the other side}$$

$$3x > 23 \qquad \text{Combining like terms}$$

$$x > \frac{23}{3}. \qquad \text{Multiplying by } \tfrac{1}{3}. \text{ The inequality symbol stays the same because } \tfrac{1}{3} \text{ is positive.}$$

The solution set is $\left\{ x \,|\, x > \frac{23}{3} \right\}$, or $\left(\frac{23}{3}, \infty \right)$.

TRY EXERCISE   53

Problem solving (Section 2.5)

Problem Solving

One of the most important uses of algebra is as a tool for problem solving. The following five steps can be used to help solve problems of many types.

> ### Five Steps for Problem Solving in Algebra
> 1. *Familiarize* yourself with the problem.
> 2. *Translate* to mathematical language. (This often means writing an equation.)
> 3. *Carry out* some mathematical manipulation. (This often means *solving* an equation.)
> 4. *Check* your possible answer in the original problem.
> 5. *State* the answer clearly, using a complete English sentence.

EXAMPLE   8   *Kitchen cabinets.*   Cherry kitchen cabinets cost 10% more than oak cabinets. Shelby Custom Cabinets designs a kitchen using $7480 worth of cherry cabinets. How much would the same kitchen cost using oak cabinets?

SOLUTION

Familiarization step (p. 110)

Percent (Section 2.4)

1. **Familiarize.** The *Familiarize* step is often the most important of the five steps, and may require a significant amount of time. Sometimes it helps to make a drawing or a table, make a guess and check it, or look up further information. For this problem, we could review percent notation. We could also make a guess. Let's suppose that the oak cabinets cost $6500. Then the cherry cabinets would cost 10% more, or an additional $(0.10)(\$6500) = \$650$. Altogether the cherry cabinets would cost $\$6500 + \$650 = \$7150$. Since $\$7150 \neq \$7480$, our guess is incorrect, but we see that 10% of the price of the oak cabinets must be added to the price of the oak cabinets to get the price of the cherry cabinets. We let $c =$ the cost of the oak cabinets.

2. **Translate.** What we learned in the *Familiarize* step leads to the translation of the problem to an equation.

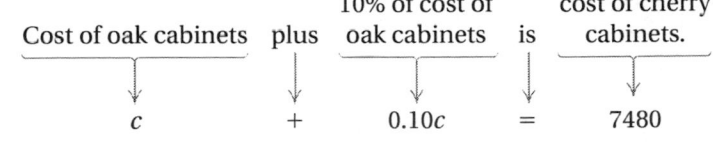

Cost of oak cabinets	plus	10% of cost of oak cabinets	is	cost of cherry cabinets.
c	$+$	$0.10c$	$=$	7480

3. **Carry out.** We solve the equation:

$$c + 0.10c = 7480$$

$1c + 0.10c = 7480$ Writing c as $1c$ before combining terms

$1.10c = 7480$ Combining like terms

$c = \dfrac{7480}{1.10}$ Dividing by 1.10

$c = 6800.$

4. **Check.** We check in the wording of the stated problem: Cherry cabinets cost 10% more, so the additional cost is

$$10\% \text{ of } \$6800 = 0.10(\$6800) = \$680.$$

The total cost of the cherry cabinets is then

$$\$6800 + \$680 = \$7480,$$

which is the amount stated in the problem.

5. **State.** The oak cabinets would cost \$6800.   **TRY EXERCISE** 63

Sometimes the translation of a problem is an inequality.

EXAMPLE 9

Long-distance telephone usage. Elyse pays a flat rate of 6¢ per minute for long-distance telephone calls. The monthly charge for her local calls is \$21.50. How many minutes can she spend calling long distance in a month and not exceed her telephone budget of \$50?

SOLUTION

1. **Familiarize.** Suppose that Elyse spends 10 hr, or 600 min, making long-distance calls one month. Then her bill would be the local service charge plus the long-distance charges, or

$$\$21.50 + \$0.06(600) = \$57.50.$$

This exceeds \$50, so we know that the number of long-distance minutes must be less than 600. We let $m =$ the number of minutes of long-distance calls in a month.

2. **Translate.** The *Familiarize* step helps us reword and translate.

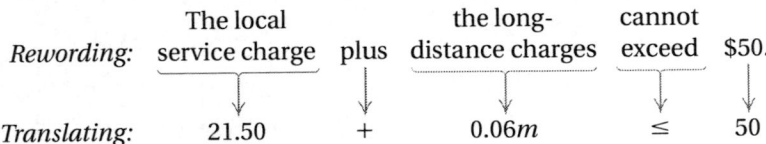

Rewording: The local service charge   plus   the long-distance charges   cannot exceed   \$50.

Translating: 21.50   +   0.06m $\leq$ 50

Solving applications with inequalities (Section 2.7)

3. **Carry out.** We solve the inequality:

$21.50 + 0.06m \leq 50$

$0.06m \leq 28.50$ Subtracting 21.50 from both sides

$m \leq 475.$ Dividing by 0.06. The inequality symbol stays the same.

4. **Check.** As a partial check, note that the telephone bill for 475 min of long-distance charges is

$$\$21.50 + \$0.06(475) = \$50.$$

Since fewer minutes will cost even less, our answer checks. We also note that 475 is less than 600 min, as noted in the *Familiarize* step.

5. **State.** Elyse will not exceed her budget if she talks long distance for no more than 475 min.   **TRY EXERCISE** 71

R.2 **EXERCISE SET**

Solve.

1. $-6 + x = 10$

2. $y + 7 = -3$

3. $t + \frac{1}{3} = \frac{1}{4}$

4. $-\frac{2}{3} + p = \frac{1}{6}$

5. $-1.9 = x - 1.1$

6. $x + 4.6 = 1.7$

7. $-x = \frac{5}{3}$

8. $-y = -\frac{2}{5}$

9. $-\frac{2}{7}x = -12$

10. $-\frac{1}{4}x = 3$

11. $\frac{-t}{5} = 1$

12. $\frac{2}{3} = -\frac{z}{8}$

13. $3y + 10 = 15$

14. $12 = 5y + 18$

15. $4x + 7 = 3 - 5x$

16. $2x = 5 + 7x$

17. $2x - 7 = 5x + 1 - x$

18. $a + 7 - 2a = 14 + 7a - 10$

19. $\frac{2}{5} + \frac{1}{3}t = 5$

20. $-\frac{5}{6} + t = \frac{1}{2}$

21. $x + 0.45 = 2.6x$

22. $1.8x + 0.16 = 4.2 - 0.05x$

23. $8(3 - m) + 7 = 47$

24. $2(5 - m) = 5(6 + m)$

25. $4 - (6 + x) = 13$

26. $18 = 9 - (3 - x)$

27. $2 + 3(4 + c) = 1 - 5(6 - c)$

28. $b + (b + 5) - 2(b - 5) = 18 + b$

29. $0.1(a - 0.2) = 1.2 + 2.4a$

30. $\frac{2}{3}\left(\frac{1}{2} - x\right) + \frac{5}{6} = \frac{3}{2}\left(\frac{2}{3}x + 1\right)$

31. $A = lw$, for l

32. $A = lw$, for w

33. $I = \frac{P}{V}$, for P

34. $b = \frac{A}{h}$, for A

35. $q = \frac{p + r}{2}$, for p

36. $q = \frac{p - r}{2}$, for r

37. $A = \pi r^2 + \pi r^2 h$, for π

38. $ax + by = c$, for a

Determine whether each number is a solution of the given inequality.

39. $x \leq -5$

  a) 5

  b) -5

  c) 0

  d) -10

40. $y > 0$

  a) -1

  b) 1

  c) 0

  d) 100

Solve and graph. Write each answer in set-builder notation and in interval notation.

41. $x + 3 \leq 15$

42. $y + 7 < -10$

43. $m - 17 > -5$

44. $x + 9 \geq -8$

45. $2x \geq -3$

46. $-\frac{1}{2}n \leq 4$

47. $-5t > 15$

48. $3x > 10$

Solve. Write each answer in set-builder notation and in interval notation.

49. $2y - 7 > 13$

50. $2 - 6y \leq 18$

51. $6 - 5a \leq a$

52. $4b + 7 > 2 - b$

53. $2(3 + 5x) \geq 7(10 - x)$

54. $2(x + 5) < 8 - 3x$

55. $\frac{2}{3}(6 - x) < \frac{1}{4}(x + 3)$

56. $\frac{2}{3}t + \frac{8}{9} \geq \frac{4}{6} - \frac{1}{4}t$

57. $0.7(2 + x) \geq 1.1x + 5.75$

58. $0.4x + 5.7 \leq 2.6 - 3(1.2x - 7)$

Solve. Use the five-step problem-solving process.

59. Three less than the sum of 2 and some number is 6. What is the number?

60. Five times some number is 10 less than the number. What is the number?

61. The sum of two consecutive even integers is 34. Find the numbers.

62. The sum of three consecutive integers is 195. Find the numbers.

63. *Reading.* Leisa is reading a 500-page book. She has twice as many pages to read as she has already finished. How many pages has she already read?

64. *Mowing.* It takes Caleb 50 min to mow his lawn. It will take him three times as many minutes to finish as he has already spent mowing. How long has he already spent mowing?

65. *Perimeter of a rectangle.* The perimeter of a rectangle is 28 cm. The width is 5 cm less than the length. Find the width and the length.

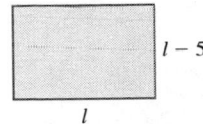

66. *Triangles.* The second angle of a triangle is one third as large as the first. The third angle is 5° more than the first. Find the measure of the second angle.

67. *Water usage.* Rural Water Company charges a monthly service fee of $9.70 plus a volume charge of $2.60 for every hundred cubic feet of water used. How much water was used if the monthly bill is $33.10?

68. *Telephone bills.* Brandon pays $4.95 a month for a long-distance telephone service that offers a flat rate of 7¢ per minute. One month his total long-distance telephone bill was $10.69. How many minutes of long-distance telephone calls were made that month?

69. *Sale price.* A can of tomatoes is on sale at 20% off for 64¢. What is the normal selling price of the tomatoes?

70. *Plywood.* The price of a piece of plywood rose 5% to $42. What was the original price of the plywood?

71. *Practice.* Dierdre's basketball coach requires each team member to average at least 15 min a day shooting baskets. One week Dierdre spent 10 min, 20 min, 5 min, 0 min, 25 min, and 15 min shooting baskets. How long must she practice shooting baskets on the seventh day if she is to meet the requirement?

72. *Perimeter of a garden.* The perimeter of Garry's rectangular garden cannot exceed the 100 ft of fencing that he purchased. He wants the length to be twice the width. What widths of the garden will meet these conditions?

73. *Meeting costs.* The Winds charges a $75 cleaning fee plus $45 an hour for the use of its meeting room. Complete Consultants has budgeted $200 to rent a room for a seminar. For how many hours can they rent the meeting room at The Winds?

74. *Meeting costs.* Spring Haven charges a $15 setup fee, a $30 cleanup fee, and $50 an hour for the use of its meeting room. For what lengths of time will Spring Haven's room be less expensive than the room at The Winds (see Exercise 73)?

R.3 Introduction to Graphing

Points and Ordered Pairs ▪ Graphs and Slope ▪ Linear Equations

Points and Ordered Pairs

We can represent, or graph, pairs of numbers such as $(2, -5)$ on a plane. To do so, we use two perpendicular number lines called **axes**. The axes cross at a point called the **origin**. Arrows on the axes show the positive directions.

Graphing ordered pairs (p. 151)

Coordinates (p. 151)

The order of the **coordinates**, or numbers in a pair, is important. The **first coordinate** indicates horizontal position and the **second coordinate** indicates vertical position. Such pairs of numbers are called **ordered pairs**. Thus the ordered pairs $(1, -2)$ and $(-2, 1)$ correspond to different points, as shown in the accompanying figure.

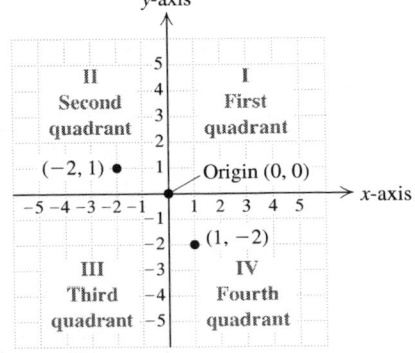

The axes divide the plane into four regions, or **quadrants**, as indicated by Roman numerals in the figure at right. Points on the axes are not considered to be in any quadrant. The horizontal axis is often labeled the *x*-axis, and the vertical axis the *y*-axis.

Quadrants (p. 153)

Graphs and Slope

Solutions of equations (p. 158)

When an equation contains two variables, solutions must be ordered pairs. Unless stated otherwise, the first number in each pair replaces the variable that occurs first alphabetically.

EXAMPLE 1   Determine whether $(1, 4)$ is a solution of $y - x = 3$.

SOLUTION   We substitute 1 for x and 4 for y since x occurs first alphabetically:

$$\begin{array}{c|c} y - x = 3 \\ \hline 4 - 1 & 3 \\ 3 \stackrel{?}{=} 3 & \text{TRUE} \end{array}$$

Since $3 = 3$ is true, the pair $(1, 4)$ *is* a solution.

`TRY EXERCISE` 9

A curve or line that represents all the solutions of an equation is called its **graph**.

EXAMPLE 2   Graph: $y = -2x + 1$.

SOLUTION   We select a value for x, calculate the corresponding value of y, and form an ordered pair.

If $x = 0$, then $y = -2 \cdot 0 + 1 = 1$, and $(0, 1)$ is a solution. Repeating this step, we find other ordered pairs and list the results in a table. We then plot the points corresponding to the pairs. They appear to form a straight line, so we draw a line through the points.

$$y = -2x + 1$$

x	y	(x, y)
0	1	$(0, 1)$
-1	3	$(-1, 3)$
3	-5	$(3, -5)$
1	-1	$(1, -1)$

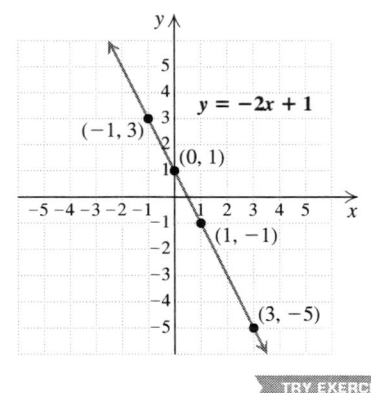

`TRY EXERCISE` 13

The graph in Example 2 is a straight line. An equation whose graph is a straight line is a **linear equation**. The *rate of change* of y with respect to x is called the **slope** of a graph. A linear graph has constant slope. It can be found using any two points on a line.

Slope (p. 187)

> ## Slope
>
> The *slope* of the line containing points (x_1, y_1) and (x_2, y_2) is given by
>
> $$m = \frac{\text{change in } y}{\text{change in } x} = \frac{\text{rise}}{\text{run}} = \frac{y_2 - y_1}{x_2 - x_1}.$$

EXAMPLE 3 Find the slope of the line containing the points $(-2, 1)$ and $(3, -4)$.

SOLUTION   From $(-2, 1)$ to $(3, -4)$, the change in y, or the rise, is $-4 - 1$, or -5. The change in x, or the run, is $3 - (-2)$, or 5. Thus

$$\text{Slope} = \frac{\text{change in } y}{\text{change in } x} = \frac{\text{rise}}{\text{run}} = \frac{-4 - 1}{3 - (-2)} = \frac{-5}{5} = -1.$$

TRY EXERCISE 17

The slope of a line indicates the direction and steepness of its slant. The larger the absolute value of the slope, the steeper the line. The direction of the slant is indicated by the sign of the slope, as shown in the figures below.

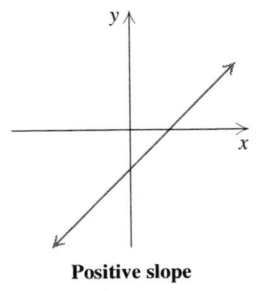
Positive slope

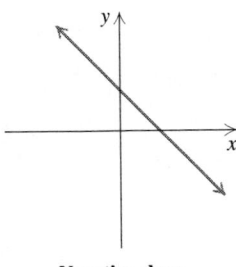
Negative slope

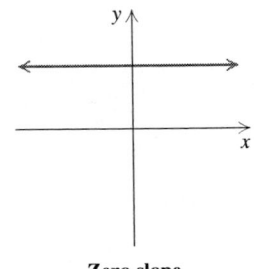
Zero slope

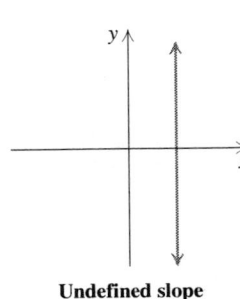
Undefined slope

x-intercept (p. 168)

y-intercept (p. 168)

The *x*-intercept of a line, if it exists, is the point at which the graph crosses the *x*-axis. To find an *x*-intercept, we replace y with 0 and calculate x.

The *y*-intercept of a line, if it exists, is the point at which the graph crosses the *y*-axis. To find a *y*-intercept, we replace x with 0 and calculate y.

Linear Equations

Any equation that can be written in the **standard form** $Ax + By = C$ is linear. Linear equations can also be written in other forms.

Forms of Linear Equations

Standard form: $Ax + By = C$

Slope–intercept form: $y = mx + b$

Point–slope form: $y - y_1 = m(x - x_1)$

The slope and *y*-intercept of a line can be read from the slope–intercept form of the line's equation.

Slope and *y*-intercept

For the graph of any equation $y = mx + b$,

• the slope is m, and

• the *y*-intercept is $(0, b)$.

EXAMPLE   4   Find the slope and the y-intercept of the line given by the equation $4x - 3y = 9$.

SOLUTION   We write the equation in slope–intercept form $y = mx + b$:

$$4x - 3y = 9 \qquad \text{We must solve for } y.$$
$$-3y = -4x + 9 \qquad \text{Adding } -4x \text{ to both sides}$$
$$y = \tfrac{4}{3}x - 3. \qquad \text{Dividing both sides by } -3$$

The slope is $\tfrac{4}{3}$ and the y-intercept is $(0, -3)$.   **TRY EXERCISE   23**

If we know an equation is a straight line, we can plot two points on the line and draw the line through those points. The intercepts are often convenient points to use.

EXAMPLE   5   Graph $2x - 5y = 10$ using intercepts.

SOLUTION   To find the x-intercept, we let $y = 0$ and solve for x:

$$2x - 5 \cdot 0 = 10 \qquad \text{Replacing } y \text{ with } 0$$
$$2x = 10$$
$$x = 5.$$

To find the y-intercept, we let $x = 0$ and solve for y:

$$2 \cdot 0 - 5y = 10 \qquad \text{Replacing } x \text{ with } 0$$
$$-5y = 10$$
$$y = -2.$$

Thus the x-intercept is $(5, 0)$ and the y-intercept is $(0, -2)$. The graph is a line, since $2x - 5y = 10$ is in the form $Ax + By = C$. It passes through these two points.

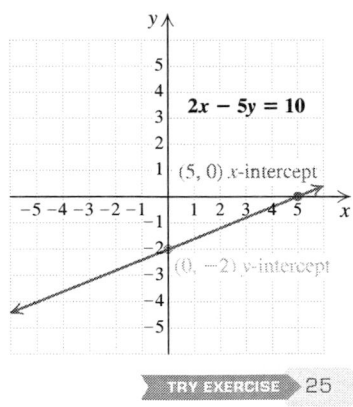

TRY EXERCISE   25

Alternatively, if we know a point on the line and its slope, we can plot the point and "count off" its slope to locate another point on the line.

EXAMPLE   6   Graph: $y = -\dfrac{1}{2}x + 3$.

SOLUTION   The equation is in slope–intercept form, so we can read the slope and y-intercept directly from the equation.

$$\text{Slope: } -\frac{1}{2}$$

y-intercept: $(0, 3)$

We plot the y-intercept and use the slope to find another point.

Another way to write the slope is $\dfrac{-1}{2}$.

This means for a run of 2 units, there is a negative rise, or a fall, of 1 unit. Starting at $(0, 3)$, we move 2 units in the positive horizontal direction and then 1 unit down, to locate the point $(2, 2)$. Then we draw the graph. A third point can be calculated and plotted as a check.

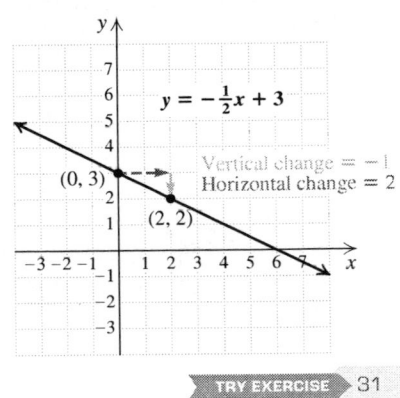

$$y = -\tfrac{1}{2}x + 3$$

Vertical change $= -1$
Horizontal change $= 2$

TRY EXERCISE 31

Horizontal and vertical lines intersect only one axis.

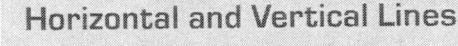

Horizontal line (p. 173)

Vertical line (p. 173)

Horizontal and Vertical Lines

Horizontal Line

$y = b$

y-intercept $(0, b)$

Slope is 0

Example: $y = -3$

Vertical Line

$x = a$

x-intercept $(a, 0)$

Undefined slope

Example: $x = 2$

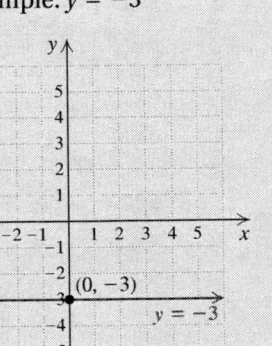

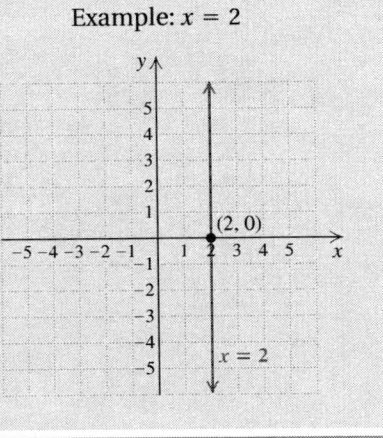

If we know the slope of a line and the coordinates of a point on the line, we can find an equation of the line, using either the slope–intercept equation $y = mx + b$, or the point–slope equation $y - y_1 = m(x - x_1)$.

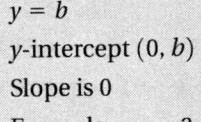 **EXAMPLE 7**

Find the slope-intercept equation of a line given the following:

a) The slope is 2, and the y-intercept is $(0, -5)$.

b) The graph contains the points $(-2, 1)$ and $(3, -4)$.

SOLUTION

a) Since the slope and the y-intercept are given, we use the slope–intercept equation:

$$y = mx + b$$
$$y = 2x - 5. \qquad \text{Substituting 2 for } m \text{ and } -5 \text{ for } b$$

b) To use the point–slope equation, we need a point on the line and its slope. The slope can be found from the points given:

Find the slope.

$$m = \frac{1 - (-4)}{-2 - 3} = \frac{5}{-5} = -1.$$

Either point can be used for (x_1, y_1). Using $(-2, 1)$, we have

Find a point–slope equation for the line.

$$y - y_1 = m(x - x_1)$$
$$y - 1 = -1(x - (-2)) \qquad \text{Substituting } -2 \text{ for } x_1, 1 \text{ for } y_1, \text{ and } -1 \text{ for } m$$
$$y - 1 = -(x + 2)$$

Find the slope–intercept equation for the line.

$$y - 1 = -x - 2$$
$$y = -x - 1. \qquad \text{This is in slope–intercept form.}$$

> TRY EXERCISE 39

We can tell from the slopes of two lines whether they are parallel or perpendicular.

Parallel lines (p. 201)

Perpendicular lines (p. 202)

> ## Parallel and Perpendicular Lines
>
> Two lines are parallel if they have the same slope.
> Two lines are perpendicular if the product of the slopes is -1.

EXAMPLE   8   Tell whether the graphs of each pair of lines are parallel, perpendicular, or neither.

a) $2x - y = 7,$
$y = 2x + 3$

b) $4x - y = 8,$
$x + 4y = 8$

SOLUTION

a) The slope of $y = 2x + 3$ is 2.
To find the slope of $2x - y = 7$, we solve for y:

$$2x - y = 7$$
$$-y = -2x + 7$$
$$y = 2x - 7.$$

The slope of $2x - y = 7$ is also 2. Since the slopes are equal, the lines are parallel.

b) We solve both equations for y in order to determine the slopes of the lines:

$$4x - y = 8$$
$$-y = -4x + 8$$
$$y = 4x - 8.$$

The slope of $4x - y = 8$ is 4.
For the second line, we have

$$x + 4y = 8$$
$$4y = -x + 8$$
$$y = -\tfrac{1}{4}x + 2.$$

The slope of $x + 4y = 8$ is $-\tfrac{1}{4}$. Since $4 \cdot \left(-\tfrac{1}{4}\right) = -1$, the lines are perpendicular.

> TRY EXERCISE 43

R.3   EXERCISE SET

For Extra Help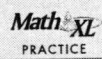

1. Plot these points.
$$(2, -3), (5, 1), (0, 2), (-1, 0),$$
$$(0, 0), (-2, -5), (-1, 1), (1, -1)$$

2. Plot these points.
$$(0, -4), (-4, 0), (5, -2), (2, 5),$$
$$(3, 3), (-3, -1), (-1, 4), (0, 1)$$

In which quadrant is each point located?

3. $(-2, 5)$

4. $(15, 27)$

5. $(3, -2.6)$

6. $(-1.7, -5.9)$

7. First coordinates are positive in quadrants ____ and ____.

8. Second coordinates are negative in quadrants ____ and ____.

Determine whether each equation has the given ordered pair as a solution.

9. $y = 2x - 5$; $(1, 3)$

10. $4x + 3y = 8$; $(-1, 4)$

11. $a - 5b = -3$; $(2, 1)$

12. $c = d + 1$; $(1, 2)$

Graph.

13. $y = \frac{1}{3}x + 3$

14. $y = -x - 2$

15. $y = -4x$

16. $y = \frac{3}{4}x + 1$

Find the slope of the line containing each given pair of points. If it is undefined, state this.

17. $(3, 6)$ and $(2, 7)$

18. $(-1, 7)$ and $(-5, 1)$

19. $\left(-2, -\frac{1}{2}\right)$ and $\left(5, -\frac{1}{2}\right)$

20. $(6.8, 7.5)$ and $(6.8, -3.2)$

Find the slope and the y-intercept of each equation.

21. $y = 2x - 5$

22. $y = 4 - x$

23. $2x + 7y = 1$

24. $x - 2y = 3$

Find the intercepts. Then graph.

25. $3 - y = 2x$

26. $2x + 5y = 10$

27. $y = 3x + 5$

28. $y = -x + 7$

29. $3x - 2y = 6$

30. $2y + 1 = x$

Determine the coordinates of the y-intercept of each equation. Then graph the equation.

31. $y = 2x - 5$

32. $y = -\frac{5}{4}x - 3$

33. $2y + 4x = 6$

34. $3y + x = 4$

Find the slope of each line, and graph.

35. $y = 4$

36. $x = -5$

37. $x = 3$

38. $y = -1$

Find the slope–intercept equation of a line given the conditions.

39. The slope is 5 and the y-intercept is $(0, 9)$.

40. The slope is $\frac{2}{3}$ and the y-intercept is $(0, -5)$.

41. The graph contains the points $(0, 3)$ and $(-1, 4)$.

42. The graph contains the points $(5, 1)$ and $(8, 0)$.

Determine whether each pair of lines is parallel, perpendicular, or neither.

43. $x + y = 5$,
$x - y = 1$

44. $2x + y = 3$,
$y = 4 - 2x$

45. $2x + 3y = 1$,
$2x - 3y = 5$

46. $y = \frac{1}{3}x - 7$,
$y + 3x = 1$

R.4 Polynomials

Exponents ■ Polynomials ■ Addition and Subtraction of Polynomials ■
Multiplication of Polynomials ■ Division of Polynomials

Exponents

We know that x^4 means $x \cdot x \cdot x \cdot x$ and that x^1 means x. Exponential notation is also defined for zero and negative exponents.

> **Zero and Negative Exponents**
>
> For any real number a, $a \neq 0$,
>
> $$a^0 = 1 \quad \text{and} \quad a^{-n} = \frac{1}{a^n}.$$

EXAMPLE 1   Simplify: **(a)** $(97)^0$; **(b)** $(-2x)^0$.

SOLUTION

The exponent zero (p. 230)

a) $(97)^0 = 1$ since any number (other than 0 itself) raised to the 0 power is 1.

b) $(-2x)^0 = 1$ for any $x \neq 0$.   **TRY EXERCISE** 1

EXAMPLE 2   Write an equivalent expression using positive exponents.

a) x^{-2} **b)** $\dfrac{1}{x^{-2}}$ **c)** $7y^{-1}$

SOLUTION

Negative exponents (p. 236)

a) $x^{-2} = \dfrac{1}{x^2}$ x^{-2} is the reciprocal of x^2.

b) $\dfrac{1}{x^{-2}} = x^{-(-2)} = x^2$ The reciprocal of x^{-2} is $x^{-(-2)}$, or x^2.

c) $7y^{-1} = 7\left(\dfrac{1}{y^1}\right) = \dfrac{7}{y}$ y^{-1} is the reciprocal of y^1.   **TRY EXERCISE** 5

The following properties hold for any integers m and n and any real numbers a and b, provided no denominators are 0 and 0^0 is not considered.

> **Properties of Exponents**
>
> | | |
> |---|---|
> | The Product Rule: | $a^m \cdot a^n = a^{m+n}$ |
> | The Quotient Rule: | $\dfrac{a^m}{a^n} = a^{m-n}$ |
> | The Power Rule: | $(a^m)^n = a^{mn}$ |
> | Raising a product to a power: | $(ab)^n = a^n b^n$ |
> | Raising a quotient to a power: | $\left(\dfrac{a}{b}\right)^n = \dfrac{a^n}{b^n}$ |

These properties are often used to simplify exponential expressions.

EXAMPLE 3 Simplify.

a) $(x^2y^{-1})(xy^{-3})$ **b)** $\dfrac{(3p)^3}{(3p)^{-2}}$ **c)** $\left(\dfrac{ab^2}{3c^3}\right)^{-4}$

SOLUTION

a) $(x^2y^{-1})(xy^{-3}) = x^2y^{-1}xy^{-3}$ Using an associative law

$= x^2x^1y^{-1}y^{-3}$ Using a commutative law; $x = x^1$

The product rule (p. 228)

$= x^{2+1}y^{-1+(-3)}$ Using the product rule: Adding exponents

$= x^3y^{-4}$, or $\dfrac{x^3}{y^4}$

The quotient rule (p. 229)

b) $\dfrac{(3p)^3}{(3p)^{-2}} = (3p)^{3-(-2)}$ Using the quotient rule: Subtracting exponents

$= (3p)^5$

The power rule (p. 231)

$= 3^5p^5$ Raising each factor to the fifth power

$= 243p^5$

Raising a product to a power (p. 232)

c) $\left(\dfrac{ab^2}{3c^3}\right)^{-4} = \dfrac{(ab^2)^{-4}}{(3c^3)^{-4}}$ Raising the numerator and the denominator to the -4 power

Raising a quotient to a power (p. 233)

$= \dfrac{a^{-4}(b^2)^{-4}}{3^{-4}(c^3)^{-4}}$ Raising each factor to the -4 power

$= \dfrac{a^{-4}b^{-8}}{3^{-4}c^{-12}}$ Multiplying exponents

$= \dfrac{3^4c^{12}}{a^4b^8}$, or $\dfrac{81c^{12}}{a^4b^8}$ Rewriting without negative exponents

TRY EXERCISE 23

Polynomials (Section 4.3)

Polynomials

Algebraic expressions like

$$2x^3 + 3x - 5, \qquad 4x, \qquad -7, \quad \text{and} \quad 2a^3b^2 + ab^3$$

are all examples of **polynomials**. All variables in a polynomial are raised to whole-number powers, and there are no variables in a denominator. The **terms** of a polynomial are separated by addition signs. The **degree of a term** is the number of variable factors in that term. The **leading term** of a polynomial is the term of highest degree. The **degree of a polynomial** is the degree of the leading term. A polynomial is written in *descending order* when the leading term appears first, followed by the term of next highest degree, and so on.

The number -2 in the term $-2y^3$ is called the **coefficient** of that term. The coefficient of the leading term is the **leading coefficient** of the polynomial. To illustrate this terminology, consider the polynomial

Term (p. 246)
Degree of a term (p. 247)
Leading term (p. 247)
Degree of a polynomial (p. 247)

Coefficient (p. 247)
Leading coefficient (p. 247)

$$4y^2 - 8y^5 + y^3 - 6y + 7.$$

The *terms* are $\qquad 4y^2, \quad -8y^5, \quad y^3, \quad -6y, \quad \text{and} \quad 7.$

The *coefficients* are $\qquad 4, \qquad -8, \quad 1, \quad -6, \quad \text{and} \quad 7.$

The *degree of each term* is $\quad 2, \qquad 5, \qquad 3, \quad 1, \qquad \text{and} \quad 0.$

The *leading term* is $-8y^5$ and the *leading coefficient* is -8.

The *degree of the polynomial* is 5.

Types of polynomials (p. 246)

Polynomials are classified by the number of terms and by degree.

A **monomial** has one term.	*Example:* $-2x^3y$
A **binomial** has two terms.	*Example:* $1.4x^2 - 10$
A **trinomial** has three terms.	*Example:* $x^2 - 3x - 6$
A **constant** polynomial has degree 0.	*Example:* 7
A **linear** polynomial has degree 1.	*Example:* $3x + 5$
A **quadratic** polynomial has degree 2.	*Example:* $5x^2 - x$
A **cubic** polynomial has degree 3.	*Example:* $x^3 + 2x^2 - \frac{1}{3}$
A **quartic** polynomial has degree 4.	*Example:* $-6x^4 - 2x^2 + 19$

Like, or *similar, terms* are either constant terms or terms containing the same variable(s) raised to the same power(s). Polynomials containing like terms can be simplified by *combining* those terms.

EXAMPLE 4   Combine like terms: $4x^2y + 2xy - x^2y + xy^2$.

SOLUTION   The like terms are $4x^2y$ and $-x^2y$. Thus we have

$$4x^2y + 2xy - x^2y + xy^2 = 4x^2y - x^2y + 2xy + xy^2$$
$$= 3x^2y + 2xy + xy^2.$$

TRY EXERCISE 37

A polynomial can be evaluated by replacing the variable or variables with a number or numbers.

EXAMPLE 5   Evaluate $-a^2 + 2ab + 5b^2$ for $a = -1$ and $b = 3$.

SOLUTION   We replace a with -1 and b with 3 and calculate the value using the rules for order of operations:

Evaluating a polynomial (p. 248)

$$-a^2 + 2ab + 5b^2 = -(-1)^2 + 2 \cdot (-1) \cdot 3 + 5 \cdot 3^2$$
$$= -1 - 6 + 45 = 38.$$

TRY EXERCISE 41

Polynomials can be added, subtracted, multiplied, and divided.

Addition and Subtraction of Polynomials

Addition of polynomials
(Section 4.4)

To add two polynomials, we write a plus sign between them and combine like terms.

EXAMPLE 6   Add: $(4x^3 + 3x^2 + 2x - 7) + (-5x^2 + x - 10)$.

SOLUTION

$$(4x^3 + 3x^2 + 2x - 7) + (-5x^2 + x - 10)$$
$$= 4x^3 + (3 - 5)x^2 + (2 + 1)x + (-7 - 10)$$
$$= 4x^3 - 2x^2 + 3x - 17$$

TRY EXERCISE 49

Opposite of a polynomial (p. 255)

To find the **opposite of a polynomial**, we replace each term with its opposite. This process is also called *changing the sign* of each term. For example, the opposite of

$$3y^4 - 7y^2 - \frac{1}{3}y + 17$$

is

$$-(3y^4 - 7y^2 - \frac{1}{3}y + 17) = -3y^4 + 7y^2 + \frac{1}{3}y - 17.$$

Subtraction of polynomials
(Section 4.4)

EXAMPLE 7

To subtract polynomials, we add the opposite of the polynomial being subtracted.

Subtract: $(3a^4 - 2a + 7) - (-a^3 + 5a - 1)$.

SOLUTION

$$(3a^4 - 2a + 7) - (-a^3 + 5a - 1)$$
$$= 3a^4 - 2a + 7 + a^3 - 5a + 1 \quad \text{Adding the opposite}$$
$$= 3a^4 + a^3 - 7a + 8 \quad \text{Combining like terms}$$

TRY EXERCISE 51

Multiplication of polynomials
(Section 4.5)

Multiplication of Polynomials

To multiply two monomials, we multiply coefficients and then multiply variables using the product rule for exponents. To multiply a monomial and a polynomial, we multiply each term of the polynomial by the monomial, using the distributive property.

EXAMPLE 8

Multiply: $4x^3(3x^4 - 2x^3 + 7x - 5)$.

SOLUTION

$$\textit{Think: } \underbrace{4x^3 \cdot 3x^4} - \underbrace{4x^3 \cdot 2x^3} + \underbrace{4x^3 \cdot 7x} - \underbrace{4x^3 \cdot 5}$$
$$4x^3(3x^4 - 2x^3 + 7x - 5) = 12x^7 \quad - \quad 8x^6 \quad + \quad 28x^4 \quad - \quad 20x^3$$

TRY EXERCISE 55

To multiply any two polynomials P and Q, we select one of the polynomials—say, P. We then multiply each term of P by every term of Q and combine like terms.

EXAMPLE 9

Multiply: $(2a^3 + 3a - 1)(a^2 - 4a)$.

SOLUTION   It is often helpful to use columns for a long multiplication. We multiply each term at the top by every term at the bottom, write like terms in columns, and add the results.

$$
\begin{array}{r}
2a^3 + 3a - 1 \\
a^2 - 4a \\
\hline
-8a^4 \qquad - 12a^2 + 4a \\
2a^5 \qquad + 3a^3 - a^2 \\
\hline
2a^5 - 8a^4 + 3a^3 - 13a^2 + 4a
\end{array}
$$

Multiplying the top row by $-4a$

Multiplying the top row by a^2

Combining like terms. Be sure that like terms are lined up in columns.

TRY EXERCISE 59

We could multiply two binomials in the same manner in which we multiplied the polynomials in Example 9. However, by observing the pattern of the products formed, we can develop a method of multiplying two binomials more efficiently.

> ## The FOIL Method
>
> To multiply two binomials, $A + B$ and $C + D$, multiply the First terms AC, the Outer terms AD, the Inner terms BC, and then the Last terms BD. Then combine like terms, if possible.
>
> $$(A + B)(C + D) = AC + AD + BC + BD$$
>
> 1. Multiply First terms: AC.
> 2. Multiply Outer terms: AD.
> 3. Multiply Inner terms: BC.
> 4. Multiply Last terms: BD.
>
>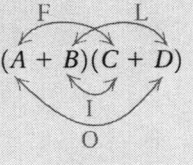
>
> FOIL

EXAMPLE 10

Multiply: $(3x + 4)(x - 2)$.

SOLUTION

FOIL (p. 270)

$$
\begin{array}{cccc}
 & F & O & I & L \\
(3x + 4)(x - 2) = & 3x^2 & - 6x & + 4x & - 8 \\
 & = 3x^2 - 2x - 8 & & & \text{Combining like terms}
\end{array}
$$

TRY EXERCISE 57

Special products occur so often that specific formulas or methods for computing them have been developed.

> ## Special Products
>
> **Multiplying sums and differences of two terms** (p. 271)
>
> The product of a sum and difference of the same two terms:
>
> $$(A + B)(A - B) = \underline{A^2 - B^2}$$
>
> This is called a *difference of squares*.
>
> **Squaring binomials** (p. 272)
>
> The square of a binomial:
>
> $$(A + B)^2 = A^2 + 2AB + B^2$$
> $$(A - B)^2 = A^2 - 2AB + B^2$$

EXAMPLE 11

Multiply: **(a)** $(x + 3y)(x - 3y)$; **(b)** $(x^3 + 2)^2$.

SOLUTION

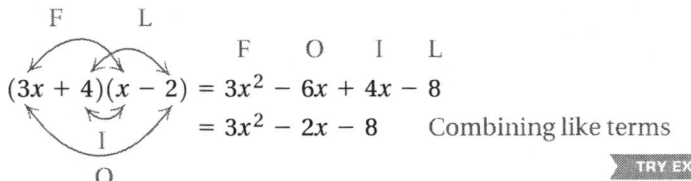

a) $(x + 3y)(x - 3y) = x^2 - (3y)^2$ $A = x$ and $B = 3y$
$$= x^2 - 9y^2$$

$$(A + B)^2 = A^2 + 2 \cdot A \cdot B + B^2$$

b) $(x^3 + 2)^2 = (x^3)^2 + 2 \cdot x^3 \cdot 2 + 2^2$ $A = x^3$ and $B = 2$
$$= x^6 + 4x^3 + 4$$

TRY EXERCISE 61

Division of polynomials
(Section 4.8)

Division of Polynomials

Polynomial division is similar to division in arithmetic. To divide a polynomial by a monomial, we divide each term by the monomial.

EXAMPLE **12**

Divide: $(3x^5 + 8x^3 - 12x) \div (4x)$.

SOLUTION   This division can be written

$$\frac{3x^5 + 8x^3 - 12x}{4x} = \frac{3x^5}{4x} + \frac{8x^3}{4x} - \frac{12x}{4x}$$ Dividing each term by $4x$

$$= \frac{3}{4}x^{5-1} + \frac{8}{4}x^{3-1} - \frac{12}{4}x^{1-1}$$ Dividing coefficients and subtracting exponents

$$= \frac{3}{4}x^4 + 2x^2 - 3.$$

To check, we multiply the quotient by $4x$:

$$\left(\tfrac{3}{4}x^4 + 2x^2 - 3\right)4x = 3x^5 + 8x^3 - 12x.$$ The answer checks.

TRY EXERCISE   69

To use long division, we write polynomials in descending order, including terms with 0 coefficients for missing terms. As shown below in Example 13, the procedure ends when the degree of the remainder is less than the degree of the divisor.

EXAMPLE **13**

Divide: $(4x^3 - 7x + 1) \div (2x + 1)$.

SOLUTION   The polynomials are already written in descending order, but there is no x^2-term in the dividend. We fill in $0x^2$ for that term.

$$
\begin{array}{r}
2x^2 \\
2x + 1\overline{)4x^3 + 0x^2 - 7x + 1} \\
\underline{4x^3 + 2x^2} \\
-2x^2
\end{array}
$$

Divide the first term of the dividend, $4x^3$, by the first term in the divisor, $2x$: $4x^3/(2x) = 2x^2$.

Multiply $2x^2$ by the divisor, $2x + 1$.

Subtract: $(4x^3 + 0x^2) - (4x^3 + 2x^2) = -2x^2.$

Then we bring down the next term of the dividend, $-7x$.

$$
\begin{array}{r}
2x^2 - x \\
2x + 1\overline{)4x^3 + 0x^2 - 7x + 1} \\
\underline{4x^3 + 2x^2} \\
-2x^2 - 7x \\
\underline{-2x^2 - x} \\
-6x
\end{array}
$$

Divide the first term of $-2x^2 - 7x$ by the first term in the divisor: $-2x^2/(2x) = -x.$

The $-7x$ has been "brought down."

Multiply $-x$ by the divisor, $2x + 1$.

Subtract: $(-2x^2 - 7x) - (-2x^2 - x) = -6x.$

Since the degree of the remainder, $-6x$, is *not* less than the degree of the divisor, we must continue dividing.

$$
\begin{array}{r}
2x^2 - x - 3 \\
2x + 1 \overline{)4x^3 + 0x^2 - 7x + 1} \\
\underline{4x^3 + 2x^2} \\
-2x^2 - 7x \\
\underline{-2x^2 - x} \\
-6x + 1 \\
\underline{-6x - 3} \\
4
\end{array}
$$

Divide the first term of $-6x + 1$ by the first term in the divisor: $-6x/(2x) = -3$.

← The 1 has been "brought down."

← Multiply -3 by $2x + 1$.

← Subtract.

The answer is $2x^2 - x - 3$ with R4, or

$$
\text{Quotient} \longrightarrow 2x^2 - x - 3 + \frac{4}{2x + 1}. \quad \begin{array}{l}\leftarrow \text{Remainder} \\ \leftarrow \text{Divisor}\end{array}
$$

Check: To check, we can multiply by the divisor and add the remainder:

$$
(2x + 1)(2x^2 - x - 3) + 4 = 4x^3 - 7x - 3 + 4
$$
$$
= 4x^3 - 7x + 1.
$$

TRY EXERCISE 71

R.4   EXERCISE SET

Solve.

1. a^0, for $a = -25$

2. y^0, for $y = 6.97$

3. $4^0 - 4^1$

4. $8^1 - 8^0$

Write an equivalent expression using positive exponents. Then, if possible, simplify.

5. 8^{-2}

6. $(-2)^{-3}$

7. $10x^{-5}$

8. $-16y^{-3}$

9. $(ab)^{-2}$

10. ab^{-2}

11. $\dfrac{1}{y^{-10}}$

12. $\dfrac{1}{x^{-t}}$

Write an equivalent expression using negative exponents.

13. $\dfrac{1}{t^4}$

14. $\dfrac{1}{a^2b^3}$

Simplify.

15. $x^5 \cdot x^{10}$

16. $a^4 \cdot a^{-2}$

17. $\dfrac{a}{a^{-5}}$

18. $\dfrac{p^{-3}}{p^{-8}}$

19. $\dfrac{(4x)^{11}}{(4x)^2}$

20. $\dfrac{a^2b^9}{a^9b^2}$

21. $(7^8)^5$

22. $(x^3)^{-7}$

23. $(x^{-2}y^{-3})^{-4}$

24. $(-2a^2)^3$

25. $\left(\dfrac{y^2}{4}\right)^3$

26. $\left(\dfrac{ab^2}{c^3}\right)^4$

27. $\left(\dfrac{2p^3}{3q^4}\right)^{-2}$

28. $\left(\dfrac{2}{x}\right)^{-5}$

Identify the terms of each polynomial.

29. $8x^3 - 6x^2 + x - 7$

30. $-a^2b + 4a^2 - 8b + 17$

Determine the coefficient and the degree of each term in each polynomial. Then find the degree of each polynomial.

31. $18x^3 + 36x^9 - 7x + 3$

32. $-8y^7 + y + 19$

33. $-x^2y + 4y^3 - 2xy$

34. $8 - x^2y^4 + y^7$

Determine the leading term and the leading coefficient of each polynomial.

35. $-p^2 + 5 + 8p^4 - 7p$

36. $13 + 20t - 30t^2 - t^3$

Combine like terms. Write each answer in descending order.

37. $3x^3 - x^2 + x^4 + x^2$

38. $5t - 8t^2 + 4t^2$

39. $3 - 2t^2 + 8t - 3t - 5t^2 + 7$

40. $8x^5 - \frac{1}{3} + \frac{4}{5}x + 1 - \frac{1}{2}x$

Evaluate each polynomial for the given replacements of the variables.

41. $3x^2 - 7x + 10$, for $x = -2$

42. $-y + 3y^2 + 2y^3$, for $y = 3$

43. $a^2b^3 + 2b^2 - 6a$, for $a = 2$ and $b = -1$

44. $2pq^3 - 5q^2 + 8p$, for $p = -4$ and $q = -2$

The distance s, in feet, traveled by a body falling freely from rest in t seconds is approximated by

$$s = 16t^2.$$

45. A pebble is dropped into a well and takes 3 sec to hit the water. How far down is the surface of the water?

46. An acorn falls from the top of an oak tree and takes 2 sec to hit the ground. How high is the tree?

The number of watts of power P generated by a particular turbine at a wind speed of x miles per hour can be approximated by the polynomial

$$P = 0.0157x^3 + 0.1163x^2 - 1.3396x + 3.7063.$$

Source: Based on data from QST, November 2006

47. Estimate the power generated by a 10-mph wind.

48. Estimate the power generated by a 30-mph wind.

Add or subtract, as indicated.

49. $(3x^3 + 2x^2 + 8x) + (x^3 - 5x^2 + 7)$

50. $(-6x^4 + 3x^2 - 16) + (4x^2 + 4x - 7)$

51. $(8y^2 - 2y - 3) - (9y^2 - 7y - 1)$

52. $(4t^2 + 6t - 7) - (t + 5)$

53. $(-x^2y + 2y^2 + y) - (3y^2 + 2x^2y - 7y)$

54. $(ab + x^2y^2) + (2ab - x^2y^2)$

Multiply.

55. $4x^2(3x^3 - 7x + 7)$

56. $a^2b(a^3 + b^2 - ab - 2b)$

57. $(2a + y)(4a + b)$

58. $(x + 7y)(y - 3x)$

59. $(x + 7)(x^2 - 3x + 1)$

60. $(2x - 3)(x^2 - x - 1)$

61. $(x + 7)(x - 7)$

62. $(2x + 1)^2$

63. $(x + y)^2$

64. $(xy + 1)(xy - 1)$

65. $(2x^2 + 7)(3x^2 - 2)$

66. $(1.1x^2 + 5)(0.1x^2 - 2)$

67. $(6a - 5y)(7a + 3y)$

68. $(3p^2 - q^3)^2$

Divide and check.

69. $(3t^5 + 9t^3 - 6t^2 + 15t) \div (-3t)$

70. $(4x^5 + 10x^4 - 16x^2) \div (4x^2)$

71. $(15x^2 - 16x - 15) \div (3x - 5)$

72. $(x^3 - 2x^2 - 14x + 1) \div (x - 5)$

73. $(2x^3 - x^2 + 1) \div (x + 1)$

74. $(2x^3 + 3x^2 - 50) \div (2x - 5)$

75. $(5x^3 + 3x^2 - 5x) \div (x^2 - 1)$

76. $(2x^3 + 3x^2 + 6x + 10) \div (x^2 + 3)$

R.5   Polynomials and Factoring

Common Factors and Factoring by Grouping   ▪   Factoring Trinomials   ▪   Factoring Special Forms   ▪   Solving Polynomial Equations by Factoring

Common Factors and Factoring by Grouping

Factor (p. 304)

To *factor* a polynomial is to find an equivalent expression that is a product. To factor a monomial, we find two monomials whose product is equivalent to the original monomial. For example, three factorizations of $50x^6$ are $5 \cdot 10x^6$, $5x^3 \cdot 10x^3$, and $2x \cdot 25x^5$.

Common factor (p. 305)

If all the terms in a polynomial share a common factor, that factor can be "factored out" of the polynomial. Whenever you are factoring a polynomial with two or more terms, try to first find the largest common factor of the terms, if one exists.

EXAMPLE   1

Factor: $3x^6 + 15x^4 - 9x^3$.

SOLUTION   The largest factor common to 3, 15, and -9 is 3. The largest power of x common to x^6, x^4, and x^3 is x^3. Thus the largest common factor of the terms of the polynomial is $3x^3$. We factor as follows:

$$3x^6 + 15x^4 - 9x^3 = 3x^3 \cdot x^3 + 3x^3 \cdot 5x - 3x^3 \cdot 3 \qquad \text{Factoring each term}$$

$$= 3x^3(x^3 + 5x - 3). \qquad \text{Factoring out } 3x^3$$

Factorizations can always be checked by multiplying:

$$3x^3(x^3 + 5x - 3) = 3x^6 + 15x^4 - 9x^3.$$

TRY EXERCISE   1

A polynomial with two or more terms can be a common factor.

EXAMPLE   2

Factor: $3x^2(x - 2) + 5(x - 2)$.

SOLUTION   The binomial $x - 2$ is a factor of both $3x^2(x - 2)$ and $5(x - 2)$. Thus we have

$$3x^2(x - 2) + 5(x - 2) = (x - 2)(3x^2 + 5). \qquad \text{Factoring out the common factor, } x - 2$$

TRY EXERCISE   5

If a polynomial with four terms can be split into two groups of terms, and both groups share a common binomial factor, the polynomial can be factored. This method is known as **factoring by grouping**.

Factoring by grouping (p. 307)

EXAMPLE   3

Factor by grouping: $2x^3 + 6x^2 - x - 3$.

SOLUTION   First, we consider the polynomial as two groups of terms, $2x^3 + 6x^2$ and $-x - 3$. Then we factor each group separately:

$$2x^3 + 6x^2 - x - 3 = 2x^2(x + 3) - 1(x + 3) \qquad \text{Factoring out } 2x^2 \text{ and } -1 \text{ to give the common binomial factor, } x + 3$$

$$= (x + 3)(2x^2 - 1).$$

The check is left to the student.

TRY EXERCISE   23

Prime polynomial (p. 316)

Not every polynomial with four terms is factorable by grouping. A polynomial that is not factorable is said to be **prime**.

Factoring trinomials of the type
$x^2 + bx + c$ (Section 5.2)

Factoring Trinomials

Many trinomials that have no common factor can be written as the product of two binomials. We look first at trinomials of the form $x^2 + bx + c$, for which the leading coefficient is 1.

Factoring trinomials involves a trial-and-error process. In order for the product of two binomials to be $x^2 + bx + c$, the binomials must look like

$$(x + p)(x + q),$$

where p and q are constants that must be determined. We look for two numbers whose product is c and whose sum is b.

EXAMPLE 4

Factor.

a) $x^2 + 10x + 16$

b) $x^2 - 8x + 15$

c) $x^2 - 2x - 24$

d) $3t^2 - 33st + 84s^2$

SOLUTION

a) The factorization is of the form

$$(x +   )(x +   ).$$

Constant term positive (p. 312)

To find the constant terms, we need a pair of factors whose product is 16 and whose sum is 10. Since 16 is positive, its factors will have the same sign as 10— that is, we need consider only positive factors of 16.

We list the possible factorizations in a table and calculate the sum of each pair of factors.

Pairs of Factors of 16	Sums of Factors
1, 16	17
2, 8	10 ←
4, 4	8

The numbers we seek are 2 and 8.

The factorization of $x^2 + 10x + 16$ is $(x + 2)(x + 8)$. To check, we multiply.

Check: $(x + 2)(x + 8) = x^2 + 8x + 2x + 16 = x^2 + 10x + 16.$

b) For $x^2 - 8x + 15$, c is positive and b is negative. Therefore, the factors of 15 will be negative. Again, we list the possible factorizations in a table.

Pairs of Factors of 15	Sums of Factors
-1, -15	-16
-3, -5	-8 ←

The numbers we need are −3 and −5.

The factorization is $(x - 3)(x - 5)$.

Check: $(x - 3)(x - 5) = x^2 - 5x - 3x + 15 = x^2 - 8x + 15.$

Constant term negative (p. 314)

c) For $x^2 - 2x - 24$, c is negative, so one factor of −24 will be negative and one will be positive. Since b is also negative, the negative factor must have the larger absolute value.

Pairs of Factors of -24	Sums of Factors
1, -24	-23
2, -12	-10
3, -8	-5
4, -6	-2 ←

The numbers we need are 4 and -6.

The factorization is $(x + 4)(x - 6)$.

Check: $(x + 4)(x - 6) = x^2 - 6x + 4x - 24 = x^2 - 2x - 24$.

d) Always look first for a common factor. There is a common factor, 3, which we factor out first:

$$3t^2 - 33st + 84s^2 = 3(t^2 - 11st + 28s^2).$$

Now we consider $t^2 - 11st + 28s^2$. Think of $28s^2$ as the "constant" term c and $-11s$ as the "coefficient" b of the middle term. We try to express $28s^2$ as the product of two factors whose sum is $-11s$. These factors are $-4s$ and $-7s$. Thus the factorization of $t^2 - 11st + 28s^2$ is

$(t - 4s)(t - 7s)$.   This is not the entire factorization
of $3t^2 - 33st + 84s^2$.

We now include the common factor, 3, and write

$3t^2 - 33st + 84s^2 = 3(t - 4s)(t - 7s)$.   This is the factorization.

Check: $3(t - 4s)(t - 7s) = 3(t^2 - 11st + 28s^2) = 3t^2 - 33st + 84s^2$.

> **TRY EXERCISE** 11

Factoring trinomials of the type $ax^2 + bx + c$ (Section 5.3)

When the leading coefficient of a trinomial is not 1, the number of trials needed to find a factorization can increase dramatically. We will consider two methods for factoring trinomials of the type $ax^2 + bx + c$: factoring with FOIL and the grouping method.

Factoring with FOIL (p. 320)

To Factor $ax^2 + bx + c$ Using FOIL

1. Make certain that all common factors have been removed. If any remain, factor out the largest common factor.
2. Find two First terms whose product is ax^2:

    $(\blacksquare x + \quad)(\blacksquare x + \quad) = ax^2 + bx + c.$
    FOIL

3. Find two Last terms whose product is c:

    $(\quad x + \blacksquare)(\quad x + \blacksquare) = ax^2 + bx + c.$
    FOIL

4. Check by multiplying to see if the sum of the Outer and Inner products is bx. If necessary, repeat steps 2 and 3 until the correct combination is found.

    $(\blacksquare x + \blacksquare)(\blacksquare x + \blacksquare) = ax^2 + bx + c.$
    I
    O
    FOIL

If no correct combination exists, state that the polynomial is prime.

EXAMPLE 5 Factor: $20x^3 - 22x^2 - 12x$.

SOLUTION

1. First, we factor out the largest common factor, $2x$:
    $$20x^3 - 22x^2 - 12x = 2x(10x^2 - 11x - 6).$$

2. Next, in order to factor the trinomial $10x^2 - 11x - 6$, we search for two terms whose product is $10x^2$. The possibilities are
    $$(x + \quad)(10x + \quad) \quad \text{or} \quad (2x + \quad)(5x + \quad).$$

3. There are four pairs of factors of -6. Since the first terms of the binomials are different, the order of the factors is important. So there are eight possibilities for the last terms:

    $$\begin{array}{cc} 1, -6 & -6, \ 1 \\ -1, \ 6 & 6, -1 \\ 2, -3 \quad \text{and} & -3, \ 2 \\ -2, \ 3 & 3, -2. \end{array}$$

4. Since each of the eight possibilities from step (3) could be used in either of the two possibilities from step (2), there are $2 \cdot 8$, or 16, possible factorizations. We check the possibilities systematically until we find one that gives the correct factorization. Let's first try factors with $(2x + \quad)(5x + \quad)$.

Pair of Factors	Corresponding Trial	Product	
1, −6	$(2x + 1)(5x - 6)$	$10x^2 - 7x - 6$	←Wrong middle term
−1, 6	$(2x - 1)(5x + 6)$	$10x^2 + 7x - 6$	←Wrong middle term. Note that changing the signs in the binomials changed the sign of middle term in the product.
2, −3	$(2x + 2)(5x - 3)$	$10x^2 + 4x - 6$	←Wrong middle term. We need not consider $(2x - 2)(5x + 3)$.
−6, 1	$(2x - 6)(5x + 1)$	$10x^2 - 28x - 6$	←Wrong middle term. We need not consider $(2x + 6)(5x - 1)$.
−3, 2	$(2x - 3)(5x + 2)$	$10x^2 - 11x - 6$	←Correct middle term

We can stop when we find a correct factorization. Including the common factor $2x$, we now have
$$20x^3 - 22x^2 - 12x = 2x(2x - 3)(5x + 2).$$

This can be checked by multiplying.

▶ TRY EXERCISE 27

The grouping method (p. 325)

With practice, some of the trials can be skipped or performed mentally.

The second method of factoring trinomials of the type $ax^2 + bx + c$ involves factoring by grouping.

> **To Factor $ax^2 + bx + c$, Using the Grouping Method**
> 1. Factor out the largest common factor, if one exists.
> 2. Multiply the leading coefficient a and the constant c.
> 3. Find a pair of factors of ac whose sum is b.
> 4. Rewrite the middle term, bx, as a sum or difference using the factors found in step (3).
> 5. Factor by grouping.
> 6. Include any common factor from step (1) and check by multiplying.

EXAMPLE **6**   Factor: $7x^2 + 31x + 12$.

SOLUTION

1. There is no common factor (other than 1 or -1).

2. We multiply the leading coefficient, 7, and the constant, 12:

   $7 \cdot 12 = 84.$

3. We look for a pair of factors of 84 whose sum is 31. Since both 84 and 31 are positive, we need consider only positive factors.

Pairs of Factors of 84	Sums of Factors
1, 84	85
2, 42	44
3, 28	31 ← ———— $3 + 28 = 31$

4. Next, we rewrite $31x$ using the factors 3 and 28:

   $31x = 3x + 28x.$

5. We now factor by grouping:

   $7x^2 + 31x + 12 = 7x^2 + 3x + 28x + 12$ Substituting $3x + 28x$ for $31x$

   $= x(7x + 3) + 4(7x + 3)$

   $= (7x + 3)(x + 4).$ Factoring out the common factor, $7x + 3$

6. *Check:* $(7x + 3)(x + 4) = 7x^2 + 31x + 12.$ **TRY EXERCISE** 15

Factoring Special Forms

We can factor certain types of polynomials directly, without using trial and error.

> **Factoring Formulas**
>
> Perfect-square trinomial: $A^2 + 2AB + B^2 = (A + B)^2,$
> $A^2 - 2AB + B^2 = (A - B)^2$
>
> Difference of squares: $A^2 - B^2 = (A + B)(A - B)$
>
> Sum of cubes: $A^3 + B^3 = (A + B)(A^2 - AB + B^2)$
>
> Difference of cubes: $A^3 - B^3 = (A - B)(A^2 + AB + B^2)$

Before using the factoring formulas, it is important to check carefully that the expression being factored is indeed in one of the forms listed. Note that there is no factoring formula for the sum of two squares.

EXAMPLE 7   Factor: (a) $2x^2 - 2$; (b) $x^2y^2 + 20xy + 100$; (c) $p^3 - 64$; (d) $3y^2 + 27$.

SOLUTION

a) We first factor out a common factor, 2:

$$2x^2 - 2 = 2(x^2 - 1).$$

Recognizing and factoring differences of squares (pp. 331, 332)

Looking at $x^2 - 1$, we see that it is a difference of squares, with $A = x$ and $B = 1$. The factorization is thus

$$2x^2 - 2 = 2(x^2 - 1) = 2(x + 1)(x - 1).$$
$$\underset{A^2 - B^2}{} \quad \underset{(A + B)(A - B)}{}$$

Recognizing and factoring perfect-square trinomials (pp. 329, 330)

b) First, we check for a common factor; there is none. The polynomial is a perfect-square trinomial, since x^2y^2 and 100 are squares; there is no minus sign before either square; and $20xy$ is $2 \cdot xy \cdot 10$, where xy and 10 are square roots of x^2y^2 and 100, respectively. The factorization is thus

$$x^2y^2 + 20xy + 100 = (xy)^2 + 2 \cdot xy \cdot 10 + 10^2 = (xy + 10)^2.$$
$$\underset{A^2 \ + \ \ 2 \cdot A \cdot \ B \ + \ B^2 \ = \ (A \ + \ B)^2}{}$$

Factoring sums or differences of cubes (Section 5.5)

c) This is a difference of cubes, with $A = p$ and $B = 4$:

$$p^3 - 64 = (p)^3 - (4)^3$$
$$= (p - 4)(p^2 + 4p + 16).$$

d) We factor out the common factor, 3:

$$3y^2 + 27 = 3(y^2 + 9).$$

Since $y^2 + 9$ is a sum of squares, no further factorization is possible.

TRY EXERCISE 7

Factoring completely (p. 333)

A polynomial is said to be *factored completely* when no factor can be factored further.

EXAMPLE 8   Factor completely: $x^4 - 1$.

SOLUTION

$$x^4 - 1 = (x^2 + 1)(x^2 - 1) \qquad \text{Factoring a difference of squares}$$
$$= (x^2 + 1)(x + 1)(x - 1) \qquad \text{The factor } x^2 - 1 \text{ is itself a difference of squares.}$$

TRY EXERCISE 21

Solving Polynomial Equations by Factoring

Polynomial equation (p. 345)
Quadratic equation (p. 345)

A **polynomial equation** is formed by setting two polynomials equal to each other. A **quadratic equation** is a polynomial equation equivalent to one of the form $ax^2 + bx + c = 0$, where $a \neq 0$. Polynomial equations that can be factored can be solved using the principle of zero products.

The principle of zero products
(p. 346)

> ## The Principle of Zero Products
>
> An equation $ab = 0$ is true if and only if $a = 0$ or $b = 0$, or both. (A product is 0 if and only if at least one factor is 0.)

If we can write an equation as a product that equals 0, we can try to use the principle of zero products to solve the equation.

EXAMPLE 9   Solve:

a) $x^2 - 11x = 12$ b) $5x^2 + 10x + 5 = 0$ c) $9x^2 = 1$

SOLUTION

a) We must have 0 on one side of the equation before using the principle of zero products:

Get 0 on one side.	$x^2 - 11x = 12$	
Factor.	$x^2 - 11x - 12 = 0$	Subtracting 12 from both sides
	$(x - 12)(x + 1) = 0$	Factoring
Use the principle of zero products.	$x - 12 = 0$ *or* $x + 1 = 0$	Using the principle of zero products
Solve.	$x = 12$ *or* $x = -1.$	

The solutions are 12 and −1. The check is left to the student.

b) We have

$$5x^2 + 10x + 5 = 0$$
$$5(x^2 + 2x + 1) = 0 \qquad \text{Factoring out a common factor}$$
$$5(x + 1)(x + 1) = 0 \qquad \text{Factoring completely}$$
$$x + 1 = 0 \quad or \quad x + 1 = 0 \qquad \text{Using the principle of zero products}$$
$$x = -1 \quad or \qquad x = -1.$$

There is only one solution, −1. The check is left to the student.

c) We have

$$9x^2 = 1$$
$$9x^2 - 1 = 0 \qquad \text{Subtracting 1 from both sides to get 0 on one side}$$
$$(3x + 1)(3x - 1) = 0 \qquad \text{Factoring a difference of squares}$$
$$3x + 1 = 0 \quad or \quad 3x - 1 = 0 \qquad \text{Using the principle of zero products}$$
$$3x = -1 \quad or \qquad 3x = 1$$
$$x = -\tfrac{1}{3} \quad or \qquad x = \tfrac{1}{3}.$$

The solutions are $\tfrac{1}{3}$ and $-\tfrac{1}{3}$. The check is left to the student.

> **TRY EXERCISE** 37

Quadratic equations can be used to solve problems. One important result that uses squared quantities is the Pythagorean theorem. It relates the lengths of the sides of a **right triangle**, that is, a triangle with a 90° angle. The side opposite the 90° angle is called the **hypotenuse**, and the other sides are called the **legs**.

The Pythagorean Theorem

The sum of the squares of the legs of a right triangle is equal to the square of the hypotenuse:

$$a^2 + b^2 = c^2.$$

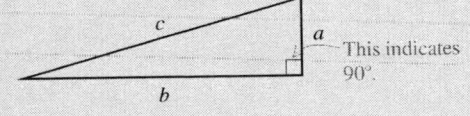

This indicates 90°.

EXAMPLE **10**   *Swing sets.*   The length of a slide on a swing set is 5 ft. The distance from the base of the ladder to the base of the slide is 1 ft more than the height of the ladder. Find the height of the ladder.

SOLUTION

1. **Familiarize.** We first make a drawing and let $x =$ the height of the ladder, in feet. We know then that the other leg of the triangle is $x + 1$, since it is 1 ft longer than the ladder. The hypotenuse has length 5 ft.

2. **Translate.** Applying the Pythagorean theorem gives us

$$a^2 + b^2 = c^2$$
$$x^2 + (x + 1)^2 = 5^2. \quad \text{Substituting}$$

3. **Carry out.** We solve the equation:

$$
\begin{aligned}
x^2 + (x + 1)^2 &= 5^2 \\
x^2 + x^2 + 2x + 1 &= 25 \qquad &&\text{Squaring } x + 1; \text{squaring } 5 \\
2x^2 + 2x + 1 &= 25 \qquad &&\text{Combining like terms} \\
2x^2 + 2x - 24 &= 0 \qquad &&\text{Getting 0 on one side} \\
2(x^2 + x - 12) &= 0 \qquad &&\text{Factoring out a common factor} \\
2(x + 4)(x - 3) &= 0 \qquad &&\text{Factoring a trinomial} \\
x + 4 = 0 \quad \text{or} \quad x - 3 &= 0 \qquad &&\text{Using the principle of zero products} \\
x = -4 \quad \text{or} \quad x &= 3.
\end{aligned}
$$

4. **Check.** We know that the integer -4 is not a solution because the height of the ladder cannot be negative. When $x = 3$, the distance from the base of the ladder to the base of the slide is $x + 1 = 4$, and $3^2 + 4^2 = 5^2$. So the solution 3 checks.

5. **State.** The ladder is 3 ft high.

TRY EXERCISE 49

R.5 EXERCISE SET

Factor completely. If a polynomial is prime, state this.

1. $18t^5 - 12t^4 + 6t^3$ **2.** $x^2y^4 - 2xy^5 + 3x^3y^6$

3. $y^2 - 6y + 9$ **4.** $4z^2 - 25$

5. $2p^3(p + 2) + (p + 2)$ **6.** $6y^2 + y - 1$

7. $x^2 + 100$ **8.** $y^3 - 1$

9. $8t^3 + 27$ **10.** $a^2b^2 + 24ab + 144$

11. $m^2 + 13m + 42$ **12.** $2x^3 - 6x^2 + x - 3$

13. $x^4 - 81$ **14.** $x^2 + x + 3$

15. $8x^2 + 22x + 15$ **16.** $4x^2 - 40x + 100$

17. $x^3 + 2x^2 - x - 2$

18. $(x + 2y)(x - 1) + (x + 2y)(x - 2)$

19. $0.001t^6 - 0.008$

20. $x^2 - 20 - x$

21. $-\frac{1}{16} + x^4$

22. $5x^8 - 5z^{16}$

23. $mn - 2m + 3n - 6$

24. $t^6 - p^6$

25. $5mn + m^2 - 150n^2$

26. $\frac{1}{27} + x^3$

27. $24x^2y - 6y - 10xy$ **28.** $-3y^2 - 12y - 12$

29. $y^2 + 121 - 22y$ **30.** $t^3 - 2t^2 - 5t + 10$

Solve.

31. $(x - 1)(x + 3) = 0$

32. $(3x - 5)(7 - 4x) = 0$

33. $8x(11 - x) = 0$

34. $(x - 3)(x + 1)(2x - 9) = 0$

35. $x^2 = 9$ **36.** $8x^2 = 2x$

37. $4x^2 - 18x = 70$ **38.** $x^2 + 6x + 9 = 0$

39. $2x^2 - 10x = 0$ **40.** $100x^2 = 9$

41. $(a + 1)(a - 5) = 7$ **42.** $d(d - 3) = 40$

43. $x^2 + 6x - 55 = 0$ **44.** $x^2 + 7x - 60 = 0$

45. $\frac{1}{2}x^2 + 5x + \frac{25}{2} = 0$ **46.** $3 + 10x^2 = 11x$

47. *Landscaping.* A triangular flower garden is 3 ft longer than it is wide. The area of the garden is 20 ft². What are the dimensions of the garden?

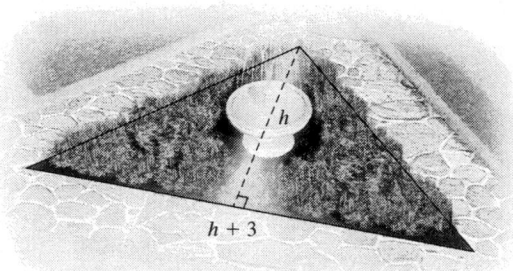

48. *Page numbers.* The product of the page numbers on two facing pages of a book is 156. Find the page numbers.

49. *Right triangles.* The hypotenuse of a right triangle is 17 ft. One leg is 1 ft shorter than twice the length of the other leg. Find the lengths of the legs.

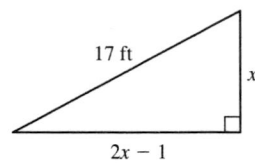

50. *Hiking.* Cheri hiked 500 ft up a steep incline. Her global positioning unit indicated that her horizontal position had changed by 100 ft more than her vertical position had changed. What was the change in altitude?

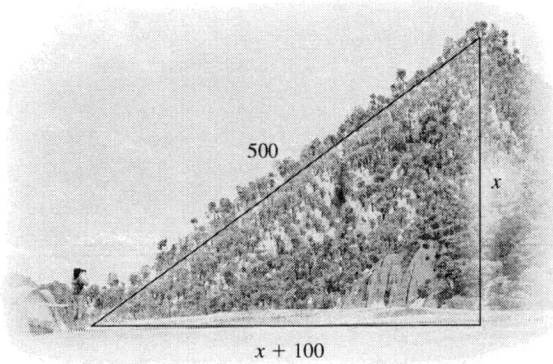

R.6   Rational Expressions and Equations

Multiplication and Division of Rational Expressions   ■   Addition and Subtraction of Rational Expressions   ■   Complex Rational Expressions   ■   Solving Rational Equations

Rational expressions (p. 376)

A **rational expression** is a quotient of two polynomials. Because division by 0 is undefined, a rational expression is undefined for any number that will make the denominator 0.

EXAMPLE   1   Find all numbers for which the rational expression

$$\frac{2x + 5}{x^2 - 9x - 10}$$

is undefined.

SOLUTION   We set the denominator equal to 0 and solve:

$$x^2 - 9x - 10 = 0$$
$$(x - 10)(x + 1) = 0 \qquad \text{Factoring}$$
$$x - 10 = 0 \quad or \quad x + 1 = 0 \qquad \text{Using the principle of zero products}$$
$$x = 10 \quad or \qquad x = -1.$$

If x is replaced with 10 or with -1, the denominator is 0. Thus,

$$\frac{2x + 5}{x^2 - 9x - 10} \text{ is undefined for } x = 10 \text{ and } x = -1.$$

TRY EXERCISE   1

Multiplication and Division of Rational Expressions

Multiplication and division of rational expressions is similar to multiplication and division with fractions.

Multiplication and division of rational expressions (Section 6.2)

The Product and the Quotient of Two Rational Expressions

To multiply two rational expressions, multiply numerators and multiply denominators:

$$\frac{A}{B} \cdot \frac{C}{D} = \frac{AC}{BD}.$$

To divide by a rational expression, multiply by its reciprocal:

$$\frac{A}{B} \div \frac{C}{D} = \frac{A}{B} \cdot \frac{D}{C} = \frac{AD}{BC}.$$

EXAMPLE   2   Simplify: $\dfrac{9x^2 + 12x}{6x^2 - 3x}$.

SOLUTION   We first factor the numerator and the denominator:

$$\frac{9x^2 + 12x}{6x^2 - 3x} = \frac{3x(3x + 4)}{3x(2x - 1)}.$$

We can now write this as a product of two rational expressions using the rule for multiplying rational expressions in reverse. Then we can simplify.

$$\frac{3x(3x + 4)}{3x(2x - 1)} = \frac{3x}{3x} \cdot \frac{3x + 4}{2x - 1} \qquad \begin{array}{l}\text{Rewriting as a product of} \\ \text{two rational expressions}\end{array}$$

$$= 1 \cdot \frac{3x + 4}{2x - 1} \qquad \frac{3x}{3x} = 1$$

$$= \frac{3x + 4}{2x - 1} \qquad \text{Removing the factor 1}$$

TRY EXERCISE 7

Only factors can be removed. Be sure that the numerator and the denominator are factored before you attempt to remove factors equal to 1.

After multiplying or dividing rational expressions, we simplify, if possible.

EXAMPLE 3

Perform each indicated operation and simplify.

a) $\dfrac{x^2 - x - 6}{3x} \cdot \dfrac{12x^3}{x + 2}$

b) $\dfrac{x^2 - 1}{x + 5} \div \dfrac{x^2 + 2x + 1}{2x + 10}$

SOLUTION

a) $\dfrac{x^2 - x - 6}{3x} \cdot \dfrac{12x^3}{x + 2} = \dfrac{(x^2 - x - 6)(12x^3)}{3x(x + 2)}$ Multiplying the numerators and the denominators

$$= \frac{(x - 3)(x + 2)(3x)(4x^2)}{3x(x + 2)} \qquad \begin{array}{l}\text{Factoring the numerator.} \\ \text{Try to go directly to this} \\ \text{step.}\end{array}$$

$$= \frac{(x - 3)\cancel{(x + 2)}\cancel{(3x)}(4x^2)}{\cancel{(3x)}\cancel{(x + 2)}} \qquad \begin{array}{l}\text{Removing a factor equal} \\ \text{to 1: } \dfrac{(x + 2)(3x)}{(x + 2)(3x)} = 1\end{array}$$

$$= 4x^2(x - 3)$$

b) $\dfrac{x^2 - 1}{x + 5} \div \dfrac{x^2 + 2x + 1}{2x + 10} = \dfrac{x^2 - 1}{x + 5} \cdot \dfrac{2x + 10}{x^2 + 2x + 1}$ Multiplying by the reciprocal of the divisor

$$= \frac{(x + 1)(x - 1)(2)(x + 5)}{(x + 5)(x + 1)(x + 1)} \qquad \begin{array}{l}\text{Multiplying rational} \\ \text{expressions and} \\ \text{factoring numerators} \\ \text{and denominators}\end{array}$$

$$= \frac{\cancel{(x + 1)}(x - 1)(2)\cancel{(x + 5)}}{\cancel{(x + 5)}\cancel{(x + 1)}(x + 1)} \qquad \begin{array}{l}\text{Removing a factor} \\ \text{equal to 1:} \\ \dfrac{(x + 1)(x + 5)}{(x + 1)(x + 5)} = 1\end{array}$$

$$= \frac{2(x - 1)}{x + 1} \qquad \begin{array}{l}\text{We leave the} \\ \text{numerator in} \\ \text{factored form.}\end{array}$$

TRY EXERCISE 13

Addition and Subtraction of Rational Expressions

Like multiplication and division, addition and subtraction of rational expressions is similar to addition and subtraction of fractions.

Addition and subtraction of rational expressions (Sections 6.3 and 6.4)

> ### The Sum and the Difference of Two Rational Expressions
>
> To add when the denominators are the same, add the numerators and keep the same denominator:
>
> $$\frac{A}{B} + \frac{C}{B} = \frac{A + C}{B}.$$
>
> To subtract when the denominators are the same, subtract the second numerator from the first and keep the same denominator:
>
> $$\frac{A}{B} - \frac{C}{B} = \frac{A - C}{B}.$$

EXAMPLE   4   Add and simplify, if possible:

$$\frac{x - 6}{x^2 - 6x + 5} + \frac{5}{x^2 - 6x + 5}.$$

SOLUTION

$$\frac{x - 6}{x^2 - 6x + 5} + \frac{5}{x^2 - 6x + 5} = \frac{x - 6 + 5}{x^2 - 6x + 5} \qquad \text{Adding numerators}$$

$$= \frac{x - 1}{(x - 5)(x - 1)} \qquad \text{Factoring the denominator}$$

$$= \frac{1(x - 1)}{(x - 5)(x - 1)} \qquad \begin{array}{l}\text{Removing a factor} \\ \text{equal to 1:} \\ \frac{x - 1}{x - 1} = 1\end{array}$$

$$= \frac{1}{x - 5} \qquad \qquad \textbf{TRY EXERCISE}\ \ 15$$

Least common denominator (p. 390)
Least common multiple (p. 390)

When two rational expressions do not have a common denominator, we must rewrite them with a common denominator before we can add or subtract them. We generally rewrite them using their **least common denominator** (**LCD**), which is the **least common multiple** (**LCM**) of their denominators.

To Find the Least Common Denominator (LCD)

1. Write the prime factorization of each denominator.
2. Select one of the factorizations and inspect it to see if it completely contains the other.

   a) If it does, it represents the LCM of the denominators.
   b) If it does not, multiply that factorization by any factors of the other denominator that it lacks. The final product is the LCM of the denominators.

The LCD is the LCM of the denominators. It should contain each factor the greatest number of times that it occurs in any of the individual factorizations.

EXAMPLE   5   Add: $\dfrac{x-3}{x^2-1} + \dfrac{4x^2}{x^2+4x+3}$.

SOLUTION   We first find the LCD. We write the prime factorization of each denominator and construct the LCM:

$$x^2 - 1 = (x+1)(x-1);$$
$$x^2 + 4x + 3 = (x+1)(x+3).$$

The LCM must contain both factorizations. We select the factorization of $x^2 - 1$. It does not contain the factor $(x+3)$ from the factorization of $x^2 + 4x + 3$. We multiply $(x+1)(x-1)$ by $(x+3)$:

$$\text{LCM} = (x+1)(x-1)(x+3).$$

The denominator $x^2 - 1 = (x+1)(x-1)$ must be multiplied by $x+3$ in order to obtain the LCD. The denominator $x^2 + 4x + 3 = (x+1)(x+3)$ must be multiplied by $x-1$ in order to obtain the LCD. We multiply each expression by a form of 1 that is made up of these "missing" factors:

$$\dfrac{x-3}{x^2-1} + \dfrac{4x^2}{x^2+4x+3} = \dfrac{x-3}{(x+1)(x-1)} \cdot \dfrac{x+3}{x+3} + \dfrac{4x^2}{(x+1)(x+3)} \cdot \dfrac{x-1}{x-1}$$

$$= \dfrac{x^2-9}{(x+1)(x-1)(x+3)} + \dfrac{4x^3-4x^2}{(x+1)(x-1)(x+3)}$$

$$= \dfrac{4x^3-3x^2-9}{(x+1)(x-1)(x+3)}.$$

TRY EXERCISE 25

EXAMPLE   6   Subtract: $\dfrac{x}{x+2} - \dfrac{2x-3}{3x-4}$.

SOLUTION   We have

$$\dfrac{x}{x+2} - \dfrac{2x-3}{3x-4}$$

Find the LCD.

$$= \dfrac{x}{x+2} \cdot \dfrac{3x-4}{3x-4} - \dfrac{2x-3}{3x-4} \cdot \dfrac{x+2}{x+2}$$
The LCD is $(x+2)(3x-4)$.

Rewrite each expression with the LCD.

$$= \dfrac{3x^2-4x}{(x+2)(3x-4)} - \dfrac{2x^2+x-6}{(x+2)(3x-4)}$$
Multiplying out the numerators (but not the denominators)

Subtract numerators. Keep the denominator.

$$= \dfrac{3x^2-4x-(2x^2+x-6)}{(x+2)(3x-4)}$$
Parentheses are important.

$$= \dfrac{3x^2-4x-2x^2-x+6}{(x+2)(3x-4)}$$
Removing parentheses in the numerator; subtracting every term

$$= \dfrac{x^2-5x+6}{(x+2)(3x-4)}$$

Simplify if possible.

$$= \dfrac{(x-2)(x-3)}{(x+2)(3x-4)}.$$
Factoring the numerator in hopes of simplifying. There are no common factors.

The result could be written as either of the last two expressions.

TRY EXERCISE 33

Factors that are opposites (p. 400)   When denominators are opposites, we can find a common denominator by multiplying either rational expression by $-1/-1$.

EXAMPLE **7**   Add: $\dfrac{a}{a-b} + \dfrac{5}{b-a}$.

SOLUTION

$$\frac{a}{a-b} + \frac{5}{b-a} = \frac{a}{a-b} + \frac{5}{b-a} \cdot \frac{-1}{-1}$$

Writing 1 as $-1/-1$ and multiplying to obtain a common denominator

$$= \frac{a}{a-b} + \frac{-5}{a-b}$$

$(b-a)(-1) = -b+a = a-b$

$$= \frac{a-5}{a-b}$$

TRY EXERCISE 27

Complex Rational Expressions

Complex rational expressions
(Section 6.5)

A **complex rational expression** is a rational expression that has one or more rational expressions within its numerator or denominator. We will consider two methods for simplifying complex rational expressions. The first involves writing the expression as a quotient of two rational expressions.

> **To Simplify a Complex Rational Expression by Dividing**
>
> 1. Add or subtract, as needed, to get a single rational expression in the numerator.
> 2. Add or subtract, as needed, to get a single rational expression in the denominator.
> 3. Divide the numerator by the denominator (invert and multiply).
> 4. If possible, simplify by removing a factor equal to 1.

EXAMPLE **8**   Simplify by dividing: $\dfrac{\dfrac{2}{x+1}}{\dfrac{1}{x+2} + \dfrac{1}{x}}$.

SOLUTION

1. There is already a single rational expression in the numerator.

2. We add to get a single rational expression in the denominator:

$$\frac{\dfrac{2}{x+1}}{\dfrac{1}{x+2} + \dfrac{1}{x}} = \frac{\dfrac{2}{x+1}}{\dfrac{1}{x+2} \cdot \dfrac{x}{x} + \dfrac{1}{x} \cdot \dfrac{x+2}{x+2}}$$

Multiplying by 1 to get the LCD, $x(x+2)$, for the denominator

$$= \frac{\dfrac{2}{x+1}}{\dfrac{x}{x(x+2)} + \dfrac{x+2}{x(x+2)}} = \frac{\dfrac{2}{x+1}}{\dfrac{2x+2}{x(x+2)}}.$$

Adding in the denominator

3. Next, we invert and multiply:

$$\frac{\dfrac{2}{x+1}}{\dfrac{2x+2}{x(x+2)}} = \frac{2}{x+1} \div \frac{2x+2}{x(x+2)} = \frac{2}{x+1} \cdot \frac{x(x+2)}{2x+2}.$$

4. Simplifying, we have:

$$\frac{2}{(x+1)} \cdot \frac{x(x+2)}{2x+2} = \frac{\cancel{2} \cdot x(x+2)}{\cancel{2}(x+1)(x+1)}$$ Factoring in the denominator and removing a factor equal to 1: $\frac{2}{2} = 1$

$$= \frac{x(x+2)}{(x+1)^2}.$$ **TRY EXERCISE** 35

A second method for simplifying complex rational expressions involves multiplying by the LCD.

To Simplify a Complex Rational Expression by Multiplying by the LCD

1. Find the LCD of *all* rational expressions within the complex rational expression.
2. Multiply the complex rational expression by a factor equal to 1. Write 1 as the LCD over itself (LCD/LCD).
3. Simplify. No fraction expressions should remain within the complex rational expression.
4. Factor and, if possible, simplify.

EXAMPLE   9   Simplify by multiplying by the LCD: $\dfrac{1+\dfrac{2}{t}}{\dfrac{4}{t^2}-1}$.

SOLUTION

1. The denominators *within* the complex rational expression are t and t^2, so the LCD is t^2.

2. We multiply by a form of 1 using t^2/t^2:

$$\frac{1+\dfrac{2}{t}}{\dfrac{4}{t^2}-1} = \frac{1+\dfrac{2}{t}}{\dfrac{4}{t^2}-1} \cdot \frac{t^2}{t^2}.$$

3. We distribute and simplify:

$$\frac{1+\dfrac{2}{t}}{\dfrac{4}{t^2}-1} \cdot \frac{t^2}{t^2} = \frac{1 \cdot t^2 + \dfrac{2}{t} \cdot t^2}{\dfrac{4}{t^2} \cdot t^2 - 1 \cdot t^2}$$

$$= \frac{t^2+2t}{4-t^2}.$$ No rational expression remains within the numerator or denominator.

4. Finally, we simplify:

$$\frac{t^2+2t}{4-t^2} = \frac{t\cancel{(t+2)}}{\cancel{(2+t)}(2-t)}$$ Factoring and simplifying; $\dfrac{t+2}{t+2} = 1$

$$= \frac{t}{2-t}.$$ **TRY EXERCISE** 41

Solving Rational Equations

Solving rational equations
(Section 6.6)

A **rational equation** is an equation containing one or more rational expressions, often with the variable in a denominator.

> **To Solve a Rational Equation**
> 1. List any restrictions that exist. Numbers that make a denominator equal 0 can never be solutions.
> 2. Clear the equation of fractions by multiplying both sides by the LCM of the denominators.
> 3. Solve the resulting equation using the addition principle, the multiplication principle, and the principle of zero products, as needed.
> 4. Check the possible solution(s) in the original equation.

Because a possible solution in step 3 may make a denominator 0, checking is essential when solving rational equations.

EXAMPLE 10

Solve: $x + \dfrac{10}{x} = 7$.

SOLUTION   First we note that x cannot be 0. The LCD is x, so we multiply both sides by x:

$$x + \frac{10}{x} = 7$$

$$x\left(x + \frac{10}{x}\right) = 7x \qquad \text{Don't forget the parentheses!}$$

$$x \cdot x + x \cdot \frac{10}{x} = 7x \qquad \text{Using the distributive law}$$

$$x^2 + 10 = 7x \qquad \text{We have a quadratic equation.}$$

$$x^2 - 7x + 10 = 0 \qquad \text{Getting 0 on one side}$$

$$(x - 2)(x - 5) = 0 \qquad \text{Factoring}$$

$$x - 2 = 0 \quad or \quad x - 5 = 0 \qquad \text{Using the principle of zero products}$$

$$x = 2 \quad or \qquad x = 5.$$

Check: For 2:

$$\begin{array}{c|c} x + \dfrac{10}{x} = 7 & \\ \hline 2 + \dfrac{10}{2} & 7 \\ 2 + 5 & \\ 7 \stackrel{?}{=} 7 & \text{TRUE} \end{array}$$

For 5:

$$\begin{array}{c|c} x + \dfrac{10}{x} = 7 & \\ \hline 5 + \dfrac{10}{5} & 7 \\ 5 + 2 & \\ 7 \stackrel{?}{=} 7 & \text{TRUE} \end{array}$$

Both numbers check, so there are two solutions, 2 and 5.   **TRY EXERCISE 45**

Work problems (p. 419)

Many problems translate to rational equations. **Work problems**, which involve the time that it takes to complete a task, can often be solved using the work principle.

> ## The Work Principle
>
> If
>
> $$a = \text{the time needed for } A \text{ to complete the work alone,}$$
> $$b = \text{the time needed for } B \text{ to complete the work alone, and}$$
> $$t = \text{the time needed for } A \text{ and } B \text{ to complete the work together,}$$
>
> then
>
> $$\frac{t}{a} + \frac{t}{b} = 1.$$
>
> The following are equivalent equations that can also be used:
>
> $$\frac{1}{a} \cdot t + \frac{1}{b} \cdot t = 1 \quad \text{and} \quad \frac{1}{a} + \frac{1}{b} = \frac{1}{t}.$$

EXAMPLE 11   *Drafting.*   It takes Kerry 30 hr to draw a set of plans for a house. It takes Jesse 45 hr to draw the same set of plans. How long would it take Kerry and Jesse, working together, to draw the set of plans?

SOLUTION

1. **Familiarize.** We could make some guesses to help us understand the problem and then list our results in a table. We could also reason that if Kerry and Jesse each drew half the plans, it would take Kerry 15 hr and Jesse $22\frac{1}{2}$ hr. So the time it takes them working together should be between 15 and $22\frac{1}{2}$ hr. We let $t = $ the time that it takes them to draw the plans, working together.

2. **Translate.** We will use the work principle to translate the problem:

$$\frac{t}{a} + \frac{t}{b} = 1 \qquad \begin{array}{l} a \text{ is the time that it takes Kerry to draw the plans;} \\ b \text{ is the time that it takes Jesse to draw the plans.} \end{array}$$

$$\frac{t}{30} + \frac{t}{45} = 1.$$

3. **Carry out.** We solve the equation:

$$\frac{t}{30} + \frac{t}{45} = 1$$

$$90\left(\frac{t}{30} + \frac{t}{45}\right) = 90 \cdot 1 \qquad \text{The LCD is } 2 \cdot 3 \cdot 3 \cdot 5, \text{ or } 90.$$

$$90 \cdot \frac{t}{30} + 90 \cdot \frac{t}{45} = 90$$

$$3t + 2t = 90$$

$$5t = 90$$

$$t = 18.$$

4. **Check.** We note that, as predicted in the *Familiarize* step, the answer is between 15 and $22\frac{1}{2}$ hr. Also, if each works 18 hr, Kerry will do $\frac{18}{30}$ of the job and Jesse will do $\frac{18}{45}$ of the job, and

$$\frac{18}{30} + \frac{18}{45} = \frac{3}{5} + \frac{2}{5} = 1. \qquad \text{The entire job will be completed.}$$

5. **State.** Together it will take them 18 hr to draw the plans.

TRY EXERCISE 51

Motion problems (p. 422)

Motion problems deal with distance, speed (or rate), and time, and can often be translated using the distance formula $d = rt$.

EXAMPLE **12**

Driving time. Karen and Eva are each driving to a sales meeting. Because of road conditions, Karen is able to drive 15 mph faster than Eva. In the same time that it takes Karen to travel 120 mi, Eva travels only 90 mi. Find their speeds.

SOLUTION

1. **Familiarize.** We let $t =$ the time, in hours, that is spent traveling and $r =$ Karen's speed, in mph. Then Eva's speed $= r - 15$. We set up a table.

$$d = r \cdot t$$

	Distance	Speed	Time
Karen	120	r	t
Eva	90	$r - 15$	t

2. **Translate.** From the distance formula, we have $t = d/r$, so we can replace the times in the table with expressions involving r.

	Distance	Speed	Time
Karen	120	r	$120/r$
Eva	90	$r - 15$	$90/(r - 15)$

Since the times are the same, we have the equation

$$\frac{120}{r} = \frac{90}{r - 15}.$$

3. **Carry out.** We solve the equation:

$$\frac{120}{r} = \frac{90}{r - 15}$$

$$r(r - 15)\frac{120}{r} = r(r - 15)\frac{90}{r - 15} \qquad \text{The LCD is } r(r - 15).$$

$$120(r - 15) = 90r \qquad \text{Simplifying}$$

$$120r - 1800 = 90r \qquad \text{Removing parentheses}$$

$$-1800 = -30r \qquad \text{Subtracting } 120r$$

$$60 = r. \qquad \text{Dividing both sides by } -30$$

4. **Check.** If $r = 60$, then $r - 15 = 45$. If Karen travels 120 mi at 60 mph, she will have traveled 2 hr. If Eva travels 90 mi at 45 mph, she will also have traveled 2 hr. Since the times are the same, the speeds check.

5. **State.** Karen is traveling at 60 mph, while Eva is traveling at 45 mph.

TRY EXERCISE 53

Ratio (p. 425)
Proportion (p. 425)

Another type of problem that translates to a rational equation involves proportions. A **ratio** of two quantities is their quotient. A **proportion** is an equation stating that two ratios are equal.

EXAMPLE 13

Baking. Rob discovers there is $2\frac{1}{2}$ cups of pancake mix left in the box. The directions on the mix indicate that $1\frac{1}{3}$ cups of milk should be added to 2 cups of mix. How much milk should Rob add to the $2\frac{1}{2}$ cups of mix?

SOLUTION   Since the problem translates directly to a proportion, we will not follow all five steps of the problem-solving process. We write the ratio of mix to milk in two ways:

$$\text{Mix} \longrightarrow \frac{2}{1\frac{1}{3}} = \frac{2\frac{1}{2}}{x} \longleftarrow \text{Mix} \atop \longleftarrow \text{Milk}$$

The LCD is $x\left(1\frac{1}{3}\right)$. We solve for x:

$$x\left(1\tfrac{1}{3}\right)\frac{2}{1\frac{1}{3}} = x\left(1\tfrac{1}{3}\right)\frac{2\frac{1}{2}}{x} \qquad \text{Multiplying by the LCD}$$

$$2x = \left(1\tfrac{1}{3}\right)\left(2\tfrac{1}{2}\right) \qquad \text{Simplifying}$$

$$2x = \tfrac{10}{3} \qquad \text{Converting to fraction notation and multiplying}$$

$$x = \tfrac{5}{3}. \qquad \text{Multiplying both sides by } \tfrac{1}{2} \text{ and simplifying}$$

Rob needs to add $\frac{5}{3}$ or $1\frac{2}{3}$ cups of milk.

TRY EXERCISE ▶ 55

R.6   EXERCISE SET

 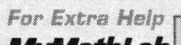
List all numbers for which each rational expression is undefined.

1. $\dfrac{x-7}{3x+1}$

2. $\dfrac{10-y}{-5y}$

3. $\dfrac{p^2-1}{p^2-4}$

4. $\dfrac{10x}{x^2+9x+8}$

Simplify by removing a factor equal to 1.

5. $\dfrac{16x^2y}{18xy^2}$

6. $\dfrac{2x+10}{6x+30}$

7. $\dfrac{t^2-2t-8}{t^2-16}$

8. $\dfrac{a^3+2a^2+a}{a^2+4a+3}$

9. $\dfrac{2-x}{x^2-4}$

10. $\dfrac{n-3}{3-n}$

Perform each indicated operation. Then, if possible, simplify.

11. $\dfrac{3x}{x+y} \cdot \dfrac{2x+2y}{x^2}$

12. $\dfrac{5}{x+7} \cdot \dfrac{x+7}{10}$

13. $\dfrac{a^2+2a+1}{a} \div \dfrac{a^2}{a^2-1}$

14. $\dfrac{x}{x+3} + \dfrac{3-x}{x+3}$

15. $\dfrac{2x}{x-7} - \dfrac{x+7}{x-7}$

16. $\dfrac{x}{x+y} \div \dfrac{y}{x+y}$

17. $\dfrac{5}{x} + \dfrac{4}{x^2}$

18. $\dfrac{x^2+4x+3}{x^2+x-2} \cdot \dfrac{x^2+3x+2}{x^2+2x-3}$

19. $\dfrac{2a+b}{a-b} - \dfrac{4}{3a-3b}$

20. $(x^2-16) \div \dfrac{4x+16}{3x^2}$

21. $\dfrac{2-x}{5x^2} \div \dfrac{x^2-4}{3x}$

22. $\dfrac{2x}{x-5} + \dfrac{3}{x+4}$

23. $\dfrac{x^3+2x^2+x}{x^2-4} \cdot \dfrac{x^2-x-2}{x^4+x^3}$

24. $\dfrac{-1}{x^2+7x+10} - \dfrac{3}{x^2+8x+15}$

25. $\dfrac{2}{(x+1)^2} + \dfrac{1}{x+1}$

26. $\dfrac{2x}{x^2 - 3x} \div (x - 3)$

27. $\dfrac{x}{x - 2} + \dfrac{2}{2 - x}$

28. $\dfrac{3}{y - 1} - \dfrac{y}{1 - y}$

29. $\dfrac{t}{t^2 - 1} - \dfrac{1}{1 - t}$

30. $\dfrac{1}{5 - x} + \dfrac{x}{2x - 10}$

31. $\dfrac{x - y}{2x} \cdot \dfrac{3x^2}{y - x}$

32. $\dfrac{1}{x + y} + \dfrac{2}{x^2 + y^2}$

33. $\dfrac{x - 2}{x + 5} - \dfrac{x + 3}{x - 4}$

34. $\dfrac{z^2 + 2z + 1}{8z} \div \dfrac{z^2 - z - 2}{4z^2 - 4}$

Simplify.

35. $\dfrac{\dfrac{2}{x} - \dfrac{1}{x^2}}{\dfrac{x}{4}}$

36. $\dfrac{\dfrac{x}{3} - \dfrac{3}{x}}{\dfrac{1}{x} + \dfrac{1}{3}}$

37. $\dfrac{\dfrac{3}{x - 7}}{\dfrac{4x + 3}{x + 1}}$

38. $\dfrac{\dfrac{a}{a - b}}{\dfrac{a^2}{a^2 - b^2}}$

39. $\dfrac{x - \dfrac{3}{x - 2}}{x - \dfrac{12}{x + 1}}$

40. $\dfrac{t + \dfrac{1}{t}}{t - \dfrac{2}{t}}$

41. $\dfrac{\dfrac{1}{2} - \dfrac{1}{x}}{\dfrac{2 - x}{2}}$

42. $\dfrac{\dfrac{x}{2y^2} + \dfrac{y}{3x^2}}{\dfrac{1}{6xy} + \dfrac{2}{x^2 y}}$

Solve.

43. $\dfrac{1}{2} + \dfrac{1}{3} = \dfrac{1}{t}$

44. $\dfrac{1}{4} + \dfrac{1}{t} = \dfrac{1}{3}$

45. $x + \dfrac{1}{x} = 2$

46. $\dfrac{x - 7}{x + 1} = \dfrac{2}{3}$

47. $\dfrac{3}{y + 7} = \dfrac{1}{y - 8}$

48. $\dfrac{x + 1}{x - 2} = \dfrac{3}{x - 2}$

49. $\dfrac{1}{x - 3} - \dfrac{x - 4}{x^2 - 9} = 1$

50. $\dfrac{3}{a + 4} = \dfrac{a - 1}{4 - a}$

51. *Painting.* Quentin can paint the turret on a Queen Anne house in 40 hr. It takes Austin 50 hr to paint the same turret. How long would it take them, working together, to paint the turret?

52. *Building fences.* Lindsay can build a fence in 6 hr. Laura can do the same job in 5 hr. How long will it take them, working together, to build the fence?

53. *Snowmobiling.* Jessica can ride her snowmobile through the fields 20 km/h faster than Josh can ride his through the woods. In the time it takes Jessica to ride 18 km, Josh travels 10 km. Find the speed of each snowmobile.

54. *Bicycling.* Ani bicycles 8 mi and Lia bicycles 12 mi to meet at a park for lunch. Because Ani's trip is mostly uphill, she rides 5 mph slower than Lia. Ani and Lia leave their homes at the same time and arrive at the park at the same time. Find the speed of each bicyclist.

55. *Elk population.* To determine the size of a park's elk population, rangers tag 15 elk and set them free. Months later, 40 elk are caught, of which 12 have tags. Estimate the size of the elk population.

56. *Manufacturing pegs.* A sample of 136 wooden pegs contained 17 defective pegs. How many defective pegs would you expect in a sample of 840 pegs?

Photo Credits

990

Appendixes

A   Mean, Median, and Mode

Mean ▪ Median ▪ Mode

One way to analyze data is to look for a single representative number, called a **center point** or **measure of central tendency**. Those most often used are the **mean** (or **average**), the **median**, and the **mode**.

Mean

Let's first consider the *mean*, or *average*.

> **Mean, or Average**
> The *mean*, or *average*, of a set of numbers is the sum of the numbers divided by the number of addends.

EXAMPLE 1   Consider the following data on revenue, in billions of dollars, for Starbucks Corporation in five recent years:

$$\$2.2, \quad \$2.6, \quad \$3.3, \quad \$4.1, \quad \$5.3.$$

What is the mean of the numbers?

SOLUTION   First, we add the numbers:

$$2.2 + 2.6 + 3.3 + 4.1 + 5.3 = 17.5.$$

Then we divide by the number of addends, 5:

$$\frac{(2.2 + 2.6 + 3.3 + 4.1 + 5.3)}{5} = \frac{17.5}{5} = 3.5.$$

The mean, or average, revenue of Starbucks for those five years is $3.5 billion.

Note that $3.5 + 3.5 + 3.5 + 3.5 + 3.5 = 17.5$. If we use this center point, 3.5, repeatedly as the addend, we get the same sum that we do when adding individual data numbers.

Median

The *median* is useful when we wish to de-emphasize extreme scores. For example, suppose five workers in a technology company manufactured the following number of computers during one day's work:

Sarah: 88
Matt: 92
Pat: 66
Jen: 94
Mark: 91

Let's first list the scores in order from smallest to largest:

66 88 91 92 94.

↑

Middle number

The middle number—in this case, 91—is the **median**.

> ## Median
> Once a set of data has been arranged from smallest to largest, the *median* of the set of data is the middle number if there is an odd number of data numbers. If there is an even number of data numbers, then there are two middle numbers and the median is the *average* of the two middle numbers.

EXAMPLE 2   Find the median of the following set of household incomes:

$76,000, $58,000, $87,000, $32,500, $64,800, $62,500.

SOLUTION   We first rearrange the numbers in order from smallest to largest.

$32,500, $58,000, $62,500, $64,800, $76,000, $87,000

↑

Median

There is an even number of numbers. We look for the middle two, which are $62,500 and $64,800. The median is the average of $62,500 and $64,800:

$$\frac{\$62,500 + \$64,800}{2} = \$63,650.$$

Mode

The last center point we consider is called the *mode*. A number that occurs most often in a set of data is sometimes considered a representative number or center point.

> ## Mode
> The *mode* of a set of data is the number or numbers that occur most often. If each number occurs the same number of times, then there is *no* mode.

EXAMPLE **3**   Find the mode of the following data:

23, 24, 27, 18, 19, 27.

SOLUTION   The number that occurs most often is 27. Thus the mode is 27.

It is easier to find the mode of a set of data if the data are ordered.

EXAMPLE **4**   Find the mode of the following data:

83, 84, 84, 84, 85, 86, 87, 87, 87, 88, 89, 90.

SOLUTION   There are two numbers that occur most often, 84 and 87. Thus the modes are 84 and 87.

EXAMPLE **5**   Find the mode of the following data:

115, 117, 211, 213, 219.

SOLUTION   Each number occurs the same number of times. The set of data has *no* mode.

A   **EXERCISE SET**

For each set of numbers, find the mean (average), the median, and any modes that exist.

1. 13, 21, 18, 13, 20

2. 5, 2, 8, 10, 7, 1, 9

3. 3, 8, 20, 3, 20, 10

4. 19, 19, 8, 16, 8, 7

5. 4.7, 2.3, 4.6, 4.9, 3.8

6. 13.4, 13.4, 12.6, 42.9

7. 234, 228, 234, 228, 234, 278

8. $29.95, $28.79, $30.95, $29.95

9. *Hurricanes.* The following bar graph shows the number of hurricanes that struck the United States

by month from 1851 to 2006. What is the average number for the 8 months given? the median? the mode?

Atlantic Storms and Hurricanes

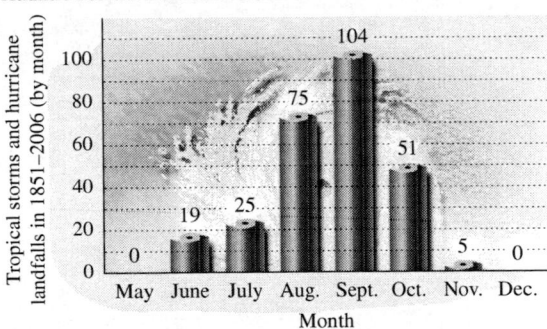

Source: Atlantic Oceanographic and Meteorological Laboratory

10. *iPod prices.* A price comparison showed the following online prices for an Apple iPod Nano:

$199, $197.97, $249.99, $179, $197.97.

What was the average price? the median price? the mode?

11. *NBA tall men.*   The following lists the heights, in inches, of the tallest men in the NBA in a recent year. Find the mean, the median, and the mode.

Zydrunas Ilgauskas	87
Yao Ming	90
Dikembe Mutombo	86
Kosta Perovic	86

Source: National Basketball Association

12. *Coffee consumption.*   The following lists the annual coffee consumption, in number of cups per person, for various countries. Find the mean, the median, and the mode.

Germany	1113
United States	610
Switzerland	1215
France	798
Italy	750

Source: Beverage Marketing Corporation

13. *PBA scores.*   Kelly Kulick rolled scores of 254, 202, 184, 269, 151, 223, 258, 222, and 202 in a recent tour trial for the Professional Bowlers Association. What was her average? her median? her mode?
Source: Professional Bowlers Association

14. *Salmon prices.*   The following prices per pound of Atlantic salmon were found at six fish markets:

$8.99, $8.49, $8.99, $9.99, $9.49, $7.99.

What was the average price per pound? the median price? the mode?

Synthesis

15. *Hank Aaron.*   Hank Aaron averaged $34\frac{7}{22}$ home runs per year over a 22-yr career. After 21 yr, Aaron had averaged $35\frac{10}{21}$ home runs per year. How many home runs did Aaron hit in his final year?

16. *Length of pregnancy.*   Marta was pregnant 270 days, 259 days, and 272 days for her first three pregnancies. In order for Marta's average length of pregnancy to equal the worldwide average of 266 days, how long must her fourth pregnancy last?
Source: David Crystal (ed.), *The Cambridge Factfinder.* Cambridge CB2 1RP: Cambridge University Press, 1993, p. 84.

17. The ordered set of data 18, 21, 24, a, 36, 37, b has a median of 30 and an average of 32. Find a and b.

18. *Male height.*   Jason's brothers are 174 cm, 180 cm, 179 cm, and 172 cm tall. The average male is 176.5 cm tall. How tall is Jason if he and his brothers have an average height of 176.5 cm?

B   Sets

Naming Sets   •   Membership   •   Subsets   •   Intersections   •   Unions

A **set** is a collection of objects. In mathematics the objects, or **elements**, of a set are generally numbers. This section provides an introduction to sets and how to combine them.

Naming Sets

To name the set of whole numbers less than 6, we can use *roster notation*, as follows:

$$\{0, 1, 2, 3, 4, 5\}.$$

The set of real numbers x for which x is less than 6 cannot be named by listing all its members because there is an infinite number of them. We name such a set using *set-builder notation*, as follows:

$$\{x \mid x < 6\}.$$

This is read

"The set of all x such that x is less than 6."

See Section 2.6 for more on this notation.

Membership

The symbol $\in$ means *is a member of* or *belongs to*, or *is an element of*. Thus,

$$x \in A$$

means

    x is a member of A,   or x belongs to A,   or x is an element of A.

EXAMPLE 1   Classify each of the following as true or false.

a) $1 \in \{1, 2, 3\}$

b) $1 \in \{2, 3\}$

c) $4 \in \{x \mid x \text{ is an even whole number}\}$

d) $5 \in \{x \mid x \text{ is an even whole number}\}$

SOLUTION

a) Since 1 is listed as a member of the set, $1 \in \{1, 2, 3\}$ is true.

b) Since 1 is *not* a member of $\{2, 3\}$, the statement $1 \in \{2, 3\}$ is false.

c) Since 4 is an even whole number, $4 \in \{x \mid x \text{ is an even whole number}\}$ is true.

d) Since 5 is *not* even, $5 \in \{x \mid x \text{ is an even whole number}\}$ is false.

 TRY EXERCISE 7

Set membership can be illustrated with a diagram, as shown below.

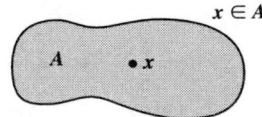

Subsets

If every element of A is also an element of B, then A is a *subset* of B. This is denoted $A \subseteq B$.

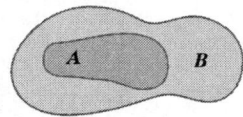

The set of whole numbers is a subset of the set of integers. The set of rational numbers is a subset of the set of real numbers.

EXAMPLE 2   Classify each of the following as true or false.

a) $\{1, 2\} \subseteq \{1, 2, 3, 4\}$

b) $\{p, q, r, w\} \subseteq \{a, p, r, z\}$

c) $\{x | x < 6\} \subseteq \{x | x \leq 11\}$

SOLUTION

a) Since every element of $\{1, 2\}$ is in the set $\{1, 2, 3, 4\}$, it follows that $\{1, 2\} \subseteq \{1, 2, 3, 4\}$ is true.

b) Since $q \in \{p, q, r, w\}$, but $q \notin \{a, p, r, z\}$, it follows that $\{p, q, r, w\} \subseteq \{a, p, r, z\}$ is false.

c) Since every number that is less than 6 is also less than 11, the statement $\{x | x < 6\} \subseteq \{x | x \leq 11\}$ is true.

> TRY EXERCISE   15

Intersections

The *intersection* of sets A and B, denoted $A \cap B$, is the set of members common to both sets.

EXAMPLE 3   Find each intersection.

a) $\{0, 1, 3, 5, 25\} \cap \{2, 3, 4, 5, 6, 7, 9\}$

b) $\{a, p, q, w\} \cap \{p, q, t\}$

SOLUTION

a) $\{0, 1, 3, 5, 25\} \cap \{2, 3, 4, 5, 6, 7, 9\} = \{3, 5\}$

b) $\{a, p, q, w\} \cap \{p, q, t\} = \{p, q\}$

> TRY EXERCISE   19

Set intersection can be illustrated with a diagram, as shown below.

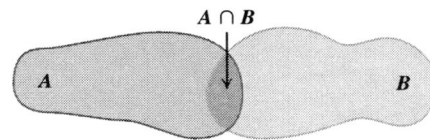

The set without members is known as the *empty set*, and is written $\varnothing$ and sometimes $\{\ \}$. Each of the following is a description of the empty set:

The set of all 12-ft–tall people;

$\{2, 3\} \cap \{5, 6, 7\}$;

$\{x | x \text{ is an even natural number}\} \cap \{x | x \text{ is an odd natural number}\}$.

Unions

Two sets A and B can be combined to form a set that contains the members of both A and B. The new set is called the *union* of A and B, denoted $A \cup B$.

EXAMPLE 4   Find each union.

a) $\{0, 5, 7, 13, 27\} \cup \{0, 2, 3, 4, 5\}$

b) $\{a, c, e, g\} \cup \{b, d, f\}$

SOLUTION

a) $\{0, 5, 7, 13, 27\} \cup \{0, 2, 3, 4, 5\} = \{0, 2, 3, 4, 5, 7, 13, 27\}$

Note that the 0 and the 5 are *not* listed twice in the solution.

b) $\{a, c, e, g\} \cup \{b, d, f\} = \{a, b, c, d, e, f, g\}$

 25

Set union can be illustrated with a diagram, as shown below.

$A \cup B$ is shaded.

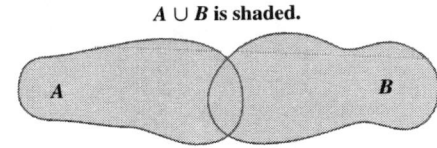

B   EXERCISE SET

Name each set using the roster method.

1. The set of whole numbers 8 through 11

2. The set of whole numbers 83 through 89

3. The set of odd numbers between 40 and 50

4. The set of multiples of 5 between 10 and 40

5. $\{x \mid \text{the square of } x \text{ is } 9\}$

6. $\{x \mid x \text{ is the cube of } \frac{1}{2}\}$

Classify each statement as either true or false.

7. $5 \in \{x \mid x \text{ is an odd number}\}$

8. $8 \in \{x \mid x \text{ is an odd number}\}$

9. Skiing $\in$ The set of all sports

10. Pharmacist $\in$ The set of all professions requiring a college degree

11. $3 \in \{-4, -3, 0, 1\}$

12. $0 \in \{-4, -3, 0, 1\}$

13. $\frac{2}{3} \in \{x \mid x \text{ is a rational number}\}$

14. $\frac{2}{3} \in \{x \mid x \text{ is a real number}\}$

15. $\{-1, 0, 1\} \subseteq \{-3, -2, -1, 1 \, 2, 3\}$

16. The set of vowels $\subseteq$ The set of consonants

17. The set of integers $\subseteq$ The set of rational numbers

18. $\{2, 4, 6\} \subseteq \{1, 2, 3, 4, 5, 6, 7\}$

Find each intersection.

19. $\{a, b, c, d, e\} \cap \{c, d, e, f, g\}$

20. $\{a, e, i, o, u\} \cap \{q, u, i, c, k\}$

21. $\{1, 2, 3, 4, 6, 12\} \cap \{1, 2, 3, 6, 9, 18\}$

22. $\{1, 2, 3, 4, 6, 12\} \cap \{1, 5, 7, 35\}$

23. $\{2, 4, 6, 8\} \cap \{1, 3, 5, 7\}$

24. $\{a, e, i, o, u\} \cap \{m, n, f, g, h\}$

Find each union.

25. $\{a, e, i, o, u\} \cup \{q, u, i, c, k\}$

26. $\{a, b, c, d, e\} \cup \{c, d, e, f, g\}$

27. $\{1, 2, 3, 4, 6, 12\} \cup \{1, 2, 3, 6, 9, 18\}$

28. $\{1, 2, 3, 4, 6, 12\} \cup \{1, 5, 7, 35\}$

29. $\{2, 4, 6, 8\} \cup \{1, 3, 5, 7\}$

30. $\{a, e, i, o, u\} \cup \{m, n, f, g, h\}$

31. What advantage(s) does set-builder notation have over roster notation?

32. What advantage(s) does roster notation have over set-builder notation?

Synthesis

33. Find the union of the set of integers and the set of whole numbers.

34. Find the intersection of the set of odd integers and the set of even integers.

35. Find the union of the set of rational numbers and the set of irrational numbers.

36. Find the intersection of the set of even integers and the set of positive rational numbers.

37. Find the intersection of the set of rational numbers and the set of irrational numbers.

38. Find the union of the set of negative integers, the set of positive integers, and the set containing 0.

39. For a set A, find each of the following.
  a) $A \cup \varnothing$
  b) $A \cup A$
  c) $A \cap A$
  d) $A \cap \varnothing$

Classify each statement as either true or false.

40. The empty set can be written $\varnothing$, { }, or {0}.

41. For any set A, $\varnothing \subseteq A$.

42. For any set A, $A \subseteq A$.

43. For any sets A and B, $A \cap B \subseteq A$.

44. A set is *closed* under an operation if, when the operation is performed on its members, the result is in the set. For example, the set of real numbers is closed under the operation of addition since the sum of any two real numbers is a real number.
  a) Is the set of even numbers closed under addition?
  b) Is the set of odd numbers closed under addition?
  c) Is the set {0, 1} closed under addition?
  d) Is the set {0, 1} closed under multiplication?
  e) Is the set of real numbers closed under multiplication?
  f) Is the set of integers closed under division?

45. Experiment with sets of various types and determine whether the following distributive law for sets is true:
$$A \cap (B \cup C) = (A \cap B) \cup (A \cap C).$$

C   Synthetic Division

Streamlining Long Division ▪ The Remainder Theorem

Streamlining Long Division

To divide a polynomial by a binomial of the type $x - a$, we can streamline the usual procedure to develop a process called *synthetic division*.

Compare the following. In each stage, we attempt to write less than in the previous stage, while retaining enough essentials to solve the problem.

STAGE 1

When a polynomial is written in descending order, the coefficients provide the essential information:

$$
\begin{array}{r}
4x^2 + 5x + 11 \\
x - 2 \overline{)\,4x^3 - 3x^2 + x + 7} \\
\underline{4x^3 - 8x^2} \\
5x^2 + x \\
\underline{5x^2 - 10x} \\
11x + 7 \\
\underline{11x - 22} \\
29
\end{array}
\qquad
\begin{array}{r}
4 + 5 + 11 \\
1 - 2\overline{)\,4 - 3 + 1 + 7} \\
\underline{4 - 8} \\
5 + 1 \\
\underline{5 - 10} \\
11 + 7 \\
\underline{11 - 22} \\
29
\end{array}
$$

Because the leading coefficient in $x - 2$ is 1, each time we multiply it by a term in the answer, the leading coefficient of that product duplicates a coefficient in the answer. In the next stage, rather than duplicate these numbers we focus on where -2 is used and drop the 1 from the divisor.

STAGE 2

$$\begin{array}{r}
4x^2 + 5x + 11 \\
x-2\overline{)4x^3 - 3x^2 + x + 7} \\
\underline{4x^3 - 8x^2} \\
5x^2 + x \\
\underline{5x^2 - 10x} \\
11x + 7 \\
\underline{11x - 22} \\
29
\end{array}$$

$$\begin{array}{r}
4 + 5 + 11 \\
-2\overline{)4 - 3 + 1 + 7} \\
- 8 \\
5 + 1 \\
- 10 \\
11 + 7 \\
- 22 \\
29
\end{array}$$

— Multiply: $-2 \cdot 4 = -8$.
Subtract: $-3 - (-8) = 5$.
— Multiply: $-2 \cdot 5 = -10$.
Subtract: $1 - (-10) = 11$.
Multiply: $-2 \cdot 11 = -22$.
Subtract: $7 - (-22) = 29$.

To simplify further, we now reverse the sign of the -2 in the divisor and, in exchange, *add* at each step in the long division.

STAGE 3

$$\begin{array}{r}
4x^2 + 5x + 11 \\
x-2\overline{)4x^3 - 3x^2 + x + 7} \\
\underline{4x^3 - 8x^2} \\
5x^2 + x \\
\underline{5x^2 - 10x} \\
11x + 7 \\
\underline{11x - 22} \\
29
\end{array}$$

$$\begin{array}{r}
4 + 5 + 11 \\
2\overline{)4 - 3 + 1 + 7} \\
8 \\
5 + 1 \\
10 \\
11 + 7 \\
22 \\
29
\end{array}$$

Replace the -2 with 2.
— Multiply: $2 \cdot 4 = 8$.
Add: $-3 + 8 = 5$.
— Multiply: $2 \cdot 5 = 10$.
Add: $1 + 10 = 11$.
— Multiply: $2 \cdot 11 = 22$.
Add: $7 + 22 = 29$.

The blue numbers can be eliminated if we look at the red numbers instead.

STAGE 4

$$\begin{array}{r}
4x^2 + 5x + 11 \\
x-2\overline{)4x^3 - 3x^2 + x + 7} \\
\underline{4x^3 - 8x^2} \\
5x^2 + x \\
\underline{5x^2 - 10x} \\
11x + 7 \\
\underline{11x - 22} \\
29
\end{array}$$

$$\begin{array}{c}
4 \quad5 \quad 11 \\
2\overline{)4 \quad -3 \quad 1 \quad 7} \\
8 \quad 10 \quad 22 \\
\overline{5 \quad 11 \quad 29}
\end{array}$$

Note that the 5 and the 11 preceding the remainder 29 coincide with the 5 and the 11 following the 4 on the top line. By writing a 4 to the left of 5 on the bottom line, we can eliminate the top line in stage 4 and read our answer from the bottom line. This final stage is commonly called **synthetic division**.

STAGE 5

$$\begin{array}{c}
4 \quad 5 \quad 11 \\
2\overline{)4 \quad -3 \quad 1 \quad 7} \\
8 \quad 10 \quad 22 \\
\overline{5 \quad 11 \quad 29}
\end{array}$$

$$\begin{array}{c}
2 \,\lfloor 4 \quad -3 \quad 1 \quad 7 \\
\;\; 8 \quad 10 \quad 22 \\
\hline
4 \quad 5 \quad 11 \,\lfloor 29
\end{array}$$

— This is the remainder.
— This is the zero-degree coefficient.
— This is the first-degree coefficient.
— This is the second-degree coefficient.

The quotient is $4x^2 + 5x + 11$ with a remainder of 29.

> Remember that for this method to work, the divisor must be of the form $x - a$, that is, a variable minus a constant.

EXAMPLE 1   Use synthetic division to divide: $(x^3 + 6x^2 - x - 30) \div (x - 2)$.

SOLUTION

$$\underline{2} \;|\; 1 \quad 6 \quad -1 \quad -30$$
$$\overline{\; 1}$$

Write the 2 of $x - 2$ and the coefficients of the dividend.

Bring down the first coefficient.

$$\underline{2} \;|\; 1 \quad 6 \quad -1 \quad -30$$
$$ 2$$
$$\overline{1 \quad 8}$$

Multiply 1 by 2 to get 2.

Add 6 and 2.

$$\underline{2} \;|\; 1 \quad 6 \quad -1 \quad -30$$
$$ 2 \quad 16$$
$$\overline{1 \quad 8 \quad 15}$$

Multiply 8 by 2.

Add -1 and 16.

$$\underline{2} \;|\; 1 \quad 6 \quad -1 \quad -30$$
$$ 2 \quad 16 \quad 30$$
$$\overline{1 \quad 8 \quad 15 \quad 0}$$

Multiply 15 by 2 and add.

The answer is $x^2 + 8x + 15$ with R 0, or just $x^2 + 8x + 15$.

> TRY EXERCISE   7

EXAMPLE 2   Use synthetic division to divide.

a) $(2x^3 + 7x^2 - 5) \div (x + 3)$

b) $(10x^2 - 13x + 3x^3 - 20) \div (4 + x)$

SOLUTION

a) $(2x^3 + 7x^2 - 5) \div (x + 3)$

The dividend has no x-term, so we need to write 0 as the coefficient of x. Note that $x + 3 = x - (-3)$, so we write -3 inside the $\rfloor$.

$$\underline{-3} \;|\; 2 \quad 7 \quad 0 \quad -5$$
$$ -6 \quad -3 \quad 9$$
$$\overline{2 \quad 1 \quad -3 \;|\; 4}$$

The answer is $2x^2 + x - 3$, with R 4, or $2x^2 + x - 3 + \dfrac{4}{x + 3}$.

b) We first rewrite $(10x^2 - 13x + 3x^3 - 20) \div (4 + x)$ in descending order:

$$(3x^3 + 10x^2 - 13x - 20) \div (x + 4).$$

Next, we use synthetic division. Note that $x + 4 = x - (-4)$.

$$\underline{-4} \;|\; 3 \quad 10 \quad -13 \quad -20$$
$$ -12 \quad 8 \quad 20$$
$$\overline{3 \quad -2 \quad -5 \;|\; 0}$$

The answer is $3x^2 - 2x - 5$.

> TRY EXERCISE   15

The Remainder Theorem

Because the remainder is 0, Example 1 shows that $x - 2$ is a factor of $x^3 + 6x^2 - x - 30$ and that $x^3 + 6x^2 - x - 30 = (x - 2)(x^2 + 8x + 15)$. Thus if $f(x) = x^3 + 6x^2 - x - 30$, then $f(2) = 0$ (since $x - 2$ is a factor of $f(x)$). Similarly, from Example 2(b), we know that if $g(x) = 10x^2 - 13x + 3x^3 - 20$, then $x + 4$ is a factor of $g(x)$ and $g(-4) = 0$. In both examples, the remainder from the division, 0, can serve as a function value. Remarkably, this pattern extends to nonzero remainders. For example, the remainder in Example 2(a) is 4, and if $f(x) = 2x^3 + 7x^2 - 5$, then $f(-3)$ is also 4 (you should check this). The fact that the remainder and the function value coincide is predicted by the remainder theorem.

> **The Remainder Theorem**
>
> The remainder obtained by dividing $P(x)$ by $x - r$ is $P(r)$.

A proof of this result is outlined in Exercise 31.

EXAMPLE 3   Let $f(x) = 8x^5 - 6x^3 + x - 8$. Use synthetic division to find $f(2)$.

SOLUTION   The remainder theorem tells us that $f(2)$ is the remainder when $f(x)$ is divided by $x - 2$. We use synthetic division to find that remainder:

$$
\begin{array}{r|rrrrrr}
2 & 8 & 0 & -6 & 0 & 1 & -8 \\
  &   & 16 & 32 & 52 & 104 & 210 \\
\hline
  & 8 & 16 & 26 & 52 & 105 & 202
\end{array}
$$

Although the bottom line can be used to find the quotient for the division $(8x^5 - 6x^3 + x - 8) \div (x - 2)$, what we are really interested in is the remainder. It tells us that $f(2) = 202$.   **TRY EXERCISE** 21

The remainder theorem is often used to check division. Thus Example 2(a) can be checked by computing $P(-3) = 2(-3)^3 + 7(-3)^2 - 5$. Since $P(-3) = 4$ and the remainder in Example 2(a) is also 4, our division was probably correct.

C   EXERCISE SET

 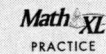

Concept Reinforcement   *Classify each statement as either true or false.*

1. If $x - 2$ is a factor of some polynomial $P(x)$, then $P(2) = 0$.

2. If $p(3) = 0$ for some polynomial $p(x)$, then $x - 3$ is a factor of $p(x)$.

3. If $P(-5) = 39$ and $P(x) = x^3 + 7x^2 + 3x + 4$, then

$$
\begin{array}{r|rrrr}
-5 & 1 & 7 & 3 & 4 \\
   &   & -5 & -10 & 35 \\
\hline
   & 1 & 2 & -7 & 39
\end{array}
$$

4. In order for $f(x)/g(x)$ to exist, $g(x)$ must be 0.

5. In order to use synthetic division, we must be sure that the divisor is of the form $x - a$.

6. Synthetic division can be used in problems in which long division could not be used.

Use synthetic division to divide.

7. $(x^3 - 4x^2 - 2x + 5) \div (x - 1)$

8. $(x^3 - 4x^2 + 5x - 6) \div (x - 3)$

9. $(a^2 + 8a + 11) \div (a + 3)$

10. $(a^2 + 8a + 11) \div (a + 5)$

11. $(2x^3 - x^2 - 7x + 14) \div (x + 2)$

12. $(3x^3 - 10x^2 - 9x + 15) \div (x - 4)$

13. $(a^3 - 10a + 12) \div (a - 2)$

14. $(a^3 - 14a + 15) \div (a - 3)$

15. $(3y^3 - 7y^2 - 20) \div (y - 3)$

16. $(2x^3 - 3x^2 + 8) \div (x + 2)$

17. $(x^5 - 32) \div (x - 2)$

18. $(y^5 - 1) \div (y - 1)$

19. $(3x^3 + 1 - x + 7x^2) \div \left(x + \frac{1}{3}\right)$

20. $(8x^3 - 1 + 7x - 6x^2) \div \left(x - \frac{1}{2}\right)$

Use synthetic division to find the indicated function value.

21. $f(x) = 5x^4 + 12x^3 + 28x + 9; \ f(-3)$

22. $g(x) = 3x^4 - 25x^2 - 18; \ g(3)$

23. $P(x) = 2x^4 - x^3 - 7x^2 + x + 2; \ P(-3)$

24. $F(x) = 3x^4 + 8x^3 + 2x^2 - 7x - 4; \ F(-2)$

25. $f(x) = x^4 - 6x^3 + 11x^2 - 17x + 20; \ f(4)$

26. $p(x) = x^4 + 7x^3 + 11x^2 - 7x - 12; \ p(2)$

27. Why is it that we *add* when performing synthetic division, but *subtract* when performing long division?

28. Explain how synthetic division could be useful when attempting to factor a polynomial.

Synthesis

29. Let $Q(x)$ be a polynomial function with $p(x)$ a factor of $Q(x)$. If $p(3) = 0$, does it follow that $Q(3) = 0$? Why or why not? If $Q(3) = 0$, does it follow that $p(3) = 0$? Why or why not?

30. What adjustments must be made if synthetic division is to be used to divide a polynomial by a binomial of the form $ax + b$, with $a > 1$?

31. To prove the remainder theorem, note that any polynomial $P(x)$ can be rewritten as $(x - r) \cdot Q(x) + R$, where $Q(x)$ is the quotient polynomial that arises when $P(x)$ is divided by $x - r$, and R is some constant (the remainder).

   a) How do we know that R must be a constant?
   b) Show that $P(r) = R$ (this says that $P(r)$ is the remainder when $P(x)$ is divided by $x - r$).

32. Let $f(x) = 6x^3 - 13x^2 - 79x + 140$. Find $f(4)$ and then solve the equation $f(x) = 0$.

33. Let $f(x) = 4x^3 + 16x^2 - 3x - 45$. Find $f(-3)$ and then solve the equation $f(x) = 0$.

34. Use the TRACE feature on a graphing calculator to check your answer to Exercise 32.

35. Use the TRACE feature on a graphing calculator to check your answer to Exercise 33.

Nested evaluation. *One way to evaluate a polynomial function like $P(x) = 3x^4 - 5x^3 + 4x^2 - 1$ is to successively factor out x as shown:*

$$P(x) = x(x(x(3x - 5) + 4) + 0) - 1.$$

Computations are then performed using this "nested" form of $P(x)$.

36. Use nested evaluation to find $f(4)$ in Exercise 32. Note the similarities to the calculations performed with synthetic division.

37. Use nested evaluation to find $f(-3)$ in Exercise 33. Note the similarities to the calculations performed with synthetic division.

Tables

TABLE 1   Fraction and Decimal Equivalents

Fraction Notation	$\frac{1}{10}$	$\frac{1}{8}$	$\frac{1}{6}$	$\frac{1}{5}$	$\frac{1}{4}$	$\frac{3}{10}$	$\frac{1}{3}$	$\frac{3}{8}$	$\frac{2}{5}$	$\frac{1}{2}$
Decimal Notation	0.1	0.125	$0.16\overline{6}$	0.2	0.25	0.3	$0.333\overline{3}$	0.375	0.4	0.5
Percent Notation	10%	12.5%, or $12\frac{1}{2}\%$	16.6$\overline{6}$%, or $16\frac{2}{3}\%$	20%	25%	30%	33.3$\overline{3}$%, or $33\frac{1}{3}\%$	37.5%, or $37\frac{1}{2}\%$	40%	50%
Fraction Notation	$\frac{3}{5}$	$\frac{5}{8}$	$\frac{2}{3}$	$\frac{7}{10}$	$\frac{3}{4}$	$\frac{4}{5}$	$\frac{5}{6}$	$\frac{7}{8}$	$\frac{9}{10}$	$\frac{1}{1}$
Decimal Notation	0.6	0.625	$0.666\overline{6}$	0.7	0.75	0.8	$0.83\overline{3}$	0.875	0.9	1
Percent Notation	60%	62.5%, or $62\frac{1}{2}\%$	66.6$\overline{6}$%, or $66\frac{2}{3}\%$	70%	75%	80%	83.3$\overline{3}$%, or $83\frac{1}{3}\%$	87.5%, or $87\frac{1}{2}\%$	90%	100%

TABLE 2   Squares and Square Roots with Approximations to Three Decimal Places

N	$\sqrt{N}$	N^2	N	$\sqrt{N}$	N^2	N	$\sqrt{N}$	N^2	N	$\sqrt{N}$	N^2
1	1	1	26	5.099	676	51	7.141	2601	76	8.718	5776
2	1.414	4	27	5.196	729	52	7.211	2704	77	8.775	5929
3	1.732	9	28	5.292	784	53	7.280	2809	78	8.832	6084
4	2	16	29	5.385	841	54	7.348	2916	79	8.888	6241
5	2.236	25	30	5.477	900	55	7.416	3025	80	8.944	6400
6	2.449	36	31	5.568	961	56	7.483	3136	81	9	6561
7	2.646	49	32	5.657	1024	57	7.550	3249	82	9.055	6724
8	2.828	64	33	5.745	1089	58	7.616	3364	83	9.110	6889
9	3	81	34	5.831	1156	59	7.681	3481	84	9.165	7056
10	3.162	100	35	5.916	1225	60	7.746	3600	85	9.220	7225
11	3.317	121	36	6	1296	61	7.810	3721	86	9.274	7396
12	3.464	144	37	6.083	1369	62	7.874	3844	87	9.327	7569
13	3.606	169	38	6.164	1444	63	7.937	3969	88	9.381	7744
14	3.742	196	39	6.245	1521	64	8	4096	89	9.434	7921
15	3.873	225	40	6.325	1600	65	8.062	4225	90	9.487	8100
16	4	256	41	6.403	1681	66	8.124	4356	91	9.539	8281
17	4.123	289	42	6.481	1764	67	8.185	4489	92	9.592	8464
18	4.243	324	43	6.557	1849	68	8.246	4624	93	9.644	8649
19	4.359	361	44	6.633	1936	69	8.307	4761	94	9.695	8836
20	4.472	400	45	6.708	2025	70	8.367	4900	95	9.747	9025
21	4.583	441	46	6.782	2116	71	8.426	5041	96	9.798	9216
22	4.690	484	47	6.856	2209	72	8.485	5184	97	9.849	9409
23	4.796	529	48	6.928	2304	73	8.544	5329	98	9.899	9604
24	4.899	576	49	7	2401	74	8.602	5476	99	9.950	9801
25	5	625	50	7.071	2500	75	8.660	5625	100	10	10,000

Answers

The complete step-by-step solutions for the exercises listed below can be found in the *Student's Solutions Manual,* ISBN 0-321-58623-9/978-0-321-58623-0, which can be purchased online or at your bookstore.

CHAPTER 1

Technology Connection, p. 7

1. 3438   **2.** 47,531

Translating for Success, p. 9

1. H   **2.** E   **3.** K   **4.** B   **5.** O   **6.** L   **7.** M   **8.** C
9. D   **10.** F

Exercise Set 1.1, pp. 10–12

1. Expression   **2.** Equation   **3.** Equation
4. Expression   **5.** Equation   **6.** Equation
7. Expression   **8.** Equation   **9.** Equation
10. Expression   **11.** Expression   **12.** Expression
13. 45   **15.** 8   **17.** 5   **19.** 4   **21.** 5   **23.** 3
25. $24 \, \text{ft}^2$ **27.** $15 \, \text{cm}^2$ **29.** 0.345   **31.** Let r represent Ron's age; $r + 5$, or $5 + r$ **33.** $6b$, or $b \cdot 6$ **35.** $c - 9$
37. $6 + q$, or $q + 6$ **39.** Let m represent Mai's speed; $8m$, or $m \cdot 8$ **41.** $y - x$ **43.** $x \div w$, or $\dfrac{x}{w}$ **45.** Let l represent the length of the box and h represent the height; $l + h$, or $h + l$ **47.** $9 \cdot 2m$, or $2m \cdot 9$ **49.** Let y represent "some number"; $\dfrac{1}{4}y - 13$, or $\dfrac{y}{4} - 13$ **51.** Let a and b represent the two numbers; $5(a - b)$ **53.** Let w represent the number of women attending; 64% of w, or $0.64w$ **55.** Yes   **57.** No   **59.** Yes   **61.** Yes
63. Let x represent the unknown number; $73 + x = 201$
65. Let x represent the unknown number; $42x = 2352$
67. Let s represent the number of unoccupied squares; $s + 19 = 64$ **69.** Let w represent the amount of solid waste generated, in millions of tons; 32% of $w = 79$, or $0.32w = 79$ **71.** (f)   **73.** (d)   **75.** (g)   **77.** (e)
79. ⟡   **81.** ⟡   **83.** $450   **85.** 2   **87.** 6   **89.** $w + 4$
91. $l + w + l + w$, or $2l + 2w$ **93.** $t + 8$ **95.** ⟡

Exercise Set 1.2, pp. 18–20

1. Commutative   **2.** Associative   **3.** Associative
4. Commutative   **5.** Distributive   **6.** Associative
7. Associative   **8.** Commutative   **9.** Commutative
10. Distributive   **11.** $t + 11$ **13.** $8x + 4$
15. $3y + 9x$ **17.** $5(1 + a)$ **19.** $x \cdot 7$ **21.** ts

23. $5 + ba$ **25.** $(a + 1)5$ **27.** $x + (8 + y)$
29. $(u + v) + 7$ **31.** $ab + (c + d)$ **33.** $8(xy)$
35. $(2a)\,b$ **37.** $(3 \cdot 2)\,(a + b)$
39. $(s + t) + 6; (t + 6) + s$ **41.** $17(ab); b(17a)$
43. $(1 + x) + 2 = (x + 1) + 2$ Commutative law
$ = x + (1 + 2)$ Associative law
$ = x + 3$ Simplifying
45. $(m \cdot 3)7 = m(3 \cdot 7)$ Associative law
$ = m \cdot 21$ Simplifying
$ = 21m$ Commutative law
47. $2x + 30$ **49.** $4 + 4a$ **51.** $24 + 8y$
53. $90x + 60$ **55.** $5r + 10 + 15t$ **57.** $2a + 2b$
59. $5x + 5y + 10$ **61.** $x, xyz, 1$ **63.** $2a, \dfrac{a}{3b}, 5b$
65. x, y **67.** $4x, 4y$ **69.** $2(a + b)$ **71.** $7(1 + y)$
73. $4(8x + 1)$ **75.** $5(x + 2 + 3y)$ **77.** $7(a + 5b)$
79. $11(4x + y + 2z)$ **81.** $5, n$ **83.** $3, (x + y)$
85. $7, a, b$ **87.** $(a - b), (x - y)$ **89.** ⟡   **91.** Let k represent Kara's salary; $\dfrac{1}{2}k$, or $\dfrac{k}{2}$ **92.** $2(m + 3)$, or $2(3 + m)$ **93.** ⟡   **95.** Yes; distributive law
97. No; for example, let $m = 1$. Then $7 \div 3 \cdot 1 = \frac{7}{3}$ and $1 \cdot 3 \div 7 = \frac{3}{7}$.   **99.** No; for example, let $x = 1$ and $y = 2$. Then $30 \cdot 2 + 1 \cdot 15 = 60 + 15 = 75$ and $5[2(1 + 3 \cdot 2)] = 5[2(7)] = 5 \cdot 14 = 70$.   **101.** ⟡

Exercise Set 1.3, pp. 27–29

1. (b)   **2.** (c)   **3.** (d)   **4.** (a)   **5.** Composite
7. Prime   **9.** Composite   **11.** Prime   **13.** Neither
15. $1 \cdot 50; 2 \cdot 25; 5 \cdot 10; 1, 2, 5, 10, 25, 50$
17. $1 \cdot 42; 2 \cdot 21; 3 \cdot 14; 6 \cdot 7; 1, 2, 3, 6, 7, 14, 21, 42$
19. $3 \cdot 13$ **21.** $2 \cdot 3 \cdot 5$ **23.** $3 \cdot 3 \cdot 3$ **25.** $2 \cdot 3 \cdot 5 \cdot 5$
27. $2 \cdot 2 \cdot 2 \cdot 5$ **29.** Prime   **31.** $2 \cdot 3 \cdot 5 \cdot 7$ **33.** $5 \cdot 23$
35. $\frac{3}{5}$ **37.** $\frac{2}{7}$ **39.** $\frac{1}{4}$ **41.** 4   **43.** $\frac{1}{4}$ **45.** 6
47. $\frac{21}{25}$ **49.** $\frac{60}{41}$ **51.** $\frac{15}{7}$ **53.** $\frac{3}{10}$ **55.** 6   **57.** $\frac{1}{2}$
59. $\frac{7}{6}$ **61.** $\dfrac{3b}{7a}$ **63.** $\dfrac{10}{n}$ **65.** $\frac{5}{6}$ **67.** 1   **69.** $\frac{5}{18}$
71. 0   **73.** $\frac{35}{18}$ **75.** $\frac{10}{3}$ **77.** 27   **79.** 1   **81.** $\frac{6}{35}$
83. 18   **85.** ⟡   **87.** $5(3 + x)$; answers may vary
88. $7 + (b + a)$, or $(a + b) + 7$ **89.** ⟡
91. Row 1: 7, 2, 36, 14, 8, 8; row 2: 9, 18, 2, 10, 12, 21
93. $\frac{2}{5}$ **95.** $\dfrac{5q}{t}$ **97.** $\frac{6}{25}$ **99.** $\dfrac{5ap}{2cm}$ **101.** $\dfrac{23r}{18t}$

103. $\frac{28}{45}$ m^2 **105.** $14\frac{2}{9}$ m   **107.** $27\frac{3}{5}$ cm

Technology Connection, p. 33

1. 2.236067977   **2.** 2.645751311   **3.** 3.605551275
4. 5.196152423   **5.** 6.164414003   **6.** 7.071067812

Exercise Set 1.4, pp. 35–37

1. Repeating   **2.** Terminating   **3.** Integer
4. Whole number   **5.** Rational number
6. Irrational number   **7.** Natural number
8. Absolute value   **9.** $-10,500, 27,482$ **11.** $136, -4$
13. $-554, 499.19$ **15.** $650, -180$ **17.** $8, -5$
19.

<---+---+---+---+---+---+---+---+---+---+---+--->
  -5 -4 -3 -2 -1 0 1 2 3 4 5
(dot at $\frac{10}{3}$)

21.
<---●---+---+---+---+---+---+---+---+---+--->
  -5 -4 -3 -2 -1 0 1 2 3 4 5
(-4.3)

23.
<---+---+---●---+---+---+---+---+---+---+--->
  -5 -4 -3 -2 -1 0 1 2 3 4 5

25. 0.875   **27.** -0.75
29. $-1.1\overline{6}$ **31.** $0.\overline{6}$ **33.** -0.5 **35.** 0.13
37.
<---+---+---+---+---+---+---●---+---+---+--->
  -5 -4 -3 -2 -1 0 1 2 3 4 5
($\sqrt{5}$)

39.
<---+---●---+---+---+---+---+---+---+---+--->
  -5 -4 -3 -2 -1 0 1 2 3 4 5
($-\sqrt{22}$)

41. $>$ **43.** $<$ **45.** $<$ **47.** $>$ **49.** $<$ **51.** $<$
53. $x < -2$ **55.** $y \geq 10$ **57.** True   **59.** False
61. True   **63.** 58   **65.** 12.2   **67.** $\sqrt{2}$ **69.** $\frac{9}{7}$ **71.** 0
73. 8   **75.** $-83, -4.7, 0, \frac{5}{9}, 2.\overline{16}, 62$ **77.** $-83, 0, 62$
79. $-83, -4.7, 0, \frac{5}{9}, 2.\overline{16}, \pi, \sqrt{17}, 62$ **81.** ✍   **83.** 42
84. $ba + 5$, or $5 + ab$ **85.** ✍   **87.** ✍
89. $-23, -17, 0, 4$ **91.** $-\frac{4}{3}, \frac{4}{9}, \frac{4}{8}, \frac{4}{6}, \frac{4}{5}, \frac{4}{3}, \frac{4}{2}$ **93.** $<$ **95.** $=$
97. $-19, 19$ **99.** $-4, -3, 3, 4$ **101.** $\frac{3}{3}$ **103.** $\frac{70}{9}$
105. $x \leq 0$ **107.** $|t| \geq 20$ **109.** ✍

Exercise Set 1.5, pp. 41–43

1. (f)   **2.** (d)   **3.** (e)   **4.** (a)   **5.** (b)   **6.** (c)
7. -3 **9.** 4   **11.** -7 **13.** -8 **15.** -35 **17.** -8
19. 0   **21.** -41 **23.** 0   **25.** 9   **27.** -2 **29.** 11
31. -43 **33.** 0   **35.** 18   **37.** -45 **39.** 0   **41.** 16
43. -0.8 **45.** -9.1 **47.** $\frac{3}{5}$ **49.** $\frac{-6}{7}$ **51.** $-\frac{1}{15}$
53. $\frac{2}{9}$ **55.** -3 **57.** 0   **59.** The price rose 29¢.
61. Her new balance was \$95.   **63.** The total gain was 20 yd.
65. The lake rose $\frac{3}{10}$ ft.   **67.** Logan owes \$85.   **69.** $17a$
71. $9x$ **73.** $25t$ **75.** $-2m$ **77.** $-10y$ **79.** $1 - 2x$
81. $12x + 17$ **83.** $7r + 8t + 16$ **85.** $18n + 16$
87. ✍   **89.** $21z + 14y + 7$ **90.** $\frac{28}{3}$ **91.** ✍
93. \$451.70   **95.** $-5y$ **97.** $-7m$ **99.** $-7t, -23$
101. 1 under par

Exercise Set 1.6, pp. 48–51

1. (d)   **2.** (g)   **3.** (f)   **4.** (h)   **5.** (a)   **6.** (c)
7. (b)   **8.** (e)   **9.** Six minus ten
11. Two minus negative twelve   **13.** Nine minus the
opposite of t **15.** The opposite of x minus y
17. Negative three minus the opposite of n **19.** -51
21. $\frac{11}{3}$ **23.** 3.14   **25.** 45   **27.** $\frac{14}{3}$ **29.** -0.101

31. 37   **33.** $-\frac{2}{5}$ **35.** 1   **37.** -15 **39.** -3 **41.** -6
43. -3 **45.** -7 **47.** -6 **49.** 0   **51.** -5
53. -10 **55.** -11 **57.** 0   **59.** 0   **61.** 8   **63.** -11
65. 16   **67.** -19 **69.** 1   **71.** 17   **73.** 3   **75.** -3
77. -21 **79.** 10   **81.** -8 **83.** -60 **85.** -23
87. -7.3 **89.** 1.1   **91.** -5.5 **93.** -0.928 **95.** $-\frac{7}{11}$
97. $-\frac{4}{5}$ **99.** $\frac{5}{17}$ **101.** $3.8 - (-5.2); 9$
103. $114 - (-79); 193$ **105.** -40 **107.** 43   **109.** 32
111. -62 **113.** -139 **115.** 0   **117.** $-3y, -8x$
119. $9, -5t, -3st$ **121.** $-3x$ **123.** $-5a + 4$
125. $-n - 9$ **127.** $-3x - 6$ **129.** $-8t - 7$
131. $-12x + 3y + 9$ **133.** $8x + 66$ **135.** 214°F
137. 30,347 ft   **139.** 116 m   **141.** ✍   **143.** 432 ft^2
144. $2 \cdot 2 \cdot 2 \cdot 2 \cdot 2 \cdot 3 \cdot 3 \cdot 3$ **145.** ✍
147. 11:00 P.M., August 14   **149.** False. For example,
let $m = -3$ and $n = -5$. Then $-3 > -5$, but
$-3 + (-5) = -8 \not> 0$.   **151.** True. For example, for
$m = 4$ and $n = -4, 4 = -(-4)$ and $4 + (-4) = 0$; for
$m = -3$ and $n = 3, -3 = -3$ and $-3 + 3 = 0$.
153. (−) (9) (−) (−) (7) [ENTER]

Exercise Set 1.7, pp. 56–58

1. 1   **2.** 0   **3.** 0   **4.** 1   **5.** 0   **6.** 1   **7.** 1   **8.** 0
9. 1   **10.** 0   **11.** -40 **13.** -56 **15.** -40 **17.** 72
19. -42 **21.** 45   **23.** 190   **25.** -132 **27.** 1200
29. -126 **31.** 11.5   **33.** 0   **35.** $-\frac{2}{7}$ **37.** $\frac{1}{12}$
39. -11.13 **41.** $-\frac{5}{12}$ **43.** 252   **45.** 0   **47.** $\frac{1}{28}$
49. 150   **51.** 0   **53.** -720 **55.** $-30,240$ **57.** -9
59. -4 **61.** -7 **63.** 4   **65.** -9 **67.** 5.1   **69.** $\frac{100}{11}$
71. -8 **73.** Undefined   **75.** -4 **77.** 0   **79.** 0
81. $-\frac{8}{3}; \frac{8}{-3}$ **83.** $-\frac{29}{35}; \frac{-29}{35}$ **85.** $\frac{-7}{3}; \frac{7}{-3}$ **87.** $-\frac{x}{2}; \frac{x}{-2}$
89. $-\frac{5}{4}$ **91.** $-\frac{10}{51}$ **93.** $-\frac{1}{10}$ **95.** $\frac{1}{4.3}$, or $\frac{10}{43}$ **97.** $-\frac{4}{9}$
99. Does not exist   **101.** $\frac{21}{20}$ **103.** -1 **105.** 1
107. $\frac{3}{11}$ **109.** $-\frac{7}{4}$ **111.** 1   **113.** $\frac{1}{10}$ **115.** $-\frac{7}{6}$
117. Undefined   **119.** $-\frac{14}{15}$ **121.** ✍   **123.** $\frac{22}{39}$
124. $12x - y - 9$ **125.** ✍   **127.** $\dfrac{1}{a + b}$
129. $-(a + b)$ **131.** $x = -x$ **133.** For 2 and 3,
the reciprocal of the sum is $1/(2 + 3)$, or 1/5. But
$1/5 \neq 1/2 + 1/3$.   **135.** 5°F   **137.** Positive
139. Positive   **141.** Positive   **143.** Distributive law;
law of opposites; multiplicative property of zero

Connecting the Concepts, p. 59

1. -10 **2.** 16   **3.** 4   **4.** -6 **5.** -120 **6.** -7
7. -23 **8.** -3 **9.** -1 **10.** -3 **11.** -0.8
12. -3.77 **13.** -7 **14.** -4.1 **15.** -12 **16.** $\frac{5}{3}$
17. 100   **18.** 77   **19.** 180   **20.** -52

Exercise Set 1.8, pp. 66–68

1. (a) Division; (b) subtraction; (c) addition;
(d) multiplication; (e) subtraction; (f) multiplication

2. (a) Multiplication; **(b)** subtraction; **(c)** addition; **(d)** subtraction; **(e)** division; **(f)** multiplication
3. x^6 **5.** $(-5)^3$ **7.** $(3t)^5$ **9.** $2n^4$ **11.** 16   **13.** 9
15. -9 **17.** 64   **19.** 625   **21.** 7   **23.** -32
25. $81t^4$ **27.** $-343x^3$ **29.** 26   **31.** 51   **33.** -6
35. 1   **37.** 298   **39.** 11   **41.** -36 **43.** 1291
45. 152   **47.** 36   **49.** 1   **51.** -44 **53.** 41   **55.** -10
57. -5 **59.** -19 **61.** -3 **63.** -75 **65.** 9   **67.** 30
69. 6   **71.** -17 **73.** $-9x - 1$ **75.** $7n - 8$
77. $-4a + 3b - 7c$ **79.** $-3x^2 - 5x + 1$ **81.** $2x - 7$
83. $-9x + 6$ **85.** $21t - r$ **87.** $9y - 25z$ **89.** $x^2 + 6$
91. $-t^3 + 4t$ **93.** $37a^2 - 23ab + 35b^2$
95. $-22t^3 - t^2 + 9t$ **97.** $2x - 25$ **99.** ✍   **101.** Let n
represent the number; $2n - 9$ **102.** Let m and n represent
the two numbers; $\frac{1}{2}(m + n)$ **103.** ✍
105. $-6r - 5t + 21$ **107.** $-2x - f$ **109.** ✍
111. True   **113.** False   **115.** 0   **117.** 17
119. 39,000   **121.** $44x^3$

Review Exercises: Chapter 1, pp. 73–74

1. True   **2.** True   **3.** False   **4.** True   **5.** False
6. False   **7.** True   **8.** False   **9.** False   **10.** True
11. 24   **12.** 4   **13.** -16 **14.** -15 **15.** $y - 7$
16. $xz + 10$, or $10 + xz$ **17.** Let b represent Brandt's
speed and w represent the wind speed; $15(b - w)$
18. No   **19.** Let d represent the number of digital prints,
in billions, made in 2006; $14.1 = d + 3.2$ **20.** $t \cdot 3 + 5$
21. $2x + (y + z)$ **22.** $(4x)y, 4(yx),(4y)x$; answers
may vary   **23.** $18x + 30y$ **24.** $40x + 24y + 16$
25. $3(7x + 5y)$ **26.** $11(2a + 9b + 1)$ **27.** $2 \cdot 2 \cdot 2 \cdot 7$
28. $\frac{5}{12}$ **29.** $\frac{9}{4}$ **30.** $\frac{19}{24}$ **31.** $\frac{3}{16}$ **32.** $\frac{3}{5}$ **33.** $\frac{27}{25}$
34. $-3600, 1350$ **35.**

$$
\begin{array}{c}
\overset{-\frac{1}{3}}{\bullet} \\
\xleftarrow{\hspace{0.3em}} \underset{-5\ -4\ -3\ -2\ -1\ \ 0\ \ 1\ \ 2\ \ 3\ \ 4\ \ 5}{} \xrightarrow{\hspace{0.3em}}
\end{array}
$$

36. $x > -3$ **37.** True   **38.** False   **39.** $-0.\overline{4}$ **40.** 1
41. -12 **42.** -10 **43.** $-\frac{7}{12}$ **44.** 0   **45.** -5 **46.** 8
47. $-\frac{7}{5}$ **48.** -7.9 **49.** 63   **50.** -9.18 **51.** $-\frac{2}{7}$
52. -140 **53.** -7 **54.** -3 **55.** $\frac{9}{4}$ **56.** 48
57. 168   **58.** $\frac{21}{8}$ **59.** 18   **60.** 53   **61.** $\frac{103}{17}$
62. $7a - b$ **63.** $-4x + 5y$ **64.** 7   **65.** $-\frac{1}{7}$
66. $(2x)^4$ **67.** $-125x^3$ **68.** $-3a + 9$ **69.** $11b - 27$
70. $3x^4 + 10x$ **71.** $17n^2 + m^2 + 20mn$ **72.** $5x + 28$
73. ✍ The value of a constant never varies. A variable can
represent a variety of numbers.   **74.** ✍ A term is one of
the parts of an expression that is separated from the other
parts by plus signs. A factor is part of a product.   **75.** ✍
The distributive law is used in factoring algebraic expressions, multiplying algebraic expressions, combining like
terms, finding the opposite of a sum, and subtracting algebraic expressions.   **76.** ✍ A negative number raised to
an even power is positive; a negative number raised to an
odd power is negative.   **77.** 25,281   **78. (a)** $\frac{3}{11}$; **(b)** $\frac{10}{11}$
79. $-\frac{5}{8}$ **80.** -2.1 **81.** (i)   **82.** (j)   **83.** (a)
84. (h)   **85.** (k)   **86.** (b)   **87.** (c)   **88.** (e)
89. (d)   **90.** (f)   **91.** (g)

Test: Chapter 1, p. 75

1. [1.1] 4   **2.** [1.1] Let x and y represent the numbers;
$xy - 9$ **3.** [1.1] 240 ft^2 **4.** [1.2] $q + 3p$
5. [1.2] $(x \cdot 4) \cdot y$ **6.** [1.1] No   **7.** [1.1] Let p represent
the maximum production capability; $p - 4250 = 45,950$
8. [1.2] $35 + 7x$ **9.** [1.7] $-5y + 10$
10. [1.2] $11(1 + 4x)$ **11.** [1.2] $7(x + 1 + 7y)$
12. [1.3] $2 \cdot 2 \cdot 3 \cdot 5 \cdot 5$ **13.** [1.3] $\frac{3}{7}$ **14.** [1.4] $<$
15. [1.4] $>$ **16.** [1.4] $\frac{9}{4}$ **17.** [1.4] 3.8   **18.** [1.6] $\frac{2}{3}$
19. [1.7] $-\frac{7}{4}$ **20.** [1.6] 10   **21.** [1.4] $-5 \geq x$
22. [1.6] 7.8   **23.** [1.5] -8 **24.** [1.6] -2.5 **25.** [1.6] $-\frac{7}{8}$
26. [1.7] -48 **27.** [1.7] $\frac{2}{9}$ **28.** [1.7] -6 **29.** [1.7] $\frac{3}{4}$
30. [1.7] -9.728 **31.** [1.8] -173 **32.** [1.6] 15
33. [1.8] -64 **34.** [1.8] 448   **35.** [1.6] $21a + 22y$
36. [1.8] $16x^4$ **37.** [1.8] $x + 7$ **38.** [1.8] $9a - 12b - 7$
39. [1.8] $-y - 16$ **40.** [1.1] 5
41. [1.8] $9 - (3 - 4) + 5 = 15$ **42.** [1.8] 15
43. [1.8] $4a$ **44.** [1.8] False

CHAPTER 2

Exercise Set 2.1, pp. 83–85

1. (c)   **2.** (b)   **3.** (f)   **4.** (a)   **5.** (d)   **6.** (e)   **7.** (d)
8. (b)   **9.** (c)   **10.** (a)   **11.** 11   **13.** -25 **15.** -31
17. 41   **19.** 19   **21.** -6 **23.** $\frac{7}{3}$ **25.** $-\frac{1}{10}$ **27.** $\frac{41}{24}$
29. $-\frac{1}{20}$ **31.** 9.1   **33.** -5 **35.** 7   **37.** 12   **39.** -38
41. 8   **43.** -7 **45.** 8   **47.** 88   **49.** 20   **51.** -54
53. $-\frac{5}{9}$ **55.** 1   **57.** $\frac{9}{2}$ **59.** -7.6 **61.** -2.5 **63.** -15
65. -5 **67.** $-\frac{7}{6}$ **69.** -128 **71.** $-\frac{1}{2}$ **73.** -15 **75.** 9
77. 310.756   **79.** ✍   **81.** -6 **82.** 2   **83.** 1
84. -16 **85.** ✍   **87.** 11.6   **89.** 2   **91.** $-23, 23$
93. 9000   **95.** 250

Technology Connection, p. 88

1. 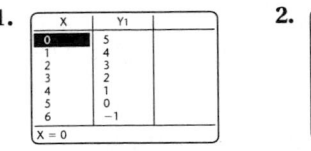   **2.**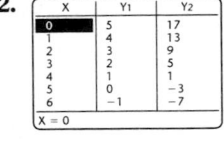

3. 4; not reliable because, depending on the choice of ΔTbl, it
is easy to scroll past a solution without realizing it.

Exercise Set 2.2, pp. 91–92

1. (c)   **2.** (e)   **3.** (a)   **4.** (f)   **5.** (b)   **6.** (d)   **7.** 8
9. 7   **11.** 5   **13.** $\frac{10}{3}$ **15.** -7 **17.** -5 **19.** -4
21. 19   **23.** -2.8 **25.** 3   **27.** 15   **29.** -6 **31.** $-\frac{25}{2}$
33. All real numbers; identity   **35.** -3 **37.** -6 **39.** 2
41. 0   **43.** 6   **45.** No solution; contradiction   **47.** $-\frac{1}{2}$
49. 0   **51.** 10   **53.** 4   **55.** 0   **57.** No solution;
contradiction   **59.** $\frac{5}{2}$ **61.** -8 **63.** $\frac{1}{6}$
65. All real numbers; identity   **67.** 2   **69.** $\frac{16}{3}$ **71.** $\frac{2}{5}$
73. 1   **75.** -4 **77.** $1.\overline{6}$ **79.** $-\frac{60}{37}$ **81.** 11   **83.** 8
85. $\frac{16}{15}$ **87.** $-\frac{1}{31}$ **89.** 2   **91.** ✍   **93.** -7 **94.** 15

95. -15 **96.** -28 **97.** 🖩   **99.** $\frac{1136}{909}$, or $1.\overline{2497}$
101. No solution; contradiction   **103.** $\frac{2}{3}$ **105.** 0
107. $\frac{52}{45}$ **109.** All real numbers; identity

Technology Connection, p. 94

1. 800

Exercise Set 2.3, pp. 97–100

1. 309.6 m   **3.** 1423 students   **5.** 8.4734   **7.** 255 mg
9. $b = \dfrac{A}{h}$ **11.** $r = \dfrac{d}{t}$ **13.** $P = \dfrac{I}{rt}$ **15.** $m = 65 - H$
17. $l = \dfrac{P - 2w}{2}$, or $l = \dfrac{P}{2} - w$ **19.** $\pi = \dfrac{A}{r^2}$
21. $h = \dfrac{2A}{b}$ **23.** $c^2 = \dfrac{E}{m}$ **25.** $d = 2Q - c$
27. $b = 3A - a - c$ **29.** $r = wf$ **31.** $C = \frac{5}{9}(F - 32)$
33. $y = 2x - 1$ **35.** $y = -\frac{2}{5}x + 2$ **37.** $y = \frac{4}{3}x - 2$
39. $y = -\frac{9}{8}x + \frac{1}{2}$ **41.** $y = \frac{3}{5}x - \frac{8}{5}$
43. $x = \dfrac{z - 13}{2} - y$, or $x = \dfrac{z - 13 - 2y}{2}$
45. $l = 4(t - 27) + w$ **47.** $t = \dfrac{A}{a + b}$ **49.** $h = \dfrac{2A}{a + b}$
51. $L = W - \dfrac{N(R - r)}{400}$, or $L = \dfrac{400W - NR + Nr}{400}$
53. 🖩   **55.** -10 **56.** -196 **57.** 0 **58.** -32
59. -13 **60.** 65 **61.** 🖩   **63.** 40 yr   **65.** 27 in³
67. $a = \dfrac{w}{c} \cdot d$ **69.** $c = \dfrac{d}{a - b}$ **71.** $a = \dfrac{c}{3 + b + d}$
73. $K = 9.632w + 19.685h - 10.54a + 102.3$

Exercise Set 2.4, pp. 104–108

1. (d)   **2.** (c)   **3.** (e)   **4.** (b)   **5.** (c)   **6.** (d)   **7.** (f)
8. (a)   **9.** (b)   **10.** (e)   **11.** 0.49   **13.** 0.01
15. 0.041   **17.** 0.2   **19.** 0.0625   **21.** 0.002   **23.** 1.75
25. 38%   **27.** 3.9%   **29.** 45%   **31.** 70%   **33.** 0.09%
35. 106%   **37.** 180%   **39.** 60%   **41.** 32%   **43.** 25%
45. 26%   **47.** $46\frac{2}{3}$, or $\frac{140}{3}$ **49.** 2.5   **51.** 10,000
53. 125%   **55.** 0.8   **57.** 50%   **59.** $33.\overline{3}\%$, or $33\frac{1}{3}\%$
61. 2.85 million Americans   **63.** 23.37 million Americans
65. 75 credits   **67.** 595 at bats   **69.** (a) 16%; (b) $29
71. $33.\overline{3}\%$, or $33\frac{1}{3}\%$; $66.\overline{6}\%$, or $66\frac{2}{3}\%$ **73.** $168
75. 285 women   **77.** $19.20 an hour   **79.** The actual
cost was 43.7% more than the estimate.   **81.** $45
83. $148.50   **85.** About 31.5 lb   **87.** About 2.45 billion
pieces of mail   **89.** About 165 calories   **91.** 🖩
93. Let l represent the length and w represent the width;
$2l + 2w$ **94.** $0.05 \cdot 180$ **95.** Let p represent the number
of points Tino scored; $p - 5$ **96.** $15 + 1.5x$ **97.** $10\left(\frac{1}{2}a\right)$
98. Let n represent the number; $3n + 10$ **99.** Let l
represent the length and w represent the width; $w = l - 2$
100. Let x represent the first number and y represent the
second number; $x = 4y$ **101.** 🖩   **103.** 18,500 people
105. About 6 ft 7 in.   **107.** About 27%   **109.** 🖩

Exercise Set 2.5, pp. 116–121

1. 11   **3.** $\frac{11}{2}$ **5.** $150   **7.** $130   **9.** About 78.4 mi
11. 160 mi   **13.** 1204 and 1205   **15.** 285 and 287
17. 32, 33, 34   **19.** Man: 103 yr; woman: 101 yr
21. Non-spam: 25 billion messages; spam: 100 billion
messages   **23.** 140 and 141   **25.** Width: 100 ft; length:
160 ft; area: 16,000 ft²   **27.** Width: 21 m; length: 25 m
29. $1\frac{3}{4}$ in. by $3\frac{1}{2}$ in.   **31.** 30°, 90°, 60°   **33.** 70°
35. Bottom: 144 ft; middle: 72 ft; top: 24 ft   **37.** 8.75 mi,
or $8\frac{3}{4}$ mi   **39.** $128\frac{1}{3}$ mi   **41.** 65°, 25°   **43.** 140°, 40°
45. Length: 27.9 cm; width: 21.6 cm   **47.** $6600
49. 830 points   **51.** $125,000   **53.** 160 chirps per
minute   **55.** 🖩   **57.** $<$ **58.** $>$ **59.** $>$ **60.** $<$
61. $-4 \le x$ **62.** $5 > x$ **63.** $y < 5$ **64.** $t \ge -10$
65. 🖩   **67.** $37   **69.** 20   **71.** Half-dollars: 5;
quarters: 10; dimes: 20; nickels: 60   **73.** $95.99
75. 5 DVDs   **77.** 6 mi   **79.** 🖩   **81.** Width: 23.31 cm;
length: 27.56 cm

Exercise Set 2.6, pp. 128–130

1. $\ge$ **2.** $\le$ **3.** $<$ **4.** $>$ **5.** Equivalent
6. Equivalent   **7.** Equivalent   **8.** Not equivalent
9. (a) Yes; (b) no; (c) no   **11.** (a) Yes; (b) no; (c) yes
13. (a) Yes; (b) yes; (c) yes   **15.** (a) No; (b) yes; (c) no
17. $y < 2$
19. $x \ge -1$
21. $0 \le t$
23. $-5 \le x < 2$
25. $-4 < x < 0$
27. $\{y \mid y < 6\}, (-\infty, 6)$
29. $\{x \mid x \ge -4\}, [-4, \infty)$
31. $\{t \mid t > -3\}, (-3, \infty)$
33. $\{x \mid x \le -7\}, (-\infty, -7]$
35. $\{x \mid x > -4\}, (-4, \infty)$ **37.** $\{x \mid x \le 2\}, (-\infty, 2]$
39. $\{x \mid x < -1\}, (-\infty, -1)$ **41.** $\{x \mid x \ge 0\}, [0, \infty)$
43. $\{y \mid y > 3\}, (3, \infty)$
45. $\{n \mid n < 17\}, (-\infty, 17)$,
47. $\{x \mid x \le -9\}, (-\infty, -9]$,
49. $\left\{y \mid y \le \frac{1}{2}\right\}, \left(-\infty, \frac{1}{2}\right]$,
51. $\left\{t \mid t > \frac{5}{8}\right\}, \left(\frac{5}{8}, \infty\right)$,
53. $\{x \mid x < 0\}, (-\infty, 0)$,
55. $\{t \mid t < 23\}, (-\infty, 23)$
57. $\{y \mid y \ge 22\}, [22, \infty)$,
59. $\{x \mid x < 7\}, (-\infty, 7)$
61. $\{t \mid t < -3\}, (-\infty, -3)$,

63. $\{n \mid n \geq -1.5\}, [-1.5, \infty),$

65. $\left\{y \mid y \geq -\frac{1}{10}\right\}, \left[-\frac{1}{10}, \infty\right)$

67. $\left\{x \mid x < -\frac{4}{5}\right\}, \left(-\infty, -\frac{4}{5}\right)$

69. $\{x \mid x < 6\},$ or $(-\infty, 6)$ **71.** $\{t \mid t \leq 7\},$ or $(-\infty, 7]$
73. $\{x \mid x > -4\},$ or $(-4, \infty)$ **75.** $\left\{y \mid y < -\frac{10}{3}\right\},$ or
$\left(-\infty, -\frac{10}{3}\right)$ **77.** $\{x \mid x > -10\},$ or $(-10, \infty)$
79. $\{y \mid y < 0\},$ or $(-\infty, 0)$ **81.** $\left\{y \mid y \geq \frac{3}{2}\right\},$ or $\left[\frac{3}{2}, \infty\right)$
83. $\{x \mid x > -4\},$ or $(-4, \infty)$ **85.** $\{t \mid t > 1\},$ or $(1, \infty)$
87. $\{x \mid x \leq -9\},$ or $(-\infty, -9]$ **89.** $\{t \mid t < 14\},$ or
$(-\infty, 14)$ **91.** $\{y \mid y \leq -4\},$ or $(-\infty, -4]$
93. $\left\{t \mid t < -\frac{5}{3}\right\},$ or $\left(-\infty, -\frac{5}{3}\right)$ **95.** $\{r \mid r > -3\},$ or $(-3, \infty)$
97. $\{x \mid x \leq 7\},$ or $(-\infty, 7]$ **99.** $\left\{x \mid x > -\frac{5}{32}\right\},$ or $\left(-\frac{5}{32}, \infty\right)$
101.   **103.** $17x - 6$ **104.** $2m - 16n$
105. $7x - 8y - 46$ **106.** $-47t + 1$
107. $35a - 20b - 17$ **108.** $-21x + 32$ **109.**
111. $\{x \mid x \text{ is a real number}\},$ or $(-\infty, \infty)$
113. $\left\{x \mid x \leq \frac{5}{6}\right\},$ or $\left(-\infty, \frac{5}{6}\right]$
115. $\{x \mid x \leq -4a\},$ or $(-\infty, -4a]$
117. $\left\{x \mid x > \dfrac{y - b}{a}\right\},$ or $\left(\dfrac{y - b}{a}, \infty\right)$
119. $\{x \mid x \text{ is a real number}\},$ or $(-\infty, \infty)$

Connecting the Concepts, pp. 130–131

1. 21   **2.** $\{x \mid x \leq 21\},$ or $(-\infty, 21]$ **3.** -6
4. $\{x \mid x > -6\},$ or $(-6, \infty)$ **5.** $\{x \mid x < 6\},$ or $(-\infty, 6)$
6. 3   **7.** $-\frac{1}{3}$ **8.** $\{y \mid y < 3\},$ or $(-\infty, 3)$
9. $\{t \mid t \leq -16\},$ or $(-\infty, -16]$ **10.** $\frac{11}{2}$
11. $\{a \mid a < -1\},$ or $(-\infty, -1)$ **12.** $\{x \mid x < 10.75\},$ or
$(-\infty, 10.75)$ **13.** $\{x \mid x \geq -11\},$ or $[-11, \infty)$
14. 105   **15.** -4.24 **16.** 15   **17.** $\{y \mid y \geq 3\},$ or $[3, \infty)$
18. $\frac{14}{3}$ **19.** $\left\{x \mid x > \frac{22}{5}\right\},$ or $\left(\frac{22}{5}, \infty\right)$
20. $\{a \mid a \geq 0\},$ or $[0, \infty)$

Translating for Success, p. 134

1. F   **2.** I   **3.** C   **4.** E   **5.** D   **6.** J   **7.** O   **8.** M
9. B   **10.** L

Exercise Set 2.7, pp. 135–138

1. $b \leq a$ **2.** $b < a$ **3.** $a \leq b$ **4.** $a < b$ **5.** $b \leq a$
6. $a \leq b$ **7.** $b < a$ **8.** $a < b$ **9.** Let n represent the
number; $n < 10$ **11.** Let t represent the temperature;
$t \leq -3$ **13.** Let d represent the number of years of
driving experience; $d \geq 5$ **15.** Let a represent the age of
the altar; $a > 1200$ **17.** Let h represent Tania's hourly
wage; $12 < h < 15$ **19.** Let w represent the wind speed;
$w > 50$ **21.** Let c represent the cost of a room; $c \leq 120$
23. More than 2.375 hr   **25.** At least 2.25   **27.** Scores
greater than or equal to 97   **29.** 8 credits or more
31. At least 3 plate appearances   **33.** Lengths greater than
6 cm   **35.** Depths less than 437.5 ft   **37.** Blue-book value

is greater than or equal to $10,625   **39.** Lengths less than
55 in.   **41.** Temperatures greater than 37°C
43. No more than 3 ft tall   **45.** A serving contains at least
16 g of fat.   **47.** Dates after September 16   **49.** No more
than 134 text messages   **51.** Years after 2012
53. Mileages less than or equal to 225   **55.**   **57.** -14
58. $-\frac{2}{3}$ **59.** -60 **60.** -11.1 **61.** 0   **62.** 5
63. -2 **64.** -1 **65.**   **67.** Temperatures between
$-15°$C and $-9\frac{4}{9}°$C   **69.** Lengths less than or equal to 8 cm
71. They contain at least 7.5 g of fat per serving.
73. At least $42   **75.**

Review Exercises: Chapter 2, pp. 142–143

1. True   **2.** False   **3.** True   **4.** True   **5.** True
6. False   **7.** True   **8.** True   **9.** -25 **10.** 7
11. -65 **12.** 3   **13.** -20 **14.** 1.11   **15.** $\frac{1}{2}$ **16.** $-\frac{3}{2}$
17. -8 **18.** -4 **19.** $-\frac{1}{3}$ **20.** 4   **21.** No solution;
contradiction   **22.** 4   **23.** 16   **24.** 1   **25.** $-\frac{7}{5}$ **26.** 0

27. All real numbers; identity   **28.** $d = \dfrac{C}{\pi}$ **29.** $B = \dfrac{3V}{h}$

30. $y = \frac{5}{2}x - 5$ **31.** $x = \dfrac{b}{t - a}$ **32.** 0.012   **33.** 44%

34. 70%   **35.** 140   **36.** No   **37.** Yes   **38.** No

39.

40.

41.   **42.** $\left\{t \mid t \geq -\frac{1}{2}\right\},$ or $\left[-\frac{1}{2}, \infty\right)$

43. $\{x \mid x \geq 7\},$ or $[7, \infty)$ **44.** $\{y \mid y > 3\},$ or $(3, \infty)$
45. $\{y \mid y \leq -4\},$ or $(-\infty, -4]$
46. $\{x \mid x < -11\},$ or $(-\infty, -11)$ **47.** $\{y \mid y > -7\},$ or
$(-7, \infty)$ **48.** $\{x \mid x > -6\},$ or $(-6, \infty)$
49. $\left\{x \mid x > -\frac{9}{11}\right\},$ or $\left(-\frac{9}{11}, \infty\right)$ **50.** $\{t \mid t \leq -12\},$ or
$(-\infty, -12]$ **51.** $\{x \mid x \leq -8\},$ or $(-\infty, -8]$
52. About 48%   **53.** 8 ft, 10 ft   **54.** Japanese students:
41,000; Chinese students: 62,000   **55.** 57, 59
56. Width: 11 cm; length: 17 cm   **57.** $160   **58.** About 109
million subscribers   **59.** 35°, 85°, 60°   **60.** No more than
55 g of fat   **61.** 14 or fewer copies   **62.** Multiplying
both sides of an equation by *any* nonzero number results in
an equivalent equation. When multiplying on both sides of
an inequality, the sign of the number being multiplied by
must be considered. If the number is positive, the direction
of the inequality symbol remains unchanged; if the number
is negative, the direction of the inequality symbol must be
reversed to produce an equivalent inequality.   **63.**
The solutions of an equation can usually each be checked.
The solutions of an inequality are normally too numerous
to check. Checking a few numbers from the solution set
found cannot guarantee that the answer is correct, although
if any number does not check, the answer found is
incorrect.   **64.** About 1 hr 36 min   **65.** Nile: 4160 mi;
Amazon: 4225 mi   **66.** $16   **67.** $-23, 23$ **68.** $-20, 20$

69. $a = \dfrac{y - 3}{2 - b}$ **70.** $F = \dfrac{0.3(12w)}{9},$ or $F = 0.4w$

st: Chapter 2, p. 144

1. [2.1] 9 **2.** [2.1] 15 **3.** [2.1] −3 **4.** [2.1] 49
5. [2.1] −12 **6.** [2.2] 2 **7.** [2.1] −8 **8.** [2.2] $-\frac{23}{67}$
9. [2.2] 7 **10.** [2.2] $\frac{23}{3}$ **11.** [2.2] All real numbers; identity
12. [2.6] $\{x \mid x > -5\}$, or $(-5, \infty)$
13. [2.6] $\{x \mid x > -13\}$, or $(-13, \infty)$
14. [2.6] $\{y \mid y \le -13\}$, or $(-\infty, -13]$
15. [2.6] $\{y \mid y \le -\frac{15}{2}\}$, or $(-\infty, -\frac{15}{2}]$
16. [2.6] $\{n \mid n < -5\}$, or $(-\infty, -5)$
17. [2.6] $\{x \mid x < -7\}$, or $(-\infty, -7)$
18. [2.6] $\{t \mid t \ge -1\}$, or $[-1, \infty)$
19. [2.6] $\{x \mid x \le -1\}$, or $(-\infty, -1]$
20. [2.3] $r = \dfrac{A}{2\pi h}$ **21.** [2.3] $l = 2w - P$ **22.** [2.4] 2.3
23. [2.4] 0.3% **24.** [2.4] 14.8 **25.** [2.4] 44%
26. [2.6]

$$y < 4$$
<−−+−−+−−+−−+−−+−−+−−+−−+−−+−−+−−>
−10 −8 −6 −4 −2 0 2 4 6 8 10

27. [2.6]

$$-2 \le x \le 2$$
<−−+−−+−−[−−+−−+−−+−−+−−]−−+−−+−−>
−5 −4 −3 −2 −1 0 1 2 3 4 5

28. [2.5] Width: 7 cm; length: 11 cm **29.** [2.5] 525 mi
from Springer Mountain and 1575 mi from Mt. Katahdin
30. [2.5] 81 mm, 83 mm, 85 mm **31.** [2.4] $65
32. [2.7] More than 36 one-way trips per month
33. [2.3] $d = \dfrac{a}{3}$ **34.** [1.4], [2.2] −15, 15 **35.** [2.7] Let
h = the number of hours of sun each day; $4 \le h \le 6$
36. [2.5] 60 tickets

Cumulative Review: Chapters 1–2, pp. 145–146

1. −12 **2.** $\frac{3}{4}$ **3.** −4.2 **4.** 10 **5.** 134 **6.** 149
7. $2x + 1$ **8.** $-10t + 12$ **9.** $-21n + 36$
10.

$$-\frac{5}{2}$$
<−−+−−+−●−+−−+−−+−−+−−+−−+−−+−−>
−5 −4 −3 −2 −1 0 1 2 3 4 5

11. 27
12. $6(2x + 3y + 5z)$ **13.** −6 **14.** 16 **15.** 9
16. $\frac{13}{18}$ **17.** 1 **18.** $-\frac{7}{2}$ **19.** $z = \dfrac{x}{4y}$ **20.** $y = \frac{4}{9}x - \frac{1}{9}$
21. $n = \dfrac{p}{a + r}$ **22.** 1.83 **23.** 37.5%
24.

$$-\frac{5}{2} \qquad t > -\frac{5}{2}$$
<−−+−−+−−+−(−+−−+−−+−−+−−+−−+−−>
−5 −4 −3 −2 −1 0 1 2 3 4 5

25. $\{t \mid t \le -2\}$, or $(-\infty, -2]$
26. $\{t \mid t < 3\}$, or $(-\infty, 3)$ **27.** $\{x \mid x < 30\}$, or $(-\infty, 30)$
28. $\{n \mid n \ge 2\}$, or $[2, \infty)$ **29.** 48 million **30.** 3.2 hr
31. $14\frac{1}{3}$ m **32.** 9 ft, 15 ft **33.** No more than $52
34. About 194% **35.** 105° **36.** For widths greater than
27 cm **37.** 4t **38.** −5, 5 **39.** $1025

CHAPTER 3

Exercise Set 3.1, pp. 154–157

1. (a) **2.** (c) **3.** (b) **4.** (d) **5.** 2 drinks
7. The person weighs more than 140 lb. **9.** About $5156

11. $231,856,000 **13.** About 29.2 million tons **15.** About
3.2 million tons **17.** About $12 billion **19.** 2001
21. 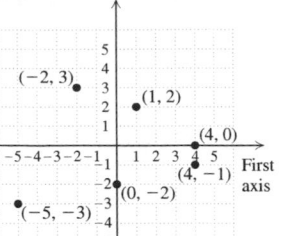 **23.**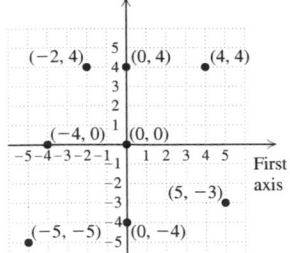

25.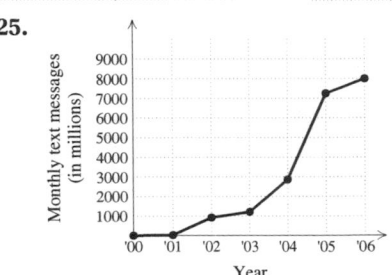

27. $A(-4, 5); B(-3, -3); C(0, 4); D(3, 4); E(3, -4)$
29. $A(4, 1); B(0, -5); C(-4, 0); D(-3, -2); E(3, 0)$
31. 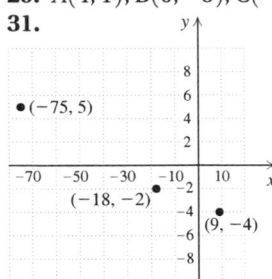 **33.**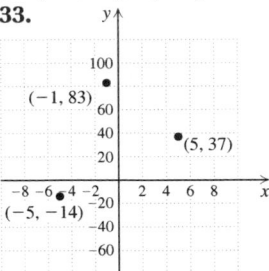

35. 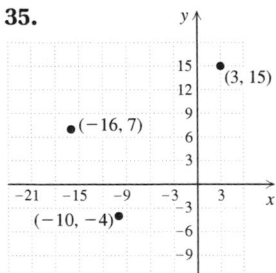 **37.**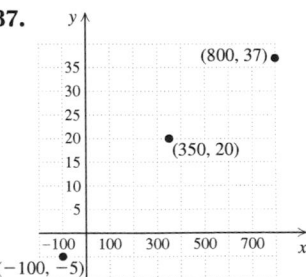

39.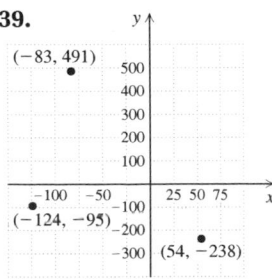

41. IV **43.** III **45.** I
47. II **49.** I and IV
51. I and III **53.**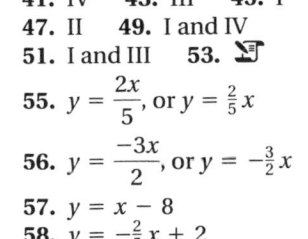
55. $y = \dfrac{2x}{5}$, or $y = \frac{2}{5}x$
56. $y = \dfrac{-3x}{2}$, or $y = -\frac{3}{2}x$
57. $y = x - 8$
58. $y = -\frac{2}{5}x + 2$
59. $y = -\frac{2}{3}x + \frac{5}{3}$

60. $y = \frac{5}{8}x - \frac{1}{8}$ **61.** ✍ **63.** II or IV **65.** $(-1, -5)$

67. Second axis

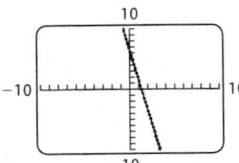

First axis

69. $\frac{65}{2}$ sq units
71. Latitude 27° North; longitude 81° West
73. ✍

19.
$$\frac{4x - 2y = 10}{\begin{array}{c|c} 4 \cdot 0 - 2(-5) & 10 \\ 0 + 10 & \end{array}}$$
$$10 \stackrel{?}{=} 10 \quad \text{True}$$
$(2, -1)$; answers may vary

$$\frac{4x - 2y = 10}{\begin{array}{c|c} 4 \cdot 4 - 2 \cdot 3 & 10 \\ 16 - 6 & \end{array}}$$
$$10 \stackrel{?}{=} 10 \quad \text{True}$$

Technology Connection, p. 164

1. $y = -5x + 6.5$

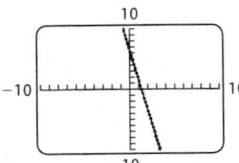

2. $y = 3x + 4.5$

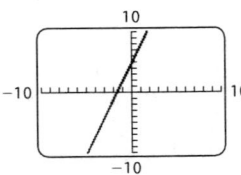

3. $7y - 4x = 22$, or $y = \frac{4}{7}x + \frac{22}{7}$

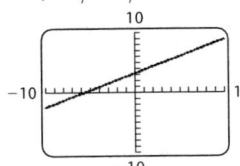

4. $5y + 11x = -20$, or $y = -\frac{11}{5}x - 4$

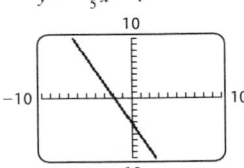

5. $2y - x^2 = 0$, or $y = 0.5x^2$

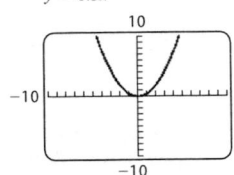

6. $y + x^2 = 8$, or $y = -x^2 + 8$

Exercise Set 3.2, pp. 165–167

1. False **2.** True **3.** True **4.** True **5.** True
6. False **7.** Yes **9.** No **11.** No
13. $y = x + 3$
$$\frac{}{\begin{array}{c|c} 2 & -1 + 3 \end{array}}$$
$$2 \stackrel{?}{=} 2 \quad \text{True}$$
$(2, 5)$; answers may vary

$y = x + 3$
$$\frac{}{\begin{array}{c|c} 7 & 4 + 3 \end{array}}$$
$$7 \stackrel{?}{=} 7 \quad \text{True}$$

15. $y = \frac{1}{2}x + 3$
$$\frac{}{\begin{array}{c|c} 5 & \frac{1}{2} \cdot 4 + 3 \\ & 2 + 3 \end{array}}$$
$$5 \stackrel{?}{=} 5 \quad \text{True}$$
$(0, 3)$; answers may vary

$y = \frac{1}{2}x + 3$
$$\frac{}{\begin{array}{c|c} 2 & \frac{1}{2}(-2) + 3 \\ & -1 + 3 \end{array}}$$
$$2 \stackrel{?}{=} 2 \quad \text{True}$$

17. $y + 3x = 7$
$$\frac{}{\begin{array}{c|c} 1 + 3 \cdot 2 & 7 \\ 1 + 6 & \end{array}}$$
$$7 \stackrel{?}{=} 7 \quad \text{True}$$
$(1, 4)$; answers may vary

$y + 3x = 7$
$$\frac{}{\begin{array}{c|c} -5 + 3 \cdot 4 & 7 \\ -5 + 12 & \end{array}}$$
$$7 \stackrel{?}{=} 7 \quad \text{True}$$

21.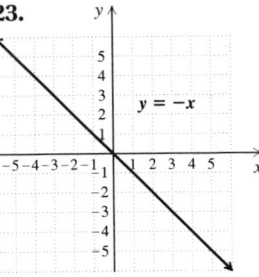
$y = x + 1$

23.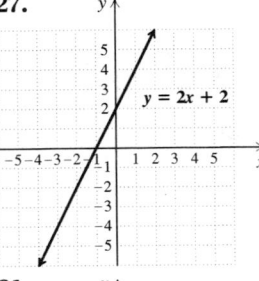
$y = -x$

25.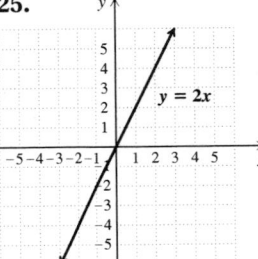
$y = 2x$

27.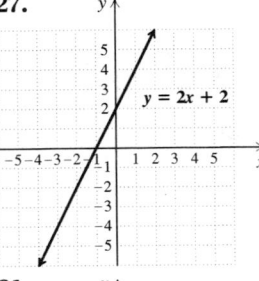
$y = 2x + 2$

29.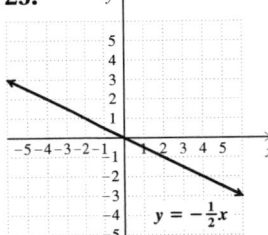
$y = -\frac{1}{2}x$

31.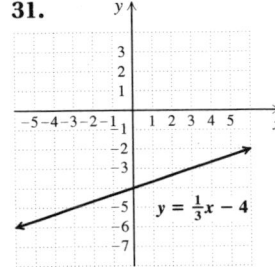
$y = \frac{1}{3}x - 4$

33.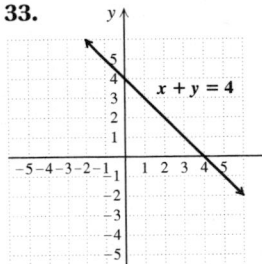
$x + y = 4$

35.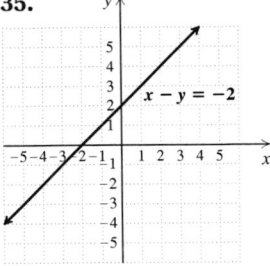
$x - y = -2$

37.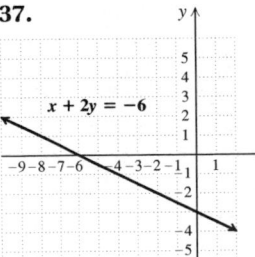
$x + 2y = -6$

39.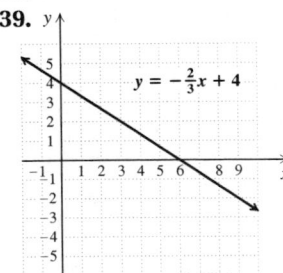
$y = -\frac{2}{3}x + 4$

41.
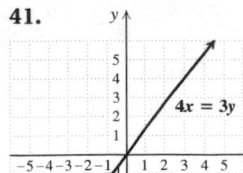

43.
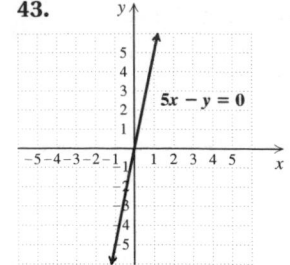

45.
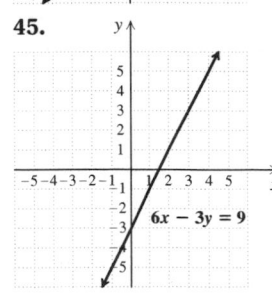

47.
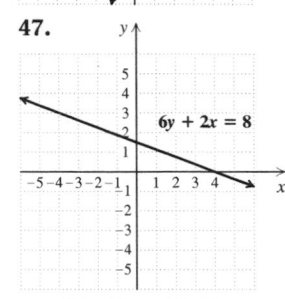

49. About $3800

51. About $49

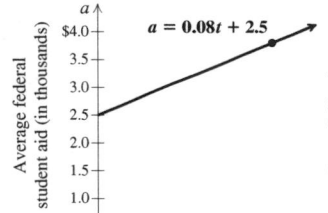

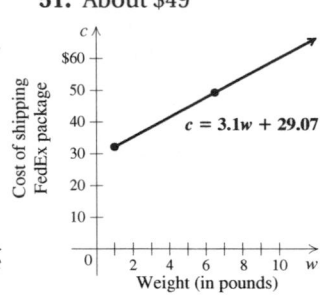

53. About $96

55. About 33 gal

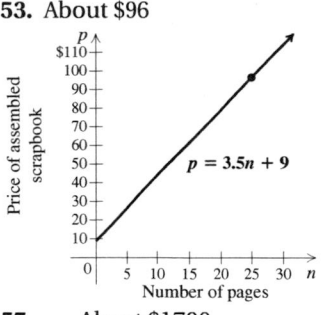

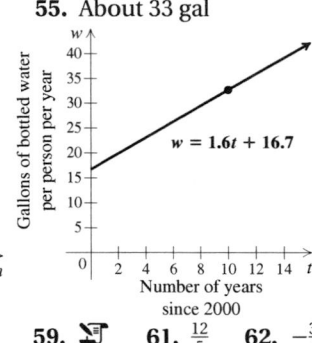

57. About $1700

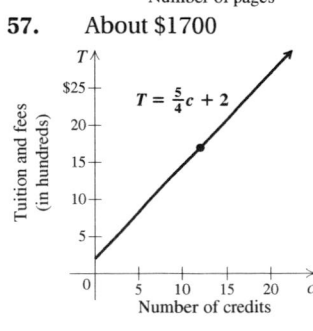

59. ✍

61. $\frac{12}{5}$

62. $-\frac{3}{4}$

63. 3

64. $-\frac{21}{5}$

65. $Q = 2A - T$

66. $p = \dfrac{w}{q + 1}$

67. $y = \dfrac{C - Ax}{B}$

68. $y = m(x - h) + k$

69. ✍

71.
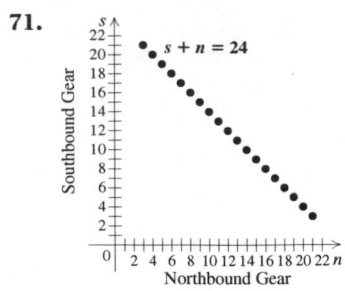
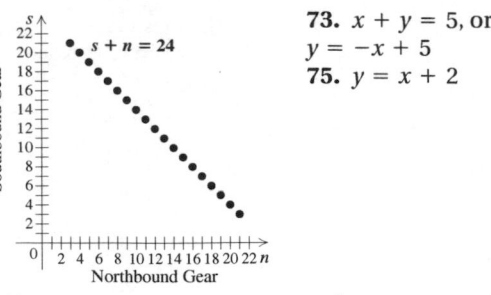

73. $x + y = 5$, or $y = -x + 5$
75. $y = x + 2$

77.
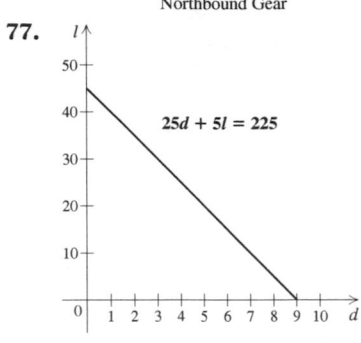

Answers may vary.
1 dinner, 40 lunches;
5 dinners, 20 lunches;
8 dinners, 5 lunches

79.
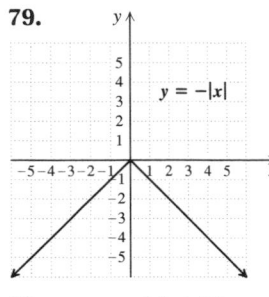

81.
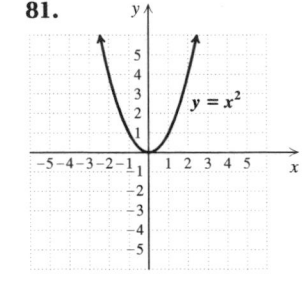

83. $y = -2.8x + 3.5$
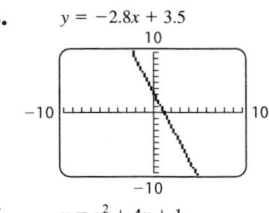

85. $y = 2.8x - 3.5$
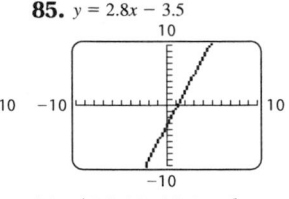

87. $y = x^2 + 4x + 1$
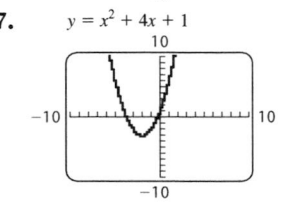

89. $56.62; 16.2 gal

Technology Connection, p. 171

1. $y = -0.72x - 15$
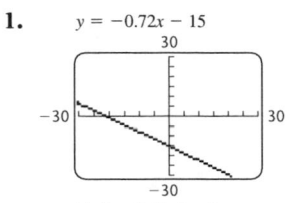
Xscl = 5, Yscl = 5

2. $y - 2.13x = 27$, or $y = 2.13x + 27$
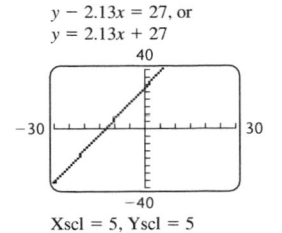
Xscl = 5, Yscl = 5

3. $5x + 6y = 84$, or
$y = -\frac{5}{6}x + 14$

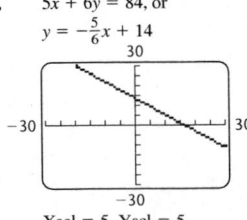

Xscl = 5, Yscl = 5

4. $2x - 7y = 150$, or
$y = \frac{2}{7}x - \frac{150}{7}$

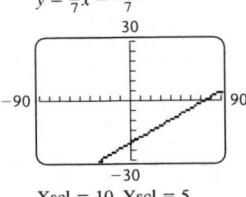

Xscl = 10, Yscl = 5

5. $19x - 17y = 200$, or
$y = \frac{19}{17}x - \frac{200}{17}$

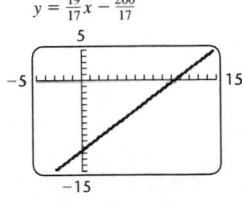

6. $6x + 5y = 159$, or
$y = -\frac{6}{5}x + \frac{159}{5}$

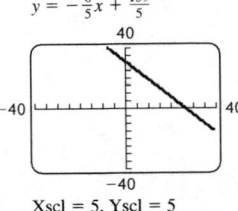

Xscl = 5, Yscl = 5

Exercise Set 3.3, pp. 173–175

1. (f)   **2.** (e)   **3.** (d)   **4.** (c)   **5.** (b)   **6.** (a)
7. (a) $(0, 5)$; **(b)** $(2, 0)$ **9. (a)** $(0, -4)$; **(b)** $(3, 0)$
11. (a) $(0, -2)$; **(b)** $(-3, 0), (3, 0)$ **13. (a)** $(0, 0)$;
(b) $(-2, 0), (0, 0), (5, 0)$ **15. (a)** $(0, 3)$; **(b)** $(5, 0)$
17. (a) $(0, -18)$; **(b)** $(4, 0)$ **19. (a)** $(0, 16)$; **(b)** $(-20, 0)$
21. (a) None; **(b)** $(12, 0)$ **23. (a)** $(0, -9)$; **(b)** none

25.

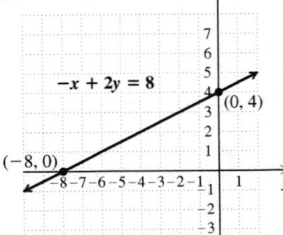

27.

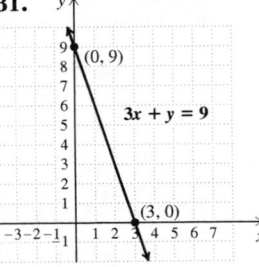

29.

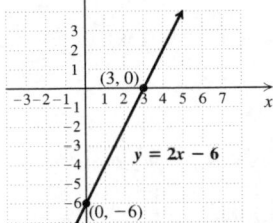

31.

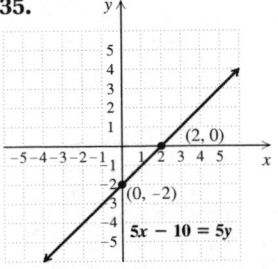

33.

35.

37.

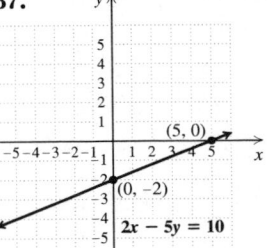

39.

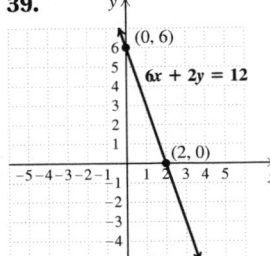

41.

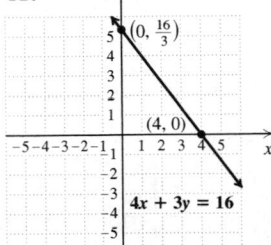

43.

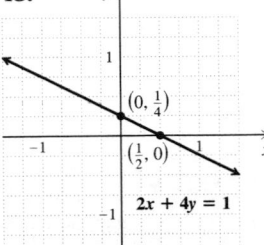

45.

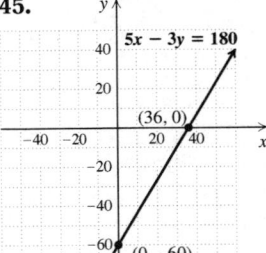

47.

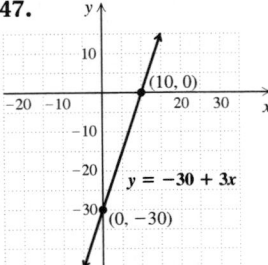

49.

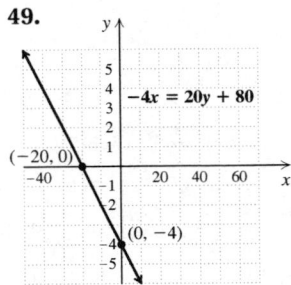

51.

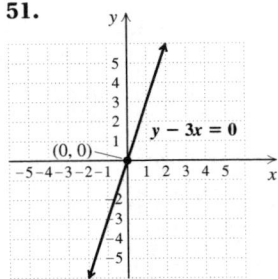

53.

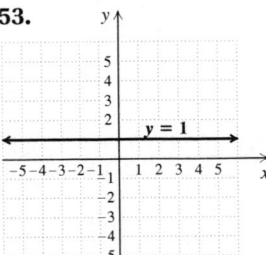

55.

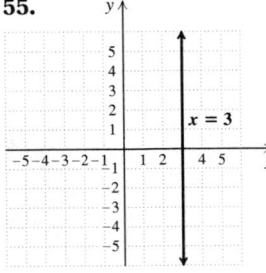

57.

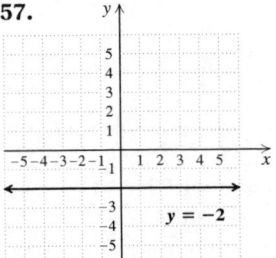

59.

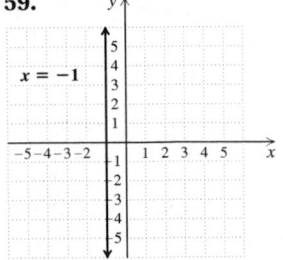

61.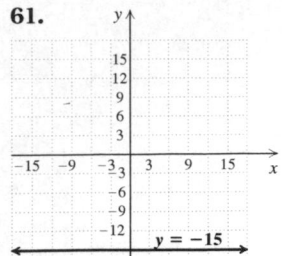

63.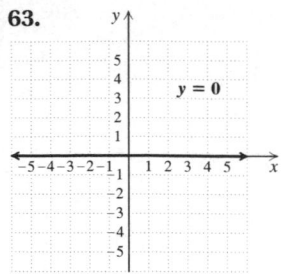

65.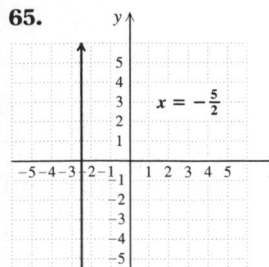

67.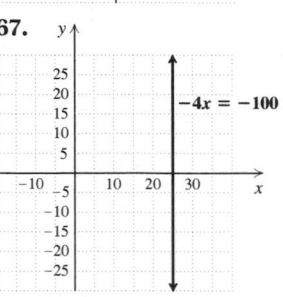

69.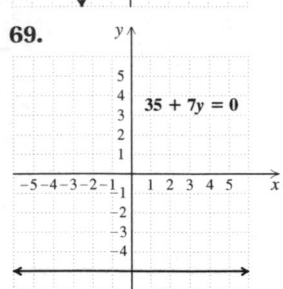

71. $y = -1$ **73.** $x = 4$
75. $x = 0$ **77.** ☜
79. $d - 7$
80. $w + 5$, or $5 + w$
81. Let n represent the number; $7 + 4n$
82. Let n represent the number; $3n$
83. Let x and y represent the numbers; $2(x + y)$
84. Let a and b represent the numbers; $\frac{1}{2}(a + b)$
85. ☜   **87.** $y = 0$ **89.** $x = -2$ **91.** $(-3, 4)$
93. $-5x + 3y = 15$, or $y = \frac{5}{3}x + 5$ **95.** -24
97. $\left(\dfrac{C - D}{A}, 0\right)$ **99.** $\left(0, -\frac{80}{7}\right)$, or $(0, -11.\overline{428571})$; $(40, 0)$
101. $(0, -9)$; $(45, 0)$ **103.** $\left(0, \frac{1}{25}\right)$, or $(0, 0.04)$; $\left(\frac{1}{50}, 0\right)$, or $(0.02, 0)$

Exercise Set 3.4, pp. 179–184

1. Miles per hour, or $\dfrac{\text{miles}}{\text{hour}}$

2. Hours per chapter, or $\dfrac{\text{hours}}{\text{chapter}}$

3. Dollars per mile, or $\dfrac{\text{dollars}}{\text{mile}}$

4. Petunias per foot, or $\dfrac{\text{petunias}}{\text{foot}}$

5. Minutes per errand, or $\dfrac{\text{minutes}}{\text{errand}}$

6. Cups of flour per cake, or $\dfrac{\text{cups of flour}}{\text{cake}}$

7. **(a)** 30 mpg; **(b)** \$39.33/day; **(c)** 130 mi/day; **(d)** 30¢/mi
9. **(a)** 7 mph; **(b)** \$7.50/hr; **(c)** \$1.07/mi
11. **(a)** \$22/hr; **(b)** 20.6 pages/hr; **(c)** \$1.07/page
13. \$568.4 billion/yr **15.** **(a)** 14.5 floors/min;
(b) 4.14 sec/floor **17.** **(a)** 23.42 ft/min; **(b)** 0.04 min/ft

19. 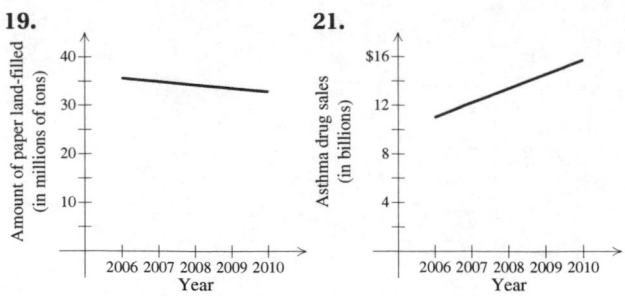 **21.**

23.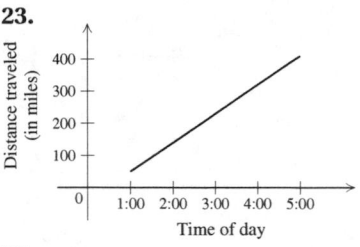

25.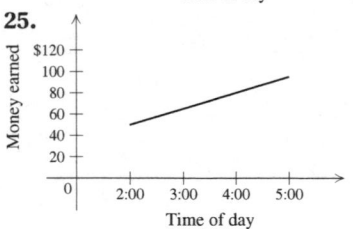

27.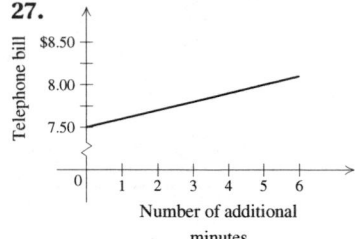

29. 20 calls/hr   **31.** 75 mi/hr   **33.** 12¢/min
35. -2000 people/yr   **37.** 0.02 gal/mi   **39.** (e)   **41.** (d)
43. (b)   **45.** ☜   **47.** 5   **48.** -6 **49.** -1 **50.** $-\frac{4}{3}$
51. $-\frac{4}{3}$ **52.** 1   **53.** 0   **54.** Undefined   **55.** ☜
57. 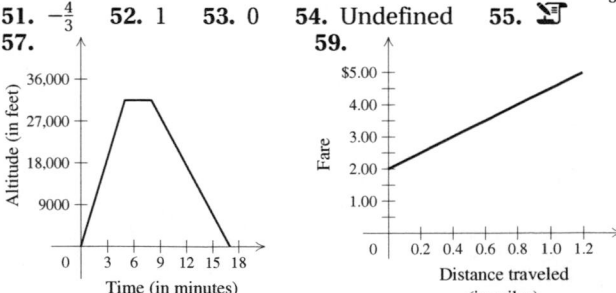   **59.**

61. 0.45 min/mi   **63.** About 41.6 min   **65.** 3.6 bu/hr

Exercise Set 3.5, pp. 190–196

1. Positive   **2.** Negative   **3.** Negative   **4.** Positive
5. Positive   **6.** Negative   **7.** Zero   **8.** Positive
9. Negative   **10.** Zero   **11.** \$60/blog   **13.** $-\$6$/month
15. 1 point/\$1000 income   **17.** About $-2.1°$/min   **19.** $\frac{4}{3}$
21. $\frac{3}{2}$ **23.** 2   **25.** -1 **27.** 0   **29.** $-\frac{1}{3}$

31. Undefined   **33.** $-\frac{3}{4}$ **35.** $\frac{1}{4}$ **37.** 0   **39.** $\frac{5}{4}$
41. $-\frac{4}{5}$ **43.** $\frac{2}{3}$ **45.** -1 **47.** $-\frac{1}{2}$ **49.** 0
51. 1   **53.** Undefined   **55.** 0   **57.** Undefined
59. Undefined   **61.** 0   **63.** 15%   **65.** 35%
67. $\frac{29}{98}$, or about 30%   **69.** About 5.1%; yes   **71.** ✍
73. $y = \dfrac{c - ax}{b}$ **74.** $r = \dfrac{p + mn}{x}$ **75.** $y = \dfrac{ax - c}{b}$
76. $t = \dfrac{q - rs}{n}$

77.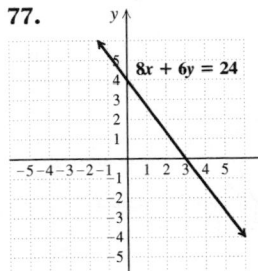

78.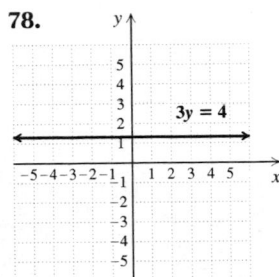

79. ✍   **81.** 0.364, or 36.4%   **83.** $\left\{m \mid m \geq \frac{5}{2}\right\}$ **85.** $\frac{1}{2}$

Technology Connection, p. 201

1.
$$y_1 = -\tfrac{3}{4}x - 2, \quad y_2 = -\tfrac{1}{5}x - 2,$$
$$y_3 = -\tfrac{3}{4}x - 5, \quad y_4 = -\tfrac{1}{5}x - 5$$

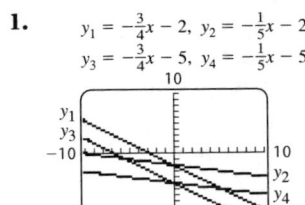

Exercise Set 3.6, pp. 203–205

1. (f)   **2.** (b)   **3.** (d)   **4.** (c)   **5.** (e)   **6.** (a)

7.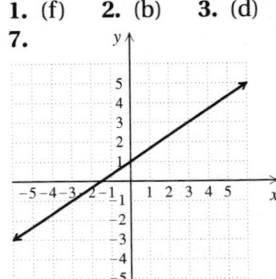

9.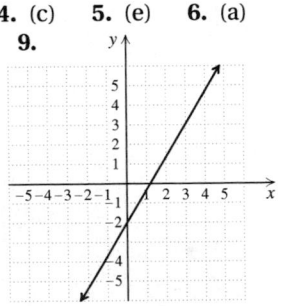

11.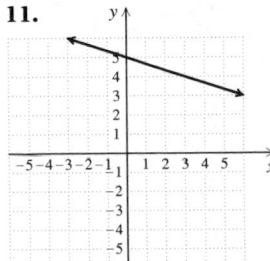

13.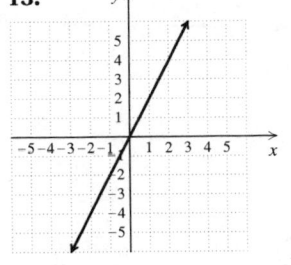

15.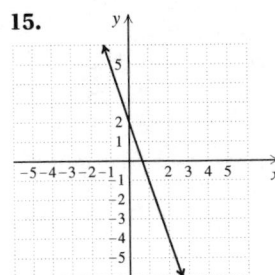

17.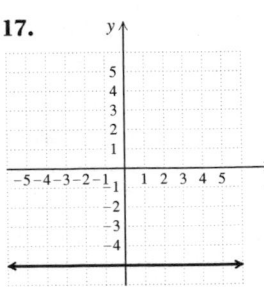

19. $-\frac{2}{7}; (0, 5)$ **21.** $\frac{1}{3}; (0, 7)$ **23.** $\frac{9}{5}; (0, -4)$ **25.** $3; (0, 7)$
27. $-2; (0, 4)$ **29.** $0; (0, 3)$ **31.** $\frac{2}{5}, \left(0, \frac{8}{5}\right)$ **33.** $\frac{9}{8}; (0, 0)$
35. $y = 5x + 7$ **37.** $y = \frac{7}{8}x - 1$ **39.** $y = -\frac{5}{3}x - 8$
41. $y = \frac{1}{3}$ **43.** $y = \frac{3}{2}x + 17$, where y is the number
of gallons per person and x is the number of years since
2000   **45.** $y = \frac{2}{5}x + 15$, where y is the number of jobs, in
millions, and x is the number of years since 2000

47.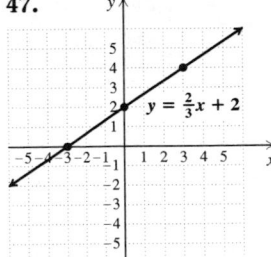

49.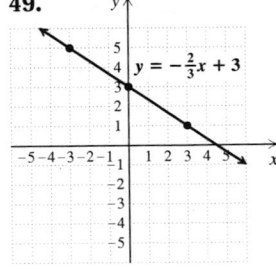

51.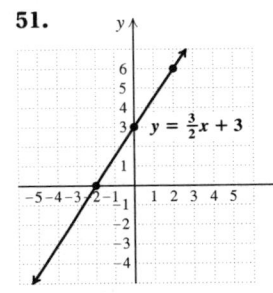

53.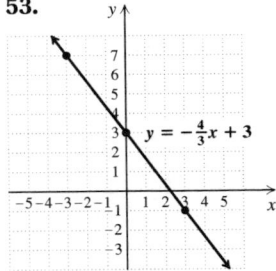

55.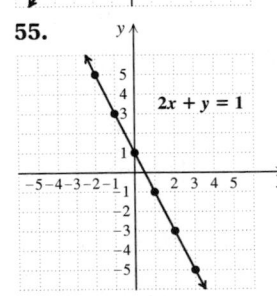

57.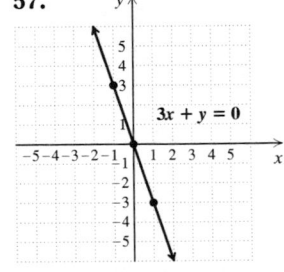

59.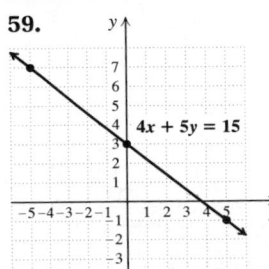

61.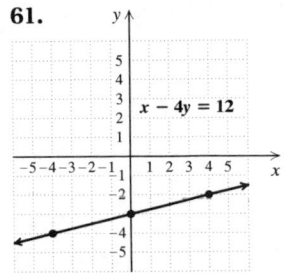

63. Yes   **65.** No   **67.** Yes   **69.** Yes   **71.** No   **73.** Yes

75. $y = 5x + 11$ **77.** $y = \frac{1}{2}x$ **79.** $y = x + 3$
81. $y = x - 4$ **83.** ✍   **85.** $y = m(x - h) + k$
86. $y = -2(x + 4) + 9$ **87.** -7 **88.** 13   **89.** -9
90. -11 **91.** ✍   **93.** When $x = 0, y = b$, so $(0, b)$ is
on the line. When $x = 1, y = m + b$, so $(1, m + b)$ is on the
line. Then

$$\text{slope} = \frac{(m + b) - b}{1 - 0} = m.$$

95. $y = \frac{1}{3}x + 3$ **97.** $y = -\frac{5}{3}x + 3$ **99.** $y = -\frac{2}{3}x$

Connecting the Concepts, p. 206

1. (a) Yes;
(b)

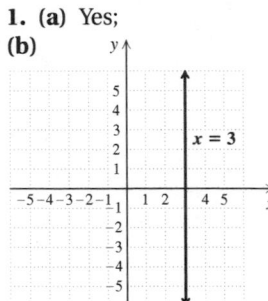

2. (a) Yes;
(b)

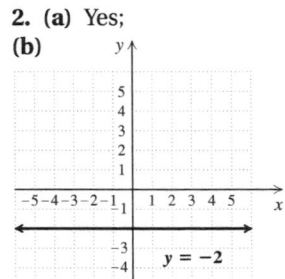

3. (a) Yes;
(b)

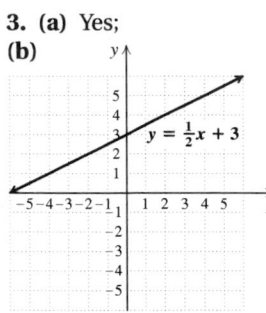

4. (a) Yes;
(b)

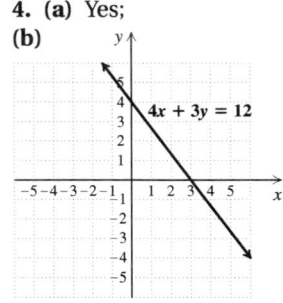

5. (a) Yes;
(b)

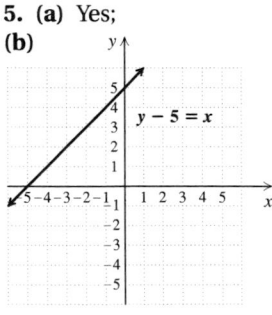

6. (a) Yes;
(b)

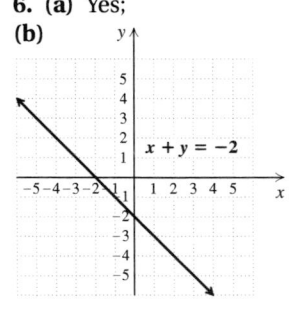

7. (a) No
8. (a) Yes;
(b)

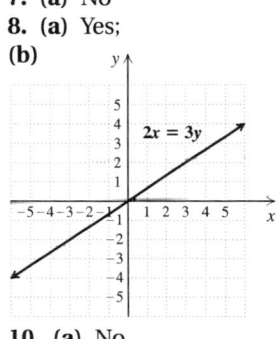

9. (a) Yes;
(b)

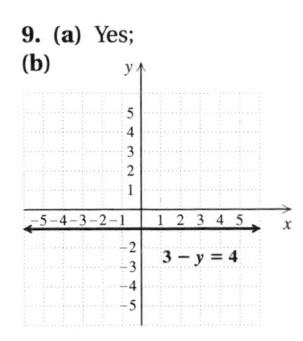

10. (a) No

11. (a) Yes;
(b)

12. (a) Yes;
(b)

13. (a) Yes;
(b)

14. (a) Yes;
(b)

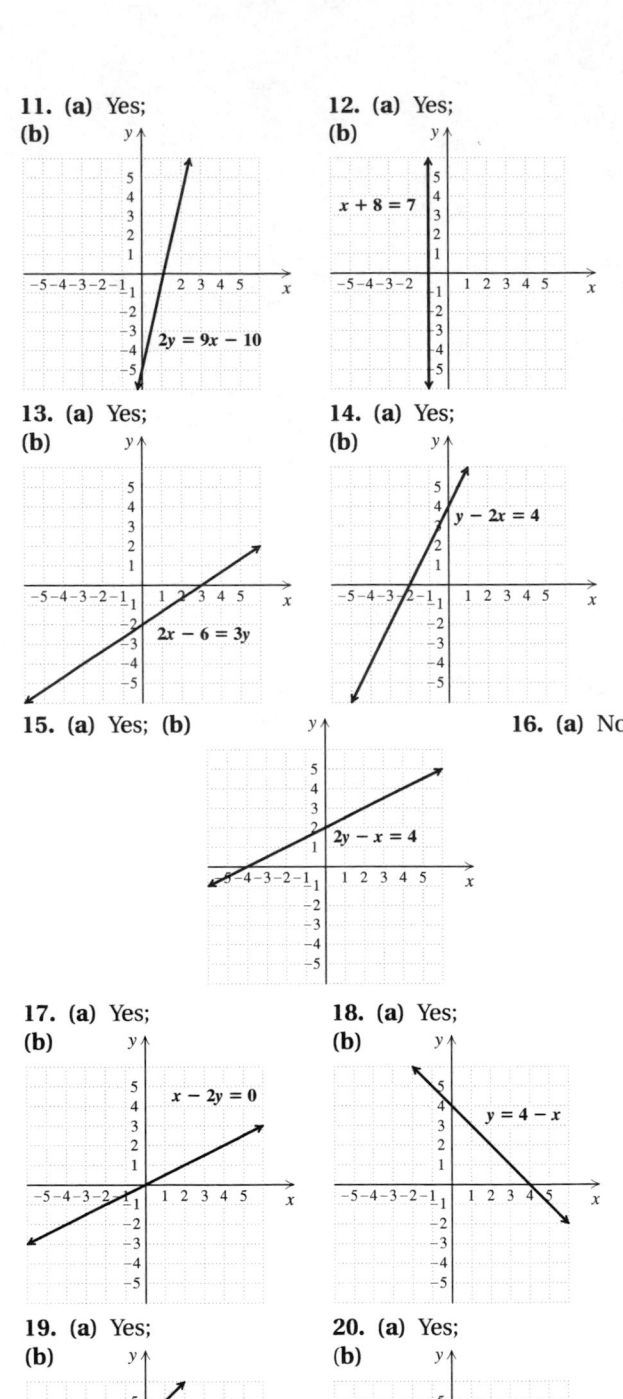

15. (a) Yes; **(b)**   **16. (a)** No

17. (a) Yes;
(b)

18. (a) Yes;
(b)

19. (a) Yes;
(b)

20. (a) Yes;
(b)

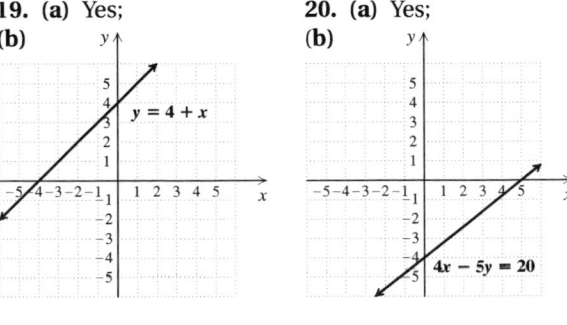

Technology Connection, p. 208

1. $y_1 = \frac{3}{4}x + 2;\ y_2 = -\frac{4}{3}x - 1$

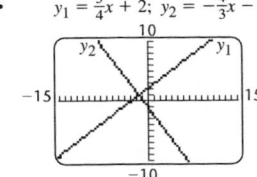

2. $y_1 = -\frac{2}{5}x - 4;\ y_2 = \frac{5}{2}x + 3$

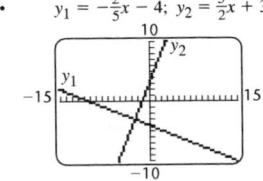

3. $y_1 = \frac{31}{40}x + 2;\ y_2 = -\frac{40}{30}x - 1$ No: $-\frac{40}{30} \neq -\frac{1}{\frac{31}{40}}$

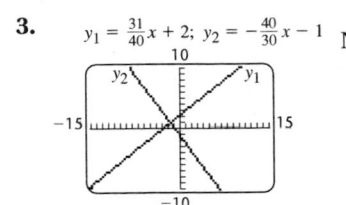

Although the lines appear to be perpendicular, they are not, because the product of their slopes is not -1:
$$\frac{31}{40}\left(-\frac{40}{30}\right) = -\frac{1240}{1200} \neq -1.$$

Visualizing for Success, p. 212

1. C **2.** G **3.** F **4.** B **5.** D **6.** A **7.** I
8. H **9.** J **10.** E

Exercise Set 3.7, pp. 213–216

1. (g) **2.** (b) **3.** (d) **4.** (h) **5.** (e) **6.** (a)
7. (f) **8.** (c) **9.** (c) **10.** (b) **11.** (d) **12.** (a)
13. $y - 6 = 3(x - 1)$ **15.** $y - 8 = \frac{3}{5}(x - 2)$
17. $y - 1 = -4(x - 3)$ **19.** $y - (-4) = \frac{3}{2}(x - 5)$
21. $y - 6 = -\frac{5}{4}(x - (-2))$
23. $y - (-1) = -2(x - (-4))$
25. $y - 8 = 1(x - (-2))$ **27.** $y = 4x - 7$
29. $y = \frac{7}{4}x - 9$ **31.** $y = -2x + 1$ **33.** $y = -4x - 9$
35. $y = \frac{2}{3}x + \frac{8}{3}$ **37.** $y = -\frac{5}{6}x + 4$ **39.** $y = \frac{1}{2}x + 4$
41. $y = 4x - 5$ **43.** $y = -\frac{2}{3}x - \frac{13}{3}$ **45.** $x = 5$
47. $y = -\frac{3}{2}x + \frac{11}{2}$ **49.** $y = x + 6$ **51.** $y = -\frac{1}{2}x + 6$
53. $x = -3$

55.
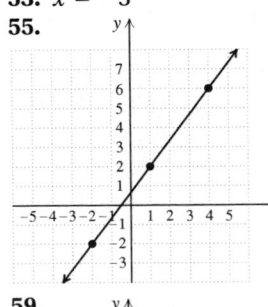

57.
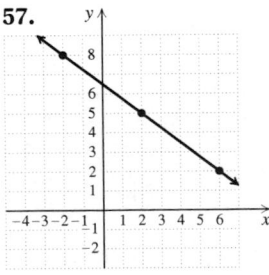

59.
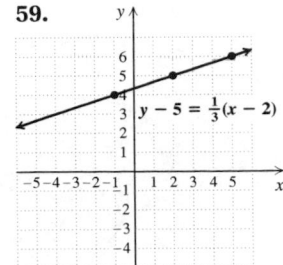

61.
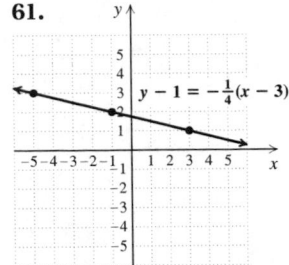

63.
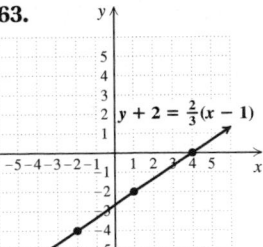

65.
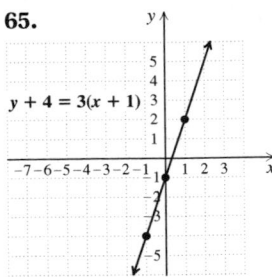

67.
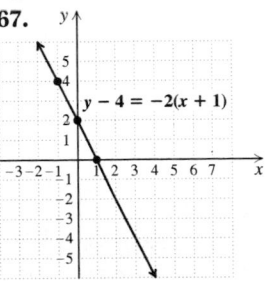

69.
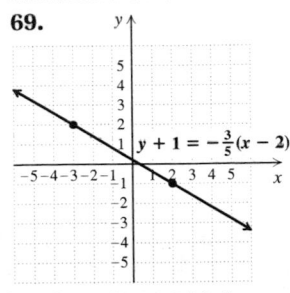

71. (a) 51.6 births per 1000 females; (b) 39.8 births per 1000 females **73.** (a) About 13.1%; (b) 4%
75. (a) 16.47 million students; (b) 18.95 million students
77. (a) 33.65 million residents; (b) about 38.6 million residents
79. $y = -x + 5$ **81.** $y = \frac{2}{3}x + 3$ **83.** $y = \frac{2}{5}x - 2$
85. $y = 2x + 7$ **87.** ✍ **89.** -125 **90.** 64 **91.** -64
92. 8 **93.** 28 **94.** -4 **95.** ✍
97.
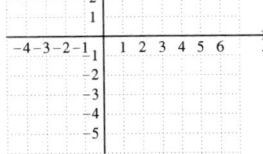

99. $y = 2x - 9$
101. $y = -\frac{4}{3}x + \frac{23}{3}$
103. $y = -4x + 7$
105. $y = \frac{10}{3}x + \frac{25}{3}$
107. $(2, 0), (0, 5)$

109. $-\frac{x}{4} + \frac{y}{3} = 1;\ (-4, 0), (0, 3)$ **111.** ✍

Connecting the Concepts, pp. 216–217

1. Slope–intercept form **2.** Standard form
3. None of these **4.** Standard form
5. Point–slope form **6.** None of these
7. $2x - 5y = 10$ **8.** $x - y = 2$
9. $-2x + y = 7$, or $2x - y = -7$ **10.** $\frac{1}{2}x + y = 3$
11. $3x - y = -23$, or $-3x + y = 23$ **12.** $x + 0y = 18$
13. $y = \frac{2}{7}x - \frac{8}{7}$ **14.** $y = -x - 8$ **15.** $y = 8x - 3$
16. $y = -\frac{3}{5}x + 3$ **17.** $y = -\frac{8}{9}x + \frac{5}{9}$ **18.** $y = -x$
19. $y = -\frac{1}{2}$ **20.** $y = \frac{1}{2}x$

Review Exercises: Chapter 3, pp. 220–222

1. True **2.** True **3.** False **4.** False **5.** True
6. True **7.** True **8.** False **9.** True **10.** True
11. About 1.3 billion searches **12.** About 1137 searches

13.–15.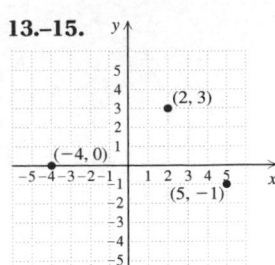

16. III   **17.** IV   **18.** II
19. $(-5,-1)$ **20.** $(-2,5)$
21. $(3,0)$

22.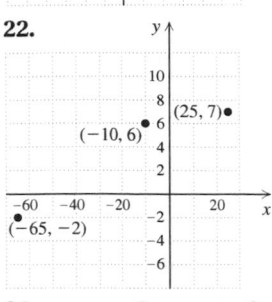

23. (a) No; (b) yes

24.

$$\begin{array}{c|c} 2x - y = 3 & \\ \hline 2 \cdot 0 - (-3) & 3 \\ 0 + 3 & \\ & 3 \overset{?}{=} 3 \quad \text{True} \end{array}$$

$$\begin{array}{c|c} 2x - y = 3 & \\ \hline 2 \cdot 2 - 1 & 3 \\ 4 - 1 & \\ & 3 \overset{?}{=} 3 \quad \text{True} \end{array}$$

$(-1,-5)$; answers may vary

25.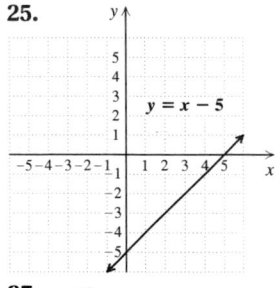

26.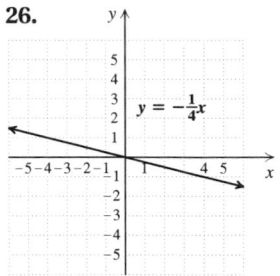

27.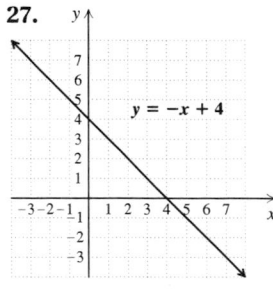

28.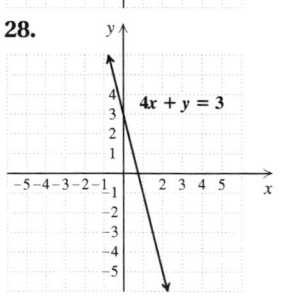

29.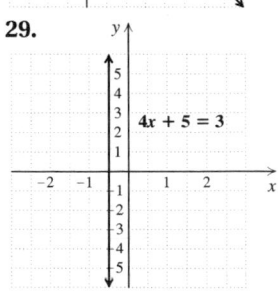

30.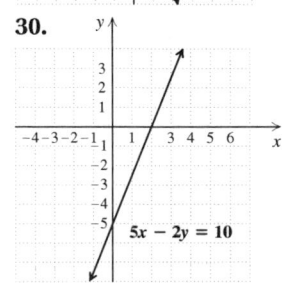

31. About 7 million viewers
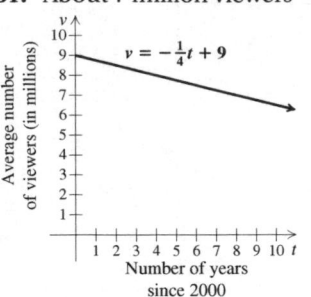

32. (a) $\frac{2}{15}$ mi/min;
(b) 7.5 min/mi
33. 12 mpg   **34.** 0
35. $\frac{7}{3}$ **36.** $-\frac{3}{7}$ **37.** $-\frac{6}{5}$
38. 0   **39.** Undefined
40. 2   **41.** $8.\overline{3}\%$
42. $(16,0),(0,-10)$
43. $-\frac{3}{5}; (0,9)$
44. Perpendicular
45. Parallel

46. $y = \frac{3}{8}x + 7$ **47.** $y - 9 = -\frac{1}{3}(x - (-2))$
48. (a) \$1725; (b) \$2701   **49.** $y = 5x - 25$
50. $y = -\frac{5}{3}x - \frac{5}{3}$

51.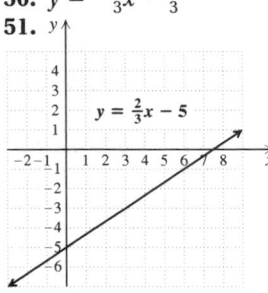

52.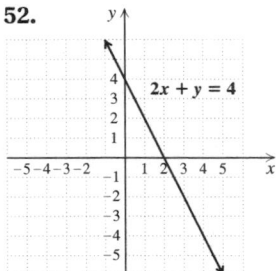

53.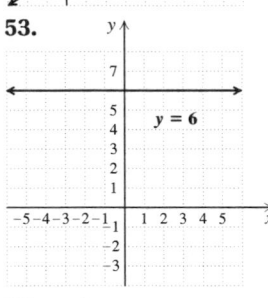

54.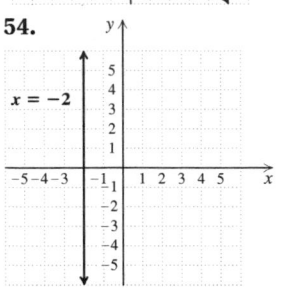

55.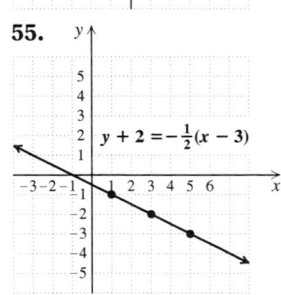

56. ✍ Two perpendicular lines share the same y-intercept if their point of intersection is on the y-axis.
57. ✍ The graph of a vertical line has only an x-intercept. The graph of a horizontal line has only a y-intercept. The graph of a nonvertical, non-horizontal line will have only one intercept if it passes through the origin: $(0,0)$ is both the x-intercept and the y-intercept.   **58.** -1
59. 19   **60.** Area: 45 sq units; perimeter: 28 units
61. $(0,4),(1,3),(-1,3)$; answers may vary

Test: Chapter 3, pp. 222–223

1. [3.1] About 95 students   **2.** [3.1] About 137 students
3. [3.1] III   **4.** [3.1] II   **5.** [3.1] $(3,4)$ **6.** [3.1] $(0,-4)$
7. [3.1] $(-5,2)$

8. [3.2]
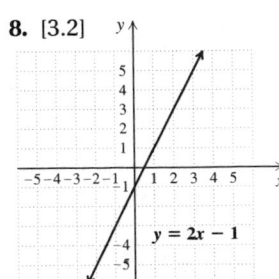
$y = 2x - 1$

9. [3.3]
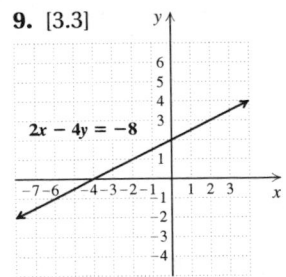
$2x - 4y = -8$

10. [3.3]
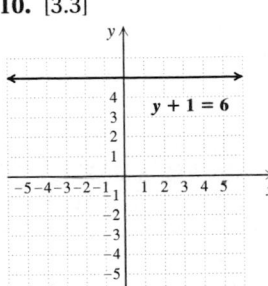
$y + 1 = 6$

11. [3.2]
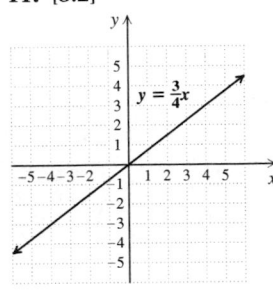
$y = \frac{3}{4}x$

12. [3.2]
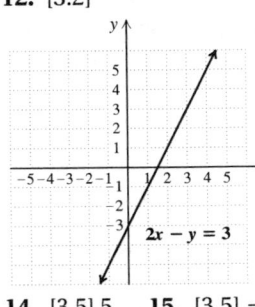
$2x - y = 3$

13. [3.3]
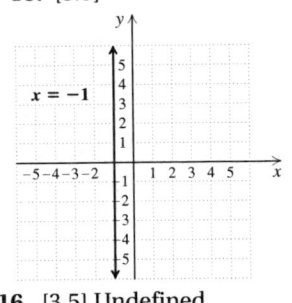
$x = -1$

14. [3.5] 5   **15.** [3.5] $-\frac{9}{4}$ **16.** [3.5] Undefined
17. [3.4] $\frac{1}{3}$ km/min   **18.** [3.5] 31.5%
19. [3.3] $(6, 0), (0, -30)$ **20.** [3.6] 8; $(0, 10)$
21. [3.6] $y = -\frac{1}{3}x - 11$ **22.** [3.6] Parallel
23. [3.6] Perpendicular   **24.** [3.7] $y = -\frac{5}{2}x - \frac{11}{2}$
25. [3.7] **(a)**   **(b)** 138 beats
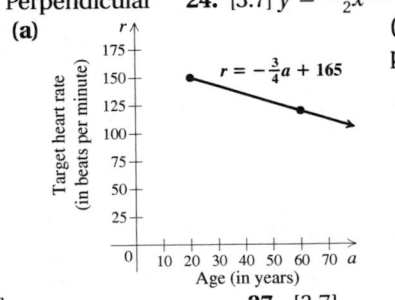
per minute
$r = -\frac{3}{4}a + 165$

26. [3.6]
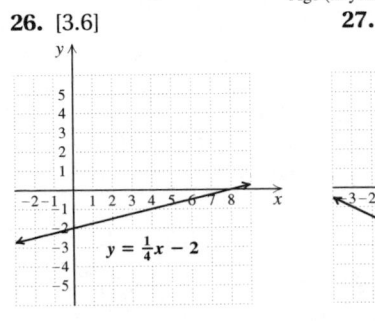
$y = \frac{1}{4}x - 2$

27. [3.7]
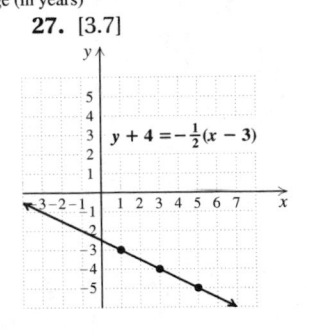
$y + 4 = -\frac{1}{2}(x - 3)$

28. [3.6] $y = \frac{2}{5}x + 9$ **29.** [3.1] Area: 25 sq units;
perimeter: 20 units   **30.** [3.2], [3.7] $(0, 12), (-3, 15), (5, 7)$

Cumulative Review: Chapters 1–3, pp. 224–225

1. 7   **2.** $12a - 6b + 18$ **3.** $4(2x - y + 1)$ **4.** $2 \cdot 3^3$
5. -0.15 **6.** 37   **7.** $\frac{1}{10}$ **8.** -10 **9.** 0.367   **10.** $\frac{11}{60}$
11. 2.6   **12.** 7.28   **13.** $-\frac{5}{12}$ **14.** -3 **15.** 27
16. $-2y - 7$ **17.** $5x + 11$ **18.** -2.6 **19.** -27
20. 16   **21.** -6 **22.** 2   **23.** $\frac{7}{9}$ **24.** -17 **25.** 2
26. $\{x \mid x < 16\}$, or $(-\infty, 16)$ **27.** $\left\{x \mid x \le -\frac{11}{8}\right\}$, or
$\left(-\infty, -\frac{11}{8}\right]$ **28.** $h = \dfrac{A - \pi r^2}{2\pi r}$ **29.** IV

30.
$-1 < x \le 2$
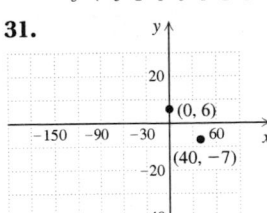

31.

$(0, 6)$
$(40, -7)$
$(-150, -40)$

32.
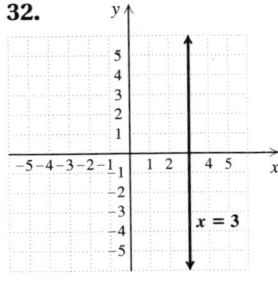
$x = 3$

33.
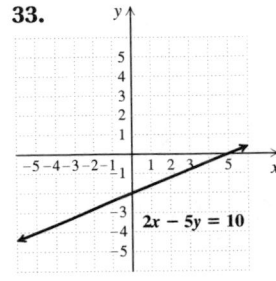
$2x - 5y = 10$

34.
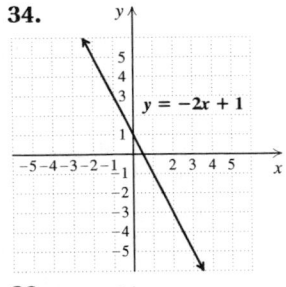
$y = -2x + 1$

35.
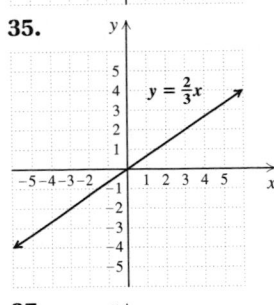
$y = \frac{2}{3}x$

36.
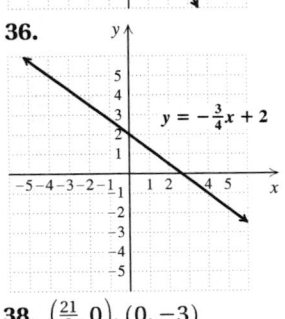
$y = -\frac{3}{4}x + 2$

37.
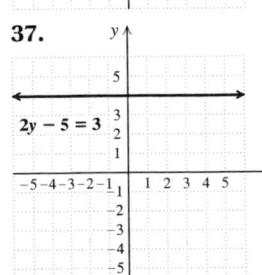
$2y - 5 = 3$

38. $\left(\frac{21}{2}, 0\right), (0, -3)$
39. $\left(-\frac{5}{4}, 0\right), (0, 5)$
40. 3; $(0, -2)$ **41.** $-\frac{1}{3}$
42. $y = \frac{2}{7}x - 4$
43. $y - 4 = -\frac{3}{8}(x - (-6))$
44. $y = -\frac{3}{8}x + \frac{7}{4}$
45. $y = 2x + 1$
46. 0.5 million bicycles per year

47. (a)

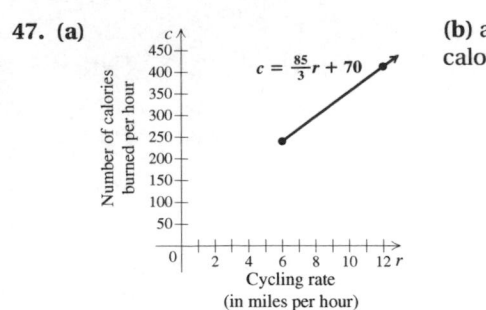

$c = \frac{85}{3}r + 70$

Number of calories burned per hour (vertical axis, 0 to 450 in increments of 50)
Cycling rate (in miles per hour) (horizontal axis, 2 to 12 r)

(b) about 353 calories per hour

48. \$210 billion   **49.** \$54,533   **50.** 21 million Americans
51. \$120   **52.** 50 m, 53 m, 40 m   **53.** 4 hr
54. \$25,000   **55.** $-4, 4$ **56.** 2   **57.** -5 **58.** 3
59. No solution   **60.** $Q = \dfrac{2 - pm}{p}$
61. $y = -\frac{7}{3}x + 7; y = -\frac{7}{3}x - 7; y = \frac{7}{3}x - 7; y = \frac{7}{3}x + 7$

CHAPTER 4

Exercise Set 4.1, pp. 234–235

1. (e)   **2.** (f)   **3.** (b)   **4.** (h)   **5.** (g)   **6.** (a)
7. (c)   **8.** (d)   **9.** Base: $2x$; exponent: 5
11. Base: x; exponent: 3   **13.** Base: $\dfrac{4}{y}$; exponent: 7
15. d^{13} **17.** a^7 **19.** 6^{15} **21.** $(3y)^{12}$ **23.** $(8n)^{10}$
25. a^5b^9 **27.** $(x + 3)^{13}$ **29.** r^{10} **31.** m^4n^9 **33.** 7^3
35. t^7 **37.** $5a$ **39.** 1   **41.** $(r + s)^8$ **43.** $\frac{4}{5}d^7$
45. $4a^7b^6$ **47.** $x^{12}y^7$ **49.** 1   **51.** 5   **53.** 2   **55.** -4
57. x^{33} **59.** 5^{32} **61.** t^{80} **63.** $100x^2$ **65.** $-8a^3$
67. $25n^{14}$ **69.** $a^{14}b^7$ **71.** $r^{17}t^{11}$ **73.** $24x^{19}$
75. $\dfrac{x^3}{125}$ **77.** $\dfrac{49}{36n^2}$ **79.** $\dfrac{a^{18}}{b^{48}}$ **81.** $\dfrac{x^8y^4}{z^{12}}$ **83.** $\dfrac{a^{12}}{16b^{20}}$
85. $-\dfrac{125x^{21}y^3}{8z^{12}}$ **87.** 1   **89.** ✍   **91.** -24 **92.** -15
93. -11 **94.** 16   **95.** -14 **96.** 4   **97.** ✍
99. ✍   **101.** Let $x = 1$; then $3x^2 = 3$, but $(3x)^2 = 9$.
103. Let $t = -1$; then $\dfrac{t^6}{t^2} = 1$, but $t^3 = -1$.   **105.** y^{6x}
107. x^t **109.** 13   **111.** $<$ **113.** $<$ **115.** $>$
117. 4,000,000; 4,194,304; 194,304   **119.** 2,000,000,000;
2,147,483,648; 147,483,648   **121.** 1,536,000 bytes, or
approximately 1,500,000 bytes

Technology Connection, p. 241

1. 1.71×10^{17} **2.** $5.\overline{370} \times 10^{-15}$ **3.** 3.68×10^{16}

Exercise Set 4.2, pp. 242–244

1. (c)   **2.** (d)   **3.** (a)   **4.** (b)   **5.** $\dfrac{1}{2^3} = \dfrac{1}{8}$
7. $\dfrac{1}{(-2)^6} = \dfrac{1}{64}$ **9.** $\dfrac{1}{t^9}$ **11.** $\dfrac{x}{y^2}$ **13.** $\dfrac{t}{r^5}$ **15.** a^8

17. $\dfrac{1}{7}$ **19.** $\left(\dfrac{5}{3}\right)^2 = \dfrac{25}{9}$ **21.** $\left(\dfrac{2}{x}\right)^5 = \dfrac{32}{x^5}$ **23.** $\left(\dfrac{t}{s}\right)^7 = \dfrac{t^7}{s^7}$
25. 9^{-2} **27.** y^{-3} **29.** 5^{-1} **31.** t^{-1} **33.** 2^3, or 8
35. $\dfrac{1}{x^{12}}$ **37.** $\dfrac{1}{t^2}$ **39.** $\dfrac{1}{n^{15}}$ **41.** t^{18} **43.** $\dfrac{1}{t^{12}}$
45. $\dfrac{1}{m^7n^7}$ **47.** $\dfrac{9}{x^8}$ **49.** $\dfrac{25t^6}{r^8}$ **51.** t^{14} **53.** $\dfrac{1}{y^4}$
55. $5y^3$ **57.** $2x^5$ **59.** $\dfrac{-3b^9}{2a^7}$ **61.** 1   **63.** $\dfrac{8y^7z}{x^3}$
65. $3s^2t^4u^4$ **67.** $\dfrac{1}{x^{12}y^{15}}$ **69.** $\dfrac{m^{10}n^6}{9}$ **71.** $\dfrac{b^5c^4}{a^8}$
73. $\dfrac{9}{a^8}$ **75.** $\dfrac{n^{12}}{m^3}$ **77.** $\dfrac{27b^{12}}{8a^6}$ **79.** 1   **81.** $\dfrac{2b^3}{a^4}$
83. $\dfrac{5y^4z^{10}}{4x^{11}}$ **85.** 4920   **87.** 0.00892   **89.** 904,000,000
91. 0.000003497   **93.** 3.6×10^7 **95.** 5.83×10^{-3}
97. 7.8×10^{10} **99.** 5.27×10^{-7} **101.** 1.032×10^{-6}
103. 6×10^{13} **105.** 2.47×10^8 **107.** 3.915×10^{-16}
109. 2.5×10^{13} **111.** 5.0×10^{-6} **113.** 3×10^{-21}
115. ✍   **117.** $8x$ **118.** $-3a - 6b$ **119.** $-2x - 7$
120. $-4t - r - 5$ **121.** 1004   **122.** 9   **123.** ✍
125. 8×10^5 **127.** 2^{-12} **129.** 5   **131.** 5^6
133. $\frac{1}{3} + \frac{1}{4} = \frac{7}{12}$ **135.** 9   **137.** $6.304347826 \times 10^{25}$
139. $1.19140625 \times 10^{-15}$ **141.** 3×10^8 mi
143. \$2.31 $\times 10^8$ **145.** 2.277×10^{10} min

Connecting the Concepts, p. 245

1. x^{14} **2.** $\dfrac{1}{x^{14}}$ **3.** $\dfrac{1}{x^{14}}$ **4.** x^{14} **5.** x^{40} **6.** x^{40}
7. c^8 **8.** $\dfrac{1}{c^8}$ **9.** $16x^{12}y^4$ **10.** $\dfrac{1}{16x^{12}y^4}$ **11.** 1
12. a^5 **13.** $\dfrac{a^{15}}{b^{20}}$ **14.** $\dfrac{b^{20}}{a^{15}}$ **15.** $\dfrac{5x^3}{2y^4}$ **16.** $\dfrac{6a^2}{7b^5}$
17. $\dfrac{7t^6}{xp^5}$ **18.** $\dfrac{16a^2}{9b^6}$ **19.** $18p^4q^{14}$ **20.** $\dfrac{9x^3}{2y^5}$

Technology Connection, pp. 249–250

1. 9.8

Exercise Set 4.3, pp. 250–254

1. (b)   **2.** (f)   **3.** (h)   **4.** (d)   **5.** (g)   **6.** (e)
7. (a)   **8.** (c)   **9.** $8x^3, -11x^2, 6x, 1$
11. $-t^6, -3t^3, 9t, -4$ **13.** Coefficients: 8, 2; degrees: 4, 1
15. Coefficients: 9, -3, 4; degrees: 2, 1, 0
17. Coefficients: 6, 9, 1; degrees: 5, 1, 3   **19.** Coefficients:
1, -1, 4, -3; degrees: 4, 3, 1, 0   **21. (a)** 1, 3, 4; **(b)** $8t^4$, 8;
(c) 4   **23. (a)** 2, 0, 4; **(b)** $2a^4$, 2; **(c)** 4
25. (a) 0, 2, 1, 5; **(b)** $-x^5$, -1; **(c)** 5

27.

Term	Coefficient	Degree of the Term	Degree of the Polynomial
$8x^5$	8	5	
$-\frac{1}{2}x^4$	$-\frac{1}{2}$	4	
$-4x^3$	-4	3	5
$7x^2$	7	2	
6	6	0	

29. Trinomial   **31.** Polynomial with no special name
33. Binomial   **35.** Monomial   **37.** $11n^2 + n$ **39.** $4a^4$
41. $7x^3 + x^2 - 6x$ **43.** $11b^3 + b^2 - b$ **45.** $-x^4 - x^3$
47. $\frac{1}{15}x^4 + 10$ **49.** $-1.1a^2 + 5.3a - 7.5$ **51.** $-3; 21$
53. $16; 34$ **55.** $-38; 148$ **57.** $159; 165$ **59.** $-39; 21$
61. \$1.93 billion   **63.** 1112 ft   **65.** 62.8 cm
67. 153.86 m^2 **69.** About 75 donations
71. About 9 words   **73.** About 6   **75.** About 16;
about 19   **77.**    **79.** $x - 3$ **80.** $-2x - 6$
81. $6a - 3$ **82.** $-t - 1$ **83.** $-t^4 + 17t$
84. $0.4a^2 - a + 11$ **85.**
87. $2x^5 + 4x^4 + 6x^3 + 8$; answers may vary   **89.** \$2510
91. $3x^6$ **93.** 3 and 8   **95.** 85.0
97.

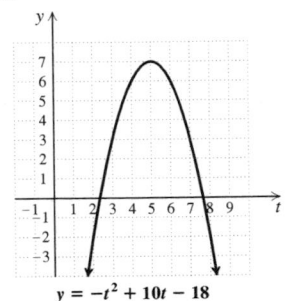

t	$-t^2 + 10t - 18$
3	3
4	6
5	7
6	6
7	3

$y = -t^2 + 10t - 18$

Technology Connection, p. 258

1. In each case, let $y_1 =$ the expression before the addition
or subtraction has been performed, $y_2 =$ the simplified
sum or difference, and $y_3 = y_2 - y_1$; and note that the
graph of y_3 coincides with the x-axis. That is, $y_3 = 0$.

Exercise Set 4.4, pp. 259–261

1. x^2 **2.** -6 **3.** $-$ **4.** $+$ **5.** $4x + 9$ **7.** $-6t + 8$
9. $-3x^2 + 6x - 2$ **11.** $9t^2 + t + 3$
13. $8m^3 - 3m - 7$ **15.** $7 + 13a - a^2 + 7a^3$
17. $2x^6 + 9x^4 + 2x^3 - 4x^2 + 5x$
19. $x^4 + \frac{1}{4}x^3 - \frac{3}{4}x^2 - \frac{5}{6}x + 3$
21. $4.2t^3 + 3.5t^2 - 6.4t - 1.8$ **23.** $-4x^3 + 4x^2 + 6x$
25. $1.3x^4 + 0.35x^3 + 9.53x^2 + 2x + 0.96$
27. $-(-3t^3 + 4t^2 - 7); 3t^3 - 4t^2 + 7$
29. $-(x^4 - 8x^3 + 6x); -x^4 + 8x^3 - 6x$
31. $-9x + 10$ **33.** $-3a^4 + 5a^2 - 1.2$

35. $4x^4 - 6x^2 - \frac{3}{4}x + 8$ **37.** $-2x - 7$
39. $-t^2 - 12t + 13$ **41.** $8a^3 + 8a^2 + a - 10$
43. $4.6x^3 + 9.2x^2 - 3.8x - 23$ **45.** 0
47. $1 + a + 12a^2 - 3a^3$ **49.** $\frac{9}{8}x^3 - \frac{1}{2}x$
51. $0.05t^3 - 0.07t^2 + 0.01t + 1$ **53.** $2x^2 + 6$
55. $-3x^4 - 8x^3 - 7x^2$ **57.** (a) $5x^2 + 4x$; (b) 145; 273
59. $16y + 26$ **61.** $(r + 11)(r + 9); 9r + 99 + 11r + r^2$
63. $(x + 3)^2; x^2 + 3x + 9 + 3x$ **65.** $m^2 - 40$
67. $\pi r^2 - 49$ **69.** $(x^2 - 12)$ ft^2 **71.** $(z^2 - 36\pi)$ ft^2
73. $\left(144 - \dfrac{d^2}{4}\pi\right)$ m^2 **75.**    **77.** $2x^2 - 2x + 6$
78. $-15x^2 + 10x + 35$ **79.** x^8 **80.** y^7 **81.** $2n^3$
82. $-6n^{12}$ **83.**    **85.** $9t^2 - 20t + 11$
87. $-6x + 14$ **89.** $250.591x^3 + 2.812x$ **91.** $20w + 42$
93. $2x^2 + 20x$ **95.** $8x + 24$ **97.**

Technology Connection, p. 266

1. Let $y_1 = (5x^4 - 2x^2 + 3x)(x^2 + 2x)$ and
$y_2 = 5x^6 + 10x^5 - 2x^4 - x^3 + 6x^2$. With the table set in
AUTO mode, note that the values in the Y_1- and Y_2-columns
match, regardless of how far we scroll up or down.
2. Use TRACE, a table, or a boldly drawn graph to confirm
that y_3 is always 0.

Exercise Set 4.5, pp. 267–269

1. (c)   **2.** (d)   **3.** (d)   **4.** (a)   **5.** (c)   **6.** (b)
7. $21x^5$ **9.** $-x^7$ **11.** x^8 **13.** $36t^4$ **15.** $-0.12x^9$
17. $-\frac{1}{20}x^{12}$ **19.** $5n^3$ **21.** $-44x^{10}$ **23.** $72y^{10}$
25. $20x^2 + 5x$ **27.** $3a^2 - 27a$ **29.** $x^5 + x^2$
31. $-6n^3 + 24n^2 - 3n$ **33.** $-15t^3 - 30t^2$
35. $4a^9 - 8a^7 - \frac{5}{2}a^4$ **37.** $x^2 + 7x + 12$
39. $t^2 + 4t - 21$ **41.** $a^2 - 1.3a + 0.42$ **43.** $x^2 - 9$
45. $28 - 15x + 2x^2$ **47.** $t^2 + \frac{17}{6}t + 2$
49. $\frac{3}{16}a^2 + \frac{5}{4}a - 2$
51.

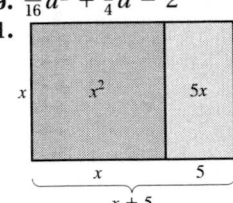

53.

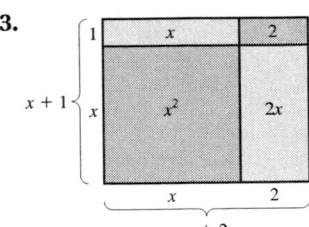

57. $x^3 + 2x + 3$

55.

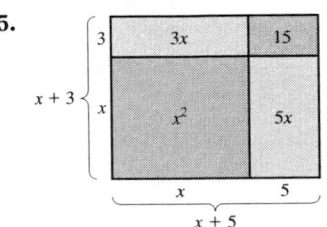

59. $2a^3 - a^2 - 11a + 10$
61. $3y^6 - 21y^4 + y^3 + 2y^2 - 7y - 14$
63. $33x^2 + 25x + 2$ **65.** $x^4 + 4x^3 - 3x^2 + 16x - 3$
67. $10t^4 + 3t^3 - 20t^2 + \frac{9}{2}t - 2$
69. $x^4 + 8x^3 + 12x^2 + 9x + 4$ **71.**    **73.** 0   **74.** 0
75. 8   **76.** 7   **77.** 32   **78.** 50   **79.**

81. $75y^2 - 45y$ **83.** 5 **85.** $V = (4x^3 - 48x^2 + 144x)$ in³; $S = (-4x^2 + 144)$ in² **87.** $(x^3 - 5x^2 + 8x - 4)$ cm³ **89.** 16 ft by 8 ft **91.** 0 **93.** $x^3 + x^2 - 22x - 40$ **95.** 0

Visualizing for Success, p. 275

1. E, F **2.** B, O **3.** S, K **4.** R, G **5.** D, M **6.** J, P **7.** C, L **8.** N, Q **9.** A, H **10.** I, T

Exercise Set 4.6, pp. 276–278

1. True **2.** False **3.** False **4.** True **5.** $x^3 + 3x^2 + 2x + 6$ **7.** $t^5 + 7t^4 - 2t - 14$ **9.** $y^2 - y - 6$ **11.** $9x^2 + 21x + 10$ **13.** $5x^2 + 17x - 12$ **15.** $15 - 13t + 2t^2$ **17.** $x^4 - 4x^2 - 21$ **19.** $p^2 - \frac{1}{16}$ **21.** $x^2 - 0.6x + 0.09$ **23.** $-3n^2 - 19n + 14$ **25.** $x^2 + 20x + 100$ **27.** $1 - 3t + 5t^2 - 15t^3$ **29.** $x^5 + 3x^3 - x^2 - 3$ **31.** $3x^6 - 2x^4 - 6x^2 + 4$ **33.** $4t^6 + 20t^3 + 25$ **35.** $8x^5 + 16x^3 + 5x^2 + 10$ **37.** $100x^4 - 9$ **39.** $x^2 - 64$ **41.** $4x^2 - 1$ **43.** $25m^4 - 16$ **45.** $81a^6 - 1$ **47.** $x^8 - 0.01$ **49.** $t^2 - \frac{9}{16}$ **51.** $x^2 + 6x + 9$ **53.** $49x^6 - 14x^3 + 1$ **55.** $a^2 - \frac{4}{5}a + \frac{4}{25}$ **57.** $t^8 + 6t^4 + 9$ **59.** $4 - 12x^4 + 9x^8$ **61.** $25 + 60t^2 + 36t^4$ **63.** $49x^2 - 4.2x + 0.09$ **65.** $14n^5 - 7n^3$ **67.** $a^3 - a^2 - 10a + 12$ **69.** $49 - 42x^4 + 9x^8$ **71.** $5x^3 + 30x^2 - 10x$ **73.** $q^{10} - 1$ **75.** $15t^5 - 3t^4 + 3t^3$ **77.** $36x^8 - 36x^5 + 9x^2$ **79.** $18a^4 + 0.8a^3 + 4.5a + 0.2$ **81.** $\frac{1}{25} - 36x^8$ **83.** $a^3 + 1$ **85.** $x^2 + 6x + 9$ **87.** $t^2 + 7t + 12$ **89.** $a^2 + 10a + 25$ **91.** $x^2 + 10x + 21$ **93.** $a^2 + 8a + 7$ **95.** $25t^2 + 20t + 4$
97. 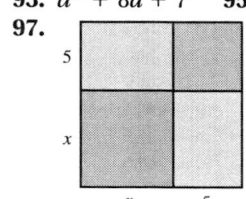 **99.**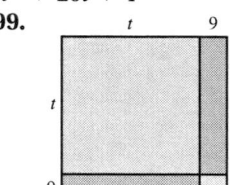
101. 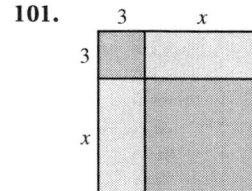 **103.** 🖘

105. Washing machine: 9 kWh/mo; refrigerator: 189 kWh/mo; freezer: 99 kWh/mo **106.** About $5.8 billion **107.** $y = \dfrac{8}{5x}$ **108.** $a = \dfrac{c}{3b}$ **109.** $x = \dfrac{by + c}{a}$ **110.** $y = \dfrac{ax - c}{b}$ **111.** 🖘 **113.** $16x^4 - 81$ **115.** $81t^4 - 72t^2 + 16$ **117.** $t^{24} - 4t^{18} + 6t^{12} - 4t^6 + 1$ **119.** 396 **121.** -7 **123.** $17F + 7(F - 17), F^2 - (F - 17)(F - 7)$; other equivalent expressions are possible. **125.** $(y + 1)(y - 1)$, $y(y + 1) - y - 1$; other equivalent expressions are possible. **127.** $y^2 - 4y + 4$ **129.** ◩

Connecting the Concepts, p. 279

1. Addition; $3x^2 + 3x + 3$ **2.** Subtraction; $6x + 13$ **3.** Multiplication; $48x^5 - 42x^3$ **4.** Multiplication; $6x^2 + x - 2$ **5.** Subtraction; $9x^3 - 5x^2 - 7x + 13$ **6.** Multiplication; $2x^3 + 3x^2 - 5x - 3$ **7.** Multiplication; $81x^2 - 1$ **8.** Addition; $9x^4 + 2x^3 - 5x$ **9.** $-6x^2 + 2x - 12$ **10.** $9x^2 + 45x + 56$ **11.** $40x^9 - 48x^8 + 16x^5$ **12.** $t^9 + 5t^7$ **13.** $4m^2 - 4m + 1$ **14.** $x^3 - 1$ **15.** $5x^3 + 3$ **16.** $c^2 - 9$ **17.** $16y^6 + 56y^3 + 49$ **18.** $3a^4 - 13a^3 - 13a^2 - 4$ **19.** $16t^4 - 25$ **20.** $a^8 - 5a^4 - 24$

Technology Connection, p. 283

1. 36.22 **2.** 22,312

Exercise Set 4.7, pp. 284–287

1. (a) **2.** (b) **3.** (b) **4.** (a) **5.** (c) **6.** (c) **7.** (a) **8.** (a) **9.** -13 **11.** -68 **13.** 3.51 L **15.** 1889 calories **17.** 73.005 in² **19.** 66.4 m **21.** Coefficients: $3, -5, 2, -11$; degrees: $3, 2, 2, 0$; 3 **23.** Coefficients: $7, -1, 1, 9$; degrees: $0, 3, 3, 3$; 3 **25.** $2r - 6s$ **27.** $5xy^2 - 2x^2y + x + 3x^2$ **29.** $9u^2v - 11uv^2 + 11u^2$ **31.** $6a^2c - 7ab^2 + a^2b$ **33.** $11x^2 - 10xy - y^2$ **35.** $-6a^4 - 8ab + 7ab^2$ **37.** $-6r^2 - 5rt - t^2$ **39.** $3x^3 - x^2y + xy^2 - 3y^3$ **41.** $-2y^4x^3 - 3y^3x$ **43.** $-8x + 8y$ **45.** $12c^2 + 5cd - 2d^2$ **47.** $x^2y^2 + 4xy - 5$ **49.** $4a^2 - b^2$ **51.** $20r^2t^2 - 23rt + 6$ **53.** $m^6n^2 + 2m^3n - 48$ **55.** $30x^2 - 28xy + 6y^2$ **57.** $0.01 - p^2q^2$ **59.** $x^2 + 2xh + h^2$ **61.** $16a^2 - 40ab + 25b^2$ **63.** $a^2b^2 - c^2d^4$ **65.** $x^3y^2 + x^2y^3 + 2x^2y^2 + 2xy^3 + 3xy + 3y^2$ **67.** $a^2 + 2ab + b^2 - c^2$ **69.** $a^2 - b^2 - 2bc - c^2$ **71.** $x^2 + 2xy + y^2$ **73.** $\frac{1}{2}a^2b^2 - 2$ **75.** $a^2 + c^2 + ab + 2ac + ad + bc + bd + cd$ **77.** $m^2 - n^2$ **79.** We draw a rectangle with dimensions $r + s$ by $u + v$. **81.**

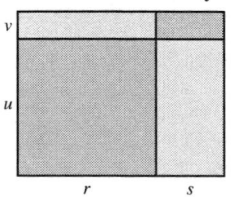 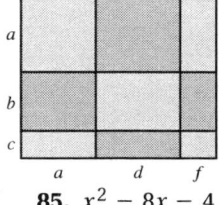

83. 🖘 **85.** $x^2 - 8x - 4$ **86.** $2x^3 - x^2 - x + 4$ **87.** $-2x + 5$ **88.** $5x^2 + x$ **89.** $13x^2 + 1$ **90.** $-x - 3$ **91.** 🖘 **93.** $4xy - 4y^2$ **95.** $2\pi ab - \pi b^2$ **97.** $x^3 + 2y^3 + x^2y + xy^2$ **99.** $2x^2 - 2\pi r^2 + 4xh + 2\pi rh$ **101.** 🖘 **103.** 40 **105.** $P + 2Pr + Pr^2$ **107.** $15,638.03

Exercise Set 4.8, pp. 292–293

1. $8x^6 - 5x^3$ **3.** $1 - 2u + u^6$ **5.** $6t^2 - 8t + 2$ **7.** $7x^3 - 6x + \frac{3}{2}$ **9.** $-4t^2 - 2t + 1$ **11.** $4x - 5 + \dfrac{1}{2x}$

13. $x + 2x^3y + 3$ **15.** $-3rs - r + 2s$ **17.** $x - 6$
19. $t - 5 + \dfrac{-45}{t - 5}$ **21.** $2x - 1 + \dfrac{1}{x + 6}$
23. $t^2 - 3t + 9$ **25.** $a + 5 + \dfrac{4}{a - 5}$
27. $x - 3 - \dfrac{3}{5x - 1}$ **29.** $3a + 1 + \dfrac{3}{2a + 5}$
31. $t^2 - 3t + 1$ **33.** $x^2 + 1$ **35.** $t^2 - 1 + \dfrac{3t - 1}{t^2 + 5}$
37. $3x^2 - 3 + \dfrac{x - 1}{2x^2 + 1}$ **39.** 📝

41.
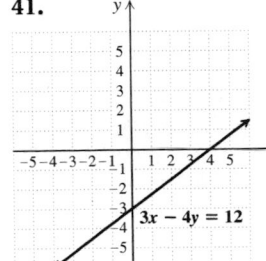
42.
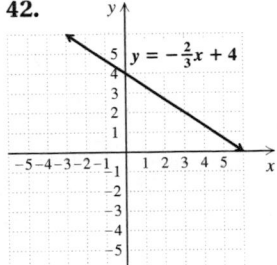

43.
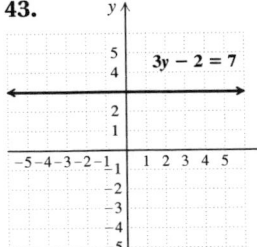
44.
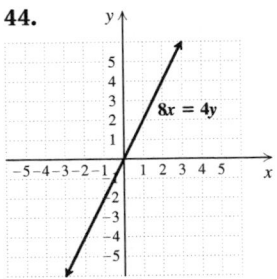

45. $-\dfrac{3}{10}$ **46.** Slope: 4; y-intercept: $\left(0, \dfrac{7}{2}\right)$
47. $y = -5x - 10$ **48.** $y = \dfrac{5}{4}x - \dfrac{9}{2}$ **49.** 📝
51. $5x^{6k} - 16x^{3k} + 14$ **53.** $3t^{2h} + 2t^h - 5$
55. $a + 3 + \dfrac{5}{5a^2 - 7a - 2}$ **57.** $2x^2 + x - 3$
59. 3   **61.** -1

Review Exercises: Chapter 4, pp. 297–298

1. True   **2.** True   **3.** True   **4.** False   **5.** False
6. False   **7.** True   **8.** True   **9.** n^{12} **10.** $(7x)^{10}$
11. t^6 **12.** 4^3, or 64   **13.** 1   **14.** $-9c^4d^2$
15. $-8x^3y^6$ **16.** $18x^5$ **17.** a^7b^6 **18.** $\dfrac{4t^{10}}{9s^8}$
19. $\dfrac{1}{8^6}$ **20.** a^{-9} **21.** $\dfrac{1}{4^2}$, or $\dfrac{1}{16}$ **22.** $\dfrac{2b^9}{a^{13}}$ **23.** $\dfrac{1}{w^{15}}$
24. $\dfrac{x^6}{4y^2}$ **25.** $\dfrac{y^3}{8x^3}$ **26.** 470,000,000   **27.** 1.09×10^{-5}
28. 2.09×10^4 **29.** 5.12×10^{-5}
30. $8x^2, -x, \dfrac{2}{3}$ **31.** $-4y^5, 7y^2, -3y, -2$ **32.** $9, -1, 7$
33. $7, -\dfrac{5}{6}, -4, 10$ **34. (a)** $2, 0, 5$; **(b)** $15t^5, 15$; **(c)** 5
35. (a) $5, 0, 2, 1$; **(b)** $-2x^5, -2$; **(c)** 5   **36.** Trinomial
37. Polynomial with no special name   **38.** Monomial
39. $-x^2 + 7x$ **40.** $-\dfrac{1}{4}x^3 + 4x^2 + 7$ **41.** $t - 1$
42. $14a^5 - 2a^2 - a - \dfrac{2}{3}$ **43.** -24 **44.** 16
45. $x^5 + 8x^4 + 6x^3 - 2x - 9$ **46.** $6a^5 - a^3 - 12a^2$
47. $-3y^2 + 8y + 3$ **48.** $x^5 - 3x^3 - 2x^2 + 8$

49. $\dfrac{3}{4}x^4 + \dfrac{1}{4}x^3 - \dfrac{1}{3}x^2 - \dfrac{7}{4}x + \dfrac{3}{8}$
50. $-x^5 + x^4 - 5x^3 - 2x^2 + 2x$ **51. (a)** $4w + 6$;
(b) $w^2 + 3w$ **52.** $-30x^5$ **53.** $49x^2 + 14x + 1$
54. $a^2 - 3a - 28$ **55.** $d^2 - 64$
56. $12x^3 - 23x^2 + 13x - 2$ **57.** $x^2 - 16x + 64$
58. $15t^5 - 6t^4 + 12t^3$ **59.** $4a^2 - 81$
60. $x^2 - 1.3x + 0.4$
61. $x^7 + x^5 - 3x^4 + 3x^3 - 2x^2 + 5x - 3$
62. $16y^6 - 40y^3 + 25$ **63.** $2t^4 - 11t^2 - 21$
64. $a^2 + \dfrac{1}{6}a - \dfrac{1}{3}$ **65.** $-49 + 4n^2$ **66.** 49
67. Coefficients: $1, -7, 9, -8$; degrees: $6, 2, 2, 0$; 6
68. Coefficients: $1, -1, 1$; degrees: $13, 22, 15$; 22
69. $-4u + 4v - 7$ **70.** $6m^3 + 4m^2n - mn^2$
71. $2a^2 - 16ab$ **72.** $11x^3y^2 - 8x^2y - 6x^2 - 6x + 6$
73. $2x^2 - xy - 15y^2$ **74.** $25a^2b^2 - 10abcd^2 + c^2d^4$
75. $\dfrac{1}{2}x^2 - \dfrac{1}{2}y^2$ **76.** $y^4 - \dfrac{1}{3}y + 4$
77. $3x^2 - 7x + 4 + \dfrac{1}{2x + 3}$ **78.** $t^3 + 2t - 3$
79. 📝 In the expression $5x^3$, the exponent refers only to the x. In the expression $(5x)^3$, the entire expression $5x$ is the base.   **80.** 📝 It is possible to determine two possibilities for the binomial that was squared by using the equation $(A - B)^2 = A^2 - 2AB + B^2$ in reverse. Since, in $x^2 - 6x + 9$, $A^2 = x^2$ and $B^2 = 9$, or 3^2, the binomial that was squared was $A - B$, or $x - 3$. If the polynomial is written $9 - 6x + x^2$, then $A^2 = 9$ and $B^2 = x^2$, so the binomial that was squared was $3 - x$. We cannot determine without further information whether the binomial squared was $x - 3$ or $3 - x$.   **81. (a)** 9; **(b)** 28   **82.** $64x^{16}$
83. $8x^4 + 4x^3 + 5x - 2$ **84.** $-16x^6 + x^2 - 10x + 25$
85. $\dfrac{94}{13}$ **86.** 2.28×10^{11} platelets

Test: Chapter 4, p. 299

1. [4.1] x^{13} **2.** [4.1] 3   **3.** [4.1] 1   **4.** [4.1] t^{45}
5. [4.1] $-40x^{19}y^4$ **6.** [4.1] $\dfrac{6}{5}a^5b^3$ **7.** [4.2] $\dfrac{1}{y^7}$
8. [4.2] 5^{-6} **9.** [4.2] $\dfrac{1}{t^9}$ **10.** [4.2] $\dfrac{3y^5}{x^5}$ **11.** [4.2] $\dfrac{b^4}{16a^{12}}$
12. [4.2] $\dfrac{c^3}{a^3b^3}$ **13.** [4.2] 3.06×10^9 **14.** [4.2] 0.00000005
15. [4.2] 1.75×10^{17} **16.** [4.2] 1.296×10^{22}
17. [4.3] Binomial   **18.** [4.3] $3, -1, \dfrac{1}{9}$ **19.** [4.3] Degrees of terms: $3, 1, 5, 0$; leading term: $7t^5$; leading coefficient: 7; degree of polynomial: 5   **20.** [4.3] -7 **21.** [4.3] $5a^2 - 6$
22. [4.3] $\dfrac{7}{4}y^2 - 4y$ **23.** [4.3] $4x^3 + 4x^2 + 3$
24. [4.4] $4x^5 + x^4 + 5x^3 - 8x^2 + 2x - 7$
25. [4.4] $5x^4 + 5x^2 + x + 5$
26. [4.4] $-2a^4 + 3a^3 - a - 7$
27. [4.4] $-t^4 + 2.5t^3 - 0.6t^2 - 9$
28. [4.5] $-6x^4 + 6x^3 + 10x^2$ **29.** [4.6] $x^2 - \dfrac{2}{3}x + \dfrac{1}{9}$
30. [4.6] $25t^2 - 49$ **31.** [4.6] $6b^2 + 7b - 5$
32. [4.6] $x^{14} - 4x^8 + 4x^6 - 16$
33. [4.6] $48 + 34y - 5y^2$ **34.** [4.5] $6x^3 - 7x^2 - 11x - 3$
35. [4.6] $64a^6 + 48a^3 + 9$ **36.** [4.7] 24
37. [4.7] $-4x^3y - x^2y^2 + xy^3 - y^3 + 19$
38. [4.7] $8a^2b^2 + 6ab + 6ab^2 + ab^3 - 4b^3$
39. [4.7] $9x^{10} - y^2$ **40.** [4.8] $4x^2 + 3x - 5$

41. [4.8] $2x^2 - 4x - 2 + \dfrac{17}{3x + 2}$ **42.** [4.5], [4.6]

$V = l(l - 2)(l - 1) = l^3 - 3l^2 + 2l$ **43.** [2.2], [4.6] $\frac{100}{21}$
44. [4.2] $\frac{1}{2} - \frac{1}{4} = \frac{1}{4}$ **45.** [4.2] About 1.4×10^7 hr

Cumulative Review: Chapters 1–4, pp. 300–301

1. 6   **2.** -8 **3.** $-\frac{7}{45}$ **4.** 6   **5.** $y + 10$ **6.** t^{12}
7. $-4x^5y^3$ **8.** $50a^4b^7$ **9.** $2(5a - 3b + 6)$ **10.** $\frac{11}{16}$
11. 6   **12.** $\frac{1}{4}t^3 - 5t^2 - 0.35$ **13.** II
14.
$$x > -1$$
$$\xleftarrow{\;\;} {\underset{-5\;-4\;-3\;-2\;-1\;\;0\;\;1\;\;2\;\;3\;\;4\;\;5}{\rule{0pt}{0pt}}}$$

15. 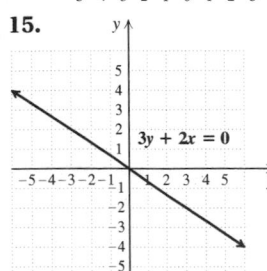   **16.**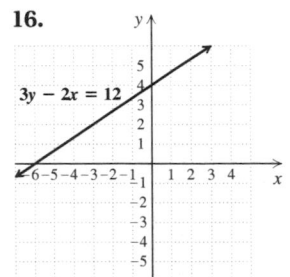

17. 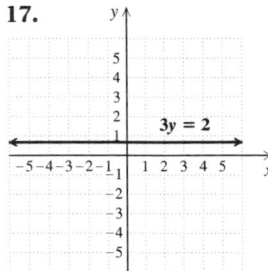   **18.**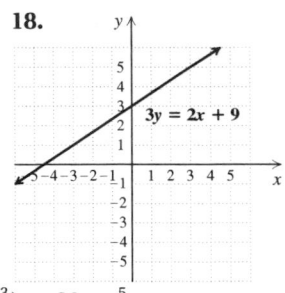

19. Slope: $\frac{1}{10}$; y-intercept: $\left(0, \frac{3}{8}\right)$ **20.** $-\frac{5}{8}$
21. $y = -\frac{2}{3}x - 10$ **22.** x-intercept: $(4, 0)$; y-intercept:
$\left(0, \frac{8}{5}\right)$ **23.** -4 **24.** $\frac{3}{5}$ **25.** $\frac{8}{3}$ **26.** 22   **27.** $\frac{5}{3}$
28. -7 **29.** $\{t \mid t \geq -8\}$, or $[-8, \infty)$ **30.** $\{x \mid x < \frac{1}{2}\}$, or
$\left(-\infty, \frac{1}{2}\right)$ **31.** $t = \dfrac{5pq}{2c}$ **32.** $7u^2v - 2uv^2 + uv + 3u^2$
33. $3x^3 - 3x^2 + 12x - 7$ **34.** $x^5 - 2x$
35. $20a - 30b + 70$ **36.** $-16x^5 - 48x^4 + 56x^3$
37. $6a^2 + 11a - 7$ **38.** $x^3 - x^2 - 7x + 10$
39. $16t^4 + 24t^2 + 9$ **40.** $\frac{1}{4}x^2 - 1$
41. $6r^4 - 5r^2s - 4s^2$ **42.** $x + \dfrac{3}{x - 1}$ **43.** $\dfrac{1}{7^{10}}$

44. $\dfrac{1}{x^7}$ **45.** $\dfrac{9}{16s^2t^{10}}$ **46.** $\dfrac{x^7y^2}{3}$ **47.** 48 thousand
megawatts   **48.** About 1298 megawatt hours
49. Washer: 20 kWh; dryer: 50 kWh
50. (a)
Kilowatt hours of electricity / Number of people in household; $w = 60n + 75$ **(b)** 375 kWh

51. No more than 6 hr   **52.** \$160 billion   **53.** About 3.6
54. $\$\frac{12}{7}$ billion per year   **55.** 0   **56.** No solution
57. $\frac{22}{9}$ **58.** $y = \frac{1}{2}x + 4$ **59.** $\frac{1}{7} + 1 = \frac{8}{7}$ **60.** $15x^{12}$

CHAPTER 5

Technology Connection, p. 310

1. Correct   **2.** Correct   **3.** Not correct
4. Not correct   **5.** Not correct   **6.** Correct
7. Not correct   **8.** Correct

Exercise Set 5.1, pp. 310–311

1. (h)   **2.** (f)   **3.** (b)   **4.** (e)   **5.** (c)   **6.** (g)
7. (d)   **8.** (a)   **9.** Answers may vary. $(14x)(x^2)$,
$(7x^2)(2x), (-2)(-7x^3)$ **11.** Answers may vary. $(-15)(a^4)$,
$(-5a)(3a^3), (-3a^2)(5a^2)$ **13.** Answers may vary.
$(5t^2)(5t^3), (25t)(t^4), (-5t)(-5t^4)$
15. $8(x + 3)$ **17.** $6(x - 5)$ **19.** $2(x^2 + x - 4)$
21. $t(3t + 1)$ **23.** $-5y(y + 2)$ **25.** $x^2(x + 6)$
27. $8a^2(2a^2 - 3)$ **29.** $-t^2(6t^4 - 9t^2 + 4)$
31. $6x^2(x^6 + 2x^4 - 4x^2 + 5)$
33. $x^2y^2(x^3y^3 + x^2y + xy - 1)$
35. $-5a^2b^2(7ab^2 - 2b + 3a)$ **37.** $(n - 6)(n + 3)$
39. $(x + 3)(x^2 - 7)$ **41.** $(2y - 9)(y^2 + 1)$
43. $(x + 2)(x^2 + 5)$ **45.** $(a + 3)(5a^2 + 2)$
47. $(3n - 2)(3n^2 + 1)$ **49.** $(t - 5)(4t^2 + 3)$
51. $(7x + 5)(x^2 - 3)$ **53.** $(6a + 7)(a^2 + 1)$
55. $(x + 6)(2x^2 - 5)$ **57.** Not factorable by grouping
59. $(y + 8)(y^2 - 2)$ **61.** $(x - 4)(2x^2 - 9)$ **63.** ✍
65. $x^2 + 9x + 14$ **66.** $x^2 - 9x + 14$ **67.** $x^2 - 5x - 14$
68. $x^2 + 5x - 14$ **69.** $a^2 - 4a + 3$ **70.** $t^2 + 8t + 15$
71. $t^2 + 5t - 50$ **72.** $a^2 - 2a - 24$ **73.** ✍
75. $(2x^3 + 3)(2x^2 + 3)$ **77.** $2x(x + 1)(x^2 - 2)$
79. $(x - 1)(5x^4 + x^2 + 3)$ **81.** Answers may vary.
$8x^4y^3 - 24x^2y^4 + 16x^3y^4$

Exercise Set 5.2, pp. 317–318

1. Positive; positive   **2.** Negative; negative
3. Negative; positive   **4.** Positive; positive
5. Positive   **6.** Negative   **7.** $(x + 4)(x + 4)$
9. $(x + 1)(x + 10)$ **11.** $(x + 3)(x + 7)$
13. $(t - 2)(t - 7)$ **15.** $(b - 4)(b - 1)$
17. $(a - 3)(a - 4)$ **19.** $(d - 2)(d - 5)$
21. $(x - 5)(x + 3)$ **23.** $(x + 5)(x - 3)$
25. $2(x + 2)(x - 9)$ **27.** $-x(x + 2)(x - 8)$
29. $(y - 5)(y + 9)$ **31.** $(x - 6)(x + 12)$
33. $-5(b - 3)(b + 10)$ **35.** $x^3(x - 2)(x + 1)$
37. Prime   **39.** $(t + 4)(t + 8)$ **41.** $(x + 9)(x + 11)$
43. $3x(x - 25)(x + 4)$ **45.** $-2(x - 24)(x + 3)$
47. $(y - 12)(y - 8)$ **49.** $-a^4(a - 6)(a + 15)$
51. $\left(t + \frac{1}{3}\right)^2$ **53.** Prime   **55.** $(p - 5q)(p - 2q)$
57. Prime   **59.** $(s - 6t)(s + 2t)$ **61.** $6a^8(a - 2)(a + 7)$
63. ✍   **65.** $6x^2 + 17x + 12$ **66.** $6x^2 + x - 12$
67. $6x^2 - x - 12$ **68.** $6x^2 - 17x + 12$

69. $5x^2 - 36x + 7$ **70.** $3x^2 + 13x - 30$
71. ☞ **73.** $-5, 5, -23, 23, -49, 49$
75. $(y + 0.2)(y - 0.4)$ **77.** $-\frac{1}{3}a(a - 3)(a + 2)$
79. $(x^m + 4)(x^m + 7)$ **81.** $(a + 1)(x + 2)(x + 1)$
83. $(x + 3)^3$, or $(x^3 + 9x^2 + 27x + 27)$ cubic meters
85. $x^2\left(\frac{3}{4}\pi + 2\right)$, or $\frac{1}{4}x^2(3\pi + 8)$ **87.** $x^2\left(9 - \frac{1}{2}\pi\right)$
89. $(x + 4)(x + 5)$

Exercise Set 5.3, pp. 327–328

1. (c) **2.** (a) **3.** (d) **4.** (b) **5.** $(2x - 1)(x + 4)$
7. $(3x + 1)(x - 6)$ **9.** $(2t + 1)(2t + 5)$
11. $(5a - 3)(3a - 1)$ **13.** $(3x + 4)(2x + 3)$
15. $2(3x + 1)(x - 2)$ **17.** $t(7t + 1)(t + 2)$
19. $(4x - 5)(3x - 2)$ **21.** $-1(7x + 4)(5x + 2)$, or
$-(7x + 4)(5x + 2)$ **23.** Prime **25.** $(5x + 4)^2$
27. $(20y - 1)(y + 3)$ **29.** $(7x + 5)(2x + 9)$
31. $-1(x - 3)(2x + 5)$, or $-(x - 3)(2x + 5)$
33. $-3(2x + 1)(x + 5)$ **35.** $2(a + 1)(5a - 9)$
37. $4(3x - 1)(x + 6)$ **39.** $(3x + 1)(x + 1)$
41. $(x + 3)(x - 2)$ **43.** $(4t - 3)(2t - 7)$
45. $(3x + 2)(2x + 5)$ **47.** $(y + 4)(2y - 1)$
49. $(3a - 4)(2a - 1)$ **51.** $(16t + 7)(t + 1)$
53. $-1(3x + 1)(3x + 5)$, or $-(3x + 1)(3x + 5)$
55. $10(x^2 + 3x - 7)$ **57.** $3x(3x - 1)(2x + 3)$
59. $(x + 1)(25x + 64)$ **61.** $3x(7x + 1)(8x + 1)$
63. $-t^2(2t - 3)(7t + 1)$ **65.** $2(2y + 9)(8y - 3)$
67. $(2a - b)(a - 2b)$ **69.** $2(s + t)(4s + 7t)$
71. $3(3x - 4y)^2$ **73.** $-2(3a - 2b)(4a - 3b)$
75. $x^2(2x + 3)(7x - 1)$ **77.** $a^6(3a + 4)(3a + 2)$
79. ☞ **81.** $x^2 - 4x + 4$ **82.** $x^2 + 4x + 4$
83. $x^2 - 4$ **84.** $25t^2 - 30t + 9$ **85.** $16a^2 + 8a + 1$
86. $4n^2 - 49$ **87.** $9c^2 - 60c + 100$
88. $1 - 10a + 25a^2$ **89.** $64n^2 - 9$ **90.** $81 - y^2$
91. ☞ **93.** $(3xy + 2)(6xy - 5)$ **95.** Prime
97. $(4t^5 - 1)^2$ **99.** $-1(5x^m - 2)(3x^m - 4)$, or
$-(5x^m - 2)(3x^m - 4)$ **101.** $(3a^{3n} + 1)(a^{3n} - 1)$
103. $[7(t - 3)^n - 2][(t - 3)^n + 1]$

Connecting the Concepts, pp. 328–329

1. $6x^2(x^3 - 3)$ **2.** $(x + 2)(x + 8)$ **3.** $(x + 7)(2x - 1)$
4. $(x + 3)(x^2 + 2)$ **5.** $5(x - 2)(x + 10)$ **6.** Prime
7. $7y(x - 4)(x + 1)$ **8.** $3a^2(5a^2 - 9b^2 + 7b)$
9. $(b - 7)^2$ **10.** $(3x - 1)(4x + 1)$
11. $(c + 1)(c + 2)(c - 2)$ **12.** $2(x - 5)(x + 20)$
13. Prime **14.** $15(d^2 - 2d + 5)$
15. $(3p + 2q)(5p + 2q)$ **16.** $-2t(t + 2)(t + 3)$
17. $(x + 11)(x - 7)$ **18.** $10(c + 1)^2$
19. $-1(2x - 5)(x + 1)$ **20.** $2n(m - 5)(m^2 - 3)$

Exercise Set 5.4, pp. 334–335

1. Prime polynomial **2.** Difference of squares
3. Difference of squares **4.** None of these
5. Perfect-square trinomial **6.** Perfect-square trinomial
7. None of these **8.** Prime polynomial
9. Difference of squares **10.** Perfect-square trinomial

11. Yes **13.** No **15.** No **17.** Yes **19.** $(x + 8)^2$
21. $(x - 5)^2$ **23.** $5(p + 2)^2$ **25.** $(1 - t)^2$, or $(t - 1)^2$
27. $2(3x + 1)^2$ **29.** $(7 - 4y)^2$, or $(4y - 7)^2$
31. $-x^3(x - 9)^2$ **33.** $2n(n + 10)^2$ **35.** $5(2x + 5)^2$
37. $(7 - 3x)^2$, or $(3x - 7)^2$ **39.** $(4x + 3)^2$
41. $2(1 + 5x)^2$, or $2(5x + 1)^2$ **43.** $(3p + 2q)^2$
45. Prime **47.** $-1(8m + n)^2$, or $-(8m + n)^2$
49. $-2(4s - 5t)^2$ **51.** Yes **53.** No **55.** Yes
57. $(x + 5)(x - 5)$ **59.** $(p + 3)(p - 3)$
61. $(7 + t)(-7 + t)$, or $(t + 7)(t - 7)$
63. $6(a + 2)(a - 2)$ **65.** $(7x - 1)^2$
67. $2(10 + t)(10 - t)$ **69.** $-5(4a + 3)(4a - 3)$
71. $5(t + 4)(t - 4)$ **73.** $2(2x + 9)(2x - 9)$
75. $x(6 + 7x)(6 - 7x)$ **77.** Prime
79. $(t^2 + 1)(t + 1)(t - 1)$ **81.** $-3x(x - 4)^2$
83. $3t(5t + 3)(5t - 3)$ **85.** $a^6(a - 1)^2$
87. $10(a + b)(a - b)$ **89.** $(4x^2 + y^2)(2x + y)(2x - y)$
91. $2(3t + 2s)(3t - 2s)$ **93.** ☞ **95.** $8x^6y^{12}$
96. $-125x^6y^3$ **97.** $x^3 + 3x^2 + 3x + 1$
98. $x^3 - 3x^2 + 3x - 1$ **99.** $p^3 + 3p^2q + 3pq^2 + q^3$
100. $p^3 - 3p^2q + 3pq^2 - q^3$ **101.** ☞
103. $(x^4 + 2^4)(x^2 + 2^2)(x + 2)(x - 2)$, or
$(x^4 + 16)(x^2 + 4)(x + 2)(x - 2)$
105. $2x\left(3x - \frac{2}{5}\right)\left(3x + \frac{2}{5}\right)$
107. $[(y - 5)^2 + z^4][(y - 5) + z^2][(y - 5) - z^2]$, or
$(y^2 - 10y + 25 + z^4)(y - 5 + z^2)(y - 5 - z^2)$
109. $-1(x^2 + 1)(x + 3)(x - 3)$, or $-(x^2 + 1)(x + 3)(x - 3)$
111. $(y + 4)^2$ **113.** $(3p + 5)(3p - 5)^2$
115. $(9 + b^{2k})(3 + b^k)(3 - b^k)$ **117.** $2x^3 - x^2 - 1$
119. $(y + x + 7)(y - x - 1)$ **121.** 16
123. $(x + 1)^2 - x^2 = [(x + 1) + x][(x + 1) - x] = 2x + 1 = (x + 1) + x$

Exercise Set 5.5, p. 339

1. Difference of cubes **2.** Sum of cubes **3.** Difference
of squares **4.** None of these **5.** Sum of cubes
6. Difference of cubes **7.** None of these **8.** Difference
of squares **9.** Difference of cubes **10.** None of these
11. $(x - 4)(x^2 + 4x + 16)$ **13.** $(z + 1)(z^2 - z + 1)$
15. $(t - 10)(t^2 + 10t + 100)$
17. $(3x + 1)(9x^2 - 3x + 1)$
19. $(4 - 5x)(16 + 20x + 25x^2)$
21. $(x - y)(x^2 + xy + y^2)$ **23.** $\left(a + \frac{1}{2}\right)\left(a^2 - \frac{1}{2}a + \frac{1}{4}\right)$
25. $8(t - 1)(t^2 + t + 1)$ **27.** $2(3x + 1)(9x^2 - 3x + 1)$
29. $rs(s + 4)(s^2 - 4s + 16)$
31. $5(x - 2z)(x^2 + 2xz + 4z^2)$
33. $\left(y - \frac{1}{10}\right)\left(y^2 + \frac{1}{10}y + \frac{1}{100}\right)$
35. $(x + 0.1)(x^2 - 0.1x + 0.01)$
37. $8(2x^2 - t^2)(4x^4 + 2x^2t^2 + t^4)$
39. $2y(3y - 4)(9y^2 + 12y + 16)$
41. $(z + 1)(z^2 - z + 1)(z - 1)(z^2 + z + 1)$
43. $(t^2 + 4y^2)(t^4 - 4t^2y^2 + 16y^4)$
45. $(x^4 - yz^4)(x^8 + x^4yz^4 + y^2z^8)$ **47.** ☞
49. $-\frac{1}{5}$ **50.** $\frac{1}{4}$

51.
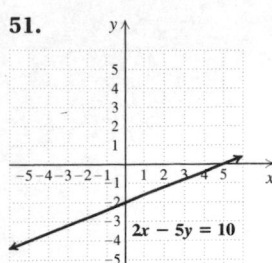
$2x - 5y = 10$

52.
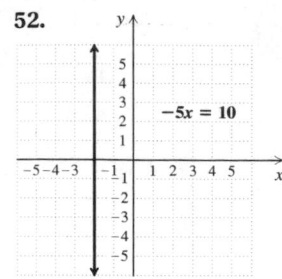
$-5x = 10$

53.
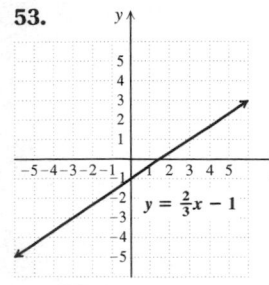
$y = \frac{2}{3}x - 1$

54.
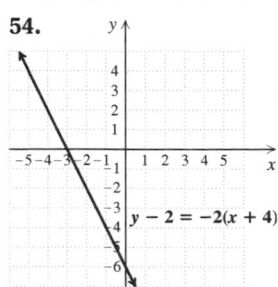
$y - 2 = -2(x + 4)$

55. ✍   **57.** $(x^{2a} - y^b)(x^{4a} + x^{2a}y^b + y^{2b})$
59. $2x(x^2 + 75)$ **61.** $5\left(xy^2 - \frac{1}{2}\right)\left(x^2y^4 + \frac{1}{2}xy^2 + \frac{1}{4}\right)$
63. $-(3x^{4a} + 3x^{2a} + 1)$ **65.** $(t - 8)(t - 1)(t^2 + t + 1)$

Exercise Set 5.6, pp. 343–344

1. Common factor   **2.** Perfect-square trinomial
3. Grouping   **4.** Multiplying   **5.** $5(a + 5)(a - 5)$
7. $(y - 7)^2$ **9.** $(3t + 7)(t + 3)$ **11.** $x(x + 9)^2$
13. $(x - 5)^2(x + 5)$ **15.** $3t(3t + 1)(3t - 1)$
17. $3x(3x - 5)(x + 3)$ **19.** Prime   **21.** $6(y - 5)(y + 8)$
23. $-2a^4(a - 2)^2$ **25.** $5x(x^2 + 4)(x + 2)(x - 2)$
27. $(t^2 + 3)(t^2 - 3)$ **29.** $-x^4(x^2 - 2x + 7)$
31. $(x - y)(x^2 + xy + y^2)$ **33.** $a(x^2 + y^2)$
35. $2\pi r(h + r)$ **37.** $(a + b)(5a + 3b)$
39. $(x + 1)(x + y)$ **41.** $(a - 2)(a - y)$
43. $(3x - 2y)(x + 5y)$ **45.** $8mn(m^2 - 4mn + 3)$
47. $(a - 2b)^2$ **49.** $(4x + 3y)^2$ **51.** Prime
53. $(a^2b^2 + 4)(ab + 2)(ab - 2)$ **55.** $4c(4d - c)(5d - c)$
57. $(2t + 1)(4t^2 - 2t + 1)(2t - 1)(4t^2 + 2t + 1)$
59. $-1(xy + 2)(xy + 6)$, or $-(xy + 2)(xy + 6)$
61. $5(pq + 6)(pq - 1)$
63. $2a(3a + 2b)(9a^2 - 6ab + 4b^2)$
65. $x^4(x + 2y)(x - y)$ **67.** $\left(6a - \frac{5}{4}\right)^2$ **69.** $\left(\frac{1}{9}x - \frac{4}{3}\right)^2$
71. $(1 + 4x^6y^6)(1 + 2x^3y^3)(1 - 2x^3y^3)$ **73.** $(2ab + 3)^2$
75. $z(z + 6)(z^2 - 6)$ **77.** ✍   **79.** $\frac{9}{8}$ **80.** $-\frac{5}{3}$
81. $-\frac{7}{2}$ **82.** $\frac{1}{4}$ **83.** 3   **84.** 11   **85.** -1 **86.** 3
87. ✍   **89.** $-x(x^2 + 9)(x^2 - 2)$
91. $-1(x^2 + 2)(x + 3)(x - 3)$, or
$-(x^2 + 2)(x + 3)(x - 3)$ **93.** $(y + 1)(y - 7)(y + 3)$
95. $(y + 4 + x)^2$ **97.** $(a + 3)^2(2a + b + 4)(a - b + 5)$
99. $(7x^2 + 1 + 5x^3)(7x^2 + 1 - 5x^3)$

Technology Connection, p. 351

1. $-4.65, 0.65$ **2.** $-0.37, 5.37$ **3.** $-8.98, -4.56$
4. No solution   **5.** $0, 2.76$

Exercise Set 5.7, pp. 351–353

1. (c)   **2.** (a)   **3.** (d)   **4.** (b)   **5.** $-9, -2$ **7.** $-6, \frac{3}{2}$
9. $\frac{1}{7}, \frac{3}{10}$ **11.** $0, 7$ **13.** $\frac{1}{21}, \frac{18}{11}$ **15.** $-\frac{8}{3}, 0$ **17.** $50, 70$
19. $-5, \frac{2}{3}, 1$ **21.** $1, 6$ **23.** $-7, 3$ **25.** $-9, -2$ **27.** $0, 10$
29. $-6, 0$ **31.** $-6, 6$ **33.** $-\frac{7}{2}, \frac{7}{2}$ **35.** -5 **37.** 8
39. $0, 2$ **41.** $-\frac{5}{4}, 3$ **43.** 3   **45.** $0, \frac{4}{3}$ **47.** $-\frac{7}{6}, \frac{7}{6}$
49. $-4, -\frac{2}{3}$ **51.** $-3, 1$ **53.** $-1, 0, \frac{3}{2}$ **55.** $-7, -\frac{8}{3}, \frac{5}{2}$
57. $-1, 4$ **59.** $-3, 2$ **61.** $(-2, 0), (3, 0)$ **63.** $(-4, 0)$,
$(2, 0)$ **65.** $(-3, 0), \left(\frac{3}{2}, 0\right)$ **67.** ✍   **69.** Let m and n
represent the numbers; $(m + n)^2$ **70.** Let m and n repre-
sent the numbers; $m^2 + n^2$ **71.** Let x represent the first
integer; then $x + 1$ represents the second integer; $x(x + 1)$
72. Mother's Day: \$13.8 billion; Father's Day: \$9 billion
73. $140°, 35°, 5°$ **74.** Length: 64 in.; width: 32 in.
75. ✍   **77.** (a) $x^2 - x - 20 = 0$; (b) $x^2 - 6x - 7 = 0$;
(c) $4x^2 - 13x + 3 = 0$; (d) $6x^2 - 5x + 1 = 0$;
(e) $12x^2 - 17x + 6 = 0$; (f) $x^3 - 4x^2 + x + 6 = 0$
79. $-5, 4$ **81.** $-\frac{3}{5}, \frac{3}{5}$ **83.** $-4, 2$
85. (a) $2x^2 + 20x - 4 = 0$; (b) $x^2 - 3x - 18 = 0$;
(c) $(x + 1)(5x - 5) = 0$; (d) $(2x + 8)(2x - 5) = 0$;
(e) $4x^2 + 8x + 36 = 0$; (f) $9x^2 - 12x + 24 = 0$
87. ✍   **89.** $2.33, 6.77$ **91.** $-9.15, -4.59$ **93.** $-3.76, 0$

Connecting the Concepts, p. 354

1. Expression   **2.** Equation   **3.** Equation
4. Expression   **5.** Expression   **6.** Equation
7. $2x^3 + x^2 - 8x$ **8.** $-2x^2 - 11$ **9.** $-10, 10$
10. $6a^2 - 19a + 10$ **11.** $(n - 1)(n - 9)$ **12.** $2, 8$
13. $-\frac{5}{2}$ **14.** $7x^3 + 2x - 7$ **15.** $(4x + 9)(4x - 9)$
16. $-3, 8$ **17.** $-4a^2 - a - 11$
18. $2x^2(9x^2 - 12x + 10)$ **19.** $-1, -\frac{2}{3}$
20. $8x^5 - 20x^4 + 12x^2$

Translating for Success, p. 361

1. O   **2.** M   **3.** K   **4.** I   **5.** G   **6.** E   **7.** C
8. A   **9.** H   **10.** B

Exercise Set 5.8, pp. 362–366

1. $-2, 3$ **3.** 6 m, 8 m, 10 m   **5.** 11, 12
7. -14 and -12; 12 and 14   **9.** Length: 30 ft; width: 6 ft
11. Length: 6 cm; width: 4 cm   **13.** Base: 12 in.; height: 9 in.
15. Foot: 7 ft; height: 12 ft   **17.** 1 min, 3 min   **19.** In 2008
21. 16 teams   **23.** 66 handshakes   **25.** 12 players
27. 9 ft   **29.** 32 ft   **31.** 300 ft by 400 ft by 500 ft
33. Dining room: 12 ft by 12 ft; kitchen: 12 ft by 10 ft
35. 20 ft   **37.** 1 sec, 2 sec   **39.** ✍   **41.** $-\frac{12}{35}$ **42.** $-\frac{21}{20}$
43. -1 **44.** $-\frac{7}{4}$ **45.** $\frac{1}{4}$ **46.** $\frac{4}{5}$ **47.** $\frac{53}{168}$ **48.** $\frac{19}{18}$
49. ✍   **51.** \$180   **53.** 39 cm   **55.** 4 in., 6 in.
57. 35 ft   **59.** 2 hr, 4.2 hr   **61.** 3 hr

Review Exercises: Chapter 5, pp. 369–371

1. False   **2.** True   **3.** True   **4.** False   **5.** False
6. True   **7.** True   **8.** False   **9.** Answers may vary.
$(4x)(5x^2), (-2x^2)(-10x), (x^3)(20)$

10. Answers may vary. $(-3x^2)(6x^3), (2x^4)(-9x),$
$(-18x)(x^4)$ **11.** $6x^3(2x-3)$ **12.** $4a(2a-3)$
13. $(10t+1)(10t-1)$ **14.** $(x+4)(x-3)$
15. $(x+7)^2$ **16.** $3x(2x+1)^2$ **17.** $(2x+3)(3x^2+1)$
18. $(6a-5)(a+1)$ **19.** $(5t-3)^2$
20. $2(24t^2-14t+3)$ **21.** $(9a^2+1)(3a+1)(3a-1)$
22. $3x(3x-5)(x+3)$ **23.** $2(x-5)(x^2+5x+25)$
24. $(x+4)(x^3-2)$ **25.** $(ab^2+8)(ab^2-8)$
26. $-4x^4(2x^2-8x+1)$ **27.** $3(2x-5)^2$
28. Prime   **29.** $-t(t+6)(t-7)$ **30.** $(2x+5)(2x-5)$
31. $(n+6)(n-10)$ **32.** $5(z^2-6z+2)$
33. $(4t+5)(t+2)$ **34.** $(2t+1)(t-4)$
35. $7x(x+1)(x+4)$ **36.** $(2y+3x^2)(4y^2-6x^2y+9x^4)$
37. $5(2x-1)^2$ **38.** $-6x(x+5)(x-5)$
39. $(5-x)(3-x)$ **40.** Prime   **41.** $(xy+8)(xy-2)$
42. $3(2a+7b)^2$ **43.** $(m+5)(m+t)$
44. $32(x^2+2y^2z^2)(x^2-2y^2z^2)$ **45.** $(2m+n)(3m+n)$
46. $(3r+5s)(2r-3s)$ **47.** $-11, 9$ **48.** $-7, 5$
49. $-\frac{3}{4}, \frac{3}{4}$ **50.** $\frac{2}{3}, 1$ **51.** $-\frac{5}{2}, 6$ **52.** $-2, 3$ **53.** $0, \frac{3}{5}$
54. 1 **55.** $-3, 4$ **56.** 10 teams   **57.** $(-1, 0), \left(\frac{5}{2}, 0\right)$
58. Height: 14 ft; base: 14 ft   **59.** 10 holes
60. ✍ Answers may vary. Because Celia did not first factor
out the largest common factor, 4, her factorization will not be
"complete" until she removes a common factor of 2 from each
binomial. The answer should be $4(x-5)(x+5)$. Awarding 3
to 7 points would seem reasonable.   **61.** ✍ The equations
solved in this chapter have an x^2-term (are quadratic),
whereas those solved previously have no x^2-term (are
linear). The principle of zero products is used to solve
quadratic equations and is not used to solve linear
equations.   **62.** 2.5 cm   **63.** 0, 2   **64.** Length: 12 cm;
width: 6 cm   **65.** 100 cm^2, 225 cm^2 **66.** $-3, 2, \frac{5}{2}$
67. No real solution

Test: Chapter 5, pp. 371–372

1. [5.1] Answers may vary. $(3x^2)(4x^2), (-2x)(-6x^3),$
$(12x^3)(x)$ **2.** [5.2] $(x-4)(x-9)$ **3.** [5.4] $(x-5)^2$
4. [5.1] $2y^2(2y^2-4y+3)$ **5.** [5.1] $(x+1)(x^2+2)$
6. [5.1] $t^5(t^2-3)$ **7.** [5.2] $a(a+4)(a-1)$
8. [5.3] $2(5x-6)(x+4)$ **9.** [5.4] $(2t+5)(2t-5)$
10. [5.2] $(x+2)(x-3)$ **11.** [5.3] $-3m(2m+1)(m+1)$
12. [5.5] $3(r-1)(r^2+r+1)$ **13.** [5.4] $5(3r+2)^2$
14. [5.4] $3(x^2+4)(x+2)(x-2)$ **15.** [5.4] $(7t+6)^2$
16. [5.1] $(x+2)(x^3-3)$ **17.** [5.2] Prime
18. [5.3] $(2x+3)(2x-5)$ **19.** [5.3] $3t(2t+5)(t-1)$
20. [5.3] $3(m-5n)(m+2n)$ **21.** [5.7] $1, 5$
22. [5.7] $-\frac{3}{2}, 5$ **23.** [5.7] $0, \frac{2}{5}$ **24.** [5.7] $-\frac{1}{5}, \frac{1}{5}$
25. [5.7] $-4, 5$ **26.** [5.7] $(-1, 0), \left(\frac{8}{3}, 0\right)$
27. [5.8] Length: 10 m; width: 4 m   **28.** [5.8] 10 people
29. [5.8] 5 ft   **30.** [5.8] 15 cm by 30 cm
31. [5.2] $(a-4)(a+8)$ **32.** [5.7] $-\frac{8}{3}, 0, \frac{2}{5}$

Cumulative Review: Chapters 1–5, pp. 372–373

1. $\frac{1}{2}$ **2.** $\frac{9}{32}$ **3.** $\frac{9}{8}$ **4.** 29   **5.** $\frac{1}{9x^4y^6}$ **6.** t^{10}
7. $3x^4+5x^3+x-10$ **8.** $-3a^2b-ab^2+2b^3$

9. $\dfrac{t^8}{4s^2}$ **10.** $-\dfrac{8x^6y^3}{27z^{12}}$ **11.** 8   **12.** -8 **13.** $-x^4$
14. $2x^3-5x^2+\frac{1}{2}x-1$ **15.** $-4t^{11}+8t^9+20t^8$
16. $9x^2-30x+25$ **17.** $100x^{10}-y^2$
18. x^3-2x^2+1 **19.** $(c+1)(c-1)$
20. $5(x+y)(1+2x)$ **21.** $(2r-t)^2$
22. $(2x-5)(3x-2)$ **23.** $10(y^2+4)$
24. $y(x-1)(x-2)$ **25.** $(3x-2y)(4x+y)$
26. $(5a+4b)(25a^2-20ab+16b^2)$ **27.** $\frac{1}{12}$
28. 1   **29.** $-\frac{9}{4}$ **30.** $\{x \mid x \geq 1\}$, or $[1, \infty)$ **31.** $-3, 1$
32. $-4, 3$ **33.** $-2, 2$ **34.** $0, 4$ **35.** $c = \dfrac{a}{b+d}$ **36.** 0
37. $-2; (0, 5)$ **38.** $y = 5x - \frac{1}{3}$ **39.** $y = 5x + \frac{5}{3}$

40.
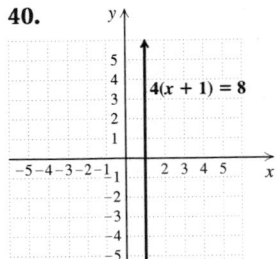

41.
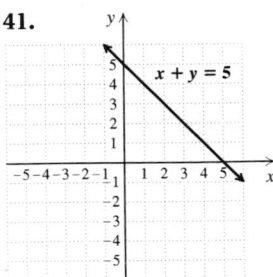

42.
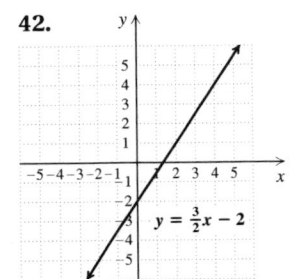

43.
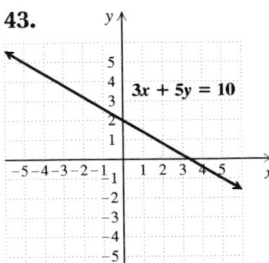

44.
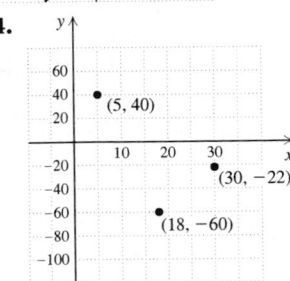

45. 372 min
46. 11,616,000 subscribers
per year   **47.** 60,000,000
users   **48.** 101,180 people
49. Bottom of ladder to
building: 5 ft; top of ladder
to ground: 12 ft
50. Length: 12 ft; width: 2 ft
51. Scores that are 9
and higher

52. (a)
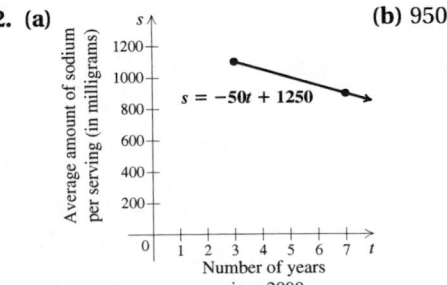

(b) 950 mg per serving

53. $b = \dfrac{2}{a+1}$ **54.** $y = -8$
55. (a) $9y^2+12y+4-x^2$; **(b)** $(3y+2+x)(3y+2-x)$
56. $-1, 0, \frac{1}{3}$

CHAPTER 6

Technology Connection, p. 379

1. Correct   **2.** Correct   **3.** Not correct   **4.** Not correct

Exercise Set 6.1, pp. 381–382

1. (e)   **2.** (a)   **3.** (d)   **4.** (b)   **5.** (c)   **6.** (f)

7. 0   **9.** −5   **11.** 5   **13.** −4, 7   **15.** −6, $\frac{1}{2}$ **17.** $\frac{5a}{4b^2}$

19. $\frac{t+2}{t-3}$ **21.** $\frac{7}{8}$ **23.** $\frac{a-3}{a+1}$ **25.** $-\frac{2x^3}{3}$ **27.** $\frac{y-3}{4y}$

29. $\frac{t-4}{t-5}$ **31.** $\frac{a+4}{2(a-4)}$ **33.** $\frac{x-4}{x+4}$ **35.** $\frac{1}{n^2+2n+4}$

37. $t-1$ **39.** $\frac{y^2+4}{y+2}$ **41.** $\frac{1}{2}$ **43.** $\frac{y}{2y+1}$

45. $\frac{2x-3}{5x+2}$ **47.** −1   **49.** −7   **51.** $-\frac{1}{4}$ **53.** $-\frac{3}{2}$

55. −1   **57.** 📖   **59.** $-\frac{4}{21}$ **60.** $-\frac{5}{3}$ **61.** $-\frac{15}{4}$
62. $-\frac{21}{16}$ **63.** $\frac{13}{63}$ **64.** $\frac{5}{48}$ **65.** 📖   **67.** $-(2y+x)$

69. $\frac{x^3+4}{(x^3+2)(x^2+2)}$ **71.** $\frac{(t-1)(t-9)^2}{(t+1)(t^2+9)}$

73. $\frac{(x-y)^3}{(x+y)^2(x-5y)}$ **75.** 📖

Technology Connection, pp. 385–386

1. Let $y_1 = ((x^2+3x+2)/(x^2+4))/(5x^2+10x)$ and $y_2 = (x+1)/((x^2+4)(5x))$. With the tables set in AUTO mode, note that the values in the Y1- and Y2-columns match except for $x = -2$.   **2.** ERROR messages occur when division by 0 is attempted. Since the simplified expression has no factor of $x+5$ or $x+1$ in a denominator, no ERROR message occurs in Y2 for $x = -5$ or −1.

Exercise Set 6.2, pp. 386–388

1. $\frac{3x(x+2)}{8(5x-1)}$ **3.** $\frac{(a-4)(a+2)}{(a+6)^2}$ **5.** $\frac{(2x+3)(x+1)}{4(x-5)}$

7. $\frac{(n-4)(n+4)}{(n^2+4)(n^2-4)}$ **9.** $\frac{(y+6)(y-3)}{(1+y)(y+3)}$ **11.** $\frac{6t}{5}$

13. $\frac{4}{c^2d}$ **15.** $\frac{(x-5)(x+2)}{x-2}$ **17.** $\frac{(n-5)(n-1)(n-6)}{(n+6)(n^2+36)}$

19. $\frac{7(a+3)}{a(a+4)}$ **21.** $\frac{3v}{v-2}$ **23.** $\frac{t-5}{t+5}$ **25.** $\frac{9(y-5)}{10(y-1)}$

27. 1   **29.** $\frac{(t-2)(t+5)}{(t-5)(t-5)}$ **31.** $(2x-1)^2$ **33.** $c(c-2)$

35. $\frac{9}{2x}$ **37.** $\frac{1}{a^4+3a}$ **39.** $\frac{20}{27}$ **41.** $\frac{x^2}{20}$ **43.** $\frac{a^3}{b^3}$

45. $\frac{4(t-3)}{3(t+1)}$ **47.** $4(y-2)$ **49.** $-\frac{a}{b}$

51. $\frac{(n+3)(n+3)}{n-2}$ **53.** $\frac{15}{16}$ **55.** $\frac{-x^2-4}{x+2}$

57. $\frac{a-5}{3(a-1)}$ **59.** $\frac{(2x-1)(2x+1)}{x-5}$

61. $\frac{(w-7)(w-8)}{(2w-7)(3w+1)}$ **63.** $\frac{1}{(c-5)(5c-3)}$

65. $\frac{(x-4y)(x-y)}{(x+y)^3}$ **67.** $\frac{x^2+4x+16}{(x+4)^2}$ **69.** $\frac{(2a+b)^2}{2(a+b)}$

71. 📖   **73.** $\frac{19}{12}$ **74.** $\frac{41}{24}$ **75.** $\frac{1}{18}$ **76.** $-\frac{1}{6}$ **77.** x^2+3

78. $-2x^2-4x+1$ **79.** 📖   **81.** $\frac{3}{7x}$ **83.** 1

85. $\frac{1}{(x+y)^3(3x+y)}$ **87.** $\frac{a^2-2b}{a^2+3b}$ **89.** $\frac{(z+4)^3}{3(z-4)^2}$

91. $\frac{a-3b}{c}$ **93.** 📖

Exercise Set 6.3, pp. 395–397

1. Numerators; denominator   **2.** Term   **3.** Least common denominator; LCD   **4.** Factorizations; denominators   **5.** $\frac{8}{t}$ **7.** $\frac{3x+5}{12}$ **9.** $\frac{9}{a+3}$

11. $\frac{8}{4x-7}$ **13.** $\frac{2y+7}{2y}$ **15.** 6   **17.** $\frac{4(x-1)}{x+3}$

19. $a+5$ **21.** $y-7$ **23.** 0   **25.** $\frac{1}{x+2}$ **27.** $\frac{t-4}{t+3}$

29. $\frac{y+2}{y-4}$ **31.** $-\frac{5}{x-4}$, or $\frac{5}{4-x}$ **33.** $-\frac{1}{x-1}$, or $\frac{1}{1-x}$
35. 180   **37.** 72   **39.** 60   **41.** $18t^5$ **43.** $30a^4b^8$
45. $6(y-3)$ **47.** $(x-5)(x+3)(x-3)$
49. $t(t-4)(t+2)^2$ **51.** $120x^2y^3z^2$
53. $(a+1)(a-1)^2$ **55.** $(2n-1)(n+1)(n+2)$
57. $12x^3(x-5)(x-3)(x-1)$

59. $2(x+1)(x-1)(x^2+x+1)$ **61.** $\frac{15}{18t^4}$, $\frac{st^2}{18t^4}$

63. $\frac{21y}{9x^4y^3}$, $\frac{4x^3}{9x^4y^3}$ **65.** $\frac{2x(x+3)}{(x-2)(x+2)(x+3)}$, $\frac{4x(x-2)}{(x-2)(x+2)(x+3)}$ **67.** 📖   **69.** $\frac{-5}{8}, \frac{5}{-8}$
70. $\frac{-4}{11}, -\frac{4}{11}$ **71.** $-x+y$, or $y-x$ **72.** $-3+a$, or $a-3$
73. $-2x+7$, or $7-2x$ **74.** $-a+b$, or $b-a$ **75.** 📖

77. $\frac{18x+5}{x-1}$ **79.** $\frac{x}{3x+1}$ **81.** 30 strands
83. 60 strands   **85.** $(2x+5)(2x-5)(3x+4)^4$
87. 30 sec   **89.** 7:55 A.M.   **91.** 📖

Exercise Set 6.4, pp. 402–404

1. LCD   **2.** Missing; denominator   **3.** Numerators; LCD
4. Simplify   **5.** $\frac{3+5x}{x^2}$ **7.** $-\frac{5}{24r}$ **9.** $\frac{3u^2+4v}{u^3v^2}$

11. $\frac{-2(xy+9)}{3x^2y^3}$ **13.** $\frac{7x+1}{24}$ **15.** $\frac{-x-4}{6}$

17. $\dfrac{a^2 + 13a - 5}{15a^2}$ **19.** $\dfrac{7z - 12}{12z}$ **21.** $\dfrac{(3c - d)(c + d)}{c^2 d^2}$

23. $\dfrac{4x^2 - 13xt + 9t^2}{3x^2 t^2}$ **25.** $\dfrac{6x}{(x + 2)(x - 2)}$

27. $\dfrac{(t - 3)(t + 1)}{(t - 1)(t + 3)}$ **29.** $\dfrac{11x + 2}{3x(x + 1)}$ **31.** $\dfrac{-5t + 3}{2t(t - 1)}$

33. $\dfrac{a^2}{(a - 3)(a + 3)}$ **35.** $\dfrac{16}{3(z + 4)}$ **37.** $\dfrac{5q - 3}{(q - 1)^2}$

39. $\dfrac{1}{t^2 + t + 1}$ **41.** $\dfrac{9a}{4(a - 5)}$ **43.** 0

45. $\dfrac{10}{(a - 3)(a + 2)}$ **47.** $\dfrac{x - 5}{(x + 5)(x + 3)}$

49. $\dfrac{3z^2 + 19z - 20}{(z - 2)^2(z + 3)}$ **51.** $\dfrac{-7}{x^2 + 25x + 24}$ **53.** $\dfrac{3x - 1}{2}$

55. $y + 3$ **57.** 0   **59.** $\dfrac{p^2 + 7p + 1}{(p - 5)(p + 5)}$

61. $\dfrac{(x + 1)(x + 3)}{(x - 4)(x + 4)}$ **63.** $\dfrac{-a - 2}{(a + 1)(a - 1)}$, or

$\dfrac{a + 2}{(1 + a)(1 - a)}$ **65.** $\dfrac{2(5x + 3y)}{(x - y)(x + y)}$ **67.** $\dfrac{2x - 3}{2 - x}$

69. 3   **71.** 0   **73.** ✍   **75.** $-\frac{3}{22}$ **76.** $\frac{7}{9}$ **77.** $\frac{9}{10}$

78. $\frac{16}{27}$ **79.** $\frac{2}{3}$ **80.** $\dfrac{(x - 3)(x + 2)}{(x - 2)(x + 3)}$ **81.** ✍

83. Perimeter: $\dfrac{2(5x - 7)}{(x - 5)(x + 4)}$; area: $\dfrac{6}{(x - 5)(x + 4)}$

85. $\dfrac{x}{3x + 1}$ **87.** $\dfrac{x^4 + 4x^3 - 5x^2 - 126x - 441}{(x + 2)^2(x + 7)^2}$

89. $\dfrac{5(a^2 + 2ab - b^2)}{(a - b)(3a + b)(3a - b)}$ **91.** $\dfrac{a}{a - b} + \dfrac{3b}{b - a}$;

answers may vary.   **93.** ✍, ▨

Connecting the Concepts, pp. 404–405

1. Addition; $\dfrac{3x + 10}{5x^2}$ **2.** Multiplication; $\dfrac{6}{5x^3}$

3. Division; $\dfrac{3x}{10}$ **4.** Subtraction; $\dfrac{3x - 10}{5x^2}$

5. Multiplication; $\dfrac{x - 3}{15(x - 2)}$ **6.** Multiplication;

$\dfrac{6}{(x + 3)(x + 4)}$ **7.** Division; $\frac{1}{3}$ **8.** Subtraction;

$\dfrac{x^2 - 2x - 2}{(x - 1)(x + 2)}$ **9.** Addition; $\dfrac{5x + 17}{(x + 3)(x + 4)}$

10. Addition; -5 **11.** Subtraction; $\dfrac{5}{x - 4}$ **12.** Division;

$\dfrac{(2x + 3)(x + 3)}{(x + 1)^2}$ **13.** Subtraction; $\frac{1}{6}$ **14.** Multiplication;

$\dfrac{x(x + 4)}{(x - 1)^2}$ **15.** Addition; $\dfrac{x + 7}{(x - 5)(x + 1)}$ **16.** Division;

$\dfrac{9(u - 1)}{16}$ **17.** Addition; $\dfrac{7t + 8}{30}$ **18.** Multiplication;

$(t + 5)^2$ **19.** Division; $\dfrac{a - 1}{(a + 2)(a - 2)^2}$

20. Subtraction; $\dfrac{-3x^2 + 9x - 14}{2x}$

Technology Connection, p. 409

1. $(1 - 1/x)/(1 - 1/x^2)$ **2.** Parentheses are needed to group separate terms into factors. When a fraction bar is replaced with a division sign, we need parentheses to preserve the groupings that had been created by the fraction bar. This holds for denominators and numerators alike.

Exercise Set 6.5, pp. 409–411

1. (d)   **2.** (a)   **3.** (b)   **4.** (c)   **5.** $\frac{5}{11}$ **7.** 10

9. $\dfrac{5x^2}{4(x^2 + 4)}$ **11.** $\dfrac{-10t}{5t - 2}$ **13.** $\dfrac{2(2a - 5)}{a - 7}$

15. $\dfrac{x^2 - 18}{2(x + 3)}$ **17.** $-\frac{1}{5}$ **19.** $\dfrac{1 + t^2}{t(1 - t)}$ **21.** $\dfrac{x}{x - y}$

23. $\dfrac{c(4c + 7)}{3(2c^2 - 1)}$ **25.** $\dfrac{15(4 - a^3)}{14a^2(9 + 2a)}$ **27.** 1

29. $\dfrac{3a^2 + 4b^3}{b^3(5 - 3a^2)}$ **31.** $\dfrac{(t - 3)(t + 3)}{t^2 + 4}$ **33.** $\dfrac{a^2 b^2}{b^2 - ab + a^2}$

35. $\dfrac{a(3ab^3 + 4)}{b^2(3 + a)}$ **37.** $\dfrac{t^2 + 5t + 3}{(t + 1)^2}$ **39.** $\dfrac{x^2 - 2x - 1}{x^2 - 5x - 4}$

41. ✍   **43.** -4 **44.** -4 **45.** $\frac{19}{3}$ **46.** $-\frac{14}{27}$ **47.** 3, 4

48. $-15, 2$ **49.** ✍   **51.** 6, 7, 8   **53.** $-3, -\frac{4}{5}, 3$

55. $\dfrac{A}{B} \div \dfrac{C}{D} = \dfrac{\dfrac{A}{B}}{\dfrac{C}{D}} = \dfrac{\dfrac{A}{B}}{\dfrac{C}{D}} \cdot \dfrac{BD}{BD} = \dfrac{AD}{BC} = \dfrac{A}{B} \cdot \dfrac{D}{C}$

57. $\dfrac{x^2 + 5x + 15}{-x^2 + 10}$ **59.** 0   **61.** $\dfrac{2z(5z - 2)}{(z + 2)(13z - 6)}$

63. ✍

Exercise Set 6.6, pp. 417–418

1. False   **2.** True   **3.** True   **4.** True   **5.** $-\frac{2}{5}$ **7.** $\frac{6}{7}$

9. $\frac{24}{5}$ **11.** $-4, -1$ **13.** $-6, 6$ **15.** 12   **17.** $\frac{14}{3}$

19. -10 **21.** $-4, -3$ **23.** $\frac{23}{2}$ **25.** $\frac{5}{2}$ **27.** -1

29. No solution   **31.** -10 **33.** $-\frac{7}{3}$ **35.** $-2, \frac{7}{3}$

37. $-3, 13$ **39.** 2   **41.** -8 **43.** No solution

45. $-6, 6$ **47.** ✍   **49.** 137, 139   **50.** 14 yd

51. Base: 9 cm; height: 12 cm   **52.** $-8, -6; 6, 8$

53. 0.06 cm per day   **54.** 0.28 in. per day   **55.** ✍

57. -2 **59.** 3   **61.** 4   **63.** 4   **65.** -2 **67.** ▨

Connecting the Concepts, pp. 418–419

1. Expression; $\dfrac{x - 2}{x + 1}$ **2.** Expression; $\dfrac{19n - 2}{5n(2n - 1)}$

3. Equation; 8   **4.** Expression; $\dfrac{(z + 1)^2(z - 1)}{z}$

5. Equation; $-\frac{1}{2}$ **6.** Expression; $\dfrac{8(t + 1)}{(t - 1)(2t - 1)}$

7. Expression; $\dfrac{2a}{a-1}$　　**8.** Equation; $-5, 3$

9. Expression; $\dfrac{3x}{10}$　　**10.** Equation; $-10, 10$

Translating for Success, p. 429

1. K　**2.** E　**3.** C　**4.** N　**5.** D　**6.** O　**7.** F　**8.** H
9. B　**10.** A

Exercise Set 6.7, pp. 430–435

1. $\frac{1}{2}$ cake per hour　**2.** $\frac{1}{3}$ cake per hour　**3.** $\frac{5}{6}$ cake per hour
4. 1 lawn per hour　**5.** $\frac{1}{3}$ lawn per hour　**6.** $\frac{2}{3}$ lawn per hour
7. $3\frac{3}{7}$ hr　**9.** $\frac{42}{13}$ min, or $3\frac{3}{13}$ min　**11.** $19\frac{1}{11}$ min
13. H470: 135 min; K5400: $67\frac{1}{2}$ min　**15.** Austin: 15 min;
Airgle: 30 min　**17.** 300 min, or 5 hr
19.

	Distance (in km)	Speed (in km/h)	Time (in hours)
B & M	330	$r - 14$	$\dfrac{330}{r-14}$
AMTRAK	400	r	$\dfrac{400}{r}$

AMTRAK: 80 km/h; B & M: 66 km/h
21. 7 mph　**23.** 5.2 ft/sec　**25.** 3 hr　**27.** 9 km/h
29. 2 km/h　**31.** 20 mph　**33.** 10.5　**35.** $\frac{8}{3}$　**37.** $3\frac{3}{4}$ in.
39. 20 ft　**41.** 15 ft　**43.** 12.6　**45.** 1440 messages
47. About 231,000 people　**49.** 18 gal　**51.** $26\frac{2}{3}$ cm
53. 52 bulbs　**55.** $7\frac{1}{2}$ oz　**57.** 90 whales
59. (a) 1.92 T; **(b)** 28.8 lb　**61.** 🖉
63.

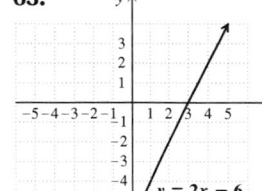

64.

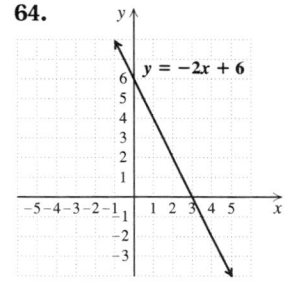

65.

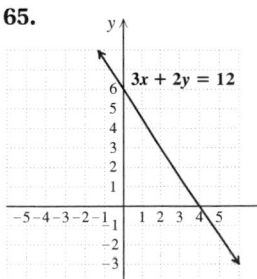

66.

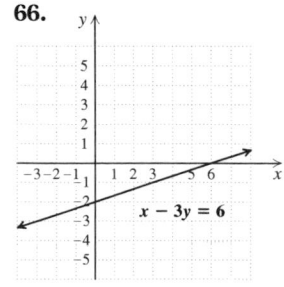

67.

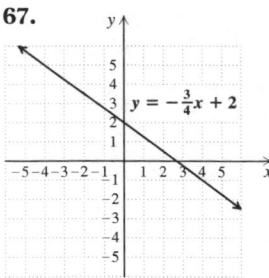

68.

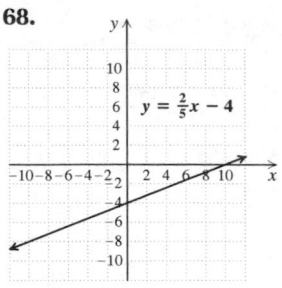

69. 🖉　**71.** $49\frac{1}{2}$ hr　**73.** 2250 people per hour
75. $14\frac{7}{8}$ mi　**77.** About 57%　**79.** Page 278
81. $\dfrac{B}{A} = \dfrac{D}{C}; \dfrac{A}{C} = \dfrac{B}{D}; \dfrac{C}{A} = \dfrac{D}{B}$　**83.** $51\frac{3}{7}$ mph　**85.** 🖉

Review Exercises: Chapter 6, pp. 439–440

1. False　**2.** True　**3.** False　**4.** True　**5.** True
6. False　**7.** False　**8.** False　**9.** 0　**10.** -5
11. $-6, 6$　**12.** $-6, 5$　**13.** -2　**14.** $\dfrac{x-3}{x+5}$　**15.** $\dfrac{7x+3}{x-3}$
16. $\dfrac{3(y-3)}{2(y+3)}$　**17.** $-5(x+2y)$　**18.** $\dfrac{a-6}{5}$
19. $\dfrac{3(y-2)^2}{4(2y-1)(y-1)}$　**20.** $-32t$　**21.** $\dfrac{2x(x-1)}{x+1}$
22. $\dfrac{(x^2+1)(2x+1)}{(x-2)(x+1)}$　**23.** $\dfrac{(t+4)^2}{t+1}$　**24.** $60a^5b^8$
25. $x^4(x-1)(x+1)$　**26.** $(y-2)(y+2)(y+1)$
27. $\dfrac{15-3x}{x+3}$　**28.** $\dfrac{4}{x-4}$　**29.** $\dfrac{x+5}{2x}$
30. $\dfrac{2a^2-21ab+15b^2}{5a^2b^2}$　**31.** $y-4$　**32.** $\dfrac{t(t-2)}{(t-1)(t+1)}$
33. $d+2$　**34.** $\dfrac{-x^2+x+26}{(x+1)(x-5)(x+5)}$　**35.** $\dfrac{2(x-2)}{x+2}$
36. $\dfrac{3(7t+2)}{4t(3t+2)}$　**37.** $\dfrac{z}{1-z}$　**38.** $\dfrac{10x}{3x^2+16}$　**39.** $c-d$
40. 4　**41.** $\frac{7}{2}$　**42.** $-6, -1$　**43.** $5\frac{1}{7}$ hr　**44.** Core 2
Duo: 45 sec; Core 2 Quad: 30 sec　**45.** Car: 105 km/h;
train: 90 km/h　**46.** 24 mph　**47.** 55 seals
48. 6　**49.** 🖉 The LCM of denominators is used to clear
fractions when simplifying a complex rational expression
using the method of multiplying by the LCD, and when
solving rational equations.　**50.** 🖉 Although multiplying
the denominators of the expressions being added results in a
common denominator, it is often not the *least* common
denominator. Using a common denominator other than the
LCD makes the expressions more complicated, requires
additional simplifying after the addition has been performed,
and leaves more room for error.　**51.** $\dfrac{5(a+3)^2}{a}$
52. $\dfrac{10a}{(a-b)(b-c)}$　**53.** 0

Test: Chapter 6, pp. 440–441

1. [6.1] 0   **2.** [6.1] −8   **3.** [6.1] −1, 1   **4.** [6.1] 1, 2

5. [6.1] $\dfrac{3x + 7}{x + 3}$ **6.** [6.2] $\dfrac{2t(t + 3)}{3(t - 1)}$

7. [6.2] $\dfrac{(5y + 1)(y + 1)}{3y(y + 2)}$ **8.** [6.2] $\dfrac{(2a + 1)(4a^2 + 1)}{4a^2(2a - 1)}$

9. [6.2] $(x + 3)(x - 3)$ **10.** [6.3] $(y - 3)(y + 3)(y + 7)$

11. [6.3] $\dfrac{-3x + 9}{x^3}$ **12.** [6.3] $\dfrac{-2t + 8}{t^2 + 1}$ **13.** [6.4] 1

14. [6.4] $\dfrac{3x - 5}{x - 3}$ **15.** [6.4] $\dfrac{11t - 8}{t(t - 2)}$

16. [6.4] $\dfrac{y^2 + 3}{(y - 1)(y + 3)^2}$ **17.** [6.4] $\dfrac{x^2 + 2x - 7}{(x + 1)(x - 1)^2}$

18. [6.5] $\dfrac{3y + 1}{y}$ **19.** [6.5] $x - 8$ **20.** [6.6] $\frac{8}{3}$

21. [6.6] −3, 5   **22.** [6.7] 12 min   **23.** [6.7] $1\frac{1}{4}$ mi

24. [6.7] Ryan: 65 km/h; Alicia: 45 km/h   **25.** [6.7] Rema: 4 hr; Pe'rez: 10 hr   **26.** [6.5] a **27.** [6.7] −1

Cumulative Review: Chapters 1–6, pp. 441–442

1. $a + cb$ **2.** −25   **3.** 25   **4.** $-3x + 33$ **5.** 10

6. −7, 7   **7.** $-\frac{5}{3}$ **8.** $\frac{8}{5}$ **9.** 4   **10.** −10, −1   **11.** −8

12. 1, 4   **13.** $\left\{ y \mid y \le -\frac{2}{3} \right\}$ **14.** −17   **15.** $-4, \frac{1}{2}$

16. $\{ x \mid x > 43 \}$ **17.** 5   **18.** $-\frac{7}{2}, 5$ **19.** −13

20. $b = 3a - c + 9$ **21.** $y = \dfrac{4z - 3x}{6}$

22.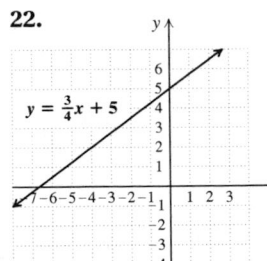

23.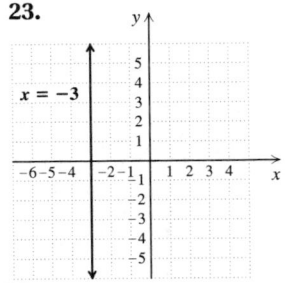

24.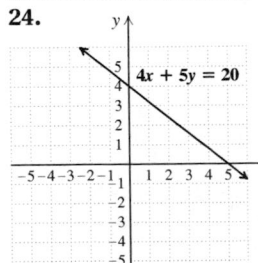

25.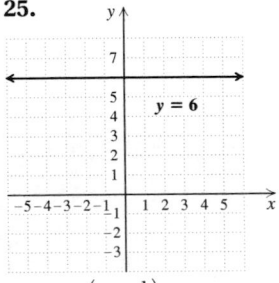

26. −2   **27.** Slope: $\frac{1}{2}$; y-intercept: $\left(0, -\frac{1}{4} \right)$

28. $y = -\frac{5}{8}x - 4$ **29.** $\dfrac{1}{x^2}$ **30.** y^{-7}, or $\dfrac{1}{y^7}$

31. $-4a^4 b^{14}$ **32.** $-y^3 - 2y^2 - 2y + 7$

33. $-15a + 10b - 5c$ **34.** $2x^5 + x^3 - 6x^2 - x + 3$

35. $36x^2 - 60xy + 25y^2$ **36.** $3n^2 - 13n - 10$

37. $4x^6 - 1$ **38.** $2x(3 - x - 12x^3)$

39. $(4x + 9)(4x - 9)$ **40.** $10(t + 1)(t^2 - t + 1)$

41. $(4x + 3)(2x + 1)$ **42.** $2(3x - 2)(x - 4)$

43. $(5t + 4)^2$ **44.** $(xy - 5)(xy + 4)$

45. $(x + 2)(x^3 - 3)$ **46.** $\dfrac{4}{t + 4}$ **47.** 1

48. $\dfrac{a^2 + 7ab + b^2}{(a + b)(a - b)}$ **49.** $\dfrac{2x + 5}{4 - x}$ **50.** $\dfrac{x}{x - 2}$

51. $\dfrac{y(3y^2 + 2)}{y^3 - 3}$ **52.** $6x^2 - 5x + 2 + \dfrac{4}{x} + \dfrac{1}{x^2}$

53. $15x^3 - 57x^2 + 177x - 529 + \dfrac{1605}{x + 3}$ **54.** 15 books

55. About 340.8 billion admissions   **56.** 33,339,507 and 33,339,508   **57.** 12 ft   **58.** $\frac{75}{4}$ min, or $18\frac{3}{4}$ min

59. 90 antelope   **60.** 150 calories   **61.** −144, 144

62. $16y^6 - y^4 + 6y^2 - 9$ **63.** −7, 4, 12   **64.** 18

CHAPTER 7

Exercise Set 7.1, pp. 450–455

1. Correspondence   **2.** Exactly   **3.** Domain

4. Range   **5.** Horizontal   **6.** Vertical   **7.** "f of 3," "f at 3," or "the value of f at 3"   **8.** Vertical   **9.** Yes   **11.** Yes

13. No   **15.** Yes   **17.** Function   **19.** Function

21. (a) −1; (b) −3   **23.** (a) 3; (b) 3   **25.** (a) 3; (b) 0

27. (a) 3; (b) −3   **29.** (a) 1; (b) 3   **31.** (a) 4; (b) −1, 3

33. (a) 2; (b) $\{ x \mid 0 < x \le 2 \}$, or $(0, 2]$ **35.** Yes   **37.** Yes

39. No   **41.** (a) 5; (b) −3; (c) −9; (d) 21;
(e) $2a + 9$; (f) $2a + 7$ **43.** (a) 0; (b) 1; (c) 57;
(d) $5t^2 + 4t$; (e) $20a^2 + 8a$; (f) 48   **45.** (a) $\frac{3}{5}$; (b) $\frac{1}{3}$; (c) $\frac{4}{7}$;
(d) 0; (e) $\dfrac{x - 1}{2x - 1}$; (f) $\dfrac{a + h - 3}{2a + 2h - 5}$

47. $4\sqrt{3}$ cm^2 ≈ 6.93 cm^2 **49.** 36π in^2 ≈ 113.10 in^2

51. 164.98 cm   **53.** 23°F   **55.** 75 heart attacks per 10,000 men   **57.** 500 movies

59. 19 watts; 30 watts

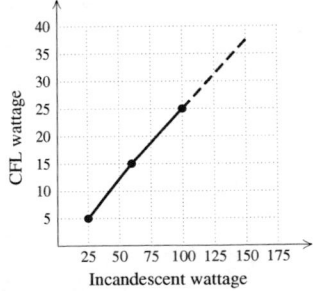

61. 3.5 drinks; 6 drinks

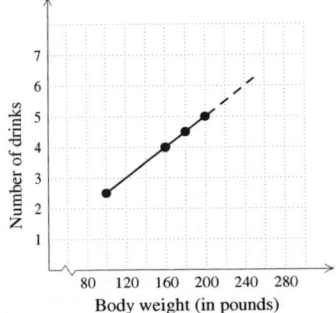

63. $257,000; $306,000

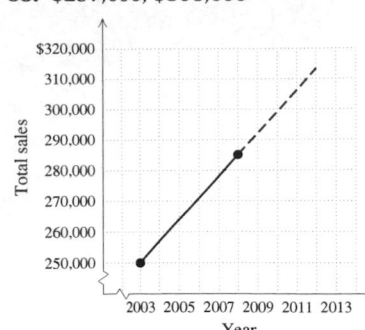

65. 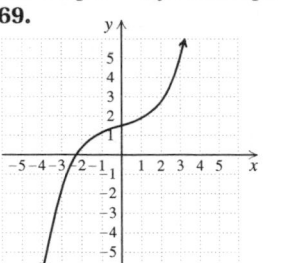   **67.** 6
68. $-6, 6$ **69.** $-\frac{1}{2}$
70. $-1, 1$
71. $-4, 3$ **72.** $\frac{9}{32}$
73. $\frac{1}{7}$ **74.** $-4, 8$
75. 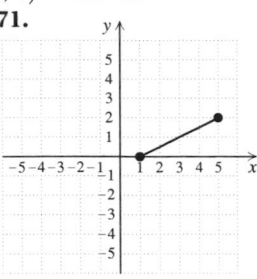   **77.** 26; 99
79. Worm
81. About 2 min 50 sec
83. 1 every 3 min

63. Slope: $\frac{2}{3}$; y-intercept: $(0, -4)$
64. Slope: $-\frac{1}{4}$; y-intercept: $(0, 6)$
65. Slope: $\frac{4}{3}$; y-intercept: $(0, 0)$
66. Slope: -5; y-intercept: $(0, 0)$ **67.**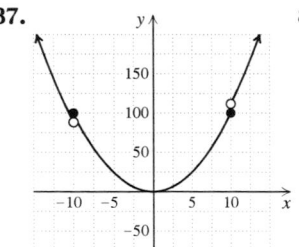
69.   **71.**

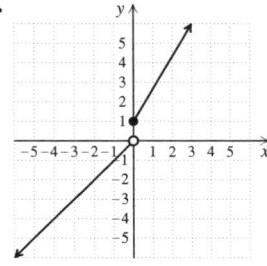

73. Domain: $\{x\,|\,x$ is a real number *and* $x \neq 0\}$; range: $\{y\,|\,y$ is a real number *and* $y \neq 0\}$
75. Domain: $\{x\,|\,x < -2 \ or \ x > 0\}$; range: $\{y\,|\,y < -2 \ or \ y > 3\}$ **77.** Domain: $\mathbb{R}$; range: $\{y\,|\,y \geq 0\}$, or $[0, \infty)$ **79.** Domain: $\{x\,|\,x$ is a real number *and* $x \neq 2\}$; range: $\{y\,|\,y$ is a real number *and* $y \neq 0\}$
81. $\{h\,|\,0 \leq h \leq 144\}$, or $[0, 144]$
83.   **85.**

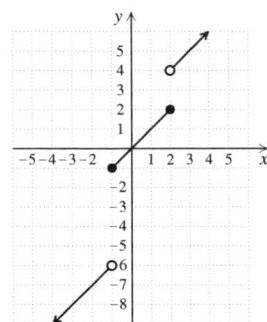

85.

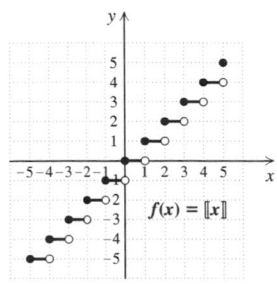

$f(x) = [\![x]\!]$

Exercise Set 7.2, pp. 461–463

1. (c)   **2.** (d)   **3.** (d)   **4.** (b)   **5.** (c)   **6.** (b)
7. Domain: $\{2, 9, -2, -4\}$; range: $\{8, 3, 10, 4\}$
9. Domain: $\{0, 4, -5, -1\}$; range: $\{0, -2\}$
11. Domain: $\{-4, -2, 0, 2, 4\}$; range: $\{-2, -1, 0, 1, 2\}$
13. Domain: $\{-5, -3, -1, 0, 2, 4\}$; range: $\{-1, 1\}$
15. Domain: $\{x\,|\,-4 \leq x \leq 3\}$, or $[-4, 3]$; range: $\{y\,|\,-3 \leq y \leq 4\}$, or $[-3, 4]$ **17.** Domain: $\{x\,|\,-4 \leq x \leq 5\}$, or $[-4, 5]$; range: $\{y\,|\,-2 \leq y \leq 4\}$, or $[-2, 4]$ **19.** Domain: $\{x\,|\,-4 \leq x \leq 4\}$, or $[-4, 4]$; range: $\{-3, -1, 1\}$ **21.** Domain: $\mathbb{R}$; range: $\mathbb{R}$
23. Domain: $\mathbb{R}$; range: $\{4\}$ **25.** Domain: $\mathbb{R}$; range: $\{y\,|\,y \geq 1\}$, or $[1, \infty)$ **27.** Domain: $\{x\,|\,x$ is a real number *and* $x \neq -2\}$; range: $\{y\,|\,y$ is a real number *and* $y \neq -4\}$
29. Domain: $\{x\,|\,x \geq 0\}$, or $[0, \infty)$; range: $\{y\,|\,y \geq 0\}$, or $[0, \infty)$ **31.** $\{x\,|\,x$ is a real number *and* $x \neq 3\}$
33. $\{x\,|\,x$ is a real number *and* $x \neq \frac{1}{2}\}$ **35.** $\mathbb{R}$ **37.** $\mathbb{R}$
39. $\{x\,|\,x$ is a real number *and* $x \neq 3 \ and \ x \neq -3\}$ **41.** $\mathbb{R}$
43. $\{x\,|\,x$ is a real number *and* $x \neq -1 \ and \ x \neq -7\}$
45. $\{t\,|\,0 \leq t < 624\}$, or $[0, 624)$
47. $\{p\,|\,\$0 \leq p \leq \$10.60\}$, or $[0, 10.60]$ **49.** $\{d\,|\,d \geq 0\}$, or $[0, \infty)$ **51.** $\{t\,|\,0 \leq t \leq 5\}$, or $[0, 5]$ **53.** (a) -5; (b) 1; (c) 21   **55.** (a) 0; (b) 2; (c) 7   **57.** (a) 100; (b) 100; (c) 131   **59.**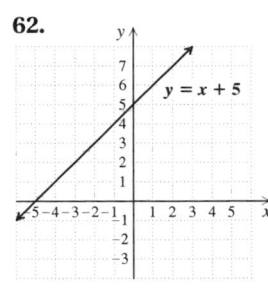
61.   **62.**

$y = x + 5$

$y = 2x - 3$

Visualizing for Success, p. 469

1. D   **2.** J   **3.** A   **4.** E   **5.** B   **6.** C   **7.** I   **8.** F
9. G   **10.** H

Exercise Set 7.3, pp. 470–473

1. False   **2.** True   **3.** False   **4.** True
5. True   **6.** True

7.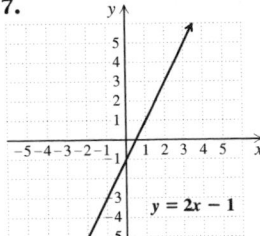
$y = 2x - 1$

9.
$y = -\frac{2}{3}x + 3$

11.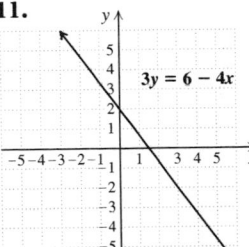
$3y = 6 - 4x$

13.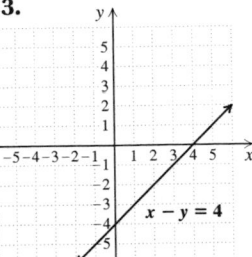
$x - y = 4$

15.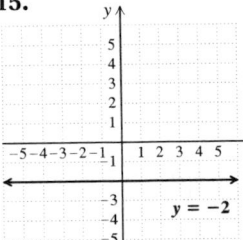
$y = -2$

17.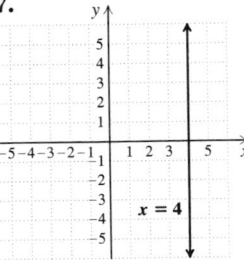
$x = 4$

19.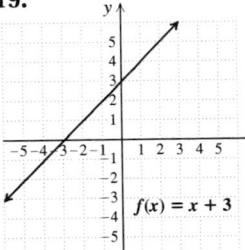
$f(x) = x + 3$

21.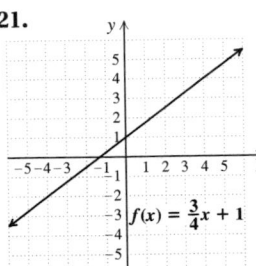
$f(x) = \frac{3}{4}x + 1$

23.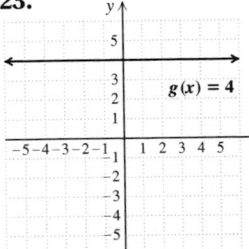
$g(x) = 4$

25. $C(d) = 0.75d + 30$; 60 miles
27. $L(t) = \frac{1}{2}t + 5$; 20 months after the haircut
29. $A(t) = 849t + 5960$; 5 years after 2006, or 2011
31. (a) $a(t) = 0.9t + 12.7$; **(b)** 24.4 million cars; **(c)** about 2014
33. (a) $E(t) = 0.14t + 78.44$; **(b)** 81.52 yr
35. (a) $A(t) = 22.525t + 236.95$; **(b)** \$462.2 million
37. (a) $N(t) = 9.4t + 16$; **(b)** 110 million Americans; **(c)** 2015   **39. (a)** $A(t) = \frac{41}{110}t + \frac{1615}{22}$; **(b)** about 80.9 million acres   **41.** Linear function; $\mathbb{R}$
43. Quadratic function; $\mathbb{R}$ **45.** Rational function; $\left\{ t \mid t \text{ is a real number } and \ t \neq -\frac{4}{3} \right\}$ **47.** Polynomial function; $\mathbb{R}$
49. Rational function; $\left\{ x \mid x \text{ is a real number } and \ x \neq \frac{5}{2} \right\}$
51. Rational function; $\{ n \mid n \text{ is a real number } and \ n \neq -1 \ and \ n \neq -2 \}$ **53.** Linear function; $\mathbb{R}$ **55.** $\{ y \mid y \geq 0 \}$, or $[0, \infty)$ **57.** $\mathbb{R}$ **59.** $\{ y \mid y \leq 0 \}$, or $(-\infty, 0]$

61.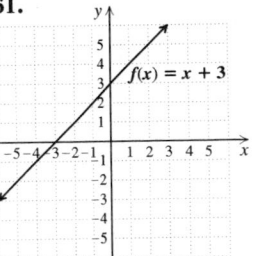
$f(x) = x + 3$
Domain: $\mathbb{R}$; range: $\mathbb{R}$

63.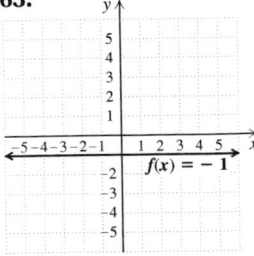
$f(x) = -1$
Domain: $\mathbb{R}$; range: $\{-1\}$

65.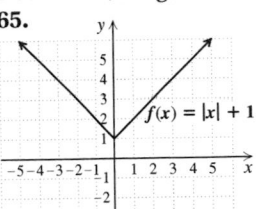
$f(x) = |x| + 1$
Domain: $\mathbb{R}$;
range: $\{ y \mid y \geq 1 \}$, or $[1, \infty)$

67.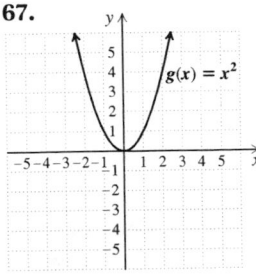
$g(x) = x^2$
Domain: $\mathbb{R}$;
range: $\{ y \mid y \geq 0 \}$, or $[0, \infty)$

69. ▧   **71.** $4x^2 + 2x - 1$ **72.** $2x^3 - x^2 - x + 7$
73. $2x^2 - 13x - 7$ **74.** $x^2 + x - 12$
75. $x^3 - 2x^2 - 3x + 5$ **76.** $x^3 + 2x^2 + x + 4$
77. ▧   **79.** False   **81.** False   **83.** 21.1°C   **85.** \$60
87. (a) $g(x) = x - 8$; **(b)** -10; **(c)** 83

Connecting the Concepts, p. 474

1. $\{-1, 0, 3, 4\}$ **2.** $\{-2, 0, 6, 8\}$ **3.** -2
4.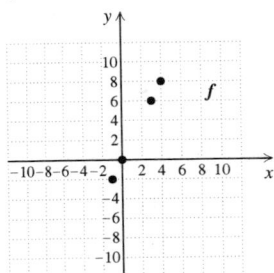
f
    5. $\mathbb{R}$

6. $\{ x \mid x \text{ is a real number } and \ x \neq 0 \}$ **7.** $\frac{1}{5}$ **8.** 2   **9.** 3
10. $\{ x \mid x \text{ is a real number } and \ x \neq 0 \ and \ x \neq 1 \}$
11. Linear function   **12.** Rational function
13. Range: $\mathbb{R}$

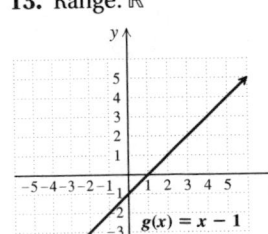
$g(x) = x - 1$

14. Yes   **15.** -4
16. $\{ x \mid x \geq -3 \}$, or $[-3, \infty)$
17. $\{ y \mid y \geq -4 \}$, or $[-4, \infty)$
18. 4   **19.** 10   **20.** 13

Exercise Set 7.4, pp. 480–483

1. Sum   **2.** Subtract   **3.** Evaluate   **4.** Domains
5. Excluding   **6.** Sum   **7.** 1   **9.** 5   **11.** -7 **13.** 1
15. -5 **17.** $x^2 - 2x - 2$ **19.** $x^2 - x + 3$ **21.** 5
23. $-a^3 + 5a^2 + 2a - 10$ **25.** $\dfrac{x^2 - 2}{5 - x}, x \neq 5$ **27.** $\frac{7}{2}$
29. -2 **31.** $1.2 + 2.9 = 4.1$ million   **33.** 4%
35. About 95 million; the number of tons of municipal solid waste that was composted or recycled in 2005   **37.** About 215 million; the number of tons of municipal solid waste in 1996   **39.** About 230 million; the number of tons of municipal solid waste that was not composted in 2004
41. $\mathbb{R}$ **43.** $\{x \mid x$ is a real number $and\, x \neq -5\}$
45. $\{x \mid x$ is a real number $and\, x \neq 0\}$
47. $\{x \mid x$ is a real number $and\, x \neq 1\}$
49. $\left\{x \mid x$ is a real number $and\, x \neq -\frac{9}{2}\, and\, x \neq 1\right\}$
51. $\{x \mid x$ is a real number $and\, x \neq 3\}$
53. $\{x \mid x$ is a real number $and\, x \neq -4\}$
55. $\{x \mid x$ is a real number $and\, x \neq 4\, and\, x \neq 5\}$
57. $\left\{x \mid x$ is a real number $and\, x \neq -1\, and\, x \neq -\frac{5}{2}\right\}$
59. 4; 3   **61.** 5; -1 **63.** $\{x \mid 0 \leq x \leq 9\};$
$\{x \mid 3 \leq x \leq 10\}; \{x \mid 3 \leq x \leq 9\}; \{x \mid 3 \leq x \leq 9\}$

65.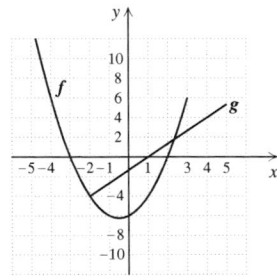

67. ✍   **69.** $c = \dfrac{b}{a}$
70. $w = \dfrac{x - y}{z}$
71. $q = \dfrac{st}{p - r}$
72. $b = \dfrac{d}{a + c}$
73. $b = \dfrac{cd + d}{a - 3}$
74. $d = \dfrac{ab - 3b}{c + 1}$

75. ✍   **77.** $\{x \mid x$ is a real number $and\, x \neq 4\, and\, x \neq 3$ $and\, x \neq 2\, and\, x \neq -2\}$
79. Answers may vary.

81. $\left\{x \mid x$ is a real number $and -1 < x < 5\, and\, x \neq \frac{3}{2}\right\}$
83. Answers may vary. $f(x) = \dfrac{1}{x + 2}, g(x) = \dfrac{1}{x - 5}$
85. ▨

Exercise Set 7.5, pp. 490–495

1. (d)   **2.** (f)   **3.** (e)   **4.** (b)   **5.** (a)   **6.** (c)
7. Inverse   **8.** Direct   **9.** Direct   **10.** Inverse
11. Inverse   **12.** Direct   **13.** $d = \dfrac{L}{f}$

15. $v_1 = \dfrac{2s}{t} - v_2,$ or $\dfrac{2s - tv_2}{t}$ **17.** $b = \dfrac{at}{a - t}$
19. $g = \dfrac{Rs}{s - R}$ **21.** $n = \dfrac{IR}{E - Ir}$ **23.** $q = \dfrac{pf}{p - f}$
25. $t_1 = \dfrac{H}{Sm} + t_2,$ or $\dfrac{H + Smt_2}{Sm}$ **27.** $r = \dfrac{Re}{E - e}$
29. $r = 1 - \dfrac{a}{S},$ or $\dfrac{S - a}{S}$ **31.** $a + b = \dfrac{f}{c^2}$
33. $r = \dfrac{A}{P} - 1,$ or $\dfrac{A - P}{P}$
35. $t_1 = t_2 - \dfrac{d_2 - d_1}{v},$ or $\dfrac{vt_2 - d_2 + d_1}{v}$ **37.** $t = \dfrac{ab}{b + a}$
39. $Q = \dfrac{2Tt - 2AT}{A - q}$ **41.** $w = \dfrac{4.15c - 98.42}{p + 0.082}$
43. $k = 6; y = 6x$ **45.** $k = 1.7; y = 1.7x$
47. $k = 10; y = 10x$ **49.** $k = 100; y = \dfrac{100}{x}$
51. $k = 44; y = \dfrac{44}{x}$ **53.** $k = 9; y = \dfrac{9}{x}$ **55.** $33\frac{1}{3}$ cm
57. 3.5 hr   **59.** 56 in.   **61.** 32 kg   **63.** 286 Hz
65. About 21 min   **67.** About 110,000,000 tons
69. $y = \frac{1}{2}x^2$ **71.** $y = \dfrac{5000}{x^2}$ **73.** $y = 1.5xz$
75. $y = \dfrac{4wx^2}{z}$ **77.** 61.3 ft   **79.** 308 cm^3
81. About 57 mph   **83.** ✍   **85.** $y = \frac{1}{6}x - \frac{1}{2}$
86. $y = \frac{3}{8}x - \frac{5}{8}$ **87.** $y = -\frac{5}{2}x - \frac{3}{2}$ **88.** $y = -\frac{1}{8}x + \frac{1}{2}$
89. Let n represent the number; $2n + 5 = 49$ **90.** Let x represent the number; $\frac{1}{2}x - 3 = 57$ **91.** Let x represent the number; $x + (x + 1) = 145$ **92.** Let n represent the number; $n - (-n) = 20$ **93.** ✍   **95.** 567 mi
97. Ratio is $\dfrac{a + 12}{a + 6}$; percent increase is $\dfrac{6}{a + 6} \cdot 100\%$, or $\dfrac{600}{a + 6}\%$ **99.** $t_1 = t_2 + \dfrac{(d_2 - d_1)(t_4 - t_3)}{a(t_4 - t_2)(t_4 - t_3) + d_3 - d_4}$
101. The intensity is halved.   **103.** About 1.7 m
105. $d(s) = \dfrac{28}{s}; 70$ yd

Review Exercises: Chapter 7, pp. 498–500

1. True   **2.** True   **3.** False   **4.** True   **5.** False
6. True   **7.** True   **8.** True   **9.** True   **10.** False
11. (a) 3; (b) $\{x \mid -2 \leq x \leq 4\}$, or $[-2, 4]$; (c) -1; (d) $\{y \mid 1 \leq y \leq 5\}$, or $[1, 5]$ **12.** $\frac{3}{2}$ **13.** $4a^2 + 4a - 3$
14. 10.53 yr   **15.** About $9.30;

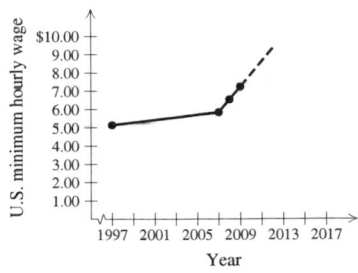

16. (a) Yes; (b) Domain: $\mathbb{R}$; range: $\{y \mid y \geq 0\}$, or $[0, \infty)$

17. (a) No   **18. (a)** No   **19. (a)** Yes; **(b)** Domain: $\mathbb{R}$;
range: $\{-2\}$ **20.** $\mathbb{R}$
21. $\{x \mid x$ is a real number $and \ x \neq 1\}$
22. $\{t \mid t$ is a real number $and \ t \neq -1 \ and \ t \neq -4\}$
23. $\{t \mid 0 \leq t \leq 60\}$, or $[0, 60]$ **24. (a)** 5; **(b)** 4;
(c) 16; **(d)** 35   **25.** $C(t) = 30t + 90$; 7 months
26. (a) $R(t) = -\frac{43}{2400}t + \frac{15{,}843}{800}$; **(b)** about 19.21 sec; about
19.09 sec   **27.** Absolute-value function   **28.** Polynomial
function   **29.** Quadratic function   **30.** Linear function
31. Rational function
32.

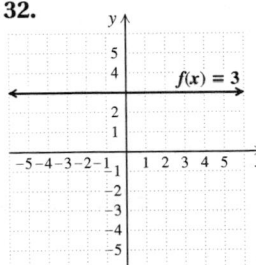

Domain: $\mathbb{R}$; range: $\{3\}$
34.

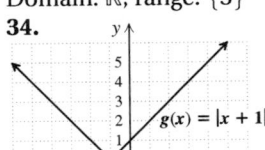

Domain: $\mathbb{R}$; range: $\{y \mid y \geq 0\}$,
or $[0, \infty)$

33.

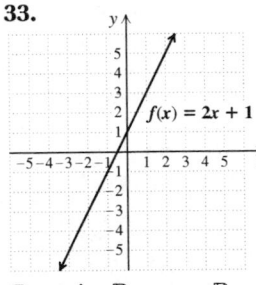

Domain: $\mathbb{R}$; range: $\mathbb{R}$
35. 102   **36.** -17
37. $-\frac{9}{2}$ **38.** $\mathbb{R}$

39. $\{x \mid x$ is a real number $and \ x \neq 2\}$ **40.** $r = \dfrac{2V - IR}{2I}$,

or $\dfrac{V}{I} - \dfrac{R}{2}$ **41.** $m = \dfrac{H}{S(t_1 - t_2)}$ **42.** $c = \dfrac{b + 3a}{2}$

43. $t_1 = \dfrac{-A}{vT} + t_2$, or $\dfrac{-A + vTt_2}{vT}$ **44.** $y = \frac{15}{2}x$

45. $y = \dfrac{\frac{3}{4}}{x}$ **46.** $y = \dfrac{1}{2}\dfrac{xw^2}{z}$ **47.** 15 min

48. 22.5 lb   **49.** About 2.9 sec   **50.** ✍ Two functions
that have the same domain and range are not necessarily
identical. For example, the functions f: $\{(-2, 1), (-3, 2)\}$
and g: $\{(-2, 2), (-3, 1)\}$ have the same domain and range
but are different functions.   **51.** ✍ Jenna is not correct.
Any value of the variable that makes a denominator 0
is not in the domain; 0 itself may or may not make a
denominator 0.   **52.** $f(x) = 10.94x + 20$ **53.** Domain:
$\{x \mid x \geq -4 \ and \ x \neq 2\}$; range: $\{y \mid y \geq 0 \ and \ y \neq 3\}$

Test: Chapter 7, pp. 501–502

1. [7.1], [7.2] **(a)** 1; **(b)** $\{x \mid -3 \leq x \leq 4\}$, or $[-3, 4]$; **(c)** 3;
(d) $\{y \mid -1 \leq y \leq 2\}$, or $[-1, 2]$ **2.** [7.1] About 49 million
international visitors   **3. (a)** [7.1] Yes; **(b)** [7.2] domain: $\mathbb{R}$;
range: $\mathbb{R}$ **4. (a)** [7.1] Yes; **(b)** [7.2] domain: $\mathbb{R}$;
range: $\{y \mid y \geq 1\}$, or $[1, \infty)$ **5. (a)** [7.1] No
6. [7.2] $\{t \mid 0 \leq t \leq 4\}$, or $[0, 4]$ **7.** [7.2] **(a)** -5; **(b)** 10
8. [7.3] $C(t) = 55t + 180$; 12 months

9. [7.3] **(a)** $C(m) = 0.3m + 25$; **(b)** \$175
10. [7.3] Linear function; $\mathbb{R}$ **11.** [7.3] Rational function;
$\{x \mid x$ is a real number $and \ x \neq -4 \ and \ x \neq 4\}$
12. [7.3] Quadratic function; $\mathbb{R}$
13. [7.3]   **14.** [7.3]

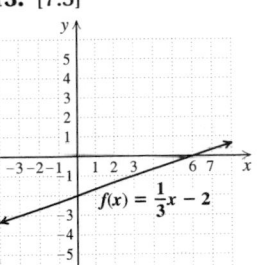   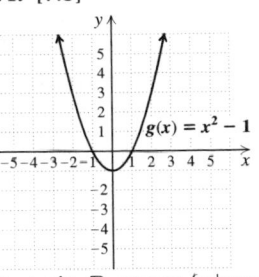

Domain: $\mathbb{R}$; range: $\mathbb{R}$ Domain: $\mathbb{R}$; range: $\{y \mid y \geq -1\}$,
or $[-1, \infty)$

15. [7.3]   **16.** [7.1] -1
                              17. [7.1] $10a + 1$
                              18. [7.4] $\frac{1}{x} + 2x + 1$

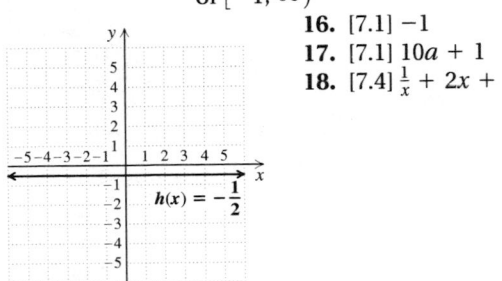

Domain: $\mathbb{R}$; range: $\left\{-\frac{1}{2}\right\}$
19. [7.1] $\{x \mid x$ is a real number $and \ x \neq 0\}$
20. [7.4] $\{x \mid x$ is a real number $and \ x \neq 0\}$
21. [7.4] $\left\{x \mid x$ is a real number $and \ x \neq 0 \ and \ x \neq -\frac{1}{2}\right\}$

22. [7.5] $s = \dfrac{Rg}{g - R}$ **23.** [7.5] $y = \frac{1}{2}x$ **24.** [7.5] 30 workers
25. [7.5] 637 in^2 **26.** [7.3] **(a)** 30 mi; **(b)** 15 mph
27. [7.4] $h(x) = 7x - 2$

Cumulative Review: Chapters 1–7, pp. 502–504

1. 10   **2.** 3.91×10^8 **3.** Slope: $\frac{7}{4}$; y-intercept: $(0, -3)$
4. $y = -2x + 5$ **5. (a)** 0; **(b)** $\{x \mid x$ is a real number and
$x \neq 5 \ and \ x \neq 6\}$
6.   **7.**

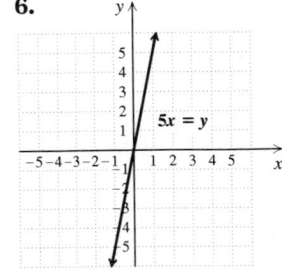   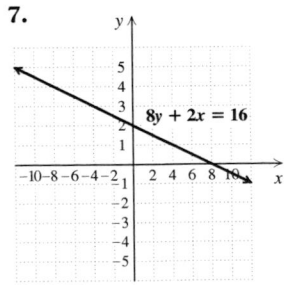

8.   **9.**

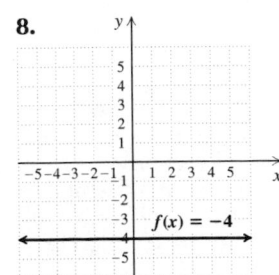   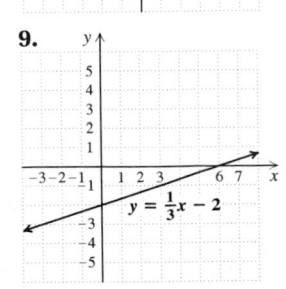

10. $-24x^4y^4$ **11.** $15x^4 - x^3 - 9x^2 + 5x - 2$
12. $9x^4 + 6x^2y + y^2$ **13.** $4x^4 - 81$

14. $-m^3n^2 - m^2n^2 - 5mn^3$ **15.** $\dfrac{y-6}{2}$ **16.** $x - 1$

17. $\dfrac{a^2 + 7ab + b^2}{(a-b)(a+b)}$ **18.** $\dfrac{-m^2 + 5m - 6}{(m+1)(m-5)}$ **19.** $\dfrac{3y^2 - 2}{3y}$

20. $\dfrac{y-x}{xy(x+y)}$ **21.** $4x(x^2 + 100)$ **22.** $(x-6)(x+14)$
23. $(4y-5)(4y+5)$ **24.** $8(2x+1)(4x^2 - 2x + 1)$
25. $(t-8)^2$ **26.** $x^2(x-1)(x+1)(x^2+1)$
27. $\left(\frac{1}{2}b - c\right)\left(\frac{1}{4}b^2 + \frac{1}{2}bc + c^2\right)$ **28.** $(3t-4)(t+7)$
29. $(x^2 - y)(x^3 + y)$ **30.** $\frac{1}{4}$ **31.** $-12, 12$
32. $\{x \,|\, x \geq -1\}$, or $[-1, \infty)$ **33.** $\frac{3}{5}$ **34.** -1

35. No solution   **36.** $a = \dfrac{Pb}{4-P}$ **37.** -5 **38.** 8

39. 0   **40.** $y = -x + 3$ **41.** 99   **42.** $\dfrac{x^2 - 1}{x+5}$

43. $\{x \,|\, x$ is a real number $and\ x \neq -6\}$
44. Domain: $\{x \,|\, -4 \leq x \leq 3\}$; or $[-4, 3]$;
range: $\{y \,|\, -3 \leq y \leq 0\ or\ y = 2\}$
45. (a) $r(t) = 45.95t + 20$; **(b)** \$1076.85 million; **(c)** in
2016–2017   **46.** 34 performances per month, or 408 performances per year   **47.** 72 in.   **48.** IQAir HealthPro:
10 min; Austin Healthmate: 15 min   **49.** 12 billion hr
50. $22\frac{1}{2}$ min   **51.** \$1.09 billion
52. $x^3 - 12x^2 + 48x - 64$ **53.** $-3, 3, -5, 5$
54. All real numbers except 9 and -5 **55.** $-\frac{1}{4}, 0, \frac{1}{4}$

56. $C(x) = \begin{cases} 12, \text{ if } x \leq 20, \\ 12 + 0.75(x - 20), \text{ if } x > 20 \end{cases}$

CHAPTER 8

Technology Connection, p. 510

1. $(1.53, 2.58)$ **2.** $(-0.26, 57.06)$ **3.** $(2.23, 1.14)$
4. $(0.87, -0.32)$

Visualizing for Success, p. 512

1. C   **2.** H   **3.** J   **4.** G   **5.** D   **6.** I   **7.** A   **8.** F
9. E   **10.** B

Exercise Set 8.1, pp. 513–515

1. False   **2.** True   **3.** True   **4.** True   **5.** True
6. False   **7.** False   **8.** True   **9.** Yes   **11.** No
13. Yes   **15.** Yes   **17.** $(3, 2)$ **19.** $(2, -1)$ **21.** $(1, 4)$
23. $(-3, -2)$ **25.** $(3, -1)$ **27.** $(3, -7)$ **29.** $(7, 2)$
31. $(4, 0)$ **33.** No solution   **35.** $\{(x, y) \,|\, y = 3 - x\}$
37. All except Exercise 33   **39.** Exercise 35
41. Let x represent the first number and y the second number; $x + y = 10, x = \frac{2}{3}y$ **43.** Let p represent the number
of personal e-mails and b the number of business e-mails;
$p + b = 578, b = p + 30$ **45.** Let x and y represent the
angles; $x + y = 180, x = 2y - 3$ **47.** Let x represent the
number of two-point shots and y the number of foul shots;
$x + y = 64, 2x + y = 100$ **49.** Let x represent the

number of hats sold and y the number of tee shirts sold;
$x + y = 45, 14.50x + 19.50y = 697.50$ **51.** Let h represent the number of vials of Humalog sold and n the number
of vials of Lantus; $h + n = 50, 83.29h + 76.76n = 3981.66$
53. Let l represent the length, in yards, and w the width, in
yards; $2l + 2w = 340; l = w + 50$ **55.** 🖾   **57.** $\frac{8}{13}$
58. -1 **59.** $-\frac{1}{10}$ **60.** 11   **61.** $y = 3x - 4$
62. $x = \frac{5}{2}y - \frac{7}{2}$ **63.** 🖾   **65.** Answers may vary.
(a) $x + y = 6, x - y = 4$; **(b)** $x + y = 1, 2x + 2y = 3$;
(c) $x + y = 1, 2x + 2y = 2$ **67.** $A = -\frac{17}{4}, B = -\frac{12}{5}$
69. Let x and y represent the number of years that Dell
and Juanita have taught at the university, respectively;
$x + y = 46, x - 2 = 2.5(y - 2)$ **71.** Let s and v represent
the number of ounces of baking soda and vinegar needed,
respectively; $s = 4v, s + v = 16$ **73.** Mineral oil: 12 oz;
vinegar: 4 oz   **75.** $(0, 0), (1, 1)$ **77.** $(0.07, -7.95)$
79. $(0.00, 1.25)$

Exercise Set 8.2, pp. 521–523

1. (d)   **2.** (e)   **3.** (a)   **4.** (f)   **5.** (c)   **6.** (b)
7. $(2, -1)$ **9.** $(-4, 3)$ **11.** $(2, -2)$
13. $\{(x, y) \,|\, 2x - 3 = y\}$ **15.** $(-2, 1)$ **17.** $\left(\frac{1}{2}, \frac{1}{2}\right)$
19. $(2, 0)$ **21.** No solution   **23.** $(1, 2)$ **25.** $(7, -2)$
27. $(-1, 2)$ **29.** $\left(\frac{49}{11}, -\frac{12}{11}\right)$ **31.** $(6, 2)$ **33.** No solution
35. $(20, 0)$ **37.** $(3, -1)$ **39.** $\{(x, y) \,|\, -4x + 2y = 5\}$
41. $\left(2, -\frac{3}{2}\right)$ **43.** $(-2, -9)$ **45.** $(30, 6)$
47. $\{(x, y) \,|\, 4x - 2y = 2\}$ **49.** No solution
51. $(140, 60)$ **53.** $\left(\frac{1}{3}, -\frac{2}{3}\right)$ **55.** 🖾   **57.** Toaster oven:
3 kWh; convection oven: 12 kWh   **58.** 90   **59.** \$105,000
60. 290 mi   **61.** First: 30 in.; second: 60 in.; third: 6 in.
62. 165 min   **63.** 🖾   **65.** $m = -\frac{1}{2}, b = \frac{5}{2}$
67. $a = 5, b = 2$ **69.** $\left(-\frac{32}{17}, \frac{38}{17}\right)$ **71.** $\left(-\frac{1}{5}, \frac{1}{10}\right)$ **73.** 🖾

Connecting the Concepts, pp. 523–524

1. $(1, 1)$ **2.** $(9, 1)$ **3.** $(4, 3)$ **4.** $(5, 7)$ **5.** $(5, 10)$
6. $\left(2, \frac{2}{5}\right)$ **7.** No solution   **8.** $\{(x, y) \,|\, x = 2 - y\}$
9. $(1, 1)$ **10.** $(0, 0)$ **11.** $(6, -1)$ **12.** No solution
13. $(3, 1)$ **14.** $\left(\frac{95}{71}, -\frac{1}{142}\right)$ **15.** $(1, 1)$ **16.** $(11, -3)$
17. $\{(x, y) \,|\, x - 2y = 5\}$ **18.** $\left(1, -\frac{1}{19}\right)$ **19.** $\left(\frac{201}{23}, -\frac{18}{23}\right)$
20. $\left(\frac{40}{9}, \frac{10}{3}\right)$

Exercise Set 8.3, pp. 532–536

1. 4, 6   **3.** Personal e-mails: 274; business e-mails: 304
5. 119°, 61°   **7.** Two-point shots: 36; foul shots: 28
9. Hats: 36; tee shirts: 9   **11.** Humalog vials: 22; Lantus
vials: 28   **13.** Length: 110 yd; width: 60 yd   **15.** Regular
paper: 32 reams; recycled paper: 84 reams   **17.** 13-watt
bulbs: 60; 18-watt bulbs: 140   **19.** HP C7115A cartridges:
180; M3908GA cartridges: 270   **21.** Mexican: 14 lb;
Peruvian: 14 lb   **23.** Custom-printed M&Ms: 64 oz; bulk
M&Ms: 256 oz   **25.** 50%-chocolate: 7.5 lb; 10%-chocolate:
12.5 lb   **27.** Deep Thought: 12 lb; Oat Dream: 8 lb
29. \$7500 at 6.5%; \$4500 at 7.2%   **31.** Steady State: 12.5 L;
Even Flow: 7.5 L   **33.** 87-octane: 2.5 gal; 95-octane: 7.5 gal
35. Whole milk: $169\frac{3}{13}$ lb; cream: $30\frac{10}{13}$ lb   **37.** 375 km

39. 14 km/h   **41.** About 1489 mi   **43.** Length: 265 ft; width: 165 ft   **45.** Wii game machines: 3.63 million; PlayStation 3 consoles: 1.21 million   **47.** $8.99 plans: 182; $4.99 plans: 68   **49.** Quarters: 17; fifty-cent pieces: 13
51. ✍   **53.** 1   **54.** $\frac{1}{2}$ **55.** −13   **56.** 17   **57.** 7
58. $\frac{13}{4}$ **59.** ✍   **61.** 0%: 20 reams; 30%: 40 reams
63. $10\frac{2}{3}$ oz   **65.** 12 sets   **67.** Brown: 0.8 gal; neutral: 0.2 gal   **69.** City: 261 mi; highway: 204 mi
71. $P(x) = \dfrac{0.1 + x}{1.5}$ (This expresses the percent as a decimal quantity.)

Exercise Set 8.4, pp. 543–544

1. True   **2.** False   **3.** False   **4.** True   **5.** True
6. False   **7.** Yes   **9.** $(3, 1, 2)$ **11.** $(1, -2, 2)$
13. $(2, -5, -6)$ **15.** No solution   **17.** $(-2, 0, 5)$
19. $(21, -14, -2)$ **21.** The equations are dependent.
23. $\left(3, \frac{1}{2}, -4\right)$ **25.** $\left(\frac{1}{2}, \frac{1}{3}, \frac{1}{6}\right)$ **27.** $\left(\frac{1}{2}, \frac{2}{3}, -\frac{5}{6}\right)$
29. $(15, 33, 9)$ **31.** $(3, 4, -1)$ **33.** $(10, 23, 50)$
35. No solution   **37.** The equations are dependent.
39. ✍   **41.** Let x and y represent the numbers: $x = \frac{1}{2}y$
42. Let x and y represent the numbers; $x - y = 2x$
43. Let x represent the first number; $x + (x + 1) + (x + 2) = 100$
44. Let x, y, and z represent the numbers; $x + y + z = 100$
45. Let x, y, and z represent the numbers; $xy = 5z$
46. Let x and y represent the numbers; $xy = 2(x + y)$
47. ✍   **49.** $(1, -1, 2)$ **51.** $(1, -2, 4, -1)$
53. $\left(-1, \frac{1}{5}, -\frac{1}{2}\right)$ **55.** 14   **57.** $z = 8 - 2x - 4y$ **59.** ✍

Exercise Set 8.5, pp. 548–551

1. 8, 15, 62   **3.** 8, 21, −3   **5.** 32°, 96°, 52°
7. Reading: 502; mathematics: 515; writing: 494
9. Bran muffin: 1.5 g; banana: 3 g; 1 cup of Wheaties: 3 g
11. Basic price: $30,610; tow package: $205; camera: $750
13. 12-oz cups: 17; 16-oz cups: 25; 20-oz cups: 13
15. Bank loan: $15,000; small-business loan: $35,000; mortgage: $70,000
17. Gold: $30/g; silver: $3/g; copper: $0.02/g
19. Roast beef: 2 servings; baked potato: 1 serving; broccoli: 2 servings
21. First mezzanine: 8 tickets; main floor: 12 tickets; second mezzanine: 20 tickets
23. Asia: 5.5 billion; Africa: 2.0 billion; rest of the world: 1.9 billion   **25.** ✍   **27.** $-4x + 6y$ **28.** $-x + 6y$
29. $7y$ **30.** $11a$ **31.** $-2a + b + 6c$
32. $-50a - 30b + 10c$ **33.** $-12x + 5y - 8z$
34. $23x - 13z$ **35.** ✍   **37.** Applicant: $87; spouse: $87; first child: $47; second child: $42   **39.** 20 yr   **41.** 35 tickets

Exercise Set 8.6, pp. 555–556

1. Matrix   **2.** Horizontal; columns   **3.** Entry
4. Matrices   **5.** Rows   **6.** First   **7.** $(3, 4)$ **9.** $(-2, 5)$
11. $\left(\frac{3}{2}, \frac{5}{2}\right)$ **13.** $\left(2, \frac{1}{2}, -2\right)$ **15.** $(2, -2, 1)$ **17.** $\left(4, \frac{1}{2}, -\frac{1}{2}\right)$
19. $(1, -3, -2, -1)$ **21.** Dimes: 18; nickels: 24
23. Dried fruit: 9 lb; macadamia nuts: 6 lb

25. $400 at 7%; $500 at 8%; $1600 at 9%   **27.** ✍
29. 17   **30.** −19   **31.** 37   **32.** 422   **33.** ✍   **35.** 1324

Exercise Set 8.7, pp. 560–561

1. True   **2.** True   **3.** True   **4.** False   **5.** False
6. False   **7.** 4   **9.** −50   **11.** 27   **13.** −3   **15.** −5
17. $(-3, 2)$ **19.** $\left(\frac{9}{19}, \frac{51}{38}\right)$ **21.** $\left(-1, -\frac{6}{7}, \frac{11}{7}\right)$
23. $(2, -1, 4)$ **25.** $(1, 2, 3)$ **27.** ✍   **29.** 9700
30. $70x - 2500$ **31.** −1800   **32.** 4500   **33.** $\frac{250}{7}$
34. $\frac{250}{7}$ **35.** ✍   **37.** 12   **39.** 10

Exercise Set 8.8, pp. 565–567

1. (b)   **2.** (f)   **3.** (h)   **4.** (a)   **5.** (e)   **6.** (d)
7. (c)   **8.** (g)
9. (a) $P(x) = 20x - 200,000$; (b) (10,000 units, $550,000)
11. (a) $P(x) = 25x - 3100$; (b) (124 units, $4960)
13. (a) $P(x) = 45x - 22,500$; (b) (500 units, $42,500)
15. (a) $P(x) = 16x - 50,000$; (b) (3125 units, $125,000)
17. (a) $P(x) = 50x - 100,000$; (b) (2000 units, $250,000)
19. ($60, 1100)   **21.** ($22, 474)   **23.** ($50, 6250)
25. ($10, 1070)   **27.** (a) $C(x) = 45,000 + 40x$;
(b) $R(x) = 130x$;   (c) $P(x) = 90x - 45,000$;
(d) $225,000 profit, $9000 loss   (e) (500 phones, $65,000)
29. (a) $C(x) = 10,000 + 30x$; (b) $R(x) = 80x$;
(c) $P(x) = 50x - 10,000$; (d) $90,000 profit, $7500 loss;
(e) (200 seats, $16,000)   **31.** ✍   **33.** 6   **34.** −2
35. $-\frac{11}{9}$ **36.** $\frac{3}{4}$ **37.** −6   **38.** −5   **39.** ✍
41. ($5, 300 yo-yo's)   **43.** (a) $8.74; (b) 24,509 units

Review Exercises: Chapter 8, pp. 571–572

1. Substitution   **2.** Elimination   **3.** Graphical
4. Dependent   **5.** Inconsistent   **6.** Contradiction
7. Parallel   **8.** Square   **9.** Determinant   **10.** Zero
11. $(4, 1)$ **12.** $(3, -2)$ **13.** $\left(\frac{8}{3}, \frac{14}{3}\right)$ **14.** No solution
15. $\left(-\frac{4}{5}, \frac{2}{5}\right)$ **16.** $\left(\frac{9}{4}, \frac{7}{10}\right)$ **17.** $\left(\frac{76}{17}, -\frac{2}{119}\right)$ **18.** $(-2, -3)$
19. $\{(x, y) \,|\, 3x + 4y = 6\}$
20. Melon: $2.49; pineapple: $3.98   **21.** 4 hr
22. 8% juice: 10 L; 15% juice: 4 L   **23.** $(4, -8, 10)$
24. The equations are dependent.   **25.** $(2, 0, 4)$
26. $\left(\frac{8}{9}, -\frac{2}{3}, \frac{10}{9}\right)$ **27.** A: 90°; B: 67.5°; C: 22.5°
28. Oil: $21\frac{1}{3}$ oz; lemon juice: $10\frac{2}{3}$ oz
29. Man: 1.4; woman: 5.3; one-year-old child: 50
30. $\left(55, -\frac{89}{2}\right)$ **31.** $(-1, 1, 3)$ **32.** −5   **33.** 9
34. $(6, -2)$ **35.** $(-3, 0, 4)$ **36.** ($3, 81)
37. (a) $C(x) = 4.75x + 54,000$; (b) $R(x) = 9.25x$;
(c) $P(x) = 4.5x - 54,000$; (d) $31,500 loss, $13,500 profit;
(e) (12,000 pints of honey, $111,000)
38. ✍ To solve a problem involving four variables, go through the *Familiarize* and *Translate* steps as usual. The resulting system of equations can be solved using the elimination method just as for three variables but likely with more steps.   **39.** ✍ A system of equations can be both dependent and inconsistent if it is equivalent to a system with fewer equations that has no solution. An example is a system of three equations in three unknowns in which two

of the equations represent the same plane, and the third represents a parallel plane.   **40.** 20,000 pints
41. Round Stic: 15 packs; Matic Grip: 9 packs
42. $(0, 2), (1, 3)$ **43.** $a = -\frac{2}{3}, b = -\frac{4}{3}, c = 3$;
$f(x) = -\frac{2}{3}x^2 - \frac{4}{3}x + 3$

Test: Chapter 8, pp. 572–573

1. [8.1] $(2, 4)$ **2.** [8.2] $\left(3, -\frac{11}{3}\right)$
3. [8.2] $\{(x, y) \,|\, x = 2y - 3\}$ **4.** [8.2] $(2, -1)$
5. [8.2] No solution   **6.** [8.2] $\left(-\frac{3}{2}, -\frac{3}{2}\right)$
7. [8.3] Length: 94 ft; width: 50 ft
8. [8.3] Pepperidge Farm Goldfish: 120 g;
Rold Gold Pretzels: 500 g   **9.** [8.3] 5.5 hr   **10.** [8.4] The equations are dependent.   **11.** [8.4] $\left(2, -\frac{1}{2}, -1\right)$
12. [8.4] No solution   **13.** [8.4] $(0, 1, 0)$
14. [8.6] $\left(\frac{22}{5}, -\frac{28}{5}\right)$ **15.** [8.6] $(3, 1, -2)$ **16.** [8.7] -14
17. [8.7] -59 **18.** [8.7] $\left(\frac{7}{13}, -\frac{17}{26}\right)$ **19.** [8.5] Electrician: 3.5 hr; carpenter: 8 hr; plumber: 10 hr   **20.** [8.8] ($3, 55)
21. [8.8] **(a)** $C(x) = 25x + 44{,}000$; **(b)** $R(x) = 80x$;
(c) $P(x) = 55x - 44{,}000$; **(d)** \$27,500 loss, \$5500 profit;
(e) (800 hammocks, \$64,000)
22. [7.3], [8.3] $m = 7, b = 10$ **23.** [8.3] $\frac{120}{7}$ lb

Cumulative Review: Chapters 1–8, pp. 574–575

1. 24   **2.** $\frac{1}{10}$ **3.** -10 **4.** $13x^2 - y$ **5.** -24
6. 2   **7.** x^{11} **8.** $-\dfrac{9x^4}{2y^6}$ **9.** $-\dfrac{2a^{11}}{5b^{33}}$ **10.** $\dfrac{81x^{36}}{256y^8}$
11. 1.87×10^6 **12.** 4×10^6 **13.** $\frac{9}{7}$ **14.** $-3, -2$
15. 2, 3   **16.** $\frac{1}{9}$ **17.** $\left\{y \,|\, y \geq -\frac{2}{3}\right\}$, or $\left[-\frac{2}{3}, \infty\right)$
18. $-10, 10$ **19.** $(1, 2)$ **20.** -11 **21.** $-\frac{1}{2}, \frac{2}{3}$
22. $(7, 3)$ **23.** $(-3, 2, -4)$ **24.** $(0, -1, 2)$
25. $p = \dfrac{3t}{q}$ **26.** $s = 2A - r$ **27.** $3a^3 + 8a^2 - 14$
28. $\dfrac{m(m + 2n)}{(m - n)(2m + n)}$ **29.** $-3a^3 + 8a^2 - 12a$
30. $\dfrac{2x + 4}{x - 2}$ **31.** $25a^4 - b^2$
32. $-15x^5 + 18x^4 + 6x^3 - 3x^2$ **33.** $4n^2 + 20n + 25$
34. $8t^5 + 5t^3 + 32t^2 + 20$ **35.** $\dfrac{(x - 1)(x + 2)}{(x - 2)^2}$
36. $2x + 1$ **37.** $\dfrac{x}{2(x + 1)(x + 2)}$ **38.** $(x + 1)(x^2 + 2)$
39. $(m^2 + 1)(m + 1)(m - 1)$ **40.** $2x(x + 4)(x + 5)$
41. $(x^2 - 3)^2$ **42.** $2(2x^2 - x - 5)$
43. $(2x - 5)(5x - 2)$
44.   **45.**

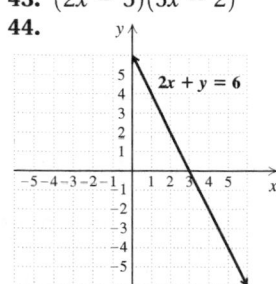

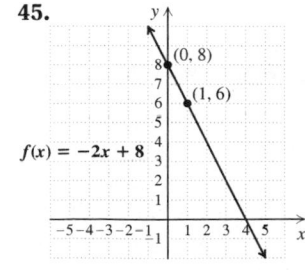

46.   **47.**

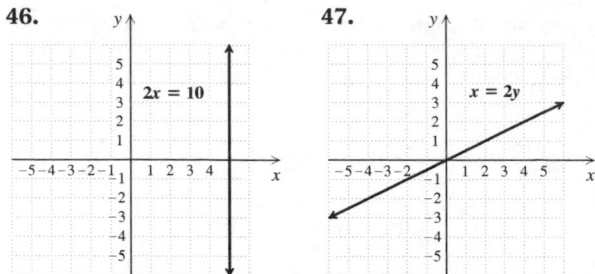

48. x-intercept: $(6, 0)$; y-intercept: $(0, -4)$
49. $y = -2x + \frac{4}{7}$ **50.** $y = -\frac{1}{10}x + \frac{12}{5}$ **51.** Parallel
52. $y = -2x + 5$ **53.** $\{-5, -3, -1, 1, 3\}$;
$\{-3, -2, 1, 4, 5\}$; -2; 3   **54.** $\{x \,|\, x$ is a real number
$and\ x \neq -10\}$ **55.** -31 **56.** 3   **57.** $2a^2 + 4a - 4$
58. 14   **59.** \$1260   **60.** Dog sled: 12 mph; snowmobile: 52 mph   **61.** At least 35 patients   **62.** 11 and 13
63. 100 min   **64.** $32.5°, 65°, 82.5°$ **65.** 42 hr
66. $x = \dfrac{t}{p - q}$ **67.** $y = 2x + 7$ **68.** $\dfrac{3t^2(2t^2 - t + 1)}{4(t - 1)}$
69. $m = -\frac{5}{9}, b = -\frac{2}{9}$ **70.** Length: 6 in.; width: $4\frac{1}{4}$ in

CHAPTER 9

Exercise Set 9.1, pp. 583–586

1. Equivalent equations   **2.** Equivalent expressions
3. Equivalent inequalities   **4.** Not equivalent
5. Not equivalent   **6.** Equivalent equations
7. Equivalent expressions   **8.** Not equivalent
9. Not equivalent   **10.** Equivalent inequalities
11. $\{x \,|\, x < 2\}$, or $(-\infty, 2)$ **13.** $\{x \,|\, x \leq -9\}$, or $(-\infty, -9]$
15. $\{x \,|\, x < -26\}$, or $(-\infty, -26)$
17. $\left\{t \,|\, t \geq -\frac{13}{3}\right\}$, or $\left[-\frac{13}{3}, \infty\right)$ **19.** $\left\{y \,|\, y \leq -\frac{3}{2}\right\}$, or $\left(-\infty, -\frac{3}{2}\right]$
21. $\left\{t \,|\, t < \frac{29}{5}\right\}$, or $\left(-\infty, \frac{29}{5}\right)$ **23.** $\left\{m \,|\, m > \frac{7}{3}\right\}$, or $\left(\frac{7}{3}, \infty\right)$
25. $\{x \,|\, x \geq 2\}$, or $[2, \infty)$ **27.** $\{x \,|\, x > 0\}$, or $(0, \infty)$
29. $\{x \,|\, x < 7\}$, or $(-\infty, 7)$ **31.** $\{x \,|\, x \geq 2\}$, or $[2, \infty)$
33. $\{x \,|\, x < 8\}$, or $(-\infty, 8)$ **35.** $\{x \,|\, x \leq 2\}$, or $(-\infty, 2]$
37. $\{x \,|\, x \geq 2\}$, or $[2, \infty)$ **39.** $\left\{x \,|\, x > \frac{2}{3}\right\}$, or $\left(\frac{2}{3}, \infty\right)$
41. $\{x \,|\, x \geq 10\}$, or $[10, \infty)$ **43.** $\{x \,|\, x \leq 3\}$, or $(-\infty, 3]$
45. $\left\{x \,|\, x \geq -\frac{7}{2}\right\}$, or $\left[-\frac{7}{2}, \infty\right)$ **47.** $\{x \,|\, x \leq 4\}$, or $(-\infty, 4]$
49. $\{x \,|\, x \geq -15\}$, or $[-15, \infty)$ **51.** $\{x \,|\, x \geq 5\}$, or $[5, \infty)$
53. Lengths of time less than $7\frac{1}{2}$ hr   **55.** At least 56 questions correct   **57.** Years after 2010   **59.** Gross sales greater than \$7000   **61.** For more than \$6000
63. **(a)** Body densities less than $\frac{99}{95}$ kg/L, or about 1.04 kg/L; **(b)** body densities less than $\frac{495}{482}$ kg/L, or about 1.03 kg/L
65. **(a)** $\left\{x \,|\, x < 3913\frac{1}{23}\right\}$, or $\{x \,|\, x \leq 3913\}$;
(b) $\left\{x \,|\, x > 3913\frac{1}{23}\right\}$, or $\{x \,|\, x \geq 3914\}$ **67.** ✍
69. $\{x \,|\, x$ is a real number $and\ x \neq 0\}$
70. $\{x \,|\, x$ is a real number $and\ x \neq 6\}$
71. $\left\{x \,|\, x$ is a real number $and\ x \neq -\frac{1}{2}\right\}$
72. $\left\{x \,|\, x$ is a real number $and\ x \neq \frac{7}{5}\right\}$
73. $\mathbb{R}$ **74.** $\{x \,|\, x$ is a real number $and\ x \neq 0\}$ **75.** ✍

77. $\left\{x \mid x \le \dfrac{2}{a-1}\right\}$ **79.** $\left\{y \mid y \ge \dfrac{2a+5b}{b(a-2)}\right\}$

81. $\left\{x \mid x > \dfrac{4m-2c}{d-(5c+2m)}\right\}$ **83.** False; $2 < 3$ and

$4 < 5$, but $2 - 4 = 3 - 5$.   **85.**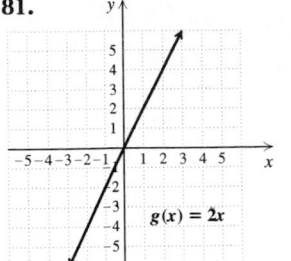

87. $\mathbb{R}$ ←————|————→
                         0

89. $\{x \mid x$ is a real number *and* $x \neq 0\}$

←——————×——————→
            0

91. $\{x \mid x \le 6\}$, or $(-\infty, 6]$ **93. (a)** $\{x \mid x < 4\}$, or $(-\infty, 4)$;
(b) $\{x \mid x \ge 2\}$, or $[2, \infty)$;   **(c)** $\{x \mid x \ge 3.2\}$, or $[3.2, \infty)$

95.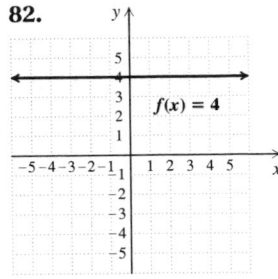

Exercise Set 9.2, pp. 593–596

1. (h)   **2.** (j)   **3.** (f)   **4.** (a)   **5.** (e)   **6.** (d)
7. (b)   **8.** (g)   **9.** (c)   **10.** (i)   **11.** $\{4, 16\}$
13. $\{0, 5, 10, 15, 20\}$ **15.** $\{b, d, f\}$ **17.** $\{u, v, x, y, z\}$
19. $\varnothing$ **21.** $\{1, 3, 5\}$

23. ←——(——)——→ $(1, 3)$
      $-2\ -1\ 0\ 1\ 2\ 3\ 4\ 5\ 6\ 7\ 8$

25. ←—[————]—→ $[-6, 0]$
      $-8\ -7\ -6\ -5\ -4\ -3\ -2\ -1\ 0\ 1\ 2$

27. ←)———(——→ $(-\infty, -1) \cup (4, \infty)$
      $-3\ -2\ -1\ 0\ 1\ 2\ 3\ 4\ 5\ 6\ 7$

29. ←——]——(——→ $(-\infty, -2] \cup (1, \infty)$
      $-5\ -4\ -3\ -2\ -1\ 0\ 1\ 2\ 3\ 4\ 5$

31. ←—(——]——→ $(-2, 4]$
      $-5\ -4\ -3\ -2\ -1\ 0\ 1\ 2\ 3\ 4\ 5$

33. ←—(——)——→ $(-2, 4)$
      $-5\ -4\ -3\ -2\ -1\ 0\ 1\ 2\ 3\ 4\ 5$

35. ←———)—(——→ $(-\infty, 5) \cup (7, \infty)$
      $-1\ 0\ 1\ 2\ 3\ 4\ 5\ 6\ 7\ 8\ 9$

37. ←—]———[——→ $(-\infty, -4] \cup [5, \infty)$
      $-5\ -4\ -3\ -2\ -1\ 0\ 1\ 2\ 3\ 4\ 5$

39. ←[———)——→ $[-3, 7)$
      $-3\ -2\ -1\ 0\ 1\ 2\ 3\ 4\ 5\ 6\ 7$

41. ←(————]——→ $(-7, 0]$
      $-8\ -7\ -6\ -5\ -4\ -3\ -2\ -1\ 0\ 1\ 2$

43. ←————)——→ $(-\infty, 5)$
      $-4\ -3\ -2\ -1\ 0\ 1\ 2\ 3\ 4\ 5\ 6$

45. $\{x \mid -5 \le x < 7\}$, or $[-5, 7)$ ←[———)→
                                                  $-5 \quad 0 \quad 7$

47. $\{t \mid 4 < t \le 8\}$, or $(4, 8]$ ←—(——]→
                                                 $0 \quad 4 \quad 8$

49. $\{a \mid -2 \le a < 2\}$, or $[-2, 2)$ ←—[——)→
                                                   $-2 \ 0 \ 2$

51. $\mathbb{R}$, or $(-\infty, \infty)$ ←————————→
                                                 0

53. $\{x \mid -3 \le x \le 2\}$, or $[-3, 2]$ ←—[——]→
                                                     $-3 \ 0 \ 2$

55. $\{x \mid 7 < x < 23\}$, or $(7, 23)$ ←—(———)→
                                                 $0 \ 7 \quad 23$

57. $\{x \mid -32 \le x \le 8\}$, or $[-32, 8]$
←—[————]→
$-32 \quad 0 \ 8$

59. $\{x \mid 1 \le x \le 3\}$, or $[1, 3]$ ←——[]→
                                                   $0 \ 1 \ 3$

61. $\left\{x \mid -\dfrac{7}{2} < x \le 7\right\}$, or $\left(-\dfrac{7}{2}, 7\right]$ ←(———]→
                                                                                             $-\frac{7}{2}\ 0 \quad 7$

63. $\{t \mid t < 0 \ or \ t > 1\}$, or $(-\infty, 0) \cup (1, \infty)$

←———)(———→
       $0 \ 1$

65. $\left\{a \mid a < \dfrac{7}{2}\right\}$, or $\left(-\infty, \dfrac{7}{2}\right)$ ←————)→
                                                                                            $0 \quad \frac{7}{2}$

67. $\{a \mid a < -5\}$, or $(-\infty, -5)$ ←———)—|→
                                                $-5 \quad 0$

69. $\varnothing$

71. $\{t \mid t \le 6\}$, or $(-\infty, 6]$ ←————]→
                                               $0 \quad 6$

73. $(-\infty, -6) \cup (-6, \infty)$ **75.** $(-\infty, 0) \cup (0, \infty)$

77. $(-\infty, 4) \cup (4, \infty)$ **79.**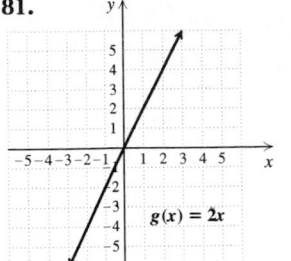

81.

82.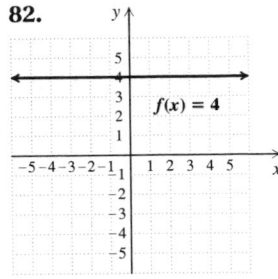

83.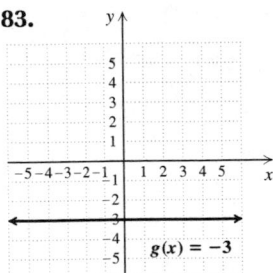

84.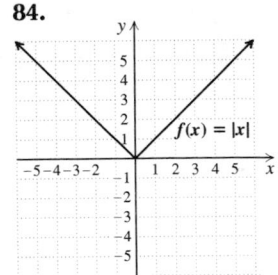

85. -1 **86.** -4 **87.**   **89.** $(-1, 6)$
91. Between 2003 and 2009   **93.** Sizes between 6 and 13
95. Densities between 1.03 kg/L and 1.04 kg/L
97. More than 12 and fewer than 125 trips
99. $\left\{m \mid m < \dfrac{6}{5}\right\}$, or $\left(-\infty, \dfrac{6}{5}\right)$ ←————→
                                                                                      $0 \ \frac{6}{5}$

101. $\left\{x \mid -\dfrac{1}{8} < x < \dfrac{1}{2}\right\}$, or $\left(-\dfrac{1}{8}, \dfrac{1}{2}\right)$ ←(—)→
                                                                                                              $-\frac{1}{8}\ 0 \quad \frac{1}{2}$

103. False   **105.** True
107. $(-\infty, -7) \cup \left(-7, \dfrac{3}{4}\right]$ **109.** 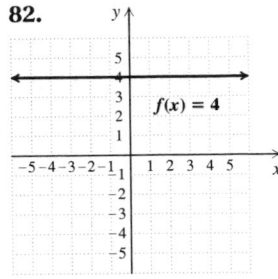   **111.**

Technology Connection, p. 602

1. The *x*-values on the graph of $y_1 = |4x + 2|$ that are *below* the line $y = 6$ solve the inequality $|4x + 2| < 6$.
2. The *x*-values on the graph of $y_1 = |3x - 2|$ that are below the line $y = 4$ are in the interval $\left(-\dfrac{2}{3}, 2\right)$.
3. The graphs of $y_1 = abs(4x + 2)$ and $y_2 = -6$ do not intersect.

Exercise Set 9.3, pp. 603–605

1. True   **2.** False   **3.** True   **4.** True   **5.** True
6. True   **7.** False   **8.** False   **9.** (g)   **10.** (h)   **11.** (d)
12. (a)   **13.** (a)   **14.** (b)   **15.** $\{-10, 10\}$ **17.** $\varnothing$
19. $\{0\}$ **21.** $\left\{-\dfrac{1}{2}, \dfrac{7}{2}\right\}$ **23.** $\varnothing$ **25.** $\{-4, 8\}$
27. $\{6, 8\}$ **29.** $\{-5.5, 5.5\}$ **31.** $\{-8, 8\}$ **33.** $\{-1, 1\}$
35. $\left\{-\dfrac{11}{2}, \dfrac{13}{2}\right\}$ **37.** $\{-2, 12\}$ **39.** $\left\{-\dfrac{1}{3}, 3\right\}$ **41.** $\{-7, 1\}$
43. $\{-8.7, 8.7\}$ **45.** $\left\{-\dfrac{9}{2}, \dfrac{11}{2}\right\}$ **47.** $\{-8, 2\}$ **49.** $\left\{-\dfrac{1}{2}\right\}$
51. $\left\{-\dfrac{3}{5}, 5\right\}$ **53.** $\mathbb{R}$ **55.** $\left\{\dfrac{1}{4}\right\}$

57. $\{a|-3 \le a \le 3\}$, or $[-3, 3]$ (number line -3 to 3)

59. $\{t|t < 0 \text{ or } t > 0\}$, or $(-\infty, 0) \cup (0, \infty)$
(number line)

61. $\{x|-3 < x < 5\}$, or $(-3, 5)$ (number line -3 to 5)

63. $\{n|-8 \le n \le 4\}$, or $[-8, 4]$ (number line -8 to 4)

65. $\{x|x < -2 \text{ or } x > 8\}$, or $(-\infty, -2) \cup (8, \infty)$
(number line -2 and 8)

67. $\mathbb{R}$, or $(-\infty, \infty)$ (number line)

69. $\left\{a|a \le -\frac{10}{3} \text{ or } a \ge \frac{2}{3}\right\}$, or $\left(-\infty, -\frac{10}{3}\right] \cup \left[\frac{2}{3}, \infty\right)$
(number line $-\frac{10}{3}$ and $\frac{2}{3}$)

71. $\{y|-9 < y < 15\}$, or $(-9, 15)$ (number line -9 to 15)

73. $\{x|x \le -8 \text{ or } x \ge 0\}$, or $(-\infty, -8] \cup [0, \infty)$
(number line -8 and 0)

75. $\left\{x|x < -\frac{1}{2} \text{ or } x > \frac{7}{2}\right\}$, or $\left(-\infty, -\frac{1}{2}\right) \cup \left(\frac{7}{2}, \infty\right)$
(number line $-\frac{1}{2}$ and $\frac{7}{2}$)

77. $\varnothing$

79. $\left\{x|x < -\frac{43}{24} \text{ or } x > \frac{9}{8}\right\}$, or $\left(-\infty, -\frac{43}{24}\right) \cup \left(\frac{9}{8}, \infty\right)$
(number line $-\frac{43}{24}$ and $\frac{9}{8}$)

81. $\{m|-9 \le m \le 3\}$, or $[-9, 3]$ (number line -9 to 3)

83. $\{a|-6 < a < 0\}$, or $(-6, 0)$ (number line -6 to 0)

85. $\left\{x|-\frac{1}{2} \le x \le \frac{7}{2}\right\}$, or $\left[-\frac{1}{2}, \frac{7}{2}\right]$ (number line $-\frac{1}{2}$ to $\frac{7}{2}$)

87. $\left\{x|x \le -\frac{7}{3} \text{ or } x \ge 5\right\}$, or $\left(-\infty, -\frac{7}{3}\right] \cup [5, \infty)$
(number line $-\frac{7}{3}$ and 5)

89. $\{x|-4 < x < 5\}$, or $(-4, 5)$ (number line -4 to 5)

91. ✍

93.
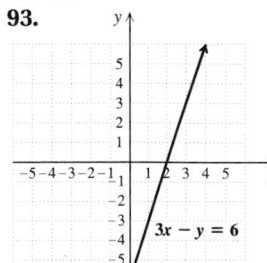

94.
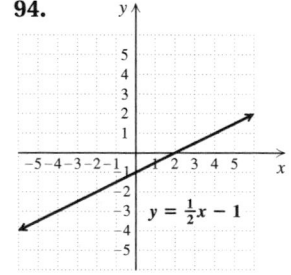

95.
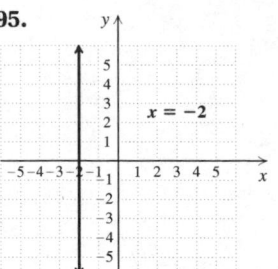

96.
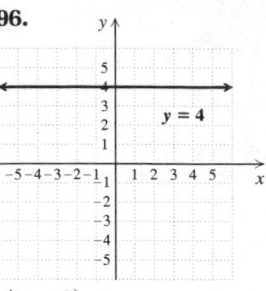

97. $\left(4, -\frac{4}{3}\right)$　**98.** $(5, 1)$　**99.** $\left(\frac{5}{7}, -\frac{18}{7}\right)$　**100.** $(-2, -5)$

101. ✍　**103.** $\left\{t|t \ge \frac{5}{3}\right\}$, or $\left[\frac{5}{3}, \infty\right)$

105. $\mathbb{R}$, or $(-\infty, \infty)$　**107.** $\left\{-\frac{1}{7}, \frac{7}{3}\right\}$　**109.** $|x| < 3$

111. $|x| \ge 6$　**113.** $|x + 3| > 5$

115. $|x - 7| < 2$, or $|7 - x| < 2$　**117.** $|x - 3| \le 4$

119. $|x + 4| < 3$　**121.** Between 80 ft and 100 ft

123. $\{x|1 \le x \le 5\}$, or $[1, 5]$　**125.** ✍, ▨

Connecting the Concepts, pp. 605–606

1. 2　**2.** $\{x|x > 3\}$, or $(3, \infty)$　**3.** $\frac{9}{2}$　**4.** $\{-4, 3\}$

5. $\{x|x \ge -6\}$, or $[-6, \infty)$　**6.** $\{t|-4 < t < 4\}$, or
$(-4, 4)$　**7.** $-\frac{11}{8}$　**8.** $\frac{62}{3}$　**9.** $\left\{-\frac{8}{3}, \frac{8}{3}\right\}$

10. $\{x|-7 \le x \le 13\}$, or $[-7, 13]$　**11.** 31　**12.** $\varnothing$

13. $\left\{x|x \le -\frac{17}{2} \text{ or } x \ge \frac{7}{2}\right\}$, or $\left(-\infty, -\frac{17}{2}\right] \cup \left[\frac{7}{2}, \infty\right)$

14. $\varnothing$　**15.** $\{m|-24 < m < 12\}$, or $(-24, 12)$

16. $\{-42, 38\}$　**17.** $\{t|t \le 4 \text{ or } t \ge 10\}$, or
$(-\infty, 4] \cup [10, \infty)$　**18.** $\frac{7}{2}$　**19.** $\{a|-7 < a < -5\}$, or
$(-7, -5)$　**20.** $\mathbb{R}$, or $(-\infty, \infty)$

Technology Connection, p. 610

1. $y > x + 3.5$
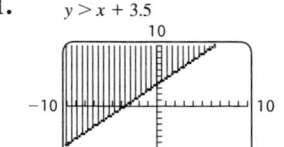

2. $7y \le 2x + 5$
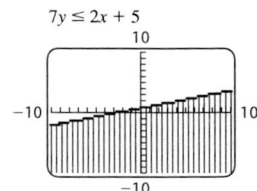

3. $8x - 2y < 11$
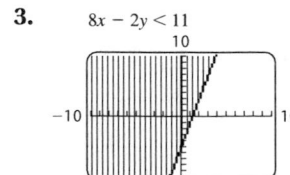

4. $11x + 13y + 4 \ge 0$
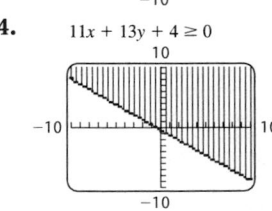

Technology Connection, p. 612

1. $y_1 \le 4 - x, \ y_2 > x - 4$
(graph with Shades, Pol-Trace, ? buttons)

Visualizing for Success, p. 613

1. B   **2.** F   **3.** J   **4.** A   **5.** E   **6.** G   **7.** C   **8.** D
9. I   **10.** H

Exercise Set 9.4, pp. 614–616

1. (e)   **2.** (c)   **3.** (d)   **4.** (a)   **5.** (b)   **6.** (f)
7. No   **9.** Yes

11.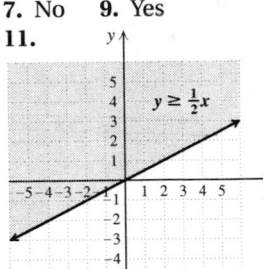

13.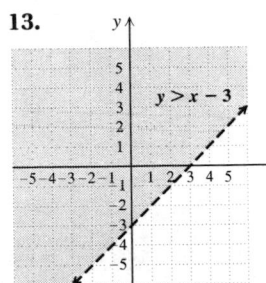

15.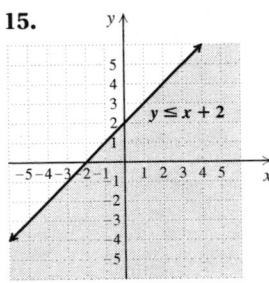

17.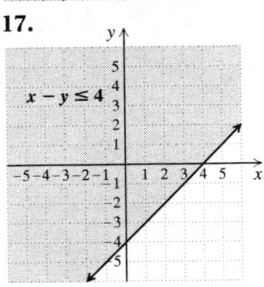

19.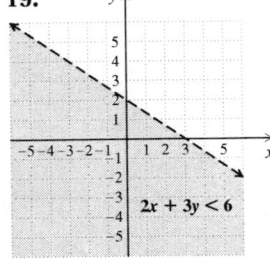

21.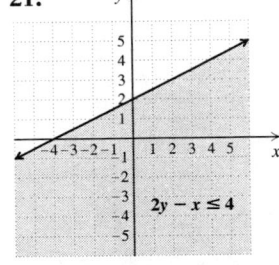

23.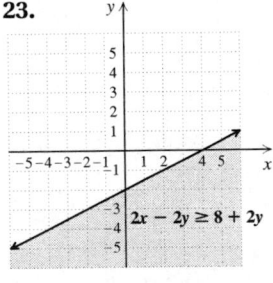

25.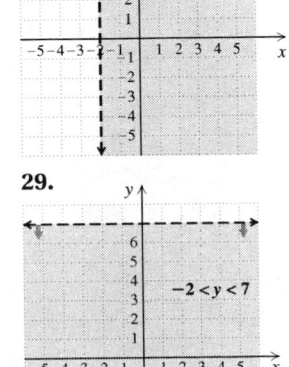

27.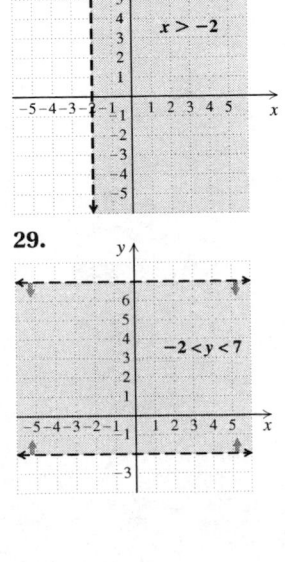

29.

31.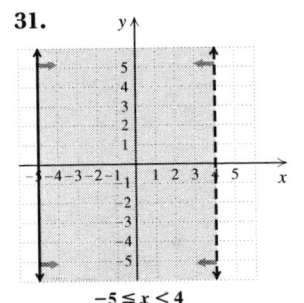
$-5 \leq x < 4$

33.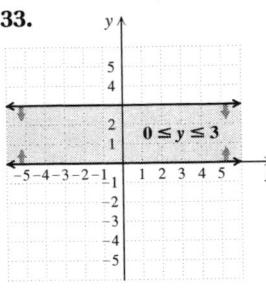
$0 \leq y \leq 3$

35.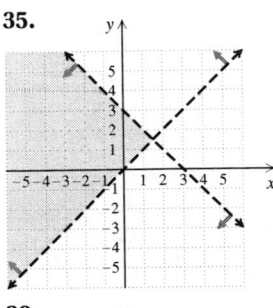

37.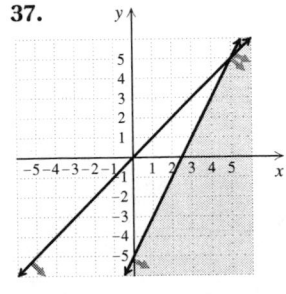

39.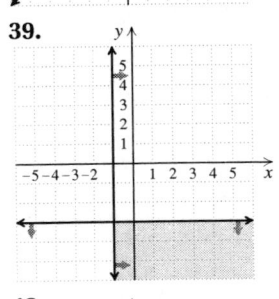

41.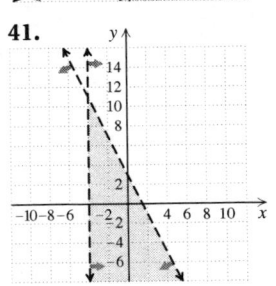

43.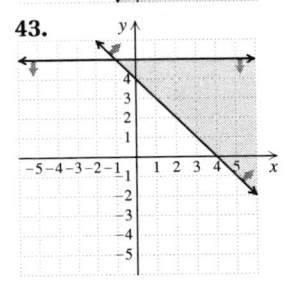

45.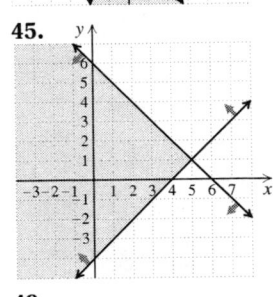

47.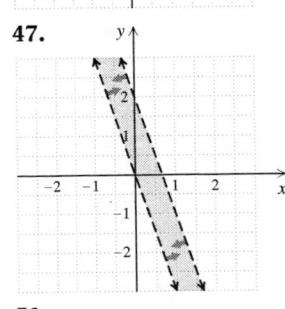

49.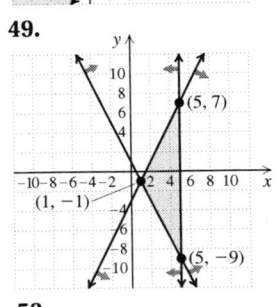

51.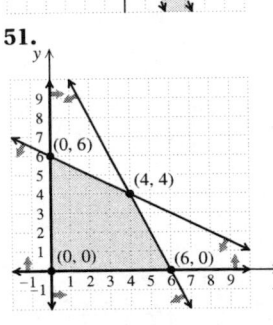

53.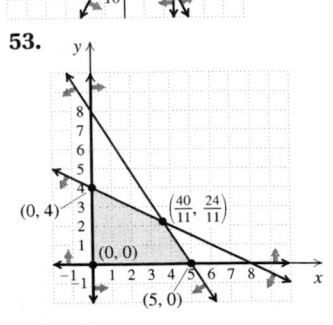

55.

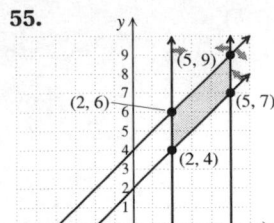

57. ✍   **59.** 3.25%   **60.** $228
61. 3%: $3600; 5%: $6400   **62.** Carrots: 12 lb;
broccoli: 8 lb   **63.** Student tickets: 62; adult tickets: 108
64. Corn: 240 acres; soybeans: 160 acres   **65.** ✍

67.

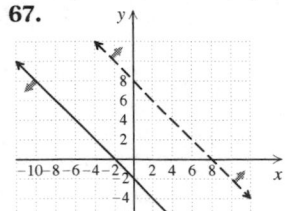

69.

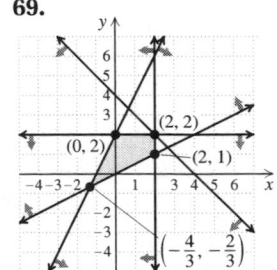

71.
$$w > 0,$$
$$h > 0,$$
$$w + h + 30 \le 62, \text{ or}$$
$$w + h \le 32,$$
$$2w + 2h + 30 \le 130, \text{ or}$$
$$w + h \le 50$$

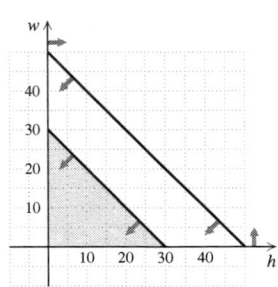

73.
$$q + v \ge 1150,$$
$$q \ge 700,$$
$$q \le 800,$$
$$v \ge 400,$$
$$v \le 800$$

75.
$$35c + 75a > 1000,$$
$$c \ge 0,$$
$$a \ge 0$$

77.
$$h < 2w,$$
$$w \le 1.5h,$$
$$h \le 3200,$$
$$h \ge 0,$$
$$w \ge 0$$

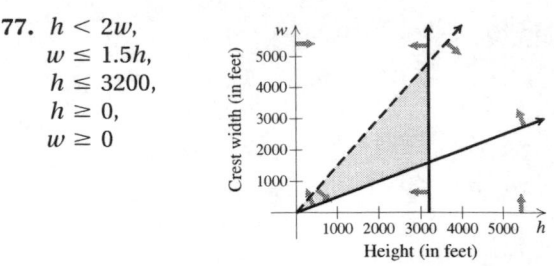

79. (a) $3x + 6y > 2$ **(b)** $x - 5y \le 10$

(c) $13x - 25y + 10 \le 0$ **(d)** $2x + 5y > 0$

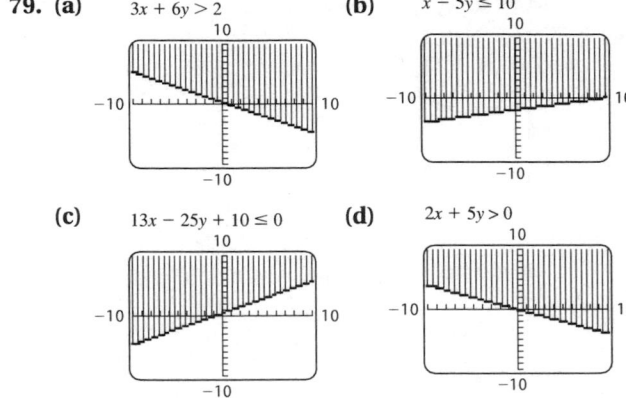

Connecting the Concepts, pp. 617–618

1. ⟵————●——→
      0   5

2. ⟵————(——→
      0   5

3. ⟵————|——→
      0   5

4. ⟵————————●——→
      0   13

5. ⟵——|——→
      -1 0

6. ⟵—(————→
     -2 0

7.

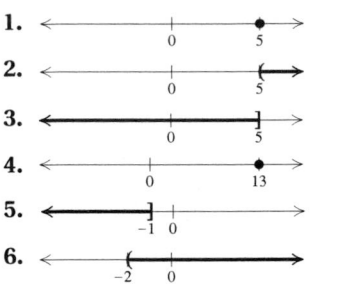

$x + y = 2$

8.

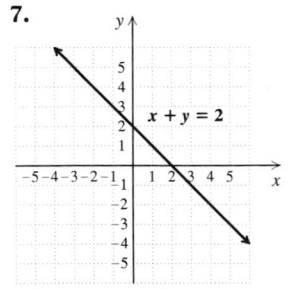

$x + y < 2$

9.

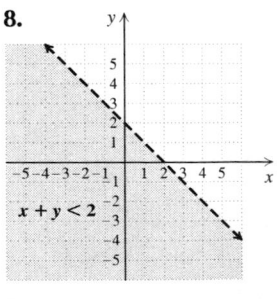

$x + y \ge 2$

10.

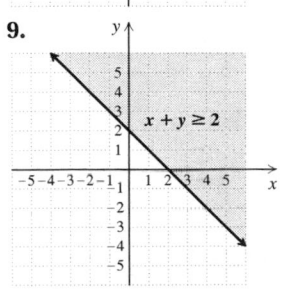

$y = 3x - 3$

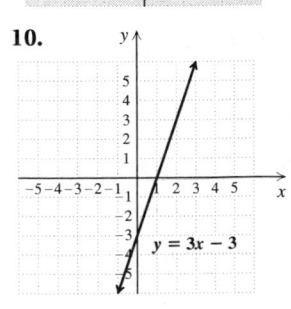

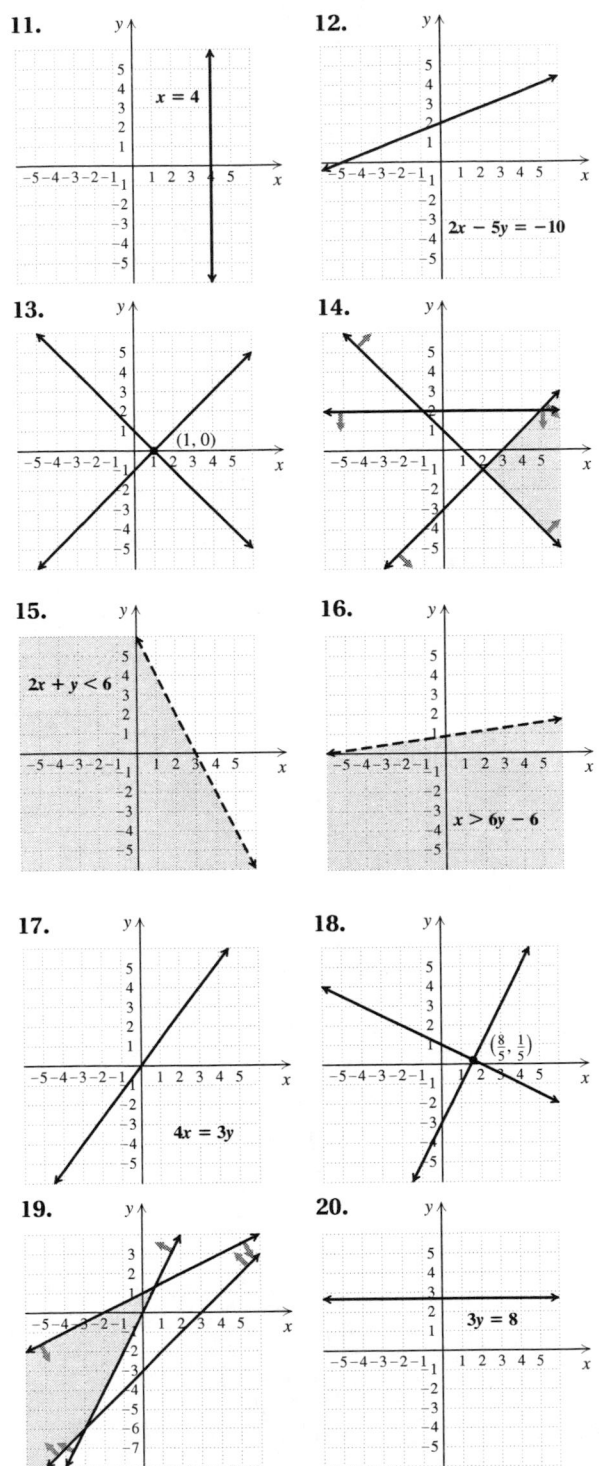

11.   **12.**   **13.**   **14.**   **15.**   **16.**   **17.**   **18.**   **19.**   **20.**

Exercise Set 9.5, pp. 622–624

1. Objective   **2.** Constraints   **3.** Corner
4. Feasible   **5.** Vertices   **6.** Vertex   **7.** Maximum
84 when $x = 0$, $y = 6$; minimum 0 when $x = 0$, $y = 0$

9. Maximum 76 when $x = 7$, $y = 0$; minimum 16 when
$x = 0$, $y = 4$ **11.** Maximum 5 when $x = 3$, $y = 7$;
minimum -15 when $x = 3$, $y = -3$ **13.** Gumbo: 40
orders; sandwiches: 50 orders   **15.** 4-photo pages: 5;
6-photo pages: 15; 110 photos   **17.** Corporate bonds:
$22,000; municipal bonds: $18,000; maximum: $3110
19. Short-answer questions: 12; essay questions: 4
21. Merlot: 80 acres; Cabernet: 160 acres
23. 2.5 servings of each   **25.** 📄   **27.** $4a - 7 + h$
28. $4a + 4h - 7$ **29.** $\{x \,|\, x$ is a real number $and\ x \neq -\frac{1}{2}\}$,
or $\left(-\infty, -\frac{1}{2}\right) \cup \left(-\frac{1}{2}, \infty\right)$ **30.** $\mathbb{R}$
31. $\{x \,|\, x \geq -4\}$, or $[-4, \infty)$
32. $\{x \,|\, x$ is a real number $and\ x \neq -1\ and\ x \neq 1\}$, or
$(-\infty, -1) \cup (-1, 1) \cup (1, \infty)$ **33.** 📄
35. T3's: 30; S5's: 10   **37.** Chairs: 25; sofas: 9

Review Exercises: Chapter 9, pp. 627–628

1. True   **2.** False   **3.** True   **4.** False   **5.** True
6. True   **7.** True   **8.** False   **9.** False   **10.** False
11. $\left\{x \,|\, x > -\frac{3}{2}\right\}$, or $(-\frac{3}{2}, \infty)$ **12.** $\{x \,|\, x < -3\}$, or
$(-\infty, -3)$ **13.** $\left\{y \,|\, y > -\frac{220}{23}\right\}$, or $(-\frac{220}{23}, \infty)$
14. $\left\{x \,|\, x \leq -\frac{5}{2}\right\}$, or $\left(-\infty, -\frac{5}{2}\right]$ **15.** $\{x \,|\, x < 5\}$, or $(-\infty, 5)$
16. $\{x \,|\, x < 1\}$, or $(-\infty, 1)$ **17.** $\{x \,|\, x \geq -4\}$, or $[-4, \infty)$
18. $\{x \,|\, x \geq 6\}$, or $[6, \infty)$ **19.** $\{x \,|\, x \leq 2\}$, or $(-\infty, 2]$
20. More than 125 hr   **21.** $3000   **22.** $\{a, c\}$
23. $\{a, b, c, d, e, f, g\}$
24. $(-3, 2]$
25. $(-\infty, \infty)$
26. $\{x \,|\, -8 < x \leq 0\}$, or $(-8, 0]$
27. $\left\{x \,|\, -\frac{5}{4} < x < \frac{5}{2}\right\}$, or $\left(-\frac{5}{4}, \frac{5}{2}\right)$
28. $\{x \,|\, x < -3\ or\ x > 1\}$, or $(-\infty, -3) \cup (1, \infty)$
29. $\{x \,|\, x < -11\ or\ x \geq -6\}$, or $(-\infty, -11) \cup [-6, \infty)$
30. $\{x \,|\, x \leq -6\ or\ x \geq 8\}$, or $(-\infty, -6] \cup [8, \infty)$
31. $\left\{x \,|\, x < -\frac{2}{5}\ or\ x > \frac{8}{5}\right\}$, or $\left(-\infty, -\frac{2}{5}\right) \cup \left(\frac{8}{5}, \infty\right)$
32. $(-\infty, -3) \cup (-3, \infty)$ **33.** $[2, \infty)$ **34.** $\left(-\infty, \frac{1}{4}\right]$
35. $\{-11, 11\}$ **36.** $\{t \,|\, t \leq -21\ or\ t \geq 21\}$, or
$(-\infty, -21] \cup [21, \infty)$ **37.** $\{5, 11\}$
38. $\left\{a \,|\, -\frac{7}{2} < a < 2\right\}$, or $\left(-\frac{7}{2}, 2\right)$
39. $\left\{x \,|\, x \leq -\frac{11}{3}\ or\ x \geq \frac{19}{3}\right\}$, or $\left(-\infty, -\frac{11}{3}\right] \cup \left[\frac{19}{3}, \infty\right)$
40. $\left\{-14, \frac{4}{3}\right\}$ **41.** $\varnothing$ **42.** $\{x \,|\, -16 \leq x \leq 8\}$, or $[-16, 8]$
43. $\{x \,|\, x < 0\ or\ x > 10\}$, or $(-\infty, 0) \cup (10, \infty)$
44. $\{x \,|\, -6 \leq x \geq 4\}$, or $[-6, 4]$ **45.** $\varnothing$

46.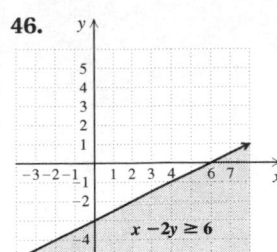

47.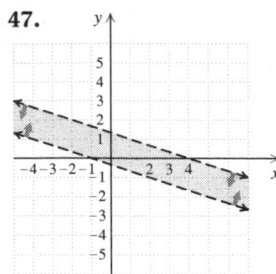

48.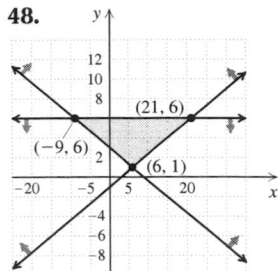

49. Maximum 40 when $x = 7$, $y = 15$; minimum 10 when $x = 1$, $y = 3$ **50.** Ohio plant: 120 computers; Oregon plant: 40 computers   **51.** ✍ The equation $|X| = p$ has two solutions when p is positive because X can be either p or $-p$. The same equation has no solution when p is negative because no number has a negative absolute value.
52. ✍ The solution set of a system of inequalities is all ordered pairs that make *all* the individual inequalities true. This consists of ordered pairs that are common to all the individual solution sets, or the intersection of the graphs.
53. $\left\{x \mid -\frac{8}{3} \le x \le -2\right\}$, or $\left[-\frac{8}{3}, -2\right]$ **54.** False: $-4 < 3$ is true, but $(-4)^2 < 9$ is false.   **55.** $|d - 2.5| \le 0.003$

Test: Chapter 9, p. 629

1. [9.1] $\{y \mid y \le -2\}$, or $(-\infty, -2]$ **2.** [9.1] $\left\{x \mid x > \frac{16}{5}\right\}$, or $\left(\frac{16}{5}, \infty\right)$ **3.** [9.1] $\left\{x \mid x \le \frac{9}{16}\right\}$, or $\left(-\infty, \frac{9}{16}\right]$
4. [9.1] $\{x \mid x > 1\}$, or $(1, \infty)$ **5.** [9.1] $\{x \mid x \ge 4\}$, or $[4, \infty)$
6. [9.1] $\{x \mid x > 1\}$, or $(1, \infty)$ **7.** [9.1] More than $187\frac{1}{2}$ mi
8. [9.1] Less than or equal to 2.5 hr   **9.** [9.2] $\{a, e\}$
10. [9.2] $\{a, b, c, d, e, i, o, u\}$ **11.** [9.1] $(-\infty, 2]$
12. [9.2] $(-\infty, 7) \cup (7, \infty)$
13. [9.2] $\left\{x \mid -\frac{3}{2} < x \le \frac{1}{2}\right\}$, or $\left(-\frac{3}{2}, \frac{1}{2}\right]$

14. [9.2] $\{x \mid x < 3 \ or \ x > 6\}$, or $(-\infty, 3) \cup (6, \infty)$

15. [9.2] $\left\{x \mid x < -4 \ or \ x \ge -\frac{5}{2}\right\}$, or $(-\infty, -4) \cup \left[-\frac{5}{2}, \infty\right)$

16. [9.2] $\{x \mid -3 \le x \le 1\}$, or $[-3, 1]$

17. [9.3] $\{-15, 15\}$

18. [9.3] $\{a \mid a < -5 \ or \ a > 5\}$, or $(-\infty, -5) \cup (5, \infty)$

19. [9.3] $\left\{x \mid -2 < x < \frac{8}{3}\right\}$, or $\left(-2, \frac{8}{3}\right)$

20. [9.3] $\left\{t \mid t \le -\frac{13}{5} \ or \ t \ge \frac{7}{5}\right\}$, or $\left(-\infty, -\frac{13}{5}\right] \cup \left[\frac{7}{5}, \infty\right)$

21. [9.3] $\varnothing$
22. [9.2] $\left\{x \mid x < \frac{1}{2} \ or \ x > \frac{7}{2}\right\}$, or $\left(-\infty, \frac{1}{2}\right) \cup \left(\frac{7}{2}, \infty\right)$

23. [9.3] $\left\{-\frac{3}{2}\right\}$
24. [9.4]

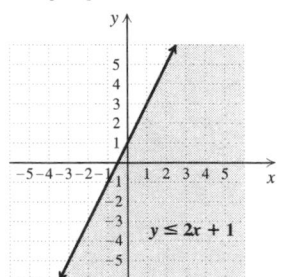

25. [9.4]

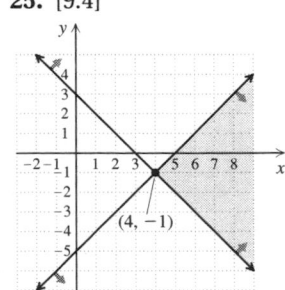

26. [9.4]

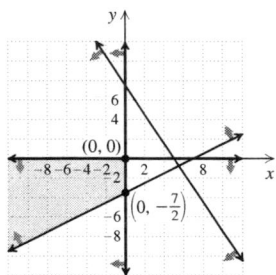

27. [9.5] Maximum 57 when $x = 6$, $y = 9$; minimum 5 when $x = 1$, $y = 0$ **28.** [9.5] Manicures: 35; haircuts: 15; maximum: \$690   **29.** [9.3] $[-1, 0] \cup [4, 6]$
30. [9.2] $\left(\frac{1}{5}, \frac{4}{5}\right)$ **31.** [9.3] $|x + 3| \le 5$

Cumulative Review: Chapters 1–9, pp. 630–631

1. 22   **2.** $c - 6$ **3.** $-\frac{1}{100}$ **4.** $-\frac{6x^4}{y^3}$ **5.** $\frac{9a^6}{4b^4}$

6. $\frac{2}{x^2 + 5x + 25}$ **7.** $x^2 - 25$ **8.** $15n^2 + 11n - 14$

9. $\frac{-10}{(x + 5)(x - 5)}$ **10.** $\frac{(x - 3)^2}{x^2(2x - 3)}$ **11.** $25(x - 1)^2$

12. $(4m + 7)(2n - 3)$ **13.** $8(t^2 + 100)$ **14.** 5
15. $\mathbb{R}$ **16.** $-2, 4$ **17.** $-4, 3$ **18.** No solution
19. $(5, 1)$ **20.** $\left\{-\frac{7}{2}, \frac{9}{2}\right\}$ **21.** $\left\{x \mid x < \frac{13}{2}\right\}$, or $\left(-\infty, \frac{13}{2}\right)$
22. $\{t \mid t < -3 \ or \ t > 3\}$, or $(-\infty, -3) \cup (3, \infty)$
23. $\left\{x \mid -2 \le x \le \frac{10}{3}\right\}$, or $\left[-2, \frac{10}{3}\right]$

24.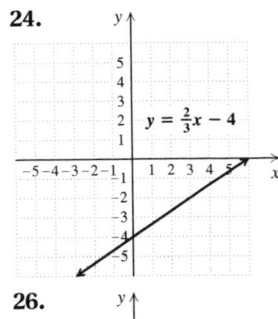

25.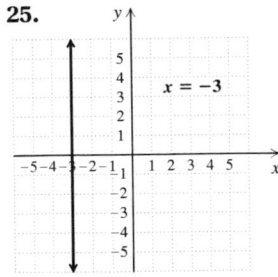

26.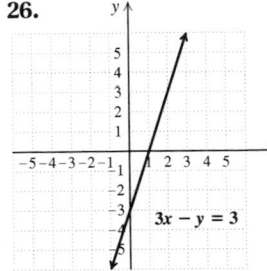

27.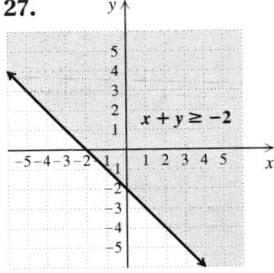

28.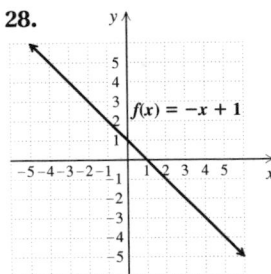

29.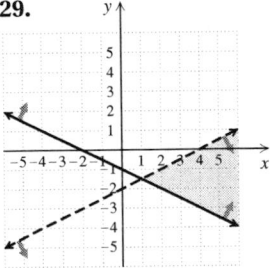

30. Slope: $\frac{4}{9}$; y-intercept: $(0, -2)$ **31.** $y = -7x - 25$
32. $y = \frac{2}{3}x + 4$ **33.** Domain: $\mathbb{R}$; range: $\{y | y \geq -2\}$,
or $[-2, \infty)$ **34.** $\{x | x \text{ is a real number } and\, x \neq -\frac{5}{2}\}$,
or $\left(-\infty, -\frac{5}{2}\right) \cup \left(-\frac{5}{2}, \infty\right)$ **35.** 22   **36.** $x^2 + 6x - 9$
37. ← [ ]→
          −1 0   4
38. $\{x | x \text{ is a real number } and\, x \neq 0 \, and\, x \neq \frac{1}{3}\}$

39. $t = \dfrac{c}{a - d}$ **40.** 183 cannons   **41.** Beef: 9300 gal;
wheat: 2300 gal   **42.** (a) $b(t) = \frac{34}{15}t + 34.6$; (b) \$55 billion;
(c) 2008   **43.** (a) More than \$40; (b) costs greater than \$30
44. Length: 10 cm; width: 6 cm   **45.** \$640
46. \$50 billion   **47.** Vegetarian dinners: 12; steak
dinners: 16   **48.** $m = \frac{1}{3}$, $b = \frac{16}{3}$ **49.** $\frac{64}{3}$
50. $[-4, 0) \cup (0, \infty)$ **51.** 2^{11a-16}

CHAPTER 10

Technology Connection, p. 636

1. False   **2.** True   **3.** False

Visualizing for Success, p. 640

1. B   **2.** H   **3.** C   **4.** I   **5.** D   **6.** A   **7.** F   **8.** J
9. G   **10.** E

Exercise Set 10.1, pp. 641–642

1. Two   **2.** Negative   **3.** Positive   **4.** Negative
5. Irrational   **6.** Real   **7.** Nonnegative   **8.** Negative
9. $8, -8$ **11.** $10, -10$ **13.** $20, -20$ **15.** $25, -25$
17. 7   **19.** -4 **21.** $\frac{6}{7}$ **23.** -13 **25.** $-\frac{4}{9}$ **27.** 0.2
29. 0.09   **31.** $p^2 + 4; 2$ **33.** $\dfrac{x}{y + 4}; 5$ **35.** $\sqrt{5}; 0$;
does not exist; does not exist   **37.** -7; does not exist; -1;
does not exist   **39.** 1; $\sqrt{2}$; $\sqrt{101}$ **41.** $10|x|$
43. $|8 - t|$ **45.** $|y + 8|$ **47.** $|2x + 7|$ **49.** -4
51. -1 **53.** $\frac{2}{3}$ **55.** $|x|$ **57.** t **59.** $6|a|$ **61.** 6
63. $|a + b|$ **65.** $|a^{11}|$ **67.** Cannot be simplified
69. $4x$ **71.** $-3t$ **73.** $5b$ **75.** $a + 1$ **77.** 3   **79.** $2x$
81. $x - 1$ **83.** $5y$ **85.** t^9 **87.** $(x - 2)^4$
89. 2; 3; -2; -4 **91.** 2; does not exist; does not exist; 3
93. $\{x | x \geq 6\}$, or $[6, \infty)$ **95.** $\{t | t \geq -8\}$, or $[-8, \infty)$
97. $\{x | x \leq 5\}$, or $(-\infty, 5]$ **99.** $\mathbb{R}$ **101.** $\{z | z \geq -\frac{2}{5}\}$, or
$\left[-\frac{2}{5}, \infty\right)$ **103.** $\mathbb{R}$ **105.** ⟐   **107.** $a^6 b^2$ **108.** $15x^3 y^9$
109. $\dfrac{125x^6}{y^9}$ **110.** $\dfrac{a^3}{8b^6 c^3}$ **111.** $\dfrac{x^3}{2y^6}$ **112.** $\dfrac{y^4 z^8}{16x^4}$
113. ⟐   **115.** About 1404 species
117. $\{x | x \geq -5\}$, or $[-5, \infty)$
119. $\{x | x \geq 0\}$, or $[0, \infty)$

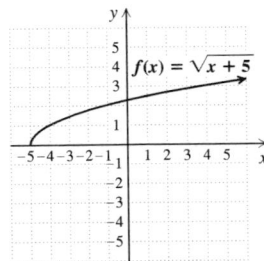 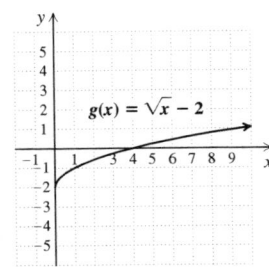

121. $\{x | -3 \leq x < 2\}$, or $[-3, 2)$
123. $\{x | x < -1 \, or\, x > 6\}$, or $(-\infty, -1) \cup (6, \infty)$
125. ▨

Technology Connection, p. 644

1. Without parentheses, the expression entered would be $\dfrac{7^2}{3}$.
2. For $x = 0$ or $x = 1$, $y_1 = y_2 = y_3$; on $(0, 1)$, $y_1 > y_2 > y_3$;
on $(1, \infty)$, $y_1 < y_2 < y_3$.

Technology Connection, p. 646

1. Many graphing calculators do not have keys for radicals
of index 3 or higher. On those graphing calculators that offer
$\sqrt[x]{\ }$ in a MATH menu, rational exponents still require fewer
keystrokes.

Exercise Set 10.2, pp. 647–649

1. (g)   **2.** (c)   **3.** (e)   **4.** (h)   **5.** (a)   **6.** (d)   **7.** (b)
8. (f)   **9.** $\sqrt[3]{y}$ **11.** 6   **13.** 2   **15.** 8   **17.** $\sqrt{xyz}$
19. $\sqrt[5]{a^2 b^2}$ **21.** $\sqrt[6]{t^5}$ **23.** 8   **25.** 625   **27.** $27\sqrt[4]{x^3}$
29. $125x^6$ **31.** $18^{1/3}$ **33.** $30^{1/2}$ **35.** $x^{7/2}$ **37.** $m^{2/5}$

39. $(pq)^{1/4}$ **41.** $(xy^2z)^{1/5}$ **43.** $(3mn)^{3/2}$
45. $(8x^2y)^{5/7}$ **47.** $\dfrac{2x}{z^{2/3}}$ **49.** $\dfrac{1}{a^{1/4}}$ **51.** $\dfrac{1}{(2rs)^{3/4}}$
53. 8   **55.** $8a^{3/5}c$ **57.** $\dfrac{2a^{3/4}c^{2/3}}{b^{1/2}}$ **59.** $\dfrac{a^3}{3^{5/2}b^{7/3}}$
61. $\left(\dfrac{3c}{2ab}\right)^{5/6}$ **63.** $\dfrac{6a}{b^{1/4}}$ **65.** $11^{5/6}$ **67.** $3^{3/4}$
69. $4.3^{1/2}$ **71.** $10^{6/25}$ **73.** $a^{23/12}$ **75.** 64   **77.** $\dfrac{m^{1/3}}{n^{1/8}}$
79. $\sqrt[3]{x}$ **81.** y^5 **83.** $\sqrt{a}$ **85.** x^2y^2 **87.** $\sqrt{7a}$
89. $\sqrt[4]{8x^3}$ **91.** $\sqrt[10]{m}$ **93.** x^3y^3 **95.** a^6b^{12}
97. $\sqrt[12]{xy}$ **99.** 🖊   **101.** x^2-25 **102.** x^3-8
103. $(2x+5)^2$ **104.** $(3a-4)^2$ **105.** $5(t-1)^2$
106. $3(n+2)^2$ **107.** 🖊   **109.** $\sqrt[6]{x^5}$
111. $\sqrt[7]{c-d},\, c \ge d$ **113.** $2^{7/12} \approx 1.498 \approx 1.5$
115. (a) 1.8 m; **(b)** 3.1 m; **(c)** 1.5 m; **(d)** 5.3 m
117. 338 cubic feet   **119.** 🖼

Technology Connection, p. 651

1. The graphs differ in appearance because the domain of y_1 is the intersection of $[-3,\infty)$ and $[3,\infty)$, or $[3,\infty)$. The domain of y_2 is $(-\infty,-3]\cup[3,\infty)$.

Exercise Set 10.3, pp. 654–655

1. True   **2.** False   **3.** False   **4.** False   **5.** True
6. True   **7.** $\sqrt{30}$ **9.** $\sqrt[3]{35}$ **11.** $\sqrt[4]{54}$ **13.** $\sqrt{26xy}$
15. $\sqrt[5]{80y^4}$ **17.** $\sqrt{y^2-b^2}$ **19.** $\sqrt[3]{0.21y^2}$
21. $\sqrt[5]{(x-2)^3}$ **23.** $\sqrt{\dfrac{6s}{11t}}$ **25.** $\sqrt[7]{\dfrac{5x-15}{4x+8}}$ **27.** $2\sqrt{3}$
29. $3\sqrt{5}$ **31.** $2x^4\sqrt{2x}$ **33.** $2\sqrt{30}$ **35.** $6a^2\sqrt{b}$
37. $2x\sqrt[3]{y^2}$ **39.** $-2x^2\sqrt[3]{2}$ **41.** $f(x)=2x^2\sqrt[3]{5}$
43. $f(x)=|7(x-3)|$, or $7|x-3|$
45. $f(x)=|x-1|\sqrt{5}$ **47.** $a^5b^5\sqrt{b}$ **49.** $xy^2z^3\sqrt[3]{x^2z}$
51. $2xy^2\sqrt[4]{xy^3}$ **53.** $x^2yz^3\sqrt[5]{x^3y^3z^2}$ **55.** $-2a^4\sqrt[3]{10a^2}$
57. $5\sqrt{2}$ **59.** $3\sqrt{22}$ **61.** 3   **63.** $24y^5$ **65.** $a\sqrt[3]{10}$
67. $2x^3\sqrt{5x}$ **69.** $s^2t^3\sqrt[3]{t}$ **71.** $(x-y)^4$
73. $2ab^3\sqrt[4]{5a}$ **75.** $x(y+z)^2\sqrt[5]{x}$ **77.** 🖊   **79.** $9abx^2$
80. $\dfrac{(x-1)^2}{(x-2)^2}$ **81.** $\dfrac{x+1}{2(x+5)}$ **82.** $\dfrac{3(4x^2+5y^3)}{50xy^2}$
83. $\dfrac{b+a}{a^2b^2}$ **84.** $\dfrac{-x-2}{4x+3}$ **85.** 🖊   **87.** 175.6 mi
89. (a) $-3.3°C$; **(b)** $-16.6°C$; **(c)** $-25.5°C$; **(d)** $-54.0°C$
91. $25x^5\sqrt[3]{25x}$ **93.** $a^{10}b^{17}\sqrt{ab}$
95.

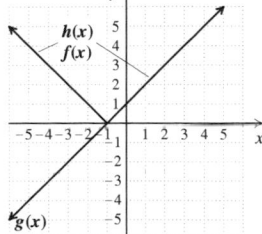

$f(x)=h(x); f(x)\ne g(x)$

97. $\{x\,|\,x\le 2\text{ or }x\ge 4\}$, or $(-\infty,2]\cup[4,\infty)$ **99.** 6
101. 🖼, 🖊

Exercise Set 10.4, pp. 660–661

1. (g)   **2.** (b)   **3.** (f)   **4.** (c)   **5.** (h)   **6.** (d)   **7.** (a)
8. (e)   **9.** $\dfrac{7}{10}$ **11.** $\dfrac{5}{2}$ **13.** $\dfrac{11}{t}$ **15.** $\dfrac{6y\sqrt{y}}{x^2}$ **17.** $\dfrac{3a\sqrt[3]{a}}{2b}$
19. $\dfrac{2a}{bc^2}$ **21.** $\dfrac{ab^2}{c^2}\sqrt[4]{\dfrac{a}{c^2}}$ **23.** $\dfrac{2x}{y^2}\sqrt[5]{\dfrac{x}{y}}$ **25.** $\dfrac{xy}{z^2}\sqrt[6]{\dfrac{y^2}{z^3}}$
27. 3   **29.** $\sqrt[3]{2}$ **31.** $y\sqrt{5y}$ **33.** $2\sqrt[3]{a^2b}$ **35.** $\sqrt{2ab}$
37. $2x^2y^3\sqrt[4]{y^3}$ **39.** $\sqrt[3]{x^2+xy+y^2}$ **41.** $\dfrac{\sqrt{10}}{5}$
43. $\dfrac{2\sqrt{15}}{21}$ **45.** $\dfrac{\sqrt[3]{10}}{2}$ **47.** $\dfrac{\sqrt[3]{75ac^2}}{5c}$ **49.** $\dfrac{y\sqrt[4]{45y^2x^3}}{3x}$
51. $\dfrac{\sqrt[3]{2xy^2}}{xy}$ **53.** $\dfrac{\sqrt{14a}}{6}$ **55.** $\dfrac{\sqrt[5]{9y^4}}{2xy}$ **57.** $\dfrac{\sqrt{5b}}{6a}$
59. $\dfrac{5}{\sqrt{55}}$ **61.** $\dfrac{12}{5\sqrt{42}}$ **63.** $\dfrac{2}{\sqrt{6x}}$ **65.** $\dfrac{7}{\sqrt[3]{98}}$
67. $\dfrac{7x}{\sqrt{21xy}}$ **69.** $\dfrac{2a^2}{\sqrt[3]{20ab}}$ **71.** $\dfrac{x^2y}{\sqrt{2xy}}$ **73.** 🖊
75. $x(3-8y+2z)$ **76.** $ac(4a+9-3a^2)$
77. a^2-b^2 **78.** a^4-4y^2 **79.** $56-11x-12x^2$
80. $6ay-2cy-3ax+cx$ **81.** 🖊   **83. (a)** 1.62 sec ;
(b) 1.99 sec ; **(c)** 2.20 sec   **85.** $9\sqrt[3]{9n^2}$ **87.** $\dfrac{-3\sqrt{a^2-3}}{a^2-3}$,
or $\dfrac{-3}{\sqrt{a^2-3}}$ **89.** Step 1: $\sqrt[n]{a}=a^{1/n}$, by definition;
Step 2: $\left(\dfrac{a}{b}\right)^n=\dfrac{a^n}{b^n}$, raising a quotient to a power;
Step 3: $a^{1/n}=\sqrt[n]{a}$, by definition   **91.** $(f/g)(x)=3x$,
where x is a real number and $x>0$
93. $(f/g)(x)=\sqrt{x+3}$, where x is a real number and $x>3$

Exercise Set 10.5, pp. 666–668

1. Radicands; indices   **2.** Indices   **3.** Bases
4. Denominators   **5.** Numerator; conjugate   **6.** Bases
7. $11\sqrt{3}$ **9.** $2\sqrt[3]{4}$ **11.** $10\sqrt[3]{y}$ **13.** $12\sqrt{2}$
15. $13\sqrt[3]{7}+\sqrt{3}$ **17.** $9\sqrt{3}$ **19.** $-7\sqrt{5}$ **21.** $9\sqrt[3]{2}$
23. $(1+12a)\sqrt{a}$ **25.** $(x-2)\sqrt[3]{6x}$ **27.** $3\sqrt{a-1}$
29. $(x+3)\sqrt{x-1}$ **31.** $5\sqrt{2}+2$ **33.** $3\sqrt{30}-3\sqrt{35}$
35. $6\sqrt{5}-4$ **37.** $3-4\sqrt[3]{63}$ **39.** $a+2a\sqrt[3]{3}$
41. $4+3\sqrt{6}$ **43.** $\sqrt{6}-\sqrt{14}+\sqrt{21}-7$ **45.** 1
47. -5 **49.** $2-8\sqrt{35}$ **51.** $23+8\sqrt{7}$ **53.** $5-2\sqrt{6}$
55. $2t+5+2\sqrt{10t}$ **57.** $14+x-6\sqrt{x+5}$
59. $6\sqrt[4]{63}+4\sqrt[4]{35}-3\sqrt[4]{54}-2\sqrt[4]{30}$ **61.** $\dfrac{18+6\sqrt{2}}{7}$
63. $\dfrac{12-2\sqrt{3}+6\sqrt{5}-\sqrt{15}}{33}$ **65.** $\dfrac{a-\sqrt{ab}}{a-b}$ **67.** -1
69. $\dfrac{12-3\sqrt{10}-2\sqrt{14}+\sqrt{35}}{6}$ **71.** $\dfrac{1}{\sqrt{5}-1}$
73. $\dfrac{2}{14+2\sqrt{3}+3\sqrt{2}+7\sqrt{6}}$ **75.** $\dfrac{x-y}{x+2\sqrt{xy}+y}$
77. $\dfrac{1}{\sqrt{a+h}+\sqrt{a}}$ **79.** $\sqrt{a}$ **81.** $b^2\sqrt[10]{b^3}$
83. $xy\sqrt[6]{xy^5}$ **85.** $3a^2b\sqrt[4]{ab}$ **87.** $a^2b^2c^2\sqrt[6]{a^2bc^2}$
89. $\sqrt[12]{a^5}$ **91.** $\sqrt[12]{x^2y^5}$ **93.** $\sqrt[10]{ab^9}$ **95.** $\sqrt[6]{(7-y)^5}$
97. $\sqrt[12]{5}+3x$ **99.** $x\sqrt[6]{xy^5}-\sqrt[15]{x^{13}y^{14}}$
101. $2m^2+m\sqrt[4]{n}+2m\sqrt[3]{n^2}+\sqrt[12]{n^{11}}$

103. $2\sqrt[4]{x^3} - \sqrt[12]{x^{11}}$ **105.** $x^2 - 7$ **107.** $11 - 6\sqrt{2}$
109. $27 + 6\sqrt{14}$ **111.** ✍   **113.** 42   **114.** $-\frac{1}{3}$
115. $-7, 3$ **116.** $-\frac{2}{5}, \frac{3}{2}$ **117.** -3 **118.** $-6, 1$
119. ✍   **121.** $f(x) = 2x\sqrt{x-1}$
123. $f(x) = (x + 3x^2)\sqrt[4]{x-1}$ **125.** $(7x^2 - 2y^2)\sqrt{x+y}$
127. $4x(y+z)^3\sqrt[6]{2x(y+z)}$ **129.** $1 - \sqrt{w}$
131. $(\sqrt{x} + \sqrt{5})(\sqrt{x} - \sqrt{5})$
133. $(\sqrt{x} + \sqrt{a})(\sqrt{x} - \sqrt{a})$ **135.** $2x - 2\sqrt{x^2-4}$

Connecting the Concepts, pp. 668–669

1. $t + 5$ **2.** $-3a^4$ **3.** $3x\sqrt{10}$ **4.** $\frac{2}{3}$ **5.** $5\sqrt{15t}$
6. $ab^2c^2\sqrt[5]{c}$ **7.** $2\sqrt{15} - 3\sqrt{22}$ **8.** $-2b\sqrt[4]{a^3b^3}$
9. $\sqrt[8]{t}$ **10.** $\dfrac{a^2}{2}$ **11.** $-8\sqrt{3}$ **12.** -4 **13.** $25 + 10\sqrt{6}$
14. $2\sqrt{x-1}$ **15.** $xy\sqrt[10]{x^7y^3}$ **16.** $15\sqrt[3]{5}$ **17.** $\sqrt[5]{x}$
18. $(x+1)\sqrt{3}$ **19.** $ab\sqrt{b}$ **20.** $6x^3y^2$

Technology Connection, p. 671

1. The x-coordinates of the points of intersection should approximate the solutions of the examples.

Exercise Set 10.6, pp. 673–675

1. False   **2.** True   **3.** True   **4.** False   **5.** True
6. True   **7.** 3   **9.** $\frac{16}{3}$ **11.** 20   **13.** -1 **15.** 5
17. 91   **19.** $0, 36$ **21.** 100   **23.** -125 **25.** 16
27. No solution   **29.** $\frac{80}{3}$ **31.** 45   **33.** $-\frac{5}{3}$ **35.** 1
37. $\frac{106}{27}$ **39.** 4   **41.** $3, 7$ **43.** $\frac{80}{9}$ **45.** -1
47. No solution   **49.** $2, 6$ **51.** 2   **53.** 4   **55.** ✍
57. Length: 200 ft; width: 15 ft   **58.** Base: 34 in.; height: 15 in.
59. Length: 14 in.; width: 10 in.
60. Length: 30 yd; width: 16 yd   **61.** $6, 8, 10$ **62.** 13 cm
63. ✍   **65.** About 68 psi   **67.** About 278 Hz
69. 524.8°C   **71.** $t = \dfrac{1}{9}\left(\dfrac{S^2 \cdot 2457}{1087.7^2} - 2617\right)$
73. 4480 rpm   **75.** $r = \dfrac{v^2h}{2gh - v^2}$ **77.** $-\frac{8}{9}$ **79.** $-8, 8$
81. $1, 8$ **83.** $\left(\frac{1}{36}, 0\right), (36, 0)$ **85.** ▨   **87.** ▨

Exercise Set 10.7, pp. 683–687

1. (d)   **2.** (c)   **3.** (e)   **4.** (b)   **5.** (f)   **6.** (a)
7. $\sqrt{34}$; 5.831   **9.** $9\sqrt{2}$; 12.728   **11.** 8   **13.** 4 m
15. $\sqrt{19}$ in.; 4.359 in.   **17.** 1 m   **19.** 250 ft
21. $\sqrt{8450}$, or $65\sqrt{2}$ ft; 91.924 ft   **23.** 24 in.
25. $(\sqrt{340} + 8)$ ft; 26.439 ft
27. $(110 - \sqrt{6500})$ paces; 29.377 paces
29. Leg $= 5$; hypotenuse $= 5\sqrt{2} \approx 7.071$
31. Shorter leg $= 7$; longer leg $= 7\sqrt{3} \approx 12.124$
33. Leg $= 5\sqrt{3} \approx 8.660$; hypotenuse $= 10\sqrt{3} \approx 17.321$
35. Both legs $= \dfrac{13\sqrt{2}}{2} \approx 9.192$
37. Leg $= 14\sqrt{3} \approx 24.249$; hypotenuse $= 28$
39. $5\sqrt{3} \approx 8.660$ **41.** $7\sqrt{2} \approx 9.899$

43. $\dfrac{15\sqrt{2}}{2} \approx 10.607$ **45.** $\sqrt{10{,}561}$ ft ≈ 102.767 ft
47. $\dfrac{1089}{4}\sqrt{3}$ ft$^2 \approx 471.551$ ft^2 **49.** $(0, -4), (0, 4)$
51. 5   **53.** $\sqrt{10} \approx 3.162$ **55.** $\sqrt{200} \approx 14.142$
57. 17.8   **59.** $\dfrac{\sqrt{13}}{6} \approx 0.601$ **61.** $\sqrt{12} \approx 3.464$
63. $\sqrt{101} \approx 10.050$ **65.** $(3, 4)$ **67.** $\left(\frac{7}{2}, \frac{7}{2}\right)$
69. $(-1, -3)$ **71.** $(0.7, 0)$ **73.** $\left(-\frac{1}{12}, \frac{1}{24}\right)$
75. $\left(\dfrac{\sqrt{2} + \sqrt{3}}{2}, \dfrac{3}{2}\right)$ **77.** ✍

79. **80.**

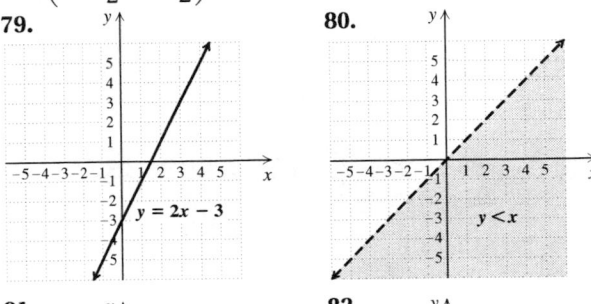

81. **82.**

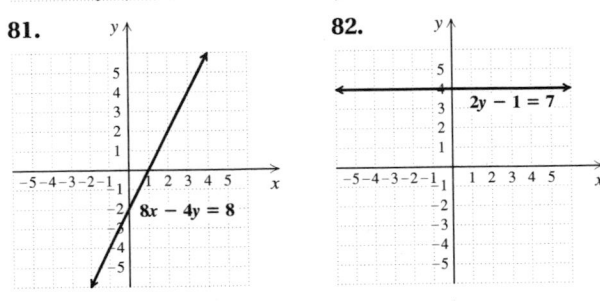

83. **84.**

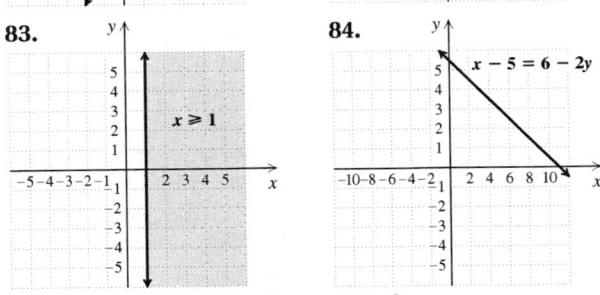

85. ✍   **87.** $36\sqrt{3}$ cm^2; 62.354 cm^2 **89.** $d = s + s\sqrt{2}$
91. 5 gal. The total area of the doors and windows is 134 ft^2 or more.   **93.** 60.28 ft by 60.28 ft   **95.** $\sqrt{75}$ cm

Exercise Set 10.8, pp. 693–694

1. False   **2.** False   **3.** True   **4.** True   **5.** True
6. True   **7.** False   **8.** True   **9.** $10i$ **11.** $i\sqrt{5}$, or $\sqrt{5}i$
13. $2i\sqrt{2}$, or $2\sqrt{2}i$ **15.** $-i\sqrt{11}$, or $-\sqrt{11}i$ **17.** $-7i$
19. $-10i\sqrt{3}$, or $-10\sqrt{3}i$ **21.** $6 - 2i\sqrt{21}$, or $6 - 2\sqrt{21}i$
23. $(-2\sqrt{19} + 5\sqrt{5})i$ **25.** $(3\sqrt{2} - 8)i$ **27.** $5 - 3i$
29. $7 + 2i$ **31.** $2 - i$ **33.** $-12 - 5i$ **35.** -40
37. -24 **39.** -18 **41.** $-\sqrt{30}$ **43.** $-3\sqrt{14}$
45. $-30 + 10i$ **47.** $28 - 21i$ **49.** $1 + 5i$ **51.** $38 + 9i$
53. $2 - 46i$ **55.** 73   **57.** 50   **59.** $12 - 16i$
61. $-5 + 12i$ **63.** $-5 - 12i$ **65.** $3 - i$ **67.** $\frac{6}{13} + \frac{4}{13}i$
69. $\frac{3}{17} + \frac{5}{17}i$ **71.** $-\frac{5}{6}i$ **73.** $-\frac{3}{4} - \frac{5}{4}i$ **75.** $1 - 2i$
77. $-\frac{23}{58} + \frac{43}{58}i$ **79.** $\frac{19}{29} - \frac{4}{29}i$ **81.** $\frac{6}{25} - \frac{17}{25}i$ **83.** 1

85. $-i$ **87.** -1 **89.** i **91.** -1 **93.** $-125i$
95. 0 **97.** 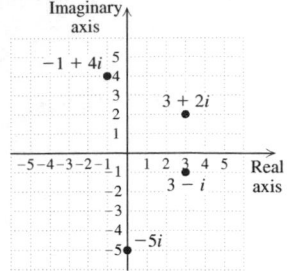   **99.** $-2, 3$ **100.** 5 **101.** $-10, 10$
102. $-5, 5$ **103.** $-\frac{2}{5}, \frac{4}{3}$ **104.** $-\frac{2}{3}, \frac{3}{2}$ **105.**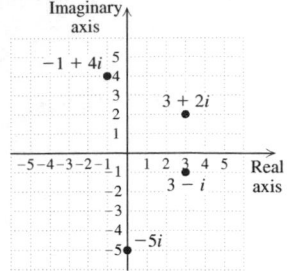
107.   **109.** 5 **111.** $\sqrt{2}$

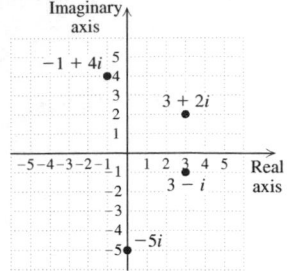

113. $-9 - 27i$ **115.** $50 - 120i$ **117.** $\frac{250}{41} + \frac{200}{41}i$
119. 8 **121.** $\frac{3}{5} + \frac{9}{5}i$ **123.** 1

Review Exercises: Chapter 10, pp. 698–699

1. True   **2.** False   **3.** False   **4.** True   **5.** True
6. True   **7.** True   **8.** False   **9.** $\frac{10}{11}$ **10.** -0.6
11. 5 **12.** $\{x \mid x \geq -10\}$, or $[-10, \infty)$ **13.** $8|t|$
14. $|c + 7|$ **15.** $|2x + 1|$ **16.** -2 **17.** $(5ab)^{4/3}$
18. $8a^4\sqrt{a}$ **19.** x^3y^5 **20.** $\sqrt[3]{x^2y}$ **21.** $\dfrac{1}{x^{2/5}}$
22. $7^{1/6}$ **23.** $f(x) = 5|x - 6|$ **24.** $2x^5y^2$
25. $5xy\sqrt{10x}$ **26.** $\sqrt{35ab}$ **27.** $3xb\sqrt[3]{x^2}$
28. $-6x^5y^4\sqrt[3]{2x^2}$ **29.** $-\dfrac{3y^4}{4}$ **30.** $y\sqrt[3]{6}$ **31.** $\dfrac{5\sqrt{x}}{2}$
32. $\dfrac{2a^2\sqrt[4]{3a^3}}{c^2}$ **33.** $7\sqrt[3]{4y}$ **34.** $\sqrt{3}$ **35.** $(2x + y^2)\sqrt[3]{x}$
36. $15\sqrt{2}$ **37.** -1 **38.** $\sqrt{15} + 4\sqrt{6} - 6\sqrt{10} - 48$
39. $\sqrt[4]{x^3}$ **40.** $\sqrt[12]{x^5}$ **41.** $4 - 4\sqrt{a} + a$
42. $-4\sqrt{10} + 4\sqrt{15}$ **43.** $\dfrac{20}{\sqrt{10} + \sqrt{15}}$ **44.** 19
45. -126 **46.** 4 **47.** 2 **48.** $5\sqrt{2}$ cm; 7.071 cm
49. $\sqrt{32}$ ft; 5.657 ft
50. Short leg $= 10$; long leg $= 10\sqrt{3} \approx 17.321$
51. $\sqrt{26} \approx 5.099$ **52.** $\left(-2, -\frac{3}{2}\right)$ **53.** $3i\sqrt{5}$, or $3\sqrt{5}i$
54. $-2 - 9i$ **55.** $6 + i$ **56.** 29 **57.** -1 **58.** $9 - 12i$
59. $\frac{13}{25} - \frac{34}{25}i$ **60.** 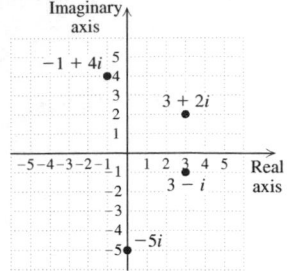 A complex number $a + bi$ is real when $b = 0$. It is imaginary when $b \neq 0$.   **61.** 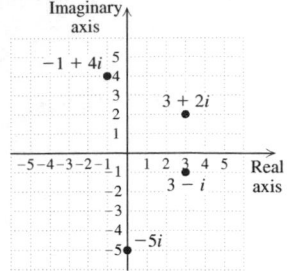 An absolute-value sign must be used to simplify $\sqrt[n]{x^n}$ when n is even, since x may be negative. If x is negative while n is even, the radical expression cannot be simplified to x, since $\sqrt[n]{x^n}$ represents the principal, or nonnegative, root. When n is odd, there is only one root, and it will be positive or negative depending on the sign of x. Thus there is no absolute-value sign when n is odd.   **62.** $\dfrac{2i}{3i}$; answers may vary
63. 3 **64.** $-\frac{2}{5} + \frac{9}{10}i$ **65.** The isosceles right triangle is larger by about 1.206 ft^2.

Test: Chapter 10, p. 700

1. [10.3] $5\sqrt{2}$ **2.** [10.4] $-\dfrac{2}{x^2}$ **3.** [10.1] $9|a|$
4. [10.1] $|x - 4|$ **5.** [10.2] $(7xy)^{1/2}$ **6.** [10.2] $\sqrt[6]{(4a^3b)^5}$

7. [10.1] $\{x \mid x \geq 5\}$, or $[5, \infty)$ **8.** [10.5] $27 + 10\sqrt{2}$
9. [10.3] $2x^3y^2\sqrt[5]{x}$ **10.** [10.3] $2\sqrt[3]{2wv^2}$ **11.** [10.4] $\dfrac{10a^2}{3b^3}$
12. [10.4] $\sqrt[5]{3x^4y}$ **13.** [10.5] $x\sqrt[4]{x}$ **14.** [10.5] $\sqrt[5]{y^2}$
15. [10.5] $6\sqrt{2}$ **16.** [10.5] $(x^2 + 3y)\sqrt{y}$
17. [10.5] $14 - 19\sqrt{x} - 3x$ **18.** [10.5] $\dfrac{5\sqrt{3} - \sqrt{6}}{23}$
19. [10.6] 4 **20.** [10.6] $-1, 2$ **21.** [10.6] 8
22. [10.7] $\sqrt{10{,}600}$ ft ≈ 102.956 ft   **23.** [10.7] 5 cm; $5\sqrt{3}$ cm ≈ 8.660 cm   **24.** [10.7] $\sqrt{17} \approx 4.123$
25. [10.7] $\left(\frac{3}{2}, -6\right)$ **26.** [10.8] $5i\sqrt{2}$, or $5\sqrt{2}i$
27. [10.8] $12 + 2i$ **28.** [10.8] $15 - 8i$ **29.** [10.8] $-\frac{11}{34} - \frac{7}{34}i$
30. [10.8] i **31.** [10.6] 3 **32.** [10.8] $-\frac{17}{4}i$ **33.** [10.6] $22{,}500$ ft

Cumulative Review: Chapters 1–10, pp. 701–702

1. -7 **2.** $-7, 5$ **3.** $-5, 5$ **4.** $\frac{5}{2}$ **5.** -1 **6.** $\frac{1}{5}$
7. $\{x \mid -3 \leq x \leq 7\}$, or $[-3, 7]$ **8.** $\mathbb{R}$, or $(-\infty, \infty)$
9. $-3, 2$ **10.** 7 **11.** $(0, 5)$ **12.** $(-1, -1, -2)$
13.   **14.**

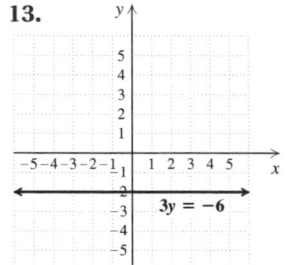   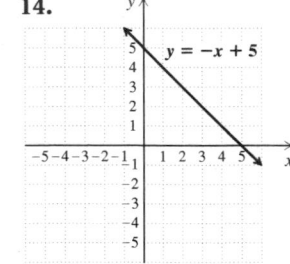

15.   **16.**

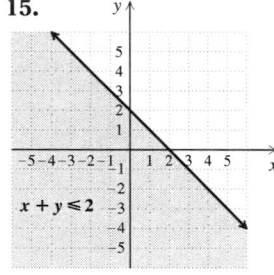   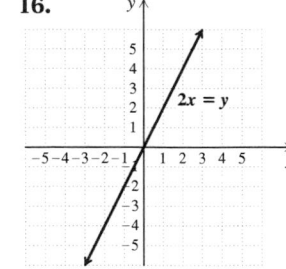

17. Slope: -1; y-intercept: $(0, -6)$
18. $y = 7x - 11$ **19.** 6 **20.** $-8xy^2$
21. $4a^2 - 20ab + 25b^2$ **22.** $c^4 - 9d^2$ **23.** $\dfrac{2x + 1}{x(x + 1)}$
24. $\dfrac{x + 13}{(x - 2)(x + 1)}$ **25.** $\dfrac{(a + 2)(2a + 1)}{(a - 3)(a - 1)}$ **26.** $\dfrac{2x + 1}{x^2}$
27. 0 **28.** $-1 + 3\sqrt{5}$ **29.** $5ab^2\sqrt{6a}$ **30.** $\sqrt[15]{y^8}$
31. $(x - 7)(x + 2)$ **32.** $4y^5(y - 1)(y^2 + y + 1)$
33. $25(2c + d)(2c - d)$ **34.** $(3t - 8)(t + 1)$
35. $3(x^2 - 2x - 7)$ **36.** $(y - x)(t - z^2)$
37. $\{x \mid x$ is a real number $and\ x \neq 3\}$, or $(-\infty, 3) \cup (3, \infty)$
38. $\left\{x \mid x \geq \frac{11}{2}\right\}$, or $\left[\frac{11}{2}, \infty\right)$ **39.** 5 **40.** $6 - 2\sqrt{5}$
41. $(f + g)(x) = x^2 + \sqrt{2x - 3}$ **42.** 4 mph
43. $2\sqrt{3}$ ft ≈ 3.464 ft   **44.** **(a)** $m(t) = 0.08t + 25.02$;
(b) 26.62; **(c)** 2037 **45.** $\$36{,}650$ **46.** Swiss chocolate: 45 oz; whipping cream: 20 oz   **47.** 4×10^5 programs
48. $\$1.54$ per year   **49.** 5 ft   **50.** $5x - 3y = -15$
51. $(0, -1), (1, 0)$ **52.** -2 **53.** 10

CHAPTER 11

Technology Connection, p. 712

1. The right-hand x-intercept should be an approximation of $4 + \sqrt{23}$. **2.** x-intercepts should be approximations of $(-5 + \sqrt{37})/2$ and $(-5 - \sqrt{37})/2$.
3. Most graphing calculators can give only rational-number approximations of the two irrational solutions. An *exact* solution cannot be found with a graphing calculator.
4. The graph of $y = x^2 - 6x + 11$ has no x-intercepts.

Exercise Set 11.1, pp. 712-714

1. $\sqrt{k}; -\sqrt{k}$ **2.** $7; -7$ **3.** $t + 3; t + 3$ **4.** 16
5. $25; 5$ **6.** $9; 3$ **7.** ± 10 **9.** $\pm 5\sqrt{2}$ **11.** $\pm\sqrt{6}$
13. $\pm\frac{7}{3}$ **15.** $\pm\sqrt{\frac{5}{6}}$, or $\pm\frac{\sqrt{30}}{6}$ **17.** $\pm i$ **19.** $\pm\frac{9}{2}i$
21. $-1, 7$ **23.** $-5 \pm 2\sqrt{3}$ **25.** $-1 \pm 3i$
27. $-\frac{3}{4} \pm \frac{\sqrt{17}}{4}$, or $\frac{-3 \pm \sqrt{17}}{4}$ **29.** $-3, 13$ **31.** $\pm\sqrt{19}$
33. $1, 9$ **35.** $-4 \pm \sqrt{13}$ **37.** $-14, 0$
39. $x^2 + 16x + 64 = (x + 8)^2$
41. $t^2 - 10t + 25 = (t - 5)^2$
43. $t^2 - 2t + 1 = (t - 1)^2$ **45.** $x^2 + 3x + \frac{9}{4} = \left(x + \frac{3}{2}\right)^2$
47. $x^2 + \frac{2}{5}x + \frac{1}{25} = \left(x + \frac{1}{5}\right)^2$
49. $t^2 - \frac{5}{6}t + \frac{25}{144} = \left(t - \frac{5}{12}\right)^2$ **51.** $-7, 1$ **53.** $5 \pm \sqrt{2}$
55. $-8, -4$ **57.** $-4 \pm \sqrt{19}$
59. $(-3 - \sqrt{2}, 0), (-3 + \sqrt{2}, 0)$
61. $\left(-\frac{9}{2} - \frac{\sqrt{181}}{2}, 0\right), \left(-\frac{9}{2} + \frac{\sqrt{181}}{2}, 0\right)$, or
$\left(\frac{-9 - \sqrt{181}}{2}, 0\right), \left(\frac{-9 + \sqrt{181}}{2}, 0\right)$
63. $(5 - \sqrt{47}, 0), (5 + \sqrt{47}, 0)$ **65.** $-\frac{4}{3}, -\frac{2}{3}$
67. $-\frac{1}{3}, 2$ **69.** $-\frac{2}{5} \pm \frac{\sqrt{19}}{5}$, or $\frac{-2 \pm \sqrt{19}}{5}$
71. $\left(-\frac{1}{4} - \frac{\sqrt{13}}{4}, 0\right), \left(-\frac{1}{4} + \frac{\sqrt{13}}{4}, 0\right)$, or $\left(\frac{-1 - \sqrt{13}}{4}, 0\right)$,
$\left(\frac{-1 + \sqrt{13}}{4}, 0\right)$ **73.** $\left(\frac{3}{4} - \frac{\sqrt{17}}{4}, 0\right), \left(\frac{3}{4} + \frac{\sqrt{17}}{4}, 0\right)$,
or $\left(\frac{3 - \sqrt{17}}{4}, 0\right), \left(\frac{3 + \sqrt{17}}{4}, 0\right)$ **75.** 10%   **77.** 4%
79. About 4.3 sec   **81.** About 11.4 sec   **83.** ⚞
85. 64   **86.** -15 **87.** $10\sqrt{2}$ **88.** $4\sqrt{6}$ **89.** $2i$
90. $5i$ **91.** $2i\sqrt{2}$, or $2\sqrt{2}i$ **92.** $2i\sqrt{6}$ or $2\sqrt{6}i$
93. ⚞   **95.** ± 18 **97.** $-\frac{7}{2}, -\sqrt{5}, 0, \sqrt{5}, 8$
99. Barge: 8 km/h; fishing boat: 15 km/h   **101.** ◪
103. ⚞, ◪

Exercise Set 11.2, pp. 719-720

1. True   **2.** True   **3.** False   **4.** False   **5.** False
6. True   **7.** $-\frac{5}{2}, 1$ **9.** $-1 \pm \sqrt{5}$ **11.** $3 \pm \sqrt{6}$
13. $\frac{3}{2} \pm \frac{\sqrt{29}}{2}$ **15.** $-1 \pm \frac{2\sqrt{3}}{3}$ **17.** $-\frac{4}{3} \pm \frac{\sqrt{19}}{3}$
19. $3 \pm i$ **21.** $\frac{1}{2} \pm \frac{\sqrt{3}}{2}i$ **23.** $-2 \pm \sqrt{2}i$ **25.** $-\frac{8}{3}, \frac{5}{4}$

27. $\frac{2}{5}$ **29.** $-\frac{11}{8} \pm \frac{\sqrt{41}}{8}$ **31.** $5, 10$ **33.** $\frac{3}{2}, 24$
35. $2 \pm \sqrt{5}i$ **37.** $2, -1 \pm \sqrt{3}i$
39. $-\frac{4}{3}, \frac{5}{2}$ **41.** $5 \pm \sqrt{53}$ **43.** $\frac{3}{2} \pm \frac{\sqrt{5}}{2}$
45. $-5.317, 1.317$ **47.** $0.764, 5.236$ **49.** $-1.266, 2.766$
51. ⚞   **53.** $x^2 + 4$ **54.** $x^2 - 180$ **55.** $x^2 - 4x - 3$
56. $x^2 + 6x + 34$ **57.** $-\frac{3}{2}$ **58.** $\frac{1}{6} \pm \frac{\sqrt{6}}{3}i$ **59.** ⚞
61. $(-2, 0), (1, 0)$ **63.** $4 - 2\sqrt{2}, 4 + 2\sqrt{2}$
65. $-1.179, 0.339$ **67.** $\frac{-5\sqrt{2} \pm \sqrt{34}}{4}$ **69.** $\frac{1}{2}$ **71.** ◪

Technology Connection, p. 723

1. $(-0.4, 0)$ is the other x-intercept of $y = 5x^2 - 13x - 6$.
2. The x-intercepts of $y = x^2 - 175$ are $(-13.22875656, 0)$ and $(13.22875656, 0)$, or $(-5\sqrt{7}, 0)$ and $(5\sqrt{7}, 0)$.
3. The x-intercepts of $y = x^3 + 3x^2 - 4x$ are $(-4, 0), (0, 0)$, and $(1, 0)$.

Exercise Set 11.3, pp. 723-725

1. (b)   **2.** (a)   **3.** (d)   **4.** (b)   **5.** (c)   **6.** (c)
7. Two irrational   **9.** Two imaginary   **11.** Two irrational
13. Two rational   **15.** Two imaginary   **17.** One rational
19. Two rational   **21.** Two irrational
23. Two imaginary   **25.** Two rational
27. Two irrational   **29.** $x^2 + x - 20 = 0$
31. $x^2 - 6x + 9 = 0$ **33.** $x^2 + 4x + 3 = 0$
35. $4x^2 - 23x + 15 = 0$ **37.** $8x^2 + 6x + 1 = 0$
39. $x^2 - 2x - 0.96 = 0$ **41.** $x^2 - 3 = 0$
43. $x^2 - 20 = 0$ **45.** $x^2 + 16 = 0$
47. $x^2 - 4x + 53 = 0$ **49.** $x^2 - 6x - 5 = 0$
51. $3x^2 - 6x - 4 = 0$ **53.** $x^3 - 4x^2 - 7x + 10 = 0$
55. $x^3 - 2x^2 - 3x = 0$ **57.** ⚞   **59.** $c = \frac{d^2}{1 - d}$
60. $b = \frac{aq}{p - q}$ **61.** $y = \frac{x - 3}{x}$, or $1 - \frac{3}{x}$
62. 10 mph   **63.** Jamal: 3.5 mph; Kade: 2 mph
64. 20 mph   **65.** ⚞   **67.** $a = 1, b = 2, c = -3$
69. (a) $-\frac{3}{5}$; (b) $-\frac{1}{3}$ **71.** (a) $9 + 9i$; (b) $3 + 3i$
73. The solutions of $ax^2 + bx + c = 0$ are
$x = \frac{-b \pm \sqrt{b^2 - 4ac}}{2a}$. When there is just one solution,
$b^2 - 4ac$ must be 0, so $x = \frac{-b \pm 0}{2a} = \frac{-b}{2a}$.
75. $a = 8, b = 20, c = -12$ **77.** $x^2 - 2 = 0$
79. $x^4 - 8x^3 + 21x^2 - 2x - 52 = 0$ **81.** ⚞, ◪

Exercise Set 11.4, pp. 729-732

1. First part: 60 mph; second part: 50 mph   **3.** 40 mph
5. Cessna: 150 mph, Beechcraft: 200 mph; or Cessna: 200 mph, Beechcraft: 250 mph   **7.** To Hillsboro: 12 mph; return trip: 9 mph   **9.** About 14 mph   **11.** 12 hr
13. About 3.24 mph   **15.** $r = \frac{1}{2}\sqrt{\frac{A}{\pi}}$

17. $r = \dfrac{-\pi h + \sqrt{\pi^2 h^2 + 2\pi A}}{2\pi}$ **19.** $r = \dfrac{\sqrt{Gm_1 m_2}}{F}$

21. $H = \dfrac{c^2}{g}$ **23.** $b = \sqrt{c^2 - a^2}$

25. $t = \dfrac{-v_0 + \sqrt{(v_0)^2 + 2gs}}{g}$ **27.** $n = \dfrac{1 + \sqrt{1 + 8N}}{2}$

29. $g = \dfrac{4\pi^2 l}{T^2}$ **31.** $t = \dfrac{-b \pm \sqrt{b^2 - 4ac}}{2a}$

33. **(a)** 10.1 sec; **(b)** 7.49 sec; **(c)** 272.5 m   **35.** 2.9 sec
37. 0.890 sec   **39.** 2.5 m/sec   **41.** 4.5%   **43.**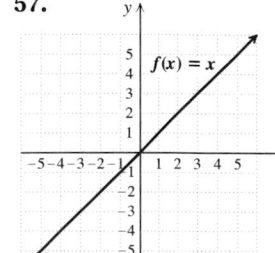

45. m^{-2}, or $\dfrac{1}{m^2}$ **46.** $t^{2/3}$ **47.** $y^{1/3}$ **48.** $z^{1/2}$ **49.** 2

50. 81   **51.**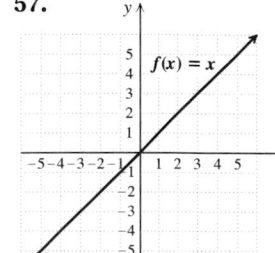

53. $t = \dfrac{-10.2 + 6\sqrt{-A^2 + 13A - 39.36}}{A - 6.5}$ **55.** $\pm\sqrt{2}$

57. $l = \dfrac{w + w\sqrt{5}}{2}$

59. $n = \pm\sqrt{\dfrac{r^2 \pm \sqrt{r^4 + 4m^4 r^2 p - 4mp}}{2m}}$

61. $A(S) = \dfrac{\pi S}{6}$

Exercise Set 11.5, pp. 737–738

1. (f)   **2.** (d)   **3.** (h)   **4.** (b)   **5.** (g)   **6.** (a)
7. (e)   **8.** (c)   **9.** $\sqrt{p}$ **10.** $x^{1/4}$ **11.** $x^2 + 3$ **12.** t^{-3}
13. $(1 + t)^2$ **14.** $w^{1/6}$ **15.** $\pm 2, \pm 3$ **17.** $\pm\sqrt{3}, \pm 2$
19. $\pm\dfrac{\sqrt{5}}{2}, \pm 1$ **21.** 4   **23.** $\pm 2\sqrt{2}, \pm 3$
25. $8 + 2\sqrt{7}$ **27.** No solution   **29.** $-\frac{1}{2}, \frac{1}{3}$ **31.** $-4, 1$
33. $-27, 8$ **35.** 729   **37.** 1   **39.** No solution   **41.** $\frac{12}{5}$
43. $\pm 2, \pm 3i$ **45.** $\pm i, \pm 2i$ **47.** $\left(\dfrac{4}{25}, 0\right)$
49. $\left(\dfrac{3}{2} + \dfrac{\sqrt{33}}{2}, 0\right), \left(\dfrac{3}{2} - \dfrac{\sqrt{33}}{2}, 0\right), (4, 0), (-1, 0)$
51. $(-243, 0), (32, 0)$ **53.** No x-intercepts   **55.**
57.   **58.**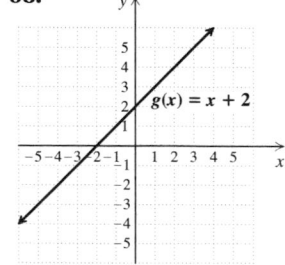

59. 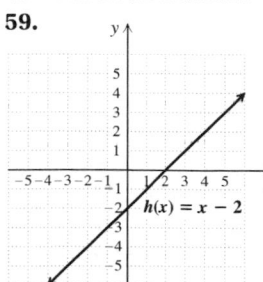   **60.**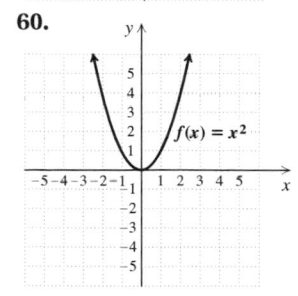

61. 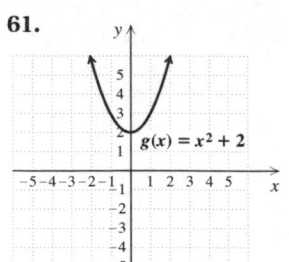   **62.**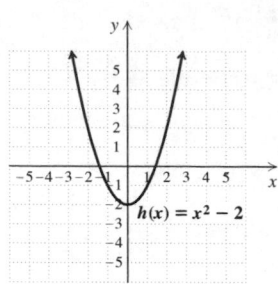

63. 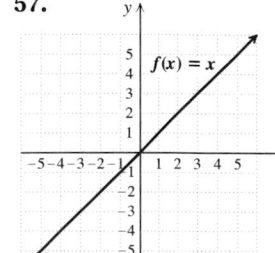   **65.** $\pm\sqrt{\dfrac{-5 \pm \sqrt{37}}{6}}$ **67.** $-2, -1, 6, 7$

69. $\dfrac{100}{99}$ **71.** $-5, -3, -2, 0, 2, 3, 5$ **73.** $1, 3, -\dfrac{1}{2} + \dfrac{\sqrt{3}}{2}i,$

$-\dfrac{1}{2} - \dfrac{\sqrt{3}}{2}i, -\dfrac{3}{2} + \dfrac{3\sqrt{3}}{2}i, -\dfrac{3}{2} - \dfrac{3\sqrt{3}}{2}i$ **75.**

77. ,

Connecting the Concepts, pp. 739–740

1. $-2, 5$ **2.** ± 11 **3.** $-3 \pm \sqrt{19}$ **4.** $-\dfrac{1}{2} \pm \dfrac{\sqrt{13}}{2}$

5. $-1 \pm \sqrt{2}$ **6.** 5   **7.** $\dfrac{1}{2} \pm \dfrac{\sqrt{5}}{2}$ **8.** $1 \pm \sqrt{7}$

9. $\pm\dfrac{\sqrt{11}}{2}$ **10.** $\frac{1}{2}, 1$ **11.** $-\dfrac{1}{2} \pm \dfrac{\sqrt{3}}{2}i$ **12.** $0, \frac{7}{16}$

13. $-\frac{5}{6}, 2$ **14.** $1 \pm \sqrt{7}i$ **15.** $\pm 1, \pm 3$ **16.** $\pm 3, \pm i$
17. $-5, 0$ **18.** $-6, 5$ **19.** $\pm\sqrt{2}, \pm 2i$
20. $\pm\dfrac{\sqrt{3}}{3}, \pm\dfrac{\sqrt{2}}{2}$

Technology Connection, p. 741

1. The graphs of $y_1, y_2,$ and y_3 open upward. The graphs of $y_4, y_5,$ and y_6 open downward. The graph of y_1 is wider than the graph of y_2. The graph of y_3 is narrower than the graph of y_2. Similarly, the graph of y_4 is wider than the graph of y_5, and the graph of y_6 is narrower than the graph of y_5.
2. If A is positive, the graph opens upward. If A is negative, the graph opens downward. Compared with the graph of $y = x^2$, the graph of $y = Ax^2$ is wider if $|A| < 1$ and narrower if $|A| > 1$.

Technology Connection, p. 743

1. Compared with the graph of $y = ax^2$, the graph of $y = a(x - h)^2$ is shifted left or right. It is shifted left if h is negative and right if h is positive.   **2.** The value of A makes the graph wider or narrower, and makes the graph open downward if A is negative. The value of B shifts the graph left or right.

Technology Connection, p. 744

1. The graph of y_2 looks like the graph of y_1 shifted up 2 units, and the graph of y_3 looks like the graph of y_1 shifted down 4 units.   **2.** Compared with the graph of $y = a(x - h)^2$, the graph of $y = a(x - h)^2 + k$ is shifted up or down. It is shifted down if k is negative and up if k is positive.

3. The value of A makes the graph wider or narrower, and makes the graph open downward if A is negative. The value of B shifts the graph left or right. The value of C shifts the graph up or down.

Exercise Set 11.6, pp. 746–748

1. (h)   **2.** (g)   **3.** (f)   **4.** (d)   **5.** (b)   **6.** (c)
7. (e)   **8.** (a)

9.
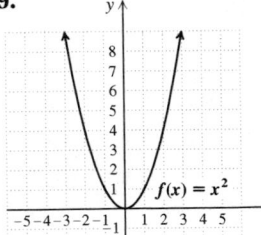

11.
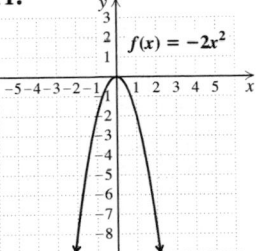

13.
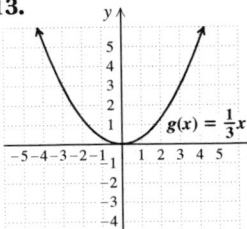

15.
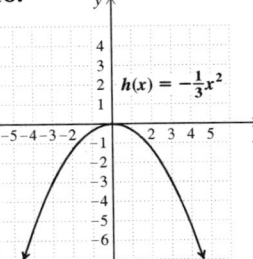

17.
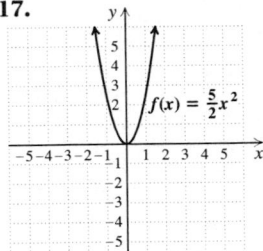

19. Vertex: $(-1, 0)$; axis of symmetry: $x = -1$
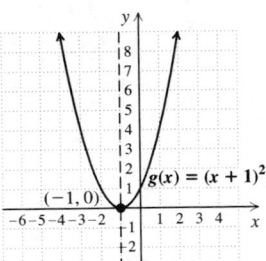

21. Vertex $(2, 0)$; axis of symmetry: $x = 2$
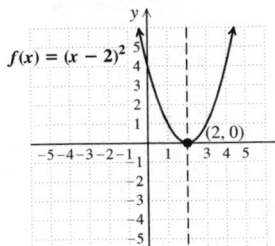

23. Vertex: $(-1, 0)$; axis of symmetry: $x = -1$
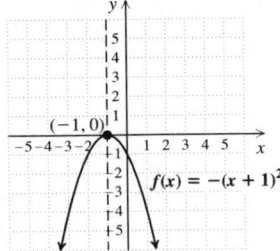

25. Vertex: $(2, 0)$; axis of symmetry: $x = 2$
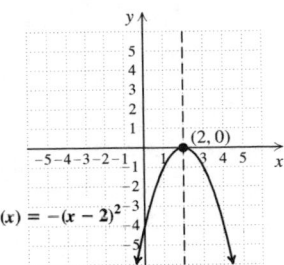

27. Vertex: $(-1, 0)$; axis of symmetry: $x = -1$
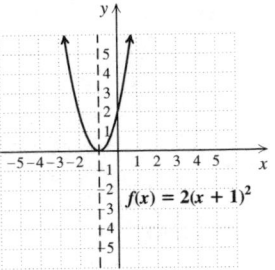

29. Vertex: $(4, 0)$; axis of symmetry: $x = 4$
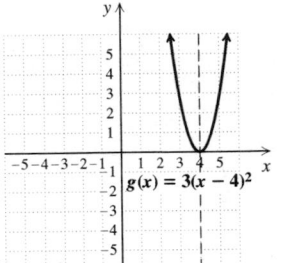

31. Vertex: $(4, 0)$; axis of symmetry: $x = 4$
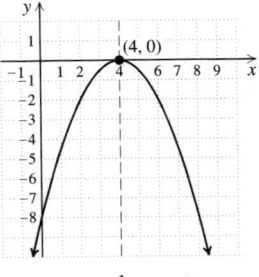

33. Vertex: $(1, 0)$; axis of symmetry: $x = 1$
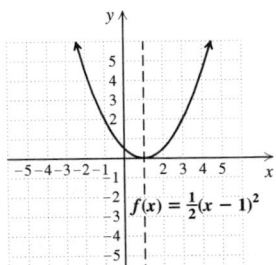

35. Vertex: $(-5, 0)$; axis of symmetry: $x = -5$
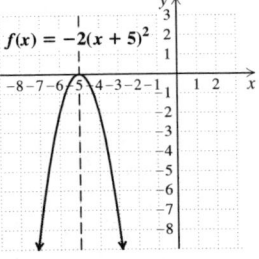

37. Vertex: $\left(\frac{1}{2}, 0\right)$; axis of symmetry: $x = \frac{1}{2}$
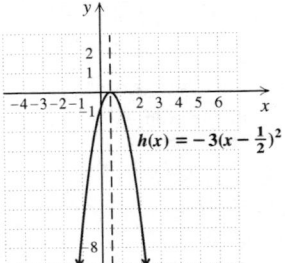

39. Vertex: $(5, 2)$; axis of symmetry: $x = 5$; minimum: 2
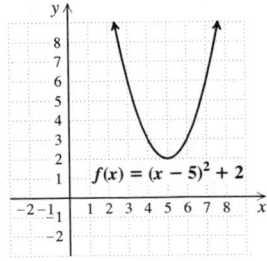

41. Vertex: $(-1, -3)$; axis of symmetry: $x = -1$; minimum: -3

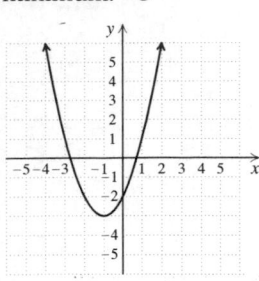

$f(x) = (x + 1)^2 - 3$

43. Vertex: $(-4, 1)$; axis of symmetry: $x = -4$; minimum: 1

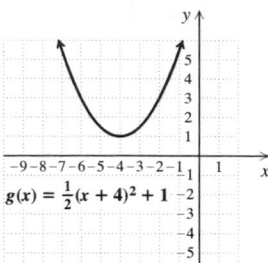

$g(x) = \frac{1}{2}(x + 4)^2 + 1$

45. Vertex: $(1, -3)$; axis of symmetry: $x = 1$; maximum: -3

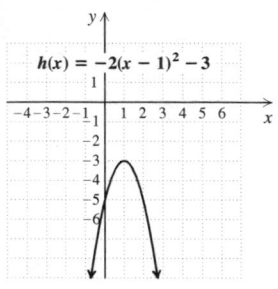

$h(x) = -2(x - 1)^2 - 3$

47. Vertex: $(-3, 1)$; axis of symmetry: $x = -3$; minimum: 1

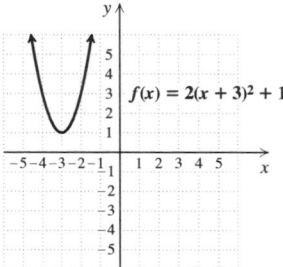

$f(x) = 2(x + 3)^2 + 1$

49. Vertex: $(2, 4)$; axis of symmetry: $x = 2$; maximum: 4

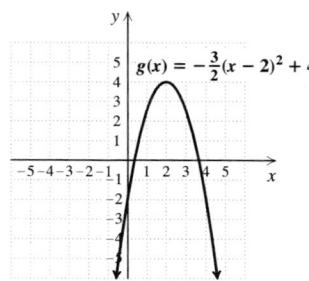

$g(x) = -\frac{3}{2}(x - 2)^2 + 4$

51. Vertex: $(3, 9)$; axis of symmetry: $x = 3$; minimum: 9
53. Vertex: $(-8, 2)$; axis of symmetry: $x = -8$; maximum: 2
55. Vertex: $\left(\frac{7}{2}, -\frac{29}{4}\right)$; axis of symmetry: $x = \frac{7}{2}$; minimum: $-\frac{29}{4}$ **57.** Vertex: $(-2.25, -\pi)$; axis of symmetry: $x = -2.25$; maximum: $-\pi$ **59.** 📓
61. x-intercept: $(3, 0)$; y-intercept: $(0, -4)$
62. x-intercept: $\left(\frac{8}{3}, 0\right)$; y-intercept: $(0, 2)$
63. $(-5, 0), (-3, 0)$ **64.** $(-1, 0), \left(\frac{3}{2}, 0\right)$
65. $x^2 - 14x + 49 = (x - 7)^2$
66. $x^2 + 7x + \frac{49}{4} = \left(x + \frac{7}{2}\right)^2$ **67.** 📓
69. $f(x) = \frac{3}{5}(x - 1)^2 + 3$ **71.** $f(x) = \frac{3}{5}(x - 4)^2 - 7$
73. $f(x) = \frac{3}{5}(x + 2)^2 - 5$ **75.** $f(x) = 2(x - 2)^2$

77. $g(x) = -2x^2 - 5$ **79.** The graph will move to the right.   **81.** The graph will be reflected across the x-axis.
83. $F(x) = 3(x - 5)^2 + 1$
85.

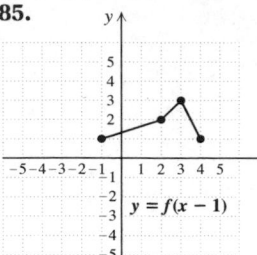

$y = f(x - 1)$

87.

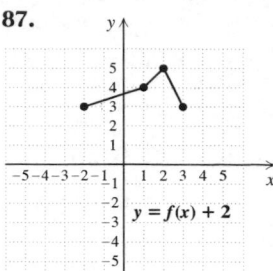

$y = f(x) + 2$

89.

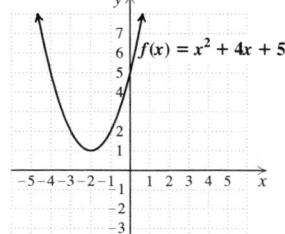

$y = f(x + 3) - 2$

91. ▨   **93.** 📓, ▨

Visualizing for Success, p. 753

1. B   **2.** E   **3.** A   **4.** H   **5.** C   **6.** J   **7.** F
8. G   **9.** I   **10.** D

Exercise Set 11.7, pp. 754–755

1. True   **2.** False   **3.** True   **4.** True   **5.** False
6. True   **7.** False   **8.** True
9. $f(x) = (x - 4)^2 + (-14)$
11. $f(x) = \left(x - \left(-\frac{3}{2}\right)\right)^2 + \left(-\frac{29}{4}\right)$
13. $f(x) = 3(x - (-1))^2 + (-5)$
15. $f(x) = -(x - (-2))^2 + (-3)$
17. $f(x) = 2\left(x - \frac{5}{4}\right)^2 + \frac{55}{8}$
19. (a) Vertex: $(-2, 1)$;   **21. (a)** Vertex: $(-4, 4)$;
axis of symmetry: $x = -2$; axis of symmetry: $x = -4$;
(b)   **(b)**

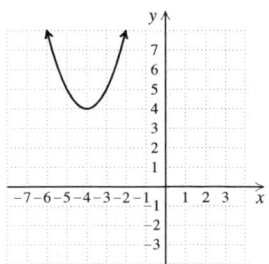

$f(x) = x^2 + 8x + 20$

23. **(a)** Vertex: $(4, -7)$; axis of symmetry: $x = 4$;

(b)

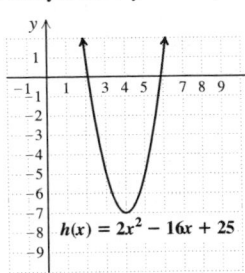

$h(x) = 2x^2 - 16x + 25$

25. **(a)** Vertex: $(1, 6)$; axis of symmetry: $x = 1$;

(b)

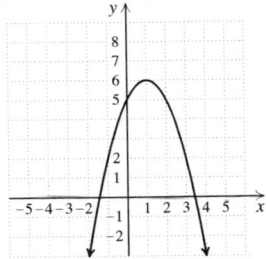

$f(x) = -x^2 + 2x + 5$

27. **(a)** Vertex: $\left(-\frac{3}{2}, -\frac{49}{4}\right)$; axis of symmetry: $x = -\frac{3}{2}$;

(b)

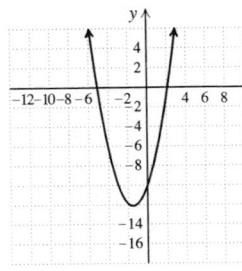

$g(x) = x^2 + 3x - 10$

29. **(a)** Vertex: $\left(-\frac{7}{2}, -\frac{49}{4}\right)$; axis of symmetry: $x = -\frac{7}{2}$;

(b)

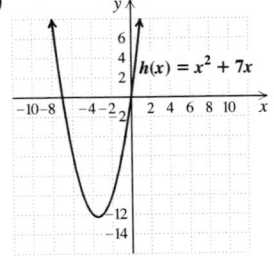

$h(x) = x^2 + 7x$

31. **(a)** Vertex: $(-1, -4)$; axis of symmetry: $x = -1$;

(b)

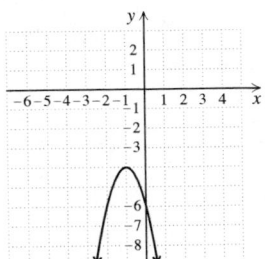

$f(x) = -2x^2 - 4x - 6$

33. **(a)** Vertex: $(3, 4)$; axis of symmetry: $x = 3$; minimum: 4;

(b)

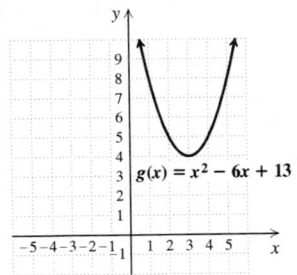

$g(x) = x^2 - 6x + 13$

35. **(a)** Vertex: $(2, -5)$; axis of symmetry: $x = 2$; minimum: -5;

(b)

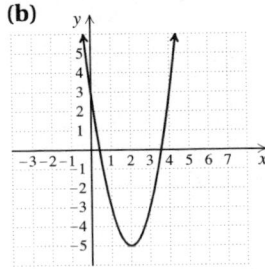

$g(x) = 2x^2 - 8x + 3$

37. **(a)** Vertex: $(4, 2)$; axis of symmetry: $x = 4$; minimum: 2;

(b)

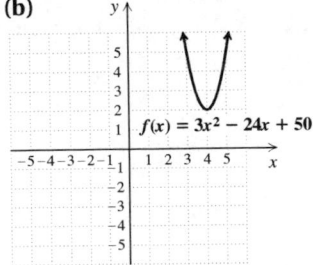

$f(x) = 3x^2 - 24x + 50$

39. **(a)** Vertex: $\left(\frac{5}{6}, \frac{1}{12}\right)$; axis of symmetry: $x = \frac{5}{6}$; maximum: $\frac{1}{12}$;

(b)

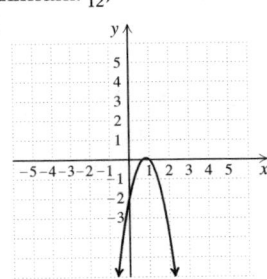

$f(x) = -3x^2 + 5x - 2$

41. **(a)** Vertex: $\left(-4, -\frac{5}{3}\right)$; axis of symmetry: $x = -4$; minimum: $-\frac{5}{3}$;

(b)

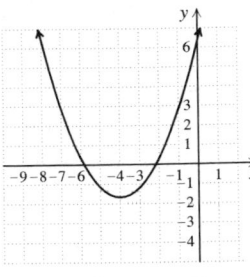

$h(x) = \frac{1}{2}x^2 + 4x + \frac{19}{3}$

43. $(3 - \sqrt{6}, 0), (3 + \sqrt{6}, 0); (0, 3)$ **45.** $(-1, 0), (3, 0); (0, 3)$ **47.** $(0, 0), (9, 0); (0, 0)$ **49.** $(2, 0); (0, -4)$
51. $\left(-\frac{1}{2} - \frac{\sqrt{21}}{2}, 0\right), \left(-\frac{1}{2} + \frac{\sqrt{21}}{2}, 0\right); (0, -5)]$
53. No x-intercept; $(0, 6)$ **55.**   **57.** $(1, 1, 1)$
58. $(-2, 5, 1)$ **59.** $(10, 5, 8)$ **60.** $(-3, 6, -5)$
61. $(2.4, -1.8, 1.5)$ **62.** $\left(\frac{1}{3}, \frac{1}{6}, \frac{1}{2}\right)$ **63.**
65. **(a)** Minimum: -6.953660714; **(b)** $(-1.056433682, 0)$, $(2.413576539, 0); (0, -5.89)$ **67.** **(a)** $-2.4, 3.4$;
(b) $-1.3, 2.3$ **69.** $f(x) = m\left(x - \frac{n}{2m}\right)^2 + \frac{4mp - n^2}{4m}$
71. $f(x) = \frac{5}{16}x^2 - \frac{15}{8}x - \frac{35}{16}$, or $f(x) = \frac{5}{16}(x - 3)^2 - 5$
73.

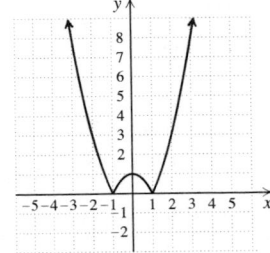

$f(x) = \left|x^2 - 1\right|$

75.

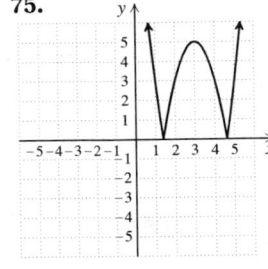

$f(x) = \left|2(x - 3)^2 - 5\right|$

Technology Connection, p. 759

1. About 607 million CDs

Exercise Set 11.8, pp. 760–765

1. (e) **2.** (b) **3.** (c) **4.** (a) **5.** (d) **6.** (f)
7. $3\frac{1}{4}$ weeks; 8.3 lb of milk per day **9.** \$120/dulcimer;
350 dulcimers **11.** 180 ft by 180 ft **13.** 450 ft²; 15 ft by 30 ft
(The house serves as a 30-ft side.) **15.** 3.5 in.
17. 81; 9 and 9 **19.** -16; 4 and -4 **21.** 25; -5 and -5
23. $f(x) = ax^2 + bx + c, a < 0$ **25.** $f(x) = mx + b$
27. Neither quadratic nor linear
29. $f(x) = ax^2 + bx + c, a > 0$
31. $f(x) = ax^2 + bx + c, a > 0$ **33.** $f(x) = mx + b$
35. $f(x) = 2x^2 + 3x - 1$ **37.** $f(x) = -\frac{1}{4}x^2 + 3x - 5$

39. (a) $A(s) = \frac{3}{16}s^2 - \frac{135}{4}s + 1750$; **(b)** about 531 accidents
41. $h(d) = -0.0068d^2 + 0.8571d$ **43.**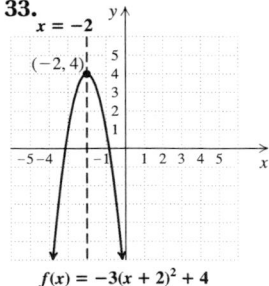
45. $\{x \mid x > 4\}$, or $(4, \infty)$ **46.** $\{x \mid x \geq -3\}$, or $[-3, \infty)$
47. $\{x \mid x \leq 7 \ or \ x \geq 11\}$, or $(-\infty, 7] \cup [11, \infty)$
48. $\left\{x \mid -3 < x < \frac{5}{2}\right\}$, or $\left(-3, \frac{5}{2}\right)$
49. $\dfrac{-4x - 23}{x + 4}$ **50.** $\dfrac{1}{x - 1}$ **51.** $-\frac{23}{4}$ **52.** No solution
53. 0   **54.** $-6, 9$ **55.** 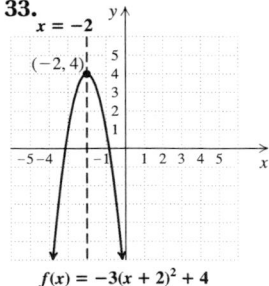   **57.** 158 ft   **59.** \$15
61. The radius of the circular portion of the window and the height of the rectangular portion should each be $\dfrac{24}{\pi + 4}$ ft.
63. (a) $h(x) = 11{,}090.60714x^2 - 29{,}069.62143x + 39{,}983.8$;
(b) 858,348 vehicles

Technology Connection, p. 770

1. $\{x \mid -0.78 \leq x \leq 1.59\}$, or $[-0.78, 1.59]$
2. $\{x \mid x \leq -0.21 \ or \ x \geq 2.47\}$, or $(-\infty, -0.21] \cup [2.47, \infty)$
3. $\{x \mid x < -1.26 \ or \ x > 2.33\}$, or $(-\infty, -1.26) \cup (2.33, \infty)$
4. $\{x \mid x > -1.37\}$, or $(-1.37, \infty)$

Exercise Set 11.9, pp. 772–775

1. True   **2.** False   **3.** True   **4.** True   **5.** False
6. True   **7.** $\left[-4, \frac{3}{2}\right]$, or $\left\{x \mid -4 \leq x \leq \frac{3}{2}\right\}$
9. $(-\infty, -2) \cup (0, 2) \cup (3, \infty)$, or $\{x \mid x < -2 \ or \ 0 < x < 2 \ or \ x > 3\}$
11. $\left(-\infty, -\frac{7}{2}\right) \cup (-2, \infty)$, or $\left\{x \mid x < -\frac{7}{2} \ or \ x > -2\right\}$
13. $(5, 6)$, or $\{x \mid 5 < x < 6\}$
15. $(-\infty, -7] \cup [2, \infty)$, or $\{x \mid x \leq -7 \ or \ x \geq 2\}$
17. $(-\infty, -1) \cup (2, \infty)$, or $\{x \mid x < -1 \ or \ x > 2\}$
19. $\varnothing$ **21.** $[2 - \sqrt{7}, 2 + \sqrt{7}]$, or $\{x \mid 2 - \sqrt{7} \leq x \leq 2 + \sqrt{7}\}$ **23.** $(-\infty, -2) \cup (0, 2)$, or $\{x \mid x < -2 \ or \ 0 < x < 2\}$ **25.** $[-2, 1] \cup [4, \infty)$, or $\{x \mid -2 \leq x \leq 1 \ or \ x \geq 4\}$ **27.** $[-2, 2]$, or $\{x \mid -2 \leq x \leq 2\}$ **29.** $(-1, 2) \cup (3, \infty)$, or $\{x \mid -1 < x < 2 \ or \ x > 3\}$ **31.** $(-\infty, 0] \cup [2, 5]$, or $\{x \mid x \leq 0 \ or \ 2 \leq x \leq 5\}$ **33.** $(-\infty, 5)$, or $\{x \mid x < 5\}$
35. $(-\infty, -1] \cup (3, \infty)$, or $\{x \mid x \leq -1 \ or \ x > 3\}$
37. $(-\infty, -6)$, or $\{x \mid x < -6\}$ **39.** $(-\infty, -1] \cup [2, 5)$, or $\{x \mid x \leq -1 \ or \ 2 \leq x < 5\}$ **41.** $(-\infty, -3) \cup [0, \infty)$, or $\{x \mid x < -3 \ or \ x \geq 0\}$ **43.** $(0, \infty)$, or $\{x \mid x > 0\}$
45. $(-\infty, -4) \cup [1, 3)$, or $\{x \mid x < -4 \ or \ 1 \leq x < 3\}$
47. $\left(-\frac{3}{4}, \frac{5}{2}\right]$, or $\left\{x \mid -\frac{3}{4} < x \leq \frac{5}{2}\right\}$ **49.** $(-\infty, 2) \cup [3, \infty)$, or $\{x \mid x < 2 \ or \ x \geq 3\}$ **51.**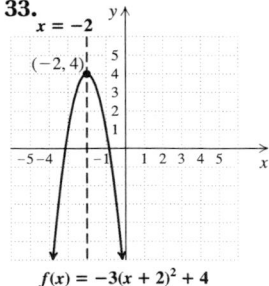
53.

$f(x) = x^3 - 2$

54.

$g(x) = \dfrac{2}{x}$

55. $\dfrac{1}{a^2} + 7$ **56.** $a - 8$ **57.** $4a^2 + 20a + 27$

58. $\sqrt{12a - 19}$ **59.** 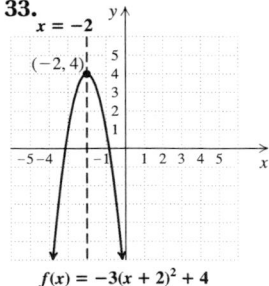   **61.** $(-1 - \sqrt{6}, -1 + \sqrt{6})$, or $\{x \mid -1 - \sqrt{6} < x < -1 + \sqrt{6}\}$ **63.** $\{0\}$
65. (a) $(10, 200)$, or $\{x \mid 10 < x < 200\}$;
(b) $[0, 10) \cup (200, \infty)$, or $\{x \mid 0 \leq x < 10 \ or \ x > 200\}$
67. $\{n \mid n$ is an integer $and \ 12 \leq n \leq 25\}$
69. $f(x) = 0$ for $x = -2, 1, 3; f(x) < 0$ for $(-\infty, -2) \cup (1, 3)$, or $\{x \mid x < -2 \ or \ 1 < x < 3\}; f(x) > 0$ for $(-2, 1) \cup (3, \infty)$, or $\{x \mid -2 < x < 1 \ or \ x > 3\}$
71. $f(x)$ has no zeros; $f(x) < 0$ for $(-\infty, 0)$, or $\{x \mid x < 0\}$; $f(x) > 0$ for $(0, \infty)$, or $\{x \mid x > 0\}$ **73.** $f(x) = 0$ for $x = -1, 0; f(x) < 0$ for $(-\infty, -3) \cup (-1, 0)$, or $\{x \mid x < -3 \ or \ -1 < x < 0\}; f(x) > 0$ for $(-3, -1) \cup (0, 2) \cup (2, \infty)$, or $\{x \mid -3 < x < -1 \ or \ 0 < x < 2 \ or \ x > 2\}$
75. $(-\infty, -5] \cup [9, \infty)$, or $\{x \mid x \leq -5 \ or \ x \geq 9\}$
77. $(-\infty, -8] \cup [0, \infty)$, or $\{x \mid x \leq -8 \ or \ x \geq 0\}$
79.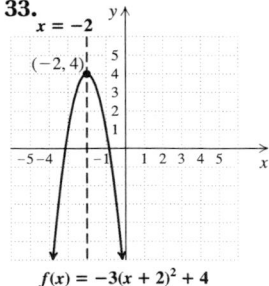

Review Exercises: Chapter 11, pp. 778–779

1. False   **2.** True   **3.** True   **4.** True   **5.** False
6. True   **7.** True   **8.** True   **9.** False   **10.** True
11. $\pm\dfrac{\sqrt{2}}{3}$ **12.** $0, -\frac{3}{4}$ **13.** $3, 9$ **14.** $2 \pm 2i$ **15.** $3, 5$
16. $-\dfrac{9}{2} \pm \dfrac{\sqrt{85}}{2}$ **17.** $-0.372, 5.372$ **18.** $-\frac{1}{4}, 1$
19. $x^2 - 18x + 81 = (x - 9)^2$
20. $x^2 + \frac{3}{5}x + \frac{9}{100} = \left(x + \frac{3}{10}\right)^2$ **21.** $3 \pm 2\sqrt{2}$
22. 4%   **23.** 8.0 sec   **24.** Two irrational real numbers
25. Two imaginary numbers   **26.** $x^2 + 9 = 0$
27. $x^2 + 10x + 25 = 0$ **28.** About 153 mph   **29.** 6 hr
30. $(-3, 0), (-2, 0), (2, 0), (3, 0)$ **31.** $-5, 3$
32. $\pm\sqrt{2}, \pm\sqrt{7}$
33.

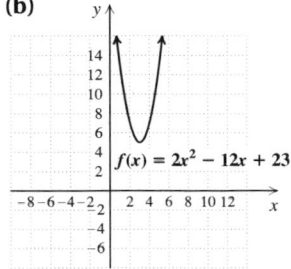

$f(x) = -3(x + 2)^2 + 4$
Maximum: 4

34. (a) Vertex: $(3, 5)$; axis of symmetry: $x = 3$;
(b)

$f(x) = 2x^2 - 12x + 23$

35. $(2, 0), (7, 0); (0, 14)$ **36.** $p = \dfrac{9\pi^2}{N^2}$

37. $T = \dfrac{1 \pm \sqrt{1 + 24A}}{6}$ **38.** Quadratic   **39.** Linear

40. 225 ft^2; 15 ft by 15 ft   **41.** **(a)** $f(x) = -\frac{3}{8}x^2 + \frac{9}{4}x + 8$;
(b) about 10%   **42.** $(-1, 0) \cup (3, \infty)$, or
$\{x | -1 < x < 0 \text{ or } x > 3\}$ **43.** $(-3, 5]$, or
$\{x | -3 < x \le 5\}$ **44.** ✍ The x-coordinate of the maximum or minimum point lies halfway between the x-coordinates of the x-intercepts.   **45.** ✍ Yes; if the discriminant is a perfect square, then the solutions are rational numbers, p/q and r/s. (Note that if the discriminant is 0, then $p/q = r/s$.) Then the equation can be written in factored form, $(qx - p)(sx - r) = 0$.   **46.** ✍ Four; let $u = x^2$. Then $au^2 + bu + c = 0$ has at most two solutions, $u = m$ and $u = n$. Now substitute x^2 for u and obtain $x^2 = m$ or $x^2 = n$. These equations yield the solutions $x = \pm\sqrt{m}$ and $x = \pm\sqrt{n}$. When $m \ne n$, the maximum number of solutions, four, occurs.   **47.** ✍ Completing the square was used to solve quadratic equations and to graph quadratic functions by rewriting the function in the form $f(x) = a(x - h)^2 + k$.   **48.** $f(x) = \frac{7}{15}x^2 - \frac{14}{15}x - 7$
49. $h = 60, k = 60$ **50.** 18, 324

Test: Chapter 11, p. 780

1. [11.1] $\pm\dfrac{\sqrt{7}}{5}$ **2.** [11.1] 2, 9   **3.** [11.2] $-1 \pm \sqrt{2}i$
4. [11.2] $1 \pm \sqrt{6}$ **5.** [11.5] $-2, \frac{2}{3}$ **6.** [11.2] $-4.193, 1.193$
7. [11.2] $-\frac{3}{4}, \frac{7}{3}$ **8.** [11.1] $x^2 - 20x + 100 = (x - 10)^2$
9. [11.1] $x^2 + \frac{2}{7}x + \frac{1}{49} = \left(x + \frac{1}{7}\right)^2$ **10.** [11.1] $-5 \pm \sqrt{10}$
11. [11.3] Two imaginary numbers   **12.** [11.3] $x^2 - 11 = 0$
13. [11.4] 16 km/h   **14.** [11.4] 2 hr   **15.** [11.5] $(-4, 0), (4, 0)$
16. [11.6]   **17.** [11.7] **(a)** $(-1, -8), x = -1$;
                                  (b)

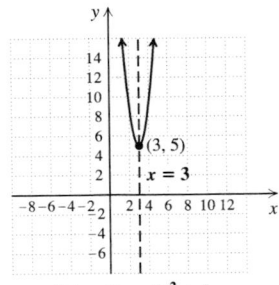
$f(x) = 4(x - 3)^2 + 5$
Minimum: 5

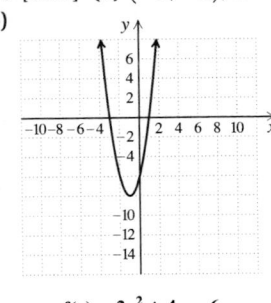
$f(x) = 2x^2 + 4x - 6$

18. [11.7] $(-2, 0), (3, 0); (0, -6)$ **19.** [11.4] $r = \sqrt{\dfrac{3V}{\pi} - R^2}$
20. [11.8] Quadratic   **21.** [11.8] Minimum: \$129/cabinet when 325 cabinets are built   **22.** [11.8] $f(x) = \frac{1}{5}x^2 - \frac{3}{5}x$
23. [11.9] $(-6, 1)$, or $\{x | -6 < x < 1\}$
24. [11.9] $[-1, 0) \cup [1, \infty)$, or $\{x | -1 \le x < 0 \text{ or } x \ge 1\}$
25. [11.3] $\frac{1}{2}$ **26.** [11.3] $x^4 + x^2 - 12 = 0$; answers may vary
27. [11.5] $\pm\sqrt{\sqrt{5} + 2}, \pm\sqrt{\sqrt{5} - 2}i$

Cumulative Review: Chapters 1–11, pp. 781–782

1. 24   **2.** $\dfrac{3a^{10}c^7}{4}$ **3.** $14x^2y - 10xy - 9xy^2$
4. $81p^4q^2 - 64t^2$ **5.** $\dfrac{t(t + 1)(t + 5)}{(3t + 4)^3}$ **6.** $-\dfrac{3}{x + 4}$

7. $3x^2\sqrt[3]{4y^2}$ **8.** $13 - \sqrt{2}i$
9. $3(2x^2 + 5y^2)(2x^2 - 5y^2)$ **10.** $x(x - 20)(x - 4)$
11. $100(m + 1)(m^2 - m + 1)(m - 1)(m^2 + m + 1)$
12. $(2t + 9)(3t + 4)$ **13.** 7   **14.** $\{x | x < 7\}$, or $(-\infty, 7)$
15. $\left(3, \frac{1}{2}\right)$ **16.** $-6, 11$ **17.** $\frac{1}{2}, 2$ **18.** 4   **19.** $-5 \pm \sqrt{2}$
20. $\dfrac{1}{6} \pm \dfrac{\sqrt{11}}{6}i$

21.

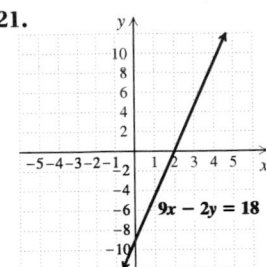
$9x - 2y = 18$

22.

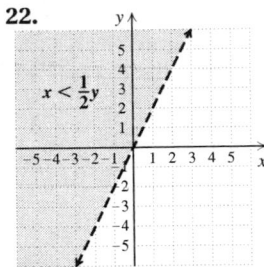
$x < \frac{1}{2}y$

23.

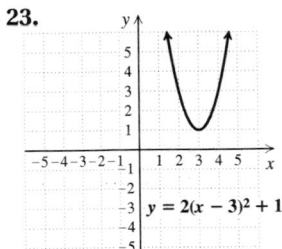
$y = 2(x - 3)^2 + 1$

24.

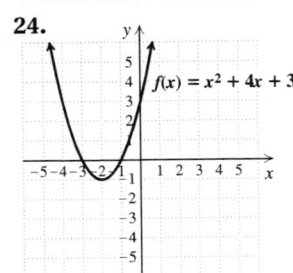
$f(x) = x^2 + 4x + 3$

25. $y = -5x + \frac{1}{2}$ **26.** $-\frac{7}{10}$ **27.** 21
28. $(-\infty, 10]$, or $\{x | x \le 10\}$
29. $\{x | x \text{ is a real number } and x \ne 4\}$, or $(-\infty, 4) \cup (4, \infty)$
30. $a = \dfrac{c}{2b - 1}$ **31.** $t = \dfrac{4r}{3p^2}$ **32.** **(a)** \$4.53 billion;
(b) 2015   **33.** **(a)** $h(t) = 33t - 47$; **(b)** 283,000 hotspots;
(c) about 2017   **34.** **(a)** 1.74 oz; **(b)** \$600 per ounce;
(c) 75%   **35.** Number tiles: 26 sets; alphabet tiles: 10 sets
36. \$125/bunk bed; 400 bunk beds
37. Deanna: 12 hr; Donna: 6 hr
38. 9 km/h   **39.** Mileages no greater than 50 mi
40. $\dfrac{1}{3} \pm \dfrac{\sqrt{2}}{6}i$ **41.** $\{0\}$ **42.** $f(x) = x + 1$
43. $(1 - \sqrt{6}, 16 - 10\sqrt{6}), (1 + \sqrt{6}, 16 + 10\sqrt{6})$

CHAPTER 12

Technology Connection, p. 786

1. To check $(f \circ g)(x)$, we let $y_1 = \sqrt{x}, y_2 = x - 1$, $y_3 = \sqrt{x - 1}$, and $y_4 = y_1(y_2)$. A table shows that we have $y_3 = y_4$. The check for $(g \circ f)(x)$ is similar. A graph can also be used.

Technology Connection, p. 791

1. Graph each pair of functions in a square window along with the line $y = x$ and determine whether the first two functions are reflections of each other across $y = x$. For further verification, examine a table of values for each pair of functions.   **2.** Yes; most graphing calculators do not require that the inverse relation be a function.

Exercise Set 12.1, pp. 792–794

1. True   **2.** True   **3.** False   **4.** False   **5.** False
6. False   **7.** True   **8.** True   **9. (a)** $(f \circ g)(1) = 5$;
(b) $(g \circ f)(1) = -1$;   **(c)** $(f \circ g)(x) = x^2 - 6x + 10$;
(d) $(g \circ f)(x) = x^2 - 2$ **11. (a)** $(f \circ g)(1) = -24$;
(b) $(g \circ f)(1) = 65$;   **(c)** $(f \circ g)(x) = 10x^2 - 34$;
(d) $(g \circ f)(x) = 50x^2 + 20x - 5$
13. (a) $(f \circ g)(1) = 8$;   **(b)** $(g \circ f)(1) = \frac{1}{64}$;

(c) $(f \circ g)(x) = \dfrac{1}{x^2} + 7$;   **(d)** $(g \circ f)(x) = \dfrac{1}{(x+7)^2}$

15. (a) $(f \circ g)(1) = 2$;   **(b)** $(g \circ f)(1) = 4$;
(c) $(f \circ g)(x) = \sqrt{x+3}$;   **(d)** $(g \circ f)(x) = \sqrt{x} + 3$
17. (a) $(f \circ g)(1) = 2$;   **(b)** $(g \circ f)(1) = \frac{1}{2}$;

(c) $(f \circ g)(x) = \sqrt{\dfrac{4}{x}}$;   **(d)** $(g \circ f)(x) = \dfrac{1}{\sqrt{4x}}$

19. (a) $(f \circ g)(1) = 4$;   **(b)** $(g \circ f)(1) = 2$;
(c) $(f \circ g)(x) = x + 3$;   **(d)** $(g \circ f)(x) = \sqrt{x^2 + 3}$
21. $f(x) = x^4; g(x) = 3x - 5$ **23.** $f(x) = \sqrt{x}$;

$g(x) = 9x + 1$ **25.** $f(x) = \dfrac{6}{x}; g(x) = 5x - 2$ **27.** Yes

29. No   **31.** Yes   **33.** No   **35. (a)** Yes;

(b) $f^{-1}(x) = x - 3$ **37. (a)** Yes;   **(b)** $f^{-1}(x) = \dfrac{x}{2}$

39. (a) Yes;   **(b)** $g^{-1}(x) = \dfrac{x+1}{3}$ **41. (a)** Yes;

(b) $f^{-1}(x) = 2x - 2$ **43. (a)** No   **45. (a)** Yes;

(b) $h^{-1}(x) = 10 - x$ **47. (a)** Yes;   **(b)** $f^{-1}(x) = \dfrac{1}{x}$

49. (a) No   **51. (a)** Yes;   **(b)** $f^{-1}(x) = \dfrac{3x - 1}{2}$

53. (a) Yes;   **(b)** $f^{-1}(x) = \sqrt[3]{x - 5}$ **55. (a)** Yes;
(b) $g^{-1}(x) = \sqrt[3]{x} + 2$ **57. (a)** Yes;
(b) $f^{-1}(x) = x^2, x \geq 0$
59.

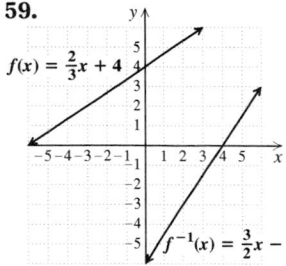

61.

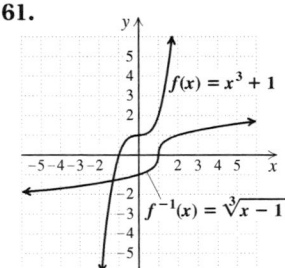

63.

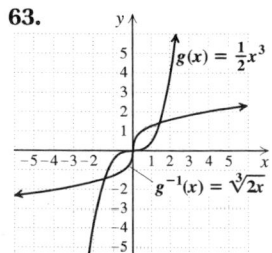

65.

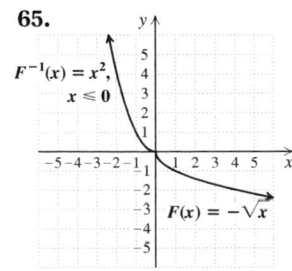

67.

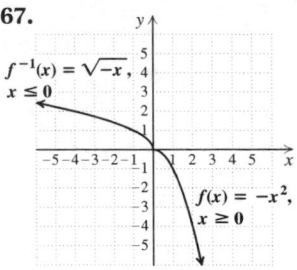

69. (1) $(f^{-1} \circ f)(x) = f^{-1}(f(x))$
$\qquad = f^{-1}\left(\sqrt[3]{x - 4}\right) = \left(\sqrt[3]{x - 4}\right)^3 + 4$
$\qquad = x - 4 + 4 = x$;
(2) $(f \circ f^{-1})(x) = f(f^{-1}(x))$
$\qquad = f(x^3 + 4) = \sqrt[3]{x^3 + 4 - 4}$
$\qquad = \sqrt[3]{x^3} = x$

71. (1) $(f^{-1} \circ f)(x) = f^{-1}(f(x)) = f^{-1}\left(\dfrac{1 - x}{x}\right)$

$\qquad = \dfrac{1}{\left(\dfrac{1 - x}{x}\right) + 1}$

$\qquad = \dfrac{1}{\dfrac{1 - x + x}{x}}$

$\qquad = x$;

(2) $(f \circ f^{-1})(x) = f(f^{-1}(x)) = f\left(\dfrac{1}{x + 1}\right)$

$\qquad = \dfrac{1 - \left(\dfrac{1}{x + 1}\right)}{\left(\dfrac{1}{x + 1}\right)}$

$\qquad = \dfrac{\dfrac{x + 1 - 1}{x + 1}}{\dfrac{1}{x + 1}} = x$

73. (a) $40, 44, 52, 60$;   **(b)** $f^{-1}(x) = (x - 24)/2$, or $\dfrac{x}{2} - 12$

(c) $8, 10, 14, 18$ **75.** 🖩   **77.** $\frac{1}{8}$ **78.** $\frac{1}{25}$ **79.** 32
80. Approximately 2.1577
81.

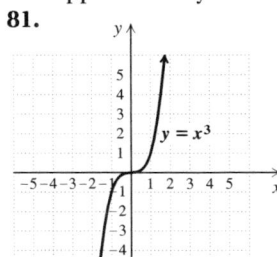

82.

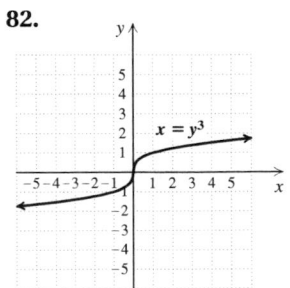

83. 🖩

85.

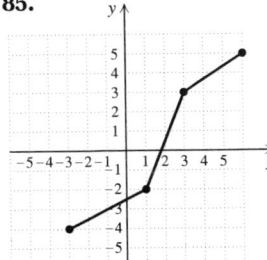

87. $g(x) = \dfrac{x}{2} + 20$ **89.** ▧

91. Suppose that $h(x) = (f \circ g)(x)$. First, note that for $I(x) = x, (f \circ I)(x) = f(I(x)) = f(x)$ for any function f.

(i) $((g^{-1} \circ f^{-1}) \circ h)(x) = ((g^{-1} \circ f^{-1}) \circ (f \circ g))(x)$
$= ((g^{-1} \circ (f^{-1} \circ f)) \circ g)(x)$
$= ((g^{-1} \circ I) \circ g)(x)$
$= (g^{-1} \circ g)(x) = x$

(ii) $(h \circ (g^{-1} \circ f^{-1}))(x) = ((f \circ g) \circ (g^{-1} \circ f^{-1}))(x)$
$= ((f \circ (g \circ g^{-1})) \circ f^{-1})(x)$
$= ((f \circ I) \circ f^{-1})(x)$
$= (f \circ f^{-1})(x) = x.$

Therefore, $(g^{-1} \circ f^{-1})(x) = h^{-1}(x)$.

93. Yes **95.** No **97.** (1) C; (2) A; (3) B; (4) D
99. ▧

Technology Connection, p. 797

1. $y_1 = \left(\dfrac{5}{2}\right)^x$; $y_2 = \left(\dfrac{2}{5}\right)^x$

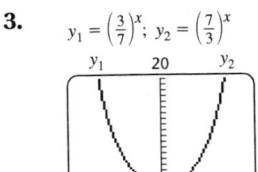

2. $y_1 = 3.2^x$; $y_2 = 3.2^{-x}$

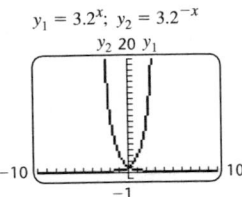

3. $y_1 = \left(\dfrac{3}{7}\right)^x$; $y_2 = \left(\dfrac{7}{3}\right)^x$

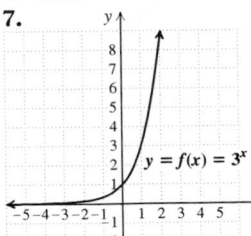

4. $y_1 = 5000(1.08)^x$; $y_2 = 5000(1.08)^{x-3}$

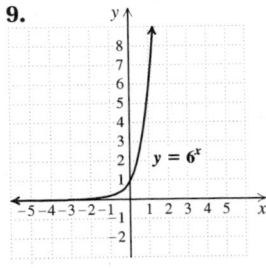
Xscl = 5, Yscl = 1000

Exercise Set 12.2, pp. 800–802

1. True **2.** True **3.** True **4.** False **5.** False
6. True

7.

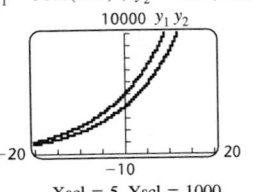

9.

11.

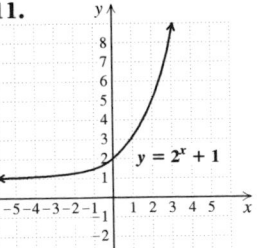

13.

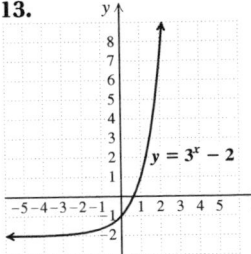

15.

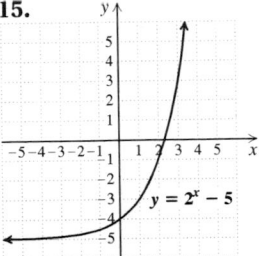

17.

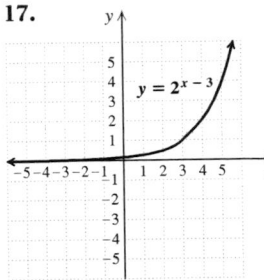

19.

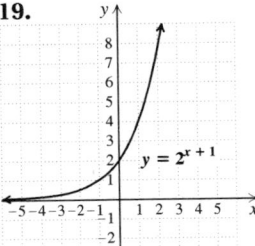

21.

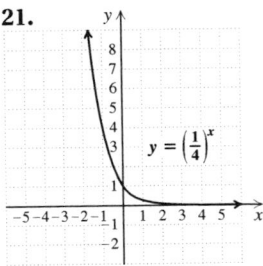

23.

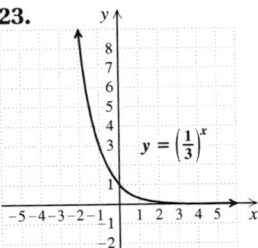

25.

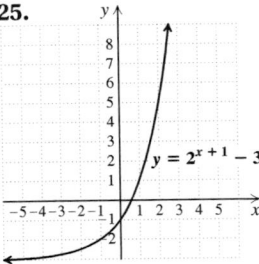

27.

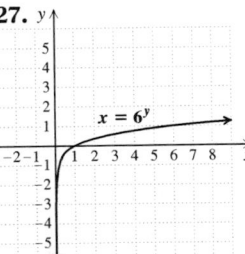

29.

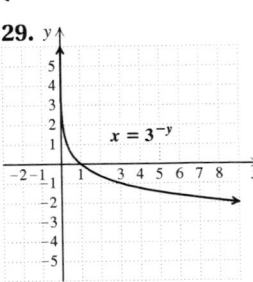

31.

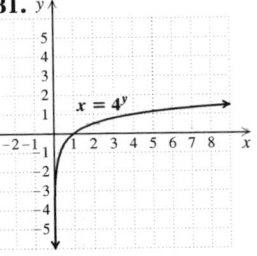

33.

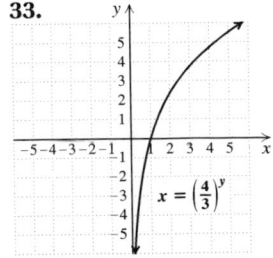

35.
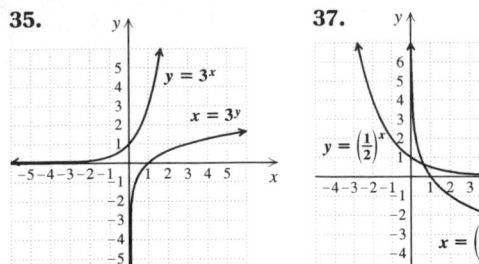

37.

39. (a) About 0.68 billion tracks; about 1.052 billion tracks; about 2.519 billion tracks;

(b)
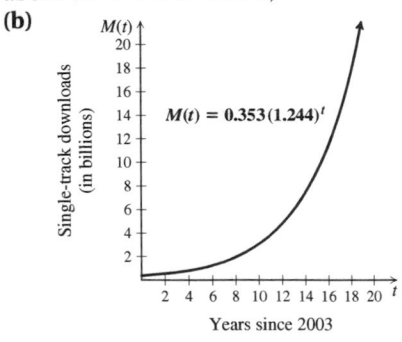

41. (a) 19.6%; 16.3%; 7.3%

(b)
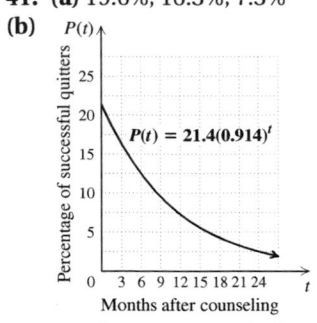

43. (a) About 44,079 whales; about 12,953 whales;

(b)
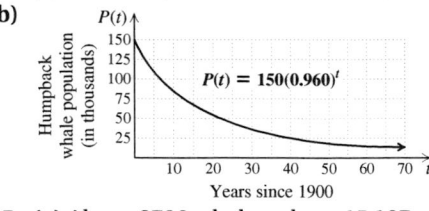

45. (a) About 8706 whales; about 15,107 whales;

(b)
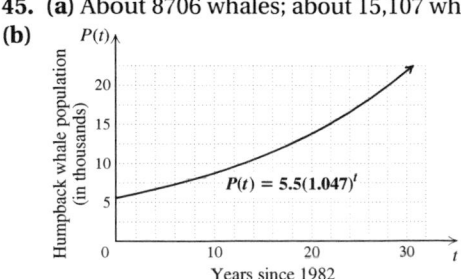

47. (a) 454,354,240 cm^2; 525,233,501,400 cm^2;

(b)
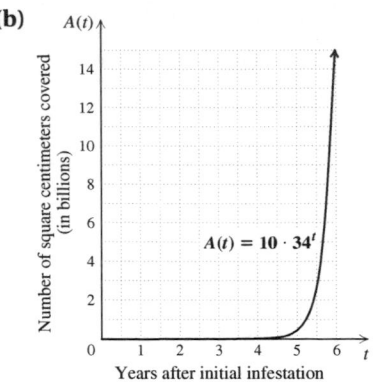

49. ✍   **51.** $3(x+4)(x-4)$ **52.** $(x-10)^2$
53. $(2x+3)(3x-4)$
54. $8(x^2-2y^2)(x^4+2x^2y^2+4y^4)$
55. $6(y-4)(y+10)$ **56.** $x(x-2)(5x^2-3)$
57. ✍   **59.** $\pi^{2.4}$

61.

63.
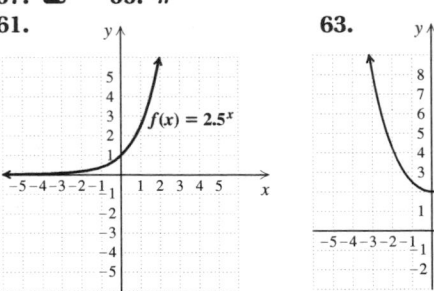

65.

67.
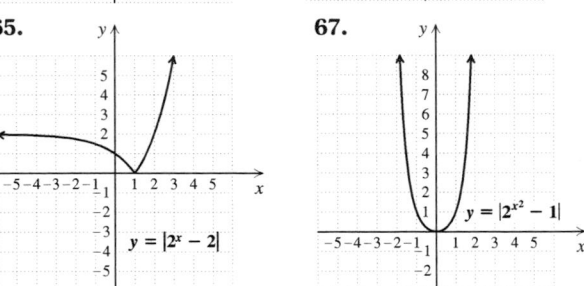

69.
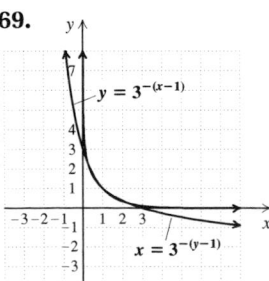

71. $N(t) = 0.464(1.778)^t$; about 464 million devices
73. ✍   **75.** ▨

Exercise Set 12.3, pp. 808–809

1. (g)   **2.** (d)   **3.** (a)   **4.** (h)   **5.** (b)   **6.** (c)
7. (e)   **8.** (f)   **9.** 3   **11.** 2   **13.** 4   **15.** −2
17. −1   **19.** 4   **21.** 1   **23.** 0   **25.** 5   **27.** −2
29. $\frac{1}{2}$ **31.** $\frac{3}{2}$ **33.** $\frac{2}{3}$ **35.** 29
37.

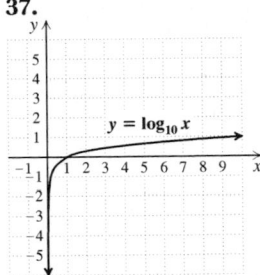

39.

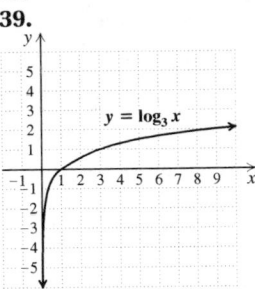

41.

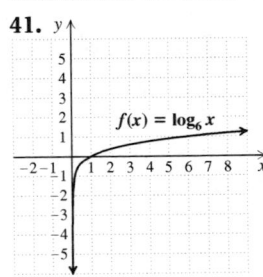

43.

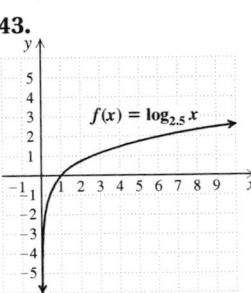

45.

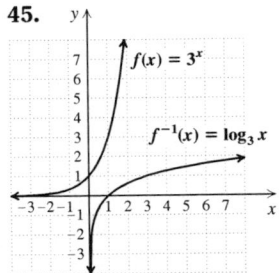

47. $10^x = 8$ **49.** $9^1 = 9$ **51.** $10^{-1} = 0.1$
53. $10^{0.845} = 7$ **55.** $c^8 = m$ **57.** $r^t = C$
59. $e^{-1.3863} = 0.25$ **61.** $r^{-x} = T$ **63.** $2 = \log_{10} 100$
65. $-3 = \log_5 \frac{1}{125}$ **67.** $\frac{1}{4} = \log_{16} 2$
69. $0.4771 = \log_{10} 3$ **71.** $m = \log_z 6$ **73.** $t = \log_p q$
75. $3 = \log_e 20.0855$ **77.** $-4 = \log_e 0.0183$ **79.** 36
81. 5   **83.** 9   **85.** 49   **87.** $\frac{1}{9}$ **89.** 4   **91.** ✍
93. $30a^2b^4$ **94.** $12 - 2\sqrt{30} + 2\sqrt{15} - 5\sqrt{2}$

95. $3\sqrt{3x}$ **96.** $\sqrt[12]{x}$ **97.** $\dfrac{x(3y-2)}{2y+x}$ **98.** $\dfrac{x+2}{x+1}$

99. ✍
101.

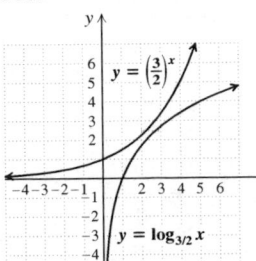

103.

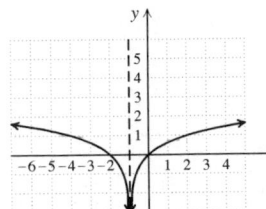

105. 6   **107.** −25, 4   **109.** −2   **111.** 0   **113.** Let $b = 0$, and suppose that $x_1 = 1$ and $x_2 = 2$. Then $0^1 = 0^2$, but $1 \neq 2$. Then let $b = 1$, and suppose that $x_1 = 1$ and $x_2 = 2$. Then $1^1 = 1^2$, but $1 \neq 2$.

Exercise Set 12.4, pp. 815–816

1. (e)   **2.** (f)   **3.** (a)   **4.** (b)   **5.** (c)   **6.** (d)
7. $\log_3 81 + \log_3 27$ **9.** $\log_4 64 + \log_4 16$
11. $\log_c r + \log_c s + \log_c t$ **13.** $\log_a (2 \cdot 10)$, or $\log_a 20$
15. $\log_c (t \cdot y)$ **17.** $8 \log_a r$ **19.** $\frac{1}{3} \log_2 y$
21. $-3 \log_b C$ **23.** $\log_2 5 - \log_2 11$
25. $\log_b m - \log_b n$ **27.** $\log_a \frac{19}{2}$ **29.** $\log_b \frac{36}{4}$, or $\log_b 9$
31. $\log_a \dfrac{x}{y}$ **33.** $\log_a x + \log_a y + \log_a z$
35. $3 \log_a x + 4 \log_a z$ **37.** $2 \log_a w - 2 \log_a x + \log_a y$
39. $5 \log_a x - 3 \log_a y - \log_a z$
41. $\log_b x + 2 \log_b y - \log_b w - 3 \log_b z$
43. $\frac{1}{2}(7 \log_a x - 5 \log_a y - 8 \log_a z)$
45. $\frac{1}{3}(6 \log_a x + 3 \log_a y - 2 - 7 \log_a z)$ **47.** $\log_a (x^8 z^3)$
49. $\log_a x$ **51.** $\log_a \dfrac{y^5}{x^{3/2}}$ **53.** $\log_a (x - 3)$ **55.** 1.953
57. −0.369   **59.** −1.161   **61.** $\frac{3}{2}$ **63.** Cannot be found
65. 10   **67.** m **69.** ✍
71.

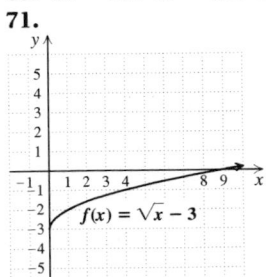

72.

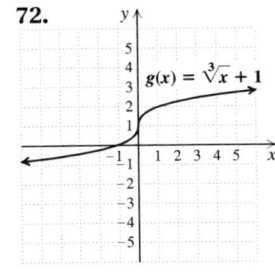

73.

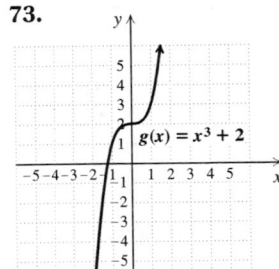

74.

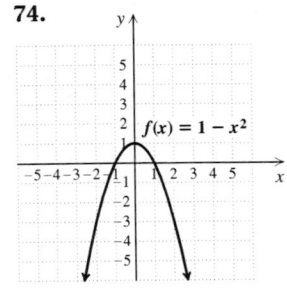

75. $(-\infty, -7) \cup (-7, \infty)$, or $\{x | x \text{ is a real number } and \, x \neq -7\}$
76. $(-\infty, -3) \cup (-3, 2) \cup (2, \infty)$, or $\{x | x \text{ is a real number } and \, x \neq -3 \, and \, x \neq 2\}$
77. $(-\infty, 10]$, or $\{x | x \leq 10\}$ **78.** $(-\infty, \infty)$, or $\mathbb{R}$
79. ✍   **81.** $\log_a (x^6 - x^4 y^2 + x^2 y^4 - y^6)$
83. $\frac{1}{2} \log_a (1 - s) + \frac{1}{2} \log_a (1 + s)$ **85.** $\frac{10}{3}$ **87.** −2
89. $\frac{2}{5}$ **91.** True

Technology Connection, p. 817

1.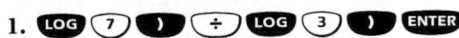

Technology Connection, p. 818

1. As x gets larger, the value of y_1 approaches 2.7182818284.... **2.** For large values of x, the graphs of y_1 and y_2 will be very close or appear to be the same curve, depending on the window chosen. **3.** Using ⟨TRACE⟩, no y-value is given for $x = 0$. Using a table, an error message appears for y_1 when $x = 0$. The domain does not include 0 because division by 0 is undefined.

Technology Connection, p. 821

1. $y = \log x / \log 7$

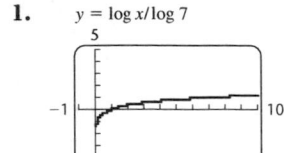

2. $y = \log (x+2) / \log 5$

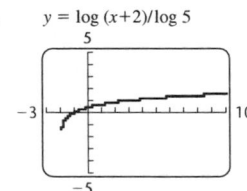

3. $y = \log x / \log 7 + 2$

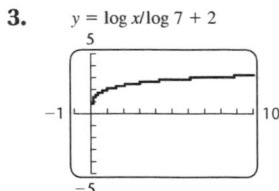

Visualizing for Success, p. 822

1. J **2.** D **3.** B **4.** G **5.** H **6.** C **7.** F **8.** I **9.** E **10.** A

Exercise Set 12.5, pp. 823–824

1. True **2.** True **3.** True **4.** False **5.** True
6. True **7.** True **8.** True **9.** True **10.** True
11. 0.8451 **13.** 1.1367 **15.** 3 **17.** −0.1249
19. 13.0014 **21.** 50.1187 **23.** 0.0011 **25.** 2.1972
27. −5.0832 **29.** 96.7583 **31.** 15.0293 **33.** 0.0305
35. 3.0331 **37.** 6.6439 **39.** 1.1610 **41.** −0.3010
43. −3.3219 **45.** 2.0115
47. Domain: $\mathbb{R}$; range: $(0, \infty)$

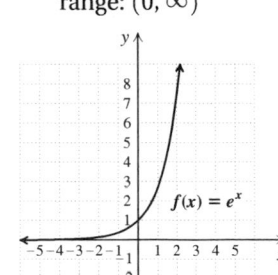

49. Domain: $\mathbb{R}$; range: $(3, \infty)$

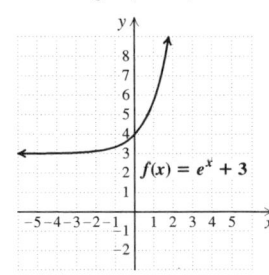

51. Domain: $\mathbb{R}$; range: $(-2, \infty)$

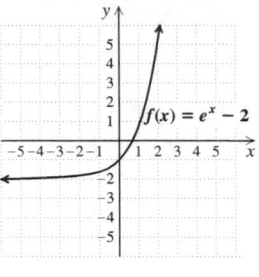

53. Domain: $\mathbb{R}$; range: $(0, \infty)$

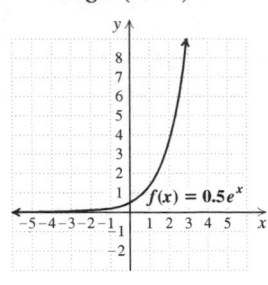

55. Domain: $\mathbb{R}$; range: $(0, \infty)$

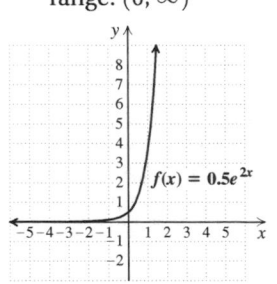

57. Domain: $\mathbb{R}$; range: $(0, \infty)$

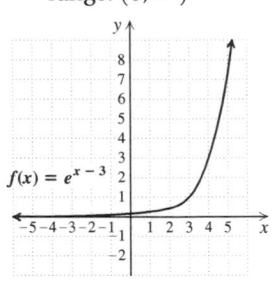

59. Domain: $\mathbb{R}$; range: $(0, \infty)$

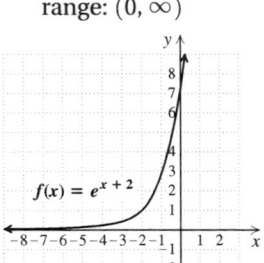

61. Domain: $\mathbb{R}$; range: $(-\infty, 0)$

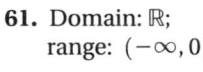
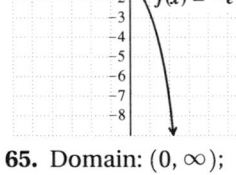

63. Domain: $(0, \infty)$; range: $\mathbb{R}$

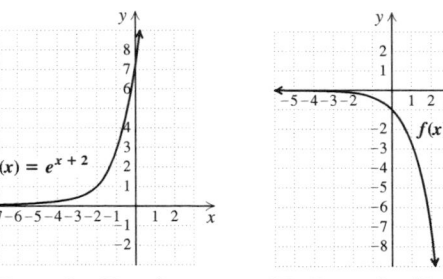

65. Domain: $(0, \infty)$; range: $\mathbb{R}$

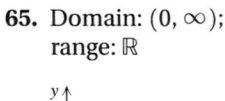
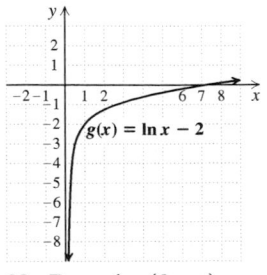

67. Domain: $(0, \infty)$; range: $\mathbb{R}$

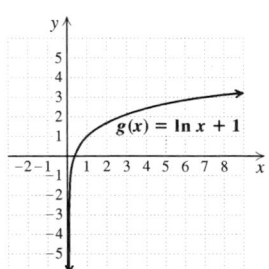

69. Domain: $(0, \infty)$; range: $\mathbb{R}$

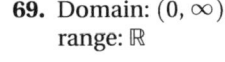
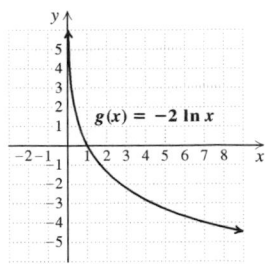

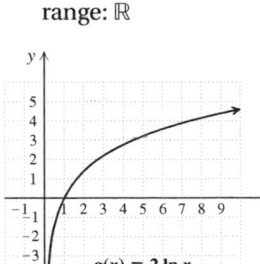

71. Domain: $(-2, \infty)$; range: $\mathbb{R}$

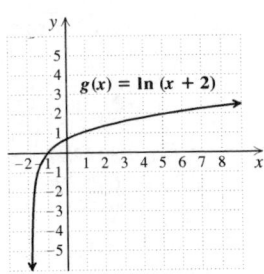

73. Domain: $(1, \infty)$; range: $\mathbb{R}$

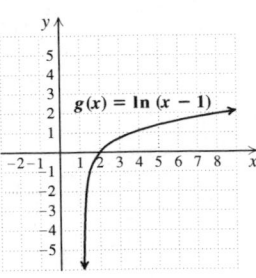

75. 📈 **77.** $-4, 7$ **78.** $0, \frac{7}{5}$ **79.** $\frac{15}{17}$ **80.** $\frac{5}{6}$ **81.** $\frac{56}{9}$
82. 4 **83.** $16, 256$ **84.** $\frac{1}{4}, 9$ **85.** 📈 **87.** 2.452
89. 1.442 **91.** $\log M = \dfrac{\ln M}{\ln 10}$ **93.** 1086.5129
95. 4.9855 **97. (a)** Domain: $\{x \mid x > 0\}$, or $(0, \infty)$; range: $\{y \mid y < 0.5135\}$, or $(-\infty, 0.5135)$; **(b)** $[-1, 5, -10, 5]$; **(c)** $y = 3.4 \ln x - 0.25e^x$

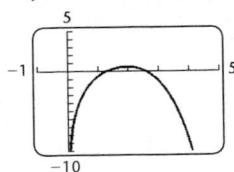

99. (a) Domain: $\{x \mid x > 0\}$, or $(0, \infty)$; range: $\{y \mid y > -0.2453\}$, or $(-0.2453, \infty)$; **(b)** $[-1, 5, -1, 10]$; **(c)** $y = 2x^3 \ln x$

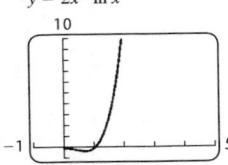

101. 📐

Connecting the Concepts, pp. 824-825

1. 2 **2.** -1 **3.** $\frac{1}{2}$ **4.** 2 **5.** 1 **6.** 0 **7.** 4 **8.** 8
9. 7 **10.** 3 **11.** $x^m = 3$ **12.** $2^{10} = 1024$
13. $t = \ln x$ **14.** $\frac{2}{3} = \log_{64} 16$ **15.** 4 **16.** $\frac{1}{3}$
17. $\log x - \frac{1}{2} \log y - \frac{3}{2} \log z$ **18.** $\log \dfrac{a}{b^2 c}$ **19.** 1.5
20. 2.8614

Technology Connection, p. 829

1. 0.38 **2.** -1.96 **3.** 0.90 **4.** -1.53 **5.** $0.13, 8.47$
6. $-0.75, 0.75$

Exercise Set 12.6, pp. 830-831

1. (e) **2.** (a) **3.** (f) **4.** (h) **5.** (b) **6.** (d)
7. (g) **8.** (c) **9.** 2 **11.** $\frac{5}{2}$ **13.** $\dfrac{\log 10}{\log 2} \approx 3.322$
15. -1 **17.** $\dfrac{\log 19}{\log 8} + 3 \approx 4.416$ **19.** $\ln 50 \approx 3.912$

21. $\dfrac{\ln 8}{-0.02} \approx -103.972$ **23.** $\dfrac{\log 87}{\log 4.9} \approx 2.810$
25. $\dfrac{\ln\left(\frac{19}{2}\right)}{4} \approx 0.563$ **27.** $\dfrac{\ln 2}{-1} \approx -0.693$ **29.** 81
31. $\frac{1}{16}$ **33.** $e^5 \approx 148.413$ **35.** $\dfrac{e^3}{4} \approx 5.021$
37. $10^{1.2} \approx 15.849$ **39.** $\dfrac{e^4 - 1}{2} \approx 26.799$
41. $e \approx 2.718$ **43.** $e^{-3} \approx 0.050$ **45.** -4 **47.** 10
49. No solution **51.** 2 **53.** $\frac{83}{15}$ **55.** 1 **57.** 6
59. 1 **61.** 5 **63.** $\frac{17}{2}$ **65.** 4 **67.** 📈
69. Length: 9.5 ft; width: 3.5 ft **70.** 25 visits or more
71. Golden Days; $23\frac{1}{3}$ lb; Snowy Friends: $26\frac{2}{3}$ lb
72. 1.5 cm **73.** $1\frac{1}{5}$ hr **74.** Approximately 2.1 ft
75. 📈 **77.** -4 **79.** 2 **81.** $\pm\sqrt{34}$ **83.** $-3, -1$
85. $-625, 625$ **87.** $\frac{1}{2}, 5000$ **89.** $-3, -1$
91. $\frac{1}{100,000}, 100,000$ **93.** $-\frac{1}{3}$ **95.** 38 **97.** 1

Exercise Set 12.7, pp. 838-843

1. (a) Approximately 2006; **(b)** 2.8 yr
3. (a) Approximately 1979; **(b)** approximately 2025
5. (a) 6.4 yr; **(b)** 23.4 yr **7. (a)** 1991; **(b)** 2013
9. (a) 2018; **(b)** 15.1 yr **11.** 4.9
13. 10^{-7} moles per liter **15.** 130 dB **17.** 7.6 W/m^2
19. Approximately 42.4 million messages per day
21. (a) $P(t) = P_0 e^{0.025t}$; **(b)** \$5126.58; \$5256.36; **(c)** 27.7 yr
23. (a) $P(t) = 304 e^{0.009t}$; **(b)** 315 million; **(c)** about 2015
25. 0.2 yr **27. (a)** About 2055; **(b)** about 2068;
(c)

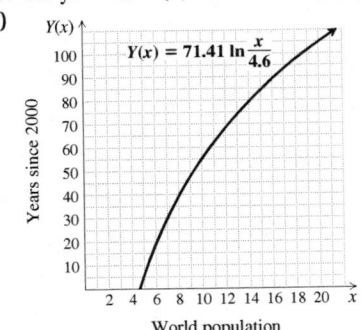

$$Y(x) = 71.41 \ln \frac{x}{4.6}$$

29. (a) 68%; **(b)** 54%, 40% **(d)** 6.9 months
(c)

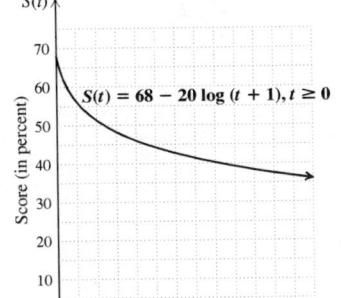

$$S(t) = 68 - 20 \log (t + 1), t \geq 0$$

31. (a) $k \approx 0.126$; $P(t) = 2000 e^{0.126t}$; **(b)** 2015

33. (a) $k \approx 0.280$; $P(t) = 8200e^{-0.280t}$; **(b)** \$215 per gigabit per second per mile; **(c)** 2029   **35.** About 1964 yr
37. 7.2 days   **39. (a)** 13.9% per hour; **(b)** 21.6 hr
41. (a) $k \approx 0.114$; $V(t) = 451{,}000e^{0.114t}$; **(b)** \$4.9 million;
(c) 6.1 yr; **(d)** 2010   **43.** 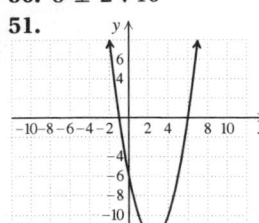   **45.** $\sqrt{2}$ **46.** 5
47. $(4, -7)$ **48.** $\left(-\frac{7}{2}, -\frac{19}{2}\right)$ **49.** $-4 \pm \sqrt{17}$
50. $5 \pm 2\sqrt{10}$

51. 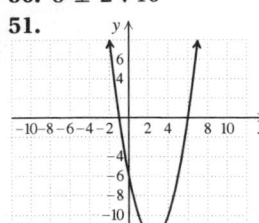   **52.**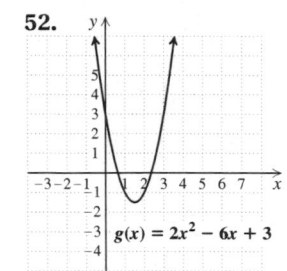

53. 🖼️   **55.** \$14.5 million   **57. (a)** -26.9;
(b) 1.58×10^{-17} W/m² **59.** Consider an exponential growth function $P(t) = P_0e^{kt}$. At time T, $P(T) = 2P_0$. Solve for T:

$$2P_0 = P_0e^{kt}$$
$$2 = e^{kt}$$
$$\ln 2 = kT$$
$$\frac{\ln 2}{k} = T.$$

61. 🖼️, 🖼️

Review Exercises: Chapter 12, pp. 847–848

1. True   **2.** True   **3.** True   **4.** False   **5.** False
6. True   **7.** False   **8.** False   **9.** True   **10.** False
11. $(f \circ g)(x) = 4x^2 - 12x + 10$; $(g \circ f)(x) = 2x^2 - 1$
12. $f(x) = \sqrt{x}$; $g(x) = 3 - x$ **13.** No

14. $f^{-1}(x) = x + 10$ **15.** $g^{-1}(x) = \dfrac{2x - 1}{3}$

16. $f^{-1}(x) = \dfrac{\sqrt[3]{x}}{3}$ **17.**

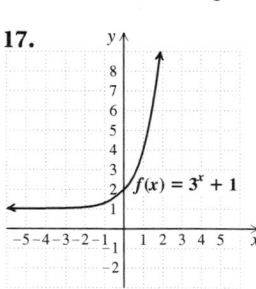

18. 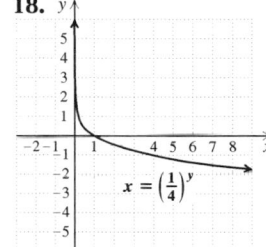   **19.**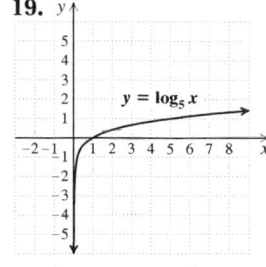

20. 2   **21.** -2 **22.** 11   **23.** $\frac{1}{2}$ **24.** $\log_2 \frac{1}{8} = -3$
25. $\log_{25} 5 = \frac{1}{2}$ **26.** $16 = 4^x$ **27.** $1 = 8^0$

28. $4\log_a x + 2\log_a y + 3\log_a z$
29. $5\log_a x - (\log_a y + 2\log_a z)$, or
$5\log_a x - \log_a y - 2\log_a z$
30. $\frac{1}{4}(2\log z - 3\log x - \log y)$ **31.** $\log_a(5 \cdot 8)$, or $\log_a 40$
32. $\log_a \frac{48}{12}$, or $\log_a 4$ **33.** $\log \dfrac{a^{1/2}}{bc^2}$ **34.** $\log a\sqrt[3]{\dfrac{x}{y^2}}$

35. 1   **36.** 0   **37.** 17   **38.** 6.93   **39.** -3.2698
40. 8.7601   **41.** 3.2698   **42.** 2.54995   **43.** -3.6602
44. 1.8751   **45.** 61.5177   **46.** -1.2040 **47.** 0.3753
48. 2.4307   **49.** 0.8982
50. Domain: $\mathbb{R}$;   **51.** Domain: $(0, \infty)$;
range: $(-1, \infty)$ range: $\mathbb{R}$

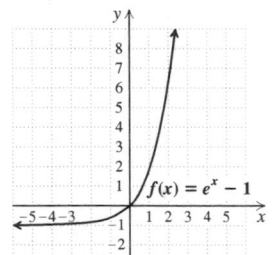   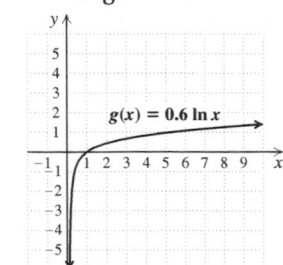

52. 3   **53.** -1 **54.** $\frac{1}{81}$ **55.** 2   **56.** $\frac{1}{1000}$
57. $e^3 \approx 20.0855$ **58.** $\frac{1}{2}\left(\dfrac{\log 19}{\log 4} + 5\right) \approx 3.5620$
59. $\dfrac{\log 12}{\log 2} \approx 3.5850$ **60.** $\dfrac{\ln 0.03}{-0.1} \approx 35.0656$
61. $e^{-3} \approx 0.0498$ **62.** $\frac{15}{2}$ **63.** 16   **64.** 5
65. (a) 82; **(b)** 66.8; **(c)** 35 months   **66. (a)** 2.3 yr;
(b) 3.1 yr   **67. (a)** $k \approx 0.043$; $A(t) = 885e^{0.043t}$;
(b) \$1.0 billion; **(c)** 2023; **(d)** 16.1 yr
68. (a) $M(t) = 3253e^{-0.137t}$; **(b)** 1640 spam messages per consumer; **(c)** 2030   **69.** 11.553% per year   **70.** 16.5 yr
71. 3463 yr   **72.** 5.1   **73.** About 114 dB
74. 🖼️ Negative numbers do not have logarithms because logarithm bases are positive, and there is no exponent to which a positive number can be raised to yield a negative number.   **75.** 🖼️ If $f(x) = e^x$, then to find the inverse function, we let $y = e^x$ and interchange x and y: $x = e^y$. If $x = e^y$, then $\log_e x = y$ by the definition of logarithms. Since $\log_e x = \ln x$, we have $y = \ln x$ or $f^{-1}(x) = \ln x$. Thus, $g(x) = \ln x$ is the inverse of $f(x) = e^x$. Another approach is to find $(f \circ g)(x)$ and $(g \circ f)(x)$:

$$(f \circ g)(x) = e^{\ln x} = x, \text{ and}$$
$$(g \circ f)(x) = \ln e^x = x.$$

Thus, g and f are inverse functions.
76. e^{e^3} **77.** $-3, -1$ **78.** $\left(\frac{8}{3}, -\frac{2}{3}\right)$

Test: Chapter 12, p. 849

1. [12.1] $(f \circ g)(x) = 2 + 6x + 4x^2$; $(g \circ f)(x) = 2x^2 + 2x + 1$
2. [12.1] $f(x) = \dfrac{1}{x}$; $g(x) = 2x^2 + 1$ **3.** [12.1] No
4. [12.1] $f^{-1}(x) = \dfrac{x - 4}{3}$ **5.** [12.1] $g^{-1}(x) = \sqrt[3]{x} - 1$

6. [12.2]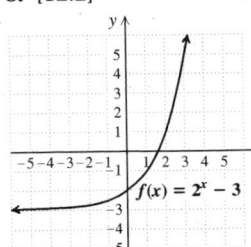

7. [12.3]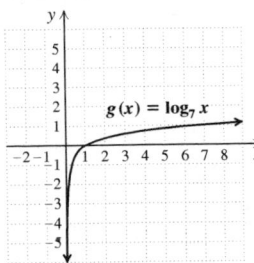

8. [12.3] 3   **9.** [12.3] $\frac{1}{2}$ **10.** [12.3] 18   **11.** [12.4] 1
12. [12.4] 0   **13.** [12.4] 19   **14.** [12.3] $\log_5 \frac{1}{625} = -4$
15. [12.3] $2^m = \frac{1}{2}$ **16.** [12.4] $3\log a + \frac{1}{2}\log b - 2\log c$
17. [12.4] $\log_a\left(z^2\sqrt[3]{x}\right)$ **18.** [12.4] 1.146   **19.** [12.4] 0.477
20. [12.4] 1.204   **21.** [12.5] 1.3979   **22.** [12.5] 0.1585
23. [12.5] −0.9163   **24.** [12.5] 121.5104   **25.** [12.5] 2.4022
26. [12.5]

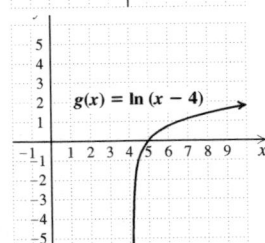

Domain: $\mathbb{R}$;
range: $(3, \infty)$

27. [12.5]

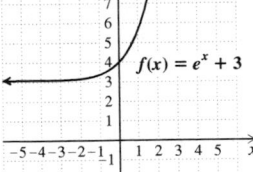

Domain: $(4, \infty)$;
range: $\mathbb{R}$

28. [12.6] −5   **29.** [12.6] 2   **30.** [12.6] $\frac{1}{100}$

31. [12.6] $-\frac{1}{3}\left(\dfrac{\log 87}{\log 5} - 4\right) \approx 0.4084$

32. [12.6] $\dfrac{\log 1.2}{\log 7} \approx 0.0937$ **33.** [12.6] $e^3 \approx 20.0855$

34. [12.6] 4   **35.** [12.7] **(a)** 2.25 ft/sec; **(b)** 2,901,000
36. [12.7] **(a)** $P(t) = 140e^{0.024t}$, where t is the number of
years after 2008 and $P(t)$ is in millions; **(b)** 154 million;
170 million; **(c)** 2023; **(d)** 28.9 yr
37. [12.7] **(a)** $k \approx 0.045$; $C(t) = 21{,}855e^{0.045t}$; **(b)** \$35,853;
(c) 2019   **38.** [12.7] 4.3%   **39.** [12.7] 4684 yr
40. [12.7] 6.3×10^6 W/m²   **41.** [12.7] 7.0
42. [12.6] −309,316   **43.** [12.4] 2

Cumulative Review: Chapters 1–12, pp. 850–851

1. 2   **2.** $\dfrac{y^{12}}{16x^8}$ **3.** $\dfrac{20x^6z^2}{y}$ **4.** $-\dfrac{y^4}{3z^5}$ **5.** 6.3×10^{-15}
6. 25   **7.** 8   **8.** $(3, -1)$ **9.** $(1, -2, 0)$ **10.** $-7, 10$
11. $\frac{9}{2}$ **12.** $\frac{3}{4}$ **13.** $\frac{1}{2}$ **14.** $\pm 4i$ **15.** $\pm 2, \pm 3$ **16.** 9
17. $\dfrac{\log 7}{5\log 3} \approx 0.3542$ **18.** $\dfrac{8e}{e-1} \approx 12.6558$

19. $(-\infty, -5) \cup (1, \infty)$, or $\{x \mid x < -5 \; or \; x > 1\}$
20. $-3 \pm 2\sqrt{5}$ **21.** $\{x \mid x \le -2 \; or \; x \ge 5\}$,
or $(-\infty, -2] \cup [5, \infty)$ **22.** $a = \dfrac{Db}{b - D}$
23. $x = \dfrac{-v \pm \sqrt{v^2 + 4ad}}{2a}$
24. $\left\{x \mid x \text{ is a real number } and \; x \ne -\frac{1}{3} \; and \; x \ne 2\right\}$, or
$\left(-\infty, -\frac{1}{3}\right) \cup \left(-\frac{1}{3}, 2\right) \cup (2, \infty)$
25. $3p^2q^3 + 11pq - 2p^2 + p + 9$ **26.** $9x^4 - 6x^2z^3 + z^6$
27. $\dfrac{1}{x - 4}$ **28.** $\dfrac{a + 2}{6}$ **29.** $\dfrac{7x + 4}{(x + 6)(x - 6)}$
30. $2y^2\sqrt[3]{y}$ **31.** $\sqrt[10]{(x + 5)^7}$ **32.** $15 - 4\sqrt{3}i$
33. $x^3 - 5x^2 + 1$ **34.** $(3 + 4n)(9 - 12n + 16n^2)$
35. $2(3x - 2y)(x + 2y)$ **36.** $(x - 4)(x^3 + 7)$
37. $2(m + 3n)^2$ **38.** $(x - 2y)(x + 2y)(x^2 + 4y^2)$
39. $\dfrac{6 + \sqrt{y} - y}{4 - y}$ **40.** $f^{-1}(x) = \dfrac{x - 9}{-2}$, or $f^{-1}(x) = \dfrac{9 - x}{2}$
41. $f(x) = -10x - 8$ **42.** $y = \frac{1}{2}x + 5$
43.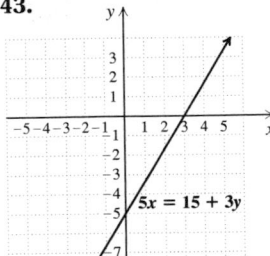

44.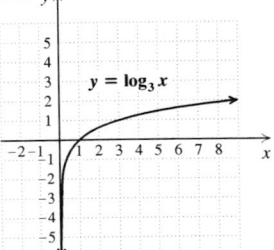

45.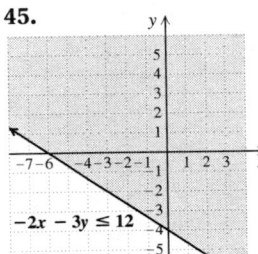

46.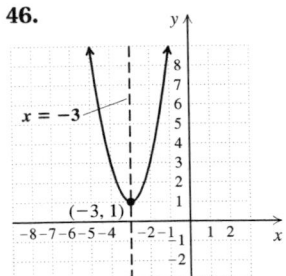

$f(x) = 2x^2 + 12x + 19$
Minimum: 1

47.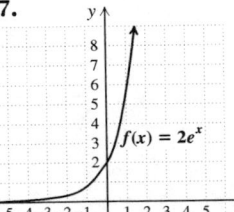

Domain: $\mathbb{R}$;
range: $(0, \infty)$

48. $\log\left(\dfrac{x^3}{y^{1/2}z^2}\right)$ **49.** 13.5 million acre-feet

50. (a) $k \approx 0.076$; $D(t) = 15e^{0.076t}$; **(b)** 79.8 million cubic
meters per day; **(c)** 2015   **51. (a)** $\frac{2}{15}$ million barrels per
day per year; **(b)** $g(t) = \frac{2}{15}t + 8.5$; **(c)** $G(t) = 8.5e^{0.015t}$
52. $5\frac{5}{11}$ min   **53.** Thick and Tasty: 6 oz; Light and Lean:
9 oz   **54.** $2\frac{7}{9}$ km/h   **55.** −49; −7 and 7

56. (a) 78; **(b)** 67.5   **57.** All real numbers except 1 and −2   **58.** $\frac{1}{3}, \frac{10,000}{3}$ **59.** 35 mph

CHAPTER 13

Technology Connection, p. 859

1. $x^2 + y^2 - 16 = 0$

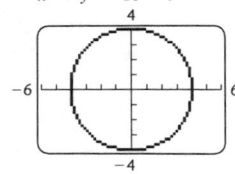

2. $(x - 1)^2 + (y - 2)^2 = 25$

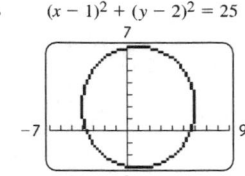

3. $(x + 3)^2 + (y - 5)^2 = 16$

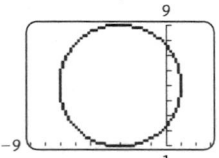

4. $(x - 5)^2 + (y + 6)^2 = 49$

Exercise Set 13.1, pp. 860–863

1. (f)   **2.** (e)   **3.** (g)   **4.** (h)   **5.** (c)   **6.** (b)
7. (d)   **8.** (a)

9.

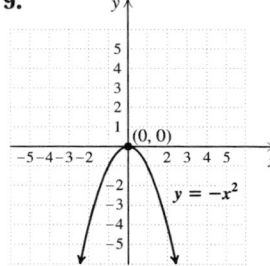

11.

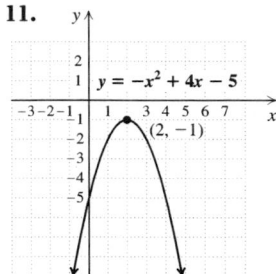

13.

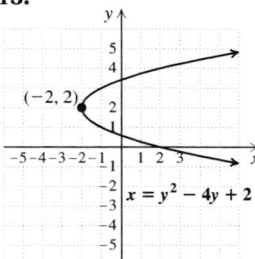

15.

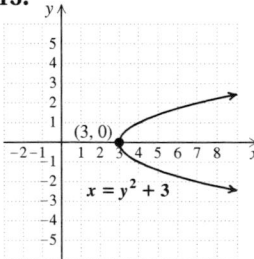

17.

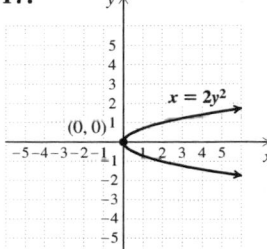

19.

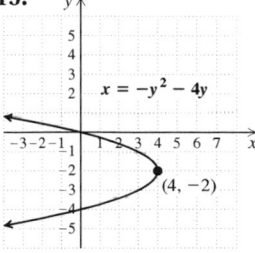

21.

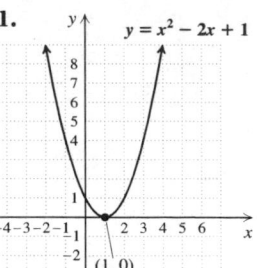

23.

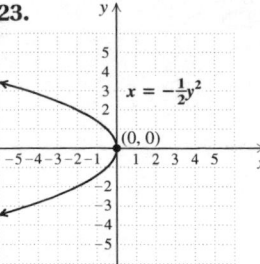

25.

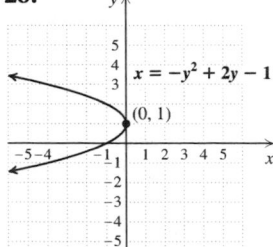

27.

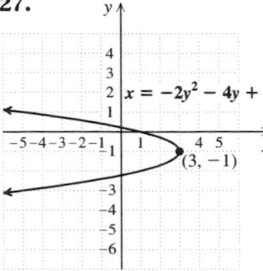

29. $x^2 + y^2 = 64$ **31.** $(x - 7)^2 + (y - 3)^2 = 6$
33. $(x + 4)^2 + (y - 3)^2 = 18$
35. $(x + 5)^2 + (y + 8)^2 = 300$
37. $x^2 + y^2 = 25$ **39.** $(x + 4)^2 + (y - 1)^2 = 20$
41. $(0, 0); 1$ **43.** $(-1, -3); 7$

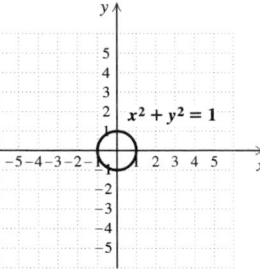

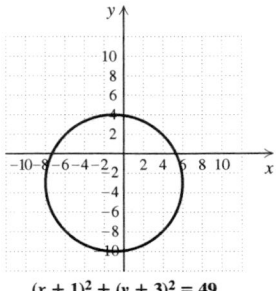

$(x + 1)^2 + (y + 3)^2 = 49$

45. $(4, -3); \sqrt{10}$ **47.** $(0, 0); 2\sqrt{2}$

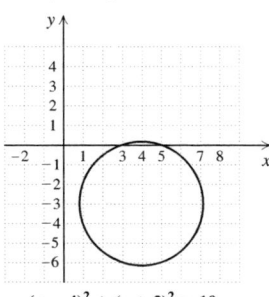

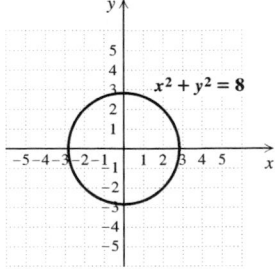

$(x - 4)^2 + (y + 3)^2 = 10$

49. $(5, 0); \frac{1}{2}$ **51.** $(-4, 3); \sqrt{40}$, or $2\sqrt{10}$

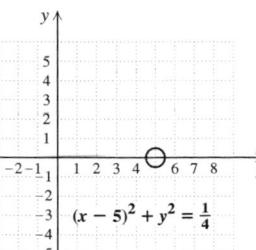

$(x - 5)^2 + y^2 = \frac{1}{4}$

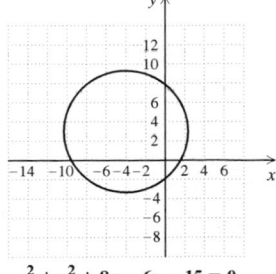

$x^2 + y^2 + 8x - 6y - 15 = 0$

53. $(4, -1); 2$

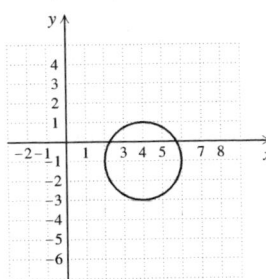

$x^2 + y^2 - 8x + 2y + 13 = 0$

55. $(0, -5); 10$

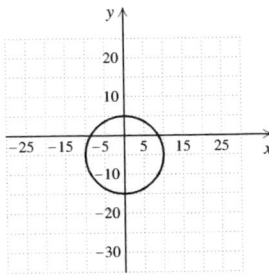

$x^2 + y^2 + 10y - 75 = 0$

57. $\left(-\dfrac{7}{2}, \dfrac{3}{2}\right); \sqrt{\dfrac{98}{4}}$, or $\dfrac{7\sqrt{2}}{2}$

59. $(0, 0); \dfrac{1}{6}$

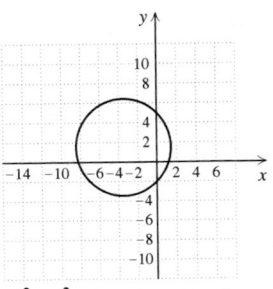

$x^2 + y^2 + 7x - 3y - 10 = 0$

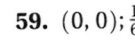

$36x^2 + 36y^2 = 1$

61. ✍   **63.** ± 4 **64.** $\pm a$ **65.** $-4, 6$

66. $-5 \pm 2\sqrt{3}$ **67.** $-3 \pm 3\sqrt{3}$ **68.** $2 \pm \dfrac{4\sqrt{2}}{3}$

69. ✍   **71.** $(x - 3)^2 + (y + 5)^2 = 9$

73. $(x - 3)^2 + y^2 = 25$ **75.** $(0, 4)$ **77.** $\dfrac{17}{4}\pi$ m^2, or approximately 13.4 m^2 **79.** 7169 mm

81. (a) $(0, -3)$;   **(b)** 5 ft   **83.** $x^2 + (y - 30.6)^2 = 590.49$

85. 7 in.   **87.** ✍, ▨

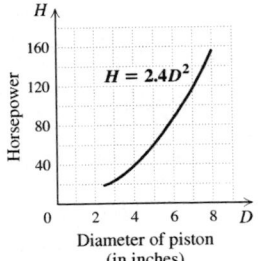

Exercise Set 13.2, pp. 867–869

1. True   **2.** False   **3.** False   **4.** False   **5.** True
6. True   **7.** True   **8.** True
9.

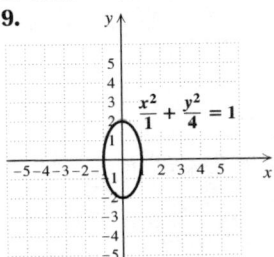

$\dfrac{x^2}{1} + \dfrac{y^2}{4} = 1$

11.

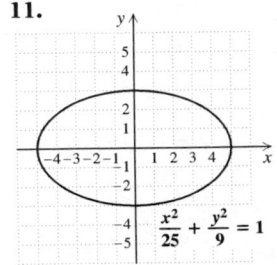

$\dfrac{x^2}{25} + \dfrac{y^2}{9} = 1$

13.

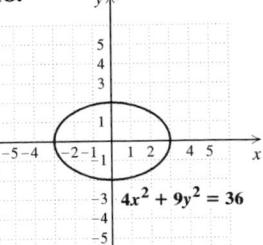

$4x^2 + 9y^2 = 36$

15.

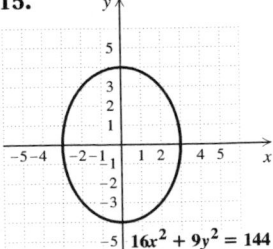

$16x^2 + 9y^2 = 144$

17.

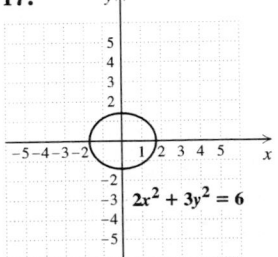

$2x^2 + 3y^2 = 6$

19.

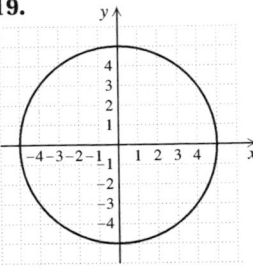

$5x^2 + 5y^2 = 125$

21.

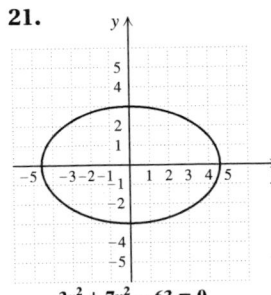

$3x^2 + 7y^2 - 63 = 0$

23.

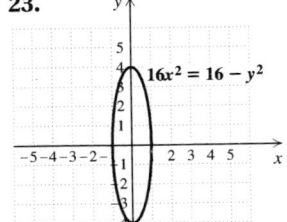

$16x^2 = 16 - y^2$

25.

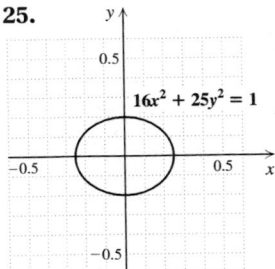

$16x^2 + 25y^2 = 1$

27.

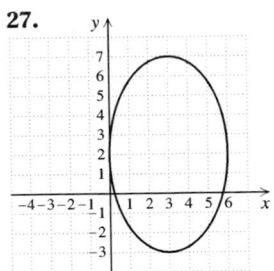

$\dfrac{(x - 3)^2}{9} + \dfrac{(y - 2)^2}{25} = 1$

29.

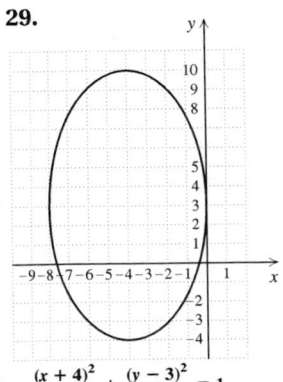

$\dfrac{(x + 4)^2}{16} + \dfrac{(y - 3)^2}{49} = 1$

31.

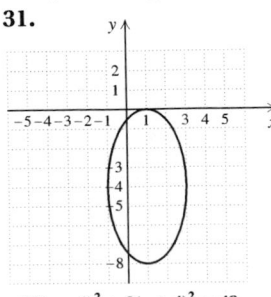

$12(x - 1)^2 + 3(y + 4)^2 = 48$

33.

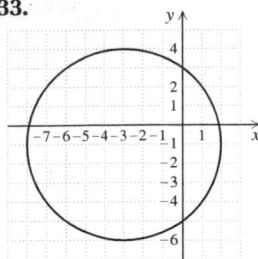

$4(x + 3)^2 + 4(y + 1)^2 - 10 = 90$

35. ⚏ **37.** $\dfrac{5}{2} \pm \dfrac{\sqrt{13}}{2}$ **38.** 3   **39.** $-\dfrac{3}{4}, 2$ **40.** $\dfrac{5}{2}$

41. $-\sqrt{11}, \sqrt{11}$ **42.** $-10, 6$ **43.** ⚏

45. $\dfrac{x^2}{81} + \dfrac{y^2}{121} = 1$ **47.** $\dfrac{(x - 2)^2}{16} + \dfrac{(y + 1)^2}{9} = 1$

49. 2.134×10^8 mi   **51. (a)** Let $F_1 = (-c, 0)$ and $F_2 = (c, 0)$. Then the sum of the distances from the foci to P is $2a$. By the distance formula,

$$\sqrt{(x + c)^2 + y^2} + \sqrt{(x - c)^2 + y^2} = 2a, \text{ or }$$
$$\sqrt{(x + c)^2 + y^2} = 2a - \sqrt{(x - c)^2 + y^2}.$$

Squaring, we get

$$(x + c)^2 + y^2 = 4a^2 - 4a\sqrt{(x - c)^2 + y^2} + (x - c)^2 + y^2,$$

or

$$x^2 + 2cx + c^2 + y^2 = 4a^2 - 4a\sqrt{(x - c)^2 + y^2} + x^2 - 2cx + c^2 + y^2.$$

Thus,

$$-4a^2 + 4cx = -4a\sqrt{(x - c)^2 + y^2}$$
$$a^2 - cx = a\sqrt{(x - c)^2 + y^2}.$$

Squaring again, we get

$$a^4 - 2a^2cx + c^2x^2 = a^2(x^2 - 2cx + c^2 + y^2)$$
$$a^4 - 2a^2cx + c^2x^2 = a^2x^2 - 2a^2cx + a^2c^2 + a^2y^2,$$

or

$$x^2(a^2 - c^2) + a^2y^2 = a^2(a^2 - c^2)$$
$$\dfrac{x^2}{a^2} + \dfrac{y^2}{a^2 - c^2} = 1.$$

(b) When P is at $(0, b)$, it follows that $b^2 = a^2 - c^2$. Substituting, we have

$$\dfrac{x^2}{a^2} + \dfrac{y^2}{b^2} = 1.$$

53. 5.66 ft   **55.**

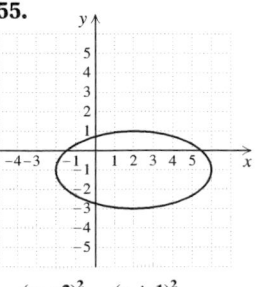

$\dfrac{(x - 2)^2}{16} + \dfrac{(y + 1)^2}{4} = 1$

57. ⚏

Technology Connection, p. 874

1. $y_1 = \dfrac{\sqrt{15x^2 - 240}}{2}$; $y_2 = -\dfrac{\sqrt{15x^2 - 240}}{2}$

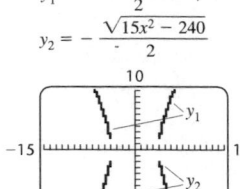

2. $y_1 = \sqrt{\dfrac{16x^2 - 64}{3}}$; $y_2 = -\sqrt{\dfrac{16x^2 - 64}{3}}$

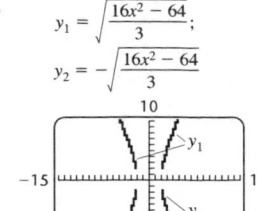

3. $y_1 = \dfrac{\sqrt{5x^2 + 320}}{4}$; $y_2 = -\dfrac{\sqrt{5x^2 + 320}}{4}$

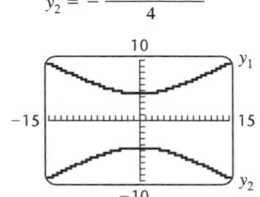

4. $y_1 = \sqrt{\dfrac{9x^2 + 441}{45}}$; $y_2 = -\sqrt{\dfrac{9x^2 + 441}{45}}$

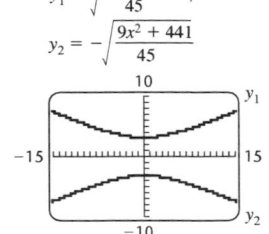

Exercise Set 13.3, pp. 876–877

1. (d)   **2.** (f)   **3.** (h)   **4.** (a)   **5.** (g)   **6.** (b)
7. (c)   **8.** (e)

9.

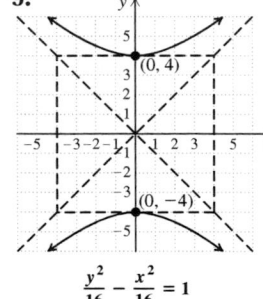

$\dfrac{y^2}{16} - \dfrac{x^2}{16} = 1$

11.

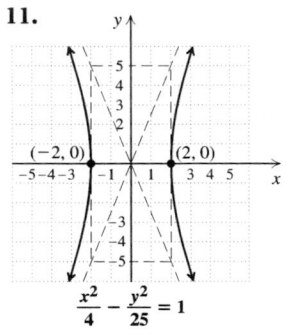

$\dfrac{x^2}{4} - \dfrac{y^2}{25} = 1$

13.

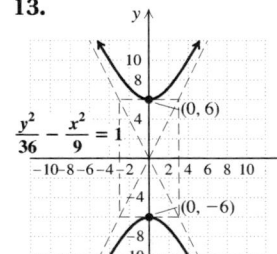

$\dfrac{y^2}{36} - \dfrac{x^2}{9} = 1$

15.

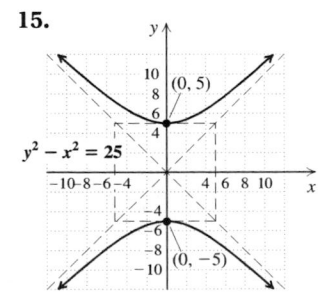

$y^2 - x^2 = 25$

17.

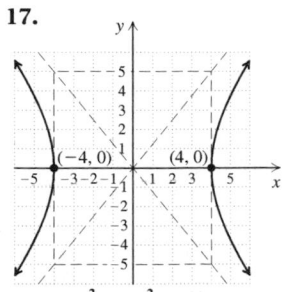

$25x^2 - 16y^2 = 400$

19.

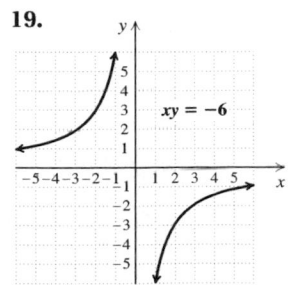

$xy = -6$

21.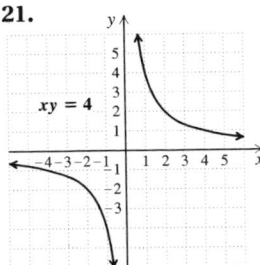

23.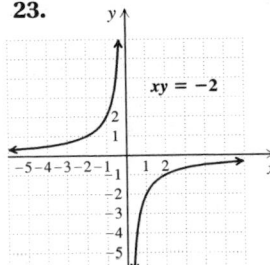

25.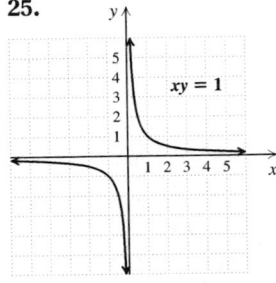

27. Circle   **29.** Ellipse   **31.** Hyperbola   **33.** Circle
35. Parabola   **37.** Hyperbola   **39.** Parabola
41. Hyperbola   **43.** Circle   **45.** Ellipse   **47.** 🖳
49. $(-3, 6)$ **50.** $\left(\frac{1}{2}, -\frac{3}{2}\right)$ **51.** $-2, 2$ **52.** $-4, \frac{2}{3}$
53. $\frac{3}{2} \pm \frac{\sqrt{13}}{2}$ **54.** $\pm 1, \pm 5$ **55.** 🖳   **57.** $\frac{y^2}{36} - \frac{x^2}{4} = 1$
59. $C: (5, 2); V: (-1, 2), (11, 2)$; asymptotes:
$y - 2 = \frac{5}{6}(x - 5), y - 2 = -\frac{5}{6}(x - 5)$

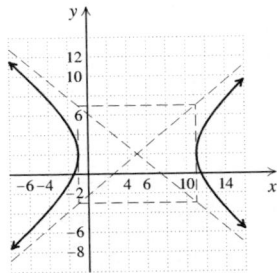

$$\frac{(x-5)^2}{36} - \frac{(y-2)^2}{25} = 1$$

61. $\dfrac{(y + 3)^2}{4} - \dfrac{(x - 4)^2}{16} = 1; C: (4, -3); V: (4, -5), (4, -1);$
asymptotes: $y + 3 = \frac{1}{2}(x - 4), y + 3 = -\frac{1}{2}(x - 4)$

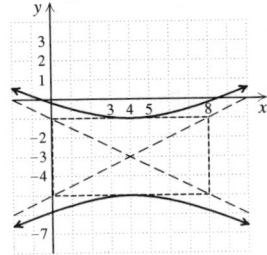

$$8(y + 3)^2 - 2(x - 4)^2 = 32$$

63. $\dfrac{(x + 3)^2}{1} - \dfrac{(y - 2)^2}{4} = 1; C: (-3, 2); V: (-4, 2), (-2, 2);$
asymptotes: $y - 2 = 2(x + 3), y - 2 = -2(x + 3)$

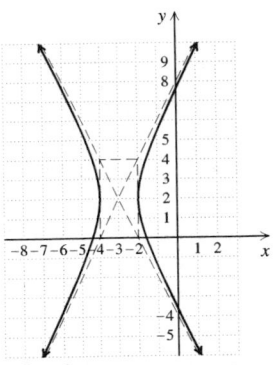

$$4x^2 - y^2 + 24x + 4y + 28 = 0$$

65. 🖳

Connecting the Concepts, p. 878

1. $(4, 1); x = 4$ **2.** $(2, -1); y = -1$ **3.** $(3, 2)$
4. $(-3, -5)$ **5.** $(-12, 0), (12, 0), (0, -9), (0, 9)$
6. $(-3, 0), (3, 0)$ **7.** $(0, -1), (0, 1)$ **8.** $y = \frac{3}{2}x, y = -\frac{3}{2}x$
9. Circle

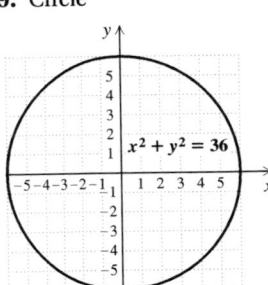

10. Parabola

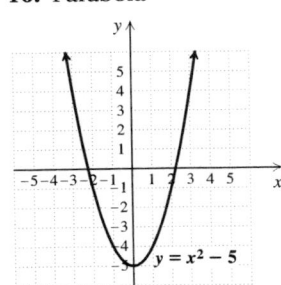

11. Ellipse

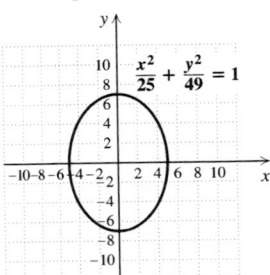

12. Hyperbola

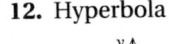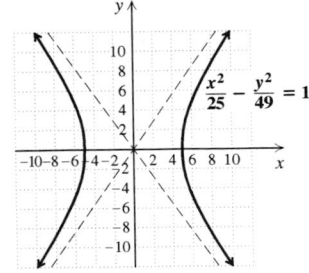

13. Parabola

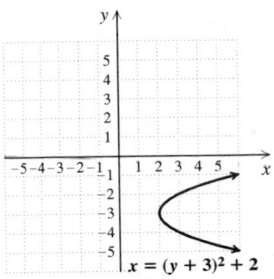

14. Ellipse

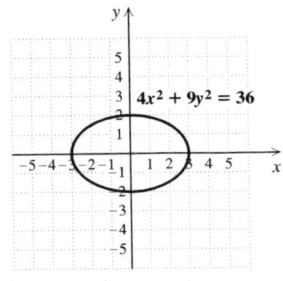

15. Hyperbola

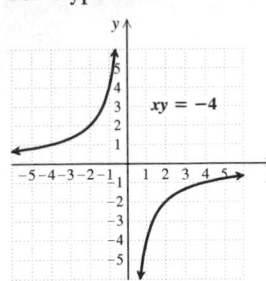

16. Circle

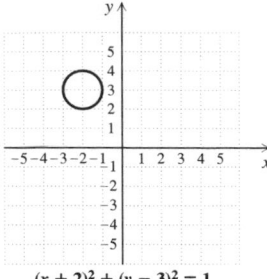

$(x + 2)^2 + (y - 3)^2 = 1$

17. Circle

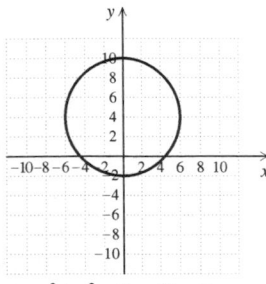

$x^2 + y^2 - 8y - 20 = 0$

18. Parabola

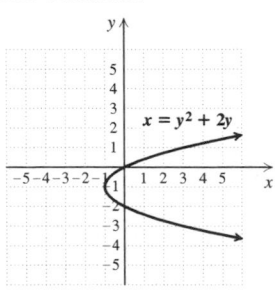

$x = y^2 + 2y$

19. Hyperbola

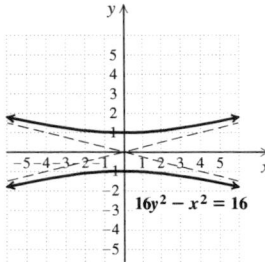

$16y^2 - x^2 = 16$

20. Hyperbola

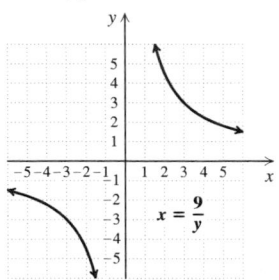

$x = \dfrac{9}{y}$

Technology Connection, p. 881

1. $(-1.50, -1.17)$; $(3.50, 0.50)$
2. $(-2.77, 2.52)$; $(-2.77, -2.52)$

Technology Connection, p. 882

1.

$y_1 = \sqrt{(20 - x^2)/4}$; $y_2 = -\sqrt{(20 - x^2)/4}$; $y_3 = 4/x$

Visualizing for Success, p. 885

1. C   **2.** A   **3.** F   **4.** B   **5.** J   **6.** D   **7.** H   **8.** I
9. G   **10.** E

Exercise Set 13.4, pp. 886–888

1. True   **2.** True   **3.** False   **4.** False   **5.** True

6. True   **7.** $(-5, -4), (4, 5)$ **9.** $(0, 2), (3, 0)$
11. $(-2, 1)$
13. $\left(\dfrac{5 + \sqrt{70}}{3}, \dfrac{-1 + \sqrt{70}}{3}\right), \left(\dfrac{5 - \sqrt{70}}{3}, \dfrac{-1 - \sqrt{70}}{30}\right)$
15. $\left(4, \dfrac{3}{2}\right), (3, 2)$ **17.** $\left(\dfrac{7}{3}, \dfrac{1}{3}\right), (1, -1)$ **19.** $\left(\dfrac{11}{4}, -\dfrac{5}{4}\right), (1, 4)$
21. $(2, 4), (4, 2)$ **23.** $(3, -5), (-1, 3)$
25. $(-5, -8), (8, 5)$ **27.** $(0, 0), (1, 1),$
$\left(-\dfrac{1}{2} + \dfrac{\sqrt{3}}{2}i, -\dfrac{1}{2} - \dfrac{\sqrt{3}}{2}i\right), \left(-\dfrac{1}{2} - \dfrac{\sqrt{3}}{2}i, -\dfrac{1}{2} + \dfrac{\sqrt{3}}{2}i\right)$
29. $(-4, 0), (4, 0)$ **31.** $(-4, -3), (-3, -4), (3, 4), (4, 3)$
33. $\left(\dfrac{16}{3}, \dfrac{5\sqrt{7}}{3}i\right), \left(\dfrac{16}{3}, -\dfrac{5\sqrt{7}}{3}i\right), \left(-\dfrac{16}{3}, \dfrac{5\sqrt{7}}{3}i\right),$
$\left(-\dfrac{16}{3}, -\dfrac{5\sqrt{7}}{3}i\right)$ **35.** $(-3, -\sqrt{5}), (-3, \sqrt{5}), (3, -\sqrt{5}),$
$(3, \sqrt{5})$ **37.** $(-3, -1), (-1, -3), (1, 3), (3, 1)$
39. $(4, 1), (-4, -1), (2, 2), (-2, -2)$ **41.** $(2, 1), (-2, -1)$
43. $\left(2, -\dfrac{4}{5}\right), \left(-2, -\dfrac{4}{5}\right), (5, 2), (-5, 2)$ **45.** $(-\sqrt{2}, \sqrt{2}),$
$(\sqrt{2}, -\sqrt{2})$ **47.** Length: 8 cm; width: 6 cm
49. Length: 2 in.; width: 1 in.   **51.** Length: 12 ft; width: 5 ft
53. 6 and 15; −6 and −15   **55.** 24 ft, 16 ft   **57.** Length:
$\sqrt{3}$ m; width: 1 m   **59.** 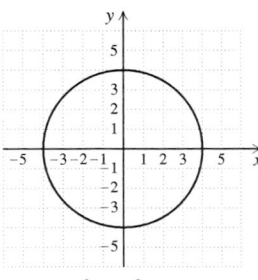   **61.** −9   **62.** −27
63. −1   **64.** $\dfrac{1}{5}$ **65.** 77   **66.** $\dfrac{21}{2}$ **67.**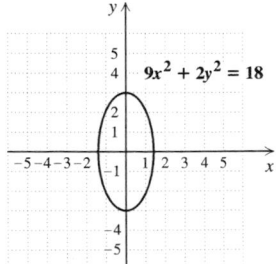
69. $(x + 2)^2 + (y - 1)^2 = 4$ **71.** $(-2, 3), (2, -3),$
$(-3, 2), (3, -2)$ **73.** Length: 55 ft; width: 45 ft
75. 10 in. by 7 in. by 5 in.   **77.** Length: 63.6 in.;
height: 35.8 in.   **79.**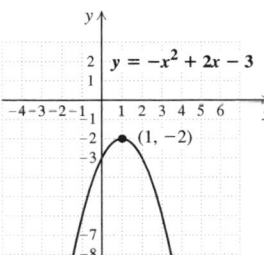

Review Exercises: Chapter 13, pp. 891–892

1. True   **2.** False   **3.** False   **4.** True   **5.** True
6. True   **7.** False   **8.** True   **9.** $(-3, 2), 4$
10. $(5, 0), \sqrt{11}$ **11.** $(3, 1), 3$ **12.** $(-4, 3), 3\sqrt{5}$
13. $(x + 4)^2 + (y - 3)^2 = 16$
14. $(x - 7)^2 + (y + 2)^2 = 20$
15. Circle

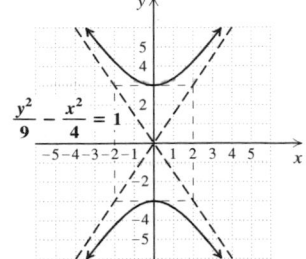

$5x^2 + 5y^2 = 80$

16. Ellipse

$9x^2 + 2y^2 = 18$

17. Parabola

$y = -x^2 + 2x - 3$

$(1, -2)$

18. Hyperbola

$\dfrac{y^2}{9} - \dfrac{x^2}{4} = 1$

19. Hyperbola

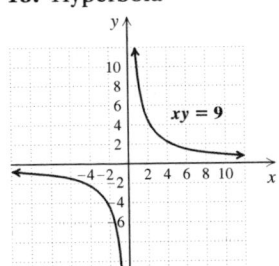

$xy = 9$

20. Parabola

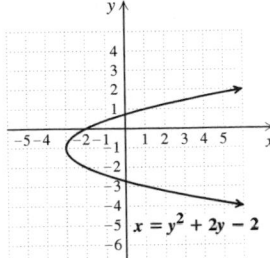

$x = y^2 + 2y - 2$

21. Ellipse

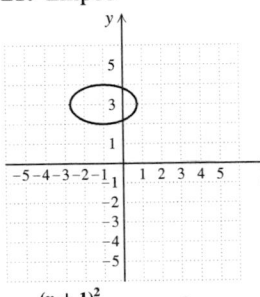

$\dfrac{(x+1)^2}{3} + (y-3)^2 = 1$

22. Circle

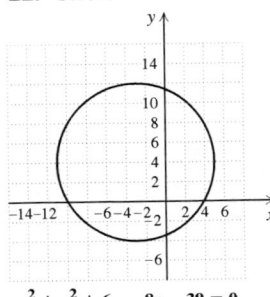

$x^2 + y^2 + 6x - 8y - 39 = 0$

23. $(5, -2)$ **24.** $(2, 2), \left(\frac{32}{9}, -\frac{10}{9}\right)$ **25.** $(0, -5), (2, -1)$
26. $(4, 3), (4, -3), (-4, 3), (-4, -3)$ **27.** $(2, 1), (\sqrt{3}, 0)$,
$(-2, 1), (-\sqrt{3}, 0)$ **28.** $(3, -3), \left(-\frac{3}{5}, \frac{21}{5}\right)$ **29.** $(6, 8)$,
$(6, -8), (-6, 8), (-6, -8)$ **30.** $(2, 2), (-2, -2)$,
$(2\sqrt{2}, \sqrt{2}), (-2\sqrt{2}, -\sqrt{2})$ **31.** Length: 12 m; width: 7 m
32. Length: 12 in.; width: 9 in.   **33.** 32 cm, 20 cm
34. 3 ft, 11 ft   **35.** ✍ The graph of a parabola has one
branch whereas the graph of a hyperbola has two branches.
A hyperbola has asymptotes, but a parabola does not.
36. ✍ Function notation rarely appears in this chapter
because many of the relations are not functions. Function
notation could be used for vertical parabolas and for hyperbolas that have the axes as asymptotes.
37. $(-5, -4\sqrt{2}), (-5, 4\sqrt{2}), (3, -2\sqrt{2}), (3, 2\sqrt{2})$
38. $(0, 6), (0, -6)$ **39.** $(x-2)^2 + (y+1)^2 = 25$
40. $\dfrac{x^2}{100} + \dfrac{y^2}{1} = 1$ **41.** $\left(\frac{9}{4}, 0\right)$

Test: Chapter 13, p. 892

1. [13.1] $(x-3)^2 + (y+4)^2 = 12$ **2.** [13.1] $(4, -1), \sqrt{5}$
3. [13.1] $(-2, 3), 3$
4. [13.1], [13.3] Parabola   **5.** [13.1], [13.3] Circle

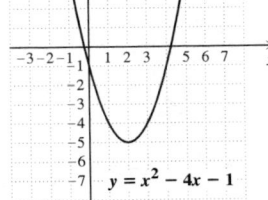

$y = x^2 - 4x - 1$

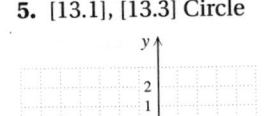

$x^2 + y^2 + 2x + 6y + 6 = 0$

6. [13.3] Hyperbola

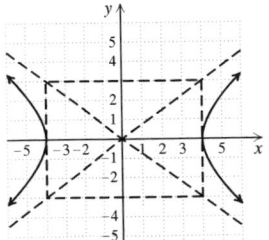

$\dfrac{x^2}{16} - \dfrac{y^2}{9} = 1$

7. [13.2], [13.3] Ellipse

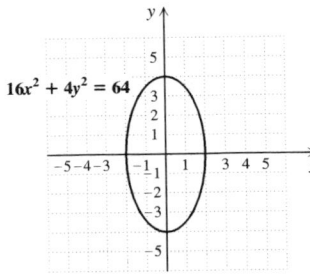

$16x^2 + 4y^2 = 64$

8. [13.3] Hyperbola

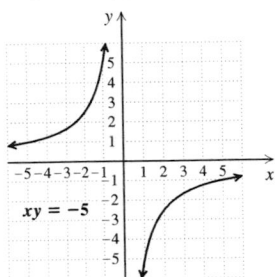

$xy = -5$

9. [13.1], [13.3] Parabola

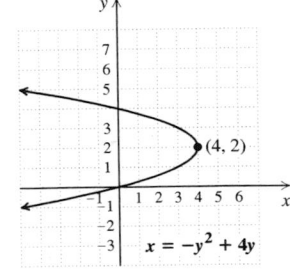

$(4, 2)$

$x = -y^2 + 4y$

10. [13.4] $(0, 6), \left(\frac{144}{25}, \frac{42}{25}\right)$ **11.** [13.4] $(-4, 13), (2, 1)$
12. [13.4] $(3, 2), (-3, -2), \left(-2\sqrt{2}\,i, \dfrac{3\sqrt{2}}{2}i\right), \left(2\sqrt{2}\,i, -\dfrac{3\sqrt{2}}{2}i\right)$
13. [13.4] $(\sqrt{6}, 2), (\sqrt{6}, -2), (-\sqrt{6}, 2), (-\sqrt{6}, -2)$
14. [13.4] 2 by 11   **15.** [13.4] $\sqrt{5}$ m, $\sqrt{3}$ m
16. [13.4] Length: 32 ft; width: 24 ft   **17.** [13.4] $1200, 6\%$
18. [13.2] $\dfrac{(x-6)^2}{25} + \dfrac{(y-3)^2}{9} = 1$ **19.** [13.1] $\left(0, -\frac{31}{4}\right)$
20. [13.4] 9   **21.** [13.2] $\dfrac{x^2}{16} + \dfrac{y^2}{49} = 1$

Cumulative Review: Chapters 1–13, pp. 893–894

1. $16t^4 - 40t^2s + 25s^2$ **2.** $\dfrac{4t-3}{3t(t-3)}$ **3.** $\dfrac{x}{a}$
4. $3t^2\sqrt{10w}$ **5.** $27a^{1/2}b^{3/16}$ **6.** -4 **7.** 25   **8.** 0
9. $-\frac{1}{64}$ **10.** $2\sqrt{3}$ **11.** $(10x - 3y)^2$
12. $3(m^2 - 2)(m^4 + 2m^2 + 4)$ **13.** $(x - y)(a - b)$
14. $(4x - 3)(8x + 1)$ **15.** $\left(-\infty, -\frac{25}{3}\right]$, or $\left\{x \mid x \le -\frac{25}{3}\right\}$
16. $0, \frac{9}{8}$ **17.** 1, 4   **18.** $\pm i$ **19.** 4
20. $\dfrac{\log 1.5}{\log 3} \approx 0.3691$ **21.** 7
22. $(-\sqrt{3}, -1), (-\sqrt{3}, 1), (\sqrt{3}, -1), (\sqrt{3}, 1)$
23.

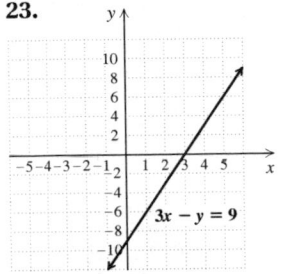

$3x - y = 9$

24.

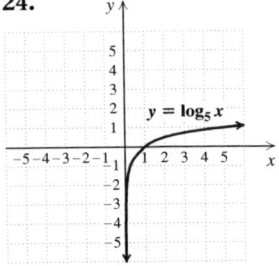

$y = \log_5 x$

25.

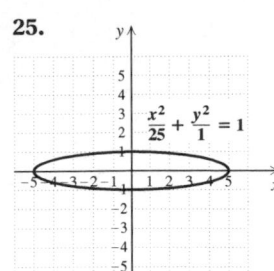

26.

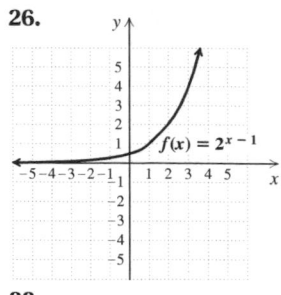

27.

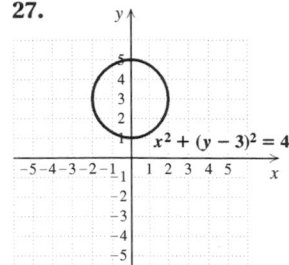

28.

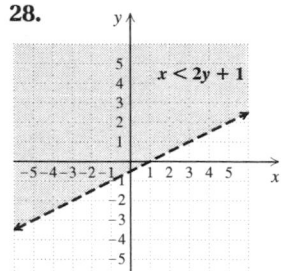

29.

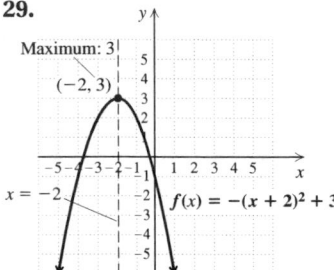

30. $\left(-\infty, \frac{5}{3}\right]$, or $\left\{x \mid x \leq \frac{5}{3}\right\}$ **31.** $c = \pm\sqrt{\dfrac{ab}{t}}$

32. $y = -x + 3$ **33.** $x^2 - 3 = 0$ **34.** $t^m = 16$

35. 2640 mi   **36.** Greg: 35 hr; Kyle: 14 hr

37. (a) $h(t) = -0.7t + 32.3$;   (b) 27.4 hr per week;
(c) approximately 2021   **38.** 1.5 in.

39. (a) $P(t) = 2.26e^{-0.0095t}$;   (b) 1.90 million;
(c) 73 yr   **40.** A: 15°; B: 45°; C: 120°   **41.** 8 in. by 8 in.

42. $\sqrt{55}$ cm $\approx$ 7.416 cm   **43.** $a = 1, b = -6$

44. $(1, -2, 0, 4)$ **45.** y is divided by 10.

46. $(-\infty, 0) \cup (0, 1]$, or $\{x \mid x < 0 \, or \, 0 < x \leq 1\}$

CHAPTER 14

Exercise Set 14.1, pp. 900–902

1. (f)   **2.** (a)   **3.** (d)   **4.** (b)   **5.** (c)   **6.** (e)   **7.** 43

9. 364   **11.** -23.5 **13.** -363 **15.** $\frac{441}{400}$

17. 2, 5, 8, 11; 29; 44   **19.** 3, 6, 11, 18; 102; 227

21. $\frac{1}{2}, \frac{2}{3}, \frac{3}{4}, \frac{4}{5}; \frac{10}{11}, \frac{15}{16}$ **23.** $1, -\frac{1}{2}, \frac{1}{4}, -\frac{1}{8}; -\frac{1}{512}; \frac{1}{16,384}$

25. $-1, \frac{1}{2}, -\frac{1}{3}, \frac{1}{4}; \frac{1}{10}; -\frac{1}{15}$ **27.** 0, 7, $-26, 63; 999; -3374$

29. $2n$ **31.** $(-1)^n$ **33.** $(-1)^{n+1} \cdot n$ **35.** $2n + 1$

37. $n^2 - 1$, or $(n + 1)(n - 1)$ **39.** $\dfrac{n}{n + 1}$

41. $(0.1)^n$, or 10^{-n} **43.** $(-1)^n \cdot n^2$ **45.** 5

47. 1.11111, or $1\frac{11,111}{100,000}$ **49.** $\dfrac{1}{2} + \dfrac{1}{4} + \dfrac{1}{6} + \dfrac{1}{8} + \dfrac{1}{10} = \dfrac{137}{120}$

51. $10^0 + 10^1 + 10^2 + 10^3 + 10^4 = 11{,}111$

53. $2 + \dfrac{3}{2} + \dfrac{4}{3} + \dfrac{5}{4} + \dfrac{6}{5} + \dfrac{7}{6} + \dfrac{8}{7} = \dfrac{1343}{140}$

55. $(-1)^2 2^1 + (-1)^3 2^2 + (-1)^4 2^3 + (-1)^5 2^4 +$
$(-1)^6 2^5 + (-1)^7 2^6 + (-1)^8 2^7 + (-1)^9 2^8 = -170$

57. $(0^2 - 2 \cdot 0 + 3) + (1^2 - 2 \cdot 1 + 3) +$
$(2^2 - 2 \cdot 2 + 3) + (3^2 - 2 \cdot 3 + 3) +$
$(4^2 - 2 \cdot 4 + 3) + (5^2 - 2 \cdot 5 + 3) = 43$

59. $\dfrac{(-1)^3}{3 \cdot 4} + \dfrac{(-1)^4}{4 \cdot 5} + \dfrac{(-1)^5}{5 \cdot 6} = -\dfrac{1}{15}$ **61.** $\displaystyle\sum_{k=1}^{5} \dfrac{k + 1}{k + 2}$

63. $\displaystyle\sum_{k=1}^{6} k^2$ **65.** $\displaystyle\sum_{k=2}^{n} (-1)^k k^2$ **67.** $\displaystyle\sum_{k=1}^{\infty} 6k$

69. $\displaystyle\sum_{k=1}^{\infty} \dfrac{1}{k(k + 1)}$ **71.** ☞   **73.** 98   **74.** -15

75. $a_1 + 4d$ **76.** $a_1 + a_n$ **77.** $3(a_1 + a_n)$, or $3a_1 + 3a_n$

78. d **79.** ☞   **81.** 1, 3, 13, 63, 313, 1563   **83.** \$2500,
\$2000, \$1600, \$1280, \$1024, \$819.20, \$655.36, \$524.29,
\$419.43, \$335.54   **85.** $S_{100} = 0$; $S_{101} = -1$

87. $i, -1, -i, 1, i; i$ **89.** 11th term

Exercise Set 14.2, pp. 908–910

1. True   **2.** True   **3.** False   **4.** False   **5.** True
6. True   **7.** False   **8.** False   **9.** $a_1 = 8, d = 5$
11. $a_1 = 7, d = -4$ **13.** $a_1 = \frac{3}{2}, d = \frac{3}{4}$
15. $a_1 = \$8.16, d = \$0.30$ **17.** 154   **19.** -94
21. $-\$1628.16$ **23.** 26th   **25.** 57th   **27.** 178
29. 5   **31.** 28   **33.** $a_1 = 8; d = -3; 8, 5, 2, -1, -4$
35. $a_1 = 1; d = 1$ **37.** 780   **39.** 31,375   **41.** 2550
43. 918   **45.** 1030   **47.** 35 musicians; 315 musicians
49. 180 stones   **51.** \$49.60   **53.** 560 seats   **55.** ☞
57. $y = \frac{1}{3}x + 10$ **58.** $y = -4x + 11$ **59.** $y = -2x + 10$
60. $y = -\frac{4}{3}x - \frac{16}{3}$ **61.** $x^2 + y^2 = 16$
62. $(x + 2)^2 + (y - 1)^2 = 20$ **63.** ☞   **65.** 33 jumps
67. Let $d =$ the common difference. Since $p, m,$ and q form
an arithmetic sequence, $m = p + d$ and $q = p + 2d$.
Then $\dfrac{p + q}{2} = \dfrac{p + (p + 2d)}{2} = p + d = m$.   **69.** 156,375

Exercise Set 14.3, pp. 917–919

1. Geometric sequence   **2.** Arithmetic sequence
3. Arithmetic sequence   **4.** Geometric sequence
5. Geometric series   **6.** Arithmetic series
7. Geometric series   **8.** None of these   **9.** 2   **11.** -0.1

13. $-\frac{1}{2}$ **15.** $\frac{1}{5}$ **17.** $\dfrac{6}{m}$ **19.** 1458   **21.** 243

23. 52,488   **25.** \$1423.31   **27.** $a_n = 5^{n-1}$
29. $a_n = (-1)^{n-1}$, or $a_n = (-1)^{n+1}$

31. $a_n = \dfrac{1}{x^n}$, or $a_n = x^{-n}$ **33.** 3066   **35.** $\frac{547}{18}$

37. $\dfrac{1 - x^8}{1 - x}$, or $(1 + x)(1 + x^2)(1 + x^4)$ **39.** \$5134.51

41. 27   **43.** $\frac{49}{4}$ **45.** No   **47.** No   **49.** $\frac{43}{99}$
51. \$25,000   **53.** $\frac{5}{9}$ **55.** $\frac{343}{99}$ **57.** $\frac{5}{33}$ **59.** $\frac{5}{1024}$ ft

61. 155,797   **63.** 2710 flies   **65.** Approximately 179.9 billion coffees   **67.** 3100.35 ft   **69.** 20.48 in.   **71.** 📈
73. $x^2 + 2xy + y^2$ **74.** $x^3 + 3x^2y + 3xy^2 + y^3$
75. $x^3 - 3x^2y + 3xy^2 - y^3$
76. $x^4 - 4x^3y + 6x^2y^2 - 4xy^3 + y^4$
77. $8x^3 + 12x^2y + 6xy^2 + y^3$
78. $8x^3 - 12x^2y + 6xy^2 - y^3$ **79.** 📈   **81.** 54
83. $\dfrac{x^2[1 - (-x)^n]}{1 + x}$ **85.** 512 cm^2 **87.** 📈, 🔲

Connecting the Concepts, p. 920

1. 300   **2.** $\dfrac{1}{n + 1}$ **3.** 78   **4.** $2^2 + 3^2 + 4^2 + 5^2 = 54$

5. $\sum_{k=1}^{6} (-1)^{k+1} \cdot k$ **6.** -3 **7.** 110   **8.** 61st   **9.** -39
10. 21   **11.** 11   **12.** 4410   **13.** $-\frac{1}{2}$ **14.** 640
15. $2(-1)^{n+1}$ **16.** \$1146.39   **17.** 1   **18.** No
19. \$465   **20.** \$1,073,741,823

Technology Connection, p. 925

1. 479,001,600   **2.** 56; 792

Visualizing for Success, p. 928

1. J   **2.** G   **3.** A   **4.** H   **5.** I   **6.** B   **7.** E   **8.** D
9. F   **10.** C

Exercise Set 14.4, pp. 929-930

1. 2^5, or 32   **2.** 8   **3.** 9   **4.** 4!   **5.** $\binom{8}{5}$, or $\binom{8}{3}$

6. a^2b^8 **7.** 1   **8.** 9 choose 5   **9.** 24   **11.** 3,628,800
13. 90   **15.** 126   **17.** 210   **19.** 1   **21.** 435   **23.** 780
25. $a^4 - 4a^3b + 6a^2b^2 - 4ab^3 + b^4$
27. $p^7 + 7p^6q + 21p^5q^2 + 35p^4q^3 + 35p^3q^4 + 21p^2q^5 + 7pq^6 + q^7$
29. $2187c^7 - 5103c^6d + 5103c^5d^2 - 2835c^4d^3 + 945c^3d^4 - 189c^2d^5 + 21cd^6 - d^7$
31. $t^{-12} + 12t^{-10} + 60t^{-8} + 160t^{-6} + 240t^{-4} + 192t^{-2} + 64$
33. $x^5 - 5x^4y + 10x^3y^2 - 10x^2y^3 + 5xy^4 - y^5$
35. $19,683s^9 + \dfrac{59,049s^8}{t} + \dfrac{78,732s^7}{t^2} + \dfrac{61,236s^6}{t^3} + \dfrac{30,618s^5}{t^4} + \dfrac{10,206s^4}{t^5} + \dfrac{2268s^3}{t^6} + \dfrac{324s^2}{t^7} + \dfrac{27s}{t^8} + \dfrac{1}{t^9}$
37. $x^{15} - 10x^{12}y + 40x^9y^2 - 80x^6y^3 + 80x^3y^4 - 32y^5$
39. $125 + 150\sqrt{5}t + 375t^2 + 100\sqrt{5}t^3 + 75t^4 + 6\sqrt{5}t^5 + t^6$
41. $x^{-3} - 6x^{-2} + 15x^{-1} - 20 + 15x - 6x^2 + x^3$
43. $15a^4b^2$ **45.** $-64,481,508a^3$ **47.** $1120x^{12}y^2$
49. $1,959,552u^5v^{10}$ **51.** y^8 **53.** 📈

55. **56.**
57. **58.**
59. **60.**

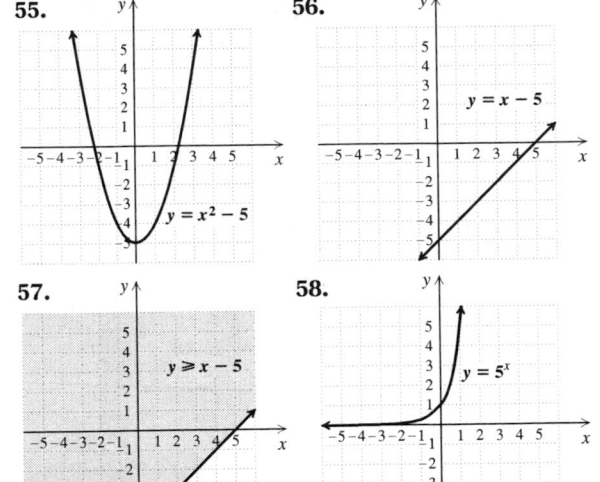
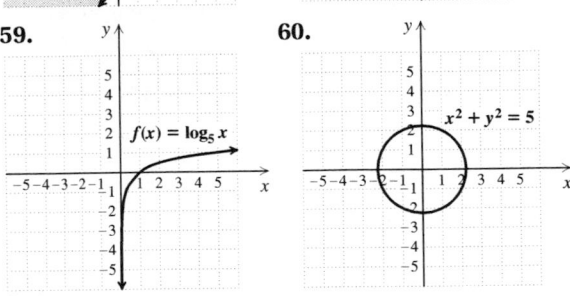

61. 📈   **63.** List all the subsets of size 3: $\{a, b, c\}$, $\{a, b, d\}$, $\{a, b, e\}$, $\{a, c, d\}$, $\{a, c, e\}$, $\{a, d, e\}$, $\{b, c, d\}$, $\{b, c, e\}$, $\{b, d, e\}$, $\{c, d, e\}$. There are exactly 10 subsets of size 3 and $\binom{5}{3} = 10$, so there are exactly $\binom{5}{3}$ ways of forming a subset of size 3 from $\{a, b, c, d, e\}$.
65. $\binom{8}{5}(0.15)^3(0.85)^5 \approx 0.084$
67. $\binom{8}{6}(0.15)^2(0.85)^6 + \binom{8}{7}(0.15)(0.85)^7 + \binom{8}{8}(0.85)^8 \approx 0.89$
69. $\binom{n}{n - r} = \dfrac{n!}{[n - (n - r)]!(n - r)!}$
$= \dfrac{n!}{r!(n - r)!} = \binom{n}{r}$
71. $\dfrac{-\sqrt[3]{q}}{2p}$ **73.** $x^7 + 7x^6y + 21x^5y^2 + 35x^4y^3 + 35x^3y^4 + 21x^2y^5 + 7xy^6 + y^7$

Review Exercises: Chapter 14, pp. 932-933

1. False   **2.** True   **3.** True   **4.** False   **5.** False
6. True   **7.** False   **8.** False   **9.** 1, 11, 21, 31; 71; 111

10. $0, \frac{1}{5}, \frac{1}{5}, \frac{3}{17}, \frac{7}{65}, \frac{11}{145}$ **11.** $a_n = -5n$
12. $a_n = (-1)^n(2n-1)$
13. $-2 + 4 + (-8) + 16 + (-32) = -22$
14. $-3 + (-5) + (-7) + (-9) + (-11) + (-13) = -48$
15. $\sum_{k=1}^{6} 7k$ **16.** $\sum_{k=1}^{5} \frac{1}{(-2)^k}$ **17.** -55 **18.** $\frac{1}{5}$
19. $a_1 = -15, d = 5$ **20.** -544 **21.** $25{,}250$
22. $1024\sqrt{2}$ **23.** $\frac{3}{4}$ **24.** $a_n = 2(-1)^n$
25. $a_n = 3\left(\frac{x}{4}\right)^{n-1}$ **26.** $11{,}718$ **27.** $-4095x$ **28.** 12
29. $\frac{49}{11}$ **30.** No   **31.** No   **32.** $\$40{,}000$ **33.** $\frac{5}{9}$ **34.** $\frac{16}{11}$
35. $\$24.30$ **36.** 903 poles   **37.** $\$15{,}791.18$ **38.** 6 m
39. 5040 **40.** 120 **41.** $190a^{18}b^2$
42. $x^4 - 8x^3y + 24x^2y^2 - 32xy^3 + 16y^4$
43. 🖎 For a geometric sequence with $|r| < 1$, as n gets larger, the absolute value of the terms gets smaller, since $|r^n|$ gets smaller.   **44.** 🖎 The first form of the binomial theorem draws the coefficients from Pascal's triangle; the second form uses factorial notation. The second form avoids the need to compute all preceding rows of Pascal's triangle, and is generally easier to use when only one term of an expansion is needed. When several terms of an expansion are needed and n is not large (say, $n \le 8$), it is often easier to use Pascal's triangle.   **45.** $\dfrac{1 - (-x)^n}{x + 1}$
46. $x^{-15} + 5x^{-9} + 10x^{-3} + 10x^3 + 5x^9 + x^{15}$

Test: Chapter 14, p. 934

1. [14.1] $\frac{1}{2}, \frac{1}{5}, \frac{1}{10}, \frac{1}{17}, \frac{1}{26}; \frac{1}{145}$ **2.** [14.1] $a_n = 4\left(\frac{1}{3}\right)^n$
3. [14.1] $-3 + (-7) + (-15) + (-31) = -56$
4. [14.1] $\sum_{k=1}^{5} (-1)^{k+1}k^3$ **5.** [14.2] $\frac{13}{2}$ **6.** [14.2] -3
7. [14.2] $a_1 = 31.2; d = -3.8$ **8.** [14.2] 2508
9. [14.3] 1536 **10.** [14.3] $\frac{2}{3}$ **11.** [14.3] 3^n
12. [14.3] 5621 **13.** [14.3] 1 **14.** [14.3] No
15. [14.3] $\frac{\$25{,}000}{23} \approx \$1086.96$ **16.** [14.3] $\frac{85}{99}$
17. [14.2] 63 seats   **18.** [14.2] $\$17{,}100$
19. [14.3] $\$5987.37$ **20.** [14.3] 36 m   **21.** [14.4] 220
22. [14.4] $x^5 - 15x^4y + 90x^3y^2 - 270x^2y^3 + 405xy^4 - 243y^5$ **23.** [14.4] $220a^9x^3$ **24.** [14.2] $n(n+1)$
25. [14.3] $\dfrac{1 - \left(\frac{1}{x}\right)^n}{1 - \frac{1}{x}}$, or $\dfrac{x^n - 1}{x^{n-1}(x-1)}$

Cumulative Review/Final Exam: Chapters 1–14, pp. 935–937

1. $\frac{7}{15}$ **2.** $-4y + 17$ **3.** 280 **4.** 8.4×10^{-15}
5. $\frac{7}{6}$ **6.** $3a^2 - 8ab - 15b^2$ **7.** $4a^2 - 1$
8. $9a^4 - 30a^2y + 25y^2$ **9.** $\frac{4}{x+2}$ **10.** $\frac{x-4}{4(x+2)}$
11. $\dfrac{(x+y)(x^2 + xy + y^2)}{x^2 + y^2}$ **12.** $x - a$ **13.** $12a^2\sqrt{b}$

14. $-27x^{10}y^{-2}$, or $-\dfrac{27x^{10}}{y^2}$ **15.** $25x^4y^{1/3}$
16. $y\sqrt[12]{x^5y^2}, y \ge 0$ **17.** $14 + 8i$
18. $(2x - 3)^2$ **19.** $(3a - 2)(9a^2 + 6a + 4)$
20. $12(s^2 + 2t)(s^2 - 2t)$ **21.** $3(y^2 + 3)(5y^2 - 4)$
22. $7x^3 + 9x^2 + 19x + 38 + \dfrac{72}{x - 2}$ **23.** 20
24. $[4, \infty)$, or $\{x | x \ge 4\}$
25. $(-\infty, 5) \cup (5, \infty)$, or $\{x | x < 5 \text{ or } x > 5\}$
26. $\dfrac{1 - 2\sqrt{x} + x}{1 - x}$ **27.** $y = 3x - 8$ **28.** $x^2 - 50 = 0$
29. $(2, -3); 6$ **30.** $\log_a \dfrac{\sqrt[3]{x^2} \cdot z^5}{\sqrt{y}}$ **31.** $a^5 = c$
32. 2.0792 **33.** 0.6826 **34.** 5 **35.** -121 **36.** 875
37. $16\left(\frac{1}{4}\right)^{n-1}$ **38.** $13{,}440a^4b^6$ **39.** $\frac{19{,}171}{64}$, or 299.546875
40. $\frac{3}{5}$ **41.** $-\frac{6}{5}, 4$ **42.** $\mathbb{R}$, or $(-\infty, \infty)$ **43.** $\left(-1, \frac{1}{2}\right)$
44. $(2, -1, 1)$ **45.** 2 **46.** $\pm 2, \pm 5$
47. $(\sqrt{5}, \sqrt{3}), (\sqrt{5}, -\sqrt{3}), (-\sqrt{5}, \sqrt{3}), (-\sqrt{5}, -\sqrt{3})$
48. 1.7925 **49.** 1005 **50.** $\frac{1}{25}$ **51.** $-\frac{1}{2}$
52. $\{x | -2 \le x \le 3\}$, or $[-2, 3]$ **53.** $\pm i\sqrt{3}$
54. $-2 \pm \sqrt{7}$ **55.** $\{y | y < -5 \text{ or } y > 2\}$, or $(-\infty, -5) \cup (2, \infty)$ **56.** $-8, 10$ **57.** 3
58. $r = \dfrac{V - P}{-Pt}$, or $\dfrac{P - V}{Pt}$ **59.** $R = \dfrac{Ir}{1 - I}$

60.

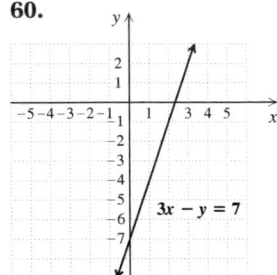

$3x - y = 7$

61.

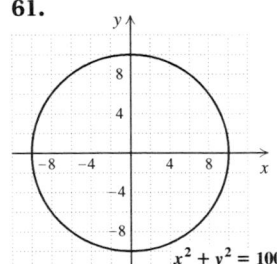

$x^2 + y^2 = 100$

62.

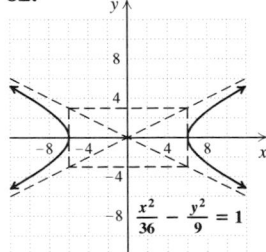

$\dfrac{x^2}{36} - \dfrac{y^2}{9} = 1$

63.

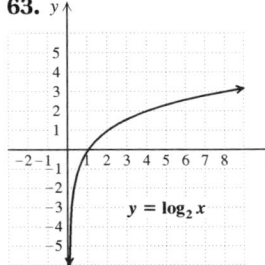

$y = \log_2 x$

64.

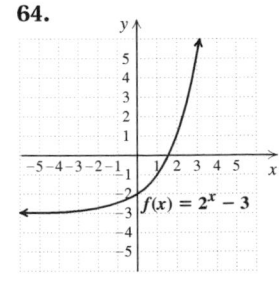

$f(x) = 2^x - 3$

65.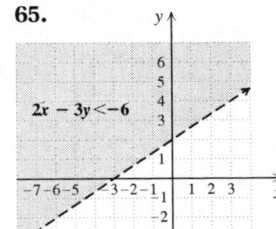

66.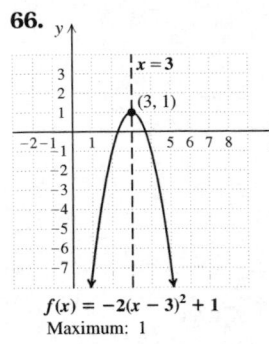
$f(x) = -2(x-3)^2 + 1$
Maximum: 1

67. 5000 ft^2 **68.** 5 ft by 12 ft   **69.** More than 25 rentals
70. 57, 59, 61   **71.** $2.68 herb: 10 oz; $4.60 herb: 14 oz
72. 350 mph   **73.** $8\frac{2}{5}$ hr, or 8 hr 24 min   **74.** 20
75. (a) The loan-to-value ratio increased 1.4% per year;
(b) $f(t) = 1.4t + 77.2$, where $f(t)$ is the loan-to-value ratio,
in percent; (c) 91.2%; (d) about 2013
76. (a) $k \approx 0.383$; $P(t) = 160e^{0.383t}$; (b) 730,273 reverse
mortgages; (c) about 2013   **77.** $14,079.98
78. All real numbers except 0 and -12 **79.** 81
80. y gets divided by 8   **81.** 84 yr

CHAPTER R

Exercise Set R.1, pp. 945–946

1. False   **3.** True   **5.** True   **7.** 22   **9.** 1.3   **11.** -25
13. $-\frac{11}{15}$ **15.** -6.5 **17.** -9 **19.** 0   **21.** $-\frac{1}{2}$ **23.** 5.8
25. -3 **27.** 39   **29.** 175   **31.** -32 **33.** 16   **35.** -6
37. 9   **39.** -3 **41.** -16 **43.** 100   **45.** 2   **47.** -23
49. 36   **51.** 10   **53.** 10   **55.** -7 **57.** 32
59. 28 cm^2 **61.** $8x + 28$ **63.** $-30 + 6x$
65. $8a + 12b - 6c$ **67.** $-6x + 3y - 3z$
69. $2(4x + 3y)$ **71.** $3(1 + w)$ **73.** $10(x + 5y + 10)$
75. p **77.** $-m + 22$ **79.** $-5x + 7$
81. $6p - 7$ **83.** $-x + 12y$ **85.** $36a - 48b$
87. $-10x + 104y + 9$ **89.** Yes   **91.** No   **93.** Yes
95. Let n represent the number; $3n = 348$
97. Let c represent the number of calories in a Taco Bell
Beef Burrito; $c + 69 = 500$ **99.** Let l represent the
amount of water used to produce 1 lb of lettuce; $42 = 2l$

Exercise Set R.2, pp. 954–955

1. 16   **3.** $-\frac{1}{12}$ **5.** -0.8 **7.** $-\frac{5}{3}$ **9.** 42   **11.** -5
13. $\frac{5}{3}$ **15.** $-\frac{4}{9}$ **17.** -4 **19.** $\frac{69}{5}$ **21.** $\frac{9}{32}$ **23.** -2
25. -15 **27.** $\frac{43}{2}$ **29.** $-\frac{61}{115}$ **31.** $l = \dfrac{A}{w}$ **33.** $P = IV$

35. $p = 2q - r$ **37.** $\pi = \dfrac{A}{r^2 + r^2 h}$

39. (a) No; (b) yes; (c) no; (d) yes
41. $\{x \mid x \le 12\}$, or $(-\infty, 12]$
43. $\{m \mid m > 12\}$, or $(12, \infty)$

45. $\left\{x \mid x \ge -\frac{3}{2}\right\}$, or $\left[-\frac{3}{2}, \infty\right)$

47. $\{t \mid t < -3\}$, or $(-\infty, -3)$

49. $\{y \mid y > 10\}$, or $(10, \infty)$
51. $\{a \mid a \ge 1\}$, or $[1, \infty)$
53. $\left\{x \mid x \ge \frac{64}{17}\right\}$, or $\left[\frac{64}{17}, \infty\right)$
55. $\left\{x \mid x > \frac{39}{11}\right\}$, or $\left(\frac{39}{11}, \infty\right)$
57. $\{x \mid x \le -10.875\}$, or $(-\infty, -10.875]$
59. 7   **61.** 16, 18   **63.** $166\frac{2}{3}$ pages   **65.** 4.5 cm, 9.5 cm
67. 900 cubic feet   **69.** 80¢   **71.** 30 min or more
73. For $2\frac{7}{9}$ hr or less

Exercise Set R.3, pp. 961

1.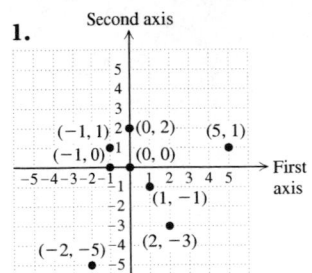

3. II   **5.** IV   **7.** I, IV
9. No   **11.** Yes

13.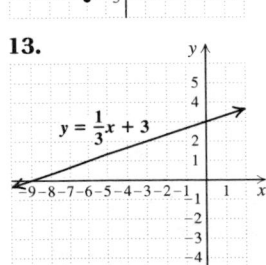

15.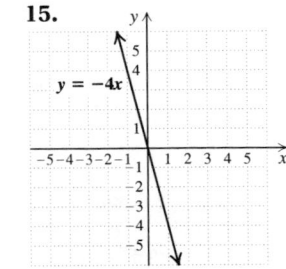

17. -1 **19.** 0   **21.** Slope: 2; y-intercept: $(0, -5)$
23. Slope: $-\frac{2}{7}$; y-intercept: $\left(0, \frac{1}{7}\right)$

25.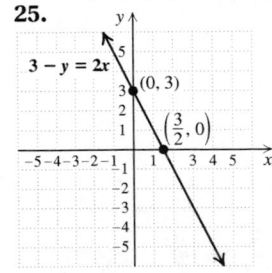

27.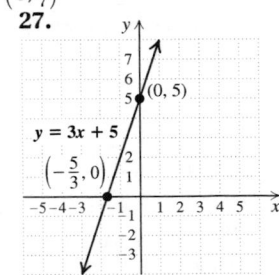

29.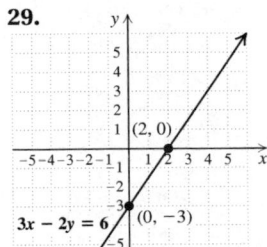

31.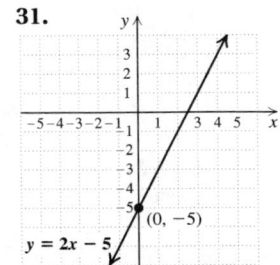

33.

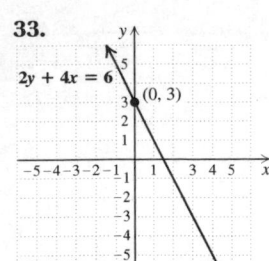

$2y + 4x = 6$ (0, 3)

35. 0

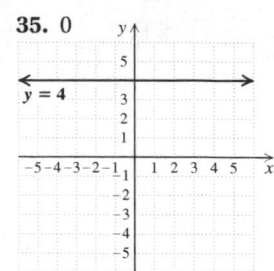

$y = 4$

37. Undefined

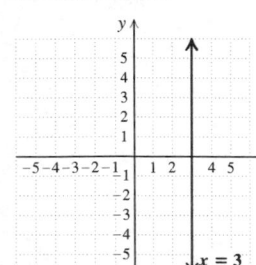

$x = 3$

39. $y = 5x + 9$
41. $y = -x + 3$
43. Perpendicular
45. Neither

Exercise Set R.4, pp. 968–969

1. 1   **3.** -3 **5.** $\dfrac{1}{8^2} = \dfrac{1}{64}$ **7.** $\dfrac{10}{x^5}$ **9.** $\dfrac{1}{(ab)^2}$

11. y^{10} **13.** t^{-4} **15.** x^{15} **17.** a^6 **19.** $(4x)^9$

21. 7^{40} **23.** $x^8 y^{12}$ **25.** $\dfrac{y^6}{64}$ **27.** $\dfrac{9q^8}{4p^6}$

29. $8x^3, -6x^2, x, -7$ **31.** 18, 36, -7, 3; 3, 9, 1, 0; 9
33. $-1, 4, -2$; 3, 3, 2; 3   **35.** $8p^4$; 8   **37.** $x^4 + 3x^3$
39. $-7t^2 + 5t + 10$ **41.** 36   **43.** -14 **45.** 144 ft
47. About 17.6 watts   **49.** $4x^3 - 3x^2 + 8x + 7$
51. $-y^2 + 5y - 2$ **53.** $-3x^2y - y^2 + 8y$
55. $12x^5 - 28x^3 + 28x^2$ **57.** $8a^2 + 2ab + 4ay + by$
59. $x^3 + 4x^2 - 20x + 7$ **61.** $x^2 - 49$
63. $x^2 + 2xy + y^2$ **65.** $6x^4 + 17x^2 - 14$
67. $42a^2 - 17ay - 15y^2$ **69.** $-t^4 - 3t^2 + 2t - 5$

71. $5x + 3$ **73.** $2x^2 - 3x + 3 + \dfrac{-2}{x+1}$

75. $5x + 3 + \dfrac{3}{x^2 - 1}$

Exercise Set R.5, p. 978

1. $6t^3(3t^2 - 2t + 1)$ **3.** $(y - 3)^2$ **5.** $(p + 2)(2p^3 + 1)$
7. Prime   **9.** $(2t + 3)(4t^2 - 6t + 9)$
11. $(m + 6)(m + 7)$ **13.** $(x^2 + 9)(x + 3)(x - 3)$
15. $(2x + 3)(4x + 5)$ **17.** $(x + 2)(x + 1)(x - 1)$
19. $(0.1t^2 - 0.2)(0.01t^4 + 0.02t^2 + 0.04)$
21. $\left(x^2 + \frac{1}{4}\right)\left(x + \frac{1}{2}\right)\left(x - \frac{1}{2}\right)$ **23.** $(n - 2)(m + 3)$
25. $(m + 15n)(m - 10n)$ **27.** $2y(3x + 1)(4x - 3)$
29. $(y - 11)^2$ **31.** $-3, 1$ **33.** 0, 11   **35.** $-3, 3$
37. $-\frac{5}{2}, 7$ **39.** 0, 5   **41.** $-2, 6$ **43.** $-11, 5$
45. -5 **47.** Base: 8 ft; height: 5 ft   **49.** 8 ft, 15 ft

Exercise Set R.6, pp. 988–989

1. $-\frac{1}{3}$ **3.** $-2, 2$ **5.** $\dfrac{8x}{9y}$ **7.** $\dfrac{t + 2}{t + 4}$ **9.** $\dfrac{-1}{x + 2}$

11. $\dfrac{6}{x}$ **13.** $\dfrac{(a + 1)^3(a - 1)}{a^3}$ **15.** 1   **17.** $\dfrac{5x + 4}{x^2}$

19. $\dfrac{6a + 3b - 4}{3a - 3b}$ **21.** $\dfrac{-3}{5x(x + 2)}$ **23.** $\dfrac{(x + 1)^2}{x^2(x + 2)}$

25. $\dfrac{x + 3}{(x + 1)^2}$ **27.** 1   **29.** $\dfrac{2t + 1}{(t + 1)(t - 1)}$

31. $\dfrac{-3x}{2}$ **33.** $\dfrac{-14x - 7}{(x + 5)(x - 4)}$ **35.** $\dfrac{8x - 4}{x^3}$

37. $\dfrac{3(x + 1)}{(x - 7)(4x + 3)}$ **39.** $\dfrac{(x + 1)^2}{(x - 2)(x + 4)}$ **41.** $\dfrac{-1}{x}$

43. $\dfrac{6}{5}$ **45.** 1   **47.** $\dfrac{31}{2}$ **49.** $-4, 4$ **51.** $22\frac{2}{9}$ hr

53. Jessica: 45 km/h; Josh: 25 km/h   **55.** 50

APPENDIXES

Exercise Set A, pp. 993–994

1. Mean: 17; median: 18; mode: 13   **3.** Mean: $10.\overline{6}$;
median: 9; mode: 3, 20   **5.** Mean: 4.06; median: 4.6;
mode: none   **7.** Mean: $239.\overline{3}$; median: 234; mode: 234
9. Average: 34.875; median: 22; mode: 0   **11.** Mean: 87.25;
median: 86.5; mode: 86   **13.** Average: $218.\overline{3}$; median: 222;
mode: 202   **15.** 10 home runs   **17.** $a = 30, b = 58$

Exercise Set B, pp. 997–998

1. $\{8, 9, 10, 11\}$ **3.** $\{41, 43, 45, 47, 49\}$ **5.** $\{-3, 3\}$
7. True   **9.** True   **11.** False   **13.** True   **15.** False
17. True   **19.** $\{c, d, e\}$ **21.** $\{1, 2, 3, 6\}$ **23.** $\varnothing$
25. $\{a, e, i, o, u, q, c, k\}$ **27.** $\{1, 2, 3, 4, 6, 9, 12, 18\}$
29. $\{1, 2, 3, 4, 5, 6, 7, 8\}$ **31.** ✒   **33.** The set of integers
35. The set of real numbers   **37.** $\varnothing$ **39.** (a) A; (b) A;
(c) A; (d) $\varnothing$ **41.** True   **43.** True   **45.** True

Exercise Set C, pp. 1001–1002

1. True   **2.** True   **3.** True   **4.** False   **5.** True

6. False   **7.** $x^2 - 3x - 5$ **9.** $a + 5 + \dfrac{-4}{a + 3}$

11. $2x^2 - 5x + 3 + \dfrac{8}{x + 2}$ **13.** $a^2 + 2a - 6$

15. $3y^2 + 2y + 6 + \dfrac{-2}{y - 3}$

17. $x^4 + 2x^3 + 4x^2 + 8x + 16$

19. $3x^2 + 6x - 3 + \dfrac{2}{x + \frac{1}{3}}$ **21.** 6   **23.** 125   **25.** 0

27. ✒   **29.** ✒
31. (a) The degree of R must be less than 1, the degree of
$x - r$; (b) Let $x = r$. Then
$$P(r) = (r - r) \cdot Q(r) + R$$
$$= 0 \cdot Q(r) + R$$
$$= R.$$

33. 0; $-3, -\frac{5}{2}, \frac{3}{2}$ **35.** ▨   **37.** 0

Glossary

A

Absolute value [1.4]   The distance that a number is from 0 on the number line.

Additive inverse [1.6]   A number's opposite. Two numbers are additive inverses of each other if their sum is zero.

Algebraic expression [1.1]   A collection of numerals and/or variables on which the operations $+$, $-$, $\cdot$, $\div$, $(\ )^n$, or $\sqrt[n]{(\ )}$ are performed.

Arithmetic sequence [14.2]   A sequence in which the difference between any two successive terms is constant.

Arithmetic series [14.2]   A series for which the associated sequence is arithmetic.

Ascending order   A polynomial written with the terms arranged according to degree of one variable, from least to greatest.

Associative law of addition [1.2]   The statement that when three numbers are added, regrouping the addends gives the same sum.

Associative law of multiplication [1.2]   The statement that when three numbers are multiplied, regrouping the factors gives the same product.

Asymptote [12.2], [13.3]   A line that a graph approaches more and more closely as x increases or as x decreases.

Average [2.7]   Most commonly, the mean of a set of numbers found by adding the numbers and dividing by the number of addends.

Axes (singular, axis) [3.1]   Two perpendicular number lines used to identify points in a plane.

Axis of symmetry [11.6]   A line that can be drawn through a graph such that the part of the graph on one side of the line is an exact reflection of the part on the opposite side.

B

Bar graph [3.1]   A graphic display of data using bars proportional in length to the numbers represented.

Base [1.8]   In exponential notation, the number or expression being raised to a power. In expressions of the form a^n, a is the base.

Binomial [4.2]   A polynomial composed of two terms.

Branches [13.3]   The two curves that comprise a hyperbola.

Break-even point [8.8]   In business, the point of intersection of the revenue function and the cost function.

C

Circle [13.1]   A set of points in a plane that are a fixed distance r, called the radius, from a fixed point (h, k), called the center.

Circle graph [3.1]   A graphic display of data using sectors of a circle to represent percents.

Circumference [2.3]   The distance around a circle.

Closed interval $[a, b]$ [2.6]   The set of all numbers x for which $a \le x \le b$. Thus, $[a, b] = \{x \mid a \le x \le b\}$.

Coefficient [2.1]   The numerical multiplier of a variable or variables.

Combined variation [7.5]   A mathematical relationship in which a variable varies directly and/or inversely, at the same time, with more than one other variable.

Common logarithm [12.5]   A logarithm with base 10.

Commutative law of addition [1.2]   The statement that when two numbers are added, changing the order in which the numbers are added does not affect the sum.

Commutative law of multiplication [1.2]   The statement that when two numbers are multiplied, changing the order in which the numbers are multiplied does not affect the product.

Complementary angles [2.5]   A pair of angles, the sum of whose measures is 90°.

Completing the square [11.1]   The procedure in which one adds a particular constant to an expression so that the resulting sum is a perfect square.

Complex number [10.8]   Any number that can be written as $a + bi$, where a and b are real numbers and $i = \sqrt{-1}$.

Complex rational expression [6.5]   A rational expression that has one or more rational expressions within its numerator and/or denominator.

Complex-number system [10.8]   A number system that contains the real-number system and is designed so that negative numbers have defined square roots.

Composite function [12.1]   A function in which a quantity depends on a variable that, in turn, depends on another variable.

Composite number [1.3]   A natural number, other than 1, that is not prime.

Compound inequality [9.2]   A statement in which two or more inequalities are combined using the word *and* or the word *or.*

Compound interest [11.1]   Interest computed on the sum of an original principal and the interest previously accrued by that principal.

Conditional equation [2.2]   An equation that is true for some replacements of a variable(s) and false for others.

Conic section [13.1]   A curve formed by the intersection of a plane and a cone.

Conjugates [10.5], [10.8]   Pairs of radical expressions, like $a\sqrt{b} + c\sqrt{d}$ and $a\sqrt{b} - c\sqrt{d}$, for which the product does not have a radical term or pairs of imaginary numbers, like $a + bi$ and $a - bi$, for which the product is real.

Conjunction [9.2]   A sentence in which two statements are joined by the word *and*.

Consecutive numbers [2.5]   Integers that are one unit apart.

Consistent system of equations [8.1], [8.4]   A system of equations that has at least one solution.

Constant [1.1]   A known number.

Constant function [7.3]   A function given by an equation of the form $f(x) = b$, where b is a real number.

Constant of proportionality [7.5]   The constant in an equation of variation.

Constraint [9.5]   A requirement imposed on a problem.

Contradiction [2.2]   An equation that is never true.

Coordinates [3.1]   The numbers in an ordered pair.

Cube root [10.1]   The number c is called the cube root of a if $c^3 = a$.

D

Data point [11.8]   A given ordered pair of a function, usually found experimentally.

Degree of a polynomial [4.3]   The degree of the term of highest degree in a polynomial.

Degree of a term [4.3]   The number of variable factors in a term.

Demand function [8.8]   A function modeling the relationship between the price of a good and the quantity of that good demanded.

Denominator [1.3], [6.1]   The number below the fraction bar in a fraction or the expression below the fraction bar in a rational expression.

Dependent equations [8.1]   Equations in a system from which one equation can be removed without changing the solution set.

Descending order [4.3]   A polynomial written with the terms arranged according to degree of one variable, from greatest to least.

Determinant [8.7]   A descriptor of a square matrix. The determinant of a two-by-two matrix $\begin{bmatrix} a & c \\ b & d \end{bmatrix}$ is denoted $\begin{vmatrix} a & c \\ b & d \end{vmatrix}$ and represents $ad - bc$.

Difference of squares [4.6], [5.4]   An expression that can be written in the form $A^2 - B^2$.

Direct variation [7.5]   A situation that translates to an equation of the form $y = kx$, with k a nonzero constant.

Discriminant [11.3]   The expression $b^2 - 4ac$ from the quadratic formula.

Disjunction [9.2]   A sentence in which two statements are joined by the word *or*.

Distributive law [1.2]   The statement that multiplying a factor by the sum of two addends gives the same result as multiplying the factor by each of the two addends and then adding.

Domain [7.2]   The set of all first coordinates of the ordered pairs in a function.

Doubling time [12.7]   The time necessary for a population to double in size.

E

e [12.5]   An irrational number that is approximately 2.7182818284, which is used in many applications.

Element [8.6]   An entry in a matrix.

Elimination method [8.2]   An algebraic method that uses the addition principle to solve a system of equations.

Ellipse [13.2]   The set of all points in a plane for which the sum of the distances from two fixed points F_1 and F_2, called foci, is constant.

Equation [1.1]   A number sentence with the verb $=$.

Equation of variation [7.5]   An equation used to represent direct, inverse, or combined variation.

Equilibrium point [8.8]   The point of intersection between the demand function and the supply function.

Equivalent equations [2.1]   Equations with the same solutions.

Equivalent expressions [1.2]   Expressions that have the same value for all allowable replacements.

Equivalent inequalities [2.6]   Inequalities that have the same solution set.

Evaluate [1.1]   To substitute a value for each occurrence of a variable in an expression and calculate the result.

Exponent [1.8]   The power to which a base is raised. In expressions of the form a^n, the number n is an exponent. For n a natural number, a^n represents n factors of a.

Exponential decay [12.7]   A decrease in quantity over time that can be modeled by an exponential equation of the form $P(t) = P_0 e^{-kt}$, $k > 0$.

Exponential equation [12.6]   An equation in which a variable appears in an exponent.

Exponential function [12.2]   A function that can be described by an exponential equation.

Exponential growth [12.7]   An increase in quantity over time that can be modeled by an exponential function of the form $P(t) = P_0 e^{kt}$, $k > 0$.

Exponential notation [1.8]   A representation of a number using a base raised to a power.

Extrapolation [3.7]   The process of predicting a future value on the basis of given data.

F

Factor [1.2]   *Verb*: to write an equivalent expression that is a product. *Noun*: a multiplier.

Finite sequence [14.1]   A function having for its domain a set of natural numbers: $\{1, 2, 3, 4, 5, \ldots, n\}$, for some natural number n.

Fixed costs [8.8]   In business, costs that are incurred regardless of how many items are produced.

Focus (plural, foci) [13.2]   One of two fixed points that determine the points of an ellipse or a hyperbola.

FOIL [4.5]   An acronym for a procedure for multiplying two binomials by multiplying the First terms, the Outer terms, the Inner terms, and the Last terms, and then adding the results.

Formula [2.3]   An equation that uses numbers and/or letters to represent a relationship between two or more quantities.

Fraction notation [1.3]   A number written using a numerator and a denominator.

Function [7.1]   A correspondence that assigns to each member of a set called the domain exactly one member of a set called the range.

G

General term of a sequence [14.1]   The nth term, denoted a_n.

Geometric sequence [14.3]   A sequence in which the ratio of every pair of successive terms is constant.

Geometric series [14.3]   A series for which the associated sequence is geometric.

Grade [3.5]   The ratio of the vertical distance a road rises over the horizontal distance it runs, expressed as a percent.

Graph [3.1]   A picture or diagram of the data in a table, or a line, a curve, a plane, or collection of points, etc., that represents all the solutions of an equation or an inequality.

H

Half-life [12.7]   The amount of time necessary for half of a quantity to decay.

Half-open interval [2.6]   An interval that includes exactly one endpoint.

Horizontal-line test [12.1]   The statement that if it is impossible to draw a horizontal line that intersects the graph of a function more than once, then that function is one-to-one.

Hyperbola [13.3]   The set of all points P in the plane such that the difference of the distance from P to two fixed points is constant.

Hypotenuse [5.8]   In a right triangle, the side opposite the right angle.

I

i [10.8]   The square root of -1. That is, $i = \sqrt{-1}$ and $i^2 = -1$.

Identity [2.2]   An equation that is always true.

Identity property of 0 [1.5]   The statement that the sum of a number and 0 is always the original number.

Identity property of 1 [1.3]   The statement that the product of a number and 1 is always the original number.

Imaginary number [10.8]   A number that can be written in the form $a + bi$, where a and b are real numbers and $b \neq 0$ and $i = \sqrt{-1}$.

Inconsistent system of equations [8.1]   A system of equations for which there is no solution.

Independent equations [8.1]   Equations that are not dependent.

Index (plural, indices) [10.1]   In the radical $\sqrt[n]{a}$, the number n is called the index.

Inequality [1.4]   A mathematical sentence using $<, >, \leq, \geq,$ or $\neq$.

Infinite geometric series [14.3]   The sum of the terms of an infinite geometric sequence.

Infinite sequence [14.1]   A function having for its domain the set of natural numbers: $\{1, 2, 3, 4, 5, \ldots\}$.

Input [7.1]   A member of the domain of a function.

Integers [1.4]   The whole numbers and their opposites.

Interpolation [3.7]   The process of estimating a value between given values.

Intersection of two sets [9.2]   The set of all elements that are common to both sets.

Interval notation [2.6]   The use of a pair of numbers inside parentheses and/or brackets to represent the set of all numbers between those two numbers. *See also* Closed, Open, and Half-open intervals.

Inverse relation [12.1]   The relation formed by interchanging the members of the domain and the range of a relation.

Inverse variation [7.5]   A situation that translates to an equation of the form $y = k/x$, with k a nonzero constant.

Irrational number [1.4]   A real number that cannot be named as a ratio of two integers. In decimal notation, irrational numbers neither terminate nor repeat.

Isosceles right triangle [10.7]   A right triangle in which both legs have the same length.

J

Joint variation [7.5]   A situation that translates to an equation of the form $y = kxz$, with k a nonzero constant.

L

Largest common factor [5.1]   The common factor of the terms of a polynomial with the largest possible coefficient and the largest possible exponent(s).

Leading coefficient [4.3]   The coefficient of the term of highest degree in a polynomial.

Leading term [4.3]   The term of highest degree in a polynomial.

Least common denominator (LCD) [6.3]   The least common multiple of the denominators of two or more rational expressions.

Least common multiple (LCM) [6.3]   The multiple of all expressions under consideration that has the smallest positive coefficient and the least possible degree.

Legs [5.8]   In a right triangle, the two sides that form the right angle.

Like radicals [10.5]   Radical expressions that have identical indices and radicands.

Like terms [1.5], [4.3]   Terms that have exactly the same variable factors.

Line graph [3.1]   A graph in which quantities are represented as points connected by straight-line segments.

Linear equation [3.2], [8.4]   In two variables, any equation that can be written in the form $y = mx + b$, or $Ax + By = C$, where x and y are variables and m, b, A, B, and C are constants and A and B are not both 0. In three variables, an equation that is equivalent to one of the form $Ax + By + Cz = D$, where x, y, and z are variables, and A, B, and C are constants that are not all 0.

Linear function [7.3]   A function that can be described by an equation of the form $f(x) = mx + b$, where m and b are constants.

Linear inequality [9.4]   An inequality whose related equation is a linear equation.

Linear programming [9.5]   A branch of mathematics involving graphs of inequalities and their constraints.

Logarithmic equation [12.6]   An equation containing a logarithmic expression.

Logarithmic function, base a [12.3]   The inverse of an exponential function with base a.

M

Matrix (plural, matrices) [8.6]   A rectangular array of numbers.

Maximum value [11.6]   The greatest function value (output) achieved by a function.

Mean [2.7]   The sum of a set of numbers divided by the number of addends.

Minimum value [11.6]   The least function value (output) achieved by a function.

Monomial [4.3]   A constant, a variable, or a product of a constant and one or more variables.

Motion problem [6.7]   A problem that deals with distance, speed, and time.

Multiplicative inverses [1.3]   Reciprocals; two numbers whose product is 1.

Multiplicative property of zero [1.7]   The statement that the product of 0 and any real number is 0.

N

Natural logarithm [12.5]   A logarithm with base e.

Natural numbers [1.3]   The counting numbers: 1, 2, 3, 4, 5, ...

Nonlinear function [7.3]   A function whose graph is not a straight line.

Numerator [1.3], [6.1]   The number above the fraction bar in a fraction or the expression above the fraction bar in a rational expression.

O

Objective function [9.5]   In linear programming, the function in which the expression being maximized or minimized appears.

One-to-one function [12.1]   A function for which all different inputs have different outputs.

Open interval (a, b) [2.6]   The set of all numbers x for which $a < x < b$. Thus, $(a, b) = \{x \mid a < x < b\}$.

Opposite [1.6]   The additive inverse of a number. Opposites are the same distance from 0 on the number line but on different sides of 0.

Ordered pair [3.1]   A pair of numbers of the form (h, k) for which the order in which the numbers are listed is important.

Origin [3.1]   The point on a graph in a coordinate plane where the two axes intersect.

Output [7.1]   A member of the range of a function.

P

Parabola [11.6], [13.1]   A graph of a second degree polynomial equation in one variable.

Parallel lines [3.6]   Lines that extend indefinitely without intersecting.

Pascal's triangle [14.4]   A triangular array of coefficients of the expansion $(a + b)^n$ for $n = 0, 1, 2, \ldots$.

Perfect square [10.1]   A rational number for which there exists a number a for which $a^2 = p$.

Perfect-square trinomial [4.6], [5.4]   A trinomial that is the square of a binomial.

Perpendicular lines [3.6]   Lines that intersect at a right angle.

Piecewise function [7.2]   A function that is defined by different equations for various parts of its domain.

Point–slope equation [3.7]   An equation of the type $y - y_1 = m(x - x_1)$, where x and y are variables, and m is the slope of the line and (x_1, y_1) is a point on the line.

Polynomial [4.2]   A monomial or a sum of monomials.

Price [8.8]   The amount a purchaser pays for an item.

Polynomial equation [5.7]   An equation in which two polynomials are set equal to each other.

Polynomial inequality [11.9]   An inequality that is equivalent to an inequality with a polynomial as one side and 0 as the other.

Prime factorization [1.3]   The factorization of a natural number into a product of its prime factors.

Prime number [1.3]   A natural number that has exactly two different natural number factors: the number itself and 1.

Principal square root [10.1]   The nonnegative square root of a number.

Proportion [6.7]   An equation stating that two ratios are equal.

Pure imaginary number [10.8]   A complex number of the form $a + bi$, with $a = 0$ and $b \neq 0$.

Pythagorean theorem [5.8]   The theorem that states that in any right triangle, if a and b are the lengths of the legs and c is the length of the hypotenuse, then $a^2 + b^2 = c^2$.

Q

Quadrants [3.1]   The four regions into which the axes divide a plane.

Quadratic equation [5.7]   An equation equivalent to one of the form $ax^2 + bx + c = 0$, where $a \neq 0$.

Quadratic formula [11.2] $x = \dfrac{-b \pm \sqrt{b^2 - 4ac}}{2a}$, which gives the solutions of $ax^2 + bx + c = 0$, where $a \neq 0$.

Quadratic function [11.1]   A second-degree polynomial function in one variable.

Quadratic inequality [11.9]   A second-degree polynomial inequality in one variable.

R

Radical equation [10.6]   An equation in which a variable appears in a radicand.

Radical expression [10.1]   An algebraic expression in which a radical sign appears.

Radical sign [10.1]   The symbol $\sqrt{}$ or $\sqrt[n]{}$, where $n > 2$.

Radical term [10.5]   A term in which a radical sign appears.

Radicand [10.1]   The expression under a radical sign.

Radius (plural, radii) [13.1]   The distance from the center of a circle to a point on the circle. Also, a segment connecting the center to a point on the circle.

Range [7.2]   The set of all second coordinates of the ordered pairs in a function.

Rate [3.4]   A ratio that indicates how two quantities change with respect to each other.

Ratio [6.7]   The quotient of two quantities. The ratio of a to b is a/b, also written $a:b$.

Rational equation [6.6]   An equation containing one or more rational expressions.

Rational expression [6.1]   A quotient of two polynomials.

Rational inequality [11.9]   An inequality containing a rational expression.

Rational number [1.4]   A number that can be written in the form $\dfrac{a}{b}$, where a and b are integers and $b \neq 0$. In decimal notation, a rational number repeats or terminates.

Rationalizing the denominator [10.4], [10.5]   A procedure for finding an equivalent expression without a radical in its denominator.

Rationalizing the numerator [10.4], [10.5]   A procedure for finding an equivalent expression without a radical in its numerator.

Real number [1.4]   Any number that is either rational or irrational.

Reciprocal [1.3]   A multiplicative inverse. Two numbers are reciprocals if their product is 1.

Reflection [11.6]   The mirror image of a graph.

Relation [7.1]   A correspondence between two sets, called the domain and the range, such that each member of the domain corresponds to at least one member of the range.

Repeating decimal [1.4]   A decimal in which a block of digits repeats indefinitely.

Right triangle [5.8]   A triangle that includes a right angle.

Row-equivalent operations [8.6]   Operations used to produce equivalent systems of equations.

S

Scientific notation [4.2]   A number written in the form $N \times 10^m$, where m is an integer, $1 \leq N < 10$, and N is expressed in decimal notation.

Sequence [14.1]   A function for which the domain is a set of consecutive natural numbers beginning with 1.

Series [14.1]   The sum of specified terms in a sequence.

Set [1.4]   A collection of objects.

Set-builder notation [2.6]   The naming of a set by describing basic characteristics of the elements in the set.

Sigma notation [14.1]   The naming of a sum using the Greek letter Σ (sigma) as part of an abbreviated form.

Similar triangles [10.7]   Triangles in which corresponding sides are proportional and corresponding angles have the same measure.

Simplify   To rewrite an expression in an equivalent, abbreviated, form.

Slope [3.5]   The ratio of the rise to the run for any two points on a line.

Slope–intercept equation [3.6]   An equation of the form $y = mx + b$, where x and y are variables, m is the slope of the line, and $(0, b)$ is its y-intercept.

Solution [1.1], [2.1], [2.6], [8.1]   A replacement or substitution that makes an equation, an inequality, or a system of equations or inequalities true.

Solution set [2.1], [2.6], [8.1]   The set of all solutions of an equation, an inequality, or a system of equations or inequalities.

Solve [2.1], [2.6], [8.1]   To find all solutions of an equation, an inequality, or a system of equations or inequalities; to find the solution(s) of a problem.

Speed [6.7]   The ratio of distance traveled to the time required to travel that distance.

Square matrix [8.7]   A matrix with the same number of rows and columns.

Square root [10.1]   The number c is a square root of a if $c^2 = a$.

Substitute [1.1]   To replace a variable with a number or an expression that represents a number.

Substitution method [8.2]   An algebraic method for solving systems of equations.

Supplementary angles [2.5]   A pair of angles, the sum of whose measure is 180°.

Supply function [8.8]   A function modeling the relationship between the price of a good and the quantity of that good supplied.

System of equations [8.1]   A set of two or more equations that are to be solved simultaneously.

T

Term [1.2], [4.3]   A number, a variable, or a product or a quotient of numbers and/or variables.

Terminating decimal [1.4]   A number in decimal notation that can be written using a finite number of decimal places.

Total cost [8.8]   The amount spent to produce a product.

Total profit [8.8]   The amount taken in less the amount spent, or total revenue minus total cost.

Total revenue [8.8]   The amount taken in from the sale of a product.

Trinomial [4.3]   A polynomial that is composed of three terms.

U

Union of A and B [9.2]   The set of all elements belonging to either A or B or both.

Undefined [1.7]   An expression that has no meaning attached to it.

V

Value [1.1]   The numerical result after a number has been substituted into an expression.

Variable [1.1]   A letter that represents an unknown number.

Variable costs [8.8]   In business, costs that vary according to the amount produced.

Variable expression [1.1]   An expression containing a variable.

Vertex (plural, vertices) [11.6], [13.1], [13.2], [13.3]   The point at which the graph of a parabola, an ellipse, or a hyperbola crosses its axis of symmetry.

Vertical-line test [7.1]   The statement that a graph represents a function if it is impossible to draw a vertical line that intersects the graph more than once.

W

Whole numbers [1.3]   The natural numbers and 0: 0, 1, 2, 3, ...

X

x-intercept [3.3]   A point at which a graph crosses the x-axis.

Y

y-intercept [3.3]   A point at which a graph crosses the y-axis.

Z

Zeros [11.9]   The x-values for which $f(x)$ is 0, for any function f.

Index

A

Abscissa, 151
Absolute value, 35, 71, 941
  on graphing calculator, 35, 71
  inequalities with, 599–602, 626
  problem solving principles with, 600
Absolute-value principle, for equations, 597–599, 626
Addition. *See also* Sum(s)
  associative law for, 15, 69, 943
  commutative law for, 14, 69, 943
  of complex numbers, 689–690
  of fractions, 26, 70
  with least common denominators, 397–398, 399, 437
  with number line, 37–39
  of polynomials, 254–255, 295, 964
  of polynomials in several variables, 282, 296
  of radical expressions, 662–663, 696
  of rational expressions, 981–983
  of rational expressions when denominators are the same, 389, 436
  of real numbers, 37–41, 71, 941
  without number line, 39–40
Addition principle
  for equations, 79–80, 83, 85–87, 139, 947
  for inequalities, 124–125, 126–128, 141, 951
Additive identity, 39, 71
Additive inverses. *See* Opposites
Algebraic expressions, 2–4, 69, 943–945
  associative laws for, 14–16, 69, 943
  commutative laws for, 14, 69, 943
  distributive law for, 16–18, 70, 943, 944
  equivalent, 13–14, 65, 69, 943
  evaluating, 2–4, 69, 943
  factoring. *See* Factoring
  polynomial. *See* Polynomial(s)
  radical. *See* Radical expressions
  rational. *See* Rational expressions
  simplifying, 23, 25, 27, 65
  solving, 65
  terms of, 17, 944
  translating to, 4–5, 69
  value of, 3, 69
  variable expressions, 2–3
Algebraic-graphical connections, 350, 416, 511, 602, 704, 772, 827
And, mathematical use of word, 588
Approximating irrational numbers using graphing calculator, 33
Arithmetic sequences, 902–904, 931
  *n*th term of, 903, 931
  problem solving with, 906–907
  sum of first *n* terms of, 904–905, 931
Arithmetic series, 904, 931

Ascending order of terms of polynomials, 255
Associative laws, 14–16, 69, 943
Asymptotes, 796
  of hyperbolas, 870–871
Average, 133, 991
Axis(es), 151, 152, 218, 955
  of hyperbolas, 870
  numbering, 152–153
  scales of, on graphing calculator, 171
  of symmetry of a parabola, 740, 741, 777

B

Bar graphs, 148–149
Bases (in exponential notation), 60, 72
  like, dividing powers with, 229–230
  like, multiplying powers with, 228–229
Bases, logarithmic. *See* Logarithmic bases
Binomial(s), 246, 247, 295, 964
  finding a specific term of, 927
  multiplication of, 966
  product of two binomials, 269–271, 295
  square of, 966
  squaring, 272–273, 296
Binomial coefficient, 927, 931
Binomial expansion
  using factorial notation, 924–927, 931
  using Pascal's triangle, 922–924
Binomial theorem, 921–927, 931–932
  binomial expansion using factorial notation and, 924–927, 931
  binomial expansion using Pascal's triangle and, 922–924
  form 1 of, 923–924
  form 2 of, 926–927, 932
Boundary, 607, 626
Branches of hyperbolas, 870
Break-even analysis, 561–563, 570
Break-even point, 563, 570

C

Calculator. *See* Graphing calculator
Canceling, 25
Cartesian coordinate plane, 151
Collecting like terms, 41, 63–64, 72, 87–88, 248, 295
Center
  of an ellipse, 863
  of a circle, 857, 889
  of a hyperbola, 870
Center points, 991–993
Change-of-base formula, 819–820
Checking
  of addition and subtraction of rational expressions, 402
  of division of rational expressions, 385–386
  by evaluating, 309

by evaluating polynomials, 266
of factorizations, 309, 310
of polynomial calculations, 258, 266
simplification of rational expressions and, 379
of solutions of inequalities, 125
of solutions of rational equations, 416
undefined rational expressions and, 377
using graphing calculator, 125, 258, 266, 310, 379, 385–386, 402, 416
Circle(s), 857–859, 889
  center of, 857, 889
  circumference of, 95
  equation of, 857, 874, 889
  radius of, 857, 889
Circle graphs, 149–150
Circumference of a circle, 95
Clearing fractions and decimals, 88–90, 139
Closed interval, 123
Coefficients, 81
  binomial, 927, 931
  of terms of polynomials, 247, 294
Collaborative Corner, 13, 20, 68, 93, 109, 158, 184, 269, 288, 319, 345, 388, 435, 483, 537, 545, 587, 596, 649, 676, 748, 766, 803, 844, 869, 921
College as resource, 83
Columns of matrices, 552, 569
Combined variation, 489–490
Combining (collecting) like terms, 41, 63–64, 72, 87–88, 248, 295
Common denominators, finding, 390–394, 437
Common difference, 903
Common factors, 17, 18
  containing variables, 306
  factoring polynomials with, 305–307, 970
  largest, 305–307, 323, 367
  in rational expressions, opposite, 380–381
Common ratio, 910–911, 931
Commutative laws, 14, 69, 943
Complete factorization, 333
Completing the square, 707–710, 775
Complex numbers, 688–692, 697
  addition of, 689–690
  conjugates of, 691–692
  division of, 691–692
  multiplication of, 690
  powers of *i* and, 692
  subtraction of, 689–690
Complex-number system, 688
Complex rational expressions, 405–409, 437, 983–984
  simplifying using division, 406–407, 437, 983–984
  simplifying using multiplication, 407–409, 437, 984

Composite functions, 784–786, 845
Composite numbers, 22, 70
Composition
   of a function, 785, 845
   inverses and, 790–791
Compound inequalities, 587, 592
Compounding interest, 710–711, 834–835, 836–837
Compound-interest formula, 711
Conditional equations, 90, 949
Conic sections, 853–890. *See also* Circle(s); Ellipses; Hyperbolas; Parabolas
   classifying graphs of equations and, 874–876
Conjugates, 663, 696
   of complex numbers, 691–692
Conjunctions of sentences, 588, 625
Connecting the Concepts, 59, 130–131, 206, 216–217, 245, 279, 328–329, 354, 404–405, 418–419, 474, 523–524, 605–606, 617–618, 668–669, 739–740, 824–825, 878, 920
Consecutive integers, 111–112
   even and odd, 112
Consistent systems of equations, 510, 541, 568
Constant(s), 2, 69, 943
   of proportionality, 486, 488
Constant functions, graphs of, 465, 496
Constant polynomials, 964
Constant term
   negative, factoring trinomials of type $x^2 + bx + c$ with, 314–315
   positive, factoring trinomials of type $x^2 + bx + c$ with, 312–314
Constraints, 618
Contradictions, 90, 949
Coordinates, 151–152, 218, 955
Corner principle, 619, 627
Costs
   fixed, 561–562
   total, 561, 562
   variable, 562
Cramer's rule
   for 3×3 matrices, 558–560, 570
   for 2×2 matrices, 557–558, 570
Cube(s)
   differences of, factoring, 974, 975
   factoring sums of, 336–338, 368
   perfect, 651
   sums of, factoring, 974, 975
Cube roots, 336, 637–638, 695
Cubic polynomials, 964
Cylinders, right, circular, surface area of, 96

D

Decay model, exponential, 837–838, 850
Decay rate, exponential, 837, 846
Decimal(s), 31–32, 71
   clearing, 89–90, 139
   irrational numbers, 32, 71
   terminating (repeating), 32, 71, 940
Decimal notation, converting between percent notation and, 100–101, 140
Degree of a polynomial, 247, 294, 963
   of polynomials in several variables, 281
Degrees of terms (of polynomials), 247, 294, 963

Denominators, 22, 23
   common, finding, 390–394, 437
   least common. *See* Least common denominators (LCDs)
   with one term, rationalizing, 658–660, 696
   opposite, rational expressions with, 400–402
   in rational expressions, 376, 377, 436
   with two terms, rationalizing, 663–664, 696
Dependent systems of equations, 511, 542–543, 568
Descartes, René, 151
Descending order of terms of polynomials, 248
Determinants of matrices, 556–557
Differences. *See also* Subtraction
   common, 903
   of cubes, factoring, 336–338, 368, 974, 975
   of functions, 475–477, 497
   of squares. *See* Differences of squares
   of two functions, 475–477, 497
   of two terms, multiplication of, 271, 295
Differences of squares, 966
   factoring, 332–333, 338, 368, 974, 975
   recognizing, 331–332
Dimensions of viewing window, 150
Direct variation, 486–487, 497
Discriminant, 720–722, 776
Disjunctions of sentences, 590–592, 626
Distance equation, 530
Distance formula, 681–682, 697. *See also* Motion problems
Distributive law, 16–18, 41, 70, 72, 943, 944
   combining (collecting) like terms, 41, 63–64, 72, 87–88, 248, 295
   factoring and, 17–18, 70
Division. *See also* Quotient(s)
   of complex numbers, 691–692
   of fractions, 23–24, 70
   involving zero, 53, 55–56, 72, 942
   of a polynomial by a binomial, 290–292, 296
   of a polynomial by a monomial, 289–290, 296
   of polynomials, 967–968
   of powers with like bases, 229–230
   of rational expressions, 384–386, 436, 979–980
   of rational terms with different indices, 664–666, 696
   of real numbers, 53–56, 72, 941
   scientific notation and, 240–241
   simplifying complex rational expressions using, 406–407, 437, 983–984
   simplifying radical expressions by, 656–657, 695
   synthetic, 998–1001
   by zero, 942
Domain(s), 625
   of a function. *See* Domain of a function
   interval notation and, 592–593
Domain of a function, 444, 445, 496
   determining, 455–459, 479, 496
   finding using inequalities, 580–581, 625
   graphs and, 477–480

   of linear functions, 466
   restrictions on, 459–460
Doubling time, 834–835, 846

E

e, 818–819
Elements of a set, 994, 995
Elimination method
   with matrices, 552–555, 569
   for solving systems of equations, 517–520, 521, 568
Ellipses, 863–867
   centered at (h, k), 865–866, 874, 889
   centered at the origin, 863–865, 874, 889
   center of, 863
   equations of, 863, 866, 874, 889
   foci of, 863
   graphing using a and b, 864
Endpoints, 457
Equality
   exponential, principle of, 825–826, 826
   words indicating, 6
Equations, 6, 69, 940
   with absolute value, 597–599, 626
   addition principle for, 79–80, 83, 85–87, 139, 947
   of an ellipse centered at $(0, 0)$, 863, 889
   of an ellipse centered at (h, k), 866, 889
   of a circle, 857, 874, 889
   conditional, 90, 949
   distance, 530
   equivalent, 79, 139, 806, 947
   exponential. *See* Exponential equations
   fraction. *See* Rational equations
   function notation and, 447–449
   of a hyperbola centered at the origin, 870, 890
   of a hyperbola in nonstandard from, 872–873
   linear. *See* Linear equations
   of lines, 464
   multiplication principle for, 81–82, 83, 85–87, 139, 947
   nonlinear. *See* Nonlinear systems of equations
   of a parabola, 855, 874, 889
   in point–slope form, 207–208, 219
   polynomial. *See* Polynomial equations
   quadratic. *See* Quadratic equations
   in quadratic form, 732–734, 776
   radical. *See* Radical equations
   rate, 530
   rational. *See* Rational equations
   in slope–intercept form, 198–199, 219
   solution of, 944
   solutions of, 6, 69, 78–79, 139, 158–159
   solving, 78, 90, 947–949
   systems of. *See* Nonlinear systems of equations; Systems of equations; Systems of equations in three variables; Systems of equations in two variables
   time, 530
   translating to, 6–7, 69
   writing from solutions, 722–723
   with x and y interchanged, 798–799
Equilibrium point, 564–565, 570
Equivalent equations, 79, 139, 806, 947

Equivalent expressions, 13–14, 65, 69
Equivalent inequalities, 124, 950
Estimations using two points, 210–211
Evaluating the expression, 2–4, 69
Evaluation
    of algebraic expressions, 2–4, 69
    checking factorizations by, 309
    checking polynomial calculations
        using, 266
    of formulas, 93–94
    of polynomials, 249–250, 266
    of polynomials in several variables,
        280, 283
Even integers, consecutive, 112
Even roots, 638–639, 695
Exponent(s), 60, 72, 228–233, 962–968.
        See also Power(s)
    definitions of, 233
    dividing powers with like bases,
        229–230
    laws of, rational exponents and,
        645–646
    logarithms as, 805
    multiplying powers with like bases,
        228–229
    negative, 236–239, 294, 962
    one as, 294
    power rule for, 962, 963
    product rule for, 962, 963
    properties of, 233, 962–963
    quotient rule for, 962, 963
    raising a power to a power and, 231, 233
    raising a product to a power and, 232,
        233, 962, 963
    raising a quotient to a power and,
        232–233, 233, 962, 963
    rational. *See* Rational exponents
    zero, 962
    zero as, 230–231, 294
Exponential decay model, 837–838, 850
Exponential decay rate, 837, 846
Exponential equality, principle of, 807,
        825–826, 826, 846
Exponential equations
    applications of, 834–838
    rewriting as logarithmic equations, 806
    solving, 825–827, 846
Exponential functions, 795–800, 845
    applications of, 799–800
    base e, graphs of, 820–821
    equations with x and y interchanged
        and, 798–799
    graphing, 795–798
    solving, 827–829, 846
Exponential growth model, 834–837, 846
Exponential growth rate, 834, 846
Exponential notation, 60–61, 72. *See also*
        Bases (in exponential notation)
Expressions. *See* Algebraic expressions;
        Polynomial(s); Radical expressions;
        Rational expressions
Extrapolation, 210–211

F

Factor(s), 17
    common. *See* Common factors
    negative exponents and, 238, 294
    opposite, rational expressions with,
        380–381

products and. *See* Exponential notation;
        Power(s)
    solving polynomial inequalities using,
        769
    terms contrasted with, 18
Factorial notation, 924–927, 931
Factoring, 303–369, 943
    checking by evaluating, 405
    choosing method for, 340–343, 368
    common factors and. *See* Common
        factors
    completely, 333
    definition of, 304, 367
    of differences of cubes, 336–338, 368,
        974, 975
    of differences of squares, 332–333, 338,
        368, 974, 975
    distributive law and, 17–18, 70
    with FOIL, 320–324, 367
    general strategy for, 340–343, 368
    by grouping, 307–309, 325–326, 367,
        970–971
    of monomials, 304
    of perfect-square trinomials, 329–331,
        368, 974, 975
    of prime polynomials, 316
    solving polynomial equations by,
        345–351, 975–977
    solving quadratic equations by, 368,
        975–977
    of sums of cubes, 336–338, 368, 974,
        975
    tips for, 307, 334
    of trinomials. *See* Factoring trinomials
    when terms have a common factor,
        305–307
Factoring trinomials, 971–974
    of trinomials of type $ax^2 + bx + c$,
        320–326, 367
    of trinomials of type $x^2 + bx + c$,
        312–317, 367
Factorizations, 18, 70
    checking, 310
    of a polynomial, 304
    prime, 22, 70
False inequalities, 125–126
Feasible region, 620
Finite sequences, 896, 931
Finite series, 898
First coordinate, 151, 955
Fixed costs, 561–562
Foci of ellipses, 863
FOIL method, 270–271, 295, 966
    factoring trinomials of type
        $ax^2 + bx + c$, 320–324, 367, 972–973
    reverse, 312–314, 367
Formulas, 93–96, 139, 484–486, 949
    change-of-base, 819–820
    compound-interest, 711
    distance, 681–682, 697. *See also* Motion
        problems
    evaluating, 93–94
    for factoring sums or differences of
        cubes, 336–338, 368
    graphing, 789–790
    for inverses, finding, 788–789, 845
    midpoint, 682, 697
    quadratic. *See* Quadratic formula
    solving for a variable, 94–96

Fraction(s). *See also* Denominators;
        Numerators; Rational expressions
    addition of, 26, 70
    clearing, 88–89, 139
    division of, 23–24, 70
    multiplication of, 23, 70
    subtraction of, 26, 70
Fraction equations. *See* Rational equations
Fraction notation, 22–23, 70
    with graphing calculator, 27
    for one, 22–23, 70
Function(s), 443–498
    composite, 784–786, 845
    composition of, 785, 845
    constant, graphs of, 465, 496
    correspondences and, 444–445
    definition of, 444, 445, 496
    difference of, 475–477, 497
    domain of. *See* Domain of a function
    exponential. *See* Exponential functions
    graphing, 445–447, 464–468, 496–497,
        789–790
    inverse. *See* Inverse functions
    linear, graphs of, 464, 496
    logarithmic. *See* Logarithmic functions
    nonlinear, graphs of, 467–468, 497
    objective, 618–619, 627
    one-to-one, 786–788, 845
    piecewise defined, 460
    polynomial, 467, 468
    product of, 475–477, 497
    quadratic. *See* Quadratic functions
    quotient of, 475–477, 497
    range of. *See* Range of a function
    rational, graphs of, 467, 468
    sum of, 475–477, 497
    zeros of, 768, 777
Function notation, 447–450
    applications using, 449–450

G

General term of a sequence, 897–898
Geometric sequences, 910–912, 931
    common ratio and, 910–911, 931
    problem solving with, 914–917
    sum of first n terms of, 912, 931
Geometric series, 912–913, 931
    infinite, 913–914
    problem solving with, 914–917
Grade, 189–190
Graphing calculator
    absolute-value functions using, 602
    absolute value on, 35, 71
    absolute-value signs and, 636
    approximating irrational numbers
        using, 33
    checking addition and subtraction of
        rational expressions using, 402
    checking division of rational
        expressions using, 385–386
    checking factorization using, 310
    checking polynomial addition or
        subtraction using, 258
    checking polynomial multiplication
        using, 266
    checking simplification of rational
        expressions using, 379
    checking solutions of inequalities
        using, 125

Graphing calculator (*continued*)
    checking solutions of rational
        equations using, 416
    common logarithms using, 817–818
    completing the square using, 709
    with complex rational expressions, 409
    composite functions and, 786
    cube and higher roots using, 639
    domains of functions using, 480
    equations that are translations of each
        other and, 798
    evaluating determinants of a matrix
        using, 559
    evaluating polynomials using, 249–250,
        283
    exponential functions using, 797
    fitting quadratic functions to data
        using, 759
    fraction notation using, 27
    functions using, 458
    function values and, 799
    graphing equations simultaneously, 201
    graphing the equation for a circle and,
        859
    hyperbolas using, 874
    inequalities using, 580, 610
    intercepts on, 171
    INTERSECT option of, 510, 829
    inverses and, 791, 805
    keypad of, 7
    linear equations using, 164
    logarithmic functions with bases other
        than 10 or *e* and, 821
    mathematical sketches and, 677
    menu of, 27
    natural logarithms using, 818–819
    negative number and subtraction keys
        on, 46
    nonlinear functions using, 468
    number *e* and, 818
    parentheses using, 61, 817
    PRB option of, 925
    quadratic formulas using, 717, 723, 741,
        743, 744
    radical expressions using, 635
    rational exponents using, 644
    rational expressions and, 377
    remainder theorem and, 1001
    row-equivalent operations using, 555
    scales of axes on, 171
    scientific notation using, 241
    screen of, 7
    second division by same number
        using, 94
    sequences using, 897
    simplification of radical expressions
        using, 646, 652
    solving polynomial equations using, 351
    solving polynomial inequalities
        using, 770
    solving quadratic equations using,
        712, 718
    solving radical equations using, 671
    studying together by phone and, 688
    systems of inequalities using, 612
    systems of nonlinear equations and,
        881, 882
    TABLE feature of, 88
    tables of values using, 757

    user's manual for, 795
    viewing window of, 150
    zooming with, 171
Graphs and graphing, 147–219, 151, 218
    algebraic-graphical connection and,
        350, 416
    axes of, 151, 152, 153, 218
    bar, 148–149
    circle, 149–150
    of constant functions, 465, 496
    domains of functions and, 477–480
    of ellipses using *a* and *b*, 864–865
    of exponential functions, base *e*,
        820–821
    functions and, 445–447
    of functions and their inverses, 789–790
    of horizontal or vertical lines,
        171–173, 218
    of inequalities, 122, 578, 949
    intercepts and, 168–173, 218
    line, 150
    of linear equations, 159–164, 218
    of linear functions, 464, 496
    of linear inequalities, 606–610, 626–627
    of logarithmic functions, 803–806
    of logarithmic functions, base *e*,
        820–821
    of nonlinear functions, 467–468, 497
    numbering axes of, 152–153
    ordered pairs and, 151–152, 218, 955
    origin of, 151, 218
    of a parabola, 856–857
    points in, 151, 955
    point-slope form and, 209–210, 219
    of polynomial functions, 467, 468
    quadrants of, 153, 218
    of quadratic functions. *See* Parabolas
    of rational functions, 467, 468
    slope and, 956–957
    slope–intercept form and, 199–201, 219
    solving systems of equations by, 508–511
Greater than or equal to symbol (≥), 34
Greater than symbol (>), 34, 71
Grouping, factoring by, 307–309, 325–326,
    367, 970–971, 974
Grouping symbols
    order of operations and, 61–63, 72
    parentheses to replace, on graphing
        calculator, 61
    simplifying and, 63–64
Growth model, exponential, 834–837, 846
Growth rate, exponential, 834, 846

H

Half-life, 837, 846
Half-open interval, 123
Half-planes, 607, 626
Horizontal hyperbolas, 874
Horizontal lines, 959
    graphing, 171–173, 218
    slope of, 189, 219
Horizontal-line test, 787, 845
Horizontal parabolas, 874
Hyperbolas, 870–876, 890
    asymptotes of, 870–871
    axis of, 870
    branches of, 870
    centered at the origin, equation of,
        870, 890

    center of, 870
    equations of, 874
    horizontal, 874
    in nonstandard form, equation of,
        872–873
    vertical, 874
    vertices of, 870
Hypotenuse of a right triangle, 358–360,
    369, 676–678, 696, 976–977

I

i, 688. *See also* Complex numbers
    powers of, 692
Identity(ies), 90, 949
    additive, 39, 71
    multiplicative, 24, 70
Identity property of one, 24, 70, 943
Identity property of zero, 39, 71, 943
Imaginary numbers, 688–689
    pure, 689
Inconsistent systems of equations, 510,
    541–542, 543, 568
Index(ices), 638
    different, multiplying or dividing terms
        with, 664–666, 696
Inequalities, 121–128, 141, 578–593, 940
    with absolute value, 599–602, 626
    addition principle for, 124–125,
        126–128, 141, 951
    compound, 587, 592
    domain and, 625
    equivalent, 124, 950
    false, 125–126
    finding domain of a radical function
        using, 580–581, 625
    graphical solutions of, 578–580, 625
    graphs of, 122, 949
    interval notation for solutions of, 123,
        141
    linear. *See* Linear inequalities
    multiplication principle for, 125–126,
        126–128, 141, 951–952
    polynomial, 766–770, 777
    problem solving using, 581–582
    quadratic, 766–770, 777
    rational, 770–772, 777
    solution set of, 578, 625
    solutions of, 121–122, 578
    solving, 578, 949–950
    solving applications with, 132–133, 141
    in two variables, 606–612, 626
Infinite geometric series, 913–914
    limit of, 914, 931
Infinite sequences, 896, 931
Infinite series, 898
Infinity symbols, 123
Instructor as resource, 83
Integers, 29–30, 71
    consecutive, 111–112
    negative, as exponents, 236–239, 294
    odd, consecutive, 112
    sets of, 30
Intercepts, 168–173, 218, 957
    finding, 169–171, 218
    with graphing calculator, 171
Interest, compounding, 710–711, 834–835,
    836–837
Interpolation, 210–211
Intersections of sets, 587–590, 625, 996

Interval(s)
  closed, 123
  half-open, 123
  open, 123
Interval notation, 123, 141, 592–593, 950
Inverse(s). *See* Opposites; Reciprocals
Inverse functions
  composition and, 790–791
  visualizing, 789
Inverse relations, 787–788
  finding formulas for, 788–789, 845
Inverse variation, 487–489, 497
Irrational numbers, 32, 71, 635, 940. *See also* Real numbers
Isosceles right triangles, 678–679, 680, 697

J

Joint variation, 489–490, 498

K

Keypad of graphing calculator, 7

L

Largest common factors, 305–307, 323, 367
Law of opposites, 45, 943
Laws of exponents, rational exponents and, 645–646
Leading coefficient, 247, 294, 963
Leading term, 963
Least common denominators (LCDs), 981–983
  addition with, 397–398, 399, 437
  finding, 390–394, 437
  simplifying complex rational expressions by multiplying by, 407–409, 437, 984
  subtraction with, 397, 398, 399–400, 437
Least common multiple (LCM), 390–391, 393–394, 437, 981–983
Legs of a right triangle, 358–360, 369, 676–678, 696, 976–977
Less than or equal to symbol ($\leq$), 34
Less than symbol ($<$), 34, 71
Like radicals, 662, 696
Like terms, 944
  combining (collecting). *See* Combining (collecting) like terms
  polynomials in several variables with, 281
Limit of an infinite geometric series, 914, 931
Line(s)
  equations of, 464
  graphing using y-intercept and slope, 197
  horizontal, 959
  parallel, 201, 219, 960
  perpendicular, 201–202, 220, 960
  vertical, 959
Linear equations, 956, 957–960
  applications using, 163–164
  graphing, 159–164, 218
  in one variable, 173
  point-slope form of, 959–960
  slope-intercept form of, 957–959
  in three variables, 537–538
Linear functions
  domain of, 466
  graphs of, 464, 496
  range of, 466

Linear inequalities
  graphs of, 607–610, 626–627
  systems of, 610–612
Linear polynomials, 964
Linear programming, 619–622, 627
Line graphs, 150
Log, meaning of, 817
Logarithm(s)
  of base to an exponent, 814
  common, on calculator, 817–818
  as exponents, 805
  natural (Napierian), on calculator, 818–819
  power rule for, 811, 812–815, 846
  of powers, 811, 812–815, 846
  product rule for, 810–811, 812–815, 846
  of products, 810–811, 812–815
  quotient rule for, 811–815, 846
  of quotients, 811–815, 846
  using properties together and, 812–815
Logarithmic bases
  change-of-base formula and, 819–820
  changing, 819–820
  e, 818–819
  of logarithmic functions, 804, 808
Logarithmic equations
  applications of, 832–833
  rewriting as exponential equations, 806
Logarithmic functions, 803–808, 810–815, 845
  base a, 804, 808
  base e, graphs of, 820–821
  equivalent equations and, 806
  graphs of, 803–806
  principle of exponential equality and, 807
  solving, 807–808
$\log_a x$, 804, 845

M

Matrices, 552–554, 569
  columns of, 552, 569
  Cramer's rule for 2×2 matrices and, 557–558, 570
  Cramer's rule for 3×3 matrices and, 558–560, 570
  determinants of, 556–557
  row-equivalent, 554
  row-equivalent operations and, 554–555, 569
  rows of, 552, 569
  square, 556
  systems using, 552–554
  2×2, determinants of, 556–557, 570
Maximum of a parabola, 743, 777
Maximum problems with quadratic functions, 756–758, 777
Mean, 133, 991
Measures of central tendency, 991–993
Median, 992
Menu of graphing calculator, 27
Midpoint formula, 682, 697
Minimum of a parabola, 743, 777
Minimum problems with quadratic functions, 756–758, 777
Mixture problems with systems of equations, 525–529, 568
Mode, 992–993

Monomials, 246, 247, 295, 964
  division of a polynomial by, 289–290, 296
  factoring, 304, 367
  multiplication of, 262
  multiplication with polynomials, 263
Motion problems
  with rational equations, 422–424, 438, 987
  with systems of equations, 530–532, 568
Multiplication. *See also* Product(s)
  associative law for, 15, 16, 69, 943
  of binomials, 966
  commutative law for, 14, 69, 943
  of complex numbers, 690
  of fractions, 23, 70
  of monomials, 262
  of monomials with polynomials, 263
  of polynomials, 262–266, 295, 965–966
  of polynomials in several variables, 282–283, 296
  of powers with like bases, 228–229
  of radical expressions, 650–651, 695
  of rational expressions, 383–384, 436, 979–980
  of rational terms with different indices, 664–666, 696
  of real numbers, 51–53, 72, 941
  scientific notation and, 240–241
  simplifying complex rational expressions using, 407–409, 437, 984
  simplifying radical expressions using, 653, 695
  of sums and differences of two terms, 271, 295
  of two polynomials, 264–266, 274
Multiplication principle
  for equations, 81–82, 83, 85–87, 139, 947
  for inequalities, 125–126, 126–128, 141, 951–952
Multiplicative identity, 24, 70
Multiplicative inverses. *See* Reciprocals
Multiplicative property of zero, 52, 943

N

Napierian logarithms, 818–819
Natural logarithms on calculator, 818–819
Natural numbers, 21–22, 70
Negative constant term, factoring trinomials of type $x^2 + bx + c$ with, 314–315
Negative exponents, 962
  factors and, 238, 294
  reciprocals and, 238–239, 294
Negative integers as exponents, 236–239, 294
Negative numbers
  with graphing calculator, 46
  product of, 52–53
  product of positive number and, 51–52
Negative one, property of, 943
Negative rational exponents, 644–645, 695
Negative sign, 45
Nonlinear functions, graphs of, 467–468, 497
Nonlinear systems of equations, 879–884, 890
  of one nonlinear equation, 879–881
  problem solving with, 883–884
  of two nonlinear equations, 881–883

Notation
decimal, converting between percent notation and, 100–101, 140
exponential, 60–61, 72
factorial, 924–927, 931
fraction, 22–23, 70
function, 447–450
interval, 123, 141, 592–593, 950
percent. *See* Percent notation
roster, 995
scientific. *See* Scientific notation
set-builder, 123, 141, 950, 995
sigma (summation), 899–900, 931
nth powers, perfect, 651
nth roots, odd and even, 638–639, 695
Number(s)
absolute value of, 35, 71
complex. *See* Complex numbers
composite, 22, 70
consecutive odd integers, 112
e, 818–819
i, 688. *See also* Complex numbers
imaginary, 688–689
integers, 29–30, 71
irrational, 32, 71, 635. *See also* Real numbers
natural, 21–22, 70
negative. *See* Negative numbers
opposites of. *See* Opposites
positive, product of negative number and, 51–52
prime, 21–22, 70
rational, 31–32, 71. *See also* Rational exponents; Real numbers
real. *See* Real numbers
sets of. *See* Set(s)
whole, 21, 70
Number line
addition with, 37–39
real numbers on, 33–34, 940
Numerators, 22
with one term, rationalizing, 658–660, 696
with two terms, rationalizing, 663–664, 696

O
Objective function, 618–619, 627
Odd integers, consecutive, 112
Odd roots, 638–639, 695
One
as an exponent, 294
fraction notation for, 22–23, 70
identity property of, 24, 70, 943
negative, property of, 943
One-to-one functions, 786–788, 845
Open interval, 123
Operations, order of, 61–63, 72, 942
Opposites, 30, 43–45, 71
addition principle for equations and, 80
law of, 45, 943
of numbers, 30
opposites of, 44
of a polynomial, 255–257, 964–965
rational expressions with opposite denominators, 400–402
reciprocals contrasted with, 56
and subtraction, 45–47, 72
of sums, 64–65, 72, 943

Or, mathematical use of word, 591, 626
Ordered pairs, 151–152, 218, 955
Order of operations, 61–63, 72, 942
Ordinate, 151
Origin, 151, 218, 955

P
Pairs, ordered, 151–152, 218, 955
Parabolas, 467, 468, 704, 740–745, 749–752, 777, 854–857, 889
axis of symmetry of, 740, 741, 777
completing the square and, 749–752
equation of, 855, 874, 889
graphing, 856–857
horizontal, 874
minimum and maximum values of, 743, 777
reflections of, 741
translation of, 743
vertex of, 740, 741, 751, 777, 855
vertical, 874
Parallel lines, 201, 219, 960
slope of, 219
Parentheses
with complex rational expressions, 409
graphing calculator to replace grouping symbols on, 61
order of operations and, 61–62, 72
Pascal's triangle, 922–924
Percent notation, 100–104, 140
converting between decimal notation and, 100–101, 140
solving problems, 101–104
translations using, 102–104, 140
Perfect cubes, 651
Perfect nth powers, 651
Perfect squares, 651
Perfect-square trinomials, 272, 296
factoring, 329–331, 368, 974, 975
recognizing, 329–330
Perpendicular lines, 201–202, 220, 960
slope of, 220
Phrases, translating to algebraic expressions, 4–5, 69
Piecewise defined functions, 460
Pie charts, 149–150
Plotting, 151, 218. *See also* Graphs and graphing
Point(s), graphing and, 955
Point-slope form, 207–211, 210–211, 220, 959–960
equations in, 207–208, 220
graphing and, 209–210, 220
Polynomial(s), 246–296, 963–964
addition of, 254–255, 295, 964
checking by evaluating, 266
coefficients of, 247, 294
combining (collecting) like terms of, 248, 295
constant, 964
cubic, 964
definition of, 246, 247, 294
degree of, 247, 294, 963
degrees of terms of. *See* Degrees of terms (of polynomials)
division by a binomial, 290–292, 296
division by a monomial, 289–290, 296
division of, 967–968
evaluating, 249–250

factoring. *See* Factoring
factorizations of, 304
linear, 964
multiplication of, 262–266, 295, 965–966
multiplication of two polynomials, 264–266, 274
multiplication with monomials, 263
opposites of, 255–257, 964–965
prime, 316, 971
problem solving with, 257–258
quadratic, 964
quotients of. *See* Rational expressions in several variables. *See* Polynomials in several variables
subtraction of, 256–257, 295, 964–965
terms of. *See* Terms of a polynomial
types of, 246–247
Polynomial equations
principle of zero products and, 346–347, 368, 976
solving by factoring, 345–350, 975–977
solving using graphing calculator, 351
Polynomial functions, graphs of, 467, 468
Polynomial inequalities, 766–770, 777
Polynomials in several variables, 280–283, 296
addition of, 282, 296
evaluating, 280
with like terms and degree, 281, 296
multiplication of, 282–283, 296
subtraction of, 282, 296
Positive constant term, factoring trinomials of type $x^2 + bx + c$ with, 312–314
Positive numbers, product of negative number and, 51–52
Positive rational exponents, 643–644, 695
Positive sign, 45
Power(s), 60. *See also* Exponent(s); Exponential *entries*
Exponential notation, 942
of i, 692
logarithms of, 811, 812–815, 846
principle of, 669–671, 696
Power rule, 231, 233
for exponents, 962, 963
for logarithms, 811, 812–815, 846
Predictions using two points, 209–211
Prime factorization, 22, 70
Prime numbers, 21–22, 70
Prime polynomials, 316, 971
Principal square root, 634–635, 695
Principle of exponential equality, 807, 825–826, 826, 846
Principle of powers, 669–671, 696
Principle of square roots, 677, 705–707, 775
Principle of zero products, 346–347, 368, 976
Problem solving
with absolute value, 600
with addition of real numbers, 40
with arithmetic sequences, 906–907
with geometric sequences, 914–917
with geometric series, 914–917
with nonlinear systems of equations, 883–884
with percent problems, 101–104
with polynomials, 257–258
with quadratic equations, 710–712, 725–727

steps for, 110–116, 140, 952–953
with subtraction of real numbers, 47–48
tips for, 116
using inequalities, 581–582
Product(s). *See also* Multiplication
with factors the same. *See* Exponential
notation; Power(s)
logarithms of, 810–811, 812–815, 846
of a monomial and a polynomial, 263
of negative number and positive
number, 51–52
raising to a power, 232, 233, 962, 963
of sum and difference of same two
terms, 966
of two binomials, 269–271, 295
of two functions, 475–477, 497
of two negative numbers, 52–53
of two or more radical terms, 663, 696
of two polynomials, 264–266
zero, principle of, 346–347, 368, 976
Product rule, 228, 233
for exponents, 962, 963
for logarithms, 810–811, 812–815, 846
Profit, total, 561
Progressions. *See* Sequences
Proportion(s), definition of, 425
Proportion problems with rational
equations, 425–428, 438, 987–988
Pure imaginary numbers, 689
Pythagorean theorem, 358–360, 369,
676–678, 696, 976–977

Q

Quadrants, 153, 218, 955
Quadratic equations, 704–712, 775
applications using, 354–359
completing the square and, 707–710, 775
definition of, 345
principle of square roots and, 705–707,
775
principle of zero products and, 368
problem solving with, 710–712, 725–727
solving by factoring, 368, 975–977
solving formulas and, 727–729
standard form of, 704, 775
Quadratic formula, 715–718, 776
approximating solutions for, 718
discriminant and, 720–722, 776
writing equations from solutions and,
722–723
Quadratic functions, 467, 468, 716
fitting to data, 758–759
graphs of, 467, 468, 740–745
minimum and maximum problems
with, 756–758, 777
Quadratic inequalities, 766–770, 777
Quadratic polynomials, 964
Quartic polynomials, 964
Quotient(s). *See also* Division
logarithms of, 811–815, 846
of polynomials. *See* Rational
expressions
raising to a power, 232–233, 233, 962, 963
of two functions, 475–477, 497
of two or more radical terms, 663, 696
Quotient rule, 229, 233
for exponents, 962, 963
for logarithms, 811–815, 846

R

Radical(s), like, 662, 696
Radical equations
principle of powers and, 669–671, 696
reducible to quadratic, 734–737
with two radical terms, 672–673, 696
Radical expressions, 635, 695
addition of, 662–663, 696
dividing and simplifying, 656–657, 695
of form $\sqrt{a^2}$, 636–637, 695
multiplying, 650–651, 695
multiplying and simplifying, 653, 695
rationalizing denominators or
numerators with one term and,
658–660, 696
simplifying by factoring, 651–653, 695
subtraction of, 662–663, 696
Radical functions, finding domain using
inequalities, 580–581, 625
Radical sign, 634
Radical terms
with differing indices, multiplying and
dividing, 664–666, 696
products or quotients of two or more
radical terms and, 663, 696
solving equations with two or more
radical terms and, 672–673, 696
Radicands, 635, 695
simplifying, 636–637
Radius of a circle, 857, 889
Range of a function, 444, 445, 496
determining, 455–459, 496
of linear functions, 466
Rate(s), 176–179, 219
of change, 166–177
slope and, 185–188
visualizing, 177–179
Rate equation, 530
Ratio(s), 987–988
common, 910–911, 931
Rational equations
applications using, 419–426, 438
definition of, 411, 438
reducible to quadratic, 734–737
solving, 411–416, 438, 985–988
solving for a specified variable, 486
Rational exponents, 643–646, 695
laws of exponents and, 645–646
negative, 644–645, 695
positive, 643–644, 695
simplifying rational expressions
and, 646
Rational expressions, 375–411, 436
addition of, 981–983
addition when denominators are the
same, 389, 436
checking addition and subtraction of,
402
complex. *See* Complex rational
expressions
definition of, 376, 436
denominators of, 376, 377, 436
division of, 384–386, 436, 979–980
with factors that are opposites, 380–381
least common denominators of. *See*
least common denominators (LCDs)
multiplication of, 383–384, 436, 979–980
with opposite denominators, 400–402

simplifying, 377–380, 436, 646
subtraction of, 981–983
subtraction when denominators are the
same, 390, 436
undefined, 376–377
Rational functions, graphs of, 467, 468
Rational inequalities, 770–772, 777
Rationalization of denominators or
numerators with two terms,
663–664, 696
Rational numbers, 31–32, 71. *See also*
Decimal(s); Fraction(s); Integers; Real
numbers
as exponents. *See* Rational exponents
Ratios, 425
Real numbers, 33–34, 71, 940–943
addition of, 37–41, 71, 941
division of, 53–56, 72, 941
multiplication of, 51–53, 72, 941
on number line, 33–34, 940
set of, 33
as square roots, 625
subtraction of, 43–48, 941
Real-number system, 33
Reciprocals, 23, 25
multiplication principle for equations
and, 81
negative exponents and, 238–239, 294
opposites contrasted with, 56
Reflections of parabolas, 741
Relations, 445
Remainder theorem, 1001
Repeating decimals, 32, 71, 940
Revenue, total, 561
Right triangles, 358–360, 369, 676–678,
696, 976–977
isosceles, 678–679, 680, 697
Roots. *See also* Radical expressions;
Square roots
cube, 637–638, 695
even, 638–639, 695
nth, odd and even, 638–639, 695
odd, 638–639, 695
square. *See* Square roots
Roster notation, 995
Row-equivalent operations,
554–555, 569
Rows of matrices, 552, 569

S

Scientific notation, 239–240, 294
division using, 240–241
with graphing calculator, 241
multiplication using, 240–241
Screen of graphing calculator, 7
Second coordinate, 151, 955
Sequences, 896–897
arithmetic. *See* Arithmetic sequences
finite, 896, 931
general term of, 897–898
infinite, 896, 931
series and. *See* Series
sum of terms of. *See* Series
Series, 898, 931
arithmetic, 904, 931
finite, 898
geometric. *See* Geometric series
infinite, 898

Set(s), 29, 71, 994–997
  elements (members) of, 994, 995
  of integers, 30
  intersections of, 587–590, 626, 996
  naming, 995
  of rational numbers, 31
  of real numbers, 33
  subsets and, 995–996
  unions of, 590–592, 626, 996–997
Set-builder notation, 123, 141, 950, 995
Sigma notation, 899–900, 931
Similar terms, combining (collecting), 41,
    63–64, 72, 87–88, 248, 295
Similar triangles, 425, 438
Simplification, 23, 25, 27
  by canceling, 25
  of complex rational expressions using
      division, 406–407, 437
  of complex rational expressions using
      multiplication, 407–409, 437
  of radical expressions, by dividing and
      simplifying, 656–657, 695
  of radical expressions, by factoring,
      651–653, 695
  of radical expressions, by multiplying
      and simplifying, 653, 695
  of a radicand, 636–637
  of rational expressions, 377–380, 436, 646
  solving expressions contrasted with, 65
Slope, 185–190, 219, 956–957
  applications using, 189–190
  graphing a line using y-intercept and, 197
  of a horizontal line, 189, 219
  point-slope form and, 207–211, 219
  rate and, 185–188
  of a vertical line, 189, 219
Slope–intercept form, 196–201, 219,
    957–959
  equations in, 198–199, 219
  graphing and, 199–201, 219
Solutions
  of an equation, 6, 69, 78–79, 139,
      158–159
  of an inequality, 121–122
  of a system of two equations in two
      variables, 508
Square(s)
  of a binomial, 272–273, 296, 966
  completing, 707–710, 775
  differences of. See Differences of
      squares
  factoring differences of, 974, 975
  perfect, 651
  perfect-square trinomials and, 272, 296,
      329–331, 368
Square matrices, 556
Square roots, 634–636, 695. See also
    Radical equations; Radical
    expressions
  principal, 634–635, 695
  principle of, 677, 705–707, 775
  real numbers as, 625
Standard form
  of the equation of a circle, 858
  of the equation of an ellipse centered at
      (h, k), 866
  of the equation of an ellipse centered at
      the origin, 863
  of a linear equation in three variables, 537
  of a quadratic equation, 704, 775

Standard viewing window of graphing
    calculator, 150
Study skills
  abbreviations and, 825
  asking questions in class and, 507
  avoiding overconfidence and, 643
  checking for accuracy and, 552
  extra-credit projects and, 650
  fall in success rate and, 527
  helping classmates and, 539
  highlighting and, 557
  instructor errors and, 656
  keeping math relevant and, 545
  learning from mistakes and, 516
  listening for announcement of topics
      that will be covered on final exam
      and, 870
  maintaining effort and, 855
  making notes in textbooks and, 607
  missed classes and, 618
  music while studying and, 711
  planning future courses and, 669
  preparation and, 740
  preparing for final exam and, 634, 863,
      879, 896, 902, 922
  reading ahead and, 561
  reasonableness of answers and, 817
  reviewing graded final and, 910
  reviewing material and, 662
  reviewing mistakes and, 597
  reviewing previous course materials
      and, 720
  rewriting equations or sentences and, 803
  rewriting problems and, 749
  second book as resource and, 589
  sleep and, 124, 756, 902
  sorting problems by type and, 832
  speed of studying and, 810
  subsections and, 784
  summarizing and, 879
  time for studying and, 726
  time management and, 771, 922
  using new words or phrases, 732
  visualizing the steps, 486
Subsets, 995–996
Substitution method, 943
  for solving systems of equations,
      516–517, 521, 568
Subtraction. See also Differences
  of complex numbers, 689–690
  of fractions, 26, 70
  with graphing calculator, 46
  with least common denominators, 397,
      398, 399–400, 437
  opposites and, 45–47, 72
  of polynomials, 256–257, 295, 964–965
  of polynomials in several variables,
      282, 296
  of radical expressions, 662–663, 696
  of rational expressions, 981–983
  of rational expressions when
      denominators are the same, 390, 436
  of real numbers, 43–48, 941
Sum(s). See also Addition
  of cubes, factoring, 336–338, 368, 974, 975
  opposites of, 64–65, 72, 943
  partial, of terms of a sequence, 898
  of terms of a sequence. See Series
  of two functions, 475–477, 497
  of two terms, multiplication of, 271, 295

Summation notation, 899–900, 931
Supply and demand problems, 564–565,
    570
Synthetic division, 998–1001
  remainder theorem and, 1001
Systems of equations
  consistent, 510, 541, 542, 543, 568
  dependency, inconsistency, and
      geometric considerations with, 510,
      511, 568
  dependent, 511, 542–543, 568
  elimination method for solving,
      517–520, 521, 568
  elimination using matrices with,
      552–555, 569
  inconsistent, 510, 541–542, 543, 568
  mixture problems using, 525–529, 568
  motion problems using, 530–532, 568
  nonlinear. See Nonlinear systems of
      equations
  substitution method for solving,
      516–517, 521, 568
  of three equations, 545–548, 569
  in three variables. See Systems of
      equations in three variables
  total-value problems using, 525–529,
      568
  in two variables. See Systems of
      equations in two variables
Systems of equations in three variables,
    537–543, 569
  dependency, inconsistency, and
      geometric considerations with,
      541–543
  identifying solutions of, 537–538
  solving, 538–541, 569
Systems of equations in two variables,
    506–511, 568
  solving graphically, 508–511, 568
  translating, 506–508
Systems of linear inequalities, 610–612

T

TABLE feature of graphing calculator, 88
Technology Connections. See Graphing
    calculator
Term(s)
  of algebraic expressions, 17, 944
  factors contrasted with, 18
  like, combining, 41, 63–64, 72, 87–88,
      248, 295
  of a polynomial. See Terms of a
      polynomial
  radical. See Radical terms
  of a sequence. See General term of a
      sequence; Series
  specific, of a binomial, finding, 927
Terminating decimals, 32, 71, 940
Terms of algebraic expressions, 17
Terms of a polynomial, 246, 294, 963
  ascending order of, 255
  coefficients of, 247, 294, 963
  constant. See Constant term
  degrees of. See Degrees of terms
      (of polynomials)
  descending order of, 248, 963
  leading, 247, 294, 963
  like, combining, 248, 295
  multiplication of sums and differences
      of, 271, 295

Test points, 768
Textbook supplements, 83
30°-60°-90° triangles, 679–680, 697
Time equation, 530
Total cost, 561, 562
Total profit, 561
Total revenue, 561
Total-value problems, with systems of
    equations, 525–529, 568
Translation
    to algebraic expressions, 4–5,
      69
    to equations, 6–7, 69
    to inequalities, 131–132
    of parabolas, 743
    percent, 102–104, 140
    as step in problem solving, 052–953,
      110, 111, 112, 113, 114, 115, 116,
      140
Triangles
    Pascal's, 922–924
    right, 358–360, 369, 976–977
    right, isosceles, 678–679, 697
    similar, 425, 438
    30°-60°-90°, 679–680, 697
Trinomials, 246, 247, 295, 964
    factoring. *See* Factoring trinomials
    perfect-square, 272, 296
    perfect-square, factoring, 329–331,
      368, 974, 975
    of type $ax^2 + bx + c$, factoring of,
      320–326, 367, 972–974
    of type $x^2 + bx + c$, factoring of,
      312–317, 367

U

Undefined answers, 55, 56, 72, 942
Undefined rational expressions, 376–377
Undefined slope of vertical line, 189, 219
Unions of sets, 590–592, 626, 996–997
University as resource, 83

V

Value
    absolute, 35, 71, 941
    of an algebraic expression, 3, 69
    solution of equation and, 944
Variable(s), 2, 69, 943
    polynomials in several variables,
      280–283, 296
Variable costs, 562
Variable expressions, 2–3
Variation, 486–490, 497–498
    combined, 489–490
    direct, 486–487, 497
    inverse, 487–489, 497
    joint, 489–490, 498
Variation constant, 486, 488
Vertex(ices)
    of a hyperbola, 870
    in linear programming, 619–620, 621, 627
    of a parabola, 740, 741, 751–752, 777, 855
Vertical hyperbolas, 874
Vertical lines, 959
    graphing, 171–173, 218
    slope of, 189, 219
Vertical-line test, 447, 496
Vertical parabolas, 874

Viewing window of graphing calculator, 150
Visualizing rates, 177–179

W

Whole numbers, 21, 70
    integers, 29–30, 71
Work principle, 422, 438
Work problems with rational equations,
    419–422, 438, 985–986

X

x-intercept, 168–173, 218, 957

Y

y-intercept, 168–173, 218, 957

Z

Zero
    as an exponent, 230–231, 233
    division involving, 53, 55–56, 72, 942
    in fractions, 23
    identity property of, 39, 71, 943
    multiplicative property of, 52, 943
    slope of, 189, 219
Zero exponents, 962
Zero products, principle of, 346–347,
    368, 976
Zeros of a function, 768, 777
Zooming with graphing calculator, 171

Index of Applications

Agriculture

Apple picking rate, 184
Composting, 761
Crop yield, 764
Decline in farmland, 841
Gardener planting trees and shrubs, 618–620
Grape growing, 623
Livestock feed, 533
Mixing fertilizers, 528–529, 568
Newborn calves, 760
Organic cotton, 470
Planting corn and soybeans, 615
Vegetable production, 946
Water usage to produce beef and wheat, 631

Astronomy

Asteroids, 838
Composition of the sun, 105
Cosmic path, 869
Distance of a planet from the sun, 853, 868
Jupiter's atmosphere, 105
Lunar eclipses, 491
Mass of Earth, 239
Meteorology, 192
Orbit of a comet, 873
Orbit time, 10
Planetary orbits, 491, 866
Rocket sections, 118
Satellite's escape velocity, 484–485, 494, 675
Stellar magnitude, 843
Weight on Mars, 434, 492
Weight on the moon, 434

Automotive

Alternative fuels, 375, 426–427, 838
Automobile maintenance, 534, 535
Automobile prices, 103–104, 549
Automobile production, 470
Automotive repair, 675
Bargaining for a used car, 921
Car depreciation, 184
Driving under the influence, 154
Fuel economy, 536
Fuel efficiency, 163–164, 167
Gas consumption, 176
Gas mileage, 182, 183, 221, 433, 623
Hybrid vehicles, 762, 765
Insurance-covered repairs, 136
Median age of cars in the United States, 498
Nighttime and daytime accidents, 763
Octane ratings, 534
Speed of a skidding car, 655
Stopping distance of a car, 493, 676
Tailgater alert, 676

Biology

Animal population, 433, 440, 442, 989
Bacteria, 800–801, 843
Cell biology, 902
Cricket chirps and temperature, 120
Ecology, 244
Endangered plant species, 505, 506–507, 524–525
Endangered species, 801
Fruit fly population, 918
Humpback whale population, 433, 801, 839, 840
Mass of a hydrogen atom, 239
Mass of water in a human, 492
Plant species, 105, 642
Threatened species, 199
Veterinary science, 433
Weight of a fish, 99
Wildlife population, 428
Wing aspect ratio, 433
Zebra mussel population, 801, 840
Zoology, 10

Business

Advertising, 277, 515, 549, 575
Blogging, 191
Book sales, 536, 631
Break-even point, 561, 565–566, 567, 570, 572, 573, 888
Broadway revenue, 503
Budget overruns, 107, 120
Call center, 181
Catering, 470, 533, 615, 631
Commercials, 535
Compact disc sales, 703, 758–759
Convention attendees, 471
Copiers, 119, 165, 397, 441
Custom embroidery, 430
Customer complaints and employees hired, 494
Digitizing books, 185–186, 197
Direct mail, 107
Discount stores, 103
E-mail marketing, 848
Employee theft, 142
Espresso-based coffee sales, 895, 918
Event promotion, 93–94
Food service, 702, 918
Hairdresser, 181
Hotel management, 244, 430, 503
Insurance claims, 584
Jewelry design, 507–508, 525–526, 568
Library mistakenly charged sales tax, 575
Making change, 535
Manufacturing, 355–356, 562–563, 566, 585, 628, 675, 989, 992
Markup, 107
Meeting costs, 955
Minimizing cost, 760, 780, 782
Mobile ad spending, 781
Number of cell phone subscribers, 373
Office supplies, 533
Operating expenses, 473
Outsourcing, 763
Packaging, 29
Photocopying, 434, 532
Production, 184, 567, 572, 573, 624
Profit, 623, 629, 760
Profits and losses, 42
Publishing, 585
Real estate, 522, 535
Refrigeration repair company, 629
Restaurant management, 549
Retail losses due to crime, 301
Retail sales, 191, 514
Retailing, 454
Revenue, cost and profit, 253
Sales meeting attendance, 361
Sales of pharmaceuticals, 514
Sales tax, 107, 225, 361, 575
Sales, 225, 533, 535, 888
Salvage value, 801
Search engine ads, 429
Selling, 114–115, 120, 146
Service agreement cancellation, 499
Shipping computers, 628
Starbucks revenue, 991
Store credit, 108
Storekeeper requesting change, 120
Telemarketing, 549
Total cost, 572, 573
Total profit, 261, 572, 573, 774
Total revenue, 572, 573
Video rentals, 535
Volume and cost, 495

Chemistry

Biochemistry, 536
Carbon dating, 837–838, 848, 849
Chemical solution, 534
Gold alloys, 550
Gold temperatures, 137
Half-life, 841
Hydrogen ion concentration, 833, 839, 848, 849
Metal alloys, 536
pH of a substance, 833, 839, 848, 849
Temperature conversion, 453, 473, 585

Temperatures of liquids, 595
Volume of a gas, 494
Zinc and copper in pennies, 433

Construction

Architecture, 196, 221, 364, 426, 432, 535, 546–547, 685, 760, 883–884
Blueprints, 143, 426, 432
Carpentry, 522
Contracting, 687
Corner on a building's foundation, 372
Cutting a beam, ribbon or wire, 142, 145, 225, 361, 888
Diagonal braces, 364, 370
Dimensions of a room, 364
Doorway construction, 862
Drafting a set of plans, 986
Fencing, 134, 936, 989
Folding sheet metal, 366
Grade of a stairway, 195
Hancock building dimensions, 118
Home construction, 841
Home remodeling, 117, 225
Home restoration, 430
Milling, 623
Molding plastics, 761
Norman window, 765
Painters scraping a house, 490
Painting, 687, 989
Paving, 431, 434
Plywood, 955
Reach of a ladder, 364, 369, 373, 977
Roofing, 115–116, 195, 365, 419–421, 687
Sanding oak floors, 439
Slope of land, 195
Two-by-four, 118
Wood stains, 536
World's tallest buildings, 7

Consumer

Appliances, 397
Average price of electricity, 780
Better pizza deal, 766
Beverage consumption, 482, 946, 994
Bills, 42, 144, 181
Bottled water consumption, 166, 204
Broadband cable and DSL subscribers, 303
Cable costs, 841
Catering costs, 132
Cell phone costs, 191, 466, 473
Cost, 12, 137, 165, 182, 204, 225, 500, 504, 702
Cost of kitchen cabinets, 952–953
Deducting sales tax, 107
Discount, 109, 120, 138
EBay purchases, 121
Energy use, 105, 277, 301, 945
Fitness center costs, 499
Frequent buyer bonus, 138
Furnace repairs, 135
Gasoline consumption, 851
Holiday spending, 353
Home video spending, 155
Insurance benefits, 584
Long distance telephone usage, 953, 955
Media usage, 762
Minimizing tolls, 595
Music club membership, 936

Ordering books, 442
Parking fees, 138
Phone costs, 501
Photography fees, 584
Pre-paid calling card, 575
Prices, 117, 143, 166, 191, 549, 571, 766, 934, 993, 994
Purchasing, 572, 732
Sale prices, 955
Sales, 109
Shipping costs, 587
Taxi fares, 119, 121, 183, 470
Telephone calls, 522
Tipping, 106, 107
Toll charges, 138
True cost of a new car, 803
U.S. wireless-phone subscribers, 143
Utility bills, 631
Vehicle rental, 119, 176–177, 179, 180, 470, 501, 522, 584, 629, 782
Water usage, 955

Economics

Crude oil, 106, 584
Currency exchange, 388
Demand, 462, 564–565, 566, 573, 843
Depreciation, 182, 184, 287, 473, 910
Equilibrium point, 564–565, 566, 567, 570, 572, 573
Federal funds rate, 97
Gasoline prices, 42
Gold prices, 782
National debt, 180
Natural gas prices, 42, 157
Poverty rate, 105
Residential fuel oil prices, 157
Russia's external debt, 301
Stock market, 36
Stock prices, 119, 760
Supply, 462, 564–565, 566, 573, 843
Tax bracket, 108
Taxable interest, 491
Value of a stock market portfolio, 848

Education

Back-to-college expenses, 251
Chinese and Japanese students enrolled in U.S. colleges, 142
Class size, 42
College admission tests, 191
College course load, 135
College enrollment, 97, 103, 215
College entrance exam scores, 584
College graduation, 106
College tuition, 105, 135, 180, 222
Cost of college, 166
Counseling, 595
Dropout rate, 108
Elementary school math proficiency, 443, 449–450
Financial aid, 133
Forgetting on a final exam, 841, 848, 851
GPA, 301
Grading, 138, 434, 621–622
Graduate school, 135, 616
High school enrollment, 215
Ordering number tiles, 782
Private four-year college costs, 849

Quiz average, 135, 373
Quiz scores, 134
Reading assignment, 134
Scholastic aptitude test, 549
School purchasing a piano, 121
Semester average, 254, 491
Standard school day, 136
Student aid, 149–150, 154–155, 165
Student loans and grants, 35, 106, 527–528, 533, 838, 933
Test scores, 120, 121, 522, 623

Engineering

Acoustics, 485–486
Antenna length, 685
Atmospheric drag, 494
Bridge design, 360, 764
Bridge expansion, 685
Cell-phone tower, 361
Coal to generate electricity, 301
Coordinates on the globe, 157
Current and resistance, 493
Desalination, 851
Design, 515, 761, 862, 886, 887, 888, 909
Distance over water, 684
Electrical safety, 500
Energy conservation, 473
Energy consumption, 522
Energy-efficient washer and dryer, 301
Europe's wind-turbine capacity, 300
Furnace output, 97, 100
Grade of a road, 189–190, 195, 223
Guy wires, 364, 678, 684
Height of a telephone pole, 366
Horsepower of an engine, 863
Intensity of a signal, 494
Ohm's law, 492
Rebuilding an engine, 421, 438
Resistance, 484
Richter scale, 840
Road design, 363, 364
Surveying, 195
Wavelength and frequency, 493
Well drilling, 136
Width of a quarry, 434
Wind power, 841, 969

Environment

Air pollution, 493
Altitude and temperature, 99
Atlantic storms, 993
Atmospheric pressure, 842
Below and above sea level, 30, 36
Colorado River, 851
Coral reefs, 244
Distance from a storm, 97
Elevations, 42, 50
Forest fires, 430
Forestry, 649
Hydrology, 765
Lake level, 42
Landfills, 181
Municipal solid waste, 481
National Park land, 472
Ocean waves, 487, 802
Ozone layer, 156
Precipitation, 761
Record temperature drop, 166

Recycling, 11, 178, 431, 471, 532, 535, 596, 801
River lengths, 143
Solid waste, 155, 595
Speed of the current, 423–424, 851
Sunshine, 761
Temperature, 1, 36, 50, 58
Ultraviolet index, 493, 500
Waste generated by a family, 500
Water from melting snow, 492
Water level, 605
Waterfalls, 616
Wave height, 363
Wind chill temperature, 655

Finance

Account balance, 42
Accumulated savings, 909
Banking, 43, 178–179, 631
Budgeting, 137, 145
Car loans, 803
Car payments, 135
Checking accounts, 585
Coin value, 556
Compound interest, 99, 287, 710–711, 731, 799–800, 818, 834, 896
Credit cards, 119
Doubling time, 834
Interest compounded continuously, 836–837, 840, 848, 849
Interest rates, 40, 615, 778
Interest, 491, 615, 713
Investment, 287, 533, 550, 556, 615, 623, 628, 711, 802, 848, 849, 887, 892, 896
Loan repayment, 915–916, 918, 933
Mortgages, 937
Online banking, 471
Outstanding mortgage debt, 30
Retirement, 937
Savings account, 36
Savings interest, 119
Savings rate, 219
Small business loans, 550

Geometry

Angle measure, 99
Angles of a triangle, 118, 143, 146, 353, 361, 549, 569, 571, 575, 894, 955
Area of a circular region, 252, 258
Area of a garden, 362
Area of a parallelogram, 11
Area of a square, 371
Area of a trapezoid, 98
Area of a triangular region, 137, 452, 685, 699
Areas of Alaska and Arizona, 107
Circumference of a circle, 252
Complementary angles, 119, 514
Court dimensions, 514, 616
Diagonal of a cube, 687, 732
Diagonal of a rectangle, 687, 700
Dimensions of a box, 366, 372, 888
Dimensions of a leaf, 356–357
Dimensions of a rectangular region, 118, 121, 134, 140, 143, 144, 268, 353, 361, 362, 364, 365, 371, 373, 429, 535, 573, 674, 684, 761, 831, 884, 886, 887, 888, 891, 892, 894, 936, 978

Dimensions of a sail, 363
Dimensions of a state, 118
Dimensions of a triangular region, 361, 362, 370, 417, 674, 699, 831
Length of a side of a square, 442, 699, 892
Lengths of the sides of a triangle, 121, 362, 894, 978
Maximizing volume, 761
Maximum area, 757–758, 761, 777, 779, 894, 936
Maximum dimensions of a postcard, 575
Minimizing area, 765
Number of diagonals, 774
Perimeter of a basketball court, 113–114, 118
Perimeter of a rectangular region, 120, 136, 146, 417, 631, 943, 955
Perimeter of a square, 891
Perimeter of a triangle, 117, 136
Perimeter of an equilateral triangle, 462
Radius of a circle, 891
Right triangles, 978
Sides of a square, 429
Supplementary angles, 119, 514
Surface area of a balloon, 502
Surface area of a box, 268
Surface area of a cube, 99
Surface area of a right circular cylinder, 280, 732
Surface area of a silo, 284, 287
Surface area of a sphere, 452, 732
Volume of a box, 268, 299
Volume of a cube, 268, 318
Width of a pool sidewalk, 366
Width of the margins in a book, 371

Health/Medicine

Absorption of ibuprofen, 97
Acid level in a person's blood, 731
Acid reflux, 366
Advil absorption, 482
Aerobic exercise, 223
Allergic reaction, 357–358
Blood alcohol level, 154, 453–454
Blood donors, 298
Blood types, 225
Body fat, 107, 491, 585, 595
Body mass index, 252–253
Body temperature, 136–137
Calories, 30, 35, 95, 97, 99, 100, 107, 191, 225, 284, 433, 441, 442, 477–478, 492, 573, 851, 946
Cholesterol-lowering drugs, 481
Cigarette smoking, 214, 215
Constricted bronchial muscles, 363
Deaths due to stroke, 838
Dehydration, 105
Diabetes, 145
Energy expenditure, 455
Exercise and pulse rate, 150, 195
Exercise, 536
Fat content, 107, 137, 143
Fitness, 191
Generic drugs, 843
Health insurance, 181, 551, 779, 831, 839, 841
Heart attacks and cholesterol, 453
Heart conditions, 363

Height, 108, 994
Hospital care, 244
Infant health, 106
Kidney transplants, 227, 252
Kissing and colds, 107
Life expectancy, 165–166, 471, 473, 483
Lithotripter, 866
Long-term care, 191
Lung capacity, 284
Medicine dosage, 100, 449, 494
Nurse seeing patients, 575
Nutrition, 95, 135, 138, 549, 550, 623–624
pH of patient's blood, 839
Pregnancy, 454–455, 994
Prescription drug sales, 181
Registered nurses, 577, 581
Treadmill, 195
Waiting list for organ transplants, 373
Weight gain, 137

Labor

Availability pay, 225
Average hourly earnings in accommodations and food services, 204
Changing work force, 762
Cost of self-employment, 106–107
Dentistry, 868–869
Earnings, 148–149, 183, 225, 486, 919
Employee contribution to health insurance premium, 763
Filing receipts, 442
Firefighting, 633, 674, 869
Health benefits, 779
Hours worked, 11, 301, 573, 628, 894
Job offers, 582, 628
Jobs in health care and social assistance, 204
Payroll, 429
Proofreading, 180
Raise, 108
Retirement age, 483
Salary, 134, 225, 702
Sales commissions, 134
Sharing the workload, 435
Sick leave, 108
Sports salaries, 843
Teller work, 535
Temporary help, 180
Union represented by Ford employees, 192
U.S. minimum hourly wage, 499
Wages with commissions, 183
Wages, 181, 584, 906, 915, 933
Women in the workforce, 105
Work experience, 515
Work rate, 491, 492
Work time, 10
Workers cleaning a stadium, 502
Working alone to complete a job, 421, 430, 431, 434, 438, 441, 778, 780, 782
Working together to complete a job, 419–421, 430, 439, 441, 442, 831, 851, 937, 986, 989

Miscellaneous

African artistry, 396
Ages, 12, 515, 551, 937
Air conditioner, 490

Apartment numbers, 117
Archaeology, 364, 841, 862, 909
Art, 732, 842, 886, 894
Baking, 433, 988
Beard growth, 418
Birthday gift, 934
Blending teas or coffees, 526–527, 533, 550, 573, 623
Caffeine, 841
Cake decorating, 430
City ordinances, 840
Countries and their capitals, 786–787
Decorating for a party, 498
Dress sizes, 595, 793, 794
Drinking water, 105
Elevators, 180, 616
E-mail, 117
Emergency shelter, 702
Escalators, 434
Filling a pool, tub, tank or bog, 429, 434, 730
Flood rescue, 702
Food, 105, 119, 121, 534
Frog jumps, 910
Gambling, 51
Garden design, 761, 887
Gardening, 418, 492, 761, 909
Gettysburg Address, 120
Hair growth, 470
High-fives, 364
Hours wasted due to spam e-mails, 299
House numbers, 575
Ink remover, 533
Keyboarding speed, 802
Landscaping, 441, 470, 702, 978
Lightbulbs, 433, 453
Lighting, 533
Memorizing words, 252
Mixing food, drinks, spices or herbs, 533, 556, 571, 831, 936
Mixing paint, 556
Mowing lawns, 430, 954
Nontoxic cleaning supplies, 514, 515, 571
Page numbers, 117, 121, 362, 978
Pet safety, 566
Phone keys, 786–787
Photo albums, 623
Photography, 108, 433
Planting bulbs, 490
Pond depth, 137
Power outages, 50–51
Predicting height, 452
Preferred viewing distance, 492
President's office, 868
Prize tee shirts, 459
Pumping rate, 492
Pumping water, 430
Quilting, 503
Radio airplay, 535
Relative aperture, 493
Safe listening, 844
Safe sight distance, 762
Safety flares, 462
Seats in an auditorium, 934
Security system installation, 108
Serial numbers on two-dollar bills, 442
Sharing raffle tickets, 551
Shoe sizes, 784–785

Sighting to the horizon, 700
Sizes of envelopes, 136
Sizes of packages, 136
Snow cannons making snow, 630
Snow removal, 180
Sodium in Chef Boyardee foods, 373
Speaker placement, 684
Sports card values, 43
Stacking objects, 918, 933
Street addresses, 117
String length and frequency, 493
Telephone pole storage, 907, 909
Toasting, 364
Value of a rare stamp, 793

Physics

Altitude of a launched object, 284, 285
Centripetal force, 937
Downward speed, 731
Falling distance, 728, 730
Free-falling objects, 711–712, 713, 714, 778
Height of a rocket, 365
Height of a thrown object, 774
Hooke's Law, 492
Intensity of light, 494–495
Intensity of sound, 839, 840, 844, 848, 849
Mass of an object, 649
Period of a pendulum, 661, 727
Pressure at sea depth, 462, 472, 595
Rebound distance of a ball, 918, 933, 934
Reverberation time, 493
Sonic boom, 873
Sound levels, 832–833
Special relativity, 731
Tension of a musical string, 495
Trajectory of a launched object, 764
Velocity of water flow, 633, 674
Wavelength of a musical note, 145

Social Sciences

Age at marriage, 616, 702
Aspects of love, 454
Average minutes per month men talk on cell phones, 373
Birth rate among teenagers, 214
Crying rate, 571
Disaster relief, 504
Educational activities vs. leisure activities, 145
Event planning, 533
Food-stamp program participation, 214
French speaking Internet users, 373
Fundraising, 514, 631
Gender, 536
Handshakes, 363, 371, 774, 902
Illegal immigration, 433
Political Action Committee contributions, 471, 473
Smoking cessation, 801, 839
Social networking, 838
Spread of a rumor, 838–839
Text messaging, 155
Time spent reading or doing homework, 143
Violent crimes, 181
Volunteering, 147, 210–211, 222, 490, 782
Widows or divorcees, 930

Sports/Entertainment

Admissions to a high school basketball game, 615
Admissions to theme parks, 442
Archery, 763
Band formations, 909
Band members setting up for a show, 490
Baseball, 105, 136, 648, 677, 684, 764, 930
Basketball, 121, 145, 514, 551
Batting average, 106
Battleship game, 158
Bicycle racer's location, 502
Broadway performances, 503
Bungee jumping, 604, 730–731, 916–917
Car racing, 117
Chess, 11, 99
Concert tickets, 2–3, 77, 144
Concerts, 840
Cover charges for a show, 764
DVD collections, 134
Fireworks displays, 462
Games in a sports league, 97, 249, 363, 370
Golf distance finder, 495
Golfing, 43
Hang time, 728, 731
Hank Aaron, 994
HDTVs, 584, 585, 888
Hiking, 144, 978
Hockey, 10, 535, 616
Lacrosse, 514
League schedules, 731
Masters tournament, 36
Mountaineering, 180, 181
Movie downloads, 488–489
Movie theatre attendance, 442
Movies released in the United States, 453
Museum attendance, 756–757
Music downloads, 703, 800
Music, 105, 136, 648, 675
NASCAR fans, 105
NBA All-Star game, 537
NBA heights, 994
Outdoor concerts, 97
Pass completions, 106
Path of the Olympic arrow, 253
PBA scores, 994
Piano concert, 550
Practice shooting baskets, 955
Price of a movie ticket, 138
Reading, 954
Race numbers, 355
Race time, 12, 120
Racing, 839
Record elevations, 47–48
Referee jogging, 700
Running, 184, 223, 397
Running records, 137, 462, 471, 499
Sailing, 365
Scrabble, 119
Skateboarding, 196
Skate-park jump, 699
Skiing, 138, 190, 862
Skydiving, 251, 252
Sled dog racing, 117
Snowboarding, 862
Snowmobiling, 989
Softball, 684

Sports costs, 946
Swimming, 107, 490, 757–758
Swing sets, 977
Team's magic number, 288
Tennis, 514
Theatrical production, 868, 892
Ticket revenue to a magic show, 551
TV viewing, 221
Unicycling, 117
Value of a sports card, 842
Walking, 684, 724, 849
Winter Olympic volunteers, 762
Women's softball, 10
Wrestling, 861
Yardage gained and lost in football, 36, 42
Zipline canopy tour, 359

Statistics/Demographics

Aging population, 215
Average number of live births, 763
Birth and death rates, 36
City population, 849
Household incomes, 992
Longest marriage, 117
Number of births in the United States, 481, 482
Number of people in a community, 108
Oldest bride, 117
Population growth, 840, 918
Population of Latvia, 894
Population of Nigeria, 849
Population of United Arab Emirates, 840
Population, 134, 182
U.S. Census Bureau, 434
U.S. senior population, 762
Urban population, 215
World population growth, 551, 839, 840

Technology

Cell phones, 802
Cells in a spreadsheet, 287
Color printers, 113, 120
Computer screens, 888
Downloads, 547–548

E-mail, 514, 840
Encoding data onto a beam of light, 244
Fax machines, 430
Flash drives, 433
Graphing calculator memory, 235
High-speed Internet, 363
Multifunction copiers, 430
Navigational devices, 802
Online searches, 220
Photo printing, 431
Photocopiers, 430
Processing a data file, 44
Spam messages, 848
Spread of a computer virus, 841
Text messaging, 155, 433, 783, 795, 835, 918
Value of a color copier, 165
Value of a laptop computer, 848
Value of a projector, 902
Value of computer software, 166
Wi-fi hotspots, 781

Transportation

Air travel, 729
Airline bumping rate, 762
Alternative-fuel vehicles, 106
Average acceleration, 491, 494
Average speed, 435, 491
Aviation, 183, 184, 364, 432, 434, 724, 893
Barge, 432
Bicycle speed, 438
Bicycling, 106, 111, 167, 195, 422–423, 429, 683, 729, 989
Boat speed, 431, 440, 780
Boating, 431, 432, 434, 534, 714, 724
Bus schedules, 397
Bus travel, 487
Canoeing, 534, 729, 782
Car speed, 440, 441, 729
Car travel, 434, 534, 729
Chartering a bus, 794
Cost of road service, 136
Crosswalks, 684
Cruise ship passengers, 835–836
Cycling distance, 429

Distance from Chicago, 501
Drag force on a boat, 494
Driving delays, 503
Driving rate, 221
Driving time, 504, 987
Filling a freighter with oil, 434
Fishing boat, 851
Ignition and lift off, 36
International visitors to the United States, 501
Interstate mile markers, 112
Jet travel, 531–532, 568
Kayaking, 431
Luggage size, 615
Mass transit, 144
Miles driven, 433
Moped speed, 432
Motorcycle travel, 725–727
Moving sidewalks, 431
Navigation, 184, 195, 729, 730
Paddleboats, 730
Parking spaces, 362
Plane speed, 778, 936
Plane travel, 181
Point of no return, 534
Radar range, 655
Rate of travel, 176–177
Road pavement messages, 648
Rowing, 730
Spaces in a parking lot, 642
Speed of a bus, 177
Speed of travel, 431
Speeds of a dog sled and snowmobile, 575
Time for a car to catch up to a truck, 573
Time for a passenger train to overtake a freight train, 571
Tractor speed, 431
Train speeds, 431, 440, 851
Train travel, 181, 182, 432, 530–531, 534, 536
Travel speed and accidents, 763
Travel to work, 11
U.S. transcontinental railroad, 551
Vehicle miles traveled, 249–250

Geometric Formulas

Plane Geometry

Rectangle
Area: $A = lw$
Perimeter: $P = 2l + 2w$

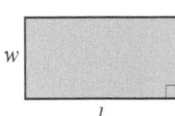

Square
Area: $A = s^2$
Perimeter: $P = 4s$

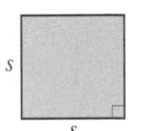

Triangle
Area: $A = \frac{1}{2}bh$

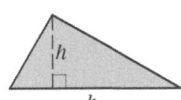

Triangle
Sum of Angle Measures:
$A + B + C = 180°$

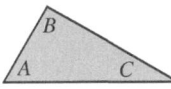

Right Triangle
Pythagorean Theorem
(Equation):
$a^2 + b^2 = c^2$

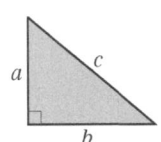

Parallelogram
Area: $A = bh$

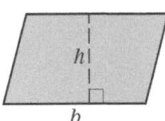

Trapezoid
Area: $A = \frac{1}{2}h(b_1 + b_2)$

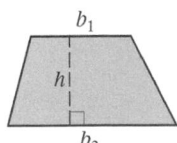

Circle
Area: $A = \pi r^2$
Circumference:
$C = \pi d = 2\pi r$
$\left(\frac{22}{7} \text{ and } 3.14 \text{ are different}\right.$
approximations for π)

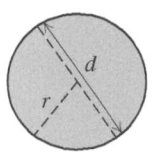

Solid Geometry

Rectangular Solid
Volume: $V = lwh$

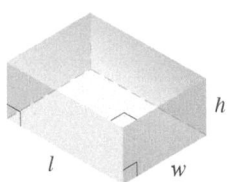

Cube
Volume: $V = s^3$

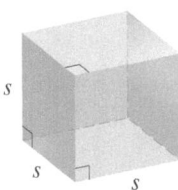

Right Circular Cylinder
Volume: $V = \pi r^2 h$
Total Surface Area:
$S = 2\pi rh + 2\pi r^2$

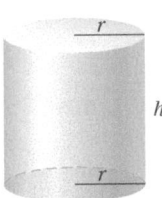

Right Circular Cone
Volume: $V = \frac{1}{3}\pi r^2 h$
Total Surface Area:
$S = \pi r^2 + \pi rs$
Slant Height:
$s = \sqrt{r^2 + h^2}$

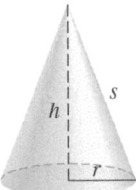

Sphere
Volume: $V = \frac{4}{3}\pi r^3$
Surface Area: $S = 4\pi r^2$

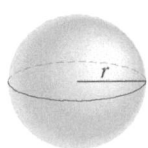

Selected Keys of the Scientific Calculator

This secondary function takes the square root of number displayed.

Squares number displayed.

Activates secondary functions printed above certain keys. Also denoted INV or 2nd.

Used when entering numbers in scientific notation. Also denoted EXP.

Finds reciprocal of number displayed.

Used to raise any base to a power. Also denoted y^x, a^x, or ⌃.

Stores number displayed in memory. Also denoted MIN or M.

Recalls number stored in memory. Also denoted MR.

This secondary function raises 10 to any power entered.

Clears all preceding numbers and operations. Also used to turn calculator on.

Used as an approximation for pi.

Used to perform indicated operation.

Used to control order in which certain operations are performed.

Clears last number displayed but not preceding operations.

Used when entering decimal notation.

Used to change sign of number displayed.

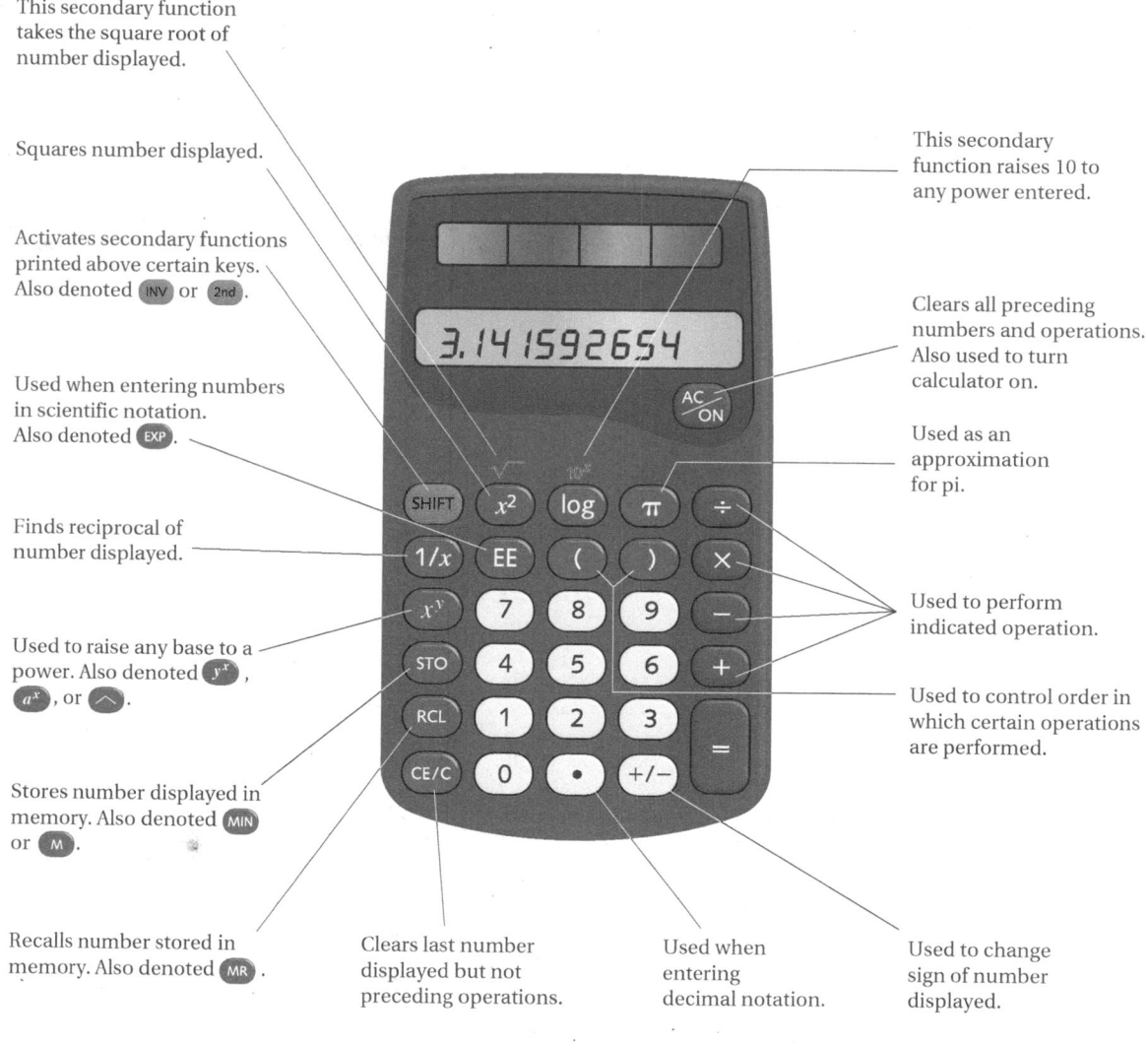